Practice "Work the Problems"

Feature	Description	Benefit	Page
"Assess Your Understanding" contains a variety of problems at the end of each section.			
'Are You Prepared?' Problems	These assess your retention of the prerequisite material you'll need. Answers are given at the end of the section exercises. This feature is related to the Preparing for This Section feature.	Do you always remember what you've learned? Working these problems is the best way to find out. If you get one wrong, you'll know exactly what you need to review and where to review it!	269, 279
Concepts and Vocabulary	These short-answer questions, mainly Fill-in-the-Blank and True/False items, assess your understanding of key definitions and concepts in the current section.	Learning math is more than memorization – it's about discovering connections. These problems help you understand the 'big ideas' before diving into skill building.	280
Skill Building	Correlated to section examples, these problems provide straightforward practice.	It's important to dig in and develop your skills. These problems provide you with ample practice to do so.	280–281
Mixed Practice	These problems offer comprehensive assessment of the skills learned in the section by asking problems that relate to more than one concept or objective. These problems may also require you to utilize skills learned in previous sections.	Learning mathematics is a building process. Many concepts are interrelated. These problems help you see how mathematics builds on itself and also see how the concepts tie together.	281
Applications and Extensions	These problems allow you to apply your skills to real-world problems. These problems also allow you to extend concepts learned in the section.	You will see that the material learned within the section has many uses in everyday life.	281–284
Discussion and Writing	"Discussion and Writing" problems are colored red. These support class discussion, verbalization of mathematical ideas, and writing and research projects.	To verbalize an idea, or to describe it clearly in writing, shows real understanding. These problems nurture that understanding. Many are challenging but you'll get out what you put in.	284
"Now Work" PROBLEMS	Many examples refer you to a related homework problem. These related problems are marked by a pencil and yellow numbers.	If you get stuck while working problems, look for the closest Now Work problem and refer back to the related example to see if it helps.	276

Review "Study for Quizzes and Tests"

Feature	Description	Benefit	Page
Chapter Reviews at the end of each chapter contain...			
"Things to Know"	A detailed list of important theorems, formulas, and definitions from the chapter.	Review these and you'll know the most important material in the chapter!	342–343
"You Should Be Able To..."	Contains a complete list of objectives by section, examples that illustrate the objective, and practice exercises that test your understanding of the objective.	Do the recommended exercises and you'll have mastery over the key material. If you get something wrong, review the suggested page numbers and try again.	343–344
Review Exercises	These provide comprehensive review and practice of key skills, matched to the Learning Objectives for each section.	Practice makes perfect. These problems combine exercises from all sections, giving you a comprehensive review in one place.	344–347
CHAPTER TEST	About 15–20 problems that can be taken as a Chapter Test. Be sure to take the Chapter Test under test conditions—no notes!	Be prepared. Take the sample practice test. This will get you ready for your instructor's test. If you get a problem wrong, watch the Chapter Test Prep video.	348
CUMULATIVE REVIEW	These problem sets appear at the end of each chapter, beginning with Chapter 2. They combine problems from previous chapters, providing an ongoing cumulative review.	These are really important. They will ensure that you are not forgetting anything as you go. These will go a long way toward keeping you constantly primed for quizzes and tests.	348–349
CHAPTER PROJECTS	The Chapter Project applies what you've learned in the chapter. Additional projects are available on the Instructor's Resource Center (IRC).	The Project gives you an opportunity to apply what you've learned in the chapter to solve a problem related to the opening article. If your instructor allows, these make excellent opportunities to work in a group, which is often the best way of learning math.	349

Precalculus

Fifth Edition

Precalculus
Enhanced with Graphing Utilities

Michael Sullivan

Chicago State University

Michael Sullivan, III

Joliet Junior College

PEARSON

Prentice
Hall

Upper Saddle River, New Jersey 07458

Senior Editor: *Adam Jaworski*
Vice President and Editorial Director, Mathematics: *Christine Hoag*
Sponsoring Editor: *Dawn Murrin*
Executive Marketing Manager: *Kate Valentine*
Editorial Assistant/Print Supplements Editor: *Joseph Colella*
Project Manager, Production: *Bob Walters, Prepress Management, Inc.*
Senior Managing Editor: *Linda Mihatov Behrens*
Senior Operations Supervisor: *Diane M. Peirano*
Executive Marketing Manager: *Becky Anderson*
Marketing Assistant: *Kathleen DeChavez*
Art Director: *Heather Scott*
Senior Art Director: *Juan R. López*
Interior Designer: *Tamara Newnam*
Cover Designer: *Tamara Newnam*
A V Project Manager: *Thomas Benfatti*
TestGen: *Mary Durnwald*

MathXL: *Phil Oslin*
Director, Image Resource Center: *Melinda Patelli*
Manager, Rights and Permissions: *Zina Arabia*
Manager, Visual Research: *Beth Brenzel*
Image Permission Coordinator: *Joanne Dippel*
Photo Researcher: *Kathy Ringrose*
Art Studios: *Laserwords/Artworks*
 Senior Managing Editor, Art Production and Management: *Patricia Burns*
 Manager, Production Technologies: *Matthew Haas*
 Manager, Illustration Production: *Sean Hogan*
 Assistant Manager, Illustration Production: *Ronda C. Whitson*
 Illustrators: *Stacy Smith, Mark Landis, and Audrey Simonetti*
 Quality Assurance: *Pamela Taylor, Timothy Nguyen, Trinell Hartranft*
Compositor: *ICC Macmillan Inc.*

 © 2009, 2006, 2003, 2000, 1996 Pearson Education, Inc.
Pearson Prentice Hall
Pearson Education, Inc.
Upper Saddle River, New Jersey 07458

Printed in the United States of America
10 9 8 7 6 5 4 3 2 1

ISBN: 978-0-13-235627-5 (Instructor's Edition)
ISBN: 0-13-235627-9 (Instructor's Edition)

ISBN: 978-0-13-601578-9 (Student Edition)
ISBN: 0-13-601578-6 (Student Edition)

Pearson Education LTD., *London*
Pearson Education Australia PTY, Limited, *Sydney*
Pearson Education Singapore, Pte. Ltd
Pearson Education North Asia Ltd. *Hong Kong*
Pearson Education Canada, Ltd., *Toronto*
Pearson Educación de Mexico, S.A. de C.V.
Pearson Education – Japan, *Tokyo*
Pearson Education Malaysia, Pte. Ltd

For the Next Generation

Shannon, Patrick, and Ryan (Murphy)   Michael S., Kevin, and Marissa (Sullivan)
Maeve and Sean (Sullivan)   Kaleigh, Billy, and Timmy (O'Hara)

Contents

To the Student   xiii

Preface to the Instructor   xv

List of Applications   xxi

Photo Credits   xxix

1   Graphs   1

1.1   Rectangular Coordinates; Graphing Utilities; Introduction to Graphing Equations   2

1.2   Intercepts; Symmetry; Graphing Key Equations   18

1.3   Solving Equations Using a Graphing Utility   26

1.4   Lines   29

1.5   Circles   44

     Chapter Review   51

     Chapter Test   54

     Chapter Projects   54

2   Functions and Their Graphs   55

2.1   Functions   56

2.2   The Graph of a Function   70

2.3   Properties of Functions   79

2.4   Library of Functions; Piecewise-defined Functions   90

2.5   Graphing Techniques: Transformations   100

2.6   Mathematical Models: Building Functions   112

     Chapter Review   118

     Chapter Test   122

     Cumulative Review   123

     Chapter Projects   124

3   Linear and Quadratic Functions   125

3.1   Linear Functions, Their Properties, and Linear Models   126

3.2   Building Linear Models from Data   136

3.3   Quadratic Functions and Their Properties   142

3.4   Building Quadratic Models from Verbal Descriptions and from Data   154

3.5   Inequalities Involving Quadratic Functions   164

     Chapter Review   168

     Chapter Test   171

     Cumulative Review   171

     Chapter Projects   172

4   Polynomial and Rational Functions — 173

4.1	Polynomial Functions and Models	174
4.2	Properties of Rational Functions	191
4.3	The Graph of a Rational Function	202
4.4	Polynomial and Rational Inequalities	213
4.5	The Real Zeros of a Polynomial Function	220
4.6	Complex Zeros; Fundamental Theorem of Algebra	234
	Chapter Review	239
	Chapter Test	243
	Cumulative Review	243
	Chapter Projects	244

5   Exponential and Logarithmic Functions — 247

5.1	Composite Functions	248
5.2	One-to-One Functions; Inverse Functions	255
5.3	Exponential Functions	269
5.4	Logarithmic Functions	284
5.5	Properties of Logarithms	297
5.6	Logarithmic and Exponential Equations	306
5.7	Financial Models	313
5.8	Exponential Growth and Decay Models; Newton's Law; Logistic Growth and Decay Models	323
5.9	Building Exponential, Logarithmic, and Logistic Models from Data	334
	Chapter Review	342
	Chapter Test	348
	Cumulative Review	348
	Chapter Projects	349

6   Trigonometric Functions — 351

6.1	Angles and Their Measure	352
6.2	Trigonometric Functions: Unit Circle Approach	365
6.3	Properties of the Trigonometric Functions	382
6.4	Graphs of the Sine and Cosine Functions	395
6.5	Graphs of the Tangent, Cotangent, Cosecant, and Secant Functions	411
6.6	Phase Shift; Sinusoidal Curve Fitting	419
	Chapter Review	430
	Chapter Test	436
	Cumulative Review	436
	Chapter Projects	437

7 Analytic Trigonometry   **439**

7.1	The Inverse Sine, Cosine, and Tangent Functions	440
7.2	The Inverse Trigonometric Functions (Continued)	453
7.3	Trigonometric Identities	459
7.4	Sum and Difference Formulas	466
7.5	Double-angle and Half-angle Formulas	476
7.6	Product-to-Sum and Sum-to-Product Formulas	485
7.7	Trigonometric Equations (I)	488
7.8	Trigonometric Equations (II)	495
	Chapter Review	502
	Chapter Test	506
	Cumulative Review	506
	Chapter Projects	507

8 Applications of Trigonometric Functions   **509**

8.1	Right Triangle Trigonometry; Applications	510
8.2	The Law of Sines	522
8.3	The Law of Cosines	533
8.4	Area of a Triangle	540
8.5	Simple Harmonic Motion; Damped Motion; Combining Waves	546
	Chapter Review	554
	Chapter Test	558
	Cumulative Review	559
	Chapter Projects	559

9 Polar Coordinates; Vectors   **561**

9.1	Polar Coordinates	562
9.2	Polar Equations and Graphs	571
9.3	The Complex Plane; De Moivre's Theorem	589
9.4	Vectors	597
9.5	The Dot Product	608
9.6	Vectors in Space	616
9.7	The Cross Product	625
	Chapter Review	631
	Chapter Test	635
	Cumulative Review	635
	Chapter Projects	636

10 Analytic Geometry 637

10.1	Conics	638
10.2	The Parabola	639
10.3	The Ellipse	648
10.4	The Hyperbola	659
10.5	Rotation of Axes; General Form of a Conic	673
10.6	Polar Equations of Conics	681
10.7	Plane Curves and Parametric Equations	687
	Chapter Review	**700**
	Chapter Test	**703**
	Cumulative Review	**703**
	Chapter Projects	**704**

11 Systems of Equations and Inequalities 705

11.1	Systems of Linear Equations: Substitution and Elimination	706
11.2	Systems of Linear Equations: Matrices	720
11.3	Systems of Linear Equations: Determinants	735
11.4	Matrix Algebra	745
11.5	Partial Fraction Decomposition	762
11.6	Systems of Nonlinear Equations	770
11.7	Systems of Inequalities	780
11.8	Linear Programming	789
	Chapter Review	**795**
	Chapter Test	**799**
	Cumulative Review	**800**
	Chapter Projects	**801**

12 Sequences; Induction; the Binomial Theorem 803

12.1	Sequences	804
12.2	Arithmetic Sequences	817
12.3	Geometric Sequences; Geometric Series	823
12.4	Mathematical Induction	833
12.5	The Binomial Theorem	837
	Chapter Review	**843**
	Chapter Test	**846**
	Cumulative Review	**847**
	Chapter Projects	**847**

13   Counting and Probability   849

13.1	Counting	850
13.2	Permutations and Combinations	855
13.3	Probability	864
	Chapter Review	874
	Chapter Test	876
	Cumulative Review	877
	Chapter Projects	877

14   A Preview of Calculus: The Limit, Derivative, and Integral of a Function   879

14.1	Finding Limits Using Tables and Graphs	880
14.2	Algebra Techniques for Finding Limits	885
14.3	One-sided Limits; Continuous Functions	892
14.4	The Tangent Problem; The Derivative	899
14.5	The Area Problem; The Integral	907
	Chapter Review	913
	Chapter Test	917
	Chapter Projects	918

Appendix A   Review   A1

A.1	Algebra Essentials	A1
A.2	Geometry Essentials	A14
A.3	Polynomials	A23
A.4	Synthetic Division	A31
A.5	Rational Expressions	A35
A.6	Solving Equations	A46
A.7	Complex Numbers; Quadratic Equations in the Complex Number System	A60
A.8	Problem Solving: Interest, Mixture, Uniform Motion, Constant Rate Jobs	A69
A.9	Interval Notation; Solving Inequalities	A78
A.10	nth Roots; Rational Exponents	A88

Appendix B   The Limit of a Sequence; Infinite Series   B1

| **Answers** | AN1 |
| **Index** | I1 |

Three Distinct Series

Students have different goals, learning styles, and levels of preparation. Instructors have different teaching philosophies, styles, and techniques. Rather than write one series to fit all, the Sullivans have written three distinct series. All share the same goal—to develop a high level of mathematical understanding and an appreciation for the way mathematics can describe the world around us. The manner of reaching that goal, however, differs from series to series.

Contemporary Series, Eighth Edition

The Contemporary Series is the most traditional in approach, yet modern in its treatment of precalculus mathematics. Graphing utility coverage is optional and can be included or excluded at the discretion of the instructor: *College Algebra, College Algebra Essentials, Algebra & Trigonometry, Trigonometry, Precalculus.*

Enhanced with Graphing Utilities Series, Fifth Edition

This series provides a more thorough integration of graphing utilities into topics, allowing students to explore mathematical concepts and foreshadow ideas usually studied in later courses. Using technology, the approach to solving certain problems differs from the Contemporary Series, while the emphasis on understanding concepts and building strong skills does not: *College Algebra, Algebra & Trigonometry, Trigonometry, A Right Triangle Approach, Precalculus.*

Concepts through Functions Series, First Edition

This series differs from the others, utilizing a functions approach that serves as the organizing principle tying concepts together. Functions are introduced early in various formats. This approach supports the Rule of Four, which states that functions are represented symbolically, numerically, graphically, and verbally. Each chapter introduces a new type of function and then develops all concepts pertaining to that particular function. The solutions of equations and inequalities, instead of being developed as stand-alone topics, are developed in the context of the underlying functions. Graphing utility coverage is optional and can be included or excluded at the discretion of the instructor: *College Algebra; Precalculus, with a Unit Circle Approach to Trigonometry; Precalculus, with a Right Triangle Approach to Trigonometry.*

To the Student

As you begin, you may feel anxious about the number of theorems, definitions, procedures, and equations. You may wonder if you can learn it all in time. Don't worry, your concerns are normal. This textbook was written with you in mind. If you attend class, work hard, and read and study this book, you will build the knowledge and skills you need to be successful. Here's how you can use the book to your benefit.

Read Carefully

When you get busy, it's easy to skip reading and go right to the problems. Don't... the book has a large number of examples and clear explanations to help you break down the mathematics into easy-to-understand steps. Reading will provide you with a clearer understanding, beyond simple memorization. Read before class (not after) so you can ask questions about anything you didn't understand. You'll be amazed at how much more you'll get out of class if you do this.

Use the Features

We use many different methods in the classroom to communicate. Those methods, when incorporated into the book, are called "features." The features serve many purposes, from providing timely review of material you learned before (just when you need it), to providing organized review sessions to help you prepare for quizzes and tests. Take advantage of the features and you will master the material.

To make this easier, we've provided a brief guide to getting the most from this book. Refer to the 'Prepare for Class,' 'Practice,' and 'Review' pages on the inside front cover of this book. Spend fifteen minutes reviewing the guide and familiarizing yourself with the features by flipping to the page numbers provided. Then, as you read, use them. This is the best way to make the most of your textbook.

Please do not hesitate to contact us, through Pearson Education, with any questions, suggestions, or comments that would improve this text. We look forward to hearing from you, and good luck with all of your studies.

Best Wishes!

Michael Sullivan

Michael Sullivan, III

Preface to the Instructor

As professors at both an urban university and a community college, Michael Sullivan and Michael Sullivan, III are aware of the varied needs of Precalculus students, ranging from those who have little mathematical background and a fear of mathematics courses, to those having a strong mathematical education and a high level of motivation. For some of your students, this will be their last course in mathematics, whereas others will further their mathematical education. This text is written for both groups.

As a teacher, and as an author of precalculus, engineering calculus, finite mathematics, and business calculus texts, Michael Sullivan understands what students must know if they are to be focused and successful in upper-level math courses. However, as a father of four, he also understands the realities of college life. As an author of a developmental mathematics series, Michael's co-author and son, Michael Sullivan, III, understands the trepidations and skills students bring to the Precalculus course. Michael, III also believes in the value of technology as a tool for learning that enhances understanding without sacrificing math skills. Together, both authors have taken great pains to ensure that the text contains solid, student-friendly examples and problems, as well as a clear and seamless writing style.

A tremendous benefit of authoring a successful series is the broad-based feedback we receive from teachers and students. We are sincerely grateful for their support. Virtually every change in this edition is the result of their thoughtful comments and suggestions. We are sincerely grateful for this support and hope that we have been able to take these ideas and, building upon a successful fourth edition, make this series an even better tool for learning and teaching. We continue to encourage you to share with us your experiences teaching from this text.

Features in the Fifth Edition

Rather than provide a list of new features here, that information can be found on the endpapers in the front of this book. This places the new features in their proper context, as building blocks of an overall learning system that has been carefully crafted over the years to help students get the most out of the time they put into studying. Please take the time to review the features listed in the front of this book and to discuss them with your students at the beginning of your course. Our experience has been that when students utilize these features, they are more successful in the course.

New to the Fifth Edition

- **Showcase Examples** are used to present examples in a guided, step-by-step format. Students can immediately see how each of the steps in a problem are employed. The "How To" examples have a two-column format in which the left column describes the step in solving the problem and the right column displays the algebra complete with annotations.

- **Model It** examples and exercises are clearly marked with a ⬤ icon. These examples and exercises are meant to develop the student's ability to build models from both verbal descriptions and data. Many of the problems involving data require the students to first determine the appropriate model (linear, quadratic, and so on) to fit to the data and justify their choice.

- **Exercise Sets** at the end of each section have been classified according to purpose. Where appropriate, more problems to challenge the better student have been added. In addition, **Mixed Practice** exercises have been added where appropriate so that students may synthesize skills from a variety of sections.

- **Applied Problems** have been updated and many new problems involving sourced information as well as data sets have been added to bring relevance and timeliness to these exercises.

- **Chapter 3 Linear and Quadratic Functions** New to this edition, this chapter gives more emphasis to linear and quadratic functions. The discussions allow for a fuller discussion of linear and quadratic functions, their properties, models involving the functions, and building models from verbal descriptions and data. A full section on quadratic inequalities is also provided with both graphical and algebraic analysis of the inequality.

- **New Content**
  - Section A.2, Geometry Essentials, now contains a discussion of congruent and similar triangles.
  - Examples and exercises that involve a more in-depth analysis of graphing and exponential and logarithmic functions are provided.
  - Examples and exercises that involve graphing a wider variety of inverse trigonometric functions are provided.

Organizational Changes in the Fifth Edition

- **Chapter 3** consolidates the discussion on linear and quadratic functions.

- **Appendix B** represents a more thorough treatment of sequences and series. This includes a presentation on the limit of a sequence and a discussion of convergent and divergent series.

Using the Fifth Edition Effectively with Your Syllabus

To meet the varied needs of diverse syllabi, this book contains more content than is likely to be covered in an Precalculus course. As the chart illustrates, this book has been organized with flexibility of use in mind. Within a given chapter, certain sections are optional (see the detail following the flowchart) and can be omitted without loss of continuity.

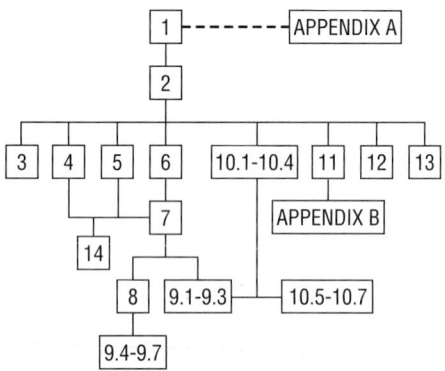

Chapter 1 Graphs
A quick coverage of this chapter, which is mainly review material, will enable you to get to Chapter 2, "Functions and Their Graphs", earlier.

Chapter 2 Functions and Their Graphs
Perhaps the most important chapter. Section 2.6 is optional.

Chapter 3 Linear and Quadratic Functions
Topic selection depends on your syllabus. Sections 3.2 and 3.4 may be omitted without a loss of continuity.

Chapter 4 Polynomial and Rational Functions
Topic selection depends on your syllabus.

Chapter 5 Exponential and Logarithmic Functions
Sections 5.1–5.6 follow in sequence. Sections 5.7, 5.8, and 5.9 are optional.

Chapter 6 Trigonometric Functions
Section 6.6 may be omitted in a brief course.

Chapter 7 Analytic Trigonometry
Sections 7.2, 7.6, and 7.8 may be omitted in a brief course.

Chapter 8 Applications of Trigonometric Functions
Sections 8.4 and 8.5 may be omitted in a brief course.

Chapter 9 Polar Coordinates; Vectors
Sections 9.1–9.3 and Sections 9.4–9.7 are independent and may be covered separately.

Chapter 10 Analytic Geometry
Sections 10.1–10.4 follow in sequence. Sections 10.5, 10.6, and 10.7 are independent of each other, but each requires Sections 10.1–10.4.

Chapter 11 Systems of Equations and Inequalities
Sections 11.2–11.7 may be covered in any order, but each requires Section 11.1. Section 11.8 requires Section 11.7.

Chapter 12 Sequences; Induction; The Binomial Theorem
There are three independent parts: Sections 12.1–12.3; Section 12.4; and Section 12.5.

Chapter 13 Counting and Probability
The sections follow in sequence.

Chapter 14 A Preview of Calculus: the Limit, Derivative, and Integral of a Function
If time permits, coverage of this chapter will provide your student with a beneficial head-start in calculus. The sections follow in sequence.

Appendix A Review
This chapter consists of review material. It may be used as the first part of the course or later as a just-in-time review when the content is required. Specific references to this chapter occur throughout the book to assist in the review process.

Appendix B The Limit of a Sequence; Infinite Series
This section represents a more thorough treatment of sequences and series.

Acknowledgments

Textbooks are written by authors but evolve from an idea to final form through the efforts of many people. It was Don Dellen who first suggested this book and series. Don is remembered for his extensive contributions to publishing and mathematics.

 Thanks are due the following people for their assistance and encouragement in the preparation of this edition:

- From Pearson Education: Adam Jaworski for his substantial contributions, ideas, and enthusiasm; Becky Anderson for her creativity and energy. Kate Valentine, who remains a huge fan and supporter; Dawn Murrin, for her unmatched talent at getting the details right; Bob Walters for his superb organizational skills in directing production; Chris Hoag for her continued support and genuine interest; Greg Tobin for his leadership and commitment to excellence; and the Pearson Math and Science Sales team, for their continued confidence and personal support of our books.

- Accuracy checkers: Kevin Bodden and Randy Gallaher, for creating the Solutions Manuals and accuracy checking answers; LaurelTech's editors, Teri Lovelace, Harold Whipple, Jill McClain-Wardynski and Peggy Irish who read the entire manuscript and checked all the answers.

- Reviewers: Debra Kopcso, *Louisiana State University;* Lynn Marecek, *Santa Ana College;* Kathleen Miranda, *SUNY at Old Westbury;* Karla Neal, *Louisiana State*

University; Leticia Oropesa, *University of Miami;* Laura Pyzdrowski, *West Virginia University;* Mike Rosenthal, *Florida International University;* Phoebe Rouse, *Louisiana State University;* Brenda Santistevan, *Salt Lake Community College;* Larissa Williamson, *University of Florida.*

Finally, we offer our grateful thanks to the dedicated users and reviewers of our books, whose collective insights form the backbone of each textbook revision.

Our list of indebtedness just grows and grows. And, if we've forgotten anyone, please accept our apology. Thank you all.

James Africh, College of DuPage
Steve Agronsky, Cal Poly State University
Grant Alexander, Joliet Junior College
Dave Anderson, South Suburban College
Joby Milo Anthony, University of Central Florida
James E. Arnold, University of Wisconsin-Milwaukee
Adel Arshaghi, Center for Educational Merit
Carolyn Autray, University of West Georgia
Agnes Azzolino, Middlesex County College
Wilson P Banks, Illinois State University
Sudeshna Basu, Howard University
Dale R. Bedgood, East Texas State University
Beth Beno, South Suburban College
Carolyn Bernath, Tallahassee Community College
William H. Beyer, University of Akron
Annette Blackwelder, Florida State University
Richelle Blair, Lakeland Community College
Kevin Bodden, Lewis and Clark College
Larry Bouldin, Roane State Community College
Bob Bradshaw, Ohlone College
Trudy Bratten, Grossmont College
Tim Bremer, Broome Community College
Tim Britt, Jackson State Community College
Joanne Brunner, Joliet Junior College
Warren Burch, Brevard Community College
Mary Butler, Lincoln Public Schools
Melanie Butler, West Virginia University
Jim Butterbach, Joliet Junior College
William J. Cable, University of Wisconsin-Stevens Point
Lois Calamia, Brookdale Community College
Jim Campbell, Lincoln Public Schools
Roger Carlsen, Moraine Valley Community College
Elena Catoiu, Joliet Junior College
Mathews Chakkanakuzhi, Palomar College
John Collado, South Suburban College
Nelson Collins, Joliet Junior College
Jim Cooper, Joliet Junior College
Denise Corbett, East Carolina University
Carlos C. Corona, San Antonio College
Theodore C. Coskey, South Seattle Community College
Donna Costello, Plano Senior High School
Paul Crittenden, University of Nebraska at Lincoln
John Davenport, East Texas State University
Faye Dang, Joliet Junior College
Antonio David, Del Mar College
Duane E. Deal, Ball State University
Timothy Deis, University of Wisconsin-Platteville
Vivian Dennis, Eastfield College
Deborah Dillon, R. L. Turner High School
Guesna Dohrman, Tallahassee Community College
Cheryl Doolittle, Iowa State University
Karen R. Dougan, University of Florida
Louise Dyson, Clark College
Paul D. East, Lexington Community College
Don Edmondson, University of Texas-Austin
Erica Egizio, Joliet Junior College
Laura Egner, Joliet Junior College
Jason Eltrevoog, Joliet Junior College

Christopher Ennis, University of Minnesota
Kathy Eppler, Salt Lake Community College
Ralph Esparza, Jr., Richland College
Garret J. Etgen, University of Houston
Scott Fallstrom, Shoreline Community College
Pete Falzone, Pensacola Junior College
W.A. Ferguson, University of Illinois-Urbana/Champaign
Iris B. Fetta, Clemson University
Mason Flake, student at Edison Community College
Timothy W. Flood, Pittsburg State University
Merle Friel, Humboldt State University
Richard A. Fritz, Moraine Valley Community College
Dewey Furness, Ricke College
Randy Gallaher, Lewis and Clark College
Tina Garn, University of Arizona
Dawit Getachew, Chicago State University
Wayne Gibson, Rancho Santiago College
Robert Gill, University of Minnesota Duluth
Sudhir Kumar Goel, Valdosta State University
Joan Goliday, Sante Fe Community College
Frederic Gooding, Goucher College
Donald Goral, Northern Virginia Community College
Sue Graupner, Lincoln Public Schools
Jennifer L. Grimsley, University of Charleston
Ken Gurganus, University of North Carolina
James E. Hall, University of Wisconsin-Madison
Judy Hall, West Virginia University
Edward R. Hancock, DeVry Institute of Technology
Julia Hassett, DeVry Institute-Dupage
Christopher Hay-Jahans, University of South Dakota
Michah Heibel, Lincoln Public Schools
LaRae Helliwell, San Jose City College
Celeste Hernandez, Richland College
Brother Herron, Brother Rice High School
Robert Hoburg, Western Connecticut State University
Lynda Hollingsworth, Northwest Missouri State University
Charla Holzbog, Denison High School
Lee Hruby, Naperville North High School
Miles Hubbard, St. Cloud State University
Kim Hughes, California State College-San Bernardino
Ron Jamison, Brigham Young University
Richard A. Jensen, Manatee Community College
Sandra G. Johnson, St. Cloud State University
Tuesday Johnson, New Mexico State University
Moana H. Karsteter, Tallahassee Community College
Donna Katula, Joliet Junior College
Arthur Kaufman, College of Staten Island
Thomas Kearns, North Kentucky University
Jack Keating, Massasoit Community College
Shelia Kellenbarger, Lincoln Public Schools
Rachael Kenney, North Carolina State University
Debra Kopcso, Louisiana State University
Lynne Kowski, Raritan Valley Community College
Keith Kuchar, Manatee Community College
Tor Kwembe, Chicago State University

Linda J. Kyle, Tarrant Country Jr. College
H.E. Lacey, Texas A & M University
Harriet Lamm, Coastal Bend College
James Lapp, Fort Lewis College
Matt Larson, Lincoln Public Schools
Christopher Lattin, Oakton Community College
Julia Ledet, Lousiana State University
Adele LeGere, Oakton Community College
Kevin Leith, University of Houston
JoAnn Lewin, Edison College
Jeff Lewis, Johnson County Community College
Janice C. Lyon, Tallahassee Community College
Jean McArthur, Joliet Junior College
Virginia McCarthy, Iowa State University
Karla McCavit, Albion College
Michael McClendon, University of Central Oklahoma
Tom McCollow, DeVry Institute of Technology
Marilyn McCollum, North Carolina State University
Jill McGowan, Howard University
Dave McGuire, Joliet Junior College
Angela McNulty, Joliet Junior College
Laurence Maher, North Texas State University
Jay A. Malmstrom, Oklahoma City Community College
Rebecca Mann, Apollo High School
Lynn Marecek, Santa Ana College
Sherry Martina, Naperville North High School
Alec Matheson, Lamar University
Nancy Matthews, University of Oklahoma
James Maxwell, Oklahoma State University-Stillwater
Marsha May, Midwestern State University
Judy Meckley, Joliet Junior College
David Meel, Bowling Green State University
Carolyn Meitler, Concordia University
Samia Metwali, Erie Community College
Rich Meyers, Joliet Junior College
Eldon Miller, University of Mississippi
James Miller, West Virginia University
Michael Miller, Iowa State University
Kathleen Miranda, SUNY at Old Westbury
Thomas Monaghan, Naperville North High School
Maria Montoya, Our Lady of the Lake University
Craig Morse, Naperville North High School
Samad Mortabit, Metropolitan State University
Pat Mower, Washburn University
A. Muhundan, Manatee Community College
Jane Murphy, Middlesex Community College
Richard Nadel, Florida International University
Gabriel Nagy, Kansas State University
Bill Naegele, South Suburban College
Karla Neal, Lousiana State University
Lawrence E. Newman, Holyoke Community College
Dwight Newsome, Pasco-Hernando Community College
James Nymann, University of Texas-El Paso

Mark Omodt, Anoka-Ramsey Community College
Seth F. Oppenheimer, Mississippi State University
Leticia Oropesa, University of Miami
Linda Padilla, Joliet Junior College
E. James Peake, Iowa State University
Kelly Pearson, Murray State University
Philip Pina, Florida Atlantic University
Michael Prophet, University of Northern Iowa
Laura Pyzdrowski, West Virginia University
Neal C. Raber, University of Akron
Thomas Radin, San Joaquin Delta College
Ken A. Rager, Metropolitan State College
Kenneth D. Reeves, San Antonio College
Elsi Reinhardt, Truckee Meadows Community College
Jane Ringwald, Iowa State University
Stephen Rodi, Austin Community College
William Rogge, Lincoln Northeast High School
Howard L. Rolf, Baylor University
Mike Rosenthal, Florida International University
Phoebe Rouse, Lousiana State University
Edward Rozema, University of Tennessee at Chattanooga
Dennis C. Runde, Manatee Community College

Alan Saleski, Loyola University of Chicago
Susan Sandmeyer, Jamestown Community College
Brenda Santistevan, Salt Lake Community College
Linda Schmidt, Greenville Technical College
A.K. Shamma, University of West Florida
Martin Sherry, Lower Columbia College
Tatrana Shubin, San Jose State University
Anita Sikes, Delgado Community College
Timothy Sipka, Alma College
Lori Smellegar, Manatee Community College
Gayle Smith, Loyola Blakefield
Vicki Smith, Nicholls State University
John Spellman, Southwest Texas State University
Karen Spike, University of North Carolina, Wilmington
Rajalakshmi Sriram, Okaloosa-Walton Community College
Becky Stamper, Western Kentucky University
Judy Staver, Florida Community College-South
Neil Stephens, Hinsdale South High School
Sonya Stephens, Florida A&M Univeristy
Patrick Stevens, Joliet Junior College
Matthew TenHuisen, University of North Carolina, Wilmington
Christopher Terry, Augusta State University

Tommy Thompson, Brookhaven College
Martha K. Tietze, Shawnee Mission Northwest High School
Richard J. Tondra, Iowa State University
Suzanne Topp, Salt Lake Community College
Marvel Townsend, University of Florida
Jim Trudnowski, Carroll College
Robert Tuskey, Joliet Junior College
Richard G. Vinson, University of South Alabama
Mary Voxman, University of Idaho
Jennifer Walsh, Daytona Beach Community College
Donna Wandke, Naperville North High School
Kathryn Wetzel, Amarillo College
Darlene Whitkenack, Northern Illinois University
Suzanne Williams, Central Piedmont Community College
Larissa Williamson, University of Florida
Christine Wilson, West Virginia University
Brad Wind, Florida International University
Mary Wolyniak, Broome Community College
Canton Woods, Auburn University
Tamara S. Worner, Wayne State College
Terri Wright, New Hampshire Community Technical College, Manchester
George Zazi, Chicago State University
Steve Zuro, Joliet Junior College

Michael Sullivan
Chicago State University

Michael Sullivan, III
Joliet Junior College

STUDENT RESOURCES

Available to students are the following supplements:

- **Student Solutions Manual (ISBN 10: 0132356228; ISBN 13: 9780132356220)**

  Fully worked solutions to odd-numbered exercises.

- **Algebra Review (ISBN 10: 0131480065; ISBN 13: 9780131480063)**

  Four chapters of Intermediate Algebra review. Perfect for a slower-paced course or for individual review.

- **CD Lecture Series (ISBN 10: 0132356252; ISBN 13: 9780132356251)**

  A comprehensive set of CD-ROMs, tied to the textbook, containing short video clips of an instructor working key book examples. The CD Lecture Series can be packaged with the book, or is available for purchase standalone.

- **Chapter Test Prep Video CDs**

  Packaged at the back of the text, these video CDs provide students with step-by-step solutions for each of the exercises in the book's chapter tests.

INSTRUCTOR RESOURCES

Instructor Resource Distribution

All instructor resources can be downloaded from the web site, **www.prenhall.com.** Select "Browse our catalog," then, click on "Mathematics;" select your course and choose your text. Under "Resources," on the left side, select "instructor" and choose the supplement you need to download. You will be required to run through a one time registration before you can complete this process.

- **TestGen®**

  TestGen enables instructors to build, edit, print, and administer tests using a computerized bank of questions developed to cover all the objectives of the text. TestGen is algorithmically based, allowing instructors to create multiple but equivalent versions of the same question or test with the click of a button. Instructors can also modify test bank questions or add new questions. Tests can be printed or administered online. The software and testbank are available for download from Pearson Education's online catalog.

- **Test Item File**

  A printed test bank derived from TestGen.

- **PowerPoint Lecture Slides**

  Fully editable slides that follow the textbook. Project in class or post to a website in an online course.

- **Instructor Solutions Manual (ISBN 10: 0132356120; ISBN 13: 9780132356121**

  Fully worked solutions to all textbook exercises and chapter projects.

- **Mini Lecture Notes**

  These include additional examples and helpful teaching tips, by section.

Instructor's Edition

Provides answers to *all* exercises in the back of the text.

MyMathLab®

MyMathLab® is a series of text-specific, easily customizable online courses for Pearson Education's textbooks in mathematics and statistics. Powered by CourseCompass™ (our online teaching and learning environment) and MathXL® (our online homework, tutorial, and assessment system), MyMathLab gives you the tools you need to deliver all or a portion of your course online, whether your students are in a lab setting or working from home. MyMathLab provides a rich and flexible set of course materials, featuring free-response exercises that are algorithmically generated for unlimited practice and mastery. Students can also use online tools, such as video lectures, animations, and a multimedia textbook, to independently improve their understanding and performance. Instructors can use MyMathLab's homework and test managers to select and assign online exercises correlated directly to the textbook, and they can also create and assign their own online exercises and import TestGen tests for added flexibility. MyMathLab's online gradebook—designed specifically for mathematics and statistics—automatically tracks students' homework and test results and gives the instructor control over how to calculate final grades. Instructors can also add offline (paper-and-pencil) grades to the gradebook. MyMathLab is available to qualified adopters. For more information, visit our website at **www.mymathlab.com** or contact your sales representative.

| STUDENT RESOURCES | INSTRUCTOR RESOURCES |

MathXL®

MathXL® is a powerful online homework, tutorial, and assessment system that accompanies Pearson Education's textbooks in mathematics or statistics. With MathXL, instructors can create, edit, and assign online homework and tests using algorithmically generated exercises correlated at the objective level to the textbook. They can also create and assign their own online exercises and import TestGen tests for added flexibility. All student work is tracked in MathXL's online gradebook. Students can take chapter tests in MathXL and receive personalized study plans based on their test results. The study plan diagnoses weaknesses and links students directly to tutorial exercises for the objectives they need to study and retest. Students can also access supplemental animations and video clips directly from selected exercises. MathXL is available to qualified adopters. For more information, visit our website at **www.mathxl.com**, or contact your sales representative.

MathXL® Tutorials on CD

This interactive tutorial CD-ROM provides algorithmically generated practice exercises that are correlated at the objective level to the exercises in the textbook. Every practice exercise is accompanied by an example and a guided solution designed to involve students in the solution process. Selected exercises may also include a video clip to help students visualize concepts. The software provides helpful feedback for incorrect answers and can generate printed summaries of students' progress.

InterAct Math Tutorial Website: www.interactmath.com

Get practice and tutorial help online! This interactive tutorial website provides algorithmically generated practice exercises that correlate directly to the exercises in the textbook. Students can retry an exercise as many times as they like with new values each time for unlimited practice and mastery. Every exercise is accompanied by an interactive guided solution that provides helpful feedback for incorrect answers, and students can also view a worked-out sample problem that steps them through an exercise similar to the one they're working on.

List of Applications

Acoustics

amplifying sound, 346
loudness of sound, 296
loudspeaker, 553
tuning fork, 553
whispering galleries, 656, 702–3

Aerodynamics

modeling aircraft motion, 636

Aeronautics

Challenger disaster, 333

Agriculture

crop allocation, 799
crop yields and fertilizer, 159
farm management, 794
field enclosure, 779
grazing area for cow, 544–45
minimizing cost, 794
removing stump, 624

Air travel

bearing of aircraft, 520
frequent flyer miles, 531
holding pattern, 494
parking at O'Hare International
   Airport, 98
revising a flight plan, 538
speed and direction of aircraft,
   626–27, 631, 635

Archaeology

age of ancient tools, 326–27
age of fossil, 332
age of tree, 332
date of prehistoric man's death, 346–47

Architecture

brick staircase, 822, 845
floor design, 821, 845
football stadium seating, 822
mosaic design, 822
Norman window, 161, A21
parabolic arch, 161
racetrack design, 658
special window, 161, 170
stadium construction, 822, 823
Taipei 101, A15
window design, 161

Area. *See also* Geometry

of Bermuda Triangle, 544
under a curve, 452–53
of isosceles triangle, 484
of sector of circle, 362
of segment of circle, 555

Astronomy

angle of elevation of Sun, 519
distances of planets from Sun, 816
planetary orbits, 656
   Earth, 659
   Jupiter, 659
   Mars, 659
   Mercury, 686
   Neptune, 704
   Pluto, 659, 704

Aviation

modeling aircraft motion, 636
orbital launches, 718

Biology

age versus total cholesterol, 341
alcohol and driving, 292, 297
bacterial growth, 324–25, 339
   E-coli, 89, 127–29
blood pressure, 493–94
blood types, 855
bone length, 170
gestation period, life expectancy vs., 141
healing of wounds, 282, 296
maternal age versus Down
   syndrome, 142
yeast biomass as function of time, 338

Business

advertising, 141, 170
automobile production, 255, 734
car rentals, 134
checkout lines, 873
cigarette exports, 339–40
cigarette production, 339–40
clothing store, 875
commissions, 169
cookie orders, 799
cost
   of can, 209–10, 212
   of commodity, 255
   of manufacturing, 219, 788, A13, A75
   marginal, 153, 170
   minimizing, 170, 794
   of production, 88, 255, 761, 799
   of theater ticket per student, 219
   of transporting goods, 98
   weekly, 187
cost equation, 42
cost function, 135
   average, 74
demand
   for jeans, 141
   for PCs, 340
demand equation, 160, 169, 244
discounts, 255

drive-thru rate
    at Burger King, 279
    at Citibank, 282, 296
    at McDonald's, 283
equipment depreciation, 831
expenses, A76
IBM personal computer price and
    demand, 340
Jiffy Lube's car arrival rate, 282–83, 296
managing a meat market, 794
McDonald's scalding coffee case, 247
new-car markup, A87
orange juice production, 734
precision ball bearings, A13
product design, 795
production scheduling, 794
product promotion, 43
profit, 761–62
    cigar company, 111
    on figurines, 799
    maximizing, 792, 794–95
    reduced, A77
profit function, 70
rate of return on, 321
restaurant management, 718
revenue, 153, 167
    advertising and, 141
    airline, 795
    of clothing store, 750
    daily, 154
    from digital music, 111
    maximizing, 153, 160
    monthly, 154
    theater, 719
salary, 823
    gross, 69
    increases in, 831, 846
sales
    commission on, A86–A87
    of movie theater ticket, 706, 711, 718
    net, 17
    per unit, A75
salvage value, 346
straight-line depreciation, 130–31, 134–35
supply and demand, 131–32, 134
tax, 219
toy truck manufacturing, 788
transporting goods, 788
truck rentals, 42, 135
unemployment, 876
wages
    of car salesperson, 42

Calculus

area under a curve, 452–53
carrying a ladder around a corner, 502
maximizing rain gutter
    construction, 501
projectile motion, 501
Simpson's rule, 162

Carpentry. *See also* Construction

pitch, 44

Chemistry

alpha particles, 672
decomposition reactions, 332, 333
drug concentration, 211
gold purity, A77
pH, 295
radioactive decay, 331–32, 339, 347
radioactivity from Chernobyl, 333
reactions, 162
salt solutions, A76, A77
sugar molecules, A77
volume of gas, A86

Combinatorics

airport codes, 856
binary codes, 876
birthday permutations, 858, 862, 863,
    869–70, 874, 876
blouses and skirts combinations, 854
book arrangements, 862, 875
box stacking, 862
code formation, 862
combination locks, 863
committee formation, 860, 862, 863, 876
    Senate committees, 863
flag arrangement, 861, 876
letter codes, 856, 876
letter combinations, 875
license plate possibilities, 862, 875, 877
light bulb wattage, 876
lining up people, 857, 862
number formation, 854, 862, 863, 876
objects selection, 863
seating arrangements, 875
shirts and ties combinations, 854
telephone numbers, 875
two-symbol codewords, 854
word formation, 860–61, 863, 876

Communications

cell phone service, 98, 124
cell phone usage, 335–36, 341
installing cable TV, 117
long distance, 135
    comparing phone companies, 169
phone charges, 134
portable phones, 55
satellite dish, 645, 647
spreading of rumors, 282, 296
Touch-Tone phones, 488, 553

Computers and computing

graphics, 623
home computers, 334
IBM PCs, 340

Construction

of box, 778
    closed, 122
    open, 117
of brick staircase, 845
of can, 242, A77
of cylindrical tube, 778

of enclosures
 maximizing area of, 156, 160, 169
of fencing, 156, 160–61, 169, 779
 minimum cost for, 211
of flashlight, 647
of headlight, 647
of highway, 520, 531–32, 556
home choices, 875
installing cable TV, 117
pitch of roof, 521
of playpen, 114–15
of rain gutter, 161, 501
of ramp, 531
 access ramp, 43
of rectangular field enclosure, 160
of stadium, 161, 822
of steel drum, 212
of swimming pool, A21, A22
of swing set, 539
of tent, 543
TV dish, 647
vent pipe installation, 658

Crime

income and, 341
male murder victims, 154
violent, 170

Cryptography

matrices in, 762

Decorating

Christmas tree, A16

Demographics

death rates, 876
diversity index, 295–96
life expectancy, A86
marital status, 855
mosquito colony growth, 332
population. *See* Population
rabbit colony growth, 815

Design

of awning, 532
of box with minimum surface area, 212
of Little League Field, 364
of water sprinkler, 363

Direction

of aircraft, 626–27, 631, 635
compass heading, 631
for crossing a river, 631
of fireworks display, 671
of lightning strikes, 672
of motorboat, 631
of swimmer, 635

Distance

Bermuda Triangle, A22
bicycle riding, 78
from Chicago to Honolulu, 453
circumference of Earth, 364

between cities, 358–59, 363
between Earth and Mercury, 532
between Earth and Venus, 533
from Earth to a star, 519
of explosion, 672
height
 of aircraft, 346, 530, 532
 of bouncing ball, 831, 845–46
 of bridge, 531
 of building, 520, 521
 of embankment, 520
 of Ferris Wheel rider, 494
 of Great Pyramid of Cheops, 532, A22
 of helicopter, 528, 556
 of hot-air balloon, 520
 of Lincoln's caricature on Mt.
  Rushmore, 520
 of mountain, 346, 527, 530
 of Sears Tower, 520
from home, 78
from Honolulu to Melbourne, Australia, 453
of hot-air balloon
 to airport, 556, 558
 from intersection, 17
from intersection, 116
length
 of guy wire, 538–39
 of ski lift, 530
limiting magnitude of telescope, 346
to the Moon, 530
pendulum swings, 828–29, 831
range of airplane, A77
of rotating beacon, 418
at sea, 528, 532, 556
to shore, 532
between skyscrapers, 521
surveying, 557
to tower, 532
traveled by wheel, A21
between two moving vehicles, 16–17
 toward intersection, 116
between two objects, 520
visibility of Gibb's Hill Lighthouse beam,
 516, 522, A22
visual, A22
walking, 78
width
 of Mississippi River, 521

Economics

Consumer Price Index (CPI), 322
demand equations, 244
federal deficit, 321
IBM personal computer price and
 demand, 340
income versus crime rate, 341
inflation, 321–22
IS-LM model in, 719
marginal propensity to consume, 832
multiplier, 832
participation rate, 70
poverty rates, 242
poverty threshold, 17

relative income of child, 762
unemployment, 876

Education

age distribution of community college, 877
college costs, 321, 815
college tuition and fees, 761
doctoral degrees awarded, 852, 873
faculty composition, 874
funding a college education, 346
grade computation, A87
IQ tests, A87
learning curve, 283, 296
maximum level achieved, 801
multiple-choice test, 862
Spring break, 794, 812
student loan, 123
  interest on, 761
test design, 875
true/false test, 862

Electricity

alternating current (ac), 435, 475
alternating current (ac) circuits, 409, 428
alternating current (ac) generators, 409–10
charging a capacitor, 553
cost of, 96
current in *RC* circuit, 283
current in *RL* circuit, 283, 296
impedance, A68
Kirchhoff's Rules, 719, 734–35
light bulbs, 877
parallel circuits
  resistance in, 201–2
rates for, 42–43, A87
resistance, 201–2, A43, A45
voltage
  alternating, 435, 475
  foreign, A13
  U.S., A13
wiring, 875

Electronics

loudspeakers, 553
microphones, 25
sawtooth curve, 484, 553
speed of laser printers, A76

Energy

nuclear power plant, 672
solar, 25, 630–31
solar heat, 647
thermostat control, 111

Engineering

bridges
  clearance, 410
  Golden Gate, 158
  parabolic arch, 170, 648, 702
  semielliptical arch, 658, 702
  suspension, 161, 647
drive wheel, 557
Gateway Arch (St. Louis), 648
grade of road, 44

lean of Leaning Tower of Pisa, 531
moment of inertia, 488
product of inertia, 484
road system, 586–87
rods and pistons, 539
searchlight, 466, 647, 702
whispering galleries, 658, 702–3

Entertainment

cable subscribers, 341
Demon Roller Coaster customer rate, 283
movie theater, 452
theater revenues, 719

Environment

lake pollution control laws, 815
oil leakage, 255

Exercise and fitness

for weight loss, A87

Finance. *See also* **Investment(s)**

balancing a checkbook, A13
bills in wallet, 876
clothes shopping, 800
college costs, 321, 815
computer system purchase, 321
cost
  of car rental, 99
  of electricity, 96
  of fast food, 718
  of land, 557
  minimizing, 170, 211
  of natural gas, 98
  of Sunday newspaper home delivery, 42
  of trans-Atlantic travel, 69, 77
  of triangular lot, 543
cost function, 135
cost minimization, 153
credit cards
  debt, 814, 846
  interest on, 321
  payment, 99, 814
demand equation, 160
depreciation, 282, 342
  of car, 312–13, 349
electricity rates, 42–43
financial planning, 718
foreign exchange, 255
future value of money, 189
gross salary, 69
life cycle hypothesis, 162
loans
  car, 814–15
  home, 815, 846
  interest on, 123, 761, A70, A75
  repayment of, 321
  student, 761
mortgages
  interest rates on, 321
  payments, 813
  second, 321
phone charges, long distance, 135
price appreciation of homes, 321

prices of fast food, 719
refunds, 718
revenue maximization, 153, 155–56
rich man's promise, 832
salary options, 832
saving
  for a car, 321
  for spring break, 812
savings accounts interest, 321
taxes, 134
  e-filing returns, 89
  federal income, 98, 268, A87
  luxury, 134
used-car purchase, 321
water bills, A87

Food and nutrition
animal, 795
candy, 140
color mix of candy, 876
cooler contents, 877
cooling time of Beer stein, 332
cooling time of pizza, 332
fast food, 718, 719
Girl Scout cookies, 873
hospital diet, 719, 734
"light" foods, A87
number of possible meals, 853
pig roasts, 333
raisins, 140

Forestry
wood product classification, 331

Games
die rolling, 877
grains of wheat on a chess board, 831–32
Powerball, 877

Gardens and gardening. *See also*
Landscaping
enclosing a garden, A76

Geography
area of Bermuda Triangle, 544
area of lake, 544, 557
inclination of hill, 632
inclination of mountain trail, 514,
  527, 556

Geology
earthquakes, 297

Geometry
angle between two lines, 475
balloon volume, 254–55
circle
  area of, 543
  circumference of, A12
  inscribed, 116, 545
  length of chord of, 539
  radius of, 778
collinear points, 745
cone volume, 255

cube
  length of edge of, 233
  surface area of, A13
  volume of, A13
cylinder
  inscribing in cone, 116–17
  inscribing in sphere, 116
  volume of, 255
Descartes's method of equal roots, 779
equation of line, 745
ladder angle, 558
quadrilateral area, 558
rectangle
  area of, 69, 113, A12
  dimensions of, 778, 779
  inscribed in semicircle, 116, 484
  perimeter of, A12
  semicircle inscribed in, 116
semicircle area, 543, 558
sphere
  surface area of, A13
  volume of, A13
square
  area of, A21
surface area
  of balloon, 254
  of cube, A13
  of sphere, A13
triangle
  area of, 543, 558, 745, A13
  circumscribing, 533
  equilateral, A13
  inscribed in circle, 116
  isosceles, 69, 559, 778, 779
  Pascal's, 816
  perimeter of, A13
  right, 518
  sides of, 559

Government
federal deficit, 347
federal income tax, 70, 98, 268, A87
  e-filing returns, 89

Health. *See also* **Medicine**
allergies, 244–45
cigarette use among teens, 43
expenditures on, 70
ideal body weight, 268
life cycle hypothesis, 162

Home improvement. *See also*
Construction
painting a house, 720

Insurance
claims for catastrophic losses, 162

Investment(s)
asset allocation, A70–A71, A75
in bonds, 795
  Treasuries, 734, 735, 786, 788, 789
  zero-coupon, 318, 322
in CDs, 795

compound interest on, 314–17, 321
diversified, 719
doubling of, 319, 322
in fixed-income securities, 322, 795
growth rate for, 321
IRA, 321, 346
    Education, 815
    Roth, 815
money market account, 317–18
return on, 321, 794, 795
in stock
    analyzing, 172
    appreciation, 321
    NASDAQ stocks, 862
    NYSE stocks, 862
    portfolios of, 855
    price of, 832
time to reach goal, 320–21, 322
tripling of, 319, 322

Landscaping. *See also* **Gardens and gardening**

pond dimensions, A76
pond enclosure, 169
rectangular pond border, 169
removing stump, 624
tree cutting, 531
tree planting, 734
watering lawn, 363

Law and law enforcement

motor vehicle thefts, 873
violent crimes, 70

Leisure and recreation

cable TV, 117
community skating rink, 123
Ferris wheel, 50, 494, 533, 553

Marketing

IBM personal computer price and
    demand, 340

Measurement

optical methods of, 466
of rainfall, 631

Mechanics. *See also* **Physics**

Medicine. *See also* **Health**

blood pressure, 493–94
drug concentration, 88, 211
drug medication, 282, 296
healing of wounds, 282, 296
spreading of disease, 347

Metallurgy

gold purity, A77

Meteorology

weather balloon height and atmospheric
    pressure, 337

Military

active duty personnel, 190

Miscellaneous

bending wire, 779
biorhythms, 410
carrying a ladder around a corner, 418, 502
citrus ladders, 822–23
cross-sectional area of beam, 69, 77
curve fitting, 719, 734, 798
drafting error, 17
McDonald's scalding coffee case, 349
pet ownership, 873
rescue at sea, 528, 530
surface area of balloon, 255
surveillance satellites, 521–22
volume of balloon, 255
wire enclosure area, 116

Mixtures. *See also* **Chemistry**

blending coffees, 788, 799, A71–A72, A75
blending teas, A75
cement, A77
mixed candy, A75
mixed nuts, 718, 788, 799, A75
water and antifreeze, A76

Motion. *See also* **Physics**

catching a train, 703
on a circle, 363
of Ferris Wheel rider, 494
minute hand of clock, 362, 435
objects approaching intersection, 699
of pendulum, 554
revolutions of circular disk, A21
simulating, 693–94
tortoise and the hare race, 778
uniform, 699

Motor vehicles

alcohol and driving, 292, 297
approaching intersection, 699
automobile production, 255, 734
brake repair with tune-up, 876
braking load, 631
crankshafts, 531
depreciation of, 312–13, 342, 349
with Global Positioning System (GPS), 347
loans for, 814–15
miles per gallon, 163
new-car markup, A87
runaway car, 167
spin balancing tires, 364, 435
stopping distance, 162, 268
used-car purchase, 321

Music

revenues from, 111

Navigation

avoiding a tropical storm, 538
bearing, 517, 538
    of aircraft, 520
    of ship, 520, 557
commercial, 531
compass heading, 631
error in
    correcting, 536, 556
    time lost due to, 531

rescue at sea, 528, 530
revising a flight plan, 538

Oceanography

tides, 429, 437
wave model, 351

Optics

angle of refraction, 494–95
bending light, 495
index of refraction, 494–95
laser beam, 519
laser projection, 484
lensmaker's equation, A45
light obliterated through glass, 282
mirrors, 672
reflecting telescope, 648

Pediatrics

height vs. head circumference, 141, 268

Pharmacy

vitamin intake, 718, 735

Physics

angle of elevation of Sun, 519
braking load, 631
damped motion, 549–50
Doppler effect, 211–12
force
  resultant, 620, 623
gravity, 201, 219
  on Earth, 69, 268
  on Jupiter, 69
harmonic motion, 548
heat transfer, 502
inclination of mountain trail, 514
moment of inertia, 488
motion of object, 548
pendulum motion, 362, 554, 828–29
  period, 111, 268, A95
product of inertia, 484
projectile motion, 157, 161, 380, 479, 484,
    488, 494, 501–2, 692, 698–700, 703
  artillery, 167, 458
  thrown object, 698
simulating motion, 693–94
static equilibrium, 620–21, 623–24, 635
tension, 620–21, 623, 635
thrown object
  ball, 162, 167
truck pulls, 624
uniform motion, 116, 699, 703, A72–A73,
    A75–A76
velocity down inclined planes, A95
vertically propelled object, 167

Play

swinging, 559
wagon pulling, 623, 629–30

Population. *See also* Demographics

bacterial, 331, 332, 333, 339
decline in, 332
E-coli growth, 89, 127–29
of endangered species, 333
of fruit fly, 329–30
as function of age, 69
growth in, 332
insect, 201, 331
of trout, 815
of United States, 312, 340, 847
of world, 312, 340–41, 347, 803

Probability

checkout lines, 873
classroom composition, 874
"Deal or No Deal" TV show, 849
exponential, 279, 282–83, 296
household annual income, 873
Monty Hall Game, 877
Poisson, 283
"Price is Right" games, 873
of winning a lottery, 874

Publishing

page design, 122

Pyrotechnics

fireworks display, 671

Rate. *See also* Speed

of car, 363
catching a bus, 698
catching a train, 698
current of stream, 718
of emptying
  of oil tankers, A77
  of pool, A77
  of tub, A77
to keep up with the Sun, 364
miles per gallon, 163
revolutions per minute
  of bicycle wheels, 363
  of pulleys, 365

Real estate

commission schedule, A86
cost of land, 557
cost of triangular lot, 543

Recreation

bungee jumping, 219
Demon Roller Coaster customer rate, 283
online gambling, 873

Security

security cameras, 519

Seismology

calibrating instruments, 703

Sequences. *See also* Combinatorics

ceramic tile floor design, 821
Drury Lane Theater, 822
football stadium seating, 822
seats in amphitheater, 823

Speed

of aircraft, 626–27, 631, 635
angular, 363, 435

average, A75, A77
of current, 363–64, 799, A75
as function of time, 78, 116
of jet stream, 799
of laser printers, A76
linear, 360–61
  on Earth, 363
of merry-go-rounds, 435
of Moon, 363
of motorboat, 635, A75
moving walkways, A76
of plane, A77
revolutions per minute of pulley, 363
of rotation of lighthouse beacons, 435
of swimmer, 635
of truck, 519
walking, A76
of wheel pulling cable cars, 364
wind, 718

Sports

baseball, 699, 863, 875
  diamond, 16
  dimensions of home plate, 543
  field, 538, 539
  Little League, 16, 364–65
  stadium, 539
  World Series, 863
basketball, 863
  free throws, 76, 521
  granny shots, 76–77
biathlon, A77
bungee jumping, 219
exacta betting, 877
football, 658, A76
golf, 494
  distance to the green, 538
  sand bunkers, 458
hammer throw, 436
hunting, 154
Olympic performance, 54, A77
races, 775–76, 778
relay runners, 875
running a race, A77
soccer, penalties in 2006 Fifa World
  Cup, 731
swimming, 558, 635
tennis court dimensions, A76
Tour de France, 506

Statistics. *See* Probability

Surveying

distance between houses, 557

Surveys

of appliance purchases, 854
data analysis, 851–52, 854
stock portfolios, 855
of summer session attendance, 854
of TV sets in a house, 873

Temperature

of air parcel, 822
body, A13
conversion of, 255, 268
cooling time of Beer stein, 332
cooling time of pizza, 332
measuring, 43
after midnight, 190
monthly, 428–29, 435
of portable heater, 347
relationship between scales, 111
sinusoidal function from, 423–24
of skillet, 347
wind chill factor, 347

Tests and testing

IQ, A87

Time

for Beer stein to cool, 332
Ferris Wheel rider height as function
  of, 494
to go from an island to a town, 117
hours of daylight, 425–26, 429, 435, 452
for pizza to cool, 332
of sunrise, 364, 452

Transportation

deicing salt, 458
Falls Incline Railway, 520

Travel. *See also* **Air travel; Navigation**

bearing, 557
drivers stopped by the police, 349
parking at O'Hare International Airport, 98

Volume

of gasoline in tank, A95
of water in cone, 117

Weapons

artillery, 167, 458

Weather

atmospheric pressure, 282, 296
avoiding a tropical storm, 538
cooling air, 822
hurricanes, 190
lightning strikes, 669–70, 672
rainfall measurement, 631
relative humidity, 283
weather satellites, 50
wind chill, 99, 347

Work, 629

computing, 629–30, 635
constant rate jobs, 799
pulling a wagon, 629–30
ramp angle, 631–32
wheelbarrow push, 623
working together to do a job, A74, A75

Photo Credits

Precalculus

1

Graphs

The First Modern Olympics: Athens, 1896

The birth of the modern Olympic Games

By John Gettings—"I hereby proclaim the opening of the first International Olympic Games at Athens." With these words on April 6, 1896, King George I of Greece welcomed the crowd that had gathered in the newly reconstructed Panathenean Stadium to the modern-day Olympic Summer Games.

The event was the idea of Baron Pierre de Coubertin of France who traveled the world to gather support for his dream to have nations come together and overcome national disputes, all in the name of sport.

The program for the Games included track and field, fencing, weightlifting, rifle and pistol shooting, tennis, cycling, swimming, gymnastics, and wrestling. Although 14 nations participated, most of the athletes were Greek.

The Games reached their high point on Day 11 with the first modern-day marathon. The idea to hold an event to commemorate the Ancient Olympic games was suggested by a friend of de Coubertin and was met with great anticipation. The race was run from Marathon to Athens (estimated at 22–26 miles), watched by more than 100,000 people and won by a Greek runner, Spiridon Louis.

Source: Adapted from John Gettings, "The First Modern Olympics: Athens, 1896," accessed at www.infoplease.com. ©2006 Pearson Education, Inc. Reprinted with permission.

—*See Chapter Project I*—

A Look Back

In Appendix A we review Algebra Essentials, Geometry Essentials, and equations in one variable.

A Look Ahead

Here we connect algebra and geometry using the rectangular coordinate system and use it to graph equations in two variables. The idea of using a system of rectangular coordinates dates back to ancient times, when such a system was used for surveying and city planning. Apollonius of Perga, in 200 BC, used a form of rectangular coordinates in his work on conics, although this use does not stand out as clearly as it does in modern treatments. Sporadic use of rectangular coordinates continued until the 1600s. By that time, algebra had developed sufficiently so that René Descartes (1596–1650) and Pierre de Fermat (1601–1665) could take the crucial step, which was the use of rectangular coordinates to translate geometry problems into algebra problems, and vice versa. This step was important for two reasons. First, it allowed both geometers and algebraists to gain new insights into their subjects, which previously had been regarded as separate, but now were seen to be connected in many important ways. Second, these insights made the development of calculus possible, which greatly enlarged the number of areas in which mathematics could be applied and made possible a much deeper understanding of these areas.

Outline

1.1 Rectangular Coordinates; Graphing Utilities; Introduction to Graphing Equations

1.2 Intercepts; Symmetry; Graphing Key Equations

1.3 Solving Equations Using a Graphing Utility

1.4 Lines

1.5 Circles

Chapter Review

Chapter Test

Chapter Project

1

1.1 Rectangular Coordinates; Graphing Utilities; Introduction to Graphing Equations

PREPARING FOR THIS SECTION   *Before getting started, review the following:*

- Algebra Essentials (Appendix A, Section A.1, pp. A1–A10)
- Geometry Essentials (Appendix A, Section A.2, pp. A14–A19)

Now Work the 'Are You Prepared?' problems on page 14.

OBJECTIVES   **1** Use the Distance Formula (p. 4)
   2 Use the Midpoint Formula (p. 7)
   3 Graph Equations by Hand by Plotting Points (p. 7)
   4 Graph Equations Using a Graphing Utility (p. 10)
   5 Use a Graphing Utility to Create Tables (p. 12)
   6 Find Intercepts from a Graph (p. 12)
   7 Use a Graphing Utility to Approximate Intercepts (p. 13)

Figure 1

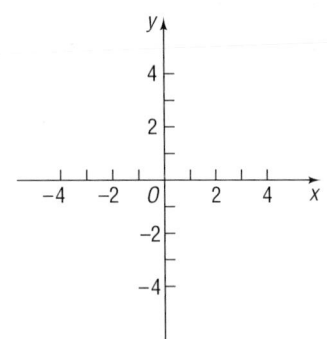

Rectangular Coordinates

We locate a point on the real number line by assigning it a single real number, called the *coordinate of the point*. For work in a two-dimensional plane, we locate points by using two numbers.

We begin with two real number lines located in the same plane: one horizontal and the other vertical. We call the horizontal line the **x-axis,** the vertical line the **y-axis,** and the point of intersection the **origin O.** See Figure 1. We assign coordinates to every point on these number lines using a convenient scale. Recall that the scale of a number line is the distance between 0 and 1. In mathematics, we usually use the same scale on each axis; in applications, a different scale is often used on each axis.

The origin O has a value of 0 on both the x-axis and y-axis. Points on the x-axis to the right of O are associated with positive real numbers, and those to the left of O are associated with negative real numbers. Points on the y-axis above O are associated with positive real numbers, and those below O are associated with negative real numbers. In Figure 1, the x-axis and y-axis are labeled as x and y, respectively, and we have used an arrow at the end of each axis to denote the positive direction.

The coordinate system described here is called a **rectangular** or **Cartesian*** **coordinate system.** The plane formed by the x-axis and y-axis is sometimes called the **xy-plane,** and the x-axis and y-axis are referred to as the **coordinate axes.**

Any point P in the xy-plane can then be located by using an **ordered pair** (x, y) of real numbers. Let x denote the signed distance of P from the y-axis (*signed* means that, if P is to the right of the y-axis, then $x > 0$, and if P is to the left of the y-axis, then $x < 0$); and let y denote the signed distance of P from the x-axis. The ordered pair (x, y), also called the **coordinates** of P, then gives us enough information to locate the point P in the plane.

Figure 2

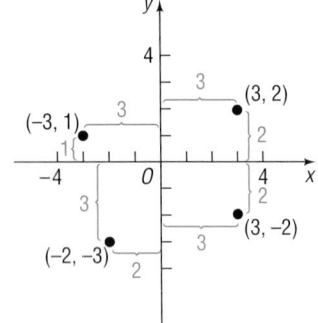

For example, to locate the point whose coordinates are $(-3, 1)$, go 3 units along the x-axis to the left of O and then go straight up 1 unit. We **plot** this point by placing a dot at this location. See Figure 2, in which the points with coordinates $(-3, 1), (-2, -3), (3, -2)$, and $(3, 2)$ are plotted.

The origin has coordinates $(0, 0)$. Any point on the x-axis has coordinates of the form $(x, 0)$, and any point on the y-axis has coordinates of the form $(0, y)$.

If (x, y) are the coordinates of a point P, then x is called the **x-coordinate,** or **abscissa,** of P and y is the **y-coordinate,** or **ordinate,** of P. We identify the point P by its coordinates (x, y) by writing $P = (x, y)$. Usually, we will simply say "the point (x, y)" rather than "the point whose coordinates are (x, y)."

The coordinate axes divide the xy-plane into four sections called **quadrants,** as shown in Figure 3. In quadrant I, both the x-coordinate and the y-coordinate of all points are positive; in quadrant II, x is negative and y is positive; in quadrant III,

*Named after René Descartes (1596–1650), a French mathematician, philosopher, and theologian.

Figure 3

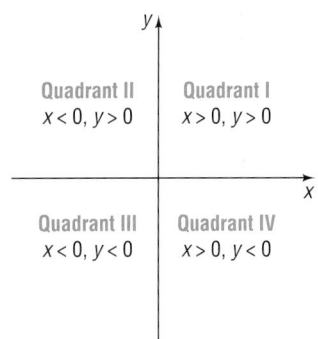

Figure 4
$Y_1 = 2x$

Figure 5

both x and y are negative; and in quadrant IV, x is positive and y is negative. Points on the coordinate axes belong to no quadrant.

Now Work PROBLEM 11

Graphing Utilities

All graphing utilities, that is, all graphing calculators and all computer software graphing packages, graph equations by plotting points on a screen. The screen itself actually consists of small rectangles, called **pixels.** The more pixels the screen has, the better the resolution. Most graphing calculators have 48 pixels per square inch; most computer screens have 32 to 108 pixels per square inch. When a point to be plotted lies inside a pixel, the pixel is turned on (lights up). The graph of an equation is a collection of lighted pixels. Figure 4 shows how the graph of $y = 2x$ looks on a TI-84 Plus graphing calculator.

The screen of a graphing utility will display the coordinate axes of a rectangular coordinate system. However, you must set the scale on each axis. You must also include the smallest and largest values of x and y that you want included in the graph. This is called **setting the viewing rectangle** or **viewing window.** Figure 5 illustrates a typical viewing window.

To select the viewing window, we must give values to the following expressions:

Xmin: the smallest value of x shown on the viewing window

Xmax: the largest value of x shown on the viewing window

Xscl: the number of units per tick mark on the x-axis

Ymin: the smallest value of y shown on the viewing window

Ymax: the largest value of y shown on the viewing window

Yscl: the number of units per tick mark on the y-axis

Figure 6 illustrates these settings and their relation to the Cartesian coordinate system.

Figure 6

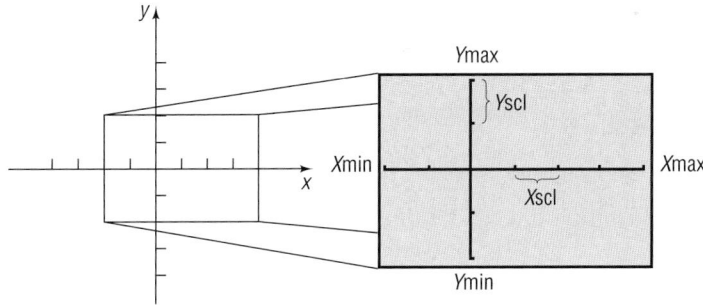

If the scale used on each axis is known, we can determine the minimum and maximum values of x and y shown on the screen by counting the tick marks. Look again at Figure 5. For a scale of 1 on each axis, the minimum and maximum values of x are -10 and 10, respectively; the minimum and maximum values of y are also -10 and 10. If the scale is 2 on each axis, then the minimum and maximum values of x are -20 and 20, respectively; and the minimum and maximum values of y are -20 and 20, respectively.

Conversely, if we know the minimum and maximum values of x and y, we can determine the scales being used by counting the tick marks displayed. We shall follow the practice of showing the minimum and maximum values of x and y in our illustrations so that you will know how the window was set. See Figure 7.

Figure 7

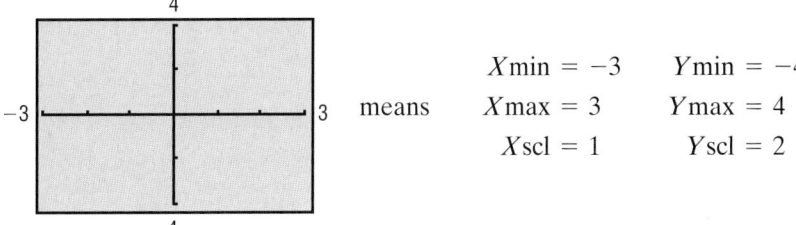

means
$$X\text{min} = -3 \qquad Y\text{min} = -4$$
$$X\text{max} = 3 \qquad Y\text{max} = 4$$
$$X\text{scl} = 1 \qquad Y\text{scl} = 2$$

EXAMPLE 1 | **Finding the Coordinates of a Point Shown on a Graphing Utility Screen**

Find the coordinates of the point shown in Figure 8. Assume the coordinates are integers.

Figure 8

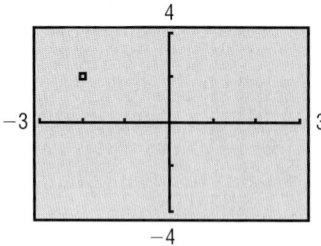

Solution | First we note that the viewing window used in Figure 8 is

$$X\text{min} = -3 \qquad Y\text{min} = -4$$
$$X\text{max} = 3 \qquad Y\text{max} = 4$$
$$X\text{scl} = 1 \qquad Y\text{scl} = 2$$

The point shown is 2 tick units to the left on the horizontal axis (scale = 1) and 1 tick up on the vertical scale (scale = 2). The coordinates of the point shown are $(-2, 2)$.

 Now Work PROBLEMS 15 AND 25

1 Use the Distance Formula

If the same units of measurement, such as inches, centimeters, and so on, are used for both the x-axis and y-axis, then all distances in the xy-plane can be measured using this unit of measurement.

EXAMPLE 2 | **Finding the Distance between Two Points**

Find the distance d between the points $(1, 3)$ and $(5, 6)$.

Solution | First we plot the points $(1, 3)$ and $(5, 6)$ and connect them with a straight line. See Figure 9(a). We are looking for length d. We begin by drawing a horizontal line from $(1, 3)$ to $(5, 3)$ and a vertical line from $(5, 3)$ to $(5, 6)$, forming a right triangle, as in Figure 9(b). One leg of the triangle is of length 4 (since $|5 - 1| = 4$) and the other is of length 3 (since $|6 - 3| = 3$). By the Pythagorean Theorem, the square of the distance d that we seek is

$$d^2 = 4^2 + 3^2 = 16 + 9 = 25$$
$$d = \sqrt{25} = 5$$

Figure 9

 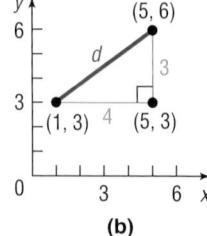

(a)　　　　　　　　(b)

The **distance formula** provides a straightforward method for computing the distance between two points.

THEOREM

Distance Formula

The distance between two points $P_1 = (x_1, y_1)$ and $P_2 = (x_2, y_2)$, denoted by $d(P_1, P_2)$, is

$$d(P_1, P_2) = \sqrt{(x_2 - x_1)^2 + (y_2 - y_1)^2} \qquad \textbf{(1)}$$

In Words

To compute the distance between two points, find the difference of the x-coordinates, square it, and add this to the square of the difference of the y-coordinates. The square root of this sum is the distance.

Figure 10 illustrates the theorem.

Proof of the Distance Formula   Let (x_1, y_1) denote the coordinates of point P_1, and let (x_2, y_2) denote the coordinates of point P_2. Assume that the line joining P_1 and P_2 is neither horizontal nor vertical. Refer to Figure 11(a). The coordinates of P_3 are (x_2, y_1). The horizontal distance from P_1 to P_3 is the absolute value of the difference of the x-coordinates, $|x_2 - x_1|$. The vertical distance from P_3 to P_2 is the absolute value of the difference of the y-coordinates, $|y_2 - y_1|$. See Figure 11(b). The distance $d(P_1, P_2)$ that we seek is the length of the hypotenuse of the right triangle, so, by the Pythagorean Theorem, it follows that

$$[d(P_1, P_2)]^2 = |x_2 - x_1|^2 + |y_2 - y_1|^2$$
$$= (x_2 - x_1)^2 + (y_2 - y_1)^2$$
$$d(P_1, P_2) = \sqrt{(x_2 - x_1)^2 + (y_2 - y_1)^2}$$

Figure 10

Figure 11

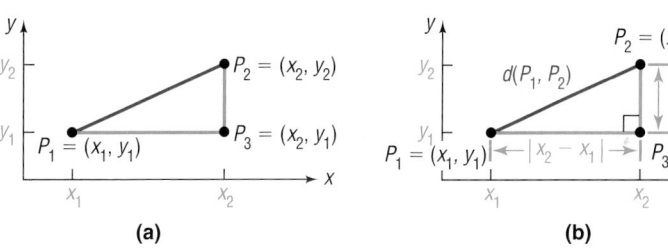

(a)   (b)

Now, if the line joining P_1 and P_2 is horizontal, then the y-coordinate of P_1 equals the y-coordinate of P_2; that is, $y_1 = y_2$. Refer to Figure 12(a). In this case, the distance formula (1) still works, because, for $y_1 = y_2$, it reduces to

$$d(P_1, P_2) = \sqrt{(x_2 - x_1)^2 + 0^2} = \sqrt{(x_2 - x_1)^2} = |x_2 - x_1|$$

Figure 12

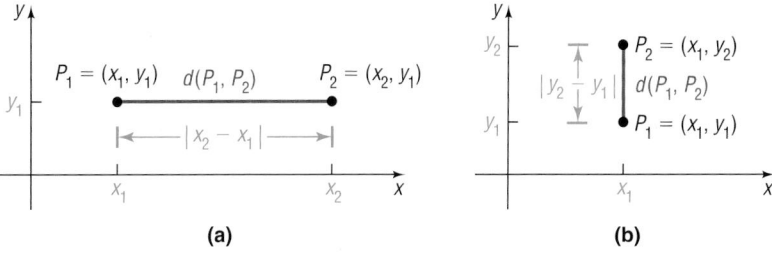

(a)   (b)

A similar argument holds if the line joining P_1 and P_2 is vertical. See Figure 12(b). The distance formula is valid in all cases. ■

EXAMPLE 3   Finding the Length of a Line Segment

Find the length of the line segment shown in Figure 13 on page 6.

Solution

Figure 13

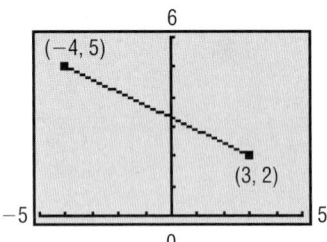

The length of the line segment is the distance between the points $P_1 = (x_1, y_1) = (-4, 5)$ and $P_2 = (x_2, y_2) = (3, 2)$. Using the distance formula (1) with $x_1 = -4$, $y_1 = 5$, $x_2 = 3$, and $y_2 = 2$, the length d is

$$d = \sqrt{(x_2 - x_1)^2 + (y_2 - y_1)^2} = \sqrt{[3 - (-4)]^2 + (2 - 5)^2}$$
$$= \sqrt{7^2 + (-3)^2} = \sqrt{49 + 9} = \sqrt{58} \approx 7.62$$

Now Work PROBLEM 31

The distance between two points $P_1 = (x_1, y_1)$ and $P_2 = (x_2, y_2)$ is never a negative number. Furthermore, the distance between two points is 0 only when the points are identical, that is, when $x_1 = x_2$ and $y_1 = y_2$. Also, because $(x_2 - x_1)^2 = (x_1 - x_2)^2$ and $(y_2 - y_1)^2 = (y_1 - y_2)^2$, it makes no difference whether the distance is computed from P_1 to P_2 or from P_2 to P_1; that is, $d(P_1, P_2) = d(P_2, P_1)$.

The introduction to this chapter mentioned that rectangular coordinates enable us to translate geometry problems into algebra problems, and vice versa. The next example shows how algebra (the distance formula) can be used to solve geometry problems.

EXAMPLE 4   **Using Algebra to Solve Geometry Problems**

Consider the three points $A = (-2, 1)$, $B = (2, 3)$, and $C = (3, 1)$.

(a) Plot each point and form the triangle ABC.
(b) Find the length of each side of the triangle.
(c) Verify that the triangle is a right triangle.
(d) Find the area of the triangle.

Solution

(a) Points A, B, C and triangle ABC are plotted in Figure 14.

Figure 14

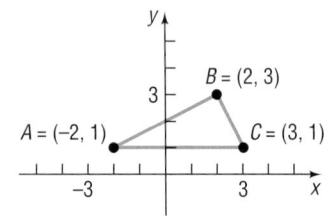

(b) $d(A, B) = \sqrt{[2 - (-2)]^2 + (3 - 1)^2} = \sqrt{16 + 4} = \sqrt{20} = 2\sqrt{5}$
    $d(B, C) = \sqrt{(3 - 2)^2 + (1 - 3)^2} = \sqrt{1 + 4} = \sqrt{5}$
    $d(A, C) = \sqrt{[3 - (-2)]^2 + (1 - 1)^2} = \sqrt{25 + 0} = 5$

(c) To show that the triangle is a right triangle, we need to show that the sum of the squares of the lengths of two of the sides equals the square of the length of the third side. (Why is this sufficient?) Looking at Figure 14, it seems reasonable to conjecture that the right angle is at vertex B. We shall check to see whether

$$[d(A, B)]^2 + [d(B, C)]^2 = [d(A, C)]^2$$

We find that

$$[d(A, B)]^2 + [d(B, C)]^2 = (2\sqrt{5})^2 + (\sqrt{5})^2$$
$$= 20 + 5 = 25 = [d(A, C)]^2$$

so it follows from the converse of the Pythagorean Theorem that triangle ABC is a right triangle.

(d) Because the right angle is at vertex B, the sides AB and BC form the base and height of the triangle. Its area is

$$\text{Area} = \frac{1}{2}(\text{Base})(\text{Height}) = \frac{1}{2}(2\sqrt{5})(\sqrt{5}) = 5 \text{ square units}$$

Now Work PROBLEM 49

2 Use the Midpoint Formula

Figure 15

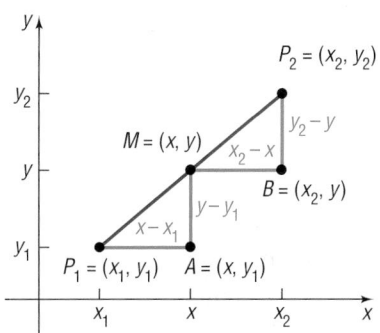

We now derive a formula for the coordinates of the **midpoint of a line segment.** Let $P_1 = (x_1, y_1)$ and $P_2 = (x_2, y_2)$ be the endpoints of a line segment, and let $M = (x, y)$ be the point on the line segment that is the same distance from P_1 as it is from P_2. See Figure 15. The triangles P_1AM and MBP_2 are congruent. [Do you see why? Angle AP_1M = angle BMP_2,* angle P_1MA = angle MP_2B, and $d(P_1, M) = d(M, P_2)$ is given. So, we have angle–side–angle.] Hence, corresponding sides are equal in length. That is,

$$x - x_1 = x_2 - x \qquad \text{and} \qquad y - y_1 = y_2 - y$$
$$2x = x_1 + x_2 \qquad\qquad 2y = y_1 + y_2$$
$$x = \frac{x_1 + x_2}{2} \qquad\qquad y = \frac{y_1 + y_2}{2}$$

THEOREM

Midpoint Formula

The midpoint $M = (x, y)$ of the line segment from $P_1 = (x_1, y_1)$ to $P_2 = (x_2, y_2)$ is

$$M = (x, y) = \left(\frac{x_1 + x_2}{2}, \frac{y_1 + y_2}{2} \right) \tag{2}$$

In Words

To find the midpoint of a line segment, average the x-coordinates and average the y-coordinates of the endpoints.

EXAMPLE 5   Finding the Midpoint of a Line Segment

Find the midpoint of a line segment from $P_1 = (-5, 5)$ to $P_2 = (3, 1)$. Plot the points P_1 and P_2 and their midpoint.

Solution   We apply the midpoint formula (2) using $x_1 = -5$, $y_1 = 5$, $x_2 = 3$, and $y_2 = 1$. Then the coordinates (x, y) of the midpoint M are

Figure 16

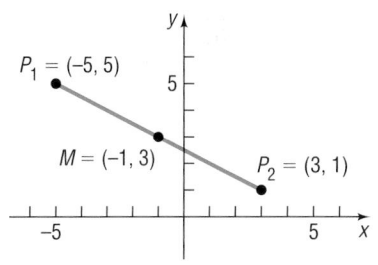

$$x = \frac{x_1 + x_2}{2} = \frac{-5 + 3}{2} = -1 \quad \text{and} \quad y = \frac{y_1 + y_2}{2} = \frac{5 + 1}{2} = 3$$

That is, $M = (-1, 3)$. See Figure 16.

Now Work PROBLEM 55

3 Graph Equations by Hand by Plotting Points

An **equation in two variables,** say x and y, is a statement in which two expressions involving x and y are equal. The expressions are called the **sides** of the equation. Since an equation is a statement, it may be true or false, depending on the value of the variables. Any values of x and y that result in a true statement are said to **satisfy** the equation.

For example, the following are all equations in two variables x and y:

$$x^2 + y^2 = 5 \qquad 2x - y = 6 \qquad y = 2x + 5 \qquad x^2 = y$$

The first of these, $x^2 + y^2 = 5$, is satisfied for $x = 1$, $y = 2$, since $1^2 + 2^2 = 1 + 4 = 5$. Other choices of x and y also satisfy this equation. It is not satisfied for $x = 2$ and $y = 3$, since $2^2 + 3^2 = 4 + 9 = 13 \neq 5$.

---

*A postulate from geometry states that the transversal $\overline{P_1P_2}$ forms congruent corresponding angles with the parallel line segments $\overline{P_1A}$ and $\overline{MB}$.

The **graph of an equation in two variables** x and y consists of the set of points in the xy-plane whose coordinates (x, y) satisfy the equation.

Graphs play an important role in helping us to visualize the relationships that exist between two variables or quantities. Figure 17 shows the relation between the level of risk in a stock portfolio and the average annual rate of return. From the graph, we can see that, when 30% of a portfolio of stocks is invested in foreign companies, risk is minimized.

Figure 17
Source: T. Rowe Price

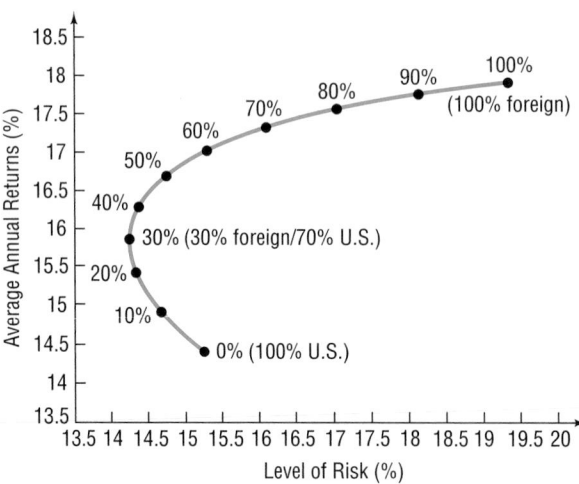

| EXAMPLE 6 | **Determining Whether a Point Is on the Graph of an Equation** |

Determine if the following points are on the graph of the equation $2x - y = 6$.

(a) $(2, 3)$ (b) $(2, -2)$

Solution

(a) For the point $(2, 3)$, we check to see if $x = 2$, $y = 3$ satisfies the equation $2x - y = 6$.

$$2x - y = 2(2) - 3 = 4 - 3 = 1 \neq 6$$

The equation is not satisfied, so the point $(2, 3)$ is not on the graph.

(b) For the point $(2, -2)$, we have

$$2x - y = 2(2) - (-2) = 4 + 2 = 6$$

The equation is satisfied, so the point $(2, -2)$ is on the graph.

Now Work PROBLEM 65

| EXAMPLE 7 | **How to Graph an Equation by Hand by Plotting Points** |

Step-by-Step Solution

Graph the equation: $y = -2x + 3$

STEP 1 Find all points (x, y) that satisfy the equation. To determine these points, choose values of x and use the equation to find the corresponding values for y. See Table 1.

Table 1

x	$y = -2x + 3$	(x, y)
-2	$-2(-2) + 3 = 7$	$(-2, 7)$
-1	$-2(-1) + 3 = 5$	$(-1, 5)$
0	$-2(0) + 3 = 3$	$(0, 3)$
1	$-2(1) + 3 = 1$	$(1, 1)$
2	$-2(2) + 3 = -1$	$(2, -1)$

STEP 2 Plot the points listed in the table as shown in Figure 18(a). Now connect the points to obtain the graph of the equation (a *line*), as shown in Figure 18(b).

Figure 18

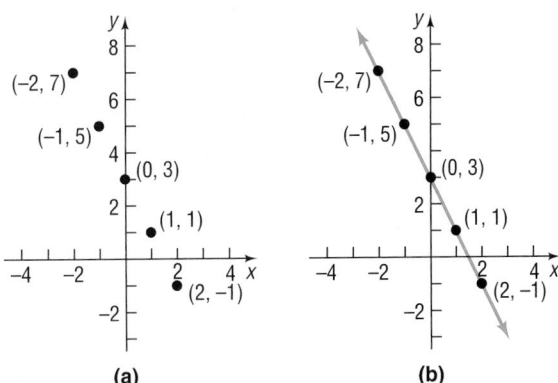

(a)   (b)

| EXAMPLE 8 | **Graphing an Equation by Hand by Plotting Points** |

Graph the equation: $y = x^2$

Solution   Table 2 provides several points on the graph. In Figure 19 we plot these points and connect them with a smooth curve to obtain the graph (a *parabola*).

Table 2

x	$(y = x^2)$	(x, y)
-4	16	$(-4, 16)$
-3	9	$(-3, 9)$
-2	4	$(-2, 4)$
-1	1	$(-1, 1)$
0	0	$(0, 0)$
1	1	$(1, 1)$
2	4	$(2, 4)$
3	9	$(3, 9)$
4	16	$(4, 16)$

Figure 19

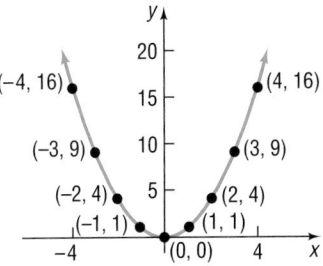

The graphs of the equations shown in Figures 18(b) and 19 do not show all the points that are on the graph. For example, in Figure 18(b), the point $(20, -37)$ is a part of the graph of $y = -2x + 3$, but it is not shown. Since the graph of $y = -2x + 3$ could be extended out as far as we please, we use arrows to indicate that the pattern shown continues. It is important when illustrating a graph to present enough of the graph so that any viewer of the illustration will "see" the rest of it as an obvious continuation of what is actually there. This is referred to as a **complete graph.**

One way to obtain a complete graph of an equation is to plot a sufficient number of points on the graph until a pattern becomes evident. Then these points are connected with a smooth curve following the suggested pattern. But how many points are sufficient? Sometimes knowledge about the equation tells us. For example, we will learn in Section 1.4 that, if an equation is of the form $y = mx + b$, then its graph is a line. In this case, two points would suffice to obtain the graph.

One purpose of this book is to investigate the properties of equations in order to decide whether a graph is complete. Sometimes we shall graph equations by plotting a sufficient number of points on the graph until a pattern becomes evident and then connect these points with a smooth curve, following the suggested pattern. (Shortly, we shall investigate various techniques that will enable us to graph an equation without plotting so many points.) Other times we shall graph equations using a graphing utility.

4 Graph Equations Using a Graphing Utility

From Examples 7 and 8, we see that a graph can be obtained by plotting points in a rectangular coordinate system and connecting them. Graphing utilities perform these same steps when graphing an equation. For example, the TI-84 Plus determines 95 evenly spaced input values,* uses the equation to determine the output values, plots these points on the screen, and finally (if in the connected mode) draws a line between consecutive points.

To graph an equation in two variables x and y using a graphing utility requires that the equation be written in the form $y = \{$expression in $x\}$. If the original equation is not in this form, replace it by equivalent equations until the form $y = \{$expression in $x\}$ is obtained. In general, there are four ways to obtain equivalent equations.

Procedures That Result in Equivalent Equations

1. Interchange the two sides of the equation:

$$\text{Replace} \quad 3x + 5 = y \quad \text{by} \quad y = 3x + 5$$

2. Simplify the sides of the equation by combining like terms, eliminating parentheses, and so on:

$$\text{Replace} \quad 2y + 2 + 6 = 2x + 5(x + 1)$$
$$\text{by} \quad 2y + 8 = 7x + 5$$

3. Add or subtract the same expression on both sides of the equation:

$$\text{Replace} \quad y + 3x - 5 = 4$$
$$\text{by} \quad y + 3x - 5 + 5 = 4 + 5$$

4. Multiply or divide both sides of the equation by the same nonzero expression:

$$\text{Replace} \quad 3y = 6 - 2x$$
$$\text{by} \quad \frac{1}{3} \cdot 3y = \frac{1}{3}(6 - 2x)$$

EXAMPLE 9	**Expressing an Equation in the Form $y = \{$expression in $x\}$**

Solve for y: $2y + 3x - 5 = 4$

Solution   We replace the original equation by a succession of equivalent equations.

$$2y + 3x - 5 = 4$$
$$2y + 3x - 5 + 5 = 4 + 5 \qquad \text{Add 5 to both sides.}$$
$$2y + 3x = 9 \qquad \text{Simplify.}$$
$$2y + 3x - 3x = 9 - 3x \qquad \text{Subtract 3x from both sides.}$$
$$2y = 9 - 3x \qquad \text{Simplify.}$$
$$\frac{2y}{2} = \frac{9 - 3x}{2} \qquad \text{Divide both sides by 2.}$$
$$y = \frac{9 - 3x}{2} \qquad \text{Simplify.}$$

Now we are ready to graph equations using a graphing utility.

---

*These input values depend on the values of Xmin and Xmax. For example, if Xmin $= -10$ and Xmax $= 10$, then the first input value will be -10 and the next input value will be $-10 + (10 - (-10))/94 = -9.7872$, and so on.

EXAMPLE 10	How to Graph an Equation Using a Graphing Utility

Use a graphing utility to graph the equation: $6x^2 + 3y = 36$

Step-by-Step Solution

STEP 1   Solve the equation for y in terms of x.

$$6x^2 + 3y = 36$$
$$3y = -6x^2 + 36 \qquad \text{Subtract } 6x^2 \text{ from both sides of the equation.}$$
$$y = -2x^2 + 12 \qquad \text{Divide both sides of the equation by 3 and simplify.}$$

STEP 2   Enter the equation to be graphed into your graphing utility. Figure 20 shows the equation to be graphed entered on a TI-84 Plus.

Figure 20

```
Plot1 Plot2 Plot3
\Y1 ■ -2X²+12
\Y2=
\Y3=
\Y4=
\Y5=
\Y6=
\Y7=
```

STEP 3   Choose an initial viewing window. Without any knowledge about the behavior of the graph, it is common to choose the standard viewing window as the initial viewing window. The standard viewing window is

$$\text{Xmin} = -10 \qquad \text{Ymin} = -10$$
$$\text{Xmax} = 10 \qquad \text{Ymax} = 10$$
$$\text{Xscl} = 1 \qquad \text{Yscl} = 1$$

See Figure 21.

Figure 21

```
WINDOW
 Xmin=-10
 Xmax=10
 Xscl=1
 Ymin=-10
 Ymax=10
 Yscl=1
 Xres=1
```

STEP 4   Graph the equation. See Figure 22.

Figure 22

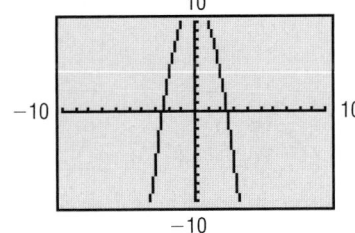

STEP 5   Adjust the viewing window until a complete graph is obtained.

The graph of $y = -2x^2 + 12$ is not complete. The value of Ymax must be increased so that the top portion of the graph is visible. After increasing the value of Ymax to 12, we obtain the graph in Figure 23. The graph is now complete.

Figure 23

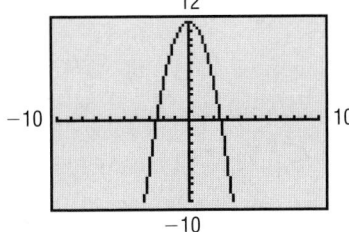

NOTE Some graphing utilities have a ZOOM-STANDARD feature that automatically sets the viewing window to the standard viewing window. In addition, some graphing utilities have a ZOOM-FIT feature that determines the appropriate Ymin and Ymax for a given Xmin and Xmax. Consult your owner's manual for the appropriate keystrokes. ■

──── **Now Work** PROBLEM 83

5 Use a Graphing Utility to Create Tables

In addition to graphing equations, graphing utilities can also be used to create a table of values that satisfy the equation. This feature is especially useful in determining an appropriate viewing window when graphing an equation.

| EXAMPLE 11 | How to Create a Table Using a Graphing Utility |

Create a table that displays the points on the graph of $6x^2 + 3y = 36$ for $x = -3, -2, -1, 0, 1, 2,$ and 3.

Step-by-Step Solution

STEP 1 Solve the equation for y in terms of x.

We solved the equation for y in terms of x in Example 10 and obtained $y = -2x^2 + 12$.

STEP 2 Enter the expression in x following the Y = prompt of the graphing utility.

See Figure 20 on page 11.

STEP 3 Set up the table. Graphing utilities typically have two modes for creating tables. In the AUTO mode, the user determines a starting point for the table (TblStart) and ΔTbl (pronounced "delta table"). The ΔTbl feature determines the increment for x in the table. The ASK mode requires the user to enter values of x, and then the utility determines the corresponding value of y.

We will create a table using AUTO mode. The table we wish to create starts at -3, so TblStart $= -3$. The increment in x is 1, so ΔTbl $= 1$. See Figure 24.

Figure 24

```
TABLE SETUP
 TblStart=-3
 ΔTbl=1
Indpnt: Auto Ask
Depend: Auto Ask
```

STEP 4 Create the table. See Table 3.

Table 3

```
  X   │ Y1
 -3   │ -6
 -2   │  4
 -1   │ 10
  0   │ 12
  1   │ 10
  2   │  4
  3   │ -6
Y1■-2X²+12
```

The user can scroll within the table if it is created in AUTO mode.

In looking at Table 3, we notice that $y = 12$ when $x = 0$. This information could have been used to help to create the initial viewing window by letting us know that Ymax needs to be at least 12 in order to get a complete graph.

6 Find Intercepts from a Graph

The points, if any, at which a graph crosses or touches the coordinate axes are called the **intercepts.** See Figure 25. The x-coordinate of a point at which the graph crosses or touches the x-axis is an **x-intercept,** and the y-coordinate of a point at which the graph crosses or touches the y-axis is a **y-intercept.** For a graph to be complete, all its intercepts must be displayed.

Figure 25

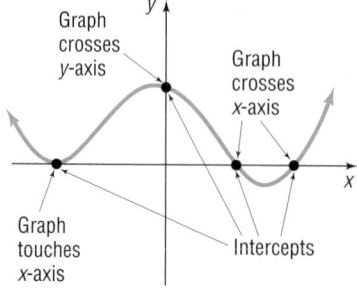

Graph crosses y-axis

Graph crosses x-axis

Graph touches x-axis

Intercepts

| EXAMPLE 12 | Finding Intercepts from a Graph |

Find the intercepts of the graph in Figure 26. What are its x-intercepts? What are its y-intercepts?

Solution

The intercepts of the graph are the points

$$(-3, 0), \quad (0, 3), \quad \left(\frac{3}{2}, 0\right), \quad \left(0, -\frac{4}{3}\right), \quad (0, -3.5), \quad (4.5, 0)$$

The x-intercepts are -3, $\frac{3}{2}$, and 4.5; the y-intercepts are -3.5, $-\frac{4}{3}$, and 3.

Figure 26

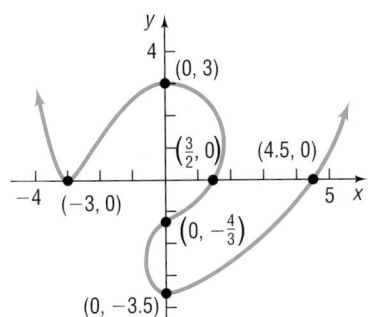

In Example 12, you should notice the following usage: If we do not specify the type of intercept (x- versus y-), then we report the intercept as an ordered pair. However, if we specify the type of intercept, then we only report the coordinate of the intercept. For x-intercepts, we report the x-coordinate of the intercept; for y-intercepts, we report the y-coordinate of the intercept.

Now Work PROBLEM 71

7 Use a Graphing Utility to Approximate Intercepts

We can use a graphing utility to approximate the intercepts of the graph of an equation.

| EXAMPLE 13 | Approximating Intercepts Using a Graphing Utility |

Use a graphing utility to approximate the intercepts of the equation $y = x^3 - 16$.

Solution

Figure 27(a) shows the graph of $y = x^3 - 16$.

The eVALUEate feature of a TI-84 Plus graphing calculator accepts as input a value of x and determines the value of y. If we let $x = 0$, we find that the y-intercept is -16. See Figure 27(b).

The ZERO feature of a TI-84 Plus is used to find the x-intercept(s). See Figure 27(c). Rounded to two decimal places, the x-intercept is 2.52.

Figure 27

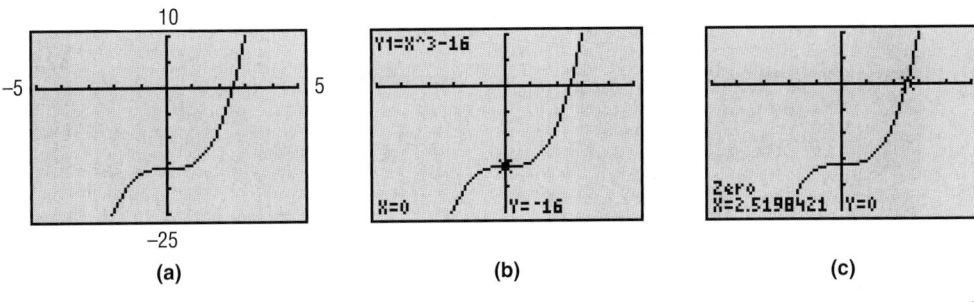

(a)   (b)   (c)

Now Work PROBLEM 93

We discuss finding intercepts algebraically in the next section.

1.1 Assess Your Understanding

'Are You Prepared?' *Answers are given at the end of these exercises. If you get a wrong answer, read the pages listed in red.*

1. If -3 and 5 are the coordinates of two points on the real number line, the distance between these points is _____. (p. A6)

2. If 3 and 4 are the legs of a right triangle, the hypotenuse is _____. (p. A14)

3. Use the converse of the Pythagorean Theorem to show that a triangle whose sides are of lengths $11, 60,$ and 61 is a right triangle. (pp. A14–A15)

4. The _____-_____-_____ case states that two triangles are congruent if two of the angles are congruent and the lengths of the corresponding sides between the two angles are equal. (p. A17)

Concepts and Vocabulary

5. If (x, y) are the coordinates of a point P in the xy-plane, then x is called the _____ of P and y is the _____ of P.

6. The coordinate axes divide the xy-plane into four sections called _____.

7. If three distinct points $P, Q,$ and R all lie on a line and if $d(P, Q) = d(Q, R)$, then Q is called the _____ of the line segment from P to R.

8. **True or False** The distance between two points is sometimes a negative number.

9. **True or False** The point $(-1, 4)$ lies in quadrant IV of the Cartesian plane.

10. **True or False** The midpoint of a line segment is found by averaging the x-coordinates and averaging the y-coordinates of the endpoints.

Skill Building

In Problems 11 and 12, plot each point in the xy-plane. Tell in which quadrant or on what coordinate axis each point lies.

11. (a) $A = (-3, 2)$
    (b) $B = (6, 0)$
    (c) $C = (-2, -2)$
    (d) $D = (6, 5)$
    (e) $E = (0, -3)$
    (f) $F = (6, -3)$

12. (a) $A = (1, 4)$
    (b) $B = (-3, -4)$
    (c) $C = (-3, 4)$
    (d) $D = (4, 1)$
    (e) $E = (0, 1)$
    (f) $F = (-3, 0)$

13. Plot the points $(2, 0), (2, -3), (2, 4), (2, 1),$ and $(2, -1)$. Describe the set of all points of the form $(2, y)$, where y is a real number.

14. Plot the points $(0, 3), (1, 3), (-2, 3), (5, 3),$ and $(-4, 3)$. Describe the set of all points of the form $(x, 3)$, where x is a real number.

In Problems 15–18, determine the coordinates of the points shown. Tell in which quadrant each point lies. Assume the coordinates are integers.

15.

16.

17.

18.
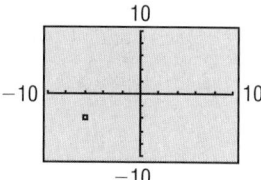

In Problems 19–24, select a setting so that each given point will lie within the viewing window.

19. $(-10, 5), (3, -2), (4, -1)$

20. $(5, 0), (6, 8), (-2, -3)$

21. $(40, 20), (-20, -80), (10, 40)$

22. $(-80, 60), (20, -30), (-20, -40)$

23. $(0, 0), (100, 5), (5, 150)$

24. $(0, -1), (100, 50), (-10, 30)$

In Problems 25–30, determine the viewing window used.

25.

26.

27.

28.

29.

30.

In Problems 31–44, find the distance $d(P_1, P_2)$ *between the points* P_1 *and* P_2.

31.

32.

33.

34.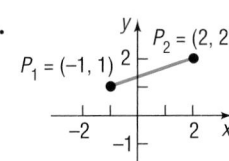

35. $P_1 = (3, -4)$; $P_2 = (5, 4)$

36. $P_1 = (-1, 0)$; $P_2 = (2, 4)$

37. $P_1 = (-5, -3)$; $P_2 = (11, 9)$

38. $P_1 = (2, -3)$; $P_2 = (10, 3)$

39. $P_1 = (4, -3)$; $P_2 = (6, 4)$

40. $P_1 = (-4, -3)$; $P_2 = (6, 2)$

41. $P_1 = (-0.2, 0.3)$; $P_2 = (1.3, 2.1)$

42. $P_1 = (1.2, 2.3)$; $P_2 = (-0.5, 1.6)$

43. $P_1 = (a, b)$; $P_2 = (0, 0)$

44. $P_1 = (a, a)$; $P_2 = (0, 0)$

In Problems 45–48, find the length of the line segment. Assume that the endpoints of each line segment have integer coordinates.

45.

46.

47.

48.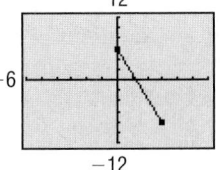

In Problems 49–54, plot each point and form the triangle ABC. Verify that the triangle is a right triangle. Find its area.

49. $A = (-2, 5)$; $B = (1, 3)$; $C = (-1, 0)$

50. $A = (-2, 5)$; $B = (12, 3)$; $C = (10, -11)$

51. $A = (-5, 3)$; $B = (6, 0)$; $C = (5, 5)$

52. $A = (-6, 3)$; $B = (3, -5)$; $C = (-1, 5)$

53. $A = (4, -3)$; $B = (0, -3)$; $C = (4, 2)$

54. $A = (4, -3)$; $B = (4, 1)$; $C = (2, 1)$

In Problems 55–64, find the midpoint of the line segment joining the points P_1 *and* P_2.

55. $P_1 = (3, -4)$; $P_2 = (5, 4)$

56. $P_1 = (-2, 0)$; $P_2 = (2, 4)$

57. $P_1 = (-5, -3)$; $P_2 = (11, 9)$

58. $P_1 = (2, -3)$; $P_2 = (10, 3)$

59. $P_1 = (4, -3)$; $P_2 = (6, 1)$

60. $P_1 = (-4, -3)$; $P_2 = (2, 2)$

61. $P_1 = (-0.2, 0.3)$; $P_2 = (1.3, 2.1)$

62. $P_1 = (1.2, 2.3)$; $P_2 = (-0.5, 1.6)$

63. $P_1 = (a, b)$; $P_2 = (0, 0)$

64. $P_1 = (a, a)$; $P_2 = (0, 0)$

In Problems 65–70, tell whether the given points are on the graph of the equation.

65. Equation: $y = x^4 - \sqrt{x}$
Points: $(0, 0); (1, 1); (-1, 0)$

66. Equation: $y = x^3 - 2\sqrt{x}$
Points: $(0, 0); (1, 1); (1, -1)$

67. Equation: $y^2 = x^2 + 9$
Points: $(0, 3); (3, 0); (-3, 0)$

68. Equation: $y^3 = x + 1$
Points: $(1, 2); (0, 1); (-1, 0)$

69. Equation: $x^2 + y^2 = 4$
Points: $(0, 2); (-2, 2); \left(\sqrt{2}, \sqrt{2}\right)$

70. Equation: $x^2 + 4y^2 = 4$
Points: $(0, 1); (2, 0); \left(2, \dfrac{1}{2}\right)$

In Problems 71–78, the graph of an equation is given. List the intercepts of the graph.

71.

72.

73.

74.

75.

76.

77.

78.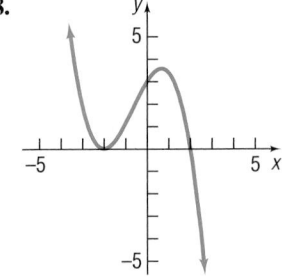

In Problems 79–90, graph each equation by hand by plotting points. Verify your results using a graphing utility.

79. $y = x + 2$ **80.** $y = x - 6$ **81.** $y = 2x + 8$ **82.** $y = 3x - 9$

83. $y = x^2 - 1$ **84.** $y = x^2 - 9$ **85.** $y = -x^2 + 4$ **86.** $y = -x^2 + 1$

87. $2x + 3y = 6$ **88.** $5x + 2y = 10$ **89.** $9x^2 + 4y = 36$ **90.** $4x^2 + y = 4$

In Problems 91–98, graph each equation using a graphing utility. Use a graphing utility to approximate the intercepts rounded to two decimal places. Use the TABLE feature to help to establish the viewing window.

91. $y = 2x - 13$ **92.** $y = -3x + 14$ **93.** $y = 2x^2 - 15$ **94.** $y = -3x^2 + 19$

95. $3x - 2y = 43$ **96.** $4x + 5y = 82$ **97.** $5x^2 + 3y = 37$ **98.** $2x^2 - 3y = 35$

Applications and Extensions

99. The **medians** of a triangle are the line segments from each vertex to the midpoint of the opposite side (see the figure). Find the lengths of the medians of the triangle with vertices at $A = (0, 0)$, $B = (6, 0)$, and $C = (4, 4)$.

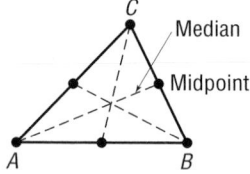

100. An **equilateral triangle** is one in which all three sides are of equal length. If two vertices of an equilateral triangle are $(0, 4)$ and $(0, 0)$, find the third vertex. How many of these triangles are possible?

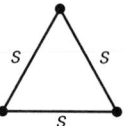

*In Problems 101–104, find the length of each side of the triangle determined by the three points P_1, P_2, and P_3. State whether the triangle is an isosceles triangle, a right triangle, neither of these, or both. (An **isosceles triangle** is one in which at least two of the sides are of equal length.)*

101. $P_1 = (2, 1)$; $P_2 = (-4, 1)$; $P_3 = (-4, -3)$ **102.** $P_1 = (-1, 4)$; $P_2 = (6, 2)$; $P_3 = (4, -5)$

103. $P_1 = (-2, -1)$; $P_2 = (0, 7)$; $P_3 = (3, 2)$ **104.** $P_1 = (7, 2)$; $P_2 = (-4, 0)$; $P_3 = (4, 6)$

105. Baseball A major league baseball "diamond" is actually a square, 90 feet on a side (see the figure). What is the distance directly from home plate to second base (the diagonal of the square)?

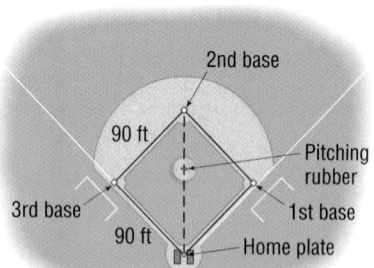

106. Little League Baseball The layout of a Little League playing field is a square, 60 feet on a side. How far is it directly from home plate to second base (the diagonal of the square)?

Source: Little League Baseball, Official Regulations and Playing Rules, 2007.

107. Baseball Refer to Problem 105. Overlay a rectangular coordinate system on a major league baseball diamond so that the origin is at home plate, the positive *x*-axis lies in the

direction from home plate to first base, and the positive *y*-axis lies in the direction from home plate to third base.

(a) What are the coordinates of first base, second base, and third base? Use feet as the unit of measurement.

(b) If the right fielder is located at $(310, 15)$, how far is it from there to second base?

(c) If the center fielder is located at $(300, 300)$, how far is it from there to third base?

108. Little League Baseball Refer to Problem 106. Overlay a rectangular coordinate system on a Little League baseball diamond so that the origin is at home plate, the positive *x*-axis lies in the direction from home plate to first base, and the positive *y*-axis lies in the direction from home plate to third base.

(a) What are the coordinates of first base, second base, and third base? Use feet as the unit of measurement.

(b) If the right fielder is located at $(180, 20)$, how far is it from there to second base?

(c) If the center fielder is located at $(220, 220)$, how far is it from there to third base?

109. Distance between Moving Objects A Dodge Neon and a Mack truck leave an intersection at the same time. The Neon heads east at an average speed of 30 miles per hour, while the truck heads south at an average speed of 40 miles per hour. Find an expression for their distance apart d (in miles) at the end of t hours.

110. Distance of a Moving Object from a Fixed Point A hot-air balloon, headed due east at an average speed of 15 miles per hour at a constant altitude of 100 feet, passes over an intersection (see the figure). Find an expression for its distance d (measured in feet) from the intersection t seconds later.

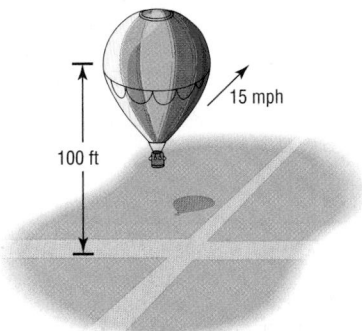

111. Drafting Error When a draftsman draws three lines that are to intersect at one point, the lines may not intersect as intended and subsequently will form an **error triangle.** If this error triangle is long and thin, one estimate for the location of the desired point is the midpoint of the shortest side. The figure shows one such error triangle.
(a) Find an estimate for the desired intersection point.
(b) Find the length of the median for the midpoint found in part (a). See Problem 99.

Source: www.uwgb.edu/dutchs/STRUCTGE/s100.htm

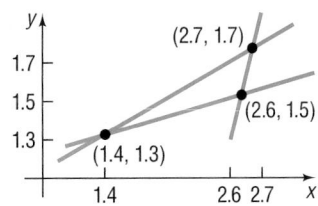

112. Net Sales The figures illustrates how net sales of Wal-Mart Stores, Inc., have grown from 2002 through 2006. Use the

midpoint formula to estimate the net sales of Wal-Mart Stores, Inc., in 2004. How does your result compare to the reported value of $256 billion?
Source: Wal-Mart Stores, Inc., 2006 Annual Report

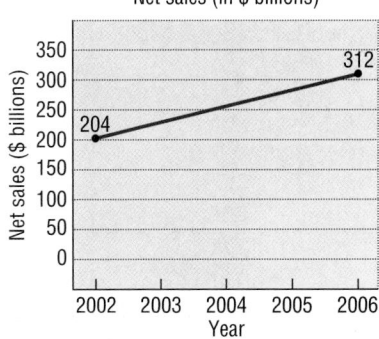

113. Poverty Threshold Poverty thresholds are determined by the U.S. Census Bureau. A poverty threshold represents the minimum annual household income for a family not to be considered poor. In 1995, the poverty threshold for a family of four with two children under the age of 18 years was $15,455. In 2005, the poverty threshold for a family of four with two children under the age of 18 years was $19,806. Assuming poverty thresholds increase in a straight-line fashion, use the midpoint formula to estimate the poverty threshold of a family of four with two children under the age of 18 in 2000. How does your result compare to the actual poverty threshold in 2000 of $17,463?
Source: U.S. Census Bureau

114. Horizontal and Vertical Shifts Suppose that $A = (2, 5)$ are the coordinates of a point in the xy-plane.
(a) Find the coordinates of the point if A is shifted 3 units to the right and 2 units down.
(b) Find the coordinates of the point if A is shifted 2 units to the left and 8 units up.

115. Completing a Line Segment Plot the points $A = (-1, 8)$ and $M = (2, 3)$ in the xy-plane. If M is the midpoint of a line segment AB, find the coordinates of B.

Discussion and Writing

In Problem 116, you may use a graphing utility, but it is not required.

116. (a) Graph $y = \sqrt{x^2}$, $y = x$, $y = |x|$, and $y = (\sqrt{x})^2$, noting which graphs are the same.
(b) Explain why the graphs of $y = \sqrt{x^2}$ and $y = |x|$ are the same.
(c) Explain why the graphs of $y = x$ and $y = (\sqrt{x})^2$ are not the same.
(d) Explain why the graphs of $y = \sqrt{x^2}$ and $y = x$ are not the same.

117. Make up an equation with the points $(2, 0)$, $(4, 0)$, and $(0, 1)$. Compare your equation with a friend's equation. Comment on any similarities.

118. Draw a graph that contains the points $(-2, -1)$, $(0, 1)$, $(1, 3)$, and $(3, 5)$. Compare your graph with those of other students. Are most of the graphs almost straight lines? How many are "curved"? Discuss the various ways that these points might be connected.

119. Explain what is meant by a complete graph.

120. Write a paragraph that describes a Cartesian plane. Then write a second paragraph that describes how to plot points in the Cartesian plane. Your paragraphs should include the terms "coordinate axes," "ordered pair," "coordinates," "plot," "x-coordinate," and "y-coordinate."

'Are You Prepared?' Answers

1. 8   **2.** 5   **3.** $11^2 + 60^2 = 61^2$ **4.** angle–side–angle

1.2 Intercepts; Symmetry; Graphing Key Equations

PREPARING FOR THIS SECTION   *Before getting started, review the following:*

- Solving Quadratic Equations (Appendix A, Section A.6, pp. A50–A55)
- Solving Linear Equations (Appendix A, Section A.6, pp. A47–A49)

Now Work the 'Are You Prepared?' problems on page 23.

OBJECTIVES   1   Find Intercepts Algebraically from an Equation (p. 18)
2   Test an Equation for Symmetry with Respect to (a) the *x*-Axis, (b) the *y*-Axis, and (c) the Origin (p. 19)
3   Know How to Graph Key Equations (p. 21)

1 Find Intercepts Algebraically from an Equation

Figure 28

In Section 1.1, we discussed how to find intercepts from a graph and how to approximate intercepts from an equation using a graphing utility. Now we discuss how to find intercepts from an equation algebraically. To help understand the procedure, we present Figure 28. From the graph, we can see that the intercepts are $(-4, 0)$, $(-1, 0)$, $(4, 0)$, and $(0, -3)$. The *x*-intercepts are -4, -1, and 4. The *y*-intercept is -3. Notice that *x*-intercepts have *y*-coordinates that equal 0; *y*-intercepts have *x*-coordinates that equal 0. This leads to the following procedure for finding intercepts.

Procedure for Finding Intercepts

1. To find the *x*-intercept(s), if any, of the graph of an equation, let $y = 0$ in the equation and solve for *x*, where *x* is a real number.
2. To find the *y*-intercept(s), if any, of the graph of an equation, let $x = 0$ in the equation and solve for *y*, where *y* is a real number.

EXAMPLE 1   **Finding Intercepts from an Equation**

Find the *x*-intercept(s) and the *y*-intercept(s) of the graph of $y = x^2 - 4$. Then graph $y = x^2 - 4$ by plotting points.

Solution   To find the *x*-intercept(s), we let $y = 0$ and obtain the equation

$$x^2 - 4 = 0 \quad \text{\small $y = x^2 - 4$ with $y = 0$}$$
$$(x + 2)(x - 2) = 0 \quad \text{\small Factor.}$$
$$x + 2 = 0 \quad \text{or} \quad x - 2 = 0 \quad \text{\small Zero-Product Property}$$
$$x = -2 \quad \text{or} \quad x = 2 \quad \text{\small Solve.}$$

The equation has two solutions, -2 and 2. The *x*-intercepts are -2 and 2.
To find the *y*-intercept(s), we let $x = 0$ in the equation.

$$y = x^2 - 4$$
$$= 0^2 - 4 = -4$$

The *y*-intercept is -4.
Since $x^2 \geq 0$ for all *x*, we deduce from the equation $y = x^2 - 4$ that $y \geq -4$ for all *x*. This information, the intercepts, and the points from Table 4 enable us to graph $y = x^2 - 4$ by hand. See Figure 29.

Table 4

x	$y = x^2 - 4$	(x, y)
-3	$(-3)^2 - 4 = 5$	$(-3, 5)$
-1	-3	$(-1, -3)$
1	-3	$(1, -3)$
3	5	$(3, 5)$

Figure 29

Now Work PROBLEM 13

2 Test an Equation for Symmetry

Another helpful tool for graphing equations by hand involves *symmetry*, particularly symmetry with respect to the *x*-axis, the *y*-axis, and the origin.

Symmetry often occurs in nature. Consider the picture of the butterfly. Do you see the symmetry?

DEFINITION

A graph is said to be **symmetric with respect to the x-axis** if, for every point (x, y) on the graph, the point $(x, -y)$ is also on the graph.

A graph is said to be **symmetric with respect to the y-axis** if, for every point (x, y) on the graph, the point $(-x, y)$ is also on the graph.

A graph is said to be **symmetric with respect to the origin** if, for every point (x, y) on the graph, the point $(-x, -y)$ is also on the graph.

Figure 30 illustrates the definition. Notice that, when a graph is symmetric with respect to the *x*-axis, the part of the graph above the *x*-axis is a reflection or mirror image of the part below it, and vice versa. When a graph is symmetric with respect to the *y*-axis, the part of the graph to the right of the *y*-axis is a reflection of the part to the left of it, and vice versa. Symmetry with respect to the origin may be viewed in two ways:

1. As a reflection about the *y*-axis, followed by a reflection about the *x*-axis

2. As a projection along a line through the origin so that the distances from the origin are equal

Figure 30

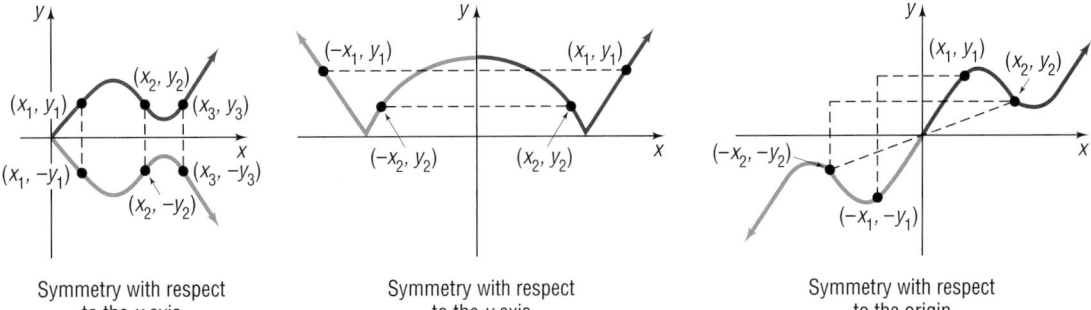

Symmetry with respect to the x-axis

Symmetry with respect to the y-axis

Symmetry with respect to the origin

EXAMPLE 2   Symmetric Points

(a) If a graph is symmetric with respect to the *x*-axis and the point $(4, 2)$ is on the graph, then the point $(4, -2)$ is also on the graph.

(b) If a graph is symmetric with respect to the y-axis and the point $(4, 2)$ is on the graph, then the point $(-4, 2)$ is also on the graph.

(c) If a graph is symmetric with respect to the origin and the point $(4, 2)$ is on the graph, then the point $(-4, -2)$ is also on the graph.

══════ **Now Work** PROBLEM 21

When the graph of an equation is symmetric with respect to the x-axis, the y-axis, or the origin, the number of points that you need to plot in order to see the pattern is reduced. For example, if the graph of an equation is symmetric with respect to the y-axis, then, once points to the right of the y-axis are plotted, an equal number of points on the graph can be obtained by reflecting them about the y-axis. Because of this, before we graph an equation, we first want to determine whether it has any symmetry. The following tests are used for this purpose.

Tests for Symmetry

To test the graph of an equation for symmetry with respect to the

x-Axis   Replace y by $-y$ in the equation. If an equivalent equation results, the graph of the equation is symmetric with respect to the x-axis.

y-Axis   Replace x by $-x$ in the equation. If an equivalent equation results, the graph of the equation is symmetric with respect to the y-axis.

Origin   Replace x by $-x$ and y by $-y$ in the equation. If an equivalent equation results, the graph of the equation is symmetric with respect to the origin.

| EXAMPLE 3 | **Finding Intercepts and Testing an Equation for Symmetry** |

For the equation $y = \dfrac{x^2 - 4}{x^2 + 1}$ (a) find the intercepts and (b) test for symmetry.

Solution   (a) To obtain the x-intercept(s), let $y = 0$ in the equation and solve for x.

$$\frac{x^2 - 4}{x^2 + 1} = 0 \quad \text{Let } y = 0.$$

$$x^2 - 4 = 0 \quad \text{Multiply both sides by } x^2 + 1.$$

$$x = -2 \quad \text{or} \quad x = 2 \quad \text{Factor and use the Zero-product Property.}$$

To obtain the y-intercept(s), let $x = 0$ in the equation and solve for y.

$$y = \frac{x^2 - 4}{x^2 + 1} = \frac{0^2 - 4}{0^2 + 1} = \frac{-4}{1} = -4$$

The x-intercepts are -2 and 2; the y-intercept is -4.

(b) We now test the equation for symmetry with respect to the x-axis, the y-axis, and the origin.

x-Axis: To test for symmetry with respect to the x-axis, replace y by $-y$. Since

$$-y = \frac{x^2 - 4}{x^2 + 1} \text{ is not equivalent to } y = \frac{x^2 - 4}{x^2 + 1}$$

the graph of the equation is not symmetric with respect to the x-axis.

y-Axis: To test for symmetry with respect to the y-axis, replace x by $-x$. Since

$$y = \frac{(-x)^2 - 4}{(-x)^2 + 1} = \frac{x^2 - 4}{x^2 + 1} \text{ is equivalent to } y = \frac{x^2 - 4}{x^2 + 1}$$

the graph of the equation is symmetric with respect to the y-axis.

Origin: To test for symmetry with respect to the origin, replace x by $-x$ and y by $-y$.

$$-y = \frac{(-x)^2 - 4}{(-x)^2 + 1} \quad \text{\small Replace x by }-x\text{ and y by }-y.$$

$$-y = \frac{x^2 - 4}{x^2 + 1} \quad \text{\small Simplify.}$$

Since the result is not equivalent to the original equation, the graph of the equation $y = \dfrac{x^2 - 4}{x^2 + 1}$ is not symmetric with respect to the origin.

Seeing the Concept

Figure 31

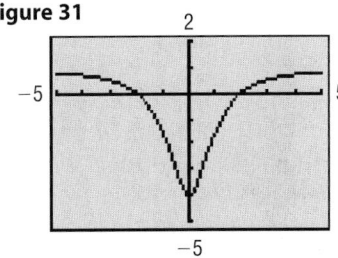

Figure 31 shows the graph of $y = \dfrac{x^2 - 4}{x^2 + 1}$ using a graphing utility. Do you see the symmetry with respect to the y-axis? Also, did you notice that the point $(2, 0)$ is on the graph along with $(-2, 0)$? How could we have found the second x-intercept using symmetry?

Now Work PROBLEM 51

3 Know How to Graph Key Equations

There are certain equations whose graphs we should be able to easily visualize in our mind's eye. We have already discussed the graph of $y = x^2$ in Example 8 in Section 1.1. The next three examples use intercepts, symmetry, and point plotting to obtain the graphs of additional key equations. It is important to know the graphs of these key equations because we use them later.

EXAMPLE 4

Graphing the Equation $y = x^3$ by Finding Intercepts and Checking for Symmetry

Graph the equation $y = x^3$ by hand by plotting points. Find any intercepts and check for symmetry first.

Figure 32

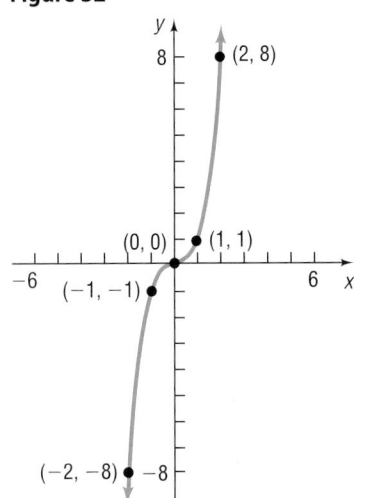

Solution

First, we seek the intercepts of $y = x^3$. When $x = 0$, then $y = 0$; and when $y = 0$, then $x = 0$. The origin $(0, 0)$ is the only intercept. Now we test $y = x^3$ for symmetry.

x-Axis: Replace y by $-y$. Since $-y = x^3$ is not equivalent to $y = x^3$, the graph is not symmetric with respect to the x-axis.

y-Axis: Replace x by $-x$. Since $y = (-x)^3 = -x^3$ is not equivalent to $y = x^3$, the graph is not symmetric with respect to the y-axis.

Origin: Replace x by $-x$ and y by $-y$. Since $-y = (-x)^3 = -x^3$ is equivalent to $y = x^3$ (multiply both sides by -1), the graph is symmetric with respect to the origin.

To graph by hand, we use the equation to obtain several points on the graph. Because of the symmetry with respect to the origin, we only need to locate points on the graph for which $x \geq 0$. See Table 5 on page 22. Points on the graph could also be obtained using the TABLE feature on a graphing utility. See Table 6. Do you see the symmetry with respect to the origin from the table? Figure 32 shows the graph.

Table 5

x	y = x³	(x, y)
0	0	(0, 0)
1	1	(1, 1)
2	8	(2, 8)
3	27	(3, 27)

Table 6

EXAMPLE 5	**Graphing the Equation** $x = y^2$

Graph the equation $x = y^2$. Find any intercepts and check for symmetry first.

Solution

The lone intercept is $(0, 0)$. The graph is symmetric with respect to the x-axis since $x = (-y)^2$ is equivalent to $x = y^2$. The graph is not symmetric with respect to the y-axis or the origin.

To graph $x = y^2$ by hand, we use the equation to obtain several points on the graph. Because the equation is solved for x, it is easier to assign values to y and use the equation to determine the corresponding values of x. Because of the symmetry, we can restrict ourselves to points whose y-coordinates are positive. We then use the symmetry to find additional points on the graph. See Table 7. For example, since $(1, 1)$ is on the graph, so is $(1, -1)$. Since $(4, 2)$ is on the graph, so is $(4, -2)$, and so on. We plot these points and connect them with a smooth curve to obtain Figure 33.

To graph the equation $x = y^2$ using a graphing utility, we must write the equation in the form $y = \{expression\ in\ x\}$. We proceed to solve for y.

$$x = y^2$$
$$y^2 = x$$
$$y = \pm\sqrt{x} \quad \text{Square Root Method}$$

To graph $x = y^2$, we need to graph both $Y_1 = \sqrt{x}$ and $Y_2 = -\sqrt{x}$ on the same screen. Figure 34 shows the result. Table 8 shows various values of y for a given value of x when $Y_1 = \sqrt{x}$ and $Y_2 = -\sqrt{x}$. Notice that when $x < 0$ we get an error. Can you explain why?

Table 7

y	x = y²	(x, y)
0	0	(0, 0)
1	1	(1, 1)
2	4	(4, 2)
3	9	(9, 3)

Figure 33

Figure 34

Table 8

Look again at either Figure 33 or 34. If we restrict y so that $y \geq 0$, the equation $x = y^2$, $y \geq 0$, may be written as $y = \sqrt{x}$. The portion of the graph of $x = y^2$ in quadrant I plus the origin is the graph of $y = \sqrt{x}$. See Figure 35.

Figure 35

EXAMPLE 6

Graphing the Equation $y = \dfrac{1}{x}$

Graph the equation $y = \dfrac{1}{x}$. Find any intercepts and check for symmetry first.

Solution

We check for intercepts first. If we let $x = 0$, we obtain a 0 in the denominator, which is not defined. We conclude that there is no y-intercept. If we let $y = 0$, we get the equation $\dfrac{1}{x} = 0$, which has no solution. We conclude that there is no x-intercept. The graph of $y = \dfrac{1}{x}$ does not cross or touch the coordinate axes.

Next we check for symmetry.

x-Axis: Replacing y by $-y$ yields $-y = \dfrac{1}{x}$, which is not equivalent to $y = \dfrac{1}{x}$.

y-Axis: Replacing x by $-x$ yields $y = \dfrac{1}{-x} = -\dfrac{1}{x}$, which is not equivalent to $y = \dfrac{1}{x}$.

Origin: Replacing x by $-x$ and y by $-y$ yields $-y = -\dfrac{1}{x}$, which is equivalent to $y = \dfrac{1}{x}$. The graph is symmetric only with respect to the origin.

We can use the equation to form Table 9 and obtain some points on the graph. Because of symmetry, we only find points (x, y) for which x is positive. From Table 9 we infer that, if x is a large and positive number, then $y = \dfrac{1}{x}$ is a positive number close to 0. We also infer that if x is a positive number close to 0 then $y = \dfrac{1}{x}$ is a large and positive number. Armed with this information, we can graph the equation. Figure 36 illustrates some of these points and the graph of $y = \dfrac{1}{x}$. Observe how the absence of intercepts and the existence of symmetry with respect to the origin were utilized. Figure 37 confirms our algebraic analysis using a TI-84 Plus.

Table 9

x	$y = \dfrac{1}{x}$	(x, y)
$\dfrac{1}{10}$	10	$\left(\dfrac{1}{10}, 10\right)$
$\dfrac{1}{3}$	3	$\left(\dfrac{1}{3}, 3\right)$
$\dfrac{1}{2}$	2	$\left(\dfrac{1}{2}, 2\right)$
1	1	$(1, 1)$
2	$\dfrac{1}{2}$	$\left(2, \dfrac{1}{2}\right)$
3	$\dfrac{1}{3}$	$\left(3, \dfrac{1}{3}\right)$
10	$\dfrac{1}{10}$	$\left(10, \dfrac{1}{10}\right)$

Figure 36

Figure 37

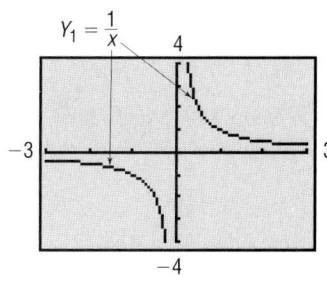

1.2 Assess Your Understanding

'Are You Prepared?'   *Answers are given at the end of these exercises. If you get a wrong answer, read the pages listed in red.*

1. Solve: $2(x + 3) - 1 = -7$ (pp. A47–A49)

2. Solve: $x^2 - 4x - 12 = 0$ (pp. A50–A51)

Concepts and Vocabulary

3. The x-intercepts of the graph of an equation are those x-values for which _____.

4. If for every point (x, y) on the graph of an equation the point $(-x, y)$ is also on the graph, then the graph is symmetric with respect to the _____.

5. If the graph of an equation is symmetric with respect to the y-axis and -4 is an x-intercept of this graph, then _____ is also an x-intercept.

6. If the graph of an equation is symmetric with respect to the origin and $(3, -4)$ is a point on the graph, then _____ is also a point on the graph.

7. **True or False** To find the y-intercepts of the graph of an equation, let $x = 0$ and solve for y.

8. **True or False** If a graph is symmetric with respect to the x-axis, then it cannot be symmetric with respect to the y-axis.

Skill Building

In Problems 9–20, find the intercepts and graph each equation by plotting points. Be sure to label the intercepts.

9. $y = x + 2$

10. $y = x - 6$

11. $y = 2x + 8$

12. $y = 3x - 9$

13. $y = x^2 - 1$

14. $y = x^2 - 9$

15. $y = -x^2 + 4$

16. $y = -x^2 + 1$

17. $2x + 3y = 6$

18. $5x + 2y = 10$

19. $9x^2 + 4y = 36$

20. $4x^2 + y = 4$

In Problems 21–30, plot each point. Then plot the point that is symmetric to it with respect to (a) the x-axis; (b) the y-axis; (c) the origin.

21. $(3, 4)$

22. $(5, 3)$

23. $(-2, 1)$

24. $(4, -2)$

25. $(5, -2)$

26. $(-1, -1)$

27. $(-3, -4)$

28. $(4, 0)$

29. $(0, -3)$

30. $(-3, 0)$

In Problems 31–38, the graph of an equation is given. Indicate whether the graph is symmetric with respect to the x-axis, the y-axis, or the origin.

31.

32.

33.

34.

35.

36.

37.

38.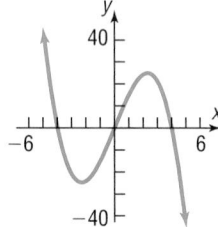

In Problems 39–42, draw a complete graph so that it has the type of symmetry indicated.

39. y-axis

40. x-axis

41. Origin

42. y-axis

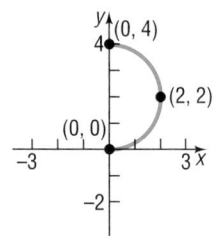

In Problems 43–46, draw a quick sketch of the equation by hand. Be sure to label all intercepts.

43. $y = x^3$

44. $x = y^2$

45. $y = \sqrt{x}$

46. $y = \dfrac{1}{x}$

In Problems 47–62, list the intercepts and test for symmetry.

47. $y^2 = x + 4$

48. $y^2 = x + 9$

49. $y = \sqrt[3]{x}$

50. $y = \sqrt[5]{x}$

51. $y = x^4 - 8x^2 - 9$

52. $y = x^4 - 2x^2 - 8$

53. $9x^2 + 4y^2 = 36$

54. $4x^2 + y^2 = 4$

55. $y = x^3 + x^2 - 9x - 9$ **56.** $y = x^3 + 2x^2 - 4x - 8$ **57.** $y = |x| - 4$ **58.** $y = |x| - 2$

59. $y = \dfrac{3x}{x^2 + 9}$ **60.** $y = \dfrac{x^2 - 4}{2x}$ **61.** $y = \dfrac{-x^3}{x^2 - 9}$ **62.** $y = \dfrac{x^4 + 1}{2x^5}$

Mixed Practice

In Problems 63–70, (a) find the intercepts of each equation, (b) test each equation for symmetry with respect to the x-axis, the y-axis, and the origin, and (c) graph each equation by hand by plotting points. Be sure to label the intercepts on the graph and use any symmetry to assist in drawing the graph. Verify your results using a graphing utility.

63. $y = x^2 - 5$ **64.** $y = x^2 - 8$ **65.** $x - y^2 = -9$ **66.** $x + y^2 = 4$

67. $x^2 + y^2 = 9$ **68.** $x^2 + y^2 = 16$ **69.** $y = x^3 - 4x$ **70.** $y = x^3 - x$

Applications and Extensions

71. Given that the point $(1, 2)$ is on the graph of an equation that is symmetric with respect to the origin, what other point is on the graph?

72. If the graph of an equation is symmetric with respect to the y-axis and 6 is an x-intercept of this graph, name another x-intercept.

73. If the graph of an equation is symmetric with respect to the origin and -4 is an x-intercept of this graph, name another x-intercept.

74. If the graph of an equation is symmetric with respect to the x-axis and 2 is a y-intercept, name another y-intercept.

75. Microphones In studios and on stages, cardioid microphones are often preferred for the richness they add to voices and for their ability to reduce the level of sound from the sides and rear of the microphone. Suppose one such cardioid pattern is given by the equation $(x^2 + y^2 - x)^2 = x^2 + y^2$.
(a) Find the intercepts of the graph of the equation.
(b) Test for symmetry with respect to the x-axis, y-axis, and origin.
Source: www.notaviva.com

76. Solar Energy The solar electric generating systems at Kramer Junction, California, use parabolic troughs to heat a heat-transfer fluid to a high temperature. This fluid is used to generate steam that drives a power conversion system to produce electricity. For troughs 7.5 feet wide, an equation for the cross section is $16y^2 = 120x - 225$.

(a) Find the intercepts of the graph of the equation.
(b) Test for symmetry with respect to the x-axis, y-axis, and origin.
Source: U.S. Department of Energy

Discussion and Writing

77. An equation is being tested for symmetry with respect to the x-axis, the y-axis, and the origin. Explain why, if two of these symmetries are present, the remaining one must also be present.

78. Draw a graph that contains the points $(-2, 5)$, $(-1, 3)$, and $(0, 2)$ that is symmetric with respect to the y-axis. Compare your graph with those of other students; comment on any similarities. Can a graph contain these points and be symmetric with respect to the x-axis? the origin? Why or why not?

'Are You Prepared?' Answers

1. $\{-6\}$ **2.** $\{-2, 6\}$

1.3 Solving Equations Using a Graphing Utility

PREPARING FOR THIS SECTION *Before getting started, review the following:*

- Solving Linear, Quadratic, and Rational Equations (Appendix A, Section A.6, pp. A46–A55)

✏ **Now Work** the 'Are You Prepared?' problems on page 28.

OBJECTIVE 1 Solve Equations Using a Graphing Utility (p. 26)

In this text, we present two methods for solving equations: algebraic and graphical. We shall see as we proceed through this book that some equations can be solved using algebraic techniques that result in *exact* solutions. For other equations, however, there are no algebraic techniques that lead to an exact solution. For such equations, a graphing utility can often be used to investigate possible solutions. When a graphing utility is used to solve an equation, usually *approximate* solutions are obtained.

One goal of this text is to determine when equations can be solved algebraically. If an algebraic method for solving an equation exists, we shall use it to obtain an exact solution. A graphing utility can then be used to support the algebraic result. However, if an equation must be solved for which no algebraic techniques are available, a graphing utility will be used to obtain approximate solutions.

1 Solve Equations Using a Graphing Utility

When a graphing utility is used to solve an equation, usually *approximate* solutions are obtained. Unless otherwise stated, we shall follow the practice of giving approximate solutions as decimals *rounded to two decimal places*.

The ZERO (or ROOT) feature of a graphing utility can be used to find the solutions of an equation when one side of the equation is 0. In using this feature to solve equations, we make use of the fact that when the graph of an equation crosses or touches the x-axis then $y = 0$. For this reason, any value of x for which $y = 0$ will be a solution to the equation. That is, solving an equation for x when one side of the equation is 0 is equivalent to finding the x-intercept of the corresponding graph of the equation.

EXAMPLE 1 | **Using ZERO (or ROOT) to Approximate Solutions of an Equation**

Find the solution(s) of the equation $x^3 - x + 1 = 0$. Round answers to two decimal places.

Solution The solutions of the equation $x^3 - x + 1 = 0$ are the same as the x-intercepts of the graph of $Y_1 = x^3 - x + 1$. Figure 38 shows the graph.

From the graph there appears to be one x-intercept (solution to the equation) between -2 and -1. Using the ZERO (or ROOT) feature of our graphing utility, we determine that the x-intercept, and thus the solution to the equation, is $x = -1.32$ rounded to two decimal places. See Figure 39.

Figure 38

Figure 39

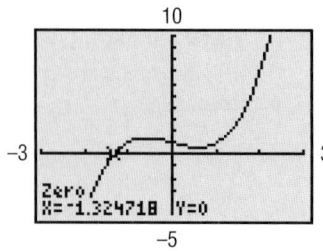

✏ **Now Work** PROBLEM 5

A second method for solving equations using a graphing utility involves the INTERSECT feature of the graphing utility. This feature is used most effectively when one side of the equation is not 0.

EXAMPLE 2 **Using INTERSECT to Approximate Solutions of an Equation**

Find the solution(s) to the equation $4x^4 - 3 = 2x + 1$. Round answers to two decimal places.

Solution   We begin by graphing each side of the equation as follows: graph $Y_1 = 4x^4 - 3$ and $Y_2 = 2x + 1$. See Figure 40.

At the point of intersection of the graphs, the value of the y-coordinate is the same. Thus, the x-coordinate of the point of intersection represents the solution to the equation. Do you see why? The INTERSECT feature on a graphing utility determines the point of intersection of the graphs. Using this feature, we find that the graphs intersect at $(-0.87, -0.73)$ and $(1.12, 3.23)$ rounded to two decimal places. See Figure 41(a) and (b). The solutions of the equation are $x = -0.87$ and $x = 1.12$ rounded to two decimal places.

Figure 40

Figure 41
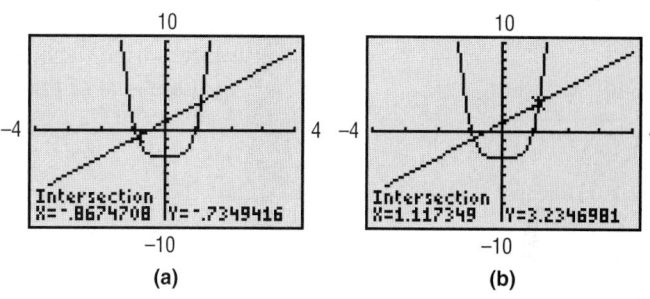

(a)   (b)

➜ **Now Work** PROBLEM 7

SUMMARY

Steps for Approximating Solutions of Equations Using ZERO (or ROOT)

STEP 1: Write the equation in the form {expression in x} $= 0$.
STEP 2: Graph $Y_1 = $ {expression in x}.
STEP 3: Use ZERO (or ROOT) to determine each x-intercept of the graph.

Steps for Approximating Solutions of Equations Using INTERSECT

STEP 1: Graph $Y_1 = $ {expression in x on the left side of the equation}
        $Y_2 = $ {expression in x on the right side of the equation}
STEP 2: Use INTERSECT to determine the x-coordinate of each point of intersection.

EXAMPLE 3 **Solving an Equation Algebraically and Graphically**

Solve the equation: $3(x - 2) = 5(x - 1)$

Algebraic Solution

$$3(x - 2) = 5(x - 1)$$
$$3x - 6 = 5x - 5 \qquad \text{Remove the parentheses.}$$
$$3x - 6 - 5x = 5x - 5 - 5x \qquad \text{Subtract 5x from each side.}$$
$$-2x - 6 = -5 \qquad \text{Simplify.}$$
$$-2x - 6 + 6 = -5 + 6 \qquad \text{Add 6 to each side.}$$
$$-2x = 1 \qquad \text{Simplify.}$$
$$\frac{-2x}{-2} = \frac{1}{-2} \qquad \text{Divide each side by } -2.$$
$$x = -\frac{1}{2} \qquad \text{Simplify.}$$

Graphing Solution

Graph $Y_1 = 3(x - 2)$ and $Y_2 = 5(x - 1)$. Using INTERSECT, we find the point of intersection to be $(-0.5, -7.5)$. See Figure 42. The solution of the equation is $x = -0.5$.

Figure 42
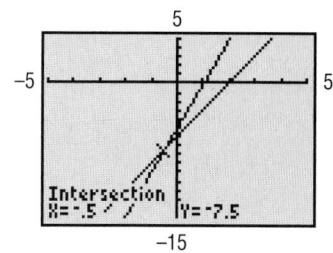

✓ Check: Let $x = -\dfrac{1}{2}$ in the expression in x on the left side of the equation and simplify. Let $x = -\dfrac{1}{2}$ in the expression in x on the right side of the equation and simplify. If the two expressions are equal, the solution checks.

$$3(x - 2) = 3\left(-\frac{1}{2} - 2\right) = 3\left(-\frac{5}{2}\right) = -\frac{15}{2}$$

$$5(x - 1) = 5\left(-\frac{1}{2} - 1\right) = 5\left(-\frac{3}{2}\right) = -\frac{15}{2}$$

Since the two expressions are equal, the solution $x = -\dfrac{1}{2}$ checks.

Now Work PROBLEM 19

1.3 Assess Your Understanding

'Are You Prepared?' *Answers are given at the end of these exercises. If you get a wrong answer, read the pages listed in red.*

1. Solve the equation $2x^2 + 5x + 2 = 0$. (pp. A50–A51)

2. Solve the equation $2x + 3 = 4(x - 1) + 1$. (pp. A47–A48)

Concepts and Vocabulary

3. To solve an equation of the form {expression in x} = 0 using a graphing utility, we graph Y_1 = {expression in x} and use _____ to determine each x-intercept of the graph.

4. *True or False* In using a graphing utility to solve an equation, exact solutions are always obtained.

Skill Building

In Problems 5–16, use a graphing utility to approximate the real solutions, if any, of each equation rounded to two decimal places. All solutions lie between −10 and 10.

5. $x^3 - 4x + 2 = 0$

6. $x^3 - 8x + 1 = 0$

7. $-2x^4 + 5 = 3x - 2$

8. $-x^4 + 1 = 2x^2 - 3$

9. $x^4 - 2x^3 + 3x - 1 = 0$

10. $3x^4 - x^3 + 4x^2 - 5 = 0$

11. $-x^3 - \dfrac{5}{3}x^2 + \dfrac{7}{2}x + 2 = 0$

12. $-x^4 + 3x^3 + \dfrac{7}{3}x^2 - \dfrac{15}{2}x + 2 = 0$

13. $-\dfrac{2}{3}x^4 - 2x^3 + \dfrac{5}{2}x = -\dfrac{2}{3}x^2 + \dfrac{1}{2}$

14. $\dfrac{1}{4}x^3 - 5x = \dfrac{1}{5}x^2 - 4$

15. $x^4 - 5x^2 + 2x + 11 = 0$

16. $-3x^4 + 8x^2 - 2x - 9 = 0$

In Problems 17–36, solve each equation algebraically. Verify your solution using a graphing utility.

17. $2(3 + 2x) = 3(x - 4)$

18. $3(2 - x) = 2x - 1$

19. $8x - (2x + 1) = 3x - 13$

20. $5 - (2x - 1) = 10 - x$

21. $\dfrac{x + 1}{3} + \dfrac{x + 2}{7} = 5$

22. $\dfrac{2x + 1}{3} + 16 = 3x$

23. $\dfrac{5}{y} + \dfrac{4}{y} = 3$

24. $\dfrac{4}{y} - 5 = \dfrac{18}{2y}$

25. $(x + 7)(x - 1) = (x + 1)^2$

26. $(x + 2)(x - 3) = (x - 3)^2$

27. $x^2 - 3x - 28 = 0$

28. $x^2 - 7x - 18 = 0$

29. $3x^2 = 4x + 4$

30. $5x^2 = 13x + 6$

31. $x^3 + x^2 - 4x - 4 = 0$

32. $x^3 + 2x^2 - 9x - 18 = 0$

33. $\sqrt{x + 1} = 4$

34. $\sqrt{x - 2} = 3$

35. $\dfrac{2}{x + 2} + \dfrac{3}{x - 1} = \dfrac{-8}{5}$

36. $\dfrac{1}{x + 1} - \dfrac{5}{x - 4} = \dfrac{21}{4}$

'Are You Prepared?' Answers

1. $\left\{-2, -\dfrac{1}{2}\right\}$ **2.** $\{3\}$

1.4 Lines

OBJECTIVES 1 Calculate and Interpret the Slope of a Line (p. 29)
2 Graph Lines Given a Point and the Slope (p. 31)
3 Find the Equation of a Vertical Line (p. 32)
4 Use the Point–Slope Form of a Line; Identify Horizontal Lines (p. 33)
5 Find the Equation of a Line Given Two Points (p. 34)
6 Write the Equation of a Line in Slope–Intercept Form (p. 34)
7 Identify the Slope and y-Intercept of a Line from Its Equation (p. 35)
8 Graph Lines Written in General Form Using Intercepts (p. 36)
9 Find Equations of Parallel Lines (p. 37)
10 Find Equations of Perpendicular Lines (p. 38)

In this section we study a certain type of equation that contains two variables, called a *linear equation,* and its graph, a *line.*

1 Calculate and Interpret the Slope of a Line

Figure 43

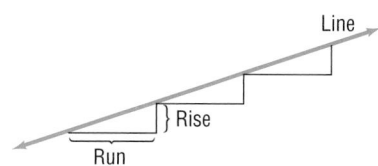

Consider the staircase illustrated in Figure 43. Each step contains exactly the same horizontal **run** and the same vertical **rise.** The ratio of the rise to the run, called the *slope,* is a numerical measure of the steepness of the staircase. For example, if the run is increased and the rise remains the same, the staircase becomes less steep. If the run is kept the same, but the rise is increased, the staircase becomes more steep. This important characteristic of a line is best defined using rectangular coordinates.

DEFINITION

Let $P = (x_1, y_1)$ and $Q = (x_2, y_2)$ be two distinct points. If $x_1 \neq x_2$, the **slope m** of the nonvertical line L containing P and Q is defined by the formula

$$m = \frac{y_2 - y_1}{x_2 - x_1} \qquad x_1 \neq x_2 \qquad (1)$$

If $x_1 = x_2$, L is a **vertical line** and the slope m of L is **undefined** (since this results in division by 0).

Figure 44(a) provides an illustration of the slope of a nonvertical line; Figure 44(b) illustrates a vertical line.

Figure 44

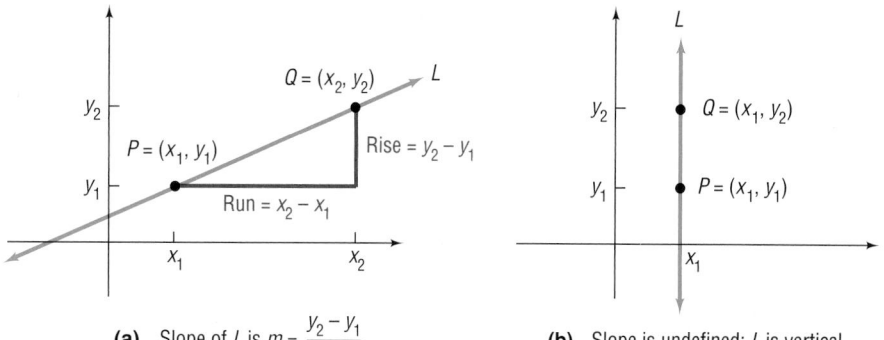

(a) Slope of L is $m = \dfrac{y_2 - y_1}{x_2 - x_1}$

(b) Slope is undefined; L is vertical

As Figure 44(a) illustrates, the slope m of a nonvertical line may be viewed as

$$m = \frac{y_2 - y_1}{x_2 - x_1} = \frac{\text{Rise}}{\text{Run}} \quad \text{or} \quad m = \frac{y_2 - y_1}{x_2 - x_1} = \frac{\text{Change in } y}{\text{Change in } x} = \frac{\Delta y}{\Delta x}$$

The slope m of a nonvertical line L measures the amount that y changes as x changes from x_1 to x_2. We call this the **average rate of change** of y with respect to x.

Two comments about computing the slope of a nonvertical line may prove helpful:

In Words

The symbol Δ is the Greek letter delta. In mathematics, we read Δ as "change in," so $\dfrac{\Delta y}{\Delta x}$ is read, "change in y divided by change in x."

1. Any two distinct points on the line can be used to compute the slope of the line. (See Figure 45 for justification.)

Figure 45

Triangles ABC and PQR are similar (equal angles). Hence, ratios of corresponding sides are proportional so that

Slope using P and $Q = \dfrac{y_2 - y_1}{x_2 - x_1}$

$= \dfrac{d(B, C)}{d(A, C)} = $ Slope using A and B

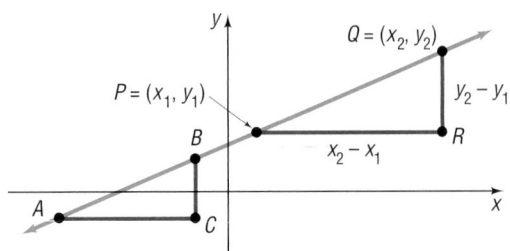

2. The slope of a line may be computed from $P = (x_1, y_1)$ to $Q = (x_2, y_2)$ or from Q to P because

$$\frac{y_2 - y_1}{x_2 - x_1} = \frac{y_1 - y_2}{x_1 - x_2}$$

EXAMPLE 1	**Finding and Interpreting the Slope of a Line Containing Two Points**

The slope m of the line containing the points $(1, 2)$ and $(5, -3)$ may be computed as

$$m = \frac{-3 - 2}{5 - 1} = \frac{-5}{4} = -\frac{5}{4} \quad \text{or as} \quad m = \frac{2 - (-3)}{1 - 5} = \frac{5}{-4} = -\frac{5}{4}$$

For every 4-unit change in x, y will change by -5 units. That is, if x increases by 4 units, then y will decrease by 5 units. The average rate of change of y with respect to x is $-\dfrac{5}{4}$.

Now Work PROBLEMS 11 AND 17

Square Screens

To get an undistorted view of slope, the same scale must be used on each axis. However, most graphing utilities have a rectangular screen. Because of this, using the same interval for both x and y will result in a distorted view. For example, Figure 46 shows the graph of the line $y = x$ connecting the points $(-4, -4)$ and $(4, 4)$. We expect the line to bisect the first and third quadrants, but it doesn't. We need to adjust the selections for Xmin, Xmax, Ymin, and Ymax so that a **square screen** results. On most graphing utilities, this is accomplished by setting the ratio of x to y at $3 : 2$.*

Figure 47 shows the graph of the line $y = x$ on a square screen using a TI-84 Plus. Notice that the line now bisects the first and third quadrants. Compare this illustration to Figure 46.

Figure 46

Figure 47

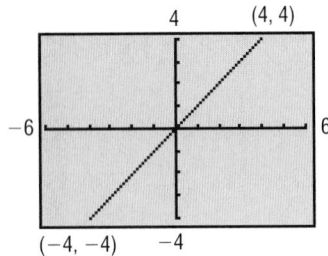

*Most graphing utilities have a feature that automatically squares the viewing window. Consult your owner's manual for the appropriate keystrokes.

To get a better idea of the meaning of the slope m of a line, consider the following:

Exploration

Figure 48

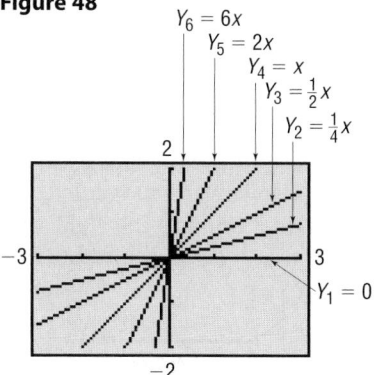

On the same square screen, graph the following equations:

$$Y_1 = 0 \qquad \textit{Slope of line is 0.}$$

$$Y_2 = \frac{1}{4}x \qquad \textit{Slope of line is } \frac{1}{4}.$$

$$Y_3 = \frac{1}{2}x \qquad \textit{Slope of line is } \frac{1}{2}.$$

$$Y_4 = x \qquad \textit{Slope of line is 1.}$$

$$Y_5 = 2x \qquad \textit{Slope of line is 2.}$$

$$Y_6 = 6x \qquad \textit{Slope of line is 6.}$$

See Figure 48.

Exploration

Figure 49

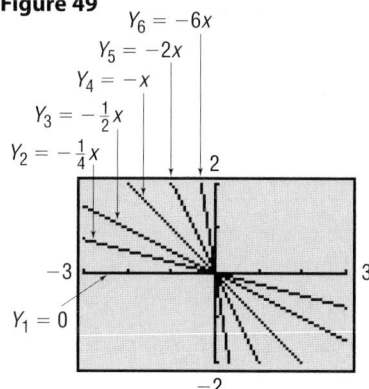

On the same square screen, graph the following equations:

$$Y_1 = 0 \qquad \textit{Slope of line is 0.}$$

$$Y_2 = -\frac{1}{4}x \qquad \textit{Slope of line is } -\frac{1}{4}.$$

$$Y_3 = -\frac{1}{2}x \qquad \textit{Slope of line is } -\frac{1}{2}.$$

$$Y_4 = -x \qquad \textit{Slope of line is } -1.$$

$$Y_5 = -2x \qquad \textit{Slope of line is } -2.$$

$$Y_6 = -6x \qquad \textit{Slope of line is } -6.$$

See Figure 49.

Figures 48 and 49 illustrate the following facts:

1. When the slope of a line is positive, the line slants upward from left to right.
2. When the slope of a line is negative, the line slants downward from left to right.
3. When the slope is 0, the line is horizontal.

Figures 48 and 49 also illustrate that the closer the line is to the vertical position, the greater the magnitude of the slope. So, a line with slope 6 will be steeper than a line whose slope is 3.

2 Graph Lines Given a Point and the Slope

The next example illustrates how the slope of a line can be used to graph the line.

EXAMPLE 2	Graphing a Line Given a Point and a Slope

Draw a graph of the line that contains the point $(3, 2)$ and has a slope of:

(a) $\dfrac{3}{4}$ \qquad\qquad (b) $-\dfrac{4}{5}$

Figure 50

Figure 51

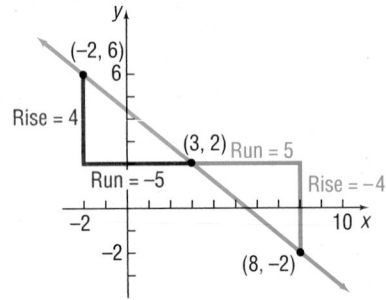

Solution

(a) Slope $= \dfrac{\text{Rise}}{\text{Run}}$. The fact that the slope is $\dfrac{3}{4}$ means that for every horizontal movement (run) of 4 units to the right there will be a vertical movement (rise) of 3 units. If we start at the given point $(3, 2)$ and move 4 units to the right and 3 units up, we reach the point $(7, 5)$. By drawing the line through this point and the point $(3, 2)$, we have the graph. See Figure 50.

(b) The fact that the slope is

$$-\frac{4}{5} = \frac{-4}{5} = \frac{\text{Rise}}{\text{Run}}$$

means that for every horizontal movement of 5 units to the right there will be a corresponding vertical movement of -4 units (a downward movement of 4 units). If we start at the given point $(3, 2)$ and move 5 units to the right and then 4 units down, we arrive at the point $(8, -2)$. By drawing the line through these points, we have the graph. See Figure 51.

Alternatively, we can set

$$-\frac{4}{5} = \frac{4}{-5} = \frac{\text{Rise}}{\text{Run}}$$

so that for every horizontal movement of -5 units (a movement to the left of 5 units) there will be a corresponding vertical movement of 4 units (upward). This approach brings us to the point $(-2, 6)$, which is also on the graph shown in Figure 51.

━ **Now Work** PROBLEM 23

3 Find the Equation of a Vertical Line

Now that we have discussed the slope of a line, we are ready to derive equations of lines. As we shall see, there are several forms of the equation of a line. Let's start with an example.

EXAMPLE 3   **Graphing a Line**

Graph the equation: $x = 3$

Solution

To graph $x = 3$ by hand, we are looking for all points (x, y) in the plane for which $x = 3$. No matter what y-coordinate is used, the corresponding x-coordinate always equals 3. Consequently, the graph of the equation $x = 3$ is a vertical line with x-intercept 3 and undefined slope. See Figure 52(a).

To use a graphing utility, we need to express the equation in the form $y = \{\text{expression in } x\}$. But $x = 3$ cannot be put into this form, so an alternative method must be used. Consult your manual to determine the methodology required to draw vertical lines. Figure 52(b) shows the graph that you should obtain.

Figure 52

$x = 3$

(a)

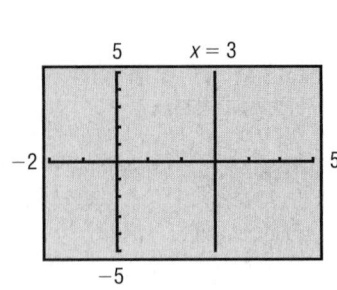

(b)

As suggested by Example 3, we have the following result:

THEOREM

Equation of a Vertical Line

A vertical line is given by an equation of the form

$$x = a$$

where a is the x-intercept.

Figure 53

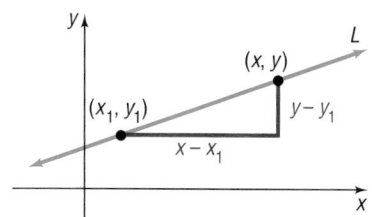

4 Use the Point–Slope Form of a Line; Identify Horizontal Lines

Now let L be a nonvertical line with slope m and containing the point (x_1, y_1). See Figure 53. For any other point (x, y) on L, we have

$$m = \frac{y - y_1}{x - x_1} \quad \text{or} \quad y - y_1 = m(x - x_1)$$

THEOREM

Point–Slope Form of an Equation of a Line

An equation of a nonvertical line of slope m that contains the point (x_1, y_1) is

$$y - y_1 = m(x - x_1) \tag{2}$$

EXAMPLE 4   **Using the Point–Slope Form of a Line**

Figure 54

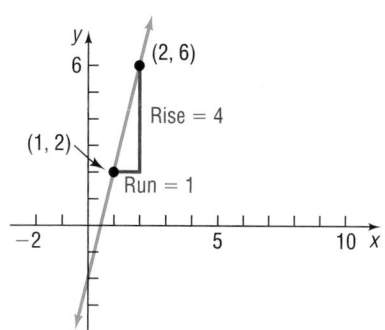

An equation of the line with slope 4 and containing the point $(1, 2)$ can be found by using the point–slope form with $m = 4$, $x_1 = 1$, and $y_1 = 2$.

$$y - y_1 = m(x - x_1) \quad \text{Point-slope form}$$
$$y - 2 = 4(x - 1) \quad m = 4, x_1 = 1, y_1 = 2$$
$$y = 4x - 2$$

See Figure 54 for the graph.

EXAMPLE 5   **Finding the Equation of a Horizontal Line**

Find an equation of the horizontal line containing the point $(3, 2)$.

Solution

Figure 55
$y = 2$

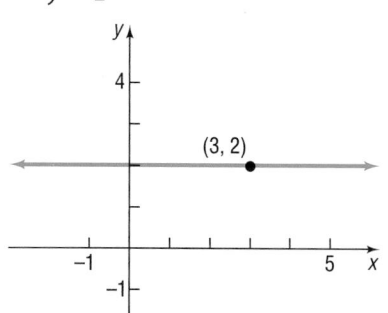

Because all the y-values are the same on a horizontal line, the slope of a horizontal line is 0. To get an equation, we use the point–slope form with $m = 0$, $x_1 = 3$, and $y_1 = 2$.

$$y - y_1 = m(x - x_1) \quad \text{Point-slope form}$$
$$y - 2 = 0 \cdot (x - 3) \quad m = 0, x_1 = 3, \text{ and } y_1 = 2$$
$$y - 2 = 0$$
$$y = 2$$

See Figure 55 for the graph.

As suggested by Example 5, we have the following result:

THEOREM **Equation of a Horizontal Line**

A horizontal line is given by an equation of the form

$$y = b$$

where b is the y-intercept.

5 Find the Equation of a Line Given Two Points

We use the slope formula and the point–slope form of a line to find an equation given two points.

EXAMPLE 6   **Finding an Equation of a Line Given Two Points**

Find an equation of the line containing the points $(2, 3)$ and $(-4, 5)$. Graph the line.

Solution   We first compute the slope of the line with $(x_1, y_1) = (2, 3)$ and $(x_2, y_2) = (-4, 5)$.

$$m = \frac{5 - 3}{-4 - 2} = \frac{2}{-6} = -\frac{1}{3} \qquad m = \frac{y_2 - y_1}{x_2 - x_1}$$

Figure 56

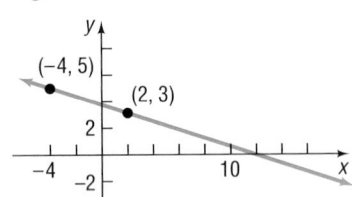

We use the point $(x_1, y_1) = (2, 3)$ and the slope $m = -\dfrac{1}{3}$ to get the point–slope form of the equation of the line.

$$y - 3 = -\frac{1}{3}(x - 2) \qquad y - y_1 = m(x - x_1)$$

See Figure 56 for the graph.

In the solution to Example 6, we could have used the other point, $(-4, 5)$, instead of the point $(2, 3)$. The equation that results, although it looks different, is equivalent to the equation that we obtained in the example. (Try it for yourself.)

Now Work   PROBLEM 37

6 Write the Equation of a Line in Slope–Intercept Form

Another useful equation of a line is obtained when the slope m and y-intercept b are known. In this event, we know both the slope m of the line and a point $(0, b)$ on the line; thus, we may use the point–slope form, equation (2), to obtain the following equation:

$$y - b = m(x - 0) \quad \text{or} \quad y = mx + b$$

THEOREM **Slope–Intercept Form of an Equation of a Line**

An equation of a line with slope m and y-intercept b is

$$y = mx + b \qquad \qquad (3)$$

Now Work   PROBLEM 45

(EXPRESS ANSWER IN SLOPE–INTERCEPT FORM)

Seeing the Concept

Figure 57
$y = mx + 2$

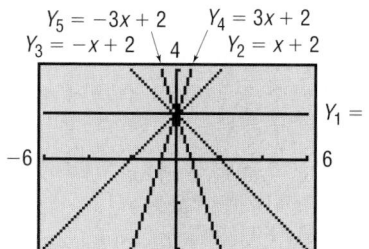

To see the role that the slope m plays, graph the following lines on the same square screen.

$$Y_1 = 2 \qquad m = 0$$
$$Y_2 = x + 2 \qquad m = 1$$
$$Y_3 = -x + 2 \qquad m = -1$$
$$Y_4 = 3x + 2 \qquad m = 3$$
$$Y_5 = -3x + 2 \qquad m = -3$$

See Figure 57. What do you conclude about the lines $y = mx + 2$?

Seeing the Concept

Figure 58
$y = 2x + b$

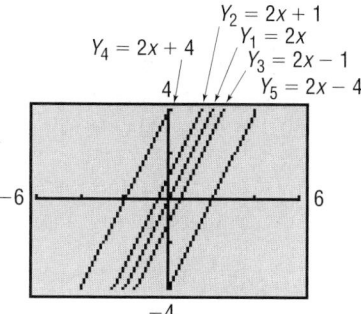

To see the role of the y-intercept b, graph the following lines on the same square screen.

$$Y_1 = 2x \qquad b = 0$$
$$Y_2 = 2x + 1 \qquad b = 1$$
$$Y_3 = 2x - 1 \qquad b = -1$$
$$Y_4 = 2x + 4 \qquad b = 4$$
$$Y_5 = 2x - 4 \qquad b = -4$$

See Figure 58. What do you conclude about the lines $y = 2x + b$?

7 Identify the Slope and y-Intercept of a Line from Its Equation

When the equation of a line is written in slope–intercept form, it is easy to find the slope m and y-intercept b of the line. For example, suppose that the equation of a line is

$$y = -2x + 3$$

Compare it to $y = mx + b$.

$$y = -2x + 3$$
$$\uparrow \qquad \uparrow$$
$$y = mx + b$$

The slope of this line is -2 and its y-intercept is 3.

━━━━━ **Now Work** PROBLEM 71

EXAMPLE 7

Finding the Slope and y-Intercept

Find the slope m and y-intercept b of the equation $2x + 4y = 8$. Graph the equation.

Solution

To obtain the slope and y-intercept, we transform the equation into its slope–intercept form by solving for y.

$$2x + 4y = 8$$
$$4y = -2x + 8$$
$$y = -\frac{1}{2}x + 2 \qquad y = mx + b$$

Figure 59

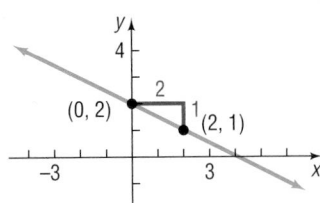

The coefficient of x, $-\dfrac{1}{2}$, is the slope, and the y-intercept is 2. We can graph the line using the fact that the y-intercept is 2 and the slope is $-\dfrac{1}{2}$. Starting at the point $(0, 2)$, go to the right 2 units and then down 1 unit to the point $(2, 1)$. See Figure 59.

Now Work PROBLEM 77

8 Graph Lines Written in General Form Using Intercepts

The form of the equation of the line in Example 7, $2x + 4y = 8$, is called the *general form*.

DEFINITION

The equation of a line is in **general form** when it is written as

$$Ax + By = C \qquad\qquad (4)$$

where A, B, and C are real numbers and A and B are not both 0.

When we want to graph a linear equation that is written in general form, we can solve the equation for y and write the equation in slope–intercept form as we did in Example 7. Another approach to graphing the equation would be to find its intercepts. Remember, the intercepts of the graph of an equation are the points where the graph crosses or touches a coordinate axis.

EXAMPLE 8

Graphing a Linear Equation Using Its Intercepts

Graph the linear equation $2x + 4y = 8$ by finding its intercepts.

Solution

To obtain the x-intercept, let $y = 0$ in the equation and solve for x.

$$\begin{aligned}
2x + 4y &= 8 \\
2x + 4(0) &= 8 \qquad \text{Let } y = 0. \\
2x &= 8 \\
x &= 4 \qquad \text{Divide both sides by 2.}
\end{aligned}$$

The x-intercept is 4 and the point $(4, 0)$ is on the graph of the equation.

To obtain the y-intercept, let $x = 0$ in the equation and solve for y.

$$\begin{aligned}
2x + 4y &= 8 \\
2(0) + 4y &= 8 \qquad \text{Let } x = 0. \\
4y &= 8 \\
y &= 2 \qquad \text{Divide both sides by 4.}
\end{aligned}$$

Figure 60

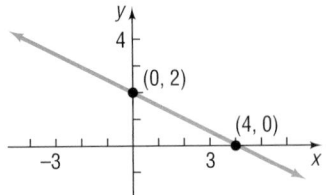

The y-intercept is 2 and the point $(0, 2)$ is on the graph of the equation.

We plot the points $(4, 0)$ and $(0, 2)$ in a Cartesian plane and draw a line through the points. See Figure 60.

Now Work PROBLEM 91

Every line has an equation that is equivalent to an equation written in general form. For example, a vertical line whose equation is

$$x = a$$

can be written in the general form

$$1 \cdot x + 0 \cdot y = a \qquad A = 1, B = 0, C = a$$

A horizontal line whose equation is

$$y = b$$

can be written in the general form

$$0 \cdot x + 1 \cdot y = b \quad A = 0, B = 1, C = b$$

Lines that are neither vertical nor horizontal have general equations of the form

$$Ax + By = C \quad A \neq 0 \text{ and } B \neq 0$$

Because the equation of every line can be written in general form, any equation equivalent to equation (4) is called a **linear equation.**

9 Find Equations of Parallel Lines

When two lines (in the plane) do not intersect (that is, they have no points in common), they are said to be **parallel.** Look at Figure 61. There we have drawn two lines and have constructed two right triangles by drawing sides parallel to the coordinate axes. These lines are parallel if and only if the right triangles are similar. (Do you see why? Two angles are equal.) And the triangles are similar if and only if the ratios of corresponding sides are equal.

This suggests the following result:

Figure 61
The distinct lines are parallel if and only if their slopes are equal.

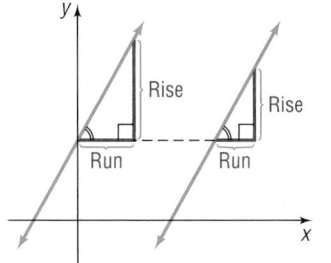

THEOREM

Criterion for Parallel Lines

Two nonvertical lines are parallel if and only if their slopes are equal and they have different *y*-intercepts.

The use of the words "if and only if" in the preceding theorem means that two statements are being made, one the converse of the other.

If two nonvertical lines are parallel, then their slopes are equal and they have different *y*-intercepts.

If two nonvertical lines have equal slopes and they have different *y*-intercepts, then they are parallel.

EXAMPLE 9

Showing That Two Lines Are Parallel

Show that the lines given by the following equations are parallel:

$$L_1: \quad 2x + 3y = 6, \qquad L_2: \quad 4x + 6y = 0$$

Solution

We need to determine whether these lines have equal slopes and different *y*-intercepts, so we write each equation in slope–intercept form:

$$L_1: \quad 2x + 3y = 6 \qquad\qquad L_2: \quad 4x + 6y = 0$$
$$3y = -2x + 6 \qquad\qquad\qquad 6y = -4x$$
$$y = -\frac{2}{3}x + 2 \qquad\qquad\qquad y = -\frac{2}{3}x$$

$$\text{Slope} = -\frac{2}{3}; \ y\text{-intercept} = 2 \qquad \text{Slope} = -\frac{2}{3}; \ y\text{-intercept} = 0$$

Because these lines have the same slope, $-\dfrac{2}{3}$, but different *y*-intercepts, the lines are parallel. See Figure 62.

Figure 62
Parallel lines

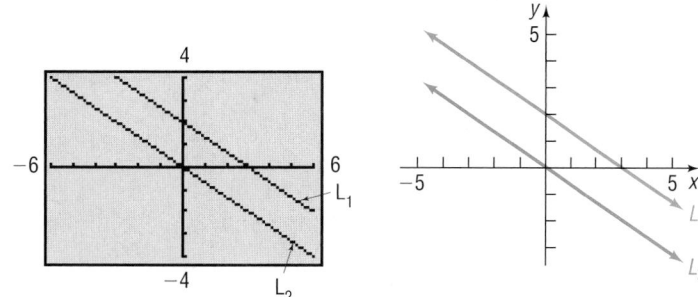

| EXAMPLE 10 | Finding a Line That Is Parallel to a Given Line |

Find an equation for the line that contains the point $(2, -3)$ and is parallel to the line $2x + y = 6$. By hand, graph the two lines.

Solution

Since the two lines are to be parallel, the slope of the line that we seek equals the slope of the line $2x + y = 6$. We begin by writing the equation of the line $2x + y = 6$ in slope–intercept form.

$$2x + y = 6$$
$$y = -2x + 6$$

The slope is -2. Since the line that we seek contains the point $(2, -3)$, we use the point–slope form to obtain

$$
\begin{aligned}
y - y_1 &= m(x - x_1) && \text{Point–slope form} \\
y - (-3) &= -2(x - 2) && m = -2, x_1 = 2, y_1 = -3 \\
y + 3 &= -2x + 4 && \text{Simplify.} \\
y &= -2x + 1 && \text{Slope–intercept form} \\
2x + y &= 1 && \text{General form}
\end{aligned}
$$

This line is parallel to the line $2x + y = 6$ and contains the point $(2, -3)$. See Figure 63.

Figure 63

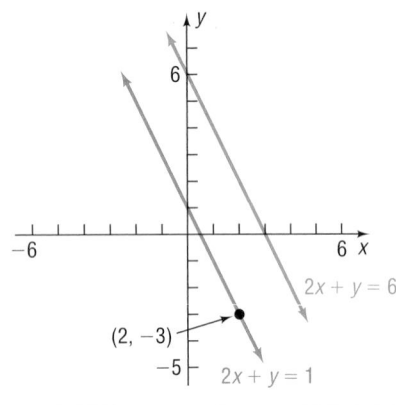

$2x + y = 6$

$(2, -3)$

$2x + y = 1$

✏️ **Now Work** PROBLEM 59

10 Find Equations of Perpendicular Lines

When two lines intersect at a right angle $(90°)$, they are said to be **perpendicular.** See Figure 64.

Figure 64
Perpendicular lines

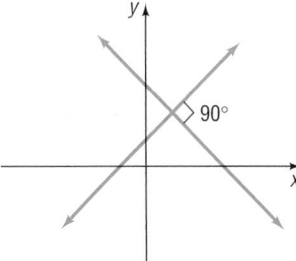

90°

The following result gives a condition, in terms of their slopes, for two lines to be perpendicular.

THEOREM

Criterion for Perpendicular Lines

Two nonvertical lines are perpendicular if and only if the product of their slopes is -1.

Here we shall prove the "only if" part of the statement:

If two nonvertical lines are perpendicular, then the product of their slopes is -1.

In Problem 128, you are asked to prove the "if" part of the theorem; that is:

If two nonvertical lines have slopes whose product is -1, then the lines are perpendicular.

Figure 65

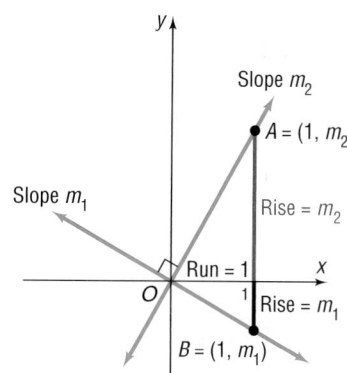

Proof   Let m_1 and m_2 denote the slopes of the two lines. There is no loss in generality (that is, neither the angle nor the slopes are affected) if we situate the lines so that they meet at the origin. See Figure 65. The point $A = (1, m_2)$ is on the line having slope m_2, and the point $B = (1, m_1)$ is on the line having slope m_1. (Do you see why this must be true?)

Suppose that the lines are perpendicular. Then triangle OAB is a right triangle. As a result of the Pythagorean Theorem, it follows that

$$[d(O, A)]^2 + [d(O, B)]^2 = [d(A, B)]^2 \qquad \textbf{(5)}$$

By the distance formula, we can write the squares of these distances as

$$[d(O, A)]^2 = (1 - 0)^2 + (m_2 - 0)^2 = 1 + m_2^2$$
$$[d(O, B)]^2 = (1 - 0)^2 + (m_1 - 0)^2 = 1 + m_1^2$$
$$[d(A, B)]^2 = (1 - 1)^2 + (m_2 - m_1)^2 = m_2^2 - 2m_1m_2 + m_1^2$$

Using these facts in equation (5), we get

$$(1 + m_2^2) + (1 + m_1^2) = m_2^2 - 2m_1m_2 + m_1^2$$

which, upon simplification, can be written as

$$m_1m_2 = -1$$

If the lines are perpendicular, the product of their slopes is -1.   ∎

You may find it easier to remember the condition for two nonvertical lines to be perpendicular by observing that the equality $m_1m_2 = -1$ means that m_1 and m_2 are negative reciprocals of each other; that is, $m_1 = -\dfrac{1}{m_2}$ and $m_2 = -\dfrac{1}{m_1}$.

EXAMPLE 11   **Finding the Slope of a Line Perpendicular to Another Line**

If a line has slope $\dfrac{3}{2}$, any line having slope $-\dfrac{2}{3}$ is perpendicular to it.

EXAMPLE 12   **Finding the Equation of a Line Perpendicular to a Given Line**

Find an equation of the line that contains the point $(1, -2)$ and is perpendicular to the line $x + 3y = 6$. Graph the two lines.

Solution   We first write the equation of the given line in slope–intercept form to find its slope.

$$x + 3y = 6$$
$$3y = -x + 6 \qquad \text{\textit{Proceed to solve for y.}}$$
$$y = -\frac{1}{3}x + 2 \qquad \text{\textit{Place in the form } y = mx + b.}$$

The given line has slope $-\dfrac{1}{3}$. Any line perpendicular to this line will have slope 3.

Because we require the point $(1, -2)$ to be on this line with slope 3, we use the point–slope form of the equation of a line.

$$y - y_1 = m(x - x_1) \qquad \text{\textit{Point–slope form}}$$
$$y - (-2) = 3(x - 1) \qquad \text{\textit{m = 3, } x_1 = 1, y_1 = -2}$$

To obtain other forms of the equation, we proceed as follows:

$$y + 2 = 3(x - 1)$$
$$y + 2 = 3x - 3 \qquad \text{\textit{Simplify}}$$
$$y = 3x - 5 \qquad \text{\textit{Slope–intercept form}}$$
$$3x - y = 5 \qquad \text{\textit{General form}}$$

Figure 66 on the next page shows the graphs.

Figure 66

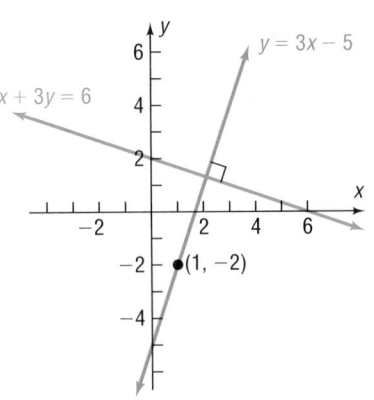

WARNING Be sure to use a square screen when you graph perpendicular lines. Otherwise, the angle between the two lines will appear distorted. ■

Now Work PROBLEM 65

1.4 Assess Your Understanding

Concepts and Vocabulary

1. The slope of a vertical line is _____; the slope of a horizontal line is _____.

2. For the line $2x + 3y = 6$, the x-intercept is _____ and the y-intercept is _____.

3. A horizontal line is given by an equation of the form _____, where b is the _____.

4. *True or False* Vertical lines have an undefined slope.

5. *True or False* The slope of the line $2y = 3x + 5$ is 3.

6. *True or False* The point $(1, 2)$ is on the line $2x + y = 4$.

7. Two nonvertical lines have slopes m_1 and m_2, respectively. The lines are parallel if _____ and the _____ are unequal; the lines are perpendicular if _____.

8. The lines $y = 2x + 3$ and $y = ax + 5$ are parallel if $a =$ _____.

9. The lines $y = 2x - 1$ and $y = ax + 2$ are perpendicular if $a =$ _____.

10. *True or False* Perpendicular lines have slopes that are reciprocals of one another.

Skill Building

In Problems 11–14, (a) find the slope of the line and (b) interpret the slope.

11.

12.

13.

14.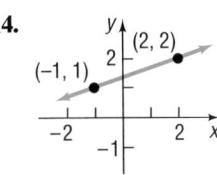

In Problems 15–22, plot each pair of points and determine the slope of the line containing them. Graph the line.

15. $(2, 3); (4, 0)$

16. $(4, 2); (3, 4)$

17. $(-2, 3); (2, 1)$

18. $(-1, 1); (2, 3)$

19. $(-3, -1); (2, -1)$

20. $(4, 2); (-5, 2)$

21. $(-1, 2); (-1, -2)$

22. $(2, 0); (2, 2)$

In Problems 23–30, graph the line containing the point P and having slope m.

23. $P = (1, 2); m = 3$

24. $P = (2, 1); m = 4$

25. $P = (2, 4); m = -\dfrac{3}{4}$

26. $P = (1, 3); m = -\dfrac{2}{5}$

27. $P = (-1, 3); m = 0$

28. $P = (2, -4); m = 0$

29. $P = (0, 3);$ slope undefined

30. $P = (-2, 0);$ slope undefined

In Problems 31–36, the slope and a point on a line are given. Use this information to locate three additional points on the line. Answers may vary.
[**Hint:** It is not necessary to find the equation of the line. See Example 2.]

31. Slope 4; point $(1, 2)$

32. Slope 2; point $(-2, 3)$

33. Slope $-\dfrac{3}{2}$; point $(2, -4)$

34. Slope $\dfrac{4}{3}$; point $(-3, 2)$

35. Slope -2; point $(-2, -3)$

36. Slope -1; point $(4, 1)$

In Problems 37–44, find an equation of the line L.

37.

38.

39.

40.

41.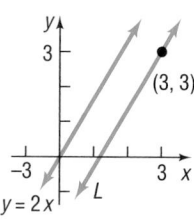

L is parallel to $y = 2x$

42.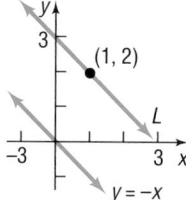

L is parallel to $y = -x$

43.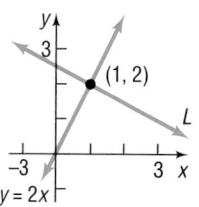

L is perpendicular to $y = 2x$

44.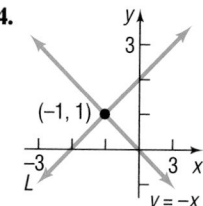

L is perpendicular to $y = -x$

In Problems 45–70, find an equation for the line with the given properties. Express your answer using either the general form or the slope–intercept form of the equation of a line, whichever you prefer.

45. Slope $= 3$; containing the point $(-2, 3)$

46. Slope $= 2$; containing the point $(4, -3)$

47. Slope $= -\dfrac{2}{3}$; containing the point $(1, -1)$

48. Slope $= \dfrac{1}{2}$; containing the point $(3, 1)$

49. Containing the points $(1, 3)$ and $(-1, 2)$

50. Containing the points $(-3, 4)$ and $(2, 5)$

51. Slope $= -3$; y-intercept $= 3$

52. Slope $= -2$; y-intercept $= -2$

53. x-intercept $= 2$; y-intercept $= -1$

54. x-intercept $= -4$; y-intercept $= 4$

55. Slope undefined; containing the point $(2, 4)$

56. Slope undefined; containing the point $(3, 8)$

57. Horizontal; containing the point $(-3, 2)$

58. Vertical; containing the point $(4, -5)$

59. Parallel to the line $y = 2x$; containing the point $(-1, 2)$

60. Parallel to the line $y = -3x$; containing the point $(-1, 2)$

61. Parallel to the line $2x - y = -2$; containing the point $(0, 0)$

62. Parallel to the line $x - 2y = -5$; containing the point $(0, 0)$

63. Parallel to the line $x = 5$; containing the point $(4, 2)$

64. Parallel to the line $y = 5$; containing the point $(4, 2)$

65. Perpendicular to the line $y = \dfrac{1}{2}x + 4$; containing the point $(1, -2)$

66. Perpendicular to the line $y = 2x - 3$; containing the point $(1, -2)$

67. Perpendicular to the line $2x + y = 2$; containing the point $(-3, 0)$

68. Perpendicular to the line $x - 2y = -5$; containing the point $(0, 4)$

69. Perpendicular to the line $x = 8$; containing the point $(3, 4)$

70. Perpendicular to the line $y = 8$; containing the point $(3, 4)$

In Problems 71–90, find the slope and y-intercept of each line. Graph the line by hand. Check your graph using a graphing utility.

71. $y = 2x + 3$

72. $y = -3x + 4$

73. $\dfrac{1}{2}y = x - 1$

74. $\dfrac{1}{3}x + y = 2$

75. $y = \dfrac{1}{2}x + 2$

76. $y = 2x + \dfrac{1}{2}$

77. $x + 2y = 4$

78. $-x + 3y = 6$

79. $2x - 3y = 6$

80. $3x + 2y = 6$

81. $x + y = 1$

82. $x - y = 2$

83. $x = -4$

84. $y = -1$

85. $y = 5$

86. $x = 2$

87. $y - x = 0$

88. $x + y = 0$

89. $2y - 3x = 0$

90. $3x + 2y = 0$

In Problems 91–100, (a) find the intercepts of the graph of each equation and (b) graph the equation.

91. $2x + 3y = 6$

92. $3x - 2y = 6$

93. $-4x + 5y = 40$

94. $6x - 4y = 24$

95. $7x + 2y = 21$

96. $5x + 3y = 18$

97. $\frac{1}{2}x + \frac{1}{3}y = 1$

98. $x - \frac{2}{3}y = 4$

99. $0.2x - 0.5y = 1$

100. $-0.3x + 0.4y = 1.2$

101. Find an equation of the *x*-axis.

102. Find an equation of the *y*-axis.

In Problems 103–106, the equations of two lines are given. Determine if the lines are parallel, perpendicular, or neither.

103. $y = 2x - 3$
$\quad\;\; y = 2x + 4$

104. $y = \frac{1}{2}x - 3$
$\qquad y = -2x + 4$

105. $y = 4x + 5$
$\qquad y = -4x + 2$

106. $y = -2x + 3$
$\qquad y = -\frac{1}{2}x + 2$

In Problems 107–110, match each graph with the correct equation:

(a) $y = x$ (b) $y = 2x$ (c) $y = \frac{x}{2}$ (d) $y = 4x$

107.

108.

109.

110.

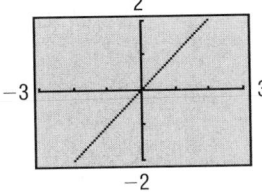

Applications and Extensions

111. Geometry Use slopes to show that the triangle whose vertices are $(-2, 5)$, $(1, 3)$, and $(-1, 0)$ is a right triangle.

112. Geometry Use slopes to show that the quadrilateral whose vertices are $(1, -1)$, $(4, 1)$, $(2, 2)$, and $(5, 4)$ is a parallelogram.

113. Geometry Use slopes to show that the quadrilateral whose vertices are $(-1, 0)$, $(2, 3)$, $(1, -2)$, and $(4, 1)$ is a rectangle.

114. Geometry Use slopes and the distance formula to show that the quadrilateral whose vertices are $(0, 0)$, $(1, 3)$, $(4, 2)$, and $(3, -1)$ is a square.

*115. Truck Rentals A truck rental company rents a moving truck for one day by charging $29 plus $0.20 per mile. Write a linear model that relates the cost C, in dollars, of renting the truck to the number x of miles driven. What is the cost of renting the truck if the truck is driven 110 miles? 230 miles?

116. Cost Equation The **fixed costs** of operating a business are the costs incurred regardless of the level of production. Fixed costs include rent, fixed salaries, and costs of leasing machinery. The **variable costs** of operating a business are the costs that change with the level of output. Variable costs include raw materials, hourly wages, and electricity. Suppose that a manufacturer of jeans has fixed daily costs of $500 and variable costs of $8 for each pair of jeans manufactured. Write a linear model that relates the daily cost C, in dollars, of manufacturing the jeans to the number x of jeans manufactured. What is the cost of manufacturing 400 pairs of jeans? 740 pairs?

117. Cost of Sunday Home Delivery The cost to the *Chicago Tribune* for Sunday home delivery is approximately $0.53 per newspaper with fixed costs of $1,070,000. Write a linear model that relates the cost C and the number x of copies delivered.
Source: Chicago Tribune, 2002.

118. Wages of a Car Salesperson Dan receives $375 per week for selling new and used cars at a car dealership in Oak Lawn, Illinois. In addition, he receives 5% of the profit on any sales that he generates. Write a linear model that relates Dan's weekly salary S when he has sales that generate a profit of x dollars.

119. Electricity Rates in Illinois Commonwealth Edison Company supplies electricity to residential customers for a monthly customer charge of $7.58 plus 8.275 cents per kilowatt-hour for up to 400 kilowatt-hours.

(a) Write a linear model that relates the monthly charge C, in dollars, to the number x of kilowatt-hours used in a month, $0 \le x \le 400$.

*This is a Model It! icon. It indicates that problems in purple require building a mathematical model.

(b) Graph this equation.

(c) What is the monthly charge for using 100 kilowatt-hours?

(d) What is the monthly charge for using 300 kilowatt-hours?

(e) Interpret the slope of the line.

Source: Commonwealth Edison Company, April 2006.

120. **Electricity Rates in Florida**   Florida Power & Light Company supplies electricity to residential customers for a monthly customer charge of $5.17 plus 10.07 cents per kilowatt-hour for up to 1000 kilowatt-hours.

(a) Write a linear model that relates the monthly charge C, in dollars, to the number x of kilowatt-hours used in a month, $0 \le x \le 1000$.

(b) Graph this equation.

(c) What is the monthly charge for using 200 kilowatt-hours?

(d) What is the monthly charge for using 500 kilowatt-hours?

(e) Interpret the slope of the line.

Source: Florida Power & Light Company, April 2006.

121. **Measuring Temperature**   The relationship between Celsius (°C) and Fahrenheit (°F) degrees for measuring temperature is linear. Find a linear equation relating °C and °F if 0°C corresponds to 32°F and 100°C corresponds to 212°F. Use the equation to find the Celsius measure of 70°F.

122. **Measuring Temperature**   The Kelvin (K) scale for measuring temperature is obtained by adding 273 to the Celsius temperature.

(a) Write a linear equation relating K and °C.

(b) Write a linear equation relating K and °F (see Problem 121).

123. **Access Ramp**   A wooden access ramp is being built to reach a platform that sits 30 inches above the floor. The proposed ramp drops 2 inches for every 25-inch run.

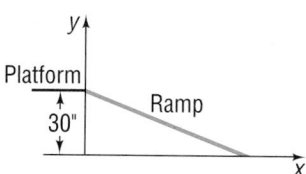

(a) Write a linear equation that relates the height y above the floor to the horizontal distance x from the platform.

(b) Find and interpret the x-intercept of the graph of your equation.

(c) Design requirements stipulate that the maximum run be 30 feet and that the maximum slope be a drop of 1 inch for each 12 inches of run. Will this ramp meet the requirements? Explain.

(d) What slopes could be used to obtain the 30-inch rise and still meet design requirements?

Source: www.adaptiveaccess.com/wood_ramps.php

124. **Cigarette Use**   A study by the Partnership for a Drug-Free America indicated that, in 1998, 42% of teens in grades 7 through 12 had recently used cigarettes. A similar study in 2005 indicated that 22% of such teens had recently used cigarettes.

(a) Write a linear model that relates the percent of teens that recently used cigarettes y to the number of years after 1998, x.

(b) Find the intercepts of the graph of your equation.

(c) Do the intercepts have any meaningful interpretation?

(d) Use your equation to predict the percent for the year 2019. Is this result reasonable?

Source: www.drugfree.org

125. **Product Promotion**   A cereal company finds that the number of people who will buy one of its products in the first month that it is introduced is linearly related to the amount of money it spends on advertising. If it spends $40,000 on advertising, then 100,000 boxes of cereal will be sold, and if it spends $60,000, then 200,000 boxes will be sold.

(a) Write a linear model that relates the amount A spent on advertising to the number x of boxes the company aims to sell.

(b) How much advertising is needed to sell 300,000 boxes of cereal?

(c) Interpret the slope.

126. Show that the line containing the points (a, b) and (b, a), $a \ne b$, is perpendicular to the line $y = x$. Also show that the midpoint of (a, b) and (b, a) lies on the line $y = x$.

127. The equation $2x - y = C$ defines a **family of lines,** one line for each value of C. On one set of coordinate axes, graph the members of the family when $C = -4, C = 0$, and $C = 2$. Can you draw a conclusion from the graph about each member of the family?

128. Prove that if two nonvertical lines have slopes whose product is -1 then the lines are perpendicular.   [**Hint:** Refer to Figure 65 and use the converse of the Pythagorean Theorem.]

Discussion and Writing

129. Which of the following equations might have the graph shown? (More than one answer is possible.)

(a) $2x + 3y = 6$

(b) $-2x + 3y = 6$

(c) $3x - 4y = -12$

(d) $x - y = 1$

(e) $x - y = -1$

(f) $y = 3x - 5$

(g) $y = 2x + 3$

(h) $y = -3x + 3$

130. Which of the following equations might have the graph shown? (More than one answer is possible.)

(a) $2x + 3y = 6$

(b) $2x - 3y = 6$

(c) $3x + 4y = 12$

(d) $x - y = 1$

(e) $x - y = -1$

(f) $y = -2x - 1$

(g) $y = -\dfrac{1}{2}x + 10$

(h) $y = x + 4$

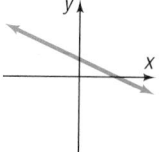

131. The figure shows the graph of two parallel lines. Which of the following pairs of equations might have such a graph?

(a) $x - 2y = 3$
$x + 2y = 7$

(b) $x + y = 2$
$x + y = -1$

(c) $x - y = -2$
$x - y = 1$

(d) $x - y = -2$
$2x - 2y = -4$

(e) $x + 2y = 2$
$x + 2y = -1$

132. The figure shows the graph of two perpendicular lines. Which of the following pairs of equations might have such a graph?

(a) $y - 2x = 2$
$y + 2x = -1$

(b) $y - 2x = 0$
$2y + x = 0$

(c) $2y - x = 2$
$2y + x = -2$

(d) $y - 2x = 2$
$x + 2y = -1$

(e) $2x + y = -2$
$2y + x = -2$

133. *m* Is for Slope   The accepted symbol used to denote the slope of a line is the letter *m*. Investigate the origin of this symbolism. Begin by consulting a French dictionary and looking up the French word *monter*. Write a brief essay on your findings.

134. Grade of a Road   The term *grade* is used to describe the inclination of a road. How does this term relate to the notion of slope of a line? Is a 4% grade very steep? Investigate the grades of some mountainous roads and determine their slopes. Write a brief essay on your findings.

135. Carpentry   Carpenters use the term *pitch* to describe the steepness of staircases and roofs. How does pitch relate to slope? Investigate typical pitches used for stairs and for roofs. Write a brief essay on your findings.

136. Can the equation of every line be written in slope–intercept form? Why?

137. Does every line have exactly one *x*-intercept and one *y*-intercept? Are there any lines that have no intercepts?

138. What can you say about two lines that have equal slopes and equal *y*-intercepts?

139. What can you say about two lines with the same *x*-intercept and the same *y*-intercept? Assume that the *x*-intercept is not 0.

140. If two distinct lines have the same slope, but different *x*-intercepts, can they have the same *y*-intercept?

141. If two distinct lines have the same *y*-intercept, but different slopes, can they have the same *x*-intercept?

142. What Went Wrong?   A student is asked to find the slope of the line joining $(-3, 2)$ and $(1, -4)$. He states that the slope is $\dfrac{3}{2}$. Is he correct? If not, what went wrong?

1.5 Circles

PREPARING FOR THIS SECTION   *Before getting started, review the following:*

- Completing the Square (Appendix A, Section A.6, pp. A52–A53)

- Square Root Method (Appendix A, Section A.6, p. A51)

Now Work the 'Are You Prepared?' problems on page 49.

OBJECTIVES   1 Write the Standard Form of the Equation of a Circle (p. 44)

2 Graph a Circle by Hand and by Using a Graphing Utility (p. 45)

3 Work with the General Form of the Equation of a Circle (p. 47)

1 Write the Standard Form of the Equation of a Circle

One advantage of a coordinate system is that it enables us to translate a geometric statement into an algebraic statement, and vice versa. Consider, for example, the following geometric statement that defines a circle.

DEFINITION   A **circle** is a set of points in the *xy*-plane that are a fixed distance r from a fixed point (h, k). The fixed distance r is called the **radius**, and the fixed point (h, k) is called the **center** of the circle.

Figure 67

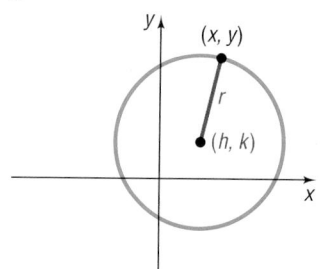

Figure 67 shows the graph of a circle. To find the equation, we let (x, y) represent the coordinates of any point on a circle with radius r and center (h, k). Then the distance between the points (x, y) and (h, k) must always equal r. That is, by the distance formula

$$\sqrt{(x - h)^2 + (y - k)^2} = r$$

After squaring both sides, we obtain

$$(x - h)^2 + (y - k)^2 = r^2$$

DEFINITION   The **standard form of an equation of a circle** with radius r and center (h, k) is

$$(x - h)^2 + (y - k)^2 = r^2 \tag{1}$$

THEOREM   The standard form of an equation of a circle of radius r with center at the origin $(0, 0)$ is

$$x^2 + y^2 = r^2$$

DEFINITION   If the radius $r = 1$, the circle whose center is at the origin is called the **unit circle** and has the equation

$$x^2 + y^2 = 1$$

See Figure 68.

Figure 68
Unit circle $x^2 + y^2 = 1$

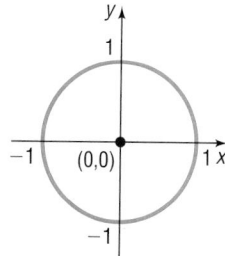

EXAMPLE 1   **Writing the Standard Form of the Equation of a Circle**

Write the standard form of the equation of the circle with radius 5 and center $(-3, 6)$.

Solution   Using the form of equation (1) and substituting the values $r = 5, h = -3$, and $k = 6$, we have

$$(x - h)^2 + (y - k)^2 = r^2$$
$$(x - (-3))^2 + (y - 6)^2 = 5^2$$
$$(x + 3)^2 + (y - 6)^2 = 25$$

Now Work PROBLEM 7

2 Graph a Circle by Hand and by Using a Graphing Utility

The graph of any equation of the form $(x - h)^2 + (y - k)^2 = r^2$ is that of a circle with radius r and center (h, k).

EXAMPLE 2   Graphing a Circle by Hand and by Using a Graphing Utility

Graph the equation: $(x + 3)^2 + (y - 2)^2 = 16$

Solution   Since the equation is in the form of equation (1), its graph is a circle. To graph the equation by hand, we first compare the given equation to the standard form of the equation of a circle. The comparison yields information about the circle.

$$(x + 3)^2 + (y - 2)^2 = 16$$
$$(x - (-3))^2 + (y - 2)^2 = 4^2$$
$$(x - h)^2 + (y - k)^2 = r^2$$

Figure 69

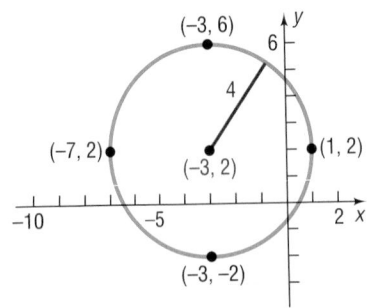

We see that $h = -3$, $k = 2$, and $r = 4$. The circle has center $(-3, 2)$ and a radius of 4 units. To graph this circle, we first plot the center $(-3, 2)$. Since the radius is 4, we can locate four points on the circle by plotting points 4 units to the left, to the right, up, and down from the center. These four points can then be used as guides to obtain the graph. See Figure 69.

To graph a circle on a graphing utility, we must write the equation in the form $y = \{$expression involving $x\}$.* We must solve for y in the equation

$$(x + 3)^2 + (y - 2)^2 = 16$$
$$(y - 2)^2 = 16 - (x + 3)^2 \qquad \text{Subtract } (x + 3)^2 \text{ from both sides.}$$
$$y - 2 = \pm\sqrt{16 - (x + 3)^2} \qquad \text{Use the Square Root Method.}$$
$$y = 2 \pm \sqrt{16 - (x + 3)^2} \qquad \text{Add 2 to both sides.}$$

Figure 70

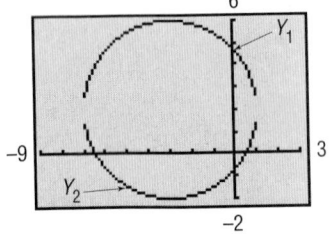

To graph the circle, we graph the top half

$$Y_1 = 2 + \sqrt{16 - (x + 3)^2}$$

and the bottom half

$$Y_2 = 2 - \sqrt{16 - (x + 3)^2}$$

Also, be sure to use a square screen. Otherwise, the circle will appear distorted. Figure 70 shows the graph on a TI-84 Plus.

━━━ **Now Work** PROBLEMS 23(a) AND (b)

EXAMPLE 3   Finding the Intercepts of a Circle

For the circle $(x + 3)^2 + (y - 2)^2 = 16$, find the intercepts, if any, of its graph.

Solution   This is the equation discussed and graphed in Example 2. To find the x-intercepts, if any, let $y = 0$ and solve for x. Then

$$(x + 3)^2 + (y - 2)^2 = 16$$
$$(x + 3)^2 + (0 - 2)^2 = 16 \qquad y = 0$$
$$(x + 3)^2 + 4 = 16 \qquad \text{Simplify.}$$
$$(x + 3)^2 = 12 \qquad \text{Subtract 4 from both sides.}$$
$$x + 3 = \pm\sqrt{12} \qquad \text{Apply the Square Root Method.}$$
$$x = -3 \pm 2\sqrt{3} \qquad \text{Solve for } x.$$

The x-intercepts are $-3 - 2\sqrt{3} \approx -6.46$ and $-3 + 2\sqrt{3} \approx 0.46$.

*Some graphing utilities (e.g., TI-83, TI-84, and TI-86) have a CIRCLE function that allows the user to enter only the coordinates of the center of the circle and its radius to graph the circle.

To find the *y*-intercepts, if any, we let $x = 0$ and solve for *y*. Then

$$(x + 3)^2 + (y - 2)^2 = 16$$
$$(0 + 3)^2 + (y - 2)^2 = 16 \qquad x = 0$$
$$9 + (y - 2)^2 = 16$$
$$(y - 2)^2 = 7$$
$$y - 2 = \pm\sqrt{7} \qquad \text{Apply the Square Root Method.}$$
$$y = 2 \pm \sqrt{7} \qquad \text{Solve for } y.$$

The *y*-intercepts are $2 - \sqrt{7} \approx -0.65$ and $2 + \sqrt{7} \approx 4.65$.

Look back at Figure 69 to verify the approximate locations of the intercepts.

— **Now Work** PROBLEM 23(c)

3 Work with the General Form of the Equation of a Circle

If we eliminate the parentheses from the standard form of the equation of the circle given in Example 3, we get

$$(x + 3)^2 + (y - 2)^2 = 16$$
$$x^2 + 6x + 9 + y^2 - 4y + 4 = 16$$

which we find, upon simplifying, is equivalent to

$$x^2 + y^2 + 6x - 4y - 3 = 0$$

It can be shown that any equation of the form

$$x^2 + y^2 + ax + by + c = 0$$

has a graph that is a circle, or a point, or has no graph at all. For example, the graph of the equation $x^2 + y^2 = 0$ is the single point $(0, 0)$. The equation $x^2 + y^2 + 5 = 0$, or $x^2 + y^2 = -5$, has no graph, because sums of squares of real numbers are never negative.

DEFINITION

When its graph is a circle, the equation

$$x^2 + y^2 + ax + by + c = 0$$

is referred to as the **general form of the equation of a circle.**

If an equation of a circle is in the general form, we use the method of completing the square to put the equation in standard form so that we can identify its center and radius.

EXAMPLE 4

Graphing a Circle Whose Equation Is in General Form

Graph the equation $x^2 + y^2 + 4x - 6y + 12 = 0$

Solution

We complete the square in both *x* and *y* to put the equation in standard form. Group the expression involving *x*, group the expression involving *y*, and put the constant on the right side of the equation. The result is

$$(x^2 + 4x) + (y^2 - 6y) = -12$$

Next, complete the square of each expression in parentheses. Remember that any number added on the left side of the equation must be added on the right.

$$(x^2 + 4x + 4) + (y^2 - 6y + 9) = -12 + 4 + 9$$

$$\underbrace{\qquad}_{\left(\frac{4}{2}\right)^2 = 4} \qquad \underbrace{\qquad}_{\left(\frac{-6}{2}\right)^2 = 9}$$

$$(x + 2)^2 + (y - 3)^2 = 1 \qquad \text{Factor}$$

We recognize this equation as the standard form of the equation of a circle with radius 1 and center $(-2, 3)$. To graph the equation by hand, use the center $(-2, 3)$ and the radius 1. See Figure 71(a).

To graph the equation using a graphing utility, we need to solve for y.

$$(y - 3)^2 = 1 - (x + 2)^2$$

$$y - 3 = \pm\sqrt{1 - (x + 2)^2} \qquad \text{Use the Square Root Method.}$$

$$y = 3 \pm \sqrt{1 - (x + 2)^2} \qquad \text{Add 3 to both sides.}$$

Figure 71(b) illustrates the graph on a TI-84 Plus graphing calculator.

Figure 71

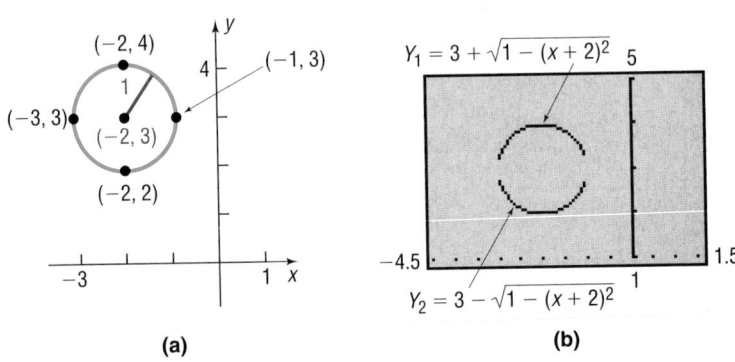

(a)   (b)

━━ **Now Work** PROBLEM 27

| EXAMPLE 5 | **Finding the General Equation of a Circle** |

Find the general equation of the circle whose center is $(1, -2)$ and whose graph contains the point $(4, -2)$.

Solution

To find the equation of a circle, we need to know its center and its radius. Here, we know that the center is $(1, -2)$. Since the point $(4, -2)$ is on the graph, the radius r will equal the distance from $(4, -2)$ to the center $(1, -2)$. See Figure 72. Thus,

Figure 72

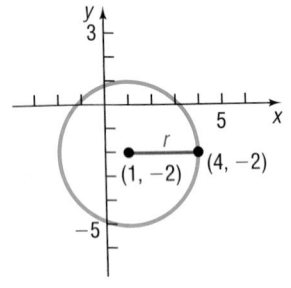

$$r = \sqrt{(4 - 1)^2 + [-2 - (-2)]^2}$$

$$= \sqrt{9} = 3$$

The standard form of the equation of the circle is

$$(x - 1)^2 + (y + 2)^2 = 9$$

Eliminating the parentheses and rearranging terms, we get the general equation

$$x^2 + y^2 - 2x + 4y - 4 = 0$$

━━ **Now Work** PROBLEM 13

Overview

The discussion in Sections 1.4 and 1.5 about lines and circles dealt with two main types of problems that can be generalized as follows:

1. Given an equation, classify it and graph it.

2. Given a graph, or information about a graph, find its equation.

This text deals with both types of problems. We shall study various equations, classify them, and graph them. The second type of problem is usually more difficult to solve than the first. In many instances a graphing utility can be used to solve problems when information about the problem (such as data) is given.

1.5 Assess Your Understanding

'Are You Prepared?' *Answers are given at the end of these exercises. If you get a wrong answer, read the pages listed in red.*

1. To complete the square of $x^2 + 10x$, you would (*add/subtract*) the number _____. (pp. A52–A53)

2. Use the Square Root Method to solve the equation $(x - 2)^2 = 9$. (p. A51)

Concepts and Vocabulary

3. *True or False* Every equation of the form
$$x^2 + y^2 + ax + by + c = 0$$
has a circle as its graph.

4. For a circle, the _____ is the distance from the center to any point on the circle.

5. *True or False* The radius of the circle $x^2 + y^2 = 9$ is 3.

6. *True or False* The center of the circle
$$(x + 3)^2 + (y - 2)^2 = 13$$
is $(3, -2)$.

Skill Building

In Problems 7–10, find the center and radius of each circle. Write the standard form of the equation.

7.

8.

9.

10.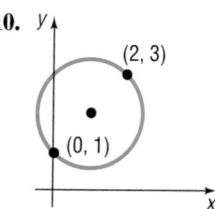

In Problems 11–20, write the standard form of the equation and the general form of the equation of each circle of radius r and center (h, k). *By hand, graph each circle.*

11. $r = 2$; $(h, k) = (0, 0)$ **12.** $r = 3$; $(h, k) = (0, 0)$ **13.** $r = 2$; $(h, k) = (0, 2)$ **14.** $r = 3$; $(h, k) = (1, 0)$

15. $r = 5$; $(h, k) = (4, -3)$ **16.** $r = 4$; $(h, k) = (2, -3)$ **17.** $r = 4$; $(h, k) = (-2, 1)$ **18.** $r = 7$; $(h, k) = (-5, -2)$

19. $r = \dfrac{1}{2}$; $(h, k) = \left(\dfrac{1}{2}, 0\right)$ **20.** $r = \dfrac{1}{2}$; $(h, k) = \left(0, -\dfrac{1}{2}\right)$

In Problems 21–34, (a) find the center (h, k) *and radius r of each circle; (b) by hand, graph each circle; (c) find the intercepts, if any.*

21. $x^2 + y^2 = 4$ **22.** $x^2 + (y - 1)^2 = 1$ **23.** $2(x - 3)^2 + 2y^2 = 8$

24. $3(x + 1)^2 + 3(y - 1)^2 = 6$ **25.** $x^2 + y^2 - 2x - 4y - 4 = 0$ **26.** $x^2 + y^2 + 4x + 2y - 20 = 0$

27. $x^2 + y^2 + 4x - 4y - 1 = 0$ **28.** $x^2 + y^2 - 6x + 2y + 9 = 0$ **29.** $x^2 + y^2 - x + 2y + 1 = 0$

30. $x^2 + y^2 + x + y - \dfrac{1}{2} = 0$ **31.** $2x^2 + 2y^2 - 12x + 8y - 24 = 0$ **32.** $2x^2 + 2y^2 + 8x + 7 = 0$

33. $2x^2 + 8x + 2y^2 = 0$ **34.** $3x^2 + 3y^2 - 12y = 0$

In Problems 35–42, find the standard form of the equation of each circle.

35. Center at the origin and containing the point $(-2, 3)$

36. Center $(1, 0)$ and containing the point $(-3, 2)$

37. Center $(2, 3)$ and tangent to the x-axis

38. Center $(-3, 1)$ and tangent to the y-axis

39. With endpoints of a diameter at $(1, 4)$ and $(-3, 2)$

40. With endpoints of a diameter at $(4, 3)$ and $(0, 1)$

41. Center $(-1, 3)$ and tangent to the line $y = 2$

42. Center $(4, -2)$ and tangent to the line $x = 1$

In Problems 43–46, match each graph with the correct equation.

(a) $(x - 3)^2 + (y + 3)^2 = 9$ (b) $(x + 1)^2 + (y - 2)^2 = 4$ (c) $(x - 1)^2 + (y + 2)^2 = 4$ (d) $(x + 3)^2 + (y - 3)^2 = 9$

43.

44.

45.

46.

Applications and Extensions

47. Find the area of the square in the figure.

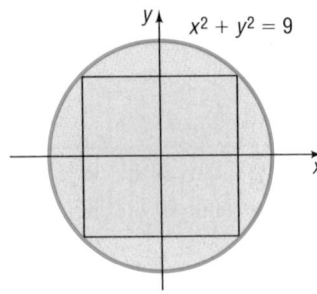

$x^2 + y^2 = 9$

48. Find the area of the blue shaded region in the figure, assuming the quadrilateral inside the circle is a square.

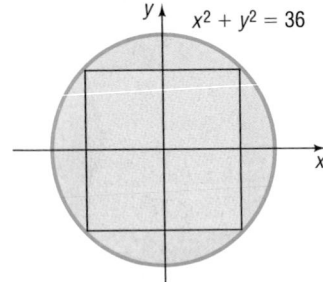

$x^2 + y^2 = 36$

49. Ferris Wheel The original Ferris wheel was built in 1893 by Pittsburg, Pennsylvania bridge builder George W. Ferris. The Ferris wheel was originally built for the 1893 World's Fair in Chicago, but was also later reconstructed for the 1904 World's Fair in St. Louis. It had a maximum height of 264 feet and a wheel diameter of 250 feet. Find an equation for the wheel if the center of the wheel is on the y-axis.

Source: inventors.about.com

50. Ferris Wheel In 2006, the Star of Nanchang (in the Jiangxi province) opened as the world's largest Ferris wheel. It has a maximum height of 160 meters and a diameter of 153 meters, with one full rotation taking approximately 30 minutes. Find an equation for the wheel if the center of the wheel is on the y-axis.

Source: AsiaOne Travel

Note: Two other even larger Ferris wheels are reportedly to be completed in Asia by 2008 in time for the 2008 summer Olympics.

51. Weather Satellites Earth is represented on a map of a portion of the solar system so that its surface is the circle with equation $x^2 + y^2 + 2x + 4y - 4091 = 0$. A weather satellite circles 0.6 unit above Earth with the center of its circular orbit at the center of Earth. Find the equation for the orbit of the satellite on this map.

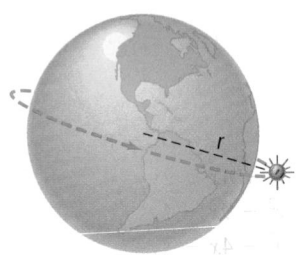

52. The **tangent line** to a circle may be defined as the line that intersects the circle in a single point, called the **point of tangency.** See the figure.

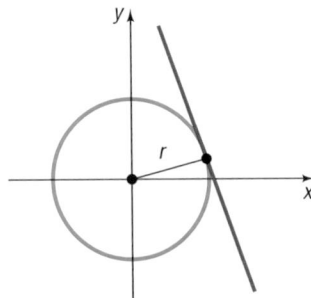

If the equation of the circle is $x^2 + y^2 = r^2$ and the equation of the tangent line is $y = mx + b$, show that:

(a) $r^2(1 + m^2) = b^2$

[Hint: The quadratic equation $x^2 + (mx + b)^2 = r^2$ has exactly one solution.]

(b) The point of tangency is $\left(\dfrac{-r^2 m}{b}, \dfrac{r^2}{b} \right)$.

(c) The tangent line is perpendicular to the line containing the center of the circle and the point of tangency.

53. The Greek Method The Greek method for finding the equation of the tangent line to a circle uses the fact that at any point on a circle the lines containing the center and the tangent line are perpendicular (see Problem 52). Use this method to find an equation of the tangent line to the circle $x^2 + y^2 = 9$ at the point $(1, 2\sqrt{2})$.

54. Use the Greek method described in Problem 53 to find an equation of the tangent line to the circle $x^2 + y^2 - 4x + 6y + 4 = 0$ at the point $(3, 2\sqrt{2} - 3)$.

55. Refer to Problem 52. The line $x - 2y + 4 = 0$ is tangent to a circle at $(0, 2)$. The line $y = 2x - 7$ is tangent to the same circle at $(3, -1)$. Find the center of the circle.

56. Find an equation of the line containing the centers of the two circles

$$x^2 + y^2 - 4x + 6y + 4 = 0$$

and

$$x^2 + y^2 + 6x + 4y + 9 = 0$$

57. If a circle of radius 2 is made to roll along the x-axis, what is an equation for the path of the center of the circle?

58. If the circumference of a circle is 6π, what is its radius?

Discussion and Writing

59. Which of the following equations might have the graph shown? (More than one answer is possible.)

(a) $(x - 2)^2 + (y + 3)^2 = 13$
(b) $(x - 2)^2 + (y - 2)^2 = 8$
(c) $(x - 2)^2 + (y - 3)^2 = 13$
(d) $(x + 2)^2 + (y - 2)^2 = 8$
(e) $x^2 + y^2 - 4x - 9y = 0$
(f) $x^2 + y^2 + 4x - 2y = 0$
(g) $x^2 + y^2 - 9x - 4y = 0$
(h) $x^2 + y^2 - 4x - 4y = 4$

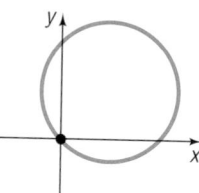

60. Which of the following equations might have the graph shown? (More than one answer is possible.)

(a) $(x - 2)^2 + y^2 = 3$
(b) $(x + 2)^2 + y^2 = 3$
(c) $x^2 + (y - 2)^2 = 3$
(d) $(x + 2)^2 + y^2 = 4$
(e) $x^2 + y^2 + 10x + 16 = 0$
(f) $x^2 + y^2 + 10x - 2y = 1$
(g) $x^2 + y^2 + 9x + 10 = 0$
(h) $x^2 + y^2 - 9x - 10 = 0$

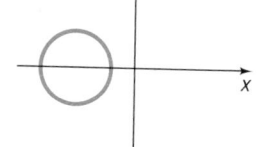

61. Explain how the center and radius of a circle can be used to graph a circle.

62. What Went Wrong? A student stated that the center and radius of the graph whose equation is $(x + 3)^2 + (y - 2)^2 = 16$ are $(3, -2)$ and 4, respectively. Why is this incorrect?

'Are You Prepared?' Answers

1. add; 25

2. $\{-1, 5\}$

CHAPTER REVIEW

Things to Know

Formulas

Distance formula (p. 5)	$d = \sqrt{(x_2 - x_1)^2 + (y_2 - y_1)^2}$
Midpoint formula (p. 7)	$(x, y) = \left(\dfrac{x_1 + x_2}{2}, \dfrac{y_1 + y_2}{2} \right)$
Slope (p. 29)	$m = \dfrac{y_2 - y_1}{x_2 - x_1}$ if $x_1 \neq x_2$; undefined if $x_1 = x_2$
Parallel lines (p. 37)	Equal slopes ($m_1 = m_2$) and different y-intercepts ($b_1 \neq b_2$)
Perpendicular lines (38)	Product of slopes is -1 ($m_1 \cdot m_2 = -1$); slopes are negative reciprocals of each other $\left(m_1 = -\dfrac{1}{m_2} \right)$

Equations of Lines and Circles

Vertical line (p. 33)	$x = a$; a is the x-intercept
Horizontal line (p. 34)	$y = b$; b is the y-intercept
Point–slope form of the equation of a line (p. 33)	$y - y_1 = m(x - x_1)$; m is the slope of the line, (x_1, y_1) is a point on the line
Slope–intercept form of the equation of a line (p. 34)	$y = mx + b$; m is the slope of the line, b is the y-intercept
General form of the equation of a line (p. 36)	$Ax + By = C$; A, B not both 0
Standard form of the equation of a circle (p. 45)	$(x - h)^2 + (y - k)^2 = r^2$; r is the radius of the circle, (h, k) is the center of the circle
Equation of the unit circle (p. 45)	$x^2 + y^2 = 1$
General form of the equation of a circle (p. 47)	$x^2 + y^2 + ax + by + c = 0$, with restrictions on $a, b,$ and c

Objectives

Section	You should be able to	Example(s)	Review Exercises
1.1	**1** Use the distance formula (p. 4)	2, 3, 4	1(a)–6(a); 51, 52(a), 54–56
	2 Use the midpoint formula (p. 7)	5	1(b)–6(b), 55
	3 Graph equations by hand by plotting points (p. 7)	6, 7, 8	9–14
	4 Graph equations using a graphing utility (p. 10)	9, 10	8, 9–14
	5 Use a graphing utility to create tables (p. 12)	11	8
	6 Find intercepts from a graph (p. 12)	12	7
	7 Use a graphing utility to approximate intercepts (p. 13)	13	8
1.2	**1** Find intercepts algebraically from an equation (p. 18)	1	9–14, 47–50
	2 Test an equation for symmetry with respect to (a) the x-axis, (b) the y-axis, and (c) the origin (p. 19)	2, 3	15–22
	3 Know how to graph key equations (p. 21)	4–6	23, 24
1.3	**1** Solve equations using a graphing utility (p. 26)	1, 2	25–28
1.4	**1** Calculate and interpret the slope of a line (p. 29)	1	1(c)–6(c), 1(d)–6(d), 53
	2 Graph lines given a point and the slope (p. 31)	2	57
	3 Find the equation of a vertical line (p. 32)	3	31
	4 Use the point–slope form of a line; identify horizontal lines (p. 33)	4, 5	29, 30
	5 Find the equation of a line given two points (p. 34)	6	32–34
	6 Write the equation of a line in slope–intercept form (p. 34)	pg. 34	29, 30, 32–38
	7 Identify the slope and y-intercept of a line from its equation (p. 35)	7	39–42
	8 Graph lines written in general form using intercepts (p. 36)	8	9, 10
	9 Find equations of parallel lines (p. 37)	9, 10	35, 36
	10 Find equations of perpendicular lines (p. 38)	11, 12	37, 38
1.5	**1** Write the standard form of the equation of a circle (p. 44)	1	43–46
	2 Graph a circle by hand and by using a graphing utility (p. 45)	2, 3	47–50
	3 Work with the general form of the equation of a circle (p. 47)	4, 5	47–50, 55

Review Exercises

In Problems 1–6, find the following for each pair of points:
  (a) The distance between the points.
  (b) The midpoint of the line segment connecting the points.
  (c) The slope of the line containing the points.
  (d) Then interpret the slope found in part (c).

1. $(0, 0); (4, 2)$

2. $(0, 0); (-4, 6)$

3. $(1, -1); (-2, 3)$

4. $(-2, 2); (1, 4)$

5. $(4, -4); (4, 8)$

6. $(-3, 4); (2, 4)$

7. List the intercepts of the following graph.

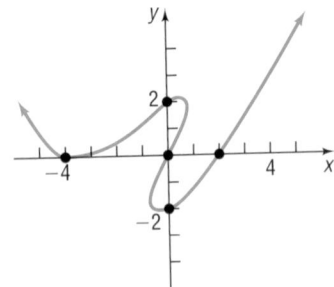

8. Graph $y = -x^2 + 15$ using a graphing utility. Create a table of values to determine a good initial viewing window. Use a graphing utility to approximate the intercepts.

In Problems 9–14, determine the intercepts and graph each equation by hand by plotting points. Verify your results using a graphing utility. Label the intercepts on the graph.

9. $2x - 3y = 6$

10. $x + 2y = 4$

11. $y = x^2 - 9$

12. $y = x^2 + 4$

13. $x^2 + 2y = 16$

14. $2x^2 - 4y = 24$

In Problems 15–22, test each equation for symmetry with respect to the x-axis, the y-axis, and the origin.

15. $2x = 3y^2$

16. $y = 5x$

17. $x^2 + 4y^2 = 16$

18. $9x^2 - y^2 = 9$

19. $y = x^4 + 2x^2 + 1$

20. $y = x^3 - x$

21. $x^2 + x + y^2 + 2y = 0$

22. $x^2 + 4x + y^2 - 2y = 0$

23. Sketch a graph of $y = x^3$.

24. Sketch a graph of $y = \sqrt{x}$.

In Problems 25–28, use a graphing utility to approximate the solutions of each equation rounded to two decimal places. All solutions lie between -10 and 10.

25. $x^3 - 5x + 3 = 0$

26. $-x^3 + 3x + 1 = 0$

27. $x^4 - 3 = 2x + 1$

28. $-x^4 + 7 = x^2 - 2$

In Problems 29–38, find an equation of the line having the given characteristics. Express your answer using either the general form or the slope–intercept form of the equation of a line, whichever you prefer. Graph the line.

29. Slope $= -2$; containing the point $(3, -1)$

30. Slope $= 0$; containing the point $(-5, 4)$

31. Slope undefined; containing the point $(-3, 4)$

32. x-intercept $= 2$; containing the point $(4, -5)$

33. y-intercept $= -2$; containing the point $(5, -3)$

34. Containing the points $(3, -4)$ and $(2, 1)$

35. Parallel to the line $2x - 3y = -4$; containing the point $(-5, 3)$

36. Parallel to the line $x + y = 2$; containing the point $(1, -3)$

37. Perpendicular to the line $x + y = 2$; containing the point $(4, -3)$

38. Perpendicular to the line $3x - y = -4$; containing the point $(-2, 4)$

In Problems 39–42, find the slope and y-intercept of each line.

39. $4x + 6y = 36$

40. $7x - 3y = 42$

41. $\frac{1}{2}x + \frac{5}{2}y = 10$

42. $-\frac{2}{3}x + \frac{1}{2}y = 2$

In Problems 43–46, find the standard form of the equation of the circle whose center and radius are given.

43. $(h, k) = (-2, 3); r = 4$

44. $(h, k) = (3, 4); r = 4$

45. $(h, k) = (-1, -2); r = 1$

46. $(h, k) = (2, -4); r = 3$

In Problems 47–50, find the center and radius of each circle. Graph each circle by hand. Determine the intercepts of the graph of each circle.

47. $x^2 + y^2 - 2x + 4y - 4 = 0$

48. $x^2 + y^2 + 4x - 4y - 1 = 0$

49. $3x^2 + 3y^2 - 6x + 12y = 0$

50. $2x^2 + 2y^2 - 4x = 0$

51. Show that the points $A = (3, 4), B = (1, 1)$, and $C = (-2, 3)$ are the vertices of an isosceles triangle.

52. Show that the points $A = (-2, 0), B = (-4, 4)$, and $C = (8, 5)$ are the vertices of a right triangle in two ways:
(a) By using the converse of the Pythagorean Theorem
(b) By using the slopes of the lines joining the vertices

53. Show that the points $A = (2, 5), B = (6, 1)$, and $C = (8, -1)$ lie on a straight line by using slopes.

54. Show that the points $A = (1, 5), B = (2, 4)$, and $C = (-3, 5)$ lie on a circle with center $(-1, 2)$. What is the radius of this circle?

55. The endpoints of the diameter of a circle are $(-3, 2)$ and $(5, -6)$. Find the center and radius of the circle. Write the general equation of this circle.

56. Find two numbers y such that the distance from $(-3, 2)$ to $(5, y)$ is 10.

57. Graph the line with slope $\frac{2}{3}$ containing the point $(1, 2)$.

58. Create four problems that you might be asked to do given the two points $(-3, 4)$ and $(6, 1)$. Each problem should involve a different concept. Be sure that your directions are clearly stated.

59. Describe each of the following graphs in the xy-plane. Give justification.
(a) $x = 0$
(b) $y = 0$
(c) $x + y = 0$
(d) $xy = 0$
(e) $x^2 + y^2 = 0$

CHAPTER TEST

1. Suppose the points $(-2, -3)$ and $(4, 5)$ are the endpoints of a line segment.
   (a) Find the distance between the two points.
   (b) Find the midpoint of the line segment connecting the two points.

In Problems 2 and 3, graph each equation by hand by plotting points. Use a graphing utility to approximate the intercepts and label them on the graph.

2. $2x - 7y = 21$

3. $y = x^2 - 5$

In Problems 4–6, use a graphing utility to approximate the real solutions of each equation rounded to two decimal places. All solutions lie between -10 and 10.

4. $2x^3 - x^2 - 2x + 1 = 0$
5. $x^4 - 5x^2 - 8 = 0$
6. $-x^3 + 7x - 2 = x^2 + 3x - 3$

7. Use $P_1 = (-1, 3)$ and $P_2 = (5, -1)$.
   (a) Find the slope of the line containing P_1 and P_2.
   (b) Interpret this slope.

8. Sketch the graph of $y^2 = x$.

9. List the intercepts and test for symmetry: $x^2 + y = 9$.

10. Write the slope–intercept form of the line with slope -2 containing the point $(3, -4)$. Graph the line.

11. Write the general form of the circle with center $(4, -3)$ and radius 5.

12. Find the center and radius of the circle $x^2 + y^2 + 4x - 2y - 4 = 0$. Graph this circle.

13. For the line $2x + 3y = 6$, find a line parallel to it containing the point $(1, -1)$. Also find a line perpendicular to it containing the point $(0, 3)$.

CHAPTER PROJECTS

I.   Predicting Olympic Performance   Measurements of human performance over time sometimes follow a strong linear relationship for reasonably short periods. In 2004, the Summer Olympic Games returned to Greece, the home of both the ancient Olympics and the first modern Olympics. The data shown represent the winning times (in hours) for men and women in the Olympic marathon.

1. Treating year as x and the winning time as y, find linear equations relating these variables (separately for men and women) using the data for the years 1992 and 1996. Compare the equations and comment on any similarities or differences.

2. Interpret the slopes in your equations from part 1. Do the y-intercepts have a reasonable interpretation? Why or why not?

3. Use your lines to predict the winning time in the 2004 Olympics. Compare your predictions to the actual results (2.18 hours for men and 2.44 hours for women). How well did your equations do in predicting the winning times?

4. Repeat parts 1 to 3 using the data for the years 1996 and 2000. How do your results compare?

5. Would your equations be useful in predicting the winning marathon times in the 2112 Summer Olympics? Why or why not?

6. Pick your favorite Winter Olympics event and find the winning value (that is, distance, time, or the like) in two Winter Olympics prior to 2006. Repeat parts 1 to 3 using your selected event and years and compare to the actual results of the 2006 Winter Olympics in Torino, Italy.

Year	Men	Women
1984	2.16	2.41
1988	2.18	2.43
1992	2.22	2.54
1996	2.21	2.43
2000	2.17	2.39

Source: www.hickoksports.com/history/olmtandf.shtml

The following projects are available on the Instructors Resource Center (IRC):

II. Project at Motorola   *How Many Cellular Phones Can I Make?*   An industrial engineer uses a model involving equations to be sure that production levels meet customer demand.

III. Isocost Lines   An isocost line is a linear equation used in economics to represent various combinations of two inputs while maintaining a constant level of expenditure. Explore various input options for labor and capital.

Functions and Their Graphs

2

A Look Back

Up to now, our discussion has focused on graphs of equations. In Section A.6, we solved equations containing one variable. In Chapter 1, we developed techniques for graphing equations containing two variables.

A Look Ahead

In this chapter, we look at a special type of equation involving two variables called a *function*. This chapter deals with what a function is, how to graph functions, properties of functions, and how functions are used in applications. The word *function* apparently was introduced by René Descartes in 1637. For him, a function simply meant any positive integral power of a variable *x*. Gottfried Wilhelm Leibniz (1646–1716), who always emphasized the geometric side of mathematics, used the word *function* to denote any quantity associated with a curve, such as the coordinates of a point on the curve. Leonhard Euler (1707–1783) employed the word to mean any equation or formula involving variables and constants. His idea of a function is similar to the one most often seen in courses that precede calculus. Later, the use of functions in investigating heat flow equations led to a very broad definition, due to Lejeune Dirichlet (1805–1859), which describes a function as a rule or correspondence between two sets. It is his definition that we use here.

Outline

2.1 Functions
2.2 The Graph of a Function
2.3 Properties of Functions
2.4 Library of Functions; Piecewise-defined Functions
2.5 Graphing Techniques: Transformations
2.6 Mathematical Models: Building Functions
Chapter Review
Chapter Test
Cumulative Review
Chapter Projects

2.1 Functions

PREPARING FOR THIS SECTION *Before getting started, review the following:*

- Intervals (Appendix A, Section A.9, pp. A78–A79)
- Evaluating Algebraic Expressions, Domain of a Variable (Appendix A, Section A.1, pp. A6–A7)
- Solving Inequalities (Appendix A, Section A.9, pp. A81–A83)

 Now Work the 'Are You Prepared?' problems on page 67.

OBJECTIVES
1 Determine Whether a Relation Represents a Function (p. 56)
2 Find the Value of a Function (p. 60)
3 Find the Domain of a Function Defined by an Equation (p. 63)
4 Form the Sum, Difference, Product, and Quotient of Two Functions (p. 65)

1 Determine Whether a Relation Represents a Function

We often see situations where one variable is somehow linked to the value of another variable. For example, an individual's level of education is linked to annual income. Engine size is linked to gas mileage. When the value of one variable is related to the value of a second variable, we have a *relation*. A **relation** is a correspondence between two sets. If x and y are two elements in these sets and if a relation exists between x and y, then we say that x **corresponds** to y or that y **depends on** x, and we write $x \rightarrow y$.

Figure 1

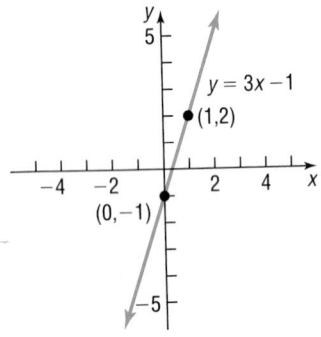

We have a number of ways to express relations between two sets. For example, the equation $y = 3x - 1$ shows a relation between x and y. It says that if we take some number x, multiply it by 3, and then subtract 1 we obtain the corresponding value of y. In this sense, x serves as the **input** to the relation and y is the **output** of the relation. We can also express this relation as a graph, as shown in Figure 1.

Not only can a relation be expressed through an equation or graph, but we can also express a relation through a technique called *mapping*. A **map** illustrates a relation by using a set of inputs and drawing arrows to the corresponding element in the set of outputs. Ordered pairs can also be used to represent $x \rightarrow y$ as (x, y). We illustrate these two concepts in Example 1.

EXAMPLE 1 Maps and Ordered Pairs as Relations

Figure 2 shows a relation between states and the number of representatives each state has in the House of Representatives. The relation might be named "number of representatives."

Figure 2

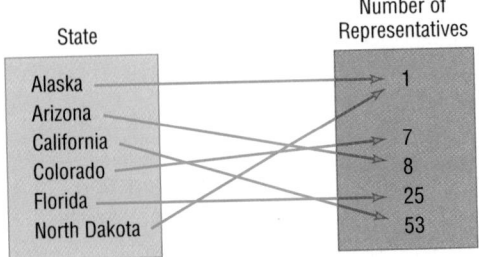

In this relation, Alaska corresponds to 1, Arizona corresponds to 8, and so on. Using ordered pairs, this relation would be expressed as

{(Alaska, 1), (Arizona, 8), (California, 53), (Colorado, 7), (Florida, 25), (North Dakota, 1)}

We now present one of the most important concepts in algebra—the *function*. A function is a special type of relation. To understand the idea behind a function, let's revisit the relation presented in Example 1. If we were to ask, "How many representatives does Alaska have?," you would respond 1. In fact, each input *state* corresponds to a single output *number of representatives*.

Let's consider a second relation where we have a correspondence between the weight of a brain (in grams) and IQ. See Figure 3. Notice the brain that weighs 1342 grams corresponds to two different IQs: 104 and 111. So, if someone asked, "What is the IQ of an individual whose brain weighs 1342 grams?," you cannot provide a single answer.

Figure 3

Let's look at one more relation. Figure 4 is a relation that shows a correspondence between *animals* and *life expectancy*. If asked to determine the life expectancy of a dog, we would all respond "11 years." If asked to determine the life expectancy of a rabbit, we would all respond "7 years."

Figure 4

Notice that the relations presented in Figures 2 and 4 have something in common. What is it? The common link between these two relations is that each input corresponds to exactly one output. This leads to the definition of a *function*.

DEFINITION

Let X and Y be two nonempty sets.* A **function** from X into Y is a relation that associates with each element of X exactly one element of Y.

The set X is called the **domain** of the function. For each element x in X, the corresponding element y in Y is called the **value** of the function at x, or the **image** of x. The set of all images of the elements in the domain is called the **range** of the function. See Figure 5.

Figure 5

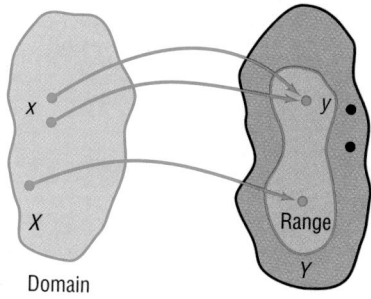

*The sets X and Y will usually be sets of real numbers, in which case a (real) function results. The two sets can also be sets of complex numbers, and then we have defined a complex function. In the broad definition (due to Lejeune Dirichlet), X and Y can be any two sets.

Since there may be some elements in Y that are not the image of some x in X, it follows that the range of a function may be a subset of Y, as shown in Figure 5.

Not all relations between two sets are functions. The next example shows how to determine whether a relation is a function.

EXAMPLE 2

Determining Whether a Relation Represents a Function

Determine which of the following relations represent a function. If the relation is a function, then state its domain and range.

(a) See Figure 6. For this relation, the domain represents the level of education and the range represents the unemployment rate.

Figure 6

Source: Statistical Abstract of the United States, 2006

(b) See Figure 7. For this relation, the domain represents the number of calories in a sandwich from a fast-food restaurant and the range represents the fat content (in grams).

Figure 7

Source: Each company's Web site

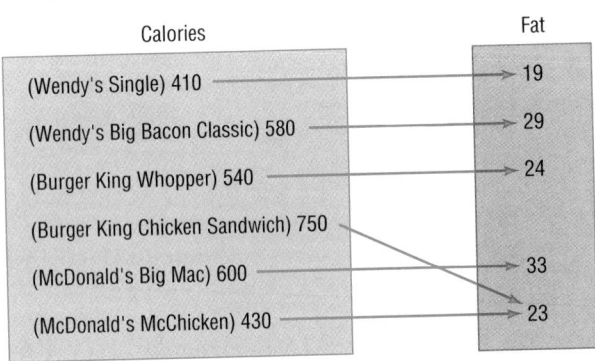

(c) See Figure 8. For this relation, the domain represents the weight (in carats) of pear-cut diamonds and the range represents the price (in dollars).

Figure 8

Source: diamonds.com

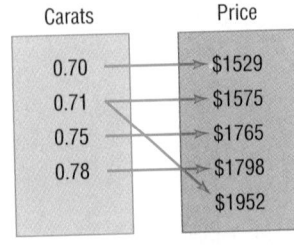

Solution

(a) The relation in Figure 6 is a function because each element in the domain corresponds to exactly one element in the range. The domain of the relation is {No High School Diploma, High School Diploma, Some College, College Graduate}, and the range of the relation is {8.5%, 5.0%, 4.2%, 2.7%}.

(b) The relation in Figure 7 is a function because each element in the domain corresponds to exactly one element in the range. The domain of the relation is {410, 580, 540, 750, 600, 430}. The range of the relation is {19, 29, 24, 33, 23}.

Figure 10

Input x

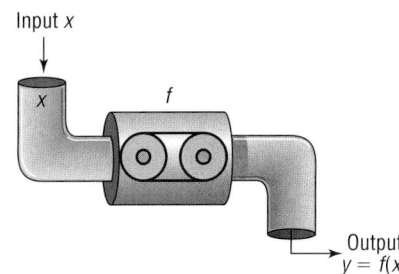

Output $y = f(x)$

Sometimes it is helpful to think of a function f as a machine that receives as input a number from the domain, manipulates it, and outputs the value. See Figure 10.

The restrictions on this input/output machine are as follows:

1. It only accepts numbers from the domain of the function.

2. For each input, there is exactly one output (which may be repeated for different inputs).

For a function $y = f(x)$, the variable x is called the **independent variable,** because it can be assigned any of the permissible numbers from the domain. The variable y is called the **dependent variable,** because its value depends on x.

Any symbol can be used to represent the independent and dependent variables. For example, if f is the *cube function,* then f can be given by $f(x) = x^3$ or $f(t) = t^3$ or $f(z) = z^3$. All three functions are the same. Each tells us to cube the independent variable to get the output. In practice, the symbols used for the independent and dependent variables are based on common usage, such as using C for cost in business.

The independent variable is also called the **argument** of the function. Thinking of the independent variable as an argument can sometimes make it easier to find the value of a function. For example, if f is the function defined by $f(x) = x^3$, then f tells us to cube the argument. Thus, $f(2)$ means to cube 2, $f(a)$ means to cube the number a, and $f(x + h)$ means to cube the quantity $x + h$.

EXAMPLE 6   **Illustrating Language Used with Functions**

Consider the function $f(p) = p^2$. The name of the function is f. The *independent variable* or *argument* of f is p. If $q = f(p)$, then q is the *dependent variable.* Since $f(3) = 9$, we say that 9 is the *value* of f at 3 or 9 is the *image* of 3. Because we can square any real number, the *domain* of the function is the set of all real numbers, or $(-\infty, \infty)$ using interval notation. Because the square of any real number is greater than or equal to zero, the *range* of f is $[0, \infty)$. In words, the function f tells us to square the argument.

◼

EXAMPLE 7   **Finding Values of a Function**

For the function f defined by $f(x) = 2x^2 - 3x$, evaluate

(a) $f(3)$ (b) $f(x) + f(3)$ (c) $3f(x)$

(d) $f(-x)$ (e) $-f(x)$ (f) $f(3x)$

(g) $f(x + 3)$ (h) $\dfrac{f(x + h) - f(x)}{h}$ $h \neq 0$

Solution   (a) We substitute 3 for x in the equation for f, $f(x) = 2x^2 - 3x$, to get
$$f(3) = 2(3)^2 - 3(3) = 18 - 9 = 9$$
The image of 3 is 9.

(b) $f(x) + f(3) = (2x^2 - 3x) + (9) = 2x^2 - 3x + 9$

(c) We multiply the equation for f by 3.
$$3f(x) = 3(2x^2 - 3x) = 6x^2 - 9x$$

(d) We substitute $-x$ for x in the equation for f and simplify.
$$f(-x) = 2(-x)^2 - 3(-x) = 2x^2 + 3x$$

(e) $-f(x) = -(2x^2 - 3x) = -2x^2 + 3x$

(f) We substitute $3x$ for x in the equation for f and simplify.
$$f(3x) = 2(3x)^2 - 3(3x) = 2(9x^2) - 9x = 18x^2 - 9x$$

(g) We substitute $x + 3$ for x in the equation for f and simplify.

$$f(x + 3) = 2(x + 3)^2 - 3(x + 3) \qquad \text{Notice the use of parentheses here.}$$

$$= 2(x^2 + 6x + 9) - 3x - 9$$

$$= 2x^2 + 12x + 18 - 3x - 9$$

$$= 2x^2 + 9x + 9$$

(h) $\dfrac{f(x + h) - f(x)}{h} \underset{\uparrow}{=} \dfrac{[2(x + h)^2 - 3(x + h)] - [2x^2 - 3x]}{h}$

$f(x + h) = 2(x + h)^2 - 3(x + h)$

$$= \dfrac{2(x^2 + 2xh + h^2) - 3x - 3h - 2x^2 + 3x}{h} \qquad \text{Simplify.}$$

$$= \dfrac{2x^2 + 4xh + 2h^2 - 3h - 2x^2}{h} \qquad \begin{array}{l}\text{Distribute and combine} \\ \text{like terms.}\end{array}$$

$$= \dfrac{4xh + 2h^2 - 3h}{h} \qquad \text{Combine like terms.}$$

$$= \dfrac{h(4x + 2h - 3)}{h} \qquad \text{Factor out } h.$$

$$= 4x + 2h - 3 \qquad \text{Divide out the } h\text{'s.}$$

Notice in Example 7 that $f(x + 3) \neq f(x) + f(3)$, $f(-x) \neq -f(x)$, and $3f(x) \neq f(3x)$.

 The expression in part (h) is called the **difference quotient** of f, an important expression in calculus.

Now Work PROBLEMS 39 AND 73

Most calculators have special keys that allow you to find the value of certain commonly used functions. For example, you should be able to find the square function $f(x) = x^2$, the square root function $f(x) = \sqrt{x}$, the reciprocal function $f(x) = \dfrac{1}{x} = x^{-1}$, and many others that will be discussed later in this book (such as $\ln x$ and $\log x$). Verify the results of Example 7, which follows, on your calculator.

EXAMPLE 8 **Finding Values of a Function on a Calculator**

(a) $f(x) = x^2$ $\qquad$ $f(1.234) = 1.234^2 = 1.522756$

(b) $F(x) = \dfrac{1}{x}$ $\qquad$ $F(1.234) = \dfrac{1}{1.234} \approx 0.8103727715$

(c) $g(x) = \sqrt{x}$ $\qquad$ $g(1.234) = \sqrt{1.234} \approx 1.110855526$

COMMENT Graphing calculators can be used to evaluate any function that you wish. Figure 11 shows the result obtained in Example 7(a) on a TI-84 Plus graphing calculator with the function to be evaluated, $f(x) = 2x^2 - 3x$, in Y_1.

Figure 11

Implicit Form of a Function

In general, when a function f is defined by an equation in x and y, we say that the function f is given **implicitly.** If it is possible to solve the equation for y in terms of x, then we write $y = f(x)$ and say that the function is given **explicitly.** For example,

Implicit Form	**Explicit Form**
$3x + y = 5$	$y = f(x) = -3x + 5$
$x^2 - y = 6$	$y = f(x) = x^2 - 6$
$xy = 4$	$y = f(x) = \dfrac{4}{x}$

COMMENT The explicit form of a function is the form required by a graphing calculator. ■

We list next a summary of some important facts to remember about a function f.

SUMMARY Important Facts about Functions

(a) For each x in a domain of a function f, there is exactly one image $f(x)$ in the range; however, an element in the range can result from more than one x in the domain.
(b) f is the symbol that we use to denote the function. It is symbolic of the equation that we use to get from an x in the domain to $f(x)$ in the range.
(c) If $y = f(x)$, then x is called the independent variable or argument of f, and y is called the dependent variable or the value of f at x.

---

3 Find the Domain of a Function Defined by an Equation

Often the domain of a function f is not specified; instead, only the equation defining the function is given. In such cases, we agree that the **domain of f** is the largest set of real numbers for which the value $f(x)$ is a real number. The domain of a function f is the same as the domain of the variable x in the expression $f(x)$.

EXAMPLE 9 | Finding the Domain of a Function

Find the domain of each of the following functions:

(a) $f(x) = x^2 + 5x$ (b) $g(x) = \dfrac{3x}{x^2 - 4}$ (c) $h(t) = \sqrt{4 - 3t}$

Solution

(a) The function tells us to square a number and then add five times the number. Since these operations can be performed on any real number, we conclude that the domain of f is the set of all real numbers.

(b) The function g tells us to divide $3x$ by $x^2 - 4$. Since division by 0 is not defined, the denominator $x^2 - 4$ can never be 0, so x can never equal -2 or 2. The domain of the function g is $\{x \mid x \neq -2, x \neq 2\}$.

(c) The function h tells us to take the square root of $4 - 3t$. But only nonnegative numbers have real square roots, so the expression under the square root (the radicand) must be nonnegative (greater than or equal to zero). This requires that

In Words
The domain of g found in Example 9(b) is $\{x \mid x \neq -2, x \neq 2\}$. This notation is read, "The domain of the function g is the set of all real numbers x such that x does not equal -2 and x does not equal 2."

$$4 - 3t \geq 0$$
$$-3t \geq -4$$
$$t \leq \frac{4}{3}$$

The domain of h is $\left\{ t \mid t \leq \dfrac{4}{3} \right\}$ or the interval $\left(-\infty, \dfrac{4}{3} \right]$.

For the functions that we will encounter in this book, the following steps may prove helpful for finding the domain of a function that is defined by an equation whose domain is a subset of real numbers.

Finding the Domain of a Function Defined by an Equation

1. Start with the domain as the set of real numbers.
2. If the equation has a denominator, exclude any numbers that give a zero denominator.
3. If the equation has a radical of even index, exclude any numbers that cause the expression inside the radical to be negative.

➤ **Now Work** PROBLEM 51

If x is in the domain of a function f, we shall say that **f is defined at x**, or **$f(x)$ exists.** If x is not in the domain of f, we say that **f is not defined at x**, or **$f(x)$ does not exist.** For example, if $f(x) = \dfrac{x}{x^2 - 1}$, then $f(0)$ exists, but $f(1)$ and $f(-1)$ do not exist. (Do you see why?)

We have not said much about finding the range of a function. The reason is that when a function is defined by an equation it is often difficult to find the range.* Therefore, we shall usually be content to find just the domain of a function when the function is defined by an equation. We shall express the domain of a function using inequalities, interval notation, set notation, or words, whichever is most convenient.

When we use functions in applications, the domain may be restricted by physical or geometric considerations. For example, the domain of the function f defined by $f(x) = x^2$ is the set of all real numbers. However, if f is used to obtain the area of a square when the length x of a side is known, then we must restrict the domain of f to the positive real numbers, since the length of a side can never be 0 or negative.

EXAMPLE 10 | **Finding the Domain in an Application**

Express the area of a circle as a function of its radius. Find the domain.

Solution

See Figure 12. We know that the formula for the area A of a circle of radius r is $A = \pi r^2$. If we use r to represent the independent variable and A to represent the dependent variable, the function expressing this relationship is

Figure 12

$$A(r) = \pi r^2$$

In this setting, the domain is $\{r \mid r > 0\}$. (Do you see why?)

Observe in the solution to Example 10 that we used the symbol A in two ways: It is used to name the function, and it is used to symbolize the dependent variable. This double use is common in applications and should not cause any difficulty.

➤ **Now Work** PROBLEM 87

---

*In Section 5.2, we discuss a way to find the range for a special class of functions.

4 Form the Sum, Difference, Product, and Quotient of Two Functions

Next we introduce some operations on functions. We shall see that functions, like numbers, can be added, subtracted, multiplied, and divided. For example, if $f(x) = x^2 + 9$ and $g(x) = 3x + 5$, then

$$f(x) + g(x) = (x^2 + 9) + (3x + 5) = x^2 + 3x + 14$$

The new function $y = x^2 + 3x + 14$ is called the *sum function* $f + g$. Similarly,

$$f(x) \cdot g(x) = (x^2 + 9)(3x + 5) = 3x^3 + 5x^2 + 27x + 45$$

The new function $y = 3x^3 + 5x^2 + 27x + 45$ is called the *product function* $f \cdot g$. The general definitions are given next.

DEFINITION

If f and g are functions:
The **sum $f + g$** is the function defined by

$$(f + g)(x) = f(x) + g(x)$$

> **In Words**
> Remember, the symbol ∩ means intersection. It means you should find the elements that are common to two sets.

The domain of $f + g$ consists of the numbers x that are in the domains of both f and g. That is, domain of $f + g$ = domain of f ∩ domain of g.

DEFINITION

The **difference $f - g$** is the function defined by

$$(f - g)(x) = f(x) - g(x)$$

The domain of $f - g$ consists of the numbers x that are in the domains of both f and g. That is, domain of $f - g$ = domain of f ∩ domain of g.

DEFINITION

The **product $f \cdot g$** is the function defined by

$$(f \cdot g)(x) = f(x) \cdot g(x)$$

The domain of $f \cdot g$ consists of the numbers x that are in the domains of both f and g. That is, domain of $f \cdot g$ = domain of f ∩ domain of g.

DEFINITION

The **quotient $\dfrac{f}{g}$** is the function defined by

$$\left(\frac{f}{g}\right)(x) = \frac{f(x)}{g(x)} \qquad g(x) \neq 0$$

The domain of $\dfrac{f}{g}$ consists of the numbers x for which $g(x) \neq 0$ that are in the domains of both f and g. That is,

$$\text{domain of } \frac{f}{g} = \{x \mid g(x) \neq 0\} \cap \text{domain of } f \cap \text{domain of } g.$$

| EXAMPLE 11 | Operations on Functions |

Let f and g be two functions defined as

$$f(x) = \frac{1}{x + 2} \quad \text{and} \quad g(x) = \frac{x}{x - 1}$$

Find the following, and determine the domain in each case.

(a) $(f + g)(x)$ (b) $(f - g)(x)$

(c) $(f \cdot g)(x)$ (d) $\left(\dfrac{f}{g}\right)(x)$

Solution   The domain of f is $\{x | x \neq -2\}$ and the domain of g is $\{x | x \neq 1\}$.

(a) $(f + g)(x) = f(x) + g(x) = \dfrac{1}{x + 2} + \dfrac{x}{x - 1}$

$$= \frac{x - 1}{(x + 2)(x - 1)} + \frac{x(x + 2)}{(x + 2)(x - 1)} = \frac{x^2 + 3x - 1}{(x + 2)(x - 1)}$$

The domain of $f + g$ consists of those numbers x that are in the domains of both f and g. Therefore, the domain of $f + g$ is $\{x | x \neq -2, x \neq 1\}$.

(b) $(f - g)(x) = f(x) - g(x) = \dfrac{1}{x + 2} - \dfrac{x}{x - 1}$

$$= \frac{x - 1}{(x + 2)(x - 1)} - \frac{x(x + 2)}{(x + 2)(x - 1)} = \frac{-(x^2 + x + 1)}{(x + 2)(x - 1)}$$

The domain of $f - g$ consists of those numbers x that are in the domains of both f and g. Therefore, the domain of $f - g$ is $\{x | x \neq -2, x \neq 1\}$.

(c) $(f \cdot g)(x) = f(x) \cdot g(x) = \dfrac{1}{x + 2} \cdot \dfrac{x}{x - 1} = \dfrac{x}{(x + 2)(x - 1)}$

The domain of $f \cdot g$ consists of those numbers x that are in the domains of both f and g. Therefore, the domain of $f \cdot g$ is $\{x | x \neq -2, x \neq 1\}$.

(d) $\left(\dfrac{f}{g}\right)(x) = \dfrac{f(x)}{g(x)} = \dfrac{\dfrac{1}{x + 2}}{\dfrac{x}{x - 1}} = \dfrac{1}{x + 2} \cdot \dfrac{x - 1}{x} = \dfrac{x - 1}{x(x + 2)}$

The domain of $\dfrac{f}{g}$ consists of the numbers x for which $g(x) \neq 0$ that are in the domains of both f and g. Since $g(x) = 0$ when $x = 0$, we exclude 0 as well as -2 and 1 from the domain. The domain of $\dfrac{f}{g}$ is $\{x | x \neq -2, x \neq 0, x \neq 1\}$.

Now Work PROBLEM 61

In calculus, it is sometimes helpful to view a complicated function as the sum, difference, product, or quotient of simpler functions. For example,

$$F(x) = x^2 + \sqrt{x} \text{ is the sum of } f(x) = x^2 \text{ and } g(x) = \sqrt{x}.$$

$$H(x) = \frac{x^2 - 1}{x^2 + 1} \text{ is the quotient of } f(x) = x^2 - 1 \text{ and } g(x) = x^2 + 1.$$

SUMMARY

We list here some of the important vocabulary introduced in this section, with a brief description of each term.

Function	A relation between two sets of real numbers so that each number x in the first set, the domain, has corresponding to it exactly one number y in the second set
	A set of ordered pairs (x, y) or $(x, f(x))$ in which no first element is paired with two different second elements
	The range is the set of y values of the function that are the images of the x values in the domain.
	A function f may be defined implicitly by an equation involving x and y or explicitly by writing $y = f(x)$.
Unspecified domain	If a function f is defined by an equation and no domain is specified, then the domain will be taken to be the largest set of real numbers for which the equation defines a real number.
Function notation	$y = f(x)$
	f is a symbol for the function.
	x is the independent variable or argument.
	y is the dependent variable.
	$f(x)$ is the value of the function at x, or the image of x.

2.1 Assess Your Understanding

'Are You Prepared?' *Answers are given at the end of these exercises. If you get a wrong answer, read the pages listed in red.*

1. The inequality $-1 < x < 3$ can be written in interval notation as _____. (pp. A78–A79)

2. If $x = -2$, the value of the expression $3x^2 - 5x + \dfrac{1}{x}$ is _____. (pp. A6–A7)

3. The domain of the variable in the expression $\dfrac{x - 3}{x + 4}$ is _____. (p. A7)

4. Solve the inequality: $3 - 2x > 5$. Graph the solution set. (pp. A81–A82)

Concepts and Vocabulary

5. If f is a function defined by the equation $y = f(x)$, then x is called the _____ variable and y is the _____ variable.

6. The set of all images of the elements in the domain of a function is called the _____.

7. If the domain of f is all real numbers in the interval $[0, 7]$ and the domain of g is all real numbers in the interval $[-2, 5]$, the domain of $f + g$ is all real numbers in the interval _____.

8. If $f(5) = 17$, then 17 is the _____ of 5.

9. If $f(x) = x + 1$ and $g(x) = x^3$, then _____ $= x^3 - (x + 1)$.

10. **True or False** Every relation is a function.

11. **True or False** The domain of $(f \cdot g)(x)$ consists of the numbers x that are in the domains of both f and g.

12. **True or False** The independent variable is sometimes referred to as the argument of the function.

13. **True or False** If no domain is specified for a function f, then the domain of f is taken to be the set of real numbers.

14. **True or False** The domain of the function $f(x) = \dfrac{x^2 - 4}{x}$ is $\{x | x \neq \pm 2\}$.

Skill Building

In Problems 15–26, determine whether each relation represents a function. For each function, state the domain and range.

15.

16.

17. Hours Worked   Salary

18. Level of Education   Average Income

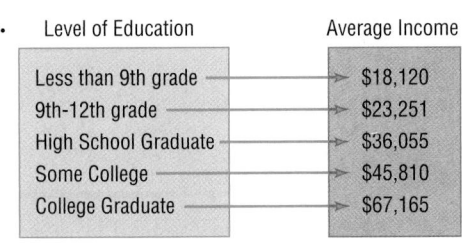

19. $\{(2, 6), (-3, 6), (4, 9), (2, 10)\}$ **20.** $\{(-2, 5), (-1, 3), (3, 7), (4, 12)\}$ **21.** $\{(1, 3), (2, 3), (3, 3), (4, 3)\}$

22. $\{(0, -2), (1, 3), (2, 3), (3, 7)\}$ **23.** $\{(-2, 4), (-2, 6), (0, 3), (3, 7)\}$ **24.** $\{(-4, 4), (-3, 3), (-2, 2), (-1, 1), (-4, 0)\}$

25. $\{(-2, 4), (-1, 1), (0, 0), (1, 1)\}$ **26.** $\{(-2, 16), (-1, 4), (0, 3), (1, 4)\}$

In Problems 27–38, determine whether the equation defines y as a function of x.

27. $y = x^2$

28. $y = x^3$

29. $y = \dfrac{1}{x}$

30. $y = |x|$

31. $y = \pm\sqrt{4 - x^2}$

32. $y = \pm\sqrt{1 - 2x}$

33. $x = y^2$

34. $x + y^2 = 1$

35. $y = 2x^2 - 3x + 4$

36. $y = \dfrac{3x - 1}{x + 2}$

37. $2x^2 + 3y^2 = 1$

38. $x^2 - 4y^2 = 1$

In Problems 39–46, find the following for each function:

   (a) $f(0)$ (b) $f(1)$ (c) $f(-1)$ (d) $f(-x)$ (e) $-f(x)$ (f) $f(x + 1)$ (g) $f(2x)$ (h) $f(x + h)$

39. $f(x) = 3x^2 + 2x - 4$

40. $f(x) = -2x^2 + x - 1$

41. $f(x) = \dfrac{x}{x^2 + 1}$

42. $f(x) = \dfrac{x^2 - 1}{x + 4}$

43. $f(x) = |x| + 4$

44. $f(x) = \sqrt{x^2 + x}$

45. $f(x) = \dfrac{2x + 1}{3x - 5}$

46. $f(x) = 1 - \dfrac{1}{(x + 2)^2}$

In Problems 47–60, find the domain of each function.

47. $f(x) = -5x + 4$

48. $f(x) = x^2 + 2$

49. $f(x) = \dfrac{x}{x^2 + 1}$

50. $f(x) = \dfrac{x^2}{x^2 + 1}$

51. $g(x) = \dfrac{x}{x^2 - 16}$

52. $h(x) = \dfrac{2x}{x^2 - 4}$

53. $F(x) = \dfrac{x - 2}{x^3 + x}$

54. $G(x) = \dfrac{x + 4}{x^3 - 4x}$

55. $h(x) = \sqrt{3x - 12}$

56. $G(x) = \sqrt{1 - x}$

57. $f(x) = \dfrac{4}{\sqrt{x - 9}}$

58. $f(x) = \dfrac{x}{\sqrt{x - 4}}$

59. $p(x) = \sqrt{\dfrac{2}{x - 1}}$

60. $q(x) = \sqrt{-x - 2}$

In Problems 61–70, for the given functions f and g, find the following. For parts (a)–(d), also find the domain.

   (a) $(f + g)(x)$ (b) $(f - g)(x)$ (c) $(f \cdot g)(x)$ (d) $\left(\dfrac{f}{g}\right)(x)$

   (e) $(f + g)(3)$ (f) $(f - g)(4)$ (g) $(f \cdot g)(2)$ (h) $\left(\dfrac{f}{g}\right)(1)$

61. $f(x) = 3x + 4; \quad g(x) = 2x - 3$

62. $f(x) = 2x + 1; \quad g(x) = 3x - 2$

63. $f(x) = x - 1; \quad g(x) = 2x^2$

64. $f(x) = 2x^2 + 3; \quad g(x) = 4x^3 + 1$

65. $f(x) = \sqrt{x}; \quad g(x) = 3x - 5$

66. $f(x) = |x|; \quad g(x) = x$

67. $f(x) = 1 + \dfrac{1}{x}; \quad g(x) = \dfrac{1}{x}$

68. $f(x) = \sqrt{x - 1}; \quad g(x) = \sqrt{4 - x}$

69. $f(x) = \dfrac{2x + 3}{3x - 2}; \quad g(x) = \dfrac{4x}{3x - 2}$

70. $f(x) = \sqrt{x + 1}; \quad g(x) = \dfrac{2}{x}$

71. Given $f(x) = 3x + 1$ and $(f + g)(x) = 6 - \dfrac{1}{2}x$, find the function g.

72. Given $f(x) = \dfrac{1}{x}$ and $\left(\dfrac{f}{g}\right)(x) = \dfrac{x + 1}{x^2 - x}$, find the function g.

⚠ *In Problems 73–80, find the difference quotient of f; that is, find* $\dfrac{f(x+h)-f(x)}{h}, h \neq 0,$ *for each function. Be sure to simplify.*

73. $f(x) = 4x + 3$

74. $f(x) = -3x + 1$

75. $f(x) = x^2 - x + 4$

76. $f(x) = x^2 + 5x - 1$

77. $f(x) = 3x^2 - 2x + 6$

78. $f(x) = 4x^2 + 5x - 7$

79. $f(x) = x^3 - 2$

80. $f(x) = \dfrac{1}{x + 3}$

Applications and Extensions

81. If $f(x) = 2x^3 + Ax^2 + 4x - 5$ and $f(2) = 5$, what is the value of A?

82. If $f(x) = 3x^2 - Bx + 4$ and $f(-1) = 12$, what is the value of B?

83. If $f(x) = \dfrac{3x + 8}{2x - A}$ and $f(0) = 2$, what is the value of A?

84. If $f(x) = \dfrac{2x - B}{3x + 4}$ and $f(2) = \dfrac{1}{2}$, what is the value of B?

85. If $f(x) = \dfrac{2x - A}{x - 3}$ and $f(4) = 0$, what is the value of A? Where is f not defined?

86. If $f(x) = \dfrac{x - B}{x - A}$, $f(2) = 0$ and $f(1)$ is undefined, what are the values of A and B?

87. **Geometry**   Express the area A of a rectangle as a function of the length x if the length of the rectangle is twice its width.

88. **Geometry**   Express the area A of an isosceles right triangle as a function of the length x of one of the two equal sides.

89. **Constructing Functions**   Express the gross salary G of a person who earns \$10 per hour as a function of the number x of hours worked.

90. **Constructing Functions**   Tiffany, a commissioned salesperson, earns \$100 base pay plus \$10 per item sold. Express her gross salary G as a function of the number x of items sold.

91. **Population as a Function of Age**   The function

$$P(a) = 0.015a^2 - 4.962a + 290.580$$

represents the population P (in millions) of Americans in 2005 that are a years of age or older.

Source: U.S. Census Bureau

(a) Identify the dependent and independent variable.

(b) Evaluate $P(20)$. Provide a verbal explanation of the meaning of $P(20)$.

(c) Evaluate $P(0)$. Provide a verbal explanation of the meaning of $P(0)$.

92. **Number of Rooms**   The function

$$N(r) = -1.44r^2 + 14.52r - 14.96$$

represents the number N of housing units (in millions) in 2005 that have r rooms, where r is an integer and $2 \leq r \leq 9$.

Source: U.S. Census Bureau

(a) Identify the dependent and independent variable.

(b) Evaluate $N(3)$. Provide a verbal explanation of the meaning of $N(3)$.

93. **Effect of Gravity on Earth**   If a rock falls from a height of 20 meters on Earth, the height H (in meters) after x seconds is approximately

$$H(x) = 20 - 4.9x^2$$

(a) What is the height of the rock when $x = 1$ second? $x = 1.1$ seconds? $x = 1.2$ seconds? $x = 1.3$ seconds?

(b) When is the height of the rock 15 meters? When is it 10 meters? When is it 5 meters?

(c) When does the rock strike the ground?

94. **Effect of Gravity on Jupiter**   If a rock falls from a height of 20 meters on the planet Jupiter, its height H (in meters) after x seconds is approximately

$$H(x) = 20 - 13x^2$$

(a) What is the height of the rock when $x = 1$ second? $x = 1.1$ seconds? $x = 1.2$ seconds?

(b) When is the height of the rock 15 meters? When is it 10 meters? When is it 5 meters?

(c) When does the rock strike the ground?

95. **Cost of Trans-Atlantic Travel**   A Boeing 747 crosses the Atlantic Ocean (3000 miles) with an airspeed of 500 miles per hour. The cost C (in dollars) per passenger is given by

$$C(x) = 100 + \dfrac{x}{10} + \dfrac{36{,}000}{x}$$

where x is the ground speed (airspeed ± wind).

(a) What is the cost per passenger for quiescent (no wind) conditions?

(b) What is the cost per passenger with a head wind of 50 miles per hour?

(c) What is the cost per passenger with a tail wind of 100 miles per hour?

(d) What is the cost per passenger with a head wind of 100 miles per hour?

96. **Cross-sectional Area**   The cross-sectional area of a beam cut from a log with radius 1 foot is given by the function $A(x) = 4x\sqrt{1 - x^2}$, where x represents the length, in feet, of half the base of the beam. See the figure. Determine the cross-sectional area of the beam if the length of half the base of the beam is as follows:

(a) One-third of a foot

(b) One-half of a foot

(c) Two-thirds of a foot

$A(x) = 4x\sqrt{1 - x^2}$

97. Economics The **participation rate** is the number of people in the labor force divided by the civilian population (excludes military). Let $L(x)$ represent the size of the labor force in year x and $P(x)$ represent the civilian population in year x. Determine a function that represents the participation rate R as a function of x.

98. Crimes Suppose that $V(x)$ represents the number of violent crimes committed in year x and $P(x)$ represents the number of property crimes committed in year x. Determine a function T that represents the combined total of violent crimes and property crimes in year x.

99. Health Care Suppose that $P(x)$ represents the percentage of income spent on health care in year x and $I(x)$ represents income in year x. Determine a function H that represents total health care expenditures in year x.

100. Income Tax Suppose that $I(x)$ represents the income of an individual in year x before taxes and $T(x)$ represents the individual's tax bill in year x. Determine a function N that represents the individual's net income (income after taxes) in year x.

101. Profit Function Suppose that the revenue R, in dollars, from selling x cell phones, in hundreds, is $R(x) = -1.2x^2 + 220x$. The cost C, in dollars, of selling x cell phones, in hundreds, is $C(x) = 0.05x^3 - 2x^2 + 65x + 500$.
(a) Find the profit function, $P(x) = R(x) - C(x)$.
(b) Find the profit if $x = 15$ hundred cell phones are sold.
(c) Interpret $P(15)$.

102. Profit Function Suppose that the revenue R, in dollars, from selling x clocks is $R(x) = 30x$. The cost C, in dollars, of selling x clocks is $C(x) = 0.1x^2 + 7x + 400$.
(a) Find the profit function, $P(x) = R(x) - C(x)$.
(b) Find the profit if $x = 30$ clocks are sold.
(c) Interpret $P(30)$.

103. Some functions f have the property that $f(a + b) = f(a) + f(b)$ for all real numbers a and b. Which of the following functions have this property?
(a) $h(x) = 2x$
(b) $g(x) = x^2$
(c) $F(x) = 5x - 2$
(d) $G(x) = \dfrac{1}{x}$

Discussion and Writing

104. Are the functions $f(x) = x - 1$ and $g(x) = \dfrac{x^2 - 1}{x + 1}$ the same? Explain.

105. Investigate when, historically, the use of the function notation $y = f(x)$ first appeared.

106. Write the equation of the following function f. The square root of three times a number x increased by 5.

107. Write the following function in words: $g(t) = t^2 - 2$.

'Are You Prepared?' Answers

1. $(-1, 3)$ **2.** 21.5 **3.** $\{x \mid x \neq -4\}$ **4.** $\{x \mid x < -1\}$

2.2 The Graph of a Function

PREPARING FOR THIS SECTION *Before getting started, review the following:*

- Graphs of Equations (Section 1.1, pp. 7–9)
- Intercepts (Section 1.2, pp. 18–19)

Now Work the 'Are You Prepared?' problems on page 74.

OBJECTIVES 1 Identify the Graph of a Function (p. 71)
2 Obtain Information from or about the Graph of a Function (p. 72)

In applications, a graph often demonstrates more clearly the relationship between two variables than, say, an equation or table would. For example, Table 1 shows the average price of gasoline in California adjusted for inflation (based on 2005 dollars) for the years 1979–2006. If we plot these data and then connect the points, we obtain Figure 13.

Table 1

Year	Price	Year	Price	Year	Price	Year	Price
1979	1.9829	1986	1.3459	1993	1.5189	2000	1.8249
1980	2.4929	1987	1.3274	1994	1.4709	2001	1.7536
1981	2.4977	1988	1.3111	1995	1.4669	2002	1.5955
1982	2.1795	1989	1.3589	1996	1.5397	2003	1.8950
1983	1.8782	1990	1.4656	1997	1.5329	2004	2.1521
1984	1.8310	1991	1.4973	1998	1.3246	2005	2.4730
1985	1.7540	1992	1.3969	1999	1.5270	2006	2.8919

Source: Statistical Abstract of the United States

Figure 13

California Gasoline Prices Based on 2005 Dollars,
Adjusted for Inflation, 1979–2006

[graph: Price (dollars per gallon) vs Year, 1978–2006]

SOURCE: *Statistical Abstact of the United States.*

We can see from the graph that the price of gasoline (adjusted for inflation) was falling from 2000 to 2002 and has been rising rapidly since 2002. The graph also shows that the lowest price occurred in 1998. To learn information such as this from an equation requires that some calculations be made.

Look again at Figure 13. The graph shows that for each date on the horizontal axis there is only one price on the vertical axis. The graph represents a function, although the exact rule for getting from date to price is not given.

When a function is defined by an equation in x and y, the **graph of the function** is the graph of the equation, that is, the set of points (x, y) in the xy-plane that satisfies the equation.

1 Identify the Graph of a Function

Not every collection of points in the xy-plane represents the graph of a function. Remember, for a function, each number x in the domain has exactly one image y in the range. This means that the graph of a function cannot contain two points with the same x-coordinate and different y-coordinates. Therefore, the graph of a function must satisfy the following **vertical-line test.**

THEOREM

Vertical-line Test

A set of points in the xy-plane is the graph of a function if and only if every vertical line intersects the graph in at most one point.

In other words, if any vertical line intersects a graph at more than one point, the graph is not the graph of a function.

EXAMPLE 1

Identifying the Graph of a Function

Which of the graphs in Figure 14 are graphs of functions?

Figure 14

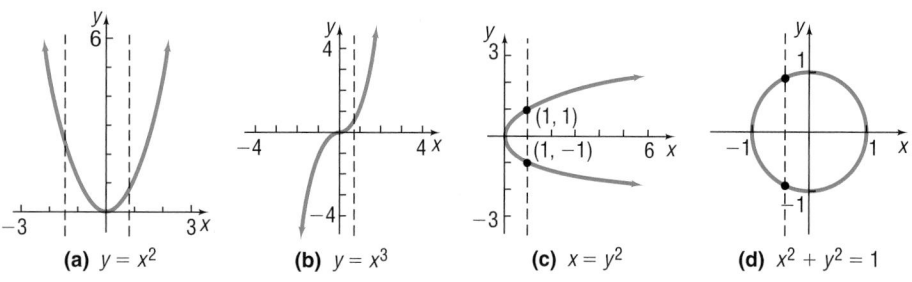

(a) $y = x^2$ **(b)** $y = x^3$ **(c)** $x = y^2$ **(d)** $x^2 + y^2 = 1$

Solution

The graphs in Figures 14(a) and 14(b) are graphs of functions, because every vertical line intersects each graph in at most one point. The graphs in Figures 14(c) and 14(d) are not graphs of functions, because there is a vertical line that intersects each graph in more than one point. Notice in Figure 14(c) that the input 1 corresponds to two outputs, −1 and 1. This is why the graph does not represent a function.

Now Work   PROBLEM 15

2 Obtain Information from or about the Graph of a Function

If (x, y) is a point on the graph of a function f, then y is the value of f at x. That is, if $y = f(x)$, then (x, y) is a point on the graph of f. The next example illustrates how to obtain information about a function if its graph is given.

EXAMPLE 2

Obtaining Information from the Graph of a Function

Let f be the function whose graph is given in Figure 15. (The graph of f might represent the distance that the bob of a pendulum is from its *at-rest* position. Negative values of y mean that the pendulum is to the left of the at-rest position, and positive values of y mean that the pendulum is to the right of the at-rest position.)

Figure 15

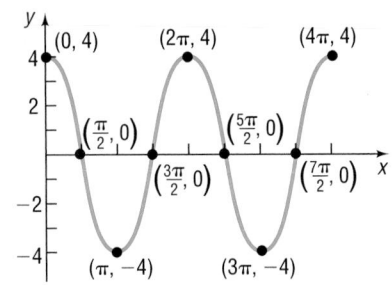

(a) What are $f(0)$, $f\left(\dfrac{3\pi}{2}\right)$, and $f(3\pi)$?

(b) What is the domain of f?

(c) What is the range of f?

(d) List the intercepts. (Recall that these are the points, if any, where the graph crosses or touches the coordinate axes.)

(e) How often does the line $y = 2$ intersect the graph?

(f) For what values of x does $f(x) = -4$?

(g) For what values of x is $f(x) > 0$?

Solution

(a) Since $(0, 4)$ is on the graph of f, the y-coordinate 4 is the value of f at the x-coordinate 0; that is, $f(0) = 4$. In a similar way, we find that when $x = \dfrac{3\pi}{2}$ then $y = 0$, so $f\left(\dfrac{3\pi}{2}\right) = 0$. When $x = 3\pi$, then $y = -4$, so $f(3\pi) = -4$.

(b) To determine the domain of f, we notice that the points on the graph of f have x-coordinates between 0 and 4π, inclusive; and for each number x between 0 and 4π, there is a point $(x, f(x))$ on the graph. The domain of f is $\{x | 0 \leq x \leq 4\pi\}$ or the interval $[0, 4\pi]$.

(c) The points on the graph all have y-coordinates between −4 and 4, inclusive; and for each such number y, there is at least one number x in the domain. The range of f is $\{y | -4 \leq y \leq 4\}$ or the interval $[-4, 4]$.

(d) The intercepts are

$$(0, 4), \left(\frac{\pi}{2}, 0\right), \left(\frac{3\pi}{2}, 0\right), \left(\frac{5\pi}{2}, 0\right), \quad \text{and} \quad \left(\frac{7\pi}{2}, 0\right)$$

(e) If we draw the horizontal line $y = 2$ on the graph in Figure 15, we find that it intersects the graph four times.

(f) Since $(\pi, -4)$ and $(3\pi, -4)$ are the only points on the graph for which $y = f(x) = -4$, we have $f(x) = -4$ when $x = \pi$ and $x = 3\pi$.

(g) To determine where $f(x) > 0$, we look at Figure 15 and determine the x-values from 0 to 4π for which the y-coordinate is positive. This occurs on $\left[0, \dfrac{\pi}{2}\right) \cup \left(\dfrac{3\pi}{2}, \dfrac{5\pi}{2}\right) \cup \left(\dfrac{7\pi}{2}, 4\pi\right]$. Using inequality notation, $f(x) > 0$ for

$$0 \le x < \dfrac{\pi}{2} \text{ or } \dfrac{3\pi}{2} < x < \dfrac{5\pi}{2} \text{ or } \dfrac{7\pi}{2} < x \le 4\pi.$$

When the graph of a function is given, its domain may be viewed as the shadow created by the graph on the x-axis by vertical beams of light. Its range can be viewed as the shadow created by the graph on the y-axis by horizontal beams of light. Try this technique with the graph given in Figure 15.

Now Work PROBLEMS **9** AND **13**

| EXAMPLE 3 | **Obtaining Information about the Graph of a Function** |

Consider the function: $f(x) = \dfrac{x+1}{x+2}$

(a) Is the point $\left(1, \dfrac{1}{2}\right)$ on the graph of f?

(b) If $x = 2$, what is $f(x)$? What point is on the graph of f?

(c) If $f(x) = 2$, what is x? What point is on the graph of f?

(d) What are the x-intercepts of the graph of f (if any)? What point(s) are on the graph of f?

Solution

(a) When $x = 1$, then

$$f(x) = \dfrac{x+1}{x+2}$$

$$f(1) = \dfrac{1+1}{1+2} = \dfrac{2}{3}$$

The point $\left(1, \dfrac{2}{3}\right)$ is on the graph of f; the point $\left(1, \dfrac{1}{2}\right)$ is not.

(b) If $x = 2$, then

$$f(x) = \dfrac{x+1}{x+2}$$

$$f(2) = \dfrac{2+1}{2+2} = \dfrac{3}{4}$$

The point $\left(2, \dfrac{3}{4}\right)$ is on the graph of f.

(c) If $f(x) = 2$, then

$$f(x) = 2$$

$$\dfrac{x+1}{x+2} = 2$$

$$x + 1 = 2(x + 2) \qquad \text{Multiply both sides by } x + 2.$$

$$x + 1 = 2x + 4 \qquad \text{Remove parentheses.}$$

$$x = -3 \qquad \text{Solve for } x.$$

If $f(x) = 2$, then $x = -3$. The point $(-3, 2)$ is on the graph of f.

(d) The x-intercepts of the graph of f are the real solutions of the equation $f(x) = 0$. The only real solution of the equation $f(x) = \dfrac{x+1}{x+2} = 0$ is $x = -1$, so -1 is the only x-intercept. Since $f(-1) = 0$, the point $(-1, 0)$ is on the graph of f.

Now Work PROBLEM **25**

| EXAMPLE 4 | Average Cost Function |

The average cost $\overline{C}$ of manufacturing x computers per day is given by the function

$$\overline{C}(x) = 0.56x^2 - 34.39x + 1212.57 + \frac{20{,}000}{x}$$

Determine the average cost of manufacturing:

(a) 30 computers per day
(b) 40 computers per day
(c) 50 computers per day
(d) Graph the function $\overline{C} = \overline{C}(x), 0 < x \le 80$.
(e) Create a TABLE with TblStart = 1 and ΔTbl = 1. Which value of x minimizes the average cost?

Solution (a) The average cost of manufacturing $x = 30$ computers is

$$\overline{C}(30) = 0.56(30)^2 - 34.39(30) + 1212.57 + \frac{20{,}000}{30} = \$1351.54$$

(b) The average cost of manufacturing $x = 40$ computers is

$$\overline{C}(40) = 0.56(40)^2 - 34.39(40) + 1212.57 + \frac{20{,}000}{40} = \$1232.97$$

(c) The average cost of manufacturing $x = 50$ computers is

$$\overline{C}(50) = 0.56(50)^2 - 34.39(50) + 1212.57 + \frac{20{,}000}{50} = \$1293.07$$

(d) See Figure 16 for the graph of $\overline{C} = \overline{C}(x)$.

(e) With the function $\overline{C} = \overline{C}(x)$ in Y_1, we create Table 2. We scroll down until we find a value of x for which Y_1 is smallest. Table 3 shows that manufacturing $x = 41$ computers minimizes the average cost at \$1231.74 per computer.

Figure 16

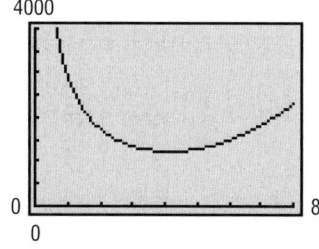

Table 2

X	Y1
1	21179
2	11146
3	7781.1
4	6084
5	5054.6
6	4359.7
7	3856.4

Y1☰.56X²-34.39X...

Table 3

X	Y1
38	1240.7
39	1235.9
40	1233
41	1231.7
42	1232.2
43	1234.4
44	1238.1

Y1=1231.74487805

Now Work PROBLEM 31

SUMMARY

Graph of a function The collection of points (x, y) that satisfies the equation $y = f(x)$.

Vertical-line test A collection of points is the graph of a function provided that every vertical line intersects the graph in at most one point.

2.2 Assess Your Understanding

'Are You Prepared?' *Answers are given at the end of these exercises. If you get a wrong answer, read the pages listed in red.*

1. The intercepts of the equation $x^2 + 4y^2 = 16$ are _____. (pp. 18–19)

2. *True or False* The point $(-2, -6)$ is on the graph of the equation $x = 2y - 2$. (pp. 7–9)

Concepts and Vocabulary

3. A set of points in the *xy*-plane is the graph of a function if and only if every _____ line intersects the graph in at most one point.

4. If the point $(5, -3)$ is a point on the graph of f, then $f(\_\_\_) = \_\_\_$.

5. If $g(-2) = 7$, then the point _____ is on the graph of g.

6. *True or False* A function can have more than one *y*-intercept.

7. *True or False* The graph of a function $y = f(x)$ always crosses the *y*-axis.

8. *True or False* The *y*-intercept of the graph of the function $y = f(x)$, whose domain is all real numbers, is $f(0)$.

Skill Building

9. Use the graph below of the function f to answer parts (a)–(n).

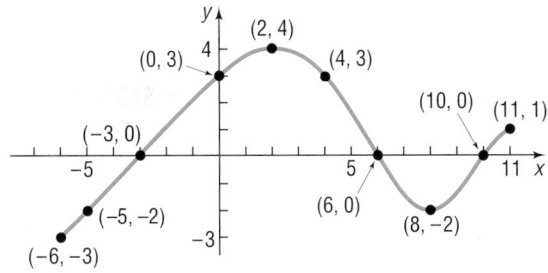

(a) Find $f(0)$ and $f(-6)$.
(b) Find $f(6)$ and $f(11)$.
(c) Is $f(3)$ positive or negative?
(d) Is $f(-4)$ positive or negative?
(e) For what values of x is $f(x) = 0$?
(f) For what values of x is $f(x) > 0$?
(g) What is the domain of f?
(h) What is the range of f?
(i) What are the *x*-intercepts?
(j) What is the *y*-intercept?
(k) How often does the line $y = \dfrac{1}{2}$ intersect the graph?
(l) How often does the line $x = 5$ intersect the graph?
(m) For what values of x does $f(x) = 3$?
(n) For what values of x does $f(x) = -2$?

10. Use the graph below of the function f to answer parts (a)–(n).

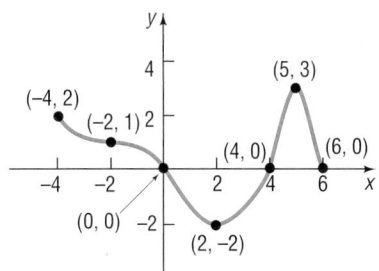

(a) Find $f(0)$ and $f(6)$.
(b) Find $f(2)$ and $f(-2)$.
(c) Is $f(3)$ positive or negative?
(d) Is $f(-1)$ positive or negative?
(e) For what values of x is $f(x) = 0$?
(f) For what values of x is $f(x) < 0$?
(g) What is the domain of f?
(h) What is the range of f?
(i) What are the *x*-intercepts?
(j) What is the *y*-intercept?
(k) How often does the line $y = -1$ intersect the graph?
(l) How often does the line $x = 1$ intersect the graph?
(m) For what value of x does $f(x) = 3$?
(n) For what value of x does $f(x) = -2$?

In Problems 11–22, determine whether the graph is that of a function by using the vertical-line test. If it is, use the graph to find:

(a) The domain and range
(b) The intercepts, if any
(c) Any symmetry with respect to the x-axis, the y-axis, or the origin

11.

12.

13.

14.

15.

16.

17.

18.

19.   **20.**   **21.**   **22.**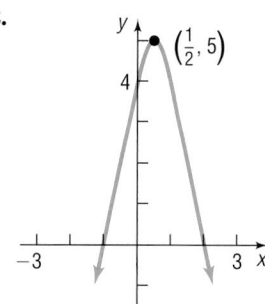

In Problems 23–28, answer the questions about the given function.

23. $f(x) = 2x^2 - x - 1$
  (a) Is the point $(-1, 2)$ on the graph of f?
  (b) If $x = -2$, what is $f(x)$? What point is on the graph of f?
  (c) If $f(x) = -1$, what is x? What point(s) are on the graph of f?
  (d) What is the domain of f?
  (e) List the x-intercepts, if any, of the graph of f.
  (f) List the y-intercept, if there is one, of the graph of f.

24. $f(x) = -3x^2 + 5x$
  (a) Is the point $(-1, 2)$ on the graph of f?
  (b) If $x = -2$, what is $f(x)$? What point is on the graph of f?
  (c) If $f(x) = -2$, what is x? What point(s) are on the graph of f?
  (d) What is the domain of f?
  (e) List the x-intercepts, if any, of the graph of f.
  (f) List the y-intercept, if there is one, of the graph of f.

25. $f(x) = \dfrac{x + 2}{x - 6}$
  (a) Is the point $(3, 14)$ on the graph of f?
  (b) If $x = 4$, what is $f(x)$? What point is on the graph of f?
  (c) If $f(x) = 2$, what is x? What point(s) are on the graph of f?
  (d) What is the domain of f?
  (e) List the x-intercepts, if any, of the graph of f.
  (f) List the y-intercept, if there is one, of the graph of f.

26. $f(x) = \dfrac{x^2 + 2}{x + 4}$
  (a) Is the point $\left(1, \dfrac{3}{5}\right)$ on the graph of f?

  (b) If $x = 0$, what is $f(x)$? What point is on the graph of f?

  (c) If $f(x) = \dfrac{1}{2}$, what is x? What point(s) are on the graph of f?

  (d) What is the domain of f?
  (e) List the x-intercepts, if any, of the graph of f.
  (f) List the y-intercept, if there is one, of the graph of f.

27. $f(x) = \dfrac{2x^2}{x^4 + 1}$
  (a) Is the point $(-1, 1)$ on the graph of f?
  (b) If $x = 2$, what is $f(x)$? What point is on the graph of f?
  (c) If $f(x) = 1$, what is x? What point(s) are on the graph of f?
  (d) What is the domain of f?
  (e) List the x-intercepts, if any, of the graph of f.
  (f) List the y-intercept, if there is one, of the graph of f.

28. $f(x) = \dfrac{2x}{x - 2}$
  (a) Is the point $\left(\dfrac{1}{2}, -\dfrac{2}{3}\right)$ on the graph of f?

  (b) If $x = 4$, what is $f(x)$? What point is on the graph of f?
  (c) If $f(x) = 1$, what is x? What point(s) are on the graph of f?
  (d) What is the domain of f?
  (e) List the x-intercepts, if any, of the graph of f.
  (f) List the y-intercept, if there is one, of the graph of f.

Applications and Extensions

29. Free-throw Shots According to physicist Peter Brancazio, the key to a successful foul shot in basketball lies in the arc of the shot. Brancazio determined the optimal angle of the arc from the free-throw line to be 45 degrees. The arc also depends on the velocity with which the ball is shot. If a player shoots a foul shot, releasing the ball at a 45-degree angle from a position 6 feet above the floor, then the path of the ball can be modeled by the function

$$h(x) = -\frac{44x^2}{v^2} + x + 6$$

where h is the height of the ball above the floor, x is the forward distance of the ball in front of the foul line, and v is the initial velocity with which the ball is shot in feet per second. Suppose a player shoots a ball with an initial velocity of 28 feet per second.
  (a) Determine the height of the ball after it has traveled 8 feet in front of the foul line.

  (b) Determine the height of the ball after it has traveled 12 feet in front of the foul line.
  (c) Find additional points and graph the path of the basketball by hand.
  (d) The center of the hoop is 10 feet above the floor and 15 feet in front of the foul line. Will the ball go through the hoop? Why or why not? If not, with what initial velocity must the ball be shot in order for the ball to go through the hoop?

Source: The Physics of Foul Shots, Discover, Vol. 21, No. 10, October 2000

30. Granny Shots The last player in the NBA to use an underhand foul shot (a "granny" shot) was Hall of Fame forward Rick Barry who retired in 1980. Barry believes that current NBA players could increase their free-throw percentage if they were to use an underhand shot. Since underhand shots are released from a lower position, the angle of the shot must be increased. If a player shoots an underhand foul shot, releasing the ball at a 70-degree angle from a position 3.5 feet above the floor, then the path of the ball can be modeled by the function $h(x) = -\dfrac{136x^2}{v^2} + 2.7x + 3.5$, where h is the height of the ball above the floor, x is the forward distance of the ball in front of the foul line, and v is the initial velocity with which the ball is shot in feet per second.

(a) The center of the hoop is 10 feet above the floor and 15 feet in front of the foul line. Determine the initial velocity with which the ball must be shot in order for the ball to go through the hoop.
(b) Write the function for the path of the ball using the velocity found in part (a).
(c) Determine the height of the ball after it has traveled 9 feet in front of the foul line.
(d) Find additional points and graph the path of the basketball by hand.

Source: The Physics of Foul Shots, Discover, Vol. 21, No. 10, October 2000

31. **Cost of Trans-Atlantic Travel**   A Boeing 747 crosses the Atlantic Ocean (3000 miles) with an airspeed of 500 miles per hour. The cost C (in dollars) per passenger is given by

$$C(x) = 100 + \frac{x}{10} + \frac{36{,}000}{x}$$

where x is the ground speed (airspeed ± wind).
(a) Use a graphing utility to graph the function $C = C(x)$.
(b) Create a TABLE with TblStart = 0 and ΔTbl = 50.
(c) To the nearest 50 miles per hour, what ground speed minimizes the cost per passenger?

32. **Cross-sectional Area**   The cross-sectional area of a beam cut from a log with radius 1 foot is given by the function $A(x) = 4x\sqrt{1 - x^2}$, where x represents the length, in feet, of half the base of the beam. See the figure.

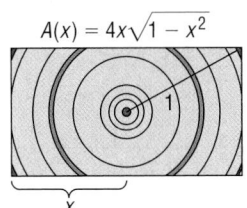

(a) Find the domain of A.
(b) Use a graphing utility to graph the function $A = A(x)$.
(c) Create a TABLE with TblStart = 0 and ΔTbl = 0.1 for $0 \le x \le 1$. Which value of x maximizes the cross-sectional area? What should be the length of the base of the beam to maximize the cross-sectional area?

33. The graphs of two functions, f and g, are illustrated. Use the graphs to answer parts (a)–(f).

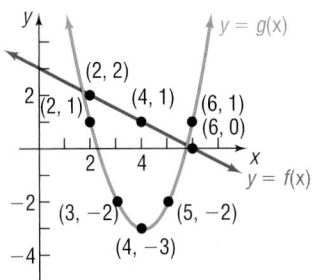

(a) $(f + g)(2)$ (b) $(f + g)(4)$ (c) $(f - g)(6)$
(d) $(g - f)(6)$ (e) $(f \cdot g)(2)$ (f) $\left(\dfrac{f}{g}\right)(4)$

34. **Reading and Interpreting Graphs**   Let C be the function whose graph is given below. This graph represents the cost C of manufacturing q computers in a day.

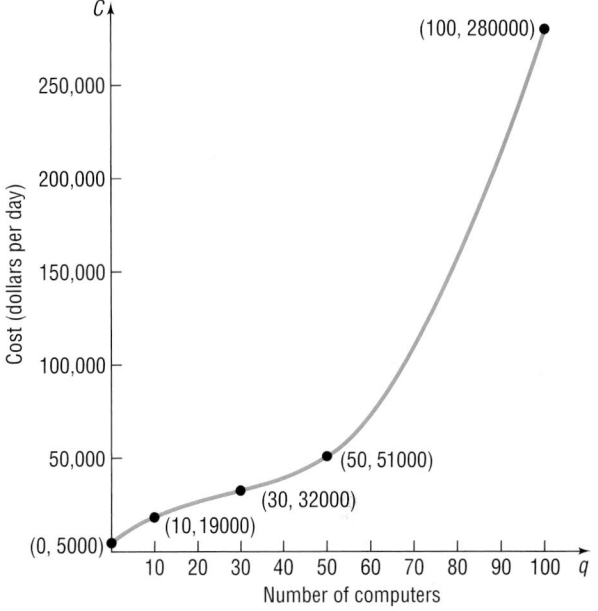

(a) Determine $C(0)$. Interpret this value.
(b) Determine $C(10)$. Interpret this value.
(c) Determine $C(50)$. Interpret this value.
(d) What is the domain of C? What does this domain imply in terms of daily production?
(e) Describe the shape of the graph.
(f) The point $(30, 32000)$ is called an *inflection point*. Describe the behavior of the graph around the inflection point.

35. **Reading and Interpreting Graphs**   Let C be the function whose graph is given below. This graph represents the cost C of using m anytime cell phone minutes in a month for a five-person family plan.

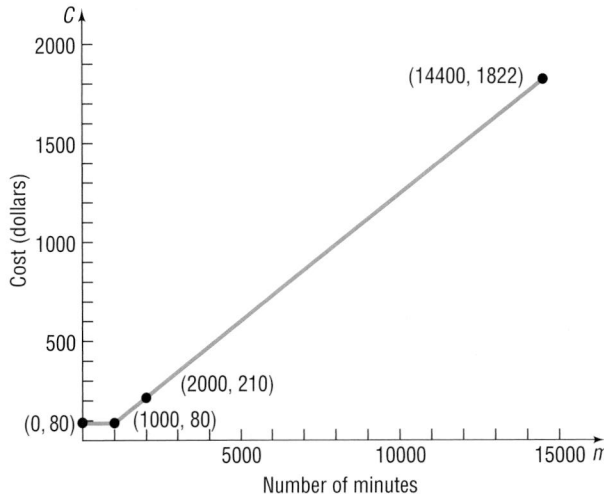

(a) Determine $C(0)$. Interpret this value.
(b) Determine $C(1000)$. Interpret this value.
(c) Determine $C(2000)$. Interpret this value.
(d) What is the domain of C? What does this domain imply in terms of the number of anytime minutes?
(e) Describe the shape of the graph.

Discussion and Writing

36. Describe how you would proceed to find the domain and range of a function if you were given its graph. How would your strategy change if you were given the equation defining the function instead of its graph?

37. How many *x*-intercepts can the graph of a function have? How many *y*-intercepts can the graph of a function have?

38. Is a graph that consists of a single point the graph of a function? Can you write the equation of such a function?

39. Match each of the following functions with the graph that best describes the situation.
  (a) The cost of building a house as a function of its square footage
  (b) The height of an egg dropped from a 300-foot building as a function of time
  (c) The height of a human as a function of time
  (d) The demand for Big Macs as a function of price
  (e) The height of a child on a swing as a function of time

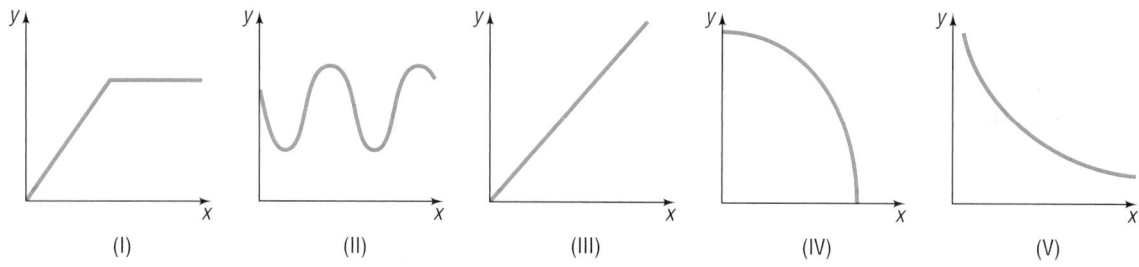

    (I)   (II)   (III)   (IV)   (V)

40. Match each of the following functions with the graph that best describes the situation.
  (a) The temperature of a bowl of soup as a function of time
  (b) The number of hours of daylight per day over a 2-year period
  (c) The population of Florida as a function of time
  (d) The distance traveled by a car going at a constant velocity as a function of time
  (e) The height of a golf ball hit with a 7-iron as a function of time

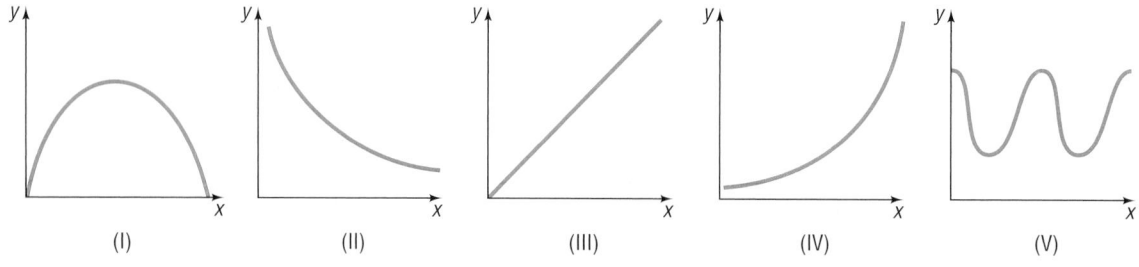

    (I)   (II)   (III)   (IV)   (V)

41. Consider the following scenario: Barbara decides to take a walk. She leaves home, walks 2 blocks in 5 minutes at a constant speed, and realizes that she forgot to lock the door. So Barbara runs home in 1 minute. While at her doorstep, it takes her 1 minute to find her keys and lock the door. Barbara walks 5 blocks in 15 minutes and then decides to jog home. It takes her 7 minutes to get home. Draw a graph of Barbara's distance from home (in blocks) as a function of time.

42. Consider the following scenario: Jayne enjoys riding her bicycle through the woods. At the forest preserve, she gets on her bicycle and rides up a 2000-foot incline in 10 minutes. She then travels down the incline in 3 minutes. The next 5000 feet are level terrain and she covers the distance in 20 minutes. She rests for 15 minutes. Jayne then travels 10,000 feet in 30 minutes. Draw a graph of Jayne's distance traveled (in feet) as a function of time.

43. The sketch to the right represents the distance *d* (in miles) that Kevin is from home as a function of time *t* (in hours). Answer the questions based on the graph. In parts (a)–(g), how many hours elapsed and how far was Kevin from home during this time?

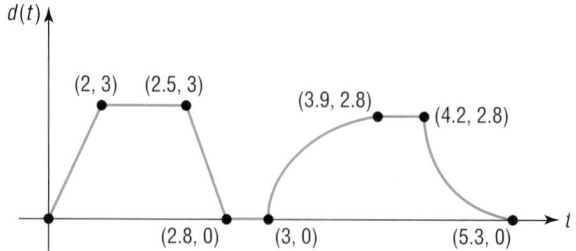

(a) From $t = 0$ to $t = 2$
(b) From $t = 2$ to $t = 2.5$
(c) From $t = 2.5$ to $t = 2.8$
(d) From $t = 2.8$ to $t = 3$
(e) From $t = 3$ to $t = 3.9$
(f) From $t = 3.9$ to $t = 4.2$
(g) From $t = 4.2$ to $t = 5.3$
(h) What is the farthest distance that Kevin is from home?
(i) How many times did Kevin return home?

44. The following sketch represents the speed v (in miles per hour) of Michael's car as a function of time t (in minutes).

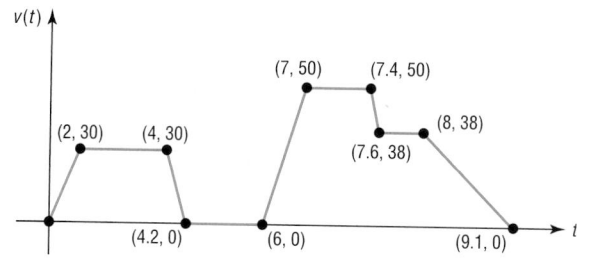

(a) Over what interval of time is Michael traveling fastest?
(b) Over what interval(s) of time is Michael's speed zero?

(c) What is Michael's speed between 0 and 2 minutes?
(d) What is Michael's speed between 4.2 and 6 minutes?
(e) What is Michael's speed between 7 and 7.4 minutes?
(f) When is Michael's speed constant?

45. Draw the graph of a function whose domain is $\{x \mid -3 \le x \le 8, \ x \ne 5\}$ and whose range is $\{y \mid -1 \le y \le 2, \ y \ne 0\}$. What point(s) in the rectangle $-3 \le x \le 8, -1 \le y \le 2$ cannot be on the graph? Compare your graph with those of other students. What differences do you see?

46. Is there a function whose graph is symmetric with respect to the x-axis? Explain.

47. Explain why the vertical-line test works.

'Are You Prepared?' Answers

1. $(-4, 0), (4, 0), (0, -2), (0, 2)$ **2.** False

2.3 Properties of Functions

PREPARING FOR THIS SECTION   *Before getting started, review the following:*

- Intervals (Appendix A, Section A.9, pp. A78–A79)
- Intercepts (Section 1.2, pp. 18–19)
- Slope of a Line (Section 1.4, pp. 29–30)
- Point–Slope Form of a Line (Section 1.4, p. 33)
- Symmetry (Section 1.2, pp. 19–21)

Now Work the 'Are You Prepared?' problems on page 86.

OBJECTIVES **1** Determine Even and Odd Functions from a Graph (p. 79)
2 Identify Even and Odd Functions from the Equation (p. 80)
3 Use a Graph to Determine Where a Function Is Increasing, Decreasing, or Constant (p. 81)
4 Use a Graph to Locate Local Maxima and Local Minima (p. 82)
5 Use a Graphing Utility to Approximate Local Maxima and Local Minima and to Determine Where a Function Is Increasing or Decreasing (p. 83)
6 Find the Average Rate of Change of a Function (p. 84)

To obtain the graph of a function $y = f(x)$, it is often helpful to know certain properties that the function has and the impact of these properties on the way that the graph will look.

1 Determine Even and Odd Functions from a Graph

The words *even* and *odd*, when applied to a function f, describe the symmetry that exists for the graph of the function.

A function f is even, if and only if, whenever the point (x, y) is on the graph of f then the point $(-x, y)$ is also on the graph. Using function notation, we define an even function as follows:

DEFINITION   A function f is **even** if, for every number x in its domain, the number $-x$ is also in the domain and

$$f(-x) = f(x)$$

A function f is odd, if and only if, whenever the point (x, y) is on the graph of f then the point $(-x, -y)$ is also on the graph. Using function notation, we define an odd function as follows:

DEFINITION
A function f is **odd** if, for every number x in its domain, the number $-x$ is also in the domain and

$$f(-x) = -f(x)$$

Refer to page 20, where the tests for symmetry are listed. The following results are then evident.

THEOREM
A function is even if and only if its graph is symmetric with respect to the y-axis. A function is odd if and only if its graph is symmetric with respect to the origin.

EXAMPLE 1   **Determining Even and Odd Functions from the Graph**

Determine whether each graph given in Figure 17 is the graph of an even function, an odd function, or a function that is neither even nor odd.

Figure 17

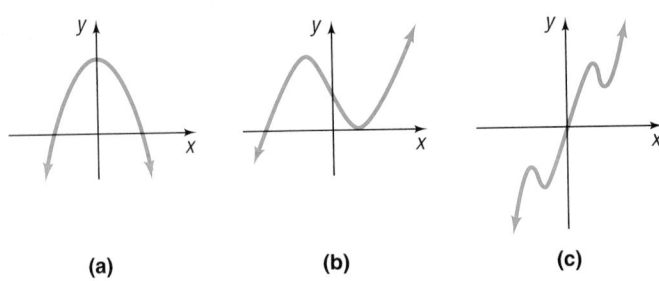

(a)   (b)   (c)

Solution   (a) The graph in Figure 17(a) is that of an even function, because the graph is symmetric with respect to the y-axis.

(b) The function whose graph is given in Figure 17(b) is neither even nor odd, because the graph is neither symmetric with respect to the y-axis nor symmetric with respect to the origin.

(c) The function whose graph is given in Figure 17(c) is odd, because its graph is symmetric with respect to the origin.

════════ **Now Work** PROBLEMS 21(a), (b), AND (d)

2 Identify Even and Odd Functions from the Equation

A graphing utility can be used to conjecture whether a function is even, odd, or neither. Remember that, when the graph of an even function contains the point (x, y), it must also contain the point $(-x, y)$. Therefore, if the graph shows evidence of symmetry with respect to the y-axis, we would conjecture that the function is even. In addition, if the graph shows evidence of symmetry with respect to the origin, we would conjecture that the function is odd.

In the next example, we use a graphing utility to conjecture whether a function is even, odd, or neither. Then we verify our conjecture algebraically.

EXAMPLE 2   Identifying Even and Odd Functions

Use a graphing utility to conjecture whether each of the following functions is even, odd, or neither. Verify the conjecture algebraically. Then state whether the graph is symmetric with respect to the y-axis or with respect to the origin.

(a) $f(x) = x^2 - 5$ (b) $g(x) = x^3 - 1$ (c) $h(x) = 5x^3 - x$

Solution

Figure 18

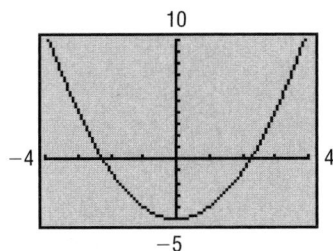

(a) Graph the function. See Figure 18. It appears that the graph is symmetric with respect to the y-axis. We conjecture that the function is even.

To algebraically verify the conjecture, we replace x by $-x$ in $f(x) = x^2 - 5$. Then

$$f(-x) = (-x)^2 - 5 = x^2 - 5 = f(x)$$

Since $f(-x) = f(x)$, we conclude that f is an even function, and the graph is symmetric with respect to the y-axis.

(b) Graph the function. See Figure 19. It appears that there is no symmetry. We conjecture that the function is neither even nor odd.

To algebraically verify that the function is not even, we find $g(-x)$ and compare the result with $g(x)$.

$$g(-x) = (-x)^3 - 1 = -x^3 - 1; \quad g(x) = x^3 - 1$$

Figure 19

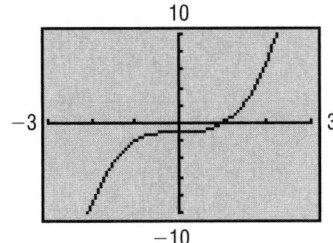

Since $g(-x) \neq g(x)$, the function is not even.

To algebraically verify that the function is not odd, we find $-g(x)$ and compare the result with $g(-x)$.

$$-g(x) = -(x^3 - 1) = -x^3 + 1; \quad g(-x) = -x^3 - 1$$

Since $g(-x) \neq -g(x)$, the function is not odd. The graph is not symmetric with respect to the y-axis nor is it symmetric with respect to the origin.

(c) Graph the function. See Figure 20. It appears that there is symmetry with respect to the origin. We conjecture that the function is odd.

To algebraically verify the conjecture, we replace x by $-x$ in $h(x) = 5x^3 - x$. Then

Figure 20

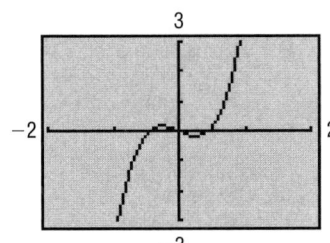

$$h(-x) = 5(-x)^3 - (-x) = -5x^3 + x = -(5x^3 - x) = -h(x)$$

Since $h(-x) = -h(x)$, h is an odd function, and the graph of h is symmetric with respect to the origin.

 Now Work PROBLEM 33

3 Use a Graph to Determine Where a Function Is Increasing, Decreasing, or Constant

Consider the graph given in Figure 21. If you look from left to right along the graph of the function, you will notice that parts of the graph are rising, parts are falling, and parts are horizontal. In such cases, the function is described as *increasing*, *decreasing*, or *constant*, respectively.

Figure 21

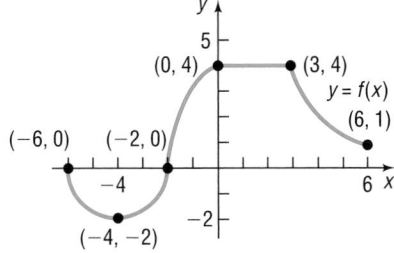

| EXAMPLE 3 | Determining Where a Function Is Increasing, Decreasing, or Constant from Its Graph |

Where is the function in Figure 21 increasing? Where is it decreasing? Where is it constant?

Solution

To answer the question of where a function is increasing, where it is decreasing, and where it is constant, we use strict inequalities involving the independent variable x, or we use open intervals* of x-coordinates. The graph in Figure 21 is rising (increasing) from the point $(-4, -2)$ to the point $(0, 4)$, so we conclude that it is

*The open interval (a, b) consists of all real numbers x for which $a < x < b$.

WARNING We describe the behavior of a graph in terms of its x-values. Do not say the graph in Figure 21 is increasing from the point $(-4, -2)$ to $(0, 4)$. Rather, say it is increasing on the interval $(-4, 0)$. ■

increasing on the open interval $(-4, 0)$ or for $-4 < x < 0$. The graph is falling (decreasing) from the point $(-6, 0)$ to the point $(-4, -2)$ and from the point $(3, 4)$ to the point $(6, 1)$. We conclude that the graph is decreasing on the open intervals $(-6, -4)$ and $(3, 6)$ or for $-6 < x < -4$ and $3 < x < 6$. The graph is constant on the open interval $(0, 3)$ or for $0 < x < 3$.

More precise definitions follow:

DEFINITIONS

A function f is **increasing** on an open interval I if, for any choice of x_1 and x_2 in I, with $x_1 < x_2$, we have $f(x_1) < f(x_2)$.

A function f is **decreasing** on an open interval I if, for any choice of x_1 and x_2 in I, with $x_1 < x_2$, we have $f(x_1) > f(x_2)$.

A function f is **constant** on an open interval I if, for all choices of x in I, the values $f(x)$ are equal.

Figure 22 illustrates the definitions. The graph of an increasing function goes up from left to right, the graph of a decreasing function goes down from left to right, and the graph of a constant function remains at a fixed height.

Figure 22

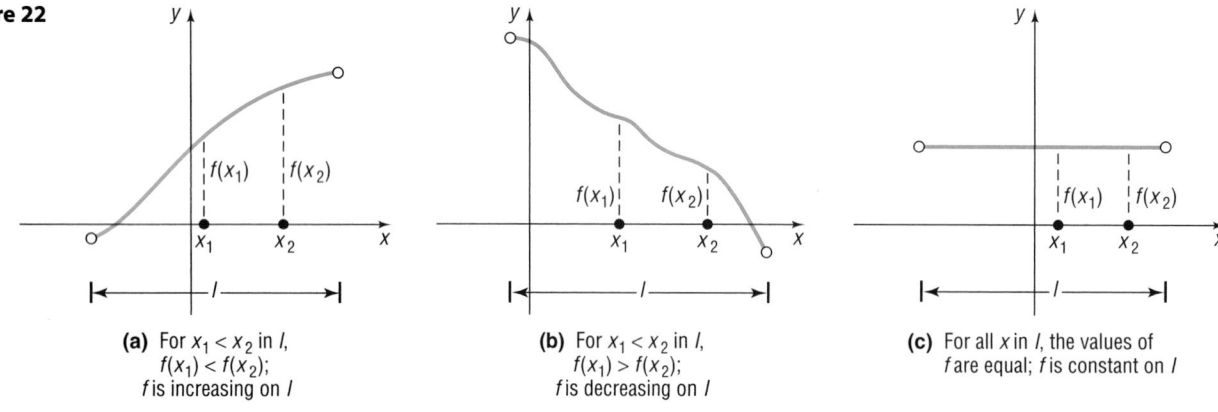

(a) For $x_1 < x_2$ in I,
$f(x_1) < f(x_2)$;
f is increasing on I

(b) For $x_1 < x_2$ in I,
$f(x_1) > f(x_2)$;
f is decreasing on I

(c) For all x in I, the values of f are equal; f is constant on I

Now Work PROBLEMS 11, 13, 15, AND 21(c)

4 Use a Graph to Locate Local Maxima and Local Minima

When the graph of a function is increasing to the left of $x = c$ and decreasing to the right of $x = c$, then at c the value of f is largest. This value is called a *local maximum* of f.* See Figure 23(a).

Figure 23

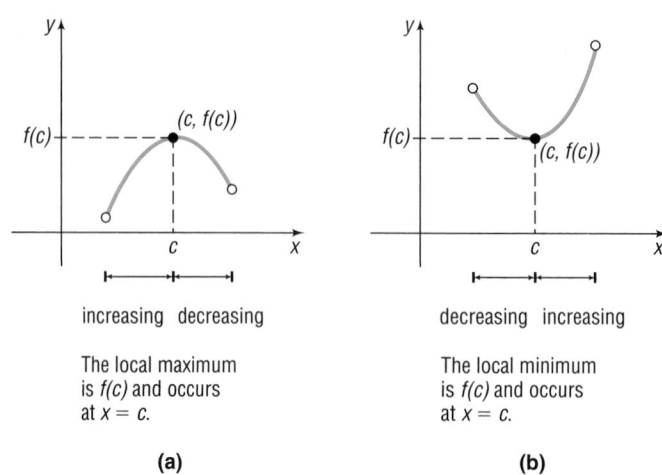

increasing decreasing

The local maximum is $f(c)$ and occurs at $x = c$.

(a)

decreasing increasing

The local minimum is $f(c)$ and occurs at $x = c$.

(b)

*Some texts will use the term *relative* instead of *local*.

When the graph of a function is decreasing to the left of $x = c$ and is increasing to the right of $x = c$, then at c the value of f is the smallest. This value is called a *local minimum* of f. See Figure 23(b).

DEFINITIONS

A function f has a **local maximum** at c if there is an open interval I containing c so that, for all x not equal to c in I, $f(x) < f(c)$. We call $f(c)$ a **local maximum of f.**

A function f has a **local minimum** at c if there is an open interval I containing c so that, for all x not equal to c in I, $f(x) > f(c)$. We call $f(c)$ a **local minimum of f.**

If f has a local maximum at c, then the value of f at c is greater than the values of f near c. If f has a local minimum at c, then the value of f at c is less than the values of f near c. The word *local* is used to suggest that it is only near c that the value $f(c)$ is largest or smallest.

EXAMPLE 4

Finding Local Maxima and Local Minima from the Graph of a Function and Determining Where the Function Is Increasing, Decreasing, or Constant

Figure 24 shows the graph of a function f.

Figure 24

(a) At what value(s) of x, if any, does f have a local maximum?
(b) What are the local maxima?
(c) At what value(s) of x, if any, does f have a local minimum?
(d) What are the local minima?
(e) List the intervals on which f is increasing. List the intervals on which f is decreasing.

Solution

WARNING The y-value is the local maximum or local minimum and it occurs at some x-value. For Figure 24, we say the local maximum is 2 and that the local maximum occurs at $x = 1$. ■

The domain of f is the set of real numbers.

(a) f has a local maximum at 1, since for all x close to 1, $x \neq 1$, we have $f(x) < f(1)$.
(b) The local maximum is $f(1) = 2$.
(c) f has a local minimum at -1 and at 3.
(d) The local minima are $f(-1) = 1$ and $f(3) = 0$.
(e) The function whose graph is given in Figure 24 is increasing for all values of x between -1 and 1 and for all values of x greater than 3. That is, the function is increasing on the intervals $(-1, 1)$ and $(3, \infty)$ or for $-1 < x < 1$ and $x > 3$. The function is decreasing for all values of x less than -1 and for all values of x between 1 and 3. That is, the function is decreasing on the intervals $(-\infty, -1)$ and $(1, 3)$ or for $x < -1$ and $1 < x < 3$.

Now Work PROBLEMS 17 AND 19

5 Use a Graphing Utility to Approximate Local Maxima and Local Minima and to Determine Where a Function Is Increasing or Decreasing

To locate the exact value at which a function f has a local maximum or a local minimum usually requires calculus. However, a graphing utility may be used to approximate these values by using the MAXIMUM and MINIMUM features.

| EXAMPLE 5 | Using a Graphing Utility to Approximate Local Maxima and Minima and to Determine Where a Function Is Increasing or Decreasing |

(a) Use a graphing utility to graph $f(x) = 6x^3 - 12x + 5$ for $-2 < x < 2$. Approximate where f has a local maximum and where f has a local minimum.

(b) Determine where f is increasing and where it is decreasing.

Solution
(a) Graphing utilities have a feature that finds the maximum or minimum point of a graph within a given interval. Graph the function f for $-2 < x < 2$. The MAXIMUM and MINIMUM commands require us to first determine the open interval I. The graphing utility will then approximate the maximum or minimum value in the interval. Using MAXIMUM we find that the local maximum is 11.53 and it occurs at $x = -0.82$, rounded to two decimal places. See Figure 25(a). Using MINIMUM, we find that the local minimum is -1.53 and it occurs at $x = 0.82$, rounded to two decimal places. See Figure 25(b).

Figure 25

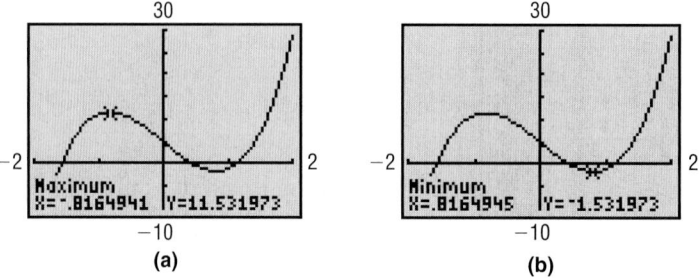

(a)   (b)

(b) Looking at Figures 25(a) and (b), we see that the graph of f is increasing from $x = -2$ to $x = -0.82$ and from $x = 0.82$ to $x = 2$, so f is increasing on the intervals $(-2, -0.82)$ and $(0.82, 2)$ or for $-2 < x < -0.82$ and $0.82 < x < 2$. The graph is decreasing from $x = -0.82$ to $x = 0.82$, so f is decreasing on the interval $(-0.82, 0.82)$ or for $-0.82 < x < 0.82$.

━━━ **Now Work** PROBLEM 45

6 Find the Average Rate of Change of a Function

In Section 1.4, we said that the slope of a line could be interpreted as the average rate of change of the line. To find the average rate of change of a function between any two points on its graph, we calculate the slope of the line containing the two points.

DEFINITION
If a and b, $a \neq b$, are in the domain of a function $y = f(x)$, the **average rate of change of f** from a to b is defined as

$$\text{Average rate of change} = \frac{\Delta y}{\Delta x} = \frac{f(b) - f(a)}{b - a} \qquad a \neq b \qquad \textbf{(1)}$$

The symbol Δy in (1) is the "change in y," and Δx is the "change in x." The average rate of change of f is the change in y divided by the change in x.

| EXAMPLE 6 | Finding the Average Rate of Change |

Find the average rate of change of $f(x) = 3x^2$:

(a) From 1 to 3   (b) From 1 to 5   (c) From 1 to 7

Solution (a) The average rate of change of $f(x) = 3x^2$ from 1 to 3 is

$$\frac{\Delta y}{\Delta x} = \frac{f(3) - f(1)}{3 - 1} = \frac{27 - 3}{3 - 1} = \frac{24}{2} = 12$$

(b) The average rate of change of $f(x) = 3x^2$ from 1 to 5 is

$$\frac{\Delta y}{\Delta x} = \frac{f(5) - f(1)}{5 - 1} = \frac{75 - 3}{5 - 1} = \frac{72}{4} = 18$$

Figure 26

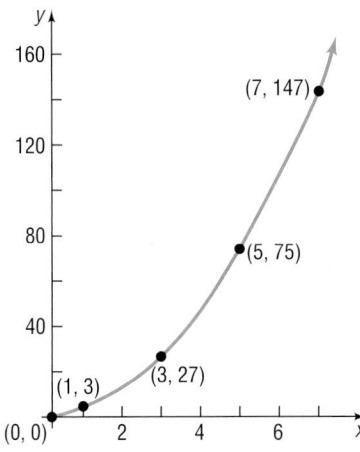

(c) The average rate of change of $f(x) = 3x^2$ from 1 to 7 is

$$\frac{\Delta y}{\Delta x} = \frac{f(7) - f(1)}{7 - 1}$$

$$= \frac{147 - 3}{7 - 1} = \frac{144}{6} = 24$$

See Figure 26 for a graph of $f(x) = 3x^2$. The function f is increasing for $x > 0$. The fact that the average rates of change are getting larger indicates that the graph is getting steeper; that is, it is increasing at an increasing rate.

Now Work PROBLEM 53

The Secant Line

The average rate of change of a function has an important geometric interpretation. Look at the graph of $y = f(x)$ in Figure 27. We have labeled two points on the graph: $(a, f(a))$ and $(b, f(b))$. The line containing these two points is called the **secant line**; its slope is

$$m_{\text{sec}} = \frac{f(b) - f(a)}{b - a}$$

Figure 27

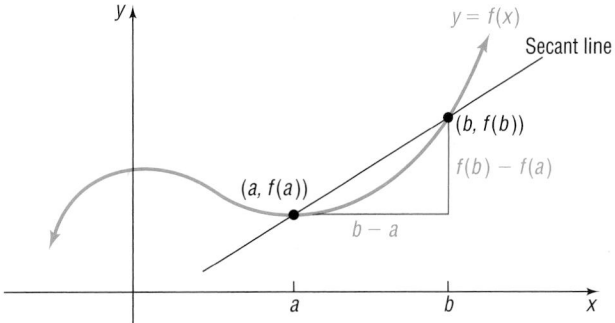

THEOREM **Slope of the Secant Line**

The average rate of change of a function from a to b equals the slope of the secant line containing two points $(a, f(a))$ and $(b, f(b))$ on its graph.

EXAMPLE 7 Finding the Equation of a Secant Line

Suppose that $g(x) = 3x^2 - 2x + 3$.

(a) Find the average rate of change of g from -2 to 1.
(b) Find an equation of the secant line containing $(-2, g(-2))$ and $(1, g(1))$.
(c) Using a graphing utility, draw the graph of g and the secant line obtained in part (b) on the same screen.

Solution

(a) The average rate of change of $g(x) = 3x^2 - 2x + 3$ from -2 to 1 is

$$\text{Average rate of change} = \frac{g(1) - g(-2)}{1 - (-2)}$$

$$= \frac{4 - 19}{3} \qquad \scriptstyle g(1) = 3(1^2) - 2(1) + 3 = 4$$

$$\scriptstyle g(-2) = 3(-2)^2 - 2(-2) + 3 = 19$$

$$= -\frac{15}{3} = -5$$

Figure 28

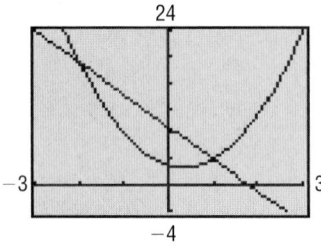

(b) The slope of the secant line containing $(-2, g(-2)) = (-2, 19)$ and $(1, g(1)) = (1, 4)$ is $m_{\text{sec}} = -5$. We use the point–slope form to find an equation of the secant line.

$$y - y_1 = m_{\text{sec}}(x - x_1) \qquad \scriptstyle \text{Point–slope form of the secant line}$$

$$y - 19 = -5(x - (-2)) \qquad \scriptstyle x_1 = -2,\ y_1 = g(-2) = 19,\ m_{\text{sec}} = -5$$

$$y - 19 = -5x - 10 \qquad \scriptstyle \text{Simplify.}$$

$$y = -5x + 9 \qquad \scriptstyle \text{Slope–intercept form of the secant line}$$

(c) Figure 28 shows the graph of g along with the secant line $y = -5x + 9$.

Now Work PROBLEM 59

2.3 Assess Your Understanding

'Are You Prepared?' *Answers are given at the end of these exercises. If you get a wrong answer, read the pages listed in* red.

1. The interval $(2, 5)$ can be written as the inequality _____. (pp. A78–A79)

2. The slope of the line containing the points $(-2, 3)$ and $(3, 8)$ is _____. (pp. 29–30)

3. Test the equation $y = 5x^2 - 1$ for symmetry with respect to the x-axis, the y-axis, and the origin. (pp. 19–21)

4. Write the point–slope form of the line with slope 5 containing the point $(3, -2)$. (p. 33)

5. The intercepts of the equation $y = x^2 - 9$ are _____. (pp. 18–19)

Concepts and Vocabulary

6. A function f is _____ on an open interval I if, for any choice of x_1 and x_2 in I, with $x_1 < x_2$, we have $f(x_1) < f(x_2)$.

7. An _____ function f is one for which $f(-x) = f(x)$ for every x in the domain of f; an _____ function f is one for which $f(-x) = -f(x)$ for every x in the domain of f.

8. **True or False** A function f is decreasing on an open interval I if, for any choice of x_1 and x_2 in I, with $x_1 < x_2$, we have $f(x_1) > f(x_2)$.

9. **True or False** A function f has a local maximum at c if there is an open interval I containing c so that, for all x not equal to c in I, $f(x) < f(c)$.

10. **True or False** Even functions have graphs that are symmetric with respect to the origin.

Skill Building

In Problems 11–20, use the given graph of the function f.

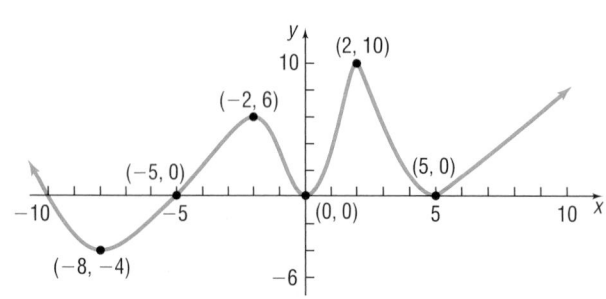

11. Is f increasing on the interval $(-8, -2)$?

12. Is f decreasing on the interval $(-8, -4)$?

13. Is f increasing on the interval $(2, 10)$?

14. Is f decreasing on the interval $(2, 5)$?

15. List the interval(s) on which f is increasing.

16. List the interval(s) on which f is decreasing.

17. Is there a local maximum at 2? If yes, what is it?

18. Is there a local maximum at 5? If yes, what is it?

19. List the numbers at which f has a local maximum. What are these local maxima?

20. List the numbers at which f has a local minimum. What are these local minima?

In Problems 21–28, the graph of a function is given. Use the graph to find:
(a) The intercepts, if any
(b) The domain and range
(c) The intervals on which it is increasing, decreasing, or constant
(d) Whether it is even, odd, or neither

21.

22.

23.

24.

25.

26.

27.

28.
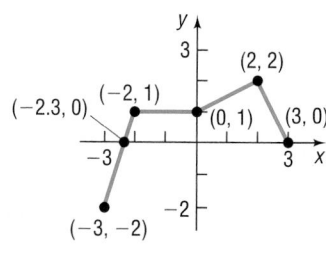

In Problems 29–32, the graph of a function f is given. Use the graph to find:
(a) The values, if any, at which f has a local maximum. What are these local maxima?
(b) The values, if any, at which f has a local minimum. What are these local minima?

29.

30.

31.

32.
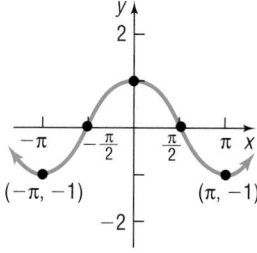

In Problems 33–44, determine algebraically whether each function is even, odd, or neither.

33. $F(x) = 4x^3 + x$

34. $f(x) = 2x^4 - x^2$

35. $g(x) = -3x^2 - 5$

36. $h(x) = 3x^5 + 5x$

37. $F(x) = \sqrt[3]{x}$

38. $G(x) = \sqrt{x}$

39. $f(x) = x + |x|$

40. $f(x) = \sqrt[3]{2x^2 + 1}$

41. $g(x) = \dfrac{1}{x^2}$

42. $h(x) = \dfrac{x}{x^2 - 1}$

43. $h(x) = \dfrac{-x^3}{3x^2 - 9}$

44. $F(x) = \dfrac{2x}{|x|}$

In Problems 45–52, use a graphing utility to graph each function over the indicated interval and approximate any local maxima and local minima. Determine where the function is increasing and where it is decreasing. Round answers to two decimal places.

45. $f(x) = x^3 - 3x + 2 \quad (-2, 2)$

46. $f(x) = x^3 - 3x^2 + 5 \quad (-1, 3)$

47. $f(x) = x^5 - x^3 \quad (-2, 2)$

48. $f(x) = x^4 - x^2 \quad (-2, 2)$

49. $f(x) = -0.2x^3 - 0.6x^2 + 4x - 6 \quad (-6, 4)$

50. $f(x) = -0.4x^3 + 0.6x^2 + 3x - 2 \quad (-4, 5)$

51. $f(x) = 0.25x^4 + 0.3x^3 - 0.9x^2 + 3 \quad (-3, 2)$

52. $f(x) = -0.4x^4 - 0.5x^3 + 0.8x^2 - 2 \quad (-3, 2)$

53. Find the average rate of change of $f(x) = -2x^2 + 4$

  (a) From 0 to 2
  (b) From 1 to 3
  (c) From 1 to 4

54. Find the average rate of change of $f(x) = -x^3 + 1$

  (a) From 0 to 2
  (b) From 1 to 3
  (c) From −1 to 1

55. Find the average rate of change of $g(x) = x^3 - 2x + 1$

  (a) From −3 to −2
  (b) From −1 to 1
  (c) From 1 to 3

56. Find the average rate of change of $h(x) = x^2 - 2x + 3$

  (a) From −1 to 1
  (b) From 0 to 2
  (c) From 2 to 5

57. $f(x) = 5x - 2$

  (a) Find the average rate of change from 1 to 3.
  (b) Find an equation of the secant line containing $(1, f(1))$ and $(3, f(3))$.

58. $f(x) = -4x + 1$

  (a) Find the average rate of change from 2 to 5.
  (b) Find an equation of the secant line containing $(2, f(2))$ and $(5, f(5))$.

59. $g(x) = x^2 - 2$

  (a) Find the average rate of change from −2 to 1.
  (b) Find an equation of the secant line containing $(-2, g(-2))$ and $(1, g(1))$.

60. $g(x) = x^2 + 1$

  (a) Find the average rate of change from −1 to 2.
  (b) Find an equation of the secant line containing $(-1, g(-1))$ and $(2, g(2))$.

61. $h(x) = x^2 - 2x$

  (a) Find the average rate of change from 2 to 4.
  (b) Find an equation of the secant line containing $(2, h(2))$ and $(4, h(4))$.

62. $h(x) = -2x^2 + x$

  (a) Find the average rate of change from 0 to 3.
  (b) Find an equation of the secant line containing $(0, h(0))$ and $(3, h(3))$.

Mixed Practice

63. $g(x) = x^3 - 4x$

  (a) Determine whether g is even, odd, or neither.
  (b) Using a graphing utility, graph g.
  (c) There is a local minimum in quadrant IV. Approximate the local minimum.
  (d) Using the results from part (a), determine the local maximum in quadrant II without using your graphing utility. Verify your result using your graphing utility.

64. $f(x) = -x^3 + 6x$

  (a) Determine whether f is even, odd, or neither.
  (b) Using a graphing utility, graph f.
  (c) There is a local maximum in quadrant I. Approximate the local maximum.
  (d) Using the results from part (a), determine the local minimum in quadrant III without using your graphing utility. Verify your result using your graphing utility.

65. $F(x) = -x^4 + 8x^2 + 8$

  (a) Determine whether F is even, odd, or neither.
  (b) Using a graphing utility, graph F.
  (c) There is a local maximum in quadrant I. Approximate the local maximum.

  (d) Using the results from part (a), determine the local maximum in quadrant II without using your graphing utility.
  (e) Suppose the area under the graph of F between $x = 0$ and $x = 3$ that is bounded below by the x-axis is 47.4 square units. Using the results from part (a), determine the area under the graph of F between $x = -3$ and $x = 0$ bounded below by the x-axis.

66. $G(x) = -x^4 + 32x^2 + 144$

  (a) Determine whether G is even, odd, or neither.
  (b) Using a graphing utility, graph G.
  (c) There is a local maximum in quadrant I. Approximate the local maximum.
  (d) Using the results from part (a), determine the local maximum in quadrant II without using your graphing utility.
  (e) Suppose the area under the graph of G between $x = 0$ and $x = 6$ that is bounded below by the x-axis is 1612.8 square units. Using the results from part (a), determine the area under the graph of F between $x = -6$ and $x = 0$ bounded below by the x-axis.

Applications and Extensions

67. Minimum Average Cost The average cost per hour in dollars, $\overline{C}$, of producing x riding lawn mowers can be modeled by the function

$$\overline{C}(x) = 0.3x^2 + 21x - 251 + \frac{2500}{x}$$

  (a) Use a graphing utility to graph $\overline{C} = \overline{C}(x)$.
  (b) Determine the number of riding lawn mowers to produce in order to minimize average cost.
  (c) What is the minimum average cost?

68. Medicine Concentration The concentration C of a medication in the bloodstream t hours after being administered is modeled by the function

$$C(t) = -0.002x^4 + 0.039t^3 - 0.285t^2 + 0.766t + 0.085$$

  (a) After how many hours will the concentration be highest?
  (b) A woman nursing a child must wait until the concentration is below 0.5 before she can feed him. After taking the medication, how long must she wait before feeding her child?

69. E-coli Growth A strain of E-coli Beu 397-recA441 is placed into a nutrient broth at 30° Celsius and allowed to grow. The data shown in the table are collected. The population is measured in grams and the time in hours. Since population P depends on time t and each input corresponds to exactly one output, we can say that population is a function of time; so $P(t)$ represents the population at time t.

(a) Find the average rate of change of the population from 0 to 2.5 hours.
(b) Find the average rate of change of the population from 4.5 to 6 hours.
(c) What is happening to the average rate of change as time passes?

Time (hours), t	Population (grams), P
0	0.09
2.5	0.18
3.5	0.26
4.5	0.35
6	0.50

70. e-Filing Tax Returns The Internal Revenue Service Restructuring and Reform Act (RRA) was signed into law by President Bill Clinton in 1998. A major objective of the RRA was to promote electronic filing of tax returns. The data in the table show the percentage of individual income tax returns filed electronically for filing years 1998–2006. Since the percentage P of returns filed electronically depends on the filing year y and each input corresponds to exactly one output, the percentage of returns filed electronically is a function of the filing year; so $P(y)$ represents the percentage of returns filed electronically for filing year y.

(a) Find the average rate of change of the percentage of e-filed returns from 1998 to 2000.
(b) Find the average rate of change of the percentage of e-filed returns from 2001 to 2003.
(c) Find the average rate of change of the percentage of e-filed returns from 2004 to 2006.

(d) What is happening to the average rate of change as time passes?

Year	Percentage of returns e-filed
1998	20.7
1999	23.5
2000	27.6
2001	30.7
2002	35.6
2003	40.2
2004	46.5
2005	51.1
2006	57.1

SOURCE: Internal Revenue Service

71. For the function $f(x) = x^2$, compute each average rate of change:
(a) From 0 to 1
(b) From 0 to 0.5
(c) From 0 to 0.1
(d) From 0 to 0.01
(e) From 0 to 0.001
(f) Use a graphing utility to graph each of the secant lines along with f.
(g) What do you think is happening to the secant lines?
(h) What is happening to the slopes of the secant lines? Is there some number that they are getting closer to? What is that number?

72. For the function $f(x) = x^2$, compute each average rate of change:
(a) From 1 to 2
(b) From 1 to 1.5
(c) From 1 to 1.1
(d) From 1 to 1.01
(e) From 1 to 1.001
(f) Use a graphing utility to graph each of the secant lines along with f.
(g) What do you think is happening to the secant lines?
(h) What is happening to the slopes of the secant lines? Is there some number that they are getting closer to? What is that number?

△ Problems 73–80 require the following discussion of a secant line. The slope of the secant line containing the two points $(x, f(x))$ and $(x + h, f(x + h))$ on the graph of a function $y = f(x)$ may be given as

$$m_{sec} = \frac{f(x + h) - f(x)}{(x + h) - x} = \frac{f(x + h) - f(x)}{h} \qquad h \neq 0$$

In calculus, this expression is called the **difference quotient of f.**

(a) Express the slope of the secant line of each function in terms of x and h. Be sure to simplify your answer.
(b) Find m_{sec} for $h = 0.5, 0.1$, and 0.01 at $x = 1$. What value does m_{sec} approach as h approaches 0?
(c) Find the equation for the secant line at $x = 1$ with $h = 0.01$.
(d) Use a graphing utility to graph f and the secant line found in part (c) on the same viewing window.

73. $f(x) = 2x + 5$ **74.** $f(x) = -3x + 2$ **75.** $f(x) = x^2 + 2x$ **76.** $f(x) = 2x^2 + x$

77. $f(x) = 2x^2 - 3x + 1$ **78.** $f(x) = -x^2 + 3x - 2$ **79.** $f(x) = \frac{1}{x}$ **80.** $f(x) = \frac{1}{x^2}$

Discussion and Writing

81. Draw the graph of a function that has the following properties: domain: all real numbers; range: all real numbers; intercepts: $(0, -3)$ and $(3, 0)$; a local maximum of -2 is at -1; a local minimum of -6 is at 2. Compare your graph with those of others. Comment on any differences.

82. Redo Problem 81 with the following additional information: increasing on $(-\infty, -1), (2, \infty)$; decreasing on $(-1, 2)$. Again compare your graph with others and comment on any differences.

83. How many x-intercepts can a function defined on an interval have if it is increasing on that interval? Explain.

84. Suppose that a friend of yours does not understand the idea of increasing and decreasing functions. Provide an explanation, complete with graphs, that clarifies the idea.

85. Can a function be both even and odd? Explain.

86. Using a graphing utility, graph $y = 5$ on the interval $(-3, 3)$. Use MAXIMUM to find the local maxima on $(-3, 3)$. Comment on the result provided by the calculator.

'Are You Prepared?' Answers

1. $2 < x < 5$ **2.** 1   **3.** symmetric with respect to the y-axis   **4.** $y + 2 = 5(x - 3)$ **5.** $(-3, 0), (3, 0), (0, -9)$

2.4 Library of Functions; Piecewise-defined Functions

PREPARING FOR THIS SECTION   *Before getting started, review the following:*

- Intercepts (Section 1.2, pp. 18–19)

- Graphs of Key Equations (Section 1.1: Example 8, p. 9; Section 1.2: Example 4, p. 21; Example 5, p. 22; Example 6, p. 23)

Now Work the 'Are You Prepared?' problems on page 96.

OBJECTIVES   **1** Graph the Functions Listed in the Library of Functions (p. 90)
2 Graph Piecewise-defined Functions (p. 95)

1 Graph the Functions Listed in the Library of Functions

We now introduce a few more functions to add to our list of important functions. We begin with the *square root function*.

On page 22, we graphed the equation $y = \sqrt{x}$. Figure 29 shows a graph of the function $f(x) = \sqrt{x}$. Based on the graph, we have the following properties:

Figure 29

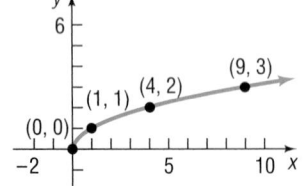

Properties of $f(x) = \sqrt{x}$

1. The domain and the range are the set of nonnegative real numbers.
2. The x-intercept of the graph of $f(x) = \sqrt{x}$ is 0. The y-intercept of the graph of $f(x) = \sqrt{x}$ is also 0.
3. The function is neither even nor odd.
4. It is increasing on the interval $(0, \infty)$.
5. It has a minimum value of 0 at $x = 0$.

EXAMPLE 1	Graphing the Cube Root Function

(a) Determine whether $f(x) = \sqrt[3]{x}$ is even, odd, or neither. State whether the graph of f is symmetric with respect to the y-axis or symmetric with respect to the origin.
(b) Determine the intercepts, if any, of the graph of $f(x) = \sqrt[3]{x}$.
(c) Graph $f(x) = \sqrt[3]{x}$.

Solution
(a) Because
$$f(-x) = \sqrt[3]{-x} = -\sqrt[3]{x} = -f(x)$$
the function is odd. The graph of f is symmetric with respect to the origin.

(b) The y-intercept is $f(0) = \sqrt[3]{0} = 0$. The x-intercept is found by solving the equation $f(x) = 0$.

$$f(x) = 0$$
$$\sqrt[3]{x} = 0 \quad \text{\small $f(x) = \sqrt[3]{x}$}$$
$$x = 0 \quad \text{\small Cube both sides of the equation.}$$

The x-intercept is also 0.

(c) We use the function to form Table 4 and obtain some points on the graph. Because of the symmetry with respect to the origin, we need to find only points (x, y) for which $x \geq 0$. Figure 30 shows the graph of $f(x) = \sqrt[3]{x}$.

Table 4

x	$y = f(x) = \sqrt[3]{x}$	(x, y)
0	0	$(0, 0)$
$\dfrac{1}{8}$	$\dfrac{1}{2}$	$\left(\dfrac{1}{8}, \dfrac{1}{2}\right)$
1	1	$(1, 1)$
2	$\sqrt[3]{2} \approx 1.26$	$(2, \sqrt[3]{2})$
8	2	$(8, 2)$

Figure 30

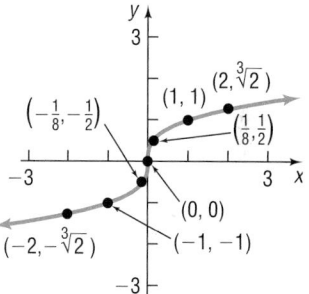

From the results of Example 1 and Figure 30, we have the following properties of the cube root function.

Properties of $f(x) = \sqrt[3]{x}$

1. The domain and the range are the set of all real numbers.
2. The x-intercept of the graph of $f(x) = \sqrt[3]{x}$ is 0. The y-intercept of the graph of $f(x) = \sqrt[3]{x}$ is also 0.
3. The graph is symmetric with respect to the origin. The function is odd.
4. It is increasing on the interval $(-\infty, \infty)$.
5. It does not have a local minimum or a local maximum.

EXAMPLE 2 | **Graphing the Absolute Value Function**

(a) Determine whether $f(x) = |x|$ is even, odd, or neither. State whether the graph of f is symmetric with respect to the y-axis or symmetric with respect to the origin.
(b) Determine the intercepts, if any, of the graph of $f(x) = |x|$.
(c) Graph $f(x) = |x|$.

Solution
(a) Because
$$f(-x) = |-x|$$
$$= |x| = f(x)$$

the function is even. The graph of f is symmetric with respect to the y-axis.

(b) The y-intercept is $f(0) = |0| = 0$. The x-intercept is found by solving the equation $f(x) = 0$ or $|x| = 0$. So the x-intercept is 0.

(c) We use the function to form Table 5 and obtain some points on the graph. Because of the symmetry with respect to the y-axis, we need to find only points (x, y) for which $x \geq 0$. Figure 31 shows the graph of $f(x) = |x|$.

Table 5

x	y = f(x) = |x|	(x, y)
0	0	(0, 0)
1	1	(1, 1)
2	2	(2, 2)
3	3	(3, 3)

Figure 31

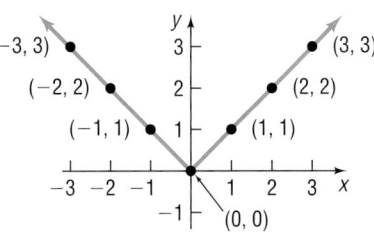

From the results of Example 2 and Figure 31, we have the following properties of the absolute value function.

> **Properties of f(x) = |x|**
>
> 1. The domain is the set of all real numbers. The range of f is $\{y | y \geq 0\}$.
> 2. The x-intercept of the graph of $f(x) = |x|$ is 0. The y-intercept of the graph of $f(x) = |x|$ is also 0.
> 3. The graph is symmetric with respect to the y-axis. The function is even.
> 4. It is decreasing on the interval $(-\infty, 0)$. It is increasing on the interval $(0, \infty)$.
> 5. It has a local minimum of 0 at $x = 0$.

Seeing the Concept

Graph $y = |x|$ on a square screen and compare what you see with Figure 31. Note that some graphing calculators use abs(x) for absolute value.

We now provide a summary of the key functions that we have encountered. In going through this list, pay special attention to the properties of each function, particularly to the shape of each graph. Knowing these graphs along with key points on the graph will lay the foundation for later graphing techniques.

Constant Function

$$f(x) = b \qquad b \text{ is a real number}$$

Figure 32
Constant Function

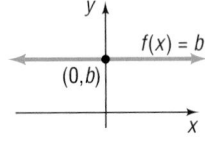

See Figure 32.

The domain of a **constant function** is the set of all real numbers; its range is the set consisting of a single number b. Its graph is a horizontal line whose y-intercept is b. The constant function is an even function whose graph is a horizontal line over its domain.

Identity Function

$$f(x) = x$$

Figure 33
Identity Function

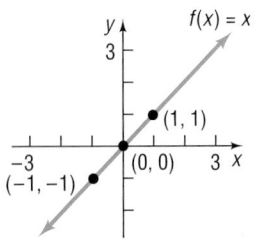

See Figure 33.

The domain and the range of the **identity function** are the set of all real numbers. Its graph is a line whose slope is $m = 1$ and whose y-intercept is 0. The line consists of all points for which the x-coordinate equals the y-coordinate. The identity function is an odd function that is increasing over its domain. Note that the graph bisects quadrants I and III.

Figure 34
Square Function

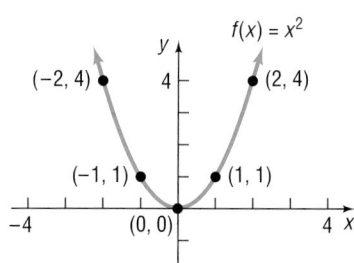

Square Function

$$f(x) = x^2$$

See Figure 34.

The domain of the **square function** f is the set of all real numbers; its range is the set of nonnegative real numbers. The graph of this function is a parabola whose intercept is at $(0, 0)$. The square function is an even function that is decreasing on the interval $(-\infty, 0)$ and increasing on the interval $(0, \infty)$.

Figure 35
Cube Function

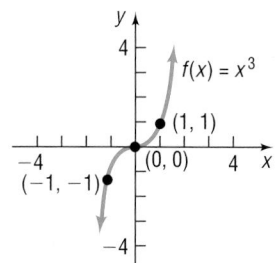

Cube Function

$$f(x) = x^3$$

See Figure 35.

The domain and the range of the **cube function** are the set of all real numbers. The intercept of the graph is at $(0, 0)$. The cube function is odd and is increasing on the interval $(-\infty, \infty)$.

Figure 36
Square Root Function

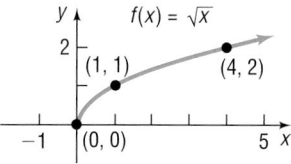

Square Root Function

$$f(x) = \sqrt{x}$$

See Figure 36.

The domain and the range of the **square root function** are the set of nonnegative real numbers. The intercept of the graph is at $(0, 0)$. The square root function is neither even nor odd and is increasing on the interval $(0, \infty)$.

Figure 37
Cube Root Function

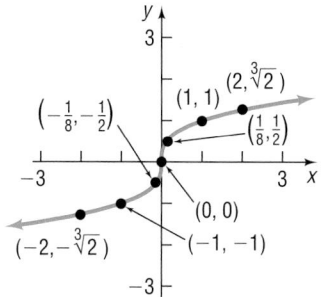

Cube Root Function

$$f(x) = \sqrt[3]{x}$$

See Figure 37.

The domain and the range of the **cube root function** are the set of all real numbers. The intercept of the graph is at $(0, 0)$. The cube root function is an odd function that is increasing on the interval $(-\infty, \infty)$.

Figure 38
Reciprocal Function

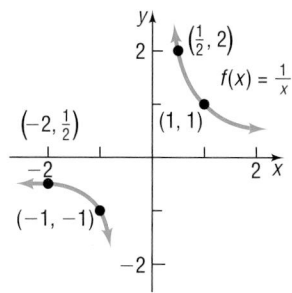

Reciprocal Function

$$f(x) = \frac{1}{x}$$

Refer to Example 6, page 23, for a discussion of the equation $y = \dfrac{1}{x}$. See Figure 38.

The domain and the range of the **reciprocal function** are the set of all nonzero real numbers. The graph has no intercepts. The reciprocal function is decreasing on the intervals $(-\infty, 0)$ and $(0, \infty)$ and is an odd function.

Absolute Value Function

$$f(x) = |x|$$

Figure 39
Absolute Value Function

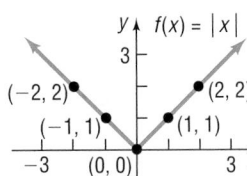

See Figure 39.

The domain of the **absolute value function** is the set of all real numbers; its range is the set of nonnegative real numbers. The intercept of the graph is at $(0, 0)$. If $x \geq 0$, then $f(x) = x$, and the graph of f is part of the line $y = x$; if $x < 0$, then $f(x) = -x$, and the graph of f is part of the line $y = -x$. The absolute value function is an even function; it is decreasing on the interval $(-\infty, 0)$ and increasing on the interval $(0, \infty)$.

The notation $\text{int}(x)$ stands for the largest integer less than or equal to x. For example,

$$\text{int}(1) = 1, \quad \text{int}(2.5) = 2, \quad \text{int}\left(\frac{1}{2}\right) = 0, \quad \text{int}\left(-\frac{3}{4}\right) = -1, \quad \text{int}(\pi) = 3$$

This type of correspondence occurs frequently enough in mathematics that we give it a name.

DEFINITION

Greatest Integer Function

$$f(x) = \text{int}(x)^* = \text{greatest integer less than or equal to } x$$

Table 6

	$y = f(x)$	
x	$= \text{int}(x)$	(x, y)
-1	-1	$(-1, -1)$
$-\dfrac{1}{2}$	-1	$\left(-\dfrac{1}{2}, -1\right)$
$-\dfrac{1}{4}$	-1	$\left(-\dfrac{1}{4}, -1\right)$
0	0	$(0, 0)$
$\dfrac{1}{4}$	0	$\left(\dfrac{1}{4}, 0\right)$
$\dfrac{1}{2}$	0	$\left(\dfrac{1}{2}, 0\right)$
$\dfrac{3}{4}$	0	$\left(\dfrac{3}{4}, 0\right)$

We obtain the graph of $f(x) = \text{int}(x)$ by plotting several points. See Table 6. For values of x, $-1 \leq x < 0$, the value of $f(x) = \text{int}(x)$ is -1; for values of x, $0 \leq x < 1$, the value of f is 0. See Figure 40 for the graph.

Figure 40
Greatest Integer Function

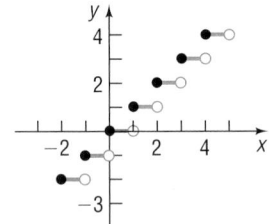

The domain of the **greatest integer function** is the set of all real numbers; its range is the set of integers. The y-intercept of the graph is 0. The x-intercepts lie in the interval $[0, 1)$. The greatest integer function is neither even nor odd. It is constant on every interval of the form $[k, k + 1)$, for k an integer. In Figure 40, we use a solid dot to indicate, for example, that at $x = 1$ the value of f is $f(1) = 1$; we use an open circle to illustrate that the function does not assume the value of 0 at $x = 1$.

Although a precise definition requires the idea of a limit, discussed in calculus, in a rough sense, a function is said to be **continuous** if its graph has no gaps or holes and can be drawn without lifting a pencil from the paper on which the graph is drawn. We contrast this with a *discontinuous* function. A function is **discontinuous** if its graph has gaps or holes so that its graph cannot be drawn without lifting a pencil from the paper.

From the graph of the greatest integer function, we can see why it is also called a **step function.** At $x = 0$, $x = \pm 1$, $x = \pm 2$, and so on, this function is discontinuous because, at integer values, the graph suddenly "steps" from one value to another without taking on any of the intermediate values. For example, to the immediate left of $x = 3$, the y-coordinates of the points on the graph are 2, and to the immediate right of $x = 3$, the y-coordinates of the points on the graph are 3. So, the graph has gaps in it.

COMMENT When graphing a function using a graphing utility, you can choose either the **connected mode,** in which points plotted on the screen are connected, making the graph appear without any breaks, or the **dot mode,** in which only the points plotted appear. When graphing the greatest integer function with a graphing utility, it is necessary to be in the dot mode. This is to prevent the utility from "connecting the dots" when $f(x)$ changes from one integer value to the next. See Figure 41.

*Some books use the notation $f(x) = [\![x]\!]$ instead of $\text{int}(x)$.

Figure 41
$f(x) = \text{int}(x)$

(a) Connected mode

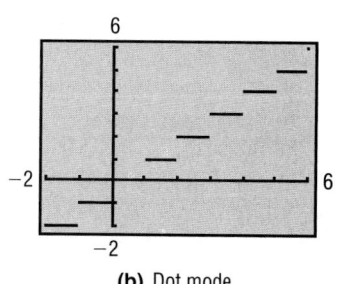
(b) Dot mode

The functions that we have discussed so far are basic. Whenever you encounter one of them, you should see a mental picture of its graph. For example, if you encounter the function $f(x) = x^2$, you should see in your mind's eye a picture like Figure 34.

—— **Now Work** PROBLEMS 9 THROUGH 16

2 Graph Piecewise-defined Functions

Sometimes a function is defined differently on different parts of its domain. For example, the absolute value function $f(x) = |x|$ is actually defined by two equations: $f(x) = x$ if $x \geq 0$ and $f(x) = -x$ if $x < 0$. For convenience, we generally combine these equations into one expression as

$$f(x) = |x| = \begin{cases} x & \text{if } x \geq 0 \\ -x & \text{if } x < 0 \end{cases}$$

When functions are defined by more than one equation, they are called **piecewise-defined** functions.

Let's look at another example of a piecewise-defined function.

EXAMPLE 3   Analyzing a Piecewise-defined Function

The function f is defined as

$$f(x) = \begin{cases} -x + 1 & \text{if } -3 \leq x < 1 \\ 2 & \text{if } x = 1 \\ x^2 & \text{if } x > 1 \end{cases}$$

(a) Find $f(0)$, $f(1)$, and $f(2)$.   (b) Determine the domain of f.
(c) Graph f.   (d) Use the graph to find the range of f.
(e) Is f continuous on its domain?

Solution   (a) To find $f(0)$, we observe that when $x = 0$ the equation for f is given by $f(x) = -x + 1$. So we have

$$f(0) = -0 + 1 = 1$$

When $x = 1$, the equation for f is $f(x) = 2$. Thus,

$$f(1) = 2$$

When $x = 2$, the equation for f is $f(x) = x^2$. So

$$f(2) = 2^2 = 4$$

Figure 42

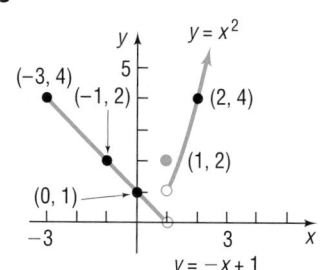

(b) To find the domain of f, we look at its definition. Since f is defined for all x greater than or equal to 3, the domain of f is $\{x \mid x \geq -3\}$, or the interval $[-3, \infty)$.
(c) To graph f, we graph "each piece." First we graph the line $y = -x + 1$ and keep only the part for which $-3 \leq x < 1$. Then we plot the point $(1, 2)$ because, when $x = 1$, $f(x) = 2$. Finally, we graph the parabola $y = x^2$ and keep only the part for which $x > 1$. See Figure 42.

(d) From the graph, we conclude that the range of f is $\{y\,|\,y > 0\}$, or the interval $(0, \infty)$.

(e) The function f is not continuous because there is a "jump" in the graph at $x = 1$.

═══════ **Now Work** PROBLEM 29

| EXAMPLE 4 | **Cost of Electricity** |

In May 2006, Commonwealth Edison Company supplied electricity to residences for a monthly customer charge of $7.58 plus 8.275¢ per kilowatt-hour (kWhr) for the first 400 kWhr supplied in the month and 6.208¢ per kWhr for all usage over 400 kWhr in the month.

(a) What is the charge for using 300 kWhr in a month?

(b) What is the charge for using 700 kWhr in a month?

(c) If C is the monthly charge for x kWhr, develop a model relating the monthly charge and kilowatt-hours used. That is, express C as a function of x.

Source: Commonwealth Edison Co., Chicago, Illinois, 2006

Solution

(a) For 300 kWhr, the charge is $7.58 plus 8.275¢ = $0.08275 per kWhr. That is,

$$\text{Charge} = \$7.58 + \$0.08275(300) = \$32.41$$

(b) For 700 kWhr, the charge is $7.58 plus 8.275¢ per kWhr for the first 400 kWhr plus 6.208¢ per kWhr for the 300 kWhr in excess of 400. That is,

$$\text{Charge} = \$7.58 + \$0.08275(400) + \$0.06208(300) = \$59.30$$

(c) Let x represent the number of kilowatt-hours used. If $0 \le x \le 400$, the monthly charge C (in dollars) can be found by multiplying x times $0.08275 and adding the monthly customer charge of $7.58. So, if $0 \le x \le 400$, then $C(x) = 0.08275x + 7.58$.

For $x > 400$, the charge is $0.08275(400) + 7.58 + 0.06208(x - 400)$, since $x - 400$ equals the usage in excess of 400 kWhr, which costs $0.06208 per kWhr. That is, if $x > 400$, then

$$C(x) = 0.08275(400) + 7.58 + 0.06208(x - 400)$$
$$= 40.68 + 0.06208(x - 400)$$
$$= 0.06208x + 15.848$$

The rule for computing C follows two equations:

$$C(x) = \begin{cases} 0.08275x + 7.58 & \text{if } 0 \le x \le 400 \\ 0.06208x + 15.848 & \text{if } x > 400 \end{cases} \quad \textit{The Model}$$

See Figure 43 for the graph.

Figure 43

2.4 Assess Your Understanding

'Are You Prepared?' *Answers are given at the end of these exercises. If you get a wrong answer, read the pages listed in red.*

1. Sketch the graph of $y = \sqrt{x}$. (p. 22)

2. Sketch the graph of $y = \dfrac{1}{x}$. (p. 23)

3. List the intercepts of the equation $y = x^3 - 8$. (pp. 18–19)

Concepts and Vocabulary

4. The function $f(x) = x^2$ is decreasing on the interval _____.

5. When functions are defined by more than one equation, they are called _____ functions.

6. *True or False* The cube function is odd and is increasing on the interval $(-\infty, \infty)$.

7. *True or False* The cube root function is odd and is decreasing on the interval $(-\infty, \infty)$.

8. *True or False* The domain and the range of the reciprocal function are the set of all real numbers.

Skill Building

In Problems 9–16, match each graph to its function.

   A. *Constant function*   B. *Identity function*   C. *Square function*
   D. *Cube function*   E. *Square root function*   F. *Reciprocal function*
   G. *Absolute value function*   H. *Cube root function*

  9.

  10.

  11.

  12.

  13.

  14.

  15.

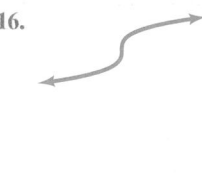 **16.**

In Problems 17–24, sketch the graph of each function. Be sure to label three points on the graph.

17. $f(x) = x$ **18.** $f(x) = x^2$ **19.** $f(x) = x^3$ **20.** $f(x) = \sqrt{x}$

21. $f(x) = \dfrac{1}{x}$ **22.** $f(x) = |x|$ **23.** $f(x) = \sqrt[3]{x}$ **24.** $f(x) = 3$

25. If $f(x) = \begin{cases} x^2 & \text{if } x < 0 \\ 2 & \text{if } x = 0 \\ 2x + 1 & \text{if } x > 0 \end{cases}$

    find: (a) $f(-2)$ (b) $f(0)$ (c) $f(2)$

26. If $f(x) = \begin{cases} -3x & \text{if } x < -1 \\ 0 & \text{if } x = -1 \\ 2x^2 + 1 & \text{if } x > -1 \end{cases}$

    find: (a) $f(-2)$ (b) $f(-1)$ (c) $f(0)$

27. If $f(x) = \begin{cases} 2x - 4 & \text{if } -1 \le x \le 2 \\ x^3 - 2 & \text{if } 2 < x \le 3 \end{cases}$

    find: (a) $f(0)$ (b) $f(1)$ (c) $f(2)$ (d) $f(3)$

28. If $f(x) = \begin{cases} x^3 & \text{if } -2 \le x < 1 \\ 3x + 2 & \text{if } 1 \le x \le 4 \end{cases}$

    find: (a) $f(-1)$ (b) $f(0)$ (c) $f(1)$ (d) $f(3)$

In Problems 29–40:

   (a) Find the domain of each function.   *(b) Locate any intercepts.*   *(c) Graph each function.*
   (d) Based on the graph, find the range.   *(e) Is f continuous on its domain?*

29. $f(x) = \begin{cases} 2x & \text{if } x \ne 0 \\ 1 & \text{if } x = 0 \end{cases}$

30. $f(x) = \begin{cases} 3x & \text{if } x \ne 0 \\ 4 & \text{if } x = 0 \end{cases}$

31. $f(x) = \begin{cases} -2x + 3 & x < 1 \\ 3x - 2 & x \ge 1 \end{cases}$

32. $f(x) = \begin{cases} x + 3 & \text{if } x < -2 \\ -2x - 3 & \text{if } x \ge -2 \end{cases}$

33. $f(x) = \begin{cases} x + 3 & \text{if } -2 \le x < 1 \\ 5 & \text{if } x = 1 \\ -x + 2 & \text{if } x > 1 \end{cases}$

34. $f(x) = \begin{cases} 2x + 5 & \text{if } -3 \le x < 0 \\ -3 & \text{if } x = 0 \\ -5x & \text{if } x > 0 \end{cases}$

35. $f(x) = \begin{cases} 1 + x & \text{if } x < 0 \\ x^2 & \text{if } x \ge 0 \end{cases}$

36. $f(x) = \begin{cases} \dfrac{1}{x} & \text{if } x < 0 \\ \sqrt[3]{x} & \text{if } x \ge 0 \end{cases}$

37. $f(x) = \begin{cases} |x| & \text{if } -2 \le x < 0 \\ x^3 & \text{if } x > 0 \end{cases}$

38. $f(x) = \begin{cases} 2 - x & \text{if } -3 \le x < 1 \\ \sqrt{x} & \text{if } x > 1 \end{cases}$

39. $f(x) = 2\,\text{int}(x)$

40. $f(x) = \text{int}(2x)$

In Problems 41–44, the graph of a piecewise-defined function is given. Write a definition for each function.

41.

42.

43.

44.

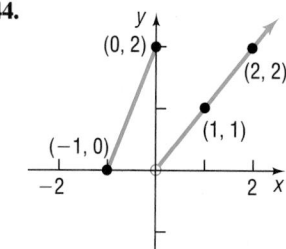

45. If $f(x) = \text{int}(2x)$, find   (a) $f(1.2)$ (b) $f(1.6)$ (c) $f(-1.8)$

46. If $f(x) = \text{int}\left(\dfrac{x}{2}\right)$, find   (a) $f(1.2)$ (b) $f(1.6)$ (c) $f(-1.8)$

Applications and Extensions

47. Cell Phone Service Sprint PCS offers a monthly cellular phone plan for $39.99. It includes 450 anytime minutes and charges $0.45 per minute for additional minutes. The following function is used to compute the monthly cost for a subscriber:

$$C(x) = \begin{cases} 39.99 & \text{if } 0 < x \le 450 \\ 0.45x - 162.51 & \text{if } x > 450 \end{cases}$$

where x is the number of anytime minutes used. Compute the monthly cost of the cellular phone for use of the following anytime minutes:

(a) 200   (b) 465   (c) 451

Source: Sprint PCS

48. Parking at O'Hare International Airport The short-term (no more than 24 hours) parking fee F (in dollars) for parking x hours at O'Hare International Airport's main parking garage can be modeled by the function

$$F(x) = \begin{cases} 3 & \text{if } 0 < x \le 3 \\ 5\,\text{int}(x+1)+1 & \text{if } 3 < x < 9 \\ 50 & \text{if } 9 \le x \le 24 \end{cases}$$

Determine the fee for parking in the short-term parking garage for
(a) 2 hours
(b) 7 hours
(c) 15 hours
(d) 8 hours and 24 minutes

Source: O'Hare International Airport

49. Cost of Natural Gas In February 2007, Peoples Energy had the following rate schedule for natural gas usage in single-family residences:

Monthly service charge $9.45
Per therm service charge
  1st 50 therms $0.36375/therm
  Over 50 therms $0.11445/therm
Gas charge $0.8738/therm

(a) What is the charge for using 50 therms in a month?
(b) What is the charge for using 500 therms in a month?
(c) Develop a model that relates the monthly charge C for x therms of gas.
(d) Graph the function found in part (c).

Source: Peoples Energy, Chicago, Illinois, 2007

50. Cost of Natural Gas In February 2007, Nicor Gas had the following rate schedule for natural gas usage in single-family residences:

Monthly customer charge $8.85
Distribution charge
  1st 20 therms $0.1473/therm
  Next 30 therms $0.0579/therm
  Over 50 therms $0.0519/therm
Gas supply charge $0.67/therm

(a) What is the charge for using 40 therms in a month?
(b) What is the charge for using 202 therms in a month?
(c) Develop a model that gives the monthly charge C for x therms of gas.
(d) Graph the function found in part (c).

Source: Nicor Gas, Aurora, Illinois, 2007

51. Federal Income Tax Two 2007 Tax Rate Schedules are given in the accompanying table. If x equals taxable income and y equals the tax due, construct a function $y = f(x)$ for Schedule X.

REVISED 2007 TAX RATE SCHEDULES											
Schedule X—Single						**Schedule Y-1—Married Filing jointly or qualifying Widow(er)**					
If Taxable Income Is over	But Not over	The Tax Is This Amount		Plus This %	Of the Excess over	If Taxable Income Is over	But Not over	The Tax Is This Amount		Plus This %	Of the Excess over
0	7825	0.00	+	10%	$0	$0	15,650	0.00	+	10%	$0
7825	31,850	782.50	+	15%	7825	15,650	63,700	1565.00	+	15%	15,650
31,850	77,100	4386.25	+	25%	31,850	63,700	128,500	8772.50	+	25%	63,700
77,100	160,850	15,698.75	+	28%	77,100	128,500	195,850	24,972.50	+	28%	128,500
160,850	349,700	39,148.75	+	33%	160,850	195,850	349,700	43,830.50	+	33%	195,850
349,700		101,469.25	+	35%	349,700	349,700	—	94,601.00	+	35%	349,700

Source: Internal Revenue Service

52. Federal Income Tax Refer to the revised 2007 tax rate schedules. If x equals taxable income and y equals the tax due, construct a function $y = f(x)$ for Schedule Y-1.

53. Cost of Transporting Goods A trucking company transports goods between Chicago and New York, a distance of 960 miles. The company's policy is to charge, for each pound, $0.50 per mile for the first 100 miles, $0.40 per mile for the

next 300 miles, $0.25 per mile for the next 400 miles, and no charge for the remaining 160 miles.
(a) Graph the relationship between the cost of transportation in dollars and mileage over the entire 960-mile route.
(b) Find the cost as a function of mileage for hauls between 100 and 400 miles from Chicago.
(c) Find the cost as a function of mileage for hauls between 400 and 800 miles from Chicago.

54. Car Rental Costs   An economy car rented in Florida from National Car Rental® on a weekly basis costs $95 per week. Extra days cost $24 per day until the day rate exceeds the weekly rate, in which case the weekly rate applies. Also, any part of a day used counts as a full day. Find the cost C of renting an economy car as a piecewise-defined function of the number x of days used, where $7 \le x \le 14$. Graph this function.

55. Minimum Payments for Credit Cards   Holders of credit cards issued by banks, department stores, oil companies, and so on, receive bills each month that state minimum amounts that must be paid by a certain due date. The minimum due depends on the total amount owed. One such credit card company uses the following rules: For a bill of less than $10, the entire amount is due. For a bill of at least $10 but less than $500, the minimum due is $10. A minimum of $30 is due on a bill of at least $500 but less than $1000, a minimum of $50 is due on a bill of at least $1000 but less than $1500, and a minimum of $70 is due on bills of $1500 or more. Find the function f that describes the minimum payment due on a bill of x dollars. Graph f.

56. Interest Payments for Credit Cards   Refer to Problem 55. The card holder may pay any amount between the minimum due and the total owed. The organization issuing the card charges the card holder interest of 1.5% per month for the first $1000 owed and 1% per month on any unpaid balance over $1000. Find the function g that gives the amount of interest charged per month on a balance of x dollars. Graph g.

57. Wind Chill   The wind chill factor represents the equivalent air temperature at a standard wind speed that would produce the same heat loss as the given temperature and wind speed.

One formula for computing the equivalent temperature is

$$W = \begin{cases} t & 0 \le v < 1.79 \\ 33 - \dfrac{(10.45 + 10\sqrt{v} - v)(33 - t)}{22.04} & 1.79 \le v \le 20 \\ 33 - 1.5958(33 - t) & v > 20 \end{cases}$$

where v represents the wind speed (in meters per second) and t represents the air temperature (°C). Compute the wind chill for the following:
(a) An air temperature of 10°C and a wind speed of 1 meter per second (m/sec)
(b) An air temperature of 10°C and a wind speed of 5 m/sec
(c) An air temperature of 10°C and a wind speed of 15 m/sec
(d) An air temperature of 10°C and a wind speed of 25 m/sec
(e) Explain the physical meaning of the equation corresponding to $0 \le v < 1.79$.
(f) Explain the physical meaning of the equation corresponding to $v > 20$.

58. Wind Chill   Redo Problem 57(a)–(d) for an air temperature of -10°C.

59. First-class Mail   In 2007 the U.S. Postal Service charged $0.80 postage for first-class mail retail flats (such as an 8.5" by 11" envelope) weighing up to 1 ounce, plus $0.17 for each additional ounce up to 13 ounces. First-class rates do not apply to flats weighing more than 13 ounces. Develop a model that relates C, the first-class postage charged, for a flat weighing x ounces. Graph the function.

Source: United States Postal Service

Discussion and Writing

In Problems 60–67, use a graphing utility.

60. Exploration   Graph $y = x^2$. Then on the same screen graph $y = x^2 + 2$, followed by $y = x^2 + 4$, followed by $y = x^2 - 2$. What pattern do you observe? Can you predict the graph of $y = x^2 - 4$? Of $y = x^2 + 5$?

61. Exploration   Graph $y = x^2$. Then on the same screen graph $y = (x - 2)^2$, followed by $y = (x - 4)^2$, followed by $y = (x + 2)^2$. What pattern do you observe? Can you predict the graph of $y = (x + 4)^2$? Of $y = (x - 5)^2$?

62. Exploration   Graph $y = |x|$. Then on the same screen graph $y = 2|x|$, followed by $y = 4|x|$, followed by $y = \frac{1}{2}|x|$. What pattern do you observe? Can you predict the graph of $y = \frac{1}{4}|x|$? Of $y = 5|x|$?

63. Exploration   Graph $y = x^2$. Then on the same screen graph $y = -x^2$. What pattern do you observe? Now try $y = |x|$ and $y = -|x|$. What do you conclude?

64. Exploration   Graph $y = \sqrt{x}$. Then on the same screen graph $y = \sqrt{-x}$. What pattern do you observe? Now try $y = 2x + 1$ and $y = 2(-x) + 1$. What do you conclude?

65. Exploration   Graph $y = x^3$. Then on the same screen graph $y = (x - 1)^3 + 2$. Could you have predicted the result?

66. Exploration   Graph $y = x^2$, $y = x^4$, and $y = x^6$ on the same screen. What do you notice is the same about each graph? What do you notice that is different?

67. Exploration   Graph $y = x^3$, $y = x^5$, and $y = x^7$ on the same screen. What do you notice is the same about each graph? What do you notice that is different?

68. Consider the equation

$$y = \begin{cases} 1 & \text{if } x \text{ is rational} \\ 0 & \text{if } x \text{ is irrational} \end{cases}$$

Is this a function? What is its domain? What is its range? What is its y-intercept, if any? What are its x-intercepts, if any? Is it even, odd, or neither? How would you describe its graph?

69. Define some functions that pass through $(0, 0)$ and $(1, 1)$ and are increasing for $x \ge 0$. Begin your list with $y = \sqrt{x}$, $y = x$, and $y = x^2$. Can you propose a general result about such functions?

'Are You Prepared?' Answers

1.

2.

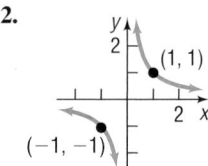

3. $(0, -8)$, $(2, 0)$

2.5 Graphing Techniques: Transformations

OBJECTIVES 1 Graph Functions Using Vertical and Horizontal Shifts (p. 100)

2 Graph Functions Using Compressions and Stretches (p. 102)

3 Graph Functions Using Reflections about the x-Axis or y-Axis (p. 104)

At this stage, if you were asked to graph any of the functions defined by $y = x$, $y = x^2$, $y = x^3$, $y = \sqrt{x}$, $y = \sqrt[3]{x}$, $y = |x|$, or $y = \dfrac{1}{x}$, your response should be, "Yes, I recognize these functions and know the general shapes of their graphs." (If this is not your answer, review the previous section, Figures 33 through 39.)

Sometimes we are asked to graph a function that is "almost" like one that we already know how to graph. In this section, we look at some of these functions and develop techniques for graphing them. Collectively, these techniques are referred to as **transformations.** We introduce the method of transformations because it is a more efficient method of graphing than point-plotting.

1 Graph Functions Using Vertical and Horizontal Shifts

Exploration

On the same screen, graph each of the following functions:

$$Y_1 = x^2$$
$$Y_2 = x^2 + 2$$
$$Y_3 = x^2 - 2$$

What do you observe? Now create a table of values for Y_1, Y_2, and Y_3. What do you observe?

Figure 44

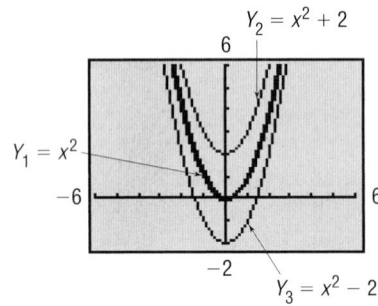

Result Figure 44 illustrates the graphs. You should have observed a general pattern. With $Y_1 = x^2$ on the screen, the graph of $Y_2 = x^2 + 2$ is identical to that of $Y_1 = x^2$, except that it is shifted vertically up 2 units. The graph of $Y_3 = x^2 - 2$ is identical to that of $Y_1 = x^2$, except that it is shifted vertically down 2 units. From Table 7(a), we see that the y-coordinates on $Y_2 = x^2 + 2$ are 2 units larger than the y-coordinates on $Y_1 = x^2$ for any given x-coordinate. From Table 7(b), we see that the y-coordinates on $Y_3 = x^2 - 2$ are 2 units smaller than the y-coordinates on $Y_1 = x^2$ for any given x-coordinate.

Table 7

X	Y₁	Y₃
-2	4	2
-1	1	-1
0	0	-2
1	1	-1
2	4	2
3	9	7
4	16	14

Y₃⊟X²-2

(a)

X	Y₁	Y₂
-2	4	6
-1	1	3
0	0	2
1	1	3
2	4	6
3	9	11
4	16	18

Y₂⊟X²+2

(b)

We are led to the following conclusions:

If a positive real number k is added to the outputs of a function $y = f(x)$, the graph of the new function $y = f(x) + k$ is the graph of f **shifted vertically up** k units.

If a positive real number k is subtracted from the outputs of a function $y = f(x)$, the graph of the new function $y = f(x) - k$ is the graph of f **shifted vertically down** k units.

EXAMPLE 1 | **Vertical Shift Down**

Use the graph of $f(x) = x^2$ to obtain the graph of $h(x) = x^2 - 4$.

Solution

Table 8 lists some points on the graphs of $Y_1 = f(x) = x^2$ and $Y_2 = h(x) = f(x) - 4 = x^2 - 4$. Notice that each y-coordinate of h is 4 units less than the corresponding y-coordinate of f.

Table 8

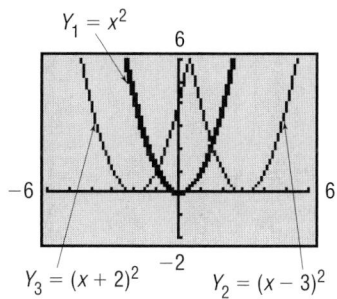

To obtain the graph of h from the graph of f, subtract 4 from each y-coordinate on the graph of f. The graph of h is identical to that of f, except that it is shifted down 4 units. See Figure 45.

Figure 45

 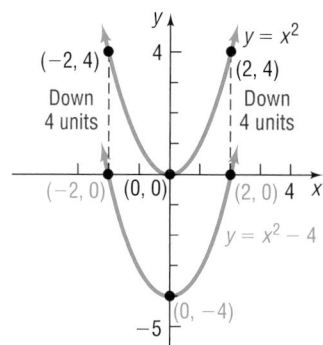

Now Work PROBLEM 39

Exploration

On the same screen, graph each of the following functions:

$$Y_1 = x^2$$
$$Y_2 = (x - 3)^2$$
$$Y_3 = (x + 2)^2$$

What do you observe?

Result Figure 46 illustrates the graphs. You should have observed the following pattern. With the graph of $Y_1 = x^2$ on the screen, the graph of $Y_2 = (x - 3)^2$ is identical to that of $Y_1 = x^2$, except it is shifted horizontally to the right 3 units. The graph of $Y_3 = (x + 2)^2$ is identical to that of $Y_1 = x^2$, except it is shifted horizontally to the left 2 units.

From Table 9(a), we see the x-coordinates on $Y_2 = (x - 3)^2$ are 3 units larger than they are for $Y_1 = x^2$ for any given y-coordinate. For example, when $Y_1 = 0$, then $x = 0$, and when $Y_2 = 0$, then $x = 3$. Also, when $Y_1 = 1$, then $x = -1$ or 1, and when $Y_2 = 1$, then $x = 2$ or 4. From Table 9(b), we see the x-coordinates on $Y_3 = (x + 2)^2$ are 2 units smaller than they are for $Y_1 = x^2$ for any given y-coordinate. For example, when $Y_1 = x^2$, then $x = 0$, and when $Y_3 = 0$, then $x = -2$. Also, when $Y_1 = 4$, then $x = -2$ or 2, and when $Y_3 = 4$, then $x = -4$ or 0.

Figure 46

$Y_1 = x^2$

$Y_3 = (x + 2)^2$ $Y_2 = (x - 3)^2$

Table 9

X	Y₁	Y₂
-1	1	16
0	0	9
1	1	4
2	4	1
3	9	0
4	16	1
5	25	4

$Y_2 = (X-3)^2$

X	Y₁	Y₃
-4	16	4
-3	9	1
-2	4	0
-1	1	1
0	0	4
1	1	9
2	4	16

$Y_3 = (X+2)^2$

(a)   (b)

We are led to the following conclusions:

If the argument x of a function f is replaced by $x - h, h > 0$, the graph of the new function $y = f(x - h)$ is the graph of f **shifted horizontally right** h units. If the argument x of a function f is replaced by $x + h, h > 0$, the graph of the new function $y = f(x + h)$ is the graph of f **shifted horizontally left** h units.

Now Work PROBLEM 43

NOTE Vertical shifts result when adding or subtracting a real number k after performing the operation suggested by the basic function, while horizontal shifts result when adding or subtracting a real number h to or from x before performing the operation suggested by the basic function. For example, the graph of $f(x) = \sqrt{x} + 3$ is obtained by shifting the graph of $y = \sqrt{x}$ up 3 units, because we evaluate the square root function first and then add 3. The graph of $g(x) = \sqrt{x + 3}$ is obtained by shifting the graph of $y = \sqrt{x}$ left 3 units, because we first add 3 to x before we evaluate the square root function. ∎

Vertical and horizontal shifts are sometimes combined.

| EXAMPLE 2 | **Combining Vertical and Horizontal Shifts** |

Graph the function $f(x) = (x + 3)^2 - 5$.

Solution

We graph f in steps. First, we note that the rule for f is basically a square function, so we begin with the graph of $y = x^2$ as shown in Figure 47(a). To get the graph of $y = (x + 3)^2$, we shift the graph of $y = x^2$ horizontally 3 units to the left. See Figure 47(b). Finally, to get the graph of $y = (x + 3)^2 - 5$, we shift the graph of $y = (x + 3)^2$ vertically down 5 units. See Figure 47(c). Note the points plotted on each graph. Using key points can be helpful in keeping track of the transformation that has taken place.

Figure 47

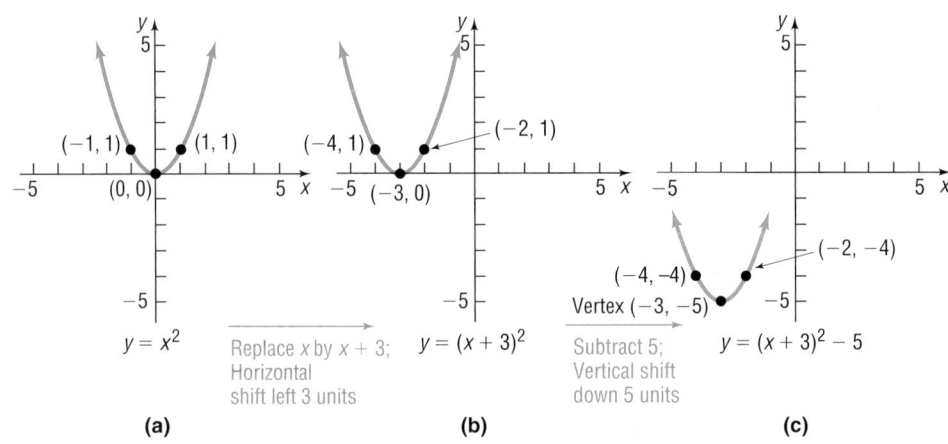

Check: Graph $Y_1 = f(x) = (x + 3)^2 - 5$ and compare the graph to Figure 47(c).

In Example 2, if the vertical shift had been done first, followed by the horizontal shift, the final graph would have been the same. (Try it for yourself.)

Now Work PROBLEMS 45 AND 77

2 Graph Functions Using Compressions and Stretches

Exploration

Figure 48

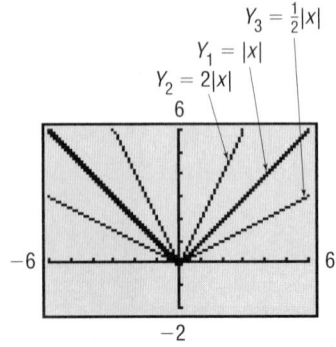

On the same screen, graph each of the following functions:

$$Y_1 = |x|$$

$$Y_2 = 2|x|$$

$$Y_3 = \frac{1}{2}|x|$$

Then create a table of values and compare the y-coordinates for any given x-coordinate.

Result Figure 48 illustrates the graphs.

Now look at Table 10, where $Y_1 = |x|$ and $Y_2 = 2|x|$. Notice that the values for Y_2 are two times the values of Y_1 for each x-value. This means that the graph of $Y_2 = 2|x|$ can be obtained from the graph of $Y_1 = |x|$ by multiplying each y-coordinate of $Y_1 = |x|$ by 2. Therefore, the graph of Y_2 will be vertically *stretched* by a factor of 2.

Look at Table 11 where $Y_1 = |x|$ and $Y_3 = \frac{1}{2}|x|$. The values of Y_3 are half the values of Y_1 for each x-value. So, the graph of $Y_3 = \frac{1}{2}|x|$ can be obtained from the graph of $Y_1 = |x|$ by multiplying each y-coordinate by $\frac{1}{2}$. Therefore, the graph of Y_3 will be vertically *compressed* by a factor of $\frac{1}{2}$.

Table 10

X	Y₁	Y₂
-2	2	4
-1	1	2
0	0	0
1	1	2
2	2	4
3	3	6
4	4	8

Y₂ ■ 2abs(X)

Table 11

X	Y₁	Y₃
-2	2	1
-1	1	.5
0	0	0
1	1	.5
2	2	1
3	3	1.5
4	4	2

Y₃ ■ .5abs(X)

Based on the Exploration, we have the following result:

When the right side of a function $y = f(x)$ is multiplied by a positive number a, the graph of the new function $y = af(x)$ is obtained by multiplying each y-coordinate on the graph of $y = f(x)$ by a. The new graph is a **vertically compressed** (if $0 < a < 1$) or a **vertically stretched** (if $a > 1$) version of the graph of $y = f(x)$.

- **Now Work** PROBLEM 47

What happens if the argument x of a function $y = f(x)$ is multiplied by a positive number a, creating a new function $y = f(ax)$? To find the answer, we look at the following Exploration.

Exploration

On the same screen, graph each of the following functions:

$$Y_1 = f(x) = \sqrt{x} \qquad Y_2 = f(2x) = \sqrt{2x} \qquad Y_3 = f\left(\frac{1}{2}x\right) = \sqrt{\frac{1}{2}x} = \sqrt{\frac{x}{2}}$$

Create a table of values to explore the relation between the x- and y-coordinates of each function.

Figure 49

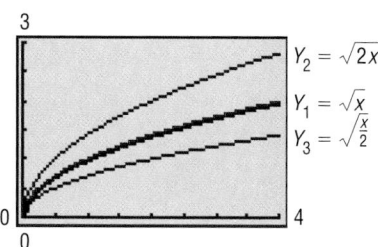

Result You should have obtained the graphs in Figure 49. Look at Table 12(a). Notice that (1, 1), (4, 2), and (9, 3) are points on the graph of $Y_1 = \sqrt{x}$. Also, (0.5, 1), (2, 2), and (4.5, 3) are points on the graph of $Y_2 = \sqrt{2x}$. For a given y-coordinate, the x-coordinate on the graph of Y_2 is $\frac{1}{2}$ of the x-coordinate on Y_1. We conclude that the graph of $Y_2 = \sqrt{2x}$ is obtained by multiplying the x-coordinate of each point on the graph of $Y_1 = \sqrt{x}$ by $\frac{1}{2}$. The graph of $Y_2 = \sqrt{2x}$ is the graph of $Y_1 = \sqrt{x}$ *compressed* horizontally.

Look at Table 12(b). Notice that (1, 1), (4, 2), and (9, 3) are points on the graph of $Y_1 = \sqrt{x}$. Also notice that (2, 1), (8, 2), and (18, 3) are points on the graph of $Y_3 = \sqrt{\frac{x}{2}}$. For a given y-coordinate, the x-coordinate on the graph of Y_3 is 2 times the x-coordinate on Y_1. We conclude that the graph of $Y_3 = \sqrt{\frac{x}{2}}$ is obtained by multiplying the x-coordinate of each point on the graph of $Y_1 = \sqrt{x}$ by 2. The graph of $Y_3 = \sqrt{\frac{x}{2}}$ is the graph of $Y_1 = \sqrt{x}$ *stretched* horizontally.

Table 12

X	Y₁	Y₂
0	0	0
.5	.70711	1
1	1	1.4142
2	1.4142	2
4	2	2.8284
4.5	2.1213	3
9	3	4.2426

Y₂ ■ √(2X)

X	Y₁	Y₃
0	0	0
1	1	.70711
2	1.4142	1
4	2	1.4142
8	2.8284	2
9	3	2.1213
18	4.2426	3

Y₃ ■ √(X/2)

(a)   (b)

Based on the results of the Exploration, we have the following result:

> If the argument x of a function $y = f(x)$ is multiplied by a positive number a, the graph of the new function $y = f(ax)$ is obtained by multiplying each x-coordinate of $y = f(x)$ by $\dfrac{1}{a}$. A **horizontal compression** results if $a > 1$, and a **horizontal stretch** occurs if $0 < a < 1$.

Let's look at an example.

EXAMPLE 3   **Graphing Using Stretches and Compressions**

The graph of $y = f(x)$ is given in Figure 50. Use this graph to find the graphs of

(a) $y = 2f(x)$ (b) $y = f(3x)$

Figure 50

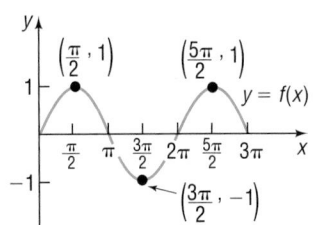

Solution   (a) The graph of $y = 2f(x)$ is obtained by multiplying each y-coordinate of $y = f(x)$ by 2. See Figure 51.

(b) The graph of $y = f(3x)$ is obtained from the graph of $y = f(x)$ by multiplying each x-coordinate of $y = f(x)$ by $\dfrac{1}{3}$. See Figure 52.

Figure 51

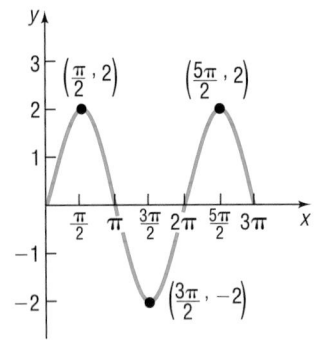

$y = 2f(x)$

Figure 52

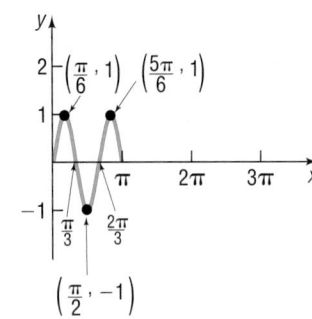

$y = f(3x)$

Now Work PROBLEMS 69(e) AND (g)

---

3 Graph Functions Using Reflections about the x-Axis or y-Axis

Exploration

Reflection about the x-axis:

(a) Graph and create a table of $Y_1 = x^2$ and $Y_2 = -x^2$.

(b) Graph and create a table of $Y_1 = |x|$ and $Y_2 = -|x|$.

(c) Graph and create a table of $Y_1 = x^2 - 4$ and $Y_2 = -(x^2 - 4) = -x^2 + 4$.

Result See Tables 13(a), (b), and (c) and Figures 53(a), (b), and (c). For each point (x, y) on the graph of Y_1, the point $(x, -y)$ is on the graph of Y_2. Put another way, Y_2 is the reflection about the x-axis of Y_1.

Table 13

(a)

(b)

(c)

Figure 53

(a)

(b)

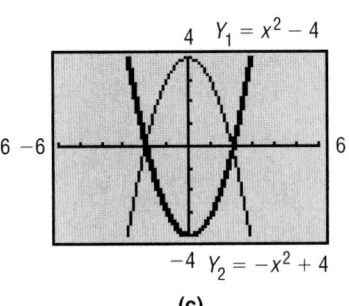

(c)

The results of the previous Exploration lead to the following result.

> When the right side of the function $y = f(x)$ is multiplied by -1, the graph of the new function $y = -f(x)$ is the **reflection about the *x*-axis** of the graph of the function $y = f(x)$.

━━━ **Now Work** PROBLEM 51

Exploration

Reflection about the y-axis:

(a) Graph $Y_1 = \sqrt{x}$, followed by $Y_2 = \sqrt{-x}$.

(b) Graph $Y_1 = x + 1$, followed by $Y_2 = -x + 1$.

(c) Graph $Y_1 = x^4 + x$, followed by $Y_2 = (-x)^4 + (-x) = x^4 - x$.

Result See Tables 14(a), (b), and (c) and Figures 54(a), (b), and (c). For each point (x, y) on the graph of Y_1, the point $(-x, y)$ is on the graph of Y_2. Put another way, Y_2 is the reflection about the y-axis of Y_1.

Table 14

(a)

(b)

(c)

Figure 54

(a)

(b)

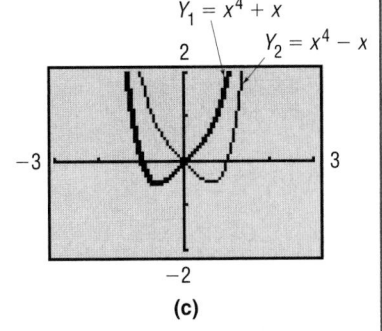

(c)

The results of the previous Exploration lead to the following result.

When the graph of the function $y = f(x)$ is known, the graph of the new function $y = f(-x)$ is the **reflection about the y-axis** of the graph of the function $y = f(x)$.

SUMMARY OF GRAPHING TECHNIQUES

To Graph:	Draw the Graph of f and:	Functional Change to $f(x)$
Vertical shifts		
$y = f(x) + k, \quad k > 0$	Raise the graph of f by k units.	Add k to $f(x)$.
$y = f(x) - k, \quad k > 0$	Lower the graph of f by k units.	Subtract k from $f(x)$.
Horizontal shifts		
$y = f(x + h), \quad h > 0$	Shift the graph of f to the left h units.	Replace x by $x + h$.
$y = f(x - h), \quad h > 0$	Shift the graph of f to the right h units.	Replace x by $x - h$.
Compressing or stretching		
$y = af(x), \quad a > 0$	Multiply each y-coordinate of $y = f(x)$ by a. Stretch the graph of f vertically if $a > 1$. Compress the graph of f vertically if $0 < a < 1$.	Multiply $f(x)$ by a.
$y = f(ax), \quad a > 0$	Multiply each x-coordinate of $y = f(x)$ by $\dfrac{1}{a}$. Stretch the graph of f horizontally if $0 < a < 1$. Compress the graph of f horizontally if $a > 1$.	Replace x by ax.
Reflection about the x-axis		
$y = -f(x)$	Reflect the graph of f about the x-axis.	Multiply $f(x)$ by -1.
Reflection about the y-axis		
$y = f(-x)$	Reflect the graph of f about the y-axis.	Replace x by $-x$.

The examples that follow combine some of the procedures outlined in this section to get the required graph.

EXAMPLE 4 **Determining the Function Obtained from a Series of Transformations**

Find the function that is finally graphed after the following three transformations are applied to the graph of $y = |x|$.

1. Shift left 2 units.
2. Shift up 3 units.
3. Reflect about the y-axis.

Solution
1. Shift left 2 units: Replace x by $x + 2$. $\qquad y = |x + 2|$
2. Shift up 3 units: Add 3. $\qquad y = |x + 2| + 3$
3. Reflect about the y-axis: Replace x by $-x$. $\qquad y = |-x + 2| + 3$

━━━━▶ **Now Work** PROBLEM **27**

| EXAMPLE 5 | **Combining Graphing Procedures** |

Graph the function $f(x) = \dfrac{3}{x - 2} + 1$. Find the domain and the range of f.

Solution   It is helpful to write f as $f(x) = 3\left(\dfrac{1}{x - 2}\right) + 1$. Now we use the following steps to obtain the graph of f:

STEP 1: $y = \dfrac{1}{x}$ *Reciprocal function*

STEP 2: $y = 3 \cdot \left(\dfrac{1}{x}\right) = \dfrac{3}{x}$ *Multiply by 3; vertical stretch of the graph of $y = \dfrac{1}{x}$ by a factor of 3.*

STEP 3: $y = \dfrac{3}{x - 2}$ *Replace x by $x - 2$; horizontal shift to the right 2 units.*

STEP 4: $y = \dfrac{3}{x - 2} + 1$ *Add 1; vertical shift up 1 unit.*

See Figure 55.

Figure 55

(a) $y = \dfrac{1}{x}$ Multiply by 3; Vertical stretch   (b) $y = \dfrac{3}{x}$ Replace x by $x - 2$; Horizontal shift right 2 units   (c) $y = \dfrac{3}{x-2}$ Add 1; Vertical shift up 1 unit   (d) $y = \dfrac{3}{x-2} + 1$

The domain of $y = \dfrac{1}{x}$ is $\{x \mid x \neq 0\}$ and its range is $\{y \mid y \neq 0\}$. Because we shifted right 2 units and up 1 unit to obtain f, the domain of f is $\{x \mid x \neq 2\}$ and its range is $\{y \mid y \neq 1\}$.

Other ordering of the steps shown in Example 5 would also result in the graph of f. For example, try this one:

HINT Although the order in which transformations are performed can be altered, you may consider using the following order for consistency:
1. Reflections
2. Compressions and stretches
3. Shifts ∎

STEP 1: $y = \dfrac{1}{x}$ *Reciprocal function*

STEP 2: $y = \dfrac{1}{x - 2}$ *Replace x by $x - 2$; horizontal shift to the right 2 units.*

STEP 3: $y = \dfrac{3}{x - 2}$ *Multiply by 3; vertical stretch of the graph of $y = \dfrac{1}{x - 2}$ by a factor of 3.*

STEP 4: $y = \dfrac{3}{x - 2} + 1$ *Add 1; vertical shift up 1 unit.*

| EXAMPLE 6 | **Combining Graphing Procedures** |

Graph the function $f(x) = \sqrt{1 - x} + 2$. Find the domain and the range of f.

Solution   Because horizontal shifts require the form $x - h$, we begin by rewriting $f(x)$ as $f(x) = \sqrt{1 - x} + 2 = \sqrt{-(x - 1)} + 2$. Now use the following steps:

STEP 1: $y = \sqrt{x}$ *Square root function*

STEP 2: $y = \sqrt{-x}$ *Replace x by $-x$; reflect about the y-axis.*

STEP 3: $y = \sqrt{-(x-1)} = \sqrt{1-x}$ Replace x by x − 1; horizontal shift to the right 1 unit.

STEP 4: $y = \sqrt{1-x} + 2$ Add 2; vertical shift up 2 units.

See Figure 56.

Figure 56

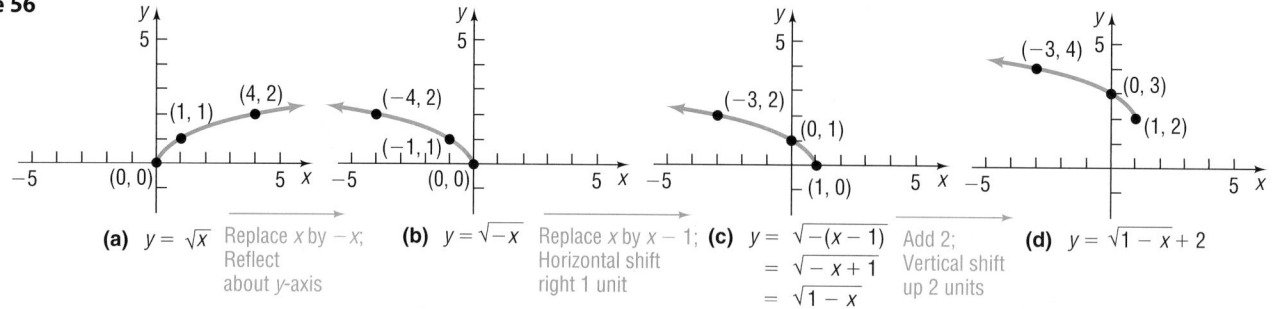

(a) $y = \sqrt{x}$ Replace x by −x;
Reflect
about y-axis

(b) $y = \sqrt{-x}$ Replace x by x − 1;
Horizontal shift
right 1 unit

(c) $y = \sqrt{-(x-1)}$ Add 2;
  $= \sqrt{-x+1}$ Vertical shift
  $= \sqrt{1-x}$ up 2 units

(d) $y = \sqrt{1-x} + 2$

The domain of f is $(-\infty, 1]$ and its range is $[2, \infty)$.

Now Work PROBLEM 61

2.5 Assess Your Understanding

Concepts and Vocabulary

1. Suppose that the graph of a function f is known. Then the graph of $y = f(x - 2)$ may be obtained by a(n) _____ shift of the graph of f to the _____ a distance of 2 units.

2. Suppose that the graph of a function f is known. Then the graph of $y = f(-x)$ may be obtained by a reflection about the _____-axis of the graph of the function $y = f(x)$.

3. Suppose that the x-intercepts of the graph of $y = f(x)$ are −2, 1, and 5. The x-intercepts of $y = f(x + 3)$ are _____, _____, and _____.

4. *True or False* The graph of $y = -f(x)$ is the reflection about the x-axis of the graph of $y = f(x)$.

5. *True or False* To obtain the graph of $y = f(x + 2) - 3$, shift the graph of $y = f(x)$ horizontally to the right 2 units and vertically down 3 units.

6. *True or False* Suppose that the x-intercepts of the graph of $y = f(x)$ are −3 and 2. Then the x-intercepts of the graph of $y = 2f(x)$ are also −3 and 2.

Skill Building

In Problems 7–18, match each graph to one of the following functions:

A. $y = x^2 + 2$

B. $y = -x^2 + 2$

C. $y = |x| + 2$

D. $y = -|x| + 2$

E. $y = (x - 2)^2$

F. $y = -(x + 2)^2$

G. $y = |x - 2|$

H. $y = -|x + 2|$

I. $y = 2x^2$

J. $y = -2x^2$

K. $y = 2|x|$

L. $y = -2|x|$

7.

8.

9.

10.

11.

12.

13.

14.

15.   **16.**   **17.**   **18.**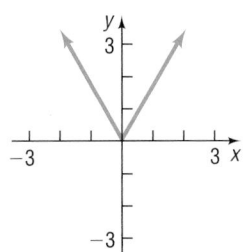

In Problems 19–26, write the function whose graph is the graph of $y = x^3$, but is:

19. Shifted to the right 4 units

20. Shifted to the left 4 units

21. Shifted up 4 units

22. Shifted down 4 units

23. Reflected about the y-axis

24. Reflected about the x-axis

25. Vertically stretched by a factor of 4

26. Horizontally stretched by a factor of 4

In Problems 27–30, find the function that is finally graphed after the following transformations are applied to the graph of $y = \sqrt{x}$.

27. (1) Shift up 2 units
   (2) Reflect about the x-axis
   (3) Reflect about the y-axis

28. (1) Reflect about the x-axis
   (2) Shift right 3 units
   (3) Shift down 2 units

29. (1) Reflect about the x-axis
   (2) Shift up 2 units
   (3) Shift left 3 units

30. (1) Shift up 2 units
   (2) Reflect about the y-axis
   (3) Shift left 3 units

31. If $(3, 6)$ is a point on the graph of $y = f(x)$, which of the following points must be on the graph of $y = -f(x)$?
   (a) $(6, 3)$
   (b) $(6, -3)$
   (c) $(3, -6)$
   (d) $(-3, 6)$

32. If $(3, 6)$ is a point on the graph of $y = f(x)$, which of the following points must be on the graph of $y = f(-x)$?
   (a) $(6, 3)$
   (b) $(6, -3)$
   (c) $(3, 6)$
   (d) $(-3, 6)$

33. If $(1, 3)$ is a point on the graph of $y = f(x)$, which of the following points must be on the graph of $y = 2f(x)$?
   (a) $(1, 3)$
   (b) $(2, 3)$
   (c) $(1, 6)$
   (d) $\left(\dfrac{1}{2}, 3\right)$

34. If $(4, 2)$ is a point on the graph of $y = f(x)$, which of the following points must be on the graph of $y = f(2x)$?
   (a) $(4, 1)$
   (b) $(8, 2)$
   (c) $(2, 2)$
   (d) $(4, 4)$

35. Suppose that the x-intercepts of the graph of $y = f(x)$ are -5 and 3.
   (a) What are the x-intercepts of the graph of $y = f(x + 2)$?
   (b) What are the x-intercepts of the graph of $y = f(x - 2)$?
   (c) What are the x-intercepts of the graph of $y = 4f(x)$?
   (d) What are the x-intercepts of the graph of $y = f(-x)$?

36. Suppose that the x-intercepts of the graph of $y = f(x)$ are -8 and 1.
   (a) What are the x-intercepts of the graph of $y = f(x + 4)$?
   (b) What are the x-intercepts of the graph of $y = f(x - 3)$?
   (c) What are the x-intercepts of the graph of $y = 2f(x)$?
   (d) What are the x-intercepts of the graph of $y = f(-x)$?

37. Suppose that the function $y = f(x)$ is increasing on the interval $(-1, 5)$.
   (a) Over what interval is the graph of $y = f(x + 2)$ increasing?
   (b) Over what interval is the graph of $y = f(x - 5)$ increasing?
   (c) What can be said about the graph of $y = -f(x)$?
   (d) What can be said about the graph of $y = f(-x)$?

38. Suppose that the function $y = f(x)$ is decreasing on the interval $(-2, 7)$.
   (a) Over what interval is the graph of $y = f(x + 2)$ decreasing?
   (b) Over what interval is the graph of $y = f(x - 5)$ decreasing?
   (c) What can be said about the graph of $y = -f(x)$?
   (d) What can be said about the graph of $y = f(-x)$?

In Problems 39–68, graph each function using the techniques of shifting, compressing, stretching, and/or reflecting. Start with the graph of the basic function (for example, $y = x^2$) and show all stages. Be sure to show at least three key points. Find the domain and the range of each function. Verify your results using a graphing utility.

39. $f(x) = x^2 - 1$

40. $f(x) = x^2 + 4$

41. $g(x) = x^3 + 1$

42. $g(x) = x^3 - 1$

43. $h(x) = \sqrt{x - 2}$

44. $h(x) = \sqrt{x + 1}$

45. $f(x) = (x - 1)^3 + 2$

46. $f(x) = (x + 2)^3 - 3$

47. $g(x) = 4\sqrt{x}$

48. $g(x) = \dfrac{1}{2}\sqrt{x}$

49. $h(x) = \dfrac{1}{2x}$

50. $h(x) = \sqrt[3]{2x}$

51. $f(x) = -\sqrt[3]{x}$

52. $f(x) = -\sqrt{x}$

53. $g(x) = \sqrt[3]{-x}$

54 $g(x) = \dfrac{1}{-x}$

55. $h(x) = -x^3 + 2$

56. $h(x) = \dfrac{1}{-x} + 2$

57. $f(x) = 2(x + 1)^2 - 3$

58. $f(x) = 3(x - 2)^2 + 1$

59. $g(x) = 2\sqrt{x - 2} + 1$

60. $g(x) = 3|x + 1| - 3$

61. $h(x) = \sqrt{-x} - 2$

62. $h(x) = \dfrac{4}{x} + 2$

63. $f(x) = -(x + 1)^3 - 1$

64. $f(x) = -4\sqrt{x - 1}$

65. $g(x) = 2|1 - x|$

66. $g(x) = 4\sqrt{2 - x}$

67. $h(x) = 2 \text{ int}(x - 1)$

68. $h(x) = \text{int}(-x)$

In Problems 69–72, the graph of a function f is illustrated. Use the graph of f as the first step toward graphing each of the following functions:

(a) $F(x) = f(x) + 3$

(b) $G(x) = f(x + 2)$

(c) $P(x) = -f(x)$

(d) $H(x) = f(x + 1) - 2$

(e) $Q(x) = \dfrac{1}{2}f(x)$

(f) $g(x) = f(-x)$

(g) $h(x) = f(2x)$

69.

70.

71.

72.

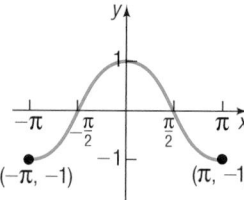

Mixed Practice

73. (a) Using a graphing utility, graph $f(x) = x^3 - 9x$ for $-4 < x < 4$.
  (b) Find the x-intercepts of the graph of f.
  (c) Approximate any local maxima and local minima.
  (d) Determine where f is increasing and where it is decreasing.
  (e) Without using a graphing utility, repeat parts (b)–(d) for $y = f(x + 2)$.
  (f) Without using a graphing utility, repeat parts (b)–(d) for $y = 2f(x)$.
  (g) Without using a graphing utility, repeat parts (b)–(d) for $y = f(-x)$.

74. (a) Using a graphing utility, graph $f(x) = x^3 - 4x$ for $-3 < x < 3$.
  (b) Find the x-intercepts of the graph of f.
  (c) Approximate any local maxima and local minima.
  (d) Determine where f is increasing and where it is decreasing.
  (e) Without using a graphing utility, repeat parts (b)–(d) for $y = f(x - 4)$.
  (f) Without using a graphing utility, repeat parts (b)–(d) for $y = f(2x)$.
  (g) Without using a graphing utility, repeat parts (b)–(d) for $y = -f(x)$.

In Problems 75–84, complete the square of each quadratic expression. Then graph each function using the technique of shifting. (If necessary, refer to Appendix A, Section A.6 to review completing the square.)

75. $f(x) = x^2 + 2x$

76. $f(x) = x^2 - 6x$

77. $f(x) = x^2 - 8x + 1$

78. $f(x) = x^2 + 4x + 2$

79. $f(x) = x^2 + x + 1$

80. $f(x) = x^2 - x + 1$

81. $f(x) = 2x^2 - 12x + 19$

82. $f(x) = 3x^2 + 6x + 1$

83. $f(x) = -3x^2 - 12x - 17$

84. $f(x) = -2x^2 - 12x - 13$

Applications and Extensions

85. The equation $y = (x - c)^2$ defines a *family of parabolas*, one parabola for each value of c. On one set of coordinate axes, graph the members of the family for $c = 0$, $c = 3$, and $c = -2$.

86. Repeat Problem 85 for the family of parabolas $y = x^2 + c$.

87. Thermostat Control Energy conservation experts estimate that homeowners can save 5% to 10% on winter heating bills by programming their thermostats 5 to 10 degrees lower while sleeping. In the given graph, the temperature T (in degrees Fahrenheit) of a home is given as a function of time t (in hours after midnight) over a 24-hour period.

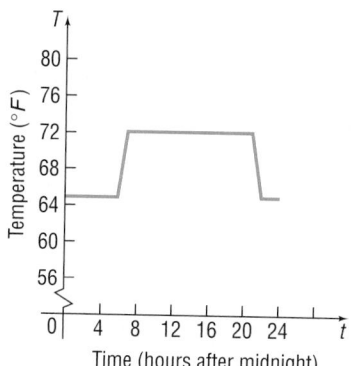

(a) At what temperature is the thermostat set during daytime hours? At what temperature is the thermostat set overnight?

(b) The homeowner reprograms the thermostat to $y = T(t) - 2$. Explain how this affects the temperature in the house. Graph this new function.

(c) The homeowner reprograms the thermostat to $y = T(t + 1)$. Explain how this affects the temperature in the house. Graph this new function.

Source: Roger Albright, 547 Ways to be Fuel Smart, 2000

88. Digital Music Revenues The total projected worldwide digital music revenues R, in millions of dollars, for the years 2005 through 2010 can be estimated by the function

$$R(x) = 170.7x^2 + 1373x + 1080$$

where x is the number of years after 2005.

(a) Find $R(0)$, $R(3)$, and $R(5)$ and explain what each value represents.

(b) Find $r = R(x - 5)$.

(c) Find $r(5)$, $r(8)$, and $r(10)$ and explain what each value represents.

(d) In the model r, what does x represent?

(e) Would there be an advantage in using the model r when estimating the projected revenues for a given year instead of the model R?

Source: eMarketer.com, May 2006

89. Temperature Measurements The relationship between the Celsius (°C) and Fahrenheit (°F) scales for measuring temperature is given by the equation

$$F = \frac{9}{5}C + 32$$

The relationship between the Celsius (°C) and Kelvin (K) scales is $K = C + 273$. Graph the equation $F = \frac{9}{5}C + 32$

using degrees Fahrenheit on the y-axis and degrees Celsius on the x-axis. Use the techniques introduced in this section to obtain the graph showing the relationship between Kelvin and Fahrenheit temperatures.

90. Period of a Pendulum The period T (in seconds) of a simple pendulum is a function of its length l (in feet) defined by the equation

$$T = 2\pi\sqrt{\frac{l}{g}}$$

where $g \approx 32.2$ feet per second per second is the acceleration of gravity.

(a) Use a graphing utility to graph the function $T = T(l)$.

(b) Now graph the functions $T = T(l + 1)$, $T = T(l + 2)$, and $T = T(l + 3)$.

(c) Discuss how adding to the length l changes the period T.

(d) Now graph the functions $T = T(2l)$, $T = T(3l)$, and $T = T(4l)$.

(e) Discuss how multiplying the length l by factors of 2, 3, and 4 changes the period T.

91. Cigar Company Profits The daily profits of a cigar company from selling x cigars are given by

$$p(x) = -0.05x^2 + 100x - 2000$$

The government wishes to impose a tax on cigars (sometimes called a *sin tax*) that gives the company the option of either paying a flat tax of $10,000 per day or a tax of 10% on profits. As chief financial officer (CFO) of the company, you need to decide which tax is the better option for the company.

(a) On the same screen, graph $Y_1 = p(x) - 10{,}000$ and $Y_2 = (1 - 0.10)p(x)$.

(b) Based on the graph, which option would you select? Why?

(c) Using the terminology learned in this section, describe each graph in terms of the graph of $p(x)$.

(d) Suppose that the government offered the options of a flat tax of $4800 or a tax of 10% on profits. Which would you select? Why?

92. The graph of a function f is illustrated in the figure.

(a) Draw the graph of $y = |f(x)|$.

(b) Draw the graph of $y = f(|x|)$.

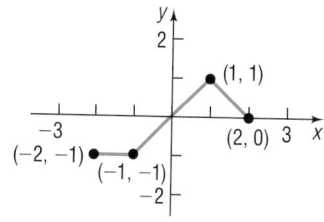

93. The graph of a function f is illustrated in the figure.

(a) Draw the graph of $y = |f(x)|$.

(b) Draw the graph of $y = f(|x|)$.

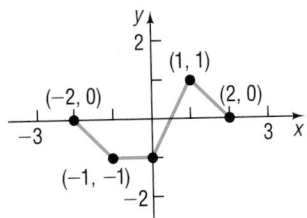

94. Suppose $(1, 3)$ is a point on the graph of $y = f(x)$.

(a) What point is on the graph of $y = f(x + 3) - 5$?

(b) What point is on the graph of $y = -2f(x - 2) + 1$?

(c) What point is on the graph of $y = f(2x + 3)$?

95. Suppose $(-3, 5)$ is a point on the graph of $y = f(x)$.

(a) What point is on the graph of $y = f(x + 1) - 3$?

(b) What point is on the graph of $y = -3f(x - 4) + 3$?

(c) What point is on the graph of $y = f(3x + 9)$?

Discussion and Writing

96. Suppose that the graph of a function f is known. Explain how the graph of $y = 4f(x)$ differs from the graph of $y = f(4x)$.

97. The area under the curve $y = \sqrt{x}$ bounded below by the x-axis, on the left by $x = 0$, and on the right by $x = 4$ is $\frac{16}{3}$

square units. Using the ideas presented in this section, what do you think is the area under the curve of $y = \sqrt{-x}$ bounded below by the x-axis, on the left by $x = -4$, and on the right by $x = 0$? Justify your answer.

2.6 Mathematical Models: Building Functions

OBJECTIVE 1 Build and Analyze Functions (p. 112)

1 Build and Analyze Functions

Real-world problems often result in mathematical models that involve functions. These functions need to be constructed or built based on the information given. In building functions, we must be able to translate the verbal description into the language of mathematics. We do this by assigning symbols to represent the independent and dependent variables and then by finding the function or rule that relates these variables.

EXAMPLE 1 **Finding the Distance from the Origin to a Point on a Graph**

Let $P = (x, y)$ be a point on the graph of $y = x^2 - 1$.

(a) Express the distance d from P to the origin O as a function of x.

(b) What is d if $x = 0$?

(c) What is d if $x = 1$?

(d) What is d if $x = \dfrac{\sqrt{2}}{2}$?

(e) Use a graphing utility to graph the function $d = d(x)$, $x \geq 0$. Rounded to two decimal places, find the value(s) of x at which d has a local minimum. [This gives the point(s) on the graph of $y = x^2 - 1$ closest to the origin.]

Solution

(a) Figure 57 illustrates the graph of $y = x^2 - 1$. The distance d from P to O is

$$d = \sqrt{(x - 0)^2 + (y - 0)^2} = \sqrt{x^2 + y^2}$$

Since P is a point on the graph of $y = x^2 - 1$, we substitute $x^2 - 1$ for y. Then

$$d(x) = \sqrt{x^2 + (x^2 - 1)^2} = \sqrt{x^4 - x^2 + 1}$$

We have expressed the distance d as a function of x.

(b) If $x = 0$, the distance d is

$$d(0) = \sqrt{0^4 - 0^2 + 1} = \sqrt{1} = 1$$

Figure 57

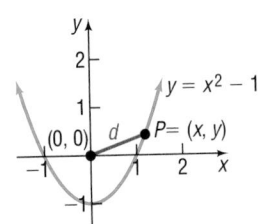

(c) If $x = 1$, the distance d is

$$d(1) = \sqrt{1^4 - 1^2 + 1} = 1$$

(d) If $x = \dfrac{\sqrt{2}}{2}$, the distance d is

Figure 58

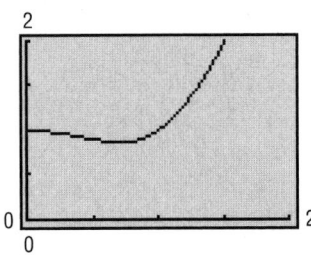

$$d\left(\frac{\sqrt{2}}{2}\right) = \sqrt{\left(\frac{\sqrt{2}}{2}\right)^4 - \left(\frac{\sqrt{2}}{2}\right)^2 + 1} = \sqrt{\frac{1}{4} - \frac{1}{2} + 1} = \frac{\sqrt{3}}{2}$$

(e) Figure 58 shows the graph of $Y_1 = \sqrt{x^4 - x^2 + 1}$. Using the MINIMUM feature on a graphing utility, we find that when $x \approx 0.71$ the value of d is smallest. The local minimum is $d \approx 0.87$ rounded to two decimal places. Since $d(x)$ is even, by symmetry, it follows that when $x \approx -0.71$ the value of d is also a local minimum. Since $(\pm 0.71)^2 - 1 = -0.50$, the points $(-0.71, -0.50)$ and $(0.71, 0.50)$ on the graph of $y = x^2 - 1$ are closest to the origin.

Now Work PROBLEM 1

EXAMPLE 2	Area of a Rectangle

Figure 59

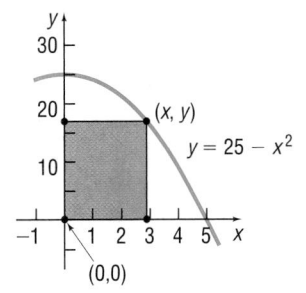

A rectangle has one corner in quadrant I on the graph of $y = 25 - x^2$, another at the origin, a third on the positive y-axis, and the fourth on the positive x-axis. See Figure 59.

(a) Express the area A of the rectangle as a function of x.
(b) What is the domain of A?
(c) Graph $A = A(x)$.
(d) For what value of x is the area largest?

Solution

(a) The area A of the rectangle is $A = xy$, where $y = 25 - x^2$. Substituting this expression for y, we obtain $A(x) = x(25 - x^2) = 25x - x^3$.

(b) Since (x, y) is in quadrant I, we have $x > 0$. Also, $y = 25 - x^2 > 0$, which implies that $x^2 < 25$, so $-5 < x < 5$. Combining these restrictions, we have the domain of A as $\{x \mid 0 < x < 5\}$, or $(0, 5)$ using interval notation.

(c) See Figure 60 for the graph of $A = A(x)$.

(d) Using MAXIMUM, we find that the maximum area is 48.11 square units at $x = 2.89$, each rounded to two decimal places. See Figure 61.

Figure 60

Figure 61

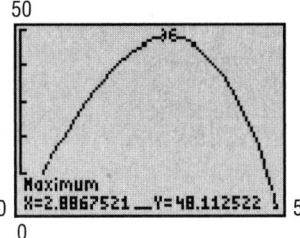

Now Work PROBLEM 7

EXAMPLE 3   **Making a Playpen***

A manufacturer of children's playpens makes a square model that can be opened at one corner and attached at right angles to a wall or, perhaps, the side of a house. If each side is 3 feet in length, the open configuration doubles the available area in which the child can play from 9 square feet to 18 square feet. See Figure 62.

Now suppose that we place hinges at the outer corners to allow for a configuration like the one shown in Figure 63.

Figure 62   **Figure 63**

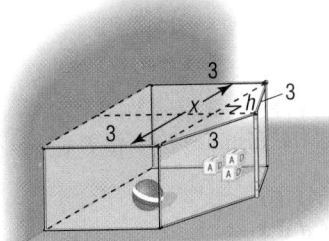

(a) Build a model that expresses the area A of the configuration shown in Figure 63 as a function of the distance x between the two parallel sides.

(b) Find the domain of A.

(c) Find A if $x = 5$.

(d) Graph $A = A(x)$. For what value of x is the area largest? What is the maximum area?

Solution   (a) Refer to Figure 63. The area A that we seek consists of the area of a rectangle (with width 3 and length x) and the area of an isosceles triangle (with base x and two equal sides of length 3). The height h of the triangle may be found using the Pythagorean Theorem.

$$h^2 + \left(\frac{x}{2}\right)^2 = 3^2$$

$$h^2 = 3^2 - \left(\frac{x}{2}\right)^2 = 9 - \frac{x^2}{4} = \frac{36 - x^2}{4}$$

$$h = \frac{1}{2}\sqrt{36 - x^2}$$

The area A enclosed by the playpen is

$$A = \text{area of rectangle} + \text{area of triangle} = 3x + \frac{1}{2}x\left(\frac{1}{2}\sqrt{36 - x^2}\right)$$

The area A expressed as a function of x is

$$A(x) = 3x + \frac{x\sqrt{36 - x^2}}{4} \qquad \textit{The Model}$$

(b) To find the domain of A, we note first that $x > 0$, since x is a length. Also, the expression under the square root must be positive, so

$$36 - x^2 > 0$$
$$x^2 < 36$$
$$-6 < x < 6$$

Combining these restrictions, we find that the domain of A is $0 < x < 6$, or $(0, 6)$ using interval notation.

*Adapted from *Proceedings, Summer Conference for College Teachers on Applied Mathematics* (University of Missouri, Rolla), 1971.

Figure 64

(c) If $x = 5$, the area is

$$A(5) = 3(5) + \frac{5}{4}\sqrt{36 - (5)^2} \approx 19.15 \text{ square feet}$$

If the length of the playpen is 5 feet, its area is 19.15 square feet.

(d) See Figure 64. The maximum area is about 19.82 square feet, obtained when x is about 5.58 feet.

2.6 Assess Your Understanding

Applications and Extensions

1. Let $P = (x, y)$ be a point on the graph of $y = x^2 - 8$.
  (a) Express the distance d from P to the origin as a function of x.
  (b) What is d if $x = 0$?
  (c) What is d if $x = 1$?
  (d) Use a graphing utility to graph $d = d(x)$.
  (e) For what values of x is d smallest?

2. Let $P = (x, y)$ be a point on the graph of $y = x^2 - 8$.
  (a) Express the distance d from P to the point $(0, -1)$ as a function of x.
  (b) What is d if $x = 0$?
  (c) What is d if $x = -1$?
  (d) Use a graphing utility to graph $d = d(x)$.
  (e) For what values of x is d smallest?

3. Let $P = (x, y)$ be a point on the graph of $y = \sqrt{x}$.
  (a) Express the distance d from P to the point $(1, 0)$ as a function of x.
  (b) Use a graphing utility to graph $d = d(x)$.
  (c) For what values of x is d smallest?

4. Let $P = (x, y)$ be a point on the graph of $y = \dfrac{1}{x}$.
  (a) Express the distance d from P to the origin as a function of x.
  (b) Use a graphing utility to graph $d = d(x)$.
  (c) For what values of x is d smallest?

5. A right triangle has one vertex on the graph of $y = x^3$, $x > 0$, at (x, y), another at the origin, and the third on the positive y-axis at $(0, y)$, as shown in the figure. Express the area A of the triangle as a function of x.

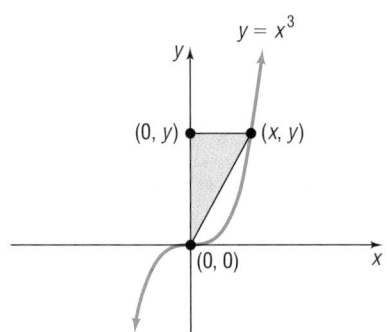

6. A right triangle has one vertex on the graph of $y = 9 - x^2$, $x > 0$, at (x, y), another at the origin, and the third on the positive x-axis at $(x, 0)$. Express the area A of the triangle as a function of x.

7. A rectangle has one corner in quadrant I on the graph of $y = 16 - x^2$, another at the origin, a third on the positive y-axis, and the fourth on the positive x-axis. See the figure.

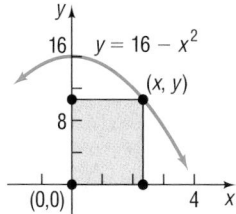

  (a) Express the area A of the rectangle as a function of x.
  (b) What is the domain of A?
  (c) Graph $A = A(x)$. For what value of x is A largest?

8. A rectangle is inscribed in a semicircle of radius 2. See the figure. Let $P = (x, y)$ be the point in quadrant I that is a vertex of the rectangle and is on the circle.

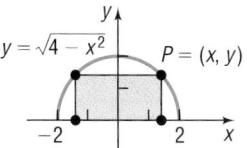

  (a) Express the area A of the rectangle as a function of x.
  (b) Express the perimeter p of the rectangle as a function of x.
  (c) Graph $A = A(x)$. For what value of x is A largest?
  (d) Graph $p = p(x)$. For what value of x is p largest?

9. A rectangle is inscribed in a circle of radius 2. See the figure. Let $P = (x, y)$ be the point in quadrant I that is a vertex of the rectangle and is on the circle.

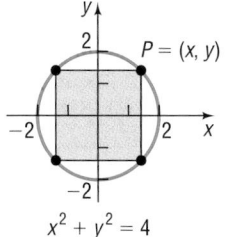

  (a) Express the area A of the rectangle as a function of x.
  (b) Express the perimeter p of the rectangle as a function of x.
  (c) Graph $A = A(x)$. For what value of x is A largest?
  (d) Graph $p = p(x)$. For what value of x is p largest?

10. A circle of radius r is inscribed in a square. See the figure.

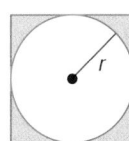

(a) Express the area A of the square as a function of the radius r of the circle.
(b) Express the perimeter p of the square as a function of r.

11. **Geometry** A wire 10 meters long is to be cut into two pieces. One piece will be shaped as a square, and the other piece will be shaped as a circle. See the figure.

(a) Express the total area A enclosed by the pieces of wire as a function of the length x of a side of the square.
(b) What is the domain of A?
(c) Graph $A = A(x)$. For what value of x is A smallest?

12. **Geometry** A wire 10 meters long is to be cut into two pieces. One piece will be shaped as an equilateral triangle, and the other piece will be shaped as a circle.
(a) Express the total area A enclosed by the pieces of wire as a function of the length x of a side of the equilateral triangle.
(b) What is the domain of A?
(c) Graph $A = A(x)$. For what value of x is A smallest?

13. A wire of length x is bent into the shape of a circle.
(a) Express the circumference of the circle as a function of x.
(b) Express the area of the circle as a function of x.

14. A wire of length x is bent into the shape of a square.
(a) Express the perimeter of the square as a function of x.
(b) Express the area of the square as a function of x.

15. **Geometry** A semicircle of radius r is inscribed in a rectangle so that the diameter of the semicircle is the length of the rectangle. See the figure.

(a) Express the area A of the rectangle as a function of the radius r of the semicircle.
(b) Express the perimeter p of the rectangle as a function of r.

16. **Geometry** An equilateral triangle is inscribed in a circle of radius r. See the figure. Express the circumference C of the circle as a function of the length x of a side of the triangle.

[**Hint:** First show that $r^2 = \dfrac{x^2}{3}$.]

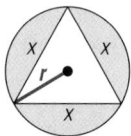

17. **Geometry** An equilateral triangle is inscribed in a circle of radius r. See the figure in Problem 16. Express the area A within the circle, but outside the triangle, as a function of the length x of a side of the triangle.

18. **Uniform Motion** Two cars leave an intersection at the same time. One is headed south at a constant speed of 30 miles per hour, and the other is headed west at a constant speed of 40 miles per hour (see the figure). Build a model that expresses the distance d between the cars as a function of the time t.

[**Hint:** At $t = 0$, the cars leave the intersection.]

19. **Uniform Motion** Two cars are approaching an intersection. One is 2 miles south of the intersection and is moving at a constant speed of 30 miles per hour. At the same time, the other car is 3 miles east of the intersection and is moving at a constant speed of 40 miles per hour.
(a) Build a model that expresses the distance d between the cars as a function of time t.

[**Hint:** At $t = 0$, the cars are 2 miles south and 3 miles east of the intersection, respectively.]

(b) Use a graphing utility to graph $d = d(t)$. For what value of t is d smallest?

20. **Inscribing a Cylinder in a Sphere** Inscribe a right circular cylinder of height h and radius r in a sphere of fixed radius R. See the illustration. Express the volume V of the cylinder as a function of h.

[**Hint:** $V = \pi r^2 h$. Note also the right triangle.]

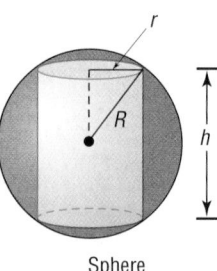

Sphere

21. **Inscribing a Cylinder in a Cone** Inscribe a right circular cylinder of height h and radius r in a cone of fixed radius R and fixed height H. See the illustration. Express the volume V of the cylinder as a function of r.

[**Hint:** $V = \pi r^2 h$. Note also the similar triangles.]

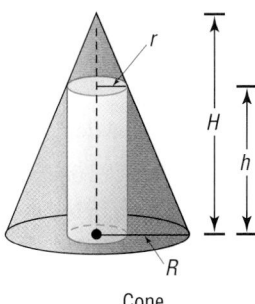

Cone

22. Installing Cable TV MetroMedia Cable is asked to provide service to a customer whose house is located 2 miles from the road along which the cable is buried. The nearest connection box for the cable is located 5 miles down the road. See the figure.

(a) If the installation cost is $500 per mile along the road and $700 per mile off the road, build a model that expresses the total cost C of installation as a function of the distance x (in miles) from the connection box to the point where the cable installation turns off the road. Give the domain.
(b) Compute the cost if $x = 1$ mile.
(c) Compute the cost if $x = 3$ miles.
(d) Graph the function $C = C(x)$. Use TRACE to see how the cost C varies as x changes from 0 to 5.
(e) What value of x results in the least cost?

23. Time Required to Go from an Island to a Town An island is 2 miles from the nearest point P on a straight shoreline. A town is 12 miles down the shore from P. See the illustration.

(a) If a person can row a boat at an average speed of 3 miles per hour and the same person can walk 5 miles per hour, build a model that expresses the time T that it takes to go from the island to town as a function of the distance x from P to where the person lands the boat.
(b) What is the domain of T?
(c) How long will it take to travel from the island to town if the person lands the boat 4 miles from P?
(d) How long will it take if the person lands the boat 8 miles from P?

24. Filling a Conical Tank Water is poured into a container in the shape of a right circular cone with radius 4 feet and height 16 feet. See the figure. Express the volume V of the water in the cone as a function of the height h of the water.

[**Hint:** The volume V of a cone of radius r and height h is $V = \frac{1}{3}\pi r^2 h$.]

25. Constructing an Open Box An open box with a square base is to be made from a square piece of cardboard 24 inches on a side by cutting out a square from each corner and turning up the sides. See the figure.

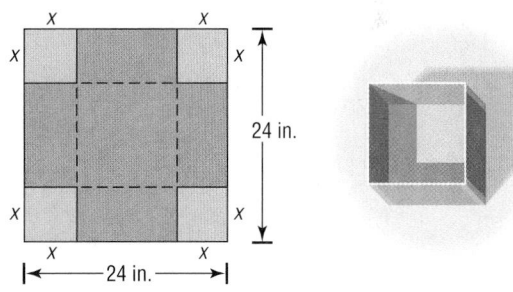

(a) Express the volume V of the box as a function of the length x of the side of the square cut from each corner.
(b) What is the volume if a 3-inch square is cut out?
(c) What is the volume if a 10-inch square is cut out?
(d) Graph $V = V(x)$. For what value of x is V largest?

26. Constructing an Open Box An open box with a square base is required to have a volume of 10 cubic feet.
(a) Express the amount A of material used to make such a box as a function of the length x of a side of the square base.
(b) How much material is required for a base 1 foot by 1 foot?
(c) How much material is required for a base 2 feet by 2 feet?
(d) Use a graphing utility to graph $A = A(x)$. For what value of x is A smallest?

CHAPTER REVIEW

Library of Functions

Constant function (p. 92)

$f(x) = b$

The graph is a horizontal line with y-intercept b.

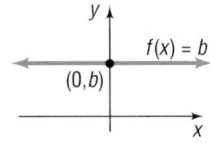

Identity function (p. 92)

$f(x) = x$

The graph is a line with slope 1 and y-intercept 0.

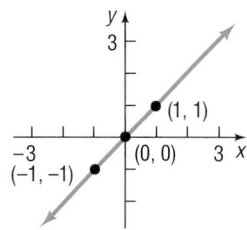

Square function (p. 93)

$f(x) = x^2$

The graph is a parabola with intercept at $(0, 0)$.

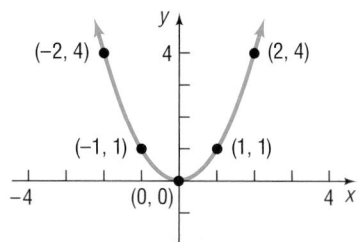

Cube function (p. 93)

$f(x) = x^3$

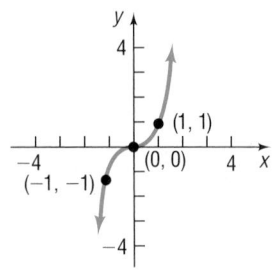

Square root function (p. 93)

$f(x) = \sqrt{x}$

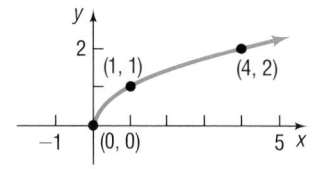

Cube root function (p. 93)

$f(x) = \sqrt[3]{x}$

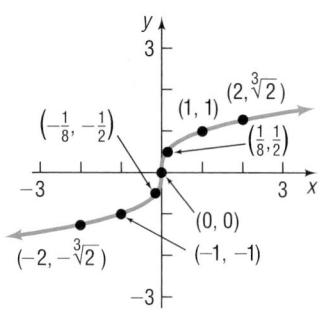

Reciprocal function (p. 93)

$f(x) = \dfrac{1}{x}$

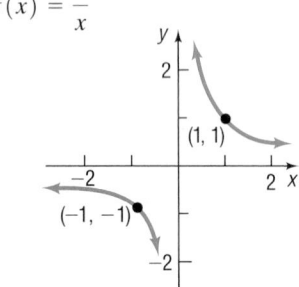

Absolute value function (p. 94)

$f(x) = |x|$

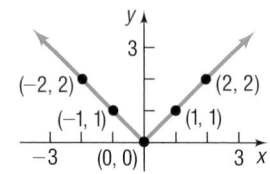

Greatest integer function (p. 94)

$f(x) = \text{int}(x)$

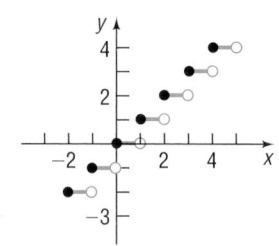

Things to Know

Function (pp. 56–60)

A relation between two sets so that each element x in the first set, the domain, has corresponding to it exactly one element y in the second set. The range is the set of y values of the function for the x values in the domain.

A function can also be characterized as a set of ordered pairs (x, y) in which no first element is paired with two different second elements.

Function notation (pp. 60–63)

$y = f(x)$

f is a symbol for the function.

x is the argument, or independent variable.

y is the dependent variable.

$f(x)$ is the value of the function at x, or the image of x.

A function f may be defined implicitly by an equation involving x and y or explicitly by writing $y = f(x)$.

Difference quotient of f (pp. 62 and 89)

$$\dfrac{f(x + h) - f(x)}{h} \qquad h \neq 0$$

Domain (pp. 57 and 63)

If unspecified, the domain of a function f is the largest set of real numbers for which $f(x)$ is a real number.

Vertical-line test (p. 71)	A set of points in the plane is the graph of a function if and only if every vertical line intersects the graph in at most one point.
Even function f (p. 79)	$f(-x) = f(x)$ for every x in the domain ($-x$ must also be in the domain).
Odd function f (p. 80)	$f(-x) = -f(x)$ for every x in the domain ($-x$ must also be in the domain).
Increasing function (p. 82)	A function f is increasing on an open interval I if, for any choice of x_1 and x_2 in I, with $x_1 < x_2$, we have $f(x_1) < f(x_2)$.
Decreasing function (p. 82)	A function f is decreasing on an open interval I if, for any choice of x_1 and x_2 in I, with $x_1 < x_2$, we have $f(x_1) > f(x_2)$.
Constant function (p. 82)	A function f is constant on an open interval I if, for all choices of x in I, the values of $f(x)$ are equal.
Local maximum (p. 83)	A function f has a local maximum at c if there is an open interval I containing c so that, for all x not equal to c in I, $f(x) < f(c)$.
Local minimum (p. 83)	A function f has a local minimum at c if there is an open interval I containing c so that, for all x not equal to c in I, $f(x) > f(c)$.
Average rate of change of a function (p. 84)	The average rate of change of f from a to b is

$$\frac{\Delta y}{\Delta x} = \frac{f(b) - f(a)}{b - a} \qquad a \neq b$$

Objectives

Section		You should be able to . . .	Examples	Review Exercises
2.1	1	Determine whether a relation represents a function (p. 56)	1–5	1, 2
	2	Find the value of a function (p. 60)	6–8	3–8, 23, 24, 71, 72
	3	Find the domain of a function defined by an equation (p. 63)	9, 10	9–16
	4	Form the sum, difference, product, and quotient of two functions (p. 65)	11	17–22
2.2	1	Identify the graph of a function (p. 71)	1	47–50
	2	Obtain information from or about the graph of a function (p. 72)	2–4	25(a)–(e), 26(a)–(e), 27(a), 27(d), 27(f), 28(a), 28(d), 28(f)
2.3	1	Determine even and odd functions from a graph (p. 79)	1	27(e), 28(e)
	2	Identify even and odd functions from the equation (p. 80)	2	29–36
	3	Use a graph to determine where a function is increasing, decreasing, or constant (p. 81)	3	27(b), 28(b)
	4	Use a graph to locate local maxima and local minima (p. 82)	4	27(c), 28(c)
	5	Use a graphing utility to approximate local maxima and local minima and to determine where a function is increasing or decreasing (p. 83)	5	37–40, 74(d), 75(b)
	6	Find the average rate of change of a function (p. 84)	6, 7	41–46
2.4	1	Graph the functions listed in the library of functions (p. 90)	1, 2	51–54
	2	Graph piecewise-defined functions (p. 95)	3, 4	67–70
2.5	1	Graph functions using vertical and horizontal shifts (p. 100)	1, 2	25(f), 26(f), 26(g) 55, 56, 59–66
	2	Graph functions using compressions and stretches (p. 102)	3	25(g), 26(h), 57, 58, 65, 66
	3	Graph functions using reflections about the x-axis or y-axis (p. 104)	4–6	25(h), 57, 61, 62, 66
2.6	1	Build and analyze functions (p. 112)	1–3	73–75

Review Exercises

In Problems 1 and 2, determine whether each relation represents a function. For each function, state the domain and the range.

1. $\{(-1, 0), (2, 3), (4, 0)\}$

2. $\{(4, -1), (2, 1), (4, 2)\}$

In Problems 3–8, find the following for each function:

  (a) $f(2)$ (b) $f(-2)$ (c) $f(-x)$ (d) $-f(x)$ (e) $f(x - 2)$ (f) $f(2x)$

3. $f(x) = \dfrac{3x}{x^2 - 1}$ **4.** $f(x) = \dfrac{x^2}{x + 1}$ **5.** $f(x) = \sqrt{x^2 - 4}$

6. $f(x) = |x^2 - 4|$

7. $f(x) = \dfrac{x^2 - 4}{x^2}$

8. $f(x) = \dfrac{x^3}{x^2 - 9}$

In Problems 9–16, find the domain of each function.

9. $f(x) = \dfrac{x}{x^2 - 9}$

10. $f(x) = \dfrac{3x^2}{x - 2}$

11. $f(x) = \sqrt{2 - x}$

12. $f(x) = \sqrt{x + 2}$

13. $h(x) = \dfrac{\sqrt{x}}{|x|}$

14. $g(x) = \dfrac{|x|}{x}$

15. $f(x) = \dfrac{x}{x^2 + 2x - 3}$

16. $F(x) = \dfrac{1}{x^2 - 3x - 4}$

In Problems 17–22, find $f + g, f - g, f \cdot g,$ and $\dfrac{f}{g}$ for each pair of functions. State the domain of each.

17. $f(x) = 2 - x;\quad g(x) = 3x + 1$

18. $f(x) = 2x - 1;\quad g(x) = 2x + 1$

19. $f(x) = 3x^2 + x + 1;\quad g(x) = 3x$

20. $f(x) = 3x;\quad g(x) = 1 + x + x^2$

21. $f(x) = \dfrac{x + 1}{x - 1};\quad g(x) = \dfrac{1}{x}$

22. $f(x) = \dfrac{1}{x - 3};\quad g(x) = \dfrac{3}{x}$

In Problems 23 and 24, find the difference quotient of each function f; that is, find

$$\dfrac{f(x + h) - f(x)}{h} \qquad h \neq 0$$

23. $f(x) = -2x^2 + x + 1$

24. $f(x) = 3x^2 - 2x + 4$

25. Using the graph of the function f shown:

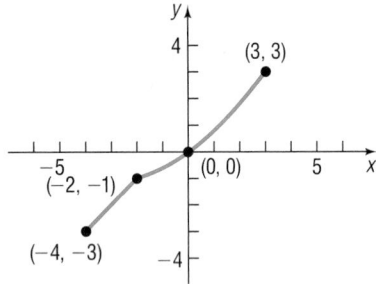

26. Using the graph of the function g shown:

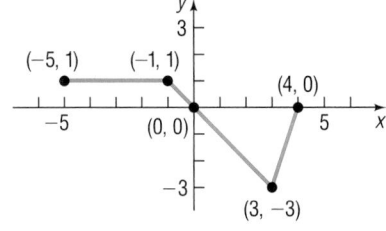

(a) Find the domain and the range of f.
(b) List the intercepts.
(c) Find $f(-2)$.
(d) For what value of x does $f(x) = -3$?
(e) Solve $f(x) > 0$.
(f) Graph $y = f(x - 3)$.

(g) Graph $y = f\left(\dfrac{1}{2}x\right)$.

(h) Graph $y = -f(x)$.

(a) Find the domain and the range of g.
(b) Find $g(-1)$.
(c) List the intercepts.
(d) For what value of x does $g(x) = -3$?
(e) Solve $g(x) > 0$.
(f) Graph $y = g(x - 2)$.
(g) Graph $y = g(x) + 1$.
(h) Graph $y = 2g(x)$.

In Problems 27 and 28, use the graph of the function f to find:
(a) The domain and the range of f.
(b) The intervals on which f is increasing, decreasing, or constant.
(c) The local minima and local maxima.
(d) Whether the graph is symmetric with respect to the x-axis, the y-axis, or the origin.
(e) Whether the function is even, odd, or neither.
(f) The intercepts, if any.

27.

28.

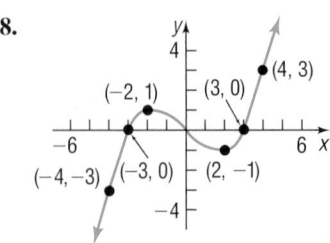

In Problems 29–36, determine (algebraically) whether the given function is even, odd, or neither.

29. $f(x) = x^3 - 4x$

30. $g(x) = \dfrac{4 + x^2}{1 + x^4}$

31. $h(x) = \dfrac{1}{x^4} + \dfrac{1}{x^2} + 1$

32. $F(x) = \sqrt{1 - x^3}$

33. $G(x) = 1 - x + x^3$

34. $H(x) = 1 + x + x^2$

35. $f(x) = \dfrac{x}{1 + x^2}$

36. $g(x) = \dfrac{1 + x^2}{x^3}$

In Problems 37–40, use a graphing utility to graph each function over the indicated interval. Approximate any local maxima and local minima. Determine where the function is increasing and where it is decreasing.

37. $f(x) = 2x^3 - 5x + 1 \quad (-3, 3)$

38. $f(x) = -x^3 + 3x - 5 \quad (-3, 3)$

39. $f(x) = 2x^4 - 5x^3 + 2x + 1 \quad (-2, 3)$

40. $f(x) = -x^4 + 3x^3 - 4x + 3 \quad (-2, 3)$

In Problems 41 and 42, find the average rate of change of f:

(a) From 1 to 2   (b) From 0 to 1   (c) From 2 to 4

41. $f(x) = 8x^2 - x$

42. $f(x) = 2x^3 + x$

In Problems 43–46, find the average rate of change from 2 to 3 for each function f. Be sure to simplify.

43. $f(x) = 2 - 5x$

44. $f(x) = 2x^2 + 7$

45. $f(x) = 3x - 4x^2$

46. $f(x) = x^2 - 3x + 2$

In Problems 47–50, is the graph shown the graph of a function?

47.

48.

49.

50.

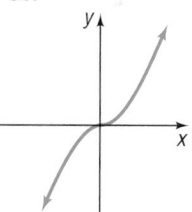

In Problems 51–54, sketch the graph of each function. Be sure to label at least three points.

51. $f(x) = |x|$

52. $f(x) = \sqrt[3]{x}$

53. $f(x) = \sqrt{x}$

54. $f(x) = \dfrac{1}{x}$

In Problems 55–66, graph each function using the techniques of shifting, compressing or stretching, and reflections. Identify any intercepts on the graph. State the domain and, based on the graph, find the range.

55. $F(x) = |x| - 4$

56. $f(x) = |x| + 4$

57. $g(x) = -2|x|$

58. $g(x) = \dfrac{1}{2}|x|$

59. $h(x) = \sqrt{x - 1}$

60. $h(x) = \sqrt{x} - 1$

61. $f(x) = \sqrt{1 - x}$

62. $f(x) = -\sqrt{x + 3}$

63. $h(x) = (x - 1)^2 + 2$

64. $h(x) = (x + 2)^2 - 3$

65. $g(x) = 3(x - 1)^3 + 1$

66. $g(x) = -2(x + 2)^3 - 8$

In Problems 67–70,

(a) Find the domain of each function.   (c) Graph each function.   (e) Is f continuous on its domain?
(b) Locate any intercepts.   (d) Based on the graph, find the range.

67. $f(x) = \begin{cases} 3x & \text{if } -2 < x \le 1 \\ x + 1 & \text{if } x > 1 \end{cases}$

68. $f(x) = \begin{cases} x - 1 & \text{if } -3 < x < 0 \\ 3x - 1 & \text{if } x \ge 0 \end{cases}$

69. $f(x) = \begin{cases} x & \text{if } -4 \le x < 0 \\ 1 & \text{if } x = 0 \\ 3x & \text{if } x > 0 \end{cases}$

70. $f(x) = \begin{cases} x^2 & \text{if } -2 \le x \le 2 \\ 2x - 1 & \text{if } x > 2 \end{cases}$

71. A function f is defined by

$$f(x) = \frac{Ax + 5}{6x - 2}$$

If $f(1) = 4$, find A.

72. A function g is defined by

$$g(x) = \frac{A}{x} + \frac{8}{x^2}$$

If $g(-1) = 0$, find A.

73. Page Design A page with dimensions of $8\frac{1}{2}$ inches by 11 inches has a border of uniform width x surrounding the printed matter of the page, as shown in the figure.

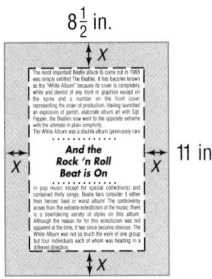

$8\frac{1}{2}$ in.

11 in.

(a) Develop a model that expresses the area A of the printed part of the page as a function of the width x of the border.
(b) Give the domain and the range of A.
(c) Find the area of printed page for borders of widths 1 inch, 1.2 inches, and 1.5 inches.

(d) Graph the function $A = A(x)$.
(e) Use a graphing utility to determine what margin should be used to obtain areas of 70 square inches and 50 square inches by solving $A(x) = 70$ and $A(x) = 50$.

74. Constructing a Closed Box A closed box with a square base is required to have a volume of 10 cubic feet.
(a) Build a model that expresses the amount A of material used to make such a box as a function of the length x of a side of the square base.
(b) How much material is required for a base 1 foot by 1 foot?
(c) How much material is required for a base 2 feet by 2 feet?
(d) Graph $A = A(x)$. For what value of x is A smallest?

75. A rectangle has one vertex in quadrant I on the graph of $y = 10 - x^2$, another at the origin, one on the positive x-axis, and one on the positive y-axis.
(a) Express the area A of the rectangle as a function of x.
(b) Find the largest area A that can be enclosed by the rectangle.

CHAPTER TEST

1. Determine whether each relation represents a function. For each function, state the domain and the range.
(a) $\{(2, 5), (4, 6), (6, 7), (8, 8)\}$
(b) $\{(1, 3), (4, -2), (-3, 5), (1, 7)\}$
(c)

(d)

In Problems 2–4, find the domain of each function and evaluate each function at $x = -1$.

2. $f(x) = \sqrt{4 - 5x}$

3. $g(x) = \dfrac{x + 2}{|x + 2|}$

4. $h(x) = \dfrac{x - 4}{x^2 + 5x - 36}$

5. Using the graph of the function f:

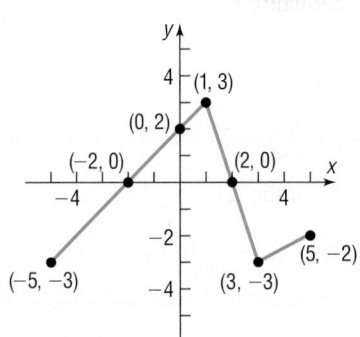

(a) Find the domain and the range of f.
(b) List the intercepts.
(c) Find $f(1)$.
(d) For what value(s) of x does $f(x) = -3$?
(e) Solve $f(x) < 0$.

6. Use a graphing utility to graph the function $f(x) = -x^4 + 2x^3 + 4x^2 - 2$ on the interval $(-5, 5)$. Approximate any local maxima and local minima rounded to two decimal places. Determine where the function is increasing and where it is decreasing.

7. Consider the function $g(x) = \begin{cases} 2x + 1 & \text{if } x < -1 \\ x - 4 & \text{if } x \geq -1 \end{cases}$

(a) Graph the function.
(b) List the intercepts.
(c) Find $g(-5)$.
(d) Find $g(2)$.

8. For the function $f(x) = 3x^2 - 2x + 4$, find the average rate of change of f from 3 to 4.

9. For the functions $f(x) = 2x^2 + 1$ and $g(x) = 3x - 2$, find the following and simplify:
(a) $f - g$ (b) $f \cdot g$
(c) $f(x + h) - f(x)$

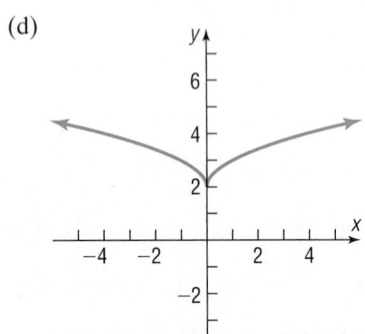

10. Graph each function using the techniques of shifting, compressing or stretching, and reflections. Start with the graph of the basic function and show all stages.

(a) $h(x) = -2(x + 1)^3 + 3$

(b) $g(x) = |x + 4| + 2$

11. The variable interest rate on a student loan changes each July 1 based on the bank prime loan rate. For the years 1992–2007, this rate can be approximated by the model $r(x) = -0.115x^2 + 1.183x + 5.623$, where x is the number of years since 1992 and r is the interest rate as a percent.

(a) Use a graphing utility to estimate the highest rate during this time period. During which year was the interest rate the highest?

(b) Use the model to estimate the rate in 2010. Does this value seem reasonable?

Source: U.S. Federal Reserve

12. A community skating rink is in the shape of a rectangle with semicircles attached at the ends. The length of the rectangle is 20 feet less than twice the width. The thickness of the ice is 0.75 inch.

(a) Build a model that expresses the ice volume, V, as a function of the width, x.

(b) How much ice is in the rink if the width is 90 feet?

CUMULATIVE REVIEW

In Problems 1–8, find the real solutions of each equation.

1. $-5x + 4 = 0$

2. $x^2 - 7x + 12 = 0$

3. $3x^2 - 5x - 2 = 0$

4. $4x^2 + 4x + 1 = 0$

5. $4x^2 - 2x + 4 = 0$

6. $\sqrt[3]{1 - x} = 2$

7. $\sqrt[3]{1 - x} = 2$

8. $|2 - 3x| = 1$

9. In the complex number system, solve $4x^2 - 2x + 4 = 0$.

10. Solve the inequality $-2 < 3x - 5 < 7$. Graph the solution set.

In Problems 11–14, graph each equation.

11. $-3x + 4y = 12$

12. $y = 3x + 12$

13. $x^2 + y^2 + 2x - 4y + 4 = 0$

14. $y = (x + 1)^2 - 3$

15. For the graph of the function f:

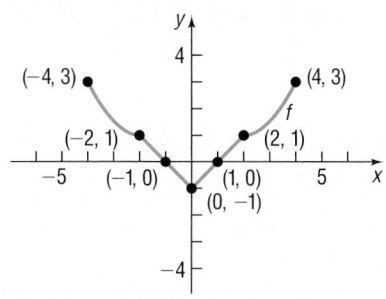

(a) Find the domain and the range of f.

(b) Find the intercepts.

(c) Is the graph of f symmetric with respect to the x-axis, the y-axis, or the origin?

(d) Find $f(2)$.

(e) For what value(s) of x is $f(x) = 3$?

(f) Solve $f(x) < 0$.

(g) Graph $y = f(x) + 2$

(h) Graph $y = f(-x)$.

(i) Graph $y = 2f(x)$.

(j) Is f even, odd, or neither?

(k) Find the interval(s) on which f is increasing.

(l) Find the interval(s) on which f is decreasing.

(m) Find the local maxima and local minima.

(n) Find the average rate of change of f from 1 to 4.

16. Find the distance between the points $P = (-1, 3)$ and $Q = (4, -2)$.

17. Which of the following points are on the graph of $y = x^3 - 3x + 1$?

(a) $(-2, -1)$ (b) $(2, 3)$ (c) $(3, 1)$

18. Determine the intercepts of $y = 3x^2 + 14x - 5$.

19. Use a graphing utility to find the solution(s) of the equation $x^4 - 3x^3 + 4x - 1 = 0$.

[**Hint:** All solutions are between $x = -10$ and $x = 10$.]

20. Find the equation of the line perpendicular to the line $y = 2x + 1$ and containing the point $(3, 5)$. Express your answer in slope–intercept form and graph both lines.

21. Determine whether the following relation represents a function: $\{(-3, 8), (1, 3), (2, 5), (3, 8)\}$.

22. For the function f defined by $f(x) = x^2 - 4x + 1$, evaluate:

(a) $f(2)$

(b) $f(x) + f(2)$

(c) $f(-x)$

(d) $-f(x)$

(e) $f(x + 2)$

(f) $\dfrac{f(x + h) - f(x)}{h}$ $h \neq 0$

23. Find the domain of $h(z) = \dfrac{3z - 1}{z^2 - 6z - 7}$.

24. Determine whether the following graph is the graph of a function:

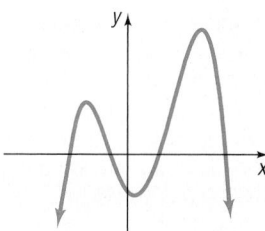

25. Consider the function $f(x) = \dfrac{x}{x + 4}$.

(a) Is the point $\left(1, \dfrac{1}{4}\right)$ on the graph of f?

(b) If $x = -2$, what is $f(x)$? What point is on the graph of f?

(c) If $f(x) = 2$, what is x? What point is on the graph of f?

26. Factor: $6x^2(x^2 + 1)^{1/2} + 2(x^2 + 1)^{3/2}$

27. Factor the expression and write it with only positive exponents: $2(x + 5)^{1/2} + x(x + 5)^{-1/2}$

CHAPTER PROJECTS

I. Cell Phone Service This month, as you were paying your bills, you noticed that your cell phone service contract had expired. Since cell phone numbers are now portable, you decided to investigate different companies. Since you regularly travel outside your local calling area, you decide to look only at plans with no roaming charges. Here are your findings:

	Anytime Minutes Included	Charge for Each Extra Minute	Mobile-to-Mobile Minutes	National Long Distance	Nights and Weekends
Company A:					
Plan A1: $39.99	450 with rollover	$0.45	Unlimited	Included	5000 (9 PM–6 AM)
Plan A2: $59.99	900 with rollover	$0.40	Unlimited	Included	Unlimited (9 PM–6 AM)
Company B:					
Plan B1: $39.99	600	$0.40	None	Included	Unlimited (9 PM–7 AM)
Plan B2: $49.99	1000	$0.40	None	Included	Unlimited (9 PM–7 AM)
Company C:					
Plan C1: $59.99	550	551–1050, $5 for each 50 minutes; above 1050, $0.10 each minute	Unlimited	Included	Unlimited (7 PM–7 AM)
Plan C2: $69.99	800	801–1300, $5 for each 50 minutes; above 1300, $0.10 each minute	Unlimited	Included	Unlimited (7 PM–7 AM)

Source: Based on rates from the Web sites of the companies Cingular, T Mobile, and Sprint PCS for the zip code 76201 on May 20, 2006. (*www.cingular.com, www.t-mobile.com,www.sprintpcs.com*)

Each plan requires a 2-year contract.

1. Determine the total cost of each plan for the life of the contract, assuming that you stay within the allotted anytime minutes provided by each contract.

2. If you expect to use 400 anytime, 200 mobile-to-mobile, and 4500 night and weekend minutes per month, which plan provides the best deal? If you expect to use 400 anytime, 200 mobile-to-mobile, and 5500 night and weekend minutes per month, which plan provides the best deal? If you expect to use 500 anytime, and 1000 mobile-to-mobile, and 2000 night and weekend minutes per month, which plan provides the best deal?

3. Ignoring any mobile-to-mobile and night and weekend usage, if you expect to use 850 anytime minutes each month, which option provides the best deal? What if you use 1050 anytime minutes per month?

4. Each monthly charge includes a specific number of peak time minutes in the monthly fee. Write a function for each option, where C is the monthly cost and x is the number of anytime minutes used.

5. Graph each function from part 4.

6. For each of the companies A, B, and C, determine the average price per minute for each plan, based on no extra minutes used. For each company, which plan is better?

7. Looking at the three plans that you found to be the best for companies A, B, and C in part 6, which of these three seems to be the best deal?

8. Based on your own cell phone usage, which plan would be the best for you?

The following projects are available on the Instructor's Resource Center (IRC):

II. Project at Motorola: *Wireless Internet Service* Use functions and their graphs to analyze the total cost of various wireless Internet service plans.

III. Cost of Cable When government regulations and customer preference influence the path of a new cable line, the Pythagorean Theorem can be used to assess the cost of installation.

IV. Oil Spill Functions are used to analyze the size and spread of an oil spill from a leaking tanker.

Linear and Quadratic Functions

3

Valuing Hewlett-Packard

17 MAY 2006—With the market focused on Hewlett-Packard Co. (HPQ) taking market share from Dell Inc. (DELL), the casual observer might be fooled into mistaking it as a computer hardware company. It's not; while the Compaq acquisition of 2002 expanded the company's hardware business, 53.4 percent of HPQ's profits still come from its imaging and printing division.

When we value stocks, we use the capital asset pricing model to price shares, which examines the volatility of the stock through beta and then projects how much earnings growth would be needed to justify the current stock price. Historically, HPQ has a beta of 2.05. The computer peripherals industry average, though, is 1.98. But the industry average beta for the computer hardware companies is 1.58.

A weighted average beta for the two industries seems appropriate for a company that walks the line between them. In this case, a beta weighted between the computer peripherals and computer hardware industries by the percentages of HPQ's profits yields an expected beta of 1.8. If we use this beta in a capital-asset-pricing model, assuming that Hewlett-Packard will maintain a price-to-earnings-to-growth ratio of 1.3 and that full fiscal year 2006 earnings per share will be at the low end of management's guidance, $2.04, then a new position taken at the current price would require an annualized, per-share earnings growth rate of 9.9% over the next five years to break even. The average long-term growth rate among the 12 analysts who provide one is 12.3% for Hewlett-Packard; this is well above what our analysis indicates that we require, implying a strong under-valuation even after the price spike.

Source: Adapted from *Paul DeMartino, "Valuing Hewlett-Packard," May 17, 2006, www.reuters.com.* Adapted with permission.

—*See Chapter Project I—*

A Look Back

Up to now, our discussion has focused on graphs of equations and the idea of a function. We have learned how to graph equations using the point-plotting method, intercepts, and the tests for symmetry. In addition, we have learned what a function is and how to identify whether a relation represents a function. We also introduced properties of functions, such as domain and range, increasing and decreasing, even and odd, and average rate of change.

A Look Ahead

Going forward, we will look at specific categories of functions. In this chapter, we focus on linear and quadratic functions, their properties and applications.

Outline

3.1 Linear Functions, Their Properties, and Linear Models

3.2 Building Linear Models from Data

3.3 Quadratic Functions and Their Properties

3.4 Building Quadratic Models from Verbal Descriptions and from Data

3.5 Inequalities Involving Quadratic Functions

Chapter Review

Chapter Test

Cumulative Review

Chapter Projects

125

3.1 Linear Functions, Their Properties, and Linear Models

PREPARING FOR THIS SECTION *Before getting started, review the following:*

- Lines (Section 1.4, pp. 29–37)
- Solve Linear Equations (Appendix A, Section A.6, pp. A47–A49)
- Functions (Section 2.1, pp. 56–64)
- The Graph of a Function (Section 2.2, pp. 70–74)
- Properties of Functions (Section 2.3, pp. 79–86)

Now Work the 'Are You Prepared?' problems on page 132.

OBJECTIVES 1 Graph Linear Functions (p. 126)
2 Use Average Rate of Change to Identify Linear Functions (p. 126)
3 Determine Whether a Linear Function Is Increasing, Decreasing, or Constant (p. 129)
4 Build Linear Models from Verbal Descriptions (p. 130)

1 Graph Linear Functions

In Section 1.4, we discussed lines. In particular, we developed the slope–intercept form of the equation of a line $y = mx + b$. When we write the slope–intercept form of a line using function notation, we have a *linear function*.

DEFINITION
A **linear function** is a function of the form

$$f(x) = mx + b$$

The graph of a linear function is a line with slope m and y-intercept b. Its domain is the set of all real numbers. If $m \neq 0$, the range of a linear function is the set of all real numbers. If $m = 0$, the range is $\{y \mid y = b\}$.

EXAMPLE 1 **Graphing a Linear Function**

Graph the linear function $f(x) = -3x + 7$. What is the domain and the range of f?

Solution
This is a linear function with slope $m = -3$ and y-intercept $b = 7$. To graph this function, we start by plotting the point $(0, 7)$, the y-intercept, and use the slope to find an additional point by moving right 1 unit and down 3 units. See Figure 1. The domain and the range of f are the set of all real numbers.

Alternatively, we could have found an additional point by evaluating the function at some $x \neq 0$. For $x = 1$, we find $f(1) = -3(1) + 7 = 4$ and obtain the point $(1, 4)$ on the graph.

Now Work PROBLEMS 13(a), (b), and (c)

Figure 1

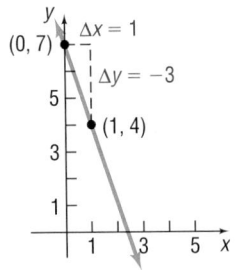

2 Use Average Rate of Change to Identify Linear Functions

Look at Table 1, which shows certain values of the independent variable x and corresponding values of the dependent variable y for the function $y = f(x) = -3x + 7$. Notice that as the value of the independent variable x increases by 1, the value of the dependent variable y decreases by 3. That is, the average rate of change of y with respect to x is a constant, -3.

Table 1

It is not a coincidence that the average rate of change of the linear function $f(x) = -3x + 7$ is the slope of the linear function. That is, $\dfrac{\Delta y}{\Delta x} = m = -3$. The following theorem states this fact.

THEOREM

Average Rate of Change of a Linear Function

Linear functions have a constant average rate of change. That is, the average rate of change of a linear function $f(x) = mx + b$ is

$$\frac{\Delta y}{\Delta x} = m$$

Proof The average rate of change of $f(x) = mx + b$ from x_1 to x_2, $x_1 \neq x_2$, is

$$\frac{\Delta y}{\Delta x} = \frac{f(x_2) - f(x_1)}{x_2 - x_1} = \frac{(mx_2 + b) - (mx_1 + b)}{x_2 - x_1}$$

$$= \frac{mx_2 - mx_1}{x_2 - x_1} = \frac{m(x_2 - x_1)}{x_2 - x_1} = m$$

∎

Based on the theorem just proved, the average rate of change of the function $g(x) = -\dfrac{2}{5}x + 5$ is $-\dfrac{2}{5}$.

━━━━ **Now Work** PROBLEM 13(d)

As it turns out, only linear functions have a constant average rate of change. Because of this, we can use the average rate of change to determine whether a particular function is linear or not. Functions that are not linear are said to be **nonlinear.**

EXAMPLE 2 | Using the Average Rate of Change to Identify
Linear Functions

(a) A strain of E-coli Beu 397-recA441 is placed into a Petri dish at 30° Celsius and allowed to grow. The data shown in Table 2 on the following page are collected. The population is measured in grams and the time in hours. Plot the ordered pairs (x, y) in the Cartesian plane and use the average rate of change to determine whether the function is linear.

(b) The data in Table 3 represent the maximum number of heartbeats that a healthy individual should have during a 15-second interval of time while exercising for different ages. Plot the ordered pairs (x, y) in the Cartesian plane and use the average rate of change to determine whether the function is linear.

Table 2

Time (hours), x	Population (grams), y	(x, y)
0	0.09	(0, 0.09)
1	0.12	(1, 0.12)
2	0.16	(2, 0.16)
3	0.22	(3, 0.22)
4	0.29	(4, 0.29)
5	0.39	(5, 0.39)

Table 3

Age, x	Maximum Number of Heart Beats, y	(x, y)
20	50	(20, 50)
30	47.5	(30, 47.5)
40	45	(40, 45)
50	42.5	(50, 42.5)
60	40	(60, 40)
70	37.5	(70, 37.5)

Source: American Heart Association

Solution

We compute the average rate of change of each function. If the average rate of change is constant, the function is linear. If the average rate of change is not constant, the function is nonlinear.

(a) Figure 2 shows the points listed in Table 2 plotted in the Cartesian plane. Notice that it is impossible to draw a straight line that contains all the points. Table 4 displays the average rate of change of population.

Figure 2

Table 4

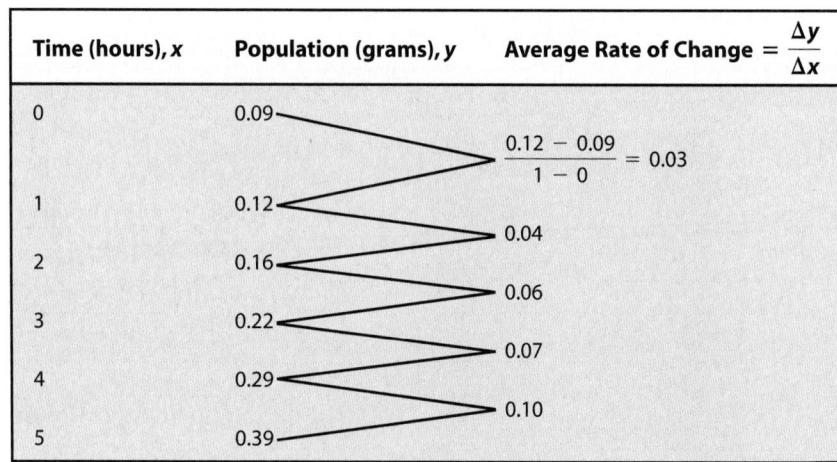

Because the average rate of change is not constant, we know that the function is not linear. In fact, because the average rate of change is increasing as the value of the independent variable increases, we say that the function is increasing at an increasing rate. So not only is the population increasing over time, but it is also growing more rapidly as time passes.

(b) Figure 3 shows the points listed in Table 3 plotted in the Cartesian plane. We can see that the data in Figure 3 lie on a straight line. Table 5 shows the average rate of change of the maximum number of heartbeats. The average rate of change of the heartbeat data is constant, -0.25 beat per year, so the function is linear. We can find the linear function using the point–slope formula with $x_1 = 20$, $y_1 = 50$, and $m = -0.25$.

$$y - y_1 = m(x - x_1)$$
$$y - 50 = -0.25(x - 20)$$
$$y - 50 = -0.25x + 5$$
$$y = -0.25x + 55$$

Figure 3

Table 5

Age, x	Maximum Number of Heartbeats, y	Average Rate of Change $= \dfrac{\Delta y}{\Delta x}$
20	50	
		$\dfrac{47.5 - 50}{30 - 20} = -0.25$
30	47.5	
		-0.25
40	45	
		-0.25
50	42.5	
		-0.25
60	40	
		-0.25
70	37.5	

▬▬▬ **Now Work** PROBLEM 21

3 Determine Whether a Linear Function Is Increasing, Decreasing, or Constant

Look back at the Explorations on page 31. We know that when the slope m of a linear function is positive $(m > 0)$ the line slants upward from left to right. When the slope m of a linear function is negative $(m < 0)$, the line slants downward from left to right. When the slope m of a linear function is zero $(m = 0)$, the line is horizontal.

Based on these results, we have the following theorem.

THEOREM

Increasing, Decreasing, and Constant Linear Functions

A linear function $f(x) = mx + b$ is increasing over its domain if its slope, m, is positive. It is decreasing over its domain if its slope, m, is negative. It is constant over its domain if its slope, m, is zero.

EXAMPLE 3   Determining Whether a Linear Function Is Increasing, Decreasing, or Constant

Determine whether the following linear functions are increasing, decreasing, or constant.

(a) $f(x) = 5x - 2$ (b) $g(x) = -2x + 8$

(c) $s(t) = \dfrac{3}{4}t - 4$ (d) $h(z) = 7$

Solution   (a) For the linear function $f(x) = 5x - 2$, the slope is 5, which is positive. The function f is increasing on the interval $(-\infty, \infty)$.

(b) For the linear function $g(x) = -2x + 8$, the slope is -2, which is negative. The function g is decreasing on the interval $(-\infty, \infty)$.

(c) For the linear function $s(t) = \dfrac{3}{4}t - 4$, the slope is $\dfrac{3}{4}$, which is positive. The function s is increasing on the interval $(-\infty, \infty)$.

(d) We can write the linear function h as $h(z) = 0z + 7$. Because the slope is 0, the function h is constant on the interval $(-\infty, \infty)$.

▬▬▬ **Now Work** PROBLEM 13(e)

4 Build Linear Models from Verbal Descriptions

When the average rate of change of a function is constant, we can use a linear function to model the relation between the two variables. For example, if your phone company charges you $0.07 per minute to talk regardless of the number of minutes used, we can model the relation between the cost C and minutes used x as the linear function $C(x) = 0.07x$, with slope $m = \dfrac{0.07\,\text{dollar}}{1\,\text{minute}}$.

Modeling with a Linear Function

If the average rate of change of a function is a constant m, a linear function f can be used to model the relation between the two variables as follows:

$$f(x) = mx + b$$

where b is the value of f at 0, that is, $f(0)$.

We illustrate how to develop a linear model in the next example.

EXAMPLE 4   Modeling Straight-line Depreciation

Book value is the value of an asset that a company uses to create its balance sheet. Some companies depreciate their assets using straight-line depreciation so that the value of the asset declines by a fixed amount each year. The amount of the decline depends on the useful life that the company places on the asset. Suppose that a company just purchased a fleet of new cars for its sales force at a cost of $28,000 per car. The company chooses to depreciate each vehicle using the straight-line method over 7 years. This means that each car will depreciate by $\dfrac{\$28{,}000}{7} = \$4000$ per year.

(a) Build a linear model that expresses the book value V of each car as a function of its age, x.

(b) What is the implied domain of the function found in part (a)?

(c) Graph the linear function.

(d) What is the book value of each car after 3 years?

(e) Interpret the slope.

(f) When will the book value of each car be $8000?
[**Hint:** Solve the equation $V(x) = 8000$.]

Solution

(a) If we let $V(x)$ represent the value of each car after x years, then $V(0)$ represents the original value of each car, so $V(0) = \$28{,}000$. The y-intercept of the linear function is $28,000. Because each car depreciates by $4000 per year, the slope of the linear function is -4000. The linear function that represents the book value V of each car after x years is

$$V(x) = -4000x + 28{,}000 \quad \text{\small The Model}$$

(b) Because x represents the age of the car, we have $x \geq 0$. Also, the value of the car cannot be negative. Since $V(7) = 0$, we have $x \leq 7$. Therefore, the domain of the function V is $\{x \mid 0 \leq x \leq 7\}$ or $[0, 7]$, using interval notation.

(c) Figure 4 shows the graph of V.

(d) The book value of each car after 3 years is

$$V(3) = -4000(3) + 28{,}000$$
$$= \$16{,}000$$

(e) Since the slope of $V(x) = -4000x + 28{,}000$ is -4000, the average rate of change of book value is $-\$4000/\text{year}$. So for each additional year that passes the book value of the car decreases by $4000.

Figure 4

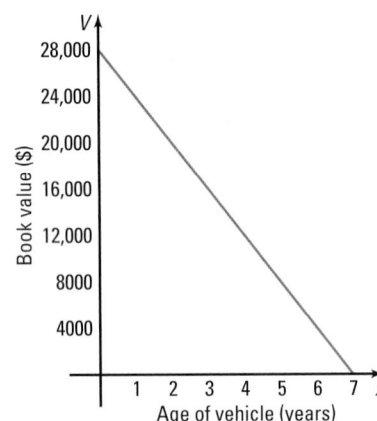

(f) To find when the book value is $8000, we solve the equation

$$V(x) = 8000$$
$$-4000x + 28{,}000 = 8000$$
$$-4000x = -20{,}000 \qquad \text{Subtract 28,000 from each side.}$$
$$x = \frac{-20{,}000}{-4000} = 5 \quad \text{Divide by } -4000.$$

The car will have a book value of $8000 when it is 5 years old.

━━━ **Now Work** PROBLEM 45

Next we look at an application from economics.

| EXAMPLE 5 | **Supply and Demand** |

The **quantity supplied** of a good is the amount of a product that a company is willing to make available for sale at a given price. The **quantity demanded** of a good is the amount of a product that consumers are willing to purchase at a given price. Suppose that the quantity supplied, S, and quantity demanded, D, of cellular telephones each month are given by the following functions:

$$S(p) = 60p - 900$$
$$D(p) = -15p + 2850$$

where p is the price (in dollars) of the telephone.

(a) The **equilibrium price** of a product is defined as the price at which quantity supplied equals quantity demanded. That is, the equilibrium price is the price at which $S(p) = D(p)$. Find the equilibrium price of cellular telephones. What is the **equilibrium quantity,** the amount demanded (or supplied) at the equilibrium price?

(b) Determine the prices for which quantity supplied is greater than quantity demanded. That is, solve the inequality $S(p) > D(p)$.

(c) Graph $S = S(p)$, $D = D(p)$ and label the equilibrium price.

Solution

(a) To find the equilibrium price, we solve the equation $S(p) = D(p)$.

$$60p - 900 = -15p + 2850 \quad \begin{array}{l} S(p) = 60p - 900; \\ D(p) = -15p + 2850 \end{array}$$
$$60p = -15p + 3750 \quad \text{Add 900 to each side.}$$
$$75p = 3750 \quad \text{Add 15p to each side.}$$
$$p = 50 \quad \text{Divide each side by 75.}$$

The equilibrium price is $50 per cellular phone. To find the equilibrium quantity, we evaluate either $S(p)$ or $D(p)$ at $p = 50$.

$$S(50) = 60(50) - 900 = 2100$$

The equilibrium quantity is 2100 cellular phones. At a price of $50 per phone, the company will produce and sell 2100 phones each month and have no shortages or excess inventory.

(b) We solve the inequality $S(p) > D(p)$.

$$60p - 900 > -15p + 2850 \quad S(p) > D(p)$$
$$60p > -15p + 3750 \quad \text{Add 900 to each side.}$$
$$75p > 3750 \quad \text{Add 15p to each side.}$$
$$p > 50 \quad \text{Divide each side by 75.}$$

If the company charges more than $50 per phone, quantity supplied will exceed quantity demanded. In this case the company will have excess phones in inventory.

(c) Figure 5 shows the graphs of $S = S(p)$ and $D = D(p)$ with the equilibrium point labeled. Notice that we only graph each function in quadrant I. Do you know why?

Figure 5

➤ **Now Work** PROBLEM 39

3.1 Assess Your Understanding

'Are You Prepared?' *Answers are given at the end of these exercises. If you get a wrong answer, read the pages listed in* red.

1. Graph $y = 2x - 3$. (pp. 35–36)

2. Find the slope of the line joining the points $(2, 5)$ and $(-1, 3)$. (pp. 29–30)

3. Find the average rate of change of $f(x) = 3x^2 - 2$ from 2 to 4. (pp. 84–85)

4. Solve: $60x - 900 = -15x + 2850$. (pp. A47–A49)

5. If $f(x) = x^2 - 4$, find $f(-2)$. (pp. 61–62)

6. **True or False** The graph of the function $f(x) = x^2$ is increasing on the interval $(0, \infty)$. (pp. 81–82)

Concepts and Vocabulary

7. For the graph of the linear function $f(x) = mx + b$, m is the _____ and b is the _____.

8. For the graph of the linear function $H(z) = -4z + 3$, the slope is _____ and the y-intercept is _____.

9. If the slope m of the graph of a linear function is _____, the function is increasing over its domain.

10. **True or False** The slope of a line is the average rate of change of the linear function.

11. **True or False** If the average rate of change of a linear function is $\dfrac{2}{3}$ then, if y increases by 3, x will increase by 2.

12. **True or False** The average rate of change of $f(x) = 2x + 8$ is 8.

Skill Building

In Problems 13–20, a linear function is given.
   (a) Determine the slope and y-intercept of each function.
   (b) Use the slope and y-intercept to graph the linear function.
   (c) Determine the domain and the range of each function.
   (d) Determine the average rate of change of each function.
   (e) Determine whether the linear function is increasing, decreasing, or constant.

13. $f(x) = 2x + 3$

14. $g(x) = 5x - 4$

15. $h(x) = -3x + 4$

16. $p(x) = -x + 6$

17. $f(x) = \dfrac{1}{4}x - 3$

18. $h(x) = -\dfrac{2}{3}x + 4$

19. $F(x) = 4$

20. $G(x) = -2$

In Problems 21–28, determine whether the given function is linear or nonlinear. If it is linear, determine the equation of the line.

21.

x	y
−2	4
−1	1
0	−2
1	−5
2	−8

22.

x	y
−2	$\frac{1}{4}$
−1	$\frac{1}{2}$
0	1
1	2
2	4

23.

x	y
−20	−8
−10	−3
0	0
10	1
20	0

24.

x	y
−20	−40
−10	0
0	40
10	80
20	120

25.

x	y
−2	−26
−1	−4
0	2
1	−2
2	−10

26.

x	y
−2	−4
−1	−3.5
0	−3
1	−2.5
2	−2

27.

x	y
−10	8
−5	8
0	8
5	8
10	8

28.

x	y
−10	0
−5	1
0	4
5	9
10	16

Applications and Extensions

29. Suppose that $f(x) = 4x − 1$ and $g(x) = −2x + 5$.
(a) Solve $f(x) = 0$.
(b) Solve $f(x) > 0$.
(c) Solve $f(x) = g(x)$.
(d) Solve $f(x) \le g(x)$.
(e) Graph $y = f(x)$ and $y = g(x)$ and label the point that represents the solution to the equation $f(x) = g(x)$.

30. Suppose that $f(x) = 3x + 5$ and $g(x) = −2x + 15$.
(a) Solve $f(x) = 0$.
(b) Solve $f(x) < 0$.
(c) Solve $f(x) = g(x)$.
(d) Solve $f(x) \ge g(x)$.
(e) Graph $y = f(x)$ and $y = g(x)$ and label the point that represents the solution to the equation $f(x) = g(x)$.

31. In parts (a)–(f), use the following figure.

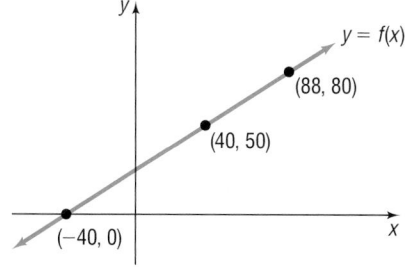

(a) Solve $f(x) = 50$.
(b) Solve $f(x) = 80$.
(c) Solve $f(x) = 0$.
(d) Solve $f(x) > 50$.
(e) Solve $f(x) \le 80$.
(f) Solve $0 < f(x) < 80$.

32. In parts (a)–(f), use the following figure.

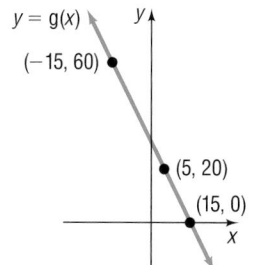

(a) Solve $g(x) = 20$.
(b) Solve $g(x) = 60$.
(c) Solve $g(x) = 0$.
(d) Solve $g(x) > 20$.
(e) Solve $g(x) \le 60$.
(f) Solve $0 < g(x) < 60$.

33. In parts (a) and (b) use the following figure.

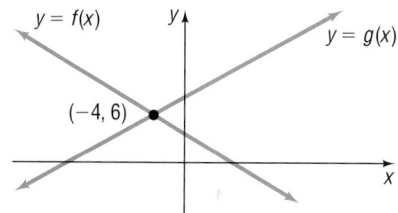

(a) Solve the equation: $f(x) = g(x)$.
(b) Solve the inequality: $f(x) > g(x)$.

34. In parts (a) and (b), use the following figure.

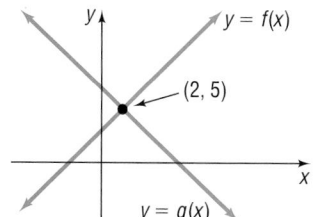

(a) Solve the equation: $f(x) = g(x)$.
(b) Solve the inequality: $f(x) \le g(x)$.

35. In parts (a) and (b), use the following figure.

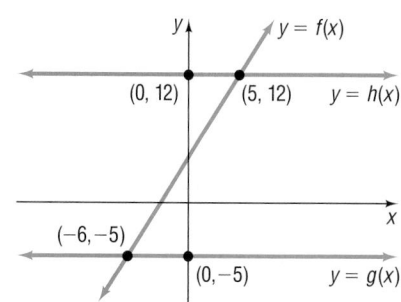

(a) Solve the equation: $f(x) = g(x)$.
(b) Solve the inequality: $g(x) \le f(x) < h(x)$.

36. In parts (a) and (b), use the following figure.

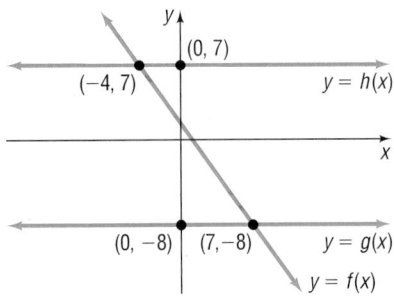

(a) Solve the equation: $f(x) = g(x)$.
(b) Solve the inequality: $g(x) < f(x) \le h(x)$.

37. Car Rentals The cost C, in dollars, of renting a moving truck for a day is modeled by the function $C(x) = 0.25x + 35$, where x is the number of miles driven.
(a) What is the cost if you drive $x = 40$ miles?
(b) If the cost of renting the moving truck is $80, how many miles did you drive?
(c) Suppose that you want the cost to be no more than $100. What is the maximum number of miles that you can drive?
(d) What is the implied domain of C?

38. Phone Charges The monthly cost C, in dollars, for international calls on a certain cellular phone plan is modeled by the function $C(x) = 0.38x + 5$, where x is the number of minutes used.
(a) What is the cost if you talk on the phone for $x = 50$ minutes?
(b) Suppose that your monthly bill is $29.32. How many minutes did you use the phone?
(c) Suppose that you budget yourself $60 per month for the phone. What is the maximum number of minutes that you can talk?
(d) What is the implied domain of C if there are 30 days in the month?

39. Supply and Demand Suppose that the quantity supplied S and quantity demanded D of T-shirts at a concert are given by the following functions:

$$S(p) = -200 + 50p$$

$$D(p) = 1000 - 25p$$

where p is the price of a T-shirt.
(a) Find the equilibrium price for T-shirts at this concert. What is the equilibrium quantity?
(b) Determine the prices for which quantity demanded is greater than quantity supplied.
(c) What do you think will eventually happen to the price of T-shirts if quantity demanded is greater than quantity supplied?

40. Supply and Demand Suppose that the quantity supplied S and quantity demanded D of hot dogs at a baseball game are given by the following functions:

$$S(p) = -2000 + 3000p$$

$$D(p) = 10,000 - 1000p$$

where p is the price of a hot dog.
(a) Find the equilibrium price for hot dogs at the baseball game. What is the equilibrium quantity?
(b) Determine the prices for which quantity demanded is less than quantity supplied.

(c) What do you think will eventually happen to the price of hot dogs if quantity demanded is less than quantity supplied?

41. Taxes The function $T(x) = 0.15(x - 7825) + 782.5$ represents the tax bill T of a single person whose adjusted gross income is x dollars for income between $7825 and $31,850, inclusive in 2007.
Source: Internal Revenue Service
(a) What is the domain of this linear function?
(b) What is a single filer's tax bill if adjusted gross income is $18,000?
(c) Which variable is independent and which is dependent?
(d) Graph the linear function over the domain specified in part (a).
(e) What is a single filer's adjusted gross income if the tax bill is $3358.75?

42. Luxury Tax In 2002, major league baseball signed a labor agreement with the players. In this agreement, any team whose payroll exceeds $136.5 million in 2006 will have to pay a luxury tax of 40% (for second offenses). The linear function $T(p) = 0.40(p - 136.5)$ describes the luxury tax T of a team whose payroll is p (in millions of dollars).
Source: Major League Baseball
(a) What is the implied domain of this linear function?
(b) What is the luxury tax for the New York Yankees whose 2006 payroll was $171.1 million?
(c) Graph the linear function.
(d) What is the payroll of a team that pays a luxury tax of $11.7 million?

*The point at which a company's profits equal zero is called the company's **break-even point**. For Problems 43 and 44, let R represent a company's revenue, let C represent the company's costs, and let x represent the number of units produced and sold each day.*
(a) Find the firm's break-even point; that is, find x so that R = C.
(b) Find the values of x such that R(x) > C(x). This represents the number of units that the company must sell to earn a profit.

43. $R(x) = 8x$
$C(x) = 4.5x + 17,500$

44. $R(x) = 12x$
$C(x) = 10x + 15,000$

45. Straight-line Depreciation Suppose that a company has just purchased a new computer for $3000. The company chooses to depreciate the computer using the straight-line method over 3 years.
(a) Write a linear model that expresses the book value V of the computer as a function of its age x.
(b) What is the implied domain of the function found in part (a)?
(c) Graph the linear function.
(d) What is the book value of the computer after 2 years?
(e) When will the computer have a book value of $2000?

46. Straight-line Depreciation Suppose that a company has just purchased a new machine for its manufacturing facility for $120,000. The company chooses to depreciate the machine using the straight-line method over 10 years.
(a) Write a linear model that expresses the book value V of the machine as a function of its age x.
(b) What is the implied domain of the function found in part (a)?
(c) Graph the linear function.

(d) What is the book value of the machine after 4 years?
(e) When will the machine have a book value of $72,000?

47. **Cost Function** The simplest cost function is the linear cost
 function, $C(x) = mx + b$, where the y-intercept b represents
the fixed costs of operating a business and the slope m represents the cost of each item produced. Suppose that a small
bicycle manufacturer has daily fixed costs of $1800 and each
bicycle costs $90 to manufacture.
   (a) Write a linear model that expresses the cost C of man-
       ufacturing x bicycles in a day.
   (b) Graph the model.
   (c) What is the cost of manufacturing 14 bicycles in a day?
   (d) How many bicycles could be manufactured for $3780?

48. **Cost Function** Refer to Problem 47. Suppose that the land-
lord of the building increases the bicycle manufacturer's rent
by $100 per month.
   (a) Assuming that the manufacturer is open for business
       20 days per month, what are the new daily fixed costs?
   (b) Write a linear model that expresses the cost C of man-
       ufacturing x bicycles in a day with the higher rent.
   (c) Graph the model.
   (d) What is the cost of manufacturing 14 bicycles in a day?
   (e) How many bicycles can be manufactured for $3780?

49. **Truck Rentals** A truck rental company rents a truck for one
day by charging $29 plus $0.07 per mile.
   (a) Write a linear model that relates the cost C, in dollars,
       of renting the truck to the number x of miles driven.
   (b) What is the cost of renting the truck if the truck is driven
       110 miles? 230 miles?

50. **Long Distance** A phone company offers a domestic long
distance package by charging $5 plus $0.05 per minute.
   (a) Write a linear model that relates the cost C, in dollars,
       of talking x minutes.
   (b) What is the cost of talking 105 minutes? 180 minutes?

51. **Developing a Linear Model from Data** The following data
represent the price p and quantity demanded per day q of an
MP3 player.

Price, p (in dollars)	Quantity Demanded, q
150	100
200	80
250	60
300	40

   (a) Plot the ordered pairs (p, q) in a Cartesian plane.
   (b) Show that quantity demanded q is a linear function of
       the price p.
   (c) Determine the linear function that describes the rela-
       tion between p and q.
   (d) What is the implied domain of the linear function?
   (e) Graph the linear function in the Cartesian plane drawn
       in part (a).
   (f) Interpret the slope.
   (g) Interpret the value of the intercepts.

52. **Developing a Linear Model from Data** The following data
represent the various combinations of soda and hot dogs that
Yolanda can buy at a baseball game with $60.

Soda, s	Hot Dogs, h
20	0
15	3
10	6
5	9

   (a) Plot the ordered pairs (s, h) in a Cartesian plane.
   (b) Show that the number of hot dogs purchased h is a
       linear function of the number of sodas purchased s.
   (c) Determine the linear function that describes the
       relation between s and h.
   (d) What is the implied domain of the linear function?
   (e) Graph the linear function in the Cartesian plane drawn
       in part (a).
   (f) Interpret the slope.
   (g) Interpret the value of the intercepts.

Discussion and Writing

53. Which of the following functions might have the graph
shown? (More than one answer is possible.)
   (a) $f(x) = 2x - 7$
   (b) $g(x) = -3x + 4$
   (c) $H(x) = 5$
   (d) $F(x) = 3x + 4$
   (e) $G(x) = \dfrac{1}{2}x + 2$

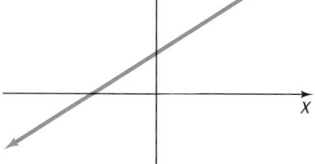

54. Which of the following functions might have the graph
shown? (More than one answer is possible.)
   (a) $f(x) = 3x + 1$
   (b) $g(x) = -2x + 3$
   (c) $H(x) = 3$
   (d) $F(x) = -4x - 1$
   (e) $G(x) = -\dfrac{2}{3}x + 3$

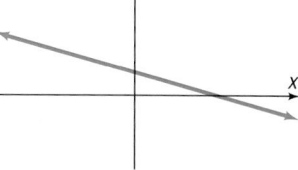

55. Under what circumstances is a linear function $f(x) = mx + b$ odd? Can a linear function ever be even?

'Are You Prepared?' Answers

1. 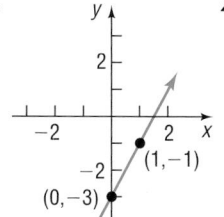   2. $\dfrac{2}{3}$ 3. 18   4. $\{50\}$ 5. 0   6. True

3.2 Building Linear Models from Data

PREPARING FOR THIS SECTION *Before getting started, review the following:*

- Rectangular Coordinates (Section 1.1, pp. 2–3)
- Functions (Section 2.1, pp. 56–64)
- Lines (Section 1.4, pp. 29–37)

Now Work the 'Are You Prepared?' problems on page 139.

OBJECTIVES **1** Draw and Interpret Scatter Diagrams (p. 136)
2 Distinguish between Linear and Nonlinear Relations (p. 137)
3 Use a Graphing Utility to Find the Line of Best Fit (p. 138)

1 Draw and Interpret Scatter Diagrams

In Section 3.1, we built linear models from verbal descriptions. Linear models can also be constructed by fitting a linear function to data. The first step in finding this relation is to plot the ordered pairs using rectangular coordinates. The resulting graph is called a **scatter diagram.**

EXAMPLE 1 Drawing and Interpreting a Scatter Diagram

In baseball, the on-base percentage for a team represents the percentage of time that the players safely reach base. The data given in Table 6 represent the number of runs scored y and the on-base percentage x for teams in the National League during the 2006 baseball season.

Table 6

Team	On-Base Percentage, x	Runs Scored, y	(x, y)
Atlanta	33.7	849	(33.7, 849)
St. Louis	33.7	781	(33.7, 781)
Colorado	34.1	813	(34.1, 813)
Houston	33.2	735	(33.2, 735)
Philadelphia	34.7	865	(34.7, 865)
San Francisco	32.4	746	(32.4, 746)
Pittsburgh	32.7	691	(32.7, 691)
Florida	33.1	758	(33.1, 758)
Chicago Cubs	31.9	716	(31.9, 716)
Arizona	33.1	773	(33.1, 773)
Milwaukee	32.7	730	(32.7, 730)
Washington	33.8	746	(33.8, 746)
Cincinnati	33.6	749	(33.6, 749)
San Diego	33.2	731	(33.2, 731)
NY Mets	33.4	834	(33.4, 834)
Los Angeles	34.8	820	(34.8, 820)

Source: espn.com

(a) Draw a scatter diagram of the data, treating on-base percentage as the independent variable.
(b) Use a graphing utility to draw a scatter diagram.
(c) Describe what happens to runs scored as the on-base percentage increases.

Solution

(a) To draw a scatter diagram, we plot the ordered pairs listed in Table 6, with the on-base percentage as the *x*-coordinate and the runs scored as the *y*-coordinate. See Figure 6(a). Notice that the points in the scatter diagram are not connected.

(b) Figure 6(b) shows a scatter diagram using a TI-84 Plus graphing calculator.

(c) We see from the scatter diagrams that, as the on-base percentage increases, the trend is that the number of runs scored also increases.

Figure 6

(a)

(b)

Now Work PROBLEM 11(a)

2 Distinguish between Linear and Nonlinear Relations

You should notice that the points in Figure 6 do not follow a perfect linear relation (as they do in Figure 3 in Section 3.1). However, the data do exhibit a linear pattern. There are numerous explanations as to why the data are not perfectly linear, but one easy explanation is the fact that other variables besides on-base percentage play a role in determining runs scored, such as number of home runs hit.

Scatter diagrams are used to help us to see the type of relation that exists between two variables. In this text, we will discuss a variety of different relations that may exist between two variables. For now, we concentrate on distinguishing between linear and nonlinear relations. See Figure 7.

Figure 7

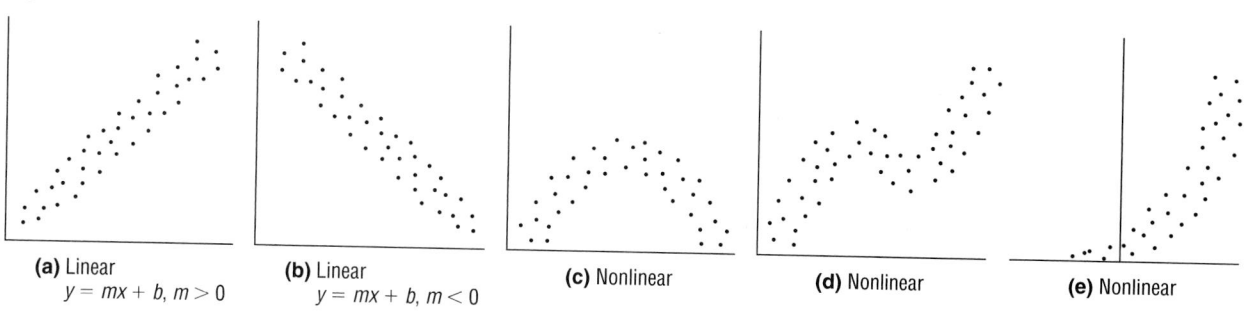

(a) Linear
$y = mx + b, m > 0$

(b) Linear
$y = mx + b, m < 0$

(c) Nonlinear

(d) Nonlinear

(e) Nonlinear

EXAMPLE 2   Distinguishing between Linear and Nonlinear Relations

Determine whether the relation between the two variables in Figure 8 is linear or nonlinear.

Figure 8

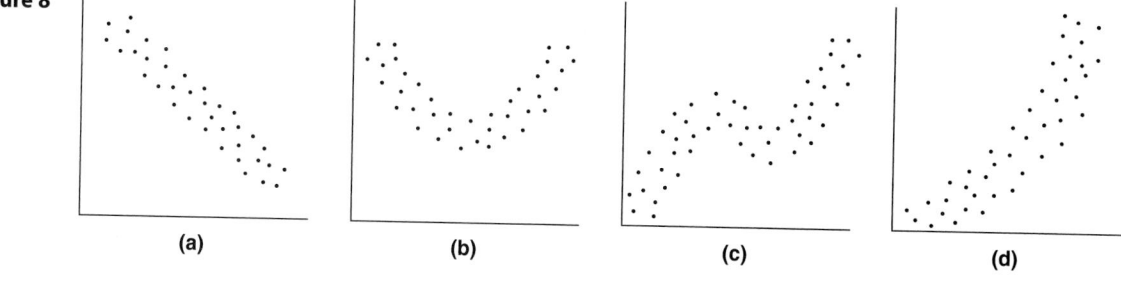

(a)

(b)

(c)

(d)

Solution   (a) Linear   (b) Nonlinear   (c) Nonlinear   (d) Nonlinear

━━━━ **Now Work** PROBLEM 5

In this section we will study data whose scatter diagrams imply that a linear relation exists between the two variables.

Suppose that the scatter diagram of a set of data appears to be linearly related as in Figure 7(a) or (b). We might wish to find an equation of a line (a model) that relates the two variables. One way to obtain a model for such data is to draw a line through two points on the scatter diagram and determine the equation of the line.

EXAMPLE 3	**Finding a Model for Linearly Related Data**

Use the data in Table 6 from Example 1 to:

(a) Select two points and find an equation of the line containing the points.
(b) Graph the line on the scatter diagram obtained in Example 1(b).

Solution   (a) Select two points, say $(32.7, 730)$ and $(34.7, 865)$. The slope of the line joining the points $(32.7, 730)$ and $(34.7, 865)$ is

$$m = \frac{865 - 730}{34.7 - 32.7} = \frac{135}{2} = 67.5$$

Figure 9

The equation of the line with slope 67.5 and passing through $(32.7, 730)$ is found using the point–slope form with $m = 67.5$, $x_1 = 32.7$, and $y_1 = 730$.

$$y - y_1 = m(x - x_1) \quad \text{Point–slope form of a line}$$
$$y - 730 = 67.5(x - 32.7) \quad x_1 = 32.7, \ y_1 = 730, \ m = 67.5$$
$$y - 730 = 67.5x - 2207.25$$
$$y = 67.5x - 1477.25 \quad \text{The Model}$$

(b) Figure 9 shows the scatter diagram with the graph of the line found in part (a).

✎ **Select two other points and complete the solution. Graph the line on the scatter diagram obtained in Figure 9.**

━━━━ **Now Work** PROBLEMS 11(b) AND (c)

3 Use a Graphing Utility to Find the Line of Best Fit

The model obtained in Example 3 depends on the selection of points, which will vary from person to person. So the model that we found might be different from the model you found. Although the model we found in Example 3 appears to fit the data well, there may be a model that "fits it better." Do you think your model fits the data better? Is there a *line of best fit*? As it turns out, there is a method for finding a model that best fits linearly related data (called the **line of best fit**).*

EXAMPLE 4	**Finding a Model for Linearly Related Data**

Use the data in Table 6 from Example 1.

(a) Use a graphing utility to find the line of best fit that models the relation between on-base percentage and runs scored.
(b) Graph the line of best fit on the scatter diagram obtained in Example 1(b).
(c) Interpret the slope.
(d) Use the line of best fit to predict the number of runs a team will score if their on-base percentage is 34.1.

---

* We shall not discuss the underlying mathematics of lines of best fit in this book.

Solution   (a) Graphing utilities contain built-in programs that find the line of best fit for a collection of points in a scatter diagram. Upon executing the LINear REGression program, we obtain the results shown in Figure 10. The output that the utility provides shows us the equation $y = ax + b$, where a is the slope of the line and b is the y-intercept. The line of best fit that relates on-base percentage to runs scored may be expressed as the line

$$y = 49.19x - 870.94 \quad \text{The Model}$$

(b) Figure 11 shows the graph of the line of best fit, along with the scatter diagram.

Figure 10

Figure 11

(c) The slope of the line of best fit is 49.19, which means that, for every 1 percent increase in the on-base percentage, runs scored increase 49.19, on average.

(d) Letting $x = 34.1$ in the equation of the line of best fit, we obtain $y = 49.19(34.1) - 870.94 \approx 806$ runs.

—————— **Now Work** PROBLEMS 11(d) AND (e)

Does the line of best fit appear to be a good fit? In other words, does the line appear to accurately describe the relation between on-base percentage and runs scored?

And just how "good" is this line of best fit? Look again at Figure 10. The last line of output is $r = 0.747$. This number, called the **correlation coefficient, r, $-1 \le r \le 1$,** is a measure of the strength of the linear relation that exists between two variables. The closer that $|r|$ is to 1, the more perfect the linear relationship is. If r is close to 0, there is little or no linear relationship between the variables. A negative value of r, $r < 0$, indicates that as x increases y decreases; a positive value of r, $r > 0$, indicates that as x increases y does also. The data given in Table 6, having a correlation coefficient of 0.747, are indicative of a relatively strong linear relationship with positive slope.

3.2 Assess Your Understanding

'Are You Prepared?' *Answers are given at the end of these exercises. If you get a wrong answer, read the pages listed in red.*

1. Plot the points $(1, 5), (2, 6), (3, 9), (1, 12)$ in the Cartesian plane. Is the relation $\{(1, 5), (2, 6), (3, 9), (1, 12)\}$ a function? Why? (pp. 2 and 59)

2. Find the equation of the line containing the points $(1, 4)$ and $(3, 8)$. (p. 34)

Concepts and Vocabulary

3. A _____ _____ is used to help us to see the type of relation, if any, that may exist between two variables.

4. *True or False* The correlation coefficient is a measure of the strength of a linear relation between two variables and must lie between -1 and 1, inclusive.

Skill Building

In Problems 5–10, examine the scatter diagram and determine whether the type of relation is linear or nonlinear.

5.

6.

7.

8.

9.

10.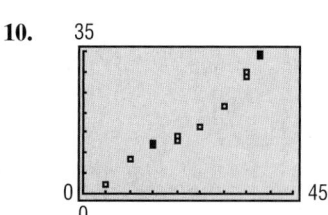

In Problems 11–16,

   (a) *Draw a scatter diagram.*
   (b) *Select two points from the scatter diagram and find the equation of the line containing the points selected.*
   (c) *Graph the line found in part (b) on the scatter diagram.*

   (d) *Use a graphing utility to find the line of best fit.*
   (e) *Use a graphing utility to draw the scatter diagram and graph the line of best fit on it.*

11.

x	3	4	5	6	7	8	9
y	4	6	7	10	12	14	16

12.

x	3	5	7	9	11	13
y	0	2	3	6	9	11

13.

x	−2	−1	0	1	2
y	−4	0	1	4	5

14.

x	−2	−1	0	1	2
y	7	6	3	2	0

15.

x	−20	−17	−15	−14	−10
y	100	120	118	130	140

16.

x	−30	−27	−25	−20	−14
y	10	12	13	13	18

Applications and Extensions

17. Candy The following data represent the weight (in grams) of various candy bars and the corresponding number of calories.

Candy Bar	Weight, x	Calories, y
Hershey's Milk Chocolate®	44.28	230
Nestle's Crunch®	44.84	230
Butterfinger®	61.30	270
Baby Ruth®	66.45	280
Almond Joy®	47.33	220
Twix® (with Caramel)	58.00	280
Snickers®	61.12	280
Heath®	39.52	210

Source: Megan Pocius, Student at Joliet Junior College

  (a) Draw a scatter diagram of the data treating weight as the independent variable.
  (b) What type of relation appears to exist between the weight of a candy bar and the number of calories?
  (c) Select two points and find a linear model that contains the points.
  (d) Graph the line on the scatter diagram drawn in part (a).
  (e) Use the linear model to predict the number of calories in a candy bar that weighs 62.3 grams.
  (f) Interpret the slope of the line found in part (c).

18. Raisins The following data represent the weight (in grams) of a box of raisins and the number of raisins in the box.

Weight (in grams), w	Number of Raisins, N
42.3	87
42.7	91
42.8	93
42.4	87
42.6	89
42.4	90
42.3	82
42.5	86
42.7	86
42.5	86

Source: Jennifer Maxwell, Student at Joliet Junior College

  (a) Does the relation defined by the set of ordered pairs (w, N) represent a function?
  (b) Draw a scatter diagram of the data treating weight as the independent variable.
  (c) Select two points and find a linear model that contains the points.
  (d) Graph the line on the scatter diagram drawn in part (b).
  (e) Express the relationship found in part (c) using function notation.
  (f) Use the linear model to predict the number of raisins in a box that weighs 42.5 grams.
  (g) Interpret the slope of the line found in part (c).

19. Height versus Head Circumference A pediatrician wanted to find a linear model that relates a child's height, H, to head circumference, C. She randomly selects nine children from her practice, measures their height and head circumference, and obtains the data shown. Let H represent the independent variable and C the dependent variable.

(a) Use a graphing utility to draw a scatter diagram.
(b) Use a graphing utility to find the line of best fit that models the relation between height and head circumference. Express the solution using function notation.
(c) Interpret the slope.
(d) Predict the head circumference of a child that is 26 inches tall.
(e) What is the height of a child whose head circumference is 17.4 inches?

Height, H (inches)	Head Circumference, C (inches)
25.25	16.4
25.75	16.9
25	16.9
27.75	17.6
26.5	17.3
27	17.5
26.75	17.3
26.75	17.5
27.5	17.5

Source: Denise Slucki, Student at Joliet Junior College

20. Gestation Period versus Life Expectancy A researcher would like to develop a linear model relating the gestation period of an animal, G, and its life expectancy, L. She collects the following data. Let G represent the independent variable and L the dependent variable.

Animal	Gestation (or incubation) Period, G (days)	Life Expectancy, L (years)
Cat	63	11
Chicken	22	7.5
Dog	63	11
Duck	28	10
Goat	151	12
Lion	108	10
Parakeet	18	8
Pig	115	10
Rabbit	31	7
Squirrel	44	9

Source: Time Almanac 2007

(a) Use a graphing utility to draw a scatter diagram.
(b) Use a graphing utility to find the line of best fit that models the relation between gestation period and life expectancy. Express the solution using function notation.
(c) Interpret the slope.
(d) Predict the life expectancy of an animal whose gestation period is 89 days.

Mixed Practice

21. Demand for Jeans The marketing manager at Levi-Strauss wishes to find a function that relates the demand D for men's jeans and p, the price of the jeans. The following data were obtained based on a price history of the jeans.

Price ($/Pair), p	Demand (Pairs of Jeans Sold per Day), D
20	60
22	57
23	56
23	53
27	52
29	49
30	44

(a) Does the relation defined by the set of ordered pairs (p, D) represent a function?
(b) Draw a scatter diagram of the data.
(c) Using a graphing utility, find the line of best fit that models the relation between price and quantity demanded.
(d) Interpret the slope.
(e) Express the relationship found in part (c) using function notation.
(f) What is the domain of the function?
(g) How many jeans will be demanded if the price is $28 a pair?

22. Advertising and Sales Revenue A marketing firm wishes to find a function that relates the sales S of a product and A, the amount spent on advertising the product. The data are obtained from past experience. Advertising and sales are measured in thousands of dollars.

Advertising Expenditures, A	Sales, S
20	335
22	339
22.5	338
24	343
24	341
27	350
28.3	351

(a) Does the relation defined by the set of ordered pairs (A, S) represent a function?
(b) Draw a scatter diagram of the data.
(c) Using a graphing utility, find the line of best fit that models the relation between advertising expenditures and sales.
(d) Interpret the slope.
(e) Express the relationship found in part (c) using function notation.
(f) What is the domain of the function?
(g) Predict sales if advertising expenditures are $25,000.

Discussion and Writing

23. **Maternal Age versus Down Syndrome** A biologist would like to know how the age of the mother affects the incidence rate of Down syndrome. The data to the right represent the age of the mother and the incidence rate of Down syndrome per 1000 pregnancies.

Draw a scatter diagram treating age of the mother as the independent variable. Would it make sense to find the line of best fit for these data? Why or why not?

24. Find the line of best fit for the ordered pairs $(1, 5)$ and $(3, 8)$. What is the correlation coefficient for these data? Why is this result reasonable?

25. What does a correlation coefficient of 0 imply?

Age of Mother, x	Incidence of Down Syndrome, y
33	2.4
34	3.1
35	4
36	5
37	6.7
38	8.3
39	10
40	13.3
41	16.7
42	22.2
43	28.6
44	33.3
45	50

Source: Hook, E.B., *Journal of the American Medical Association*, 249, 2034-2038, 1983.

'Are You Prepared?' Answers

1.

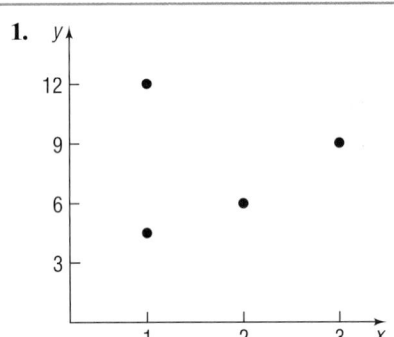

2. $y = 2x + 2$

No, because an input, 1, corresponds to two different outputs.

3.3 Quadratic Functions and Their Properties

PREPARING FOR THIS SECTION *Before getting started, review the following:*

- Intercepts (Section 1.2, pp. 18–19)
- Graphing Techniques: Transformations (Section 2.5, pp. 100–108)
- Completing the Square (Appendix A, Section A.6, p. A52)
- Quadratic Equations (Appendix A, Section A.6, pp. A50–A55)

Now Work the 'Are You Prepared?' problems on page 151.

OBJECTIVES **1** Graph a Quadratic Function Using Transformations (p. 144)
2 Identify the Vertex and Axis of Symmetry of a Quadratic Function (p. 146)
3 Graph a Quadratic Function Using Its Vertex, Axis, and Intercepts (p. 146)
4 Find the Maximum or Minimum Value of a Quadratic Function (p. 150)

Quadratic Functions

Here are some examples of quadratic functions.

$$F(x) = 3x^2 - 5x + 1 \qquad g(x) = -6x^2 + 1 \qquad H(x) = \frac{1}{2}x^2 + \frac{2}{3}x$$

Do you see what is similar among these three functions?

DEFINITION

In Words
A quadratic function is a function defined by a second-degree polynomial in one variable.

A **quadratic function** is a function of the form

$$f(x) = ax^2 + bx + c$$

where a, b, and c are real numbers and $a \neq 0$. The domain of a quadratic function is the set of all real numbers.

Many applications require a knowledge of quadratic functions. For example, suppose that Texas Instruments collects the data shown in Table 7, which relate the number of calculators sold at the price p (in dollars) per calculator. Since the price of a product determines the quantity that will be purchased, we treat price as the independent variable. The relationship between the number x of calculators sold and the price p per calculator can be modeled by the linear equation

$$x = 21{,}000 - 150p$$

Table 7

Price per Calculator, p (Dollars)	Number of Calculators, x
60	12,000
65	11,250
70	10,500
75	9,750
80	9,000
85	8,250
90	7,500

Figure 12

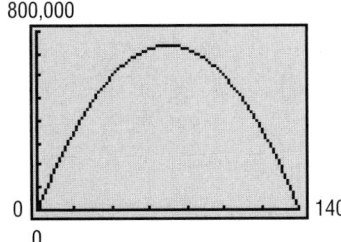

Then the revenue R derived from selling x calculators at the price p per calculator is equal to the unit selling price p of the calculator times the number x of units actually sold. That is,

$$R = xp$$
$$R(p) = (21{,}000 - 150p)p \quad \scriptstyle x = 21{,}000 - 150p$$
$$= -150p^2 + 21{,}000p$$

So the revenue R is a quadratic function of the price p. Figure 12 illustrates the graph of this revenue function, whose domain is $0 \leq p \leq 140$, since both x and p must be nonnegative. In the next section we shall determine the price p that maximizes revenue.

A second situation in which a quadratic function appears involves the motion of a projectile. Based on Newton's Second Law of Motion (force equals mass times acceleration, $F = ma$), it can be shown that, ignoring air resistance, the path of a projectile propelled upward at an inclination to the horizontal is the graph of a quadratic function. See Figure 13 for an illustration. In the next section we shall analyze the path of a projectile.

Figure 13
Path of a cannonball

1 Graph a Quadratic Function Using Transformations

We know how to graph the square function $f(x) = x^2$. Figure 14 shows the graph of three functions of the form $f(x) = ax^2, a > 0$, for $a = 1, a = \dfrac{1}{2}$, and $a = 3$. Notice that the larger the value of a, the "narrower" the graph is, and the smaller the value of a, the "wider" the graph is.

Figure 15 shows graphs of $f(x) = ax^2$ for $a < 0$. Notice that these graphs are reflections about the x-axis of the graphs in Figure 15. Based on the results of these two figures, we can draw some general conclusions about the graph of $f(x) = ax^2$. First, as $|a|$ increases, the graph becomes "taller" (a vertical stretch), and as $|a|$ gets closer to zero, the graph gets "shorter" (a vertical compression). Second, if a is positive, the graph opens "up," and if a is negative, the graph opens "down."

Figure 14

Figure 15

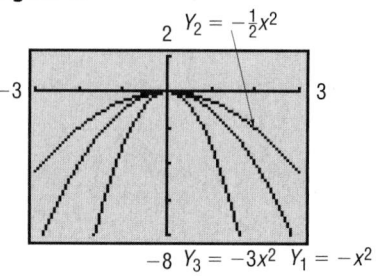

Figure 16

Graphs of a quadratic function,
$f(x) = ax^2 + bx + c, a \neq 0$

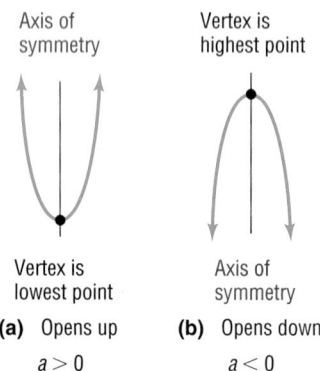

The graphs in Figures 14 and 15 are typical of the graphs of all quadratic functions, which we call **parabolas.*** Refer to Figure 16, where two parabolas are pictured. The one on the left **opens up** and has a lowest point; the one on the right **opens down** and has a highest point. The lowest or highest point of a parabola is called the **vertex**. The vertical line passing through the vertex in each parabola in Figure 16 is called the **axis of symmetry** (usually abbreviated to **axis**) of the parabola. Because the parabola is symmetric about its axis, the axis of symmetry of a parabola can be used to find additional points on the parabola.

The parabolas shown in Figure 16 are the graphs of a quadratic function $f(x) = ax^2 + bx + c, a \neq 0$. Notice that the coordinate axes are not included in the figure. Depending on the values of a, b, and c, the axes could be placed anywhere. The important fact is that the shape of the graph of a quadratic function will look like one of the parabolas in Figure 16.

In the following example, we use techniques from Section 2.5 to graph a quadratic function $f(x) = ax^2 + bx + c, a \neq 0$. In so doing, we shall complete the square and write the function f in the form $f(x) = a(x - h)^2 + k$.

EXAMPLE 1   Graphing a Quadratic Function Using Transformations

Graph the function $f(x) = 2x^2 + 8x + 5$. Find the vertex and axis of symmetry.

Solution   We begin by completing the square on the right side.

$$f(x) = 2x^2 + 8x + 5$$
$$= 2(x^2 + 4x) + 5 \qquad \text{Factor out the 2 from } 2x^2 + 8x.$$
$$= 2(x^2 + 4x + 4) + 5 - 8 \qquad \text{Complete the square of } x^2 + 4x \text{ by adding 4.}$$
$$= 2(x + 2)^2 - 3 \qquad \text{Notice that the factor of 2 requires that 8 be added and subtracted.}$$

---

*We shall study parabolas using a geometric definition later in this book.

The graph of f can be obtained in three stages, as shown in Figure 17. Now compare this graph to the graph in Figure 16(a). The graph of $f(x) = 2x^2 + 8x + 5$ is a parabola that opens up and has its vertex (lowest point) at $(-2, -3)$. Its axis of symmetry is the line $x = -2$.

Figure 17

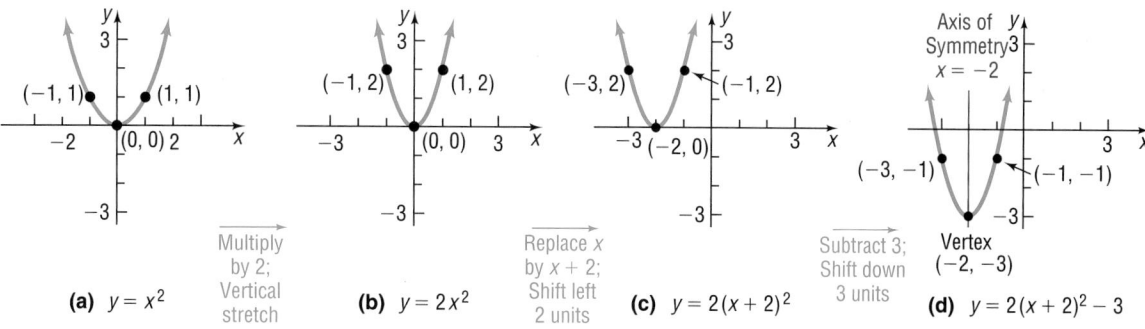

(a) $y = x^2$ Multiply by 2; Vertical stretch   **(b)** $y = 2x^2$ Replace x by $x + 2$; Shift left 2 units   **(c)** $y = 2(x + 2)^2$ Subtract 3; Shift down 3 units   **(d)** $y = 2(x + 2)^2 - 3$ Vertex $(-2, -3)$

✓ **Check:** Use a graphing utility to graph $Y_1 = f(x) = 2x^2 + 8x + 5$ and use the MINIMUM command to locate its vertex.

✏ **Now Work** PROBLEM 21

The method used in Example 1 can be used to graph any quadratic function $f(x) = ax^2 + bx + c, a \neq 0$, as follows:

$f(x) = ax^2 + bx + c$

$= a\left(x^2 + \dfrac{b}{a}x\right) + c$ Factor out a from $ax^2 + bx$.

$= a\left(x^2 + \dfrac{b}{a}x + \dfrac{b^2}{4a^2}\right) + c - a\left(\dfrac{b^2}{4a^2}\right)$ Complete the square by adding $\dfrac{b^2}{4a^2}$. Look closely at this step!

$= a\left(x + \dfrac{b}{2a}\right)^2 + c - \dfrac{b^2}{4a}$ Factor; Simplify

$= a\left(x + \dfrac{b}{2a}\right)^2 + \dfrac{4ac - b^2}{4a}$ $c - \dfrac{b^2}{4a} = c \cdot \dfrac{4a}{4a} - \dfrac{b^2}{4a} = \dfrac{4ac - b^2}{4a}$

$= a\left(x - \left(-\dfrac{b}{2a}\right)\right)^2 + \dfrac{4ac - b^2}{4a}$

Based on these results, we conclude the following:

If $h = -\dfrac{b}{2a}$ and $k = \dfrac{4ac - b^2}{4a}$, then

$$f(x) = ax^2 + bx + c = a(x - h)^2 + k \qquad \textbf{(1)}$$

The graph of $f(x) = a(x - h)^2 + k$ is the parabola $y = ax^2$ shifted horizontally h units (replace x by $x - h$) and vertically k units (add k). As a result, the vertex is at (h, k), and the graph opens up if $a > 0$ and down if $a < 0$. The axis of symmetry is the vertical line $x = h$.

For example, compare equation (1) with the solution given in Example 1.

$$f(x) = 2(x + 2)^2 - 3$$
$$= 2(x - (-2))^2 + (-3)$$
$$= a(x - \quad h)^2 + \quad k$$

We conclude that $a = 2$, so the graph opens up. Also, we find that $h = -2$ and $k = -3$, so its vertex is at $(-2, -3)$.

2 Identify the Vertex and Axis of Symmetry of a Quadratic Function

We do not need to complete the square to obtain the vertex. In almost every case, it is easier to obtain the vertex of a quadratic function f by remembering that its x-coordinate is $h = -\dfrac{b}{2a}$. The y-coordinate k can then be found by evaluating f at $-\dfrac{b}{2a}$. That is, $k = f\left(-\dfrac{b}{2a}\right)$.

We summarize these remarks as follows:

Properties of the Graph of a Quadratic Function

$$f(x) = ax^2 + bx + c \qquad a \neq 0$$

$$\text{Vertex} = \left(-\frac{b}{2a}, f\left(-\frac{b}{2a}\right)\right) \quad \text{Axis of symmetry: the line } x = -\frac{b}{2a} \qquad \textbf{(2)}$$

Parabola opens up if $a > 0$; the vertex is a minimum point.
Parabola opens down if $a < 0$; the vertex is a maximum point.

EXAMPLE 2	Locating the Vertex without Graphing

Without graphing, locate the vertex and axis of symmetry of the parabola defined by $f(x) = -3x^2 + 6x + 1$. Does it open up or down?

Solution For this quadratic function, $a = -3, b = 6$, and $c = 1$. The x-coordinate of the vertex is

$$h = -\frac{b}{2a} = -\frac{6}{-6} = 1$$

The y-coordinate of the vertex is

$$k = f\left(-\frac{b}{2a}\right) = f(1) = -3(1)^2 + 6(1) + 1 = 4$$

The vertex is located at the point $(1, 4)$. The axis of symmetry is the line $x = 1$. Because $a = -3 < 0$, the parabola opens down.

✓ **Check:** Use a graphing utility to graph $Y_1 = f(x) = -3x^2 + 6x + 1$ and use the MAXIMUM command to locate its vertex.

3 Graph a Quadratic Function Using Its Vertex, Axis, and Intercepts

The location of the vertex and the location of the intercepts, along with knowledge as to whether the graph of the quadratic function opens up or down, usually provide enough information to graph $f(x) = ax^2 + bx + c, a \neq 0$.

The y-intercept is the value of f at $x = 0$; that is, the y-intercept is $f(0) = c$.

The x-intercepts, if there are any, are found by solving the quadratic equation

$$ax^2 + bx + c = 0$$

This equation has two, one, or no real solutions, depending on whether the discriminant $b^2 - 4ac$ is positive, 0, or negative. Depending on the value of the discriminant, the graph of f has x-intercepts, as follows:

The x-Intercepts of a Quadratic Function

1. If the discriminant $b^2 - 4ac > 0$, the graph of $f(x) = ax^2 + bx + c$ has two distinct x-intercepts, so it crosses the x-axis in two places.
2. If the discriminant $b^2 - 4ac = 0$, the graph of $f(x) = ax^2 + bx + c$ has one x-intercept, so it touches the x-axis at its vertex.
3. If the discriminant $b^2 - 4ac < 0$, the graph of $f(x) = ax^2 + bx + c$ has no x-intercept, so it does not cross or touch the x-axis.

Figure 18 illustrates these possibilities for parabolas that open up.

Figure 18

$f(x) = ax^2 + bx + c, a > 0$

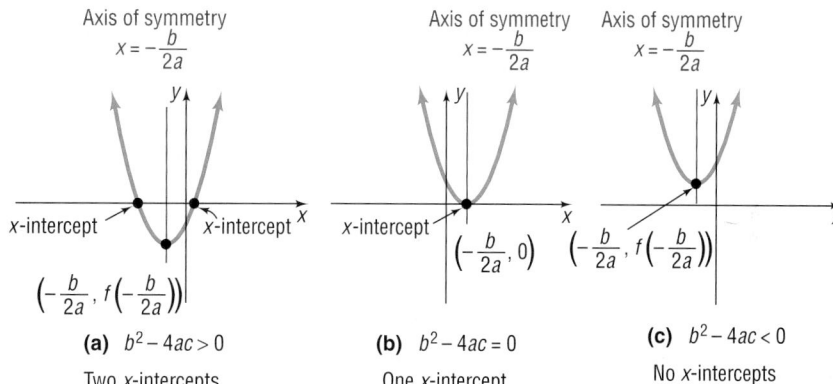

(a) $b^2 - 4ac > 0$
Two x-intercepts

(b) $b^2 - 4ac = 0$
One x-intercept

(c) $b^2 - 4ac < 0$
No x-intercepts

| EXAMPLE 3 | How to Graph a Quadratic Function by Hand Using Its Properties |

Graph $f(x) = -3x^2 + 6x + 1$ using its properties. Determine the domain and the range of f. Determine where f is increasing and where it is decreasing.

Step-by-Step Solution

STEP 1 Determine whether the graph of f opens up or down.

In Example 2, we determined that the graph of $f(x) = -3x^2 + 6x + 1$ opens down because $a = -3 < 0$.

STEP 2 Determine the vertex and axis of symmetry of the graph of f.

In Example 2, we found the vertex to be at the point whose coordinates are $(1, 4)$. The axis of symmetry is the line $x = 1$.

STEP 3 Determine the intercepts of the graph of f.

The y-intercept is found by letting $x = 0$. The y-intercept is $f(0) = 1$. The x-intercepts are found by solving the equation $f(x) = 0$.

$$f(x) = 0$$
$$-3x^2 + 6x + 1 = 0 \quad a = -3, b = 6, c = 1$$

The discriminant $b^2 - 4ac = 6^2 - 4(-3)(1) = 36 + 12 = 48 > 0$, so the equation has two real solutions and the graph has two x-intercepts. Using the quadratic formula, we find that

$$x = \frac{-b + \sqrt{b^2 - 4ac}}{2a} = \frac{-6 + \sqrt{48}}{2(-3)} = \frac{-6 + 4\sqrt{3}}{-6} \approx -0.15$$

and

$$x = \frac{-b - \sqrt{b^2 - 4ac}}{2a} = \frac{-6 - \sqrt{48}}{2(-3)} = \frac{-6 - 4\sqrt{3}}{-6} \approx 2.15$$

The x-intercepts are approximately -0.15 and 2.15.

STEP 4 Use the information in Steps 1 through 3 to graph f.

The graph is illustrated in Figure 19. Notice how we use the y-intercept and the axis of symmetry, $x = 1$, to obtain the additional point $(2, 1)$ on the graph.

Figure 19

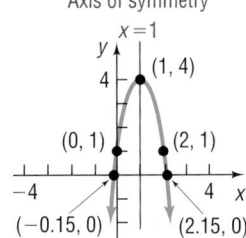

Axis of symmetry
$x = 1$

The domain of f is the set of all real numbers. Based on the graph, the range of f is the interval $(-\infty, 4]$. The function f is increasing on the interval $(-\infty, 1)$ and decreasing on the interval $(1, \infty)$.

Graph the function in Example 3 by completing the square and using transformations. Which method do you prefer?

Now Work PROBLEM 29

If the graph of a quadratic function has only one x-intercept or no x-intercepts, it is usually necessary to plot an additional point to obtain the graph.

EXAMPLE 4

Graphing a Quadratic Function Using Its Vertex, Axis, and Intercepts

(a) Graph $f(x) = x^2 - 6x + 9$ by determining whether the graph opens up or down and by finding its vertex, axis of symmetry, y-intercept, and x-intercepts, if any.
(b) Determine the domain and the range of f.
(c) Determine where f is increasing and where it is decreasing.

Solution

(a) **STEP 1:** For $f(x) = x^2 - 6x + 9$, we have $a = 1, b = -6$, and $c = 9$. Since $a = 1 > 0$, the parabola opens up.

STEP 2: The x-coordinate of the vertex is

$$h = -\frac{b}{2a} = -\frac{-6}{2(1)} = 3$$

Figure 20

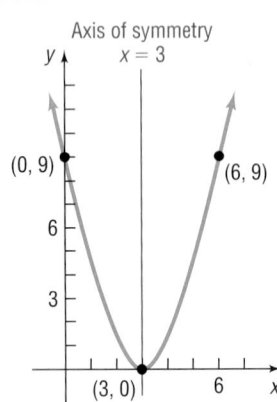

Axis of symmetry
$x = 3$

The y-coordinate of the vertex is

$$k = f(3) = (3)^2 - 6(3) + 9 = 0$$

So the vertex is at $(3, 0)$. The axis of symmetry is the line $x = 3$.

STEP 3: The y-intercept is $f(0) = 9$. Since the vertex $(3, 0)$ lies on the x-axis, the graph touches the x-axis at the x-intercept.

STEP 4: By using the axis of symmetry and the y-intercept at $(0, 9)$, we can locate the additional point $(6, 9)$ on the graph. See Figure 20.

(b) The domain of f is the set of all real numbers. Based on the graph, the range of f is the interval $[0, \infty)$.
(c) The function f is decreasing on the interval $(-\infty, 3)$ and increasing on the interval $(3, \infty)$.

Now Work PROBLEM 35

| EXAMPLE 5 | Graphing a Quadratic Function Using Its Vertex, Axis, and Intercepts |

(a) Graph $f(x) = 2x^2 + x + 1$ by determining whether the graph opens up or down and by finding its vertex, axis of symmetry, y-intercept, and x-intercepts, if any.

(b) Determine the domain and the range of f.

(c) Determine where f is increasing and where it is decreasing.

Solution   (a) **STEP 1:** For $f(x) = 2x^2 + x + 1$, we have $a = 2, b = 1$, and $c = 1$. Since $a = 2 > 0$, the parabola opens up.

STEP 2: The x-coordinate of the vertex is

$$h = -\frac{b}{2a} = -\frac{1}{4}$$

The y-coordinate of the vertex is

$$k = f\left(-\frac{1}{4}\right) = 2\left(\frac{1}{16}\right) + \left(-\frac{1}{4}\right) + 1 = \frac{7}{8}$$

NOTE In Example 5, since the vertex is above the x-axis and the parabola opens up, we can conclude that the graph of the quadratic function will have no x-intercepts. ∎

So the vertex is at $\left(-\frac{1}{4}, \frac{7}{8}\right)$. The axis of symmetry is the line $x = -\frac{1}{4}$.

STEP 3: The y-intercept is $f(0) = 1$. The x-intercept(s), if any, obey the equation $2x^2 + x + 1 = 0$. Since the discriminant $b^2 - 4ac = (1)^2 - 4(2)(1) = -7 < 0$, this equation has no real solutions, and therefore the graph has no x-intercepts.

STEP 4: We use the point $(0, 1)$ and the axis of symmetry $x = -\frac{1}{4}$ to locate the additional point $\left(-\frac{1}{2}, 1\right)$ on the graph. See Figure 21.

Figure 21

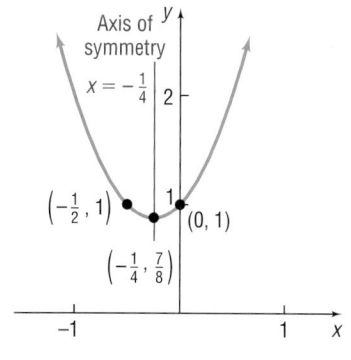

(b) The domain of f is the set of all real numbers. Based on the graph, the range of f is the interval $\left[\frac{7}{8}, \infty\right)$.

(c) The function f is decreasing on the interval $\left(-\infty, -\frac{1}{4}\right)$ and is increasing on the interval $\left(-\frac{1}{4}, \infty\right)$.

Now Work PROBLEM 39

SUMMARY   Steps for Graphing a Quadratic Function $f(x) = ax^2 + bx + c, a \neq 0$, by Hand

Option 1

STEP 1: Complete the square in x to write the quadratic function in the form $f(x) = a(x - h)^2 + k$.

STEP 2: Graph the function in stages using transformations.

Option 2

STEP 1: Determine whether the graph of f opens up or down.

STEP 2: Determine the vertex $\left(-\frac{b}{2a}, f\left(-\frac{b}{2a}\right)\right)$ and the axis of symmetry, $x = -\frac{b}{2a}$.

STEP 3: Determine the y-intercept, $f(0)$. Determine the x-intercept(s), if any.

   (a) If $b^2 - 4ac > 0$, then the graph of the quadratic function has two x-intercepts, which are found by solving the equation $ax^2 + bx + c = 0$.

   (b) If $b^2 - 4ac = 0$, the vertex is the x-intercept.

   (c) If $b^2 - 4ac < 0$, there are no x-intercepts.

STEP 4: Determine an additional point by using the y-intercept and the axis of symmetry. Plot the points and draw the graph.

Given the vertex (h, k) and one additional point on the graph of a quadratic function $f(x) = ax^2 + bx + c, a \neq 0$, we can use

$$f(x) = a(x - h)^2 + k \qquad (3)$$

to obtain the quadratic function.

EXAMPLE 6 **Finding the Quadratic Function Given Its Vertex and One Other Point**

Determine the quadratic function whose vertex is $(1, -5)$ and whose y-intercept is -3. The graph of the parabola is shown in Figure 22.

Solution The vertex is $(1, -5)$, so $h = 1$ and $k = -5$. Substitute these values into equation (3).

Figure 22

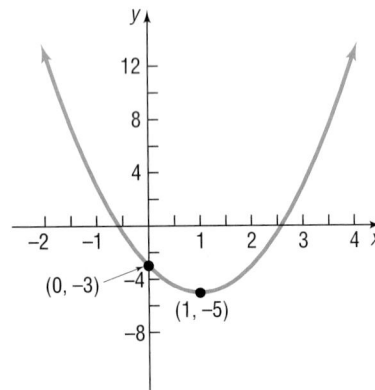

$$f(x) = a(x - h)^2 + k \quad \text{Equation (3)}$$
$$f(x) = a(x - 1)^2 - 5 \quad h = 1, k = -5$$

To determine the value of a, we use the fact that $f(0) = -3$ (the y-intercept).

$$f(x) = a(x - 1)^2 - 5$$
$$-3 = a(0 - 1)^2 - 5 \quad x = 0, y = f(0) = -3$$
$$-3 = a - 5$$
$$a = 2$$

The quadratic function whose graph is shown in Figure 22 is

$$f(x) = a(x - h)^2 + k = 2(x - 1)^2 - 5 = 2x^2 - 4x - 3$$

✓ **Check:** Figure 23 shows the graph $f(x) = 2x^2 - 4x - 3$ using a graphing utility.

Figure 23

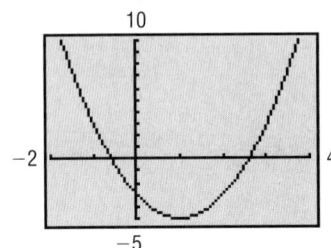

━━━ **Now Work** PROBLEM 43

4 Find the Maximum or Minimum Value of a Quadratic Function

The graph of a quadratic function

$$f(x) = ax^2 + bx + c, \qquad a \neq 0$$

is a parabola with vertex at $\left(-\dfrac{b}{2a}, f\left(-\dfrac{b}{2a}\right)\right)$. This vertex is the highest point on the graph if $a < 0$ and the lowest point on the graph if $a > 0$. If the vertex is the highest point ($a < 0$), then $f\left(-\dfrac{b}{2a}\right)$ is the **maximum value** of f. If the vertex is the lowest point ($a > 0$), then $f\left(-\dfrac{b}{2a}\right)$ is the **minimum value** of f.

| EXAMPLE 7 | Finding the Maximum or Minimum Value of a Quadratic Function |

Determine whether the quadratic function

$$f(x) = x^2 - 4x - 5$$

has a maximum or minimum value. Then find the maximum or minimum value.

Solution We compare $f(x) = x^2 - 4x - 5$ to $f(x) = ax^2 + bx + c$. We conclude that $a = 1, b = -4$, and $c = -5$. Since $a > 0$, the graph of f opens up, so the vertex is a minimum point. The minimum value occurs at

$$x = -\frac{b}{2a} \underset{\substack{\uparrow \\ a = 1, b = -4}}{=} -\frac{-4}{2(1)} = \frac{4}{2} = 2$$

The minimum value is

$$f\left(-\frac{b}{2a}\right) = f(2) = 2^2 - 4(2) - 5 = 4 - 8 - 5 = -9$$

Table 8

Y₁ ◼ X²−4X−5

✓ **Check:** We can support the algebraic solution using the TABLE feature on a graphing utility. Create Table 8 by letting $Y_1 = x^2 - 4x - 5$. From the table we see that the smallest value of y occurs when $x = 2$, leading us to investigate the number 2 further. The symmetry about $x = 2$ confirms that 2 is the x-coordinate of the vertex of the parabola. We conclude that the minimum value is -9 and occurs at $x = 2$. ∎

━━━ **Now Work** PROBLEM 51

3.3 Assess Your Understanding

'Are You Prepared?' *Answers are given at the end of these exercises. If you get a wrong answer, read the pages listed in red.*

1. List the intercepts of the graph of $y = x^2 - 9$. (pp. 18–19)

2. Find the real solutions of the equation $2x^2 + 7x - 4 = 0$. (pp. A50–A51)

3. To complete the square of $x^2 - 5x$, you add the number _____. (p. A52)

4. To graph $y = (x - 4)^2$, you shift the graph of $y = x^2$ to the _____ a distance of _____ units. (pp. 101–102)

Concepts and Vocabulary

5. The graph of a quadratic function is called a(n) _____.

6. The vertical line passing through the vertex of a parabola is called the _____.

7. The x-coordinate of the vertex of $f(x) = ax^2 + bx + c$, $a \neq 0$, is _____.

8. *True or False* The graph of $f(x) = 2x^2 + 3x - 4$ opens up.

9. *True or False* The y-coordinate of the vertex of $f(x) = -x^2 + 4x + 5$ is $f(2)$.

10. *True or False* If the discriminant $b^2 - 4ac = 0$, the graph of $f(x) = ax^2 + bx + c, a \neq 0$, will touch the x-axis at its vertex.

Skill Building

In Problems 11–18, match graphs A–H to one the following functions.

11. $f(x) = x^2 - 1$

12. $f(x) = -x^2 - 1$

13. $f(x) = x^2 - 2x + 1$

14. $f(x) = x^2 + 2x + 1$

15. $f(x) = x^2 - 2x + 2$

16. $f(x) = x^2 + 2x$

17. $f(x) = (x - 1)^2 - 1$

18. $f(x) = (x + 1)^2 + 1$

A.

B.

C.

D.
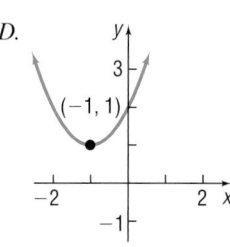

E.

F.

G.

H.

In Problems 19–28, graph the function f by starting with the graph of $y = x^2$ and using transformations (shifting, compressing, stretching, and/or reflection). Verify your results using a graphing utility.

[**Hint:** If necessary, write f in the form $f(x) = a(x - h)^2 + k$.]

19. $f(x) = \frac{1}{4}x^2 - 2$ **20.** $f(x) = 2x^2 + 4$ **21.** $f(x) = (x + 2)^2 - 2$ **22.** $f(x) = (x - 3)^2 - 10$

23. $f(x) = 2(x - 1)^2 - 1$ **24.** $f(x) = 3(x + 1)^2 - 3$ **25.** $f(x) = -x^2 - 2x$ **26.** $f(x) = -2x^2 + 6x + 2$

27. $f(x) = 2x^2 + 4x - 2$ **28.** $f(x) = 3x^2 + 12x + 5$

In Problems 29–42, (a) graph each quadratic function by determining whether its graph opens up or down and by finding its vertex, axis of symmetry, y-intercept, and x-intercepts, if any. (b) Determine the domain and the range of the function. (c) Determine where the function is increasing and where it is decreasing. Verify your results using a graphing utility.

29. $f(x) = x^2 + 2x$ **30.** $f(x) = x^2 - 4x$ **31.** $f(x) = -x^2 - 6x$ **32.** $f(x) = -x^2 + 4x$

33. $f(x) = x^2 + 2x - 8$ **34.** $f(x) = x^2 - 2x - 3$ **35.** $f(x) = x^2 + 2x + 1$ **36.** $f(x) = x^2 + 6x + 9$

37. $f(x) = 2x^2 - x + 2$ **38.** $f(x) = 4x^2 - 2x + 1$ **39.** $f(x) = -2x^2 + 2x - 3$ **40.** $f(x) = -3x^2 + 3x - 2$

41. $f(x) = -4x^2 - 6x + 2$ **42.** $f(x) = 3x^2 - 8x + 2$

In Problems 43–48, determine the quadratic function whose graph is given. Verify your results using a graphing utility.

43.

44.

45.

46.

47.

48.

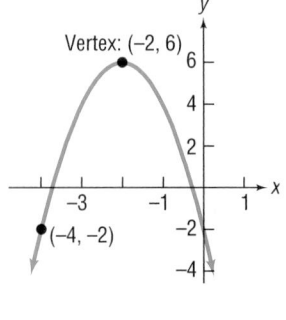

In Problems 49–56, determine, without graphing, whether the given quadratic function has a maximum value or a minimum value and then find the value. Use a graphing utility to verify your result.

49. $f(x) = 2x^2 + 12x$ **50.** $f(x) = -2x^2 + 12x$ **51.** $f(x) = 2x^2 + 12x - 3$ **52.** $f(x) = 4x^2 - 8x + 3$

53. $f(x) = -x^2 + 10x - 4$ **54.** $f(x) = -2x^2 + 8x + 3$ **55.** $f(x) = -3x^2 + 12x + 1$ **56.** $f(x) = 4x^2 - 4x$

Mixed Practice

In Problems 57–68, (a) graph each function. (b) Determine the domain and the range of the function. (c) Determine where the function is increasing and where it is decreasing.

57. $f(x) = x^2 - 2x - 15$

58. $g(x) = x^2 - 2x - 8$

59. $F(x) = 2x - 5$

60. $f(x) = \frac{3}{2}x - 2$

61. $g(x) = -2(x - 3)^2 + 2$

62. $h(x) = -3(x + 1)^2 + 4$

63. $f(x) = 2x^2 + x + 1$

64. $G(x) = 3x^2 + 2x + 5$

65. $h(x) = -\frac{2}{5}x + 4$

66. $f(x) = -3x + 2$

67. $H(x) = -4x^2 - 4x - 1$

68. $F(x) = -4x^2 + 20x - 25$

Applications and Extensions

69. The graph of the function $f(x) = ax^2 + bx + c$ has vertex at $(0, 2)$ and passes through the point $(1, 8)$. Find a, b, and c.

70. The graph of the function $f(x) = ax^2 + bx + c$ has vertex at $(1, 4)$ and passes through the point $(-1, -8)$. Find a, b, and c.

In Problems 71–76, for the given functions f and g,
  (a) Graph f and g on the same Cartesian plane.
  (b) Solve $f(x) = g(x)$.
  (c) Use the result of part (b) to label the points of intersection of the graphs of f and g.
  (d) Shade the region above f and below g between the points of intersection.

71. $f(x) = 2x - 1$; $g(x) = x^2 - 4$

72. $f(x) = -2x - 1$; $g(x) = x^2 - 9$

73. $f(x) = -x^2 + 4$; $g(x) = -2x + 1$

74. $f(x) = -x^2 + 9$; $g(x) = 2x + 1$

75. $f(x) = -x^2 + 5x$; $g(x) = x^2 + 3x - 4$

76. $f(x) = -x^2 + 7x - 6$; $g(x) = x^2 + x - 6$

Answer Problems 77 and 78 using the following: A quadratic function of the form $f(x) = ax^2 + bx + c$ with $b^2 - 4ac > 0$ may also be written in the form $f(x) = a(x - r_1)(x - r_2)$, where r_1 and r_2 are the x-intercepts of the graph of the quadratic function.

77. (a) Find a quadratic function whose x-intercepts are -3 and 1 with $a = 1; a = 2; a = -2; a = 5$.
  (b) How does the value of a affect the intercepts?
  (c) How does the value of a affect the axis of symmetry?
  (d) How does the value of a affect the vertex?
  (e) Compare the x-coordinate of the vertex with the midpoint of the x-intercepts. What might you conclude?

78. (a) Find a quadratic function whose x-intercepts are -5 and 3 with $a = 1; a = 2; a = -2; a = 5$.
  (b) How does the value of a affect the intercepts?
  (c) How does the value of a affect the axis of symmetry?
  (d) How does the value of a affect the vertex?
  (e) Compare the x-coordinate of the vertex with the midpoint of the x-intercepts. What might you conclude?

79. Suppose that $f(x) = x^2 + 4x - 21$.
  (a) What is the vertex of f?
  (b) What are the x-intercepts of the graph of f?
  (c) Solve $f(x) = -21$ for x. What points are on the graph of f?
  (d) Use the information obtained in parts (a)–(c) to graph $f(x) = x^2 + 4x - 21$.

80. Suppose that $f(x) = x^2 + 2x - 8$.
  (a) What is the vertex of f?
  (b) What are the x-intercepts of the graph of f?
  (c) Solve $f(x) = -8$ for x. What points are on the graph of f?
  (d) Use the information obtained in parts (a)–(c) to graph $f(x) = x^2 + 2x - 8$.

81. Find the point on the line $y = x$ that is closest to the point $(3, 1)$.

  [**Hint:** Express the distance d from the point to the line as a function of x, and then find the minimum value of $[d(x)]^2$.]

82. Find the point on the line $y = x + 1$ that is closest to the point $(4, 1)$.

83. Maximizing Revenue   Suppose that the manufacturer of a gas clothes dryer has found that, when the unit price is p dollars, the revenue R (in dollars) is

$$R(p) = -4p^2 + 4000p$$

What unit price should be established for the dryer to maximize revenue? What is the maximum revenue?

84. Maximizing Revenue   The John Deere company has found that the revenue, in dollars, from sales of heavy-duty tractors is a function of the unit price p, in dollars, that it charges. If the revenue R is

$$R(p) = -\frac{1}{2}p^2 + 1900p$$

what unit price p should be charged to maximize revenue? What is the maximum revenue?

85. Minimizing Marginal Cost   The **marginal cost** of a product can be thought of as the cost of producing one additional unit of output. For example, if the marginal cost of producing the 50th product is $6.20, it cost $6.20 to increase production from 49 to 50 units of output. Suppose the marginal cost C (in dollars) to produce x thousand mp3 players is given by the function

$$C(x) = x^2 - 140x + 7400$$

  (a) How many players should be produced to minimize the marginal cost?
  (b) What is the minimum marginal cost?

86. Minimizing Marginal Cost   (See Problem 85.) The marginal cost C (in dollars) of manufacturing x cell phones (in thousands) is given by

$$C(x) = 5x^2 - 200x + 4000$$

  (a) How many cell phones should be manufactured to minimize the marginal cost?
  (b) What is the minimum marginal cost?

87. Hunting The function

$$H(x) = -3.24x^2 + 242.1x - 738.4$$

models the number of individuals whose age is x and who engage in hunting activities.
(a) What is the age at which there are the most hunters? Approximately how many hunters are this age?
(b) Are the number of hunters increasing or decreasing for individuals who are between 40 and 45 years of age?

Source: National Sporting Goods Association

88. Male Murder Victims The function

$$M(x) = 1.00x^2 - 136.74x + 4764.89$$

models the number of male murder victims who are x years of age ($20 \le x < 90$).
(a) Use the model to approximate the number of male murder victims who are $x = 23$ years of age.
(b) At what age is the number of male murder victims 1456?
(c) Describe what happens to the number of male murder victims as age increases from 20 to 65.

Source: Federal Bureau of Investigation

89. Business The monthly revenue R achieved by selling x wristwatches is modeled by $R(x) = 75x - 0.2x^2$. The monthly cost C of selling x wristwatches is $C(x) = 32x + 1750$.

(a) How many wristwatches must the firm sell to maximize revenue? What is the maximum revenue?
(b) Profit is given as $P(x) = R(x) - C(x)$. What is the profit function?
(c) How many wristwatches must the firm sell to maximize profit? What is the maximum profit?
(d) Provide a reasonable explanation as to why the answers found in parts (a) and (c) differ. Explain why a quadratic function is a reasonable model for revenue.

90. Business The daily revenue R achieved by selling x boxes of candy is modeled by $R(x) = 9.5x - 0.04x^2$. The daily cost C of selling x boxes of candy is $C(x) = 1.25x + 250$.

(a) How many boxes of candy must the firm sell to maximize revenue? What is the maximum revenue?
(b) Profit is given as $P(x) = R(x) - C(x)$. What is the profit function?
(c) How many boxes of candy must the firm sell to maximize profit? What is the maximum profit?
(d) Provide a reasonable explanation as to why the answers found in parts (a) and (c) differ. Explain why a quadratic function is a reasonable model for revenue.

91. Let $f(x) = ax^2 + bx + c$, where a, b, and c are odd integers. If x is an integer, show that $f(x)$ must be an odd integer.

[**Hint:** x is either an even integer or an odd integer.]

Discussion and Writing

92. Make up a quadratic function that opens down and has only one x-intercept. Compare yours with others in the class. What are the similarities? What are the differences?

93. On one set of coordinate axes, graph the family of parabolas $f(x) = x^2 + 2x + c$ for $c = -3, c = 0$, and $c = 1$. Describe the characteristics of a member of this family.

94. On one set of coordinate axes, graph the family of parabolas $f(x) = x^2 + bx + 1$ for $b = -4, b = 0$, and $b = 4$. Describe the general characteristics of this family.

95. State the circumstances that cause the graph of a quadratic function $f(x) = ax^2 + bx + c$ to have no x-intercepts.

96. Why does the graph of a quadratic function open up if $a > 0$ and down if $a < 0$?

97. Can a quadratic function have a range of $(-\infty, \infty)$? Justify your answer.

98. What are the possibilities for the number of times the graphs of two different quadratic functions intersect?

'Are You Prepared?' Answers

1. $(0, -9), (-3, 0), (3, 0)$ **2.** $\left\{-4, \dfrac{1}{2}\right\}$ **3.** $\dfrac{25}{4}$ **4.** right; 4

3.4 Building Quadratic Models from Verbal Descriptions and from Data

PREPARING FOR THIS SECTION *Before getting started, review the following:*

• Problem Solving (Appendix A, Section A.8, pp. A69–A74)

Now Work the 'Are You Prepared?' problems on page 160.

OBJECTIVES 1 Build Quadratic Models from Verbal Descriptions (p. 155)
2 Build Quadratic Models from Data (p. 158)

In this section we will first discuss models that lead to a quadratic function when a verbal description of the problem is given. We end the section by fitting a quadratic function to data, which is another form of modeling.

When a mathematical model leads to a quadratic function, the properties of the graph of the quadratic function can provide important information about the model. In particular, we can use the quadratic function to determine the maximum or minimum value of the function. The fact that the graph of a quadratic function has a maximum or minimum value enables us to answer questions involving **optimization,** that is, finding the maximum or minimum values in models involving quadratic functions.

1 Build Quadratic Models from Verbal Descriptions

In economics, revenue R, in dollars, is defined as the amount of money received from the sale of an item and is equal to the unit selling price p, in dollars, of the item times the number x of units actually sold. That is,

$$R = xp$$

In economics, the Law of Demand states that p and x are related: As one increases, the other decreases. The equation that relates p and x is called the **demand equation.**

| EXAMPLE 1 | Maximizing Revenue |

The marketing department at Texas Instruments has found that, when certain calculators are sold at a price of p dollars per unit, the number x of calculators sold is given by the demand equation

$$x = 21{,}000 - 150p$$

(a) Find a model that expresses the revenue R as a function of the price p.
(b) What is the domain of R?
(c) What unit price should be used to maximize revenue?
(d) If this price is charged, what is the maximum revenue?
(e) How many units are sold at this price?
(f) Graph R.

Solution

(a) The revenue R is $R = xp$, where $x = 21{,}000 - 150p$.

$$R = xp = (21{,}000 - 150p)p = -150p^2 + 21{,}000p \quad \text{The Model}$$

(b) Because x represents the number of calculators sold, we have $x \geq 0$, so $21{,}000 - 150p \geq 0$. Solving this linear inequality, we find that $p \leq 140$. In addition, Texas Instruments will only charge a positive price for the calculator, so $p > 0$. Combining these inequalities, we have the domain of R is $\{p \,|\, 0 < p \leq 140\}$.

(c) The function R is a quadratic function with $a = -150, b = 21{,}000$, and $c = 0$. Because $a < 0$, the vertex is the highest point on the parabola. The revenue R is therefore a maximum when the price p is

$$p = -\frac{b}{2a} \underset{\uparrow}{=} -\frac{21{,}000}{2(-150)} = -\frac{21{,}000}{-300} = \$70.00$$

$$a = -150, b = 21{,}000$$

(d) The maximum revenue R is

$$R(70) = -150(70)^2 + 21{,}000(70) = \$735{,}000$$

(e) The number of calculators sold is given by the demand equation $x = 21{,}000 - 150p$. At a price of $p = \$70$,

$$x = 21{,}000 - 150(70) = 10{,}500$$

calculators are sold.

(f) See Figure 24 for the graph of R.

Figure 24

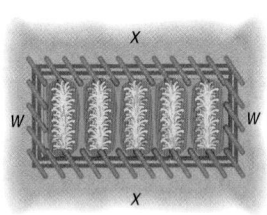

▬▬➤ **Now Work** PROBLEM 3

| EXAMPLE 2 | **Maximizing the Area Enclosed by a Fence** |

A farmer has 2000 yards of fence to enclose a rectangular field. What are the dimensions of the rectangle that encloses the most area?

Solution

Figure 25

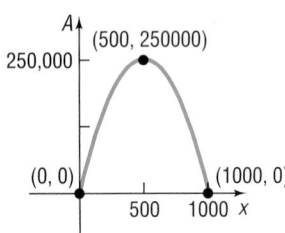

Figure 25 illustrates the situation. The available fence represents the perimeter of the rectangle. If x is the length and w is the width, then

$$2x + 2w = 2000 \qquad \textbf{(1)}$$

The area A of the rectangle is

$$A = xw$$

To express A in terms of a single variable, we solve equation (1) for w and substitute the result in $A = xw$. Then A involves only the variable x. [You could also solve equation (1) for x and express A in terms of w alone. Try it!]

$$2x + 2w = 2000$$
$$2w = 2000 - 2x$$
$$w = \frac{2000 - 2x}{2} = 1000 - x$$

Then the area A is

$$A = xw = x(1000 - x) = -x^2 + 1000x$$

Now, A is a quadratic function of x.

$$A(x) = -x^2 + 1000x \qquad a = -1, b = 1000, c = 0$$

Figure 26

Figure 26 shows a graph of $A(x) = -x^2 + 1000x$. Since $a < 0$, the vertex is a maximum point on the graph of A. The maximum value occurs at

$$x = -\frac{b}{2a} = -\frac{1000}{2(-1)} = 500$$

The maximum value of A is

$$A\left(-\frac{b}{2a}\right) = A(500) = -500^2 + 1000(500) = -250{,}000 + 500{,}000 = 250{,}000$$

The largest rectangle that can be enclosed by 2000 yards of fence has an area of 250,000 square yards. Its dimensions are 500 yards by 500 yards.

▬▬➤ **Now Work** PROBLEM 7

| EXAMPLE 3 | Analyzing the Motion of a Projectile |

A projectile is fired from a cliff 500 feet above the water at an inclination of 45° to the horizontal, with a muzzle velocity of 400 feet per second. In physics, it is established that the height h of the projectile above the water can be modeled by

$$h(x) = \frac{-32x^2}{(400)^2} + x + 500$$

where x is the horizontal distance of the projectile from the base of the cliff. See Figure 27.

Figure 27

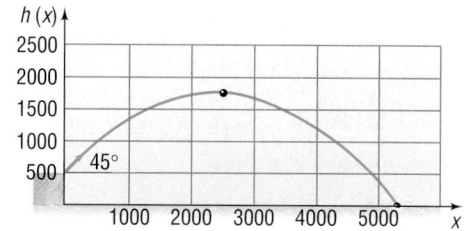

(a) Find the maximum height of the projectile.

(b) How far from the base of the cliff will the projectile strike the water?

Solution

(a) The height of the projectile is given by a quadratic function.

$$h(x) = \frac{-32x^2}{(400)^2} + x + 500 = \frac{-1}{5000}x^2 + x + 500$$

We are looking for the maximum value of h. Since $a < 0$, the maximum value is obtained at the vertex. We compute

$$x = -\frac{b}{2a} = -\frac{1}{2\left(-\frac{1}{5000}\right)} = \frac{5000}{2} = 2500$$

The maximum height of the projectile is

$$h(2500) = \frac{-1}{5000}(2500)^2 + 2500 + 500 = -1250 + 2500 + 500 = 1750 \text{ ft}$$

(b) The projectile will strike the water when the height is zero. To find the distance x traveled, we need to solve the equation

$$h(x) = \frac{-1}{5000}x^2 + x + 500 = 0$$

We find the discriminant first.

$$b^2 - 4ac = 1^2 - 4\left(\frac{-1}{5000}\right)(500) = 1.4$$

Then

$$x = \frac{-b \pm \sqrt{b^2 - 4ac}}{2a} = \frac{-1 \pm \sqrt{1.4}}{2\left(-\frac{1}{5000}\right)} \approx \begin{cases} -458 \\ 5458 \end{cases}$$

We discard the negative solution and find that the projectile will strike the water at a distance of about 5458 feet from the base of the cliff.

Seeing the Concept

Graph

$$h(x) = \frac{-1}{5000}x^2 + x + 500$$

$$0 \le x \le 5500$$

Use MAXIMUM to find the maximum height of the projectile, and use ROOT or ZERO to find the distance from the base of the cliff to where it strikes the water. Compare your results with those obtained in Example 3.

━━━━▶ **Now Work** PROBLEM 11

| EXAMPLE 4 | **The Golden Gate Bridge** |

The Golden Gate Bridge, a suspension bridge, spans the entrance to San Francisco Bay. Its 746-foot-tall towers are 4200 feet apart. The bridge is suspended from two huge cables more than 3 feet in diameter; the 90-foot-wide roadway is 220 feet above the water. The cables are parabolic in shape* and touch the road surface at the center of the bridge. Find the height of the cable above the road at a distance of 1000 feet from the center.

Solution

See Figure 28. We begin by choosing the placement of the coordinate axes so that the x-axis coincides with the road surface and the origin coincides with the center of the bridge. As a result, the twin towers will be vertical (height $746 - 220 = 526$ feet above the road) and located 2100 feet from the center. Also, the cable, which has the shape of a parabola, will extend from the towers, open up, and have its vertex at $(0, 0)$. The choice of placement of the axes enables us to identify the equation of the parabola as $y = ax^2, a > 0$. We can also see that the points $(-2100, 526)$ and $(2100, 526)$ are on the graph.

Figure 28

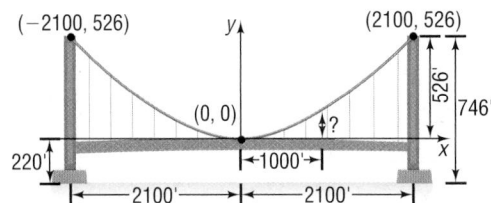

Based on these facts, we can find the value of a in $y = ax^2$.

$$y = ax^2$$
$$526 = a(2100)^2 \qquad \text{x = 2100, y = 526}$$
$$a = \frac{526}{(2100)^2}$$

The equation of the parabola is therefore

$$y = \frac{526}{(2100)^2}x^2$$

The height of the cable when $x = 1000$ is

$$y = \frac{526}{(2100)^2}(1000)^2 \approx 119.3 \text{ feet}$$

The cable is 119.3 feet above the road at a distance of 1000 feet from the center of the bridge.

 Now Work PROBLEM 13

2 Build Quadratic Models from Data

In Section 3.2, we found the line of best fit for data that appeared to be linearly related. It was noted that data may also follow a nonlinear relation. Figures 29(a) and (b) show scatter diagrams of data that follow a quadratic relation.

*A cable suspended from two towers is in the shape of a **catenary,** but when a horizontal roadway is suspended from the cable, the cable takes the shape of a parabola.

Figure 29

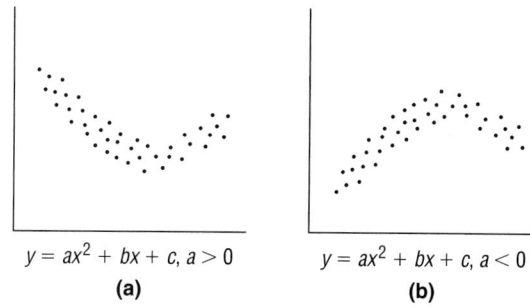

$y = ax^2 + bx + c, a > 0$

(a)

$y = ax^2 + bx + c, a < 0$

(b)

EXAMPLE 5 | Fitting a Quadratic Function to Data

A farmer collected the data given in Table 9, which shows crop yields Y for various amounts x of fertilizer used.

(a) Use a graphing utility to draw a scatter diagram of the data. Comment on the type of relation that may exist between the two variables.

(b) Use a graphing utility to find the quadratic function of best fit that models the relation between amount of fertilizer and crop yield.

(c) Use the function found in part (b) to determine the optimal amount of fertilizer to apply.

(d) Use the function found in part (b) to predict crop yield when the optimal amount of fertilizer is applied.

(e) Draw the quadratic function of best fit on the scatter diagram.

Solution

(a) Figure 30 shows the scatter diagram, from which it appears that the data follow a quadratic relation, with $a < 0$.

(b) Upon executing the QUADratic REGression program, we obtain the results shown in Figure 31. The output that the utility provides shows us the equation $y = ax^2 + bx + c$. The quadratic function of best fit is

$$Y(x) = -0.0171x^2 + 1.0765x + 3.8939 \quad \text{The Model}$$

where x represents the amount of fertilizer used and Y represents crop yield.

Table 9

Plot	Fertilizer, x (Pounds/100 ft²)	Yield, Y (Bushels)
1	0	4
2	0	6
3	5	10
4	5	7
5	10	12
6	10	10
7	15	15
8	15	17
9	20	18
10	20	21
11	25	20
12	25	21
13	30	21
14	30	22
15	35	21
16	35	20
17	40	19
18	40	19

Figure 30

Figure 31

```
QuadReg
y=ax²+bx+c
a=-.0171212121
b=1.076515152
c=3.893939394
```

(c) Based on the quadratic function of best fit, the optimal amount of fertilizer to apply is

$$x = -\frac{b}{2a} = -\frac{1.0765}{2(-0.0171)} \approx 31.5 \text{ pounds of fertilizer per 100 square feet}$$

(d) We evaluate the function $Y(x)$ for $x = 31.5$.

$$Y(31.5) = -0.0171(31.5)^2 + 1.0765(31.5) + 3.8939 \approx 20.8 \text{ bushels}$$

If we apply 31.5 pounds of fertilizer per 100 square feet, the crop yield will be 20.8 bushels according to the quadratic function of best fit.

(e) Figure 32 shows the graph of the quadratic function found in part (b) drawn on the scatter diagram.

Figure 32

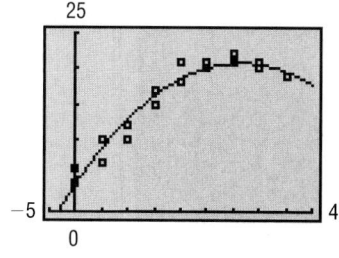

Look again at Figure 31. Notice that the output given by the graphing calculator does not include r, the correlation coefficient. Recall that the correlation coefficient is a measure of the strength of a linear relation that exists between two variables. The graphing calculator does not provide an indication of how well the function fits the data in terms of r since a quadratic function cannot be expressed as a linear function.

Now Work PROBLEM 27

3.4 Assess Your Understanding

'Are You Prepared?' *Answers are given at the end of these exercises. If you get a wrong answer, read the pages listed in* red.

1. Translate the following sentence to a mathematical equation: The total revenue R from selling x hot dogs is $3 times the number of hot dogs sold. (p. A69)

2. Translate the following sentence to a mathematical equation: The perimeter P of a rectangle is the sum of twice the length l and twice the width w. (p. A69)

Applications and Extensions

3. **Maximizing Revenue** The price p (in dollars) and the quantity x sold of a certain product obey the demand equation

$$p = -\frac{1}{6}x + 100$$

(a) Find a model that expresses the revenue R as a function of x. (Remember, $R = xp$.)
(b) What is the domain of R?
(c) What is the revenue if 200 units are sold?
(d) What quantity x maximizes revenue? What is the maximum revenue?
(e) What price should the company charge to maximize revenue?

4. **Maximizing Revenue** The price p (in dollars) and the quantity x sold of a certain product obey the demand equation

$$p = -\frac{1}{3}x + 100$$

(a) Find a model that expresses the revenue R as a function of x.
(b) What is the domain of R?
(c) What is the revenue if 100 units are sold?
(d) What quantity x maximizes revenue? What is the maximum revenue?
(e) What price should the company charge to maximize revenue?

5. **Maximizing Revenue** The price p (in dollars) and the quantity x sold of a certain product obey the demand equation

$$x = -5p + 100 \qquad 0 < p \le 20$$

(a) Express the revenue R as a function of x.
(b) What is the revenue if 15 units are sold?
(c) What quantity x maximizes revenue? What is the maximum revenue?
(d) What price should the company charge to maximize revenue?

6. **Maximizing Revenue** The price p (in dollars) and the quantity x sold of a certain product obey the demand equation

$$x = -20p + 500 \qquad 0 < p \le 25$$

(a) Express the revenue R as a function of x.
(b) What is the revenue if 20 units are sold?
(c) What quantity x maximizes revenue? What is the maximum revenue?
(d) What price should the company charge to maximize revenue?

7. **Enclosing a Rectangular Field** David has 400 yards of fencing and wishes to enclose a rectangular area.
(a) Express the area A of the rectangle as a function of the width w of the rectangle.
(b) For what value of w is the area largest?
(c) What is the maximum area?

8. **Enclosing a Rectangular Field** Beth has 3000 feet of fencing available to enclose a rectangular field.
(a) Express the area A of the rectangle as a function of x, where x is the length of the rectangle.
(b) For what value of x is the area largest?
(c) What is the maximum area?

9. **Enclosing the Most Area with a Fence** A farmer with 4000 meters of fencing wants to enclose a rectangular plot that borders on a river. If the farmer does not fence the side along the river, what is the largest area that can be enclosed? (See the figure.)

$4000 - 2x$

10. **Enclosing the Most Area with a Fence**   A farmer with 2000 meters of fencing wants to enclose a rectangular plot that borders on a straight highway. If the farmer does not fence the side along the highway, what is the largest area that can be enclosed?

11. **Analyzing the Motion of a Projectile**   A projectile is fired from a cliff 200 feet above the water at an inclination of 45° to the horizontal, with a muzzle velocity of 50 feet per second. The height h of the projectile above the water is modeled by

$$h(x) = \frac{-32x^2}{(50)^2} + x + 200$$

where x is the horizontal distance of the projectile from the face of the cliff.

(a) At what horizontal distance from the face of the cliff is the height of the projectile a maximum?

(b) Find the maximum height of the projectile.

(c) At what horizontal distance from the face of the cliff will the projectile strike the water?

(d) Using a graphing utility, graph the function h, $0 \le x \le 200$.

(e) Use a graphing utility to verify the solutions found in parts (b) and (c).

(f) When the height of the projectile is 100 feet above the water, how far is it from the cliff?

12. **Analyzing the Motion of a Projectile**   A projectile is fired at an inclination of 45° to the horizontal, with a muzzle velocity of 100 feet per second. The height h of the projectile is modeled by

$$h(x) = \frac{-32x^2}{(100)^2} + x$$

where x is the horizontal distance of the projectile from the firing point.

(a) At what horizontal distance from the firing point is the height of the projectile a maximum?

(b) Find the maximum height of the projectile.

(c) At what horizontal distance from the firing point will the projectile strike the ground?

(d) Using a graphing utility, graph the function h, $0 \le x \le 350$.

(e) Use a graphing utility to verify the results obtained in parts (b) and (c).

(f) When the height of the projectile is 50 feet above the ground, how far has it traveled horizontally?

13. **Suspension Bridge**   A suspension bridge with weight uniformly distributed along its length has twin towers that extend 75 meters above the road surface and are 400 meters apart. The cables are parabolic in shape and are suspended from the tops of the towers. The cables touch the road surface at the center of the bridge. Find the height of the cables at a point 100 meters from the center. (Assume that the road is level.)

14. **Architecture**   A parabolic arch has a span of 120 feet and a maximum height of 25 feet. Choose suitable rectangular coordinate axes and find the equation of the parabola. Then calculate the height of the arch at points 10 feet, 20 feet, and 40 feet from the center.

15. **Constructing Rain Gutters**   A rain gutter is to be made of aluminum sheets that are 12 inches wide by turning up the edges 90°. See the illustration. What depth will provide maximum cross-sectional area and hence allow the most water to flow?

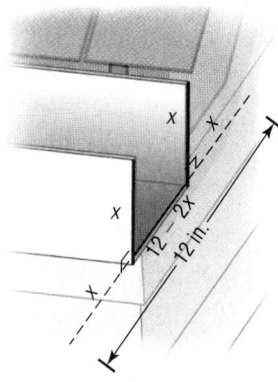

16. **Norman Windows**   **A Norman window** has the shape of a rectangle surmounted by a semicircle of diameter equal to the width of the rectangle. See the figure. If the perimeter of the window is 20 feet, what dimensions will admit the most light (maximize the area)?

[**Hint:** Circumference of a circle $= 2\pi r$; area of a circle $= \pi r^2$, where r is the radius of the circle.]

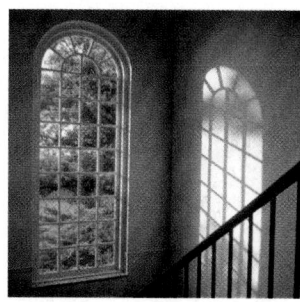

17. **Constructing a Stadium**   A track and field playing area is in the shape of a rectangle with semicircles at each end. See the figure. The inside perimeter of the track is to be 1500 meters. What should the dimensions of the rectangle be so that the area of the rectangle is a maximum?

18. **Architecture**   A special window has the shape of a rectangle surmounted by an equilateral triangle. See the figure. If the perimeter of the window is 16 feet, what dimensions will admit the most light?

[**Hint:** Area of an equilateral triangle $= \left(\frac{\sqrt{3}}{4}\right)x^2$, where x is the length of a side of the triangle.]

19. Stopping Distance An accepted relationship between stopping distance, d (in feet), and the speed of a car, v (in mph), is $d = 1.1v + 0.06v^2$ on dry, level concrete.
(a) How many feet will it take a car traveling 45 mph to stop on dry, level concrete?
(b) If an accident occurs 200 feet ahead of you, what is the maximum speed you can be traveling to avoid being involved?
(c) What might the term $1.1v$ represent?

Source: www2.nsta.org/Energy/fn_braking.html

20. Insurance Claims The years 1999 to 2005 were particularly costly for insurance companies, with 7 of the 10 most costly catastrophes in U.S. history (as of 2005). For the United States Automobile Association (USAA) and its affiliates, the total cost of claims for catastrophic losses, in millions, can be modeled by $C(x) = 34.87x^2 - 98.1x + 258.3$, where $x = 0$ for 1999, $x = 1$ for 2000, $x = 2$ for 2001, and so on.
(a) Estimate the total cost of claims for the year 2003.
(b) According to the model, during which year were catastrophic loss claims at a minimum?
(c) Would $C(x)$ be useful for predicting total catastrophic loss claims for the year 2015? Why or why not?

Source: USAA Report to Members 2005

21. Chemical Reactions A self-catalytic chemical reaction results in the formation of a compound that causes the formation ratio to increase. If the reaction rate V is modeled by

$$V(x) = kx(a - x), \qquad 0 \le x \le a$$

where k is a positive constant, a is the initial amount of the compound, and x is the variable amount of the compound, for what value of x is the reaction rate a maximum?

22. Calculus: Simpson's Rule The figure shows the graph of $y = ax^2 + bx + c$. Suppose that the points $(-h, y_0)$, $(0, y_1)$, and (h, y_2) are on the graph. It can be shown that the area enclosed by the parabola, the x-axis, and the lines $x = -h$ and $x = h$ is

$$\text{Area} = \frac{h}{3}(2ah^2 + 6c)$$

Show that this area may also be given by

$$\text{Area} = \frac{h}{3}(y_0 + 4y_1 + y_2)$$

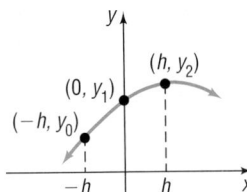

23. Use the result obtained in Problem 22 to find the area enclosed by $f(x) = -5x^2 + 8$, the x-axis, and the lines $x = -1$ and $x = 1$.

24. Use the result obtained in Problem 22 to find the area enclosed by $f(x) = 2x^2 + 8$, the x-axis, and the lines $x = -2$ and $x = 2$.

25. Use the result obtained in Problem 22 to find the area enclosed by $f(x) = x^2 + 3x + 5$, the x-axis, and the lines $x = -4$ and $x = 4$.

26. Use the result obtained in Problem 22 to find the area enclosed by $f(x) = -x^2 + x + 4$, the x-axis, and the lines $x = -1$ and $x = 1$.

27. Life Cycle Hypothesis An individual's income varies with his or her age. The following table shows the median income I of individuals of different age groups within the United States for 2003. For each age group, let the class midpoint represent the independent variable, x. For the class "65 years and older," we will assume that the class midpoint is 69.5.

Age	Class Midpoint, x	Median Income, I
15–24 years	19.5	$9,961
25–34 years	29.5	$30,562
35–44 years	39.5	$39,195
45–54 years	49.5	$42,079
55–64 years	59.5	$38,915
65 years and older	69.5	$20,363

Source: U.S. Census Bureau

(a) Use a graphing utility to draw a scatter diagram of the data. Comment on the type of relation that may exist between the two variables.
(b) Use a graphing utility to find the quadratic function of best fit that models the relation between age and median income.
(c) Use the function found in part (b) to determine the age at which an individual can expect to earn the most income.
(d) Use the function found in part (b) to predict the peak income earned.
(e) With a graphing utility, graph the quadratic function of best fit on the scatter diagram.

28. Height of a Ball A shot-putter throws a ball at an inclination of 45° to the horizontal. The following data represent the height of the ball h at the instant that it has traveled x feet horizontally.

Distance, x	Height, h
20	25
40	40
60	55
80	65
100	71
120	77
140	77
160	75
180	71
200	64

(a) Use a graphing utility to draw a scatter diagram of the data. Comment on the type of relation that may exist between the two variables.
(b) Use a graphing utility to find the quadratic function of best fit that models the relation between distance and height.
(c) Use the function found in part (b) to determine how far the ball will travel before it reaches its maximum height.
(d) Use the function found in part (b) to find the maximum height of the ball.
(e) With a graphing utility, graph the quadratic function of best fit on the scatter diagram.

Mixed Practice

29. Which Model? The following data represent the square footage and rents (dollars per month) for apartments in the Del Mar area of San Diego, California.

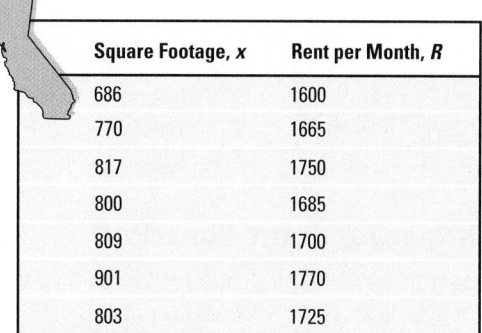

Square Footage, x	Rent per Month, R
686	1600
770	1665
817	1750
800	1685
809	1700
901	1770
803	1725

Source: apartments.com

(a) Using a graphing utility, draw a scatter diagram of the data treating square footage as the independent variable. What type of relation appears to exist between square footage and rent?
(b) Based on your response to part (a), find either a linear or quadratic model that describes the relation between square footage and rent.
(c) Use your model to predict the rent of an apartment in San Diego that is 850 square feet.

30. Which Model? An engineer collects the following data showing the speed s of a Toyota Camry and its average miles per gallon, M.

Speed, s	Miles per Gallon, M
30	18
35	20
40	23
40	25
45	25
50	28
55	30
60	29
65	26
65	25
70	25

(a) Using a graphing utility, draw a scatter diagram of the data treating speed as the independent variable. What type of relation appears to exist between speed and miles per gallon?
(b) Based on your response to part (a), find either a linear or quadratic model that describes the relation between speed and miles per gallon.
(c) Use your model to predict the miles per gallon for a Camry that is traveling 63 miles per hour.

31. Which Model? The following data represent the percentage of the U.S. population aged 25 years or older whose age is x who do not have a high school diploma as of March 2005.

Age, a	Percentage without a High School Diploma, P
30	13.3
40	11.6
50	10.9
60	13.7
70	22.3
80	30.2

Source: U.S. Census Bureau

(a) Using a graphing utility, draw a scatter diagram of the data treating age as the independent variable. What type of relation appears to exist between age and percentage of the population without a high school diploma?
(b) Based on your response to part (a), find either a linear or quadratic model that describes the relation between age and percentage of the population that do not have a high school diploma.
(c) Use your model to predict the percentage of 35-year-olds that do not have a high school diploma.

32. Which Model? Crickets make a chirping noise by sliding their wings rapidly over each other. Perhaps you have noticed that the number of chirps seems to increase with the temperature. The following data list the temperature (in degrees Fahrenheit) and the number of chirps per second for the striped ground cricket.

Temperature, x	Chirps per Second, C
88.6	20.0
93.3	19.8
80.6	17.1
69.7	14.7
69.4	15.4
79.6	15.0
80.6	16.0
76.3	14.4
75.2	15.5

Source: Pierce, George W. *The Songs of Insects.* Cambridge, MA Harvard University Press, 1949, pp. 12 – 21

(a) Using a graphing utility, draw a scatter diagram of the data treating temperature as the independent variable. What type of relation appears to exist between temperature and chirps per second?
(b) Based on your response to part (a), find either a linear or quadratic model that best describes the relation between temperature and chirps per second.
(c) Use your model to predict the chirps per second if the temperature is 80°F.

'Are You Prepared?' Answers

1. $R = 3x$ **2.** $P = 2l + 2w$

3.5 Inequalities Involving Quadratic Functions

PREPARING FOR THIS SECTION *Before getting started, review the following:*

- Solve Inequalities (Appendix A, Section A.9, pp. A81–A84)
- Use Interval Notation (Appendix A, Section A.9, pp. A78–A79)

Now Work the 'Are You Prepared?' problems on page 166.

OBJECTIVE   1 Solve Inequalities Involving a Quadratic Function (p. 164)

1 Solve Inequalities Involving a Quadratic Function

In this section we solve inequalities that involve quadratic functions. We will accomplish this by using their graphs. For example, to solve the inequality

$$ax^2 + bx + c > 0 \qquad a \neq 0$$

we graph the function $f(x) = ax^2 + bx + c$ and, from the graph, determine where it is above the x-axis, that is, where $f(x) > 0$. To solve the inequality $ax^2 + bx + c < 0, a \neq 0$, we graph the function $f(x) = ax^2 + bx + c$ and determine where the graph is below the x-axis. If the inequality is not strict, we include the x-intercepts in the solution.

Let's look at an example.

| EXAMPLE 1 | **Solving an Inequality** |

Solve the inequality $x^2 - 4x - 12 \leq 0$ and graph the solution set.

By Hand Solution

We graph the function $f(x) = x^2 - 4x - 12$. The intercepts are

y-intercept: $\qquad\qquad f(0) = -12$ Evaluate f at 0.

x-intercepts (if any): $\quad x^2 - 4x - 12 = 0$ Solve f(x) = 0.

$\qquad\qquad (x - 6)(x + 2) = 0$ Factor.

$\qquad\quad x - 6 = 0 \quad \text{or} \quad x + 2 = 0$ Apply the Zero-Product Property.

$\qquad\qquad x = 6 \quad \text{or} \qquad x = -2$

The y-intercept is -12; the x-intercepts are -2 and 6.

The vertex is at $x = -\dfrac{b}{2a} = -\dfrac{-4}{2(1)} = 2$. Since $f(2) = -16$, the vertex is $(2, -16)$. See Figure 33 for the graph.

Figure 33

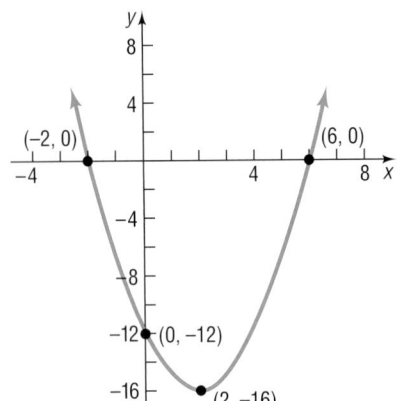

Graphing Utility Solution

We graph $Y_1 = x^2 - 4x - 12$. See Figure 34. Using the ZERO command, we find that the x-intercepts of Y_1 are -2 and 6. Since the inequality is not strict, the solution set is $\{x \mid -2 \leq x \leq 6\}$ or, using interval notation, $[-2, 6]$.

Figure 34

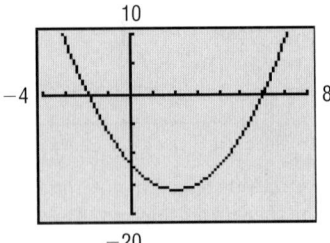

The graph is below the x-axis for $-2 < x < 6$. Since the original inequality is not strict, we include the x-intercepts. The solution set is $\{x \mid -2 \leq x \leq 6\}$ or, using interval notation, $[-2, 6]$.

Figure 35

See Figure 35 for the graph of the solution set.

Now Work PROBLEM 9

| EXAMPLE 2 | **Solving an Inequality** |

Solve the inequality $2x^2 < x + 10$ and graph the solution set.

Solution **Option 1** We rearrange the inequality so that 0 is on the right side.

$$2x^2 < x + 10$$

$$2x^2 - x - 10 < 0 \qquad \text{Subtract } x + 10 \text{ from both sides.}$$

This inequality is equivalent to the one that we wish to solve.

Next we graph the function $f(x) = 2x^2 - x - 10$. We want to determine where the graph is below the x-axis. The intercepts are

y-intercept: $\qquad\qquad\qquad f(0) = -10 \qquad\qquad$ Evaluate f at 0.

x-intercepts (if any): $\qquad 2x^2 - x - 10 = 0 \qquad\qquad$ Solve $f(x) = 0$.

$$(2x - 5)(x + 2) = 0 \qquad\qquad \text{Factor.}$$

$$2x - 5 = 0 \quad \text{or} \quad x + 2 = 0 \quad \text{Apply the Zero-Product Property.}$$

$$x = \frac{5}{2} \quad \text{or} \qquad x = -2$$

Figure 36

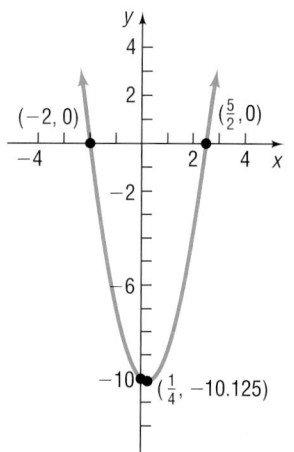

The y-intercept is -10; the x-intercepts are -2 and $\frac{5}{2}$.

The vertex is at $x = -\dfrac{b}{2a} = -\dfrac{-1}{2(2)} = \dfrac{1}{4}$. Since $f\left(\dfrac{1}{4}\right) = -10.125$, the vertex is $\left(\dfrac{1}{4}, -10.125\right)$. See Figure 36 for the graph.

The graph is below the x-axis between $x = -2$ and $x = \dfrac{5}{2}$. Since the inequality is strict, the solution set is $\left\{ x \mid -2 < x < \dfrac{5}{2} \right\}$ or, using interval notation, $\left(-2, \dfrac{5}{2}\right)$.

✓ **Check:** Verify the result of Method 1 by graphing $Y_1 = 2x^2 - x - 10$ and using the ZERO feature.

Option 2 If $f(x) = 2x^2$ and $g(x) = x + 10$, the inequality that we wish to solve is $f(x) < g(x)$. We graph the functions $f(x) = 2x^2$ and $g(x) = x + 10$. See Figure 37. The graphs intersect where $f(x) = g(x)$. Then

Figure 37

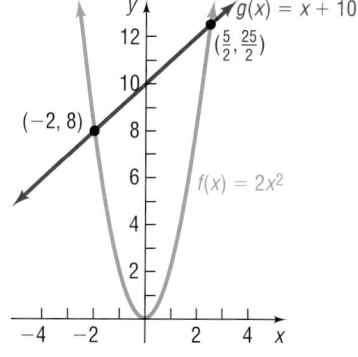

$$2x^2 = x + 10 \qquad\qquad f(x) = g(x)$$

$$2x^2 - x - 10 = 0$$

$$(2x - 5)(x + 2) = 0 \qquad\qquad \text{Factor.}$$

$$2x - 5 = 0 \quad \text{or} \quad x + 2 = 0 \quad \text{Apply the Zero-Product Property.}$$

$$x = \frac{5}{2} \quad \text{or} \qquad x = -2$$

The graphs intersect at the points $(-2, 8)$ and $\left(\dfrac{5}{2}, \dfrac{25}{2}\right)$. The inequality that we wish to solve is $f(x) < g(x)$, so we seek where the graph of f is below that of g.

Figure 38

$$\begin{array}{ccccc} & & & & \\ \hline -4 & -2 & 0 & 2 & 4 \end{array}$$

This happens between the points of intersection. Since the inequality is strict, the solution set is $\left\{x \mid -2 < x < \dfrac{5}{2}\right\}$ or, using interval notation, $\left(-2, \dfrac{5}{2}\right)$.

See Figure 38 for the graph of the solution set.

✓ Check: Verify the result of Option 2 by graphing $Y_1 = 2x^2$ and $Y_2 = x + 10$ on the same screen. Use INTERSECT to find the x-coordinates of the points of intersection. Determine where Y_1 is below Y_2 to solve $Y_1 < Y_2$.

━━━━━ **Now Work** PROBLEMS 5 AND 13

3.5 Assess Your Understanding

'Are You Prepared?' *Answers are given at the end of these exercises. If you get a wrong answer, read the pages listed in red.*

1. Solve the inequality $-3x - 2 < 7$. (pp. A81–A82)

2. Write $(-2, 7]$ using inequality notation and graph the inequality. (pp. A78–A79)

Skill Building

In Problems 3–6, use the figure to solve each inequality.

3.
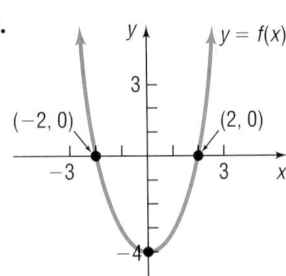

(a) $f(x) > 0$
(b) $f(x) \le 0$

4.
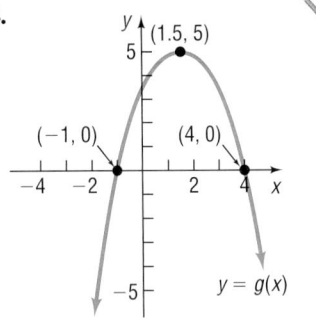

(a) $g(x) < 0$
(b) $g(x) \ge 0$

5.
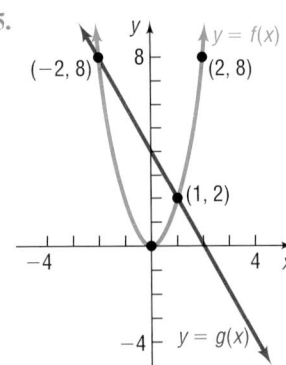

(a) $g(x) \ge f(x)$
(b) $f(x) > g(x)$

6.
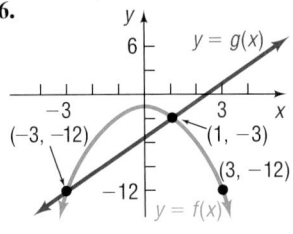

(a) $f(x) < g(x)$
(b) $f(x) \ge g(x)$

In Problems 7–22, solve each inequality. Verify your results using a graphing utility.

7. $x^2 - 3x - 10 \le 0$

8. $x^2 + 3x - 10 > 0$

9. $x^2 - 4x > 0$

10. $x^2 + 8x \le 0$

11. $x^2 - 9 < 0$

12. $x^2 - 1 < 0$

13. $x^2 + x > 12$

14. $x^2 + 7x < -12$

15. $2x^2 \le 5x + 3$

16. $6x^2 \le 6 + 5x$

17. $x(x - 7) > 8$

18. $x(x + 1) > 20$

19. $4x^2 + 9 < 6x$

20. $25x^2 + 16 < 40x$

21. $6(x^2 + 1) \ge 5x$

22. $2(2x^2 - 3x) \ge -9$

Mixed Practice

23. What is the domain of the function $f(x) = \sqrt{x^2 - 16}$?

24. What is the domain of the function $f(x) = \sqrt{x - 3x^2}$?

In Problems 25–32, use the given functions f and g.

    (a) *Solve* $f(x) = 0$.
    (b) *Solve* $g(x) = 0$.
    (c) *Solve* $f(x) = g(x)$.
    (d) *Solve* $f(x) > 0$.
    (e) *Solve* $g(x) \le 0$.
    (f) *Solve* $f(x) > g(x)$.
    (g) *Solve* $f(x) \ge 1$.

25. $f(x) = x^2 - 1$
$g(x) = 3x + 3$

26. $f(x) = -x^2 + 3$
$g(x) = -3x + 3$

27. $f(x) = -x^2 + 1$
$g(x) = 4x + 1$

28. $f(x) = -x^2 + 4$
$g(x) = -x - 2$

29. $f(x) = x^2 - 4$
$g(x) = -x^2 + 4$

30. $f(x) = x^2 - 2x + 1$
$g(x) = -x^2 + 1$

31. $f(x) = x^2 - x - 2$
$g(x) = x^2 + x - 2$

32. $f(x) = -x^2 - x + 1$
$g(x) = -x^2 + x + 6$

Applications and Extensions

33. Physics A ball is thrown vertically upward with an initial velocity of 80 feet per second. The distance s (in feet) of the ball from the ground after t seconds is $s(t) = 80t - 16t^2$.

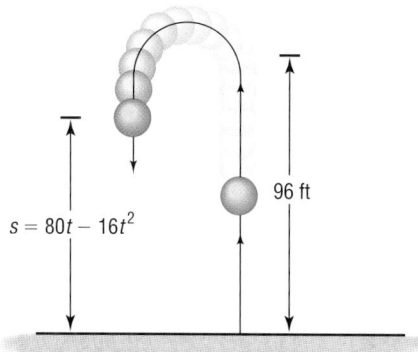

$s = 80t - 16t^2$ 96 ft

(a) At what time t will the ball strike the ground?
(b) For what time t is the ball more than 96 feet above the ground?

34. Physics A ball is thrown vertically upward with an initial velocity of 96 feet per second. The distance s (in feet) of the ball from the ground after t seconds is $s(t) = 96t - 16t^2$.
(a) At what time t will the ball strike the ground?
(b) For what time t is the ball more than 128 feet above the ground?

35. Revenue Suppose that the manufacturer of a gas clothes dryer has found that, when the unit price is p dollars, the revenue R (in dollars) is

$$R(p) = -4p^2 + 4000p$$

(a) At what prices p is revenue zero?
(b) For what range of prices will revenue exceed $800,000?

36. Revenue The John Deere company has found that the revenue from sales of heavy-duty tractors is a function of the unit price p, in dollars, that it charges. The revenue R, in dollars, is

$$R(p) = -\frac{1}{2}p^2 + 1900p$$

(a) At what prices p is revenue zero?
(b) For what range of prices will revenue exceed $1,200,000?

37. Artillery A projectile fired from the point $(0, 0)$ at an angle to the positive x-axis has a trajectory given by

$$y = cx - (1 + c^2)\left(\frac{g}{2}\right)\left(\frac{x}{v}\right)^2$$

where

x = horizontal distance in meters
y = height in meters
v = initial muzzle velocity in meters per second (m/sec)
g = acceleration due to gravity = 9.81 meters per second squared (m/sec^2)
$c > 0$ is a constant determined by the angle of elevation.

A howitzer fires an artillery round with a muzzle velocity of 897 m/sec.
(a) If the round must clear a hill 200 meters high at a distance of 2000 meters in front of the howitzer, what values of c are permitted in the trajectory equation?
(b) If the goal in part (a) is to hit a target on the ground 75 kilometers away, is it possible to do so? If so, for what values of c? If not, what is the maximum distance the round will travel?

Source: www.answers.com

38. Runaway Car Using Hooke's Law, we can show that the *work* done in compressing a spring a distance of x feet from its at-rest position is $W = \frac{1}{2}kx^2$, where k is a stiffness constant depending on the spring. It can also be shown that the work done by a body in motion before it comes to rest is given by $\widetilde{W} = \frac{w}{2g}v^2$, where w = weight of the object (lb), g = acceleration due to gravity (32.2 ft/sec^2), and v = object's velocity (in ft/sec). A parking garage has a spring shock absorber at the end of a ramp to stop runaway cars. The spring has a stiffness constant $k = 9450$ lb/ft and must be able to stop a 4000-lb car traveling at 25 mph. What is the least compression required of the spring? Express your answer using feet to the nearest tenth. [**Hint:** Solve $W > \widetilde{W}, x \geq 0$].

Source: www.sciforums.com

Discussion and Writing

39. Show that the inequality $(x - 4)^2 \leq 0$ has exactly one solution.

40. Show that the inequality $(x - 2)^2 > 0$ has one real number that is not a solution.

41. Explain why the inequality $x^2 + x + 1 > 0$ has all real numbers as the solution set.

42. Explain why the inequality $x^2 - x + 1 < 0$ has the empty set as solution set.

'Are You Prepared?' Answers

1. $\{x | x > -3\}$ or $(-3, \infty)$ **2.** $-2 < x \leq 7$

CHAPTER REVIEW

Things to Know

Linear function (p. 126)

$$f(x) = mx + b$$

Average rate of change $= m$
The graph is a line with slope m and y-intercept b.

Quadratic function (pp. 143–146)

$$f(x) = ax^2 + bx + c, a \neq 0$$

The graph is a parabola that opens up if $a > 0$ and opens down if $a < 0$.

Vertex: $\left(-\dfrac{b}{2a}, f\left(-\dfrac{b}{2a} \right) \right)$

Axis of symmetry: $x = -\dfrac{b}{2a}$

y-intercept: $f(0) = c$

x-intercept(s): If any, found by finding the real solutions of the equation
$$ax^2 + bx + c = 0$$

Objectives

Section		You should be able to . . .	Example(s)	Review Exercises
3.1	1	Graph linear functions (p. 126)	1	1(a)–6(a), 1(b)–6(b)
	2	Use average rate of change to identify linear functions (p. 126)	2	7, 8
	3	Determine whether a linear function is increasing, decreasing, or constant (p. 129)	3	1(e)–6(e)
	4	Build linear models from verbal descriptions (p. 130)	4, 5	35, 36
3.2	1	Draw and interpret scatter diagrams (p. 136)	1	45(a), 46(a)
	2	Distinguish between linear and nonlinear relations (p. 137)	2	45(b), 46(a)
	3	Use a graphing utility to find the line of best fit (p. 138)	4	45(c)
3.3	1	Graph a quadratic function using transformations (p. 144)	1	9–14
	2	Identify the vertex and axis of symmetry of a quadratic function (p. 146)	2	15–24
	3	Graph a quadratic function using its vertex, axis, and intercepts (p. 146)	3–5	15–24
	4	Find the maximum or minimum value of a quadratic function (p. 150)	7	25–30, 37–42
3.4	1	Build quadratic models from verbal descriptions (p. 155)	1–4	37–44
	2	Build quadratic models from data (p. 158)	5	46
3.5	1	Solve inequalities involving a quadratic function (p. 164)	1, 2	31–34

Review Exercises

In Problems 1–6:

    (a) Determine the slope and y-intercept of each linear function.
    (b) Graph each function. Label the intercepts.
    (c) Determine the domain and the range of each function.
    (d) Determine the average rate of change of each function.
    (e) Determine whether the function is increasing, decreasing, or constant.

1. $f(x) = 2x - 5$

2. $g(x) = -4x + 7$

3. $h(x) = \dfrac{4}{5}x - 6$

4. $F(x) = -\dfrac{1}{3}x + 1$

5. $G(x) = 4$

6. $H(x) = -3$

In Problems 7 and 8, determine whether the function is linear or nonlinear. If the function is linear, determine the equation of the line.

7.

x	y
−1	−2
0	3
1	8
2	13
3	18

8.

x	y
−1	−3
0	4
1	7
2	6
3	1

In Problems 9–14, graph each quadratic function using transformations (shifting, compressing, stretching, and/or reflecting). Verify your results using a graphing utility.

9. $f(x) = (x - 2)^2 + 2$

10. $f(x) = (x + 1)^2 - 4$

11. $f(x) = -(x - 4)^2$

12. $f(x) = (x - 1)^2 - 3$

13. $f(x) = 2(x + 1)^2 + 4$

14. $f(x) = -3(x + 2)^2 + 1$

In Problems 15–24, (a) graph each quadratic function by determining whether its graph opens up or down and by finding its vertex, axis of symmetry, y-intercept, and x-intercepts, if any. (b) Determine the domain and the range of the function. (c) Determine where the function is increasing and where it is decreasing. Verify your results using a graphing utility.

15. $f(x) = (x - 2)^2 + 2$

16. $f(x) = (x + 1)^2 - 4$

17. $f(x) = \frac{1}{4}x^2 - 16$

18. $f(x) = -\frac{1}{2}x^2 + 2$

19. $f(x) = -4x^2 + 4x$

20. $f(x) = 9x^2 - 6x + 3$

21. $f(x) = \frac{9}{2}x^2 + 3x + 1$

22. $f(x) = -x^2 + x + \frac{1}{2}$

23. $f(x) = 3x^2 + 4x - 1$

24. $f(x) = -2x^2 - x + 4$

In Problems 25–30, determine whether the given quadratic function has a maximum value or a minimum value, and then find the value. Verify your results using a graphing utility.

25. $f(x) = 3x^2 - 6x + 4$

26. $f(x) = 2x^2 + 8x + 5$

27. $f(x) = -x^2 + 8x - 4$

28. $f(x) = -x^2 - 10x - 3$

29. $f(x) = -3x^2 + 12x + 4$

30. $f(x) = -2x^2 + 4$

In Problems 31–34, solve each quadratic inequality. Verify your results using a graphing utility.

31. $x^2 + 6x - 16 < 0$

32. $3x^2 - 2x - 1 \geq 0$

33. $3x^2 \geq 14x + 5$

34. $4x^2 < 13x - 3$

---

35. Comparing Phone Companies   Marissa must decide between one of two companies as her long-distance phone provider. Company A charges a monthly fee of $7.00 plus $0.06 per minute, while Company B does not have a monthly fee, but charges $0.08 per minute.

(a) Find a linear function that relates cost, C, to total minutes on the phone, x, for each company.

(b) Determine the number of minutes for which the bill from Company A will equal the bill from Company B.

(c) Over what interval of minutes will the bill from Company B be less than the bill from Company A?

36. Sales Commissions   Bill was just offered a sales position for a computer company. His salary would be $15,000 per year plus 1% of his total annual sales.

(a) Find a linear function that relates Bill's annual salary, S, to his total annual sales, x.

(b) In 2005, Bill had total annual sales of $1,000,000. What was Bill's salary?

(c) What would Bill have to sell to earn $100,000?

(d) Determine the sales required of Bill for his salary to exceed $150,000.

37. Demand Equation   The price p (in dollars) and the quantity x sold of a certain product obey the demand equation

$$p = -\frac{1}{10}x + 150 \qquad 0 \leq x \leq 1500$$

(a) Express the revenue R as a function of x.

(b) What is the revenue if 100 units are sold?

(c) What quantity x maximizes revenue? What is the maximum revenue?

(d) What price should the company charge to maximize revenue?

38. Landscaping   A landscape engineer has 200 feet of border to enclose a rectangular pond. What dimensions will result in the largest pond?

39. Enclosing the Most Area with a Fence   A farmer with 10,000 meters of fencing wants to enclose a rectangular field and then divide it into two plots with a fence parallel to one of the sides. See the figure. What is the largest area that can be enclosed?

40. Architecture A special window in the shape of a rectangle with semicircles at each end is to be constructed so that the outside dimensions are 100 feet in length. See the illustration. Find the dimensions of the rectangle that maximizes its area.

41. Minimizing Marginal Cost Callaway Golf Company has determined that the marginal cost C of manufacturing x Big Bertha drivers may be expressed by the quadratic function

$$C(x) = 4.9x^2 - 617.4x + 19,600$$

(a) How many drivers should be manufactured to minimize the marginal cost?
(b) At this level of production, what is the marginal cost?

42. Violent Crimes The function

$$V(t) = 5.0t^2 - 87.3t + 1761.1$$

models the number V (in thousands) of violent crimes committed in the United States t years after 1995, based on data obtained from the Federal Bureau of Investigation. So $t = 0$ represents 1995, $t = 1$ represents 1996, and so on.
(a) Determine the year in which the fewest violent crimes were committed.
(b) Approximately how many violent crimes were committed during this year?
(c) Using a graphing utility, graph $V = V(t)$. Were the number of violent crimes increasing or decreasing during the years 1995 to 2003?

43. A rectangle has one vertex on the line $y = 10 - x$, $x > 0$, another at the origin, one on the positive x-axis, and one on the positive y-axis. Express the area A of the rectangle as a function of x. Find the largest area A that can be enclosed by the rectangle.

44. Parabolic Arch Bridge A horizontal bridge is in the shape of a parabolic arch. Given the information shown in the figure, what is the height h of the arch 2 feet from shore?

45. Bone Length Research performed at NASA, led by Dr. Emily R. Morey-Holton, measured the lengths of the right humerus and right tibia in 11 rats that were sent to space on Spacelab Life Sciences 2. The following data were collected.
(a) Draw a scatter diagram of the data treating length of the right humerus as the independent variable.

Right Humerus (mm), x	Right Tibia (mm), y
24.80	36.05
24.59	35.57
24.59	35.57
24.29	34.58
23.81	34.20
24.87	34.73
25.90	37.38
26.11	37.96
26.63	37.46
26.31	37.75
26.84	38.50

Source: NASA Life Sciences Data Archive

(b) Based on the scatter diagram, do you think that there is a linear relation between the length of the right humerus and the length of the right tibia?
(c) Use a graphing utility to find the line of best fit relating length of the right humerus and length of the right tibia.
(d) Predict the length of the right tibia on a rat whose right humerus is 26.5 millimeters (mm).

46. Advertising A small manufacturing firm collected the following data on advertising expenditures A (in thousands of dollars) and total revenue R (in thousands of dollars).

Advertising	Total Revenue
20	$6101
22	$6222
25	$6350
25	$6378
27	$6453
28	$6423
29	$6360
31	$6231

(a) Draw a scatter diagram of the data. Comment on the type of relation that may exist between the two variables.
(b) Use a graphing utility to find the quadratic function of best fit that models the relation between advertising and total revenue.
(c) Use the function found in part (b) to determine the optimal level of advertising.
(d) Use the function found in part (b) to predict the total revenue when the optimal level of advertising is spent.
(e) Use a graphing utility to draw a scatter diagram of the data, and then graph the quadratic function of best fit on the scatter diagram.

CHAPTER TEST

1. For the linear function $f(x) = -4x + 3$,
   (a) Find the slope and y-intercept.
   (b) Determine whether f is increasing, decreasing, or constant.
   (c) Graph f.

2. Determine whether the given function is linear or nonlinear If it is linear, determine the equation of the line.

x	y
−2	12
−1	7
0	2
1	−3
2	−8

3. Graph $f(x) = (x - 3)^2 - 2$ using transformations.

In Problems 4 and 5,
(a) Determine whether the graph opens up or down.
(b) Determine the vertex of the graph of the quadratic function.
(c) Determine the axis of symmetry of the graph of the quadratic function.
(d) Determine the intercepts of the graph of the quadratic function.
(e) Use the information in parts (a)–(d) to graph the quadratic function.
(f) Based on the graph, determine the domain and the range of the quadratic function.
(g) Based on the graph, determine where the function is increasing and where it is decreasing.

4. $f(x) = 3x^2 - 12x + 4$

5. $g(x) = -2x^2 + 4x - 5$

6. Determine the quadratic function for the given graph.

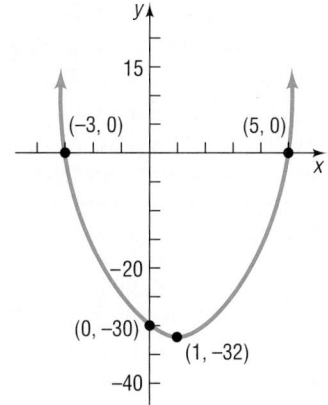

7. Determine whether $f(x) = -2x^2 + 12x + 3$ has a maximum or minimum value. Then find the maximum or minimum value.

8. Solve $x^2 - 10x + 24 \geq 0$.

9. The weekly rental cost of a 20-foot recreational vehicle is $129.50 plus $0.15 per mile.
   (a) Find a linear function that expresses the cost C as a function of miles driven m.
   (b) What is the rental cost if 860 miles are driven?
   (c) How many miles were driven if the rental cost is $213.80?

10. The price p (in dollars) and the quantity x sold of a certain product obey the demand equation $p = -\dfrac{1}{10}x + 1000$.
   (a) Find a model that expresses the revenue R as a function of x.
   (b) What is the revenue if 400 units are sold?
   (c) What quantity x maximizes revenue? What is the maximum revenue?
   (d) What price should the company charge to maximize revenue?

11. Consider these two data sets:

Set A

x	−2	−1	0	0	1	2	2
y	5	2	1	−3	−8	−12	−10

Set B

x	−2	−1	0	0	1	2	2
y	10	4	2	3	5	10	12

One data set follows a linear pattern and one data set follows a quadratic relation.
   (a) Draw a scatter diagram of each data set. Determine which is linear and which is quadratic. For the linear data, indicate whether the relation shows a positive or negative slope. For the quadratic relation, indicate whether the quadratic function of best fit will open up or down.
   (b) For the linear data set, find the line of best fit.
   (c) For the quadratic data set, find the quadratic function of best fit.

CUMULATIVE REVIEW

1. For the function f defined by $f(x) = x^2 - 4x + 1$, find:
   (a) $f(2)$ (b) $f(x) + f(2)$ (c) $f(-x)$
   (d) $-f(x)$ (e) $f(x + 2)$ (f) $\dfrac{f(x + h) - f(x)}{h}$ $h \neq 0$

2. Find the domain of $h(z) = \dfrac{3z - 1}{6z - 7}$.

3. Is the following graph the graph of a function?

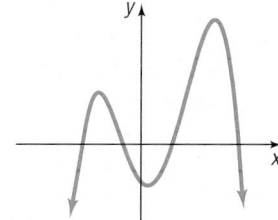

4. Consider the function $f(x) = \dfrac{x}{x + 4}$.

(a) Is the point $\left(1, \dfrac{1}{4}\right)$ on the graph of f?

(b) If $x = -2$, what is $f(x)$? What point is on the graph of f?

(c) If $f(x) = 2$, what is x? What point is on the graph of f?

5. Is the function $f(x) = \dfrac{x^2}{2x + 1}$ even, odd, or neither?

6. Approximate the local maxima and local minima of $f(x) = x^3 - 5x + 1$ on $(-4, 4)$. Determine where the function is increasing and where it is decreasing.

7. If $f(x) = 3x + 5$ and $g(x) = 2x + 1$,

(a) Solve $f(x) = g(x)$.

(b) Solve $f(x) > g(x)$.

8. Given that $f(x) = x^2 + 3x$ and $g(x) = 5x + 3$,

(a) Solve $f(x) = g(x)$.   (b) Solve $f(x) > g(x)$.

9. For the graph of the function f to the right,

(a) Find the domain and the range of f.

(b) Find the intercepts.

(c) Is the graph of f symmetric with respect to the x-axis, the y-axis, or the origin?

(d) Find $f(2)$.

(e) For what value(s) of x is $f(x) = 3$?

(f) Solve $f(x) < 0$.

(g) Graph $y = f(x) + 2$

(h) Graph $y = f(-x)$.

(i) Graph $y = 2f(x)$.

(j) Is f even, odd, or neither?

(k) Find the interval(s) on which f is increasing.

CHAPTER PROJECTS

I. **Analyzing a Stock** The beta, β, of a stock represents the relative risk of a stock compared with a market basket of stocks, such as Standard and Poor's 500 Index of stocks. Beta is computed by finding the slope of the line of best fit between the rate of return of the stock and rate of return of the S&P 500. The rates of return are computed on a weekly basis.

1. Find the weekly closing price of your favorite stock and the S&P 500 for 20 weeks. One good source is on the Internet at *finance.yahoo.com.*

2. Compute the rate of return by computing the weekly percentage change in the closing price of your stock and the weekly percentage change in the S&P 500 using the following formula:

$$\text{Weekly \% change} = \frac{P_2 - P_1}{P_1}$$

where P_1 is last week's closing price and P_2 is this week's closing price.

3. Using a graphing utility, find the line of best fit, treating the weekly rate of return of the S&P 500 as the independent variable and the weekly rate of return of your stock as the dependent variable.

4. What is the beta of your stock?

5. Compare your result with that of the Value Line Investment Survey found in your library. What might account for any differences?

The following projects are available on the Instructor's Resource Center (IRC):

II. **Cannons** A battery commander uses the weight of a missile, its initial velocity, and the position of its gun to determine where the missile will travel.

III. **First and Second Differences** Finite differences provide a numerical method that is used to estimate the graph of an unknown function.

IV. **CBL Experiment** Computer simulation is used to study the physical properties of a bouncing ball.

Polynomial and Rational Functions

4

We Don't Want to Be Number One Again—in Tree Pollen

LEXINGTON, Ky. (March 29, 2006)—Were your allergies especially bothersome last spring? It's no wonder. In the spring of 2005, Lexington, Ky., was the tree pollen capital of the U.S. No allergy sufferer is rooting for the Bluegrass to earn that title again in 2006. Either way, allergy sufferers should be prepared. The spring allergy season is here.

If you can't stop sneezing, blowing your nose, and rubbing your itchy eyes, you may have allergic rhinitis, as do 40 million other Americans. The pollens of trees such as maple, oak and walnut trigger much of the allergic rhinitis, commonly referred to as hay fever, in the early spring. Pollinating grasses and weeds are responsible for summer hay fever. Perennial allergic rhinitis can be triggered any time of year by indoor allergens, such as animal dander, mold or dust mites.

"Spring can be the start of misery for many allergy sufferers because they have multiple pollen allergies," said Dr. Beth Miller, director of the UK Asthma, Allergy and Sinus Clinics.

Source: Adapted from *Melanie Jackson, "We Don't Want to Be Number One Again—In Tree Pollen," University of Kentucky News, March 29, 2006, http://news.uky.edu.*

—See Chapter Project I—

A Look Back

In Chapter 2, we began our discussion of functions. We defined domain and range and independent and dependent variables; we found the value of a function and graphed functions. We continued our study of functions by listing the properties that a function might have, such as being even or odd, and we created a library of functions, naming key functions and listing their properties, including their graphs.

In Chapter 3, we discussed linear functions and quadratic functions, which belong to the class of *polynomial functions*.

A Look Ahead

In this chapter, we look at two general classes of functions, polynomial functions and rational functions, and examine their properties. Polynomial functions are arguably the simplest expressions in algebra. For this reason, they are often used to approximate other, more complicated functions. Rational functions are ratios of polynomial functions.

Outline

4.1 Polynomial Functions and Models
4.2 Properties of Rational Functions
4.3 The Graph of a Rational Function
4.4 Polynomial and Rational Inequalities
4.5 The Real Zeros of a Polynomial Function
4.6 Complex Zeros; Fundamental Theorem of Algebra
Chapter Review
Chapter Test
Cumulative Review
Chapter Projects

4.1 Polynomial Functions and Models

PREPARING FOR THIS SECTION *Before getting started, review the following:*

- Polynomials (Appendix A, Section A.3, pp. A23–A29)
- Using a Graphing Utility to Approximate Local Maxima and Local Minima (Section 2.3, pp. 83–84)

- Intercepts of a Function (Section 2.2, pp. 72–73)
- Graphing Techniques: Transformations (Section 2.5, pp. 100–108)
- Intercepts (Section 1.2, pp. 18–19)

Now Work the 'Are You Prepared?' problems on page 187.

OBJECTIVES 1 Identify Polynomial Functions and Their Degree (p. 174)
2 Graph Polynomial Functions Using Transformations (p. 177)
3 Identify the Real Zeros of a Polynomial Function and Their Multiplicity (p. 178)
4 Analyze the Graph of a Polynomial Function (p. 183)
5 Build Cubic Models from Data (p. 186)

1 Identify Polynomial Functions and Their Degree

In Chapter 3 we studied the linear function $f(x) = mx + b$, which we can write as

$$f(x) = a_1 x + a_0$$

and we studied the quadratic function $f(x) = ax^2 + bx + c$, $a \neq 0$, which we can write as

$$f(x) = a_2 x^2 + a_1 x + a_0, \qquad a_2 \neq 0$$

Each of these functions is an example of a *polynomial function*.

DEFINITION

A **polynomial function** is a function of the form

$$f(x) = a_n x^n + a_{n-1} x^{n-1} + \cdots + a_1 x + a_0 \qquad \textbf{(1)}$$

where $a_n, a_{n-1}, \ldots, a_1, a_0$ are real numbers and n is a nonnegative integer. The domain of a polynomial function is the set of all real numbers.

In Words
A polynomial function is the sum of monomials.

A polynomial function is a function whose rule is given by a polynomial in one variable. The **degree** of a polynomial function is the largest power of x that appears. The zero polynomial function $f(x) = 0 + 0x + 0x^2 + \cdots + 0x^n$ is not assigned a degree.

Polynomial functions are among the simplest expressions in algebra. They are easy to evaluate: only addition and repeated multiplication are required. Because of this, they are often used to approximate other, more complicated functions. In this section, we investigate properties of this important class of functions.

EXAMPLE 1 **Identifying Polynomial Functions**

Determine which of the following are polynomial functions. For those that are, state the degree; for those that are not, tell why not.

(a) $f(x) = 2 - 3x^4$ (b) $g(x) = \sqrt{x}$ (c) $h(x) = \dfrac{x^2 - 2}{x^3 - 1}$

(d) $F(x) = 0$ (e) $G(x) = 8$ (f) $H(x) = -2x^3(x - 1)^2$

Solution (a) f is a polynomial function of degree 4.

(b) g is not a polynomial function because $g(x) = \sqrt{x} = x^{\frac{1}{2}}$, so the variable x is raised to the $\dfrac{1}{2}$ power, which is not a nonnegative integer.

(c) h is not a polynomial function. It is the ratio of two polynomials, and the polynomial in the denominator is of positive degree.

(d) F is the zero polynomial function; it is not assigned a degree.

(e) G is a nonzero constant function. It is a polynomial function of degree 0 since $G(x) = 8 = 8x^0$.

(f) $H(x) = -2x^3(x - 1)^2 = -2x^3(x^2 - 2x + 1) = -2x^5 + 4x^4 - 2x^3$. So H is a polynomial function of degree 5. Do you see a way to find the degree of H without multiplying out?

 Now Work PROBLEMS 11 AND 15

We have already discussed in detail polynomial functions of degrees 0, 1, and 2. See Table 1 for a summary of the properties of the graphs of these polynomial functions.

Table 1

Degree	Form	Name	Graph
No degree	$f(x) = 0$	Zero function	The x-axis
0	$f(x) = a_0, \quad a_0 \neq 0$	Constant function	Horizontal line with y-intercept a_0
1	$f(x) = a_1x + a_0, \quad a_1 \neq 0$	Linear function	Nonvertical, nonhorizontal line with slope a_1 and y-intercept a_0
2	$f(x) = a_2x^2 + a_1x + a_0, \quad a_2 \neq 0$	Quadratic function	Parabola: graph opens up if $a_2 > 0$; graph opens down if $a_2 < 0$

One objective of this section is to analyze the graph of a polynomial function. If you take a course in calculus, you will learn that the graph of every polynomial function is both smooth and continuous. By **smooth,** we mean that the graph contains no sharp corners or cusps; by **continuous,** we mean that the graph has no gaps or holes and can be drawn without lifting pencil from paper. See Figures 1(a) and (b).

Figure 1

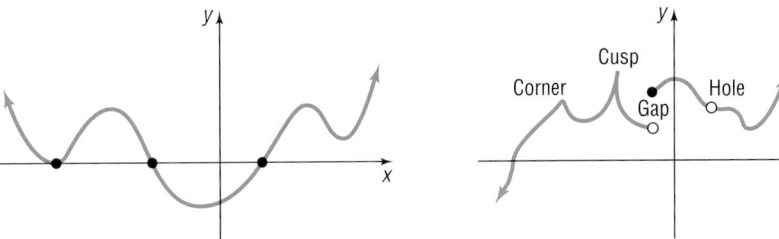

(a) Graph of a polynomial function: smooth, continuous

(b) Cannot be the graph of a polynomial function

Power Functions

We begin the analysis of the graph of a polynomial function by discussing *power functions,* a special kind of polynomial function.

DEFINITION

A **power function of degree n** is a monomial of the form

$$f(x) = ax^n \qquad (2)$$

where a is a real number, $a \neq 0$, and $n > 0$ is an integer.

In Words

A power function is defined by a single monomial.

Examples of power functions are

$$f(x) = 3x \qquad f(x) = -5x^2 \qquad f(x) = 8x^3 \qquad f(x) = -5x^4$$

degree 1 $\qquad$ degree 2 $\qquad$ degree 3 $\qquad$ degree 4

The graph of a power function of degree 1, $f(x) = ax$, is a straight line, with slope a, that passes through the origin. The graph of a power function of degree 2, $f(x) = ax^2$, is a parabola, with vertex at the origin, that opens up if $a > 0$ and down if $a < 0$.

If we know how to graph a power function of the form $f(x) = x^n$, a compression or stretch and, perhaps, a reflection about the x-axis will enable us to obtain the graph of $g(x) = ax^n$. Consequently, we shall concentrate on graphing power functions of the form $f(x) = x^n$.

We begin with power functions of even degree of the form $f(x) = x^n$, $n \geq 2$ and n even.

Exploration

Using your graphing utility and the viewing window $-2 \leq x \leq 2, -4 \leq y \leq 16$, graph the function $Y_1 = f(x) = x^4$. On the same screen, graph $Y_2 = g(x) = x^8$. Now, also on the same screen, graph $Y_3 = h(x) = x^{12}$. What do you notice about the graphs as the magnitude of the exponent increases? Repeat this procedure for the viewing window $-1 \leq x \leq 1, 0 \leq y \leq 1$. What do you notice?

Result   See Figures 2(a) and (b).

Figure 2

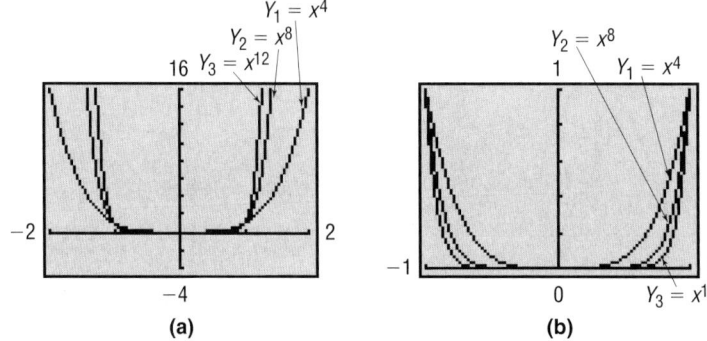

(a)   (b)

Table 2

X	Y2	Y3
-1	1	1
1	1	1
.5	.00391	2.4E-4
.1	1E-8	1E-12
.01	1E-16	1E-24
.001	1E-24	1E-36
0	0	0

Y2■X^8

NOTE Don't forget how graphing calculators express scientific notation. In Table 2, 1E −8 means 1×10^{-8}. ■

The domain of $f(x) = x^n$, $n \geq 2$ and n even, is the set of all real numbers, and the range is the set of nonnegative real numbers. Such a power function is an even function (do you see why?), so its graph is symmetric with respect to the y-axis. Its graph always contains the origin $(0, 0)$ and the points $(-1, 1)$ and $(1, 1)$.

If $n = 2$, the graph is the parabola $y = x^2$ that opens up, with vertex at the origin. For large n, it appears that the graph coincides with the x-axis near the origin, but it does not; the graph actually touches the x-axis only at the origin. See Table 2, where $Y_2 = x^8$ and $Y_3 = x^{12}$. For x close to 0, the values of y are positive and close to 0. Also, for large n, it may appear that for $x < -1$ or for $x > 1$ the graph is vertical, but it is not; it is only increasing very rapidly. If you TRACE along one of the graphs, these distinctions will be clear.

To summarize:

Properties of Power Functions, $f(x) = x^n$, n Is an Even Integer

1. The graph is symmetric with respect to the y-axis, so f is even.
2. The domain is the set of all real numbers. The range is the set of nonnegative real numbers.
3. The graph always contains the points $(0, 0)$, $(1, 1)$, and $(-1, 1)$.
4. As the exponent n increases in magnitude, the graph becomes more vertical when $x < -1$ or $x > 1$; but for x near the origin, the graph tends to flatten out and lie closer to the x-axis.

Now we consider power functions of odd degree of the form $f(x) = x^n$, n odd.

Exploration

Using your graphing utility and the viewing window $-2 \leq x \leq 2, -16 \leq y \leq 16$, graph the function $Y_1 = f(x) = x^3$. On the same screen, graph $Y_2 = g(x) = x^7$ and $Y_3 = h(x) = x^{11}$. What do you notice about the graphs as the magnitude of the exponent increases? Repeat this procedure for the viewing window $-1 \leq x \leq 1, -1 \leq y \leq 1$. What do you notice?

Result   The graphs on your screen should look like Figures 3(a) and (b).

Figure 3

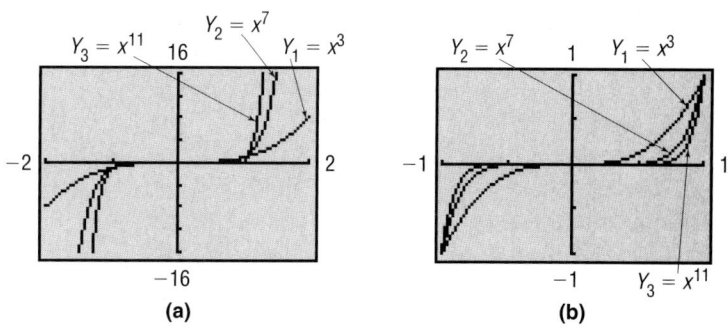

(a)   (b)

The domain and the range of $f(x) = x^n, n \geq 3$ and n odd, are the set of real numbers. Such a power function is an odd function (do you see why?), so its graph is symmetric with respect to the origin. Its graph always contains the origin $(0, 0)$ and the points $(-1, -1)$ and $(1, 1)$.

It appears that the graph coincides with the x-axis near the origin, but it does not; the graph actually crosses the x-axis only at the origin. Also, it appears that as x increases the graph is vertical, but it is not; it is increasing very rapidly. TRACE along the graphs to verify these distinctions.

To summarize:

Properties of Power Functions, $f(x) = x^n$, n Is an Odd Integer

1. The graph is symmetric with respect to the origin, so f is odd.
2. The domain and the range are the set of all real numbers.
3. The graph always contains the points $(0, 0)$, $(1, 1)$, and $(-1, -1)$.
4. As the exponent n increases in magnitude, the graph becomes more vertical when $x < -1$ or $x > 1$, but for x near the origin, the graph tends to flatten out and lie closer to the x-axis.

2 Graph Polynomial Functions Using Transformations

The methods of shifting, compression, stretching, and reflection studied in Section 2.5, when used with the facts just presented, will enable us to graph polynomial functions that are transformations of power functions.

EXAMPLE 2   **Graphing Polynomial Functions Using Transformations**

Graph: $f(x) = 1 - x^5$

Solution   It is helpful to rewrite f as $f(x) = -x^5 + 1$. Figure 4 shows the required stages.

Figure 4

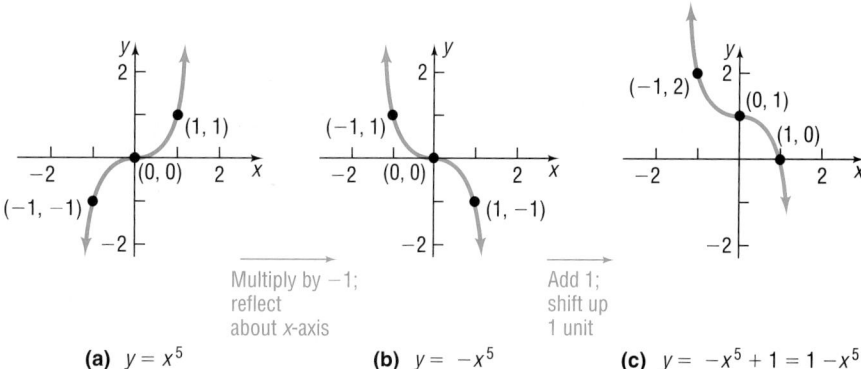

Multiply by -1;
reflect
about x-axis

Add 1;
shift up
1 unit

(a) $y = x^5$ **(b)** $y = -x^5$ **(c)** $y = -x^5 + 1 = 1 - x^5$

✓ **Check:**   Verify the graph of f by graphing $Y_1 = 1 - x^5$.

EXAMPLE 3 | Graphing Polynomial Functions Using Transformations

Graph: $f(x) = \dfrac{1}{2}(x - 1)^4$

Solution   Figure 5 shows the required stages.

Figure 5

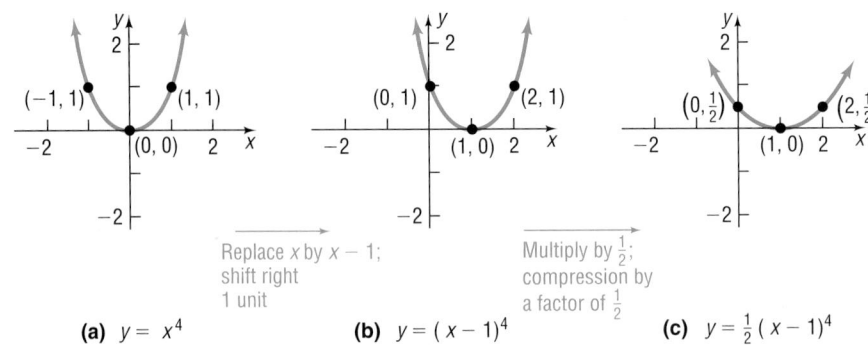

Replace x by $x - 1$;
shift right
1 unit

Multiply by $\frac{1}{2}$;
compression by
a factor of $\frac{1}{2}$

(a) $y = x^4$ **(b)** $y = (x - 1)^4$ **(c)** $y = \frac{1}{2}(x - 1)^4$

✓ Check: Verify the graph of f by graphing $Y_1 = \dfrac{1}{2}(x - 1)^4$.

Now Work PROBLEMS 23 AND 29

3 Identify the Real Zeros of a Polynomial Function and Their Multiplicity

Figure 6 shows the graph of a polynomial function with four x-intercepts. Notice that at the x-intercepts the graph must either cross the x-axis or touch the x-axis. Consequently, between consecutive x-intercepts the graph is either above the x-axis or below the x-axis. We will make use of this property of the graph of a polynomial function shortly.

Figure 6

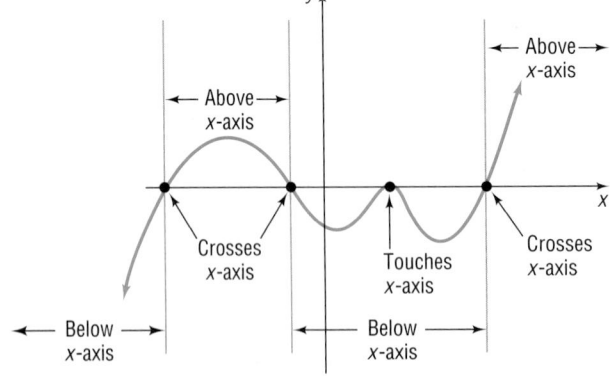

If a polynomial function f is factored completely, it is easy to solve the equation $f(x) = 0$ using the Zero-Product Property and locate the x-intercepts of the graph. For example, if $f(x) = (x - 1)^2(x + 3)$, then the solutions of the equation

$$f(x) = (x - 1)^2(x + 3) = 0$$

are 1 and -3. So, if $x = 1$ or $x = -3$, the value of the function is zero. This leads to the following definition.

DEFINITION   If f is a function and r is a real number for which $f(r) = 0$, then r is called a **real zero of f**.

As a consequence of this definition, the following statements are equivalent.

1. r is a real zero of a polynomial function f.
2. r is an x-intercept of the graph of f.
3. $x - r$ is a factor of f.
4. r is a solution to the equation $f(x) = 0$.

So the real zeros of a polynomial function are the x-intercepts of its graph, and they are found by solving the equation $f(x) = 0$.

| EXAMPLE 4 | **Finding a Polynomial from Its Zeros** |

(a) Find a polynomial of degree 3 whose zeros are $-3, 2$, and 5.
(b) Use a graphing utility to graph the polynomial found in part (a) to verify your result.

Solution   (a) If r is a real zero of a polynomial f, then $x - r$ is a factor of f. This means that $x - (-3) = x + 3$, $x - 2$, and $x - 5$ are factors of f. As a result, any polynomial of the form

$$f(x) = a(x + 3)(x - 2)(x - 5)$$

where a is any nonzero real number, qualifies. The value of a causes a stretch, compression, or reflection, but does not affect the x-intercepts. Do you know why?

(b) We choose to graph f with $a = 1$. Then

$$f(x) = (x + 3)(x - 2)(x - 5) = x^3 - 4x^2 - 11x + 30$$

Figure 7 shows the graph of f. Notice that the x-intercepts are $-3, 2$, and 5.

Figure 7

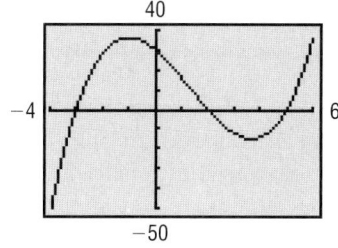

Seeing the Concept
Graph the function found in Example 4 for $a = 2$ and $a = -1$. Does the value of a affect the zeros of f? How does the value of a affect the graph of f?

━━━━━ **Now Work** PROBLEM 37

If the same factor $x - r$ occurs more than once, r is called a **repeated,** or **multiple, zero of f.** More precisely, we have the following definition.

DEFINITION   If $(x - r)^m$ is a factor of a polynomial f and $(x - r)^{m+1}$ is not a factor of f, then r is called a **zero of multiplicity m of f.*

| EXAMPLE 5 | **Identifying Zeros and Their Multiplicities** |

For the polynomial

$$f(x) = 5(x - 2)(x + 3)^2\left(x - \frac{1}{2}\right)^4$$

2 is a zero of multiplicity 1 because the exponent on the factor $x - 2$ is 1.
-3 is a zero of multiplicity 2 because the exponent on the factor $x + 3$ is 2.
$\dfrac{1}{2}$ is a zero of multiplicity 4 because the exponent on the factor $x - \dfrac{1}{2}$ is 4.

━━━━━ **Now Work** PROBLEM 45(a)

*Some books use the terms **multiple root** and **root of multiplicity** m.

In Example 5 notice that, if you add the multiplicities $(1 + 2 + 4 = 7)$, you obtain the degree of the polynomial.

Suppose that it is possible to factor completely a polynomial function and, as a result, locate all the x-intercepts of its graph (the real zeros of the function). The following example illustrates the role that the multiplicity of an x-intercept plays.

EXAMPLE 6	**Investigating the Role of Multiplicity**

For the polynomial $f(x) = x^2(x - 2)$:

(a) Find the x- and y-intercepts of the graph of f.
(b) Using a graphing utility, graph the polynomial.
(c) For each x-intercept, determine whether it is of odd or even multiplicity.

Solution

(a) The y-intercept is $f(0) = 0^2(0 - 2) = 0$. The x-intercepts satisfy the equation

$$f(x) = x^2(x - 2) = 0$$

from which we find that

$$x^2 = 0 \quad \text{or} \quad x - 2 = 0$$
$$x = 0 \quad \text{or} \quad x = 2$$

The x-intercepts are 0 and 2.

(b) See Figure 8 for the graph of f.

(c) We can see from the factored form of f that 0 is a zero or root of multiplicity 2, and 2 is a zero or root of multiplicity 1; so 0 is of even multiplicity and 2 is of odd multiplicity.

Figure 8

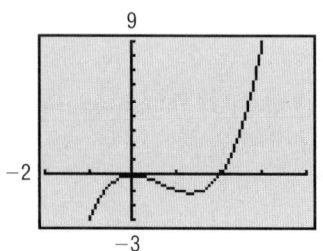

We can use a TABLE to further analyze the graph. See Table 3. The sign of $f(x)$ is the same on each side of $x = 0$, and the graph of f just *touches* the x-axis at $x = 0$ (a zero of *even* multiplicity). The sign of $f(x)$ changes from one side of $x = 2$ to the other, and the graph of f *crosses* the x-axis at $x = 2$ (a zero of *odd* multiplicity). These observations suggest the following result:

Table 3

If *r* Is a Zero of Even Multiplicity

Sign of $f(x)$ does not change from one side of r to the other side of r.

Graph **touches** x-axis at r.

If *r* Is a Zero of Odd Multiplicity

Sign of $f(x)$ changes from one side of r to the other side of r.

Graph **crosses** x-axis at r.

Now Work PROBLEM 45(b)

Figure 9

Turning Points

Points on the graph where the graph changes from an increasing function to a decreasing function, or vice versa, are called **turning points.***

Look at Figure 9. The graph of $f(x) = x^2(x - 2) = x^3 - 2x^2$ has a turning point at $(0, 0)$. After utilizing MINIMUM, we find that the graph also has a turning point at $(1.33, -1.19)$, rounded to two decimal places.

---

*Graphing utilities can be used to approximate turning points. Calculus is needed to find the exact location of turning points.

Exploration

Graph $Y_1 = x^3$, $Y_2 = x^3 - x$ and $Y_3 = x^3 + 3x^2 + 4$. How many turning points do you see? Graph $Y_1 = x^4$, $Y_2 = x^4 - \dfrac{4}{3}x^3$, and $Y_3 = x^4 - 2x^2$. How many turning points do you see? How does the number of turning points compare to the degree?

 The following theorem from calculus supplies the answer to the question posed in the Exploration.

THEOREM

Turning Points

If f is a polynomial function of degree n, then f has at most $n - 1$ turning points.

If the graph of a polynomial function f has $n - 1$ turning points, the degree of f is at least n.

For example, a polynomial function of degree 5 will have at most $5 - 1 = 4$ turning points. If a polynomial function has 3 turning points, then its degree must be at least 4.

EXAMPLE 7

Identifying the Graph of a Polynomial Function

Which of the graphs in Figure 10 could be the graph of a polynomial function? For those that could, list the real zeros and state the least degree the polynomial can have. For those that could not, say why not.

Figure 10

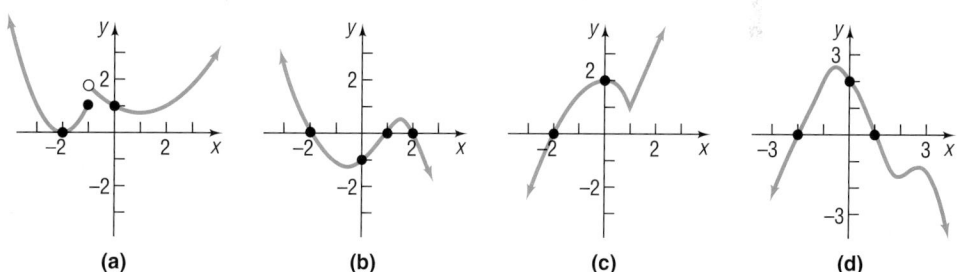

(a) (b) (c) (d)

Solution (a) The graph in Figure 10(a) cannot be the graph of a polynomial function because of the gap that occurs at $x = -1$. Remember, the graph of a polynomial function is continuous—no gaps or holes.

(b) The graph in Figure 10(b) could be the graph of a polynomial function. It has three real zeros, at -2, 1, and 2. Since the graph has two turning points, the degree of the polynomial function must be at least 3.

(c) The graph in Figure 10(c) cannot be the graph of a polynomial function because of the cusp at $x = 1$. Remember, the graph of a polynomial function is smooth.

(d) The graph in Figure 10(d) could be the graph of a polynomial function. It has two real zeros, at -2 and 1. Since the graph has three turning points, the degree of the polynomial function is at least 4.

Now Work PROBLEMS 45(c) AND 57

End Behavior

One last remark about Figure 8. For very large values of x, either positive or negative, the graph of $f(x) = x^2(x - 2)$ looks like the graph of $y = x^3$. To see why, we write f in the form

$$f(x) = x^2(x - 2) = x^3 - 2x^2 = x^3\left(1 - \frac{2}{x}\right)$$

Now, for large values of x, either positive or negative, the term $\dfrac{2}{x}$ is close to 0, so for large values of x

$$f(x) = x^3 - 2x^2 = x^3\left(1 - \frac{2}{x}\right) \approx x^3$$

The behavior of the graph of a function for large values of x, either positive or negative, is referred to as its **end behavior.** The end behavior of $f(x) = x^2(x - 2)$ is $y = x^3$.

THEOREM

End Behavior

For large values of x, either positive or negative, the graph of the polynomial

$$f(x) = a_n x^n + a_{n-1} x^{n-1} + \cdots + a_1 x + a_0$$

resembles the graph of the power function

$$y = a_n x^n$$

Seeing the Concept

For each pair of functions Y_1 and Y_2 given in parts (a), (b), and (c), graph Y_1 and Y_2 on the same viewing window. Create a TABLE or TRACE for large positive and large negative values of x. What do you notice about the graphs of Y_1 and Y_2 as x becomes very large and positive or very large and negative?

(a) $Y_1 = x^2(x - 2)$; $Y_2 = x^3$
(b) $Y_1 = x^4 - 3x^3 + 7x - 3$; $Y_2 = x^4$
(c) $Y_1 = -2x^3 + 4x^2 - 8x + 10$; $Y_2 = -2x^3$

Look back at Figures 2(a) and 3(a). Based on the preceding theorem and the previous discussion on power functions, the end behavior of a polynomial can only be of four types. See Figure 11.

Figure 11
End Behavior of $f(x) = a_n x^n + a_{n-1} x^{n-1} + \cdots + a_1 x + a_0$

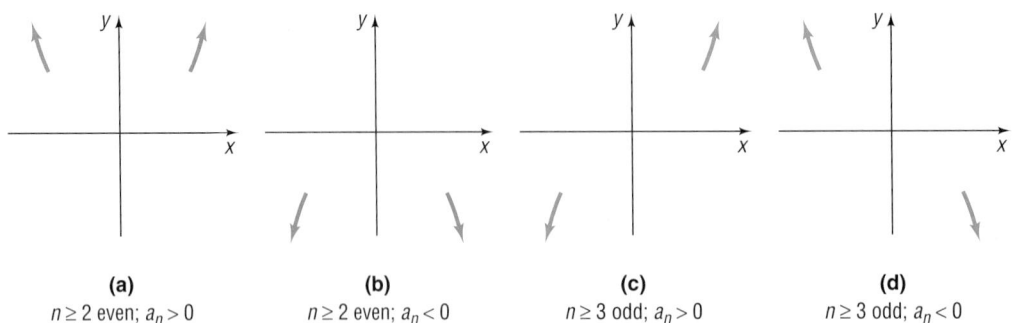

(a)	(b)	(c)	(d)
$n \geq 2$ even; $a_n > 0$	$n \geq 2$ even; $a_n < 0$	$n \geq 3$ odd; $a_n > 0$	$n \geq 3$ odd; $a_n < 0$

For example, if $f(x) = -2x^4 + x^3 + 4x^2 - 7x + 1$, the graph of f will resemble the graph of the power function $y = -2x^4$ for large $|x|$. Therefore, the graph of f will behave like Figure 11(b) for large $|x|$.

Now Work PROBLEM 45(d)

| EXAMPLE 8 | **Identifying the Graph of a Polynomial Function** |

Which of the graphs in Figure 12 could be the graph of

$$f(x) = x^4 + 5x^3 + 5x^2 - 5x - 6?$$

Figure 12

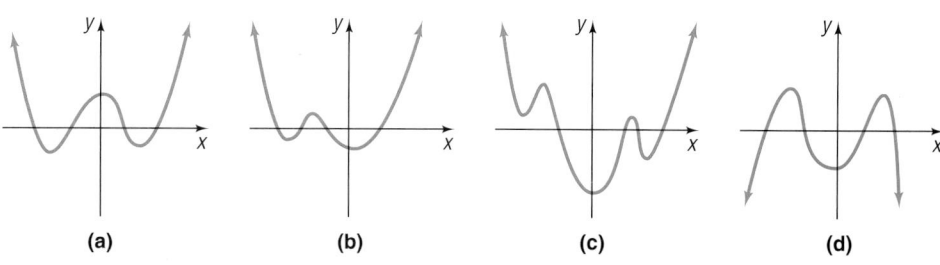

(a)   (b)   (c)   (d)

Solution   The y-intercept of f is $f(0) = -6$. We can eliminate the graph in Figure 12(a), whose y-intercept is positive.

We don't have any methods for finding the x-intercepts of f, so we move on to investigate the turning points of each graph. Since f is of degree 4, the graph of f has at most 3 turning points. We eliminate the graph in Figure 12(c) since that graph has 5 turning points.

Now we look at end behavior. For large values of x, the graph of f will behave like the graph of $y = x^4$. This eliminates the graph in Figure 12(d), whose end behavior is like the graph of $y = -x^4$.

Only the graph in Figure 12(b) could be (and, in fact, is) the graph of $f(x) = x^4 + 5x^3 + x^2 - 5x - 6$.

━━━ **Now Work** PROBLEM 61

SUMMARY Graph of a Polynomial Function $f(x) = a_n x^n + a_{n-1} x^{n-1} + \cdots + a_1 x + a_0$ $a_n \neq 0$

Degree of the polynomial f: n
Maximum number of turning points: $n - 1$
At a zero of even multiplicity: The graph of f touches the x-axis.
At a zero of odd multiplicity: The graph of f crosses the x-axis.
Between zeros, the graph of f is either above or below the x-axis.
End behavior: For large $|x|$, the graph of f behaves like the graph of $y = a_n x^n$.

---

4 Analyze the Graph of a Polynomial Function

| EXAMPLE 9 | **How to Analyze the Graph of a Polynomial Function** |

Analyze the graph of the polynomial function $f(x) = (2x + 1)(x - 3)^2$.

Step-by-Step Solution

STEP 1   *Determine the end behavior of the graph of the function.*

First, we expand the polynomial to write it in the form

$$f(x) = a_n x^n + a_{n-1} x^{n-1} + \cdots + a_1 x + a_0$$

$$f(x) = (2x + 1)(x - 3)^2$$
$$= (2x + 1)(x^2 - 6x + 9)$$
$$= 2x^3 - 12x^2 + 18x + x^2 - 6x + 9 \quad \text{Multiply.}$$
$$= 2x^3 - 11x^2 + 12x + 9 \quad\quad \text{Combine like terms.}$$

The polynomial function f is of degree 3. The graph of f behaves like $y = 2x^3$ for large values of $|x|$.

STEP 2   Find the x- and y-intercepts of the graph of the function.

The y-intercept is $f(0) = 9$. To find the x-intercepts, we solve $f(x) = 0$.

$$f(x) = 0$$
$$(2x + 1)(x - 3)^2 = 0$$
$$2x + 1 = 0 \quad \text{or} \quad (x - 3)^2 = 0$$
$$x = -\frac{1}{2} \quad \text{or} \quad x - 3 = 0$$
$$x = 3$$

The x-intercepts are $-\frac{1}{2}$ and 3.

STEP 3   Determine the zeros of the function and their multiplicity. Use this information to determine whether the graph crosses or touches the x-axis at each x-intercept.

The zeros of f are $-\frac{1}{2}$ and 3. The zero $-\frac{1}{2}$ is a zero of multiplicity 1, so the graph of f crosses the x-axis at $x = -\frac{1}{2}$. The zero 3 is a zero of multiplicity 2, so the graph of f touches the x-axis at $x = 3$.

STEP 4   Use a graphing utility to graph the function.

See Figure 13 for the graph of f.

Figure 13

STEP 5   Approximate the turning points of the graph.

From the graph of f shown in Figure 13, we can see that f has two turning points. Using MAXIMUM, one turning point is at (0.67, 12.70), rounded to two decimal places. Using MINIMUM, the other turning point is at $(3, 0)$.

STEP 6   Use the information in Steps 1 to 5 to draw a complete graph of the function by hand.

Figure 14 shows a graph of f using the information in Steps 1 through 5.

Figure 14

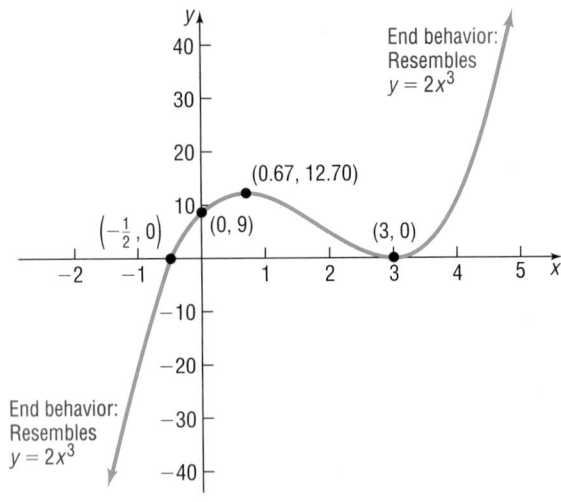

STEP 7   Find the domain and the range of the function.

The domain and the range of f is the set of all real numbers.

STEP 8   Use the graph to determine where the function is increasing and where it is decreasing.

Based on the graph, f is increasing on the intervals $(-\infty, 0.67)$ and $(3, \infty)$. Also, f is decreasing on the interval $(0.67, 3)$.

SUMMARY   Analyzing the Graph of a Polynomial Function

STEP 1: Determine the end behavior of the graph of the function.

STEP 2: Find the *x*- and *y*-intercepts of the graph of the function.

STEP 3: Determine the zeros of the function and their multiplicity. Use this information to determine whether the graph crosses or touches the *x*-axis at each *x*-intercept.

STEP 4: Use a graphing utility to graph the function.

STEP 5: Approximate the turning points of the graph.

STEP 6: Use the information in Steps 1 through 5 to draw a complete graph of the function by hand.

STEP 7: Find the domain and the range of the function.

STEP 8: Use the graph to determine where the function is increasing and where it is decreasing.

Now Work PROBLEM 65

For polynomial functions that have noninteger coefficients and for polynomials that are not easily factored, we utilize the graphing utility early in the analysis. This is because the amount of information that can be obtained from algebraic analysis is limited.

EXAMPLE 10 **How to Use a Graphing Utility to Analyze the Graph of a Polynomial Function**

Analyze the graph of the polynomial function

$$f(x) = x^3 + 2.48x^2 - 4.3155x + 2.484406$$

Step-by-Step Solution

STEP 1 *Determine the end behavior of the graph of the function.*

The polynomial function *f* is of degree 3. The graph of *f* behaves like $y = x^3$ for large values of $|x|$.

STEP 2 *Graph the function using a graphing utility.*

See Figure 15 for the graph of *f*.

Figure 15

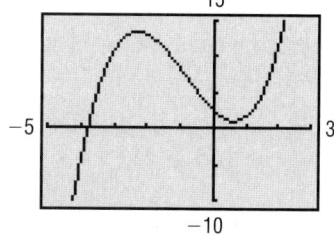

STEP 3 *Use a graphing utility to approximate the x- and y-intercepts of the graph.*

The *y*-intercept is $f(0) = 2.484406$. In Example 9 the polynomial function was factored, so it was easy to find the *x*-intercepts algebraically. However, it is not readily apparent how to factor *f* in this example. Therefore, we use a graphing utility's ZERO (or ROOT or SOLVE) feature and find the lone *x*-intercept to be -3.79, rounded to two decimal places.

STEP 4 *Use a graphing utility to create a TABLE to find points on the graph around each x-intercept.*

Table 4 shows values of *x* around the *x*-intercept. The points $(-4, -4.57)$ and $(-2, 13.04)$ are on the graph.

Table 4

X	Y1
-4	-4.574
-2	13.035

Y1◼X^3+2.48X²-4...

STEP 5 Approximate the turning points of the graph.

From the graph of f shown in Figure 15, we can see that f has two turning points. Using MAXIMUM, one turning point is at $(-2.28, 13.36)$, rounded to two decimal places. Using MINIMUM, the other turning point is at $(0.63, 1)$, rounded to two decimal places.

STEP 6 Use the information in Steps 1 through 5 to draw a complete graph of the function by hand.

Figure 16 shows a graph of f using the information in Steps 1 to 5.

Figure 16

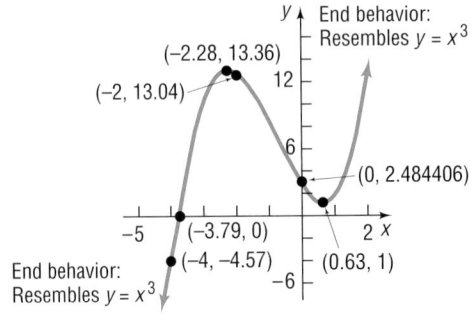

STEP 7 Find the domain and the range of the function.

The domain and the range of f are the set of all real numbers.

STEP 8 Use the graph to determine where the function is increasing and where it is decreasing.

Based on the graph, f is increasing on the intervals $(-\infty, -2.28)$ and $(0.63, \infty)$. Also, f is decreasing on the interval $(-2.28, 0.63)$.

SUMMARY Using a Graphing Utility to Analyze the Graph of a Polynomial Function

STEP 1: Determine the end behavior of the graph of the function.

STEP 2: Graph the function using a graphing utility.

STEP 3: Use a graphing utility to approximate the x- and y-intercepts of the graph.

STEP 4: Use a graphing utility to create a TABLE to find points on the graph around each x-intercept.

STEP 5: Approximate the turning points of the graph.

STEP 6: Use the information in Steps 1 through 5 to draw a complete graph of the function by hand.

STEP 7: Find the domain and the range of the function.

STEP 8: Use the graph to determine where the function is increasing and where it is decreasing.

Now Work PROBLEM 83

5 Build Cubic Models from Data

In Section 3.2 we found the line of best fit from data, and in Section 3.4 we found the quadratic function of best fit. It is also possible to find polynomial functions of best fit. However, most statisticians do not recommend finding polynomials of best fit of degree higher than 3.

Data that follow a cubic relation should look like Figure 17(a) or (b).

Figure 17

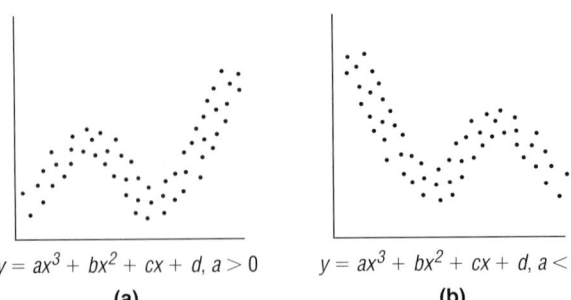

$y = ax^3 + bx^2 + cx + d, a > 0$ $y = ax^3 + bx^2 + cx + d, a < 0$

(a)   (b)

| EXAMPLE 11 | A Cubic Function of Best Fit |

Table 5

Number of Text Books, x	Cost, C
0	100
5	128.1
10	144
13	153.5
17	161.2
18	162.6
20	166.3
23	178.9
25	190.2
27	221.8

The data in Table 5 represent the weekly cost C (in thousands of dollars) of printing x thousand textbooks.

(a) Draw a scatter diagram of the data using x as the independent variable and C as the dependent variable. Comment on the type of relation that may exist between the two variables x and C.

(b) Using a graphing utility, find the cubic function of best fit $C = C(x)$ that models the relation between number of texts and cost.

(c) Graph the cubic function of best fit on your scatter diagram.

(d) Use the function found in part (b) to predict the cost of printing 22 thousand texts per week.

Solution

(a) Figure 18 shows the scatter diagram. A cubic relation may exist between the two variables.

(b) Upon executing the CUBIC REGression program, we obtain the results shown in Figure 19. The output the utility provides shows us the equation $y = ax^3 + bx^2 + cx + d$. The cubic function of best fit to the data is $C(x) = 0.0179x^3 - 0.7279x^2 + 11.3079x + 88.3169$.

(c) Figure 20 shows the graph of the cubic function of best fit on the scatter diagram. The function fits the data reasonably well.

Figure 18

Figure 19

Figure 20

(d) We evaluate the function $C(x)$ at $x = 22$.

$$C(22) = 0.0179(22)^3 - 0.7279(22)^2 + 11.3079(22) + 88.3169 \approx 175.4$$

The model predicts that the cost of printing 22 thousand textbooks in a week will be 175.4 thousand dollars, that is, $175,400.

4.1 Assess Your Understanding

'Are You Prepared?' *Answers are given at the end of these exercises. If you get a wrong answer, read the pages listed in* red.

1. The intercepts of the equation $9x^2 + 4y = 36$ are _____. (pp. 18–19)

2. *True or False* The expression $4x^3 - 3.6x^2 - \sqrt{2}$ is a polynomial. (pp. A24–A25)

3. To graph $y = x^2 - 4$, you would shift the graph of $y = x^2$ _____ a distance of _____ units. (pp. 100–101)

4. Use a graphing utility to approximate (rounded to two decimal places) the local maxima and local minima of $f(x) = x^3 - 2x^2 - 4x + 5$, for $-3 < x < 3$. (pp. 83–84)

Concepts and Vocabulary

5. The graph of every polynomial function is both _____ and _____.

6. A real number r for which $f(r) = 0$ is called a(n) _____ of the function f.

7. If r is a real zero of even multiplicity of a function f, the graph of f _____ the x-axis at r.

8. *True or False* The graph of $f(x) = x^2(x - 3)(x + 4)$ has exactly three x-intercepts.

9. *True or False* The x-intercepts of the graph of a polynomial function are called turning points.

10. *True or False* End behavior: the graph of the function $f(x) = 3x^4 - 6x^2 + 2x + 5$ resembles $y = x^4$ for large values of $|x|$.

Skill Building

In Problems 11–22, determine which functions are polynomial functions. For those that are, state the degree. For those that are not, tell why not.

11. $f(x) = 4x + x^3$

12. $f(x) = 5x^2 + 4x^4$

13. $g(x) = \dfrac{1 - x^2}{2}$

14. $h(x) = 3 - \dfrac{1}{2}x$

15. $f(x) = 1 - \dfrac{1}{x}$

16. $f(x) = x(x - 1)$

17. $g(x) = x^{3/2} - x^2 + 2$

18. $h(x) = \sqrt{x}(\sqrt{x} - 1)$

19. $F(x) = 5x^4 - \pi x^3 + \dfrac{1}{2}$

20. $F(x) = \dfrac{x^2 - 5}{x^3}$

21. $G(x) = 2(x - 1)^2(x^2 + 1)$

22. $G(x) = -3x^2(x + 2)^3$

In Problems 23–36, use transformations of the graph of $y = x^4$ or $y = x^5$ to graph each function. Verify your results using a graphing utility.

23. $f(x) = (x + 1)^4$

24. $f(x) = (x - 2)^5$

25. $f(x) = x^5 - 3$

26. $f(x) = x^4 + 2$

27. $f(x) = \dfrac{1}{2}x^4$

28. $f(x) = 3x^5$

29. $f(x) = -x^5$

30. $f(x) = -x^4$

31. $f(x) = (x - 1)^5 + 2$

32. $f(x) = (x + 2)^4 - 3$

33. $f(x) = 2(x + 1)^4 + 1$

34. $f(x) = \dfrac{1}{2}(x - 1)^5 - 2$

35. $f(x) = 4 - (x - 2)^5$

36. $f(x) = 3 - (x + 2)^4$

In Problems 37–44, form a polynomial whose real zeros and degree are given. Answers will vary depending on the choice of a leading coefficient. Graph the function using a graphing utility to verify your results.

37. Zeros: $-1, 1, 3$;   degree 3

38. Zeros: $-2, 2, 3$;   degree 3

39. Zeros: $-3, 0, 4$;   degree 3

40. Zeros: $-4, 0, 2$;   degree 3

41. Zeros: $-4, -1, 2, 3$;   degree 4

42. Zeros: $-3, -1, 2, 5$;   degree 4

43. Zeros: -1, multiplicity 1;   3, multiplicity 2;   degree 3

44. Zeros: -2, multiplicity 2;   4, multiplicity 1;   degree 3

In Problems 45–56, for each polynomial function:

(a) List each real zero and its multiplicity.
(b) Determine whether the graph crosses or touches the x-axis at each x-intercept.
(c) Determine the maximum number of turning points on the graph.
(d) Determine the end behavior; that is, find the power function that the graph of f resembles for large values of $|x|$.

45. $f(x) = 3(x - 7)(x + 3)^2$

46. $f(x) = 4(x + 4)(x + 3)^3$

47. $f(x) = 4(x^2 + 1)(x - 2)^3$

48. $f(x) = 2(x - 3)(x^2 + 4)^3$

49. $f(x) = -2\left(x + \dfrac{1}{2}\right)^2(x + 4)^3$

50. $f(x) = \left(x - \dfrac{1}{3}\right)^2(x - 1)^3$

51. $f(x) = (x - 5)^3(x + 4)^2$

52. $f(x) = \left(x + \sqrt{3}\right)^2(x - 2)^4$

53. $f(x) = 3(x^2 + 8)(x^2 + 9)^2$

54. $f(x) = -2(x^2 + 3)^3$

55. $f(x) = -2x^2(x^2 - 2)$

56. $f(x) = 4x(x^2 - 3)$

In Problems 57–60, identify which of the graphs could be the graph of a polynomial function. For those that could, list the real zeros and state the least degree the polynomial can have. For those that could not, say why not.

57.

58.

59.

60.
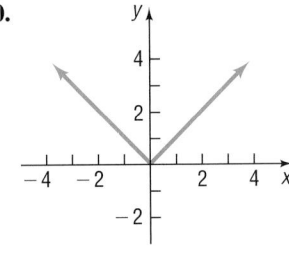

In Problems 61–64, construct a polynomial function that might have the given graph. (More than one answer may be possible.)

61.

62.

63.

64.

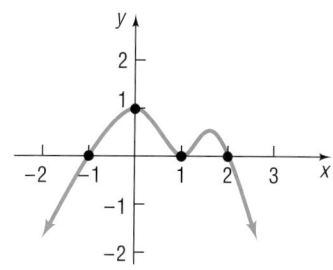

In Problems 65–82, analyze each polynomial function by following Steps 1 through 8 on page 185.

65. $f(x) = x^2(x - 3)$

66. $f(x) = x(x + 2)^2$

67. $f(x) = (x + 4)(x - 2)^2$

68. $f(x) = (x - 1)(x + 3)^2$

69. $f(x) = -2(x + 2)(x - 2)^3$

70. $f(x) = -\dfrac{1}{2}(x + 4)(x - 1)^3$

71. $f(x) = (x + 1)(x - 2)(x + 4)$

72. $f(x) = (x - 1)(x + 4)(x - 3)$

73. $f(x) = x^2(x - 2)(x + 2)$

74. $f(x) = x^2(x - 3)(x + 4)$

75. $f(x) = (x + 1)^2(x - 2)^2$

76. $f(x) = (x + 1)^3(x - 3)$

77. $f(x) = x^2(x - 3)(x + 1)$

78. $f(x) = x^2(x - 3)(x - 1)$

79. $f(x) = (x + 2)^2(x - 4)^2$

80. $f(x) = (x - 2)^2(x + 2)(x + 4)$

81. $f(x) = x^2(x - 2)(x^2 + 3)$

82. $f(x) = x^2(x^2 + 1)(x + 4)$

In Problems 83–90, analyze each polynomial function f by following Steps 1 through 8 on page 186.

83. $f(x) = x^3 + 0.2x^2 - 1.5876x - 0.31752$

84. $f(x) = x^3 - 0.8x^2 - 4.6656x + 3.73248$

85. $f(x) = x^3 + 2.56x^2 - 3.31x + 0.89$

86. $f(x) = x^3 - 2.91x^2 - 7.668x - 3.8151$

87. $f(x) = x^4 - 2.5x^2 + 0.5625$

88. $f(x) = x^4 - 18.5x^2 + 50.2619$

89. $f(x) = 2x^4 - \pi x^3 + \sqrt{5}x - 4$

90. $f(x) = -1.2x^4 + 0.5x^2 - \sqrt{3}x + 2$

Mixed Practice

In Problems 91–98, analyze each polynomial function by following Steps 1 through 8 on page 185.
[Hint: You will need to first factor the polynomial.]

91. $f(x) = 4x - x^3$

92. $f(x) = x - x^3$

93. $f(x) = x^3 + x^2 - 12x$

94. $f(x) = x^3 + 2x^2 - 8x$

95. $f(x) = 2x^4 + 12x^3 - 8x^2 - 48x$

96. $f(x) = 4x^3 + 10x^2 - 4x - 10$

97. $f(x) = -x^5 - x^4 + x^3 + x^2$

98. $f(x) = -x^5 + 5x^4 + 4x^3 - 20x^2$

Applications and Extensions

99. Future Value of Money Suppose you make deposits of $500 at the beginning of every year into an Individual Retirement Account (IRA). At the beginning of the first year, the value of the account will be 500 dollars; at the beginning of the second year, the value of the account, in dollars, will be

$$\underbrace{500 + 500r}_{\text{Value of 1st deposit}} + \underbrace{500}_{\text{Value of 2nd deposit}} = 500(1 + r) + 500 = 500r + 1000$$

(a) Verify that the value of the account at the beginning of the third year is $T(r) = 500r^2 + 1500r + 1500$.

(b) The account value at the beginning of the fourth year is $F(r) = 500r^3 + 2000r^2 + 3000r + 2000$. If the annual rate of interest is 5% = 0.05, what will be the value of the account at the beginning of the fourth year?

100. A Geometric Series In calculus, you will learn that certain functions can be approximated by polynomial functions. We will explore one such function now.

(a) Using a graphing utility, create a table of values with $Y_1 = f(x) = \dfrac{1}{1 - x}$ and $Y_2 = g_2(x) = 1 + x + x^2 + x^3$ for $-1 < x < 1$ with ΔTbl = 0.1.

(b) Using a graphing utility, create a table of values with $Y_1 = f(x) = \dfrac{1}{1 - x}$ and $Y_3 = g_3(x) = 1 + x + x^2 + x^3 + x^4$ for $-1 < x < 1$ with ΔTbl = 0.1.

(c) Using a graphing utility, create a table of values with $Y_1 = f(x) = \dfrac{1}{1 - x}$ and $Y_4 = g_4(x) = 1 + x + x^2 + x^3 + x^4 + x^5$ for $-1 < x < 1$ with ΔTbl = 0.1.

(d) What do you notice about the values of the function as more terms are added to the polynomial? Are there some values of *x* for which the approximation is better?

101. Hurricanes In 2005, hurricane Katrina struck the Gulf Coast of the United States, killing 1289 people and causing an estimated $200 billion in damage. The following data represent the number of major hurricane strikes in the United States (category 3, 4, or 5) each decade from 1921 to 2000.

Decade, x	Major Hurricanes Striking United States, H
1921–1930, 1	5
1931–1940, 2	8
1941–1950, 3	10
1951–1960, 4	8
1961–1970, 5	6
1971–1980, 6	4
1981–1990, 7	5
1991–2000, 8	5

Source: National Oceanic & Atmospheric Administration

(a) Draw a scatter diagram of the data. Comment on the type of relation that may exist between the two variables.
(b) Use a graphing utility to find the cubic function of best fit that models the relation between decade and number of major hurricanes.
(c) Use the model found in part (b) to predict the number of major hurricanes that struck the United States between 1961 and 1970.
(d) With a graphing utility, draw a scatter diagram of the data and then graph the cubic function of best fit on the scatter diagram.
(e) Concern has risen about the increase in the number and intensity of hurricanes, but some scientists believe this is just a natural fluctuation that could last another

decade or two. Use your model to predict the number of major hurricanes that will strike the United States between 2001 and 2010. Does your result appear to agree with what these scientists believe?
(f) From 2001 through 2005, five major hurricanes struck the United States. Does this support or contradict your prediction in part (e)?

102. Active Duty The following data represent the number of active duty military personnel (in millions) in the four major branches of the U.S. military for the years 1998 to 2005, where 1 represents 1998, 2 represents 1999, and so on.

Year, x	Active Duty Personnel, N
1998, 1	1.41
1999, 2	1.39
2000, 3	1.38
2001, 4	1.39
2002, 5	1.41
2003, 6	1.42
2004, 7	1.41
2005, 8	1.39

Source: infoplease.com

(a) Draw a scatter diagram of the data. Comment on the type of relation that may exist between the two variables.
(b) Use a graphing utility to find the cubic function of best fit that models the relation between year and active duty personnel.
(c) Use the model found in part (b) to predict the number of active duty military personnel in 2002.
(d) With a graphing utility, draw a scatter diagram of the data and then graph the cubic function of best fit on the scatter diagram.
(e) Do you think that the function given in part (b) will be useful in predicting the number of active duty military personnel in 2010? Explain.

Mixed Practice

103. Temperature The following data represent the temperature *T* (°Fahrenheit) in Kansas City, Missouri, *x* hours after midnight on May 15, 2005.

Hours after Midnight, x	Temperature (°F), T
3	45.0
6	44.1
9	51.1
12	57.9
15	63.0
18	63.0
21	59.0
24	54.0

Source: The Weather Underground

(a) Draw a scatter diagram of the data. Comment on the type of relation that may exist between the two variables.
(b) Find the average rate of change in temperature from 9 AM to 12 noon.
(c) What is the average rate of change in temperature from 3 PM to 6 PM?
(d) Decide on a function of best fit to these data (linear, quadratic, or cubic) and use this function to predict the temperature at 5 PM.
(e) With a graphing utility, draw a scatter diagram of the data and then graph the function of best fit on the scatter diagram.
(f) Interpret the *y*-intercept.

Discussion and Writing

104. Can the graph of a polynomial function have no y-intercept? Can it have no x-intercepts? Explain.

105. Write a few paragraphs that provide a general strategy for graphing a polynomial function. Be sure to mention the following: degree, intercepts, end behavior, and turning points.

106. Make up a polynomial that has the following characteristics: crosses the x-axis at -1 and 4, touches the x-axis at 0 and 2, and is above the x-axis between 0 and 2. Give your polynomial to a fellow classmate and ask for a written critique of your polynomial.

107. Make up two polynomials, not of the same degree, with the following characteristics: crosses the x-axis at -2, touches the x-axis at 1, and is above the x-axis between -2 and 1. Give your polynomials to a fellow classmate and ask for a written critique of your polynomials.

108. The graph of a polynomial function is always smooth and continuous. Name a function studied earlier that is smooth and not continuous. Name one that is continuous, but not smooth.

109. Which of the following statements are true regarding the graph of the cubic polynomial $f(x) = x^3 + bx^2 + cx + d$? (Give reasons for your conclusions.)

(a) It intersects the y-axis in one and only one point.
(b) It intersects the x-axis in at most three points.
(c) It intersects the x-axis at least once.
(d) For $|x|$ very large, it behaves like the graph of $y = x^3$.
(e) It is symmetric with respect to the origin.
(f) It passes through the origin.

110. The illustration shows the graph of a polynomial function.

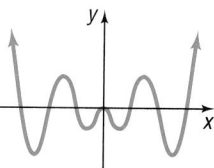

(a) Is the degree of the polynomial even or odd?
(b) Is the leading coefficient positive or negative?
(c) Is the function even, odd, or neither?
(d) Why is x^2 necessarily a factor of the polynomial?
(e) What is the minimum degree of the polynomial?
(f) Formulate five different polynomials whose graphs could look like the one shown. Compare yours to those of other students. What similarities do you see? What differences?

111. Design a polynomial function with the following characteristics: degree 6; four distinct real zeros, one of multiplicity 3; y-intercept 3; behaves like $y = -5x^6$ for large values of $|x|$. Is this polynomial unique? Compare your polynomial with those of other students. What terms will be the same as everyone else's? Add some more characteristics, such as symmetry or naming the real zeros. How does this modify the polynomial?

'Are You Prepared?' Answers

1. $(-2, 0), (2, 0), (0, 9)$ **2.** True   **3.** down; 4   **4.** Local maximum 6.48 at $x = -0.67$; local minimum -3 at $x = 2$

4.2 Properties of Rational Functions

PREPARING FOR THIS SECTION   *Before getting started, review the following:*

- Rational Expressions (Appendix A, Section A.5, pp. A35–A43)

- Polynomial Division (Appendix A, Section A.3, pp. A26–A28)

- Graph of $f(x) = \dfrac{1}{x}$ (Section 1.2, Example 6, p. 23)

- Graphing Techniques: Transformations (Section 2.5, pp. 100–108)

Now Work the 'Are You Prepared?' problems on page 200.

OBJECTIVES   **1** Find the Domain of a Rational Function (p. 192)
   2 Find the Vertical Asymptotes of a Rational Function (p. 195)
   3 Find the Horizontal or Oblique Asymptotes of a Rational Function (p. 196)

Ratios of integers are called *rational numbers*. Similarly, ratios of polynomial functions are called *rational functions*. Examples of rational functions are

$$R(x) = \frac{x^2 - 4}{x^2 + x + 1} \qquad F(x) = \frac{x^3}{x^2 - 4} \qquad G(x) = \frac{3x^2}{x^4 - 1}$$

DEFINITION

A **rational function** is a function of the form

$$R(x) = \frac{p(x)}{q(x)}$$

where p and q are polynomial functions and q is not the zero polynomial. The domain of a rational function is the set of all real numbers except those for which the denominator q is 0.

1 Find the Domain of a Rational Function

EXAMPLE 1 | Finding the Domain of a Rational Function

(a) The domain of $R(x) = \dfrac{2x^2 - 4}{x + 5}$ is the set of all real numbers x except -5; that is, $\{x | x \neq -5\}$.

(b) The domain of $R(x) = \dfrac{1}{x^2 - 4}$ is the set of all real numbers x except -2 and 2; that is, $\{x | x \neq -2, x \neq 2\}$.

(c) The domain of $R(x) = \dfrac{x^3}{x^2 + 1}$ is the set of all real numbers.

(d) The domain of $R(x) = \dfrac{-x^2 + 2}{3}$ is the set of all real numbers.

(e) The domain of $R(x) = \dfrac{x^2 - 1}{x - 1}$ is the set of all real numbers x except 1; that is, $\{x | x \neq 1\}$.

It is important to observe that the functions

$$R(x) = \frac{x^2 - 1}{x - 1} \quad \text{and} \quad f(x) = x + 1$$

are not equal, since the domain of R is $\{x | x \neq 1\}$ and the domain of f is the set of all real numbers.

━━━━━ **Now Work** PROBLEM 13

If $R(x) = \dfrac{p(x)}{q(x)}$ is a rational function and if p and q have no common factors, then the rational function R is said to be in **lowest terms.** For a rational function $R(x) = \dfrac{p(x)}{q(x)}$ in lowest terms, the zeros, if any, of the numerator are the x-intercepts of the graph of R and so will play a major role in the graph of R. The zeros of the denominator of R [that is, the numbers x, if any, for which $q(x) = 0$], although not in the domain of R, also play a major role in the graph of R. We will discuss this role shortly.

We have already discussed the properties of the rational function $f(x) = \dfrac{1}{x}$. (Refer to Example 6, page 23.) The next rational function that we take up is $H(x) = \dfrac{1}{x^2}$.

EXAMPLE 2 | Graphing $y = \dfrac{1}{x^2}$

Analyze the graph of $H(x) = \dfrac{1}{x^2}$.

Solution   The domain of $H(x) = \dfrac{1}{x^2}$ consists of all real numbers x except 0. The graph has no y-intercept, because x can never equal 0. The graph has no x-intercept because the equation $H(x) = 0$ has no solution. Therefore, the graph of H will not cross either coordinate axis.

Because

$$H(-x) = \frac{1}{(-x)^2} = \frac{1}{x^2} = H(x)$$

H is an even function, so its graph is symmetric with respect to the y-axis.

Figure 21

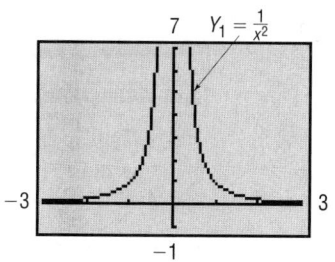

See Figure 21. Notice that the graph confirms the conclusions just reached. But what happens to the graph as the values of x get closer and closer to 0? We use a TABLE to answer the question. See Table 6. The first four rows show that as x approaches 0 the values of $H(x)$ become larger and larger positive numbers. When this happens, we say that $H(x)$ is **unbounded in the positive direction.** We symbolize this by writing $H(x) \to \infty$ [read as "$H(x)$ **approaches infinity**"]. In calculus, **limits** are used to convey these ideas. There we use the symbolism $\lim\limits_{x \to 0} H(x) = \infty$, read as "the limit of $H(x)$ as x approaches 0 is infinity" to mean that $H(x) \to \infty$ as $x \to 0$.

Look at the last three rows of Table 6. As $x \to \infty$, the values of $H(x)$ approach 0 (the end behavior of the graph). This is symbolized in calculus by writing $\lim\limits_{x \to \infty} H(x) = 0$.

Table 6

X	Y1
.1	100
.01	10000
.001	1E6
1E-4	1E8
10	.01
100	1E-4
1000	1E-6

Y1 ◻ 1/X²

Figure 22 shows the graph of $H(x) = \dfrac{1}{x^2}$ drawn by hand.

Figure 22

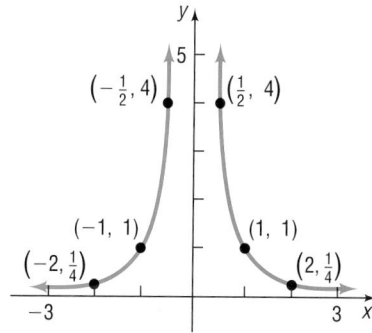

Sometimes transformations (shifting, compressing, stretching, and reflection) can be used to graph a rational function.

EXAMPLE 3   **Using Transformations to Graph a Rational Function**

Graph the rational function: $R(x) = \dfrac{1}{(x-2)^2} + 1$

Solution   First, notice that the domain of R is the set of all real numbers except $x = 2$. To graph R, we start with the graph of $y = \dfrac{1}{x^2}$. See Figure 23 for the stages.

Figure 23

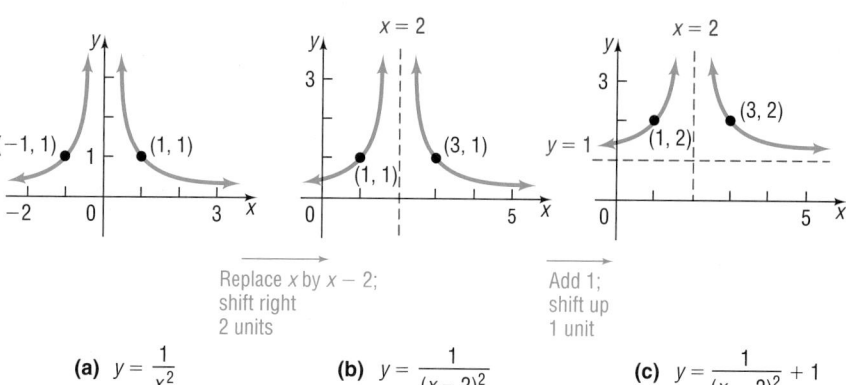

(a) $y = \dfrac{1}{x^2}$ Replace x by $x - 2$; shift right 2 units   (b) $y = \dfrac{1}{(x-2)^2}$ Add 1; shift up 1 unit   (c) $y = \dfrac{1}{(x-2)^2} + 1$

Check: Graph $Y_1 = \dfrac{1}{(x-2)^2} + 1$ using a graphing utility to verify the graph obtained in Figure 23(c).

Now Work PROBLEM 31

Asymptotes

Notice that the y-axis in Figure 23(a) is transformed into the vertical line $x = 2$ in Figure 23(c), and the x-axis in Figure 23(a) is transformed into the horizontal line $y = 1$ in Figure 23(c). The **Exploration** that follows will help us analyze the role of these lines.

Exploration

(a) Using a graphing utility and the TABLE feature, evaluate the function $H(x) = \dfrac{1}{(x-2)^2} + 1$ at $x = 10, 100, 1000,$ and $10,000.$ What happens to the values of H as x becomes unbounded in the positive direction, symbolized by $\lim\limits_{x \to \infty} H(x)$?

(b) Evaluate H at $x = -10, -100, -1000,$ and $-10,000.$ What happens to the values of H as x becomes unbounded in the negative direction, symbolized by $\lim\limits_{x \to -\infty} H(x)$?

(c) Evaluate H at $x = 1.5, 1.9, 1.99, 1.999,$ and $1.9999.$ What happens to the values of H as x approaches $2, x < 2,$ symbolized by $\lim\limits_{x \to 2^-} H(x)$?

(d) Evaluate H at $x = 2.5, 2.1, 2.01, 2.001,$ and $2.0001.$ What happens to the values of H as x approaches $2, x > 2,$ symbolized by $\lim\limits_{x \to 2^+} H(x)$?

Result

(a) Table 7 shows the values of $Y_1 = H(x)$ as x approaches $\infty.$ Notice that the values of H are approaching $1,$ so $\lim\limits_{x \to \infty} H(x) = 1.$

(b) Table 8 shows the values of $Y_1 = H(x)$ as x approaches $-\infty.$ Again the values of H are approaching $1,$ so $\lim\limits_{x \to -\infty} H(x) = 1.$

(c) From Table 9 we see that, as x approaches $2, x < 2,$ the values of H are increasing without bound, so $\lim\limits_{x \to 2^-} H(x) = \infty.$

(d) Finally, Table 10 reveals that, as x approaches $2, x > 2,$ the values of H are increasing without bound, so $\lim\limits_{x \to 2^+} H(x) = \infty.$

Table 7

X	Y1
10	1.0156
100	1.0001
1000	1
10000	1

Y1$\boxdot$1/(X–2)²+1

Table 8

X	Y1
-10	1.0069
-100	1.0001
-1000	1
-10000	1

Y1$\boxdot$1/(X–2)²+1

Table 9

X	Y1
1.5	5
1.9	101
1.99	10001
1.999	1E6
1.9999	1E8

Y1$\boxdot$1/(X–2)²+1

Table 10

X	Y1
2.5	5
2.1	101
2.01	10001
2.001	1E6
2.0001	1E8

Y1$\boxdot$1/(X–2)²+1

The results of the Exploration reveal an important property of rational functions. The vertical line $x = 2$ and the horizontal line $y = 1$ are called *asymptotes* of the graph of H, which we define as follows:

DEFINITION

Let R denote a function:

If, as $x \to -\infty$ or as $x \to \infty$, the values of $R(x)$ approach some fixed number L, then the line $y = L$ is a **horizontal asymptote** of the graph of R. [Refer to Figures 24(a) and (b).]

If, as x approaches some number c, the values $|R(x)| \to \infty$, then the line $x = c$ is a **vertical asymptote** of the graph of R. The graph of R never intersects a vertical asymptote. [Refer to Figures 24(c) and (d).]

Figure 24

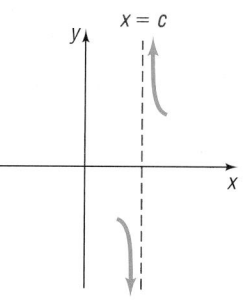

(a) End behavior:
As $x \to \infty$, the values of $R(x)$ approach L [symbolized by $\lim\limits_{x \to \infty} R(x) = L$]. That is, the points on the graph of R are getting closer to the line $y = L$; $y = L$ is a horizontal asymptote.

(b) End behavior:
As $x \to -\infty$, the values of $R(x)$ approach L [symbolized by $\lim\limits_{x \to -\infty} R(x) = L$]. That is, the points on the graph of R are getting closer to the line $y = L$; $y = L$ is a horizontal asymptote.

(c) As x approaches c, the values of $R(x) \to \infty$ [for $x < c$, this is symbolized by $\lim\limits_{x \to c^-} R(x) = \infty$; for $x > c$, this is symbolized by $\lim\limits_{x \to c^+} R(x) = \infty$]. That is, the points on the graph of R are getting closer to the line $x = c$; $x = c$ is a vertical asymptote.

(d) As x approaches c, the values of $|R(x)| \to \infty$ [for $x < c$, this is symbolized by $\lim\limits_{x \to c^-} R(x) = -\infty$; for $x > c$, this is symbolized by $\lim\limits_{x \to c^+} R(x) = \infty$]. That is, the points on the graph of R are getting closer to the line $x = c$; $x = c$ is a vertical asymptote.

A horizontal asymptote, when it occurs, describes the end behavior of the graph as $x \to \infty$ or as $x \to -\infty$. **The graph of a function may intersect a horizontal asymptote.**

A vertical asymptote, when it occurs, describes the behavior of the graph when x is close to some number c. **The graph of a function will never intersect a vertical asymptote.**

There is a third possibility. If, as $x \to -\infty$ or as $x \to \infty$, the value of a rational function $R(x)$ approaches a linear expression $ax + b$, $a \neq 0$, then the line $y = ax + b$, $a \neq 0$, is an **oblique asymptote** of R. Figure 25 shows an oblique asymptote. An oblique asymptote, when it occurs, describes the end behavior of the graph. **The graph of a function may intersect an oblique asymptote.**

Figure 25

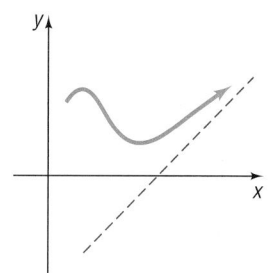

Now Work PROBLEM 23

2 Find the Vertical Asymptotes of a Rational Function

The vertical asymptotes of a rational function $R(x) = \dfrac{p(x)}{q(x)}$, in lowest terms, are located at the real zeros of the denominator of $q(x)$. Suppose that r is a real zero of q, so $x - r$ is a factor of q. As x approaches r, symbolized as $x \to r$, the values of $x - r$ approach 0, causing the ratio to become unbounded; that is, $|R(x)| \to \infty$. Based on the definition, we conclude that the line $x = r$ is a vertical asymptote.

THEOREM

Locating Vertical Asymptotes

A rational function $R(x) = \dfrac{p(x)}{q(x)}$, *in lowest terms,* will have a vertical asymptote $x = r$ if r is a real zero of the denominator q. That is, if $x - r$ is a factor of the denominator q of a rational function $R(x) = \dfrac{p(x)}{q(x)}$, in lowest terms, R will have the vertical asymptote $x = r$.

WARNING If a rational function is not in lowest terms, an application of this theorem may result in an incorrect listing of vertical asymptotes. ■

EXAMPLE 4   Finding Vertical Asymptotes

Find the vertical asymptotes, if any, of the graph of each rational function.

(a) $R(x) = \dfrac{x}{x^2 - 4}$

(b) $F(x) = \dfrac{x + 3}{x - 1}$

(c) $H(x) = \dfrac{x^2}{x^2 + 1}$

(d) $G(x) = \dfrac{x^2 - 9}{x^2 + 4x - 21}$

Solution

(a) R is in lowest terms, and the zeros of the denominator $x^2 - 4$ are -2 and 2. The lines $x = -2$ and $x = 2$ are the vertical asymptotes of the graph of R.

(b) F is in lowest terms, and the only zero of the denominator is 1. The line $x = 1$ is the vertical asymptote of the graph of F.

(c) H is in lowest terms, and the denominator has no real zeros, because the equation $x^2 + 1$ has no real solutions. The graph of H has no vertical asymptotes.

(d) Factor $G(x)$ to determine if it is in lowest terms.

WARNING In Example 4(a), the vertical asymptotes are $x = -2$ and $x = 2$. Do not say that the vertical asymptotes are -2 and 2. ∎

$$G(x) = \frac{x^2 - 9}{x^2 + 4x - 21} = \frac{(x + 3)(x - 3)}{(x + 7)(x - 3)} = \frac{x + 3}{x + 7} \qquad x \neq 3$$

The only zero of the denominator of $G(x)$ in lowest terms is -7. The line $x = -7$ is the only vertical asymptote of the graph of G.

As Example 4 points out, rational functions can have no vertical asymptotes, one vertical asymptote, or more than one vertical asymptote. However, the graph of a rational function will never intersect any of its vertical asymptotes. (Do you know why?)

Exploration

Graph each of the following rational functions:

$$R(x) = \frac{1}{x - 1} \qquad R(x) = \frac{1}{(x - 1)^2} \qquad R(x) = \frac{1}{(x - 1)^3} \qquad R(x) = \frac{1}{(x - 1)^4}$$

Each has the vertical asymptote $x = 1$. What happens to the value of $R(x)$ as x approaches 1 from the right side of the vertical asymptote; that is, what is $\lim\limits_{x \to 1^+} R(x)$? What happens to the value of $R(x)$ as x approaches 1 from the left side of the vertical asymptote; that is, what is $\lim\limits_{x \to 1^-} R(x)$? How does the multiplicity of the zero in the denominator affect the graph of R?

Now Work PROBLEM 45 (FIND THE VERTICAL ASYMPTOTES, IF ANY)

3 Find the Horizontal or Oblique Asymptotes of a Rational Function

The procedure for finding horizontal and oblique asymptotes is somewhat more involved. To find such asymptotes, we need to know how the value of a function behaves as $x \to -\infty$ or as $x \to \infty$.

If a rational function $R(x)$ is **proper,** that is, if the degree of the numerator is less than the degree of the denominator, then as $x \to -\infty$ or as $x \to \infty$ the value of $R(x)$ approaches 0. Consequently, the line $y = 0$ (the x-axis) is a horizontal asymptote of the graph.

THEOREM

If a rational function is proper, the line $y = 0$ is a horizontal asymptote of its graph.

EXAMPLE 5 **Finding Horizontal Asymptotes**

Find the horizontal asymptotes, if any, of the graph of

$$R(x) = \frac{x - 12}{4x^2 + x + 1}$$

Solution

Since the degree of the numerator, 1, is less than the degree of the denominator, 2, the rational function R is proper. We conclude that the line $y = 0$ is a horizontal asymptote of the graph of R.

To see why $y = 0$ is a horizontal asymptote of the function R in Example 5, we need to investigate the behavior of R as $x \to -\infty$ and $x \to \infty$. When $|x|$ is unbounded, the numerator of R, which is $x - 12$, can be approximated by the power function $y = x$, while the denominator of R, which is $4x^2 + x + 1$, can be approximated by the power function $y = 4x^2$. Applying these ideas to $R(x)$, we find

$$R(x) = \frac{x - 12}{4x^2 + x + 1} \approx \frac{x}{4x^2} = \frac{1}{4x} \to 0$$

For $|x|$ unbounded   As $x \to -\infty$ or $x \to \infty$

This shows that the line $y = 0$ is a horizontal asymptote of the graph of R.

Table 11

(a)

(b)

We verify these results in Tables 11(a) and (b). Notice, as $x \to -\infty$ [Table 11(a)] or $x \to \infty$ [Table 11(b)], respectively, that the value of $R(x)$ approaches 0.

If a rational function $R(x) = \dfrac{p(x)}{q(x)}$ is **improper,** that is, if the degree of the numerator is greater than or equal to the degree of the denominator, we must use long division to write the rational function as the sum of a polynomial $f(x)$ plus a proper rational function $\dfrac{r(x)}{q(x)}$ using long division. That is, we write

$$R(x) = \frac{p(x)}{q(x)} = f(x) + \frac{r(x)}{q(x)}$$

where $f(x)$ is a polynomial and $\dfrac{r(x)}{q(x)}$ is a proper rational function. Since $\dfrac{r(x)}{q(x)}$ is proper, then $\dfrac{r(x)}{q(x)} \to 0$ as $x \to -\infty$ or as $x \to \infty$. As a result,

$$R(x) = \frac{p(x)}{q(x)} \to f(x), \qquad \text{as } x \to -\infty \text{ or as } x \to \infty$$

The possibilities are listed next.

1. If $f(x) = b$, a constant, then the line $y = b$ is a horizontal asymptote of the graph of R.

2. If $f(x) = ax + b, a \neq 0$, then the line $y = ax + b$ is an oblique asymptote of the graph of R.

3. In all other cases, the graph of R approaches the graph of f, and there are no horizontal or oblique asymptotes.

We illustrate each of these possibilities in Examples 6 through 8.

EXAMPLE 6   **Finding Horizontal or Oblique Asymptotes**

Find the horizontal or oblique asymptotes, if any, of the graph of

$$H(x) = \frac{3x^4 - x^2}{x^3 - x^2 + 1}$$

Solution   Since the degree of the numerator, 4, is larger than the degree of the denominator, 3, the rational function H is improper. To find any horizontal or oblique asymptotes, we use long division.

$$
\begin{array}{r}
3x + 3 \\
x^3 - x^2 + 1 \overline{)3x^4 - x^2 } \\
\underline{3x^4 - 3x^3 + 3x } \\
3x^3 - x^2 - 3x \\
\underline{3x^3 - 3x^2 + 3} \\
2x^2 - 3x - 3
\end{array}
$$

As a result,

$$H(x) = \frac{3x^4 - x^2}{x^3 - x^2 + 1} = 3x + 3 + \frac{2x^2 - 3x - 3}{x^3 - x^2 + 1}$$

As $x \to -\infty$ or as $x \to \infty$,

$$\frac{2x^2 - 3x - 3}{x^3 - x^2 + 1} \approx \frac{2x^2}{x^3} = \frac{2}{x} \to 0$$

As $x \to -\infty$ or as $x \to \infty$, we have $H(x) \to 3x + 3$. We conclude that the graph of the rational function H has an oblique asymptote $y = 3x + 3$.

We verify these results in Tables 12(a) and (b) with $Y_1 = H(x)$ and $Y_2 = 3x + 3$. As $x \to -\infty$ or $x \to \infty$, the difference in the values between Y_1 and Y_2 is indistinguishable.

Table 12

X	Y1	Y2
-10	-27.21	-27
-100	-297	-297
-1000	-2997	-2997
-10000	-29997	-29997
-1E5	-3E5	-3E5
-1E6	-3E6	-3E6
-1E7	-3E7	-3E7

Y1⬛(3X^4-X²)/(X...

(a)

X	Y1	Y2
10	33.185	33
100	303.02	303
1000	3003	3003
10000	30003	30003
100000	300003	300003
1E6	3E6	3E6
1E7	3E7	3E7

Y1⬛(3X^4-X²)/(X...

(b)

EXAMPLE 7 | Finding Horizontal or Oblique Asymptotes

Find the horizontal or oblique asymptotes, if any, of the graph of

$$R(x) = \frac{8x^2 - x + 2}{4x^2 - 1}$$

Solution Since the degree of the numerator, 2, equals the degree of the denominator, 2, the rational function R is improper. To find any horizontal or oblique asymptotes, we use long division.

$$\begin{array}{r} 2 \\ 4x^2 - 1 \overline{)8x^2 - x + 2} \\ \underline{8x^2 - 2} \\ -x + 4 \end{array}$$

As a result,

$$R(x) = \frac{8x^2 - x + 2}{4x^2 - 1} = 2 + \frac{-x + 4}{4x^2 - 1}$$

Then, as $x \to -\infty$ or as $x \to \infty$,

$$\frac{-x + 4}{4x^2 - 1} \approx \frac{-x}{4x^2} = \frac{-1}{4x} \to 0$$

As $x \to -\infty$ or as $x \to \infty$, we have $R(x) \to 2$. We conclude that $y = 2$ is a horizontal asymptote of the graph.

✓**Check:** Verify the results by creating a TABLE with $Y_1 = R(x)$ and $Y_2 = 2$.

In Example 7, we note that the quotient 2 obtained by long division is the quotient of the leading coefficients of the numerator polynomial and the denominator polynomial $\left(\frac{8}{4}\right)$. This means that we can avoid the long division process for rational functions whose numerator and denominator *are of the same degree* and conclude that the quotient of the leading coefficients will give us the horizontal asymptote.

Now Work PROBLEMS 41 AND 43

| EXAMPLE 8 | Finding Horizontal or Oblique Asymptotes |

Find the horizontal or oblique asymptotes, if any, of the graph of

$$G(x) = \frac{2x^5 - x^3 + 2}{x^3 - 1}$$

Solution Since the degree of the numerator, 5, is larger than the degree of the denominator, 3, the rational function G is improper. To find any horizontal or oblique asymptotes, we use long division.

$$
\begin{array}{r}
2x^2 - 1 \\
x^3 - 1\overline{)2x^5 - x^3 \qquad + 2} \\
\underline{2x^5 \qquad - 2x^2} \\
-x^3 + 2x^2 + 2 \\
\underline{-x^3 \qquad + 1} \\
2x^2 + 1
\end{array}
$$

As a result,

$$G(x) = \frac{2x^5 - x^3 + 2}{x^3 - 1} = 2x^2 - 1 + \frac{2x^2 + 1}{x^3 - 1}$$

Then, as $x \to -\infty$ or as $x \to \infty$,

$$\frac{2x^2 + 1}{x^3 - 1} \approx \frac{2x^2}{x^3} = \frac{2}{x} \to 0$$

As $x \to -\infty$ or as $x \to \infty$, we have $G(x) \to 2x^2 - 1$. We conclude that, for large values of $|x|$, the graph of G approaches the graph of $y = 2x^2 - 1$. That is, the graph of G will look like the graph of $y = 2x^2 - 1$ as $x \to -\infty$ or $x \to \infty$. Since $y = 2x^2 - 1$ is not a linear function, G has no horizontal or oblique asymptotes.

We now summarize the procedure for finding horizontal and oblique asymptotes.

SUMMARY Finding Horizontal and Oblique Asymptotes of a Rational Function *R*

Consider the rational function

$$R(x) = \frac{p(x)}{q(x)} = \frac{a_n x^n + a_{n-1}x^{n-1} + \cdots + a_1 x + a_0}{b_m x^m + b_{m-1}x^{m-1} + \cdots + b_1 x + b_0}$$

in which the degree of the numerator is n and the degree of the denominator is m.

1. If $n < m$ (the degree of the numerator is less than the degree of the denominator), then R is a proper rational function, and the graph of R will have the horizontal asymptote $y = 0$ (the x-axis).

2. If $n \geq m$ (the degree of the numerator is greater than or equal to the degree of the denominator), then R is improper. Here long division is used.

(a) If $n = m$ (the degree of the numerator equals the degree of the denominator), the quotient obtained will be the number $\dfrac{a_n}{b_m}$, and the line $y = \dfrac{a_n}{b_m}$ is a horizontal asymptote.

(b) If $n = m + 1$ (the degree of the numerator is one more than the degree of the denominator), the quotient obtained is of the form $ax + b$ (a polynomial of degree 1), and the line $y = ax + b$ is an oblique asymptote.

(c) If $n \geq m + 2$ (the degree of the numerator is two or more greater than the degree of the denominator), the quotient obtained is a polynomial of degree 2 or higher, and R has neither a horizontal nor an oblique asymptote. In this case, for $|x|$ unbounded, the graph of R will behave like the graph of the quotient.

NOTE The graph of a rational function either has one horizontal or one oblique asymptote or else has no horizontal and no oblique asymptote. ∎

4.2 Assess Your Understanding

'Are You Prepared?' *Answers are given at the end of these exercises. If you get a wrong answer, read the pages listed in* red.

1. **True or False** The quotient of two polynomial expressions is a rational expression. (p. A35)

2. What is the quotient and remainder when $3x^4 - x^2$ is divided by $x^3 - x^2 + 1$? (pp. A26–A28)

3. Graph $y = \dfrac{1}{x}$. (p. 23)

4. Graph $y = 2(x + 1)^2 - 3$ using transformations. (pp. 100–108)

Concepts and Vocabulary

5. The line _____ is a horizontal asymptote of $R(x) = \dfrac{x^3 - 1}{x^3 + 1}$.

6. The line _____ is a vertical asymptote of $R(x) = \dfrac{x - 1}{x + 1}$.

7. For a rational function R, if the degree of the numerator is less than the degree of the denominator, then R is _____.

8. **True or False** The domain of every rational function is the set of all real numbers.

9. **True or False** If an asymptote is neither horizontal nor vertical, it is called oblique.

10. **True or False** If the degree of the numerator of a rational function equals the degree of the denominator, then the ratio of the leading coefficients gives rise to the horizontal asymptote.

Skill Building

In Problems 11–22, find the domain of each rational function.

11. $R(x) = \dfrac{4x}{x - 3}$

12. $R(x) = \dfrac{5x^2}{3 + x}$

13. $H(x) = \dfrac{-4x^2}{(x - 2)(x + 4)}$

14. $G(x) = \dfrac{6}{(x + 3)(4 - x)}$

15. $F(x) = \dfrac{3x(x - 1)}{2x^2 - 5x - 3}$

16. $Q(x) = \dfrac{-x(1 - x)}{3x^2 + 5x - 2}$

17. $R(x) = \dfrac{x}{x^3 - 8}$

18. $R(x) = \dfrac{x}{x^4 - 1}$

19. $H(x) = \dfrac{3x^2 + x}{x^2 + 4}$

20. $G(x) = \dfrac{x - 3}{x^4 + 1}$

21. $R(x) = \dfrac{3(x^2 - x - 6)}{4(x^2 - 9)}$

22. $F(x) = \dfrac{-2(x^2 - 4)}{3(x^2 + 4x + 4)}$

In Problems 23–28, use the graph shown to find:
   (a) The domain and range of each function
   (d) Vertical asymptotes, if any
   (b) The intercepts, if any
   (e) Oblique asymptotes, if any
   (c) Horizontal asymptotes, if any

23.

24.

25.

26.

27.

28.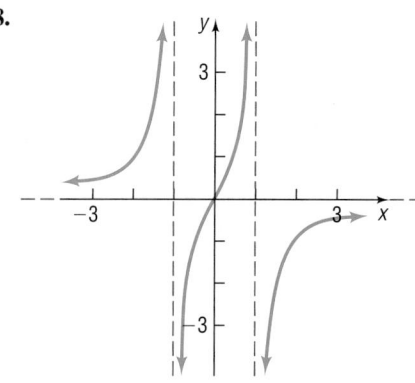

In Problems 29–40, graph each rational function using transformations. Verify your results using a graphing utility.

29. $F(x) = 2 + \dfrac{1}{x}$

30. $Q(x) = 3 + \dfrac{1}{x^2}$

31. $R(x) = \dfrac{1}{(x-1)^2}$

32. $R(x) = \dfrac{3}{x}$

33. $H(x) = \dfrac{-2}{x+1}$

34. $G(x) = \dfrac{2}{(x+2)^2}$

35. $R(x) = \dfrac{-1}{x^2 + 4x + 4}$

36. $R(x) = \dfrac{1}{x-1} + 1$

37. $G(x) = 1 + \dfrac{2}{(x-3)^2}$

38. $F(x) = 2 - \dfrac{1}{x+1}$

39. $R(x) = \dfrac{x^2 - 4}{x^2}$

40. $R(x) = \dfrac{x-4}{x}$

In Problems 41–52, find the vertical, horizontal, and oblique asymptotes, if any, of each rational function.

41. $R(x) = \dfrac{3x}{x+4}$

42. $R(x) = \dfrac{3x+5}{x-6}$

43. $H(x) = \dfrac{x^3 - 8}{x^2 - 5x + 6}$

44. $G(x) = \dfrac{x^3 + 1}{x^2 - 5x + 6}$

45. $T(x) = \dfrac{x^3}{x^4 - 1}$

46. $P(x) = \dfrac{4x^2}{x^3 - 1}$

47. $Q(x) = \dfrac{2x^2 - 5x - 12}{3x^2 - 11x - 4}$

48. $F(x) = \dfrac{x^2 + 6x + 5}{2x^2 + 7x + 5}$

49. $R(x) = \dfrac{6x^2 + 7x - 5}{3x + 5}$

50. $R(x) = \dfrac{8x^2 + 26x - 7}{4x - 1}$

51. $G(x) = \dfrac{x^4 - 1}{x^2 - x}$

52. $F(x) = \dfrac{x^4 - 16}{x^2 - 2x}$

Applications and Extensions

53. Gravity In physics, it is established that the acceleration due to gravity, g (in meters/sec^2), at a height h meters above sea level is given by

$$g(h) = \frac{3.99 \times 10^{14}}{(6.374 \times 10^6 + h)^2}$$

where 6.374×10^6 is the radius of Earth in meters.
(a) What is the acceleration due to gravity at sea level?
(b) The Sears Tower in Chicago, Illinois, is 443 meters tall. What is the acceleration due to gravity at the top of the Sears Tower?
(c) The peak of Mount Everest is 8848 meters above sea level. What is the acceleration due to gravity on the peak of Mount Everest?
(d) Find the horizontal asymptote of $g(h)$.
(e) Solve $g(h) = 0$. How do you interpret your answer?

54. Population Model A rare species of insect was discovered in the Amazon Rain Forest. To protect the species,

environmentalists declare the insect endangered and transplant the insect into a protected area. The population P of the insect t months after being transplanted is

$$P(t) = \frac{50(1 + 0.5t)}{(2 + 0.01t)}$$

(a) How many insects were discovered? In other words, what was the population when $t = 0$?
(b) What will the population be after 5 years?
(c) Determine the horizontal asymptote of $P(t)$. What is the largest population that the protected area can sustain?

55. Resistance in Parallel Circuits From Ohm's law for circuits, it follows that the total resistance R_{tot} of two components hooked in parallel is given by the equation

$$R_{tot} = \frac{R_1 R_2}{R_1 + R_2}$$

where R_1 and R_2 are the individual resistances.

(a) Let $R_1 = 10$ ohms, and graph R_{tot} as a function of R_2.
(b) Find and interpret any asymptotes of the graph obtained in part (a).
(c) If $R_2 = 2\sqrt{R_1}$, what value of R_1 will yield an R_{tot} of 17 ohms?

Source: en.wikipedia.org/wiki/Series_and_parallel_circuits

56. Newton's Method In calculus you will learn that, if

$$p(x) = a_n x^n + a_{n-1}x^{n-1} + \cdots + a_1 x + a_0$$

is a polynomial, then the *derivative* of $p(x)$ is

$$p'(x) = na_n x^{n-1} + (n-1)a_{n-1}x^{n-2} + \cdots + 2a_2 x + a_1$$

Newton's Method is an efficient method for finding the *x*-intercepts (or real zeros) of a function, such as $p(x)$. The following steps outline Newton's Method.

STEP 1: Select an initial value x_0 that is somewhat close to the *x*-intercept being sought.

STEP 2: Find values for x using the relation

$$x_{n+1} = x_n - \frac{p(x_n)}{p'(x_n)} \quad n = 1, 2, \ldots$$

until you get two consecutive values x_n and x_{n+1} that agree to whatever decimal place accuracy you desire.

STEP 3: The approximate zero will be x_{n+1}.

Consider the polynomial $p(x) = x^3 - 7x - 40$.

(a) Evaluate $p(5)$ and $p(-3)$.
(b) What might we conclude about a zero of p? Explain.
(c) Use Newton's Method to approximate an *x*-intercept, r, $-3 < r < 5$, of $p(x)$ to four decimal places.
(d) Use a graphing utility to graph $p(x)$ and verify your answer in part (c).
(e) Using a graphing utility, evaluate $p(r)$ to verify your result.

Discussion and Writing

57. If the graph of a rational function R has the vertical asymptote $x = 4$, the factor $x - 4$ must be present in the denominator of R. Explain why.

58. If the graph of a rational function R has the horizontal asymptote $y = 2$, the degree of the numerator of R equals the degree of the denominator of R. Explain why.

59. Can the graph of a rational function have both a horizontal and an oblique asymptote? Explain.

60. Make up a rational function that has $y = 2x + 1$ as an oblique asymptote. Explain the methodology that you used.

'Are You Prepared?' Answers

1. True   **2.** Quotient: $3x + 3$; remainder: $2x^2 - 3x - 3$ **3.**

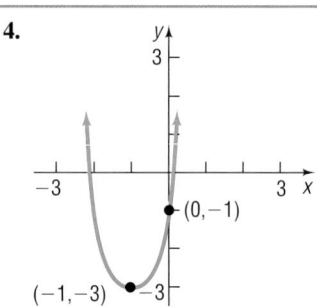

4.

4.3 The Graph of a Rational Function

PREPARING FOR THIS SECTION *Before getting started, review the following:*

- Finding Intercepts (Section 1.2, pp. 18–19)
- Even or Odd Functions (Section 2.3, pp. 79–81)
- Solving Rational Equations (Appendix A, Section A.6, p. A49)

Now Work the 'Are You Prepared?' problems on page 210.

> **OBJECTIVES** **1** Analyze the Graph of a Rational Function (p. 202)
> **2** Solve Applied Problems Involving Rational Functions (p. 209)

1 Analyze the Graph of a Rational Function

Graphing utilities make the task of graphing rational functions less time consuming. However, the results of algebraic analysis must be taken into account before drawing conclusions based on the graph provided by the utility. In the next example we illustrate how to use the information collected in the last section in conjunction with the graphing utility to analyze the graph of a rational function $R(x) = \dfrac{p(x)}{q(x)}$.

| EXAMPLE 1 | **How to Analyze the Graph of a Rational Function** |

Analyze the graph of the rational function: $\quad R(x) = \dfrac{x-1}{x^2-4}$

Step-by-Step Solution

STEP 1 Factor the numerator and denominator of R. Find the domain of the rational function.

$$R(x) = \frac{x-1}{x^2-4} = \frac{x-1}{(x+2)(x-2)}$$

The domain of R is $\{x \mid x \neq -2, x \neq 2\}$.

STEP 2 Write R in lowest terms.

Because there are no common factors between the numerator and denominator, R is in lowest terms.

STEP 3 Locate the intercepts of the graph.

The x-intercepts are found by determining the real zeros of the numerator of R written in lowest terms. By solving $x - 1 = 0$, we find the only real zero of the numerator is 1, so the only x-intercept of the graph of R is 1. Since 0 is in the domain of R, the y-intercept is $R(0) = \dfrac{1}{4}$.

STEP 4 Test for symmetry. If $R(-x) = R(x)$, the function is even and its graph will be symmetric with respect to the y-axis. If $R(-x) = -R(x)$, the function is odd and its graph will be symmetric with respect to the origin.

Because

$$R(-x) = \frac{-x-1}{(-x)^2-4} = \frac{-x-1}{x^2-4} = -\frac{x+1}{x^2-4}$$

we conclude that $R(-x) \neq R(x)$, so R is not even. Because $R(-x) \neq -R(x)$, R is not odd. So there is no symmetry with respect to the y-axis or the origin.

STEP 5 Locate the vertical asymptotes.

We locate the vertical asymptotes by finding the zeros of the denominator with the rational function in lowest terms. With R written in lowest terms, we find that the graph of R has two vertical asymptotes: the lines $x = -2$ and $x = 2$.

STEP 6 Locate the horizontal or oblique asymptotes. Determine points, if any, at which the graph of R intersects these asymptotes.

Because the degree of the numerator is less than the degree of the denominator, R is proper and the line $y = 0$ (the x-axis) is a horizontal asymptote of the graph. To determine if the graph of R intersects the horizontal asymptote, we solve the equation $R(x) = 0$:

$$\frac{x-1}{x^2-4} = 0$$
$$x - 1 = 0$$
$$x = 1$$

The only solution is $x = 1$, so the graph of R intersects the horizontal asymptote at $(1, 0)$.

STEP 7 Graph R using a graphing utility.

The analysis in Steps 1 through 6 helps us to determine an appropriate viewing window to obtain a complete graph. Figure 26(a) shows the graph of $R(x) = \dfrac{x-1}{x^2-4}$ in connected mode, and Figure 26(b) shows it in dot mode. Notice in Figure 26(a) that the graph has vertical lines at $x = -2$ and $x = 2$. This is due to the fact that, when the graphing utility is in connected mode, it will "connect the dots" between consecutive pixels. We know that the graph of R does not cross the lines $x = -2$ and $x = 2$, since R is not defined at $x = -2$ or $x = 2$. When graphing rational functions, dot mode should be used if extraneous vertical lines appear. You should confirm that all the algebraic conclusions that we came to in Steps 1 through 6 are part of the graph.

For example, the graph has a horizontal asymptote at $y = 0$ and vertical asymptotes at $x = -2$ and $x = 2$. The y-intercept is $\frac{1}{4}$ and the x-intercept is 1.

Figure 26

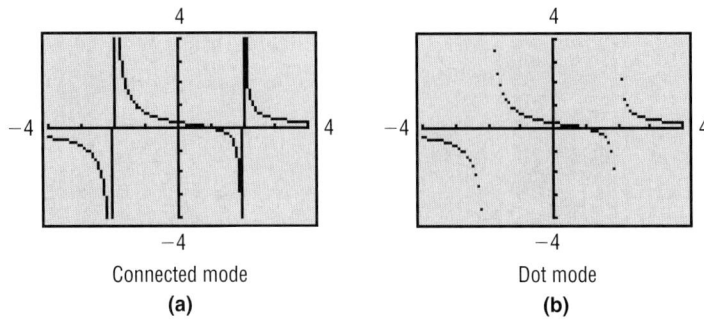

Connected mode
(a)

Dot mode
(b)

STEP 8 Use the results obtained in Steps 1 through 7 to graph R by hand.

Figure 27 shows the graph of R.

Figure 27

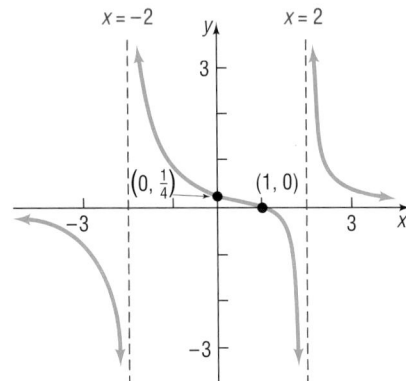

Below we summarize the steps to be used when analyzing a rational function.

Analyzing the Graph of a Rational Function

STEP 1: Factor the numerator and denominator of R. Find the domain of the rational function.

STEP 2: Write R in lowest terms.

STEP 3: Locate the intercepts of the graph. The x-intercepts, if any, of $R(x) = \dfrac{p(x)}{q(x)}$ in lowest terms satisfy the equation $p(x) = 0$. The y-intercept, if there is one, is $R(0)$.

STEP 4: Test for symmetry. Replace x by $-x$ in $R(x)$. If $R(-x) = R(x)$, there is symmetry with respect to the y-axis; if $R(-x) = -R(x)$, there is symmetry with respect to the origin.

STEP 5: Locate the vertical asymptotes. The vertical asymptotes, if any, of $R(x) = \dfrac{p(x)}{q(x)}$ in lowest terms are found by identifying the real zeros of $q(x)$. Each zero of the denominator gives rise to a vertical asymptote.

STEP 6: Locate the horizontal or oblique asymptotes, if any, using the procedure given in Section 4.2. Determine points, if any, at which the graph of R intersects these asymptotes.

STEP 7: Graph R using a graphing utility.

STEP 8: Use the results obtained in Steps 1 through 7 to graph R by hand.

Now Work PROBLEM 7

| EXAMPLE 2 | Analyzing the Graph of a Rational Function |

Analyze the graph of the rational function: $R(x) = \dfrac{x^2 - 1}{x}$

Solution **STEP 1:** $R(x) = \dfrac{x^2 - 1}{x} = \dfrac{(x + 1)(x - 1)}{x}$

The domain of R is $\{x \mid x \neq 0\}$.

STEP 2: R is in lowest terms.

STEP 3: The graph has two x-intercepts: -1 and 1. There is no y-intercept, since x cannot equal 0.

STEP 4: Since $R(-x) = -R(x)$, the function is odd and the graph is symmetric with respect to the origin.

STEP 5: The real zero of the denominator with R in lowest terms is 0, so the graph of $R(x)$ has the line $x = 0$ (the y-axis) as a vertical asymptote.

STEP 6: Since the degree of the numerator, 2, is one more than the degree of the denominator, 1, the rational function R is improper and will have an oblique asymptote. To find the oblique asymptote, we use long division.

$$
\begin{array}{r}
x \\
x\overline{)x^2 - 1} \\
\underline{x^2 } \\
-1
\end{array}
$$

NOTE *Because the denominator of the rational function is a monomial, we can also find the oblique asymptote as follows:*

$$\frac{x^2 - 1}{x} = \frac{x^2}{x} - \frac{1}{x} = x - \frac{1}{x}$$

Since $\dfrac{1}{x} \to 0$ *as* $x \to \infty$, $y = x$ *is an oblique asymptote.* ∎

The quotient is x, so the line $y = x$ is an oblique asymptote of the graph. To determine whether the graph of R intersects the asymptote $y = x$, we solve the equation $R(x) = x$.

$$R(x) = \frac{x^2 - 1}{x} = x$$
$$x^2 - 1 = x^2$$
$$-1 = 0 \quad \text{Impossible.}$$

We conclude that the equation $\dfrac{x^2 - 1}{x} = x$ has no solution, so the graph of $R(x)$ does not intersect the line $y = x$.

STEP 7: See Figure 28. We see from the graph that there is no y-intercept and there are two x-intercepts, -1 and 1. The symmetry with respect to the origin is also evident. We can also see that there is a vertical asymptote at $x = 0$. Finally, it is not necessary to graph this function in dot mode since no extraneous vertical lines are present.

STEP 8: Using the information gathered in Steps 1 through 7, we obtain the graph of R shown in Figure 29. Notice how the oblique asymptote is used as a guide in graphing the rational function by hand.

Figure 28

Figure 29

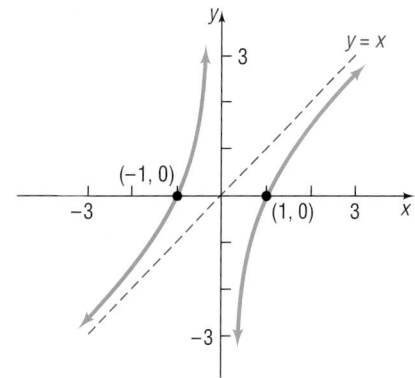

Now Work PROBLEM 15

| EXAMPLE 3 | Analyzing the Graph of a Rational Function |

Analyze the graph of the rational function: $R(x) = \dfrac{3x^2 - 3x}{x^2 + x - 12}$

Solution **STEP 1:** We factor R to get

$$R(x) = \frac{3x(x - 1)}{(x + 4)(x - 3)}$$

The domain of R is $\{x \mid x \neq -4, x \neq 3\}$.

STEP 2: R is in lowest terms.

STEP 3: The graph has two x-intercepts: 0 and 1. The y-intercept is $R(0) = 0$.

STEP 4: Because

$$R(-x) = \frac{3(-x)^2 - 3(-x)}{(-x)^2 + (-x) - 12} = \frac{3x^2 + 3x}{x^2 - x - 12}$$

we conclude that R is neither even nor odd. There is no symmetry with respect to the y-axis or the origin.

STEP 5: The real zeros of the denominator of R with R in lowest terms are -4 and 3. So the graph of R has two vertical asymptotes: $x = -4$ and $x = 3$.

STEP 6: Since the degree of the numerator equals the degree of the denominator, the graph has a horizontal asymptote. To find it, we form the quotient of the leading coefficient of the numerator, 3, and the leading coefficient of the denominator, 1. The graph of R has the horizontal asymptote $y = 3$. To find out whether the graph of R intersects the asymptote, we solve the equation $R(x) = 3$.

$$R(x) = \frac{3x^2 - 3x}{x^2 + x - 12} = 3$$
$$3x^2 - 3x = 3x^2 + 3x - 36$$
$$-6x = -36$$
$$x = 6$$

The graph intersects the line $y = 3$ at $x = 6$, and $(6, 3)$ is a point on the graph of R.

STEP 7: Figure 30(a) shows the graph of R in connected mode. Notice the extraneous vertical lines at $x = -4$ and $x = 3$ (the vertical asymptotes). As a result, we also graph R in dot mode. See Figure 30(b).

STEP 8: Figure 30 does not display the graph between the two x-intercepts, 0 and 1. However, because the zeros in the numerator, 0 and 1, are of odd multiplicity (both are multiplicity 1), we know that the graph of R crosses the x-axis at 0 and 1. Therefore, the graph of R is above the x-axis for $0 < x < 1$. To see this part better, we graph R for $-1 \le x \le 2$ in Figure 31. Using MAXIMUM, we approximate the turning point to be $(0.52, 0.07)$, rounded to two decimal places.

Figure 30

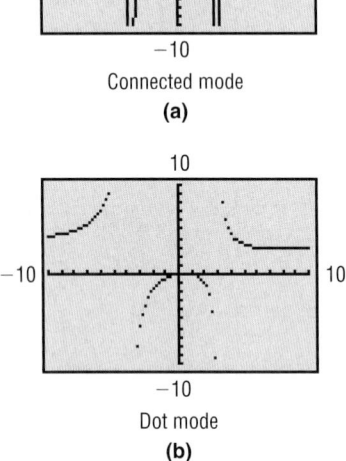

Connected mode
(a)

Dot mode
(b)

Figure 31

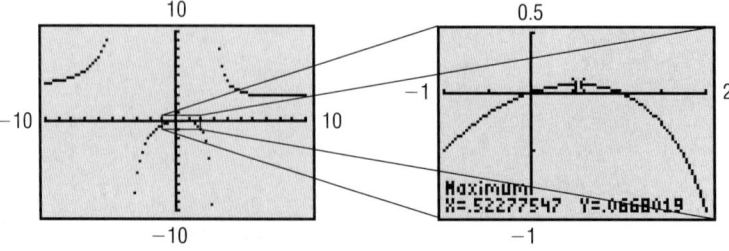

Figure 30 also does not display the graph of R crossing the horizontal asymptote at $(6, 3)$. To see this part better, we graph R for $4 \leq x \leq 60$ in Figure 32. Using MINIMUM, we approximate the turning point to be $(11.48, 2.75)$, rounded to two decimal places.

Figure 32

Using this information along with the information gathered in Steps 1 through 7, we obtain the graph of R shown in Figure 33.

Figure 33

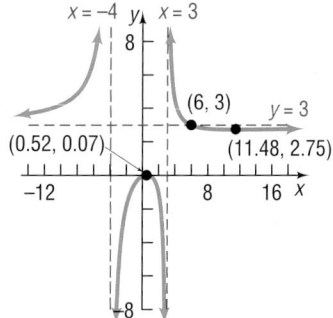

EXAMPLE 4	**Analyzing the Graph of a Rational Function with a Hole**

Analyze the graph of the rational function: $R(x) = \dfrac{2x^2 - 5x + 2}{x^2 - 4}$

Solution **STEP 1:** We factor R and obtain

$$R(x) = \frac{(2x - 1)(x - 2)}{(x + 2)(x - 2)}$$

The domain of R is $\{x \mid x \neq -2, x \neq 2\}$.

STEP 2: In lowest terms,

$$R(x) = \frac{2x - 1}{x + 2} \qquad x \neq 2$$

STEP 3: The graph has one x-intercept: 0.5. The y-intercept is $R(0) = -0.5$.

STEP 4: Because

$$R(-x) = \frac{2x^2 + 5x + 2}{x^2 - 4}$$

we conclude that R is neither even nor odd. There is no symmetry with respect to the y-axis or the origin.

STEP 5: Since $x + 2$ is the only factor of the denominator of $R(x)$ *in lowest terms,* the graph has one vertical asymptote, $x = -2$. However, the rational function is undefined at both $x = 2$ and $x = -2$.

STEP 6: Since the degree of the numerator equals the degree of the denominator, the graph has a horizontal asymptote. To find it, we form the quotient of the leading coefficient of the numerator, 2, and the leading coefficient of the denominator, 1. The graph of R has the horizontal asymptote $y = 2$. To find whether the graph of R intersects the asymptote, we solve the equation $R(x) = 2$.

$$R(x) = \frac{2x - 1}{x + 2} = 2$$

$$2x - 1 = 2(x + 2)$$

$$2x - 1 = 2x + 4$$

$$-1 = 4 \qquad \text{Impossible}$$

The graph does not intersect the line $y = 2$.

STEP 7: Figure 34 shows the graph of $R(x)$. Notice that the graph has one vertical asymptote at $x = -2$. Also, the function appears to be continuous at $x = 2$.

STEP 8: The analysis presented thus far does not explain the behavior of the graph at $x = 2$. We use the TABLE feature of our graphing utility to determine the behavior of the graph of R as x approaches 2. See Table 13. From the table, we conclude that the value of R approaches 0.75 as x approaches 2. This result is further verified by evaluating R in lowest terms at $x = 2$. We conclude that there is a hole in the graph at $(2, 0.75)$. Using the information gathered in Steps 1 through 7, we obtain the graph of R shown in Figure 35.

Figure 34

Table 13

Figure 35

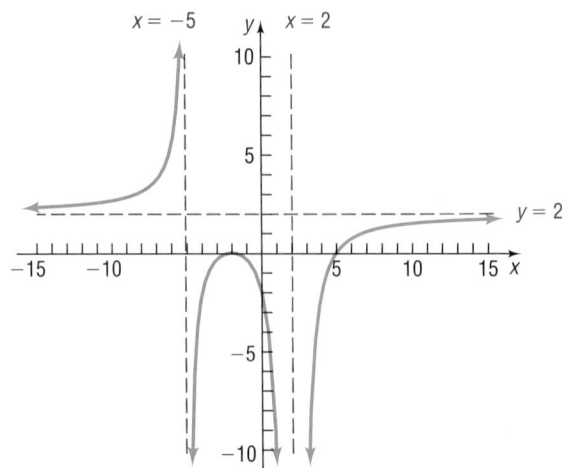

As Example 4 shows, **the values excluded from the domain of a rational function give rise to either vertical asymptotes or holes.**

➤ **Now Work** PROBLEM 33

| EXAMPLE 5 | **Constructing a Rational Function from Its Graph** |

Make up a rational function that might have the graph shown in Figure 36.

Figure 36

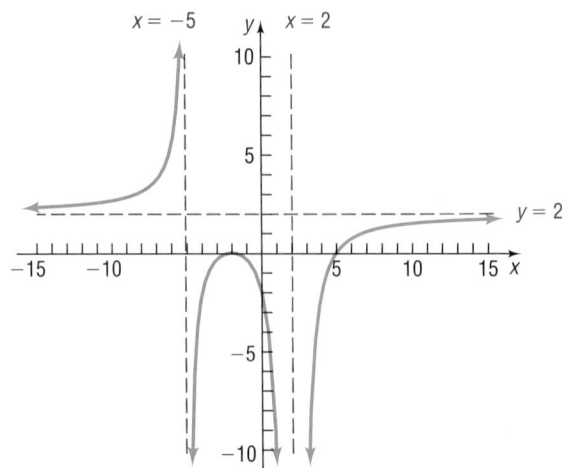

Solution   The numerator of a rational function $R(x) = \dfrac{p(x)}{q(x)}$ in lowest terms determines the
x-intercepts of its graph. The graph shown in Figure 36 has x-intercepts -2 (even
multiplicity; graph touches the x-axis) and 5 (odd multiplicity; graph crosses the
x-axis). So one possibility for the numerator is $p(x) = (x + 2)^2(x - 5)$.

The denominator of a rational function in lowest terms determines the vertical
asymptotes of its graph. The vertical asymptotes of the graph are $x = -5$ and $x = 2$.
Since $R(x)$ approaches ∞ from the left of $x = -5$ and $R(x)$ approaches $-\infty$ from
the right of $x = -5$, we know that $(x + 5)$ is a factor of odd multiplicity in $q(x)$.
Also, $R(x)$ approaches $-\infty$ from both sides of $x = 2$, so $(x - 2)$ is a factor of even
multiplicity in $q(x)$. A possibility for the denominator is $q(x) = (x + 5)(x - 2)^2$.

So far we have $R(x) = \dfrac{(x + 2)^2(x - 5)}{(x + 5)(x - 2)^2}$. However, the horizontal asymptote

Figure 37

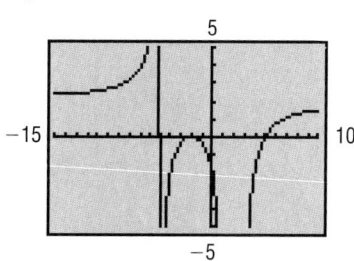

of the graph given in Figure 36 is $y = 2$, so we know that the degree of the numerator must equal the degree of the denominator, and the quotient of leading

coefficients must be $\dfrac{2}{1}$. This leads to $R(x) = \dfrac{2(x + 2)^2(x - 5)}{(x + 5)(x - 2)^2}$. Figure 37 shows

the graph of R drawn on a graphing utility. Since Figure 37 looks similar to Figure 36,
we have found a rational function R for the graph in Figure 36.

 Now Work PROBLEM 51

2 Solve Applied Problems Involving Rational Functions

EXAMPLE 6 | **Finding the Least Cost of a Can**

Reynolds Metal Company manufactures aluminum cans in the shape of a cylinder
with a capacity of 500 cubic centimeters (cm^3), or $\dfrac{1}{2}$ liter. The top and bottom of
the can are made of a special aluminum alloy that costs 0.05¢/per square cen-
timeter (cm^2). The sides of the can are made of material that costs 0.02¢/cm^2.

(a) Express the cost of material for the can as a function of the radius r of the can.
(b) Use a graphing utility to graph the function $C = C(r)$.
(c) What value of r will result in the least cost?
(d) What is this least cost?

Solution   (a) Figure 38 illustrates the situation. Notice that the material required to produce
a cylindrical can of height h and radius r consists of a rectangle of area $2\pi rh$
and two circles, each of area πr^2. The total cost C (in cents) of manufacturing
the can is therefore

Figure 38

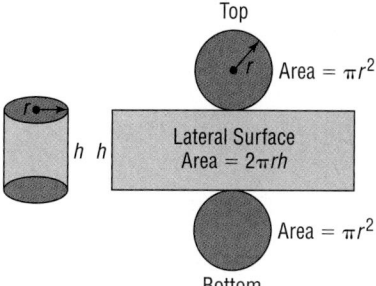

$$C = \text{Cost of the top and bottom} + \text{Cost of the side}$$
$$= \underbrace{2(\pi r^2)}_{\substack{\text{Total area} \\ \text{of top and} \\ \text{bottom}}} \underbrace{(0.05)}_{\substack{\text{Cost/unit} \\ \text{area}}} + \underbrace{(2\pi rh)}_{\substack{\text{Total} \\ \text{area of} \\ \text{side}}} \underbrace{(0.02)}_{\substack{\text{Cost/unit} \\ \text{area}}}$$
$$= 0.10\pi r^2 + 0.04\pi rh$$

But we have the additional restriction that the height h and radius r must be
chosen so that the volume V of the can is 500 cm^3. Since $V = \pi r^2 h$, we have

$$500 = \pi r^2 h \quad \text{or} \quad h = \frac{500}{\pi r^2}$$

Figure 39

Substituting this expression for h, the cost C, in cents, as a function of the radius r, is

$$C(r) = 0.10\pi r^2 + 0.04\pi r \frac{500}{\pi r^2} = 0.10\pi r^2 + \frac{20}{r} = \frac{0.10\pi r^3 + 20}{r}$$

(b) See Figure 39 for the graph of $C = C(r)$.

(c) Using the MINIMUM command, the cost is least for a radius of about 3.17 cm.

(d) The least cost is $C(3.17) \approx 9.47¢$.

Now Work PROBLEM 61

4.3 Assess Your Understanding

'Are You Prepared?' *The answers are given at the end of these exercises. If you get a wrong answer, read the pages listed in* red.

1. (a) Find the intercepts of the graph of the function $f(x) = \dfrac{x^2 - 1}{x^2 - 4}$. (pp. 18–19; 73)

   (b) Is the function in part (a) even, odd, or neither? (pp. 79–81)

2. Solve $\dfrac{x - 3}{x^2 + 1} = -2$. (p. A49)

Concepts and Vocabulary

3. If the numerator and the denominator of a rational function have no common factors, the rational function is _____.

4. *True or False* The graph of a rational function never intersects a horizontal asymptote.

5. *True or False* The graph of a rational function sometimes intersects a vertical asymptote.

6. *True or False* The graph of a rational function sometimes has a hole.

Skill Building

In Problems 7–44, follow Steps 1 through 8 on page 204 to analyze the graph of each function.

7. $R(x) = \dfrac{x + 1}{x(x + 4)}$

8. $R(x) = \dfrac{x}{(x - 1)(x + 2)}$

9. $R(x) = \dfrac{3x + 3}{2x + 4}$

10. $R(x) = \dfrac{2x + 4}{x - 1}$

11. $R(x) = \dfrac{3}{x^2 - 4}$

12. $R(x) = \dfrac{6}{x^2 - x - 6}$

13. $P(x) = \dfrac{x^4 + x^2 + 1}{x^2 - 1}$

14. $Q(x) = \dfrac{x^4 - 1}{x^2 - 4}$

15. $H(x) = \dfrac{x^3 - 1}{x^2 - 9}$

16. $G(x) = \dfrac{x^3 + 1}{x^2 + 2x}$

17. $R(x) = \dfrac{x^2}{x^2 + x - 6}$

18. $R(x) = \dfrac{x^2 + x - 12}{x^2 - 4}$

19. $G(x) = \dfrac{x}{x^2 - 4}$

20. $G(x) = \dfrac{3x}{x^2 - 1}$

21. $R(x) = \dfrac{3}{(x - 1)(x^2 - 4)}$

22. $R(x) = \dfrac{-4}{(x + 1)(x^2 - 9)}$

23. $H(x) = \dfrac{4(x^2 - 1)}{x^4 - 16}$

24. $H(x) = \dfrac{x^2 + 4}{x^4 - 1}$

25. $F(x) = \dfrac{x^2 - 3x - 4}{x + 2}$

26. $F(x) = \dfrac{x^2 + 3x + 2}{x - 1}$

27. $R(x) = \dfrac{x^2 + x - 12}{x - 4}$

28. $R(x) = \dfrac{x^2 - x - 12}{x + 5}$

29. $F(x) = \dfrac{x^2 + x - 12}{x + 2}$

30. $G(x) = \dfrac{x^2 - x - 12}{x + 1}$

31. $R(x) = \dfrac{x(x - 1)^2}{(x + 3)^3}$

32. $R(x) = \dfrac{(x - 1)(x + 2)(x - 3)}{x(x - 4)^2}$

33. $R(x) = \dfrac{x^2 + x - 12}{x^2 - x - 6}$

34. $R(x) = \dfrac{x^2 + 3x - 10}{x^2 + 8x + 15}$

35. $R(x) = \dfrac{6x^2 - 7x - 3}{2x^2 - 7x + 6}$

36. $R(x) = \dfrac{8x^2 + 26x + 15}{2x^2 - x - 15}$

37. $R(x) = \dfrac{x^2 + 5x + 6}{x + 3}$

38. $R(x) = \dfrac{x^2 + x - 30}{x + 6}$

39. $f(x) = x + \dfrac{1}{x}$

40. $f(x) = 2x + \dfrac{9}{x}$

41. $f(x) = x^2 + \dfrac{1}{x}$

42. $f(x) = 2x^2 + \dfrac{9}{x}$

43. $f(x) = x + \dfrac{1}{x^3}$

44. $f(x) = 2x + \dfrac{9}{x^3}$

In Problems 45–50, graph each function using a graphing utility; then use MINIMUM to obtain the minimum value, rounded to two decimal places.

45. $f(x) = x + \dfrac{1}{x}, \quad x > 0$

46. $f(x) = 2x + \dfrac{9}{x}, \quad x > 0$

47. $f(x) = x^2 + \dfrac{1}{x}, \quad x > 0$

48. $f(x) = 2x^2 + \dfrac{9}{x}, \quad x > 0$

49. $f(x) = x + \dfrac{1}{x^3}, \quad x > 0$

50. $f(x) = 2x + \dfrac{9}{x^3}, \quad x > 0$

In Problems 51–54, find a rational function that might have the given graph. (More than one answer might be possible.)

51.

52.

53.

54.

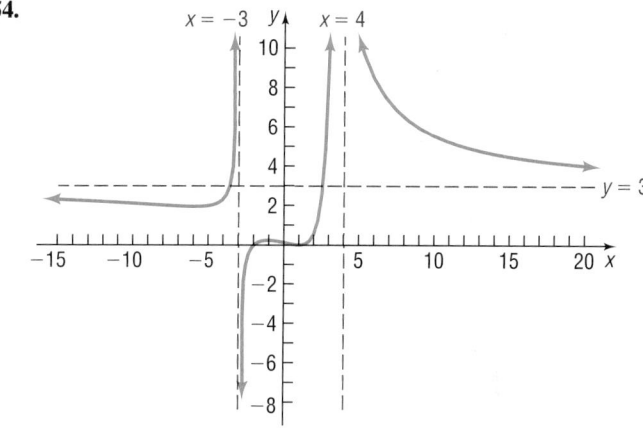

Applications and Extensions

55. Drug Concentration The concentration C of a certain drug in a patient's bloodstream t hours after injection is given by

$$C(t) = \frac{t}{2t^2 + 1}$$

(a) Find the horizontal asymptote of $C(t)$. What happens to the concentration of the drug as t increases?
(b) Using your graphing utility, graph $C = C(t)$.
(c) Determine the time at which the concentration is highest.

56. Drug Concentration The concentration C of a certain drug in a patient's bloodstream t minutes after injection is given by

$$C(t) = \frac{50t}{t^2 + 25}$$

(a) Find the horizontal asymptote of $C(t)$. What happens to the concentration of the drug as t increases?
(b) Using your graphing utility, graph $C = C(t)$.
(c) Determine the time at which the concentration is highest.

57. Minimum Cost A rectangular area adjacent to a river is to be fenced in; no fence is needed on the river side. The enclosed area is to be 1000 square feet. Fencing for the side parallel to the river is $5 per linear foot, and fencing for the other two sides is $8 per linear foot; the four corner posts are $25

apiece. Let x be the length of one of the sides perpendicular to the river.
(a) Write a function $C(x)$ that describes the cost of the project.
(b) What is the domain of C?
(c) Use a graphing utility to graph $C = C(x)$.
(d) Find the dimensions of the cheapest enclosure.

Source: www.uncwil.edu/courses/math111hb/PandR/rational/ rational.html

58. Doppler Effect The Doppler effect (named after Christian Doppler) is the change in the pitch (frequency) of the sound from a source (s) as heard by an observer (o) when one or both are in motion. If we assume both the source and the observer are moving in the same direction, the relationship is

$$f' = f_a \left(\frac{v - v_o}{v - v_s} \right)$$

where f' = perceived pitch by the observer
         f_a = actual pitch of the source
         v = speed of sound in air (assume 772.4 mph)
         v_o = speed of the observer
         v_s = speed of the source

Suppose you are traveling down the road at 45 mph and you hear an ambulance (with siren) coming toward you from the rear. The actual pitch of the siren is 600 hertz (Hz).

(a) Write a function $f'(v_s)$ that describes this scenario.
(b) If $f' = 620$ Hz, find the speed of the ambulance.
(c) Use a graphing utility to graph the function.
(d) Verify your answer from part (b).

Source: www.kettering.edu/~drussell/

59. **Minimizing Surface Area** United Parcel Service has contracted you to design a closed box with a square base that has a volume of 10,000 cubic inches. See the illustration.

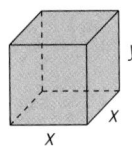

(a) Express the surface area S of the box as a function of x.
(b) Using a graphing utility, graph the function found in part (a).
(c) What is the minimum amount of cardboard that can be used to construct the box?
(d) What are the dimensions of the box that minimize the surface area?
(e) Why might UPS be interested in designing a box that minimizes the surface area?

60. **Minimizing Surface Area** United Parcel Service has contracted you to design an open box with a square base that has a volume of 5000 cubic inches. See the illustration.

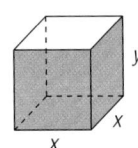

(a) Express the surface area S of the box as a function of x.
(b) Using a graphing utility, graph the function found in part (a).
(c) What is the minimum amount of cardboard that can be used to construct the box?
(d) What are the dimensions of the box that minimize the surface area?
(e) Why might UPS be interested in designing a box that minimizes the surface area?

61. **Cost of a Can** A can in the shape of a right circular cylinder is required to have a volume of 500 cubic centimeters. The top and bottom are made of material that costs 6¢ per square centimeter, while the sides are made of material that costs 4¢ per square centimeter.
(a) Express the total cost C of the material as a function of the radius r of the cylinder. (Refer to Figure 38.)
(b) Graph $C = C(r)$. For what value of r is the cost C a minimum?

62. **Material Needed to Make a Drum** A steel drum in the shape of a right circular cylinder is required to have a volume of 100 cubic feet.

(a) Express the amount A of material required to make the drum as a function of the radius r of the cylinder.
(b) How much material is required if the drum's radius is 3 feet?
(c) How much material is required if the drum's radius is 4 feet?
(d) How much material is required if the drum's radius is 5 feet?
(e) Graph $A = A(r)$. For what value of r is A smallest?

Discussion and Writing

63. Graph each of the following functions:

$$y = \frac{x^2 - 1}{x - 1} \qquad y = \frac{x^3 - 1}{x - 1}$$

$$y = \frac{x^4 - 1}{x - 1} \qquad y = \frac{x^5 - 1}{x - 1}$$

Is $x = 1$ a vertical asymptote? Why not? What is happening for $x = 1$? What do you conjecture about $y = \dfrac{x^n - 1}{x - 1}$, $n \geq 1$ an integer, for $x = 1$?

64. Graph each of the following functions:

$$y = \frac{x^2}{x - 1} \qquad y = \frac{x^4}{x - 1} \qquad y = \frac{x^6}{x - 1} \qquad y = \frac{x^8}{x - 1}$$

What similarities do you see? What differences?

65. Write a few paragraphs that provide a general strategy for graphing a rational function. Be sure to mention the following: proper, improper, intercepts, and asymptotes.

66. Create a rational function that has the following characteristics: crosses the x-axis at 2; touches the x-axis at -1; one vertical asymptote at $x = -5$ and another at $x = 6$; and one horizontal asymptote, $y = 3$. Compare your function to a fellow classmate's. How do they differ? What are their similarities?

67. Create a rational function that has the following characteristics: crosses the x-axis at 3; touches the x-axis at -2; one vertical asymptote, $x = 1$; and one horizontal asymptote, $y = 2$. Give your rational function to a fellow classmate and ask for a written critique of your rational function.

68. Create a rational function with the following characteristics: three real zeros, one of multiplicity 2; y-intercept 1; vertical asymptotes, $x = -2$ and $x = 3$; oblique asymptote, $y = 2x + 1$. Is this rational function unique? Compare your function with those of other students. What will be the same as everyone else's? Add some more characteristics, such as symmetry or naming the real zeros. How does this modify the rational function?

69. Explain the circumstances under which the graph of a rational function will have a hole.

'Are You Prepared?' Answers

1. (a) $\left(0, \frac{1}{4}\right), (1, 0), (-1, 0)$ (b) Even   **2.** $\left\{-1, \frac{1}{2}\right\}$

4.4 Polynomial and Rational Inequalities

PREPARING FOR THIS SECTION *Before getting started, review the following:*

• Solving Linear Inequalities (Appendix A, Section A.9, pp. A81–A83)

• Solving Quadratic Inequalities (Section 3.5, pp. 164–166)

 Now Work the 'Are You Prepared?' problem on page 217.

OBJECTIVES 1 Solve Polynomial Inequalities Algebraically and Graphically (p. 213)
2 Solve Rational Inequalities Algebraically and Graphically (p. 215)

1 Solve Polynomial Inequalities Algebraically and Graphically

In this section we solve inequalities that involve polynomials of degree 3 and higher, along with inequalities that involve rational functions. To help understand the algebraic procedure for solving such inequalities, we use the information obtained in the previous three sections about the graphs of polynomial and rational functions. The approach follows the same logic as we used to solve inequalities involving quadratic functions.

EXAMPLE 1 **Solving a Polynomial Inequality Using Its Graph**

Solve $(x + 3)(x - 1)^2 > 0$ by graphing $f(x) = (x + 3)(x - 1)^2$.

By Hand Graphical Solution

We graph $f(x) = (x + 3)(x - 1)^2$ and determine the intervals of x for which the graph is above the x-axis. Do you see why? These values of x result in $f(x)$ being positive. Using Steps 1 through 8 on page 185, we obtain the graph shown in Figure 40.

Figure 40

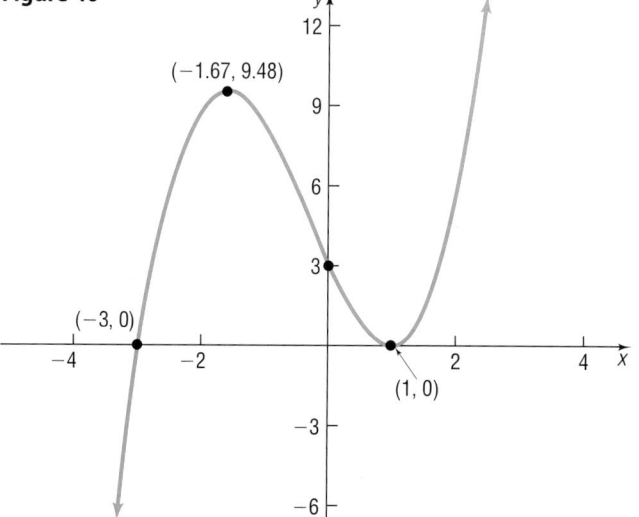

From the graph, we can see that $f(x) > 0$ for $-3 < x < 1$ or $x > 1$. The solution set is $\{x \mid -3 < x < 1 \text{ or } x > 1\}$ or, using interval notation, $(-3, 1) \cup (1, \infty)$.

Graphing Utility Solution

We graph $Y_1 = (x + 3)(x - 1)^2$. See Figure 41. Using the ZERO command, we find that the x-intercepts of the graph of Y_1 are -3 and 1. The graph of Y_1 is above the x-axis (and therefore f is positive) for $-3 < x < 1$ or $x > 1$. Therefore, the solution set is $\{x \mid -3 < x < 1 \text{ or } x > 1\}$ or, using interval notation, $(-3, 1) \cup (1, \infty)$.

Figure 41

 Now Work PROBLEM 9

The results of Example 1 lead to the following approach to solving polynomial inequalities algebraically. Suppose that the polynomial or rational inequality is in one of the forms

$$f(x) < 0 \qquad f(x) > 0 \qquad f(x) \le 0 \qquad f(x) \ge 0$$

Locate the zeros (x-intercepts of the graph) of the polynomial function f. We know that the sign of f can change on either side of an x-intercept, so we use these zeros to divide the real number line into intervals. Then we know that on each interval the graph of f is either above $[f(x) > 0]$ or below $[f(x) < 0]$ the x-axis.

EXAMPLE 2	**How to Solve a Polynomial Inequality Algebraically**

Solve the inequality $x^4 > x$ algebraically, and graph the solution set.

Step-by-Step Solution

STEP 1 Write the inequality so that a polynomial expression f is on the left side and zero is on the right side.

Rearrange the inequality so that 0 is on the right side.

$$x^4 > x$$

$$x^4 - x > 0 \qquad \text{Subtract } x \text{ from both sides of the inequality.}$$

This inequality is equivalent to the one we wish to solve.

STEP 2 Determine the real zeros (x-intercepts of the graph) of f.

Find the zeros of $f(x) = x^4 - x$ by solving $x^4 - x = 0$.

$$x^4 - x = 0$$

$$x(x^3 - 1) = 0 \qquad \text{Factor out } x.$$

$$x(x - 1)(x^2 + x + 1) = 0 \qquad \text{Factor the difference of two cubes.}$$

$$x = 0 \quad \text{or} \quad x - 1 = 0 \quad \text{or} \quad x^2 + x + 1 = 0 \qquad \text{Set each factor to zero and solve.}$$

$$x = 0 \quad \text{or} \qquad x = 1$$

The equation $x^2 + x + 1 = 0$ has no real solutions. Do you see why?

STEP 3 Use the zeros found in Step 2 to divide the real number line into intervals.

We use the zeros to separate the real number line into three intervals:

$$(-\infty, 0) \qquad (0, 1) \qquad (1, \infty)$$

STEP 4 Select a number in each interval, evaluate f at the number, and determine whether f is positive or negative. If f is positive, all values of x in the interval are positive. If f is negative, all values of x in the interval are negative.

Note: If the inequality is not strict ($\le$ or $\ge$), include the solutions of $f(x) = 0$ in the solution set.

We select a test number in each interval found in Step 3 and evaluate $f(x) = x^4 - x$ at each number to determine if $f(x)$ is positive or negative. See Table 14.

Table 14

Interval	$(-\infty, 0)$	$(0, 1)$	$(1, \infty)$
Number chosen	-1	$\dfrac{1}{2}$	2
Value of f	$f(-1) = 2$	$f\left(\dfrac{1}{2}\right) = -\dfrac{7}{16}$	$f(2) = 14$
Conclusion	Positive	Negative	Positive

Since we want to know where $f(x)$ is positive, we conclude that $f(x) > 0$ for all numbers x for which $x < 0$ or $x > 1$. Because the original inequality is strict, numbers x that satisfy the equation $x^4 = x$ are not solutions. The solution set of the inequality $x^4 > x$ is $\{x \mid x < 0 \text{ or } x > 1\}$ or, using interval notation, $(-\infty, 0) \cup (1, \infty)$.

Figure 42 shows the graph of the solution set.

Figure 42

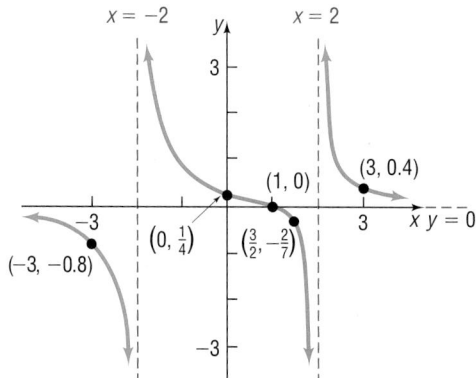

$-2\ -1\ \ 0\ \ 1\ \ 2$

✓**Check:** Graph $Y_1 = x^4$ and $Y_2 = x$ on the same screen. Use INTERSECT to find where $Y_1 = Y_2$. Then determine where $Y_1 > Y_2$.

➤ **Now Work** PROBLEM 21

2 Solve Rational Inequalities Algebraically and Graphically

Just as we presented a graphical approach to help understand the algebraic procedure for solving inequalities involving polynomials, we present a graphical approach to help understand the algebraic procedure for solving inequalities involving rational expressions.

| EXAMPLE 3 | Solving a Rational Inequality Using Its Graph |

Solve $\dfrac{x-1}{x^2-4} \geq 0$ by graphing $R(x) = \dfrac{x-1}{x^2-4}$.

By Hand Graphical Solution

We graph $R(x) = \dfrac{x-1}{x^2-4}$ and determine the intervals of x such that the graph is above or on the x-axis. Do you see why? These values of x result in $R(x)$ being positive or zero. We graphed $R(x) = \dfrac{x-1}{x^2-4}$ in Example 1 from Section 4.3 (p. 203). We reproduce the graph in Figure 43.

Figure 43

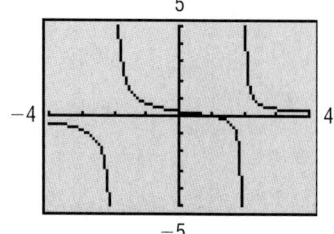

From the graph, we can see that $R(x) \geq 0$ for $-2 < x \leq 1$ or $x > 2$. The solution set is $\{x \mid -2 < x \leq 1 \text{ or } x > 2\}$ or, using interval notation, $(-2, 1] \cup (2, \infty)$.

Graphing Utility Solution

We graph $Y_1 = \dfrac{x-1}{x^2-4}$. See Figure 44. Using the ZERO command, we find that the x-intercept of the graph of Y_1 is 1. The graph of Y_1 is above the x-axis (and therefore R is positive) for $-2 < x < 1$ or $x > 2$. Since the inequality is not strict, we include 1 in the solution set. Therefore, the solution set is $\{x \mid -2 < x \leq 1 \text{ or } x > 2\}$ or, using interval notation, $(-2, 1] \cup (2, \infty)$.

Figure 44

➤ **Now Work** PROBLEM 33

To solve a rational inequality algebraically, we follow the same approach that we used to solve a polynomial inequality graphically. However, we must also identify the zeros of the denominator of the rational function, because the sign of a rational function may change on either side of a vertical asymptote. Convince yourself of this by looking at Figure 43. Notice the function values are negative for $x < -2$ and are positive for $x > -2$ (but less than 1).

| EXAMPLE 4 | **How to Solve a Rational Inequality Algebraically** |

Solve the inequality $\dfrac{4x + 5}{x + 2} \geq 3$ algebraically, and graph the solution set.

Step-by-Step Solution

STEP 1 Write the inequality so that a rational expression f is on the left side and zero is on the right side.

Rearrange the inequality so that 0 is on the right side.

$$\frac{4x + 5}{x + 2} \geq 3$$

$$\frac{4x + 5}{x + 2} - 3 \geq 0 \quad \text{Subtract 3 from both sides of the inequality.}$$

$$\frac{4x + 5}{x + 2} - 3 \cdot \frac{x + 2}{x + 2} \geq 0 \quad \text{Multiply 3 by } \frac{x + 2}{x + 2}$$

$$\frac{4x + 5 - 3x - 6}{x + 2} \geq 0 \quad \text{Write as a single quotient.}$$

$$\frac{x - 1}{x + 2} \geq 0 \quad \text{Combine like terms.}$$

STEP 2 Determine the real zeros (x-intercepts of the graph) of f and the real numbers for which f is undefined.

The zero of $f(x) = \dfrac{x - 1}{x + 2}$ is 1. Also, f is undefined for $x = -2$.

STEP 3 Use the zeros and undefined values found in Step 2 to divide the real number line into intervals.

We use the zeros and undefined values to separate the real number line into three intervals:

$$(-\infty, -2) \quad (-2, 1) \quad (1, \infty)$$

STEP 4 Select a number in each interval, evaluate f at the number, and determine whether f is positive or negative. If f is positive, all values of f in the interval are positive. If f is negative, all values of f in the interval are negative.

Note: If the inequality is not strict ($\leq$ or $\geq$), include the solutions of $f(x) = 0$ in the solution set.

We select a test number in each interval found in Step 3 and evaluate $f(x) = \dfrac{x - 1}{x + 2}$ at each number to determine if $f(x)$ is positive or negative. See Table 15.

Table 15

Interval	$(-\infty, -2)$	$(-2, 1)$	$(1, \infty)$
Number chosen	-3	0	2
Value of f	$f(-3) = 4$	$f(0) = -\dfrac{1}{2}$	$f(2) = \dfrac{1}{4}$
Conclusion	Positive	Negative	Positive

Since we want to know where $f(x)$ is positive or zero, we conclude that $f(x) \geq 0$ for all numbers x for which $x < -2$ or $x \geq 1$. Notice we do not include -2 in the solution because -2 is not in the domain of f. The solution set of the inequality $\dfrac{4x + 5}{x + 2} \geq 3$ is $\{x \mid x < -2 \text{ or } x \geq 1\}$ or, using interval notation, $(-\infty, -2) \cup [1, \infty)$.

Figure 45 shows the graph of the solution set.

Figure 45

$$\xleftarrow{\hspace{1cm}} \begin{array}{c|c|c|c|c} \hline -4 & -2 & 0 & 2 & 4 \end{array} \xrightarrow{\hspace{1cm}}$$

✓**Check:** Graph $Y_1 = \dfrac{4x + 5}{x + 2}$ and $Y_2 = 3$ on the same screen. Use INTERSECT to find where $Y_1 = Y_2$. Then determine where $Y_1 \geq Y_2$.

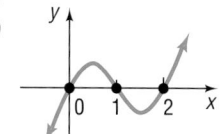 **Now Work** PROBLEM 39

Next we summarize the steps for solving a polynomial or rational inequality algebraically.

SUMMARY   Steps for Solving Polynomial and Rational Inequalities Algebraically

STEP 1: Write the inequality so that a polynomial or rational expression f is on the left side and zero is on the right side in one of the following forms:

$$f(x) > 0 \qquad f(x) \geq 0 \qquad f(x) < 0 \qquad f(x) \leq 0$$

For rational expressions, be sure that the left side is written as a single quotient and find the domain of f.

STEP 2: Determine the real numbers at which the expression f equals zero and, if the expression is rational, the real numbers at which the expression f is undefined.

STEP 3: Use the numbers found in Step 2 to separate the real number line into intervals.

STEP 4: Select a number in each interval and evaluate f at the number.
   (a) If the value of f is positive, then $f(x) > 0$ for all numbers x in the interval.
   (b) If the value of f is negative, then $f(x) < 0$ for all numbers x in the interval.

If the inequality is not strict ($\geq$ or $\leq$), include the solutions of $f(x) = 0$ in the solution set. Be careful to exclude values of x where f is undefined.

4.4 Assess Your Understanding

'Are You Prepared?' *Answers are given at the end of these exercises. If you get a wrong answer, read the pages listed in red.*

1. Solve the inequality $3 - 4x > 5$. Graph the solution set. (pp. A81–A83)

2. Solve the inequality $x^2 - 5x \leq 24$. Graph the solution set. (pp. 164–166)

Concepts and Vocabulary

3. *True or False* A test number for the interval $-2 < x < 5$ could be 4.

4. *True or False* The graph of $f(x) = \dfrac{x}{x - 3}$ is above the

x-axis for $x < 0$ or $x > 3$, so the solution set of the inequality $\dfrac{x}{x - 3} \geq 0$ is $\{x \mid x \leq 0 \text{ or } x \geq 3\}$.

Skill Building

In Problems 5–8, use the graph of the function f to solve the inequality.

5. (a) $f(x) > 0$
   (b) $f(x) \leq 0$

6. (a) $f(x) < 0$
   (b) $f(x) \geq 0$

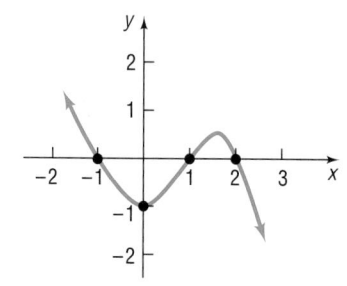

7. (a) $f(x) < 0$
   (b) $f(x) \geq 0$

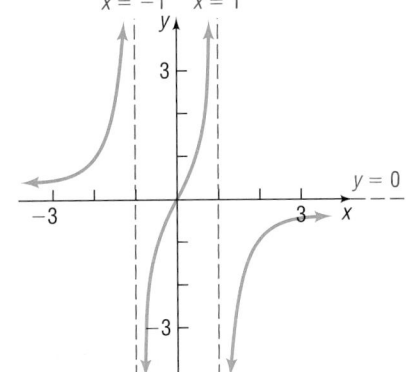

8. (a) $f(x) > 0$
   (b) $f(x) \leq 0$

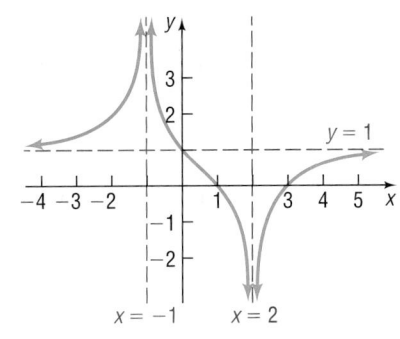

In Problems 9–14, solve the inequality by using the graph of the function.
[Hint: The graphs were drawn in Problems 65–70 of Section 4.1.]

  9. Solve $f(x) < 0$, where $f(x) = x^2(x - 3)$.

10. Solve $f(x) \leq 0$, where $f(x) = x(x + 2)^2$.

11. Solve $f(x) \geq 0$, where $f(x) = (x + 4)(x - 2)^2$.

12. Solve $f(x) > 0$, where $f(x) = (x - 1)(x + 3)^2$.

13. Solve $f(x) \leq 0$, where $f(x) = -2(x + 2)(x - 2)^3$.

14. Solve $f(x) < 0$, where $f(x) = -\frac{1}{2}(x + 4)(x - 1)^3$.

In Problems 15–18, solve the inequality by using the graph of the function.
[Hint: The graphs were drawn in Problems 7–10 of Section 4.3.]

15. Solve $R(x) > 0$, where $R(x) = \dfrac{x + 1}{x(x + 4)}$.

16. Solve $R(x) < 0$, where $R(x) = \dfrac{x}{(x - 1)(x + 2)}$.

17. Solve $R(x) \leq 0$, where $R(x) = \dfrac{3x + 3}{2x + 4}$.

18. Solve $R(x) \geq 0$, where $R(x) = \dfrac{2x + 4}{x - 1}$.

In Problems 19–48, solve each inequality algebraically. Verify your results using a graphing utility.

19. $(x - 5)^2(x + 2) < 0$

20. $(x - 5)(x + 2)^2 > 0$

21. $x^3 - 4x^2 > 0$

22. $x^3 + 8x^2 < 0$

23. $2x^3 > -8x^2$

24. $3x^3 < -15x^2$

25. $(x - 1)(x - 2)(x - 3) \leq 0$

26. $(x + 1)(x + 2)(x + 3) \leq 0$

27. $x^3 - 2x^2 - 3x > 0$

28. $x^3 + 2x^2 - 3x > 0$

29. $x^4 > x^2$

30. $x^4 < 9x^2$

31. $x^4 > 1$

32. $x^3 > 1$

33. $\dfrac{x + 1}{x - 1} > 0$

34. $\dfrac{x - 3}{x + 1} > 0$

35. $\dfrac{(x - 1)(x + 1)}{x} \leq 0$

36. $\dfrac{(x - 3)(x + 2)}{x - 1} \leq 0$

37. $\dfrac{(x - 2)^2}{x^2 - 1} \geq 0$

38. $\dfrac{(x + 5)^2}{x^2 - 4} \geq 0$

39. $\dfrac{x + 4}{x - 2} \leq 1$

40. $\dfrac{x + 2}{x - 4} \geq 1$

41. $\dfrac{3x - 5}{x + 2} \leq 2$

42. $\dfrac{x - 4}{2x + 4} \geq 1$

43. $\dfrac{1}{x - 2} < \dfrac{2}{3x - 9}$

44. $\dfrac{5}{x - 3} > \dfrac{3}{x + 1}$

45. $\dfrac{x^2(3 + x)(x + 4)}{(x + 5)(x - 1)} \geq 0$

46. $\dfrac{x(x^2 + 1)(x - 2)}{(x - 1)(x + 1)} \geq 0$

47. $\dfrac{(3 - x)^3(2x + 1)}{x^3 - 1} < 0$

48. $\dfrac{(2 - x)^3(3x - 2)}{x^3 + 1} < 0$

Mixed Practice

In Problems 49–60, solve each inequality algebraically. Verify your results using a graphing utility.

49. $(x + 1)(x - 3)(x - 5) > 0$

50. $(2x - 1)(x + 2)(x + 5) < 0$

51. $7x - 4 \geq -2x^2$

52. $x^2 + 3x \geq 10$

53. $\dfrac{x + 1}{x - 3} \leq 2$

54. $\dfrac{x - 1}{x + 2} \geq -2$

55. $3(x^2 - 2) < 2(x - 1)^2 + x^2$

56. $(x - 3)(x + 2) < x^2 + 3x + 5$

57. $6x - 5 < \dfrac{6}{x}$

58. $x + \dfrac{12}{x} < 7$

59. $x^3 - 9x \leq 0$

60. $x^3 - x \geq 0$

Applications and Extensions

61. For what positive numbers will the cube of a number exceed four times its square?

62. For what positive numbers will the cube of a number be less than the number?

63. What is the domain of the function $f(x) = \sqrt{x^4 - 16}$?

64. What is the domain of the function $f(x) = \sqrt{x^3 - 3x^2}$?

65. What is the domain of the function $f(x) = \sqrt{\dfrac{x - 2}{x + 4}}$?

66. What is the domain of the function $f(x) = \sqrt{\dfrac{x - 1}{x + 4}}$?

In Problems 67–70, determine where the graph of f is below the graph of g by solving the inequality $f(x) \leq g(x)$. Graph f and g together.

67. $f(x) = x^4 - 1$
$g(x) = -2x^2 + 2$

68. $f(x) = x^4 - 1$
$g(x) = x - 1$

69. $f(x) = x^4 - 4$
$g(x) = 3x^2$

70. $f(x) = x^4$
$g(x) = 2 - x^2$

71. Average Cost Suppose that the daily cost C of manufacturing bicycles is given by $C(x) = 80x + 5000$. Then the average daily cost $\overline{C}$ is given by $\overline{C}(x) = \dfrac{80x + 5000}{x}$. How many bicycles must be produced each day for the average cost to be no more than $100?

72. Average Cost See Problem 71. Suppose that the government imposes a $1000 per day tax on the bicycle manufacturer so that the daily cost C of manufacturing x bicycles is now given by $C(x) = 80x + 6000$. Now the average daily cost $\overline{C}$ is given by $\overline{C}(x) = \dfrac{80x + 6000}{x}$. How many bicycles must be produced each day for the average cost to be no more than $100?

73. Bungee Jumping Originating on Pentecost Island in the Pacific, the practice of a person jumping from a high place harnessed to a flexible attachment was introduced to Western culture in 1979 by the Oxford University Dangerous Sport Club. One important parameter to know before attempting a bungee jump is the amount the cord will stretch at the

bottom of the fall. The stiffness of the cord is related to the amount of stretch by the equation

$$K = \frac{2W(S + L)}{S^2}$$

where W = weight of the jumper (pounds)

K = cord's stiffness (pounds per foot)

L = free length of the cord (feet)

S = stretch (feet)

(a) A 150-pound person plans to jump off a ledge attached to a cord of length 42 feet. If the stiffness of the cord is no less than 16 pounds per foot, how much will the cord stretch?

(b) If safety requirements will not permit the jumper to get any closer than 3 feet to the ground, what is the minimum height required for the ledge in part (a)?

Source: American Institute of Physics, Physics News Update, No. 150, November 5, 1993

74. Gravitational Force According to Newton's Law of universal gravitation, the attractive force F between two bodies is given by

$$F = G\frac{m_1 m_2}{r^2}$$

where m_1, m_2 = the masses of the two bodies

r = distance between the two bodies

G = gravitational constant 6.6742×10^{-11} newtons meter^2 kilogram^{-2}

Suppose an object is traveling directly from Earth to the moon. The mass of Earth is 5.9742×10^{24} kilograms, the mass of the moon is 7.349×10^{22} kilograms, and the mean distance from Earth to the moon is 384,400 kilometers. For an object between Earth and the moon, how far from Earth is the force on the object due to the moon greater than the force on the object due to Earth?

Source: www.solarviews.com;en.wikipedia.org

75. Field Trip Mrs. West has decided to take her fifth grade class to a play. The manager of the theater agreed to discount the regular $40 price of the ticket by $0.20 for each ticket sold. The cost of the bus, $500, will be split equally among each of the students. How many students must attend to keep the cost per student at or below $40?

Discussion and Writing

76. Make up an inequality that has no solution. Make up one that has exactly one solution.

77. The inequality $x^4 + 1 < -5$ has no solution. Explain why.

78. A student attempted to solve the inequality $\dfrac{x + 4}{x - 3} \leq 0$ by multiplying both sides of the inequality by $x - 3$ to get

$x + 4 \leq 0$. This led to a solution of $\{x \mid x \leq -4\}$. Is the student correct? Explain.

79. Write a rational inequality whose solution set is $\{x \mid -3 < x \leq 5\}$.

'Are You Prepared?'

1. $\left\{x \mid x < -\dfrac{1}{2}\right\}$ or $\left(-\infty, -\dfrac{1}{2}\right)$

2. $\{x \mid -3 \leq x \leq 8\}$ or $[-3, 8]$

4.5 The Real Zeros of a Polynomial Function

PREPARING FOR THIS SECTION *Before getting started, review the following:*

- Classification of Numbers (Appendix A, Section A.1, p. A3)
- Factoring Polynomials (Appendix A, Section A.3, pp. A28–A29)
- Synthetic Division (Appendix A, Section A.4, pp. A31–A34)

- Polynomial Division (Appendix A, Section A.3, pp. A26–A28)
- Quadratic Formula (Appendix A, Section A.6, pp. A53–A55)
- Evaluate Functions (Section 2.1, pp. 60–62)

Now Work the 'Are You Prepared?' problems on page 231.

OBJECTIVES 1 Use the Remainder and Factor Theorems (p. 220)
2 Use the Rational Zeros Theorem to List the Potential Rational Zeros of a Polynomial Function (p. 223)
3 Find the Real Zeros of a Polynomial Function (p. 224)
4 Solve Polynomial Equations (p. 226)
5 Use the Theorem for Bounds on Zeros (p. 227)
6 Use the Intermediate Value Theorem (p. 230)

In Section 4.1, we were able to identify the real zeros of a polynomial function because either the polynomial function was in factored form or it could be easily factored. But how do we find the real zeros of a polynomial function if it is not factored or cannot be easily factored?

Recall that if r is a real zero of a polynomial function f then $f(r) = 0$, r is an x-intercept of the graph of f, $x - r$ is a factor of f, and r is a solution of the equation $f(x) = 0$. For example, if $x - 4$ is a factor of f, then 4 is a real zero of f and 4 is a solution to the equation $f(x) = 0$. For polynomial and rational functions, we have seen the importance of the real zeros for graphing. In most cases, however, the real zeros of a polynomial function are difficult to find using algebraic methods. No nice formulas like the quadratic formula are available to help us find zeros for polynomials of degree 3 or higher. Formulas do exist for solving any third- or fourth-degree polynomial equation, but they are somewhat complicated. No general formulas exist for polynomial equations of degree 5 or higher. Refer to the Historical Feature at the end of this section for more information.

1 Use the Remainder and Factor Theorems

When we divide one polynomial (the dividend) by another (the divisor), we obtain a quotient polynomial and a remainder, the remainder being either the zero polynomial or a polynomial whose degree is less than the degree of the divisor. To check our work, we verify that

$$(\text{Quotient})(\text{Divisor}) + \text{Remainder} = \text{Dividend}$$

This checking routine is the basis for a famous theorem called the **division algorithm* for polynomials,** which we now state without proof.

THEOREM **Division Algorithm for Polynomials**

If $f(x)$ and $g(x)$ denote polynomial functions and if $g(x)$ is a polynomial whose degree is greater than zero, then there are unique polynomial functions

---

*A systematic process in which certain steps are repeated a finite number of times is called an **algorithm.** For example, long division is an algorithm.

$q(x)$ and $r(x)$ such that

$$\frac{f(x)}{g(x)} = q(x) + \frac{r(x)}{g(x)} \quad \text{or} \quad f(x) = q(x)g(x) + r(x) \qquad \textbf{(1)}$$

$$\uparrow \qquad \uparrow \quad \uparrow \qquad \uparrow$$
$$\text{dividend} \quad \text{quotient} \quad \text{divisor} \quad \text{remainder}$$

where $r(x)$ is either the zero polynomial or a polynomial of degree less than that of $g(x)$.

In equation (1), $f(x)$ is the **dividend,** $g(x)$ is the **divisor,** $q(x)$ is the **quotient,** and $r(x)$ is the **remainder.**

If the divisor $g(x)$ is a first-degree polynomial of the form

$$g(x) = x - c \qquad c \text{ a real number}$$

then the remainder $r(x)$ is either the zero polynomial or a polynomial of degree 0. As a result, for such divisors, the remainder is some number, say R, and we may write

$$f(x) = (x - c)q(x) + R \qquad \textbf{(2)}$$

This equation is an identity in x and is true for all real numbers x. Suppose that $x = c$. Then equation (2) becomes

$$f(c) = (c - c)q(c) + R$$
$$f(c) = R$$

Substitute $f(c)$ for R in equation (2) to obtain

$$f(x) = (x - c)q(x) + f(c) \qquad \textbf{(3)}$$

We have now proved the **Remainder Theorem.**

REMAINDER THEOREM

Let f be a polynomial function. If $f(x)$ is divided by $x - c$, then the remainder is $f(c)$.

| EXAMPLE 1 | **Using the Remainder Theorem** |

Find the remainder if $f(x) = x^3 - 4x^2 - 5$ is divided by
(a) $x - 3$ (b) $x + 2$

Solution
(a) We could use long division or synthetic division, but it is easier to use the Remainder Theorem, which says that the remainder is $f(3)$.

$$f(3) = (3)^3 - 4(3)^2 - 5 = 27 - 36 - 5 = -14$$

The remainder is -14.

(b) To find the remainder when $f(x)$ is divided by $x + 2 = x - (-2)$, we evaluate $f(-2)$.

$$f(-2) = (-2)^3 - 4(-2)^2 - 5 = -8 - 16 - 5 = -29$$

The remainder is -29.

Figure 46

Compare the method used in Example 1(a) with the method used in Example 1 on page A33 (synthetic division). Which method do you prefer? Give reasons.

NOTE A graphing utility provides another way to find the value of a function, using the eVALUEate feature. Consult your manual for details. See Figure 46 for the result of Example 1(a). ■

An important and useful consequence of the Remainder Theorem is the **Factor Theorem.**

FACTOR THEOREM   Let f be a polynomial function. Then $x - c$ is a factor of $f(x)$ if and only if $f(c) = 0$.

The Factor Theorem actually consists of two separate statements:

1. If $f(c) = 0$, then $x - c$ is a factor of $f(x)$.
2. If $x - c$ is a factor of $f(x)$, then $f(c) = 0$.

The proof requires two parts.

Proof

1. Suppose that $f(c) = 0$. Then, by equation (3), we have

$$f(x) = (x - c)q(x) + f(c)$$
$$= (x - c)q(x) + 0$$
$$= (x - c)q(x)$$

for some polynomial $q(x)$. That is, $x - c$ is a factor of $f(x)$.

2. Suppose that $x - c$ is a factor of $f(x)$. Then there is a polynomial function q such that

$$f(x) = (x - c)q(x)$$

Replacing x by c, we find that

$$f(c) = (c - c)q(c) = 0 \cdot q(c) = 0$$

This completes the proof.   ∎

One use of the Factor Theorem is to determine whether a polynomial has a particular factor.

| EXAMPLE 2 | **Using the Factor Theorem** |

Use the Factor Theorem to determine whether the function

$$f(x) = 2x^3 - x^2 + 2x - 3$$

has the factor
(a) $x - 1$ (b) $x + 2$

Solution   The Factor Theorem states that if $f(c) = 0$ then $x - c$ is a factor.

(a) Because $x - 1$ is of the form $x - c$ with $c = 1$, we find the value of $f(1)$. We choose to use substitution.

$$f(1) = 2(1)^3 - (1)^2 + 2(1) - 3 = 2 - 1 + 2 - 3 = 0$$

See also Figure 47(a). By the Factor Theorem, $x - 1$ is a factor of $f(x)$.

(b) We first need to write $x + 2$ in the form $x - c$. Since $x + 2 = x - (-2)$, we find the value of $f(-2)$. See Figure 47(b). Because $f(-2) = -27 \neq 0$, we conclude from the Factor Theorem that $x - (-2) = x + 2$ is not a factor of $f(x)$.

Figure 47

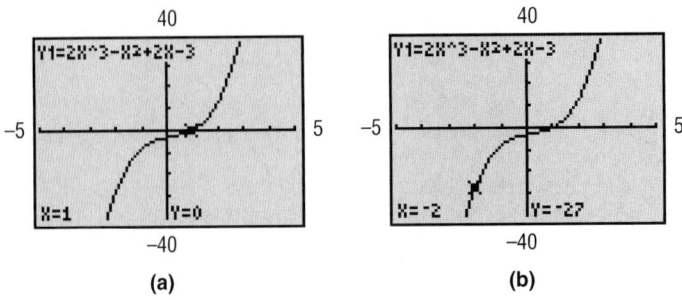

(a)   (b)

In Example 2, we found that $x - 1$ was a factor of f. To write f in factored form, we can use long division or synthetic division. Using synthetic division, we find that

$$
\begin{array}{r}
1\overline{\smash{)}2 \quad -1 \quad\ \ 2 \quad -3} \\
2 \quad\ \ 1 \quad\ \ 3 \\
\hline
2 \quad\ \ 1 \quad\ \ 3 \quad\ \ 0
\end{array}
$$

The quotient is $q(x) = 2x^2 + x + 3$ with a remainder of 0, as expected. We can write f in factored form as

$$f(x) = 2x^3 - x^2 + 2x - 3 = (x - 1)(2x^2 + x + 3)$$

▬▬▬ **Now Work** PROBLEM 11

The next theorem concerns the number of real zeros that a polynomial function may have. In counting the zeros of a polynomial, we count each zero as many times as its multiplicity.

THEOREM

Number of Real Zeros

A polynomial function of degree n, $n \geq 1$, has at most n real zeros.

Proof   The proof is based on the Factor Theorem. If r is a zero of a polynomial function f, then $f(r) = 0$ and, hence, $x - r$ is a factor of $f(x)$. Each zero corresponds to a factor of degree 1. Because f cannot have more first-degree factors than its degree, the result follows. ∎

2 Use the Rational Zeros Theorem to List the Potential Rational Zeros of a Polynomial Function

The next result, called the **Rational Zeros Theorem**, provides information about the rational zeros of a polynomial *with integer coefficients*.

THEOREM

Rational Zeros Theorem

Let f be a polynomial function of degree 1 or higher of the form

$$f(x) = a_n x^n + a_{n-1} x^{n-1} + \cdots + a_1 x + a_0 \qquad a_n \neq 0, a_0 \neq 0$$

where each coefficient is an integer. If $\dfrac{p}{q}$, in lowest terms, is a rational zero of f, then p must be a factor of a_0, and q must be a factor of a_n.

EXAMPLE 3   Listing Potential Rational Zeros

List the potential rational zeros of

$$f(x) = 2x^3 + 11x^2 - 7x - 6$$

Solution   Because f has integer coefficients, we may use the Rational Zeros Theorem. First, we list all the integers p that are factors of $a_0 = -6$ and all the integers q that are factors of the leading coefficient $a_3 = 2$.

$$p: \quad \pm 1, \pm 2, \pm 3, \pm 6$$
$$q: \quad \pm 1, \pm 2$$

Now we form all possible quotients $\dfrac{p}{q}$.

$$\frac{p}{q}: \quad \pm 1, \pm 2, \pm 3, \pm 6, \pm \frac{1}{2}, \pm \frac{3}{2}$$

If f has a rational zero, it will be found in this list, which contains 12 possibilities.

Now Work PROBLEM 21

Be sure that you understand what the Rational Zeros Theorem says: For a polynomial with integer coefficients, *if* there is a rational zero, it is one of those listed. It may be the case that the function does not have any rational zeros.

The Rational Zeros Theorem provides a list of potential rational zeros of a function f. If we graph f, we can get a better sense of the location of the x-intercepts and test to see if they are rational. We can also use the potential rational zeros to select our initial viewing window to graph f and then adjust the window based on the results. The graphs shown throughout the text will be those obtained after setting the final viewing window.

> **In Words**
>
> For the polynomial function
>
> $f(x) = 2x^3 + 11x^2 - 7x - 6$
>
> we know 5 is not a zero, because 5 is not in the list of potential rational zeros. However, −1 may or may not be a zero.

3 Find the Real Zeros of a Polynomial Function

EXAMPLE 4 **How to Find the Real Zeros of a Polynomial Function**

Find the real zeros of the polynomial function $f(x) = 2x^3 + 11x^2 - 7x - 6$. Write f in factored form.

Step-by-Step Solution

STEP 1 Use the degree of the polynomial to determine the maximum number of zeros.

Since f is a polynomial of degree 3, there are at most three real zeros.

STEP 2 If the polynomial has integer coefficients, use the Rational Zeros Theorem to identify those rational numbers that potentially can be zeros.

We list the potential rational zeros obtained in Example 3:

$$\pm 1, \pm 2, \pm 3, \pm 6, \pm \frac{1}{2}, \pm \frac{3}{2}$$

STEP 3 Using a graphing utility, graph the polynomial function.

Figure 48 shows the graph of f. We see that f has three zeros: one near −6, one between −1 and 0, and one near 1.

Figure 48

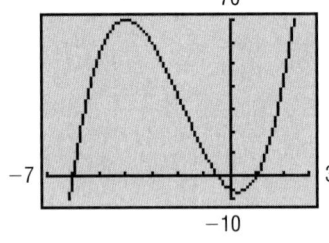

STEP 4 Use the Factor Theorem to determine if the potential rational zero is a zero. If it is, use synthetic division or long division to factor the polynomial function. Repeat Step 4 until all the zeros of the polynomial function have been identified and the polynomial function is completely factored.

From our list of potential rational zeros, we will test −6 to determine if it is a zero of f. Because

$$\begin{aligned}
f(-6) &= 2(-6)^3 + 11(-6)^2 - 7(-6) - 6 \\
&= 2(-216) + 11(36) + 42 - 6 \\
&= -432 + 396 + 36 \\
&= 0
\end{aligned}$$

we know that −6 is a zero and $x - (-6) = x + 6$ is a factor of f. We can use long division or synthetic division to factor f. (We will not show the division here, but you are encouraged to verify the results shown.) After dividing f by $x + 6$, we find that the quotient is $2x^2 - x - 1$, so

$$\begin{aligned}
f(x) &= 2x^3 + 11x^2 - 7x - 6 \\
&= (x + 6)(2x^2 - x - 1)
\end{aligned}$$

Now any solution of the equation $2x^2 - x - 1 = 0$ will be a zero of f. Because of this, we call the equation $2x^2 - x - 1 = 0$ a **depressed equation** of f. Because any zero of f is a solution to the equation $2x^2 - x - 1 = 0$, we work with the depressed equation to find the zeros of f.

The depressed equation $2x^2 - x - 1 = 0$ is a quadratic equation with discriminant $b^2 - 4ac = (-1)^2 - 4(2)(-1) = 9 > 0$. The equation has two real solutions, which can be found by factoring.

$$2x^2 - x - 1 = (2x + 1)(x - 1) = 0$$
$$2x + 1 = 0 \quad \text{or} \quad x - 1 = 0$$
$$x = -\frac{1}{2} \quad \text{or} \quad x = 1$$

The zeros of f are $-6, -\frac{1}{2}$, and 1.

We completely factor f as follows:

$$f(x) = 2x^3 + 11x^2 - 7x - 6 = (x + 6)(2x^2 - x - 1) = (x + 6)(2x + 1)(x - 1)$$

Notice that the three zeros of f are in the list of potential rational zeros in Step 2.

We summarize the steps used in Example 4 next.

SUMMARY Steps for Finding the Real Zeros of a Polynomial Function

STEP 1: Use the degree of the polynomial to determine the maximum number of zeros.

STEP 2: If the polynomial has integer coefficients, use the Rational Zeros Theorem to identify those rational numbers that potentially can be zeros.

STEP 3: Using a graphing utility, graph the polynomial function.

STEP 4: Use the Factor Theorem to determine if the potential rational zero is a zero. If it is, use synthetic division or long division to factor the polynomial function. Each time that a zero (and thus a factor) is found, repeat Step 4 on the depressed equation. In attempting to find the zeros, remember to use (if possible) the factoring techniques that you already know (special products, factoring by grouping, and so on).

| EXAMPLE 5 | Finding the Real Zeros of a Polynomial Function |

Find the real zeros of $f(x) = x^5 - x^4 - 4x^3 + 8x^2 - 32x + 48$. Write f in factored form.

Solution

STEP 1: There are at most five real zeros.

STEP 2: To obtain the list of potential rational zeros, we write the factors p of $a_0 = 48$ and the factors q of the leading coefficient $a_5 = 1$.

$$p: \quad \pm 1, \pm 2, \pm 3, \pm 4, \pm 6, \pm 8, \pm 12, \pm 16, \pm 24, \pm 48$$
$$q: \quad \pm 1$$

Figure 49

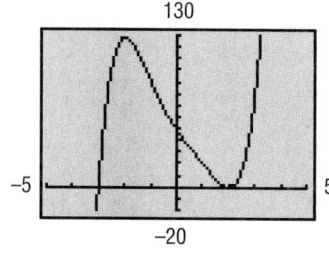

The potential rational zeros consist of all possible quotients $\frac{p}{q}$:

$$\frac{p}{q}: \quad \pm 1, \pm 2, \pm 3, \pm 4, \pm 6, \pm 8, \pm 12, \pm 16, \pm 24, \pm 48$$

STEP 3: Figure 49 shows the graph of f. The graph has the characteristics that we expect of the given polynomial of degree 5: no more than four turning points, y-intercept 48, and it behaves like $y = x^5$ for large $|x|$.

STEP 4: Since -3 appears to be a zero and -3 is a potential rational zero, we evaluate $f(-3)$ and find that $f(-3) = 0$. By the Factor Theorem, $x + 3$ is a factor of f. We use synthetic division to factor f.

$$
\begin{array}{r|rrrrrr}
-3 & 1 & -1 & -4 & 8 & -32 & 48 \\
  &   & -3 & 12 & -24 & 48 & -48 \\
\hline
  & 1 & -4 & 8 & -16 & 16 & 0
\end{array}
$$

We can factor f as

$$f(x) = x^5 - x^4 - 4x^3 + 8x^2 - 32x + 48 = (x + 3)(x^4 - 4x^3 + 8x^2 - 16x + 16)$$

We now work with the first depressed equation:

$$q_1(x) = x^4 - 4x^3 + 8x^2 - 16x + 16 = 0$$

Repeat Step 4: In looking back at Figure 49, it appears that 2 might be a zero of even multiplicity. We check the potential rational zero 2 and find that $f(2) = 0$. Using synthetic division,

$$
\begin{array}{r|rrrrr}
2 & 1 & -4 & 8 & -16 & 16 \\
  &   & 2 & -4 & 8 & -16 \\
\hline
  & 1 & -2 & 4 & -8 & 0
\end{array}
$$

Now we can factor f as

$$f(x) = (x + 3)(x - 2)(x^3 - 2x^2 + 4x - 8)$$

Repeat Step 4: The depressed equation $q_2(x) = x^3 - 2x^2 + 4x - 8 = 0$ can be factored by grouping.

$$
\begin{aligned}
x^3 - 2x^2 + 4x - 8 = (x^3 - 2x^2) + (4x - 8) &= x^2(x - 2) + 4(x - 2) \\
&= (x - 2)(x^2 + 4) = 0 \\
x - 2 = 0 \quad &\text{or} \quad x^2 + 4 = 0 \\
x = 2 &
\end{aligned}
$$

Since $x^2 + 4 = 0$ has no real solutions, the real zeros of f are -3 and 2, with 2 being a zero of multiplicity 2. The factored form of f is

$$
\begin{aligned}
f(x) &= x^5 - x^4 - 4x^3 + 8x^2 - 32x + 48 \\
&= (x + 3)(x - 2)^2(x^2 + 4)
\end{aligned}
$$

— **Now Work** PROBLEM 39

4 Solve Polynomial Equations

| EXAMPLE 6 | Solving a Polynomial Equation |

Solve the equation: $x^5 - x^4 - 4x^3 + 8x^2 - 32x + 48 = 0$

Solution The solutions of this equation are the zeros of the polynomial function

$$f(x) = x^5 - x^4 - 4x^3 + 8x^2 - 32x + 48$$

Using the result of Example 5, the real zeros are -3 and 2. These are the real solutions of the equation $x^5 - x^4 - 4x^3 + 8x^2 - 32x + 48 = 0$.

— **Now Work** PROBLEM 63

In Example 5, the quadratic factor $x^2 + 4$ that appears in the factored form of $f(x)$ is called *irreducible*, because the polynomial $x^2 + 4$ cannot be factored over the real numbers. In general, we say that a quadratic factor $ax^2 + bx + c$ is **irreducible** if it cannot be factored over the real numbers, that is, if it is prime over the real numbers.

Refer back to Examples 4 and 5. The polynomial function of Example 4 has three real zeros, and its factored form contains three linear factors. The polynomial function of Example 5 has two distinct real zeros, and its factored form contains two distinct linear factors and one irreducible quadratic factor.

THEOREM   Every polynomial function (with real coefficients) can be uniquely factored into a product of linear factors and/or irreducible quadratic factors.

We shall prove this result in Section 4.6, and, in fact, we shall draw several additional conclusions about the zeros of a polynomial function. One conclusion is worth noting now. If a polynomial (with real coefficients) is of odd degree, then it must contain at least one linear factor. (Do you see why?) This means that it must have at least one real zero.

COROLLARY   A polynomial function (with real coefficients) of odd degree has at least one real zero.

5 Use the Theorem for Bounds on Zeros

One challenge in using a graphing utility is to set the viewing window so that a complete graph is obtained. The next theorem is a tool that can be used to find bounds on the zeros. This will assure that the function does not have any zeros outside these bounds. Then using these bounds to set Xmin and Xmax assures that all the x-intercepts appear in the viewing window.

A positive number M is a **bound** on the zeros of a polynomial if every zero r lies between $-M$ and M, inclusive. That is, M is a bound to the zeros of a polynomial f if

$$-M \leq \text{any zero of } f \leq M$$

THEOREM   **Bounds on Zeros**

Let f denote a polynomial function whose leading coefficient is 1.

$$f(x) = x^n + a_{n-1}x^{n-1} + \cdots + a_1 x + a_0$$

A bound M on the zeros of f is the smaller of the two numbers

$$\text{Max}\{1, |a_0| + |a_1| + \cdots + |a_{n-1}|\}, \quad 1 + \text{Max}\{|a_0|, |a_1|, \ldots, |a_{n-1}|\} \quad \textbf{(4)}$$

where Max { } means "choose the largest entry in { }."

An example will help to make the theorem clear.

| EXAMPLE 7 | Using the Theorem for Finding Bounds on Zeros |

Find a bound to the zeros of each polynomial.

(a) $f(x) = x^5 + 3x^3 - 9x^2 + 5$ (b) $g(x) = 4x^5 - 2x^3 + 2x^2 + 1$

Solution   (a) The leading coefficient of f is 1.

$$f(x) = x^5 + 3x^3 - 9x^2 + 5 \qquad a_4 = 0, a_3 = 3, a_2 = -9, a_1 = 0, a_0 = 5$$

We evaluate the expressions in formula (4).

$$\text{Max}\{1, |a_0| + |a_1| + \cdots + |a_{n-1}|\} = \text{Max}\{1, |5| + |0| + |-9| + |3| + |0|\}$$

$$= \text{Max}\{1, 17\} = 17$$

$$1 + \text{Max}\{|a_0|, |a_1|, \ldots, |a_{n-1}|\} = 1 + \text{Max}\{|5|, |0|, |-9|, |3|, |0|\}$$

$$= 1 + 9 = 10$$

The smaller of the two numbers, 10, is the bound. Every zero of f lies between -10 and 10.

(b) First we write g so that its leading coefficient is 1.

$$g(x) = 4x^5 - 2x^3 + 2x^2 + 1 = 4\left(x^5 - \frac{1}{2}x^3 + \frac{1}{2}x^2 + \frac{1}{4}\right)$$

Next we evaluate the two expressions in formula (4) with $a_4 = 0$, $a_3 = -\frac{1}{2}$, $a_2 = \frac{1}{2}$, $a_1 = 0$, and $a_0 = \frac{1}{4}$.

$$\text{Max}\{1, |a_0| + |a_1| + \cdots + |a_{n-1}|\} = \text{Max}\left\{1, \left|\frac{1}{4}\right| + |0| + \left|\frac{1}{2}\right| + \left|-\frac{1}{2}\right| + |0|\right\}$$

$$= \text{Max}\left\{1, \frac{5}{4}\right\} = \frac{5}{4}$$

$$1 + \text{Max}\{|a_0|, |a_1|, \ldots, |a_{n-1}|\} = 1 + \text{Max}\left\{\left|\frac{1}{4}\right|, |0|, \left|\frac{1}{2}\right|, \left|-\frac{1}{2}\right|, |0|\right\}$$

$$= 1 + \frac{1}{2} = \frac{3}{2}$$

The smaller of the two numbers, $\frac{5}{4}$, is the bound. Every zero of g lies between $-\frac{5}{4}$ and $\frac{5}{4}$.

| EXAMPLE 8 | Obtaining Graphs Using Bounds on Zeros |

Obtain a graph for each polynomial.

(a) $f(x) = x^5 + 3x^3 - 9x^2 + 5$ (b) $g(x) = 4x^5 - 2x^3 + 2x^2 + 1$

Solution

(a) Based on Example 7(a), every zero lies between -10 and 10. Using $X\min = -10$ and $X\max = 10$, we graph $Y_1 = f(x) = x^5 + 3x^3 - 9x^2 + 5$. Figure 50(a) shows the graph obtained using ZOOM-FIT. Figure 50(b) shows the graph after adjusting the viewing window to improve the graph.

Figure 50

(a)   (b)

Figure 51

(b) Based on Example 7(b), every zero lies between $-\dfrac{5}{4}$ and $\dfrac{5}{4}$. Using $X\min = -\dfrac{5}{4}$ and $X\max = \dfrac{5}{4}$, we graph $Y_1 = g(x) = 4x^5 - 2x^3 + 2x^2 + 1$. Figure 51 shows the graph after using ZOOM-FIT. Here no adjustment of the viewing window is needed.

──── **Now Work** PROBLEM 33

The next example shows how to proceed when some of the coefficients of the polynomial are not integers.

EXAMPLE 9 | **Finding the Real Zeros of a Polynomial**

Find all the real zeros of the polynomial function

$$f(x) = x^5 - 1.8x^4 - 17.79x^3 + 31.672x^2 + 37.95x - 8.7121$$

Round answers to two decimal places.

Solution

STEP 1: There are at most five real zeros.

STEP 2: Since there are noninteger coefficients, the Rational Zeros Theorem does not apply.

Figure 52

(a)

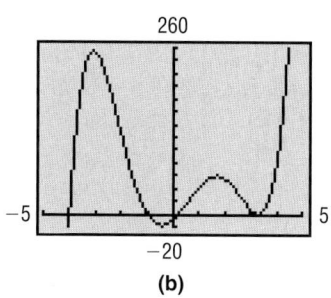

(b)

STEP 3: We determine the bounds of f. The leading coefficient of f is 1 with $a_4 = -1.8$, $a_3 = -17.79$, $a_2 = 31.672$, $a_1 = 37.95$, and $a_0 = -8.7121$. We evaluate the expressions using formula (4).

$$\text{Max}\{1, |-8.7121| + |37.95| + |31.672| + |-17.79| + |-1.8|\} = \text{Max}\{1, 97.9241\}$$
$$= 97.9241$$

$$1 + \text{Max}\{|-8.7121|, |37.95|, |31.672|, |-17.79|, |-1.8|\} = 1 + 37.95$$
$$= 38.95$$

The smaller of the two numbers, 38.95, is the bound. Every real zero of f lies between -38.95 and 38.95. Figure 52(a) shows the graph of f with $X\min = -38.95$ and $X\max = 38.95$. Figure 52(b) shows a graph of f after adjusting the viewing window to improve the graph.

STEP 4: From Figure 52(b), we see that f appears to have four x-intercepts: one near -4, one near -1, one between 0 and 1, and one near 3. The x-intercept near 3 might be a zero of even multiplicity since the graph seems to touch the x-axis at that point.

We use the Factor Theorem to determine if -4 and -1 are zeros. We find that $f(-4) = f(-1) = 0$. As a result -4 and -1 are zeros. Using ZERO (or ROOT), we find that the remaining zeros are 0.20 and 3.30, rounded to two decimal places.

There are no real zeros on the graph that have not already been identified. So either 3.30 is a zero of multiplicity 2 or there are two distinct zeros, each of which is 3.30, rounded to two decimal places. (Example 10 will explain how to determine which is true.)

Now Work PROBLEM 57

6 Use the Intermediate Value Theorem

 The Intermediate Value Theorem requires that the function be *continuous*. Although calculus is needed to explain the meaning precisely, we have already said that, very basically, a function f is continuous when its graph can be drawn without lifting pencil from paper, that is, when the graph contains no holes or jumps or gaps. Every polynomial function is continuous.

INTERMEDIATE VALUE THEOREM Let f denote a continuous function. If $a < b$ and if $f(a)$ and $f(b)$ are of opposite sign, then f has at least one zero between a and b.

Although the proof of this result requires advanced methods in calculus, it is easy to "see" why the result is true. Look at Figure 53.

Figure 53
If $f(a) < 0$ and $f(b) > 0$ and if f is continuous, there is at least one zero between a and b.

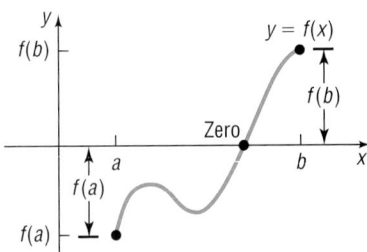

The Intermediate Value Theorem together with the TABLE feature of a graphing utility provides a basis for finding zeros.

EXAMPLE 10 **Using the Intermediate Value Theorem and a Graphing Utility to Locate Zeros**

Continue working with Example 9 to determine whether there is a repeated zero or two distinct zeros near 3.30.

Table 16

X	Y1
3.27	.08567
3.28	.03829
3.29	.00956
3.3	⁻1E⁻⁴
3.31	.0097
3.32	.03936
3.33	.08931

Y1☐X^5-1.8X^4-1...

Solution We use the TABLE feature of a graphing utility. See Table 16. Since $f(3.29) = 0.00956 > 0$ and $f(3.30) = -0.0001 < 0$, by the Intermediate Value Theorem there is a zero between 3.29 and 3.30. Similarly, since $f(3.30) = -0.0001 < 0$ and $f(3.31) = 0.0097 > 0$, there is another zero between 3.30 and 3.31. Now we know that the five zeros of f are distinct.

Now Work PROBLEM 75

Historical Feature

ormulas for the solution of third- and fourth-degree polynomial equations exist, and, while not very practical, they do have an interesting history.

In the 1500s in Italy, mathematical contests were a popular pastime, and persons possessing methods for solving problems kept them secret. (Solutions that were published were already common knowledge.) Niccolo of Brescia (1499–1557), commonly referred to as Tartaglia ("the stammerer"), had the secret for solving cubic (third-degree) equations, which gave him a decided advantage in the contests. Girolamo Cardano (1501–1576) found out that Tartaglia had the secret, and, being interested in cubics, he requested it from Tartaglia. The reluctant Tartaglia hesitated for some time, but finally, swearing Cardano to secrecy with midnight oaths by candlelight, told him the secret. Cardano then pub-

lished the solution in his book *Ars Magna* (1545), giving Tartaglia the credit but rather compromising the secrecy. Tartaglia exploded into bitter recriminations, and each wrote pamphlets that reflected on the other's mathematics, moral character, and ancestry.

The quartic (fourth-degree) equation was solved by Cardano's student Lodovico Ferrari, and this solution also was included, with credit and this time with permission, in the *Ars Magna*.

Attempts were made to solve the fifth-degree equation in similar ways, all of which failed. In the early 1800s, P. Ruffini, Niels Abel, and Evariste Galois all found ways to show that it is not possible to solve fifth-degree equations by formula, but the proofs required the introduction of new methods. Galois's methods eventually developed into a large part of modern algebra.

Historical Problems

Problems 1–8 develop the Tartaglia–Cardano solution of the cubic equation and show why it is not altogether practical.

1. Show that the general cubic equation $y^3 + by^2 + cy + d = 0$ can be transformed into an equation of the form $x^3 + px + q = 0$ by using the substitution $y = x - \dfrac{b}{3}$.

2. In the equation $x^3 + px + q = 0$, replace x by $H + K$. Let $3HK = -p$, and show that $H^3 + K^3 = -q$.

3. Based on Problem 2, we have the two equations

$$3HK = -p \quad \text{and} \quad H^3 + K^3 = -q$$

Solve for K in $3HK = -p$ and substitute into $H^3 + K^3 = -q$. Then show that

$$H = \sqrt[3]{\dfrac{-q}{2} + \sqrt{\dfrac{q^2}{4} + \dfrac{p^3}{27}}}$$

[**Hint:** Look for an equation that is quadratic in form.]

4. Use the solution for H from Problem 3 and the equation $H^3 + K^3 = -q$ to show that

$$K = \sqrt[3]{\dfrac{-q}{2} - \sqrt{\dfrac{q^2}{4} + \dfrac{p^3}{27}}}$$

5. Use the results from Problems 2 to 4 to show that the solution of $x^3 + px + q = 0$ is

$$x = \sqrt[3]{\dfrac{-q}{2} + \sqrt{\dfrac{q^2}{4} + \dfrac{p^3}{27}}} + \sqrt[3]{\dfrac{-q}{2} - \sqrt{\dfrac{q^2}{4} + \dfrac{p^3}{27}}}$$

6. Use the result of Problem 5 to solve the equation $x^3 - 6x - 9 = 0$.

7. Use a calculator and the result of Problem 5 to solve the equation $x^3 + 3x - 14 = 0$.

8. Use the methods of this chapter to solve the equation $x^3 + 3x - 14 = 0$.

4.5 Assess Your Understanding

'Are You Prepared?' *Answers are given at the end of these exercises. If you get a wrong answer, read the pages listed in* red.

1. Find $f(-1)$ if $f(x) = 2x^2 - x$. (pp. 60–62)
2. Factor the expression $6x^2 + x - 2$. (pp. A28–A29)
3. Find the quotient and remainder if $3x^4 - 5x^3 + 7x - 4$ is divided by $x - 3$. (pp. A26–A28 or A33)
4. Solve the equation $x^2 + x - 3 = 0$. (pp. A53–A55)

Concepts and Vocabulary

5. In the process of polynomial division, (Divisor)(Quotient) + _____ = _____.

6. When a polynomial function f is divided by $x - c$, the remainder is _____.

7. If a function f, whose domain is all real numbers, is even and if 4 is a zero of f, then _____ is also a zero.

8. *True or False* Every polynomial function of degree 3 with real coefficients has exactly three real zeros.

9. *True or False* The only potential rational zeros of $f(x) = 2x^5 - x^3 + x^2 - x + 1$ are $\pm 1, \pm 2$.

10. *True or False* If f is a polynomial function of degree 4 and if $f(2) = 5$, then

$$\dfrac{f(x)}{x - 2} = p(x) + \dfrac{5}{x - 2}$$

where $p(x)$ is a polynomial of degree 3.

Skill Building

In Problems 11–20, use the Remainder Theorem to find the remainder when $f(x)$ is divided by $x - c$. Then use the Factor Theorem to determine whether $x - c$ is a factor of $f(x)$. If $x - c$ is a factor of f, write f in factored form; that is, write f in the form $f(x) = (x - c)$ (quotient).

11. $f(x) = 4x^3 - 3x^2 - 8x + 4;\quad x - 2$

12. $f(x) = -4x^3 + 5x^2 + 8;\quad x + 3$

13. $f(x) = 3x^4 - 6x^3 - 5x + 10;\quad x - 2$

14. $f(x) = 4x^4 - 15x^2 - 4;\quad x - 2$

15. $f(x) = 3x^6 + 82x^3 + 27;\quad x + 3$

16. $f(x) = 2x^6 - 18x^4 + x^2 - 9;\quad x + 3$

17. $f(x) = 4x^6 - 64x^4 + x^2 - 15;\quad x + 4$

18. $f(x) = x^6 - 16x^4 + x^2 - 16;\quad x + 4$

19. $f(x) = 2x^4 - x^3 + 2x - 1;\quad x - \dfrac{1}{2}$

20. $f(x) = 3x^4 + x^3 - 3x + 1;\quad x + \dfrac{1}{3}$

In Problems 21–32, determine the maximum number of real zeros that each polynomial function may have. Then list the potential rational zeros of each polynomial function. Do not attempt to find the zeros.

21. $f(x) = 3x^4 - 3x^3 + x^2 - x + 1$

22. $f(x) = x^5 - x^4 + 2x^2 + 3$

23. $f(x) = x^5 - 6x^2 + 9x - 3$

24. $f(x) = 2x^5 - x^4 - x^2 + 1$

25. $f(x) = -4x^3 - x^2 + x + 2$

26. $f(x) = 6x^4 - x^2 + 2$

27. $f(x) = 6x^4 - x^2 + 9$

28. $f(x) = -4x^3 + x^2 + x + 6$

29. $f(x) = 2x^5 - x^3 + 2x^2 + 12$

30. $f(x) = 3x^5 - x^2 + 2x + 18$

31. $f(x) = 6x^4 + 2x^3 - x^2 + 20$

32. $f(x) = -6x^3 - x^2 + x + 10$

In Problems 33–38, find the bounds to the zeros of each polynomial function. Use the bounds to obtain a complete graph of f.

33. $f(x) = 2x^3 + x^2 - 1$

34. $f(x) = 3x^3 - 2x^2 + x + 4$

35. $f(x) = x^3 - 5x^2 - 11x + 11$

36. $f(x) = 2x^3 - x^2 - 11x - 6$

37. $f(x) = x^4 + 3x^3 - 5x^2 + 9$

38. $f(x) = 4x^4 - 12x^3 + 27x^2 - 54x + 81$

In Problems 39–56, find the real zeros of f. Use the real zeros to factor f.

39. $f(x) = x^3 + 2x^2 - 5x - 6$

40. $f(x) = x^3 + 8x^2 + 11x - 20$

41. $f(x) = 2x^3 - 13x^2 + 24x - 9$

42. $f(x) = 2x^3 - 5x^2 - 4x + 12$

43. $f(x) = 3x^3 + 4x^2 + 4x + 1$

44. $f(x) = 3x^3 - 7x^2 + 12x - 28$

45. $f(x) = x^3 - 8x^2 + 17x - 6$

46. $f(x) = x^3 + 6x^2 + 6x - 4$

47. $f(x) = x^4 + x^3 - 3x^2 - x + 2$

48. $f(x) = x^4 - x^3 - 6x^2 + 4x + 8$

49. $f(x) = 2x^4 + 17x^3 + 35x^2 - 9x - 45$

50. $f(x) = 4x^4 - 15x^3 - 8x^2 + 15x + 4$

51. $f(x) = 2x^4 - 3x^3 - 21x^2 - 2x + 24$

52. $f(x) = 2x^4 + 11x^3 - 5x^2 - 43x + 35$

53. $f(x) = 4x^4 + 7x^2 - 2$

54. $f(x) = 4x^4 + 15x^2 - 4$

55. $f(x) = 4x^5 - 8x^4 - x + 2$

56. $f(x) = 4x^5 + 12x^4 - x - 3$

In Problems 57–62, find the real zeros of f. If necessary, round to two decimal places.

57. $f(x) = x^3 + 3.2x^2 - 16.83x - 5.31$

58. $f(x) = x^3 + 3.2x^2 - 7.25x - 6.3$

59. $f(x) = x^4 - 1.4x^3 - 33.71x^2 + 23.94x + 292.41$

60. $f(x) = x^4 + 1.2x^3 - 7.46x^2 - 4.692x + 15.2881$

61. $f(x) = x^3 + 19.5x^2 - 1021x + 1000.5$

62. $f(x) = x^3 + 42.2x^2 - 664.8x + 1490.4$

In Problems 63–72, find the real solutions of each equation.

63. $x^4 - x^3 + 2x^2 - 4x - 8 = 0$

64. $2x^3 + 3x^2 + 2x + 3 = 0$

65. $3x^3 + 4x^2 - 7x + 2 = 0$

66. $2x^3 - 3x^2 - 3x - 5 = 0$

67. $3x^3 - x^2 - 15x + 5 = 0$

68. $2x^3 - 11x^2 + 10x + 8 = 0$

69. $x^4 + 4x^3 + 2x^2 - x + 6 = 0$

70. $x^4 - 2x^3 + 10x^2 - 18x + 9 = 0$

71. $x^3 - \dfrac{2}{3}x^2 + \dfrac{8}{3}x + 1 = 0$

72. $x^3 - \dfrac{2}{3}x^2 + 3x - 2 = 0$

In Problems 73–78, use the Intermediate Value Theorem to show that each function has a zero in the given interval. Approximate the zero rounded to two decimal places.

73. $f(x) = 8x^4 - 2x^2 + 5x - 1$; $[0, 1]$

74. $f(x) = x^4 + 8x^3 - x^2 + 2$; $[-1, 0]$

75. $f(x) = 2x^3 + 6x^2 - 8x + 2$; $[-5, -4]$

76. $f(x) = 3x^3 - 10x + 9$; $[-3, -2]$

77. $f(x) = x^5 - x^4 + 7x^3 - 7x^2 - 18x + 18$; $[1.4, 1.5]$

78. $f(x) = x^5 - 3x^4 - 2x^3 + 6x^2 + x + 2$; $[1.7, 1.8]$

Mixed Practice

In Problems 79–84, analyze each polynomial function using Steps 1 through 8 on page 185 in Section 4.1.

79. $f(x) = x^3 + 2x^2 - 5x - 6$
[**Hint:** See Problem 39.]

80. $f(x) = x^3 + 8x^2 + 11x - 20$
[**Hint:** See Problem 40.]

81. $f(x) = x^4 + x^3 - 3x^2 - x + 2$
[**Hint:** See Problem 47.]

82. $f(x) = x^4 - x^3 - 6x^2 + 4x + 8$
[**Hint:** See Problem 48.]

83. $f(x) = 4x^5 - 8x^4 - x + 2$
[**Hint:** See Problem 55.]

84. $f(x) = 4x^5 + 12x^4 - x - 3$
[**Hint:** See Problem 56.]

Applications and Extensions

85. Find k such that $f(x) = x^3 - kx^2 + kx + 2$ has the factor $x - 2$.

86. Find k such that $f(x) = x^4 - kx^3 + kx^2 + 1$ has the factor $x + 2$.

87. What is the remainder when $f(x) = 2x^{20} - 8x^{10} + x - 2$ is divided by $x - 1$?

88. What is the remainder when $f(x) = -3x^{17} + x^9 - x^5 + 2x$ is divided by $x + 1$?

89. Use the Factor Theorem to prove that $x - c$ is a factor of $x^n - c^n$ for any positive integer n.

90. Use the Factor Theorem to prove that $x + c$ is a factor of $x^n + c^n$ if $n \geq 1$ is an odd integer.

91. One solution of the equation $x^3 - 8x^2 + 16x - 3 = 0$ is 3. Find the sum of the remaining solutions.

92. One solution of the equation $x^3 + 5x^2 + 5x - 2 = 0$ is -2. Find the sum of the remaining solutions.

93. Geometry What is the length of the edge of a cube if, after a slice 1 inch thick is cut from one side, the volume remaining is 294 cubic inches?

94. Geometry What is the length of the edge of a cube if its volume could be doubled by an increase of 6 centimeters in one edge, an increase of 12 centimeters in a second edge, and a decrease of 4 centimeters in the third edge?

95. Let $f(x)$ be a polynomial function whose coefficients are integers. Suppose that r is a real zero of f and that the leading coefficient of f is 1. Use the Rational Zeros Theorem to show that r is either an integer or an irrational number.

96. Prove the Rational Zeros Theorem.
[**Hint:** Let $\dfrac{p}{q}$, where p and q have no common factors except 1 and -1, be a zero of the polynomial function

$$f(x) = a_n x^n + a_{n-1} x^{n-1} + \cdots + a_1 x + a_0$$

whose coefficients are all integers. Show that

$$a_n p^n + a_{n-1} p^{n-1} q + \cdots + a_1 p q^{n-1} + a_0 q^n = 0$$

Now, because p is a factor of the first n terms of this equation, p must also be a factor of the term $a_0 q^n$. Since p is not a factor of q (why?), p must be a factor of a_0. Similarly, q must be a factor of a_n.]

97. Bisection Method for Approximating Zeros of a Function f
We begin with two consecutive integers, a and $a + 1$, such that $f(a)$ and $f(a + 1)$ are of opposite sign. Evaluate f at the midpoint m_1 of a and $a + 1$. If $f(m_1) = 0$, then m_1 is the zero of f, and we are finished. Otherwise, $f(m_1)$ is of opposite sign to either $f(a)$ or $f(a + 1)$. Suppose that it is $f(a)$ and $f(m_1)$ that are of opposite sign. Now evaluate f at the midpoint m_2 of a and m_1. Repeat this process until the desired degree of accuracy is obtained. Note that each iteration places the zero in an interval whose length is half that of the previous interval. Use the bisection method to approximate the zero of $f(x) = 8x^4 - 2x^2 + 5x - 1$ in the interval $[0, 1]$, correct to three decimal places. Verify your result using a graphing utility.

[**Hint:** The process ends when both endpoints agree to the desired number of decimal places.]

Discussion and Writing

98. Is $\dfrac{1}{3}$ a zero of $f(x) = 2x^3 + 3x^2 - 6x + 7$? Explain.

99. Is $\dfrac{1}{3}$ a zero of $f(x) = 4x^3 - 5x^2 - 3x + 1$? Explain.

100. Is $\dfrac{3}{5}$ a zero of $f(x) = 2x^6 - 5x^4 + x^3 - x + 1$? Explain.

101. Is $\dfrac{2}{3}$ a zero of $f(x) = x^7 + 6x^5 - x^4 + x + 2$? Explain.

'Are You Prepared?' Answers

1. 3 **2.** $(3x + 2)(2x - 1)$ **3.** Quotient: $3x^3 + 4x^2 + 12x + 43$; remainder: 125 **4.** $\left\{ \dfrac{-1 - \sqrt{13}}{2}, \dfrac{-1 + \sqrt{13}}{2} \right\}$

4.6 Complex Zeros; Fundamental Theorem of Algebra

PREPARING FOR THIS SECTION *Before getting started, review the following:*

- Complex Numbers (Appendix A, Section A.7, pp. A60–A64)
- Quadratic Equations in the Complex Number System (Appendix A, Section A.7, pp. A65–A67)

Now Work the 'Are You Prepared?' problems on page 238.

OBJECTIVES 1 Use the Conjugate Pairs Theorem (p. 235)
2 Find a Polynomial Function with Specified Zeros (p. 236)
3 Find the Complex Zeros of a Polynomial Function (p. 237)

In Appendix A, Section A.6, we found the real solutions of a quadratic equation. That is, we found the real zeros of a polynomial function of degree 2. Then, in Appendix A, Section A.7, we found the solutions of a quadratic equation in the complex number system; that is, we found the *complex zeros* of a polynomial function of degree 2.

In Section 4.5 we found the real zeros of polynomial functions of degree 3 or higher. In this section we will find the *complex zeros* of polynomial functions of degree 3 or higher.

DEFINITION

A variable in the complex number system is referred to as a **complex variable.** A **complex polynomial function** f of degree n is a function of the form

$$f(x) = a_n x^n + a_{n-1} x^{n-1} + \cdots + a_1 x + a_0 \qquad (1)$$

where $a_n, a_{n-1}, \ldots, a_1, a_0$ are complex numbers, $a_n \neq 0$, n is a nonnegative integer, and x is a complex variable. As before, a_n is called the **leading coefficient** of f. A complex number r is called a **complex zero** of f if $f(r) = 0$.

In most of our work the coefficients in (1) will be real numbers.

We have learned that some quadratic equations have no real solutions, but that in the complex number system every quadratic equation has a solution, either real or complex. The next result, proved by Karl Friedrich Gauss (1777–1855) when he was 22 years old,* gives an extension to complex polynomials. In fact, this result is so important and useful that it has become known as the **Fundamental Theorem of Algebra.**

FUNDAMENTAL THEOREM OF ALGEBRA

Every complex polynomial function $f(x)$ of degree $n \geq 1$ has at least one complex zero.

We shall not prove this result, as the proof is beyond the scope of this book. However, using the Fundamental Theorem of Algebra and the Factor Theorem, we can prove the following result:

THEOREM

Every complex polynomial function $f(x)$ of degree $n \geq 1$ can be factored into n linear factors (not necessarily distinct) of the form

$$f(x) = a_n(x - r_1)(x - r_2) \cdot \cdots \cdot (x - r_n) \qquad (2)$$

where $a_n, r_1, r_2, \ldots, r_n$ are complex numbers. That is, every complex polynomial function of degree $n \geq 1$ has exactly n complex zeros, some of which may repeat.

*In all, Gauss gave four different proofs of this theorem, the first one in 1799 being the subject of his doctoral dissertation.

Proof Let

$$f(x) = a_nx^n + a_{n-1}x^{n-1} + \cdots + a_1x + a_0$$

By the Fundamental Theorem of Algebra, f has at least one zero, say r_1. Then, by the Factor Theorem, $x - r_1$ is a factor, and

$$f(x) = (x - r_1)q_1(x)$$

where $q_1(x)$ is a complex polynomial of degree $n - 1$ whose leading coefficient is a_n. Repeating this argument n times, we arrive at

$$f(x) = (x - r_1)(x - r_2) \cdot \cdots \cdot (x - r_n)q_n(x)$$

where $q_n(x)$ is a complex polynomial of degree $n - n = 0$ whose leading coefficient is a_n. That is, $q_n(x) = a_nx^0 = a_n$, and so

$$f(x) = a_n(x - r_1)(x - r_2) \cdot \cdots \cdot (x - r_n)$$

We conclude that every complex polynomial function $f(x)$ of degree $n \geq 1$ has exactly n (not necessarily distinct) zeros. ∎

1 Use the Conjugate Pairs Theorem

We can use the Fundamental Theorem of Algebra to obtain valuable information about the complex zeros of polynomials whose coefficients are real numbers.

CONJUGATE PAIRS THEOREM

Let $f(x)$ be a polynomial whose coefficients are real numbers. If $r = a + bi$ is a zero of f, the complex conjugate $\bar{r} = a - bi$ is also a zero of f.

In other words, for polynomials whose coefficients are real numbers, the complex zeros occur in conjugate pairs. This result should not be all that surprising since the complex zeros of a quadratic function occurred in conjugate pairs.

Proof Let

$$f(x) = a_nx^n + a_{n-1}x^{n-1} + \cdots + a_1x + a_0$$

where $a_n, a_{n-1}, \ldots, a_1, a_0$ are real numbers and $a_n \neq 0$. If $r = a + bi$ is a zero of f, then $f(r) = f(a + bi) = 0$, so

$$a_nr^n + a_{n-1}r^{n-1} + \cdots + a_1r + a_0 = 0$$

We take the conjugate of both sides to get

$$\overline{a_nr^n + a_{n-1}r^{n-1} + \cdots + a_1r + a_0} = \bar{0}$$

$$\overline{a_nr^n} + \overline{a_{n-1}r^{n-1}} + \cdots + \overline{a_1r} + \overline{a_0} = \bar{0} \qquad \text{The conjugate of a sum equals the sum of the conjugates (see Section A.7).}$$

$$\overline{a_n}(\bar{r})^n + \overline{a_{n-1}}(\bar{r})^{n-1} + \cdots + \overline{a_1}\bar{r} + \overline{a_0} = \bar{0} \qquad \text{The conjugate of a product equals the product of the conjugates.}$$

$$a_n(\bar{r})^n + a_{n-1}(\bar{r})^{n-1} + \cdots + a_1\bar{r} + a_0 = 0 \qquad \text{The conjugate of a real number equals the real number.}$$

This last equation states that $f(\bar{r}) = 0$; that is, $\bar{r} = a - bi$ is a zero of f. ∎

The importance of this result should be clear. Once we know that, say, $3 + 4i$ is a zero of a polynomial with real coefficients, then we know that $3 - 4i$ is also a zero. This result has an important corollary.

COROLLARY

A polynomial f of odd degree with real coefficients has at least one real zero.

Proof   Because complex zeros occur as conjugate pairs in a polynomial with real coefficients, there will always be an even number of zeros that are not real numbers. Consequently, since f is of odd degree, one of its zeros has to be a real number. ■

For example, the polynomial $f(x) = x^5 - 3x^4 + 4x^3 - 5$ has at least one zero that is a real number, since f is of degree 5 (odd) and has real coefficients.

| EXAMPLE 1 | **Using the Conjugate Pairs Theorem** |

A polynomial f of degree 5 whose coefficients are real numbers has the zeros 1, $5i$, and $1 + i$. Find the remaining two zeros.

Solution   Since f has coefficients that are real numbers, complex zeros appear as conjugate pairs. It follows that $-5i$, the conjugate of $5i$, and $1 - i$, the conjugate of $1 + i$, are the two remaining zeros.

━━━ **Now Work** PROBLEM 7

2 Find a Polynomial Function with Specified Zeros

| EXAMPLE 2 | **Finding a Polynomial Function Whose Zeros Are Given** |

(a) Find a polynomial f of degree 4 whose coefficients are real numbers and that has the zeros 1, 1, and $-4 + i$.

(b) Graph the polynomial found in part (a) to verify your result.

Solution   (a) Since $-4 + i$ is a zero, by the Conjugate Pairs Theorem, $-4 - i$ must also be a zero of f. Because of the Factor Theorem, if $f(c) = 0$, then $x - c$ is a factor of $f(x)$. So we can now write f as

$$f(x) = a(x - 1)(x - 1)[x - (-4 + i)][x - (-4 - i)]$$

where a is any real number. If we let $a = 1$, we obtain

$$
\begin{aligned}
f(x) &= (x - 1)(x - 1)[x - (-4 + i)][x - (-4 - i)] \\
&= (x^2 - 2x + 1)[x^2 - (-4 + i)x - (-4 - i)x + (-4 + i)(-4 - i)] \\
&= (x^2 - 2x + 1)(x^2 + 4x - ix + 4x + ix + 16 + 4i - 4i - i^2) \\
&= (x^2 - 2x + 1)(x^2 + 8x + 17) \\
&= x^4 + 8x^3 + 17x^2 - 2x^3 - 16x^2 - 34x + x^2 + 8x + 17 \\
&= x^4 + 6x^3 + 2x^2 - 26x + 17
\end{aligned}
$$

(b) A quick analysis of the polynomial f tells us what to expect:

At most three turning points

For large $|x|$, the graph will behave like $y = x^4$.

A repeated real zero at 1 so that the graph will touch the x-axis at 1

The only x-intercept is at 1.

Figure 54 shows the complete graph. (Do you see why? The graph has exactly three turning points and the degree of the polynomial is 4.)

Figure 54

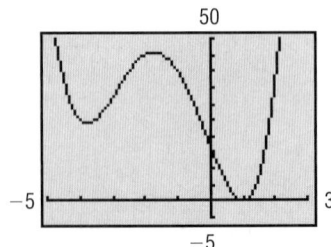

━━━ **Now Work** PROBLEM 17

Exploration

Graph the function found in Example 2 for $a = 2$ and $a = -1$. Does the value of a affect the zeros of f? How does the value of a affect the graph of f?

Now we can prove the theorem we conjectured earlier in Section 4.5.

THEOREM   Every polynomial function with real coefficients can be uniquely factored over the real numbers into a product of linear factors and/or irreducible quadratic factors.

Proof   Every complex polynomial f of degree n has exactly n zeros and can be factored into a product of n linear factors. If its coefficients are real, then those zeros that are complex numbers will always occur as conjugate pairs. As a result, if $r = a + bi$ is a complex zero, then so is $\bar{r} = a - bi$. Consequently, when the linear factors $x - r$ and $x - \bar{r}$ of f are multiplied, we have

$$(x - r)(x - \bar{r}) = x^2 - (r + \bar{r})x + r\bar{r} = x^2 - 2ax + a^2 + b^2$$

This second-degree polynomial has real coefficients and is irreducible (over the real numbers). Thus, the factors of f are either linear or irreducible quadratic factors. ∎

3 Find the Complex Zeros of a Polynomial Function

The steps for finding the complex zeros of a polynomial function are the same as those for finding the real zeros.

| EXAMPLE 3 | Finding the Complex Zeros of a Polynomial Function |

Find the complex zeros of the polynomial function

$$f(x) = 3x^4 + 5x^3 + 25x^2 + 45x - 18$$

Write f in factored form.

Solution   **STEP 1:** The degree of f is 4. So f will have four complex zeros.

STEP 2: The Rational Zeros Theorem provides information about the potential rational zeros of polynomials with integer coefficients. For this polynomial (which has integer coefficients), the potential rational zeros are

$$\pm\frac{1}{3}, \pm\frac{2}{3}, \pm 1, \pm 2, \pm 3, \pm 6, \pm 9, \pm 18$$

STEP 3: Figure 55 shows the graph of f. The graph has the characteristics that we expect of this polynomial of degree 4: It behaves like $y = 3x^4$ for large $|x|$ and has y-intercept -18. There are x-intercepts near -2 and between 0 and 1.

STEP 4: Because $f(-2) = 0$, we know that -2 is a zero of f and $x - (-2) = x + 2$ is a factor of f. We can use long division or synthetic division to factor f. Using synthetic division, we factor f.

Figure 55

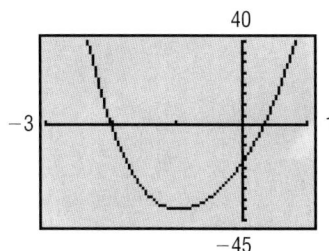

$$
\begin{array}{r}
-2\overline{)}\;\;3\quad\;\;5\quad\;\;25\quad\;\;45\quad -18 \\
\underline{\qquad\;\; -6\quad\;\;\;2\quad -54\quad\;\;\;18} \\
3\quad -1\quad\;\;27\quad\;\; -9\quad\;\;\;\;\;0
\end{array}
$$

So $f(x) = (x + 2)(3x^3 - x^2 + 27x - 9)$. The depressed equation is

$$q_1(x) = 3x^3 - x^2 + 27x - 9 = 0$$

Repeat Step 4: The depressed equation $3x^3 - x^2 + 27x - 9 = 0$ can be factored by grouping.

$$3x^3 - x^2 + 27x - 9 = 0$$

$$x^2(3x - 1) + 9(3x - 1) = 0 \qquad \text{Factor } x^2 \text{ from } 3x^3 - x^2 \text{ and } 9 \text{ from } 27x - 9.$$

$$(x^2 + 9)(3x - 1) = 0 \qquad \text{Factor out the common factor } 3x - 1.$$

$$x^2 + 9 = 0 \qquad \text{or} \quad 3x - 1 = 0 \qquad \text{Apply the Zero-Product Property.}$$
$$x^2 = -9 \qquad \text{or} \qquad 3x = 1$$

$$x = -3i, \quad x = 3i \quad \text{or} \qquad x = \frac{1}{3}$$

The four complex zeros of f are $\left\{ -3i, 3i, -2, \dfrac{1}{3} \right\}$.

The factored form of f is

$$\begin{aligned} f(x) &= 3x^4 + 5x^3 + 25x^2 + 45x - 18 \\ &= (x + 3i)(x - 3i)(x + 2)(3x - 1) \\ &= 3(x + 3i)(x - 3i)(x + 2)\left(x - \frac{1}{3} \right) \end{aligned}$$

─ **Now Work** PROBLEM 33

4.6 Assess Your Understanding

'Are You Prepared?' *Answers are given at the end of these exercises. If you get the wrong answer, read the pages listed in red.*

1. Find the sum and the product of the complex numbers $3 - 2i$ and $-3 + 5i$. (pp. A60–A62)

2. In the complex number system, solve $x^2 + 2x + 2 = 0$. (pp. A65–A67)

Concepts and Vocabulary

3. Every polynomial function of odd degree with real coefficients will have at least _____ real zero(s).

4. If $3 + 4i$ is a zero of a polynomial function of degree 5 with real coefficients, then so is _____.

5. *True or False* A polynomial function of degree n with real coefficients has exactly n complex zeros. At most n of them are real zeros.

6. *True or False* A polynomial function of degree 4 with real coefficients could have $-3, 2 + i, 2 - i$, and $-3 + 5i$ as its zeros.

Skill Building

In Problems 7–16, information is given about a polynomial $f(x)$ whose coefficients are real numbers. Find the remaining zeros of f.

7. Degree 3;   zeros: $3, 4 - i$

8. Degree 3;   zeros: $4, 3 + i$

9. Degree 4;   zeros: $i, 1 + i$

10. Degree 4;   zeros: $1, 2, 2 + i$

11. Degree 5;   zeros: $1, i, 2i$

12. Degree 5;   zeros: $0, 1, 2, i$

13. Degree 4;   zeros: $i, 2, -2$

14. Degree 4;   zeros: $2 - i, -i$

15. Degree 6;   zeros: $2, 2 + i, -3 - i, 0$

16. Degree 6;   zeros: $i, 3 - 2i, -2 + i$

In Problems 17–22, form a polynomial $f(x)$ with real coefficients having the given degree and zeros. Answers will vary depending on the choice of leading coefficient.

17. Degree 4;   zeros: $3 + 2i$; 4, multiplicity 2

18. Degree 4;   zeros: $i, 1 + 2i$

19. Degree 5;   zeros: $2; -i; 1 + i$

20. Degree 6;   zeros: $i, 4 - i; 2 + i$

21. Degree 4;   zeros: 3, multiplicity 2; $-i$

22. Degree 5;   zeros: 1, multiplicity 3; $1 + i$

In Problems 23–30, use the given zero to find the remaining zeros of each function.

23. $f(x) = x^3 - 4x^2 + 4x - 16$;   zero: $2i$

24. $g(x) = x^3 + 3x^2 + 25x + 75$;   zero: $-5i$

25. $f(x) = 2x^4 + 5x^3 + 5x^2 + 20x - 12$;   zero: $-2i$

26. $h(x) = 3x^4 + 5x^3 + 25x^2 + 45x - 18$;   zero: $3i$

27. $h(x) = x^4 - 9x^3 + 21x^2 + 21x - 130$;   zero: $3 - 2i$

28. $f(x) = x^4 - 7x^3 + 14x^2 - 38x - 60$;   zero: $1 + 3i$

29. $h(x) = 3x^5 + 2x^4 + 15x^3 + 10x^2 - 528x - 352$;   zero: $-4i$

30. $g(x) = 2x^5 - 3x^4 - 5x^3 - 15x^2 - 207x + 108$;   zero: $3i$

In Problems 31–40, find the complex zeros of each polynomial function. Write f in factored form.

31. $f(x) = x^3 - 1$

32. $f(x) = x^4 - 1$

33. $f(x) = x^3 - 8x^2 + 25x - 26$

34. $f(x) = x^3 + 13x^2 + 57x + 85$

35. $f(x) = x^4 + 5x^2 + 4$

36. $f(x) = x^4 + 13x^2 + 36$

37. $f(x) = x^4 + 2x^3 + 22x^2 + 50x - 75$

38. $f(x) = x^4 + 3x^3 - 19x^2 + 27x - 252$

39. $f(x) = 3x^4 - x^3 - 9x^2 + 159x - 52$

40. $f(x) = 2x^4 + x^3 - 35x^2 - 113x + 65$

Discussion and Writing

In Problems 41 and 42, explain why the facts given are contradictory.

41. $f(x)$ is a polynomial of degree 3 whose coefficients are real numbers; its zeros are $4 + i, 4 - i$, and $2 + i$.

42. $f(x)$ is a polynomial of degree 3 whose coefficients are real numbers; its zeros are $2, i$, and $3 + i$.

43. $f(x)$ is a polynomial of degree 4 whose coefficients are real numbers; three of its zeros are $2, 1 + 2i$, and $1 - 2i$. Explain why the remaining zero must be a real number.

44. $f(x)$ is a polynomial of degree 4 whose coefficients are real numbers; two of its zeros are -3 and $4 - i$. Explain why one of the remaining zeros must be a real number. Write down one of the missing zeros.

'Are You Prepared?' Answers

1. Sum: $3i$; product: $1 + 21i$

2. $-1 - i, -1 + i$

CHAPTER REVIEW

Things to Know

Power function (pp. 175–177)

$f(x) = x^n, \quad n \geq 2$ even

Domain: all real numbers   Range: nonnegative real numbers

Passes through $(-1, 1), (0, 0), (1, 1)$

Even function

Decreasing on $(-\infty, 0)$, increasing on $(0, \infty)$

$f(x) = x^n, \quad n \geq 3$ odd

Domain: all real numbers   Range: all real numbers

Passes through $(-1, -1), (0, 0), (1, 1)$

Odd function

Increasing on $(-\infty, \infty)$

Polynomial function (pp. 174, 180–185)

$f(x) = a_n x^n + a_{n-1} x^{n-1}$
$\quad + \cdots + a_1 x + a_0, \quad a_n \neq 0$

Domain: all real numbers

At most $n - 1$ turning points

End behavior: Behaves like $y = a_n x^n$ for large $|x|$

Real zeros of a polynomial function f (pp. 178–179)

Real number r for which $f(r) = 0$; if r is a real zero of f, then r is an x-intercept of the graph of f and $x - r$ is a factor of f.

Rational function (pp. 191–199)

$$R(x) = \frac{p(x)}{q(x)}$$

p, q are polynomial functions.

Domain: $\{x \mid q(x) \neq 0\}$

Vertical asymptotes: With $R(x)$ in lowest terms, if $q(r) = 0$ for some real number, then $x = r$ is a vertical asymptote.

Horizontal or oblique asymptotes: See the summary on page 199.

Remainder Theorem (p. 221)

If a polynomial function $f(x)$ is divided by $x - c$, then the remainder is $f(c)$.

Factor Theorem (p. 222)

$x - c$ is a factor of a polynomial function $f(x)$ if and only if $f(c) = 0$.

Rational Zeros Theorem (p. 223)

Let f be a polynomial function of degree 1 or higher of the form

$$f(x) = a_n x^n + a_{n-1} x^{n-1} + \cdots + a_1 x + a_0 \quad a_n \neq 0, a_0 \neq 0$$

where each coefficient is an integer. If $\dfrac{p}{q}$, in lowest terms, is a rational zero of f, then p must be a factor of a_0, and q must be a factor of a_n.

Bounds on Zeros (p. 227)

Let f denote a polynomial function whose leading coefficient is 1, so $f(x) = x^n + a_{n-1} x^{n-1} + \cdots + a_1 x + a_0$. A bound M on the zeros of f is the smaller of the two numbers

$$\text{Max} \{1, |a_0| + |a_1| + \cdots + |a_{n-1}|\}, \quad 1 + \text{Max} \{|a_0|, |a_1|, \ldots, |a_{n-1}|\}$$

Intermediate Value Theorem (p. 230)

Let f be a continuous function. If $a < b$ and $f(a)$ and $f(b)$ are of opposite sign, then there is at least one real zero of f between a and b.

Fundamental Theorem of Algebra (p. 234)

Every complex polynomial function $f(x)$ of degree $n \geq 1$ has at least one complex zero.

Conjugate Pairs Theorem (p. 235)

Let f be a polynomial whose coefficients are real numbers. If $r = a + bi$ is a zero of f, then its complex conjugate $\bar{r} = a - bi$ is also a zero of f.

Objectives

Section	You should be able to ...	Examples	Review Exercises
4.1	**1** Identify polynomial functions and their degree (p. 174)	1	1–4
	2 Graph polynomial functions using transformations (p. 177)	2, 3	5–10
	3 Identify the real zeros of a polynomial function and their multiplicity (p. 178)	4–6	11–18
	4 Analyze the graph of a polynomial function (p. 183)	9, 10	11–18
	5 Build cubic models from data (p. 186)	11	88
4.2	**1** Find the domain of a rational function (p. 192)	1	19–22
	2 Find the vertical asymptotes of a rational function (p. 195)	4	19–22
	3 Find the horizontal or oblique asymptotes of a rational function (p. 196)	5–8	19–22
4.3	**1** Analyze the graph of a rational function (p. 202)	1–5	23–34
	2 Solve applied problems involving rational functions (p. 209)	6	87
4.4	**1** Solve polynomial inequalities algebraically and graphically (p. 213)	1, 2	35, 36
	2 Solve rational inequalities algebraically and graphically (p. 215)	3, 4	37–44
4.5	**1** Use the Remainder and Factor Theorems (p. 220)	1, 2	45–50
	2 Use the Rational Zeros Theorem to list the potential rational zeros of a polynomial function (p. 223)	3	51, 52
	3 Find the real zeros of a polynomial function (p. 224)	4, 5, 9	53–62
	4 Solve polynomial equations (p. 226)	6	63–66
	5 Use the Theorem for Bounds on Zeros (p. 227)	7, 8	67–70
	6 Use the Intermediate Value Theorem (p. 230)	10	71–74
4.6	**1** Use the Conjugate Pairs Theorem (p. 235)	1	75–78
	2 Find a polynomial function with specified zeros (p. 236)	2	75–78
	3 Find the complex zeros of a polynomial function (p. 237)	3	79–86

Review Exercises

In Problems 1–4, determine which functions are polynomial functions. For those that are, state the degree. For those that are not, tell why not.

1. $f(x) = 4x^5 - 3x^2 + 5x - 2$ **2.** $f(x) = \dfrac{3x^5}{2x + 1}$ **3.** $f(x) = 3x^2 + 5x^{1/2} - 1$ **4.** $f(x) = 3$

In Problems 5–10, graph each function using transformations (shifting, compressing, stretching, and reflection). Show all the stages.

5. $f(x) = (x + 2)^3$ **6.** $f(x) = -x^3 + 3$ **7.** $f(x) = -(x - 1)^4$

8. $f(x) = (x - 1)^4 - 2$ **9.** $f(x) = (x - 1)^4 + 2$ **10.** $f(x) = (1 - x)^3$

In Problems 11–18, analyze the graph of each polynomial function by following Steps 1 through 8 on page 185.

11. $f(x) = x(x + 2)(x + 4)$ **12.** $f(x) = x(x - 2)(x - 4)$ **13.** $f(x) = (x - 2)^2(x + 4)$

14. $f(x) = (x - 2)(x + 4)^2$ **15.** $f(x) = x^3 - 4x^2$ **16.** $f(x) = x^3 + 4x$

17. $f(x) = (x - 1)^2(x + 3)(x + 1)$ **18.** $f(x) = (x - 4)(x + 2)^2(x - 2)$

In Problems 19–22, find the domain of each rational function. Find any horizontal, vertical, or oblique asymptotes.

19. $R(x) = \dfrac{x + 2}{x^2 - 9}$ **20.** $R(x) = \dfrac{x^2 + 4}{x - 2}$ **21.** $R(x) = \dfrac{2x^2 + 3x + 2}{(x + 2)^2}$ **22.** $R(x) = \dfrac{-4x^3}{x^3 - 1}$

In Problems 23–34, analyze each rational function following Steps 1 through 8 on page 204.

23. $R(x) = \dfrac{2x - 6}{x}$ **24.** $R(x) = \dfrac{4 - x}{x}$ **25.** $H(x) = \dfrac{x + 2}{x(x - 2)}$ **26.** $H(x) = \dfrac{x}{x^2 - 1}$

27. $R(x) = \dfrac{x^2 + x - 6}{x^2 - x - 6}$ **28.** $R(x) = \dfrac{x^2 - 6x + 9}{x^2}$ **29.** $F(x) = \dfrac{x^3}{x^2 - 4}$ **30.** $F(x) = \dfrac{3x^3}{(x - 1)^2}$

31. $R(x) = \dfrac{2x^4}{(x - 1)^2}$ **32.** $R(x) = \dfrac{x^4}{x^2 - 9}$ **33.** $G(x) = \dfrac{x^2 - 4}{x^2 - x - 2}$ **34.** $F(x) = \dfrac{(x - 1)^2}{x^2 - 1}$

In Problems 35–44, solve each inequality. Graph the solution set.

35. $x^3 + x^2 < 4x + 4$ **36.** $x^3 + 4x^2 \geq x + 4$ **37.** $\dfrac{6}{x + 3} \geq 1$ **38.** $\dfrac{-2}{1 - 3x} < 1$

39. $\dfrac{2x - 6}{1 - x} < 2$ **40.** $\dfrac{3 - 2x}{2x + 5} \geq 2$ **41.** $\dfrac{(x - 2)(x - 1)}{x - 3} \geq 0$ **42.** $\dfrac{x + 1}{x(x - 5)} \leq 0$

43. $\dfrac{x^2 - 8x + 12}{x^2 - 16} > 0$ **44.** $\dfrac{x(x^2 + x - 2)}{x^2 + 9x + 20} \leq 0$

In Problems 45–48, find the remainder R when f(x) is divided by g(x). Is g a factor of f?

45. $f(x) = 8x^3 - 3x^2 + x + 4;$ $g(x) = x - 1$ **46.** $f(x) = 2x^3 + 8x^2 - 5x + 5;$ $g(x) = x - 2$

47. $f(x) = x^4 - 2x^3 + 15x - 2;$ $g(x) = x + 2$ **48.** $f(x) = x^4 - x^2 + 2x + 2;$ $g(x) = x + 1$

49. Find the value of $f(x) = 12x^6 - 8x^4 + 1$ at $x = 4$.

50. Find the value of $f(x) = -16x^3 + 18x^2 - x + 2$ at $x = -2$.

In Problems 51 and 52, determine the maximum number of zeros each polynomial function may have. Then list the potential rational zeros of each polynomial function. Do not attempt to find the zeros.

51. $f(x) = 12x^8 - x^7 + 8x^4 - 2x^3 + x + 3$ **52.** $f(x) = -6x^5 + x^4 + 5x^3 + x + 1$

In Problems 53–58, use the Rational Zeros Theorem to find all the real zeros of each polynomial function. Use the zeros to factor f over the real numbers.

53. $f(x) = x^3 - 3x^2 - 6x + 8$ **54.** $f(x) = x^3 - x^2 - 10x - 8$

55. $f(x) = 4x^3 + 4x^2 - 7x + 2$ **56.** $f(x) = 4x^3 - 4x^2 - 7x - 2$

57. $f(x) = x^4 - 4x^3 + 9x^2 - 20x + 20$ **58.** $f(x) = x^4 + 6x^3 + 11x^2 + 12x + 18$

In Problems 59–62, determine the real zeros of the polynomial function. Approximate all irrational zeros rounded to two decimal places.

59. $f(x) = 2x^3 - 11.84x^2 - 9.116x + 82.46$ **60.** $f(x) = 12x^3 + 39.8x^2 - 4.4x - 3.4$

61. $g(x) = 15x^4 - 21.5x^3 - 1718.3x^2 + 5308x + 3796.8$ **62.** $g(x) = 3x^4 + 67.93x^3 + 486.265x^2 + 1121.32x + 412.195$

In Problems 63–66, solve each equation in the real number system.

63. $2x^4 + 2x^3 - 11x^2 + x - 6 = 0$

64. $3x^4 + 3x^3 - 17x^2 + x - 6 = 0$

65. $2x^4 + 7x^3 + x^2 - 7x - 3 = 0$

66. $2x^4 + 7x^3 - 5x^2 - 28x - 12 = 0$

In Problems 67–70, find bounds to the real zeros of each polynomial function. Obtain a complete graph of f using a graphing utility.

67. $f(x) = x^3 - x^2 - 4x + 2$

68. $f(x) = x^3 + x^2 - 10x - 5$

69. $f(x) = 2x^3 - 7x^2 - 10x + 35$

70. $f(x) = 3x^3 - 7x^2 - 6x + 14$

In Problems 71–74, use the Intermediate Value Theorem to show that each polynomial has a zero in the given interval.

71. $f(x) = 3x^3 - x - 1$; $[0, 1]$

72. $f(x) = 2x^3 - x^2 - 3$; $[1, 2]$

73. $f(x) = 8x^4 - 4x^3 - 2x - 1$; $[0, 1]$

74. $f(x) = 3x^4 + 4x^3 - 8x - 2$; $[1, 2]$

In Problems 75–78, information is given about a complex polynomial f(x) whose coefficients are real numbers. Find the remaining zeros of f. Then find a polynomial with real coefficients that has the zeros.

75. Degree 3; zeros: $4 + i, 6$

76. Degree 3; zeros: $3 + 4i, 5$

77. Degree 4; zeros: $i, 1 + i$

78. Degree 4; zeros: $1, 2, 1 + i$

In Problems 79–86, find the complex zeros of each polynomial function f(x). Write f in factored form.

79. $f(x) = x^3 - 3x^2 - 6x + 8$

80. $f(x) = x^3 - x^2 - 10x - 8$

81. $f(x) = 4x^3 + 4x^2 - 7x + 2$

82. $f(x) = 4x^3 - 4x^2 - 7x - 2$

83. $f(x) = x^4 - 4x^3 + 9x^2 - 20x + 20$

84. $f(x) = x^4 + 6x^3 + 11x^2 + 12x + 18$

85. $f(x) = 2x^4 + 2x^3 - 11x^2 + x - 6$

86. $f(x) = 3x^4 + 3x^3 - 17x^2 + x - 6$

---

87. Making a Can A can in the shape of a right circular cylinder is required to have a volume of 250 cubic centimeters.

(a) Express the amount A of material to make the can as a function of the radius r of the cylinder.

(b) How much material is required if the can is of radius 3 centimeters?

(c) How much material is required if the can is of radius 5 centimeters?

(d) Graph $A = A(r)$. For what value of r is A smallest?

88. Model It: Poverty Rates The following data represent the percentage of families in the United States whose income is below the poverty level.

Year, t	Percent below Poverty Level, p
1990, 1	10.9
1991, 2	11.5
1992, 3	11.9
1993, 4	12.3
1994, 5	11.6
1995, 6	10.8
1996, 7	11.0
1997, 8	10.3
1998, 9	10.0
1999, 10	9.3
2000, 11	8.7
2001, 12	9.2
2002, 13	9.6
2003, 14	10.0
2004, 15	10.2

Source: U.S. Census Bureau

(a) With a graphing utility, draw a scatter diagram of the data. Comment on the type of relation that appears to exist between the two variables.

(b) Decide on a function of best fit to these data (linear, quadratic, or cubic), and use this function to predict the percentage of U.S. families that were below the poverty level in 2005 ($t = 16$).

(c) Draw the function of best fit on the scatter diagram drawn in part (a).

89. Design a polynomial function with the following characteristics: degree 6; four real zeros, one of multiplicity 3; y-intercept 3; behaves like $y = -5x^6$ for large values of $|x|$. Is this polynomial unique? Compare your polynomial with those of other students. What terms will be the same as everyone else's? Add some more characteristics, such as symmetry or naming the real zeros. How does this modify the polynomial?

90. Design a rational function with the following characteristics: three real zeros, one of multiplicity 2; y-intercept 1; vertical asymptotes $x = -2$ and $x = 3$; oblique asymptote $y = 2x + 1$. Is this rational function unique? Compare yours with those of other students. What will be the same as everyone else's? Add some more characteristics, such as symmetry or naming the real zeros. How does this modify the rational function?

CHAPTER TEST

1. Graph $f(x) = (x - 3)^4 - 2$ using transformations.

2. For the polynomial function $g(x) = 2x^3 + 5x^2 - 28x - 15$,
   (a) Determine the maximum number of real zeros that the function may have.
   (b) Find bounds to the zeros of the function.
   (c) List the potential rational zeros.
   (d) Determine the real zeros of g. Factor g over the reals.
   (e) Find the x- and y-intercepts of the graph of g.
   (f) Determine whether the graph crosses or touches the x-axis at each x-intercept.
   (g) Find the power function that the graph of g resembles for large values of $|x|$.
   (h) Approximate the turning points on the graph of g.
   (i) Put all the information together to obtain the graph of g.

3. Find the complex zeros of $f(x) = x^3 - 4x^2 + 25x - 100$.

4. Solve $3x^3 + 2x - 1 = 8x^2 - 4$ in the complex number system.

In Problems 5 and 6, find the domain of each function. Find any horizontal, vertical, or oblique asymptotes.

5. $g(x) = \dfrac{2x^2 - 14x + 24}{x^2 + 6x - 40}$

6. $r(x) = \dfrac{x^2 + 2x - 3}{x + 1}$

7. Sketch the graph of the function in Problem 6. Label all intercepts, vertical asymptotes, horizontal asymptotes, and oblique asymptotes.

In Problems 8 and 9, write a function that meets the given conditions.

8. Fourth-degree polynomial with real coefficients; zeros: $-2, 0, 3 + i$.

9. Rational function; asymptotes: $y = 2, x = 4$; domain: $\{x | x \neq 4, x \neq 9\}$.

10. Use the Intermediate Value Theorem to show that the function $f(x) = -2x^2 - 3x + 8$ has at least one real zero on the interval $[0, 4]$.

11. Solve: $\dfrac{x + 2}{x - 3} < 2$

CUMULATIVE REVIEW

1. Find the distance between the points $P = (1, 3)$ and $Q = (-4, 2)$.

2. Solve the inequality $x^2 \geq x$ and graph the solution set.

3. Solve the inequality $x^2 - 3x < 4$ and graph the solution set.

4. Find a linear function with slope -3 that contains the point $(-1, 4)$. Graph the function.

5. Find the equation of the line parallel to the line $y = 2x + 1$ and containing the point $(3, 5)$. Express your answer in slope–intercept form and graph the line.

6. Graph the equation $y = x^3$.

7. Does the relation $\{(3, 6), (1, 3), (2, 5), (3, 8)\}$ represent a function? Why or why not?

8. Solve the equation $x^3 - 6x^2 + 8x = 0$.

9. Solve the inequality $3x + 2 \leq 5x - 1$ and graph the solution set.

10. Find the center and radius of the circle $x^2 + 4x + y^2 - 2y - 4 = 0$. Graph the circle.

11. For the equation $y = x^3 - 9x$, determine the intercepts and test for symmetry.

12. Find an equation of the line perpendicular to $3x - 2y = 7$ that contains the point $(1, 5)$.

13. Is the following graph the graph of a function? Why or why not?

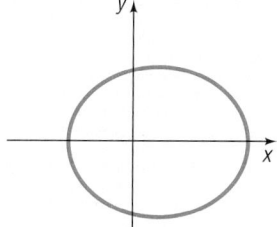

14. For the function $f(x) = x^2 + 5x - 2$, find
    (a) $f(3)$ (b) $f(-x)$
    (c) $-f(x)$ (d) $f(3x)$
    (e) $\dfrac{f(x + h) - f(x)}{h}$ $h \neq 0$

15. Answer the following questions regarding the function
    $$f(x) = \dfrac{x + 5}{x - 1}$$
    (a) What is the domain of f?
    (b) Is the point $(2, 6)$ on the graph of f?
    (c) If $x = 3$, what is $f(x)$? What point is on the graph of f?
    (d) If $f(x) = 9$, what is x? What point is on the graph of f?

16. Graph the function $f(x) = -3x + 7$.

17. Graph $f(x) = 2x^2 - 4x + 1$ by determining whether its graph opens up or down and by finding its vertex, axis of symmetry, y-intercept, and x-intercepts, if any.

18. Find the average rate of change of $f(x) = x^2 + 3x + 1$ from 1 to 2. Use this result to find the equation of the secant line containing $(1, f(1))$ and $(2, f(2))$.

19. In parts (a) to (f), use the following graph.

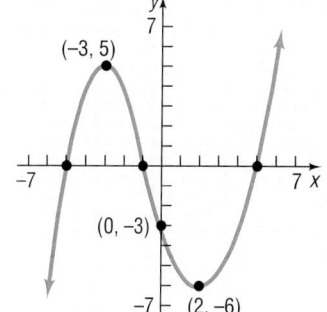

(a) Determine the intercepts.
(b) Based on the graph, tell whether the graph is symmetric with respect to the *x*-axis, the *y*-axis, and/or the origin.
(c) Based on the graph, tell whether the function is even, odd, or neither.
(d) List the intervals on which *f* is increasing. List the intervals on which *f* is decreasing.
(e) List the numbers, if any, at which *f* has a local maximum. What are these local maxima?
(f) List the numbers, if any, at which *f* has a local minimum. What are these local minima?

20. Determine algebraically whether the function

$$f(x) = \frac{5x}{x^2 - 9}$$

is even, odd, or neither.

21. For the function $f(x) = \begin{cases} 2x + 1 & \text{if } -3 < x < 2 \\ -3x + 4 & \text{if } x \geq 2 \end{cases}$

(a) Find the domain of *f*.
(b) Locate any intercepts.
(c) Graph the function.
(d) Based on the graph, find the range.

22. Graph the function $f(x) = -3(x + 1)^2 + 5$ using transformations.

23. Suppose that $f(x) = x^2 - 5x + 1$ and $g(x) = -4x - 7$.
(a) Find $f + g$ and state its domain.
(b) Find $\dfrac{f}{g}$ and state its domain.

24. The price *p* (in dollars) and the quantity *x* sold of a certain product obey the demand equation

$$p = -\frac{1}{10}x + 150, \quad 0 \leq x \leq 1500$$

(a) Express the revenue *R* as a function of *x*.
(b) What is the revenue if 100 units are sold?
(c) What quantity *x* maximizes revenue? What is the maximum revenue?
(d) What price should the company charge to maximize revenue?

CHAPTER PROJECTS

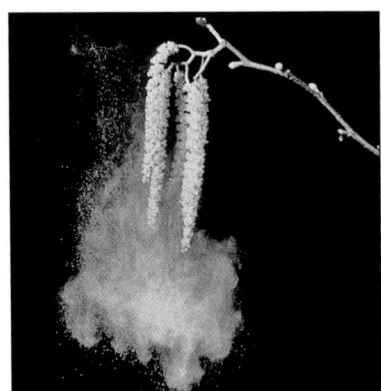

I. **Weed Pollen** The table shows the tree pollen count for Lexington, Kentucky, from April 1, 2006, to May 16, 2006, during the prime season for tree pollen.

Date	Count	Date	Count	Date	Count	Date	Count	Date	Count
4/1	76	4/10	19	4/19	1162	4/29	359	5/8	63
4/2	43	4/11	207	4/20	924	4/30	164	5/9	91
4/3	114	4/12	903	4/21	1030	5/1	65	5/10	166
4/4	73	4/13	1058	4/22	82	5/2	69	5/11	80
4/5	140	4/14	981	4/23	1514	5/3	30	5/12	153
4/6	138	4/15	1832	4/25	724	5/4	181	5/13	71
4/7	153	4/16	2058	4/26	102	5/5	95	5/14	63
4/8	264	4/17	1387	4/27	110	5/6	300	5/15	13
4/9	203	4/18	1188	4/28	320	5/7	91	5/16	9

Source: National Allergy Bureau at the American Academy of Allergy, Asthma and Immunology Web site. Used with permission.

1. Let the independent variable D represent the date, where $D = 1$ on 4/1, $D = 2$ on 4/2, $D = 3$ on 4/3, and $D = 46$ on 5/16. Let the dependent variable P represent the number of grains per cubic meter of weed pollen. Draw a scatter diagram of the data using your graphing utility and by hand on graph paper.

2. In the hand-drawn scatter diagram, sketch a smooth curve that fits the data. Try to have the curve pass through as many of the points as closely as possible. How many turning points are there? What does this tell you about the degree of the polynomial that could model the data? If the ends of the graph on the left and on the right are extended downward, how many real zeros are indicated by the graph? How many complex? Why?

3. Use a graphing utility to determine the quartic function of best fit. Graph it on your graphing utility. Does it look like what you expected from your hand-drawn graph? Explain.

4. Use a graphing utility to determine the cubic function of best fit. Graph it on your graphing utility. Does it look like what you expected from your hand-drawn graph? Explain.

5. Use a graphing utility to determine the quadratic function of best fit. Graph it on your graphing utility. Does it look like what you expected from your hand-drawn graph? Explain.

6. Which of the three functions seems to fit the best? Explain your reasoning.

7. Investigate weed pollen counts at other times of the year. (Go to the National Allergy Bureau at www.aaaai.org.) Would the polynomial you found in part (3) work for other 6-week periods? Why or why not? What about for the same period of time in other years?

The following project is available at the Instructor's Resource Center (IRC):

II. Theory of Equations   The coefficients of a polynomial function can be found if its zeros are known, an advantage of using polynomials in modeling.

Exponential and Logarithmic Functions

5

The McDonald's Scalding Coffee Case

April 3, 1996—There is a lot of hype about the McDonald's scalding coffee case. No one is in favor of frivolous cases or outlandish results; however, it is important to understand some points that were not reported in most of the stories about the case. McDonald's coffee was not only hot, it was scalding, capable of almost instantaneous destruction of skin, flesh, and muscle.

Plaintiff's expert, a scholar in thermodynamics applied to human skin burns, testified that liquids at 180 degrees will cause a full thickness burn to human skin in two to seven seconds. Other testimony showed that, as the temperature decreases toward 155 degrees, the extent of the burn relative to that temperature decreases exponentially. Thus, if (the) spill had involved coffee at 155 degrees, the liquid would have cooled and given her time to avoid a serious burn.

Source: ATLA fact sheet © 1995, 1996 Consumer Attorneys of CA. Used with permission of the Association of Trial Lawyers of America.

—See Chapter Project 1—

A Look Back

Until now, our study of functions has concentrated on polynomial and rational functions. These functions belong to the class of **algebraic functions,** that is, functions that can be expressed in terms of sums, differences, products, quotients, powers, or roots of polynomials. Functions that are not algebraic are termed **transcendental** (they transcend, or go beyond, algebraic functions).

A Look Ahead

In this chapter, we study two transcendental functions: the exponential function and the logarithmic function. These functions occur frequently in a wide variety of applications, such as biology, chemistry, economics, and psychology.

The chapter begins with a discussion of composite, one-to-one, and inverse functions, concepts needed to see the relationship between exponential and logarithmic functions.

Outline

5.1 Composite Functions

5.2 One-to-One Functions; Inverse Functions

5.3 Exponential Functions

5.4 Logarithmic Functions

5.5 Properties of Logarithms

5.6 Logarithmic and Exponential Equations

5.7 Financial Models

5.8 Exponential Growth and Decay Models; Newton's Law; Logistic Growth and Decay Models

5.9 Building Exponential, Logarithmic, and Logistic Models from Data

Chapter Review

Chapter Test

Cumulative Review

Chapter Projects

5.1 Composite Functions

PREPARING FOR THIS SECTION *Before getting started, review the following:*

- Finding Values of a Function (Section 2.1, pp. 60–62)
- Domain of a Function (Section 2.1, pp. 63–64)

Now Work the 'Are You Prepared?' problems on page 253.

OBJECTIVES 1 Form a Composite Function (p. 248)
2 Find the Domain of a Composite Function (p. 249)

1 Form a Composite Function

Figure 1

Suppose that an oil tanker is leaking oil and you want to determine the area of the circular oil patch around the ship. See Figure 1. It is determined that the oil is leaking from the tanker in such a way that the radius of the circular patch of oil around the ship is increasing at a rate of 3 feet per minute. Therefore, the radius r of the oil patch at any time t, in minutes, is given by $r(t) = 3t$. So after 20 minutes the radius of the oil patch is $r(20) = 3(20) = 60$ feet.

The area A of a circle as a function of the radius r is given by $A(r) = \pi r^2$. The area of the circular patch of oil after 20 minutes is $A(60) = \pi(60)^2 = 3600\pi$ square feet. Notice that $60 = r(20)$, so $A(60) = A(r(20))$. The argument of the function A is itself a function!

In general, we can find the area of the oil patch as a function of time t by evaluating $A(r(t))$. The function $A(r(t))$ is a special type of function called a *composite function*.

As another example, consider the function $y = (2x + 3)^2$. If we write $y = f(u) = u^2$ and $u = g(x) = 2x + 3$, then, by a substitution process, we can obtain the original function: $y = f(u) = f(g(x)) = (2x + 3)^2$.

In general, suppose that f and g are two functions and that x is a number in the domain of g. By evaluating g at x, we get $g(x)$. If $g(x)$ is in the domain of f, then we may evaluate f at $g(x)$ and obtain the expression $f(g(x))$. The correspondence from x to $f(g(x))$ is called a *composite function* $f \circ g$.

DEFINITION

Given two functions f and g, the **composite function,** denoted by $f \circ g$ (read as "f composed with g"), is defined by

$$(f \circ g)(x) = f(g(x))$$

The domain of $f \circ g$ is the set of all numbers x in the domain of g such that $g(x)$ is in the domain of f.

Look carefully at Figure 2. Only those x's in the domain of g for which $g(x)$ is in the domain of f can be in the domain of $f \circ g$. The reason is that if $g(x)$ is not in the domain of f then $f(g(x))$ is not defined. Because of this, the domain of $f \circ g$ is a subset of the domain of g; the range of $f \circ g$ is a subset of the range of f.

Figure 2

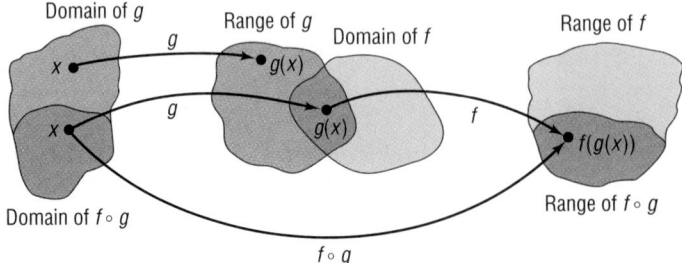

Figure 3 provides a second illustration of the definition. Here x is the input to the function g, yielding $g(x)$. Then $g(x)$ is the input to the function f, yielding $f(g(x))$. Notice that the "inside" function g in $f(g(x))$ is done first.

Figure 3

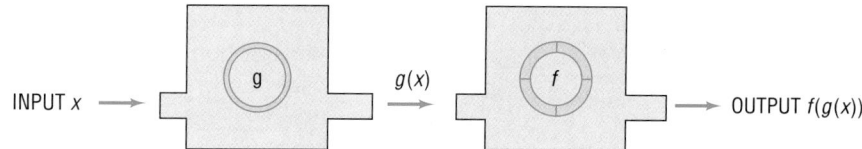

INPUT x g $g(x)$ f OUTPUT $f(g(x))$

Let's look at some examples.

| EXAMPLE 1 | **Evaluating a Composite Function** |

Suppose that $f(x) = 2x^2 - 3$ and $g(x) = 4x$. Find:

(a) $(f \circ g)(1)$ (b) $(g \circ f)(1)$ (c) $(f \circ f)(-2)$ (d) $(g \circ g)(-1)$

Solution   (a) $(f \circ g)(1) = f(g(1)) = f(4) = 2 \cdot 4^2 - 3 = 29$

$$g(x) = 4x \quad f(x) = 2x^2 - 3$$
$$g(1) = 4$$

(b) $(g \circ f)(1) = g(f(1)) = g(-1) = 4 \cdot (-1) = -4$

$$f(x) = 2x^2 - 3 \quad g(x) = 4x$$
$$f(1) = -1$$

(c) $(f \circ f)(-2) = f(f(-2)) = f(5) = 2 \cdot 5^2 - 3 = 47$

$$f(-2) = 2(-2)^2 - 3 = 5$$

(d) $(g \circ g)(-1) = g(g(-1)) = g(-4) = 4 \cdot (-4) = -16$

$$g(-1) = -4$$

Figure 4

Y₁(Y₂(1))
           29

COMMENT Graphing calculators can be used to evaluate composite functions.* Let $Y_1 = f(x) = 2x^2 - 3$ and $Y_2 = g(x) = 4x$. Then, using a TI-84 Plus graphing calculator, $(f \circ g)(1)$ is found as shown in Figure 4. Notice that this is the result obtained in Example 1(a). ∎

➤ **Now Work** PROBLEM 11

2 Find the Domain of a Composite Function

| EXAMPLE 2 | **Finding a Composite Function and Its Domain** |

Suppose that $f(x) = x^2 + 3x - 1$ and $g(x) = 2x + 3$.

Find: (a) $f \circ g$ (b) $g \circ f$

Then find the domain of each composite function.

Solution   The domain of f and the domain of g are the set of all real numbers.

(a) $(f \circ g)(x) = f(g(x)) = f(2x + 3) = (2x + 3)^2 + 3(2x + 3) - 1$

$$f(x) = x^2 + 3x - 1$$

$$= 4x^2 + 12x + 9 + 6x + 9 - 1 = 4x^2 + 18x + 17$$

Since the domains of both f and g are the set of all real numbers, the domain of $f \circ g$ is the set of all real numbers.

---

*Consult your owner's manual for the appropriate keystrokes.

(b) $(g \circ f)(x) = g(f(x)) = g(x^2 + 3x - 1) = 2(x^2 + 3x - 1) + 3$

$$\uparrow$$
$$g(x) = 2x + 3$$

$$= 2x^2 + 6x - 2 + 3 = 2x^2 + 6x + 1$$

Since the domains of both f and g are the set of all real numbers, the domain of $g \circ f$ is the set of all real numbers.

∎

Look back at Figure 2. In determining the domain of the composite function $(f \circ g)(x) = f(g(x))$, keep the following two thoughts in mind about the input x.

1. $g(x)$ must be defined so that any x not in the domain of g must be excluded.
2. $f(g(x))$ must be defined so that any x for which $g(x)$ is not in the domain of f must be excluded.

EXAMPLE 3	**Finding the Domain of $f \circ g$**

Find the domain of $(f \circ g)(x)$ if $f(x) = \dfrac{1}{x + 2}$ and $g(x) = \dfrac{4}{x - 1}$.

Solution For $(f \circ g)(x) = f(g(x))$, we first note that the domain of g is $\{x | x \neq 1\}$, so we exclude 1 from the domain of $f \circ g$. Next we note that the domain of f is $\{x | x \neq -2\}$, which means that $g(x)$ cannot equal -2. We solve the equation $g(x) = -2$ to determine what values of x to exclude.

$$\frac{4}{x - 1} = -2 \qquad\qquad g(x) = -2$$

$$4 = -2(x - 1)$$

$$4 = -2x + 2$$

$$2x = -2$$

$$x = -1$$

We also exclude -1 from the domain of $f \circ g$. The domain of $f \circ g$ is $\{x | x \neq -1, x \neq 1\}$.

✓**Check:** For $x = 1$, $g(x) = \dfrac{4}{x - 1}$ is not defined, so $(f \circ g)(x) = f(g(x))$ is not defined.

For $x = -1$, $g(-1) = \dfrac{4}{-2} = -2$, and $(f \circ g)(-1) = f(g(-1)) = f(-2)$ is not defined.

∎

🖉 **Now Work** PROBLEM 21

EXAMPLE 4	**Finding a Composite Function and Its Domain**

Suppose that $f(x) = \dfrac{1}{x + 2}$ and $g(x) = \dfrac{4}{x - 1}$

Find: (a) $f \circ g$ (b) $f \circ f$

Then find the domain of each composite function.

Solution The domain of f is $\{x | x \neq -2\}$ and the domain of g is $\{x | x \neq 1\}$.

(a) $(f \circ g)(x) = f(g(x)) = f\left(\dfrac{4}{x - 1}\right) = \dfrac{1}{\dfrac{4}{x - 1} + 2} = \dfrac{x - 1}{4 + 2(x - 1)} = \dfrac{x - 1}{2x + 2} = \dfrac{x - 1}{2(x + 1)}$

$$\uparrow \qquad\qquad\qquad \uparrow$$
$$f(x) = \frac{1}{x+2} \qquad \text{Multiply by } \frac{x-1}{x-1}.$$

In Example 3, we found the domain of $f \circ g$ to be $\{x | x \neq -1, x \neq 1\}$.

We could also find the domain of $f \circ g$ by first looking at the domain of g: $\{x \mid x \neq 1\}$. We exclude 1 from the domain of $f \circ g$ as a result. Then we look at $f \circ g$ and notice that x cannot equal -1, since $x = -1$ results in division by 0. So we also exclude -1 from the domain of $f \circ g$. Therefore, the domain of $f \circ g$ is $\{x \mid x \neq -1, x \neq 1\}$.

(b) $(f \circ f)(x) = f(f(x)) = f\left(\dfrac{1}{x + 2}\right) = \dfrac{1}{\dfrac{1}{x+2} + 2} = \dfrac{x+2}{1 + 2(x+2)} = \dfrac{x+2}{2x+5}$

$\uparrow$ $\qquad\qquad\qquad\qquad$ $\uparrow$

$f(x) = \dfrac{1}{x+2}$ $\qquad\qquad$ Multiply by $\dfrac{x+2}{x+2}$.

The domain of $f \circ f$ consists of those x in the domain of f, $\{x \mid x \neq -2\}$, for which

$$f(x) = \dfrac{1}{x+2} \neq -2 \qquad \dfrac{1}{x+2} = -2$$

$$1 = -2(x+2)$$
$$1 = -2x - 4$$
$$2x = -5$$
$$x = -\dfrac{5}{2}$$

or, equivalently,

$$x \neq -\dfrac{5}{2}$$

The domain of $f \circ f$ is $\left\{ x \mid x \neq -\dfrac{5}{2}, x \neq -2 \right\}$.

We could also find the domain of $f \circ f$ by recognizing that -2 is not in the domain of f and so should be excluded from the domain of $f \circ f$. Then, looking at $f \circ f$, we see that x cannot equal $-\dfrac{5}{2}$. Do you see why? Therefore, the domain of $f \circ f$ is $\left\{ x \mid x \neq -\dfrac{5}{2}, x \neq -2 \right\}$.

━━━━━━━ **Now Work** PROBLEMS **33** AND **35**

Look back at Example 2, which illustrates that, in general, $f \circ g \neq g \circ f$. Sometimes $f \circ g$ does equal $g \circ f$, as shown in the next example.

EXAMPLE 5 | **Showing That Two Composite Functions Are Equal**

If $f(x) = 3x - 4$ and $g(x) = \dfrac{1}{3}(x + 4)$, show that

$$(f \circ g)(x) = (g \circ f)(x) = x$$

for every x in the domain of $f \circ g$ and $g \circ f$.

Solution $(f \circ g)(x) = f(g(x))$

$= f\left(\dfrac{x+4}{3}\right)$ $\qquad$ $g(x) = \dfrac{1}{3}(x+4) = \dfrac{x+4}{3}$

$= 3\left(\dfrac{x+4}{3}\right) - 4$ $\qquad$ Substitute $g(x)$ into the rule for f, $f(x) = 3x - 4$.

$= x + 4 - 4 = x$

Using a graphing calculator, let

$$Y_1 = f(x) = 3x - 4$$

$$Y_2 = g(x) = \frac{1}{3}(x + 4)$$

$$Y_3 = f \circ g, Y_4 = g \circ f$$

Using the viewing window $-3 \le x \le 3$, $-2 \le y \le 2$, graph only Y_3 and Y_4. What do you see? TRACE to verify that $Y_3 = Y_4$.

$$(g \circ f)(x) = g(f(x))$$

$$= g(3x - 4) \qquad f(x) = 3x - 4$$

$$= \frac{1}{3}[(3x - 4) + 4] \qquad \text{Substitute } f(x) \text{ into the rule for } g, g(x) = \frac{1}{3}(x + 4).$$

$$= \frac{1}{3}(3x) = x$$

We conclude that $(f \circ g)(x) = (g \circ f)(x) = x$.

In Section 5.2, we shall see that there is an important relationship between functions f and g for which $(f \circ g)(x) = (g \circ f)(x) = x$.

➤ **Now Work** PROBLEM 45

Calculus Application

 Some techniques in calculus require that we be able to determine the components of a composite function. For example, the function $H(x) = \sqrt{x + 1}$ is the composition of the functions f and g, where $f(x) = \sqrt{x}$ and $g(x) = x + 1$, because $H(x) = (f \circ g)(x) = f(g(x)) = f(x + 1) = \sqrt{x + 1}$.

EXAMPLE 6 **Finding the Components of a Composite Function**

Find functions f and g such that $f \circ g = H$ if $H(x) = (x^2 + 1)^{50}$.

Solution The function H takes $x^2 + 1$ and raises it to the power 50. A natural way to decompose H is to raise the function $g(x) = x^2 + 1$ to the power 50. If we let $f(x) = x^{50}$ and $g(x) = x^2 + 1$, then

Figure 5

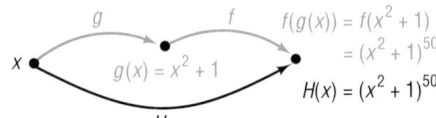

$$(f \circ g)(x) = f(g(x))$$

$$= f(x^2 + 1)$$

$$= (x^2 + 1)^{50} = H(x)$$

See Figure 5.

Other functions f and g may be found for which $f \circ g = H$ in Example 6. For example, if $f(x) = x^2$ and $g(x) = (x^2 + 1)^{25}$, then

$$(f \circ g)(x) = f(g(x)) = f((x^2 + 1)^{25}) = [(x^2 + 1)^{25}]^2 = (x^2 + 1)^{50}$$

Although the functions f and g found as a solution to Example 6 are not unique, there is usually a "natural" selection for f and g that comes to mind first.

EXAMPLE 7 **Finding the Components of a Composite Function**

Find functions f and g such that $f \circ g = H$ if $H(x) = \dfrac{1}{x + 1}$.

Solution Here H is the reciprocal of $g(x) = x + 1$. If we let $f(x) = \dfrac{1}{x}$ and $g(x) = x + 1$, we find that

$$(f \circ g)(x) = f(g(x)) = f(x + 1) = \frac{1}{x + 1} = H(x)$$

➤ **Now Work** PROBLEM 53

5.1 Assess Your Understanding

'Are You Prepared?' *Answers are given at the end of these exercises. If you get a wrong answer, read the pages listed in red.*

1. Find $f(3)$ if $f(x) = -4x^2 + 5x$. (pp. 61–62)

2. Find $f(3x)$ if $f(x) = 4 - 2x^2$. What is the argument of f? (pp. 61–62)

3. Find the domain of the function $f(x) = \dfrac{x^2 - 1}{x^2 - 25}$. (pp. 63–64)

Concepts and Vocabulary

4. If $f(x) = x + 1$ and $g(x) = x^3$, then _____ $= (x + 1)^3$.

5. *True or False* $f(g(x)) = f(x) \cdot g(x)$.

6. *True or False* The domain of the composite function $(f \circ g)(x)$ is the same as the domain of $g(x)$.

Skill Building

In Problems 7 and 8, evaluate each expression using the values given in the table.

7.

x	−3	−2	−1	0	1	2	3
f(x)	−7	−5	−3	−1	3	5	5
g(x)	8	3	0	−1	0	3	8

  (a) $(f \circ g)(1)$ (b) $(f \circ g)(-1)$ (c) $(g \circ f)(-1)$ (d) $(g \circ f)(0)$ (e) $(g \circ g)(-2)$ (f) $(f \circ f)(-1)$

8.

x	−3	−2	−1	0	1	2	3
f(x)	11	9	7	5	3	1	−1
g(x)	−8	−3	0	1	0	−3	−8

  (a) $(f \circ g)(1)$ (b) $(f \circ g)(2)$ (c) $(g \circ f)(2)$ (d) $(g \circ f)(3)$ (e) $(g \circ g)(1)$ (f) $(f \circ f)(3)$

In Problems 9 and 10, evaluate each expression using the graphs of $y = f(x)$ and $y = g(x)$ shown in the figure.

9. (a) $(g \circ f)(-1)$ (b) $(g \circ f)(0)$
    (c) $(f \circ g)(-1)$ (d) $(f \circ g)(4)$

10. (a) $(g \circ f)(1)$ (b) $(g \circ f)(5)$
    (c) $(f \circ g)(0)$ (d) $(f \circ g)(2)$

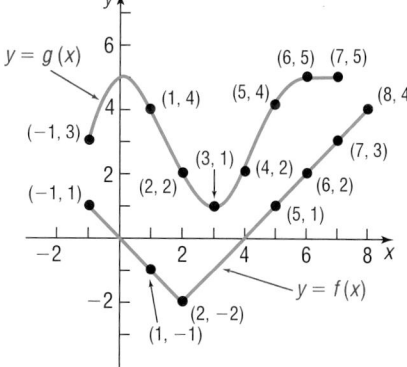

In Problems 11–20, for the given functions f and g, find:

  (a) $(f \circ g)(4)$ *(b) $(g \circ f)(2)$*   *(c) $(f \circ f)(1)$*   *(d) $(g \circ g)(0)$*

11. $f(x) = 2x$; $g(x) = 3x^2 + 1$

12. $f(x) = 3x + 2$; $g(x) = 2x^2 - 1$

13. $f(x) = 4x^2 - 3$; $g(x) = 3 - \dfrac{1}{2}x^2$

14. $f(x) = 2x^2$; $g(x) = 1 - 3x^2$

15. $f(x) = \sqrt{x}$; $g(x) = 2x$

16. $f(x) = \sqrt{x + 1}$; $g(x) = 3x$

17. $f(x) = |x|$; $g(x) = \dfrac{1}{x^2 + 1}$

18. $f(x) = |x - 2|$; $g(x) = \dfrac{3}{x^2 + 2}$

19. $f(x) = \dfrac{3}{x + 1}$; $g(x) = \sqrt[3]{x}$

20. $f(x) = x^{3/2}$; $g(x) = \dfrac{2}{x + 1}$

In Problems 21–28, find the domain of the composite function $f \circ g$.

21. $f(x) = \dfrac{3}{x - 1}$; $g(x) = \dfrac{2}{x}$

22. $f(x) = \dfrac{1}{x + 3}$; $g(x) = -\dfrac{2}{x}$

23. $f(x) = \dfrac{x}{x-1}$; $g(x) = -\dfrac{4}{x}$

24. $f(x) = \dfrac{x}{x+3}$; $g(x) = \dfrac{2}{x}$

25. $f(x) = \sqrt{x}$; $g(x) = 2x + 3$

26. $f(x) = x - 2$; $g(x) = \sqrt{1-x}$

27. $f(x) = x^2 + 1$; $g(x) = \sqrt{x-1}$

28. $f(x) = x^2 + 4$; $g(x) = \sqrt{x-2}$

In Problems 29–44, for the given functions f and g, find:

    (a) $f \circ g$ (b) $g \circ f$ (c) $f \circ f$ (d) $g \circ g$

State the domain of each composite function.

29. $f(x) = 2x + 3$; $g(x) = 3x$

30. $f(x) = -x$; $g(x) = 2x - 4$

31. $f(x) = 3x + 1$; $g(x) = x^2$

32. $f(x) = x + 1$; $g(x) = x^2 + 4$

33. $f(x) = x^2$; $g(x) = x^2 + 4$

34. $f(x) = x^2 + 1$; $g(x) = 2x^2 + 3$

35. $f(x) = \dfrac{3}{x-1}$; $g(x) = \dfrac{2}{x}$

36. $f(x) = \dfrac{1}{x+3}$; $g(x) = -\dfrac{2}{x}$

37. $f(x) = \dfrac{x}{x-1}$; $g(x) = -\dfrac{4}{x}$

38. $f(x) = \dfrac{x}{x+3}$; $g(x) = \dfrac{2}{x}$

39. $f(x) = \sqrt{x}$; $g(x) = 2x + 3$

40. $f(x) = \sqrt{x-2}$; $g(x) = 1 - 2x$

41. $f(x) = x^2 + 1$; $g(x) = \sqrt{x-1}$

42. $f(x) = x^2 + 4$; $g(x) = \sqrt{x-2}$

43. $f(x) = \dfrac{x-5}{x+1}$; $g(x) = \dfrac{x+2}{x-3}$

44. $f(x) = \dfrac{2x-1}{x-2}$; $g(x) = \dfrac{x+4}{2x-5}$

In Problems 45–52, show that $(f \circ g)(x) = (g \circ f)(x) = x$.

45. $f(x) = 2x$; $g(x) = \dfrac{1}{2}x$

46. $f(x) = 4x$; $g(x) = \dfrac{1}{4}x$

47. $f(x) = x^3$; $g(x) = \sqrt[3]{x}$

48. $f(x) = x + 5$; $g(x) = x - 5$

49. $f(x) = 2x - 6$; $g(x) = \dfrac{1}{2}(x+6)$

50. $f(x) = 4 - 3x$; $g(x) = \dfrac{1}{3}(4-x)$

51. $f(x) = ax + b$; $g(x) = \dfrac{1}{a}(x - b)$ $a \neq 0$

52. $f(x) = \dfrac{1}{x}$; $g(x) = \dfrac{1}{x}$

In Problems 53–58, find functions f and g so that $f \circ g = H$.

53. $H(x) = (2x + 3)^4$

54. $H(x) = (1 + x^2)^3$

55. $H(x) = \sqrt{x^2 + 1}$

56. $H(x) = \sqrt{1 - x^2}$

57. $H(x) = |2x + 1|$

58. $H(x) = |2x^2 + 3|$

Applications and Extensions

59. If $f(x) = 2x^3 - 3x^2 + 4x - 1$ and $g(x) = 2$, find $(f \circ g)(x)$ and $(g \circ f)(x)$.

60. If $f(x) = \dfrac{x+1}{x-1}$, find $(f \circ f)(x)$.

61. If $f(x) = 2x^2 + 5$ and $g(x) = 3x + a$, find a so that the graph of $f \circ g$ crosses the y-axis at 23.

62. If $f(x) = 3x^2 - 7$ and $g(x) = 2x + a$, find a so that the graph of $f \circ g$ crosses the y-axis at 68.

In Problems 63 and 64, use the functions f and g to find:

    (a) $f \circ g$ (b) $g \circ f$

    (c) the domain of $f \circ g$ and of $g \circ f$ (d) the conditions for which $f \circ g = g \circ f$

63. $f(x) = ax + b$; $g(x) = cx + d$

64. $f(x) = \dfrac{ax + b}{cx + d}$; $g(x) = mx$

65. Surface Area of a Balloon The surface area S (in square meters) of a hot-air balloon is given by

$$S(r) = 4\pi r^2$$

where r is the radius of the balloon (in meters). If the radius r is increasing with time t (in seconds) according to the

formula $r(t) = \dfrac{2}{3}t^3$, $t \geq 0$, find the surface area S of the balloon as a function of the time t.

66. Volume of a Balloon The volume V (in cubic meters) of the hot-air balloon described in Problem 65 is given by

$V(r) = \dfrac{4}{3}\pi r^3$. If the radius r is the same function of t as in Problem 65, find the volume V as a function of the time t.

67. Automobile Production The number N of cars produced at a certain factory in 1 day after t hours of operation is given by $N(t) = 100t - 5t^2$, $0 \le t \le 10$. If the cost C (in dollars) of producing N cars is $C(N) = 15{,}000 + 8000N$, find the cost C as a function of the time t of operation of the factory.

68. Environmental Concerns The spread of oil leaking from a tanker is in the shape of a circle. If the radius r (in feet) of the spread after t hours is $r(t) = 200\sqrt{t}$, find the area A of the oil slick as a function of the time t.

69. Production Cost The price p, in dollars, of a certain product and the quantity x sold obey the demand equation

$$p = -\dfrac{1}{4}x + 100 \quad 0 \le x \le 400$$

Suppose that the cost C, in dollars, of producing x units is

$$C = \dfrac{\sqrt{x}}{25} + 600$$

Assuming that all items produced are sold, find the cost C as a function of the price p.

[**Hint:** Solve for x in the demand equation and then form the composite.]

70. Cost of a Commodity The price p, in dollars, of a certain commodity and the quantity x sold obey the demand equation

$$p = -\dfrac{1}{5}x + 200 \quad 0 \le x \le 1000$$

Suppose that the cost C, in dollars, of producing x units is

$$C = \dfrac{\sqrt{x}}{10} + 400$$

Assuming that all items produced are sold, find the cost C as a function of the price p.

71. Volume of a Cylinder The volume V of a right circular cylinder of height h and radius r is $V = \pi r^2 h$. If the height is twice the radius, express the volume V as a function of r.

72. Volume of a Cone The volume V of a right circular cone is $V = \dfrac{1}{3}\pi r^2 h$. If the height is twice the radius, express the volume V as a function of r.

73. Foreign Exchange Traders often buy foreign currency in hope of making money when the currency's value changes. For example, on April 3, 2007, one U.S. dollar could purchase 0.7480 Euros, and one Euro could purchase 158.7160 yen. Let $f(x)$ represent the number of Euros you can buy with x dollars, and let $g(x)$ represent the number of yen you can buy with x Euros.
(a) Find a function that relates dollars to Euros.
(b) Find a function that relates Euros to yen.
(c) Use the results of parts (a) and (b) to find a function that relates dollars to yen. That is, find $(g \circ f)(x) = g(f(x))$.
(d) What is $g(f(1000))$?

74. Temperature Conversion The function $C(F) = \dfrac{5}{9}(F - 32)$ converts a temperature in degrees Fahrenheit, F, to a temperature in degrees Celsius, C. The function $K(C) = C + 273$, converts a temperature in degrees Celsius to a temperature in kelvins, K.
(a) Find a function that converts a temperature in degrees Fahrenheit to a temperature in kelvins.
(b) Determine 80 degrees Fahrenheit in kelvins.

75. Discounts The manufacturer of a computer is offering two discounts on last year's model computer. The first discount is a $200 rebate and the second discount is 20% off the regular price, p.
(a) Write a function f that represents the sale price if only the rebate applies.
(b) Write a function g that represents the sale price if only the 20% discount applies.
(c) Find $f \circ g$ and $g \circ f$. What does each of these functions represent? Which combination of discounts represents a better deal for the consumer? Why?

76. If f and g are odd functions, show that the composite function $f \circ g$ is also odd.

77. If f is an odd function and g is an even function, show that the composite functions $f \circ g$ and $g \circ f$ are both even.

'Are You Prepared?' Answers

1. -21 **2.** $4 - 18x^2$; $3x$ **3.** $\{x \mid x \ne -5, x \ne 5\}$

5.2 One-to-One Functions; Inverse Functions

PREPARING FOR THIS SECTION *Before getting started, review the following:*

- Functions (Section 2.1, pp. 56–64)
- Increasing/Decreasing Functions (Section 2.3, pp. 81–84)

Now Work the 'Are You Prepared?' problems on page 265.

OBJECTIVES   **1** Determine Whether a Function Is One-to-One (p. 256)
       2 Determine the Inverse of a Function Defined by a Map or a Set of Ordered Pairs (p. 258)
       3 Obtain the Graph of the Inverse Function from the Graph of the Function (p. 260)
       4 Find the Inverse of a Function Defined by an Equation (p. 261)

1 Determine Whether a Function Is One-to-One

In Section 2.1, we presented four different ways to represent a function: as (1) a map, (2) a set of ordered pairs, (3) a graph, and (4) an equation. For example, Figures 6 and 7 illustrate two different functions represented as mappings. The function in Figure 6 shows the correspondence between states and their population (in millions). The function in Figure 7 shows a correspondence between animals and life expectancy (in years).

Figure 6

Figure 7

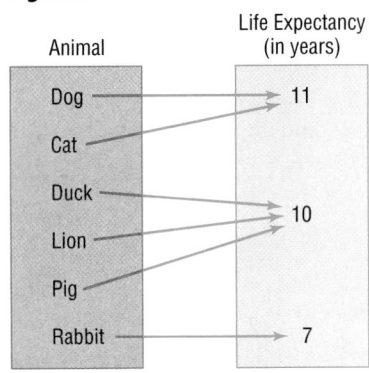

Suppose we asked a group of people to name the state that has a population of 0.8 million based on the function in Figure 6. Everyone in the group would respond South Dakota. Now, if we asked the same group of people to name the animal whose life expectancy is 11 years based on the function in Figure 7, some would respond dog, while others would respond cat. What is the difference between the functions in Figures 6 and 7? In Figure 6, we can see that no two elements in the domain corresponds to the same element in the range. In Figure 7, this is not the case: two different elements in the domain correspond to the same element in the range. We give functions such as the one in Figure 6 a special name.

DEFINITION

A function is **one-to-one** if any two different inputs in the domain correspond to two different outputs in the range. That is, if x_1 and x_2 are two different inputs of a function f, then f is one-to-one if $f(x_1) \neq f(x_2)$.

> **In Words**
> A function is not one-to-one if two different inputs correspond to the same output.

Put another way, a function f is one-to-one if no y in the range is the image of more than one x in the domain. A function is not one-to-one if two different elements in the domain correspond to the same element in the range. So the function in Figure 7 is not one-to-one because two different elements in the domain, *dog* and *cat*, both correspond to 11. Figure 8 illustrates the distinction of one-to-one functions, functions that are not one-to-one, and nonfunctions.

Figure 8

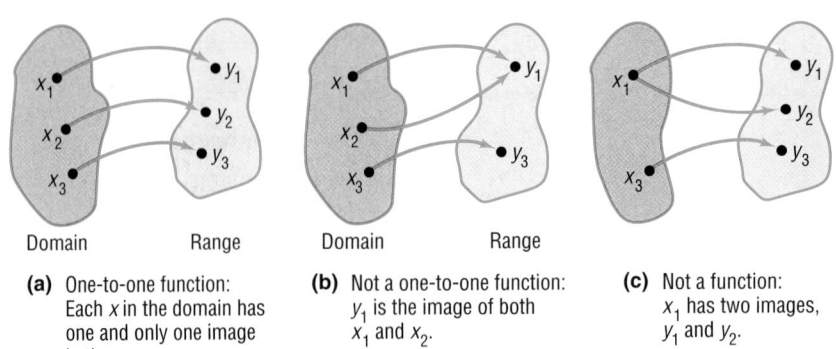

(a) One-to-one function: Each x in the domain has one and only one image in the range

(b) Not a one-to-one function: y_1 is the image of both x_1 and x_2.

(c) Not a function: x_1 has two images, y_1 and y_2.

| EXAMPLE 1 | **Determining Whether a Function Is One-to-One** |

Determine whether the following functions are one-to-one.

(a) For the following function, the domain represents the age of five males and the range represents their HDL (good) cholesterol (mg/dL).

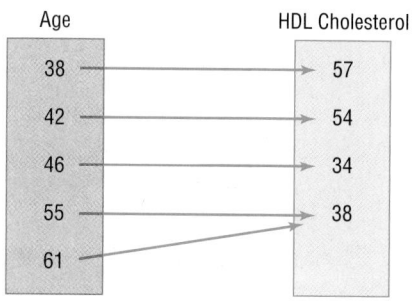

(b) $\{(-2, 6), (-1, 3), (0, 2), (1, 5), (2, 8)\}$

Solution

(a) The function is not one-to-one because there are two different inputs, 55 and 61, that correspond to the same output, 38.

(b) The function is one-to-one because there are no two distinct inputs that correspond to the same output.

➤ **Now Work** PROBLEMS 9 AND 13

For functions defined by an equation $y = f(x)$ and for which the graph of f is known, there is a simple test, called the **horizontal-line test,** to determine whether f is one-to-one.

THEOREM

Figure 9
$f(x_1) = f(x_2) = h$ and $x_1 \neq x_2$; f is not a one-to-one function.

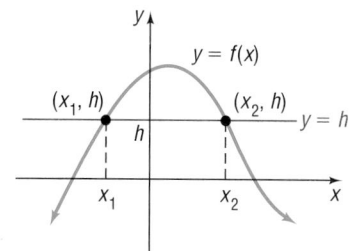

Horizontal-line Test

If every horizontal line intersects the graph of a function f in at most one point, then f is one-to-one.

The reason that this test works can be seen in Figure 9, where the horizontal line $y = h$ intersects the graph at two distinct points, (x_1, h) and (x_2, h). Since h is the image of both x_1 and x_2 and $x_1 \neq x_2$, f is not one-to-one. Based on Figure 9, we can state the horizontal-line test in another way: If the graph of any horizontal line intersects the graph of a function f at more than one point, then f is not one-to-one.

| EXAMPLE 2 | **Using the Horizontal-line Test** |

For each function, use its graph to determine whether the function is one-to-one.

(a) $f(x) = x^2$ (b) $g(x) = x^3$

Solution

(a) Figure 10(a) on page 258 illustrates the horizontal-line test for $f(x) = x^2$. The horizontal line $y = 1$ intersects the graph of f twice, at $(1, 1)$ and at $(-1, 1)$, so f is not one-to-one.

(b) Figure 10(b) illustrates the horizontal-line test for $g(x) = x^3$. Because every horizontal line intersects the graph of g exactly once, it follows that g is one-to-one.

Figure 10

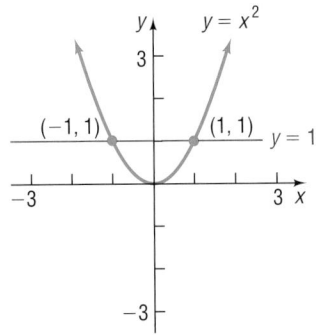

(a) A horizontal line intersects the graph twice; *f* is not one-to-one

(b) Every horizontal line intersects the graph exactly once; *g* is one-to-one

Now Work PROBLEM 17

Let's look more closely at the one-to-one function $g(x) = x^3$. This function is an increasing function. Because an increasing (or decreasing) function will always have different *y*-values for unequal *x*-values, it follows that a function that is increasing (or decreasing) over its domain is also a one-to-one function.

THEOREM

A function that is increasing on an interval *I* is a one-to-one function on *I*.

A function that is decreasing on an interval *I* is a one-to-one function on *I*.

2 Determine the Inverse of a Function Defined by a Map or a Set of Ordered Pairs

We begin with the definition.

DEFINITION

Suppose *f* is a one-to-one function. Then, to each *x* in the domain of *f*, there is exactly one *y* in the range (because *f* is a function); and to each *y* in the range of *f*, there is exactly one *x* in the domain (because *f* is one-to-one). The correspondence from the range of *f* back to the domain of *f* is called the **inverse function of *f*.** We use the symbol f^{-1} to denote the inverse of *f*.

In Words

Suppose we have a one-to-one function *f* where the input 5 corresponds to the output 10. In the inverse function f^{-1}, the input 10 would correspond to the output 5.

Recall that we have a variety of ways of representing functions. We will discuss how to find inverses for all four representations of functions: (1) maps, (2) sets of ordered pairs (3) graphs, and (4) equations. We begin with finding inverses of functions represented by maps or sets of ordered pairs.

EXAMPLE 3

Finding the Inverse of a Function Defined by a Map

Find the inverse of the following function. Let the domain of the function represent certain states, and let the range represent the state's population (in millions). State the domain and the range of the inverse function.

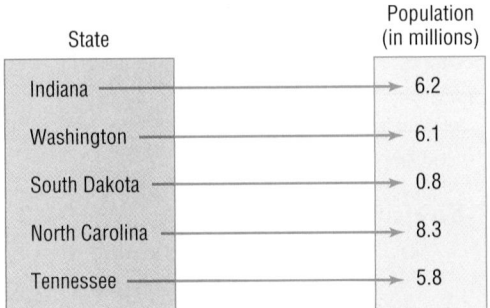

Solution

The function is one-to-one. To find the inverse function, we interchange the elements in the domain with the elements in the range. For example, the function receives as input Indiana and outputs 6.2 million. So the inverse receives as input 6.2 million and outputs Indiana. The inverse function is shown next.

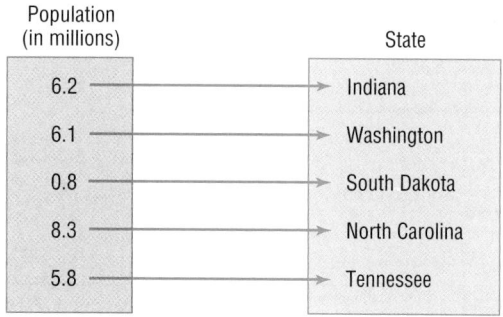

The domain of the inverse function is $\{6.2, 6.1, 0.8, 8.3, 5.8\}$. The range of the inverse function is $\{$Indiana, Washington, South Dakota, North Carolina, Tennessee$\}$.

If the function f is a set of ordered pairs (x, y), then the inverse of f, denoted f^{-1}, is the set of ordered pairs (y, x).

EXAMPLE 4	**Finding the Inverse of a Function Defined by a Set of Ordered Pairs**

Find the inverse of the following one-to-one function:

$$\{(-3, -27), (-2, -8), (-1, -1), (0, 0), (1, 1), (2, 8), (3, 27)\}$$

State the domain and the range of the function and its inverse.

Solution The inverse of the given function is found by interchanging the entries in each ordered pair and so is given by

$$\{(-27, -3), (-8, -2), (-1, -1), (0, 0), (1, 1), (8, 2), (27, 3)\}$$

The domain of the function is $\{-3, -2, -1, 0, 1, 2, 3\}$. The range of the function is $\{-27, -8, -1, 0, 1, 8, 27\}$. The domain of the inverse function is $\{-27, -8, -1, 0, 1, 8, 27\}$. The range of the inverse function is $\{-3, -2, -1, 0, 1, 2, 3\}$.

Now Work PROBLEMS 23 AND 27

Figure 11

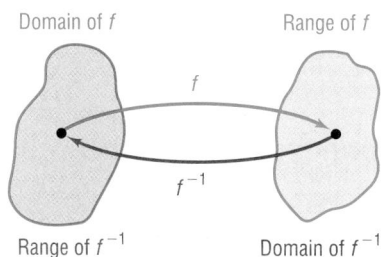

Domain of f Range of f

Range of f^{-1} Domain of f^{-1}

WARNING Be careful! f^{-1} is a symbol for the inverse function of f. The -1 used in f^{-1} is not an exponent. That is, f^{-1} does not mean the reciprocal of f; $f^{-1}(x)$ is not equal to $\dfrac{1}{f(x)}$. ∎

Remember, if f is a one-to-one function, it has an inverse function, f^{-1}. See Figure 11.

Based on the results of Example 4 and Figure 11, two facts are now apparent about a one-to-one function f and its inverse f^{-1}.

Domain of f = Range of f^{-1} Range of f = Domain of f^{-1}

Look again at Figure 11 to visualize the relationship. If we start with x, apply f, and then apply f^{-1}, we get x back again. If we start with x, apply f^{-1}, and then apply f, we get the number x back again. To put it simply, what f does, f^{-1} undoes, and vice versa. See the illustration that follows.

Input x from domain of f $\xrightarrow{\text{Apply } f}$ $f(x)$ $\xrightarrow{\text{Apply } f^{-1}}$ $f^{-1}(f(x)) = x$

Input x from domain of f^{-1} $\xrightarrow{\text{Apply } f^{-1}}$ $f^{-1}(x)$ $\xrightarrow{\text{Apply } f}$ $f(f^{-1}(x)) = x$

In other words,

$$f^{-1}(f(x)) = x \quad \text{where } x \text{ is in the domain of } f$$
$$f(f^{-1}(x)) = x \quad \text{where } x \text{ is in the domain of } f^{-1}$$

Consider the function $f(x) = 2x$, which multiplies the argument x by 2. The inverse function f^{-1} undoes whatever f does. So the inverse function of f is $f^{-1}(x) = \dfrac{1}{2}x$, which divides the argument by 2. For example, $f(3) = 2(3) = 6$ and $f^{-1}(6) = \dfrac{1}{2}(6) = 3$, so f^{-1} undoes what f did. We can verify this by showing that

$$f^{-1}(f(x)) = f^{-1}(2x) = \frac{1}{2}(2x) = x \quad \text{and} \quad f(f^{-1}(x)) = f\left(\frac{1}{2}x\right) = 2\left(\frac{1}{2}x\right) = x$$

See Figure 12.

Figure 12

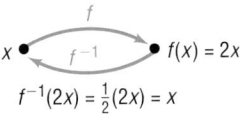

$f^{-1}(2x) = \frac{1}{2}(2x) = x$

EXAMPLE 5 — Verifying Inverse Functions

Exploration

Simultaneously graph $Y_1 = x$, $Y_2 = x^3$, and $Y_3 = \sqrt[3]{x}$ on a square screen with $-3 \le x \le 3$. What do you observe about the graphs of $Y_2 = x^3$, its inverse $Y_3 = \sqrt[3]{x}$, and the line $Y_1 = x$?

Repeat this experiment by simultaneously graphing $Y_1 = x$, $Y_2 = 2x + 3$, and $Y_3 = \dfrac{1}{2}(x - 3)$ on a square screen with $-6 \le x \le 3$. Do you see the symmetry of the graph of Y_2 and its inverse Y_3 with respect to the line $Y_1 = x$?

(a) We verify that the inverse of $g(x) = x^3$ is $g^{-1}(x) = \sqrt[3]{x}$ by showing that

$$g^{-1}(g(x)) = g^{-1}(x^3) = \sqrt[3]{x^3} = x \qquad \text{for all } x \text{ in the domain of } g$$
$$g(g^{-1}(x)) = g(\sqrt[3]{x}) = (\sqrt[3]{x})^3 = x \quad \text{for all } x \text{ in the domain of } g^{-1}$$

(b) We verify that the inverse of $f(x) = 2x + 3$ is $f^{-1}(x) = \dfrac{1}{2}(x - 3)$ by showing that

$$f^{-1}(f(x)) = f^{-1}(2x + 3) = \frac{1}{2}[(2x + 3) - 3] = \frac{1}{2}(2x) = x \qquad \text{for all } x \text{ in the domain of } f$$

$$f(f^{-1}(x)) = f\left(\frac{1}{2}(x - 3)\right) = 2\left[\frac{1}{2}(x - 3)\right] + 3 = (x - 3) + 3 = x \quad \text{for all } x \text{ in the domain of } f^{-1}$$

EXAMPLE 6 — Verifying Inverse Functions

Verify that the inverse of $f(x) = \dfrac{1}{x - 1}$ is $f^{-1}(x) = \dfrac{1}{x} + 1$. For what values of x is $f^{-1}(f(x)) = x$? For what values of x is $f(f^{-1}(x)) = x$?

Solution The domain of f is $\{x \mid x \ne 1\}$ and the domain of f^{-1} is $\{x \mid x \ne 0\}$. Now

$$f^{-1}(f(x)) = f^{-1}\left(\frac{1}{x - 1}\right) = \frac{1}{\dfrac{1}{x - 1}} + 1 = x - 1 + 1 = x \qquad \text{provided } x \ne 1$$

$$f(f^{-1}(x)) = f\left(\frac{1}{x} + 1\right) = \frac{1}{\dfrac{1}{x} + 1 - 1} = \frac{1}{\dfrac{1}{x}} = x \qquad \text{provided } x \ne 0$$

Now Work PROBLEM 31

3 Obtain the Graph of the Inverse Function from the Graph of the Function

For the functions in Example 5(b), we list points on the graph of $f = Y_1$ and on the graph of $f^{-1} = Y_2$ in Table 1. We notice that whenever (a, b) is on the graph of f then (b, a) is on the graph of f^{-1}. Figure 13 shows these points plotted. Also shown is the graph of $y = x$, which you should observe is a line of symmetry of the points.

Table 1

Figure 13

Figure 14

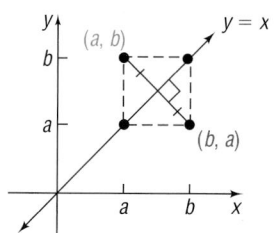

Suppose that (a, b) is a point on the graph of a one-to-one function f defined by $y = f(x)$. Then $b = f(a)$. This means that $a = f^{-1}(b)$, so (b, a) is a point on the graph of the inverse function f^{-1}. The relationship between the point (a, b) on f and the point (b, a) on f^{-1} is shown in Figure 14. The line segment containing (a, b) and (b, a) is perpendicular to the line $y = x$ and is bisected by the line $y = x$. (Do you see why?) It follows that the point (b, a) on f^{-1} is the reflection about the line $y = x$ of the point (a, b) on f.

THEOREM

The graph of a function f and the graph of its inverse f^{-1} are symmetric with respect to the line $y = x$.

Figure 15 illustrates this result. Notice that, once the graph of f is known, the graph of f^{-1} may be obtained by reflecting the graph of f about the line $y = x$.

Figure 15

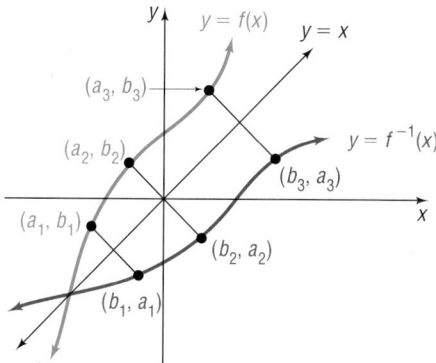

EXAMPLE 7   **Graphing the Inverse Function**

The graph in Figure 16(a) is that of a one-to-one function $y = f(x)$. Draw the graph of its inverse.

Solution   We begin by adding the graph of $y = x$ to Figure 16(a). Since the points $(-2, -1), (-1, 0)$, and $(2, 1)$ are on the graph of f, we know that the points $(-1, -2), (0, -1)$, and $(1, 2)$ must be on the graph of f^{-1}. Keeping in mind that the graph of f^{-1} is the reflection about the line $y = x$ of the graph of f, we can draw f^{-1}. See Figure 16(b).

Figure 16

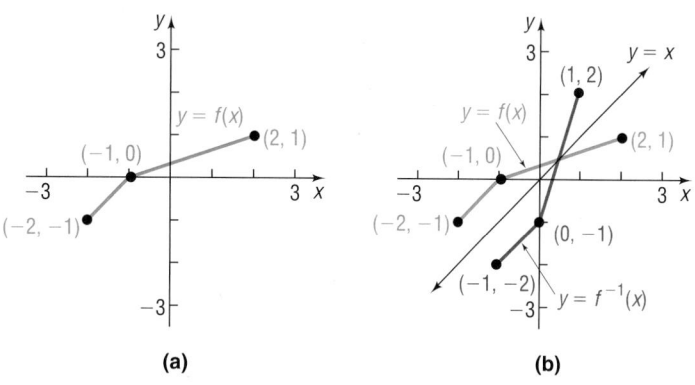

(a)   (b)

━━━▶ **Now Work** PROBLEM 41

4 Find the Inverse of a Function Defined by an Equation

The fact that the graphs of a one-to-one function f and its inverse function f^{-1} are symmetric with respect to the line $y = x$ tells us more. It says that we can obtain f^{-1}

by interchanging the roles of x and y in f. Look again at Figure 11. If f is defined by the equation

$$y = f(x)$$

then f^{-1} is defined by the equation

$$x = f(y)$$

The equation $x = f(y)$ defines f^{-1} *implicitly*. If we can solve this equation for y, we will have the *explicit* form of f^{-1}, that is,

$$y = f^{-1}(x)$$

Let's use this procedure to find the inverse of $f(x) = 2x + 3$. (Since f is a linear function and is increasing, we know that f is one-to-one and so has an inverse function.)

| EXAMPLE 8 | **How to Find the Inverse Function** |

Find the inverse of $f(x) = 2x + 3$. Graph f and f^{-1} on the same coordinate axes.

Step-by-Step Solution

STEP 1   Replace $f(x)$ with y. In $y = f(x)$, interchange the variables x and y to obtain $x = f(y)$. This equation defines the inverse function f^{-1} implicitly.

We replace $f(x)$ with y in $f(x) = 2x + 3$ and obtain $y = 2x + 3$. Now we interchange the variables x and y to obtain

$$x = 2y + 3$$

This equation defines the inverse f^{-1} implicitly.

STEP 2   If possible, solve the implicit equation for y in terms of x to obtain the explicit form of f^{-1}, $y = f^{-1}(x)$.

To find the explicit form of the inverse, we solve $x = 2y + 3$ for y.

$$x = 2y + 3$$
$$2y + 3 = x \qquad \text{Reflexive Property, If } a = b, \text{ then } b = a.$$
$$2y = x - 3 \qquad \text{Subtract 3 from both sides.}$$
$$y = \frac{1}{2}(x - 3) \qquad \text{Divide both sides by 2.}$$

The explicit form of the inverse f^{-1} is therefore

$$f^{-1}(x) = \frac{1}{2}(x - 3)$$

STEP 3   Check the result by showing that $f^{-1}(f(x)) = x$ and $f(f^{-1}(x)) = x$.

We verified that f and f^{-1} are inverses in Example 5(b) on page 260.

The graphs of $f(x) = 2x + 3$ and its inverse $f^{-1}(x) = \frac{1}{2}(x - 3)$ are shown in Figure 17. Note the symmetry of the graphs with respect to the line $y = x$.

Figure 17

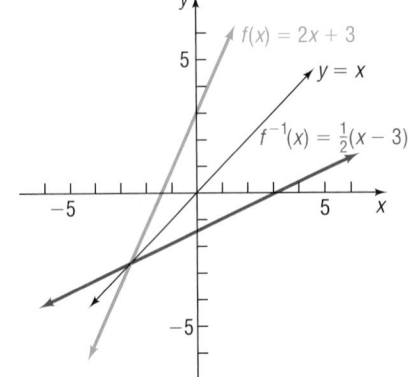

We now list the steps to follow for finding the inverse of a one-to-one function.

Procedure for Finding the Inverse of a One-to-One Function

Step 1: In $y = f(x)$, interchange the variables x and y to obtain

$$x = f(y)$$

This equation defines the inverse function f^{-1} implicitly.

Step 2: If possible, solve the implicit equation for y in terms of x to obtain the explicit form of f^{-1}:

$$y = f^{-1}(x)$$

Step 3: Check the result by showing that

$$f^{-1}(f(x)) = x \quad \text{and} \quad f(f^{-1}(x)) = x$$

EXAMPLE 9   **Finding the Inverse Function**

The function

$$f(x) = \frac{2x + 1}{x - 1} \qquad x \neq 1$$

is one-to-one. Find its inverse and check the result.

Solution   **Step 1:** Replace $f(x)$ with y and interchange the variables x and y in

$$y = \frac{2x + 1}{x - 1}$$

to obtain

$$x = \frac{2y + 1}{y - 1}$$

Step 2: Solve for y.

$$x = \frac{2y + 1}{y - 1}$$

$$x(y - 1) = 2y + 1 \qquad \text{Multiply both sides by } y - 1.$$

$$xy - x = 2y + 1 \qquad \text{Apply the Distributive Property.}$$

$$xy - 2y = x + 1 \qquad \text{Subtract } 2y \text{ from both sides; add } x \text{ to both sides.}$$

$$(x - 2)y = x + 1 \qquad \text{Factor.}$$

$$y = \frac{x + 1}{x - 2} \qquad \text{Divide by } x - 2.$$

The inverse is

$$f^{-1}(x) = \frac{x + 1}{x - 2} \quad x \neq 2 \quad \text{Replace } y \text{ by } f^{-1}(x).$$

Step 3: ✓ Check:

$$f^{-1}(f(x)) = f^{-1}\left(\frac{2x + 1}{x - 1}\right) = \frac{\dfrac{2x + 1}{x - 1} + 1}{\dfrac{2x + 1}{x - 1} - 2} = \frac{2x + 1 + x - 1}{2x + 1 - 2(x - 1)} = \frac{3x}{3} = x \quad x \neq 1$$

$$f(f^{-1}(x)) = f\left(\frac{x + 1}{x - 2}\right) = \frac{2\left(\dfrac{x + 1}{x - 2}\right) + 1}{\dfrac{x + 1}{x - 2} - 1} = \frac{2(x + 1) + x - 2}{x + 1 - (x - 2)} = \frac{3x}{3} = x \quad x \neq 2$$

■

Exploration

In Example 9, we found that, if $f(x) = \dfrac{2x+1}{x-1}$, then $f^{-1}(x) = \dfrac{x+1}{x-2}$. Compare the vertical and horizontal asymptotes of f and f^{-1}.

Result The vertical asymptote of f is $x = 1$, and the horizontal asymptote is $y = 2$. The vertical asymptote of f^{-1} is $x = 2$, and the horizontal asymptote is $y = 1$.

━━━━━━━➤ **Now Work** PROBLEM 49

We said in Chapter 2 that finding the range of a function f is not easy. However, if f is one-to-one, we can find its range by finding the domain of the inverse function f^{-1}.

EXAMPLE 10 **Finding the Range of a Function**

Find the domain and the range of

$$f(x) = \frac{2x+1}{x-1}$$

Solution The domain of f is $\{x | x \neq 1\}$. To find the range of f, we use the fact that the domain of f^{-1} equals the range of f. Based on Example 9, we have

$$f^{-1}(x) = \frac{x+1}{x-2}$$

The domain of f^{-1} is $\{x | x \neq 2\}$, so the range of f is $\{y | y \neq 2\}$. Also, because the domain of f is $\{x | x \neq 1\}$, the range of f^{-1} is $\{y | y \neq 1\}$.

━━━━━━━➤ **Now Work** PROBLEM 63

If a function is not one-to-one, it has no inverse function. Sometimes, though, an appropriate restriction on the domain of such a function will yield a new function that is one-to-one. Then the function defined on the restricted domain has an inverse function. Let's look at an example of this common practice.

EXAMPLE 11 **Finding the Inverse of a Domain-restricted Function**

Find the inverse of $y = f(x) = x^2$ if $x \geq 0$.

Solution The function $y = x^2$ is not one-to-one. [Refer to Example 2(a).] However, if we restrict the domain of this function to $x \geq 0$, as indicated, we have a new function that is increasing and therefore is one-to-one. As a result, the function defined by $y = f(x) = x^2$, $x \geq 0$, has an inverse function, f^{-1}.

We follow the steps given previously to find f^{-1}.

STEP 1: In the equation $y = x^2$, $x \geq 0$, interchange the variables x and y. The result is

$$x = y^2 \qquad y \geq 0$$

This equation defines (implicitly) the inverse function.

Figure 18

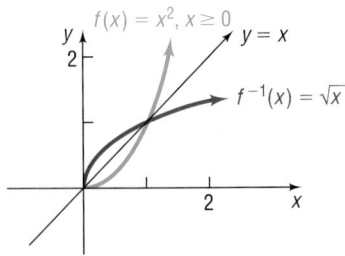

STEP 2: We solve for y to get the explicit form of the inverse. Since $y \geq 0$, only one solution for y is obtained: $y = \sqrt{x}$. So $f^{-1}(x) = \sqrt{x}$.

STEP 3: ✓ Check: $f^{-1}(f(x)) = f^{-1}(x^2) = \sqrt{x^2} = |x| = x$ since $x \geq 0$

$$f(f^{-1}(x)) = f(\sqrt{x}) = (\sqrt{x})^2 = x$$

Figure 18 illustrates the graphs of $f(x) = x^2$, $x \geq 0$, and $f^{-1}(x) = \sqrt{x}$.

SUMMARY

1. If a function f is one-to-one, then it has an inverse function f^{-1}.
2. Domain of f = Range of f^{-1}; Range of f = Domain of f^{-1}.
3. To verify that f^{-1} is the inverse of f, show that $f^{-1}(f(x)) = x$ for every x in the domain of f and $f(f^{-1}(x)) = x$ for every x in the domain of f^{-1}.
4. The graphs of f and f^{-1} are symmetric with respect to the line $y = x$.
5. To find the range of a one-to-one function f, find the domain of its inverse function f^{-1}.

5.2 Assess Your Understanding

'Are You Prepared?' *Answers are given at the end of these exercises. If you get a wrong answer, read the pages listed in red.*

1. Is the set of ordered pairs $\{(1, 3), (2, 3), (-1, 2)\}$ a function? Why or why not? (pp. 56–59)
2. Where is the function $f(x) = x^2$ increasing? Where is it decreasing? (pp. 81–82)
3. What is the domain of $f(x) = \dfrac{x + 5}{x^2 + 3x - 18}$? (pp. 63–64)

Concepts and Vocabulary

4. If every horizontal line intersects the graph of a function f at no more than one point, f is a(n) _____ function.
5. If f^{-1} denotes the inverse of a function f, then the graphs of f and f^{-1} are symmetric with respect to the line _____.
6. If the domain of a one-to-one function f is $[4, \infty)$, the range of its inverse, f^{-1}, is _____.

7. *True or False* If f and g are inverse functions, the domain of f is the same as the domain of g.
8. *True or False* If f and g are inverse functions, their graphs are symmetric with respect to the line $y = x$.

Skill Building

In Problems 9–16, determine whether the function is one-to-one.

9.

10.

11.

12.

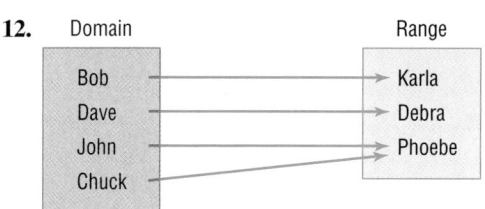

13. $\{(2, 6), (-3, 6), (4, 9), (1, 10)\}$

14. $\{(-2, 5), (-1, 3), (3, 7), (4, 12)\}$

15. $\{(0, 0), (1, 1), (2, 16), (3, 81)\}$

16. $\{(1, 2), (2, 8), (3, 18), (4, 32)\}$

In Problems 17–22, the graph of a function f is given. Use the horizontal-line test to determine whether f is one-to-one.

17.

18.

19.

20.

21.

22.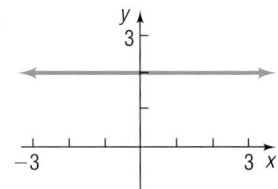

In Problems 23–30, find the inverse of each one-to-one function. State the domain and the range of each inverse function.

23.

Location	Annual Rainfall (inches)
Mt Waialeale, Hawaii	460.00
Monrovia, Liberia	202.01
Pago Pago, American Samoa	196.46
Moulmein, Burma	191.02
Lae, Papua New Guinea	182.87

Source: Information Please Almanac

24.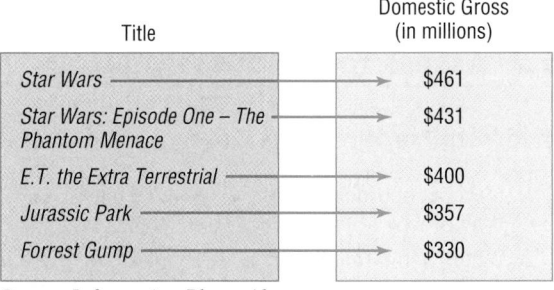

Title	Domestic Gross (in millions)
Star Wars	$461
Star Wars: Episode One – The Phantom Menace	$431
E.T. the Extra Terrestrial	$400
Jurassic Park	$357
Forrest Gump	$330

Source: Information Please Almanac

25.

Age	Monthly Cost of Life Insurance
30	$7.09
40	$8.40
45	$11.29

Source: eterm.com

26.

State	Unemployment Rate
Virginia	11%
Nevada	5.5%
Tennessee	5.1%
Texas	6.3%

Source: United States Statistical Abstract

27. $\{(-3, 5), (-2, 9), (-1, 2), (0, 11), (1, -5)\}$

28. $\{(-2, 2), (-1, 6), (0, 8), (1, -3), (2, 9)\}$

29. $\{(-2, 1), (-3, 2), (-10, 0), (1, 9), (2, 4)\}$

30. $\{(-2, -8), (-1, -1), (0, 0), (1, 1), (2, 8)\}$

In Problems 31–40, verify that the functions f and g are inverses of each other by showing that $f(g(x)) = x$ and $g(f(x)) = x$. Give any values of x that need to be excluded from the domain.

31. $f(x) = 3x + 4;\quad g(x) = \dfrac{1}{3}(x - 4)$

32. $f(x) = 3 - 2x;\quad g(x) = -\dfrac{1}{2}(x - 3)$

33. $f(x) = 4x - 8;\quad g(x) = \dfrac{x}{4} + 2$

34. $f(x) = 2x + 6;\quad g(x) = \dfrac{1}{2}x - 3$

35. $f(x) = x^3 - 8;\quad g(x) = \sqrt[3]{x + 8}$

36. $f(x) = (x - 2)^2, x \geq 2;\quad g(x) = \sqrt{x} + 2$

37. $f(x) = \dfrac{1}{x};\quad g(x) = \dfrac{1}{x}$

38. $f(x) = x;\quad g(x) = x$

39. $f(x) = \dfrac{2x + 3}{x + 4};\quad g(x) = \dfrac{4x - 3}{2 - x}$

40. $f(x) = \dfrac{x - 5}{2x + 3};\quad g(x) = \dfrac{3x + 5}{1 - 2x}$

In Problems 41–46, the graph of a one-to-one function f is given. Draw the graph of the inverse function f^{-1}. For convenience (and as a hint), the graph of $y = x$ is also given.

41.

42.

43.

44.

45.

46.

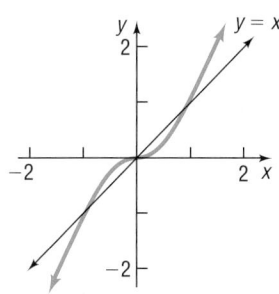

In Problems 47–58, the function f is one-to-one. Find its inverse and check your answer. Graph f, f^{-1}, and y = x on the same coordinate axes.

47. $f(x) = 3x$

48. $f(x) = -4x$

49. $f(x) = 4x + 2$

50. $f(x) = 1 - 3x$

51. $f(x) = x^3 - 1$

52. $f(x) = x^3 + 1$

53. $f(x) = x^2 + 4 \quad x \geq 0$

54. $f(x) = x^2 + 9 \quad x \geq 0$

55. $f(x) = \dfrac{4}{x}$

56. $f(x) = -\dfrac{3}{x}$

57. $f(x) = \dfrac{1}{x - 2}$

58. $f(x) = \dfrac{4}{x + 2}$

In Problems 59–70, the function f is one-to-one. Find its inverse and check your answer. State the domain and the range of f and f^{-1}.

59. $f(x) = \dfrac{2}{3 + x}$

60. $f(x) = \dfrac{4}{2 - x}$

61. $f(x) = \dfrac{3x}{x + 2}$

62. $f(x) = -\dfrac{2x}{x - 1}$

63. $f(x) = \dfrac{2x}{3x - 1}$

64. $f(x) = -\dfrac{3x + 1}{x}$

65. $f(x) = \dfrac{3x + 4}{2x - 3}$

66. $f(x) = \dfrac{2x - 3}{x + 4}$

67. $f(x) = \dfrac{2x + 3}{x + 2}$

68. $f(x) = \dfrac{-3x - 4}{x - 2}$

69. $f(x) = \dfrac{x^2 - 4}{2x^2} \quad x > 0$

70. $f(x) = \dfrac{x^2 + 3}{3x^2} \quad x > 0$

Applications and Extensions

71. Use the graph of $y = f(x)$ given in Problem 41 to evaluate the following:
(a) $f(-1)$ (b) $f(1)$ (c) $f^{-1}(1)$ (d) $f^{-1}(2)$

72. Use the graph of $y = f(x)$ given in Problem 42 to evaluate the following:
(a) $f(2)$ (b) $f(1)$ (c) $f^{-1}(0)$ (d) $f^{-1}(-1)$

73. If $f(7) = 13$ and f is one-to-one, what is $f^{-1}(13)$?

74. If $g(-5) = 3$ and g is one-to-one, what is $g^{-1}(3)$?

75. The domain of a one-to-one function f is $[5, \infty)$, and its range is $[-2, \infty)$. State the domain and the range of f^{-1}.

76. The domain of a one-to-one function f is $[0, \infty)$, and its range is $[5, \infty)$. State the domain and the range of f^{-1}.

77. The domain of a one-to-one function g is the set of all real numbers, and its range is $[0, \infty)$. State the domain and the range of g^{-1}.

78. The domain of a one-to-one function g is $[0, 15]$, and its range is $(0, 8)$. State the domain and the range of g^{-1}.

79. A function $y = f(x)$ is increasing on the interval $(0, 5)$. What conclusions can you draw about the graph of $y = f^{-1}(x)$?

80. A function $y = f(x)$ is decreasing on the interval $(0, 5)$. What conclusions can you draw about the graph of $y = f^{-1}(x)$?

81. Find the inverse of the linear function

$$f(x) = mx + b \quad m \neq 0$$

82. Find the inverse of the function

$$f(x) = \sqrt{r^2 - x^2} \quad 0 \leq x \leq r$$

83. A function f has an inverse function. If the graph of f lies in quadrant I, in which quadrant does the graph of f^{-1} lie?

84. A function f has an inverse function. If the graph of f lies in quadrant II, in which quadrant does the graph of f^{-1} lie?

85. The function $f(x) = |x|$ is not one-to-one. Find a suitable restriction on the domain of f so that the new function that results is one-to-one. Then find the inverse of f.

86. The function $f(x) = x^4$ is not one-to-one. Find a suitable restriction on the domain of f so that the new function that results is one-to-one. Then find the inverse of f.

In applications, the symbols used for the independent and dependent variables are often based on common usage. So, rather than using y = f(x) to represent a function, an applied problem might use C = C(q) to represent the cost C of manufacturing q units of a good since, in economics, q is used for output. Because of this, the inverse notation f^{-1} used in a pure mathematics problem is not used when finding inverses of applied problems. Rather, the inverse of a function such as C = C(q) will be q = q(C). So C = C(q) is a function that represents the cost C as a function of the output q, while q = q(C) is a function that represents the output q as a function of the cost C. Problems 87–90 illustrate this idea.

87. Vehicle Stopping Distance Taking into account reaction time, the distance d (in feet) that a car requires to come to a complete stop while traveling r miles per hour is given by the function

$$d(r) = 6.97r - 90.39$$

(a) Express the speed r at which the car is traveling as a function of the distance d required to come to a complete stop.

(b) Verify that $r = r(d)$ is the inverse of $d = d(r)$ by showing that $r(d(r)) = r$ and $d(r(d)) = d$.

(c) Predict the speed that a car was traveling if the distance required to stop was 300 feet.

88. Height and Head Circumference The head circumference C of a child is related to the height H of the child (both in inches) through the function

$$H(C) = 2.15C - 10.53$$

(a) Express the head circumference C as a function of height H.

(b) Verify that $C = C(H)$ is the inverse of $H = H(C)$ by showing that $H(C(H)) = H$ and $C(H(C)) = C$.

(c) Predict the head circumference of a child who is 26 inches tall.

89. Ideal Body Weight One model for the ideal body weight W for men (in kilograms) as a function of height h (in inches) is given by the function

$$W(h) = 50 + 2.3(h - 60)$$

(a) What is the ideal weight of a 6-foot male?

(b) Express the height h as a function of weight W.

(c) Verify that $h = h(W)$ is the inverse of $W = W(h)$ by showing that $h(W(h)) = h$ and $W(h(W)) = W$.

(d) What is the height of a male who is at his ideal weight of 80 kilograms?

[**Note:** The ideal body weight W for women (in kilograms) as a function of height h (in inches) is given by $W(h) = 45.5 + 2.3(h - 60)$.]

90. Temperature Conversion The function $F(C) = \dfrac{9}{5}C + 32$ converts a temperature from C degrees Celsius to F degrees Fahrenheit.

(a) Express the temperature in degrees Celsius C as a function of the temperature in degrees Fahrenheit F.

(b) Verify that $C = C(F)$ is the inverse of $F = F(C)$ by showing that $C(F(C)) = C$ and $F(C(F)) = F$.

(c) What is the temperature in degrees Celsius if it is 70 degrees Fahrenheit?

91. Income Taxes The function

$$T(g) = 4386.25 + 0.25(g - 31,850)$$

represents the 2007 federal income tax T (in dollars) due for a "single" filer whose modified adjusted gross income is g dollars, where $31,850 \le g \le 77,100$.

(a) What is the domain of the function T?

(b) Given that the tax due T is an increasing linear function of modified adjusted gross income g, find the range of the function T.

(c) Find adjusted gross income g as a function of federal income tax T. What are the domain and the range of this function?

92. Income Taxes The function

$$T(g) = 1565 + 0.15(g - 15,650)$$

represents the 2007 federal income tax T (in dollars) due for a "married filing jointly" filer whose modified adjusted gross income is g dollars, where $15,650 \le g \le 63,700$.

(a) What is the domain of the function T?

(b) Given that the tax due T is an increasing linear function of modified adjusted gross income g, find the range of the function T.

(c) Find adjusted gross income g as a function of federal income tax T. What are the domain and the range of this function?

93. Gravity on Earth If a rock falls from a height of 100 meters on Earth, the height H (in meters) after t seconds is approximately

$$H(t) = 100 - 4.9t^2$$

(a) In general, quadratic functions are not one-to-one. However, the function $H(t)$ is one-to-one. Why?

(b) Find the inverse of H and verify your result.

(c) How long will it take a rock to fall 80 meters?

94. Period of a Pendulum The period T (in seconds) of a simple pendulum as a function of its length l (in feet) is given by

$$T(l) = 2\pi\sqrt{\dfrac{l}{32.2}}$$

(a) Express the length l as a function of the period T.

(b) How long is a pendulum whose period is 3 seconds?

95. Given

$$f(x) = \dfrac{ax + b}{cx + d}$$

find $f^{-1}(x)$. If $c \ne 0$, under what conditions on $a, b, c,$ and d is $f = f^{-1}$?

Discussion and Writing

96. Can a one-to-one function and its inverse be equal? What must be true about the graph of f for this to happen? Give some examples to support your conclusion.

97. Draw the graph of a one-to-one function that contains the points $(-2, -3)$, $(0, 0)$, and $(1, 5)$. Now draw the graph of its inverse. Compare your graph to those of other students. Discuss any similarities. What differences do you see?

98. Give an example of a function whose domain is the set of real numbers and that is neither increasing nor decreasing on its domain, but is one-to-one.

[**Hint:** Use a piecewise-defined function.]

99. Is every odd function one-to-one? Explain.

100. Suppose $C(g)$ represents the cost C, in dollars, of manufacturing g cars. Explain what $C^{-1}(800,000)$ represents.

'Are You Prepared?' Answers

1. Yes; for each input x there is one output y.

2. Increasing on $(0, \infty)$; decreasing on $(-\infty, 0)$

3. $\{x | x \neq -6, x \neq 3\}$

5.3 Exponential Functions

PREPARING FOR THIS SECTION *Before getting started, review the following:*

- Exponents (Appendix A, Section A.1, pp. A7–A9, and Appendix A, Section A.10, pp. A91–A92)
- Graphing Techniques: Transformations (Section 2.5, pp. 100–108)
- Average Rate of Change (Section 2.3, pp. 84–85)

- Solving Linear and Quadratic Equations (Appendix A, Section A.6, pp. A47–A49 and A50–A56)
- Linear Functions (Section 3.1, pp. 126–129)
- Horizontal Asymptotes (Section 4.2, pp. 196–199)

Now Work the 'Are You Prepared?' problems on page 279.

OBJECTIVES
1 Evaluate Exponential Functions (p. 269)
2 Graph Exponential Functions (p. 273)
3 Define the Number e (p. 276)
4 Solve Exponential Equations (p. 278)

1 Evaluate Exponential Functions

In Appendix A, Section A.10, we give a definition for raising a real number a to a rational power. Based on that discussion, we gave meaning to expressions of the form

$$a^r$$

where the base a is a positive real number and the exponent r is a rational number. But what is the meaning of a^x, where the base a is a positive real number and the exponent x is an irrational number? Although a rigorous definition requires methods discussed in calculus, the basis for the definition is easy to follow: Select a rational number r that is formed by truncating (removing) all but a finite number of digits from the irrational number x. Then it is reasonable to expect that

$$a^x \approx a^r$$

For example, take the irrational number $\pi = 3.14159\ldots$. Then an approximation to a^π is

$$a^\pi \approx a^{3.14}$$

where the digits after the hundredths position have been removed from the value for π. A better approximation would be

$$a^\pi \approx a^{3.14159}$$

where the digits after the hundred-thousandths position have been removed. Continuing in this way, we can obtain approximations to a^π to any desired degree of accuracy.

Most calculators have an $\boxed{x^y}$ key or a caret key $\boxed{\wedge}$ for working with exponents. To evaluate expressions of the form a^x, enter the base a, then press the $\boxed{x^y}$ key (or the $\boxed{\wedge}$ key), enter the exponent x, and press $\boxed{=}$ (or $\boxed{\text{ENTER}}$).

| EXAMPLE 1 | Using a Calculator to Evaluate Powers of 2 |

Using a calculator, evaluate:

(a) $2^{1.4}$ (b) $2^{1.41}$ (c) $2^{1.414}$ (d) $2^{1.4142}$ (e) $2^{\sqrt{2}}$

Solution

Figure 19

```
2^1.4
        2.639015822
```

Figure 19 shows the solution to part (a) using a TI-84 Plus graphing calculator.

(a) $2^{1.4} \approx 2.639015822$ (b) $2^{1.41} \approx 2.657371628$

(c) $2^{1.414} \approx 2.66474965$ (d) $2^{1.4142} \approx 2.665119089$

(e) $2^{\sqrt{2}} \approx 2.665144143$

Now Work PROBLEM 11

It can be shown that the familiar laws for rational exponents hold for real exponents.

THEOREM

Laws of Exponents

If s, t, a, and b are real numbers with $a > 0$ and $b > 0$, then

$$a^s \cdot a^t = a^{s+t} \qquad (a^s)^t = a^{st} \qquad (ab)^s = a^s \cdot b^s$$

$$1^s = 1 \qquad a^{-s} = \frac{1}{a^s} = \left(\frac{1}{a}\right)^s \qquad a^0 = 1 \qquad \textbf{(1)}$$

Introduction to Exponential Growth

Let's examine a function f that has the following two properties:

1. The value of f doubles with every 1-unit increase in the independent variable x.
2. The value of f at $x = 0$ is 5, so $f(0) = 5$.

Table 2

x	f(x)
0	5
1	10
2	20
3	40
4	80

Table 2 shows values of the function f for $x = 0, 1, 2, 3$, and 4.

We seek an equation $y = f(x)$ that describes this function f. The key is the fact that the value of f doubles for every 1-unit increase in x.

$f(0) = 5$

$f(1) = 2f(0) = 2 \cdot 5 = 5 \cdot 2^1$ *We double the value of f at 0 to get the value at 1.*

$f(2) = 2f(1) = 2(5 \cdot 2) = 5 \cdot 2^2$ *We double the value of f at 1 to get the value at 2.*

$f(3) = 2f(2) = 2(5 \cdot 2^2) = 5 \cdot 2^3$

$f(4) = 2f(3) = 2(5 \cdot 2^3) = 5 \cdot 2^4$

The pattern leads us to

$$f(x) = 2f(x - 1) = 2(5 \cdot 2^{x-1}) = 5 \cdot 2^x$$

We are now ready for the following definition.

DEFINITION

An **exponential function** is a function of the form

$$f(x) = Ca^x$$

where a is a positive real number $(a > 0)$ and $a \neq 1$, and $C \neq 0$ is a real number. The domain of f is the set of all real numbers. The base a is the **growth factor,** and because $f(0) = Ca^0 = C$, we call C the **initial value.**

WARNING It is important to distinguish a power function, $g(x) = ax^n$, $n \geq 2$, an integer, from an exponential function, $f(x) = C \cdot a^x$, $a \neq 1$, $a > 0$. In a power function, the base is a variable and the exponent is a constant. In an exponential function, the base is a constant and the exponent is a variable. ∎

In the definition of an exponential function, we exclude the base $a = 1$ because this function is simply the constant function $f(x) = C \cdot 1^x = C$. We also need to exclude bases that are negative; otherwise, we would have to exclude many values of x from the domain, such as $x = \dfrac{1}{2}$ and $x = \dfrac{3}{4}$. [Recall that $(-2)^{1/2} = \sqrt{-2}$, $(-3)^{3/4} = \sqrt[4]{(-3)^3} = \sqrt[4]{-27}$, and so on, are not defined in the set of real numbers.]

Some examples of exponential functions are

$$f(x) = 2^x \qquad F(x) = \left(\frac{1}{3}\right)^x \qquad G(x) = 2 \cdot 3^x$$

Notice for each function that the base is a constant and the exponent is a variable.

In the function $f(x) = 5 \cdot 2^x$, notice that the ratio of consecutive outputs is constant for 1-unit increases in the input. This ratio equals the constant 2, the base of the exponential function. In other words,

$$\frac{f(1)}{f(0)} = \frac{5 \cdot 2^1}{5} = 2 \qquad \frac{f(2)}{f(1)} = \frac{5 \cdot 2^2}{5 \cdot 2^1} = 2 \qquad \frac{f(3)}{f(2)} = \frac{5 \cdot 2^3}{5 \cdot 2^2} = 2 \quad \text{and so on}$$

This leads to the following result.

THEOREM

For an exponential function $f(x) = C \cdot a^x$, $a > 0$, $a \neq 1$, if x is any real number, then

$$\frac{f(x+1)}{f(x)} = a \quad \text{or} \quad f(x+1) = af(x)$$

In Words
For 1-unit changes in the input x of an exponential function $f(x) = C \cdot a^x$, the ratio of consecutive outputs is the constant a.

Proof

$$\frac{f(x+1)}{f(x)} = \frac{Ca^{x+1}}{Ca^x} = a^{x+1-x} = a^1 = a \qquad ∎$$

EXAMPLE 2 **Identifying Linear or Exponential Functions**

Determine whether the given function is linear, exponential, or neither. For those that are linear, find a linear function that models the data. For those that are exponential, find an exponential function that models the data.

(a)

x	y
−1	5
0	2
1	−1
2	−4
3	−7

(b)

x	y
−1	2
0	4
1	7
2	11
3	15

(c)

x	y
−1	32
0	16
1	8
2	4
3	2

Solution

For each function we compute the average rate of change of y with respect to x. If the average rate of change is constant, then the function is linear. Also, we compute the ratio of consecutive outputs. If the ratio is constant, then the function is exponential.

(a) See Table 3(a). The average rate of change for every 1-unit increase in x is –3. Therefore, the function is a linear function. In a linear function the average rate of change is the slope m, so $m = -3$. The y-intercept b is the value of the function at $x = 0$, so $b = 2$. The linear function that models the data is $f(x) = mx + b = -3x + 2$.

Table 3

x	y	Average Rate of Change	Ratio of Consecutive Outputs
−1	5		
		$\dfrac{\Delta y}{\Delta x} = \dfrac{2-5}{0-(-1)} = -3$	$\dfrac{2}{5}$
0	2		
		−3	$-\dfrac{1}{2}$
1	−1		
		−3	4
2	−4		
		−3	$\dfrac{7}{4}$
3	−7		

(a)

x	y	Average Rate of Change	Ratio of Consecutive Outputs
−1	2		
		$\dfrac{\Delta y}{\Delta x} = \dfrac{4-2}{0-(-1)} = 2$	2
0	4		
		3	$\dfrac{7}{4}$
1	7		
		4	$\dfrac{11}{7}$
2	11		
		5	$\dfrac{16}{11}$
3	16		

(b)

x	y	Average Rate of Change	Ratio of Consecutive Outputs
−1	32		
		$\dfrac{\Delta y}{\Delta x} = \dfrac{16-32}{0-(-1)} = -16$	$\dfrac{16}{32} = \dfrac{1}{2}$
0	16		
		−8	$\dfrac{8}{16} = \dfrac{1}{2}$
1	8		
		−4	$\dfrac{4}{8} = \dfrac{1}{2}$
2	4		
		−2	$\dfrac{2}{4} = \dfrac{1}{2}$
3	2		

(c)

(b) See Table 3(b). In this function the average rate of change from −1 to 0 is 2, and the average rate of change from 0 to 1 is 3. Because the average rate of change is not constant, the function is not a linear function. In this function, the ratio of consecutive outputs from −1 to 0 is 2, and the ratio of consecutive outputs from 0 to 1 is $\dfrac{7}{4}$. Because the ratio of consecutive outputs is not a constant, the function is not an exponential function.

(c) See Table 3(c). In this function the average rate of change from −1 to 0 is −16, and the average rate of change from 0 to 1 is −8. Because the average rate of change is not constant, the function is not a linear function. The ratio of consecutive outputs for a 1-unit increase in the inputs is a constant, $\dfrac{1}{2}$. Because the ratio of consecutive outputs is constant, the function is an exponential function with growth factor $a = \dfrac{1}{2}$. The initial value of the exponential function is $C = 16$. Therefore, the exponential function that models the data is
$$g(x) = Ca^x = 16 \cdot \left(\dfrac{1}{2}\right)^x.$$

Now Work PROBLEM 21

2 Graph Exponential Functions

If we know how to graph an exponential function of the form $f(x) = a^x$, then a compression, stretch, and perhaps reflection about the x-axis will enable us to obtain the graph of $f(x) = C \cdot a^x$.

First, we graph the exponential function $f(x) = 2^x$.

| EXAMPLE 3 | Graphing an Exponential Function |

Graph the exponential function: $f(x) = 2^x$

Solution

Table 4

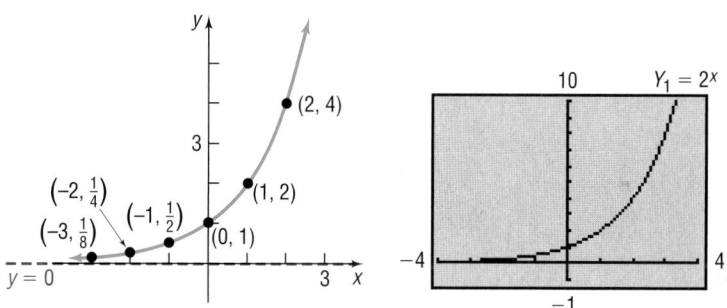

The domain of $f(x) = 2^x$ is the set of all real numbers. We begin by locating some points on the graph of $f(x) = 2^x$, as listed in Table 4.

Since $2^x > 0$ for all x, the range of f is $(0, \infty)$. From this, we conclude that the graph has no x-intercepts, and, in fact, the graph will lie above the x-axis for all x. As Table 4 indicates, the y-intercept is 1. Table 4 also indicates that as $x \to -\infty$ the value of $f(x) = 2^x$ gets closer and closer to 0. We conclude that the x-axis ($y = 0$) is a horizontal asymptote to the graph as $x \to -\infty$. This gives us the end behavior for x large and negative.

To determine the end behavior for x large and positive, look again at Table 4. As $x \to \infty$, $f(x) = 2^x$ grows very quickly, causing the graph of $f(x) = 2^x$ to rise very rapidly. It is apparent that f is an increasing function and hence is one-to-one.

Figure 20 shows the graph of $f(x) = 2^x$. Notice that all the conclusions given earlier are confirmed by the graph.

Figure 20

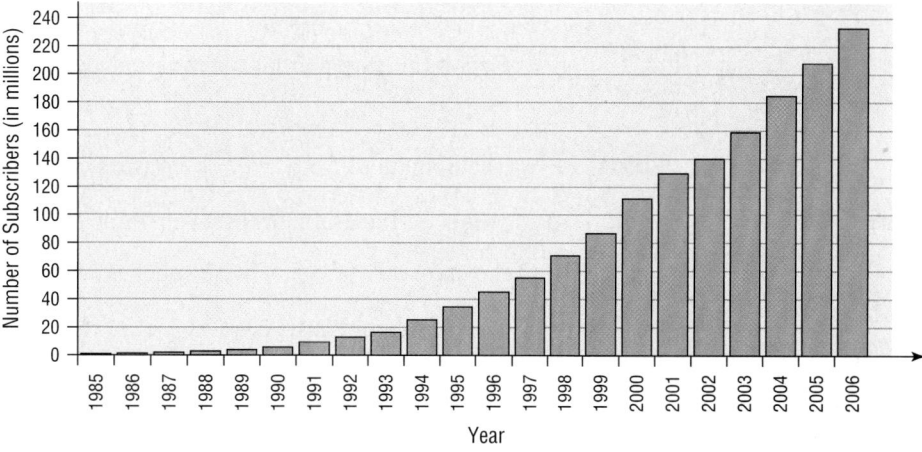

As we shall see, graphs that look like the one in Figure 20 occur very frequently in a variety of situations. For example, look at the graph in Figure 21, which illustrates the number of cellular telephone subscribers at the end of each year from 1985 to 2006. We might conclude from this graph that the number of cellular telephone subscribers is growing *exponentially*.

Figure 21

Number of Cellular Phone Subscribers at Year End

Source: ©2006 CTIA–The Wireless Association®. All Rights Reserved.

We shall have more to say about situations that lead to exponential growth later in this chapter. For now, we continue to seek properties of the exponential functions.

The graph of $f(x) = 2^x$ in Figure 20 is typical of all exponential functions of the form $f(x) = a^x$ with $a > 1$. Such functions are increasing functions and hence are one-to-one. Their graphs lie above the x-axis, pass through the point $(0, 1)$, and thereafter rise rapidly as $x \to \infty$. As $x \to -\infty$, the x-axis $(y = 0)$ is a horizontal asymptote. There are no vertical asymptotes. Finally, the graphs are smooth and continuous, with no corners or gaps.

Figures 22 and 23 illustrate the graphs of two more exponential functions whose bases are larger than 1. Notice the larger the base, the steeper the graph is when $x > 0$, and when $x < 0$, the larger the base, the closer the graph of the equation is to the x-axis.

Figure 22

Figure 23

(a)

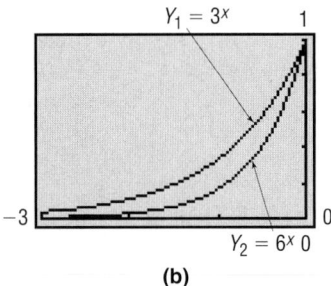
(b)

The following display summarizes the information that we have about $f(x) = a^x, a > 1$.

Properties of the Exponential Function $f(x) = a^x$, $a > 1$

1. The domain is the set of all real numbers; the range is the set of positive real numbers.

2. There are no x-intercepts; the y-intercept is 1.

3. The x-axis $(y = 0)$ is a horizontal asymptote as $x \to -\infty$.

4. $f(x) = a^x, a > 1$, is an increasing function and is one-to-one.

5. The graph of f contains the points $(0, 1)$, $(1, a)$, and $\left(-1, \dfrac{1}{a}\right)$.

6. The graph of f is smooth and continuous, with no corners or gaps. See Figure 24.

Figure 24
$f(x) = a^x, a > 1$

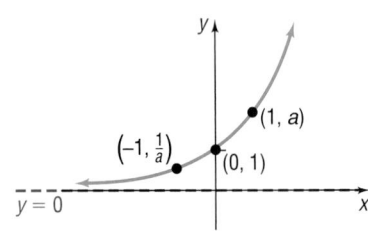

Now we consider $f(x) = a^x$ when $0 < a < 1$.

| EXAMPLE 4 | Graphing an Exponential Function |

Graph the exponential function: $f(x) = \left(\dfrac{1}{2}\right)^x$

Solution

The domain of $f(x) = \left(\dfrac{1}{2}\right)^x$ consists of all real numbers. As before, we locate some

Table 5

points on the graph, as listed in Table 5. Since $\left(\dfrac{1}{2}\right)^x > 0$ for all x, the range of f is

the interval $(0, \infty)$. The graph lies above the x-axis and so has no x-intercepts.

The y-intercept is 1. As $x \to -\infty$, $f(x) = \left(\dfrac{1}{2}\right)^x$ grows very quickly. As $x \to \infty$, the

values of $f(x)$ approach 0. The x-axis $(y = 0)$ is a horizontal asymptote as $x \to \infty$. It is apparent that f is a decreasing function and hence is one-to-one. Figure 25 illustrates the graph.

Figure 25

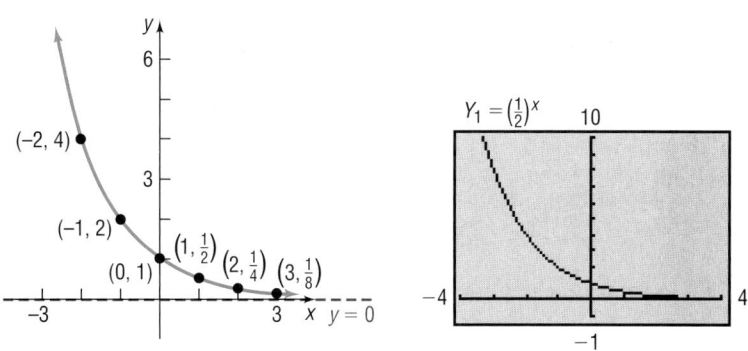

Seeing the Concept

Using a graphing utility, simultaneously graph:

(a) $Y_1 = 3^x$, $Y_2 = \left(\dfrac{1}{3}\right)^x$

(b) $Y_1 = 6^x$, $Y_2 = \left(\dfrac{1}{6}\right)^x$

Conclude that the graph of $Y_2 = \left(\dfrac{1}{a}\right)^x$, for $a > 0$, is the reflection about the y-axis of the graph of $Y_1 = a^x$.

We could have obtained the graph of $y = \left(\dfrac{1}{2}\right)^x$ from the graph of $y = 2^x$ using transformations. The graph of $y = \left(\dfrac{1}{2}\right)^x = 2^{-x}$ is a reflection about the y-axis of the graph of $y = 2^x$. Compare Figures 20 and 25.

The graph of $f(x) = \left(\dfrac{1}{2}\right)^x$ in Figure 25 is typical of all exponential functions of the form $f(x) = a^x$ with $0 < a < 1$. Such functions are decreasing and one-to-one. Their graphs lie above the x-axis and pass through the point $(0, 1)$. The graphs rise rapidly as $x \to -\infty$. As $x \to \infty$, the x-axis ($y = 0$) is a horizontal asymptote. There are no vertical asymptotes. Finally, the graphs are smooth and continuous, with no corners or gaps.

Figures 26 and 27 illustrate the graphs of two more exponential functions whose bases are between 0 and 1. Notice the smaller the base, the steeper the graph when $x < 0$, and when $x > 0$, the smaller the base, the closer the graph of the equation is to the x-axis.

The following display summarizes the information that we have about the function $f(x) = a^x$, $0 < a < 1$.

Figure 26

Figure 27

(a)

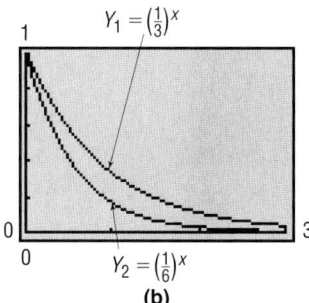

(b)

Figure 28

$f(x) = a^x$, $0 < a < 1$

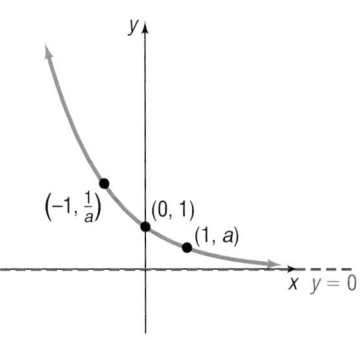

Properties of the Exponential Function $f(x) = a^x$, $0 < a < 1$

1. The domain is the set of all real numbers; the range is the set of positive real numbers.

2. There are no x-intercepts; the y-intercept is 1.

3. The x-axis ($y = 0$) is a horizontal asymptote as $x \to \infty$.

4. $f(x) = a^x$, $0 < a < 1$, is a decreasing function and is one-to-one.

5. The graph of f contains the points $(0, 1)$, $(1, a)$, and $\left(-1, \dfrac{1}{a}\right)$.

6. The graph of f is smooth and continuous, with no corners or gaps. See Figure 28.

| EXAMPLE 5 | **Graphing Exponential Functions Using Transformations** |

Graph $f(x) = 2^{-x} - 3$ and determine the domain, range, and horizontal asymptote of f.

Solution We begin with the graph of $y = 2^x$. Figure 29 shows the stages.

Figure 29

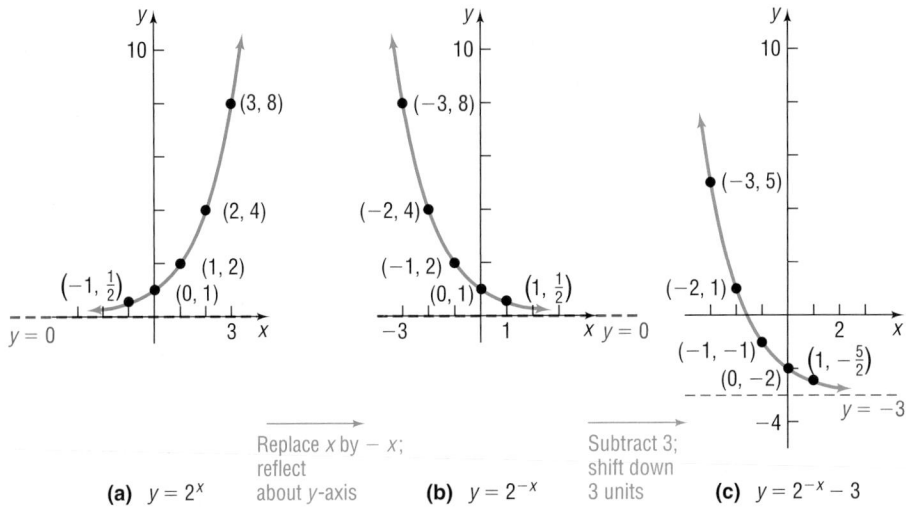

(a) $y = 2^x$ Replace x by $-x$; reflect about y-axis

(b) $y = 2^{-x}$ Subtract 3; shift down 3 units

(c) $y = 2^{-x} - 3$

As Figure 29(c) illustrates, the domain of $f(x) = 2^{-x} - 3$ is the interval $(-\infty, \infty)$, and the range is the interval $(-3, \infty)$. The horizontal asymptote of f is the line $y = -3$.

✓**Check:** Graph $Y_1 = 2^{-x} - 3$ to verify the graph obtained in Figure 29(c).

━━━━━━ **Now Work** PROBLEM 37

3 Define the Number *e*

As we shall see shortly, many problems that occur in nature require the use of an exponential function whose base is a certain irrational number, symbolized by the letter e.

Let's look at one way of arriving at this important number e.

DEFINITION The **number *e*** is defined as the number that the expression

$$\left(1 + \frac{1}{n}\right)^n \tag{2}$$

 approaches as $n \to \infty$. In calculus, this is expressed using limit notation as

$$e = \lim_{n \to \infty}\left(1 + \frac{1}{n}\right)^n$$

Table 6 illustrates what happens to the defining expression (2) as n takes on increasingly large values. The last number in the right column in the table is correct to nine decimal places and is the same as the entry given for e on your calculator (if expressed correctly to nine decimal places).

Table 6

n	$\dfrac{1}{n}$	$1 + \dfrac{1}{n}$	$\left(1 + \dfrac{1}{n}\right)^n$
1	1	2	2
2	0.5	1.5	2.25
5	0.2	1.2	2.48832
10	0.1	1.1	2.59374246
100	0.01	1.01	2.704813829
1,000	0.001	1.001	2.716923932
10,000	0.0001	1.0001	2.718145927
100,000	0.00001	1.00001	2.718268237
1,000,000	0.000001	1.000001	2.718280469
1,000,000,000	10^{-9}	$1 + 10^{-9}$	2.718281827

Table 7

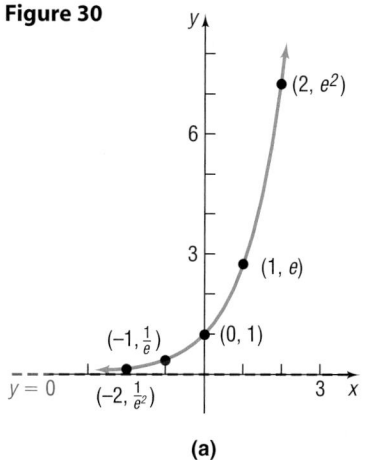

The exponential function $f(x) = e^x$, whose base is the number e, occurs with such frequency in applications that it is usually referred to as *the* exponential function. Graphing calculators have the key $\boxed{e^x}$ or $\boxed{\exp(x)}$, which may be used to evaluate the exponential function for a given value of x. Use your calculator to find e^x for $x = -2$, $x = -1$, $x = 0$, $x = 1$, and $x = 2$, as we have done to create Table 7. The graph of the exponential function $f(x) = e^x$ is given in Figures 30(a) and 30(b). Since $2 < e < 3$, the graph of $y = e^x$ is increasing and lies between the graphs of $y = 2^x$ and $y = 3^x$. [See Figure 30(c).]

Figure 30

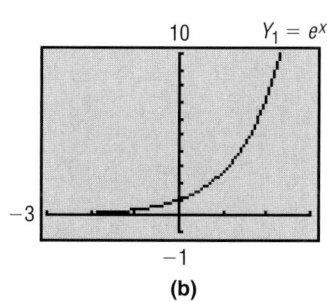

(a)

(b)

(c)

EXAMPLE 6 **Graphing Exponential Functions Using Transformations**

Graph $f(x) = -e^{x-3}$ and determine the domain, range, and horizontal asymptote of f.

Solution We begin with the graph of $y = e^x$. Figure 31 shows the stages.

Figure 31

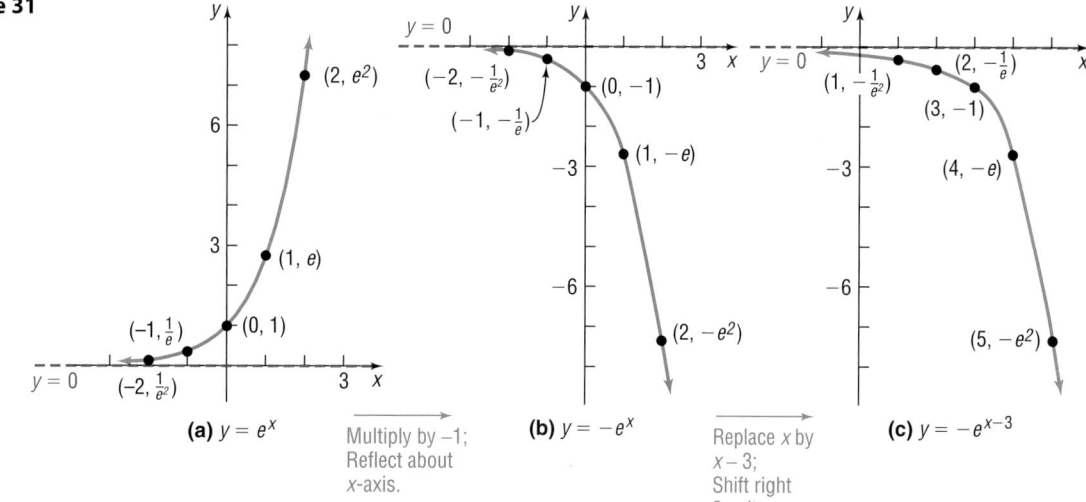

(a) $y = e^x$

Multiply by -1;
Reflect about
x-axis.

(b) $y = -e^x$

Replace x by
$x - 3$;
Shift right
3 units.

(c) $y = -e^{x-3}$

As Figure 31(c) illustrates, the domain of $f(x) = -e^{x-3}$ is the interval $(-\infty, \infty)$, and the range is the interval $(-\infty, 0)$. The horizontal asymptote is the line $y = 0$.

✓ **Check:** Graph $Y_1 = -e^{x-3}$ to verify the graph obtained in Figure 31(c).

> **Now Work** PROBLEM 49

4 Solve Exponential Equations

Equations that involve terms of the form a^x, $a > 0$, $a \neq 1$, are referred to as **exponential equations.** Such equations can sometimes be solved by appropriately applying the Laws of Exponents and property (3):

> **In Words**
> When two exponential expressions with the same base are equal, then their exponents are equal.

$$\text{If} \quad a^u = a^v, \quad \text{then} \quad u = v \qquad \textbf{(3)}$$

Property (3) is a consequence of the fact that exponential functions are one-to-one. To use property (3), each side of the equality must be written with the same base.

| EXAMPLE 7 | Solving an Exponential Equation |

Solve: $3^{x+1} = 81$

Algebraic Solution

$$3^{x+1} = 81$$
$$3^{x+1} = 3^4 \quad \text{\small $81 = 3^4$}$$

Now we have the same base, 3, on each side of the equation, so we can set the exponents equal to each other to obtain

$$x + 1 = 4$$
$$x = 3$$

The solution set is $\{3\}$.

Graphing Solution

Graph $Y_1 = 3^{x+1}$ and $Y_2 = 81$. Use INTERSECT to determine the point of intersection. See Figure 32.

Figure 32

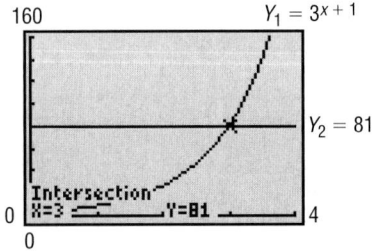

The graphs intersect at $(3, 81)$, so the solution set is $\{3\}$.

> **Now Work** PROBLEM 59

| EXAMPLE 8 | Solving an Exponential Equation |

Solve: $e^{-x^2} = (e^x)^2 \cdot \dfrac{1}{e^3}$

Solution

We use the Laws of Exponents first to get the base e on the right side.

$$(e^x)^2 \cdot \frac{1}{e^3} = e^{2x} \cdot e^{-3} = e^{2x-3}$$

As a result,

$$e^{-x^2} = e^{2x-3}$$
$$-x^2 = 2x - 3 \quad \text{\small Apply Property (3).}$$
$$x^2 + 2x - 3 = 0 \quad \text{\small Place the quadratic equation in standard form.}$$
$$(x + 3)(x - 1) = 0 \quad \text{\small Factor.}$$
$$x = -3 \quad \text{or} \quad x = 1 \quad \text{\small Use the Zero-Product Property.}$$

The solution set is $\{-3, 1\}$.

✓ **Check:** Verify these solutions using a graphing utility.

Many applications involve the exponential function. Let's look at one.

EXAMPLE 9   **Exponential Probability**

Between 9:00 PM and 10:00 PM cars arrive at Burger King's drive-thru at the rate of 12 cars per hour (0.2 car per minute). The following formula from statistics can be used to determine the probability that a car will arrive within t minutes of 9:00 PM.

$$F(t) = 1 - e^{-0.2t}$$

(a) Determine the probability that a car will arrive within 5 minutes of 9 PM (that is, before 9:05 PM).

(b) Determine the probability that a car will arrive within 30 minutes of 9 PM (before 9:30 PM).

(c) Graph F using your graphing utility.

(d) What value does F approach as t becomes unbounded in the positive direction?

Solution   (a) The probability that a car will arrive within 5 minutes is found by evaluating $F(t)$ at $t = 5$.

$$F(5) = 1 - e^{-0.2(5)} \approx 0.63212$$

Figure 33

We evaluate this expression in Figure 33. We conclude that there is a 63% probability that a car will arrive within 5 minutes.

(b) The probability that a car will arrive within 30 minutes is found by evaluating $F(t)$ at $t = 30$.

$$F(30) = 1 - e^{-0.2(30)} \approx 0.9975$$
↑
Use a calculator.

Figure 34

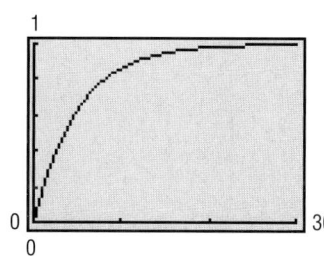

There is a 99.75% probability that a car will arrive within 30 minutes.

(c) See Figure 34 for the graph of F.

(d) As time passes, the probability that a car will arrive increases. The value that F approaches can be found by letting $t \to \infty$. Since $e^{-0.2t} = \dfrac{1}{e^{0.2t}}$, it follows that $e^{-0.2t} \to 0$ as $t \to \infty$. We conclude that F approaches 1 as t gets large.

⟶ **Now Work** PROBLEM **101**

SUMMARY   Properties of the Exponential Function

$f(x) = a^x, \quad a > 1$ Domain: the interval $(-\infty, \infty)$; Range: the interval $(0, \infty)$
x-intercepts: none; y-intercept: 1
Horizontal asymptote: x-axis ($y = 0$) as $x \to -\infty$
Increasing; one-to-one; smooth; continuous
See Figure 24 for a typical graph.

$f(x) = a^x, \quad 0 < a < 1$ Domain: the interval $(-\infty, \infty)$; Range: the interval $(0, \infty)$
x-intercepts: none; y-intercept: 1
Horizontal asymptote: x-axis ($y = 0$) as $x \to \infty$
Decreasing; one-to-one; smooth; continuous
See Figure 28 for a typical graph.

If $a^u = a^v$, then $u = v$.

5.3 Assess Your Understanding

'Are You Prepared?'   *Answers are given at the end of these exercises. If you get a wrong answer, read the pages listed in red.*

1. (a) $4^3 =$ _____   (b) $8^{2/3} =$ _____   (c) $3^{-2} =$ _____   **2.** Solve: (a) $5x - 2 = 3$ (pp. A47–A49)
(d) $(x^2)^3 =$ _____   (e) $a^3 \cdot a^5 =$ _____ (pp. A7–A9 and A91)   (b) $2x^2 + 3x = 14$ (pp. A50–A55)

3. *True or False* To graph $y = (x - 2)^3$, shift the graph of $y = x^3$ to the left 2 units. (pp. 101–102)

4. Find the average rate of change of $f(x) = 3x - 5$ from $x = 0$ to $x = 4$. (pp. 84–85 and 126–129)

5. *True or False* The function $f(x) = \dfrac{2x}{x - 3}$ has $y = 2$ as a horizontal asymptote. (pp. 196–199)

Concepts and Vocabulary

6. The graph of every exponential function $f(x) = a^x$, $a > 0, a \neq 1$, passes through three points: _____, _____, and _____.

7. If the graph of the exponential function $f(x) = a^x$, $a > 0, a \neq 1$, is decreasing, then a must be less than _____.

8. If $3^x = 3^4$, then $x =$ _____.

9. *True or False* The graphs of $y = 3^x$ and $y = \left(\dfrac{1}{3}\right)^x$ are identical.

10. *True or False* The range of the exponential function $f(x) = a^x, a > 0, a \neq 1$, is the set of all real numbers.

Skill Building

In Problems 11–20, approximate each number using a calculator. Express your answer rounded to three decimal places.

11. (a) $3^{2.2}$ (b) $3^{2.23}$ (c) $3^{2.236}$ (d) $3^{\sqrt{5}}$

12. (a) $5^{1.7}$ (b) $5^{1.73}$ (c) $5^{1.732}$ (d) $5^{\sqrt{3}}$

13. (a) $2^{3.14}$ (b) $2^{3.141}$ (c) $2^{3.1415}$ (d) 2^{π}

14. (a) $2^{2.7}$ (b) $2^{2.71}$ (c) $2^{2.718}$ (d) 2^{e}

15. (a) $3.1^{2.7}$ (b) $3.14^{2.71}$ (c) $3.141^{2.718}$ (d) π^{e}

16. (a) $2.7^{3.1}$ (b) $2.71^{3.14}$ (c) $2.718^{3.141}$ (d) e^{π}

17. $e^{1.2}$

18. $e^{-1.3}$

19. $e^{-0.85}$

20. $e^{2.1}$

In Problems 21–28, determine whether the given function is linear, exponential, or neither. For those that are linear functions, find a linear function that models the data; for those that are exponential, find an exponential function that models the data.

21.

x	f(x)
−1	3
0	6
1	12
2	18
3	30

22.

x	g(x)
−1	2
0	5
1	8
2	11
3	14

23.

x	H(x)
−1	$\frac{1}{4}$
0	1
1	4
2	16
3	64

24.

x	F(x)
−1	$\frac{2}{3}$
0	1
1	$\frac{3}{2}$
2	$\frac{9}{4}$
3	$\frac{27}{8}$

25.

x	f(x)
−1	$\frac{3}{2}$
0	3
1	6
2	12
3	24

26.

x	g(x)
−1	6
0	1
1	0
2	3
3	10

27.

x	H(x)
−1	2
0	4
1	6
2	8
3	10

28.

x	F(x)
−1	$\frac{1}{2}$
0	$\frac{1}{4}$
1	$\frac{1}{8}$
2	$\frac{1}{16}$
3	$\frac{1}{32}$

In Problems 29–36, the graph of an exponential function is given. Match each graph to one of the following functions.

(a) $y = 3^x$

(b) $y = 3^{-x}$

(c) $y = -3^x$

(d) $y = -3^{-x}$

(e) $y = 3^x - 1$

(f) $y = 3^{x-1}$

(g) $y = 3^{1-x}$

(h) $y = 1 - 3^x$

29.

30.

31.

32.

33.   **34.**   **35.**   **36.**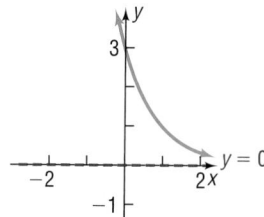

In Problems 37–48, use transformations to graph each function. Determine the domain, range, and horizontal asymptote of each function.

37. $f(x) = 2^x + 1$

38. $f(x) = 3^x - 2$

39. $f(x) = 3^{x-1}$

40. $f(x) = 2^{x+2}$

41. $f(x) = 3 \cdot \left(\dfrac{1}{2}\right)^x$

42. $f(x) = 4 \cdot \left(\dfrac{1}{3}\right)^x$

43. $f(x) = 3^{-x} - 2$

44. $f(x) = -3^x + 1$

45. $f(x) = 2 + 4^{x-1}$

46. $f(x) = 1 - 2^{x+3}$

47. $f(x) = 2 + 3^{x/2}$

48. $f(x) = 1 - 2^{-x/3}$

In Problems 49–56, begin with the graph of $y = e^x$ (Figure 30(a)) and use transformations to graph each function. Determine the domain, range, and horizontal asymptote of each function.

49. $f(x) = e^{-x}$

50. $f(x) = -e^x$

51. $f(x) = e^{x+2}$

52. $f(x) = e^x - 1$

53. $f(x) = 5 - e^{-x}$

54. $f(x) = 9 - 3e^{-x}$

55. $f(x) = 2 - e^{-x/2}$

56. $f(x) = 7 - 3e^{2x}$

In Problems 57–76, solve each equation. Verify your results using a graphing utility.

57. $7^x = 7^3$

58. $5^x = 5^{-6}$

59. $2^{-x} = 16$

60. $3^{-x} = 81$

61. $\left(\dfrac{1}{5}\right)^x = \dfrac{1}{25}$

62. $\left(\dfrac{1}{4}\right)^x = \dfrac{1}{64}$

63. $2^{2x-1} = 4$

64. $5^{x+3} = \dfrac{1}{5}$

65. $3^{x^3} = 9^x$

66. $4^{x^2} = 2^x$

67. $8^{-x+14} = 16^x$

68. $9^{-x+15} = 27^x$

69. $3^{x^2-7} = 27^{2x}$

70. $5^{x^2+8} = 125^{2x}$

71. $4^x \cdot 2^{x^2} = 16^2$

72. $9^{2x} \cdot 27^{x^2} = 3^{-1}$

73. $e^x = e^{3x+8}$

74. $e^{3x} = e^{2-x}$

75. $e^{x^2} = e^{3x} \cdot \dfrac{1}{e^2}$

76. $(e^4)^x \cdot e^{x^2} = e^{12}$

77. If $4^x = 7$, what does 4^{-2x} equal?

78. If $2^x = 3$, what does 4^{-x} equal?

79. If $3^{-x} = 2$, what does 3^{2x} equal?

80. If $5^{-x} = 3$, what does 5^{3x} equal?

In Problems 81–84, determine the exponential function whose graph is given.

81.

82.

83.

84.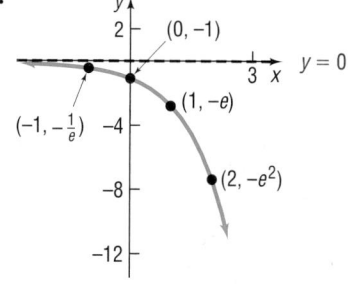

Mixed Practice

85. Suppose that $f(x) = 2^x$.
   (a) What is $f(4)$? What point is on the graph of f?
   (b) If $f(x) = \dfrac{1}{16}$, what is x? What point is on the graph of f?

86. Suppose that $f(x) = 3^x$.
   (a) What is $f(4)$? What point is on the graph of f?
   (b) If $f(x) = \dfrac{1}{9}$, what is x? What point is on the graph of f?

87. Suppose that $g(x) = 4^x + 2$.
   (a) What is $g(-1)$? What point is on the graph of g?
   (b) If $g(x) = 66$, what is x? What point is on the graph of g?

88. Suppose that $g(x) = 5^x - 3$.
   (a) What is $g(-1)$? What point is on the graph of g?
   (b) If $g(x) = 122$, what is x? What point is on the graph of g?

89. Suppose that $H(x) = \left(\dfrac{1}{2}\right)^x - 4$.
   (a) What is $H(-6)$? What point is on the graph of H?
   (b) If $H(x) = 12$, what is x? What point is on the graph of H?
   (c) Find the zero of H.

90. Suppose that $F(x) = \left(\dfrac{1}{3}\right)^x - 3$.
   (a) What is $F(-5)$? What point is on the graph of F?
   (b) If $F(x) = 24$, what is x? What point is on the graph of F?
   (c) Find the zero of F.

In Problems 91–94, graph each function. Based on the graph, state the domain and the range and find any intercepts.

91. $f(x) = \begin{cases} e^{-x} & \text{if } x < 0 \\ e^x & \text{if } x \geq 0 \end{cases}$

92. $f(x) = \begin{cases} e^x & \text{if } x < 0 \\ e^{-x} & \text{if } x \geq 0 \end{cases}$

93. $f(x) = \begin{cases} -e^x & \text{if } x < 0 \\ -e^{-x} & \text{if } x \geq 0 \end{cases}$

94. $f(x) = \begin{cases} -e^{-x} & \text{if } x < 0 \\ -e^x & \text{if } x \geq 0 \end{cases}$

Applications and Extensions

95. Optics   If a single pane of glass obliterates 3% of the light passing through it, the percent p of light that passes through n successive panes is given approximately by the function

$$p(n) = 100(0.97)^n$$

   (a) What percent of light will pass through 10 panes?
   (b) What percent of light will pass through 25 panes?

96. Atmospheric Pressure   The atmospheric pressure p on a balloon or plane decreases with increasing height. This pressure, measured in millimeters of mercury, is related to the height h (in kilometers) above sea level by the function

$$p(h) = 760e^{-0.145h}$$

   (a) Find the atmospheric pressure at a height of 2 kilometers (over a mile).
   (b) What is it at a height of 10 kilometers (over 30,000 feet)?

97. Depreciation   The price p, in dollars, of a Honda Civic DX Sedan that is x years old is modeled by

$$p(x) = 16,630(0.90)^x$$

   (a) How much does a 3-year-old Civic DX Sedan cost?
   (b) How much does a 9-year-old Civic DX Sedan cost?

98. Healing of Wounds   The normal healing of wounds can be modeled by an exponential function. If A_0 represents the original area of the wound and if A equals the area of the wound, then the function

$$A(n) = A_0 e^{-0.35n}$$

describes the area of a wound after n days following an injury when no infection is present to retard the healing. Suppose that a wound initially had an area of 100 square millimeters.
   (a) If healing is taking place, how large will the area of the wound be after 3 days?
   (b) How large will it be after 10 days?

99. Drug Medication   The function

$$D(h) = 5e^{-0.4h}$$

can be used to find the number of milligrams D of a certain drug that is in a patient's bloodstream h hours after the drug has been administered. How many milligrams will be present after 1 hour? After 6 hours?

100. Spreading of Rumors   A model for the number N of people in a college community who have heard a certain rumor is

$$N = P(1 - e^{-0.15d})$$

where P is the total population of the community and d is the number of days that have elapsed since the rumor began. In a community of 1000 students, how many students will have heard the rumor after 3 days?

101. Exponential Probability   Between 12:00 PM and 1:00 PM, cars arrive at Citibank's drive-thru at the rate of 6 cars per hour (0.1 car per minute). The following formula from probability can be used to determine the probability that a car will arrive within t minutes of 12:00 PM:

$$F(t) = 1 - e^{-0.1t}$$

   (a) Determine the probability that a car will arrive within 10 minutes of 12:00 PM (that is, before 12:10 PM).
   (b) Determine the probability that a car will arrive within 40 minutes of 12:00 PM (before 12:40 PM).
   (c) What value does F approach as t becomes unbounded in the positive direction?
   (d) Graph F using a graphing utility.
   (e) Using INTERSECT, determine how many minutes are needed for the probability to reach 50%.

102. Exponential Probability   Between 5:00 PM and 6:00 PM, cars arrive at Jiffy Lube at the rate of 9 cars per hour (0.15 car per minute). The following formula from probability can be used to determine the probability that a car will arrive within t minutes of 5:00 PM:

$$F(t) = 1 - e^{-0.15t}$$

(a) Determine the probability that a car will arrive within 15 minutes of 5:00 PM (that is, before 5:15 PM).
(b) Determine the probability that a car will arrive within 30 minutes of 5:00 PM (before 5:30 PM).
(c) What value does F approach as t becomes unbounded in the positive direction?
(d) Graph F using a graphing utility.
(e) Using INTERSECT, determine how many minutes are needed for the probability to reach 60%.

103. Poisson Probability Between 5:00 PM and 6:00 PM, cars arrive at McDonald's drive-thru at the rate of 20 cars per hour. The following formula from probability can be used to determine the probability that x cars will arrive between 5:00 PM and 6:00 PM.

$$P(x) = \frac{20^x e^{-20}}{x!}$$

where

$$x! = x \cdot (x - 1) \cdot (x - 2) \cdot \cdots \cdot 3 \cdot 2 \cdot 1$$

(a) Determine the probability that $x = 15$ cars will arrive between 5:00 PM and 6:00 PM.
(b) Determine the probability that $x = 20$ cars will arrive between 5:00 PM and 6:00 PM.

104. Poisson Probability People enter a line for the *Demon Roller Coaster* at the rate of 4 per minute. The following formula from probability can be used to determine the probability that x people will arrive within the next minute.

$$P(x) = \frac{4^x e^{-4}}{x!}$$

where

$$x! = x \cdot (x - 1) \cdot (x - 2) \cdot \cdots \cdot 3 \cdot 2 \cdot 1$$

(a) Determine the probability that $x = 5$ people will arrive within the next minute.
(b) Determine the probability that $x = 8$ people will arrive within the next minute.

105. Relative Humidity The relative humidity is the ratio (expressed as a percent) of the amount of water vapor in the air to the maximum amount that it can hold at a specific temperature. The relative humidity, R, is found using the following formula:

$$R = 10^{\left(\frac{4221}{T+459.4} - \frac{4221}{D+459.4} + 2 \right)}$$

where T is the air temperature (in °F) and D is the dew point temperature (in °F).

(a) Determine the relative humidity if the air temperature is 50° Fahrenheit and the dew point temperature is 41° Fahrenheit.
(b) Determine the relative humidity if the air temperature is 68° Fahrenheit and the dew point temperature is 59° Fahrenheit.
(c) What is the relative humidity if the air temperature and the dew point temperature are the same?

106. Learning Curve Suppose that a student has 500 vocabulary words to learn. If the student learns 15 words after 5 minutes, the function

$$L(t) = 500(1 - e^{-0.0061t})$$

approximates the number of words L that the student will learn after t minutes.

(a) How many words will the student learn after 30 minutes?
(b) How many words will the student learn after 60 minutes?

107. Current in a *RL* Circuit The equation governing the amount of current I (in amperes) after time t (in seconds) in a single *RL* circuit consisting of a resistance R (in ohms), an inductance L (in henrys), and an electromotive force E (in volts) is

$$I = \frac{E}{R}\left[1 - e^{-(R/L)t}\right]$$

(a) If $E = 120$ volts, $R = 10$ ohms, and $L = 5$ henrys, how much current I_1 is flowing after 0.3 second? After 0.5 second? After 1 second?
(b) What is the maximum current?
(c) Graph the function $I = I_1(t)$, measuring I along the y-axis and t along the x-axis.
(d) If $E = 120$ volts, $R = 5$ ohms, and $L = 10$ henrys, how much current I_2 is flowing after 0.3 second? After 0.5 second? After 1 second?
(e) What is the maximum current?
(f) Graph the function $I = I_2(t)$ on the same coordinate axes as $I_1(t)$.

108. Current in a *RC* Circuit The equation governing the amount of current I (in amperes) after time t (in microseconds) in a single *RC* circuit consisting of a resistance R (in ohms), a capacitance C (in microfarads), and an electromotive force E (in volts) is

$$I = \frac{E}{R}e^{-t/(RC)}$$

(a) If $E = 120$ volts, $R = 2000$ ohms, and $C = 1.0$ microfarad, how much current I_1 is flowing initially ($t = 0$)? After 1000 microseconds? After 3000 microseconds?
(b) What is the maximum current?
(c) Graph the function $I = I_1(t)$, measuring I along the y-axis and t along the x-axis.
(d) If $E = 120$ volts, $R = 1000$ ohms, and $C = 2.0$ microfarads, how much current I_2 is flowing initially? After 1000 microseconds? After 3000 microseconds?
(e) What is the maximum current?
(f) Graph the function $I = I_2(t)$ on the same coordinate axes as $I_1(t)$.

109. Another Formula for *e* Use a calculator to compute the values of

$$2 + \frac{1}{2!} + \frac{1}{3!} + \cdots + \frac{1}{n!}$$

for $n = 4, 6, 8$, and 10. Compare each result with e.
[**Hint:** $1! = 1, 2! = 2 \cdot 1, 3! = 3 \cdot 2 \cdot 1$,
$n! = n(n - 1) \cdots (3)(2)(1)$.]

110. Another Formula for e Use a calculator to compute the various values of the expression. Compare the values to e.

$$2 + \cfrac{1}{1 + \cfrac{1}{2 + \cfrac{2}{3 + \cfrac{3}{4 + \cfrac{4}{\text{etc.}}}}}}$$

111. Difference Quotient If $f(x) = a^x$, show that

$$\frac{f(x + h) - f(x)}{h} = a^x \cdot \frac{a^h - 1}{h} \quad h \neq 0$$

112. If $f(x) = a^x$, show that $f(A + B) = f(A) \cdot f(B)$.

113. If $f(x) = a^x$, show that $f(-x) = \dfrac{1}{f(x)}$.

114. If $f(x) = a^x$, show that $f(\alpha x) = [f(x)]^{\alpha}$.

Problems 115 and 116 provide definitions for two other transcendental functions.

115. The **hyperbolic sine function,** designated by sinh x, is defined as

$$\sinh x = \frac{1}{2}(e^x - e^{-x})$$

(a) Show that $f(x) = \sinh x$ is an odd function.
(b) Graph $f(x) = \sinh x$ using a graphing utility.

116. The **hyperbolic cosine function,** designated by cosh x, is defined as

$$\cosh x = \frac{1}{2}(e^x + e^{-x})$$

(a) Show that $f(x) = \cosh x$ is an even function.
(b) Graph $f(x) = \cosh x$ using a graphing utility.
(c) Refer to Problem 115. Show that, for every x,

$$(\cosh x)^2 - (\sinh x)^2 = 1$$

117. Historical Problem Pierre de Fermat (1601–1665) conjectured that the function

$$f(x) = 2^{(2^x)} + 1$$

for $x = 1, 2, 3, \ldots$, would always have a value equal to a prime number. But Leonhard Euler (1707–1783) showed that this formula fails for $x = 5$. Use a calculator to determine the prime numbers produced by f for $x = 1, 2, 3, 4$. Then show that $f(5) = 641 \times 6,700,417$, which is not prime.

Discussion and Writing

118. The bacteria in a 4-liter container double every minute. After 60 minutes the container is full. How long did it take to fill half the container?

119. Explain in your own words what the number e is. Provide at least two applications that use this number.

120. Do you think that there is a power function that increases more rapidly than an exponential function whose base is greater than 1? Explain.

121. As the base a of an exponential function $f(x) = a^x$, $a > 1$, increases, what happens to the behavior of its graph for $x > 0$? What happens to the behavior of its graph for $x < 0$?

122. The graphs of $y = a^{-x}$ and $y = \left(\dfrac{1}{a}\right)^x$ are identical. Why?

'Are You Prepared?' Answers

1. (a) 64   (b) 4   (c) $\dfrac{1}{9}$ (d) x^6 (e) a^8 **2.** (a) {1}   (b) $\left\{-\dfrac{7}{2}, 2\right\}$ **3.** False   **4.** 3   **5.** True

5.4 Logarithmic Functions

PREPARING FOR THIS SECTION *Before getting started, review the following:*

- Solving Inequalities (Appendix A, Section A.9, pp. A81–A82)
- Quadratic Inequalities (Section 3.5, pp. 164–166)
- Polynomial and Rational Inequalities (Section 4.4, pp. 213–217)

Now Work the 'Are You Prepared?' problems on page 293.

OBJECTIVES   **1** Change Exponential Statements to Logarithmic Statements and Logarithmic Statements to Exponential Statements (p. 285)
     2 Evaluate Logarithmic Expressions (p. 285)
     3 Determine the Domain of a Logarithmic Function (p. 286)
     4 Graph Logarithmic Functions (p. 287)
     5 Solve Logarithmic Equations (p. 291)

Recall that a one-to-one function $y = f(x)$ has an inverse function that is defined (implicitly) by the equation $x = f(y)$. In particular, the exponential function $y = f(x) = a^x$, $a > 0$, $a \neq 1$, is one-to-one and hence has an inverse function that is defined implicitly by the equation

$$x = a^y, \qquad a > 0, \qquad a \neq 1$$

This inverse function is so important that it is given a name, the *logarithmic function*.

DEFINITION

The **logarithmic function to the base a,** where $a > 0$ and $a \neq 1$, is denoted by $y = \log_a x$ (read as "y is the logarithm to the base a of x") and is defined by

$$y = \log_a x \quad \text{if and only if} \quad x = a^y$$

The domain of the logarithmic function $y = \log_a x$ is $x > 0$.

As this definition illustrates, a *logarithm* is a name for a certain exponent.

EXAMPLE 1 **Relating Logarithms to Exponents**

(a) If $y = \log_3 x$, then $x = 3^y$. For example, $4 = \log_3 81$ is equivalent to $81 = 3^4$.

(b) If $y = \log_5 x$, then $x = 5^y$. For example, $-1 = \log_5\left(\dfrac{1}{5}\right)$ is equivalent to $\dfrac{1}{5} = 5^{-1}$.

---

1 Change Exponential Statements to Logarithmic Statements and Logarithmic Statements to Exponential Statements

We can use the definition of a logarithm to convert from exponential form to logarithmic form, and vice versa, as the following two examples illustrate.

EXAMPLE 2 **Changing Exponential Statements to Logarithmic Statements**

Change each exponential statement to an equivalent statement involving a logarithm.

(a) $1.2^3 = m$ (b) $e^b = 9$ (c) $a^4 = 24$

Solution We use the fact that $y = \log_a x$ and $x = a^y$, $a > 0$, $a \neq 1$, are equivalent.

(a) If $1.2^3 = m$, then $3 = \log_{1.2} m$.   (b) If $e^b = 9$, then $b = \log_e 9$.

(c) If $a^4 = 24$, then $4 = \log_a 24$.

═══ **Now Work** PROBLEM 9

EXAMPLE 3 **Changing Logarithmic Statements to Exponential Statements**

Change each logarithmic statement to an equivalent statement involving an exponent.

(a) $\log_a 4 = 5$ (b) $\log_e b = -3$ (c) $\log_3 5 = c$

Solution (a) If $\log_a 4 = 5$, then $a^5 = 4$.   (b) If $\log_e b = -3$, then $e^{-3} = b$.

(c) If $\log_3 5 = c$, then $3^c = 5$.

═══ **Now Work** PROBLEM 17

---

2 Evaluate Logarithmic Expressions

To find the exact value of a logarithm, we write the logarithm in exponential notation and use the fact that if $a^u = a^v$ then $u = v$.

| EXAMPLE 4 | **Finding the Exact Value of a Logarithmic Expression** |

Find the exact value of:

(a) $\log_2 16$

(b) $\log_3 \dfrac{1}{27}$

Solution

(a) $y = \log_2 16$

$2^y = 16$ *Change to exponential form.*

$2^y = 2^4$ *$16 = 2^4$*

$y = 4$ *Equate exponents.*

Therefore, $\log_2 16 = 4$.

> **In Words**
>
> The expression $\log_2 16$ means, "give me the exponent y such that $2^y = 16$."

(b) $y = \log_3 \dfrac{1}{27}$

$3^y = \dfrac{1}{27}$ *Change to exponential form.*

$3^y = 3^{-3}$ *$\dfrac{1}{27} = \dfrac{1}{3^3} = 3^{-3}$*

$y = -3$ *Equate exponents.*

Therefore, $\log_3 \dfrac{1}{27} = -3$.

═══ **Now Work** PROBLEM 25

3 Determine the Domain of a Logarithmic Function

The logarithmic function $y = \log_a x$ has been defined as the inverse of the exponential function $y = a^x$. That is, if $f(x) = a^x$, then $f^{-1}(x) = \log_a x$. Based on the discussion given in Section 5.2 on inverse functions, for a function f and its inverse f^{-1}, we have

$$\text{Domain of } f^{-1} = \text{Range of } f \quad \text{and} \quad \text{Range of } f^{-1} = \text{Domain of } f$$

Consequently, it follows that

> Domain of the logarithmic function $=$ Range of the exponential function $= (0, \infty)$
>
> Range of the logarithmic function $=$ Domain of the exponential function $= (-\infty, \infty)$

In the next box, we summarize some properties of the logarithmic function:

> $y = \log_a x$ (defining equation: $x = a^y$)
>
> Domain: $0 < x < \infty$ Range: $-\infty < y < \infty$

The domain of a logarithmic function consists of the *positive* real numbers, so the argument of a logarithmic function must be greater than zero.

| EXAMPLE 5 | **Finding the Domain of a Logarithmic Function** |

Find the domain of each logarithmic function.

(a) $F(x) = \log_2(x + 3)$ (b) $g(x) = \log_5\left(\dfrac{1 + x}{1 - x}\right)$ (c) $h(x) = \log_{1/2}|x|$

Solution

(a) The domain of F consists of all x for which $x + 3 > 0$, that is, $x > -3$. Using interval notation, the domain of f is $(-3, \infty)$.

(b) The domain of g is restricted to

$$\frac{1 + x}{1 - x} > 0$$

Solving this inequality, we find that the domain of g consists of all x between -1 and 1, that is, $-1 < x < 1$ or, using interval notation, $(-1, 1)$.

(c) Since $|x| > 0$, provided that $x \neq 0$, the domain of h consists of all real numbers except zero or, using interval notation, $(-\infty, 0) \cup (0, \infty)$.

═══ **Now Work** PROBLEMS 39 AND 45

4 Graph Logarithmic Functions

Since exponential functions and logarithmic functions are inverses of each other, the graph of the logarithmic function $y = \log_a x$ is the reflection about the line $y = x$ of the graph of the exponential function $y = a^x$, as shown in Figure 35.

Figure 35

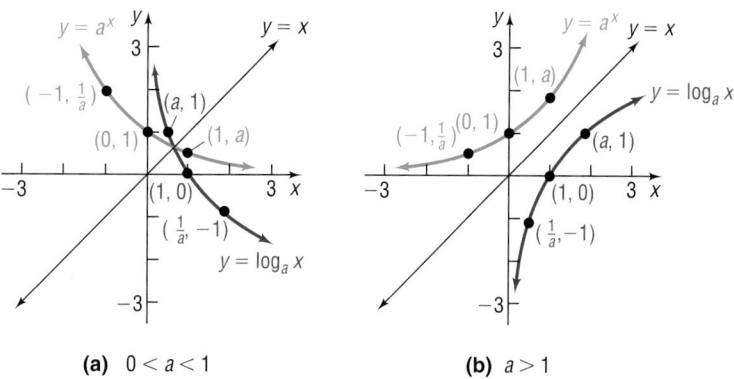

(a) $0 < a < 1$ (b) $a > 1$

For example, to graph $y = \log_2 x$, graph $y = 2^x$ and reflect it about the line $y = x$. See Figure 36. To graph $y = \log_{1/3} x$, graph $y = \left(\dfrac{1}{3}\right)^x$ and reflect it about the line $y = x$. See Figure 37.

Figure 36

Figure 37

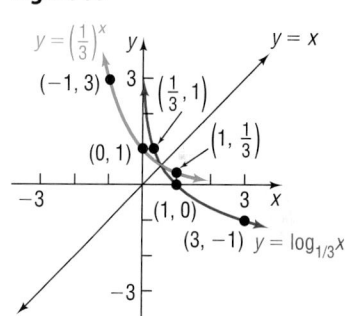

Now Work PROBLEM 59

The graphs of $y = \log_a x$ in Figures 35(a) and (b) lead to the following properties.

Properties of the Logarithmic Function $f(x) = \log_a x$

1. The domain is the set of positive real numbers; the range is the set of all real numbers.

2. The x-intercept of the graph is 1. There is no y-intercept.

3. The y-axis ($x = 0$) is a vertical asymptote of the graph.

4. A logarithmic function is decreasing if $0 < a < 1$ and increasing if $a > 1$.

5. The graph of f contains the points $(1, 0)$, $(a, 1)$, and $\left(\dfrac{1}{a}, -1\right)$.

6. The graph is smooth and continuous, with no corners or gaps.

If the base of a logarithmic function is the number e, then we have the **natural logarithm function.** This function occurs so frequently in applications that it is given a special symbol, **ln** (from the Latin, *logarithmus naturalis*). That is,

In Words
$y = \log_e x$ is written $y = \ln x$

$$y = \ln x \quad \text{if and only if} \quad x = e^y \tag{1}$$

Since $y = \ln x$ and the exponential function $y = e^x$ are inverse functions, we can obtain the graph of $y = \ln x$ by reflecting the graph of $y = e^x$ about the line $y = x$. See Figure 38.

Table 8 displays other points on the graph of $f(x) = \ln x$. Notice for $x \leq 0$ that we obtain an error message. Do you recall why?

Figure 38

Table 8

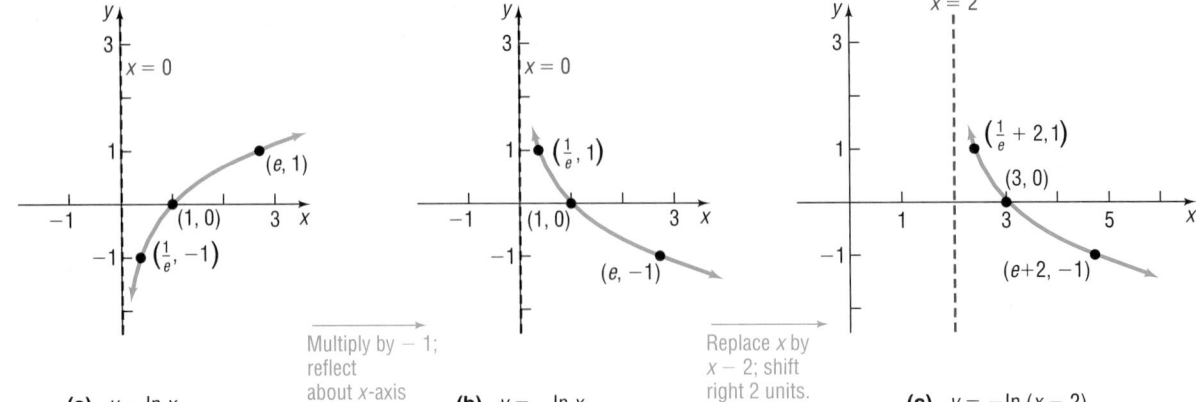

| EXAMPLE 6 | **Graphing a Logarithmic Function and Its Inverse** |

(a) Find the domain of the logarithmic function $f(x) = -\ln(x - 2)$.

(b) Graph f.

(c) From the graph, determine the range and vertical asymptote of f.

(d) Find f^{-1}, the inverse of f.

(e) Use f^{-1} to confirm the range of f found in part (c). From the domain of f, find the range of f^{-1}.

(f) Graph f^{-1}.

Solution

(a) The domain of f consists of all x for which $x - 2 > 0$ or, equivalently, $x > 2$. The domain of f is $\{x \mid x > 2\}$ or $(2, \infty)$.

(b) To obtain the graph of $y = -\ln(x - 2)$, we begin with the graph of $y = \ln x$ and use transformations. See Figure 39.

Figure 39

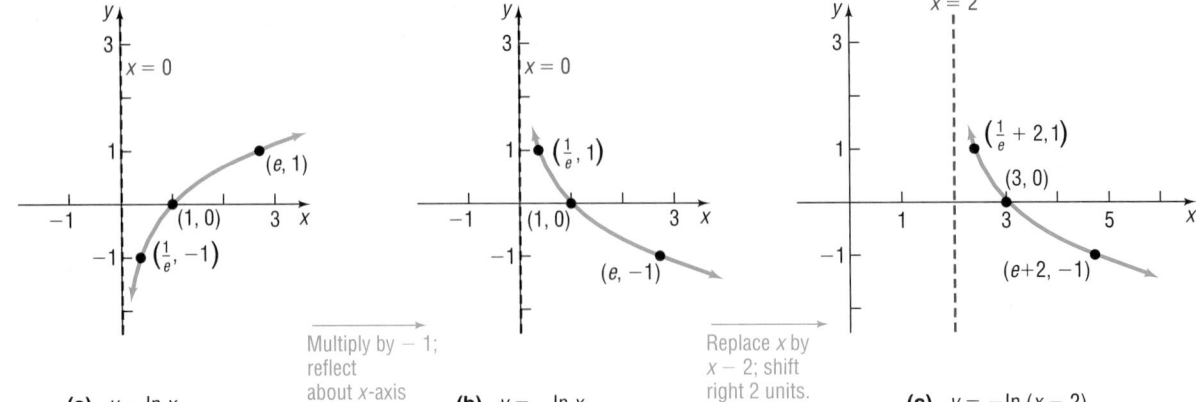

(c) The range of $f(x) = -\ln(x - 2)$ is the set of all real numbers. The vertical asymptote is $x = 2$. [Do you see why? The original asymptote $(x = 0)$ is shifted to the right 2 units.]

(d) We begin with $y = -\ln(x - 2)$. The inverse function is defined (implicitly) by the equation

$$x = -\ln(y - 2)$$

We proceed to solve for y.

$$-x = \ln(y - 2) \quad \text{Isolate the logarithm.}$$
$$e^{-x} = y - 2 \quad \text{Change to an exponential expression.}$$
$$y = e^{-x} + 2 \quad \text{Solve for y.}$$

The inverse of f is $f^{-1}(x) = e^{-x} + 2$.

(e) The range of f is the domain of f^{-1}, which is the set of all real numbers, confirming what we found from the graph of f. The range of f^{-1} is the domain of f, which is $(2, \infty)$.

(f) To graph f^{-1}, we use the graph of f in Figure 39(c) and reflect it about the line $y = x$. See Figure 40. We could also graph $f^{-1}(x) = e^{-x} + 2$ using transformations.

Figure 40

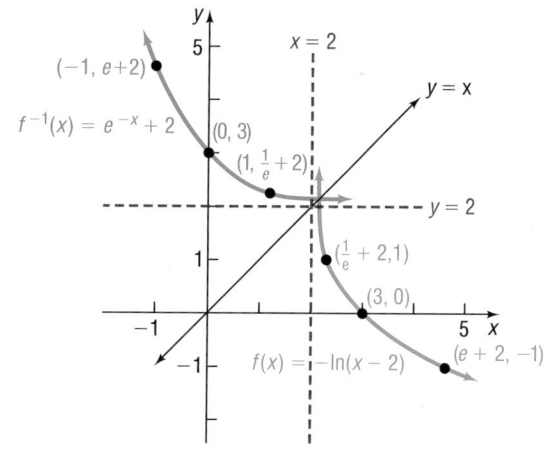

$f^{-1}(x) = e^{-x} + 2$

$(-1, e+2)$

$x = 2$

$y = x$

$(0, 3)$

$(1, \frac{1}{e} + 2)$

$y = 2$

$(\frac{1}{e} + 2, 1)$

$(3, 0)$

$f(x) = -\ln(x - 2)$

$(e + 2, -1)$

Figure 41

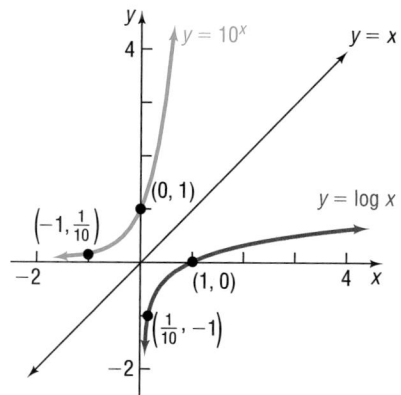

$y = 10^x$

$y = x$

$(0, 1)$

$y = \log x$

$(-1, \frac{1}{10})$

$(1, 0)$

$(\frac{1}{10}, -1)$

Now Work PROBLEM 71

If the base of a logarithmic function is the number 10, then we have the **common logarithm function.** If the base a of the logarithmic function is not indicated, it is understood to be 10. That is,

$$y = \log x \quad \text{if and only if} \quad x = 10^y$$

Since $y = \log x$ and the exponential function $y = 10^x$ are inverse functions, we can obtain the graph of $y = \log x$ by reflecting the graph of $y = 10^x$ about the line $y = x$. See Figure 41.

EXAMPLE 7   **Graphing a Logarithmic Function and Its Inverse**

(a) Find the domain of the logarithmic function $f(x) = 3 \log (x - 1)$.
(b) Graph f.
(c) From the graph, determine the range and vertical asymptote of f.
(d) Find f^{-1}, the inverse of f.
(e) Use f^{-1} to confirm the range of f found in part (c). From the domain of f, find the range of f^{-1}.
(f) Graph f^{-1}.

Solution (a) The domain of f consists of all x for which $x - 1 > 0$ or, equivalently, $x > 1$. The domain of f is $\{x \,|\, x > 1\}$ or $(1, \infty)$.

(b) To obtain the graph of $y = 3 \log(x - 1)$, we begin with the graph of $y = \log x$ and use transformations. See Figure 42 on page 290.

Figure 42

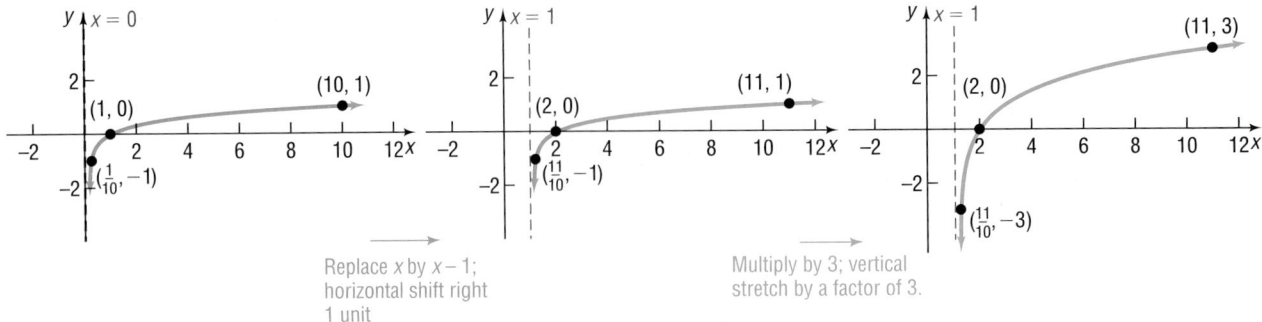

(a) $y = \log x$ **(b)** $y = \log(x - 1)$ **(c)** $y = 3\log(x - 1)$

(c) The range of $f(x) = 3\log(x - 1)$ is the set of all real numbers. The vertical asymptote is $x = 1$.

(d) We begin with $y = 3\log(x - 1)$. The inverse function is defined (implicitly) by the equation

$$x = 3\log(y - 1)$$

We proceed to solve for y.

$$\frac{x}{3} = \log(y - 1) \qquad \text{Isolate the logarithm.}$$
$$10^{x/3} = y - 1 \qquad \text{Change to an exponential expression.}$$
$$y = 10^{x/3} + 1 \qquad \text{Solve for } y.$$

The inverse of f is $f^{-1}(x) = 10^{x/3} + 1$.

(e) The range of f is the domain of f^{-1}, which is the set of all real numbers, confirming what we found from the graph of f. The range of f^{-1} is the domain of f, which is $(1, \infty)$.

(f) To graph f^{-1}, we use the graph of f in Figure 42(c) and reflect it about the line $y = x$. See Figure 43. We could also graph $f^{-1}(x) = 10^{x/3} + 1$ using transformations.

Figure 43

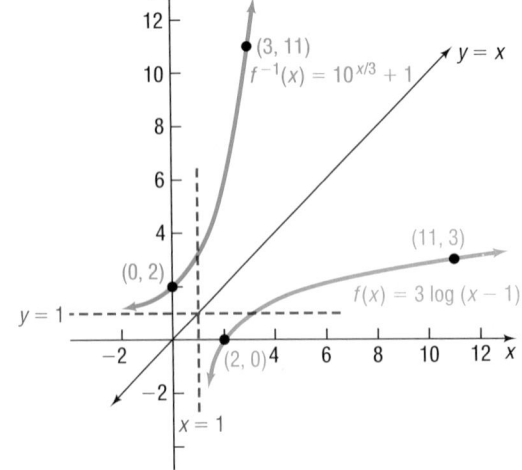

5 Solve Logarithmic Equations

Equations that contain logarithms are called **logarithmic equations.** Care must be taken when solving logarithmic equations algebraically. In the expression $\log_a M$, remember that a and M are positive and $a \neq 1$. Be sure to check each apparent solution in the original equation and discard any that are extraneous.

Some logarithmic equations can be solved by changing from a logarithmic expression to an exponential expression.

EXAMPLE 8   **Solving a Logarithmic Equation**

Solve: (a) $\log_3(4x - 7) = 2$ (b) $\log_x 64 = 2$

Solution   (a) We can obtain an exact solution by changing the logarithmic equation to exponential form.

$$\log_3(4x - 7) = 2$$
$$4x - 7 = 3^2 \quad \text{Change to an exponential equation.}$$
$$4x - 7 = 9$$
$$4x = 16$$
$$x = 4$$

✓ Check: $\log_3(4x - 7) = \log_3(4 \cdot 4 - 7) = \log_3 9 = 2 \quad 3^2 = 9$

The solution set is {4}.

(b) We can obtain an exact solution by changing the logarithmic equation to exponential form.

$$\log_x 64 = 2$$
$$x^2 = 64 \qquad \text{Change to an exponential equation.}$$
$$x = \pm\sqrt{64} = \pm 8 \quad \text{Square Root Method}$$

The base of a logarithm is always positive. As a result, we discard -8. We check the solution 8.

✓ Check: $\log_8 64 = 2 \quad 8^2 = 64$

The solution set is {8}.

EXAMPLE 9   **Using Logarithms to Solve Exponential Equations**

Solve: $e^{2x} = 5$

Solution   We can obtain an exact solution by changing the exponential equation to logarithmic form.

$$e^{2x} = 5$$
$$\ln 5 = 2x \quad \text{Change to a logarithmic equation using the}$$
$$\text{fact that if } e^y = x \text{ then } y = \ln x.$$

$$x = \frac{\ln 5}{2} \quad \text{Exact solution}$$

$$\approx 0.805 \quad \text{Approximate solution}$$

The solution set is $\left\{\dfrac{\ln 5}{2}\right\}$.

Now Work PROBLEMS 87 AND 99

EXAMPLE 10	Alcohol and Driving

The blood alcohol concentration (BAC) is the amount of alcohol in a person's bloodstream. A BAC of 0.04% means that a person has 4 parts alcohol per 10,000 parts blood in the body. Relative risk is defined as the likelihood of one event occurring divided by the likelihood of a second event occurring. For example, if an individual with a BAC of 0.02% is 1.4 times as likely to have a car accident as an individual who has not been drinking, the relative risk of an accident with a BAC of 0.02% is 1.4. Recent medical research suggests that the relative risk R of having an accident while driving a car can be modeled by the equation

$$R = e^{kx}$$

where x is the percent of concentration of alcohol in the bloodstream and k is a constant.

(a) Research indicates that the relative risk of a person having an accident with a BAC of 0.02% is 1.4. Find the constant k in the equation.

(b) Using this value of k, what is the relative risk if the concentration is 0.17%?

(c) Using this same value of k, what BAC corresponds to a relative risk of 100?

(d) If the law asserts that anyone with a relative risk of 5 or more should not have driving privileges, at what concentration of alcohol in the bloodstream should a driver be arrested and charged with a DUI (driving under the influence)?

Solution

(a) For a concentration of alcohol in the blood of 0.02% and a relative risk of 1.4, we let $x = 0.02$ and $R = 1.4$ in the equation and solve for k.

$$R = e^{kx}$$
$$1.4 = e^{k(0.02)} \qquad R = 1.4; x = 0.02$$
$$0.02k = \ln 1.4 \qquad \text{Change to a logarithmic expression.}$$
$$k = \frac{\ln 1.4}{0.02} \approx 16.82 \quad \text{Solve for } k.$$

(b) For a concentration of 0.17%, we have $x = 0.17$. Using $k = 16.82$ in the equation, we find the relative risk R to be

$$R = e^{kx} = e^{(16.82)(0.17)} \approx 17.5$$

For a concentration of alcohol in the blood of 0.17%, the relative risk of an accident is about 17.5. That is, a person with a BAC of 0.17% is 17.5 times as likely to have a car accident as a person with no alcohol in the bloodstream.

(c) For a relative risk of 100, we have $R = 100$. Using $k = 16.82$ in the equation $R = e^{kx}$, we find the concentration x of alcohol in the blood obeys

$$100 = e^{16.82x} \qquad R = e^{kx}, R = 100; k = 16.82$$
$$16.82x = \ln 100 \qquad \text{Change to a logarithmic expression.}$$
$$x = \frac{\ln 100}{16.82} \approx 0.27 \quad \text{Solve for } x.$$

For a concentration of alcohol in the blood of 0.27%, the relative risk of an accident is 100.

NOTE A BAC of 0.30% results in a loss of consciousness in most people. ∎

(d) For a relative risk of 5, we have $R = 5$. Using $k = 16.82$ in the equation $R = e^{kx}$, we find the concentration x of alcohol in the bloodstream obeys

$$5 = e^{16.82x}$$
$$16.82x = \ln 5$$
$$x = \frac{\ln 5}{16.82} \approx 0.096$$

NOTE Most states use 0.08% or 0.10% as the blood alcohol content at which a DUI citation is given. ∎

A driver with a BAC of 0.096% or more should be arrested and charged with DUI.

SUMMARY Properties of the Logarithmic Function

$f(x) = \log_a x, \quad a > 1$
($y = \log_a x$ means $x = a^y$)

Domain: the interval $(0, \infty)$; Range: the interval $(-\infty, \infty)$
x-intercept: 1; y-intercept: none; vertical asymptote: $x = 0$ (y-axis); increasing; one-to-one
See Figure 44(a) for a typical graph.

$f(x) = \log_a x, \quad 0 < a < 1$
($y = \log_a x$ means $x = a^y$)

Domain: the interval $(0, \infty)$; Range: the interval $(-\infty, \infty)$
x-intercept: 1; y-intercept: none; vertical asymptote: $x = 0$ (y-axis); decreasing; one-to-one
See Figure 44(b) for a typical graph.

Figure 44

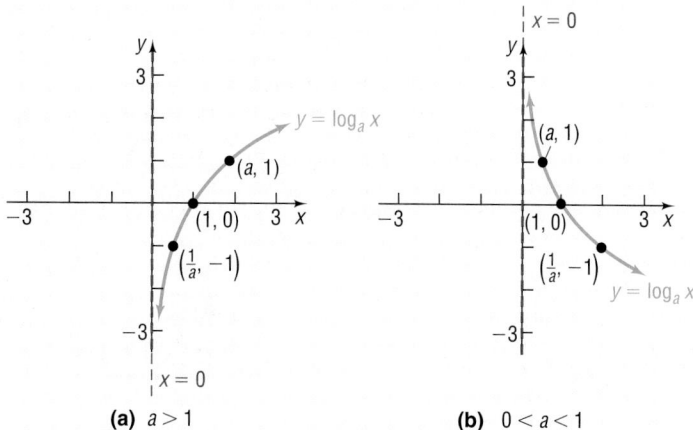

(a) $a > 1$ **(b)** $0 < a < 1$

5.4 Assess Your Understanding

'Are You Prepared?' *Answers are given at the end of these exercises. If you get a wrong answer, read the pages listed in red.*

1. Solve the inequality: $3x - 7 \le 8 - 2x$ (pp. A81–A82)

2. Solve the inequality: $x^2 - x - 6 > 0$ (pp. 164–166)

3. Solve the inequality: $\dfrac{x - 1}{x + 4} > 0$ (pp. 215–217)

Concepts and Vocabulary

4. The domain of the logarithmic function $f(x) = \log_a x$ is _____.

5. The graph of every logarithmic function $f(x) = \log_a x$, $a > 0, a \ne 1$, passes through three points: _____, _____, and _____.

6. If the graph of a logarithmic function $f(x) = \log_a x$, $a > 0, a \ne 1$, is increasing, then its base must be larger than _____.

7. *True or False* If $y = \log_a x$, then $y = a^x$.

8. *True or False* The graph of $f(x) = \log_a x, a > 0, a \ne 1$, has an x-intercept equal to 1 and no y-intercept.

Skill Building

In Problems 9–16, change each exponential statement to an equivalent statement involving a logarithm.

9. $9 = 3^2$ **10.** $16 = 4^2$ **11.** $a^2 = 1.6$ **12.** $a^3 = 2.1$

13. $2^x = 7.2$ **14.** $3^x = 4.6$ **15.** $e^x = 8$ **16.** $e^{2.2} = M$

In Problems 17–24, change each logarithmic statement to an equivalent statement involving an exponent.

17. $\log_2 8 = 3$ **18.** $\log_3\left(\dfrac{1}{9}\right) = -2$ **19.** $\log_a 3 = 6$ **20.** $\log_b 4 = 2$

21. $\log_3 2 = x$ **22.** $\log_2 6 = x$ **23.** $\ln 4 = x$ **24.** $\ln x = 4$

In Problems 25–36, find the exact value of each logarithm without using a calculator.

25. $\log_2 1$

26. $\log_8 8$

27. $\log_5 25$

28. $\log_3\left(\dfrac{1}{9}\right)$

29. $\log_{1/2} 16$

30. $\log_{1/3} 9$

31. $\log_{10} \sqrt{10}$

32. $\log_5 \sqrt[3]{25}$

33. $\log_{\sqrt{2}} 4$

34. $\log_{\sqrt{3}} 9$

35. $\ln \sqrt{e}$

36. $\ln e^3$

In Problems 37–48, find the domain of each function.

37. $f(x) = \ln(x - 3)$

38. $g(x) = \ln(x - 1)$

39. $F(x) = \log_2 x^2$

40. $H(x) = \log_5 x^3$

41. $f(x) = 3 - 2\log_4\left[\dfrac{x}{2} - 5\right]$

42. $g(x) = 8 + 5\ln(2x + 3)$

43. $f(x) = \ln\left(\dfrac{1}{x + 1}\right)$

44. $g(x) = \ln\left(\dfrac{1}{x - 5}\right)$

45. $g(x) = \log_5\left(\dfrac{x + 1}{x}\right)$

46. $h(x) = \log_3\left(\dfrac{x}{x - 1}\right)$

47. $f(x) = \sqrt{\ln x}$

48. $g(x) = \dfrac{1}{\ln x}$

In Problems 49–56, use a calculator to evaluate each expression. Round your answer to three decimal places.

49. $\ln\dfrac{5}{3}$

50. $\dfrac{\ln 5}{3}$

51. $\dfrac{\ln\dfrac{10}{3}}{0.04}$

52. $\dfrac{\ln\dfrac{2}{3}}{-0.1}$

53. $\dfrac{\ln 4 + \ln 2}{\log 4 + \log 2}$

54. $\dfrac{\log 15 + \log 20}{\ln 15 + \ln 20}$

55. $\dfrac{2\ln 5 + \log 50}{\log 4 - \ln 2}$

56. $\dfrac{3\log 80 - \ln 5}{\log 5 + \ln 20}$

57. Find a so that the graph of $f(x) = \log_a x$ contains the point $(2, 2)$.

58. Find a so that the graph of $f(x) = \log_a x$ contains the point $\left(\dfrac{1}{2}, -4\right)$.

In Problems 59–62, graph each function and its inverse on the same Cartesian plane.

59. $f(x) = 3^x; f^{-1}(x) = \log_3 x$

60. $f(x) = 4^x; f^{-1}(x) = \log_4 x$

61. $f(x) = \left(\dfrac{1}{2}\right)^x; f^{-1}(x) = \log_{\frac{1}{2}} x$

62. $f(x) = \left(\dfrac{1}{3}\right)^x; f^{-1}(x) = \log_{\frac{1}{3}} x$

In Problems 63–70, the graph of a logarithmic function is given. Match each graph to one of the following functions:

(a) $y = \log_3 x$

(b) $y = \log_3(-x)$

(c) $y = -\log_3 x$

(d) $y = -\log_3(-x)$

(e) $y = \log_3 x - 1$

(f) $y = \log_3(x - 1)$

(g) $y = \log_3(1 - x)$

(h) $y = 1 - \log_3 x$

63.

64.

65.

66.

67.

68.

69.

70.

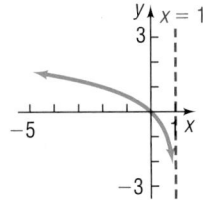

In Problems 71–86, use the given function f to:

(a) Find the domain of f.

(b) Graph f.

(c) From the graph, determine the range and any asymptotes of f.

(d) Find f^{-1}, the inverse of f.
(e) Use f^{-1} to confirm the range of f found in part (c). From the domain of f, find the range of f^{-1}.
(f) Graph f^{-1}.

71. $f(x) = \ln(x + 4)$ **72.** $f(x) = \ln(x - 3)$ **73.** $f(x) = 2 + \ln x$ **74.** $f(x) = -\ln(-x)$

75. $f(x) = \ln(2x) - 3$ **76.** $f(x) = -2\ln(x + 1)$ **77.** $f(x) = \log(x - 4) + 2$ **78.** $f(x) = \frac{1}{2}\log x - 5$

79. $f(x) = \frac{1}{2}\log(2x)$ **80.** $f(x) = \log(-2x)$ **81.** $f(x) = 3 + \log_3(x + 2)$ **82.** $f(x) = 2 - \log_3(x + 1)$

83. $f(x) = e^{x+2} - 3$ **84.** $f(x) = 3e^x + 2$ **85.** $f(x) = 2^{x/3} + 4$ **86.** $f(x) = -3^{x+1}$

In Problems 87–110, solve each equation.

87. $\log_3 x = 2$ **88.** $\log_5 x = 3$ **89.** $\log_2(2x + 1) = 3$ **90.** $\log_3(3x - 2) = 2$

91. $\log_x 4 = 2$ **92.** $\log_x\left(\frac{1}{8}\right) = 3$ **93.** $\ln e^x = 5$ **94.** $\ln e^{-2x} = 8$

95. $\log_4 64 = x$ **96.** $\log_5 625 = x$ **97.** $\log_3 243 = 2x + 1$ **98.** $\log_6 36 = 5x + 3$

99. $e^{3x} = 10$ **100.** $e^{-2x} = \frac{1}{3}$ **101.** $e^{2x+5} = 8$ **102.** $e^{-2x+1} = 13$

103. $\log_3(x^2 + 1) = 2$ **104.** $\log_5(x^2 + x + 4) = 2$ **105.** $\log_2 8^x = -3$ **106.** $\log_3 3^x = -1$

107. $5e^{0.2x} = 7$ **108.** $8 \cdot 10^{2x-7} = 3$ **109.** $2 \cdot 10^{2-x} = 5$ **110.** $4e^{x+1} = 5$

Mixed Practice

111. Suppose that $G(x) = \log_3(2x + 1) - 2$.
(a) What is the domain of G?
(b) What is $G(40)$? What point is on the graph of G?
(c) If $G(x) = 3$, what is x? What point is on the graph of G?
(d) What is the zero of G?

112. Suppose that $F(x) = \log_2(x + 1) - 3$.
(a) What is the domain of F?
(b) What is $F(7)$? What point is on the graph of F?
(c) If $F(x) = -1$, what is x? What point is on the graph of F?
(d) What is the zero of F?

In Problems 113–116, graph each function. Based on the graph, state the domain and the range and find any intercepts.

113. $f(x) = \begin{cases} \ln(-x) & \text{if } x < 0 \\ \ln x & \text{if } x > 0 \end{cases}$

114. $f(x) = \begin{cases} \ln(-x) & \text{if } x \leq -1 \\ -\ln(-x) & \text{if } -1 < x < 0 \end{cases}$

115. $f(x) = \begin{cases} -\ln x & \text{if } 0 < x < 1 \\ \ln x & \text{if } x \geq 1 \end{cases}$

116. $f(x) = \begin{cases} \ln x & \text{if } 0 < x < 1 \\ -\ln x & \text{if } x \geq 1 \end{cases}$

Applications and Extensions

117. Chemistry The pH of a chemical solution is given by the formula

$$\text{pH} = -\log_{10}[\text{H}^+]$$

where $[\text{H}^+]$ is the concentration of hydrogen ions in moles per liter. Values of pH range from 0 (acidic) to 14 (alkaline).
(a) What is the pH of a solution for which $[\text{H}^+]$ is 0.1?
(b) What is the pH of a solution for which $[\text{H}^+]$ is 0.01?
(c) What is the pH of a solution for which $[\text{H}^+]$ is 0.001?
(d) What happens to pH as the hydrogen ion concentration decreases?
(e) Determine the hydrogen ion concentration of an orange (pH = 3.5).
(f) Determine the hydrogen ion concentration of human blood (pH = 7.4).

118. Diversity Index **Shannon's diversity index** is a measure of the diversity of a population. The diversity index is given by the formula

$$H = -(p_1 \log p_1 + p_2 \log p_2 + \cdots + p_n \log p_n)$$

where p_1 is the proportion of the population that is species 1, p_2 is the proportion of the population that is species 2, and so on.
(a) According to the U.S. Census Bureau, the distribution of race in the United States in 2000 was as follows:

Race	Proportion
American Indian or Native Alaskan	0.014
Asian	0.041
Black or African American	0.128
Hispanic	0.124
Native Hawaiian or Pacific Islander	0.003
White	0.690

Source: U.S. Census Bureau

Compute the diversity index of the United States in 2000.

(b) The largest value of the diversity index is given by $H_{max} = \log(S)$, where S is the number of categories of race. Compute H_{max}.

(c) The **evenness ratio** is given by $E_H = \dfrac{H}{H_{max}}$, where $0 \le E_H \le 1$. If $E_H = 1$, there is complete evenness. Compute the evenness ratio for the United States.

(d) Obtain the distribution of race for the United States in 1990 from the Census Bureau. Compute Shannon's diversity index. Is the United States becoming more diverse? Why?

119. **Atmospheric Pressure** The atmospheric pressure p on a balloon or an aircraft decreases with increasing height. This pressure, measured in millimeters of mercury, is related to the height h (in kilometers) above sea level by the function

$$p(h) = 760e^{-0.145h}$$

(a) Find the height of an aircraft if the atmospheric pressure is 320 millimeters of mercury.

(b) Find the height of a mountain if the atmospheric pressure is 667 millimeters of mercury.

120. **Healing of Wounds** The normal healing of wounds can be modeled by an exponential function. If A_0 represents the original area of the wound and if A equals the area of the wound, then the function

$$A(n) = A_0 e^{-0.35n}$$

describes the area of a wound after n days following an injury when no infection is present to retard the healing. Suppose that a wound initially had an area of 100 square millimeters.

(a) If healing is taking place, after how many days will the wound be one-half its original size?

(b) How long before the wound is 10% of its original size?

121. **Exponential Probability** Between 12:00 PM and 1:00 PM, cars arrive at Citibank's drive-thru at the rate of 6 cars per hour (0.1 car per minute). The following formula from statistics can be used to determine the probability that a car will arrive within t minutes of 12:00 PM.

$$F(t) = 1 - e^{-0.1t}$$

(a) Determine how many minutes are needed for the probability to reach 50%.

(b) Determine how many minutes are needed for the probability to reach 80%.

(c) Is it possible for the probability to equal 100%? Explain.

122. **Exponential Probability** Between 5:00 PM and 6:00 PM, cars arrive at Jiffy Lube at the rate of 9 cars per hour (0.15 car per minute). The following formula from statistics can be used

to determine the probability that a car will arrive within t minutes of 5:00 PM.

$$F(t) = 1 - e^{-0.15t}$$

(a) Determine how many minutes are needed for the probability to reach 50%.

(b) Determine how many minutes are needed for the probability to reach 80%.

123. **Drug Medication** The formula

$$D = 5e^{-0.4h}$$

can be used to find the number of milligrams D of a certain drug that is in a patient's bloodstream h hours after the drug was administered. When the number of milligrams reaches 2, the drug is to be administered again. What is the time between injections?

124. **Spreading of Rumors** A model for the number N of people in a college community who have heard a certain rumor is

$$N = P(1 - e^{-0.15d})$$

where P is the total population of the community and d is the number of days that have elapsed since the rumor began. In a community of 1000 students, how many days will elapse before 450 students have heard the rumor?

125. **Current in a RL Circuit** The equation governing the amount of current I (in amperes) after time t (in seconds) in a simple RL circuit consisting of a resistance R (in ohms), an inductance L (in henrys), and an electromotive force E (in volts) is

$$I = \frac{E}{R}[1 - e^{-(R/L)t}]$$

If $E = 12$ volts, $R = 10$ ohms, and $L = 5$ henrys, how long does it take to obtain a current of 0.5 ampere? Of 1.0 ampere? Graph the equation.

126. **Learning Curve** Psychologists sometimes use the function

$$L(t) = A(1 - e^{-kt})$$

to measure the amount L learned at time t. The number A represents the amount to be learned, and the number k measures the rate of learning. Suppose that a student has an amount A of 200 vocabulary words to learn. A psychologist determines that the student learned 20 vocabulary words after 5 minutes.

(a) Determine the rate of learning k.

(b) Approximately how many words will the student have learned after 10 minutes?

(c) After 15 minutes?

(d) How long does it take for the student to learn 180 words?

Loudness of Sound *Problems 127–130 use the following discussion: The **loudness** $L(x)$, measured in decibels, of a sound of intensity x, measured in watts per square meter, is defined as $L(x) = 10 \log \dfrac{x}{I_0}$, where $I_0 = 10^{-12}$ watt per square meter is the least intense sound that a human ear can detect. Determine the loudness, in decibels, of each of the following sounds.*

127. Normal conversation: intensity of $x = 10^{-7}$ watt per square meter

128. Amplified rock music: intensity of 10^{-1} watt per square meter

129. Heavy city traffic: intensity of $x = 10^{-3}$ watt per square meter

130. Diesel truck traveling 40 miles per hour 50 feet away: intensity 10 times that of a passenger car traveling 50 miles per hour 50 feet away whose loudness is 70 decibels

The Richter Scale *Problems 131 and 132 use the following discussion: The **Richter scale** is one way of converting seismographic readings into numbers that provide an easy reference for measuring the magnitude M of an earthquake. All earthquakes are compared to a **zero-level earthquake** whose seismographic reading measures 0.001 millimeter at a distance of 100 kilometers from the epicenter. An earthquake whose seismographic reading measures x millimeters has **magnitude** M(x), given by*

$$M(x) = \log\left(\frac{x}{x_0}\right)$$

where $x_0 = 10^{-3}$ is the reading of a zero-level earthquake the same distance from its epicenter. In Problems 131 and 132, determine the magnitude of each earthquake.

131. Magnitude of an Earthquake Mexico City in 1985: seismographic reading of 125,892 millimeters 100 kilometers from the center

132. Magnitude of an Earthquake San Francisco in 1906: seismographic reading of 50,119 millimeters 100 kilometers from the center

133. Alcohol and Driving The concentration of alcohol in a person's bloodstream is measurable. Suppose that the relative risk R of having an accident while driving a car can be modeled by the equation

$$R = e^{kx}$$

where x is the percent of concentration of alcohol in the bloodstream and k is a constant.

(a) Suppose that a concentration of alcohol in the bloodstream of 0.03 percent results in a relative risk of an accident of 1.4. Find the constant k in the equation.

(b) Using this value of k, what is the relative risk if the concentration is 0.17 percent?

(c) Using the same value of k, what concentration of alcohol corresponds to a relative risk of 100?

(d) If the law asserts that anyone with a relative risk of having an accident of 5 or more should not have driving privileges, at what concentration of alcohol in the bloodstream should a driver be arrested and charged with a DUI?

(e) Compare this situation with that of Example 10. If you were a lawmaker, which situation would you support? Give your reasons.

Discussion and Writing

134. Is there any function of the form $y = x^\alpha, 0 < \alpha < 1$, that increases more slowly than a logarithmic function whose base is greater than 1? Explain.

135. In the definition of the logarithmic function, the base a is not allowed to equal 1. Why?

136. Critical Thinking In buying a new car, one consideration might be how well the price of the car holds up over time. Different makes of cars have different depreciation rates. One way to compute a depreciation rate for a car is given here. Suppose that the current prices of a certain automobile are as shown in the table.

	Age in Years				
New	**1**	**2**	**3**	**4**	**5**
$38,000	$36,600	$32,400	$28,750	$25,400	$21,200

Use the formula New = Old(e^{Rt}) to find R, the annual depreciation rate, for a specific time t. When might be the best time to trade in the car? Consult the NADA ("blue") book and compare two like models that you are interested in. Which has the better depreciation rate?

'Are You Prepared?' Answers

1. $x \le 3$ **2.** $x < -2$ or $x > 3$ **3.** $x < -4$ or $x > 1$

5.5 Properties of Logarithms

OBJECTIVES 1 Work with the Properties of Logarithms (p. 297)

2 Write a Logarithmic Expression as a Sum or Difference of Logarithms (p. 299)

3 Write a Logarithmic Expression as a Single Logarithm (p. 300)

4 Evaluate Logarithms Whose Base Is Neither 10 Nor e (p. 301)

5 Graph Logarithmic Functions Whose Base Is Neither 10 Nor e (p. 303)

1 Work with the Properties of Logarithms

Logarithms have some very useful properties that can be derived directly from its definition and the laws of exponents.

EXAMPLE 1   Establishing Properties of Logarithms

(a) Show that $\log_a 1 = 0$.   (b) Show that $\log_a a = 1$.

Solution (a) This fact was established when we graphed $y = \log_a x$ (see Figure 35). To show the result algebraically, let $y = \log_a 1$. Then

$$y = \log_a 1$$
$$a^y = 1 \qquad \textit{Change to an exponential expression.}$$
$$a^y = a^0 \qquad \textit{$a^0 = 1$ since $a > 0, a \neq 1$}$$
$$y = 0 \qquad \textit{Solve for y.}$$
$$\log_a 1 = 0 \qquad \textit{$y = \log_a 1$}$$

(b) Let $y = \log_a a$. Then

$$y = \log_a a$$
$$a^y = a \qquad \textit{Change to an exponential expression.}$$
$$a^y = a^1 \qquad \textit{$a = a^1$}$$
$$y = 1 \qquad \textit{Solve for y.}$$
$$\log_a a = 1 \qquad \textit{$y = \log_a a$}$$

To summarize:

$$\log_a 1 = 0 \qquad \log_a a = 1$$

THEOREM

Properties of Logarithms

In the properties given next, M and a are positive real numbers, $a \neq 1$, and r is any real number.

The number $\log_a M$ is the exponent to which a must be raised to obtain M. That is,

$$a^{\log_a M} = M \tag{1}$$

The logarithm to the base a of a raised to a power equals that power. That is,

$$\log_a a^r = r \tag{2}$$

The proof uses the fact that $y = a^x$ and $y = \log_a x$ are inverses.

Proof of Property (1) For inverse functions,

$$f(f^{-1}(x)) = x \quad \text{for all } x \text{ in the domain of } f^{-1}$$

Using $f(x) = a^x$ and $f^{-1}(x) = \log_a x$, we find

$$f(f^{-1}(x)) = a^{\log_a x} = x \quad \text{for } x > 0$$

Now let $x = M$ to obtain $a^{\log_a M} = M$, where $M > 0$. ∎

Proof of Property (2) For inverse functions,

$$f^{-1}(f(x)) = x \quad \text{for all } x \text{ in the domain of } f$$

Using $f(x) = a^x$ and $f^{-1}(x) = \log_a x$, we find

$$f^{-1}(f(x)) = \log_a a^x = x \quad \text{for all real numbers } x$$

Now let $x = r$ to obtain $\log_a a^r = r$, where r is any real number. ∎

| EXAMPLE 2 | **Using Properties (1) and (2)** |

(a) $2^{\log_2 \pi} = \pi$ (b) $\log_{0.2} 0.2^{-\sqrt{2}} = -\sqrt{2}$ (c) $\ln e^{kt} = kt$

◾

Now Work PROBLEM 9

Other useful properties of logarithms are given next.

THEOREM

Properties of Logarithms

In the following properties, M, N, and a are positive real numbers, $a \neq 1$, and r is any real number.

The Log of a Product Equals the Sum of the Logs

$$\log_a(MN) = \log_a M + \log_a N \qquad (3)$$

The Log of a Quotient Equals the Difference of the Logs

$$\log_a\left(\frac{M}{N}\right) = \log_a M - \log_a N \qquad (4)$$

The Log of a Power Equals the Product of the Power and the Log

$$\log_a M^r = r \log_a M \qquad (5)$$

We shall derive properties (3) and (5) and leave the derivation of property (4) as an exercise (see Problem 103).

Proof of Property (3) Let $A = \log_a M$ and let $B = \log_a N$. These expressions are equivalent to the exponential expressions

$$a^A = M \quad \text{and} \quad a^B = N$$

Now

$$
\begin{aligned}
\log_a(MN) = \log_a(a^A a^B) &= \log_a a^{A+B} &&\text{Law of Exponents} \\
&= A + B &&\text{Property (2) of logarithms} \\
&= \log_a M + \log_a N &&
\end{aligned}
$$

◾

Proof of Property (5) Let $A = \log_a M$. This expression is equivalent to

$$a^A = M$$

Now

$$
\begin{aligned}
\log_a M^r = \log_a(a^A)^r &= \log_a a^{rA} &&\text{Law of Exponents} \\
&= rA &&\text{Property (2) of logarithms} \\
&= r \log_a M &&
\end{aligned}
$$

◾

Now Work PROBLEM 13

2 Write a Logarithmic Expression as a Sum or Difference of Logarithms

Logarithms can be used to transform products into sums, quotients into differences, and powers into factors. Such transformations prove useful in certain types of calculus problems.

EXAMPLE 3 | **Writing a Logarithmic Expression as a Sum of Logarithms**

Write $\log_a(x\sqrt{x^2 + 1})$, $x > 0$, as a sum of logarithms. Express all powers as factors.

Solution

$$\log_a(x\sqrt{x^2 + 1}) = \log_a x + \log_a \sqrt{x^2 + 1} \qquad \log_a(M \cdot N) = \log_a M + \log_a N$$

$$= \log_a x + \log_a(x^2 + 1)^{1/2}$$

$$= \log_a x + \frac{1}{2}\log_a(x^2 + 1) \qquad \log_a M^r = r\log_a M$$

EXAMPLE 4 | **Writing a Logarithmic Expression as a Difference of Logarithms**

Write

$$\ln \frac{x^2}{(x - 1)^3} \qquad x > 1$$

as a difference of logarithms. Express all powers as factors.

Solution

$$\ln \frac{x^2}{(x - 1)^3} = \ln x^2 - \ln(x - 1)^3 = 2\ln x - 3\ln(x - 1)$$

$$\uparrow \qquad\qquad\qquad \uparrow$$

$$\log_a\left(\frac{M}{N}\right) = \log_a M - \log_a N \qquad \log_a M^r = r\log_a M$$

EXAMPLE 5 | **Writing a Logarithmic Expression as a Sum and Difference of Logarithms**

Write

$$\log_a \frac{\sqrt{x^2 + 1}}{x^3(x + 1)^4} \qquad x > 0$$

as a sum and difference of logarithms. Express all powers as factors.

Solution

WARNING In using properties (3) through (5), be careful about the values that the variable may assume. For example, the domain of the variable for $\log_a x$ is $x > 0$ and for $\log_a(x - 1)$ it is $x > 1$. If we add these functions, the domain is $x > 1$. That is, the equality

$$\log_a x + \log_a(x - 1) = \log_a[x(x - 1)]$$

is true only for $x > 1$. ∎

$$\log_a \frac{\sqrt{x^2 + 1}}{x^3(x + 1)^4} = \log_a \sqrt{x^2 + 1} - \log_a[x^3(x + 1)^4] \qquad \text{Property (4)}$$

$$= \log_a \sqrt{x^2 + 1} - [\log_a x^3 + \log_a(x + 1)^4] \qquad \text{Property (3)}$$

$$= \log_a(x^2 + 1)^{1/2} - \log_a x^3 - \log_a(x + 1)^4$$

$$= \frac{1}{2}\log_a(x^2 + 1) - 3\log_a x - 4\log_a(x + 1) \qquad \text{Property (5)}$$

━━━ **Now Work** PROBLEM 45

3 Write a Logarithmic Expression as a Single Logarithm

Another use of properties (3) through (5) is to write sums and/or differences of logarithms with the same base as a single logarithm. This skill will be needed to solve certain logarithmic equations discussed in the next section.

EXAMPLE 6 | **Writing Expressions as a Single Logarithm**

Write each of the following as a single logarithm.

(a) $\log_a 7 + 4\log_a 3$

(b) $\frac{2}{3}\ln 8 - \ln(3^4 - 8)$

(c) $\log_a x + \log_a 9 + \log_a(x^2 + 1) - \log_a 5$

Solution (a) $\log_a 7 + 4 \log_a 3 = \log_a 7 + \log_a 3^4$ $r \log_a M = \log_a M^r$

$$= \log_a 7 + \log_a 81$$

$$= \log_a(7 \cdot 81)$$ $\log_a M + \log_a N = \log_a(M \cdot N)$

$$= \log_a 567$$

(b) $\dfrac{2}{3} \ln 8 - \ln(3^4 - 8) = \ln 8^{2/3} - \ln(81 - 8)$ $r \log_a M = \log_a M^r$

$$= \ln 4 - \ln 73$$ $8^{2/3} = (\sqrt[3]{8})^2 = 2^2 = 4$

$$= \ln\left(\frac{4}{73}\right)$$ $\log_a M - \log_a N = \log_a\left(\dfrac{M}{N}\right)$

(c) $\log_a x + \log_a 9 + \log_a(x^2 + 1) - \log_a 5 = \log_a(9x) + \log_a(x^2 + 1) - \log_a 5$

$$= \log_a[9x(x^2 + 1)] - \log_a 5$$

$$= \log_a\left[\frac{9x(x^2 + 1)}{5}\right]$$

WARNING A common error made by some students is to express the logarithm of a sum as the sum of logarithms.

$$\log_a(M + N) \quad \textit{is not equal to} \quad \log_a M + \log_a N$$

Correct statement $\log_a(MN) = \log_a M + \log_a N$ Property (3)

Another common error is to express the difference of logarithms as the quotient of logarithms.

$$\log_a M - \log_a N \quad \textit{is not equal to} \quad \frac{\log_a M}{\log_a N}$$

Correct statement $\log_a M - \log_a N = \log_a\left(\dfrac{M}{N}\right)$ Property (4)

A third common error is to express a logarithm raised to a power as the product of the power times the logarithm.

$$(\log_a M)^r \quad \textit{is not equal to} \quad r \log_a M$$

Correct statement $\log_a M^r = r \log_a M$ Property (5)   ∎

Now Work PROBLEM 51

Two other properties of logarithms that we need to know are consequences of the fact that the logarithmic function $y = \log_a x$ is a one-to-one function.

THEOREM **Properties of Logarithms**

In the following properties, M, N, and a are positive real numbers, $a \neq 1$.

> If $M = N$, then $\log_a M = \log_a N$.   **(6)**
>
> If $\log_a M = \log_a N$, then $M = N$.   **(7)**

When property (6) is used, we start with the equation $M = N$ and say "take the logarithm of both sides" to obtain $\log_a M = \log_a N$.

Properties (6) and (7) are useful for solving *exponential and logarithmic equations*, a topic discussed in the next section.

4 Evaluate Logarithms Whose Base Is Neither 10 Nor *e*

Logarithms to the base 10, common logarithms, were used to facilitate arithmetic computations before the widespread use of calculators. (See the Historical Feature at the end of this section.) Natural logarithms, that is, logarithms whose base is the number *e*, remain very important because they arise frequently in the study of natural phenomena.

Common logarithms are usually abbreviated by writing **log,** with the base understood to be 10, just as natural logarithms are abbreviated by **ln,** with the base understood to be e.

Most calculators have both $\boxed{\log}$ and $\boxed{\ln}$ keys to calculate the common logarithm and natural logarithm of a number. Let's look at an example to see how to approximate logarithms having a base other than 10 or e.

EXAMPLE 7	**Approximating a Logarithm Whose Base Is Neither 10 Nor e**

Approximate $\log_2 7$. Round the answer to four decimal places.

Solution   Let $y = \log_2 7$. Then $2^y = 7$, so

$$2^y = 7$$
$$\ln 2^y = \ln 7 \qquad \textit{Property (6)}$$
$$y \ln 2 = \ln 7 \qquad \textit{Property (5)}$$
$$y = \frac{\ln 7}{\ln 2} \qquad \textit{Exact value}$$
$$y \approx 2.8074 \qquad \textit{Approximate value rounded to four decimal places}$$

Example 7 shows how to approximate a logarithm whose base is 2 by changing to logarithms involving the base e. In general, we use the **Change-of-Base Formula.**

THEOREM   **Change-of-Base Formula**

If $a \neq 1$, $b \neq 1$, and M are positive real numbers, then

$$\boxed{\log_a M = \frac{\log_b M}{\log_b a}} \qquad (8)$$

Proof   We derive this formula as follows: Let $y = \log_a M$. Then

$$a^y = M$$
$$\log_b a^y = \log_b M \qquad \textit{Property (6)}$$
$$y \log_b a = \log_b M \qquad \textit{Property (5)}$$
$$y = \frac{\log_b M}{\log_b a} \qquad \textit{Solve for y.}$$
$$\log_a M = \frac{\log_b M}{\log_b a} \qquad y = \log_a M \qquad \blacksquare$$

Since calculators have keys only for $\boxed{\log}$ and $\boxed{\ln}$, in practice, the Change-of-Base Formula uses either $b = 10$ or $b = e$. That is,

$$\log_a M = \frac{\log M}{\log a} \quad \text{and} \quad \log_a M = \frac{\ln M}{\ln a} \qquad (9)$$

EXAMPLE 8	**Using the Change-of-Base Formula**

Approximate: (a) $\log_5 89$

                   (b) $\log_{\sqrt{2}} \sqrt{5}$

Round answers to four decimal places.

Solution (a) $\log_5 89 = \dfrac{\log 89}{\log 5} \approx \dfrac{1.949390007}{0.6989700043} \approx 2.7889$

or

$\log_5 89 = \dfrac{\ln 89}{\ln 5} \approx \dfrac{4.48863637}{1.609437912} \approx 2.7889$

(b) $\log_{\sqrt{2}} \sqrt{5} = \dfrac{\log \sqrt{5}}{\log \sqrt{2}} = \dfrac{\frac{1}{2}\log 5}{\frac{1}{2}\log 2} = \dfrac{\log 5}{\log 2} \approx 2.3219$

or

$\log_{\sqrt{2}} \sqrt{5} = \dfrac{\ln \sqrt{5}}{\ln \sqrt{2}} = \dfrac{\frac{1}{2}\ln 5}{\frac{1}{2}\ln 2} = \dfrac{\ln 5}{\ln 2} \approx 2.3219$

────── Now Work PROBLEMS 17 AND 65

5 Graph Logarithmic Functions Whose Base Is Neither 10 Nor *e*

We also use the Change-of-Base Formula to graph logarithmic functions whose base is neither 10 nor *e*.

EXAMPLE 9 | Graphing a Logarithmic Function Whose Base Is Neither 10 Nor *e*

Use a graphing utility to graph $y = \log_2 x$.

Figure 45

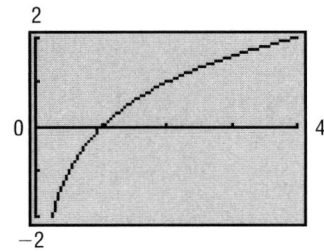

Solution Since graphing utilities only have logarithms with the base 10 or the base *e*, we need to use the Change-of-Base Formula to express $y = \log_2 x$ in terms of logarithms with base 10 or base *e*. We can graph either $y = \dfrac{\ln x}{\ln 2}$ or $y = \dfrac{\log x}{\log 2}$ to obtain the graph of $y = \log_2 x$. See Figure 45.

✓ Check: Verify that $y = \dfrac{\ln x}{\ln 2}$ and $y = \dfrac{\log x}{\log 2}$ result in the same graph by graphing each on the same screen.

────── Now Work PROBLEM 73

SUMMARY   Properties of Logarithms

In the list that follows, a, b, M, N, and r are real numbers. Also, $a > 0, a \neq 1, b > 0, b \neq 1, M > 0$, and $N > 0$.

Definition $y = \log_a x$ means $x = a^y$

Properties of logarithms

$\log_a 1 = 0; \quad \log_a a = 1$ $\log_a M^r = r \log_a M$

$a^{\log_a M} = M; \quad \log_a a^r = r$ If $M = N$, then $\log_a M = \log_a N$.

$\log_a(MN) = \log_a M + \log_a N$ If $\log_a M = \log_a N$, then $M = N$.

$\log_a\left(\dfrac{M}{N}\right) = \log_a M - \log_a N$

Change-of-Base Formula $\log_a M = \dfrac{\log_b M}{\log_b a}$

Historical Feature

John Napier (1550–1617)

Logarithms were invented about 1590 by John Napier (1550–1617) and Joost Bürgi (1552–1632), working independently. Napier, whose work had the greater influence, was a Scottish lord, a secretive man whose neighbors were inclined to believe him to be in league with the devil. His approach to logarithms was very different from ours; it was based on the relationship between arithmetic and geometric sequences, discussed in a later chapter, and not on the inverse function relationship of logarithms to exponential functions (described in

Section 5.4). Napier's tables, published in 1614, listed what would now be called *natural logarithms* of sines and were rather difficult to use. A London professor, Henry Briggs, became interested in the tables and visited Napier. In their conversations, they developed the idea of common logarithms, which were published in 1617. Their importance for calculation was immediately recognized, and by 1650 they were being printed as far away as China. They remained an important calculation tool until the advent of the inexpensive handheld calculator about 1972, which has decreased their calculational, but not their theoretical, importance.

A side effect of the invention of logarithms was the popularization of the decimal system of notation for real numbers.

5.5 Assess Your Understanding

Concepts and Vocabulary

1. The logarithm of a product equals the _____ of the logarithms.

2. If $\log_8 M = \dfrac{\log_5 7}{\log_5 8}$, then $M =$ _____.

3. $\log_a M^r =$ _____.

4. *True or False* $\ln(x + 3) - \ln(2x) = \dfrac{\ln(x + 3)}{\ln(2x)}$

5. *True or False* $\log_2(3x^4) = 4\log_2(3x)$

6. *True or False* $\log_2 16 = \dfrac{\ln 16}{\ln 2}$

Skill Building

In Problems 7–22, use properties of logarithms to find the exact value of each expression. Do not use a calculator.

7. $\log_3 3^{71}$

8. $\log_2 2^{-13}$

9. $\ln e^{-4}$

10. $\ln e^{\sqrt{2}}$

11. $2^{\log_2 7}$

12. $e^{\ln 8}$

13. $\log_8 2 + \log_8 4$

14. $\log_6 9 + \log_6 4$

15. $\log_6 18 - \log_6 3$

16. $\log_8 16 - \log_8 2$

17. $\log_2 6 \cdot \log_6 4$

18. $\log_3 8 \cdot \log_8 9$

19. $3^{\log_3 5 - \log_3 4}$

20. $5^{\log_5 6 + \log_5 7}$

21. $e^{\log_{e^2} 16}$

22. $e^{\log_{e^2} 9}$

In Problems 23–30, suppose that $\ln 2 = a$ and $\ln 3 = b$. Use properties of logarithms to write each logarithm in terms of a and b.

23. $\ln 6$

24. $\ln \dfrac{2}{3}$

25. $\ln 1.5$

26. $\ln 0.5$

27. $\ln 8$

28. $\ln 27$

29. $\ln \sqrt[5]{6}$

30. $\ln \sqrt[4]{\dfrac{2}{3}}$

In Problems 31–50, write each expression as a sum and/or difference of logarithms. Express powers as factors.

31. $\log_5(25x)$

32. $\log_3 \dfrac{x}{9}$

33. $\log_2 z^3$

34. $\log_7(x^5)$

35. $\ln(ex)$

36. $\ln \dfrac{e}{x}$

37. $\ln(xe^x)$

38. $\ln \dfrac{x}{e^x}$

39. $\log_a(u^2 v^3)$ $u > 0, v > 0$

40. $\log_2\left(\dfrac{a}{b^2}\right)$ $a > 0, b > 0$

41. $\ln\left(x^2\sqrt{1 - x}\right)$ $0 < x < 1$

42. $\ln\left(x\sqrt{1 + x^2}\right)$ $x > 0$

43. $\log_2\left(\dfrac{x^3}{x - 3}\right)$ $x > 3$

44. $\log_5\left(\dfrac{\sqrt[3]{x^2 + 1}}{x^2 - 1}\right)$ $x > 1$

45. $\log\left[\dfrac{x(x + 2)}{(x + 3)^2}\right]$ $x > 0$

46. $\log\left[\dfrac{x^3\sqrt{x + 1}}{(x - 2)^2}\right]$ $x > 2$

47. $\ln\left[\dfrac{x^2 - x - 2}{(x + 4)^2}\right]^{1/3}$ $x > 2$

48. $\ln\left[\dfrac{(x - 4)^2}{x^2 - 1}\right]^{2/3}$ $x > 4$

49. $\ln \dfrac{5x\sqrt{1 + 3x}}{(x - 4)^3}$ $x > 4$

50. $\ln\left[\dfrac{5x^2\sqrt[3]{1 - x}}{4(x + 1)^2}\right]$ $0 < x < 1$

In Problems 51–64, write each expression as a single logarithm.

51. $3\log_5 u + 4\log_5 v$

52. $2\log_3 u - \log_3 v$

53. $\log_3 \sqrt{x} - \log_3 x^3$

54. $\log_2\left(\dfrac{1}{x}\right) + \log_2\left(\dfrac{1}{x^2}\right)$

55. $\log_4(x^2 - 1) - 5\log_4(x + 1)$

56. $\log(x^2 + 3x + 2) - 2\log(x + 1)$

57. $\ln\left(\dfrac{x}{x-1}\right) + \ln\left(\dfrac{x+1}{x}\right) - \ln(x^2-1)$ **58.** $\log\left(\dfrac{x^2+2x-3}{x^2-4}\right) - \log\left(\dfrac{x^2+7x+6}{x+2}\right)$ **59.** $8\log_2\sqrt{3x-2} - \log_2\left(\dfrac{4}{x}\right) + \log_2 4$

60. $21\log_3\sqrt[3]{x} + \log_3(9x^2) - \log_3 9$ **61.** $2\log_a(5x^3) - \dfrac{1}{2}\log_a(2x+3)$ **62.** $\dfrac{1}{3}\log(x^3+1) + \dfrac{1}{2}\log(x^2+1)$

63. $2\log_2(x+1) - \log_2(x+3) - \log_2(x-1)$ **64.** $3\log_5(3x+1) - 2\log_5(2x-1) - \log_5 x$

In Problems 65–72, use the Change-of-Base Formula and a calculator to evaluate each logarithm. Round your answer to three decimal places.

65. $\log_3 21$ **66.** $\log_5 18$ **67.** $\log_{1/3} 71$ **68.** $\log_{1/2} 15$

69. $\log_{\sqrt{2}} 7$ **70.** $\log_{\sqrt{5}} 8$ **71.** $\log_\pi e$ **72.** $\log_\pi \sqrt{2}$

In Problems 73–78, graph each function using a graphing utility and the Change-of-Base Formula.

73. $y = \log_4 x$ **74.** $y = \log_5 x$ **75.** $y = \log_2(x+2)$

76. $y = \log_4(x-3)$ **77.** $y = \log_{x-1}(x+1)$ **78.** $y = \log_{x+2}(x-2)$

Mixed Practice

79. If $f(x) = \ln x$, $g(x) = e^x$, and $h(x) = x^2$, find:
(a) $(f \circ g)(x)$. What is the domain of $f \circ g$?
(b) $(g \circ f)(x)$. What is the domain of $g \circ f$?
(c) $(f \circ g)(5)$
(d) $(f \circ h)(x)$. What is the domain of $f \circ h$?
(e) $(f \circ h)(e)$

80. If $f(x) = \log_2 x$, $g(x) = 2^x$, and $h(x) = 4x$, find:
(a) $(f \circ g)(x)$. What is the domain of $f \circ g$?
(b) $(g \circ f)(x)$. What is the domain of $g \circ f$?
(c) $(f \circ g)(3)$
(d) $(f \circ h)(x)$. What is the domain of $f \circ h$?
(e) $(f \circ h)(8)$

Applications and Extensions

In Problems 81–90, express y as a function of x. The constant C is a positive number.

81. $\ln y = \ln x + \ln C$ **82.** $\ln y = \ln(x + C)$

83. $\ln y = \ln x + \ln(x+1) + \ln C$ **84.** $\ln y = 2\ln x - \ln(x+1) + \ln C$

85. $\ln y = 3x + \ln C$ **86.** $\ln y = -2x + \ln C$

87. $\ln(y-3) = -4x + \ln C$ **88.** $\ln(y+4) = 5x + \ln C$

89. $3\ln y = \dfrac{1}{2}\ln(2x+1) - \dfrac{1}{3}\ln(x+4) + \ln C$ **90.** $2\ln y = -\dfrac{1}{2}\ln x + \dfrac{1}{3}\ln(x^2+1) + \ln C$

91. Find the value of $\log_2 3 \cdot \log_3 4 \cdot \log_4 5 \cdot \log_5 6 \cdot \log_6 7 \cdot \log_7 8$.

92. Find the value of $\log_2 4 \cdot \log_4 6 \cdot \log_6 8$.

93. Find the value of $\log_2 3 \cdot \log_3 4 \cdot \cdots \cdot \log_n(n+1) \cdot \log_{n+1} 2$.

94. Find the value of $\log_2 2 \cdot \log_2 4 \cdot \cdots \cdot \log_2 2^n$.

95. Show that $\log_a\left(x + \sqrt{x^2 - 1}\right) + \log_a\left(x - \sqrt{x^2 - 1}\right) = 0$.

96. Show that $\log_a\left(\sqrt{x} + \sqrt{x - 1}\right) + \log_a\left(\sqrt{x} - \sqrt{x - 1}\right) = 0$.

97. Show that $\ln(1 + e^{2x}) = 2x + \ln(1 + e^{-2x})$.

98. Difference Quotient If $f(x) = \log_a x$, show that $\dfrac{f(x+h) - f(x)}{h} = \log_a\left(1 + \dfrac{h}{x}\right)^{1/h}$, $h \neq 0$.

99. If $f(x) = \log_a x$, show that $-f(x) = \log_{1/a} x$.

100. If $f(x) = \log_a x$, show that $f(AB) = f(A) + f(B)$.

101. If $f(x) = \log_a x$, show that $f\left(\dfrac{1}{x}\right) = -f(x)$.

102. If $f(x) = \log_a x$, show that $f(x^\alpha) = \alpha f(x)$.

103. Show that $\log_a\left(\dfrac{M}{N}\right) = \log_a M - \log_a N$, where a, M, and N are positive real numbers and $a \neq 1$.

104. Show that $\log_a\left(\dfrac{1}{N}\right) = -\log_a N$, where a and N are positive real numbers and $a \neq 1$.

Discussion and Writing

105. Graph $Y_1 = \log(x^2)$ and $Y_2 = 2\log(x)$ using a graphing utility. Are they equivalent? What might account for any differences in the two functions?

106. Write an example that illustrates why $(\log_a x)^r \neq r\log_a x$.

107. Write an example that illustrates why $\log_2(x + y) \neq \log_2 x + \log_2 y$.

108. Does $3^{\log_3(-5)} = -5$? Why or why not?

5.6 Logarithmic and Exponential Equations

PREPARING FOR THIS SECTION *Before getting started, review the following:*

- Solving Equations Using a Graphing Utility (Section 1.3, pp. 26–28)
- Solving Quadratic Equations (Appendix A, Section A.6, pp. A50–A55)
- Equations Quadratic in Form (Appendix A, Section A.6, pp. A55–A56)

Now Work the 'Are You Prepared?' problems on page 310.

OBJECTIVES 1 Solve Logarithmic Equations (p. 306)

2 Solve Exponential Equations (p. 308)

3 Solve Logarithmic and Exponential Equations Using a Graphing Utility (p. 310)

1 Solve Logarithmic Equations

In Section 5.4 we solved logarithmic equations by changing a logarithmic equation to an exponential equation. That is, we used the definition of a logarithm:

$$y = \log_a x \quad \text{is equivalent to} \quad x = a^y \qquad a > 0, a \neq 1$$

For example, to solve the equation $\log_2(1 - 2x) = 3$, we use the equivalent exponential equation $1 - 2x = 2^3$ and solve for x.

$$\log_2(1 - 2x) = 3$$
$$1 - 2x = 2^3 \qquad \text{Change to an exponential expression.}$$
$$-2x = 7 \qquad \text{Simplify.}$$
$$x = -\frac{7}{2} \qquad \text{Divide both sides by } -2.$$

You should check this solution for yourself.

For most logarithmic equations, some manipulation of the equation (usually using properties of logarithms) is required to obtain a solution. Also, to avoid extraneous solutions with logarithmic equations, we determine the domain of the variable first.

Our practice will be to solve equations, whenever possible, by finding exact solutions using algebraic methods and exact or approximate solutions using a graphing utility. When algebraic methods cannot be used, approximate solutions will be obtained using a graphing utility. The reader is encouraged to pay particular attention to the form of equations for which exact solutions are possible.

We begin with an example of a logarithmic equation that requires using the fact that a logarithmic function is a one-to-one function.

$$\text{If } \log_a M = \log_a N, \text{ then } M = N \qquad M, N, \text{ and } a \text{ are positive and } a \neq 1$$

EXAMPLE 1 **Solving a Logarithmic Equation**

Solve: $2 \log_5 x = \log_5 9$

Algebraic Solution

We note that the domain of the variable in this equation is $x > 0$. Because each logarithm is to the same base, 5, we can obtain an exact solution as follows:

$$2 \log_5 x = \log_5 9$$

$$\log_5 x^2 = \log_5 9 \quad \text{\small $\log_a M^r = r \log_a M$}$$

$$x^2 = 9 \quad \text{\small If $\log_a M = \log_a N$, then $M = N$.}$$

$$x = 3 \quad \text{or} \quad x = -3 \quad \text{\small Recall that the domain of the variable is $x > 0$.}$$
$$\text{\small Therefore, -3 is extraneous and we discard it.}$$

✓Check:
$$2 \log_5 3 \overset{?}{=} \log_5 9$$
$$\log_5 3^2 \overset{?}{=} \log_5 9 \quad \text{\small $r \log_a M = \log_a M^r$}$$
$$\log_5 9 = \log_5 9$$

The solution set is {3}.

Graphing Solution

To solve the equation using a graphing utility, graph

$$Y_1 = 2 \log_5 x = \frac{2 \log x}{\log 5} \quad \text{and} \quad Y_2 = \log_5 9 = \frac{\log 9}{\log 5},$$

and determine the point of intersection. See Figure 46. The point of intersection is (3, 1.3652124), so $x = 3$ is the only solution. The solution set is {3}.

Figure 46

—————— **Now Work** PROBLEM 13

EXAMPLE 2	Solving a Logarithmic Equation

Solve: $\log_5(x + 6) + \log_5(x + 2) = 1$

Algebraic Solution

The domain of the variable requires that $x + 6 > 0$ and $x + 2 > 0$, so $x > -6$ and $x > -2$. This means any solution must satisfy $x > -2$. To obtain an exact solution, we express the left side as a single logarithm. Then we will change the equation to exponential form.

$$\log_5(x + 6) + \log_5(x + 2) = 1$$

$$\log_5[(x + 6)(x + 2)] = 1 \quad \text{\small $\log_a M + \log_a N =$}$$
$$\text{\small $\log_a(MN)$}$$

$$(x + 6)(x + 2) = 5^1 = 5 \quad \text{\small Change to an}$$
$$\text{\small exponential equation.}$$

$$x^2 + 8x + 12 = 5 \quad \text{\small Simplify.}$$

$$x^2 + 8x + 7 = 0 \quad \text{\small Place the quadratic}$$
$$\text{\small equation in standard}$$
$$\text{\small form.}$$

$$(x + 7)(x + 1) = 0 \quad \text{\small Factor.}$$

$$x = -7 \quad \text{or} \quad x = -1 \quad \text{\small Zero-Product Property}$$

Only $x = -1$ satisfies the restriction that $x > -2$, so $x = -7$ is extraneous. The solution set is {−1}, which you should check.

Graphing Solution

Graph $Y_1 = \log_5(x + 6) + \log_5(x + 2) = \dfrac{\log(x + 6)}{\log 5} +$

$\dfrac{\log(x + 2)}{\log 5}$ and $Y_2 = 1$ and determine the point(s) of intersection. See Figure 47. The point of intersection is $(-1, 1)$, so $x = -1$ is the only solution. The solution set is {−1}.

Figure 47

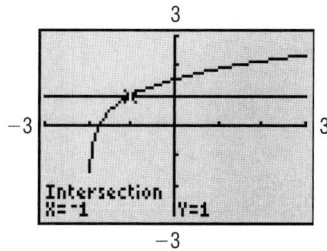

WARNING A negative solution is not automatically extraneous. You must determine whether the potential solution causes the argument of any logarithmic expression in the equation to be negative. ■

—————— **Now Work** PROBLEM 21

| EXAMPLE 3 | Solving a Logarithmic Equation |

Solve: $\ln x + \ln(x - 4) = \ln(x + 6)$

Algebraic Solution

The domain of the variable requires that $x > 0$, $x - 4 > 0$, and $x + 6 > 0$. As a result, the domain of the variable is $x > 4$. We begin the solution using the log of a product property.

$\ln x + \ln(x - 4) = \ln(x + 6)$

$\quad \ln[x(x - 4)] = \ln(x + 6)$ $\ln M + \ln N = \ln(MN)$

$\quad\quad\quad x(x - 4) = x + 6$ If $\ln M = \ln N$, then $M = N$.

$\quad\quad\quad\quad x^2 - 4x = x + 6$ Simplify.

$\quad\quad x^2 - 5x - 6 = 0$ Place the quadratic equation in standard form.

$\quad (x - 6)(x + 1) = 0$ Factor.

$\quad\quad x = 6 \quad \text{or} \quad x = -1$ Zero-Product Property

Since the domain of the variable is $x > 4$, we discard -1 as extraneous. The solution set is $\{6\}$, which you should check.

Graphing Solution

Graph $Y_1 = \ln x + \ln(x - 4)$ and $Y_2 = \ln(x + 6)$ and determine the point(s) of intersection. See Figure 48. The x-coordinate of the point of intersection is 6, so the solution set is $\{6\}$.

Figure 48

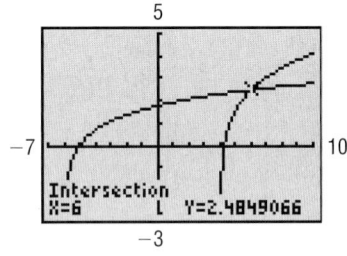

Intersection
X=6   Y=2.4849066

━━━━━▶ **Now Work** PROBLEM 31

2 Solve Exponential Equations

In Sections 5.3 and 5.4, we solved exponential equations algebraically by expressing each side of the equation using the same base. That is, we used the one-to-one property of the exponential function:

$$\text{If } a^u = a^v, \quad \text{then} \quad u = v \quad a > 0, a \neq 1$$

For example, to solve the exponential equation $4^{2x+1} = 16$, we notice that $16 = 4^2$ and apply the property above to obtain $2x + 1 = 2$, from which we find $x = \dfrac{1}{2}$.

For most exponential equations, we cannot express each side of the equation using the same base. In such cases, algebraic techniques can sometimes be used to obtain exact solutions. When algebraic techniques cannot be used, we use a graphing utility to obtain approximate solutions. You should pay particular attention to the form of equations for which exact solutions are obtained.

In the next two examples we solve exponential equations by changing the exponential expression to a logarithmic expression.

| EXAMPLE 4 | Solving an Exponential Equation |

Solve: $2^x = 5$

Algebraic Solution

Since 5 cannot be written as an integer power of 2, we write the exponential equation as the equivalent logarithmic equation.

$$2^x = 5$$

$$x = \log_2 5 = \frac{\ln 5}{\ln 2}$$

$\uparrow$

Change-of-Base Formula (9), Section 5.5

Graphing Solution

Graph $Y_1 = 2^x$ and $Y_2 = 5$ and determine the x-coordinate of the point of intersection. See Figure 49.

Figure 49

Intersection
X=2.3219281   Y=5

Alternatively, we can solve the equation $2^x = 5$ by taking the natural logarithm (or common logarithm) of each side. Taking the natural logarithm,

$$2^x = 5$$

$$\ln 2^x = \ln 5 \qquad \text{If } M = N, \text{ then } \ln M = \ln N.$$

$$x \ln 2 = \ln 5 \qquad \ln M^r = r \ln M$$

$$x = \frac{\ln 5}{\ln 2} \qquad \text{Exact solution}$$

$$\approx 2.322 \qquad \text{Approximate solution}$$

The solution set is $\left\{ \dfrac{\ln 5}{\ln 2} \right\}$.

The approximate solution, rounded to three decimal places, is 2.322.

─── **Now Work** PROBLEM 35

───────────────────────────────

| EXAMPLE 5 | Solving an Exponential Equation |

Solve: $8 \cdot 3^x = 5$

Algebraic Solution

We wish to isolate the exponential expression and then rewrite the statement as an equivalent logarithm.

$$8 \cdot 3^x = 5$$

$$3^x = \frac{5}{8} \qquad \text{Solve for } 3^x.$$

$$x = \log_3\left(\frac{5}{8}\right) = \frac{\ln\left(\frac{5}{8}\right)}{\ln 3} \qquad \text{Exact solution}$$

$$\approx -0.428 \qquad \text{Approximate solution}$$

The solution set is $\left\{ \log_3\left(\dfrac{5}{8}\right) \right\}$.

Graphing Solution

Graph $Y_1 = 8 \cdot 3^x$ and $Y_2 = 5$ and determine the x-coordinate of the point of intersection. See Figure 50.

Figure 50

The approximate solution, rounded to three decimal places, is −0.428.

───────────────────────────────

| EXAMPLE 6 | Solving an Exponential Equation |

Solve: $5^{x-2} = 3^{3x+2}$

Algebraic Solution

Because the bases are different, we first apply Property (6), Section 5.5 (take the natural logarithm of each side), and then use appropriate properties of logarithms. The result is a linear equation in x that we can solve.

$$5^{x-2} = 3^{3x+2}$$

$$\ln 5^{x-2} = \ln 3^{3x+2} \qquad \text{If } M = N, \ln M = \ln N.$$

$$(x - 2)\ln 5 = (3x + 2)\ln 3 \qquad \ln M^r = r \ln M$$

$$(\ln 5)x - 2\ln 5 = (3\ln 3)x + 2\ln 3 \qquad \text{Distribute. The equation is now linear in } x.$$

$$(\ln 5)x - (3\ln 3)x = 2\ln 3 + 2\ln 5 \qquad \text{Place terms involving } x \text{ on the left.}$$

$$(\ln 5 - 3\ln 3)x = 2(\ln 3 + \ln 5) \qquad \text{Factor.}$$

$$x = \frac{2(\ln 3 + \ln 5)}{\ln 5 - 3\ln 3} \qquad \text{Exact solution}$$

$$\approx -3.212 \qquad \text{Approximate solution}$$

Graphing Solution

Graph $Y_1 = 5^{x-2}$ and $Y_2 = 3^{3x+2}$ and determine the x-coordinate of the point of intersection. See Figure 51.

Figure 51

The approximate solution, rounded to three decimal places, is −3.212.

─── **Now Work** PROBLEM 41

The next example deals with an exponential equation that is quadratic in form.

| EXAMPLE 7 | **Solving an Exponential Equation That Is Quadratic in Form** |

Solve: $4^x - 2^x - 12 = 0$

Algebraic Solution

We note that $4^x = (2^2)^x = 2^{2x} = (2^x)^2$, so the equation is actually quadratic in form, and we can rewrite it as

$$(2^x)^2 - 2^x - 12 = 0 \quad \text{Let } u = 2^x; \text{ then } u^2 - u - 12 = 0.$$

Now we can factor as usual.

$$(2^x - 4)(2^x + 3) = 0 \quad (u - 4)(u + 3) = 0$$
$$2^x - 4 = 0 \quad \text{or} \quad 2^x + 3 = 0 \quad u - 4 = 0 \quad \text{or} \quad u + 3 = 0$$
$$2^x = 4 \qquad\qquad 2^x = -3 \quad u = 2^x = 4 \qquad u = 2^x = -3$$

The equation on the left has the solution $x = 2$, since $2^x = 4 = 2^2$; the equation on the right has no solution, since $2^x > 0$ for all x. The only solution is 2. The solution set is $\{2\}$.

Graphing Solution

Graph $Y_1 = 4^x - 2^x - 12$ and determine the x-intercept. See Figure 52. The x-intercept is 2, so the solution set is $\{2\}$.

Figure 52

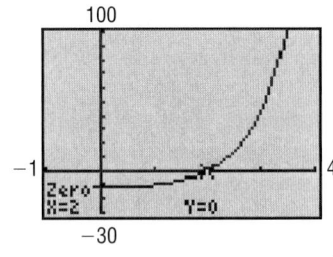

━━━━━━ **Now Work** PROBLEM 53

3 Solve Logarithmic and Exponential Equations Using a Graphing Utility

 The algebraic techniques introduced in this section to obtain exact solutions apply only to certain types of logarithmic and exponential equations. Solutions for other types are usually studied in calculus, using numerical methods. For such types, we can use a graphing utility to approximate the solution.

| EXAMPLE 8 | **Solving Equations Using a Graphing Utility** |

Solve: $x + e^x = 2$

Express the solution(s) rounded to two decimal places.

Solution

The solution is found by graphing $Y_1 = x + e^x$ and $Y_2 = 2$. Since Y_1 is an increasing function (do you know why?), there is only one point of intersection for Y_1 and Y_2. Figure 53 shows the graphs of Y_1 and Y_2. Using the INTERSECT command, the solution is 0.44 rounded to two decimal places.

Figure 53

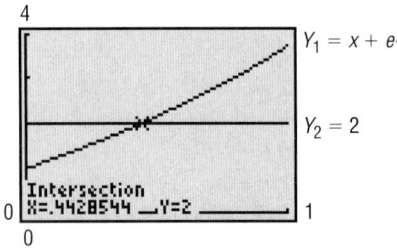

━━━━━━ **Now Work** PROBLEM 63

5.6 Assess Your Understanding

'Are You Prepared?' *Answers are given at the end of these exercises. If you get a wrong answer, read the pages listed in red.*

1. Solve $x^2 - 7x - 30 = 0$. (pp. A50–A51)

2. Solve $(x + 3)^2 - 4(x + 3) + 3 = 0$. (pp. A55–A56)

3. Approximate the solution(s) to $x^3 = x^2 - 5$ using a graphing utility. (pp. A26–A27)

4. Approximate the solution(s) to $x^3 - 2x + 2 = 0$ using a graphing utility. (pp. A26–A27)

Skill Building

In Problems 5–32, solve each logarithmic equation. Express irrational solutions in exact form and as a decimal rounded to 3 decimal places. Verify your results using a graphing utility.

5. $\log_4 x = 2$

6. $\log(x + 6) = 1$

7. $\log_2(5x) = 4$

8. $\log_3(3x - 1) = 2$

9. $\log_4(x + 2) = \log_4 8$

10. $\log_5(2x + 3) = \log_5 3$

11. $\frac{1}{2} \log_3 x = 2 \log_3 2$

12. $-2 \log_4 x = \log_4 9$

13. $3 \log_2 x = -\log_2 27$

14. $2 \log_5 x = 3 \log_5 4$

15. $3 \log_2(x - 1) + \log_2 4 = 5$

16. $2 \log_3(x + 4) - \log_3 9 = 2$

17. $\log x + \log(x + 15) = 2$

18. $\log x + \log (x - 21) = 2$

19. $\log(2x + 1) = 1 + \log(x - 2)$

20. $\log(2x) - \log(x - 3) = 1$

21. $\log_2(x + 7) + \log_2(x + 8) = 1$

22. $\log_6(x + 4) + \log_6(x + 3) = 1$

23. $\log_8(x + 6) = 1 - \log_8(x + 4)$

24. $\log_5(x + 3) = 1 - \log_5(x - 1)$

25. $\ln x + \ln(x + 2) = 4$

26. $\ln(x + 1) - \ln x = 2$

27. $\log_3(x + 1) + \log_3(x + 4) = 2$

28. $\log_2(x + 1) + \log_2(x + 7) = 3$

29. $\log_{1/3}(x^2 + x) - \log_{1/3}(x^2 - x) = -1$

30. $\log_4(x^2 - 9) - \log_4(x + 3) = 3$

31. $\log_a(x - 1) - \log_a(x + 6) = \log_a(x - 2) - \log_a(x + 3)$

32. $\log_a x + \log_a(x - 2) = \log_a(x + 4)$

In Problems 33–60, solve each exponential equation. Express irrational solutions in exact form and as a decimal rounded to 3 decimal places. Verify your results using a graphing utility.

33. $2^{x-5} = 8$

34. $5^{-x} = 25$

35. $2^x = 10$

36. $3^x = 14$

37. $8^{-x} = 1.2$

38. $2^{-x} = 1.5$

39. $5(2^{3x}) = 8$

40. $0.3(4^{0.2x}) = 0.2$

41. $3^{1-2x} = 4^x$

42. $2^{x+1} = 5^{1-2x}$

43. $\left(\frac{3}{5}\right)^x = 7^{1-x}$

44. $\left(\frac{4}{3}\right)^{1-x} = 5^x$

45. $1.2^x = (0.5)^{-x}$

46. $0.3^{1+x} = 1.7^{2x-1}$

47. $\pi^{1-x} = e^x$

48. $e^{x+3} = \pi^x$

49. $2^{2x} + 2^x - 12 = 0$

50. $3^{2x} + 3^x - 2 = 0$

51. $3^{2x} + 3^{x+1} - 4 = 0$

52. $2^{2x} + 2^{x+2} - 12 = 0$

53. $16^x + 4^{x+1} - 3 = 0$

54. $9^x - 3^{x+1} + 1 = 0$

55. $25^x - 8 \cdot 5^x = -16$

56. $36^x - 6 \cdot 6^x = -9$

57. $3 \cdot 4^x + 4 \cdot 2^x + 8 = 0$

58. $2 \cdot 49^x + 11 \cdot 7^x + 5 = 0$

59. $4^x - 10 \cdot 4^{-x} = 3$

60. $3^x - 14 \cdot 3^{-x} = 5$

In Problems 61–74, use a graphing utility to solve each equation. Express your answer rounded to two decimal places.

61. $\log_5(x + 1) - \log_4(x - 2) = 1$

62. $\log_2(x - 1) - \log_6(x + 2) = 2$

63. $e^x = -x$

64. $e^{2x} = x + 2$

65. $e^x = x^2$

66. $e^x = x^3$

67. $\ln x = -x$

68. $\ln(2x) = -x + 2$

69. $\ln x = x^3 - 1$

70. $\ln x = -x^2$

71. $e^x + \ln x = 4$

72. $e^x - \ln x = 4$

73. $e^{-x} = \ln x$

74. $e^{-x} = -\ln x$

In Problems 75–86, solve each equation. Express irrational solutions in exact form and as a decimal rounded to 3 decimal places. Verify your results using a graphing utility.

75. $\log_2(x + 1) - \log_4 x = 1$
[**Hint:** Change $\log_4 x$ to base 2.]

76. $\log_2(3x + 2) - \log_4 x = 3$

77. $\log_{16} x + \log_4 x + \log_2 x = 7$

78. $\log_9 x + 3 \log_3 x = 14$

79. $\left(\sqrt[3]{2}\right)^{2-x} = 2^{x^2}$

80. $\log_2 x^{\log_2 x} = 4$

81. $\frac{e^x + e^{-x}}{2} = 1$
[**Hint:** Multiply each side by e^x.]

82. $\frac{e^x + e^{-x}}{2} = 3$

83. $\frac{e^x - e^{-x}}{2} = 2$

84. $\frac{e^x - e^{-x}}{2} = -2$

85. $\log_5 x + \log_3 x = 1$
[**Hint:** Use the Change-of-Base Formula and factor out $\ln x$.]

86. $\log_2 x + \log_6 x = 3$

Mixed Practice

87. $f(x) = \log_2(x + 3)$ and $g(x) = \log_2(3x + 1)$.
   (a) Solve $f(x) = 3$. What point is on the graph of f?
   (b) Solve $g(x) = 4$. What point is on the graph of g?
   (c) Solve $f(x) = g(x)$. Do the graphs of f and g intersect? If so, where?
   (d) Solve $(f + g)(x) = 7$.
   (e) Solve $(f - g)(x) = 2$.

88. $f(x) = \log_3(x + 5)$ and $g(x) = \log_3(x - 1)$.
   (a) Solve $f(x) = 2$. What point is on the graph of f?
   (b) Solve $g(x) = 3$. What point is on the graph of g?
   (c) Solve $f(x) = g(x)$. Do the graphs of f and g intersect? If so, where?
   (d) Solve $(f + g)(x) = 3$.
   (e) Solve $(f - g)(x) = 2$.

89. (a) If $f(x) = 3^{x+1}$ and $g(x) = 2^{x+2}$, graph f and g on the same Cartesian plane.
   (b) Find the point(s) of intersection of the graphs of f and g by solving $f(x) = g(x)$. Round answers to three decimal places. Label this point on the graph drawn in part (a).
   (c) Based on the graph, solve $f(x) > g(x)$.

90. (a) If $f(x) = 5^{x-1}$ and $g(x) = 2^{x+1}$, graph f and g on the same Cartesian plane.
   (b) Find the point(s) of intersection of the graphs of f and g by solving $f(x) = g(x)$. Label this point on the graph drawn in part (a).
   (c) Based on the graph, solve $f(x) > g(x)$.

91. (a) Graph $f(x) = 3^x$ and $g(x) = 10$ on the same Cartesian plane.
   (b) Shade the region bounded by the y-axis, $f(x) = 3^x$, and $g(x) = 10$ on the graph drawn in part (a).
   (c) Solve $f(x) = g(x)$ and label the point of intersection on the graph drawn in part (a).

92. (a) Graph $f(x) = 2^x$ and $g(x) = 12$ on the same Cartesian plane.
   (b) Shade the region bounded by the y-axis, $f(x) = 2^x$, and $g(x) = 12$ on the graph drawn in part (a).
   (c) Solve $f(x) = g(x)$ and label the point of intersection on the graph drawn in part (a).

93. (a) Graph $f(x) = 2^{x+1}$ and $g(x) = 2^{-x+2}$ on the same Cartesian plane.
   (b) Shade the region bounded by the y-axis, $f(x) = 2^{x+1}$, and $g(x) = 2^{-x+2}$ on the graph drawn in part (a).
   (c) Solve $f(x) = g(x)$ and label the point of intersection on the graph drawn in part (a).

94. (a) Graph $f(x) = 3^{-x+1}$ and $g(x) = 3^{x-2}$ on the same Cartesian plane.
   (b) Shade the region bounded by the y-axis, $f(x) = 3^{-x+1}$, and $g(x) = 3^{x-2}$ on the graph drawn in part (a).
   (c) Solve $f(x) = g(x)$ and label the point of intersection on the graph drawn in part (a).

95. (a) Graph $f(x) = 2^x - 4$.
   (b) Find the zero of f.
   (c) Based on the graph, solve $f(x) < 0$.

96. (a) Graph $g(x) = 3^x - 9$.
   (b) Find the zero of g.
   (c) Based on the graph, solve $g(x) > 0$.

Applications and Extensions

97. A Population Model The resident population of the United States in 2006 was 298 million people and was growing at a rate of 0.9% per year. Assuming that this growth rate continues, the model $P(t) = 298(1.009)^{t-2006}$ represents the population P (in millions of people) in year t.
   (a) According to this model, when will the population of the United States be 310 million people?
   (b) According to this model, when will the population of the United States be 360 million people?
Source: Statistical Abstract of the United States, 125th ed., 2006.

98. A Population Model The population of the world in 2006 was 6.53 billion people and was growing at a rate of 1.14% per year. Assuming that this growth rate continues, the model $P(t) = 6.53(1.0114)^{t-2006}$ represents the population P (in billions of people) in year t.
   (a) According to this model, when will the population of the world be 9.25 billion people?
   (b) According to this model, when will the population of the world be 11.75 billion people?
Source: U.S. Census Bureau.

99. Depreciation The value V of a Chevy Cobalt that is t years old can be modeled by $V(t) = 14{,}512(0.82)^t$.
   (a) According to the model, when will the car be worth $9000?
   (b) According to the model, when will the car be worth $4000?
   (c) According to the model, when will the car be worth $2000?
Source: Kelley Blue Book

100. Depreciation The value V of a Dodge Stratus that is t years old can be modeled by $V(t) = 19{,}282(0.84)^t$.
 (a) According to the model, when will the car be worth $15,000?
 (b) According to the model, when will the car be worth $8000?
 (c) According to the model, when will the car be worth $2000?
 Source: Kelley Blue Book

Discussion and Writing

101. Fill in reasons for each step in the following two solutions.
Solve: $\log_3(x - 1)^2 = 2$

Solution A

$\log_3(x - 1)^2 = 2$
$(x - 1)^2 = 3^2 = 9$ _____
$(x - 1) = \pm 3$ _____
$x - 1 = -3$ or $x - 1 = 3$ _____
$x = -2$ or $x = 4$ _____

Solution B

$\log_3(x - 1)^2 = 2$
$2\log_3(x - 1) = 2$ _____
$\log_3(x - 1) = 1$ _____
$x - 1 = 3^1 = 3$ _____
$x = 4$ _____

Both solutions given in Solution A check. Explain what caused the solution $x = -2$ to be lost in Solution B.

'Are You Prepared?' Answers

1. $\{-3, 10\}$ **2.** $\{-2, 0\}$ **3.** $\{-1.43\}$ **4.** $\{-1.77\}$

5.7 Financial Models

PREPARING FOR THIS SECTION *Before getting started, review the following:*

* Simple Interest (Appendix A, Section A.8, p. A70)

Now Work the 'Are You Prepared?' problems on page 320.

OBJECTIVES 1 Determine the Future Value of a Lump Sum of Money (p. 313)
2 Calculate Effective Rates of Return (p. 317)
3 Determine the Present Value of a Lump Sum of Money (p. 318)
4 Determine the Rate of Interest or Time Required to Double a Lump Sum of Money (p. 319)

1 Determine the Future Value of a Lump Sum of Money

Interest is money paid for the use of money. The total amount borrowed (whether by an individual from a bank in the form of a loan or by a bank from an individual in the form of a savings account) is called the **principal**. The **rate of interest,** expressed as a percent, is the amount charged for the use of the principal for a given period of time, usually on a yearly (that is, per annum) basis.

THEOREM **Simple Interest Formula**

If a principal of P dollars is borrowed for a period of t years at a per annum interest rate r, expressed as a decimal, the interest I charged is

$$I = Prt \qquad\qquad (1)$$

Interest charged according to formula (1) is called **simple interest.**

In working with problems involving interest, we define the term **payment period** as follows:

Annually:	Once per year	**Monthly:**	12 times per year
Semiannually:	Twice per year	**Daily:**	365 times per year*
Quarterly:	Four times per year		

When the interest due at the end of a payment period is added to the principal so that the interest computed at the end of the next payment period is based on this new principal amount (old principal + interest), the interest is said to have been **compounded.** **Compound interest** is interest paid on principal and previously earned interest.

EXAMPLE 1	**Computing Compound Interest**

A credit union pays interest of 8% per annum compounded quarterly on a certain savings plan. If $1000 is deposited in such a plan and the interest is left to accumulate, how much is in the account after 1 year?

Solution   We use the simple interest formula, $I = Prt$. The principal P is $1000 and the rate of interest is 8% $= 0.08$. After the first quarter of a year, the time t is $\frac{1}{4}$ year, so the interest earned is

$$I = Prt = (\$1000)(0.08)\left(\frac{1}{4}\right) = \$20$$

The new principal is $P + I = \$1000 + \$20 = \$1020$. At the end of the second quarter, the interest on this principal is

$$I = (\$1020)(0.08)\left(\frac{1}{4}\right) = \$20.40$$

At the end of the third quarter, the interest on the new principal of $1020 + $20.40 = $1040.40 is

$$I = (\$1040.40)(0.08)\left(\frac{1}{4}\right) = \$20.81$$

Finally, after the fourth quarter, the interest is

$$I = (\$1061.21)(0.08)\left(\frac{1}{4}\right) = \$21.22$$

After 1 year the account contains $1061.21 + $21.22 = $1082.43.

The pattern of the calculations performed in Example 1 leads to a general formula for compound interest. To fix our ideas, let P represent the principal to be invested at a per annum interest rate r that is compounded n times per year, so the time of each compounding period is $\frac{1}{n}$ years. (For computing purposes, r is expressed as a decimal.) The interest earned after each compounding period is given by formula (1).

$$\text{Interest} = \text{principal} \times \text{rate} \times \text{time} = P \cdot r \cdot \frac{1}{n} = P \cdot \left(\frac{r}{n}\right)$$

The amount A after one compounding period is

$$A = P + P \cdot \left(\frac{r}{n}\right) = P \cdot \left(1 + \frac{r}{n}\right)$$

*Most banks use a 360-day "year." Why do you think they do?

After two compounding periods, the amount A, based on the new principal $P \cdot \left(1 + \dfrac{r}{n}\right)$, is

$$A = \underbrace{P \cdot \left(1 + \frac{r}{n}\right)}_{\substack{\text{New} \\ \text{principal}}} + \underbrace{P \cdot \left(1 + \frac{r}{n}\right)\left(\frac{r}{n}\right)}_{\substack{\text{Interest on} \\ \text{new principal}}} = \underset{\underset{\text{Factor out } P \cdot \left(1 + \frac{r}{n}\right)}{\uparrow}}{P \cdot \left(1 + \frac{r}{n}\right)\left(1 + \frac{r}{n}\right)} = P \cdot \left(1 + \frac{r}{n}\right)^2$$

After three compounding periods, the amount A is

$$A = P \cdot \left(1 + \frac{r}{n}\right)^2 + P \cdot \left(1 + \frac{r}{n}\right)^2 \left(\frac{r}{n}\right) = P \cdot \left(1 + \frac{r}{n}\right)^2 \cdot \left(1 + \frac{r}{n}\right) = P \cdot \left(1 + \frac{r}{n}\right)^3$$

Continuing this way, after n compounding periods (1 year), the amount A is

$$A = P \cdot \left(1 + \frac{r}{n}\right)^n$$

Because t years will contain $n \cdot t$ compounding periods, after t years we have

$$A = P \cdot \left(1 + \frac{r}{n}\right)^{nt}$$

THEOREM

Compound Interest Formula

The amount A after t years due to a principal P invested at an annual interest rate r compounded n times per year is

$$A = P \cdot \left(1 + \frac{r}{n}\right)^{nt} \qquad \qquad \textbf{(2)}$$

Exploration

To see the effects of compounding interest monthly on an initial deposit of \$1, graph $Y_1 = \left(1 + \dfrac{r}{12}\right)^{12x}$ with $r = 0.06$ and $r = 0.12$ for $0 \le x \le 30$. What is the future value of \$1 in 30 years when the interest rate per annum is $r = 0.06$ (6%)? What is the future value of \$1 in 30 years when the interest rate per annum is $r = 0.12$ (12%)? Does doubling the interest rate double the future value?

For example, to rework Example 1, we would use $P = \$1000$, $r = 0.08$, $n = 4$ (quarterly compounding), and $t = 1$ year to obtain

$$A = P \cdot \left(1 + \frac{r}{n}\right)^{nt} = 1000\left(1 + \frac{0.08}{4}\right)^{4 \cdot 1} = \$1082.43$$

In equation (2), the amount A is typically referred to as the **future value** of the account, while P is called the **present value**.

➤ **Now Work** PROBLEM 3

EXAMPLE 2	**Comparing Investments Using Different Compounding Periods**

Investing \$1000 at an annual rate of 10% compounded annually, semiannually, quarterly, monthly, and daily will yield the following amounts after 1 year:

Annual compounding ($n = 1$): $A = P \cdot (1 + r)$
$$= (\$1000)(1 + 0.10) = \$1100.00$$

Semiannual compounding ($n = 2$): $A = P \cdot \left(1 + \dfrac{r}{2}\right)^2$
$$= (\$1000)(1 + 0.05)^2 = \$1102.50$$

Quarterly compounding ($n = 4$): $A = P \cdot \left(1 + \dfrac{r}{4}\right)^4$
$$= (\$1000)(1 + 0.025)^4 = \$1103.81$$

Monthly compounding ($n = 12$): $A = P \cdot \left(1 + \dfrac{r}{12}\right)^{12}$
$$= (\$1000)\left(1 + \frac{0.10}{12}\right)^{12} = \$1104.71$$

Daily compounding ($n = 365$):
$$A = P \cdot \left(1 + \frac{r}{365}\right)^{365}$$
$$= (\$1000)\left(1 + \frac{0.10}{365}\right)^{365} = \$1105.16$$

From Example 2, we can see that the effect of compounding more frequently is that the amount after 1 year is higher: $1000 compounded 4 times a year at 10% results in $1103.81, $1000 compounded 12 times a year at 10% results in $1104.71, and $1000 compounded 365 times a year at 10% results in $1105.16. This leads to the following question: What would happen to the amount after 1 year if the number of times that the interest is compounded were increased without bound?

Let's find the answer. Suppose that P is the principal, r is the per annum interest rate, and n is the number of times that the interest is compounded each year. The amount after 1 year is

$$A = P \cdot \left(1 + \frac{r}{n}\right)^{n}$$

Rewrite this expression as follows:

$$A = P \cdot \left(1 + \frac{r}{n}\right)^{n} = P \cdot \left(1 + \frac{1}{\frac{n}{r}}\right)^{n} = P \cdot \left[\left(1 + \frac{1}{\frac{n}{r}}\right)^{n/r}\right]^{r} = P \cdot \left[\left(1 + \frac{1}{h}\right)^{h}\right]^{r} \quad \textbf{(3)}$$
$$\uparrow$$
$$h = \frac{n}{r}$$

Now suppose that the number n of times that the interest is compounded per year gets larger and larger; that is, suppose that $n \rightarrow \infty$. Then $h = \frac{n}{r} \rightarrow \infty$, and the expression in brackets in Equation (3) equals e. That is, $A \rightarrow Pe^{r}$.

Table 9 compares $\left(1 + \frac{r}{n}\right)^{n}$, for large values of n, to e^{r} for $r = 0.05$, $r = 0.10$, $r = 0.15$, and $r = 1$. The larger that n gets, the closer $\left(1 + \frac{r}{n}\right)^{n}$ gets to e^{r}.

No matter how frequent the compounding, the amount after 1 year has the definite ceiling Pe^{r}.

Table 9

	$\left(1 + \frac{r}{n}\right)^{n}$			
	$n = 100$	$n = 1000$	$n = 10,000$	e^{r}
$r = 0.05$	1.0512580	1.0512698	1.051271	1.0512711
$r = 0.10$	1.1051157	1.1051654	1.1051704	1.1051709
$r = 0.15$	1.1617037	1.1618212	1.1618329	1.1618342
$r = 1$	2.7048138	2.7169239	2.7181459	2.7182818

When interest is compounded so that the amount after 1 year is Pe^{r}, we say the interest is **compounded continuously.**

THEOREM

Continuous Compounding

The amount A after t years due to a principal P invested at an annual interest rate r compounded continuously is

$$A = Pe^{rt} \quad \textbf{(4)}$$

EXAMPLE 3   Using Continuous Compounding

The amount A that results from investing a principal P of $1000 at an annual rate r of 10% compounded continuously for a time t of 1 year is

$$A = \$1000e^{0.10} = (\$1000)(1.10517) = \$1105.17$$

Now Work PROBLEM 11

2 Calculate Effective Rates of Return

Suppose you have $1000 and a bank offers to pay you 3% annual interest on a savings account compounded monthly. What annual interest rate would you need to earn if the interest was compounded annually (once per year)? To answer this question, we first determine the value of the $1000 in the account that earns 3% compounded monthly.

$$A = \$1000\left(1 + \frac{0.03}{12}\right)^{12} \quad \text{Use } A = P\left(1 + \frac{r}{n}\right)^{n} \text{ with } P = \$1000, \, r = 0.03, \, n = 12.$$

$$= \$1030.42$$

So the interest earned is $30.42. Using $I = Prt$ with $t = 1$, $I = \$30.42$, and $P = \$1000$, we find the annual simple interest rate is $0.03042 = 3.042\%$. This interest rate is known as the *effective rate of interest*.

The **effective rate of interest** is the equivalent annual simple interest rate that would yield the same amount as compounding n times per year, or continuously, after 1 year. We can determine the effective rate of interest using the following.

THEOREM   **Effective Rate of Interest**

The effective rate of interest r_e of an investment earning an annual interest rate r is given by

$$\text{Compounding } n \text{ times per year:} \quad r_e = \left(1 + \frac{r}{n}\right)^{n} - 1$$

$$\text{Continuous compounding:} \quad r_e = e^{r} - 1$$

EXAMPLE 4   Computing the Effective Rate of Interest—Which Is the Best Deal?

Suppose you want to open a money market account. You visit three banks to determine their money market rates. Bank A offers you 6% annual interest compounded daily and Bank B offers you 6.02% compounded quarterly. Bank C offers 5.98% compounded continuously. Determine which bank is offering the best deal.

Solution   The bank that offers the best deal is the one with the highest effective interest rate.

Bank A	**Bank B**	**Bank C**
$r_e = \left(1 + \dfrac{0.06}{365}\right)^{365} - 1$	$r_e = \left(1 + \dfrac{0.0602}{4}\right)^{4} - 1$	$r_e = e^{0.0598} - 1$
$\approx 1.06183 - 1$	$\approx 1.06157 - 1$	$\approx 1.06162 - 1$
$= 0.06183$	$= 0.06157$	$= 0.06162$
$= 6.183\%$	$= 6.157\%$	$= 6.162\%$

Since the effective rate of interest is highest for Bank A, Bank A is offering the best deal.

Now Work PROBLEM 23

3 Determine the Present Value of a Lump Sum of Money

When people engaged in finance speak of the "time value of money," they are usually referring to the *present value* of money. The **present value** of A dollars to be received at a future date is the principal that you would need to invest now so that it will grow to A dollars in the specified time period. The present value of money to be received at a future date is always less than the amount to be received, since the amount to be received will equal the present value (money invested now) *plus* the interest accrued over the time period.

We use the compound interest formula (2) to get a formula for present value. If P is the present value of A dollars to be received after t years at a per annum interest rate r compounded n times per year, then, by formula (2),

$$A = P \cdot \left(1 + \frac{r}{n}\right)^{nt}$$

To solve for P, we divide both sides by $\left(1 + \frac{r}{n}\right)^{nt}$. The result is

$$\frac{A}{\left(1 + \frac{r}{n}\right)^{nt}} = P \quad \text{or} \quad P = A \cdot \left(1 + \frac{r}{n}\right)^{-nt}$$

THEOREM

Present Value Formulas

The present value P of A dollars to be received after t years, assuming a per annum interest rate r compounded n times per year, is

$$P = A \cdot \left(1 + \frac{r}{n}\right)^{-nt} \tag{5}$$

If the interest is compounded continuously,

$$P = Ae^{-rt} \tag{6}$$

To prove (6), solve formula (4) for P.

EXAMPLE 5

Computing the Value of a Zero-coupon Bond

A zero-coupon (noninterest-bearing) bond can be redeemed in 10 years for $1000. How much should you be willing to pay for it now if you want a return of

(a) 8% compounded monthly?

(b) 7% compounded continuously?

Solution

(a) We are seeking the present value of $1000. We use formula (5) with $A = \$1000$, $n = 12, r = 0.08$, and $t = 10$.

$$P = A \cdot \left(1 + \frac{r}{n}\right)^{-nt} = \$1000\left(1 + \frac{0.08}{12}\right)^{-12(10)} = \$450.52$$

For a return of 8% compounded monthly, you should pay $450.52 for the bond.

(b) Here we use formula (6) with $A = \$1000, r = 0.07$, and $t = 10$.

$$P = Ae^{-rt} = \$1000e^{-(0.07)(10)} = \$496.59$$

For a return of 7% compounded continuously, you should pay $496.59 for the bond.

Now Work PROBLEM 13

4 Determine the Rate of Interest or Time Required to Double a Lump Sum of Money

| EXAMPLE 6 | Rate of Interest Required to Double an Investment |

What annual rate of interest compounded annually should you seek if you want to double your investment in 5 years?

Solution   If P is the principal and we want P to double, the amount A will be $2P$. We use the compound interest formula with $n = 1$ and $t = 5$ to find r.

$$A = P \cdot \left(1 + \frac{r}{n}\right)^{nt}$$

$$2P = P \cdot (1 + r)^5 \qquad \text{\small $A = 2P, n = 1, t = 5$}$$

$$2 = (1 + r)^5 \qquad \text{\small Divide both sides by P.}$$

$$1 + r = \sqrt[5]{2} \qquad \text{\small Take the fifth root of each side.}$$

$$r = \sqrt[5]{2} - 1 \approx 1.148698 - 1 = 0.148698$$

The annual rate of interest needed to double the principal in 5 years is 14.87%.

━━━ **Now Work** PROBLEM 31

| EXAMPLE 7 | Time Required to Double or Triple an Investment |

(a) How long will it take for an investment to double in value if it earns 5% compounded continuously?

(b) How long will it take to triple at this rate?

Solution   (a) If P is the initial investment and we want P to double, the amount A will be $2P$. We use formula (4) for continuously compounded interest with $r = 0.05$. Then

$$A = Pe^{rt}$$

$$2P = Pe^{0.05t} \qquad \text{\small $A = 2P, r = 0.05$}$$

$$2 = e^{0.05t} \qquad \text{\small Divide both sides by P.}$$

$$0.05t = \ln 2 \qquad \text{\small Rewrite as a logarithm.}$$

$$t = \frac{\ln 2}{0.05} \approx 13.86 \quad \text{\small Solve for t.}$$

It will take about 14 years to double the investment.

(b) To triple the investment, we set $A = 3P$ in formula (4).

$$A = Pe^{rt}$$

$$3P = Pe^{0.05t} \qquad \text{\small $A = 3P, r = 0.05$}$$

$$3 = e^{0.05t} \qquad \text{\small Divide both sides by P.}$$

$$0.05t = \ln 3 \qquad \text{\small Rewrite as a logarithm.}$$

$$t = \frac{\ln 3}{0.05} \approx 21.97 \quad \text{\small Solve for t.}$$

It will take about 22 years to triple the investment.

━━━ **Now Work** PROBLEM 35

5.7 Assess Your Understanding

'Are You Prepared?' *Answers are given at the end of these exercises. If you get a wrong answer, read the pages listed in red.*

1. What is the interest due if $500 is borrowed for 6 months at a simple interest rate of 6% per annum? (p. A70)

2. If you borrow $5000 and, after 9 months, pay off the loan in the amount of $5500, what per annum rate of interest was charged? (p. A70)

Skill Building

In Problems 3–12, find the amount that results from each investment.

3. $100 invested at 4% compounded quarterly after a period of 2 years

4. $50 invested at 6% compounded monthly after a period of 3 years

5. $500 invested at 8% compounded quarterly after a period of $2\frac{1}{2}$ years

6. $300 invested at 12% compounded monthly after a period of $1\frac{1}{2}$ years

7. $600 invested at 5% compounded daily after a period of 3 years

8. $700 invested at 6% compounded daily after a period of 2 years

9. $10 invested at 11% compounded continuously after a period of 2 years

10. $40 invested at 7% compounded continuously after a period of 3 years

11. $100 invested at 10% compounded continuously after a period of $2\frac{1}{4}$ years

12. $100 invested at 12% compounded continuously after a period of $3\frac{3}{4}$ years

In Problems 13–22, find the principal needed now to get each amount; that is, find the present value.

13. To get $100 after 2 years at 6% compounded monthly

14. To get $75 after 3 years at 8% compounded quarterly

15. To get $1000 after $2\frac{1}{2}$ years at 6% compounded daily

16. To get $800 after $3\frac{1}{2}$ years at 7% compounded monthly

17. To get $600 after 2 years at 4% compounded quarterly

18. To get $300 after 4 years at 3% compounded daily

19. To get $80 after $3\frac{1}{4}$ years at 9% compounded continuously

20. To get $800 after $2\frac{1}{2}$ years at 8% compounded continuously

21. To get $400 after 1 year at 10% compounded continuously

22. To get $1000 after 1 year at 12% compounded continuously

In Problems 23–26, find the effective rate of interest.

23. For 5% compounded quarterly

24. For 6% compounded monthly

25. For 5% compounded continuously

26. For 6% compounded continuously

In Problems 27–30, determine the rate that represents the better deal.

27. 6% compounded quarterly or $6\frac{1}{4}$% compounded annually

28. 9% compounded quarterly of $9\frac{1}{4}$% compounded annually

29. 9% compounded monthly or 8.8% compounded daily

30. 8% compounded semiannually or 7.9% compounded daily

31. What rate of interest compounded annually is required to double an investment in 3 years?

32. What rate of interest compounded annually is required to double an investment in 6 years?

33. What rate of interest compounded annually is required to triple an investment in 5 years?

34. What rate of interest compounded annually is required to triple an investment in 10 years?

35. (a) How long does it take for an investment to double in value if it is invested at 8% compounded monthly?
    (b) How long does it take if the interest is compounded continuously?

36. (a) How long does it take for an investment to triple in value if it is invested at 6% compounded monthly?
    (b) How long does it take if the interest is compounded continuously?

37. What rate of interest compounded quarterly will yield an effective interest rate of 7%?

38. What rate of interest compounded continuously will yield an effective interest rate of 6%?

Applications and Extensions

39. **Time Required to Reach a Goal** If Tanisha has $100 to invest at 8% per annum compounded monthly, how long will it be before she has $150? If the compounding is continuous, how long will it be?

40. **Time Required to Reach a Goal** If Angela has $100 to invest at 10% per annum compounded monthly, how long will it be before she has $175? If the compounding is continuous, how long will it be?

41. Time Required to Reach a Goal How many years will it take for an initial investment of $10,000 to grow to $25,000? Assume a rate of interest of 6% compounded continuously.

42. Time Required to Reach a Goal How many years will it take for an initial investment of $25,000 to grow to $80,000? Assume a rate of interest of 7% compounded continuously.

43. Price Appreciation of Homes What will a $90,000 condominium cost 5 years from now if the price appreciation for condos over that period averages 3% compounded annually?

44. Credit Card Interest A department store charges 1.25% per month on the unpaid balance for customers with charge accounts (interest is compounded monthly). A customer charges $200 and does not pay her bill for 6 months. What is the bill at that time?

45. Saving for a Car Jerome will be buying a used car for $15,000 in 3 years. How much money should he ask his parents for now so that, if he invests it at 5% compounded continuously, he will have enough to buy the car?

46. Paying off a Loan John requires $3000 in 6 months to pay off a loan that has no prepayment privileges. If he has the $3000 now, how much of it should he save in an account paying 3% compounded monthly so that in 6 months he will have exactly $3000?

47. Return on a Stock George contemplates the purchase of 100 shares of a stock selling for $15 per share. The stock pays no dividends. The history of the stock indicates that it should grow at an annual rate of 15% per year. How much will the 100 shares of stock be worth in 5 years?

48. Return on an Investment A business purchased for $650,000 in 2005 is sold in 2008 for $850,000. What is the annual rate of return for this investment?

49. Comparing Savings Plans Jim places $1000 in a bank account that pays 5.6% compounded continuously. After 1 year, will he have enough money to buy a computer system that costs $1060? If another bank will pay Jim 5.9% compounded monthly, is this a better deal?

50. Savings Plans On January 1, Kim places $1000 in a certificate of deposit that pays 6.8% compounded continuously and matures in 3 months. Then Kim places the $1000 and the interest in a passbook account that pays 5.25% compounded monthly. How much does Kim have in the passbook account on May 1?

51. Comparing IRA Investments Will invests $2000 in his IRA in a bond trust that pays 9% interest compounded semiannually. His friend Henry invests $2000 in his IRA in a certificate of deposit that pays $8\frac{1}{2}$% compounded continuously. Who has more money after 20 years, Will or Henry?

52. Comparing Two Alternatives Suppose that April has access to an investment that will pay 10% interest compounded continuously. Which is better: to be given $1000 now so that she can take advantage of this investment opportunity or to be given $1325 after 3 years?

53. College Costs The average annual cost of college at 4-year private colleges was $29,026 in 2005. This was a 5.5% increase from the previous year.

Source: Trends in College Pricing 2005, College Board

(a) If the cost of college increases by 5.5% each year, what will be the average cost of college at a 4-year private college in 2015?

(b) College savings plans, such as a 529 plan, allow individuals to put money aside now to help pay for college later. If one such plan offers a rate of 4% compounded continuously, how much should be put in a college savings plan in 2005 to pay for 1 year of the cost of college at a 4-year private college in 2015?

54. Analyzing Interest Rates on a Mortgage Colleen and Bill have just purchased a house for $650,000, with the seller holding a second mortgage of $100,000. They promise to pay the seller $100,000 plus all accrued interest 5 years from now. The seller offers them three interest options on the second mortgage:

(a) Simple interest at 12% per annum

(b) $11\frac{1}{2}$% interest compounded monthly

(c) $11\frac{1}{4}$% interest compounded continuously

Which option is best; that is, which results in the least interest on the loan?

55. Federal Deficit At the end of fiscal year 2005, the federal budget deficit was $319 billion. At that time, 20-year Series EE bonds had a fixed rate of 3.2% compounded semiannually. If the federal government financed this deficit through EE bonds, how much would it have to pay back in 2025?

Source: U.S. Treasury Department

56. Federal Deficit On February 6, 2006, President Bush proposed the fiscal year 2007 federal budget. The proposal projected a fiscal year 2006 deficit of $423 billion and a fiscal year 2007 deficit of $354 billion. Assuming the deficit decreases at the same rate each year, when will the deficit be cut to $100 billion?

Source: Office of Management and Budget

Inflation *Problems 57–62 require the following discussion.* **Inflation** *is a term used to describe the erosion of the purchasing power of money. For example, suppose the annual inflation rate is 3%. Then $1000 worth of purchasing power now will have only $970 worth of purchasing power in 1 year because 3% of the original $1000 (0.03 × 1000 = 30) has been eroded due to inflation. In general, if the rate of inflation averages r% over n years, the amount A that $P will purchase after n years is*

$$A = P \cdot (1 - r)^n$$

where r is expressed as a decimal.

57. Inflation If the inflation rate averages 3%, how much will $1000 purchase in 2 years?

58. Inflation If the inflation rate averages 2%, how much will $1000 purchase in 3 years?

59. Inflation If the amount that $1000 will purchase is only $950 after 2 years, what was the average inflation rate?

60. Inflation If the amount that $1000 will purchase is only $930 after 2 years, what was the average inflation rate?

61. Inflation If the average inflation rate is 2%, how long is it until purchasing power is cut in half?

62. Inflation If the average inflation rate is 4%, how long is it until purchasing power is cut in half?

*Problems 63–66 involve zero-coupon bonds. A **zero-coupon bond** is a bond that is sold now at a discount and will pay its face value at the time when it matures; no interest payments are made.*

63. **Zero-Coupon Bonds** A zero-coupon bond can be redeemed in 20 years for $10,000. How much should you be willing to pay for it now if you want a return of:

   (a) 10% compounded monthly?

   (b) 10% compounded continuously?

64. **Zero-Coupon Bonds** A child's grandparents are considering buying a $40,000 face-value, zero-coupon bond at birth so that she will have enough money for her college education 17 years later. If they want a rate of return of 8% compounded annually, what should they pay for the bond?

65. **Zero-Coupon Bonds** How much should a $10,000 face-value, zero-coupon bond, maturing in 10 years, be sold for now if its rate of return is to be 8% compounded annually?

66. **Zero-Coupon Bonds** If Pat pays $12,485.52 for a $25,000 face-value, zero-coupon bond that matures in 8 years, what is his annual rate of return?

67. **Time to Double or Triple an Investment** The formula

$$t = \frac{\ln m}{n \ln\left(1 + \dfrac{r}{n}\right)}$$

can be used to find the number of years t required to multiply an investment m times when r is the per annum interest rate compounded n times a year.

   (a) How many years will it take to double the value of an IRA that compounds annually at the rate of 12%?

   (b) How many years will it take to triple the value of a savings account that compounds quarterly at an annual rate of 6%?

   (c) Give a derivation of this formula.

68. **Time to Reach an Investment Goal** The formula

$$t = \frac{\ln A - \ln P}{r}$$

can be used to find the number of years t required for an investment P to grow to a value A when compounded continuously at an annual rate r.

   (a) How long will it take to increase an initial investment of $1000 to $8000 at an annual rate of 10%?

   (b) What annual rate is required to increase the value of a $2000 IRA to $30,000 in 35 years?

   (c) Give a derivation of this formula.

*Problems 69–72, require the following discussion. The **Consumer Price Index (CPI)** indicates the relative change in price over time for a fixed basket of goods and services. It is a cost of living index that helps measure the effect of inflation on the cost of goods and services. The CPI uses the base period 1982–1984 for comparison (the CPI for this period is 100). The CPI for January 2006 was 198.3. This means that $100 in the period 1982–1984 had the same purchasing power as $198.30 in January 2006. In general, if the rate of inflation averages r% over n years, then the CPI index after n years is*

$$\text{CPI} = \text{CPI}_0\left(1 + \frac{r}{100}\right)^n$$

where CPI_0 is the CPI index at the beginning of the n-year period. Source: U.S. Bureau of Labor Statistics

69. **Consumer Price Index**

   (a) The CPI was 152.4 for 1995 and 195.3 for 2005. Assuming that annual inflation remained constant for this time period, determine the average annual inflation rate.

   (b) Using the inflation rate from part (a), in what year will the CPI reach 300?

70. **Consumer Price Index** If the current CPI is 234.2 and the average annual inflation rate is 2.8%, what will be the CPI in 5 years?

71. **Consumer Price Index** If the average annual inflation rate is 3.1%, how long will it take for the CPI index to double? (A doubling of the CPI index means purchasing power is cut in half).

72. **Consumer Price Index** The base period for the CPI changed in 1998. Under the previous weight and item structure, the CPI for 1995 was 456.5. If the average annual inflation rate was 5.57%, what year was used as the base period for the CPI?

Discussion and Writing

73. Explain in your own words what the term *compound interest* means. What does *continuous compounding* mean?

74. Explain in your own words the meaning of *present value*.

75. **Critical Thinking** You have just contracted to buy a house and will seek financing in the amount of $100,000. You go to several banks. Bank 1 will lend you $100,000 at the rate of 8.75% amortized over 30 years with a loan origination fee of 1.75%. Bank 2 will lend you $100,000 at the rate of 8.375% amortized over 15 years with a loan origination fee of 1.5%. Bank 3 will lend you $100,000 at the rate of 9.125% amortized over 30 years with no loan origination fee. Bank 4 will lend you $100,000 at the rate of 8.625% amortized over 15 years with no loan origination fee. Which loan would you take? Why? Be sure to have sound reasons for your choice.

Use the information in the table to assist you. If the amount of the monthly payment does not matter to you, which loan would you take? Again, have sound reasons for your choice. Compare your final decision with others in the class. Discuss.

	Monthly Payment	Loan Origination Fee
Bank 1	$786.70	$1,750.00
Bank 2	$977.42	$1,500.00
Bank 3	$813.63	$0.00
Bank 4	$990.68	$0.00

'Are You Prepared?' Answers

1. $15

2. $13\frac{1}{3}\%$

5.8 Exponential Growth and Decay Models; Newton's Law; Logistic Growth and Decay Models

> **OBJECTIVES** 1 Find Equations of Populations That Obey the Law of Uninhibited Growth (p. 323)
>
> 2 Find Equations of Populations That Obey the Law of Decay (p. 325)
>
> 3 Use Newton's Law of Cooling (p. 327)
>
> 4 Use Logistic Models (p. 328)

1 Find Equations of Populations That Obey the Law of Uninhibited Growth

Many natural phenomena have been found to follow the law that an amount A varies with time t according to the function

$$A(t) = A_0 e^{kt} \tag{1}$$

Here A_0 is the original amount ($t = 0$) and $k \neq 0$ is a constant.

If $k > 0$, then equation (1) states that the amount A is increasing over time; if $k < 0$, the amount A is decreasing over time. In either case, when an amount A varies over time according to equation (1), it is said to follow the **exponential law** or the **law of uninhibited growth** ($k > 0$) **or decay** ($k < 0$). See Figure 54.

Figure 54

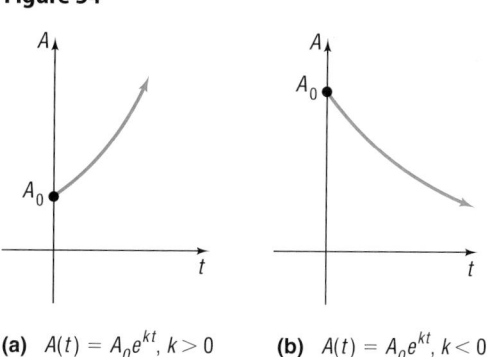

(a) $A(t) = A_0 e^{kt}$, $k > 0$ **(b)** $A(t) = A_0 e^{kt}$, $k < 0$

For example, we saw in Section 5.7 that continuously compounded interest follows the law of uninhibited growth. In this section we shall look at three additional phenomena that follow the exponential law.

Cell division is the growth process of many living organisms, such as amoebas, plants, and human skin cells. Based on an ideal situation in which no cells die and no by-products are produced, the number of cells present at a given time follows the law of uninhibited growth. Actually, however, after enough time has passed, growth at an exponential rate will cease due to the influence of factors such as lack of living space and dwindling food supply. The law of uninhibited growth accurately models only the early stages of the cell division process.

The cell division process begins with a culture containing N_0 cells. Each cell in the culture grows for a certain period of time and then divides into two identical cells. We assume that the time needed for each cell to divide in two is constant and does not change as the number of cells increases. These new cells then grow, and eventually each divides in two, and so on.

Uninhibited Growth of Cells

A model that gives the number N of cells in a culture after a time t has passed (in the early stages of growth) is

$$N(t) = N_0 e^{kt} \qquad k > 0 \tag{2}$$

where N_0 is the initial number of cells and k is a positive constant that represents the growth rate of the cells.

In using formula (2) to model the growth of cells, we are using a function that yields positive real numbers, even though we are counting the number of cells, which must be an integer. This is a common practice in many applications.

| EXAMPLE 1 | Bacterial Growth |

A colony of bacteria grows according to the law of uninhibited growth according to the function $N(t) = 100e^{0.045t}$, where N is measured in grams and t is measured in days.

(a) Determine the initial amount of bacteria.
(b) What is the growth rate of the bacteria?
(c) Graph the function using a graphing utility.
(d) What is the population after 5 days?
(e) How long will it take for the population to reach 140 grams?
(f) What is the doubling time for the population?

Solution

(a) The initial amount of bacteria, N_0, is obtained when $t = 0$, so

$$N_0 = N(0) = 100e^{0.045(0)} = 100 \text{ grams}$$

(b) Compare $N(t) = 100e^{0.045t}$ to $N(t) = 100e^{kt}$. The value of k, 0.045, indicates a growth rate of 4.5%.

(c) Figure 55 shows the graph of $N(t) = 100e^{0.045t}$.

(d) The population after 5 days is $N(5) = 100e^{0.045(5)} \approx 125.2$ grams.

(e) To find how long it takes for the population to reach 140 grams, we solve the equation $N(t) = 140$.

$$100e^{0.045t} = 140$$
$$e^{0.045t} = 1.4 \qquad \text{Divide both sides of the equation by 100.}$$
$$0.045t = \ln 1.4 \qquad \text{Rewrite as a logarithm.}$$
$$t = \frac{\ln 1.4}{0.045} \qquad \text{Divide both sides of the equation by 0.045.}$$
$$\approx 7.5 \text{ days}$$

Figure 55

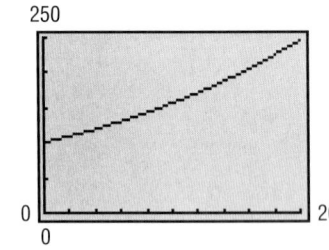

(f) The population doubles when $N(t) = 200$ grams, so we find the doubling time by solving the equation $200 = 100e^{0.045t}$ for t.

$$200 = 100e^{0.045t}$$
$$2 = e^{0.045t} \qquad \text{Divide both sides of the equation by 100.}$$
$$\ln 2 = 0.045t \qquad \text{Rewrite as a logarithm.}$$
$$t = \frac{\ln 2}{0.045} \qquad \text{Divide both sides of the equation by 0.045.}$$
$$\approx 15.4 \text{ days}$$

The population doubles approximately every 15.4 days.

Now Work PROBLEM 1

EXAMPLE 2	**Bacterial Growth**

A colony of bacteria grows according to the law of uninhibited growth.

(a) If N is the number of cells and t is the time in hours, express N as a function of t.

(b) If the number of bacteria doubles in 3 hours, find the function that gives the number of cells in the culture.

(c) How long will it take for the size of the colony to triple?

(d) How long will it take for the population to double a second time (that is, increase four times)?

Solution (a) Using formula (2), the number N of cells at a time t is

$$N(t) = N_0 e^{kt}$$

where N_0 is the initial number of bacteria present and k is a positive number.

(b) We seek the number k. The number of cells doubles in 3 hours, so we have

$$N(3) = 2N_0$$

But $N(3) = N_0 e^{k(3)}$, so

$$N_0 e^{k(3)} = 2N_0$$
$$e^{3k} = 2 \qquad \text{Divide both sides by } N_0.$$
$$3k = \ln 2 \qquad \text{Write the exponential equation as a logarithm.}$$
$$k = \frac{1}{3} \ln 2$$

The function that models this growth process is therefore

$$N(t) = N_0 e^{\left(\frac{1}{3} \ln 2\right)t}$$

(c) The time t needed for the size of the colony to triple requires that $N = 3N_0$. We substitute $3N_0$ for N to get

$$3N_0 = N_0 e^{\left(\frac{1}{3} \ln 2\right)t}$$
$$3 = e^{\left(\frac{1}{3} \ln 2\right)t} \qquad \text{Divide both sides by } N_0.$$
$$\left(\frac{1}{3} \ln 2\right)t = \ln 3 \qquad \text{Write the exponential equation as a logarithm.}$$
$$t = \frac{3 \ln 3}{\ln 2} \approx 4.755 \text{ hours}$$

It will take about 4.755 hours or 4 hours, 45 minutes for the size of the colony to triple.

(d) If a population doubles in 3 hours, it will double a second time in 3 more hours, for a total time of 6 hours.

2 Find Equations of Populations That Obey the Law of Decay

Radioactive materials follow the law of uninhibited decay.

Uninhibited Radioactive Decay

The amount A of a radioactive material present at time t is given by

$$A(t) = A_0 e^{kt} \qquad k < 0 \qquad \text{(3)}$$

where A_0 is the original amount of radioactive material and k is a negative number that represents the rate of decay.

All radioactive substances have a specific **half-life,** which is the time required for half of the radioactive substance to decay. In **carbon dating,** we use the fact that all living organisms contain two kinds of carbon, carbon 12 (a stable carbon) and carbon 14 (a radioactive carbon with a half-life of 5600 years). While an organism is living, the ratio of carbon 12 to carbon 14 is constant. But when an organism dies, the original amount of carbon 12 present remains unchanged, whereas the amount of carbon 14 begins to decrease. This change in the amount of carbon 14 present relative to the amount of carbon 12 present makes it possible to calculate when the organism died.

EXAMPLE 3

Estimating the Age of Ancient Tools

Traces of burned wood along with ancient stone tools in an archeological dig in Chile were found to contain approximately 1.67% of the original amount of carbon 14.

(a) If the half-life of carbon 14 is 5600 years, approximately when was the tree cut and burned?

(b) Using a graphing utility, graph the relation between the percentage of carbon 14 remaining and time.

(c) Determine the time that elapses until half of the carbon 14 remains. This answer should equal the half-life of carbon 14.

(d) Use a graphing utility to verify the answer found in part (a).

Solution

(a) Using formula (3), the amount A of carbon 14 present at time t is

$$A(t) = A_0 e^{kt}$$

where A_0 is the original amount of carbon 14 present and k is a negative number. We first seek the number k. To find it, we use the fact that after 5600 years half of the original amount of carbon 14 remains, so $A(5600) = \dfrac{1}{2}A_0$. Then

$$\frac{1}{2}A_0 = A_0 e^{k(5600)}$$

$$\frac{1}{2} = e^{5600k} \qquad\qquad \text{Divide both sides of the equation by } A_0.$$

$$5600k = \ln\frac{1}{2} \qquad\qquad \text{Rewrite as a logarithm.}$$

$$k = \frac{1}{5600}\ln\frac{1}{2} \approx -0.000124$$

Formula (3) therefore becomes

$$A(t) = A_0 e^{\frac{\ln\frac{1}{2}}{5600}t}$$

If the amount A of carbon 14 now present is 1.67% of the original amount, it follows that

$$0.0167A_0 = A_0 e^{\frac{\ln\frac{1}{2}}{5600}t}$$

$$0.0167 = e^{\frac{\ln\frac{1}{2}}{5600}t} \qquad\qquad \text{Divide both sides of the equation by } A_0.$$

$$\frac{\ln\frac{1}{2}}{5600}t = \ln 0.0167 \qquad\qquad \text{Rewrite as a logarithm.}$$

$$t = \frac{5600}{\ln\frac{1}{2}}\ln 0.0167 \approx 33{,}062 \text{ years}$$

The tree was cut and burned about 33,062 years ago. Some archeologists use this conclusion to argue that humans lived in the Americas 33,000 years ago, much earlier than is generally accepted.

Figure 56

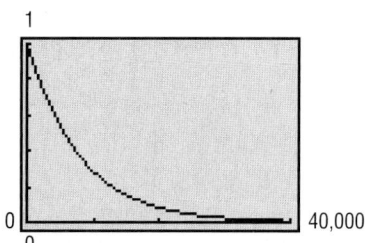

(b) Figure 56 shows the graph of $y = e^{\frac{\ln\frac{1}{2}}{5600}x}$, where y is the fraction of carbon 14 present and x is the time.

(c) By graphing $Y_1 = 0.5$ and $Y_2 = e^{\frac{\ln\frac{1}{2}}{5600}x}$, where x is time, and using INTERSECT, we find that it takes 5600 years until half the carbon 14 remains. The half-life of carbon 14 is 5600 years.

(d) By graphing $Y_1 = 0.0167$ and $Y_2 = e^{\frac{\ln\frac{1}{2}}{5600}x}$, where x is time, and using INTERSECT, we find that it takes 33,062 years until 1.67% of the carbon 14 remains.

— **Now Work** PROBLEM 3

3 Use Newton's Law of Cooling

Newton's Law of Cooling* states that the temperature of a heated object decreases exponentially over time toward the temperature of the surrounding medium.

Newton's Law of Cooling

The temperature u of a heated object at a given time t can be modeled by the following function:

$$u(t) = T + (u_0 - T)e^{kt} \qquad k < 0 \tag{4}$$

where T is the constant temperature of the surrounding medium, u_0 is the initial temperature of the heated object, and k is a negative constant.

| EXAMPLE 4 | **Using Newton's Law of Cooling** |

An object is heated to 100°C (degrees Celsius) and is then allowed to cool in a room whose air temperature is 30°C.

(a) If the temperature of the object is 80°C after 5 minutes, when will its temperature be 50°C?

(b) Using a graphing utility, graph the relation found between the temperature and time.

(c) Using a graphing utility, verify the results from part (a).

(d) Using a graphing utility, determine the elapsed time before the object is 35°C.

(e) What do you notice about the temperature as time passes?

Solution

(a) Using formula (4) with $T = 30$ and $u_0 = 100$, the temperature (in degrees Celsius) of the object at time t (in minutes) is

$$u(t) = 30 + (100 - 30)e^{kt} = 30 + 70e^{kt}$$

where k is a negative constant. To find k, we use the fact that $u = 80$ when $t = 5$. Then

$$80 = 30 + 70e^{k(5)}$$
$$50 = 70e^{5k}$$
$$e^{5k} = \frac{50}{70}$$
$$5k = \ln\frac{5}{7}$$
$$k = \frac{1}{5}\ln\frac{5}{7} \approx -0.0673$$

*Named after Sir Isaac Newton (1642–1727), one of the cofounders of calculus.

Formula (4) therefore becomes

$$u(t) = 30 + 70e^{\frac{\ln\frac{5}{7}}{5}t}$$

We want to find t when $u = 50°C$, so

$$50 = 30 + 70e^{\frac{\ln\frac{5}{7}}{5}t}$$

$$20 = 70e^{\frac{\ln\frac{5}{7}}{5}t}$$

$$e^{\frac{\ln\frac{5}{7}}{5}t} = \frac{20}{70}$$

$$\frac{\ln\frac{5}{7}}{5}t = \ln\frac{2}{7}$$

$$t = \frac{5}{\ln\frac{5}{7}}\ln\frac{2}{7} \approx 18.6 \text{ minutes}$$

The temperature of the object will be 50°C after about 18.6 minutes or 18 minutes, 37 seconds.

Figure 57

100

0

50

0

(b) Figure 57 shows the graph of $y = 30 + 70e^{\frac{\ln\frac{5}{7}}{5}x}$, where y is the temperature and x is the time.

(c) By graphing $Y_1 = 50$ and $Y_2 = 30 + 70e^{\frac{\ln\frac{5}{7}}{5}x}$, where x is time, and using INTERSECT, we find that it takes $x = 18.6$ minutes (18 minutes, 37 seconds) for the temperature to cool to 50°C.

(d) By graphing $Y_1 = 35$ and $Y_2 = 30 + 70e^{\frac{\ln\frac{5}{7}}{5}x}$, where x is time, and using INTERSECT, we find that it takes $x = 39.22$ minutes (39 minutes, 13 seconds) for the temperature to cool to 35°C.

(e) As x increases, the value of $e^{\frac{\ln\frac{5}{7}}{5}x}$ approaches zero, so the value of y, the temperature of the object, approaches 30°C, the air temperature of the room.

Now Work PROBLEM 13

4 Use Logistic Models

The exponential growth model $A(t) = A_0e^{kt}$, $k > 0$, assumes uninhibited growth, meaning that the value of the function grows without limit. Recall that we stated that cell division could be modeled using this function, assuming that no cells die and no by-products are produced. However, cell division eventually is limited by factors such as living space and food supply. The **logistic model,** given next, can describe situations where the growth or decay of the dependent variable is limited.

Logistic Model

In a logistic model, the population P after time t is given by the function

$$P(t) = \frac{c}{1 + ae^{-bt}} \qquad (5)$$

where a, b, and c are constants with $c > 0$. The model is a growth model if $b > 0$; the model is a decay model if $b < 0$.

The number c is called the **carrying capacity** (for growth models) because the value $P(t)$ approaches c as t approaches infinity; that is, $\lim\limits_{t \to \infty} P(t) = c$. The number $|b|$ is the growth rate for $b > 0$ and the decay rate for $b < 0$. Figure 58(a) shows the graph of a typical logistic growth function, and Figure 58(b) shows the graph of a typical logistic decay function.

Figure 58

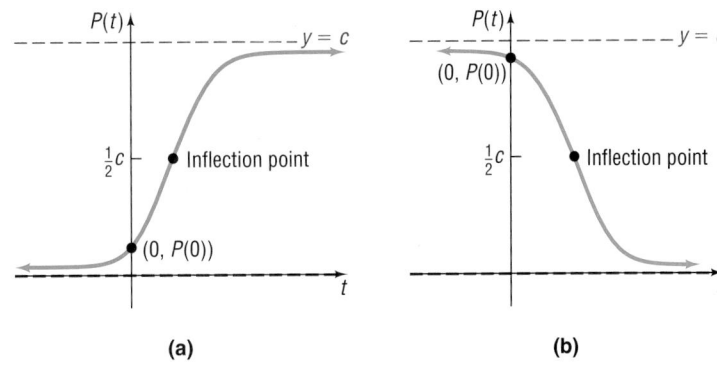

(a)   (b)

Based on the figures, we have the following properties of logistic growth functions.

Properties of the Logistic Model

1. The domain is the set of all real numbers. The range is the interval $(0, c)$, where c is the carrying capacity.
2. There are no x-intercepts; the y-intercept is $P(0)$.
3. There are two horizontal asymptotes: $y = 0$ and $y = c$.
4. $P(t)$ is an increasing function if $b > 0$ and a decreasing function if $b < 0$.
5. There is an **inflection point** where $P(t)$ equals $\dfrac{1}{2}$ of the carrying capacity. The inflection point is the point on the graph where the graph changes from being curved upward to curved downward for growth functions and the point where the graph changes from being curved downward to curved upward for decay functions.
6. The graph is smooth and continuous, with no corners or gaps.

EXAMPLE 5	Fruit Fly Population

Fruit flies are placed in a half-pint milk bottle with a banana (for food) and yeast plants (for food and to provide a stimulus to lay eggs). Suppose that the fruit fly population after t days is given by

$$P(t) = \frac{230}{1 + 56.5e^{-0.37t}}$$

(a) State the carrying capacity and the growth rate.
(b) Determine the initial population.
(c) What is the population after 5 days?
(d) How long does it take for the population to reach 180?
(e) Use a graphing utility to determine how long it takes for the population to reach one-half of the carrying capacity.

Solution

(a) As $t \to \infty$, $e^{-0.37t} \to 0$ and $P(t) \to \dfrac{230}{1}$. The carrying capacity of the half-pint bottle is 230 fruit flies. The growth rate is $|b| = |0.37| = 37\%$ per day.

(b) To find the initial number of fruit flies in the half-pint bottle, we evaluate $P(0)$.

$$P(0) = \frac{230}{1 + 56.5e^{-0.37(0)}}$$

$$= \frac{230}{1 + 56.5}$$

$$= 4$$

So, initially, there were 4 fruit flies in the half-pint bottle.

(c) To find the number of fruit flies in the half-pint bottle after 5 days, we evaluate $P(5)$.

$$P(5) = \frac{230}{1 + 56.5e^{-0.37(5)}} \approx 23 \text{ fruit flies}$$

After 5 days, there are approximately 23 fruit flies in the bottle.

(d) To determine when the population of fruit flies will be 180, we solve the equation $P(t) = 180$.

$$\frac{230}{1 + 56.5e^{-0.37t}} = 180$$

$$230 = 180(1 + 56.5e^{-0.37t})$$

$$1.2778 = 1 + 56.5e^{-0.37t} \qquad \text{Divide both sides by 180.}$$

$$0.2778 = 56.5e^{-0.37t} \qquad \text{Subtract 1 from both sides.}$$

$$0.0049 = e^{-0.37t} \qquad \text{Divide both sides by 56.5.}$$

$$\ln(0.0049) = -0.37t \qquad \text{Rewrite as a logarithmic expression.}$$

$$t \approx 14.4 \text{ days} \qquad \text{Divide both sides by } -0.37.$$

It will take approximately 14.4 days (14 days, 10 hours) for the population to reach 180 fruit flies.

(e) One-half of the carrying capacity is 115 fruit flies. We solve $P(t) = 115$ by graphing $Y_1 = \dfrac{230}{1 + 56.5e^{-0.37x}}$ and $Y_2 = 115$ and using INTERSECT. See Figure 59. The population will reach one-half of the carrying capacity in about 10.9 days (10 days, 22 hours).

Figure 59

Look back at Figure 59. Notice the point where the graph reaches 115 fruit flies (one-half of the carrying capacity): the graph changes from being curved upward to being curved downward. Using the language of calculus, we say the graph changes from increasing at an increasing rate to increasing at a decreasing rate. For any logistic growth function, when the population reaches one-half the carrying capacity, the population growth starts to slow down.

Exploration

On the same viewing rectangle, graph

$$Y_1 = \frac{500}{1 + 24e^{-0.03x}} \text{ and } Y_2 = \frac{500}{1 + 24e^{-0.08x}}$$

What effect does the growth rate $|b|$ have on the logistic growth function?

━━━ **Now Work** PROBLEM 23

| EXAMPLE 6 | Wood Products |

The EFISCEN wood product model classifies wood products according to their life-span. There are four classifications: short (1 year), medium short (4 years), medium long (16 years), and long (50 years). Based on data obtained from the European Forest Institute, the percentage of remaining wood products after t years for wood products with long life-spans (such as those used in the building industry) is given by

$$P(t) = \frac{100.3952}{1 + 0.0316e^{0.0581t}}$$

(a) What is the decay rate?
(b) What is the percentage of remaining wood products after 10 years?
(c) How long does it take for the percentage of remaining wood products to reach 50%?
(d) Explain why the numerator given in the model is reasonable.

Solution
(a) The decay rate is $|b| = |-0.0581| = 5.81\%$.
(b) Evaluate $P(10)$.

$$P(10) = \frac{100.3952}{1 + 0.0316e^{0.0581(10)}} \approx 95.0$$

So 95% of long-life-span wood products remains after 10 years.
(c) Solve the equation $P(t) = 50$.

$$\frac{100.3952}{1 + 0.0316e^{0.0581t}} = 50$$

$$100.3952 = 50(1 + 0.0316e^{0.0581t})$$

$2.0079 = 1 + 0.0316e^{0.0581t}$ Divide both sides by 50.

$1.0079 = 0.0316e^{0.0581t}$ Subtract 1 from both sides.

$31.8957 = e^{0.0581t}$ Divide both sides by 0.0316.

$\ln(31.8957) = 0.0581t$ Rewrite as a logarithmic expression.

$t \approx 59.6 \text{ years}$ Divide both sides by 0.0581.

It will take approximately 59.6 years for the percentage of long-life-span wood products remaining to reach 50%.
(d) The numerator of 100.3952 is reasonable because the maximum percentage of wood products remaining that is possible is 100%.

 Now Work PROBLEM 27

5.8 Assess Your Understanding

Applications and Extensions

1. **Growth of an Insect Population** The size P of a certain insect population at time t (in days) obeys the model $P(t) = 500e^{0.02t}$.
   (a) Determine the number of insects at $t = 0$ days.
   (b) What is the growth rate of the insect population?
   (c) Graph the function using a graphing utility.
   (d) What is the population after 10 days?
   (e) When will the insect population reach 800?
   (f) When will the insect population double?

2. **Growth of Bacteria** The number N of bacteria present in a culture at time t (in hours) obeys the model $N(t) = 1000e^{0.01t}$.
   (a) Determine the number of bacteria at $t = 0$ hours.
   (b) What is the growth rate of the bacteria?

   (c) Graph the function using a graphing utility.
   (d) What is the population after 4 hours?
   (e) When will the number of bacteria reach 1700?
   (f) When will the number of bacteria double?

3. **Radioactive Decay** Strontium 90 is a radioactive material that decays according to the function $A(t) = A_0 e^{-0.0244t}$, where A_0 is the initial amount present and A is the amount present at time t (in years). Assume that a scientist has a sample of 500 grams of strontium 90.
   (a) What is the decay rate of strontium 90?
   (b) Graph the function using a graphing utility.
   (c) How much strontium 90 is left after 10 years?
   (d) When will 400 grams of strontium 90 be left?
   (e) What is the half-life of strontium 90?

4. Radioactive Decay Iodine 131 is a radioactive material that decays according to the function $A(t) = A_0 e^{-0.087t}$, where A_0 is the initial amount present and A is the amount present at time t (in days). Assume that a scientist has a sample of 100 grams of iodine 131.
  (a) What is the decay rate of iodine 131?
  (b) Graph the function using a graphing utility.
  (c) How much iodine 131 is left after 9 days?
  (d) When will 70 grams of iodine 131 be left?
  (e) What is the half-life of iodine 131?

5. Growth of a Colony of Mosquitoes The population of a colony of mosquitoes obeys the law of uninhibited growth.
  (a) If N is the population of the colony and t is the time in days, express N as a function of t.
  (b) If there are 1000 mosquitoes initially and there are 1800 after 1 day, what is the size of the colony after 3 days?
  (c) How long is it until there are 10,000 mosquitoes?

6. Bacterial Growth A culture of bacteria obeys the law of uninhibited growth.
  (a) If N is the number of bacteria in the culture and t is the time in hours, express N as a function of t.
  (b) If 500 bacteria are present initially and there are 800 after 1 hour, how many will be present in the culture after 5 hours?
  (c) How long is it until there are 20,000 bacteria?

7. Population Growth The population of a southern city follows the exponential law.
  (a) If N is the population of the city and t is the time in years, express N as a function of t.
  (b) If the population doubled in size over an 18-month period and the current population is 10,000, what will the population be 2 years from now?

8. Population Decline The population of a midwestern city follows the exponential law.
  (a) If N is the population of the city and t is the time in years, express N as a function of t.
  (b) If the population decreased from 900,000 to 800,000 from 2005 to 2007, what will the population be in 2009?

9. Radioactive Decay The half-life of radium is 1690 years. If 10 grams are present now, how much will be present in 50 years?

10. Radioactive Decay The half-life of radioactive potassium is 1.3 billion years. If 10 grams are present now, how much will be present in 100 years? In 1000 years?

11. Estimating the Age of a Tree A piece of charcoal is found to contain 30% of the carbon 14 that it originally had.
  (a) When did the tree from which the charcoal came die? Use 5600 years as the half-life of carbon 14.
  (b) Using a graphing utility, graph the relation between the percentage of carbon 14 remaining and time.
  (c) Using INTERSECT, determine the time that elapses until half of the carbon 14 remains.
  (d) Verify the answer found in part (a).

12. Estimating the Age of a Fossil A fossilized leaf contains 70% of its normal amount of carbon 14.
  (a) How old is the fossil?
  (b) Using a graphing utility, graph the relation between the percentage of carbon 14 remaining and time.
  (c) Using INTERSECT, determine the time that elapses until half of the carbon 14 remains.
  (d) Verify the answer found in part (a).

13. Cooling Time of a Pizza A pizza baked at 450°F is removed from the oven at 5:00 PM into a room that is a constant 70°F. After 5 minutes, the pizza is at 300°F.
  (a) At what time can you begin eating the pizza if you want its temperature to be 135°F?
  (b) Using a graphing utility, graph the relation between temperature and time.
  (c) Using INTERSECT, determine the time that needs to elapse before the pizza is 160°F.
  (d) TRACE the function for large values of time. What do you notice about y, the temperature?

14. Newton's Law of Cooling A thermometer reading 72°F is placed in a refrigerator where the temperature is a constant 38°F.
  (a) If the thermometer reads 60°F after 2 minutes, what will it read after 7 minutes?
  (b) How long will it take before the thermometer reads 39°F?
  (c) Using a graphing utility, graph the relation between temperature and time.
  (d) Using INTERSECT, determine the time needed to elapse before the thermometer reads 45°F.
  (e) TRACE the function for large values of time. What do you notice about y, the temperature?

15. Newton's Law of Heating A thermometer reading 8°C is brought into a room with a constant temperature of 35°C.
  (a) If the thermometer reads 15°C after 3 minutes, what will it read after being in the room for 5 minutes? For 10 minutes?
  (b) Graph the relation between temperature and time. TRACE to verify that your answers are correct.
  [**Hint:** You need to construct a formula similar to equation (4).]

16. Warming Time of a Beer Stein A beer stein has a temperature of 28°F. It is placed in a room with a constant temperature of 70°F. After 10 minutes, the temperature of the stein has risen to 35°F. What will the temperature of the stein be after 30 minutes? How long will it take the stein to reach a temperature of 45°F? (See the hint given for Problem 15.)

17. Decomposition of Chlorine in a Pool Under certain water conditions, the free chlorine (hypochlorous acid, HOCl) in a swimming pool decomposes according to the law of uninhibited decay. After shocking his pool, Ben tested the water and found the amount of free chlorine to be 2.5 parts per million (ppm). Twenty-four hours later, Ben tested the water again and found the amount of free chlorine to be 2.2 ppm. What will be the reading after 3 days (that is, 72 hours)? When the chlorine level reaches 1.0 ppm, Ben must shock the pool again. How long can Ben go before he must shock the pool again?

18. Decomposition of Dinitrogen Pentoxide At 45°C, dinitrogen pentoxide (N_2O_5) decomposes into nitrous dioxide (NO_2) and oxygen (O_2) according to the law of uninhibited decay. An initial amount of 0.25 mole of dinitrogen pentoxide decomposes to 0.15 mole in 17 minutes. How much dinitrogen pentoxide will remain after 30 minutes? How long will it take until 0.01 mole of dinitrogen pentoxide remains?

19. Decomposition of Sucrose Reacting with water in an acidic solution at 35°C, sucrose ($C_{12}H_{22}O_{11}$) decomposes into glucose ($C_6H_{12}O_6$) and fructose ($C_6H_{12}O_6$)* according to the law of uninhibited decay. An initial amount of 0.40 mole of sucrose decomposes to 0.36 mole in 30 minutes. How much sucrose will remain after 2 hours? How long will it take until 0.10 mole of sucrose remains?

20. Decomposition of Salt in Water Salt (NaCl) decomposes in water into sodium (Na^+) and chloride (Cl^-) ions according to the law of uninhibited decay. If the initial amount of salt is 25 kilograms and, after 10 hours, 15 kilograms of salt is left, how much salt is left after 1 day? How long does it take until $\frac{1}{2}$ kilogram of salt is left?

21. Radioactivity from Chernobyl After the release of radioactive material into the atmosphere from a nuclear power plant at Chernobyl (Ukraine) in 1986, the hay in Austria was contaminated by iodine 131 (half-life 8 days). If it is safe to feed the hay to cows when 10% of the iodine 131 remains, how long did the farmers need to wait to use this hay?

22. Pig Roasts The hotel Bora-Bora is having a pig roast. At noon, the chef put the pig in a large earthen oven. The pig's original temperature was 75°F. At 2:00 PM the chef checked the pig's temperature and was upset because it had reached only 100°F. If the oven's temperature remains a constant 325°F, at what time may the hotel serve its guests, assuming that pork is done when it reaches 175°F?

23. Population of a Bacteria Culture The logistic growth model

$$P(t) = \frac{1000}{1 + 32.33e^{-0.439t}}$$

represents the population (in grams) of a bacterium after t hours.
(a) Determine the carrying capacity of the environment.
(b) What is the growth rate of the bacteria?
(c) Determine the initial population size.
(d) Use a graphing utility to graph $P = P(t)$.
(e) What is the population after 9 hours?
(f) When will the population be 700 grams?
(g) How long does it take for the population to reach one-half of the carrying capacity?

24. Population of an Endangered Species Often environmentalists capture an endangered species and transport the species to a controlled environment where the species can produce offspring and regenerate its population. Suppose

*Author's Note: Surprisingly, the chemical formulas for glucose and fructose are the same. This is not a typo.

that six American bald eagles are captured, transported to Montana, and set free. Based on experience, the environmentalists expect the population to grow according to the model

$$P(t) = \frac{500}{1 + 82.33e^{-0.162t}}$$

where t is measured in years.

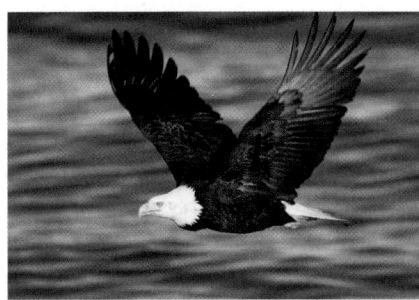

(a) Determine the carrying capacity of the environment.
(b) What is the growth rate of the bald eagle?
(c) Use a graphing utility to graph $P = P(t)$.
(d) What is the population after 3 years?
(e) When will the population be 300 eagles?
(f) How long does it take for the population to reach one-half of the carrying capacity?

25. The *Challenger* Disaster After the *Challenger* disaster in 1986, a study was made of the 23 launches that preceded the fatal flight. A mathematical model was developed involving the relationship between the Fahrenheit temperature x around the O-rings and the number y of eroded or leaky primary O-rings. The model stated that

$$y = \frac{6}{1 + e^{-(5.085 - 0.1156x)}}$$

where the number 6 indicates the 6 primary O-rings on the spacecraft.
(a) What is the predicted number of eroded or leaky primary O-rings at a temperature of 100°F?
(b) What is the predicted number of eroded or leaky primary O-rings at a temperature of 60°F?
(c) What is the predicted number of eroded or leaky primary O-rings at a temperature of 30°F?
(d) Graph the equation. At what temperature is the predicted number of eroded or leaky O-rings 1? 3? 5?

Source: Linda Tappin, "Analyzing Data Relating to the *Challenger* Disaster," *Mathematics Teacher,* Vol. 87, No. 6, September 1994, pp. 423–426.

26. Word Users According to a survey by Olsten Staffing Services, the percentage of companies reporting usage of Microsoft Word t years since 1984 is given by

$$P(t) = \frac{99.744}{1 + 3.014e^{-0.799t}}$$

(a) What is the growth rate in the percentage of Microsoft Word users?
(b) Use a graphing utility to graph $P = P(t)$.
(c) What was the percentage of Microsoft Word users in 1990?
(d) During what year did the percentage of Microsoft Word users reach 90%?
(e) Explain why the numerator given in the model is reasonable. What does it imply?

27. Home Computers The logistic model

$$P(t) = \frac{95.4993}{1 + 0.0405e^{0.1968t}}$$

represents the percentage of households that do not own a personal computer t years since 1984.

(a) Evaluate and interpret $P(0)$.
(b) Use a graphing utility to graph $P = P(t)$.
(c) What percentage of households did not own a personal computer in 1995?
(d) In what year will the percentage of households that do not own a personal computer reach 10%?

Source: U.S. Department of Commerce

28. Farmers The logistic model

$$W(t) = \frac{14,656.248}{1 + 0.059e^{0.057t}}$$

represents the number of farm workers in the United States t years after 1910.

(a) Evaluate and interpret $W(0)$.
(b) Use a graphing utility to graph $W = W(t)$.

(c) How many farm workers were there in the United States in 1990?
(d) When did the number of farm workers in the United States reach 10,000?
(e) According to this model, what happens to the number of farm workers in the United States as t approaches ∞? Based on this result, do you think that it is reasonable to use this model to predict the number of farm workers in the United States in 2060? Why?

Source: U.S. Department of Agriculture

29. Birthdays The logistic model

$$P(n) = \frac{113.3198}{1 + 0.115e^{0.0912n}}$$

models the probability that, in a room of n people, no two people share the same birthday.

(a) Use a graphing utility to graph $P = P(n)$.
(b) In a room of $n = 15$ people, what is the probability that no two share the same birthday?
(c) How many people must be in a room before the probability that no two people share the same birthday falls below 10%?
(d) What happens to the probability as n increases? Explain what this result means.

30. Bank Failures The logistic model

$$F(t) = \frac{130.118}{1 + 0.00022e^{3.042t}}$$

models the number of bank failures in the United States t years since 1991.

(a) Evaluate and interpret $F(0)$.
(b) Use a graphing utility to graph $F = F(t)$.
(c) How many bank failures were there in 1994 ($t = 3$)?
(d) In what year did the number of bank failures reach 10?
(e) What does the model imply will happen to the number of bank failures as time passes?

Source: Federal Deposit Insurance Corporation

5.9 Building Exponential, Logarithmic, and Logistic Models from Data

PREPARING FOR THIS SECTION *Before getting started, review the following:*

- Building Linear Models from Data (Section 3.2, pp. 136–139)
- Building Cubic Models from Data (Section 4.1, pp. 186–187)
- Building Quadratic Models from Data (Section 3.4, pp. 158–160)

OBJECTIVES 1 Build an Exponential Model from Data (p. 335)
2 Build a Logarithmic Model from Data (p. 336)
3 Build a Logistic Model from Data (p. 337)

 In Section 3.2, we discussed how to find the linear function of best fit ($y = ax + b$), in Section 3.4, we discussed how to find the quadratic function of best fit ($y = ax^2 + bx + c$), and in Section 4.1, we discussed how to find the cubic function of best fit ($y = ax^3 + bx^2 + cx + d$).

In this section we will discuss how to use a graphing utility to find equations of best fit that describe the relation between two variables when the relation is thought to be exponential ($y = ab^x$), logarithmic ($y = a + b \ln x$), or logistic $\left(y = \dfrac{c}{1 + ae^{-bx}} \right)$. As before, we draw a scatter diagram of the data to help to determine the appropriate model to use.

Figure 60 shows scatter diagrams that will typically be observed for the three models. Below each scatter diagram are any restrictions on the values of the parameters.

Figure 60

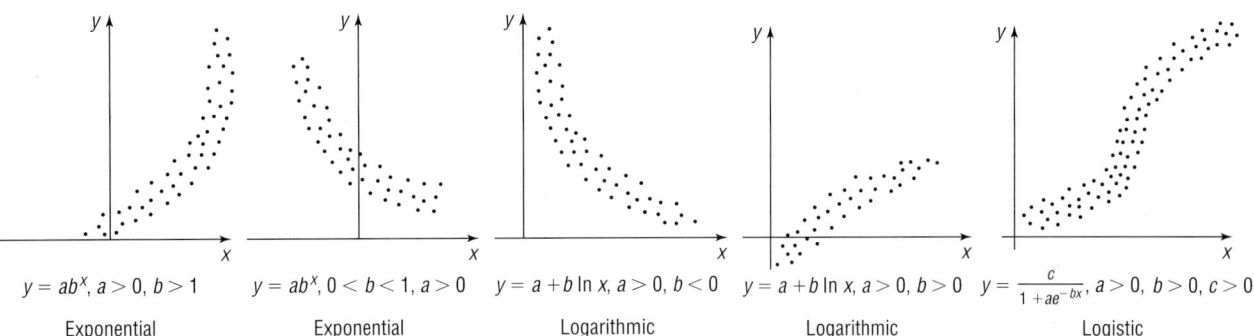

$y = ab^x, a > 0, b > 1$
Exponential

$y = ab^x, 0 < b < 1, a > 0$
Exponential

$y = a + b \ln x, a > 0, b < 0$
Logarithmic

$y = a + b \ln x, a > 0, b > 0$
Logarithmic

$y = \dfrac{c}{1 + ae^{-bx}}, a > 0, b > 0, c > 0$
Logistic

Most graphing utilities have REGression options that fit data to a specific type of curve. Once the data have been entered and a scatter diagram obtained, the type of curve that you want to fit to the data is selected. Then that REGression option is used to obtain the curve of *best fit* of the type selected.

The correlation coefficient r will appear only if the model can be written as a linear expression. As it turns out, r will appear for the linear, power, exponential, and logarithmic models, since these models can be written as a linear expression. Remember, the closer $|r|$ is to 1, the better the fit.

Let's look at some examples.

1 Build an Exponential Model from Data

We saw in Section 5.7 that the future value of money behaves exponentially, and we saw in Section 5.8 that growth and decay models also behave exponentially. The next example shows how data can lead to an exponential model.

| EXAMPLE 1 | **Fitting an Exponential Function to Data** |

Kathleen is interested in finding a function that explains the growth of cell phone usage in the United States. She gathers data on the number (in millions) of U.S. cell phone subscribers from 1985 through 2005. The data are shown in Table 10.

(a) Using a graphing utility, draw a scatter diagram with year as the independent variable.

(b) Using a graphing utility, build an exponential model from the data.

(c) Express the function found in part (b) in the form $A = A_0 e^{kt}$.

(d) Graph the exponential function found in part (b) or (c) on the scatter diagram.

(e) Using the solution to part (b) or (c), predict the number of U.S. cell phone subscribers in 2009.

(f) Interpret the value of k found in part (c).

Solution

Table 10

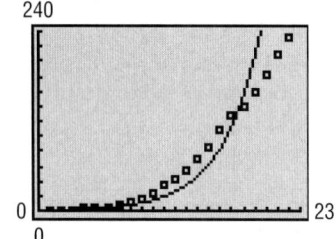

Year, x	Number of Subscribers (in millions), y
1985 (x = 1)	0.34
1986 (x = 2)	0.68
1987 (x = 3)	1.23
1988 (x = 4)	2.07
1989 (x = 5)	3.51
1990 (x = 6)	5.28
1991 (x = 7)	7.56
1992 (x = 8)	11.03
1993 (x = 9)	16.01
1994 (x = 10)	24.13
1995 (x = 11)	33.76
1996 (x = 12)	44.04
1997 (x = 13)	55.31
1998 (x = 14)	69.21
1999 (x = 15)	86.05
2000 (x = 16)	109.48
2001 (x = 17)	128.37
2002 (x = 18)	140.77
2003 (x = 19)	158.72
2004 (x = 20)	182.14
2005 (x = 21)	207.90
2006 (x = 22)	233.00

Source: ©2006 CTIA–The Wireless Association®. All Rights Reserved.

Figure 63

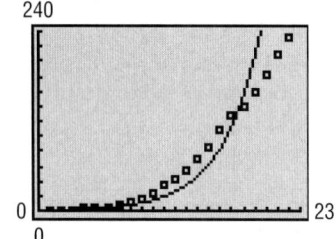

(a) Enter the data into the graphing utility, letting 1 represent 1985, 2 represent 1986, and so on. We obtain the scatter diagram shown in Figure 61.

(b) A graphing utility fits the data in Figure 61 to an exponential function of the form $y = ab^x$ using the EXPonential REGression option. From Figure 62 we find that $y = ab^x = 0.72673(1.3470)^x$. Notice that $|r|$ is close to 1, indicating a good fit.

Figure 61

Figure 62

(c) To express $y = ab^x$ in the form $A = A_0 e^{kt}$, where $x = t$ and $y = A$, we proceed as follows:

$$ab^x = A_0 e^{kt} \quad x = t$$

When $x = t = 0$, we find that $a = A_0$. This leads to

$$a = A_0 \quad b^x = e^{kt}$$
$$b^x = (e^k)^t$$
$$b = e^k \qquad x = t$$

Since $y = ab^x = 0.72673(1.3470)^x$, we find that $a = 0.72673$ and $b = 1.3470$.

$$a = A_0 = 0.72673 \quad \text{and} \quad b = e^k = 1.3470$$

We want to find k, so we rewrite $e^k = 1.3470$ as a logarithm and obtain

$$k = \ln(1.3470) \approx 0.2979$$

As a result, $A = A_0 e^{kt} = 0.72673 e^{0.2979t}$.

(d) See Figure 63 for the graph of the exponential function of best fit.

(e) Let $t = 25$ (end of 2009) in the function found in part (c). The predicted number (in millions) of cell phone subscribers in the United States in 2009 is

$$A_0 e^{kt} = 0.72673 e^{0.2979(25)} \approx 1247$$

This prediction (1247 millon) far exceeds what the U.S. population will be in 2009 (currently the U.S. population is about 300 million). See the answer in part (f).

(f) The value of $k = 0.2979$ represents the growth rate of the number of cell phone subscribers in the United States. Over the period 1985 through 2006, the number of cell phone subscribers has grown at an annual rate of 29.79% compounded continuously. This growth rate is not sustainable as we learned in part (e). In Problem 10 you are asked to build a better model from this data.

Now Work PROBLEM 1

2 Build a Logarithmic Model from Data

Many relations between variables do not follow an exponential model; instead, the independent variable is related to the dependent variable using a logarithmic model.

<table>
<tr><td>EXAMPLE 2</td><td>**Fitting a Logarithmic Function to Data**</td></tr>
</table>

Jodi, a meteorologist, is interested in finding a function that explains the relation between the height of a weather balloon (in kilometers) and the atmospheric pressure (measured in millimeters of mercury) on the balloon. She collects the data shown in Table 11.

Table 11

Atmospheric Pressure, p	Height, h
760	0
740	0.184
725	0.328
700	0.565
650	1.079
630	1.291
600	1.634
580	1.862
550	2.235

(a) Using a graphing utility, draw a scatter diagram of the data with atmospheric pressure as the independent variable.

(b) It is known that the relation between atmospheric pressure and height follows a logarithmic model. Using a graphing utility, build a logarithmic model from the data.

(c) Draw the logarithmic function found in part (b) on the scatter diagram.

(d) Use the function found in part (b) to predict the height of the weather balloon if the atmospheric pressure is 560 millimeters of mercury.

Solution

(a) After entering the data into the graphing utility, we obtain the scatter diagram shown in Figure 64.

(b) A graphing utility fits the data in Figure 64 to a logarithmic function of the form $y = a + b \ln x$ by using the LOGarithm REGression option. See Figure 65. The logarithmic model from the data is

$$h(p) = 45.7863 - 6.9025 \ln p$$

where h is the height of the weather balloon and p is the atmospheric pressure. Notice that $|r|$ is close to 1, indicating a good fit.

(c) Figure 66 shows the graph of $h(p) = 45.7863 - 6.9025 \ln p$ on the scatter diagram.

Figure 64

Figure 65

Figure 66

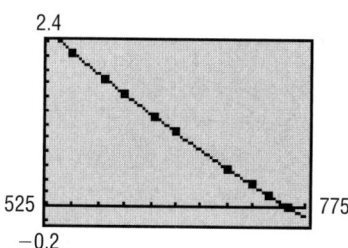

(d) Using the function found in part (b), Jodi predicts the height of the weather balloon when the atmospheric pressure is 560 to be

$$h(560) = 45.7863 - 6.9025 \ln 560$$
$$\approx 2.108 \text{ kilometers}$$

═══ **Now Work** PROBLEM 5

3 Build a Logistic Model from Data

Logistic growth models can be used to model situations for which the value of the dependent variable is limited. Many real-world situations conform to this scenario. For example, the population of the human race is limited by the availability of natural resources such as food and shelter. When the value of the dependent variable is limited, a logistic growth model is often appropriate.

| EXAMPLE 3 | Fitting a Logistic Function to Data |

The data in Table 12 represent the amount of yeast biomass in a culture after t hours.

Table 12

Time (in hours)	Yeast Biomass	Time (in hours)	Yeast Biomass
0	9.6	10	513.3
1	18.3	11	559.7
2	29.0	12	594.8
3	47.2	13	629.4
4	71.1	14	640.8
5	119.1	15	651.1
6	174.6	16	655.9
7	257.3	17	659.6
8	350.7	18	661.8
9	441.0		

Source: Tor Carlson (Über Geschwindigkeit und Grösse der Hefevermehrung in Würze, Biochemische Zeitschrift, Bd. 57, pp. 313–334, 1913)

(a) Using a graphing utility, draw a scatter diagram of the data with time as the independent variable.
(b) Using a graphing utility, build a logistic model from the data.
(c) Using a graphing utility, graph the function found in part (b) on the scatter diagram.
(d) What is the predicted carrying capacity of the culture?
(e) Use the function found in part (b) to predict the population of the culture at $t = 19$ hours.

Solution

(a) See Figure 67 for a scatter diagram of the data.

Figure 67

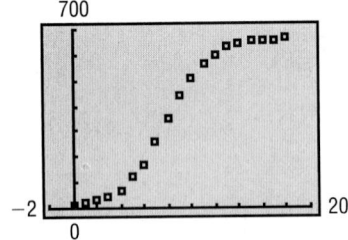

(b) A graphing utility fits a logistic growth model of the form $y = \dfrac{c}{1 + ae^{-bx}}$ by using the LOGISTIC regression option. See Figure 68. The logistic model from the data is

$$y = \frac{663.0}{1 + 71.6e^{-0.5470x}}$$

where y is the amount of yeast biomass in the culture and x is the time.

(c) See Figure 69 for the graph of the logistic model.

Figure 68

Figure 69

(d) Based on the logistic growth model found in part (b), the carrying capacity of the culture is 663.

(e) Using the logistic growth model found in part (b), the predicted amount of yeast biomass at $t = 19$ hours is

$$y = \frac{663.0}{1 + 71.6e^{-0.5470(19)}} \approx 661.5$$

Now Work PROBLEM 7

5.9 Assess Your Understanding

Applications and Extensions

1. **Biology**   A strain of E-coli Beu 397-recA441 is placed into a nutrient broth at 30° Celsius and allowed to grow. The following data are collected. Theory states that the number of bacteria in the petri dish will initially grow according to the law of uninhibited growth. The population is measured using an optical device in which the amount of light that passes through the petri dish is measured.

Time (hours), x	Population, y
0	0.09
2.5	0.18
3.5	0.26
4.5	0.35
6	0.50

Source: Dr. Polly Lavery, Joliet Junior College

(a) Draw a scatter diagram treating time as the independent variable.
(b) Using a graphing utility, build an exponential model from the data.
(c) Express the function found in part (b) in the form $N(t) = N_0 e^{kt}$.
(d) Graph the exponential function found in part (b) or (c) on the scatter diagram.
(e) Use the exponential function from part (b) or (c) to predict the population at $x = 7$ hours.
(f) Use the exponential function from part (b) or (c) to predict when the population will reach 0.75.

2. **Biology**   A strain of E-coli SC18del-recA718 is placed into a nutrient broth at 30° Celsius and allowed to grow. The following data are collected. Theory states that the number of bacteria in the petri dish will initially grow according to the law of uninhibited growth. The population is measured using an optical device in which the amount of light that passes through the petri dish is measured.

Time (hours), x	Population, y
2.5	0.175
3.5	0.38
4.5	0.63
4.75	0.76
5.25	1.20

Source: Dr. Polly Lavery, Joliet Junior College

(a) Draw a scatter diagram treating time as the independent variable.
(b) Using a graphing utility, build an exponential model from the data.
(c) Express the function found in part (b) in the form $N(t) = N_0 e^{kt}$.
(d) Graph the exponential function found in part (b) or (c) on the scatter diagram.

(e) Use the exponential function from part (b) or (c) to predict the population at $x = 6$ hours.
(f) Use the exponential function from part (b) or (c) to predict when the population will reach 2.1.

3. **Chemistry**   A chemist has a 100-gram sample of a radioactive material. He records the amount of radioactive material every week for 6 weeks and obtains the following data:

Week	Weight (in Grams)
0	100.0
1	88.3
2	75.9
3	69.4
4	59.1
5	51.8
6	45.5

(a) Using a graphing utility, draw a scatter diagram with week as the independent variable.
(b) Using a graphing utility, build an exponential model from the data.
(c) Express the function found in part (b) in the form $A(t) = A_0 e^{kt}$.
(d) Graph the exponential function found in part (b) or (c) on the scatter diagram.
(e) From the result found in part (b), determine the half-life of the radioactive material.
(f) How much radioactive material will be left after 50 weeks?
(g) When will there be 20 grams of radioactive material?

4. **Cigarette Exports**   The following data represent the number of cigarettes (in billions) exported from the United States by year.

Year	Cigarette Exports (in billions of pieces)
1995	231.1
1998	201.3
1999	151.4
2000	147.9
2001	133.9
2002	127.4
2003	121.5
2004	118.7

Source: Statistical Abstract of the United States, 2006

(a) Let t = the number of years since 1995. Using a graphing utility, draw a scatter diagram of the data using t as the independent variable and number of cigarettes as the dependent variable.

(b) Using a graphing utility, build an exponential model from the data.

(c) Express the function found in part (b) in the form $A(t) = A_0 e^{kt}$.

(d) Graph the exponential function found in part (b) or (c) on the scatter diagram.

(e) Use the exponential function from part (b) or (c) to predict the number of cigarettes that will be exported from the United States in 2010.

(f) Use the exponential function from part (b) or (c) to predict when the number of cigarettes exported from the United States will decrease to 50 billion.

5. Economics and Marketing The following data represent the price and quantity demanded in 2007 for Dell personal computers.

Price ($/Computer)	Quantity Demanded
2300	152
2000	159
1700	164
1500	171
1300	176
1200	180
1000	189

(a) Using a graphing utility, draw a scatter diagram of the data with price as the dependent variable.

(b) Using a graphing utility, build a logarithmic model from the data.

(c) Using a graphing utility, draw the logarithmic function found in part (b) on the scatter diagram.

(d) Use the function found in part (b) to predict the number of Dell personal computers that will be demanded if the price is $1650.

6. Economics and Marketing The following data represent the price and quantity supplied in 2007 for Dell personal computers.

Price ($/Computer)	Quantity Supplied
2300	180
2000	173
1700	160
1500	150
1300	137
1200	130
1000	113

(a) Using a graphing utility, draw a scatter diagram of the data with price as the dependent variable.

(b) Using a graphing utility, build a logarithmic model from the data.

(c) Using a graphing utility, draw the logarithmic function found in part (b) on the scatter diagram.

(d) Use the function found in part (b) to predict the number of Dell personal computers that will be supplied if the price is $1650.

7. Population Model The following data represent the population of the United States. An ecologist is interested in building a model that describes the population of the United States.

Year	Population
1900	76,212,168
1910	92,228,496
1920	106,021,537
1930	123,202,624
1940	132,164,569
1950	151,325,798
1960	179,323,175
1970	203,302,031
1980	226,542,203
1990	248,709,873
2000	281,421,906

Source: U.S. Census Bureau

(a) Using a graphing utility, draw a scatter diagram of the data using years since 1900 as the independent variable and population as the dependent variable.

(b) Using a graphing utility, build a logistic model from the data.

(c) Using a graphing utility, draw the function found in part (b) on the scatter diagram.

(d) Based on the function found in part (b), what is the carrying capacity of the United States?

(e) Use the function found in part (b) to predict the population of the United States in 2004.

(f) When will the United States population be 300,000,000?

(g) Compare actual U.S. Census figures to the predictions found in parts (e) and (f). Discuss any differences.

8. Population Model The following data represent the world population. An ecologist is interested in building a model that describes the world population.

Year	Population (in Billions)
1993	5.531
1994	5.611
1995	5.691
1996	5.769
1997	5.847
1998	5.925
1999	6.003
2000	6.080
2001	6.157

Source: U.S. Census Bureau

(a) Using a graphing utility, draw a scatter diagram of the data using years since 1992 as the independent variable and population as the dependent variable.

(b) Using a graphing utility, build a logistic model from the data.

(c) Using a graphing utility, draw the function found in part (b) on the scatter diagram.

(d) Based on the function found in part (b), what is the carrying capacity of the world?

(e) Use the function found in part (b) to predict the population of the world in 2004.

(f) When will world population be 7 billion?
(g) Compare actual U.S. Census figures to the prediction found in part (e). Discuss any differences.

9. Cable Subscribers The following data represent the number of basic cable TV subscribers in the United States. A market

Year	Subscribers (1,000)
1975 ($t = 5$)	9,800
1980 ($t = 10$)	17,500
1985 ($t = 15$)	35,440
1990 ($t = 20$)	50,520
1992 ($t = 22$)	54,300
1994 ($t = 24$)	58,373
1996 ($t = 26$)	62,300
1998 ($t = 28$)	64,650
2000 ($t = 30$)	66,250
2002 ($t = 32$)	66,472
2004 ($t = 34$)	65,853

Source: Statistical Abstract of the United States, 2006

researcher believes that external factors, such as satellite TV, have affected the growth of cable subscribers. She is interested in building a model that can be used to describe the number of cable TV subscribers in the United States.
(a) Using a graphing utility, draw a scatter diagram of the data using the number of years after 1970, t, as the independent variable and number of subscribers as the dependent variable.
(b) Using a graphing utility, build a logistic model from the data.
(c) Using a graphing utility, draw the function found in part (b) on the scatter diagram.
(d) Based on the model found in part (b), what is the carrying capacity of the cable TV market in the United States?
(e) Use the model found in part (b) to predict the number of cable TV subscribers in the United States in 2015.

10. Cell Phone Users Refer to the data in Table 10 (p. 336).
(a) Using a graphing utility, build a logistic model from the data.
(b) Graph the logistic function found in part (b) on a scatter diagram of the data.
(c) What is the predicted carrying capacity of U.S. cell phone subscribers?
(d) Use the model found in part (b) to predict the number of U.S. cell phone subscribers at the end of 2009.
(e) Compare the answer to part (d) above with the answer to Example 1, part (e). How do you explain the different predictions?

Mixed Practice

11. Age versus Total Cholesterol The following data represent the age and average total cholesterol for adult males at various ages.

Age	Total Cholesterol
27	189
40	205
50	215
60	210
70	210
80	194

(a) Using a graphing utility, draw a scatter diagram of the data using age, x, as the independent variable and total cholesterol, y, as the dependent variable.
(b) Based on the scatter diagram drawn in part (a), decide on a model (linear, quadratic, cubic, exponential, logarithmic, or logistic) that you think best describes the relation between age and total cholesterol. Be sure to justify your choice of model.
(c) Using a graphing utility, find the model of best fit.
(d) Using a graphing utility, draw the model of best fit on the scatter diagram drawn in part (a).
(e) Use your model to predict the total cholesterol of a 35-year-old male.

12. Income versus Crime Rate The following data represent crime rate against individuals (crimes per 1000 population) and their income in the United States in 2003.

Income	Crime Rate
$5000	51.1
11,250	31.9
20,000	27.0
30,000	25.8
42,500	22.0
62,500	23.3
85,000	18.5

Source: Statistical Abstract of the United States, 2006

(a) Using a graphing utility, draw a scatter diagram of the data using income, x, as the independent variable and crime rate, y, as the dependent variable.
(b) Based on the scatter diagram drawn in part (a), decide on a model (linear, quadratic, cubic, exponential, logarithmic, or logistic) that you think best describes the relation between income and crime rate. Be sure to justify your choice of model.
(c) Using a graphing utility, find the model of best fit.
(d) Using a graphing utility, draw the model of best fit on the scatter diagram drawn in part (a).
(e) Use your model to predict the crime rate of an individual whose income is $55,000.

13. Depreciation of a Chevrolet Impala The following data represent the asking price and age of a Chevrolet Impala SS.

Age	Asking Price
1	$27,417
1	26,750
2	22,995
2	23,195
3	17,999
4	16,995
4	16,490

Source: cars.com

(a) Using a graphing utility, draw a scatter diagram of the data using age, x, as the independent variable and asking price, y, as the dependent variable.
(b) Based on the scatter diagram drawn in part (a), decide on a model (linear, quadratic, cubic, exponential, logarithmic, or logistic) that you think best describes the relation between age and asking price. Be sure to justify your choice of model.
(c) Using a graphing utility, find the model of best fit.
(d) Using a graphing utility, draw the model of best fit on the scatter diagram drawn in part (a).
(e) Use your model to predict the asking price of a Chevrolet Impala SS that is 5 years old.

CHAPTER REVIEW

Things to Know

Composite function (p. 248)

$(f \circ g)(x) = f(g(x))$ The domain of $f \circ g$ is the set of all numbers x in the domain of g for which $g(x)$ is in the domain of f.

One-to-one function f (p. 256)

A function for which any two different inputs in the domain correspond to two different outputs in the range.
For any choice of elements x_1, x_2 in the domain of f, if $x_1 \neq x_2$, then $f(x_1) \neq f(x_2)$.

Horizontal-line test (p. 257)

If every horizontal line intersects the graph of a function f in at most one point, f is one-to-one.

Inverse function f^{-1} of f (pp. 258–261)

Domain of f = range of f^{-1};   range of f = domain of f^{-1}
$f^{-1}(f(x)) = x$ for all x in the domain of f
$f(f^{-1}(x)) = x$ for all x in the domain of f^{-1}
The graphs of f and f^{-1} are symmetric with respect to the line $y = x$.

Properties of the exponential function (pp. 273–275)

$f(x) = Ca^x, \quad a > 1$

Domain: the interval $(-\infty, \infty)$

Range: the interval $(0, \infty)$

x-intercepts: none; y-intercept: 1

Horizontal asymptote: x-axis ($y = 0$) as $x \to -\infty$

Increasing; one-to-one; smooth; continuous

See Figure 24 for a typical graph.

$f(x) = Ca^x, \quad 0 < a < 1$

Domain: the interval $(-\infty, \infty)$

Range: the interval $(0, \infty)$

x-intercepts: none; y-intercept: 1

Horizontal asymptote: x-axis ($y = 0$) as $x \to \infty$

Decreasing; one-to-one; smooth; continuous

See Figure 28 for a typical graph.

Number e (p. 276)

Value approached by the expression $\left(1 + \dfrac{1}{n}\right)^n$ as $n \to \infty$; that is, $\displaystyle\lim_{n \to \infty} \left(1 + \dfrac{1}{n}\right)^n = e$

Property of exponents (p. 278)

If $a^u = a^v$, then $u = v$.

Properties of the logarithmic function (p. 287)

$f(x) = \log_a x, \quad a > 1$
($y = \log_a x$ means $x = a^y$)

Domain: the interval $(0, \infty)$

Range: the interval $(-\infty, \infty)$

x-intercept: 1; y-intercept; none

Vertical asymptote: $x = 0$ (y-axis)

Increasing; one-to-one; smooth; continuous

See Figure 44(a) for a typical graph.

$$f(x) = \log_a x, \quad 0 < a < 1$$
$$(y = \log_a x \text{ means } x = a^y)$$

Domain: the interval $(0, \infty)$
Range: the interval $(-\infty, \infty)$
x-intercept: 1; y-intercept; none
Vertical asymptote: $x = 0$ (y-axis)
Decreasing; one-to-one; smooth; continuous
See Figure 44(b) for a typical graph.

Natural logarithm (p. 287)

$y = \ln x$ means $x = e^y$.

Properties of logarithms (pp. 297–299, 301)

$\log_a 1 = 0 \quad \log_a a = 1 \quad a^{\log_a M} = M \quad \log_a a^r = r$

$\log_a(MN) = \log_a M + \log_a N \qquad \log_a\left(\dfrac{M}{N}\right) = \log_a M - \log_a N$

$\log_a M^r = r \log_a M$

If $M = N$, then $\log_a M = \log_a N$.

If $\log_a M = \log_a N$, then $M = N$.

Formulas

Change-of-Base Formula (p. 302)

$\log_a M = \dfrac{\log_b M}{\log_b a}$

Compound Interest Formula (p. 315)

$A = P \cdot \left(1 + \dfrac{r}{n}\right)^{nt}$

Continuous compounding (p. 316)

$A = Pe^{rt}$

Effective rate of interest (p. 317)

Compounding n times per year: $r_e = \left(1 + \dfrac{r}{n}\right)^n - 1$

Continuous Compounding $r_e = e^r - 1$

Present Value Formulas (p. 318)

$P = A \cdot \left(1 + \dfrac{r}{n}\right)^{-nt} \quad \text{or} \quad P = Ae^{-rt}$

Growth and decay (p. 323)

$A(t) = A_0 e^{kt}$

Newton's Law of Cooling (p. 327)

$u(t) = T + (u_0 - T)e^{kt} \quad k < 0$

Logistic model (p. 328)

$P(t) = \dfrac{c}{1 + ae^{-bt}}$

Objectives

Section		You should be able to . . .	Example(s)	Review Exercises
5.1	1	Form a composite function (p. 248)	1, 4, 5	1–12
	2	Find the domain of a composite function (p. 249)	2–4	7–12
5.2	1	Determine whether a function is one-to-one (p. 256)	1, 2	13(a), 14(a), 15, 16
	2	Determine the inverse of a function defined by a map or a set of ordered pairs (p. 258)	3, 4	13(b), 14(b)
	3	Obtain the graph of the inverse function from the graph of the function (p. 260)	7	15, 16
	4	Find the inverse of a function defined by an equation (p. 261)	8, 9, 11	17–22
5.3	1	Evaluate exponential functions (p. 269)	1	23(a), (c), 24(a), (c), 87(a)
	2	Graph exponential functions (p. 273)	3–6	55–60
	3	Define the number e (p. 276)	pg. 276	59, 60
	4	Solve exponential equations (p. 278)	7, 8	63–66, 71, 72, 74–76, 87(b)
5.4	1	Change exponential statements to logarithmic statements and logarithmic statements to exponential statements (p. 285)	2, 3	25–28
	2	Evaluate logarithmic expressions (p. 285)	4	23(b), (d), 24(b), (d), 33, 34, 83(b), 84(b), 85, 86, 88(a), 89
	3	Determine the domain of a logarithmic function (p. 286)	5	29–32, 61(a), 62(a)
	4	Graph logarithmic functions (p. 287)	6, 7	61, 62, 83(a), 84(a)
	5	Solve logarithmic equations (p. 291)	8, 9	67, 68, 73, 83(c), 84(c), 88(b)

5.5	**1**	Work with the properties of logarithms (p. 297)	1, 2	35–38
	2	Write a logarithmic expression as a sum or difference of logarithms (p. 299)	3–5	39–44
	3	Write a logarithmic expression as a single logarithm (p. 300)	6	45–50
	4	Evaluate logarithms whose base is neither 10 nor e (p. 301)	7, 8	51, 52
	5	Graph logarithmic functions whose base is neither 10 nor e (p. 303)	9	53, 54
5.6	**1**	Solve logarithmic equations (p. 306)	1–3	67, 77, 78
	2	Solve exponential equations (p. 308)	4–7	63–66, 69, 70, 74–76, 79–82
	3	Solve logarithmic and exponential equations using a graphing utility (p. 310)	8	69–82
5.7	**1**	Determine the future value of a lump sum of money (p. 313)	1–3	90, 92, 97
	2	Calculate effective rates of return (p. 317)	4	90
	3	Determine the present value of a lump sum of money (p. 318)	5	91
	4	Determine the rate of interest or time required to double a lump sum of money (p. 319)	6, 7	90
5.8	**1**	Find equations of populations that obey the law of uninhibited growth (p. 323)	1, 2	95
	2	Find equations of populations that obey the law of decay (p. 325)	3	93, 96
	3	Use Newton's Law of Cooling (p. 327)	4	94
	4	Use logistic models (p. 328)	5, 6	98
5.9	**1**	Build an exponential model from data (p. 335)	1	99
	2	Build a logarithmic model from data (p. 336)	2	100
	3	Build a logistic model from data (p. 337)	3	101

Review Exercises

In Problems 1–6, for the given functions f and g find:

(a) $(f \circ g)(2)$ (b) $(g \circ f)(-2)$ (c) $(f \circ f)(4)$ (d) $(g \circ g)(-1)$

1. $f(x) = 3x - 5$; $g(x) = 1 - 2x^2$ **2.** $f(x) = 4 - x$; $g(x) = 1 + x^2$

3. $f(x) = \sqrt{x + 2}$; $g(x) = 2x^2 + 1$ **4.** $f(x) = 1 - 3x^2$; $g(x) = \sqrt{4 - x}$

5. $f(x) = e^x$; $g(x) = 3x - 2$ **6.** $f(x) = \dfrac{2}{1 + 2x^2}$; $g(x) = 3x$

In Problems 7–12, find $f \circ g$, $g \circ f$, $f \circ f$, and $g \circ g$ for each pair of functions. State the domain of each composite function.

7. $f(x) = 2 - x$; $g(x) = 3x + 1$ **8.** $f(x) = 2x - 1$; $g(x) = 2x + 1$

9. $f(x) = 3x^2 + x + 1$; $g(x) = |3x|$ **10.** $f(x) = \sqrt{3x}$; $g(x) = 1 + x + x^2$

11. $f(x) = \dfrac{x + 1}{x - 1}$; $g(x) = \dfrac{1}{x}$ **12.** $f(x) = \sqrt{x - 3}$; $g(x) = \dfrac{3}{x}$

In Problems 13 and 14, (a) verify that the function is one-to-one, and (b) find the inverse of the given function.

13. $\{(1, 2), (3, 5), (5, 8), (6, 10)\}$ **14.** $\{(-1, 4), (0, 2), (1, 5), (3, 7)\}$

In Problems 15 and 16, state why the graph of the function is one-to-one. Then draw the graph of the inverse function f^{-1}. For convenience (and as a hint), the graph of $y = x$ is also given.

15.

16.

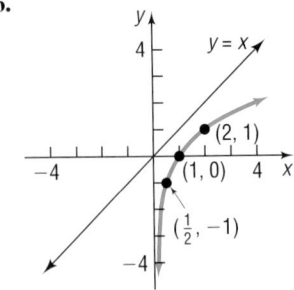

In Problems 17–22, the function f is one-to-one. Find the inverse of each function and check your answer. Find the domain and the range of f and f^{-1}.

17. $f(x) = \dfrac{2x + 3}{5x - 2}$

18. $f(x) = \dfrac{2 - x}{3 + x}$

19. $f(x) = \dfrac{1}{x - 1}$

20. $f(x) = \sqrt{x - 2}$

21. $f(x) = \dfrac{3}{x^{1/3}}$

22. $f(x) = x^{1/3} + 1$

In Problems 23 and 24, $f(x) = 3^x$ and $g(x) = \log_3 x$.

23. Evaluate: (a) $f(4)$ (b) $g(9)$ (c) $f(-2)$ (d) $g\left(\dfrac{1}{27}\right)$

24. Evaluate: (a) $f(1)$ (b) $g(81)$ (c) $f(-4)$ (d) $g\left(\dfrac{1}{243}\right)$

In Problems 25 and 26, convert each exponential statement to an equivalent statement involving a logarithm. In Problems 27 and 28, convert each logarithmic statement to an equivalent statement involving an exponent.

25. $5^2 = z$

26. $a^5 = m$

27. $\log_5 u = 13$

28. $\log_a 4 = 3$

In Problems 29–32, find the domain of each logarithmic function.

29. $f(x) = \log(3x - 2)$

30. $F(x) = \log_5(2x + 1)$

31. $H(x) = \log_2(x^2 - 3x + 2)$

32. $F(x) = \ln(x^2 - 9)$

In Problems 33–38, evaluate each expression. Do not use a calculator.

33. $\log_2\left(\dfrac{1}{8}\right)$

34. $\log_3 81$

35. $\ln e^{\sqrt{2}}$

36. $e^{\ln 0.1}$

37. $2^{\log_2 0.4}$

38. $\log_2 2^{\sqrt{3}}$

In Problems 39–44, write each expression as the sum and/or difference of logarithms. Express powers as factors.

39. $\log_3\left(\dfrac{uv^2}{w}\right), \quad u > 0, v > 0, w > 0$

40. $\log_2\left(a^2\sqrt{b}\right)^4, \quad a > 0, b > 0$

41. $\log\left(x^2\sqrt{x^3 + 1}\right), \quad x > 0$

42. $\log_5\left(\dfrac{x^2 + 2x + 1}{x^2}\right), \quad x > 0$

43. $\ln\left(\dfrac{x\sqrt[3]{x^2 + 1}}{x - 3}\right), \quad x > 3$

44. $\ln\left(\dfrac{2x + 3}{x^2 - 3x + 2}\right)^2, \quad x > 2$

In Problems 45–50, write each expression as a single logarithm.

45. $3\log_4 x^2 + \dfrac{1}{2}\log_4 \sqrt{x}$

46. $-2\log_3\left(\dfrac{1}{x}\right) + \dfrac{1}{3}\log_3 \sqrt{x}$

47. $\ln\left(\dfrac{x - 1}{x}\right) + \ln\left(\dfrac{x}{x + 1}\right) - \ln(x^2 - 1)$

48. $\log(x^2 - 9) - \log(x^2 + 7x + 12)$

49. $2\log 2 + 3\log x - \dfrac{1}{2}[\log(x + 3) + \log(x - 2)]$

50. $\dfrac{1}{2}\ln(x^2 + 1) - 4\ln\dfrac{1}{2} - \dfrac{1}{2}[\ln(x - 4) + \ln x]$

In Problems 51 and 52, use the Change-of-Base Formula and a calculator to evaluate each logarithm. Round your answer to three decimal places.

51. $\log_4 19$

52. $\log_2 21$

In Problems 53 and 54, graph each function using a graphing utility and the Change-of-Base Formula.

53. $y = \log_3 x$

54. $y = \log_7 x$

In Problems 55–62, use the given function f to:
  (a) Find the domain of f.
  (b) Graph f.
  (c) From the graph, determine the range and any asymptotes of f.
  (d) Find f^{-1}, the inverse of f.
  (e) Use f^{-1} to find the range of f.
  (f) Graph f^{-1}.

55. $f(x) = 2^{x-3}$

56. $f(x) = -2^x + 3$

57. $f(x) = \dfrac{1}{2}(3^{-x})$

58. $f(x) = 1 + 3^{-x}$

59. $f(x) = 1 - e^{-x}$

60. $f(x) = 3e^{x-2}$

61. $f(x) = \dfrac{1}{2}\ln(x + 3)$

62. $f(x) = 3 + \ln(2x)$

In Problems 63–82, solve each equation. Express irrational solutions in exact form and as a decimal rounded to 3 decimal places.

63. $4^{1-2x} = 2$

64. $8^{6+3x} = 4$

65. $3^{x^2+x} = \sqrt{3}$

66. $4^{x-x^2} = \dfrac{1}{2}$

67. $\log_x 64 = -3$

68. $\log_{\sqrt{2}} x = -6$

69. $5^x = 3^{x+2}$

70. $5^{x+2} = 7^{x-2}$

71. $9^{2x} = 27^{3x-4}$

72. $25^{2x} = 5^{x^2-12}$

73. $\log_3 \sqrt{x-2} = 2$

74. $2^{x+1} \cdot 8^{-x} = 4$

75. $8 = 4^{x^2} \cdot 2^{5x}$

76. $2^x \cdot 5 = 10^x$

77. $\log_6(x+3) + \log_6(x+4) = 1$

78. $\log(7x - 12) = 2 \log x$

79. $e^{1-x} = 5$

80. $e^{1-2x} = 4$

81. $9^x + 4 \cdot 3^x - 3 = 0$

82. $4^x - 14 \cdot 4^{-x} = 5$

83. Suppose that $f(x) = \log_2(x - 2) + 1$.
(a) Graph f.
(b) What is $f(6)$? What point is on the graph of f?
(c) Solve $f(x) = 4$. What point is on the graph of f?
(d) Based on the graph drawn in part (a), solve $f(x) > 0$.
(e) Find $f^{-1}(x)$. Graph f^{-1} on the same Cartesian plane as f.

84. Suppose that $f(x) = \log_3(x + 1) - 4$.
(a) Graph f.
(b) What is $f(8)$? What point is on the graph of f?
(c) Solve $f(x) = -3$. What point is on the graph of f?
(d) Based on the graph drawn in part (a), solve $f(x) < 0$.
(e) Find $f^{-1}(x)$. Graph f^{-1} on the same Cartesian plane as f.

In Problems 85 and 86, use the following result: If x is the atmospheric pressure (measured in millimeters of mercury), then the formula for the altitude h(x) (measured in meters above sea level) is

$$h(x) = (30T + 8000) \log\left(\frac{P_0}{x}\right)$$

where T is the temperature (in degrees Celsius) and P_0 is the atmospheric pressure at sea level, which is approximately 760 millimeters of mercury.

85. Finding the Altitude of an Airplane At what height is a Piper Cub whose instruments record an outside temperature of 0°C and a barometric pressure of 300 millimeters of mercury?

86. Finding the Height of a Mountain How high is a mountain if instruments placed on its peak record a temperature of 5°C and a barometric pressure of 500 millimeters of mercury?

87. Amplifying Sound An amplifier's power output P (in watts) is related to its decibel voltage gain d by the formula

$$P = 25e^{0.1d}$$

(a) Find the power output for a decibel voltage gain of 4 decibels.
(b) For a power output of 50 watts, what is the decibel voltage gain?

88. Limiting Magnitude of a Telescope A telescope is limited in its usefulness by the brightness of the star that it is aimed at and by the diameter of its lens. One measure of a star's brightness is its *magnitude;* the dimmer the star, the larger its magnitude. A formula for the limiting magnitude L of a telescope, that is, the magnitude of the dimmest star that it can be used to view, is given by

$$L = 9 + 5.1 \log d$$

where d is the diameter (in inches) of the lens.
(a) What is the limiting magnitude of a 3.5-inch telescope?
(b) What diameter is required to view a star of magnitude 14?

89. Salvage Value The number of years n for a piece of machinery to depreciate to a known salvage value can be found using the formula

$$n = \frac{\log s - \log i}{\log(1 - d)}$$

where s is the salvage value of the machinery, i is its initial value, and d is the annual rate of depreciation.
(a) How many years will it take for a piece of machinery to decline in value from $90,000 to $10,000 if the annual rate of depreciation is 0.20 (20%)?

(b) How many years will it take for a piece of machinery to lose half of its value if the annual rate of depreciation is 15%?

90. Funding a College Education A child's grandparents purchase a $10,000 bond fund that matures in 18 years to be used for her college education. The bond fund pays 4% interest compounded semiannually. How much will the bond fund be worth at maturity? What is the effective rate of interest? How long will it take the bond to double in value under these terms?

91. Funding a College Education A child's grandparents wish to purchase a bond that matures in 18 years to be used for her college education. The bond pays 4% interest compounded semiannually. How much should they pay so that the bond will be worth $85,000 at maturity?

92. Funding an IRA First Colonial Bankshares Corporation advertised the following IRA investment plans.

Target IRA Plans

For each $5000 Maturity Value Desired	
Deposit:	**At a Term of:**
$620.17	20 Years
$1045.02	15 Years
$1760.92	10 Years
$2967.26	5 Years

(a) Assuming continuous compounding, what annual rate of interest did they offer?
(b) First Colonial Bankshares claims that $4000 invested today will have a value of over $32,000 in 20 years. Use the answer found in part (a) to find the actual value of $4000 in 20 years. Assume continuous compounding.

93. Estimating the Date That a Prehistoric Man Died The bones of a prehistoric man found in the desert of New Mexico contain approximately 5% of the original amount of carbon 14. If the half-life of carbon 14 is 5600 years, approximately how long ago did the man die?

94. **Temperature of a Skillet**   A skillet is removed from an oven whose temperature is 450°F and placed in a room whose temperature is 70°F. After 5 minutes, the temperature of the skillet is 400°F. How long will it be until its temperature is 150°F?

95. **World Population**   The annual growth rate of the world's population in 2005 was $k = 1.15\% = 0.0115$. The population of the world in 2005 was 6,451,058,790. Letting $t = 0$ represent 2005, use the uninhibited growth model to predict the world's population in the year 2015.

    Source: U.S. Census Bureau

96. **Radioactive Decay**   The half-life of radioactive cobalt is 5.27 years. If 100 grams of radioactive cobalt is present now, how much will be present in 20 years? In 40 years?

97. **Federal Deficit**   In fiscal year 2005, the federal deficit was $319 billion. At that time, 10-year treasury notes were paying 4.25% interest per annum. If the federal government financed this deficit through 10-year notes, how much would it have to pay back in 2015?

    Source: U.S. Treasury Department

98. **Logistic Growth**   The logistic growth model

    $$P(t) = \frac{0.8}{1 + 1.67e^{-0.16t}}$$

    represents the proportion of new cars with a global positioning system (GPS). Let $t = 0$ represent 2006, $t = 1$ represent 2007, and so on.
    (a) What proportion of new cars in 2006 had a GPS?
    (b) Determine the maximum proportion of new cars that have a GPS.
    (c) Using a graphing utility, graph $P = P(t)$.
    (d) When will 75% of new cars have a GPS?

99. **CBL Experiment**   The following data were collected by placing a temperature probe in a portable heater, removing the probe, and then recording temperature over time.

Time (sec.)	Temperature (°F)
0	165.07
1	164.77
2	163.99
3	163.22
4	162.82
5	161.96
6	161.20
7	160.45
8	159.35
9	158.61
10	157.89
11	156.83
12	156.11
13	155.08
14	154.40
15	153.72

According to Newton's Law of Cooling, these data should follow an exponential model.
(a) Using a graphing utility, draw a scatter diagram for the data.

(b) Using a graphing utility, build an exponential model from the data.
(c) Graph the exponential function found in part (b) on the scatter diagram.
(d) Predict how long it will take for the probe to reach a temperature of 110°F.

100. **Wind Chill Factor**   The following data represent the wind speed (mph) and wind chill factor at an air temperature of 15°F.

Wind Speed (mph)	Wind Chill Factor (°F)
5	7
10	3
15	0
20	−2
25	−4
30	−5
35	−7

Source: U.S. National Weather Service

(a) Using a graphing utility, draw a scatter diagram with wind speed as the independent variable.
(b) Using a graphing utility, build a logarithmic model from the data.
(c) Using a graphing utility, draw the logarithmic function found in part (b) on the scatter diagram.
(d) Use the function found in part (b) to predict the wind chill factor if the air temperature is 15°F and the wind speed is 23 mph.

101. **Spreading of a Disease**   Jack and Diane live in a small town of 50 people. Unfortunately, both Jack and Diane have a cold. Those who come in contact with someone who has this cold will themselves catch the cold. The following data represent the number of people in the small town who have caught the cold after t days.

Days, t	Number of People with Cold, C
0	2
1	4
2	8
3	14
4	22
5	30
6	37
7	42
8	44

(a) Using a graphing utility, draw a scatter diagram of the data. Comment on the type of relation that appears to exist between the days and number of people with a cold.
(b) Using a graphing utility, build a logistic model from the data.
(c) Graph the function found in part (b) on the scatter diagram.
(d) According to the function found in part (b), what is the maximum number of people who will catch the cold? In reality, what is the maximum number of people who could catch the cold?
(e) Sometime between the second and third day, 10 people in the town had a cold. According to the model found in part (b), when did 10 people have a cold?
(f) How long will it take for 46 people to catch the cold?

CHAPTER TEST

1. Given $f(x) = \dfrac{x + 2}{x - 2}$ and $g(x) = 2x + 5$, find:
   (a) $f \circ g$ and state its domain
   (b) $(g \circ f)(-2)$
   (c) $(f \circ g)(-2)$

2. Determine whether the function is one-to-one.
   (a) $y = 4x^2 + 3$
   (b) $y = \sqrt{x + 3} - 5$

3. Find the inverse of $f(x) = \dfrac{2}{3x - 5}$ and check your answer. State the domain and the range of f and f^{-1}.

4. If the point $(3, -5)$ is on the graph of a one-to-one function f, what point must be on the graph of f^{-1}?

In Problems 5–7, solve each equation algebraically.

5. $3^x = 243$ 6. $\log_b 16 = 2$ 7. $\log_5 x = 4$

In Problems 8–11, use a calculator to evaluate each expression. Round your answer to three decimal places.

8. $e^3 + 2$ 9. $\log 20$
10. $\log_3 21$ 11. $\ln 133$

In Problems 12 and 13, use the given function f to:
   (a) Find the domain of f.
   (b) Graph f.
   (c) From the graph, determine the range and any asymptotes of f.
   (d) Find f^{-1}, the inverse of f.
   (e) Use f^{-1} to find the range of f.
   (f) Graph f^{-1}.

12. $f(x) = 4^{x+1} - 2$

13. $f(x) = 1 - \log_5(x - 2)$

In Problems 14–19, solve each equation.

14. $5^{x+2} = 125$ 15. $\log(x + 9) = 2$
16. $8 - 2e^{-x} = 4$ 17. $\log(x^2 + 3) = \log(x + 6)$
18. $7^{x+3} = e^x$ 19. $\log_2(x - 4) + \log_2(x + 4) = 3$

20. Write $\log_2\left(\dfrac{4x^3}{x^2 - 3x - 18}\right)$ as the sum and/or difference of logarithms. Express powers as factors.

21. A 50-mg sample of a radioactive substance decays to 34 mg after 30 days. How long will it take for there to be 2 mg remaining?

22. (a) If $1000 is invested at 5% compounded monthly, how much is there after 8 months?
    (b) If you want to have $1000 in 9 months, how much do you need to place in a savings account now that pays 5% compounded quarterly?
    (c) How long does it take to double your money if you can invest it at 6% compounded annually?

23. The decibel level, D, of sound is given by the equation
    $D = 10 \log\left(\dfrac{I}{I_0}\right)$, where I is the intensity of the sound and
    $I_0 = 10^{-12}$ watt per square meter.
    (a) If the shout of a single person measures 80 decibels, how loud will the sound be if two people shout at the same time? That is, how loud would the sound be if the intensity doubled?
    (b) The pain threshold for sound is 125 decibels. If the Athens Olympic Stadium 2004 (Olympiako Stadio Athinas 'Spyros Louis') can seat 74,400 people, how many people in the crowd need to shout at the same time for the resulting sound level to meet or exceed the pain threshold? (Ignore any possible sound dampening.)

CUMULATIVE REVIEW

1. Is the following graph the graph of a function? If it is, is the function one-to-one?

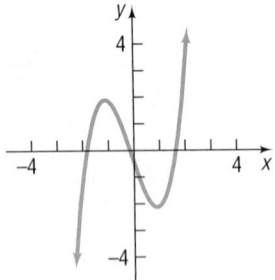

2. For the function $f(x) = 2x^2 - 3x + 1$, find the following:
   (a) $f(3)$ (b) $f(-x)$ (c) $f(x + h)$

3. Determine which of the following points are on the graph of $x^2 + y^2 = 1$.
   (a) $\left(\dfrac{1}{2}, \dfrac{1}{2}\right)$ (b) $\left(\dfrac{1}{2}, \dfrac{\sqrt{3}}{2}\right)$

4. Solve the equation $3(x - 2) = 4(x + 5)$.

5. Graph the line $2x - 4y = 16$.

6. (a) Graph the quadratic function $f(x) = -x^2 + 2x - 3$ by determining whether its graph opens up or down and by finding its vertex, axis of symmetry, y-intercept, and x-intercept(s), if any.
   (b) Solve $f(x) \leq 0$.

7. Determine the quadratic function whose graph is given in the figure.

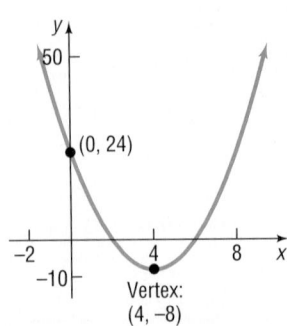

8. Graph $f(x) = 3(x + 1)^3 - 2$ using transformations.

9. Given that $f(x) = x^2 + 2$ and $g(x) = \dfrac{2}{x-3}$, find $f(g(x))$ and state its domain. What is $f(g(5))$?

10. For the polynomial function $f(x) = 4x^3 + 9x^2 - 30x - 8$:
   (a) Find the real zeros of f.
   (b) Determine the intercepts of the graph of f.
   (c) Use a graphing utility to approximate the local maxima and local minima.
   (d) Draw a complete graph of f. Be sure to label the intercepts and turning points.

11. For the function $g(x) = 3^x + 2$:
   (a) Graph g using transformations. State the domain, range, and horizontal asymptote of g.
   (b) Determine the inverse of g. State the domain, range, and vertical asymptote of g^{-1}.
   (c) On the same graph as g, graph g^{-1}.

12. Solve the equation $4^{x-3} = 8^{2x}$.

13. Solve the equation: $\log_3(x + 1) + \log_3(2x - 3) = \log_9 9$

14. Suppose that $f(x) = \log_3(x + 2)$. Solve:
   (a) $f(x) = 0$ (b) $f(x) > 0$ (c) $f(x) = 3$

15. Data Analysis The following data represent the percent of all drivers by age that have been stopped by the police for any reason within the past year. The median age represents the midpoint of the upper and lower limit for the age range.

Age Range	Median Age, x	Percentage Stopped, y
16–19	17.5	18.2
20–29	24.5	16.8
30–39	34.5	11.3
40–49	44.5	9.4
50–59	54.5	7.7
≥60	69.5	3.8

   (a) Using your graphing utility, draw a scatter diagram of the data treating median age, x, as the independent variable.
   (b) Determine a model that you feel best describes the relation between median age and percentage stopped. You may choose from among linear, quadratic, cubic, exponential, logarithmic, or logistic models.
   (c) Provide a justification for the model that you selected in part (b).

CHAPTER PROJECTS

I. Hot Coffee   A fast-food restaurant wants a special container to hold coffee. The restaurant wishes the container to quickly cool the coffee from 200° to 130°F and keep the liquid between 110° and 130°F as long as possible. The restaurant has three containers to select from.

1. The CentiKeeper Company has a container that reduces the temperature of a liquid from 200° to 100°F in 30 minutes by maintaining a constant temperature of 70°F.

2. The TempControl Company has a container that reduces the temperature of a liquid from 200° to 110°F in 25 minutes by maintaining a constant temperature of 60°F.

3. The Hot'n'Cold Company has a container that reduces the temperature of a liquid from 200° to 120°F in 20 minutes by maintaining a constant temperature of 65°F.

   You need to recommend which container the restaurant should purchase.

(a) Use Newton's Law of Cooling to find a function relating the temperature of the liquid over time for each container.

(b) How long does it take each container to lower the coffee temperature from 200° to 130°F?

(c) How long will the coffee temperature remain between 110° and 130°F? This temperature is considered the optimal drinking temperature.

(d) Graph each function using a graphing utility.

(e) Which company would you recommend to the restaurant? Why?

(f) How might the cost of the container affect your decision?

The following projects are available on the Instructor's Resource Center (IRC):

II. Project at Motorola   *Thermal Fatigue of Solder Connections*   Product reliability is a major concern of a manufacturer. Here a logarithmic transformation is used to simplify the analysis of a cell phone's ability to withstand temperature change.

III. Depreciation of a New Car   Resale value is a factor to consider when purchasing a car, and exponential functions provide a way to compare the depreciation rates of different makes and models.

Trigonometric Functions

Surf's Up: Using Models To Predict Huge Waves

GALVESTON, Feb. 15, 2005—If you are a ship captain and there might be 50-foot waves headed your way, you would appreciate some information about them, right?

That's the idea behind a wave model system a Texas A&M University at Galveston professor has developed. His detailed wave prediction system is currently in use in the Gulf of Mexico and the Gulf of Maine.

Vijay Panchang, head of the Department of Maritime Systems Engineering, doesn't make waves; he predicts what they will do, when they will do it, and how high they will get.

Using data provided daily from NOAA [National Oceanic and Atmospheric Administration] and his own complex mathematical models, Panchang and research engineer Doncheng Li provide daily wave model predictions for much of the Texas coast, the Gulf of Mexico, and the Gulf of Maine. Their simulations, updated every 12 hours, provide a forecast for two days ahead.

Because the models use wind data, tsunamis that are created by undersea earthquakes cannot be predicted. But that is not to say his modeling system does not come up with some big waves.

His wave model predicted big waves in November 2003 in the Gulf of Maine, and it was accurate; waves as high as 30 feet were recorded during one storm even in coastal regions.

Last summer during Hurricane Ivan, a buoy located 60 miles south of the Alabama coast recorded a whopping 60-foot wave. "There may have been higher waves because right after recording the 60-foot wave, the buoy snapped and stopped functioning," he says.

Source: Science Daily www.sciencedaily.com/releases/2005/02/050222193810.htm. Posted February 23, 2005.

—*See Chapter Project I—*

A Look Back

In Chapter 2, we began our discussion of functions. We defined domain and range and independent and dependent variables; we found the value of a function and graphed functions. We continued our study of functions by listing properties that a function might have, like being even or odd, and we created a library of functions, naming key functions and listing their properties, including the graph.

A Look Ahead

In this chapter we define the trigonometric functions, six functions that have wide application. We shall talk about their domain and range, see how to find values, graph them, and develop a list of their properties.

There are two widely accepted approaches to the development of the trigonometric functions: one uses right triangles; the other uses circles, especially the unit circle. In this book, we develop the trigonometric functions using the unit circle. In Section 8.1, we introduce trigonometric functions using right triangles.

Outline

6.1 Angles and Their Measure
6.2 Trigonometric Functions: Unit Circle Approach
6.3 Properties of the Trigonometric Functions
6.4 Graphs of the Sine and Cosine Functions
6.5 Graphs of the Tangent, Cotangent, Cosecant, and Secant Functions
6.6 Phase Shift; Sinusoidal Curve Fitting
      Chapter Review
      Chapter Test
      Cumulative Review
      Chapter Projects

6.1 Angles and Their Measure

PREPARING FOR THIS SECTION *Before getting started, review the following:*

- Circumference and Area of a Circle (Appendix A, Section A.2, p. A16)
- Uniform Motion (Appendix A, Section A.8, p. A72)

Now Work the 'Are You Prepared?' problems on page 361.

OBJECTIVES 1 Convert between Decimals and Degrees, Minutes, Seconds Forms for Angles (p. 354)
2 Find the Arc Length of a Circle (p. 356)
3 Convert from Degrees to Radians and from Radians to Degrees (p. 356)
4 Find the Area of a Sector of a Circle (p. 359)
5 Find the Linear Speed of an Object Traveling in Circular Motion (p. 360)

Figure 1

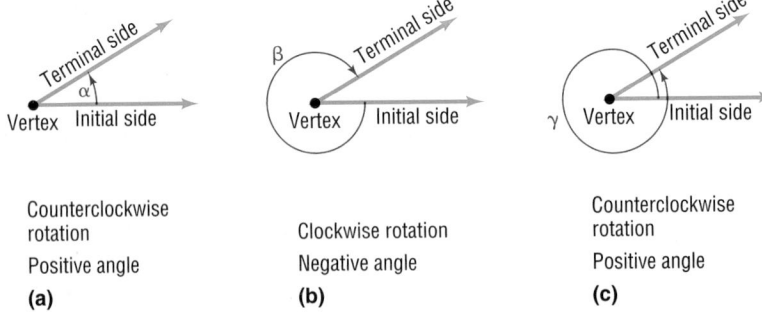

A **ray,** or **half-line,** is that portion of a line that starts at a point V on the line and extends indefinitely in one direction. The starting point V of a ray is called its **vertex.** See Figure 1.

If two rays are drawn with a common vertex, they form an **angle.** We call one ray of an angle the **initial side** and the other the **terminal side.** The angle formed is identified by showing the direction and amount of rotation from the initial side to the terminal side. If the rotation is in the counterclockwise direction, the angle is **positive;** if the rotation is clockwise, the angle is **negative.** See Figure 2.

Figure 2

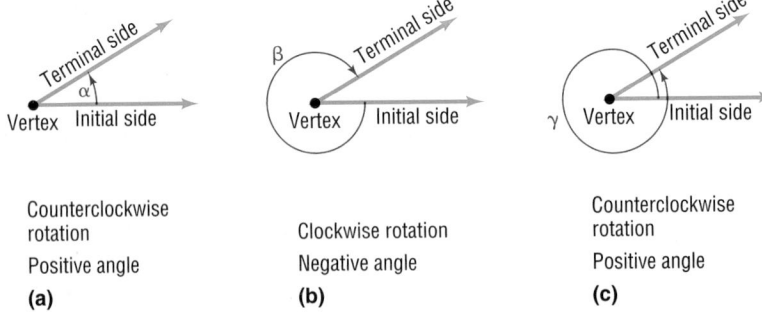

Lowercase Greek letters, such as α (alpha), β (beta), γ (gamma), and θ (theta), will often be used to denote angles. Notice in Figure 2(a) that the angle α is positive because the direction of the rotation from the initial side to the terminal side is counterclockwise. The angle β in Figure 2(b) is negative because the rotation is clockwise. The angle γ in Figure 2(c) is positive. Notice that the angle α in Figure 2(a) and the angle γ in Figure 2(c) have the same initial side and the same terminal side. However, α and γ are unequal, because the amount of rotation required to go from the initial side to the terminal side is greater for angle γ than for angle α.

An angle θ is said to be in **standard position** if its vertex is at the origin of a rectangular coordinate system and its initial side coincides with the positive x-axis. See Figure 3.

Figure 3

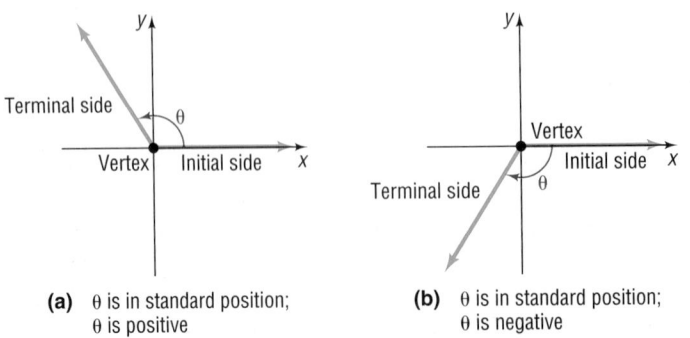

(a) θ is in standard position; θ is positive

(b) θ is in standard position; θ is negative

When an angle θ is in standard position, the terminal side will lie either in a quadrant, in which case we say that θ **lies in that quadrant,** or the terminal side will lie on the x-axis or the y-axis, in which case we say that θ is a **quadrantal angle.** For example, the angle θ in Figure 4(a) lies in quadrant II, the angle θ in Figure 4(b) lies in quadrant IV, and the angle θ in Figure 4(c) is a quadrantal angle.

Figure 4

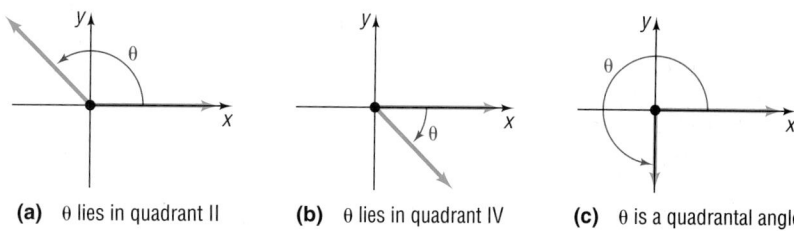

(a) θ lies in quadrant II   (b) θ lies in quadrant IV   (c) θ is a quadrantal angle

We measure angles by determining the amount of rotation needed for the initial side to become coincident with the terminal side. The two commonly used measures for angles are *degrees* and *radians*.

Degrees

HISTORICAL NOTE *One counterclockwise rotation is 360° due to the Babylonian year, which had 360 days in it.* ∎

The angle formed by rotating the initial side exactly once in the counterclockwise direction until it coincides with itself (1 revolution) is said to measure 360 degrees, abbreviated 360°. **One degree, 1°,** is $\dfrac{1}{360}$ revolution. A **right angle** is an angle that measures 90°, or $\dfrac{1}{4}$ revolution; a **straight angle** is an angle that measures 180°, or $\dfrac{1}{2}$ revolution. See Figure 5. As Figure 5(b) shows, it is customary to indicate a right angle by using the symbol ⌐.

Figure 5

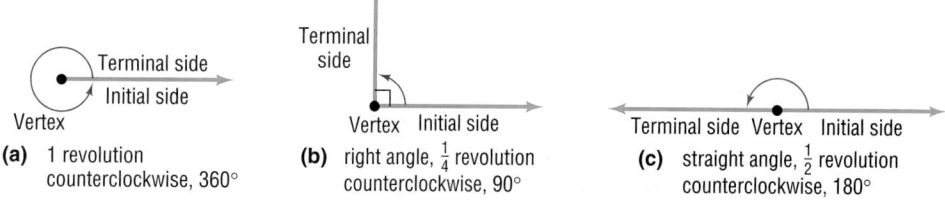

(a) 1 revolution counterclockwise, 360°   (b) right angle, $\frac{1}{4}$ revolution counterclockwise, 90°   (c) straight angle, $\frac{1}{2}$ revolution counterclockwise, 180°

It is also customary to refer to an angle that measures θ degrees as an angle *of* θ degrees.

EXAMPLE 1   **Drawing an Angle**

Draw each angle.
(a) 45°   (b) −90°   (c) 225°   (d) 405°

Solution   (a) An angle of 45° is $\dfrac{1}{2}$ of a right angle.   (b) An angle of −90° is $\dfrac{1}{4}$ revolution in
See Figure 6.   the clockwise direction. See Figure 7.

Figure 6   **Figure 7**

(c) An angle of 225° consists of a rotation through 180° followed by a rotation through 45°. See Figure 8.

(d) An angle of 405° consists of 1 revolution (360°) followed by a rotation through 45°. See Figure 9.

Figure 8

Figure 9

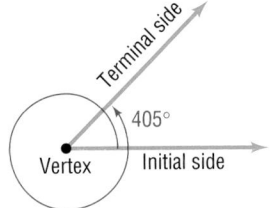

Now Work PROBLEM 11

1 Convert between Decimals and Degrees, Minutes, Seconds Forms for Angles

Although subdivisions of a degree may be obtained by using decimals, we also may use the notion of *minutes* and *seconds*. **One minute,** denoted by **1'**, is defined as $\frac{1}{60}$ degree. **One second,** denoted by **1''**, is defined as $\frac{1}{60}$ minute, or equivalently, $\frac{1}{3600}$ degree. An angle of, say, 30 degrees, 40 minutes, 10 seconds is written compactly as 30°40'10''. To summarize:

$$
\begin{array}{c}
\text{1 counterclockwise revolution} = 360° \\
1° = 60' \qquad 1' = 60''
\end{array}
\tag{1}
$$

It is sometimes necessary to convert from the degree, minute, second notation (D°M'S'') to a decimal form, and vice versa. Check your calculator; it should be capable of doing the conversion for you.

Before using your calculator, though, you must set the mode to degrees because there are two common ways to measure angles: degree mode and radian mode. (We will define radians shortly.) Usually, a menu is used to change from one mode to another. Check your owner's manual to find out how your particular calculator works.

Now let's see how to convert from the degree, minute, second notation (D°M'S'') to a decimal form, and vice versa, by looking at some examples:

$$
15°30' = 15.5° \quad \text{because} \quad 30' = 30 \cdot 1' = 30 \cdot \left(\frac{1}{60}\right)° = 0.5°
$$

$$
1' = \left(\frac{1}{60}\right)°
$$

$$
32.25° = 32°15' \quad \text{because} \quad 0.25° = \left(\frac{1}{4}\right)° = \frac{1}{4} \cdot 1° = \frac{1}{4}(60') = 15'
$$

$$
1° = 60'
$$

EXAMPLE 2 | **Converting between Degrees, Minutes, Seconds, and Decimal Forms**

(a) Convert 50°6'21'' to a decimal in degrees. Round the answer to four decimal places.

(b) Convert 21.256° to the D°M'S'' form. Round the answer to the nearest second.

Algebraic Solution

(a) Because $1' = \left(\dfrac{1}{60}\right)^{\circ}$ and $1'' = \left(\dfrac{1}{60}\right)' = \left(\dfrac{1}{60} \cdot \dfrac{1}{60}\right)^{\circ}$, we convert as follows:

$$50°6'21'' = 50° + 6' + 21''$$

$$= 50° + 6 \cdot \left(\frac{1}{60}\right)^{\circ} + 21 \cdot \left(\frac{1}{60} \cdot \frac{1}{60}\right)^{\circ}$$

$$\approx 50° + 0.1° + 0.0058°$$

$$= 50.1058°$$

(b) We proceed as follows:

$$21.256° = 21° + 0.256°$$

$$= 21° + (0.256)(60') \quad \text{Convert fraction of degree to minutes; } 1° = 60'.$$

$$= 21° + 15.36'$$

$$= 21° + 15' + 0.36'$$

$$= 21° + 15' + (0.36)(60'') \quad \text{Convert fraction of minute to seconds; } 1' = 60''.$$

$$= 21° + 15' + 21.6''$$

$$\approx 21°15'22'' \quad \text{Round to the nearest second.}$$

Graphing Solution

(a) Figure 10 shows the solution using a TI-84 Plus graphing calculator.

Figure 10

So $50°6'21'' = 51.1058°$ rounded to four decimal places.

(b) Figure 11 shows the solution using a TI-84 Plus graphing calculator.

Figure 11

So $21.256° = 21°15'22''$ rounded to the nearest second.

 Now Work PROBLEMS 23 AND 29

In many applications, such as describing the exact location of a star or the precise position of a ship at sea, angles measured in degrees, minutes, and even seconds are used. For calculation purposes, these are transformed to decimal form. In other applications, especially those in calculus, angles are measured using *radians*.

Radians

A **central angle** is a positive angle whose vertex is at the center of a circle. The rays of a central angle subtend (intersect) an arc on the circle. If the radius of the circle is r and the length of the arc subtended by the central angle is also r, then the measure of the angle is **1 radian.** See Figure 12(a).

For a circle of radius 1, the rays of a central angle with measure 1 radian subtend an arc of length 1. For a circle of radius 3, the rays of a central angle with measure 1 radian subtend an arc of length 3. See Figure 12(b).

Figure 12

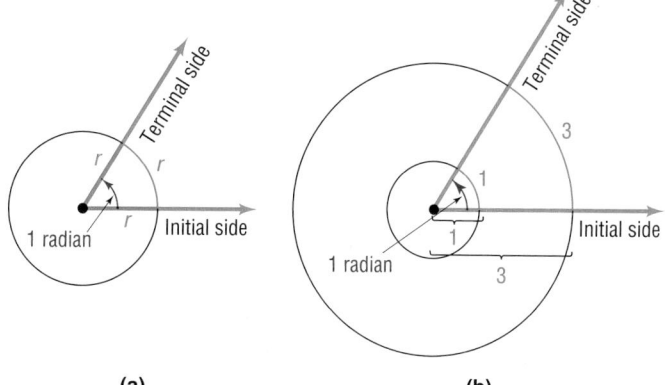

(a)   (b)

2 Find the Arc Length of a Circle

Figure 13

$\dfrac{\theta}{\theta_1} = \dfrac{s}{s_1}$

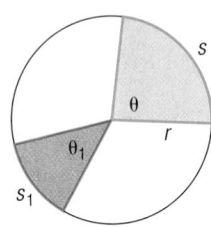

Now consider a circle of radius r and two central angles, θ and θ_1, measured in radians. Suppose that these central angles subtend arcs of lengths s and s_1, respectively, as shown in Figure 13. From geometry, we know that the ratio of the measures of the angles equals the ratio of the corresponding lengths of the arcs subtended by these angles; that is,

$$\frac{\theta}{\theta_1} = \frac{s}{s_1} \qquad\qquad (2)$$

Suppose that $\theta_1 = 1$ radian. Refer again to Figure 12(a). The length s_1 of the arc subtended by the central angle $\theta_1 = 1$ radian equals the radius r of the circle. Then $s_1 = r$, so equation (2) reduces to

$$\frac{\theta}{1} = \frac{s}{r} \quad \text{or} \quad s = r\theta \qquad\qquad (3)$$

THEOREM **Arc Length**

For a circle of radius r, a central angle of θ radians subtends an arc whose length s is

$$s = r\theta \qquad\qquad (4)$$

NOTE Formulas must be consistent with regard to the units used. In equation (4), we write

$$s = r\theta$$

To see the units, however, we must go back to equation (3) and write

$$\frac{\theta \text{ radians}}{1 \text{ radian}} = \frac{s \text{ length units}}{r \text{ length units}}$$

$$s \text{ length units} = r \text{ length units} \frac{\theta \text{ radians}}{1 \text{ radian}}$$

Since the radians cancel, we are left with

$$s \text{ length units} = (r \text{ length units})\theta \qquad s = r\theta$$

where θ appears to be "dimensionless" but, in fact, is measured in radians. So, in using the formula $s = r\theta$, the dimension for θ is radians, and any convenient unit of length (such as inches or meters) may be used for s and r. ∎

EXAMPLE 3 **Finding the Length of an Arc of a Circle**

Find the length of the arc of a circle of radius 2 meters subtended by a central angle of 0.25 radian.

Solution We use equation (4) with $r = 2$ meters and $\theta = 0.25$. The length s of the arc is

$$s = r\theta = 2(0.25) = 0.5 \text{ meter}$$

 Now Work PROBLEM 71

3 Convert from Degrees to Radians and from Radians to Degrees

Figure 14

1 revolution $= 2\pi$ radians

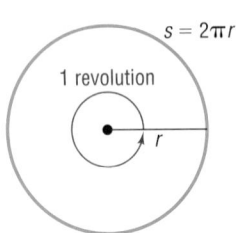

Next we discuss the relationship between angles measured in degrees and angles measured in radians. Consider a circle of radius r. A central angle of 1 revolution will subtend an arc equal to the circumference of the circle (Figure 14). Because the circumference of a circle equals $2\pi r$, we use $s = 2\pi r$ in equation (4) to find that, for an angle θ of 1 revolution,

$$s = r\theta$$
$$2\pi r = r\theta \qquad \theta = 1 \text{ revolution}; s = 2\pi r$$
$$\theta = 2\pi \text{ radians} \qquad \text{Solve for } \theta.$$

From this we have,

$$
1 \text{ revolution} = 2\pi \text{ radians} \tag{5}
$$

Since 1 revolution = 360°, we have

$$
360° = 2\pi \text{ radians}
$$

Dividing both sides by 2 yields

$$
180° = \pi \text{ radians} \tag{6}
$$

Divide both sides of equation (6) by 180. Then

$$
1 \text{ degree} = \frac{\pi}{180} \text{ radian}
$$

Divide both sides of (6) by π. Then

$$
\frac{180}{\pi} \text{ degrees} = 1 \text{ radian}
$$

We have the following two conversion formulas:

$$
1 \text{ degree} = \frac{\pi}{180} \text{ radian} \qquad 1 \text{ radian} = \frac{180}{\pi} \text{ degrees} \tag{7}
$$

EXAMPLE 4 **Converting from Degrees to Radians**

Convert each angle in degrees to radians.
(a) 60°   (b) 150°   (c) −45°   (d) 90°   (e) 107°

Solution (a) $60° = 60 \cdot 1 \text{ degree} = 60 \cdot \dfrac{\pi}{180} \text{ radian} = \dfrac{\pi}{3} \text{ radians}$

(b) $150° = 150 \cdot 1° = 150 \cdot \dfrac{\pi}{180} \text{ radian} = \dfrac{5\pi}{6} \text{ radians}$

(c) $-45° = -45 \cdot \dfrac{\pi}{180} \text{ radian} = -\dfrac{\pi}{4} \text{ radian}$

(d) $90° = 90 \cdot \dfrac{\pi}{180} \text{ radian} = \dfrac{\pi}{2} \text{ radians}$

(e) $107° = 107 \cdot \dfrac{\pi}{180} \text{ radian} \approx 1.868 \text{ radians}$

Example 4, parts (a)–(d), illustrates that angles that are "nice" fractions of a revolution are expressed in radian measure as fractional multiples of π, rather than as decimals. For example, a right angle, as in Example 4(d), is left in the form $\dfrac{\pi}{2}$ radians, which is exact, rather than using the approximation $\dfrac{\pi}{2} \approx \dfrac{3.1416}{2} = 1.5708$ radians. When the fractions are not "nice," we use the decimal approximation of the angle, as in Example 4(e).

Now Work PROBLEMS **35 AND 61**

| EXAMPLE 5 | **Converting Radians to Degrees** |

Convert each angle in radians to degrees.

(a) $\dfrac{\pi}{6}$ radian   (b) $\dfrac{3\pi}{2}$ radians   (c) $-\dfrac{3\pi}{4}$ radians

(d) $\dfrac{7\pi}{3}$ radians   (e) 3 radians

Solution

(a) $\dfrac{\pi}{6}$ radian $= \dfrac{\pi}{6} \cdot 1$ radian $= \dfrac{\pi}{6} \cdot \dfrac{180}{\pi}$ degrees $= 30°$

(b) $\dfrac{3\pi}{2}$ radians $= \dfrac{3\pi}{2} \cdot \dfrac{180}{\pi}$ degrees $= 270°$

(c) $-\dfrac{3\pi}{4}$ radians $= -\dfrac{3\pi}{4} \cdot \dfrac{180}{\pi}$ degrees $= -135°$

(d) $\dfrac{7\pi}{3}$ radians $= \dfrac{7\pi}{3} \cdot \dfrac{180}{\pi}$ degrees $= 420°$

(e) 3 radians $= 3 \cdot \dfrac{180}{\pi}$ degrees $\approx 171.89°$

Now Work PROBLEM 47

Table 1 lists the degree and radian measures of some commonly encountered angles. You should learn to feel equally comfortable using degree or radian measure for these angles.

Table 1

Degrees	0°	30°	45°	60°	90°	120°	135°	150°	180°
Radians	0	$\dfrac{\pi}{6}$	$\dfrac{\pi}{4}$	$\dfrac{\pi}{3}$	$\dfrac{\pi}{2}$	$\dfrac{2\pi}{3}$	$\dfrac{3\pi}{4}$	$\dfrac{5\pi}{6}$	π
Degrees		210°	225°	240°	270°	300°	315°	330°	360°
Radians		$\dfrac{7\pi}{6}$	$\dfrac{5\pi}{4}$	$\dfrac{4\pi}{3}$	$\dfrac{3\pi}{2}$	$\dfrac{5\pi}{3}$	$\dfrac{7\pi}{4}$	$\dfrac{11\pi}{6}$	2π

| EXAMPLE 6 | **Finding the Distance between Two Cities** |

See Figure 15(a). The latitude of a location L is the angle formed by a ray drawn from the center of Earth to the Equator and a ray drawn from the center of Earth to L. See Figure 15(b). Glasgow, Montana, is due north of Albuquerque, New Mexico. Find the distance between Glasgow (48°9′ north latitude) and Albuquerque (35°5′ north latitude). Assume that the radius of Earth is 3960 miles.

Figure 15

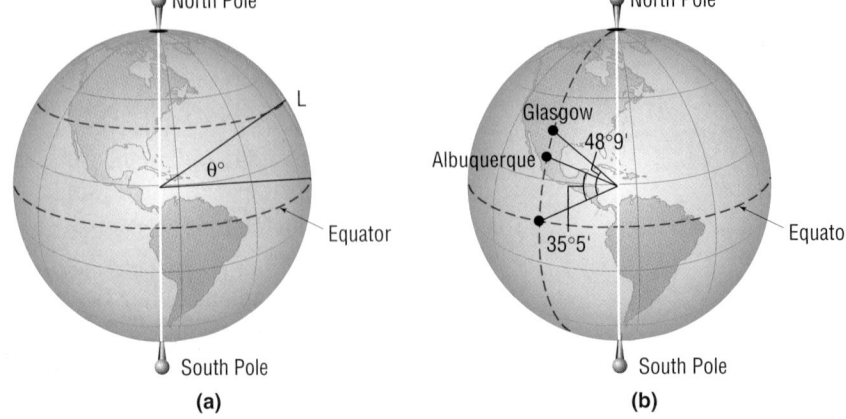

(a)   (b)

Solution   The measure of the central angle between the two cities is $48°9' - 35°5' = 13°4'$. We use equation (4), $s = r\theta$, but first we must convert the angle of $13°4'$ to radians.

$$\theta = 13°4' \approx 13.0667° = 13.0667 \cdot \frac{\pi}{180} \text{ radian} \approx 0.228 \text{ radian}$$

$$4' = \left(\frac{4}{60}\right)°$$

We use $\theta = 0.228$ radian and $r = 3960$ miles in equation (4). The distance between the two cities is

$$s = r\theta = 3960 \cdot 0.228 \approx 903 \text{ miles}$$

NOTE If the measure of an angle is given as 5, it is understood to mean 5 radians; if the measure of an angle is given as 5°, it means 5 degrees. ∎

When an angle is measured in degrees, the degree symbol will always be shown. However, when an angle is measured in radians, we will follow the usual practice and omit the word *radians*. So, if the measure of an angle is given as $\frac{\pi}{6}$, it is understood to mean $\frac{\pi}{6}$ radian.

─── **Now Work** PROBLEM 101

Figure 16

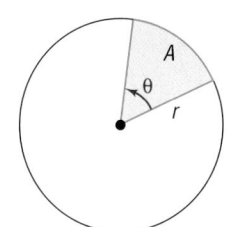

4 Find the Area of a Sector of a Circle

Consider a circle of radius r. Suppose that θ, measured in radians, is a central angle of this circle. See Figure 16. We seek a formula for the area A of the sector (shown in blue) formed by the angle θ.

Now consider a circle of radius r and two central angles θ and θ_1, both measured in radians. See Figure 17. From geometry, we know the ratio of the measures of the angles equals the ratio of the corresponding areas of the sectors formed by these angles. That is,

Figure 17

$$\frac{\theta}{\theta_1} = \frac{A}{A_1}$$

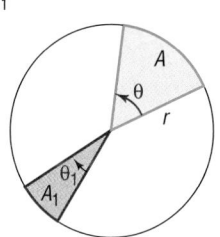

$$\frac{\theta}{\theta_1} = \frac{A}{A_1}$$

Suppose that $\theta_1 = 2\pi$ radians. Then $A_1 =$ area of the circle $= \pi r^2$. Solving for A, we find

$$A = A_1 \frac{\theta}{\theta_1} = \pi r^2 \frac{\theta}{2\pi} = \frac{1}{2} r^2 \theta$$

$$A_1 = \pi r^2$$
$$\theta_1 = 2\pi$$

THEOREM   **Area of a Sector**

The area A of the sector of a circle of radius r formed by a central angle of θ radians is

$$A = \frac{1}{2} r^2 \theta \qquad \textbf{(8)}$$

EXAMPLE 7   Finding the Area of a Sector of a Circle

Find the area of the sector of a circle of radius 2 feet formed by an angle of $30°$. Round the answer to two decimal places.

Solution   We use equation (8) with $r = 2$ feet and $\theta = 30° = \frac{\pi}{6}$ radian. [Remember, in equation (8), θ must be in radians.]

$$A = \frac{1}{2} r^2 \theta = \frac{1}{2}(2)^2 \frac{\pi}{6} = \frac{\pi}{3}$$

The area A of the sector is 1.05 square feet, rounded to two decimal places.

─── **Now Work** PROBLEM 79

5 Find the Linear Speed of an Object Traveling in Circular Motion

We have already defined the average speed of an object as the distance traveled divided by the elapsed time in Appendix A, Section A.8.

Figure 18

$$v = \frac{s}{t}$$

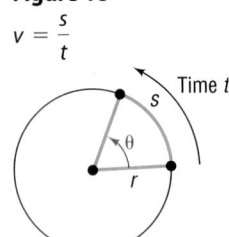

DEFINITION   Suppose that an object moves around a circle of radius r at a constant speed. If s is the distance traveled in time t around this circle, then the **linear speed** v of the object is defined as

$$v = \frac{s}{t} \qquad (9)$$

As this object travels around the circle, suppose that θ (measured in radians) is the central angle swept out in time t. See Figure 18.

DEFINITION   The **angular speed** ω (the Greek letter omega) of this object is the angle θ (measured in radians) swept out, divided by the elapsed time t; that is,

$$\omega = \frac{\theta}{t} \qquad (10)$$

Angular speed is the way the turning rate of an engine is described. For example, an engine idling at 900 rpm (revolutions per minute) is one that rotates at an angular speed of

$$900 \frac{\text{revolutions}}{\text{minute}} = 900 \frac{\text{revolutions}}{\text{minute}} \cdot 2\pi \frac{\text{radians}}{\text{revolution}} = 1800\pi \frac{\text{radians}}{\text{minute}}$$

There is an important relationship between linear speed and angular speed:

$$\text{linear speed} = v = \underset{\underset{(9)}{\uparrow}}{\frac{s}{t}} = \underset{\underset{s \,=\, r\theta}{\uparrow}}{\frac{r\theta}{t}} = r\left(\frac{\theta}{t}\right) = \underset{\underset{(10)}{\uparrow}}{r \cdot \omega}$$

So

$$v = r\omega \qquad (11)$$

where ω is measured in radians per unit time.

When using equation (11), remember that $v = \frac{s}{t}$ (the linear speed) has the dimensions of length per unit of time (such as feet per second or miles per hour), r (the radius of the circular motion) has the same length dimension as s, and ω (the angular speed) has the dimensions of radians per unit of time. If the angular speed is given in terms of *revolutions* per unit of time (as is often the case), be sure to convert it to *radians* per unit of time using the fact that 1 revolution = 2π radians before attempting to use equation (11).

EXAMPLE 8   **Finding Linear Speed**

A child is spinning a rock at the end of a 2-foot rope at the rate of 180 revolutions per minute (rpm). Find the linear speed of the rock when it is released.

Solution   Look at Figure 19. The rock is moving around a circle of radius $r = 2$ feet. The angular speed ω of the rock is

$$\omega = 180 \frac{\text{revolutions}}{\text{minute}} = 180 \frac{\text{revolutions}}{\text{minute}} \cdot 2\pi \frac{\text{radians}}{\text{revolution}} = 360\pi \frac{\text{radians}}{\text{minute}}$$

Figure 19

From equation (11), the linear speed v of the rock is

$$v = r\omega = 2 \text{ feet} \cdot 360\pi \frac{\text{radians}}{\text{minute}} = 720\pi \frac{\text{feet}}{\text{minute}} \approx 2262 \frac{\text{feet}}{\text{minute}}$$

The linear speed of the rock when it is released is 2262 ft/min $\approx$ 25.7 mi/hr.

Now Work PROBLEM 97

Historical Feature

Trigonometry was developed by Greek astronomers, who regarded the sky as the inside of a sphere, so it was natural that triangles on a sphere were investigated early (by Menelaus of Alexandria about AD 100) and that triangles in the plane were studied much later. The first book containing a systematic treatment of plane and spherical trigonometry was written by the Persian astronomer Nasir Eddin (about AD 1250).

Regiomontanus (1436–1476) is the person most responsible for moving trigonometry from astronomy into mathematics. His work was improved by Copernicus (1473–1543) and Copernicus's student

Rhaeticus (1514–1576). Rhaeticus's book was the first to define the six trigonometric functions as ratios of sides of triangles, although he did not give the functions their present names. Credit for this is due to Thomas Finck (1583), but Finck's notation was by no means universally accepted at the time. The notation was finally stabilized by the textbooks of Leonhard Euler (1707–1783).

Trigonometry has since evolved from its use by surveyors, navigators, and engineers to present applications involving ocean tides, the rise and fall of food supplies in certain ecologies, brain wave patterns, and many other phenomena.

6.1 Assess Your Understanding

'Are You Prepared?' *Answers are given at the end of these exercises. If you get a wrong answer, read the pages listed in* red.

1. What is the formula for the circumference C of a circle of radius r? What is the formula for the area A of a circle of radius r? (p. A16)

2. What is the formula for uniform motion? (p. A72)

Concepts and Vocabulary

3. An angle θ is in _____ _____ if its vertex is at the origin of a rectangular coordinate system and its initial side coincides with the positive x-axis.

4. On a circle of radius r, a central angle of θ radians subtends an arc of length $s =$ _____; the area of the sector formed by this angle θ is $A =$ _____.

5. An object travels around a circle of radius r with constant speed. If s is the distance traveled in time t around the circle and θ is the central angle (in radians) swept out in time t, then the linear speed of the object is $v =$ _____ and the angular speed of the object is $\omega =$ _____.

6. *True or False* $\pi = 180$.

7. *True or False* $180° = \pi$ radians.

8. *True or False*   On the unit circle, if s is the length of the arc subtended by a central angle θ, measured in radians, then $s = \theta$.

9. *True or False*   The area A of the sector of a circle of radius r formed by a central angle of θ degrees is $A = \dfrac{1}{2}r^2\theta$.

10. *True or False*   For circular motion on a circle of radius r, linear speed equals angular speed divided by r.

Skill Building

In Problems 11–22, draw each angle.

11. $30°$
12. $60°$
13. $135°$
14. $-120°$
15. $450°$
16. $540°$

17. $\dfrac{3\pi}{4}$
18. $\dfrac{4\pi}{3}$
19. $-\dfrac{\pi}{6}$
20. $-\dfrac{2\pi}{3}$
21. $\dfrac{16\pi}{3}$
22. $\dfrac{21\pi}{4}$

In Problems 23–28, convert each angle to a decimal in degrees. Round your answer to two decimal places.

23. $40°10'25''$
24. $61°42'21''$
25. $1°2'3''$
26. $73°40'40''$
27. $9°9'9''$
28. $98°22'45''$

In Problems 29–34, convert each angle to $D°M'S''$ form. Round your answer to the nearest second.

29. $40.32°$
30. $61.24°$
31. $18.255°$
32. $29.411°$
33. $19.99°$
34. $44.01°$

In Problems 35–46, convert each angle in degrees to radians. Express your answer as a multiple of π.

35. 30°   **36.** 120°   **37.** 240°   **38.** 330°   **39.** −60°   **40.** −30°

41. 180°   **42.** 270°   **43.** −135°   **44.** −225°   **45.** −90°   **46.** −180°

In Problems 47–58, convert each angle in radians to degrees.

47. $\dfrac{\pi}{3}$ **48.** $\dfrac{5\pi}{6}$ **49.** $-\dfrac{5\pi}{4}$ **50.** $-\dfrac{2\pi}{3}$ **51.** $\dfrac{\pi}{2}$ **52.** 4π

53. $\dfrac{\pi}{12}$ **54.** $\dfrac{5\pi}{12}$ **55.** $-\dfrac{\pi}{2}$ **56.** $-\pi$ **57.** $-\dfrac{\pi}{6}$ **58.** $-\dfrac{3\pi}{4}$

In Problems 59–64, convert each angle in degrees to radians. Express your answer in decimal form, rounded to two decimal places.

59. 17°   **60.** 73°   **61.** −40°   **62.** −51°   **63.** 125°   **64.** 350°

In Problems 65–70, convert each angle in radians to degrees. Express your answer in decimal form, rounded to two decimal places.

65. 3.14   **66.** 0.75   **67.** 2   **68.** 3   **69.** 6.32   **70.** $\sqrt{2}$

In Problems 71–78, s denotes the length of the arc of a circle of radius r subtended by the central angle θ. Find the missing quantity. Round answers to three decimal places.

71. $r = 10$ meters, $\theta = \dfrac{1}{2}$ radian, $s = ?$

72. $r = 6$ feet, $\theta = 2$ radians, $s = ?$

73. $\theta = \dfrac{1}{3}$ radian, $s = 2$ feet, $r = ?$

74. $\theta = \dfrac{1}{4}$ radian, $s = 6$ centimeters, $r = ?$

75. $r = 5$ miles, $s = 3$ miles, $\theta = ?$

76. $r = 6$ meters, $s = 8$ meters, $\theta = ?$

77. $r = 2$ inches, $\theta = 30°$, $s = ?$

78. $r = 3$ meters, $\theta = 120°$, $s = ?$

In Problems 79–86, A denotes the area of the sector of a circle of radius r formed by the central angle θ. Find the missing quantity. Round answers to three decimal places.

79. $r = 10$ meters, $\theta = \dfrac{1}{2}$ radian, $A = ?$

80. $r = 6$ feet, $\theta = 2$ radians, $A = ?$

81. $\theta = \dfrac{1}{3}$ radian, $A = 2$ square feet, $r = ?$

82. $\theta = \dfrac{1}{4}$ radian, $A = 6$ square centimeters, $r = ?$

83. $r = 5$ miles, $A = 3$ square miles, $\theta = ?$

84. $r = 6$ meters, $A = 8$ square meters, $\theta = ?$

85. $r = 2$ inches, $\theta = 30°$, $A = ?$

86. $r = 3$ meters, $\theta = 120°$, $A = ?$

In Problems 87–90, find the length s and area A. Round answers to three decimal places.

87.

88.

89.

90.

Applications and Extensions

91. Movement of a Minute Hand   The minute hand of a clock is 6 inches long. How far does the tip of the minute hand move in 15 minutes? How far does it move in 25 minutes? Round answers to two decimal places.

92. Movement of a Pendulum   A pendulum swings through an angle of 20° each second. If the pendulum is 40 inches long, how far does its tip move each second? Round answers to two decimal places.

93. Area of a Sector   Find the area of the sector of a circle of radius 4 meters formed by an angle of 45°. Round the answer to two decimal places.

94. Area of a Sector   Find the area of the sector of a circle of radius 3 centimeters formed by an angle of 60°. Round the answer to two decimal places.

95. Watering a Lawn A water sprinkler sprays water over a distance of 30 feet while rotating through an angle of 135°. What area of lawn receives water?

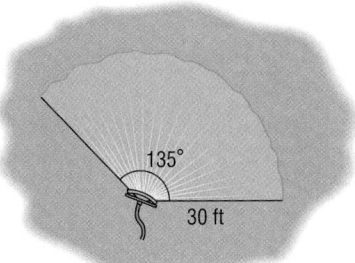

96. Designing a Water Sprinkler An engineer is asked to design a water sprinkler that will cover a field of 100 square yards that is in the shape of a sector of a circle of radius 15 yards. Through what angle should the sprinkler rotate?

97. Motion on a Circle An object is traveling around a circle with a radius of 5 centimeters. If in 20 seconds a central angle of $\frac{1}{3}$ radian is swept out, what is the angular speed of the object? What is its linear speed?

98. Motion on a Circle An object is traveling around a circle with a radius of 2 meters. If in 20 seconds the object travels 5 meters, what is its angular speed? What is its linear speed?

99. Bicycle Wheels The diameter of each wheel of a bicycle is 26 inches. If you are traveling at a speed of 35 miles per hour on this bicycle, through how many revolutions per minute are the wheels turning?

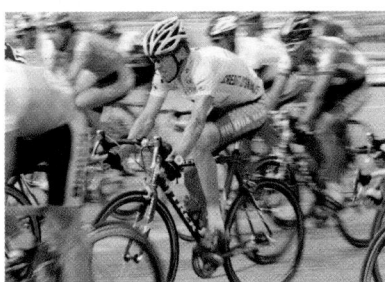

100. Car Wheels The radius of each wheel of a car is 15 inches. If the wheels are turning at the rate of 3 revolutions per second, how fast is the car moving? Express your answer in inches per second and in miles per hour.

In Problems 101–104, the latitude of a location L is the angle formed by a ray drawn from the center of Earth to the Equator and a ray drawn from the center of Earth to L. See the figure.

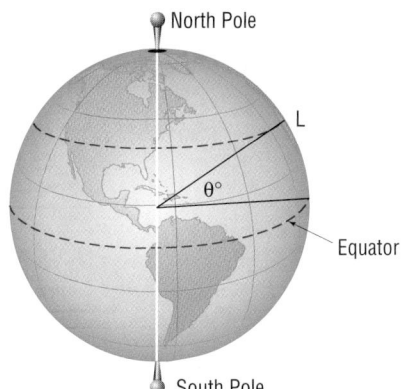

101. Distance between Cities Memphis, Tennessee, is due north of New Orleans, Louisiana. Find the distance between Memphis (35°9′ north latitude) and New Orleans (29°57′ north latitude). Assume that the radius of Earth is 3960 miles.

102. Distance between Cities Charleston, West Virginia, is due north of Jacksonville, Florida. Find the distance between Charleston (38°21′ north latitude) and Jacksonville (30°20′ north latitude). Assume that the radius of Earth is 3960 miles.

103. Linear Speed on Earth Earth rotates on an axis through its poles. The distance from the axis to a location on Earth 30° north latitude is about 3429.5 miles. Therefore, a location on Earth at 30° north latitude is spinning on a circle of radius 3429.5 miles. Compute the linear speed on the surface of Earth at 30° north latitude.

104. Linear Speed on Earth Earth rotates on an axis through its poles. The distance from the axis to a location on Earth 40° north latitude is about 3033.5 miles. Therefore, a location on Earth at 40° north latitude is spinning on a circle of radius 3033.5 miles. Compute the linear speed on the surface of Earth at 40° north latitude.

105. Speed of the Moon The mean distance of the moon from Earth is 2.39×10^5 miles. Assuming that the orbit of the moon around Earth is circular and that 1 revolution takes 27.3 days, find the linear speed of the moon. Express your answer in miles per hour.

106. Speed of Earth The mean distance of Earth from the Sun is 9.29×10^7 miles. Assuming that the orbit of Earth around the Sun is circular and that 1 revolution takes 365 days, find the linear speed of Earth. Express your answer in miles per hour.

107. Pulleys Two pulleys, one with radius 2 inches and the other with radius 8 inches, are connected by a belt. (See the figure.) If the 2-inch pulley is caused to rotate at 3 revolutions per minute, determine the revolutions per minute of the 8-inch pulley.

[**Hint:** The linear speeds of the pulleys are the same; both equal the speed of the belt.]

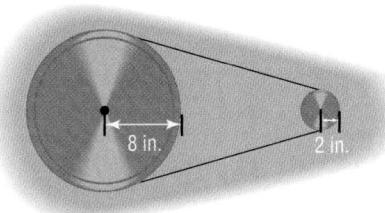

108. Ferris Wheels A neighborhood carnival has a Ferris wheel whose radius is 30 feet. You measure the time it takes for one revolution to be 70 seconds. What is the linear speed (in feet per second) of this Ferris wheel? What is the angular speed in radians per second?

109. Computing the Speed of a River Current To approximate the speed of the current of a river, a circular paddle wheel with radius 4 feet is lowered into the water. If the current causes the wheel to rotate at a speed of 10 revolutions per minute, what is the speed of the current? Express your answer in miles per hour.

110. Spin Balancing Tires A spin balancer rotates the wheel of a car at 480 revolutions per minute. If the diameter of the wheel is 26 inches, what road speed is being tested? Express your answer in miles per hour. At how many revolutions per minute should the balancer be set to test a road speed of 80 miles per hour?

111. The Cable Cars of San Francisco At the Cable Car Museum you can see the four cable lines that are used to pull cable cars up and down the hills of San Francisco. Each cable travels at a speed of 9.55 miles per hour, caused by a rotating wheel whose diameter is 8.5 feet. How fast is the wheel rotating? Express your answer in revolutions per minute.

112. Difference in Time of Sunrise Naples, Florida, is approximately 90 miles due west of Ft. Lauderdale. How much sooner would a person in Ft. Lauderdale first see the rising Sun than a person in Naples? See the hint.

[**Hint:** Consult the figure. When a person at Q sees the first rays of the Sun, a person at P is still in the dark. The person at P sees the first rays after Earth has rotated so that P is at the location Q. Now use the fact that at the latitude of Ft. Lauderdale in 24 hours an arc of length $2\pi(3559)$ miles is subtended.]

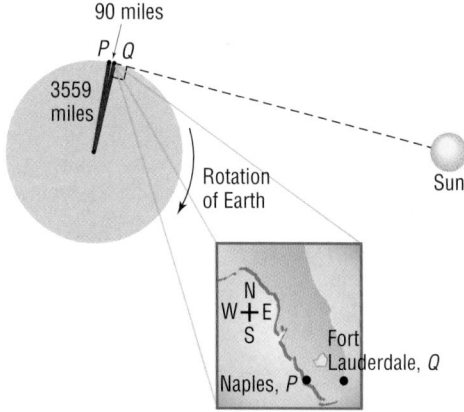

113. Keeping Up with the Sun How fast would you have to travel on the surface of Earth at the equator to keep up with the Sun (that is, so that the Sun would appear to remain in the same position in the sky)?

114. Nautical Miles A **nautical mile** equals the length of arc subtended by a central angle of 1 minute on a great circle* on the surface of Earth. (See the figure on the top, right of the page.) If the radius of Earth is taken as 3960 miles, express 1 nautical mile in terms of ordinary, or **statute,** miles.

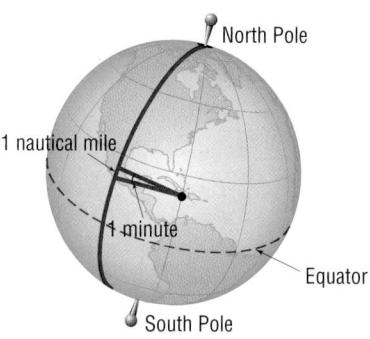

115. Approximating the Circumference of Earth Eratosthenes of Cyrene (276–194 BC) was a Greek scholar who lived and worked in Cyrene and Alexandria. One day while visiting in Syene he noticed that the Sun's rays shone directly down a well. On this date 1 year later, in Alexandria, which is 500 miles due north of Syene he measured the angle of the Sun to be about 7.2 degrees. See the figure. Use this information to approximate the radius and circumference of Earth.

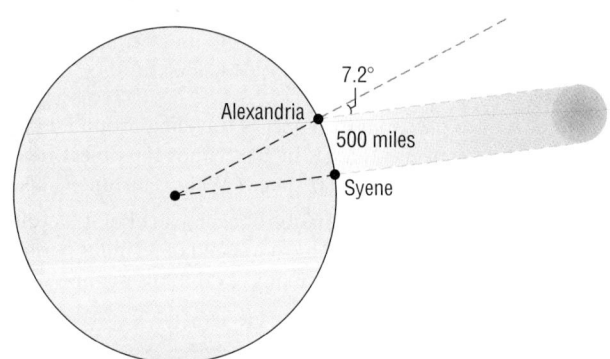

116. Designing a Little League Field For a 60-foot Little League Baseball field, the distance from home base to the nearest fence (or other obstruction) on fair territory should be a minimum of 200 feet. The commissioner of parks and recreation is making plans for a new 60-foot field. Because of limited ground availability, he will use the minimum required distance to the outfield fence. To increase safety, however, he plans to include a 10-foot wide warning track on the inside of the fence. To further increase safety, the fence and warning track will extend both directions into foul territory. In total the arc formed by the outfield fence (including the extensions into the foul territories) will be subtended by a central angle at home plate measuring 96°, as illustrated.
(a) Determine the length of the outfield fence.
(b) Determine the area of the warning track.

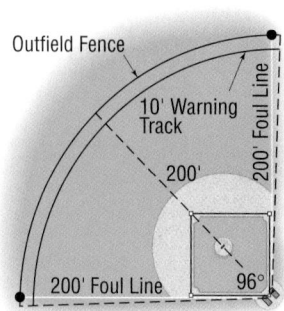

Source: www.littleleague.org

*Any circle drawn on the surface of Earth that divides Earth into two equal hemispheres.

[**Note:** There is a 90° angle between the two foul lines. Then there are two 3° angles between the foul lines and the dotted lines shown. The angle between the two dotted lines outside the 200-foot foul lines is 96°.]

117. Pulleys   Two pulleys, one with radius r_1 and the other with radius r_2, are connected by a belt. The pulley with radius r_1 rotates at ω_1 revolutions per minute, whereas the pulley with radius r_2 rotates at ω_2 revolutions per minute. Show that

$$\frac{r_1}{r_2} = \frac{\omega_2}{\omega_1}.$$

Discussion and Writing

118. Do you prefer to measure angles using degrees or radians? Provide justification and a rationale for your choice.

119. What is 1 radian? What is 1°?

120. Which angle has the larger measure: 1 degree or 1 radian? Or are they equal?

121. Explain the difference between linear speed and angular speed.

122. For a circle of radius r, a central angle of θ degrees subtends an arc whose length s is $s = \dfrac{\pi}{180} r\theta$. Discuss whether this is a true or false statement. Give reasons to defend your position.

123. Discuss why ships and airplanes use nautical miles to measure distance. Explain the difference between a nautical mile and a statute mile.

124. Investigate the way that speed bicycles work. In particular, explain the differences and similarities between 5-speed and 9-speed derailleurs. Be sure to include a discussion of linear speed and angular speed.

125. In Example 6, we found that the distance between Albuquerque, New Mexico, and Glasgow, Montana, is approximately 903 miles. According to *mapquest.com*, the distance is approximately 1300 miles. What might account for the difference?

'Are You Prepared?' Answers

1. $C = 2\pi r; A = \pi r^2$ **2.** $d = r \cdot t$

6.2 Trigonometric Functions: Unit Circle Approach

PREPARING FOR THIS SECTION   *Before getting started, review the following:*

- Geometry Essentials (Appendix A, Section A.2, pp. A14–A19)
- Unit Circle (Section 1.5, p. 45)
- Symmetry (Section 1.2, pp. 19–21)
- Functions (Section 2.1, pp. 56–64)

Now Work the 'Are You Prepared?' problems on page 378.

OBJECTIVES   **1** Find the Exact Values of the Trigonometric Functions Using a Point on the Unit Circle (p. 367)

2 Find the Exact Values of the Trigonometric Functions of Quadrantal Angles (p. 368)

3 Find the Exact Values of the Trigonometric Functions of $\dfrac{\pi}{4} = 45°$ (p. 370)

4 Find the Exact Values of the Trigonometric Functions of $\dfrac{\pi}{6} = 30°$ and $\dfrac{\pi}{3} = 60°$ (p. 371)

5 Find the Exact Values of the Trigonometric Functions for Integer Multiples of $\dfrac{\pi}{6} = 30°, \dfrac{\pi}{4} = 45°,$ and $\dfrac{\pi}{3} = 60°$ (p. 374)

6 Use a Calculator to Approximate the Value of a Trigonometric Function (p. 375)

7 Use a Circle of Radius r to Evaluate the Trigonometric Functions (p. 376)

We are now ready to introduce trigonometric functions. The approach that we take uses the unit circle.

The Unit Circle

Recall that the unit circle is a circle whose radius is 1 and whose center is at the origin of a rectangular coordinate system. Also recall that any circle of radius r has circumference of length $2\pi r$. Therefore, the unit circle (radius $= 1$) has a circumference of length 2π. In other words, for 1 revolution around the unit circle the length of the arc is 2π units.

The following discussion sets the stage for defining the trigonometric functions using the unit circle.

Let t be any real number. We position the t-axis so that it is vertical with the positive direction up. We place this t-axis in the xy-plane so that $t = 0$ is located at the point $(1, 0)$ in the xy-plane.

If $t \geq 0$, let s be the distance from the origin to t on the t-axis. See the red portion of Figure 20(a).

Now look at the unit circle in Figure 20(a). Beginning at the point $(1, 0)$ on the unit circle, travel $s = t$ units in the counterclockwise direction along the circle, to arrive at the point $P = (x, y)$. In this sense, the length $s = t$ units is being **wrapped** around the unit circle.

If $t < 0$, we begin at the point $(1, 0)$ on the unit circle and travel $s = |t|$ units in the clockwise direction to arrive at the point $P = (x, y)$. See Figure 20(b).

Figure 20

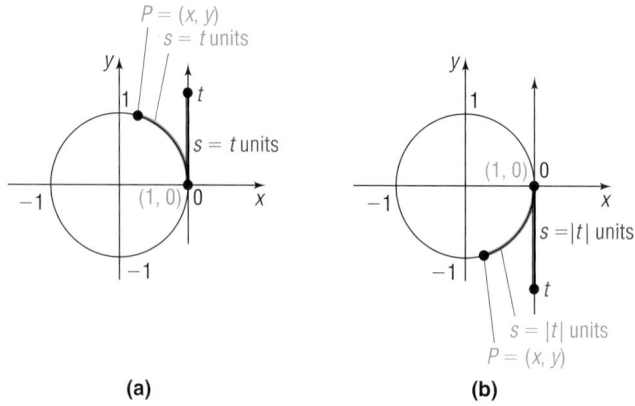

(a)　　　　(b)

If $t > 2\pi$ or if $t < -2\pi$, it will be necessary to travel around the unit circle more than once before arriving at the point P. Do you see why?

Let's describe this process another way. Picture a string of length $s = |t|$ units being wrapped around a circle of radius 1 unit. We start wrapping the string around the circle at the point $(1, 0)$. If $t \geq 0$, we wrap the string in the counterclockwise direction; if $t < 0$, we wrap the string in the clockwise direction. The point $P = (x, y)$ is the point where the string ends.

This discussion tells us that, for any real number t, we can locate a unique point $P = (x, y)$ on the unit circle. We call P **the point on the unit circle that corresponds to t.** This is the important idea here. No matter what real number t is chosen, there is a unique point P on the unit circle corresponding to it. We use the coordinates of the point $P = (x, y)$ on the unit circle corresponding to the real number t to define the **six trigonometric functions of t.**

DEFINITION

Let t be a real number and let $P = (x, y)$ be the point on the unit circle that corresponds to t.

The **sine function** associates with t the y-coordinate of P and is denoted by

$$\sin t = y$$

In Words

The sine function takes as input
a real number t that corresponds to a point P = (x, y) on
the unit circle and outputs the
y-coordinate. The cosine function
takes as input a real number t
that corresponds to a point
P = (x, y) on the unit circle and
outputs the x-coordinate.

The **cosine function** associates with t the x-coordinate of P and is denoted by

$$\cos t = x$$

If $x \neq 0$, the **tangent function** associates with t the ratio of the y-coordinate to the x-coordinate of P and is denoted by

$$\tan t = \frac{y}{x}$$

If $y \neq 0$, the **cosecant function** is defined as

$$\csc t = \frac{1}{y}$$

If $x \neq 0$, the **secant function** is defined as

$$\sec t = \frac{1}{x}$$

If $y \neq 0$, the **cotangent function** is defined as

$$\cot t = \frac{x}{y}$$

Notice in these definitions that if $x = 0$, that is, if the point P is on the y-axis, then the tangent function and the secant function are undefined. Also, if $y = 0$, that is, if the point P is on the x-axis, then the cosecant function and the cotangent function are undefined.

Because we use the unit circle in these definitions of the trigonometric functions, they are sometimes referred to as **circular functions.**

1 Find the Exact Values of the Trigonometric Functions Using a Point on the Unit Circle

EXAMPLE 1   Finding the Values of the Six Trigonometric Functions Using a Point on the Unit Circle

Let t be a real number and let $P = \left(-\frac{1}{2}, \frac{\sqrt{3}}{2} \right)$ be the point on the unit circle that corresponds to t. Find the values of $\sin t$, $\cos t$, $\tan t$, $\csc t$, $\sec t$, and $\cot t$.

Figure 21

Solution   See Figure 21. We follow the definition of the six trigonometric functions, using $P = \left(-\frac{1}{2}, \frac{\sqrt{3}}{2} \right) = (x, y)$. Then, with $x = -\frac{1}{2}$ and $y = \frac{\sqrt{3}}{2}$, we have

$P = \left(-\frac{1}{2}, \frac{\sqrt{3}}{2} \right)$

$(1, 0)$ x

$$\sin t = y = \frac{\sqrt{3}}{2} \qquad \cos t = x = -\frac{1}{2} \qquad \tan t = \frac{y}{x} = \frac{\frac{\sqrt{3}}{2}}{-\frac{1}{2}} = -\sqrt{3}$$

WARNING When writing the values of the trigonometric functions, do not forget the argument of the function.

$$\csc t = \frac{1}{y} = \frac{1}{\frac{\sqrt{3}}{2}} = \frac{2\sqrt{3}}{3} \qquad \sec t = \frac{1}{x} = \frac{1}{-\frac{1}{2}} = -2 \qquad \cot t = \frac{x}{y} = \frac{-\frac{1}{2}}{\frac{\sqrt{3}}{2}} = -\frac{\sqrt{3}}{3}$$

$\sin t = \frac{\sqrt{3}}{2}$ *correct*

$\sin = \frac{\sqrt{3}}{2}$ *incorrect*   ∎

Now Work PROBLEM 11

Trigonometric Functions of Angles

Let $P = (x, y)$ be the point on the unit circle corresponding to the real number t. See Figure 22(a). Let θ be the angle in standard position, measured in radians, whose terminal side is the ray from the origin through P. See Figure 22(b). Since the unit circle has radius 1 unit, if $s = |t|$ units, then from the arc length formula $s = r\theta$, we have $\theta = t$ radians. See Figures 22(c) and (d).

Figure 22

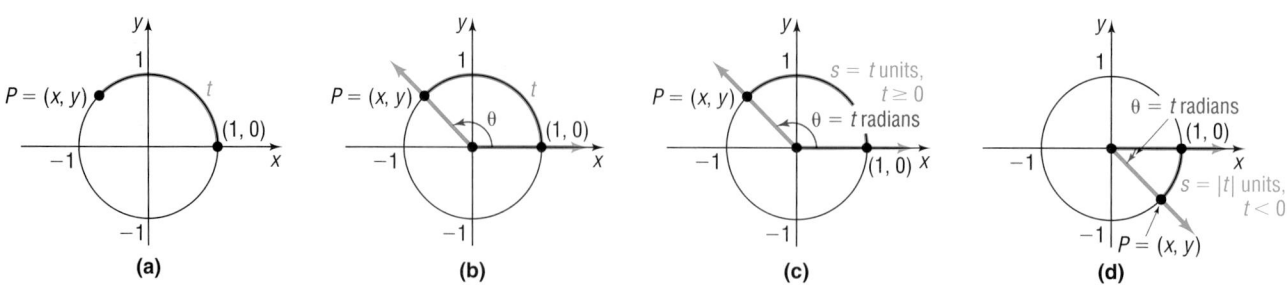

(a)   (b)   (c)   (d)

The point $P = (x, y)$ on the unit circle that corresponds to the real number t is the point P on the terminal side of the angle $\theta = t$ radians. As a result, we can say that

$$\sin t = \sin \theta$$

Real number $\theta = t$ radians

and so on. We can now define the trigonometric functions of the angle θ.

DEFINITION

If $\theta = t$ radians, the **six trigonometric functions of the angle θ** are defined as

$\sin \theta = \sin t$	$\cos \theta = \cos t$	$\tan \theta = \tan t$
$\csc \theta = \csc t$	$\sec \theta = \sec t$	$\cot \theta = \cot t$

Even though the trigonometric functions can be viewed both as functions of real numbers and as functions of angles, it is customary to refer to trigonometric functions of real numbers and trigonometric functions of angles collectively as the *trigonometric functions*. We shall follow this practice from now on.

If an angle θ is measured in degrees, we shall use the degree symbol when writing a trigonometric function of θ, as, for example, in $\sin 30°$ and $\tan 45°$. If an angle θ is measured in radians, then no symbol is used when writing a trigonometric function of θ, as, for example, in $\cos \pi$ and $\sec \dfrac{\pi}{3}$.

Finally, since the values of the trigonometric functions of an angle θ are determined by the coordinates of the point $P = (x, y)$ on the unit circle corresponding to θ, the units used to measure the angle θ are irrelevant. For example, it does not matter whether we write $\theta = \dfrac{\pi}{2}$ radians or $\theta = 90°$. The point on the unit circle corresponding to this angle is $P = (0, 1)$. As a result,

$$\sin \frac{\pi}{2} = \sin 90° = 1 \quad \text{and} \quad \cos \frac{\pi}{2} = \cos 90° = 0$$

2 Find the Exact Values of the Trigonometric Functions of Quadrantal Angles

To find the exact value of a trigonometric function of an angle θ or a real number t requires that we locate the point $P = (x, y)$ on the unit circle that corresponds to t. This is not always easy to do. In the examples that follow, we will evaluate the trigonometric functions of certain angles or real numbers for which this process is relatively easy. A calculator will be used to evaluate the trigonometric functions of most other angles.

EXAMPLE 2

Finding the Exact Values of the Six Trigonometric Functions of Quadrantal Angles

Find the exact values of the six trigonometric functions of:

(a) $\theta = 0 = 0°$

(b) $\theta = \dfrac{\pi}{2} = 90°$

(c) $\theta = \pi = 180°$

(d) $\theta = \dfrac{3\pi}{2} = 270°$

Solution

(a) The point on the unit circle that corresponds to $\theta = 0 = 0°$ is $P = (1, 0)$. See Figure 23(a). Then

$$\sin 0 = \sin 0° = y = 0 \qquad \cos 0 = \cos 0° = x = 1$$

$$\tan 0 = \tan 0° = \frac{y}{x} = 0 \qquad \sec 0 = \sec 0° = \frac{1}{x} = 1$$

Since the y-coordinate of P is 0, $\csc 0$ and $\cot 0$ are not defined.

(b) The point on the unit circle that corresponds to $\theta = \dfrac{\pi}{2} = 90°$ is $P = (0, 1)$. See Figure 23(b). Then

$$\sin \frac{\pi}{2} = \sin 90° = y = 1 \qquad \cos \frac{\pi}{2} = \cos 90° = x = 0$$

$$\csc \frac{\pi}{2} = \csc 90° = \frac{1}{y} = 1 \qquad \cot \frac{\pi}{2} = \cot 90° = \frac{x}{y} = 0$$

Since the x-coordinate of P is 0, $\tan \dfrac{\pi}{2}$ and $\sec \dfrac{\pi}{2}$ are not defined.

(c) The point on the unit circle that corresponds to $\theta = \pi = 180°$ is $P = (-1, 0)$. See Figure 23(c). Then

$$\sin \pi = \sin 180° = y = 0 \qquad \cos \pi = \cos 180° = x = -1$$

$$\tan \pi = \tan 180° = \frac{y}{x} = 0 \qquad \sec \pi = \sec 180° = \frac{1}{x} = -1$$

Since the y-coordinate of P is 0, $\csc \pi$ and $\cot \pi$ are not defined.

(d) The point on the unit circle that corresponds to $\theta = \dfrac{3\pi}{2} = 270°$ is $P = (0, -1)$. See Figure 23(d). Then

$$\sin \frac{3\pi}{2} = \sin 270° = y = -1 \qquad \cos \frac{3\pi}{2} = \cos 270° = x = 0$$

$$\csc \frac{3\pi}{2} = \csc 270° = \frac{1}{y} = -1 \qquad \cot \frac{3\pi}{2} = \cot 270° = \frac{x}{y} = 0$$

Since the x-coordinate of P is 0, $\tan \dfrac{3\pi}{2}$ and $\sec \dfrac{3\pi}{2}$ are not defined.

Figure 23

(a)

(b)

(c)

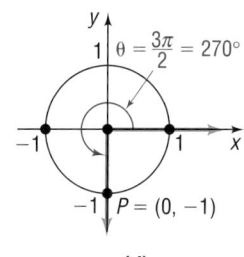

(d)

Table 2 on the next page summarizes the values of the trigonometric functions found in Example 2.

Table 2

				Quadrantal Angles				
θ (Radians)	θ (Degrees)	sin θ	cos θ	tan θ	csc θ	sec θ	cot θ
0	0°	0	1	0	Not defined	1	Not defined
$\dfrac{\pi}{2}$	90°	1	0	Not defined	1	Not defined	0
π	180°	0	−1	0	Not defined	−1	Not defined
$\dfrac{3\pi}{2}$	270°	−1	0	Not defined	−1	Not defined	0

There is no need to memorize Table 2. To find the value of a trigonometric function of a quadrantal angle, draw the angle and apply the definition, as we did in Example 2.

EXAMPLE 3 | **Finding Exact Values of the Trigonometric Functions of Angles That Are Integer Multiples of Quadrantal Angles**

Find the exact value of:

(a) $\sin(3\pi)$

(b) $\cos(-270°)$

Solution

(a) See Figure 24(a). The point P on the unit circle that corresponds to $\theta = 3\pi$ is $P = (-1, 0)$, so $\sin(3\pi) = y = 0$.

(b) See Figure 24(b). The point P on the unit circle that corresponds to $\theta = -270°$ is $P = (0, 1)$, so $\cos(-270°) = x = 0$.

Figure 24

(a)

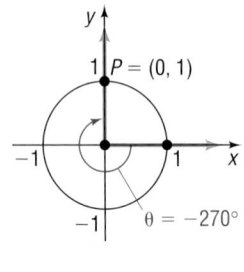

(b)

━━━ **Now Work** PROBLEMS **19** AND **59**

3 Find the Exact Values of the Trigonometric Functions of $\dfrac{\pi}{4} = 45°$

EXAMPLE 4 | **Finding the Exact Values of the Trigonometric Functions of $\dfrac{\pi}{4} = 45°$**

Find the exact values of the six trigonometric functions of $\dfrac{\pi}{4} = 45°$.

Solution

We seek the coordinates of the point $P = (x, y)$ on the unit circle that corresponds to $\theta = \dfrac{\pi}{4} = 45°$. See Figure 25. First, we observe that P lies on the line $y = x$. (Do

Figure 25

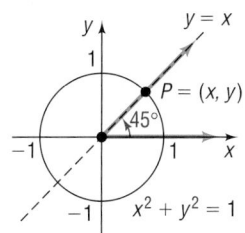

you see why? Since $\theta = 45° = \frac{1}{2} \cdot 90°$, P must lie on the line that bisects quadrant I.)

Since $P = (x, y)$ also lies on the unit circle, $x^2 + y^2 = 1$, it follows that

$$x^2 + y^2 = 1$$
$$x^2 + x^2 = 1 \quad y = x, x > 0, y > 0$$
$$2x^2 = 1$$

$$x = \frac{1}{\sqrt{2}} = \frac{\sqrt{2}}{2} \qquad y = \frac{\sqrt{2}}{2}$$

Then

$$\sin \frac{\pi}{4} = \sin 45° = \frac{\sqrt{2}}{2} \qquad \cos \frac{\pi}{4} = \cos 45° = \frac{\sqrt{2}}{2} \qquad \tan \frac{\pi}{4} = \tan 45° = \frac{\frac{\sqrt{2}}{2}}{\frac{\sqrt{2}}{2}} = 1$$

$$\csc \frac{\pi}{4} = \csc 45° = \frac{1}{\frac{\sqrt{2}}{2}} = \sqrt{2} \qquad \sec \frac{\pi}{4} = \sec 45° = \frac{1}{\frac{\sqrt{2}}{2}} = \sqrt{2} \qquad \cot \frac{\pi}{4} = \cot 45° = \frac{\frac{\sqrt{2}}{2}}{\frac{\sqrt{2}}{2}} = 1$$

EXAMPLE 5   **Finding the Exact Value of a Trigonometric Expression**

Find the exact value of each expression.

(a) $\sin 45° \cos 180°$

(b) $\tan \frac{\pi}{4} - \sin \frac{3\pi}{2}$

(c) $\left(\sec \frac{\pi}{4} \right)^2 + \csc \frac{\pi}{2}$

Solution   (a) $\sin 45° \cos 180° = \frac{\sqrt{2}}{2} \cdot (-1) = -\frac{\sqrt{2}}{2}$

                      ↑   ↑

          From Example 4   From Table 2

(b) $\tan \frac{\pi}{4} - \sin \frac{3\pi}{2} = 1 - (-1) = 2$

            ↑   ↑

        From Example 4   From Table 2

(c) $\left(\sec \frac{\pi}{4} \right)^2 + \csc \frac{\pi}{2} = \left(\sqrt{2} \right)^2 + 1 = 2 + 1 = 3$

Now Work PROBLEM 33

4 Find the Exact Values of the Trigonometric Functions of $\frac{\pi}{6} = 30°$ and $\frac{\pi}{3} = 60°$

Consider a right triangle in which one of the angles is $\frac{\pi}{6} = 30°$. It then follows that the third angle is $\frac{\pi}{3} = 60°$. Figure 26(a) illustrates such a triangle with hypotenuse of length 1. Our problem is to determine a and b.

We begin by placing next to this triangle another triangle congruent to the first, as shown in Figure 26(b). Notice that we now have a triangle whose angles are each 60°. This triangle is therefore equilateral, so each side is of length 1.

Figure 26

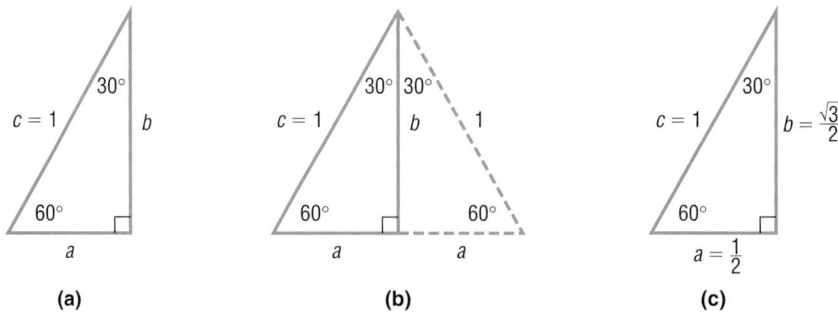

(a)　　　　　　　　(b)　　　　　　　　(c)

This means the base is $2a = 1$, and so $a = \dfrac{1}{2}$. By the Pythagorean Theorem, b satisfies the equation $a^2 + b^2 = c^2$, so we have

$$a^2 + b^2 = c^2$$

$$\frac{1}{4} + b^2 = 1 \qquad\qquad a = \frac{1}{2}, c = 1$$

$$b^2 = 1 - \frac{1}{4} = \frac{3}{4}$$

$$b = \frac{\sqrt{3}}{2} \qquad\qquad \begin{array}{l}b > 0 \text{ because it}\\ \text{is the length of the}\\ \text{side of a triangle.}\end{array}$$

This results in Figure 26(c).

EXAMPLE 6　**Finding the Exact Values of the Trigonometric Functions of $\dfrac{\pi}{3} = 60°$**

Find the exact values of the six trigonometric functions of $\dfrac{\pi}{3} = 60°$.

Solution　Position the triangle in Figure 26(c) so that the 60° angle is in the standard position. See Figure 27. The point on the unit circle that corresponds to $\theta = \dfrac{\pi}{3} = 60°$ is $P = \left(\dfrac{1}{2}, \dfrac{\sqrt{3}}{2}\right)$. Then

Figure 27

$$\sin\frac{\pi}{3} = \sin 60° = \frac{\sqrt{3}}{2} \qquad\qquad \cos\frac{\pi}{3} = \cos 60° = \frac{1}{2}$$

$$\csc\frac{\pi}{3} = \csc 60° = \frac{1}{\dfrac{\sqrt{3}}{2}} = \frac{2}{\sqrt{3}} = \frac{2\sqrt{3}}{3} \qquad\qquad \sec\frac{\pi}{3} = \sec 60° = \frac{1}{\dfrac{1}{2}} = 2$$

$$\tan\frac{\pi}{3} = \tan 60° = \frac{\dfrac{\sqrt{3}}{2}}{\dfrac{1}{2}} = \sqrt{3} \qquad\qquad \cot\frac{\pi}{3} = \cot 60° = \frac{\dfrac{1}{2}}{\dfrac{\sqrt{3}}{2}} = \frac{1}{\sqrt{3}} = \frac{\sqrt{3}}{3}$$

EXAMPLE 7　**Finding the Exact Values of the Trigonometric Functions of $\dfrac{\pi}{6} = 30°$**

Find the exact values of the trigonometric functions of $\dfrac{\pi}{6} = 30°$.

Figure 28

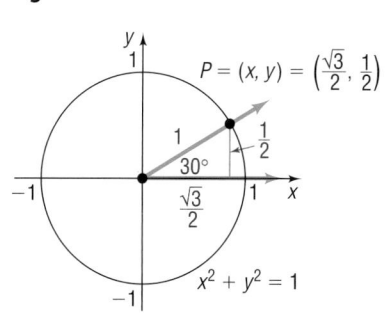

Solution   Position the triangle in Figure 26(c) so that the 30° angle is in the standard position. See Figure 28. The point on the unit circle that corresponds to $\theta = \dfrac{\pi}{6} = 30°$ is

$$P = \left(\frac{\sqrt{3}}{2}, \frac{1}{2}\right). \text{ Then}$$

$$\sin\frac{\pi}{6} = \sin 30° = \frac{1}{2} \qquad\qquad \cos\frac{\pi}{6} = \cos 30° = \frac{\sqrt{3}}{2}$$

$$\csc\frac{\pi}{6} = \csc 30° = \frac{1}{\frac{1}{2}} = 2 \qquad\qquad \sec\frac{\pi}{6} = \sec 30° = \frac{1}{\frac{\sqrt{3}}{2}} = \frac{2}{\sqrt{3}} = \frac{2\sqrt{3}}{3}$$

$$\tan\frac{\pi}{6} = \tan 30° = \frac{\frac{1}{2}}{\frac{\sqrt{3}}{2}} = \frac{1}{\sqrt{3}} = \frac{\sqrt{3}}{3} \qquad \cot\frac{\pi}{6} = \cot 30° = \frac{\frac{\sqrt{3}}{2}}{\frac{1}{2}} = \sqrt{3}$$

Table 3 summarizes the information just derived for $\dfrac{\pi}{6} = 30°, \dfrac{\pi}{4} = 45°$, and $\dfrac{\pi}{3} = 60°$. Until you memorize the entries in Table 3, you should draw an appropriate diagram to determine the values given in the table.

Table 3

θ (Radians)	θ (Degrees)	$\sin\theta$	$\cos\theta$	$\tan\theta$	$\csc\theta$	$\sec\theta$	$\cot\theta$
$\dfrac{\pi}{6}$	30°	$\dfrac{1}{2}$	$\dfrac{\sqrt{3}}{2}$	$\dfrac{\sqrt{3}}{3}$	2	$\dfrac{2\sqrt{3}}{3}$	$\sqrt{3}$
$\dfrac{\pi}{4}$	45°	$\dfrac{\sqrt{2}}{2}$	$\dfrac{\sqrt{2}}{2}$	1	$\sqrt{2}$	$\sqrt{2}$	1
$\dfrac{\pi}{3}$	60°	$\dfrac{\sqrt{3}}{2}$	$\dfrac{1}{2}$	$\sqrt{3}$	$\dfrac{2\sqrt{3}}{3}$	2	$\dfrac{\sqrt{3}}{3}$

━━━ **Now Work** PROBLEM 39

EXAMPLE 8   **Constructing a Rain Gutter**

A rain gutter is to be constructed of aluminum sheets 12 inches wide. After marking off a length of 4 inches from each edge, this length is bent up at an angle θ. See Figure 29. The area A of the opening may be expressed as a function of θ as

$$A(\theta) = 16\sin\theta(\cos\theta + 1)$$

Find the area A of the opening for $\theta = 30°, \theta = 45°$, and $\theta = 60°$.

Solution   For $\theta = 30°$: $A(30°) = 16\sin 30°(\cos 30° + 1)$

Figure 29

|← ———— 12 in ———— →|

4 in   4 in   4 in

4 in   4 in
θ θ

$$= 16\left(\frac{1}{2}\right)\left(\frac{\sqrt{3}}{2} + 1\right) = 4\sqrt{3} + 8 \approx 14.9$$

The area of the opening for $\theta = 30°$ is about 14.9 square inches.

For $\theta = 45°$: $A(45°) = 16\sin 45°(\cos 45° + 1)$

$$= 16\left(\frac{\sqrt{2}}{2}\right)\left(\frac{\sqrt{2}}{2} + 1\right) = 8 + 8\sqrt{2} \approx 19.3$$

The area of the opening for $\theta = 45°$ is about 19.3 square inches.

For $\theta = 60°$: $A(60°) = 16 \sin 60° (\cos 60° + 1)$

$$= 16\left(\frac{\sqrt{3}}{2}\right)\left(\frac{1}{2} + 1\right) = 12\sqrt{3} \approx 20.8$$

The area of the opening for $\theta = 60°$ is about 20.8 square inches.

5 Find the Exact Values of the Trigonometric Functions for Integer Multiples of $\frac{\pi}{6} = 30°$, $\frac{\pi}{4} = 45°$, and $\frac{\pi}{3} = 60°$

We know the exact values of the trigonometric functions of $\frac{\pi}{4} = 45°$. Using symmetry, we can find the exact values of the trigonometric functions of $\frac{3\pi}{4} = 135°$, $\frac{5\pi}{4} = 225°$, and $\frac{7\pi}{4} = 315°$.

Figure 30

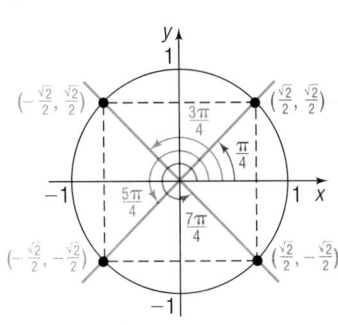

See Figure 30. Using symmetry with respect to the y-axis, the point $\left(-\frac{\sqrt{2}}{2}, \frac{\sqrt{2}}{2}\right)$ is the point on the unit circle that corresponds to the angle $\frac{3\pi}{4} = 135°$.

Similarly, using symmetry with respect to the origin, the point $\left(-\frac{\sqrt{2}}{2}, -\frac{\sqrt{2}}{2}\right)$ is the point on the unit circle that corresponds to the angle $\frac{5\pi}{4} = 225°$. Finally, using symmetry with respect to the x-axis, the point $\left(\frac{\sqrt{2}}{2}, -\frac{\sqrt{2}}{2}\right)$ is the point on the unit circle that corresponds to the angle $\frac{7\pi}{4} = 315°$.

EXAMPLE 9

Finding Exact Values for Multiples of $\frac{\pi}{4} = 45°$

Find the exact value of each expression.

(a) $\cos\frac{5\pi}{4}$ (b) $\sin 135°$ (c) $\tan 315°$

Solution   (a) From Figure 30, we see the point $\left(-\frac{\sqrt{2}}{2}, -\frac{\sqrt{2}}{2}\right)$ corresponds to $\frac{5\pi}{4}$, so

$$\cos\frac{5\pi}{4} = x = -\frac{\sqrt{2}}{2}.$$

(b) Since $135° = \frac{3\pi}{4}$, the point $\left(-\frac{\sqrt{2}}{2}, \frac{\sqrt{2}}{2}\right)$ corresponds to $135°$, so

$$\sin 135° = \frac{\sqrt{2}}{2}.$$

(c) Since $315° = \frac{7\pi}{4}$, the point $\left(\frac{\sqrt{2}}{2}, -\frac{\sqrt{2}}{2}\right)$ corresponds to $315°$, so

$$\tan 315° = \frac{-\dfrac{\sqrt{2}}{2}}{\dfrac{\sqrt{2}}{2}} = -1.$$

Figure 30 can also be used to find exact values for other multiples of $\frac{\pi}{4} = 45°$. For example, the point $\left(\frac{\sqrt{2}}{2}, -\frac{\sqrt{2}}{2} \right)$ is the point on the unit circle that corresponds to the angle $-\frac{\pi}{4} = -45°$; the point $\left(\frac{\sqrt{2}}{2}, \frac{\sqrt{2}}{2} \right)$ is the point on the unit circle that corresponds to the angle $\frac{9\pi}{4} = 405°$.

--- **Now Work** PROBLEMS 49 AND 53

The use of symmetry also provides information about certain integer multiples of the angles $\frac{\pi}{6} = 30°$ and $\frac{\pi}{3} = 60°$. See Figures 31 and 32.

Figure 31

Figure 32

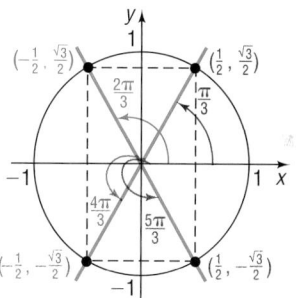

EXAMPLE 10

Finding Exact Values for Multiples of $\frac{\pi}{6} = 30°$ or $\frac{\pi}{3} = 60°$

Based on Figures 31 and 32, we see that

(a) $\cos 210° = \cos \dfrac{7\pi}{6} = -\dfrac{\sqrt{3}}{2}$

(b) $\sin(-60°) = \sin\left(-\dfrac{\pi}{3}\right) = -\dfrac{\sqrt{3}}{2}$

(c) $\tan \dfrac{5\pi}{3} = \dfrac{-\dfrac{\sqrt{3}}{2}}{\dfrac{1}{2}} = -\sqrt{3}$

--- **Now Work** PROBLEM 45

6 Use a Calculator to Approximate the Value of a Trigonometric Function

Before getting started, you must first decide whether to enter the angle in the calculator using radians or degrees and then set the calculator to the correct MODE. Check your instruction manual to find out how your calculator handles degrees and radians. Your calculator has keys marked $\boxed{\sin}$, $\boxed{\cos}$, and $\boxed{\tan}$. To find the values of the remaining three trigonometric functions, secant, cosecant, and cotangent, we use the fact that, if $P = (x, y)$ is a point on the unit circle on the terminal side of θ, then

WARNING On your calculator the second functions $\sin^{-1}$, $\cos^{-1}$, and $\tan^{-1}$ do not represent the reciprocal of sin, cos, and tan. ∎

$$\sec \theta = \frac{1}{x} = \frac{1}{\cos \theta} \qquad \csc \theta = \frac{1}{y} = \frac{1}{\sin \theta} \qquad \cot \theta = \frac{x}{y} = \frac{1}{\dfrac{y}{x}} = \frac{1}{\tan \theta}$$

EXAMPLE 11	Using a Calculator to Approximate the Value of a Trigonometric Function

Use a calculator to find the approximate value of:

(a) $\cos 48°$ (b) $\csc 21°$ (c) $\tan \dfrac{\pi}{12}$

Express your answer rounded to two decimal places.

Solution   (a) First, we set the MODE to receive degrees. See Figure 33(a). Figure 33(b) shows the solution using a TI-84 Plus graphing calculator.

Figure 33

     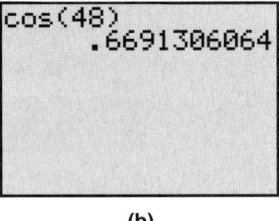

(a)   (b)

Rounded to two decimal places,

$$\cos 48° = 0.67$$

(b) Most calculators do not have a csc key. The manufacturers assume the user knows some trigonometry. To find the value of $\csc 21°$, we use the fact that $\csc 21° = \dfrac{1}{\sin 21°}$. Figure 34 shows the solution using a TI-84 Plus graphing calculator. Rounded to two decimal places,

$$\csc 21° = 2.79$$

(c) Set the MODE to receive radians. Figure 35 shows the solution using a TI-84 Plus graphing calculator. Rounded to two decimal places,

$$\tan \dfrac{\pi}{12} = 0.27$$

Figure 34   **Figure 35**

Now Work PROBLEM 63

Figure 36

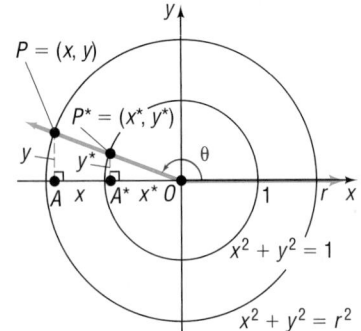

7 Use a Circle of Radius r to Evaluate the Trigonometric Functions

Until now, to find the exact value of a trigonometric function of an angle θ required that we locate the corresponding point $P = (x, y)$ on the unit circle. In fact, though, any circle whose center is at the origin can be used.

Let θ be any nonquadrantal angle placed in standard position. Let $P = (x, y)$ be the point on the circle $x^2 + y^2 = r^2$ that corresponds to θ, and let $P^* = (x^*, y^*)$ be the point on the unit circle that corresponds to θ. See Figure 36, where θ is shown in quadrant II.

Notice that the triangles $OA*P*$ and OAP are similar; as a result, the ratios of corresponding sides are equal.

$$\frac{y*}{1} = \frac{y}{r} \qquad \frac{x*}{1} = \frac{x}{r} \qquad \frac{y*}{x*} = \frac{y}{x}$$

$$\frac{1}{y*} = \frac{r}{y} \qquad \frac{1}{x*} = \frac{r}{x} \qquad \frac{x*}{y*} = \frac{x}{y}$$

These results lead us to formulate the following theorem:

THEOREM

For an angle θ in standard position, let $P = (x, y)$ be the point on the terminal side of θ that is also on the circle $x^2 + y^2 = r^2$. Then

$$\sin \theta = \frac{y}{r} \qquad\qquad \cos \theta = \frac{x}{r} \qquad\qquad \tan \theta = \frac{y}{x} \quad x \neq 0$$

$$\csc \theta = \frac{r}{y} \quad y \neq 0 \qquad \sec \theta = \frac{r}{x} \quad x \neq 0 \qquad \cot \theta = \frac{x}{y} \quad y \neq 0$$

EXAMPLE 12 **Finding the Exact Values of the Six Trigonometric Functions**

Find the exact values of each of the six trigonometric functions of an angle θ if $(4, -3)$ is a point on its terminal side.

Figure 37

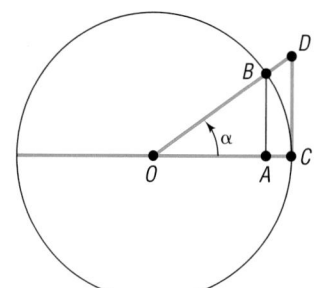

Solution See Figure 37. The point $(4, -3)$ is on a circle of radius $r = \sqrt{4^2 + (-3)^2} = \sqrt{16 + 9} = \sqrt{25} = 5$ with the center at the origin.

For the point $(x, y) = (4, -3)$, we have $x = 4$ and $y = -3$. Since $r = 5$, we find

$$\sin \theta = \frac{y}{r} = -\frac{3}{5} \qquad \cos \theta = \frac{x}{r} = \frac{4}{5} \qquad \tan \theta = \frac{y}{x} = -\frac{3}{4}$$

$$\csc \theta = \frac{r}{y} = -\frac{5}{3} \qquad \sec \theta = \frac{r}{x} = \frac{5}{4} \qquad \cot \theta = \frac{x}{y} = -\frac{4}{3}$$

Now Work PROBLEM 75

Historical Feature

The name *sine* for the sine function is due to a medieval confusion. The name comes from the Sanskrit word *jīva* (meaning chord), first used in India by Araybhata the Elder (AD 510). He really meant half-chord, but abbreviated it. This was brought into Arabic as *jiba*, which was meaningless. Because the proper Arabic word *jaib* would be written the same way (short vowels are not written out in Arabic), *jiba* was pronounced as *jaib*, which meant bosom or hollow, and *jiba* remains as the Arabic word for sine to this day. Scholars translating the Arabic works into Latin found that the word *sinus* also meant bosom or hollow, and from *sinus* we get the word *sine*.

The name *tangent*, due to Thomas Finck (1583), can be understood by looking at Figure 38. The line segment $\overline{DC}$ is tangent to the circle at C. If $d(O, B) = d(O, C) = 1$, then the length of the line segment $\overline{DC}$ is

$$d(D, C) = \frac{d(D, C)}{1} = \frac{d(D, C)}{d(O, C)} = \tan \alpha$$

The old name for the tangent is *umbra versa* (meaning turned shadow), referring to the use of the tangent in solving height problems with shadows.

The names of the remaining functions came about as follows. If α and β are complementary angles, then $\cos \alpha = \sin \beta$. Because β is the complement of α, it was natural to write the cosine of α as *sin co* α. Probably for reasons involving ease of pronunciation, the *co* migrated to the front, and then cosine received a three-letter abbreviation to match sin, sec, and tan. The two other cofunctions were similarly treated, except that the long forms *cotan* and *cosec* survive to this day in some countries.

Figure 38

6.2 Assess Your Understanding

'Are You Prepared?' *Answers are given at the end of these exercises. If you get a wrong answer, read the pages listed in red.*

1. In a right triangle, with legs a and b and hypotenuse c, the Pythagorean Theorem states that _____. (p. A14)

2. The value of the function $f(x) = 3x - 7$ at 5 is _____. (pp. 60–62)

3. *True or False* For a function $y = f(x)$, for each x in the domain, there is exactly one element y in the range. (pp. 56–60)

4. If two triangles are similar, then corresponding angles are _____ and the lengths of corresponding sides are _____. (p. A17)

5. What point is symmetric with respect to the y-axis to the point $\left(\dfrac{1}{2}, \dfrac{\sqrt{3}}{2}\right)$? (pp. 19–20)

6. If (x, y) is a point on the unit circle in quadrant IV and if $x = \dfrac{\sqrt{3}}{2}$, what is y? (p. 45)

Concepts and Vocabulary

7. $\tan\dfrac{\pi}{4} + \sin 30° =$ _____.

8. Using a calculator, $\sin 2 =$ _____, rounded to two decimal places.

9. *True or False* Exact values can be found for the trigonometric functions of 60°.

10. *True or False* Exact values can be found for the sine of any angle.

Skill Building

In Problems 11–18, t is a real number and P = (x, y) is the point on the unit circle that corresponds to t. Find the exact values of the six trigonometric functions of t.

11. $\left(\dfrac{\sqrt{3}}{2}, \dfrac{1}{2}\right)$

12. $\left(\dfrac{1}{2}, -\dfrac{\sqrt{3}}{2}\right)$

13. $\left(-\dfrac{2}{5}, \dfrac{\sqrt{21}}{5}\right)$

14. $\left(-\dfrac{1}{5}, \dfrac{2\sqrt{6}}{5}\right)$

15. $\left(-\dfrac{\sqrt{2}}{2}, \dfrac{\sqrt{2}}{2}\right)$

16. $\left(\dfrac{\sqrt{2}}{2}, \dfrac{\sqrt{2}}{2}\right)$

17. $\left(\dfrac{2\sqrt{2}}{3}, -\dfrac{1}{3}\right)$

18. $\left(-\dfrac{\sqrt{5}}{3}, -\dfrac{2}{3}\right)$

In Problems 19–28, find the exact value. Do not use a calculator.

19. $\sin\dfrac{11\pi}{2}$

20. $\cos(7\pi)$

21. $\tan(6\pi)$

22. $\cot\dfrac{7\pi}{2}$

23. $\csc\dfrac{11\pi}{2}$

24. $\sec(8\pi)$

25. $\cos\left(-\dfrac{3\pi}{2}\right)$

26. $\sin(-3\pi)$

27. $\sec(-\pi)$

28. $\tan(-5\pi)$

In Problems 29–44, find the exact value of each expression. Do not use a calculator.

29. $\sin 45° + \cos 60°$

30. $\sin 30° - \cos 45°$

31. $\sin 90° + \tan 45°$

32. $\cos 180° - \sin 180°$

33. $\sin 45° \cos 45°$

34. $\tan 45° \cos 30°$

35. $\csc 45° \tan 60°$

36. $\sec 30° \cot 45°$

37. $4 \sin 90° - 3 \tan 180°$

38. $5 \cos 90° - 8 \sin 270°$

39. $2 \sin\dfrac{\pi}{3} - 3 \tan\dfrac{\pi}{6}$

40. $2 \sin\dfrac{\pi}{4} + 3 \tan\dfrac{\pi}{4}$

41. $2 \sec\dfrac{\pi}{4} + 4 \cot\dfrac{\pi}{3}$

42. $3 \csc\dfrac{\pi}{3} + \cot\dfrac{\pi}{4}$

43. $\csc\dfrac{\pi}{2} + \cot\dfrac{\pi}{2}$

44. $\sec \pi - \csc\dfrac{\pi}{2}$

In Problems 45–62, find the exact values of the six trigonometric functions of the given angle. If any are not defined, say "not defined." Do not use a calculator.

45. $\dfrac{2\pi}{3}$

46. $\dfrac{5\pi}{6}$

47. $210°$

48. $240°$

49. $\dfrac{3\pi}{4}$

50. $\dfrac{11\pi}{4}$

51. $\dfrac{8\pi}{3}$

52. $\dfrac{13\pi}{6}$

53. $405°$

54. $390°$

55. $-\dfrac{\pi}{6}$

56. $-\dfrac{\pi}{3}$

57. $-135°$

58. $-240°$

59. $\dfrac{5\pi}{2}$

60. 5π

61. $720°$

62. $630°$

In Problems 63–74, use a calculator to find the approximate value of each expression rounded to two decimal places.

63. $\sin 28°$

64. $\cos 14°$

65. $\sec 21°$

66. $\cot 70°$

67. $\tan\dfrac{\pi}{10}$

68. $\sin\dfrac{\pi}{8}$

69. $\cot\dfrac{\pi}{12}$

70. $\csc\dfrac{5\pi}{13}$

71. $\sin 1$

72. $\tan 1$

73. $\sin 1°$

74. $\tan 1°$

In Problems 75–82, a point on the terminal side of an angle θ in standard position is given. Find the exact values of the six trigonometric functions of θ.

75. $(-3, 4)$ **76.** $(5, -12)$ **77.** $(2, -3)$ **78.** $(-1, -2)$

79. $(-2, -2)$ **80.** $(-1, 1)$ **81.** $\left(\dfrac{1}{3}, \dfrac{1}{4}\right)$ **82.** $(0.3, 0.4)$

83. Find the exact value of:

$$\sin 45° + \sin 135° + \sin 225° + \sin 315°$$

84. Find the exact value of:

$$\tan 60° + \tan 150°$$

85. Find the exact value of:

$$\sin 40° + \sin 130° + \sin 220° + \sin 310°$$

86. Find the exact value of:

$$\tan 40° + \tan 140°$$

87. If $f(\theta) = \sin \theta = 0.1$, find $f(\theta + \pi)$.

88. If $f(\theta) = \cos \theta = 0.3$, find $f(\theta + \pi)$.

89. If $f(\theta) = \tan \theta = 3$, find $f(\theta + \pi)$.

90. If $f(\theta) = \cot \theta = -2$, find $f(\theta + \pi)$.

91. If $\sin \theta = \dfrac{1}{5}$, find $\csc \theta$.

92. If $\cos \theta = \dfrac{2}{3}$, find $\sec \theta$.

In Problems 93–104, $f(\theta) = \sin \theta$ and $g(\theta) = \cos \theta$. Find the exact value of each function below if $\theta = 60°$. Do not use a calculator.

93. $f(\theta)$ **94.** $g(\theta)$ **95.** $f\left(\dfrac{\theta}{2}\right)$ **96.** $g\left(\dfrac{\theta}{2}\right)$

97. $[f(\theta)]^2$ **98.** $[g(\theta)]^2$ **99.** $f(2\theta)$ **100.** $g(2\theta)$

101. $2f(\theta)$ **102.** $2g(\theta)$ **103.** $f(-\theta)$ **104.** $g(-\theta)$

Mixed Practice

In Problems 105–112, $f(x) = \sin x$, $g(x) = \cos x$, $h(x) = 2x$, and $p(x) = \dfrac{x}{2}$. Find the value of each of the following:

105. $(f + g)(30°)$ **106.** $(f - g)(60°)$ **107.** $(f \cdot g)\left(\dfrac{3\pi}{4}\right)$ **108.** $(f \cdot g)\left(\dfrac{4\pi}{3}\right)$

109. $(f \circ h)\left(\dfrac{\pi}{6}\right)$ **110.** $(g \circ p)(60°)$ **111.** $(p \circ g)(315°)$ **112.** $(h \circ f)\left(\dfrac{5\pi}{6}\right)$

113. (a) Find $f\left(\dfrac{\pi}{4}\right)$. What point is on the graph of f?

(b) Using the result of part (a), what point is on the graph of f^{-1}?

(c) What point is on the graph of $y = f\left(x + \dfrac{\pi}{4}\right) - 3$ if $x = \dfrac{\pi}{4}$?

114. (a) Find $g\left(\dfrac{\pi}{6}\right)$. What point is on the graph of g?

(b) Using the result of part (a), what point is on the graph of g^{-1}?

(c) What point is on the graph of $y = 2g\left(x - \dfrac{\pi}{6}\right)$ if $x = \dfrac{\pi}{6}$?

Applications and Extensions

115. Use a calculator in radian mode to complete the following table.

What can you conclude about the value of $f(\theta) = \dfrac{\sin \theta}{\theta}$ as θ approaches 0?

θ	0.5	0.4	0.2	0.1	0.01	0.001	0.0001	0.00001
$\sin \theta$								
$f(\theta) = \dfrac{\sin \theta}{\theta}$								

⚠ **116.** Use a calculator in radian mode to complete the following table.

What can you conclude about the value of $g(\theta) = \dfrac{\cos \theta - 1}{\theta}$ as θ approaches 0?

θ	0.5	0.4	0.2	0.1	0.01	0.001	0.0001	0.00001
$\cos \theta - 1$								
$g(\theta) = \dfrac{\cos \theta - 1}{\theta}$								

For Problems 117–120, use the following discussion.

Projectile Motion *The path of a projectile fired at an inclination θ to the horizontal with initial speed v_0 is a parabola (see the figure).*

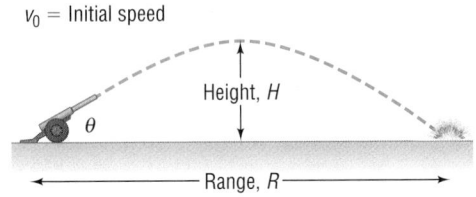

v_0 = Initial speed

Height, H

θ

Range, R

The range R of the projectile, that is, the horizontal distance that the projectile travels, is found by using the function

$$R(\theta) = \frac{v_0^2 \sin(2\theta)}{g}$$

where $g \approx 32.2$ feet per second per second ≈ 9.8 meters per second per second is the acceleration due to gravity. The maximum height H of the projectile is given by the function

$$H(\theta) = \frac{v_0^2 (\sin \theta)^2}{2g}$$

In Problems 117–120, find the range R and maximum height H.

117. The projectile is fired at an angle of 45° to the horizontal with an initial speed of 100 feet per second.

118. The projectile is fired at an angle of 30° to the horizontal with an initial speed of 150 meters per second.

119. The projectile is fired at an angle of 25° to the horizontal with an initial speed of 500 meters per second.

120. The projectile is fired at an angle of 50° to the horizontal with an initial speed of 200 feet per second.

121. Inclined Plane See the figure.

θ a

If friction is ignored, the time t (in seconds) required for a block to slide down an inclined plane is given by the function

$$t(\theta) = \sqrt{\frac{2a}{g \sin \theta \cos \theta}}$$

where a is the length (in feet) of the base and $g \approx 32$ feet per second per second is the acceleration due to gravity. How long does it take a block to slide down an inclined plane with base $a = 10$ feet when:
(a) $\theta = 30°$?   (b) $\theta = 45°$?   (c) $\theta = 60°$?

122. Piston Engines In a certain piston engine, the distance x (in centimeters) from the center of the drive shaft to the head of the piston is given by the function

$$x(\theta) = \cos \theta + \sqrt{16 + 0.5 \cos(2\theta)}$$

where θ is the angle between the crank and the path of the piston head. See the figure. Find x when $\theta = 30°$ and when $\theta = 45°$.

θ

x

123. Calculating the Time of a Trip Two oceanfront homes are located 8 miles apart on a straight stretch of beach, each a distance of 1 mile from a paved road that parallels the ocean. See the figure.

Ocean

4 mi   4 mi

Beach   1 mi

θ θ

Paved path

x

River

Sally can jog 8 miles per hour along the paved road, but only 3 miles per hour in the sand on the beach. Because of a river directly between the two houses, it is necessary to jog in the sand to the road, continue on the road, and then jog directly back in the sand to get from one house to the other. The time T to get from one house to the other as a function of the angle θ shown in the illustration is

$$T(\theta) = 1 + \frac{2}{3 \sin \theta} - \frac{1}{4 \tan \theta}, \qquad 0° < \theta < 90°$$

(a) Calculate the time T for $\theta = 30°$. How long is Sally on the paved road?
(b) Calculate the time T for $\theta = 45°$. How long is Sally on the paved road?
(c) Calculate the time T for $\theta = 60°$. How long is Sally on the paved road?
(d) Calculate the time T for $\theta = 90°$. Describe the path taken. Why can't the formula for T be used?

124. **Designing Fine Decorative Pieces** A designer of decorative art plans to market solid gold spheres encased in clear crystal cones. Each sphere is of fixed radius R and will be enclosed in a cone of height h and radius r. See the illustration. Many cones can be used to enclose the sphere, each having a different slant angle θ. The volume V of the cone can be expressed as a function of the slant angle θ of the cone as

$$V(\theta) = \frac{1}{3}\pi R^3 \frac{(1 + \sec \theta)^3}{(\tan \theta)^2} \qquad 0° < \theta < 90°$$

What volume V is required to enclose a sphere of radius 2 centimeters in a cone whose slant angle θ is 30°? 45°? 60°?

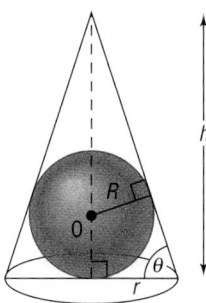

125. **Projectile Motion** An object is propelled upward at an angle θ, $45° < \theta < 90°$, to the horizontal with an initial velocity of v_0 feet per second from the base of an inclined plane that makes an angle of 45° with the horizontal. See the illustration. If air resistance is ignored, the distance R that it travels up the inclined plane as a function of θ is given by

$$R(\theta) = \frac{v_0^2 \sqrt{2}}{32} [\sin(2\theta) - \cos(2\theta) - 1]$$

(a) Find the distance R that the object travels along the inclined plane if the initial velocity is 32 feet per second and $\theta = 60°$.

(b) Graph $R = R(\theta)$ if the initial velocity is 32 feet per second.
(c) What value of θ makes R largest?

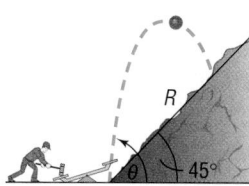

126. If θ, $0 < \theta < \pi$, is the angle between the positive x-axis and a nonhorizontal, nonvertical line L, show that the slope m of L equals $\tan \theta$. The angle θ is called the **inclination** of L.

[**Hint:** See the illustration, where we have drawn the line M parallel to L and passing through the origin. Use the fact that M intersects the unit circle at the point $(\cos \theta, \sin \theta)$.]

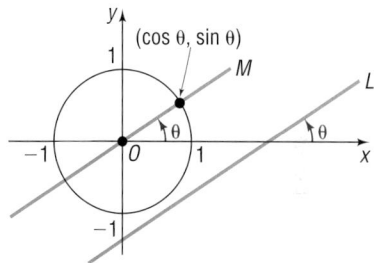

In Problems 127–128, use the figure to approximate the value of the six trigonometric functions at t to the nearest tenth. Then use a calculator to approximate each of the six trigonometric functions at t.

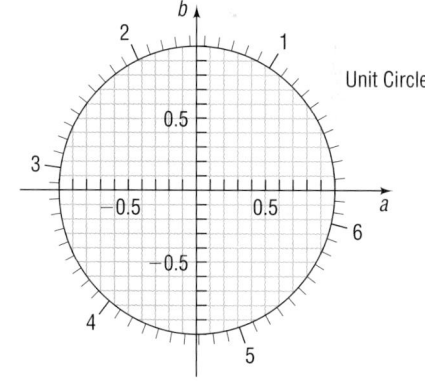

127. (a) $t = 1$ (b) $t = 5.1$
128. (a) $t = 2$ (b) $t = 4$

Discussion and Writing

129. Write a brief paragraph that explains how to quickly compute the trigonometric functions of 30°, 45°, and 60°.

130. Write a brief paragraph that explains how to quickly compute the trigonometric functions of 0°, 90°, 180°, and 270°.

131. How would you explain the meaning of the sine function to a fellow student who has just completed college algebra?

'Are You Prepared?' Answers

1. $c^2 = a^2 + b^2$ 2. 8   3. True   4. equal; proportional   5. $\left(-\frac{1}{2}, \frac{\sqrt{3}}{2}\right)$ 6. $-\frac{1}{2}$

6.3 Properties of the Trigonometric Functions

PREPARING FOR THIS SECTION   *Before getting started, review the following:*

- Functions (Section 2.1, pp. 56–64)
- Identity (Appendix A, Section A.6, p. A46)
- Even and Odd Functions (Section 2.3, pp. 79–81)

Now Work the *'Are You Prepared?'* problems on page 392.

OBJECTIVES 1 Determine the Domain and the Range of the Trigonometric Functions (p. 382)

2 Determine the Period of the Trigonometric Functions (p. 384)

3 Determine the Signs of the Trigonometric Functions in a Given Quadrant (p. 386)

4 Find the Values of the Trigonometric Functions Using Fundamental Identities (p. 386)

5 Find the Exact Values of the Trigonometric Functions of an Angle Given One of the Functions and the Quadrant of the Angle (p. 389)

6 Use Even–Odd Properties to Find the Exact Values of the Trigonometric Functions (p. 391)

1 Determine the Domain and the Range of the Trigonometric Functions

Let θ be an angle in standard position, and let $P = (x, y)$ be the point on the unit circle that corresponds to θ. See Figure 39. Then, by the definition given earlier,

Figure 39

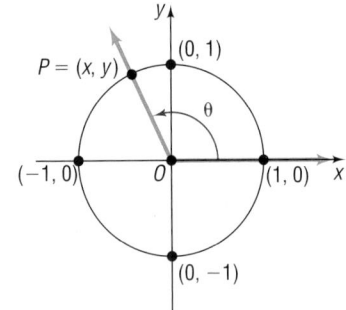

$$\sin \theta = y \qquad \cos \theta = x \qquad \tan \theta = \frac{y}{x} \quad x \neq 0$$

$$\csc \theta = \frac{1}{y} \quad y \neq 0 \qquad \sec \theta = \frac{1}{x} \quad x \neq 0 \qquad \cot \theta = \frac{x}{y} \quad y \neq 0$$

For $\sin \theta$ and $\cos \theta$, θ can be any angle, so it follows that the domain of the sine function and cosine function is the set of all real numbers.

> The domain of the sine function is the set of all real numbers.
>
> The domain of the cosine function is the set of all real numbers.

If $x = 0$, then the tangent function and the secant function are not defined. That is, for the tangent function and secant function, the x-coordinate of $P = (x, y)$ cannot be 0. See Figure 39. On the unit circle, there are two such points $(0, 1)$ and $(0, -1)$. These two points correspond to the angles $\dfrac{\pi}{2}(90°)$ and $\dfrac{3\pi}{2}(270°)$ or, more generally, to any angle that is an odd integer multiple of $\dfrac{\pi}{2}(90°)$, such as $\pm\dfrac{\pi}{2}(\pm 90°)$, $\pm\dfrac{3\pi}{2}(\pm270°)$, $\pm\dfrac{5\pi}{2}(\pm450°)$, and so on. Such angles must therefore be excluded from the domain of the tangent function and secant function.

> The domain of the tangent function is the set of all real numbers, except odd integer multiples of $\frac{\pi}{2}(90°)$.
>
> The domain of the secant function is the set of all real numbers, except odd integer multiples of $\frac{\pi}{2}(90°)$.

If $y = 0$, then the cotangent function and the cosecant function are not defined. For the cotangent function and cosecant function, the y-coordinate of $P = (x, y)$ cannot be 0. See Figure 39. On the unit circle, there are two such points, $(1, 0)$ and $(-1, 0)$. These two points correspond to the angles $0(0°)$ and $\pi(180°)$ or, more generally, to any angle that is an integer multiple of $\pi(180°)$, such as $0(0°)$, $\pm\pi(\pm180°)$, $\pm2\pi(\pm360°)$, $\pm3\pi(\pm540°)$, and so on. Such angles must therefore be excluded from the domain of the cotangent function and cosecant function.

> The domain of the cotangent function is the set of all real numbers, except integer multiples of $\pi(180°)$.
>
> The domain of the cosecant function is the set of all real numbers, except integer multiples of $\pi(180°)$.

Next we determine the range of each of the six trigonometric functions. Refer again to Figure 39. Let $P = (x, y)$ be the point on the unit circle that corresponds to the angle θ. It follows that $-1 \le x \le 1$ and $-1 \le y \le 1$. Since $\sin \theta = y$ and $\cos \theta = x$, we have

$$-1 \le \sin \theta \le 1 \qquad -1 \le \cos \theta \le 1$$

The range of both the sine function and the cosine function consists of all real numbers between -1 and 1, inclusive. Using absolute value notation, we have $|\sin \theta| \le 1$ and $|\cos \theta| \le 1$.

If θ is not an integer multiple of $\pi(180°)$, then $\csc \theta = \frac{1}{y}$. Since $y = \sin \theta$ and $|y| = |\sin \theta| \le 1$, it follows that $|\csc \theta| = \frac{1}{|\sin \theta|} = \frac{1}{|y|} \ge 1$. The range of the cosecant function consists of all real numbers less than or equal to -1 or greater than or equal to 1. That is,

$$\csc \theta \le -1 \quad \text{or} \quad \csc \theta \ge 1$$

NOTE If $|y| \le 1$, then $\frac{1}{|y|} \ge 1$. For example, $\left|-\frac{1}{2}\right| < 1$ and $\frac{1}{\left|-\frac{1}{2}\right|} = 2 > 1$. ∎

If θ is not an odd integer multiple of $\frac{\pi}{2}(90°)$, then, $\sec \theta = \frac{1}{x}$. Since $x = \cos \theta$ and $|x| = |\cos \theta| \le 1$, it follows that $|\sec \theta| = \frac{1}{|\cos \theta|} = \frac{1}{|x|} \ge 1$. The range of the secant function consists of all real numbers less than or equal to -1 or greater than or equal to 1. That is,

$$\sec \theta \le -1 \quad \text{or} \quad \sec \theta \ge 1$$

The range of both the tangent function and the cotangent function is the set of all real numbers.

$$-\infty < \tan \theta < \infty \qquad -\infty < \cot \theta < \infty$$

You are asked to prove this in Problems 121 and 122.

Table 4 summarizes these results.

Table 4

Function	Symbol	Domain	Range
sine	$f(\theta) = \sin\theta$	All real numbers	All real numbers from -1 to 1, inclusive
cosine	$f(\theta) = \cos\theta$	All real numbers	All real numbers from -1 to 1, inclusive
tangent	$f(\theta) = \tan\theta$	All real numbers, except odd integer multiples of $\frac{\pi}{2}(90°)$	All real numbers
cosecant	$f(\theta) = \csc\theta$	All real numbers, except integer multiples of $\pi(180°)$	All real numbers greater than or equal to 1 or less than or equal to -1
secant	$f(\theta) = \sec\theta$	All real numbers, except odd integer multiples of $\frac{\pi}{2}(90°)$	All real numbers greater than or equal to 1 or less than or equal to -1
cotangent	$f(\theta) = \cot\theta$	All real numbers, except integer multiples of $\pi(180°)$	All real numbers

Now Work PROBLEM 97

2 Determine the Period of the Trigonometric Functions

Look at Figure 40. This figure shows that for an angle of $\dfrac{\pi}{3}$ radians the corresponding point P on the unit circle is $\left(\dfrac{1}{2}, \dfrac{\sqrt{3}}{2}\right)$. Notice that, for an angle of $\dfrac{\pi}{3} + 2\pi$ radians, the corresponding point P on the unit circle is also $\left(\dfrac{1}{2}, \dfrac{\sqrt{3}}{2}\right)$. Then

Figure 40

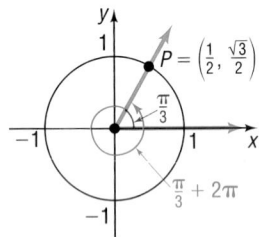

$$\sin\frac{\pi}{3} = \frac{\sqrt{3}}{2} \quad \text{and} \quad \sin\left(\frac{\pi}{3} + 2\pi\right) = \frac{\sqrt{3}}{2}$$

$$\cos\frac{\pi}{3} = \frac{1}{2} \quad \text{and} \quad \cos\left(\frac{\pi}{3} + 2\pi\right) = \frac{1}{2}$$

Figure 41

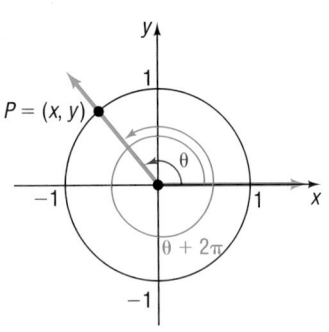

This example illustrates a more general situation. For a given angle θ, measured in radians, suppose that we know the corresponding point $P = (x, y)$ on the unit circle. Now add 2π to θ. The point on the unit circle corresponding to $\theta + 2\pi$ is identical to the point P on the unit circle corresponding to θ. See Figure 41. The values of the trigonometric functions of $\theta + 2\pi$ are equal to the values of the corresponding trigonometric functions of θ.

If we add (or subtract) integer multiples of 2π to θ, the values of the sine and cosine function remain unchanged. That is, for all θ

$$\sin(\theta + 2\pi k) = \sin\theta \qquad \cos(\theta + 2\pi k) = \cos\theta \tag{1}$$
$$\text{where } k \text{ is any integer.}$$

Functions that exhibit this kind of behavior are called *periodic functions*.

DEFINITION

A function f is called **periodic** if there is a positive number p such that, whenever θ is in the domain of f, so is $\theta + p$, and

$$f(\theta + p) = f(\theta)$$

If there is a smallest such number p, this smallest value is called the **(fundamental) period** of f.

Based on equation (1), the sine and cosine functions are periodic. In fact, the sine and cosine functions have period 2π. You are asked to prove this fact in Problems 123 and 124. The secant and cosecant functions are also periodic with period 2π, and the tangent and cotangent functions are periodic with period π. You are asked to prove these statements in Problems 125 through 128.

These facts are summarized as follows:

Periodic Properties

$$\sin(\theta + 2\pi) = \sin\theta \quad \cos(\theta + 2\pi) = \cos\theta \quad \tan(\theta + \pi) = \tan\theta$$
$$\csc(\theta + 2\pi) = \csc\theta \quad \sec(\theta + 2\pi) = \sec\theta \quad \cot(\theta + \pi) = \cot\theta$$

Because the sine, cosine, secant, and cosecant functions have period 2π, once we know their values over an interval of length 2π, we know all their values; similarly, since the tangent and cotangent functions have period π, once we know their values over an interval of length π, we know all their values.

EXAMPLE 1

Finding Exact Values Using Periodic Properties

Find the exact value of:

(a) $\sin\dfrac{17\pi}{4}$ (b) $\cos(5\pi)$ (c) $\tan\dfrac{5\pi}{4}$

Solution

(a) It is best to sketch the angle first, as shown in Figure 42(a). Since the period of the sine function is 2π, each full revolution can be ignored. This leaves the angle $\dfrac{\pi}{4}$. Then

$$\sin\frac{17\pi}{4} = \sin\left(\frac{\pi}{4} + 4\pi\right) = \sin\frac{\pi}{4} = \frac{\sqrt{2}}{2}$$

(b) See Figure 42(b). Since the period of the cosine function is 2π, each full revolution can be ignored. This leaves the angle π. Then

$$\cos(5\pi) = \cos(\pi + 4\pi) = \cos\pi = -1$$

(c) See Figure 42(c). Since the period of the tangent function is π, each half-revolution can be ignored. This leaves the angle $\dfrac{\pi}{4}$. Then

$$\tan\frac{5\pi}{4} = \tan\left(\frac{\pi}{4} + \pi\right) = \tan\frac{\pi}{4} = 1$$

Figure 42

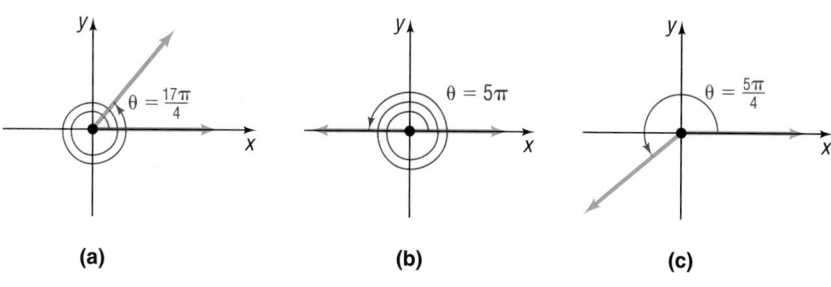

(a)   (b)   (c)

The periodic properties of the trigonometric functions will be very helpful to us when we study their graphs later in the chapter.

Now Work PROBLEM 11

3 Determine the Signs of the Trigonometric Functions in a Given Quadrant

Let $P = (x, y)$ be the point on the unit circle that corresponds to the angle θ. If we know in which quadrant the point P lies, then we can determine the signs of the trigonometric functions of θ. For example, if $P = (x, y)$ lies in quadrant IV, as shown in Figure 43, then we know that $x > 0$ and $y < 0$. Consequently,

Figure 43

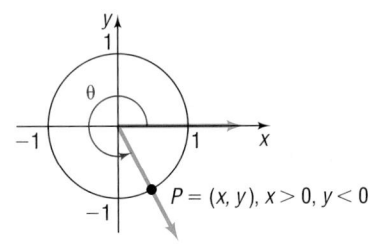

$$\sin \theta = y < 0 \qquad \cos \theta = x > 0 \qquad \tan \theta = \frac{y}{x} < 0$$

$$\csc \theta = \frac{1}{y} < 0 \qquad \sec \theta = \frac{1}{x} > 0 \qquad \cot \theta = \frac{x}{y} < 0$$

$P = (x, y), x > 0, y < 0$

Table 5 lists the signs of the six trigonometric functions for each quadrant. See also Figure 44.

Table 5

Quadrant of P	sin θ, csc θ	cos θ, sec θ	tan θ, cot θ
I	Positive	Positive	Positive
II	Positive	Negative	Negative
III	Negative	Negative	Positive
IV	Negative	Positive	Negative

Figure 44

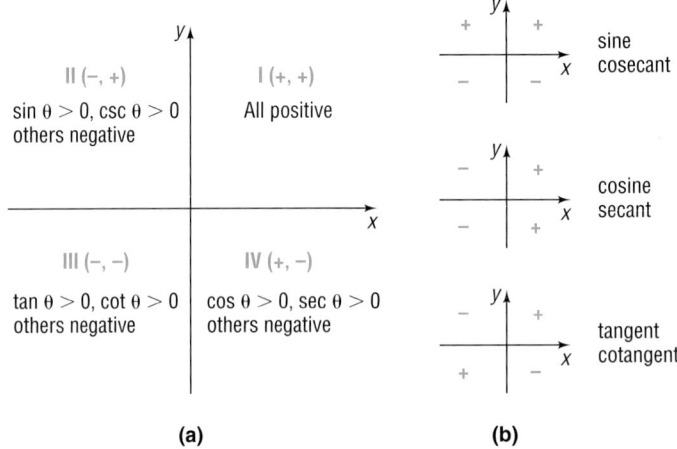

II $(-, +)$
$\sin \theta > 0, \csc \theta > 0$
others negative

I $(+, +)$
All positive

III $(-, -)$
$\tan \theta > 0, \cot \theta > 0$
others negative

IV $(+, -)$
$\cos \theta > 0, \sec \theta > 0$
others negative

sine cosecant

cosine secant

tangent cotangent

(a)   (b)

EXAMPLE 2 **Finding the Quadrant in Which an Angle θ Lies**

If $\sin \theta < 0$ and $\cos \theta < 0$, name the quadrant in which the angle θ lies.

Solution Let $P = (x, y)$ be the point on the unit circle corresponding to θ. Then $\sin \theta = y < 0$ and $\cos \theta = x < 0$. Because points in quadrant III have $x < 0$ and $y < 0$, θ lies in quadrant III.

Now Work PROBLEM 27

4 Find the Values of the Trigonometric Functions Using Fundamental Identities

If $P = (x, y)$ is the point on the unit circle corresponding to θ, then

$$\sin \theta = y \qquad\qquad \cos \theta = x \qquad\qquad \tan \theta = \frac{y}{x} \ \text{ if } x \neq 0$$

$$\csc \theta = \frac{1}{y} \ \text{ if } y \neq 0 \qquad \sec \theta = \frac{1}{x} \ \text{ if } x \neq 0 \qquad \cot \theta = \frac{x}{y} \ \text{ if } y \neq 0$$

Based on these definitions, we have the **reciprocal identities:**

Reciprocal Identities

$$\csc\theta = \frac{1}{\sin\theta} \qquad \sec\theta = \frac{1}{\cos\theta} \qquad \cot\theta = \frac{1}{\tan\theta} \qquad \textbf{(2)}$$

Two other fundamental identities are the **quotient identities.**

Quotient Identities

$$\tan\theta = \frac{\sin\theta}{\cos\theta} \qquad \cot\theta = \frac{\cos\theta}{\sin\theta} \qquad \textbf{(3)}$$

The proofs of identities (2) and (3) follow from the definitions of the trigonometric functions. (See Problems 129 and 130.)

If $\sin\theta$ and $\cos\theta$ are known, identities (2) and (3) make it easy to find the values of the remaining trigonometric functions.

| EXAMPLE 3 | **Finding Exact Values Using Identities when Sine and Cosine Are Given** |

Given $\sin\theta = \dfrac{\sqrt{5}}{5}$ and $\cos\theta = \dfrac{2\sqrt{5}}{5}$, find the exact values of the four remaining trigonometric functions of θ using identities.

Solution Based on a quotient identity from (3), we have

$$\tan\theta = \frac{\sin\theta}{\cos\theta} = \frac{\dfrac{\sqrt{5}}{5}}{\dfrac{2\sqrt{5}}{5}} = \frac{1}{2}$$

Then we use the reciprocal identities from (2) to get

$$\csc\theta = \frac{1}{\sin\theta} = \frac{1}{\dfrac{\sqrt{5}}{5}} = \frac{5}{\sqrt{5}} = \sqrt{5} \qquad \sec\theta = \frac{1}{\cos\theta} = \frac{1}{\dfrac{2\sqrt{5}}{5}} = \frac{5}{2\sqrt{5}} = \frac{\sqrt{5}}{2} \qquad \cot\theta = \frac{1}{\tan\theta} = \frac{1}{\dfrac{1}{2}} = 2$$

- **Now Work** PROBLEM 35

The equation of the unit circle is $x^2 + y^2 = 1$, or equivalently,

$$y^2 + x^2 = 1$$

If $P = (x, y)$ is the point on the unit circle that corresponds to the angle θ, then $y = \sin\theta$ and $x = \cos\theta$, so we have

$$(\sin\theta)^2 + (\cos\theta)^2 = 1 \qquad \textbf{(4)}$$

It is customary to write $\sin^2\theta$ instead of $(\sin\theta)^2$, $\cos^2\theta$ instead of $(\cos\theta)^2$, and so on. With this notation, we can rewrite equation (4) as

$$\sin^2\theta + \cos^2\theta = 1 \qquad \textbf{(5)}$$

If $\cos \theta \neq 0$, we can divide each side of equation (5) by $\cos^2 \theta$.

$$\frac{\sin^2 \theta}{\cos^2 \theta} + \frac{\cos^2 \theta}{\cos^2 \theta} = \frac{1}{\cos^2 \theta}$$

$$\left(\frac{\sin \theta}{\cos \theta} \right)^2 + 1 = \left(\frac{1}{\cos \theta} \right)^2$$

Now use identities (2) and (3) to get

$$\tan^2 \theta + 1 = \sec^2 \theta \qquad \textbf{(6)}$$

Similarly, if $\sin \theta \neq 0$, we can divide equation (5) by $\sin^2 \theta$ and use identities (2) and (3) to get $1 + \cot^2 \theta = \csc^2 \theta$, which we write as

$$\cot^2 \theta + 1 = \csc^2 \theta \qquad \textbf{(7)}$$

Collectively, the identities in (5), (6), and (7) are referred to as the **Pythagorean identities.**

Let's pause here to summarize the fundamental identities.

Fundamental Identities

$$\tan \theta = \frac{\sin \theta}{\cos \theta} \qquad\qquad \cot \theta = \frac{\cos \theta}{\sin \theta}$$

$$\csc \theta = \frac{1}{\sin \theta} \qquad \sec \theta = \frac{1}{\cos \theta} \qquad \cot \theta = \frac{1}{\tan \theta}$$

$$\sin^2 \theta + \cos^2 \theta = 1 \qquad \tan^2 \theta + 1 = \sec^2 \theta \qquad \cot^2 \theta + 1 = \csc^2 \theta$$

EXAMPLE 4 **Finding the Exact Value of a Trigonometric Expression Using Identities**

Find the exact value of each expression. Do not use a calculator.

(a) $\tan 20° - \dfrac{\sin 20°}{\cos 20°}$ (b) $\sin^2 \dfrac{\pi}{12} + \dfrac{1}{\sec^2 \dfrac{\pi}{12}}$

Solution (a) $\tan 20° - \dfrac{\sin 20°}{\cos 20°} = \tan 20° - \tan 20° = 0$

$\qquad\qquad\qquad\qquad \uparrow$
$\qquad\qquad\quad \dfrac{\sin \theta}{\cos \theta} = \tan \theta$

(b) $\sin^2 \dfrac{\pi}{12} + \dfrac{1}{\sec^2 \dfrac{\pi}{12}} = \sin^2 \dfrac{\pi}{12} + \cos^2 \dfrac{\pi}{12} = 1$

$\qquad\qquad\qquad\quad \uparrow \qquad\qquad\qquad \uparrow$
$\qquad\qquad \cos \theta = \dfrac{1}{\sec \theta} \qquad \sin^2 \theta + \cos^2 \theta = 1$

$\text{-----} \blacktriangleright$ **Now Work** PROBLEM **79**

5 Find the Exact Values of the Trigonometric Functions of an Angle Given One of the Functions and the Quadrant of the Angle

Many problems require finding the exact values of the remaining trigonometric functions when the value of one of them is known and the quadrant in which θ lies can be found. There are two approaches to solving such problems. One approach uses a circle of radius r; the other uses identities.

When using identities, sometimes a rearrangement is required. For example, the Pythagorean identity

$$\sin^2\theta + \cos^2\theta = 1$$

can be solved for $\sin\theta$ in terms of $\cos\theta$ (or vice versa) as follows:

$$\sin^2\theta = 1 - \cos^2\theta$$

$$\sin\theta = \pm\sqrt{1 - \cos^2\theta}$$

where the $+$ sign is used if $\sin\theta > 0$ and the $-$ sign is used if $\sin\theta < 0$. Similarly, in $\tan^2\theta + 1 = \sec^2\theta$, we can solve for $\tan\theta$ (or $\sec\theta$), and in $\cot^2\theta + 1 = \csc^2\theta$, we can solve for $\cot\theta$ (or $\csc\theta$).

| EXAMPLE 5 | **Given One Value of a Trigonometric Function and the Sign of Another, Find the Remaining Ones** |

Given that $\sin\theta = \dfrac{1}{3}$ and $\cos\theta < 0$, find the exact value of each of the remaining five trigonometric functions.

Solution 1 Using a Circle

Suppose that $P = (x, y)$ is the point on a circle that corresponds to θ. Since $\sin\theta = \dfrac{1}{3} > 0$ and $\cos\theta < 0$, the point $P = (x, y)$ is in quadrant II. Because $\sin\theta = \dfrac{1}{3} = \dfrac{y}{r}$, we let $y = 1$ and $r = 3$. The point $P = (x, y) = (x, 1)$ that corresponds to θ lies on the circle of radius 3: $x^2 + y^2 = 9$. See Figure 45.

To find x, we use the fact that $x^2 + y^2 = 9$, $y = 1$, and P is in quadrant II (so $x < 0$).

Figure 45

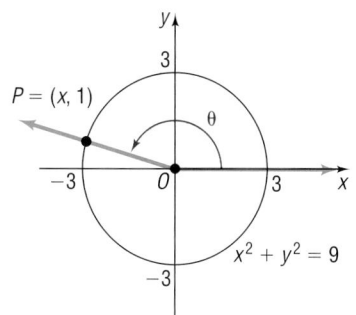

$$x^2 + y^2 = 9$$
$$x^2 + 1^2 = 9 \qquad y = 1$$
$$x^2 = 8$$
$$x = -2\sqrt{2} \qquad x < 0$$

Since $x = -2\sqrt{2}$, $y = 1$, and $r = 3$, we find that

$$\cos\theta = \frac{x}{r} = -\frac{2\sqrt{2}}{3} \qquad \tan\theta = \frac{y}{x} = \frac{1}{-2\sqrt{2}} = -\frac{\sqrt{2}}{4}$$

$$\csc\theta = \frac{r}{y} = \frac{3}{1} = 3 \qquad \sec\theta = \frac{r}{x} = \frac{3}{-2\sqrt{2}} = -\frac{3\sqrt{2}}{4} \qquad \cot\theta = \frac{x}{y} = \frac{-2\sqrt{2}}{1} = -2\sqrt{2}$$

Solution 2 Using Identities

First, we solve the identity $\sin^2\theta + \cos^2\theta = 1$ for $\cos\theta$.

$$\sin^2\theta + \cos^2\theta = 1$$
$$\cos^2\theta = 1 - \sin^2\theta$$
$$\cos\theta = \pm\sqrt{1 - \sin^2\theta}$$

Because $\cos \theta < 0$, we choose the minus sign and use the fact that $\sin \theta = \dfrac{1}{3}$.

$$\cos \theta = -\sqrt{1 - \sin^2 \theta} = -\sqrt{1 - \frac{1}{9}} = -\sqrt{\frac{8}{9}} = -\frac{2\sqrt{2}}{3}$$
$$\uparrow$$
$$\sin \theta = \frac{1}{3}$$

Now we know the values of $\sin \theta$ and $\cos \theta$, so we can use quotient and reciprocal identities to get

$$\tan \theta = \frac{\sin \theta}{\cos \theta} = \frac{\dfrac{1}{3}}{\dfrac{-2\sqrt{2}}{3}} = \frac{1}{-2\sqrt{2}} = -\frac{\sqrt{2}}{4} \qquad \cot \theta = \frac{1}{\tan \theta} = -2\sqrt{2}$$

$$\sec \theta = \frac{1}{\cos \theta} = \frac{1}{\dfrac{-2\sqrt{2}}{3}} = \frac{-3}{2\sqrt{2}} = -\frac{3\sqrt{2}}{4} \qquad \csc \theta = \frac{1}{\sin \theta} = \frac{1}{\dfrac{1}{3}} = 3$$

Finding the Values of the Trigonometric Functions of θ when One Is Known and the Quadrant of θ Is Known

Given the value of one trigonometric function and the quadrant in which θ lies, the exact value of each of the remaining five trigonometric functions can be found in either of two ways.

Method 1 Using a Circle of Radius r

STEP 1: Assign a value to two of the three variables x, y, r based on the value of the given trigonometric function and the location of P.

STEP 2: Draw a circle showing the location of the angle θ and the point $P = (x, y)$ that corresponds to θ. The radius of the circle that contains $P = (x, y)$ is $r = \sqrt{x^2 + y^2}$.

STEP 3: Use the fact that P lies on the circle $x^2 + y^2 = r^2$ to find the value of the missing variable.

STEP 4: Apply the theorem on page 377 to find the values of the remaining trigonometric functions.

Method 2 Using Identities

Use appropriately selected identities to find the value of each of the remaining trigonometric functions.

EXAMPLE 6	**Given One Value of a Trigonometric Function and the Sign of Another, Find the Remaining Ones**

Given that $\tan \theta = \dfrac{1}{2}$ and $\sin \theta < 0$, find the exact value of each of the remaining five trigonometric functions of θ.

**Solution 1
Using a Circle**

STEP 1: Since $\tan \theta = \dfrac{1}{2} > 0$ and $\sin \theta < 0$, the point $P = (x, y)$ that corresponds to θ lies in quadrant III. Since $\tan \theta = \dfrac{1}{2} = \dfrac{y}{x}$ and θ lies in quadrant III, we let $x = -2$ and $y = -1$.

STEP 2: Figure 46 shows a circle with the point $P = (-2, -1)$ and the angle θ labeled.

Figure 46

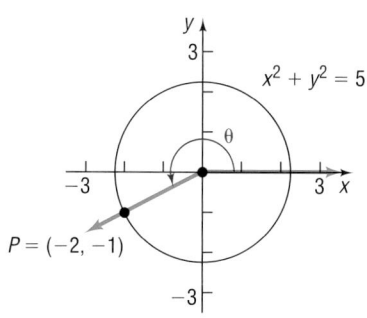

$P = (-2, -1)$

STEP 3: We know $x = -2$ and $y = -1$, so $r = \sqrt{x^2 + y^2} = \sqrt{(-2)^2 + (-1)^2} = \sqrt{5}$, and P lies on the circle $x^2 + y^2 = 5$.

STEP 4: Now apply the theorem on page 377 using $x = -2$, $y = -1$, and $r = \sqrt{5}$.

$$\sin\theta = \frac{y}{r} = \frac{-1}{\sqrt{5}} = -\frac{\sqrt{5}}{5} \qquad \cos\theta = \frac{x}{r} = \frac{-2}{\sqrt{5}} = -\frac{2\sqrt{5}}{5}$$

$$\csc\theta = \frac{r}{y} = \frac{\sqrt{5}}{-1} = -\sqrt{5} \qquad \sec\theta = \frac{r}{x} = \frac{\sqrt{5}}{-2} = -\frac{\sqrt{5}}{2} \qquad \cot\theta = \frac{x}{y} = \frac{-2}{-1} = 2$$

Solution 2
Using Identities

Because we know the value of $\tan\theta$, we use the Pythagorean identity that involves $\tan\theta$, that is, $\tan^2\theta + 1 = \sec^2\theta$. Since $\tan\theta = \frac{1}{2} > 0$ and $\sin\theta < 0$, then θ lies in quadrant III, where $\sec\theta < 0$.

$$\tan^2\theta + 1 = \sec^2\theta \qquad \text{Pythagorean identity}$$

$$\left(\frac{1}{2}\right)^2 + 1 = \sec^2\theta \qquad \tan\theta = \frac{1}{2}$$

$$\sec^2\theta = \frac{1}{4} + 1 = \frac{5}{4} \qquad \text{Proceed to solve for } \sec\theta.$$

$$\sec\theta = -\frac{\sqrt{5}}{2} \qquad \sec\theta < 0$$

Now we know $\tan\theta = \frac{1}{2}$ and $\sec\theta = -\frac{\sqrt{5}}{2}$. Using reciprocal identities, we find

$$\cos\theta = \frac{1}{\sec\theta} = \frac{1}{-\dfrac{\sqrt{5}}{2}} = -\frac{2}{\sqrt{5}} = -\frac{2\sqrt{5}}{5}$$

$$\cot\theta = \frac{1}{\tan\theta} = \frac{1}{\dfrac{1}{2}} = 2$$

To find $\sin\theta$, we use the following reasoning:

$$\tan\theta = \frac{\sin\theta}{\cos\theta} \quad \text{so} \quad \sin\theta = \tan\theta \cdot \cos\theta = \left(\frac{1}{2}\right) \cdot \left(-\frac{2\sqrt{5}}{5}\right) = -\frac{\sqrt{5}}{5}$$

$$\csc\theta = \frac{1}{\sin\theta} = \frac{1}{-\dfrac{\sqrt{5}}{5}} = -\frac{5}{\sqrt{5}} = -\sqrt{5}$$

Now Work PROBLEM 43

6 Use Even–Odd Properties to Find the Exact Values of the Trigonometric Functions

Recall that a function f is even if $f(-\theta) = f(\theta)$ for all θ in the domain of f; a function f is odd if $f(-\theta) = -f(\theta)$ for all θ in the domain of f. We will now show that the trigonometric functions sine, tangent, cotangent, and cosecant are odd functions and the functions cosine and secant are even functions.

In Words
Cosine and secant are even functions; the others are odd functions.

Even–Odd Properties

$$\sin(-\theta) = -\sin\theta \qquad \cos(-\theta) = \cos\theta \qquad \tan(-\theta) = -\tan\theta$$

$$\csc(-\theta) = -\csc\theta \qquad \sec(-\theta) = \sec\theta \qquad \cot(-\theta) = -\cot\theta$$

Figure 47

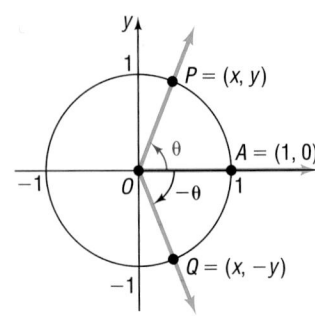

Proof   Let $P = (x, y)$ be the point on the unit circle that corresponds to the angle θ. See Figure 47. Using symmetry, the point Q on the unit circle that corresponds to the angle $-\theta$ will have coordinates $(x, -y)$. Using the definition of the trigonometric functions, we have

$$\sin \theta = y \text{ and } \sin(-\theta) = -y \qquad \qquad \cos \theta = x \text{ and } \cos(-\theta) = x$$
$$= -\sin \theta \qquad \qquad \qquad \qquad = \cos \theta$$

Now, using these results and some of the fundamental identities, we have

$$\tan(-\theta) = \frac{\sin(-\theta)}{\cos(-\theta)} = \frac{-\sin \theta}{\cos \theta} = -\tan \theta \qquad \cot(-\theta) = \frac{1}{\tan(-\theta)} = \frac{1}{-\tan \theta} = -\cot \theta$$

$$\sec(-\theta) = \frac{1}{\cos(-\theta)} = \frac{1}{\cos \theta} = \sec \theta \qquad \csc(-\theta) = \frac{1}{\sin(-\theta)} = \frac{1}{-\sin \theta} = -\csc \theta$$

EXAMPLE 7	**Finding Exact Values Using Even–Odd Properties**

Find the exact value of:

(a) $\sin(-45°)$ (b) $\cos(-\pi)$ (c) $\cot\left(-\dfrac{3\pi}{2}\right)$ (d) $\tan\left(-\dfrac{37\pi}{4}\right)$

Solution   (a) $\sin(-45°) = \underset{\substack{\uparrow \\ \text{Odd function}}}{-\sin 45°} = -\dfrac{\sqrt{2}}{2}$ (b) $\cos(-\pi) = \underset{\substack{\uparrow \\ \text{Even function}}}{\cos \pi} = -1$

(c) $\cot\left(-\dfrac{3\pi}{2}\right) = \underset{\substack{\uparrow \\ \text{Odd function}}}{-\cot \dfrac{3\pi}{2}} = 0$

(d) $\tan\left(-\dfrac{37\pi}{4}\right) = \underset{\substack{\uparrow \\ \text{Odd function}}}{-\tan \dfrac{37\pi}{4}} = -\tan\left(\dfrac{\pi}{4} + 9\pi\right) = \underset{\substack{\uparrow \\ \text{Period is } \pi.}}{-\tan \dfrac{\pi}{4}} = -1$

Now Work PROBLEM 59

6.3 Assess Your Understanding

'Are You Prepared?'   *Answers are given at the end of these exercises. If you get a wrong answer, read the pages listed in red.*

1. The domain of the function $f(x) = \dfrac{x + 1}{2x + 1}$ is _____. (pp. 63–64)

2. A function for which $f(x) = f(-x)$ for all x in the domain of f is called an _____ function. (pp. 79–81)

3. *True or False*   The function $f(x) = \sqrt{x}$ is even. (pp. 79–81)

4. *True or False*   The equation $x^2 + 2x = (x + 1)^2 - 1$ is an identity. (p. A46)

Concepts and Vocabulary

5. The sine, cosine, cosecant, and secant functions have period _____; the tangent and cotangent functions have period _____.

6. The domain of the tangent function is _____.

7. The range of the sine function is _____.

8. *True or False*   The only even trigonometric functions are the cosine and secant functions.

9. *True or False*   All the trigonometric functions are periodic, with period 2π.

10. *True or False*   The range of the secant function is the set of positive real numbers.

Skill Building

In Problems 11–26, use the fact that the trigonometric functions are periodic to find the exact value of each expression. Do not use a calculator.

11. $\sin 405°$ **12.** $\cos 420°$ **13.** $\tan 405°$ **14.** $\sin 390°$ **15.** $\csc 450°$ **16.** $\sec 540°$

17. $\cot 390°$ **18.** $\sec 420°$ **19.** $\cos \dfrac{33\pi}{4}$ **20.** $\sin \dfrac{9\pi}{4}$ **21.** $\tan(21\pi)$ **22.** $\csc \dfrac{9\pi}{2}$

23. $\sec \dfrac{17\pi}{4}$ **24.** $\cot \dfrac{17\pi}{4}$ **25.** $\tan \dfrac{19\pi}{6}$ **26.** $\sec \dfrac{25\pi}{6}$

In Problems 27–34, name the quadrant in which the angle θ lies.

27. $\sin \theta > 0, \quad \cos \theta < 0$ **28.** $\sin \theta < 0, \quad \cos \theta > 0$ **29.** $\sin \theta < 0, \quad \tan \theta < 0$ **30.** $\cos \theta > 0, \quad \tan \theta > 0$

31. $\cos \theta > 0, \quad \tan \theta < 0$ **32.** $\cos \theta < 0, \quad \tan \theta > 0$ **33.** $\sec \theta < 0, \quad \sin \theta > 0$ **34.** $\csc \theta > 0, \quad \cos \theta < 0$

In Problems 35–42, $\sin \theta$ and $\cos \theta$ are given. Find the exact value of each of the four remaining trigonometric functions.

35. $\sin \theta = -\dfrac{3}{5}, \quad \cos \theta = \dfrac{4}{5}$ **36.** $\sin \theta = \dfrac{4}{5}, \quad \cos \theta = -\dfrac{3}{5}$ **37.** $\sin \theta = \dfrac{2\sqrt{5}}{5}, \quad \cos \theta = \dfrac{\sqrt{5}}{5}$

38. $\sin \theta = -\dfrac{\sqrt{5}}{5}, \quad \cos \theta = -\dfrac{2\sqrt{5}}{5}$ **39.** $\sin \theta = \dfrac{1}{2}, \quad \cos \theta = \dfrac{\sqrt{3}}{2}$ **40.** $\sin \theta = \dfrac{\sqrt{3}}{2}, \quad \cos \theta = \dfrac{1}{2}$

41. $\sin \theta = -\dfrac{1}{3}, \quad \cos \theta = \dfrac{2\sqrt{2}}{3}$ **42.** $\sin \theta = \dfrac{2\sqrt{2}}{3}, \quad \cos \theta = -\dfrac{1}{3}$

In Problems 43–58, find the exact value of each of the remaining trigonometric functions of θ.

43. $\sin \theta = \dfrac{12}{13}, \quad \theta$ in quadrant II   **44.** $\cos \theta = \dfrac{3}{5}, \quad \theta$ in quadrant IV   **45.** $\cos \theta = -\dfrac{4}{5}, \quad \theta$ in quadrant III

46. $\sin \theta = -\dfrac{5}{13}, \quad \theta$ in quadrant III   **47.** $\sin \theta = \dfrac{5}{13}, \quad 90° < \theta < 180°$ **48.** $\cos \theta = \dfrac{4}{5}, \quad 270° < \theta < 360°$

49. $\cos \theta = -\dfrac{1}{3}, \quad \dfrac{\pi}{2} < \theta < \pi$ **50.** $\sin \theta = -\dfrac{2}{3}, \quad \pi < \theta < \dfrac{3\pi}{2}$ **51.** $\sin \theta = \dfrac{2}{3}, \quad \tan \theta < 0$

52. $\cos \theta = -\dfrac{1}{4}, \quad \tan \theta > 0$ **53.** $\sec \theta = 2, \quad \sin \theta < 0$ **54.** $\csc \theta = 3, \quad \cot \theta < 0$

55. $\tan \theta = \dfrac{3}{4}, \quad \sin \theta < 0$ **56.** $\cot \theta = \dfrac{4}{3}, \quad \cos \theta < 0$ **57.** $\tan \theta = -\dfrac{1}{3}, \quad \sin \theta > 0$

58. $\sec \theta = -2, \quad \tan \theta > 0$

In Problems 59–76, use the even–odd properties to find the exact value of each expression. Do not use a calculator.

59. $\sin(-60°)$ **60.** $\cos(-30°)$ **61.** $\tan(-30°)$ **62.** $\sin(-135°)$ **63.** $\sec(-60°)$ **64.** $\csc(-30°)$

65. $\sin(-90°)$ **66.** $\cos(-270°)$ **67.** $\tan\left(-\dfrac{\pi}{4}\right)$ **68.** $\sin(-\pi)$ **69.** $\cos\left(-\dfrac{\pi}{4}\right)$ **70.** $\sin\left(-\dfrac{\pi}{3}\right)$

71. $\tan(-\pi)$ **72.** $\sin\left(-\dfrac{3\pi}{2}\right)$ **73.** $\csc\left(-\dfrac{\pi}{4}\right)$ **74.** $\sec(-\pi)$ **75.** $\sec\left(-\dfrac{\pi}{6}\right)$ **76.** $\csc\left(-\dfrac{\pi}{3}\right)$

In Problems 77–88, use properties of the trigonometric functions to find the exact value of each expression. Do not use a calculator.

77. $\sin^2 40° + \cos^2 40°$ **78.** $\sec^2 18° - \tan^2 18°$ **79.** $\sin 80° \csc 80°$ **80.** $\tan 10° \cot 10°$

81. $\tan 40° - \dfrac{\sin 40°}{\cos 40°}$ **82.** $\cot 20° - \dfrac{\cos 20°}{\sin 20°}$ **83.** $\cos 400° \cdot \sec 40°$ **84.** $\tan 200° \cdot \cot 20°$

85. $\sin\left(-\dfrac{\pi}{12}\right) \csc \dfrac{25\pi}{12}$ **86.** $\sec\left(-\dfrac{\pi}{18}\right) \cdot \cos \dfrac{37\pi}{18}$ **87.** $\dfrac{\sin(-20°)}{\cos 380°} + \tan 200°$ **88.** $\dfrac{\sin 70°}{\cos(-430°)} + \tan(-70°)$

89. If $\sin \theta = 0.3$, find the value of:
$$\sin \theta + \sin(\theta + 2\pi) + \sin(\theta + 4\pi)$$

90. If $\cos \theta = 0.2$, find the value of:
$$\cos \theta + \cos(\theta + 2\pi) + \cos(\theta + 4\pi)$$

91. If $\tan \theta = 3$, find the value of:
$$\tan \theta + \tan(\theta + \pi) + \tan(\theta + 2\pi)$$

92. If $\cot \theta = -2$, find the value of:
$$\cot \theta + \cot(\theta - \pi) + \cot(\theta - 2\pi)$$

93. Find the exact value of:
$$\sin 1° + \sin 2° + \sin 3° + \cdots + \sin 358° + \sin 359°$$

94. Find the exact value of:
$$\cos 1° + \cos 2° + \cos 3° + \cdots + \cos 358° + \cos 359°$$

95. What is the domain of the sine function?

96. What is the domain of the cosine function?

97. For what numbers θ is $f(\theta) = \tan \theta$ not defined?

98. For what numbers θ is $f(\theta) = \cot \theta$ not defined?

99. For what numbers θ is $f(\theta) = \sec \theta$ not defined?

100. For what numbers θ is $f(\theta) = \csc \theta$ not defined?

101. What is the range of the sine function?

102. What is the range of the cosine function?

103. What is the range of the tangent function?

104. What is the range of the cotangent function?

105. What is the range of the secant function?

106. What is the range of the cosecant function?

107. Is the sine function even, odd, or neither? Is its graph symmetric? With respect to what?

108. Is the cosine function even, odd, or neither? Is its graph symmetric? With respect to what?

109. Is the tangent function even, odd, or neither? Is its graph symmetric? With respect to what?

110. Is the cotangent function even, odd, or neither? Is its graph symmetric? With respect to what?

111. Is the secant function even, odd, or neither? Is its graph symmetric? With respect to what?

112. Is the cosecant function even, odd, or neither? Is its graph symmetric? With respect to what?

Applications and Extensions

In Problems 113–118, use the periodic and even–odd properties.

113. If $f(\theta) = \sin \theta$ and $f(a) = \dfrac{1}{3}$, find the exact value of:

    (a) $f(-a)$ (b) $f(a) + f(a + 2\pi) + f(a + 4\pi)$

114. If $f(\theta) = \cos \theta$ and $f(a) = \dfrac{1}{4}$, find the exact value of:

    (a) $f(-a)$ (b) $f(a) + f(a + 2\pi) + f(a - 2\pi)$

115. If $f(\theta) = \tan \theta$ and $f(a) = 2$, find the exact value of:

    (a) $f(-a)$ (b) $f(a) + f(a + \pi) + f(a + 2\pi)$

116. If $f(\theta) = \cot \theta$ and $f(a) = -3$, find the exact value of:

    (a) $f(-a)$ (b) $f(a) + f(a + \pi) + f(a + 4\pi)$

117. If $f(\theta) = \sec \theta$ and $f(a) = -4$, find the exact value of:

    (a) $f(-a)$ (b) $f(a) + f(a + 2\pi) + f(a + 4\pi)$

118. If $f(\theta) = \csc \theta$ and $f(a) = 2$, find the exact value of:

    (a) $f(-a)$ (b) $f(a) + f(a + 2\pi) + f(a + 4\pi)$

119. Calculating the Time of a Trip From a parking lot, you want to walk to a house on the beach. The house is located 1500 feet down a paved path that parallels the ocean, which is 500 feet away. See the illustration. Along the path you can walk 300 feet per minute, but in the sand on the beach you can only walk 100 feet per minute.

    The time T to get from the parking lot to the beach house can be expressed as a function of the angle θ shown in the illustration and is

$$T(\theta) = 5 - \frac{5}{3 \tan \theta} + \frac{5}{\sin \theta} \qquad 0 < \theta < \frac{\pi}{2}$$

Calculate the time T if you walk directly from the parking lot to the house.

[Hint: $\tan \theta = \dfrac{500}{1500}$.]

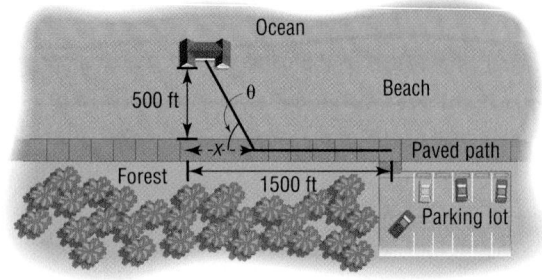

120. Calculating the Time of a Trip Two oceanfront homes are located 8 miles apart on a straight stretch of beach, each a distance of 1 mile from a paved road that parallels the ocean. Sally can jog 8 miles per hour along the paved road, but only 3 miles per hour in the sand on the beach. Because a river flows directly between the two houses, it is necessary to jog in the sand to the road, continue on the road, and then jog directly back in the sand to get from one house to the other. See the illustration. The time T to get from one house to the other as a function of the angle θ shown in the illustration is

$$T(\theta) = 1 + \frac{2}{3 \sin \theta} - \frac{1}{4 \tan \theta} \qquad 0 < \theta < \frac{\pi}{2}$$

    (a) Calculate the time T for $\tan \theta = \dfrac{1}{4}$.

    (b) Describe the path taken.

    (c) Explain why θ must be larger than $14°$.

121. Show that the range of the tangent function is the set of all real numbers.

122. Show that the range of the cotangent function is the set of all real numbers.

123. Show that the period of $f(\theta) = \sin \theta$ is 2π.

    [Hint: Assume that $0 < p < 2\pi$ exists so that $\sin(\theta + p) = \sin \theta$ for all θ. Let $\theta = 0$ to find p. Then let $\theta = \dfrac{\pi}{2}$ to obtain a contradiction.]

124. Show that the period of $f(\theta) = \cos \theta$ is 2π.

125. Show that the period of $f(\theta) = \sec \theta$ is 2π.

126. Show that the period of $f(\theta) = \csc \theta$ is 2π.

127. Show that the period of $f(\theta) = \tan\theta$ is π.

128. Show that the period of $f(\theta) = \cot\theta$ is π.

129. Prove the reciprocal identities given in formula (2).

130. Prove the quotient identities given in formula (3).

131. Establish the identity:

$$(\sin\theta\cos\phi)^2 + (\sin\theta\sin\phi)^2 + \cos^2\theta = 1$$

Discussion and Writing

132. Write down five properties of the tangent function. Explain the meaning of each.

133. Describe your understanding of the meaning of a periodic function.

134. Explain how to find the value of $\sin 390°$ using periodic properties.

135. Explain how to find the value of $\cos(-45°)$ using even–odd properties.

'Are You Prepared?' Answers

1. $\left\{ x \mid x \neq -\dfrac{1}{2} \right\}$ **2.** Even   **3.** False   **4.** True

6.4 Graphs of the Sine and Cosine Functions*

PREPARING FOR THIS SECTION *Before getting started, review the following:*

- Graphing Techniques: Transformations (Section 2.5, pp. 100–108)

Now Work the 'Are You Prepared?' problems on page 406.

OBJECTIVES
1 Graph Functions of the Form $y = A\sin(\omega x)$ Using Transformations (p. 397)
2 Graph Functions of the Form $y = A\cos(\omega x)$ Using Transformations (p. 398)
3 Determine the Amplitude and Period of Sinusoidal Functions (p. 400)
4 Graph Sinusoidal Functions Using Key Points (p. 401)
5 Find an Equation for a Sinusoidal Graph (p. 405)

Since we want to graph the trigonometric functions in the *xy*-plane, we shall use the traditional symbols *x* for the independent variable (or argument) and *y* for the dependent variable (or value at *x*) for each function. So we write the six trigonometric functions as

$$
\begin{array}{ccc}
y = f(x) = \sin x & y = f(x) = \cos x & y = f(x) = \tan x \\
y = f(x) = \csc x & y = f(x) = \sec x & y = f(x) = \cot x
\end{array}
$$

 Here the independent variable *x* represents an angle, measured in radians. In calculus, *x* will usually be treated as a real number. As we said earlier, these are equivalent ways of viewing *x*.

The Graph of the Sine Function $y = \sin x$

Since the sine function has period 2π, we need to graph $y = \sin x$ only on the interval $[0, 2\pi]$. The remainder of the graph will consist of repetitions of this portion of the graph.

*For those who wish to include phase shifts here, Section 6.6 can be covered immediately after Section 6.4 without loss of continuity.

Table 6

x	y = sin x	(x, y)
0	0	(0, 0)
$\dfrac{\pi}{6}$	$\dfrac{1}{2}$	$\left(\dfrac{\pi}{6}, \dfrac{1}{2}\right)$
$\dfrac{\pi}{2}$	1	$\left(\dfrac{\pi}{2}, 1\right)$
$\dfrac{5\pi}{6}$	$\dfrac{1}{2}$	$\left(\dfrac{5\pi}{6}, \dfrac{1}{2}\right)$
π	0	$(\pi, 0)$
$\dfrac{7\pi}{6}$	$-\dfrac{1}{2}$	$\left(\dfrac{7\pi}{6}, -\dfrac{1}{2}\right)$
$\dfrac{3\pi}{2}$	-1	$\left(\dfrac{3\pi}{2}, -1\right)$
$\dfrac{11\pi}{6}$	$-\dfrac{1}{2}$	$\left(\dfrac{11\pi}{6}, -\dfrac{1}{2}\right)$
2π	0	$(2\pi, 0)$

We begin by constructing Table 6, which lists some points on the graph of $y = \sin x$, $0 \le x \le 2\pi$. As the table shows, the graph of $y = \sin x$, $0 \le x \le 2\pi$, begins at the origin. As x increases from 0 to $\dfrac{\pi}{2}$, the value of $y = \sin x$ increases from 0 to 1; as x increases from $\dfrac{\pi}{2}$ to π to $\dfrac{3\pi}{2}$, the value of y decreases from 1 to 0 to -1; as x increases from $\dfrac{3\pi}{2}$ to 2π, the value of y increases from -1 to 0. If we plot the points listed in Table 6 and connect them with a smooth curve, we obtain the graph shown in Figure 48.

Figure 48
$y = \sin x$, $0 \le x \le 2\pi$

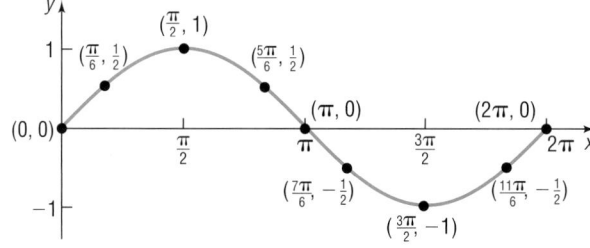

The graph in Figure 48 is one period, or **cycle,** of the graph of $y = \sin x$. To obtain a more complete graph of $y = \sin x$, we continue the graph in each direction, as shown in Figure 49(a). Figure 49(b) shows the graph on a TI-84 Plus graphing calculator.

Figure 49
$y = \sin x$, $-\infty < x < \infty$

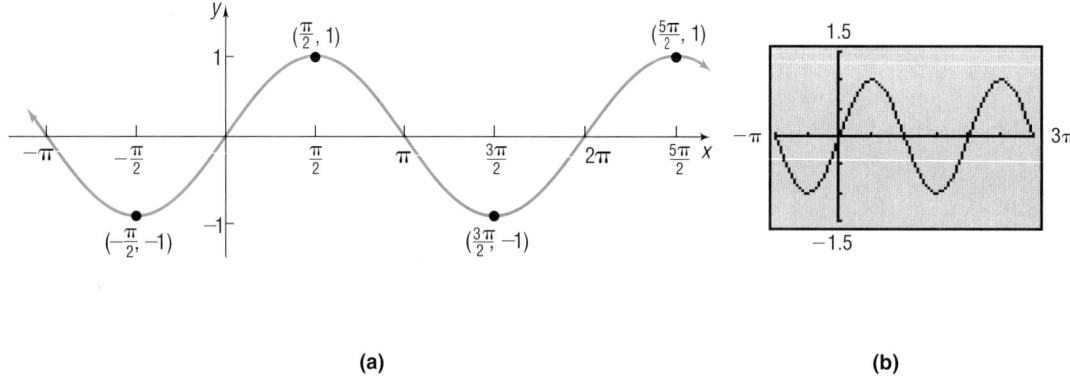

(a)   (b)

The graph of $y = \sin x$ illustrates some of the facts that we already know about the sine function.

Properties of the Sine Function $y = \sin x$

1. The domain is the set of all real numbers.
2. The range consists of all real numbers from -1 to 1, inclusive.
3. The sine function is an odd function, as the symmetry of the graph with respect to the origin indicates.
4. The sine function is periodic, with period 2π.
5. The x-intercepts are $\ldots, -2\pi, -\pi, 0, \pi, 2\pi, 3\pi, \ldots$; the y-intercept is 0.
6. The maximum value is 1 and occurs at $x = \ldots, -\dfrac{3\pi}{2}, \dfrac{\pi}{2}, \dfrac{5\pi}{2}, \dfrac{9\pi}{2}, \ldots$;

   the minimum value is -1 and occurs at $x = \ldots, -\dfrac{\pi}{2}, \dfrac{3\pi}{2}, \dfrac{7\pi}{2}, \dfrac{11\pi}{2}, \ldots$.

⟿ **Now Work** PROBLEMS **9**, **11**, AND **13**

1 Graph Functions of the Form $y = A \sin(\omega x)$ Using Transformations

| EXAMPLE 1 | **Graphing Functions of the Form $y = A \sin(\omega x)$ Using Transformations** |

Graph $y = 3 \sin x$ using transformations. Use the graph to determine the domain and the range of $y = 3 \sin x$.

Solution Figure 50 illustrates the steps.

Figure 50

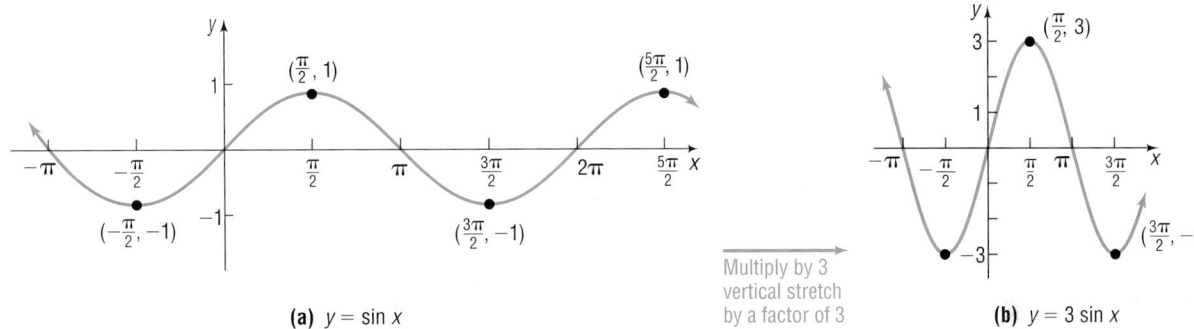

(a) $y = \sin x$ — Multiply by 3 vertical stretch by a factor of 3 — **(b)** $y = 3 \sin x$

The domain of $y = 3 \sin x$ is the set of all real numbers or $(-\infty, \infty)$. The range of $y = 3 \sin x$ is $\{y \mid -3 \le y \le 3\}$ or $[-3, 3]$.

✓**Check:** Graph $Y_1 = 3 \sin x$ to verify the graph shown in Figure 50(b).

| EXAMPLE 2 | **Graphing Functions of the Form $y = A \sin(\omega x)$ Using Transformations** |

Graph $y = -\sin(2x)$ using transformations. Use the graph to determine the domain and the range of $y = -\sin(2x)$.

Solution Figure 51 illustrates the steps.

Figure 51

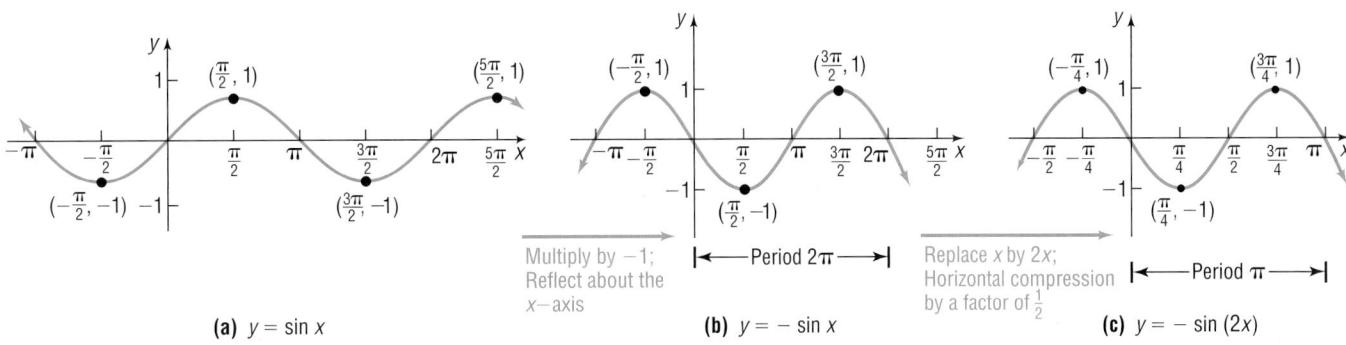

(a) $y = \sin x$ — Multiply by -1; Reflect about the x-axis — **(b)** $y = -\sin x$ — Replace x by $2x$; Horizontal compression by a factor of $\frac{1}{2}$ — **(c)** $y = -\sin(2x)$

The domain of $y = -\sin(2x)$ is the set of all real numbers. The range of $y = -\sin(2x)$ is $\{y \mid -1 \le y \le 1\}$ or $[-1, 1]$.

Notice in Figure 51(c) that the period of the function $y = -\sin(2x)$ is π due to the horizontal compression of the original period 2π by a factor of $\frac{1}{2}$.

✓**Check:** Graph $Y_1 = -\sin(2x)$ to verify the graph shown in Figure 51(c).

Now Work PROBLEM 45 USING TRANSFORMATIONS

Table 7

x	y = cos x	(x, y)
0	1	(0, 1)
$\frac{\pi}{3}$	$\frac{1}{2}$	$\left(\frac{\pi}{3}, \frac{1}{2}\right)$
$\frac{\pi}{2}$	0	$\left(\frac{\pi}{2}, 0\right)$
$\frac{2\pi}{3}$	$-\frac{1}{2}$	$\left(\frac{2\pi}{3}, -\frac{1}{2}\right)$
π	-1	$(\pi, -1)$
$\frac{4\pi}{3}$	$-\frac{1}{2}$	$\left(\frac{4\pi}{3}, -\frac{1}{2}\right)$
$\frac{3\pi}{2}$	0	$\left(\frac{3\pi}{2}, 0\right)$
$\frac{5\pi}{3}$	$\frac{1}{2}$	$\left(\frac{5\pi}{3}, \frac{1}{2}\right)$
2π	1	$(2\pi, 1)$

The Graph of the Cosine Function

The cosine function also has period 2π. We proceed as we did with the sine function by constructing Table 7, which lists some points on the graph of $y = \cos x$, $0 \le x \le 2\pi$. As the table shows, the graph of $y = \cos x$, $0 \le x \le 2\pi$, begins at the point $(0, 1)$. As x increases from 0 to $\frac{\pi}{2}$ to π, the value of y decreases from 1 to 0 to -1; as x increases from π to $\frac{3\pi}{2}$ to 2π, the value of y increases from -1 to 0 to 1. As before, we plot the points in Table 7 to get one period or cycle of the graph. See Figure 52.

Figure 52
$y = \cos x, 0 \le x \le 2\pi$

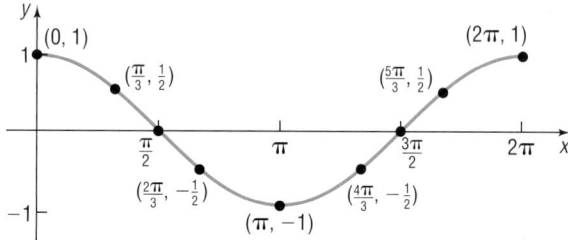

A more complete graph of $y = \cos x$ is obtained by continuing the graph in each direction, as shown in Figure 53(a). Figure 53(b) shows the graph on a TI-84 Plus graphing calculator.

Figure 53
$y = \cos x, -\infty < x < \infty$

$y = \cos x$

(a)

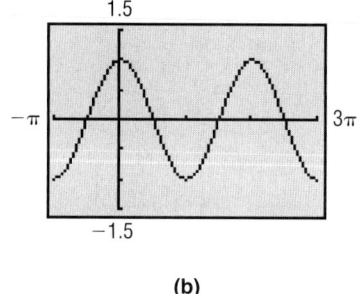

(b)

The graph of $y = \cos x$ illustrates some of the facts that we already know about the cosine function.

Properties of the Cosine Function

1. The domain is the set of all real numbers.
2. The range consists of all real numbers from -1 to 1, inclusive.
3. The cosine function is an even function, as the symmetry of the graph with respect to the y-axis indicates.
4. The cosine function is periodic, with period 2π.
5. The x-intercepts are $\ldots, -\frac{3\pi}{2}, -\frac{\pi}{2}, \frac{\pi}{2}, \frac{3\pi}{2}, \frac{5\pi}{2}, \ldots$; the y-intercept is 1.
6. The maximum value is 1 and occurs at $x = \ldots, -2\pi, 0, 2\pi, 4\pi, 6\pi, \ldots$; the minimum value is -1 and occurs at $x = \ldots, -\pi, \pi, 3\pi, 5\pi, \ldots$.

2 Graph Functions of the Form $y = A \cos(\omega x)$ Using Transformations

EXAMPLE 3   Graphing Functions of the Form $y = A \cos(\omega x)$ Using Transformations

Graph $y = 2 \cos(3x)$ using transformations. Use the graph to determine the domain and the range of $y = 2 \cos(3x)$.

Solution   Figure 54 shows the steps.

Figure 54

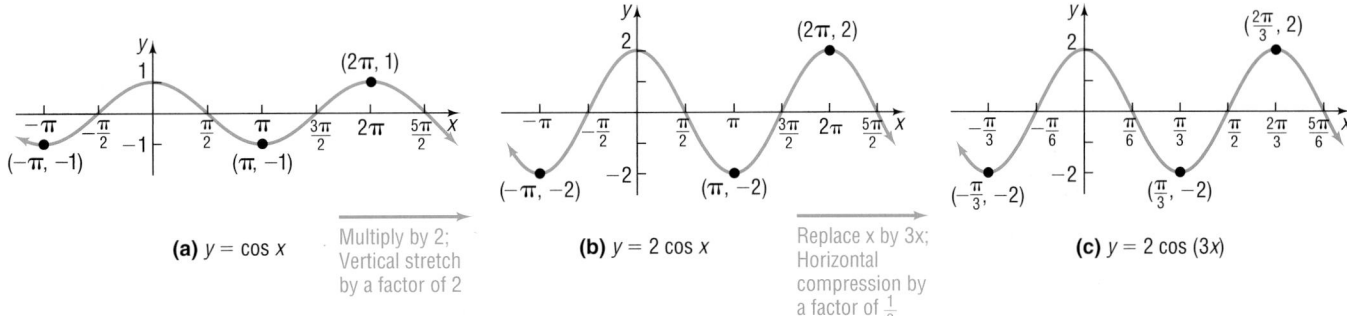

(a) $y = \cos x$ Multiply by 2; Vertical stretch by a factor of 2   **(b)** $y = 2\cos x$ Replace x by 3x; Horizontal compression by a factor of $\frac{1}{3}$ **(c)** $y = 2\cos(3x)$

The domain of $y = 2\cos(3x)$ is the set of all real numbers or $(-\infty, \infty)$. The range of $y = 2\cos(3x)$ is $\{y \mid -2 \le y \le 2\}$ or $[-2, 2]$.

✓**Check:** Graph $Y_1 = 2\cos(3x)$ to verify the graph shown in Figure 54(c).

Notice in Figure 54(c) that the period of the function $y = 2\cos(3x)$ is $\dfrac{2\pi}{3}$ due to the compression of the original period 2π by a factor of $\dfrac{1}{3}$.

━━━ **Now Work**   PROBLEM **53** USING TRANSFORMATIONS

Sinusoidal Graphs

Shift the graph of $y = \cos x$ to the right $\dfrac{\pi}{2}$ units to obtain the graph of $y = \cos\left(x - \dfrac{\pi}{2}\right)$. See Figure 55(a). Now look at the graph of $y = \sin x$ in Figure 55(b). We see that the graph of $y = \sin x$ is the same as the graph of $y = \cos\left(x - \dfrac{\pi}{2}\right)$.

Figure 55

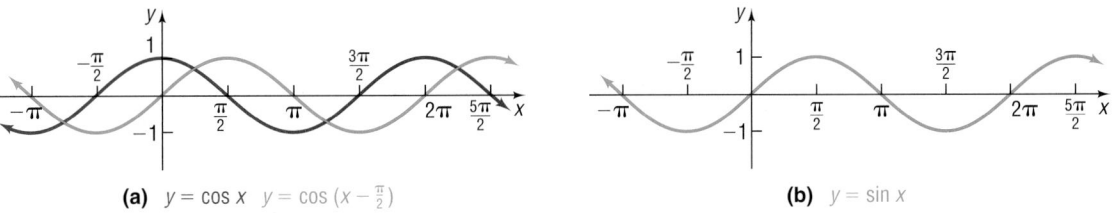

(a) $y = \cos x$ $y = \cos\left(x - \frac{\pi}{2}\right)$ **(b)** $y = \sin x$

Based on Figure 55, we conjecture that

$$\sin x = \cos\left(x - \frac{\pi}{2}\right)$$

Seeing the Concept

Graph $Y_1 = \sin x$ and $Y_2 = \cos\left(x - \dfrac{\pi}{2}\right)$.

How many graphs do you see?

(We shall prove this fact in Chapter 7.) Because of this relationship, the graphs of functions of the form $y = A\sin(\omega x)$ or $y = A\cos(\omega x)$ are referred to as **sinusoidal graphs.**

Let's look at some general properties of sinusoidal graphs.

3 Determine the Amplitude and Period of Sinusoidal Functions

In Figure 56(b) we show the graph of $y = 2 \cos x$. Notice that the values of $y = 2 \cos x$ lie between -2 and 2, inclusive.

Figure 56

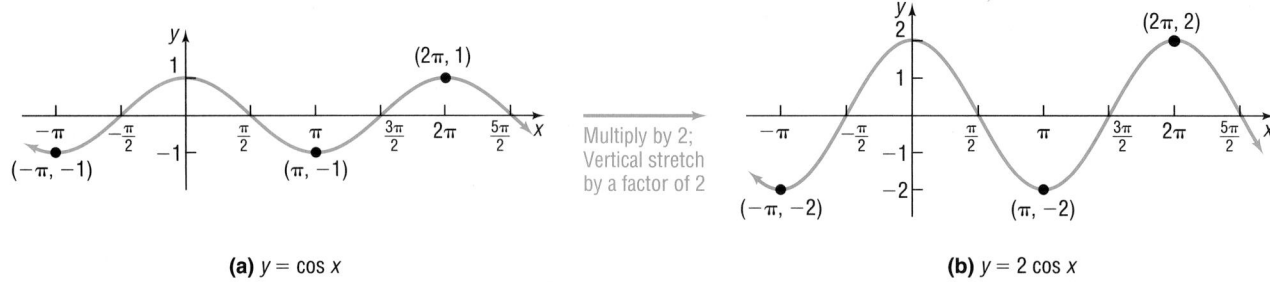

(a) $y = \cos x$ **(b)** $y = 2 \cos x$

In general, the values of the functions $y = A \sin x$ and $y = A \cos x$, where $A \neq 0$, will always satisfy the inequalities

$$-|A| \leq A \sin x \leq |A| \quad \text{and} \quad -|A| \leq A \cos x \leq |A|$$

respectively. The number $|A|$ is called the **amplitude** of $y = A \sin x$ or $y = A \cos x$. See Figure 57.

Figure 57

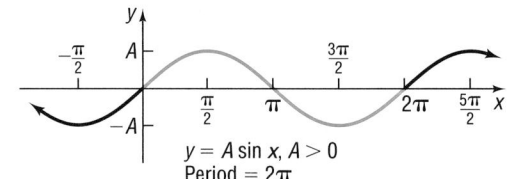

$y = A \sin x, A > 0$
Period $= 2\pi$

In Figure 58(a), we show the graph of $y = \cos x$. In Figure 58(b), we show the graph of $y = \cos(3x)$. Notice that the period of the function $y = \cos(3x)$ is $\dfrac{2\pi}{3}$, due to the horizontal compression of the period of $y = \cos x$, 2π, by a factor of $\dfrac{1}{3}$.

Figure 58

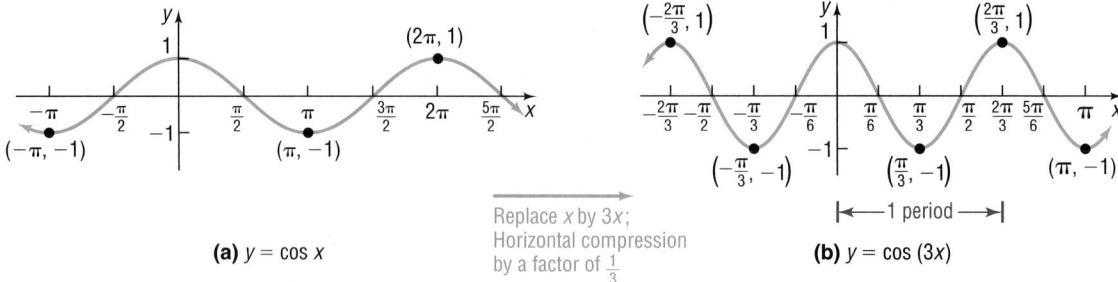

(a) $y = \cos x$ **(b)** $y = \cos(3x)$

In general, if $\omega > 0$, the functions $y = \sin(\omega x)$ and $y = \cos(\omega x)$ will have period $T = \dfrac{2\pi}{\omega}$. To see why, recall that the graph of $y = \sin(\omega x)$ is obtained from the graph of $y = \sin x$ by performing a horizontal compression or stretch by a factor $\dfrac{1}{\omega}$. This horizontal compression replaces the interval $[0, 2\pi]$, which contains one period of the graph of $y = \sin x$, by the interval $\left[0, \dfrac{2\pi}{\omega}\right]$, which contains one period of the graph of $y = \sin(\omega x)$.

For example, for the function $y = \cos(3x)$, graphed in Figure 58(b), $\omega = 3$, so the period is $\dfrac{2\pi}{\omega} = \dfrac{2\pi}{3}$.

One period of the graph of $y = A\sin(\omega x)$ or $y = A\cos(\omega x)$ is called a **cycle**. Figure 59 illustrates the general situation. The blue portion of the graph is one cycle.

Figure 59

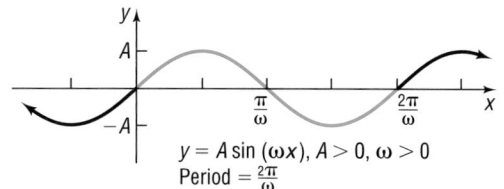

$y = A\sin(\omega x), A > 0, \omega > 0$
Period $= \frac{2\pi}{\omega}$

NOTE A function f is even if $f(-x) = f(x)$; a function is odd if $f(-x) = -f(x)$. Since the sine function is odd, $\sin(-\theta) = -\sin\theta$; since the cosine function is even, $\cos(-\theta) = \cos\theta$. ∎

If $\omega < 0$ in $y = A\sin(\omega x)$ or $y = A\cos(\omega x)$, we use the Even–Odd Properties of the sine and cosine functions. Since the sine function is an odd function and the cosine function is an even function, we have

$$A\sin(-\omega x) = -A\sin(\omega x) \quad \text{and} \quad A\cos(-\omega x) = A\cos(\omega x)$$

This gives us an equivalent form in which the coefficient of x in the argument is positive. For example,

$$\sin(-2x) = -\sin(2x) \quad \text{and} \quad \cos(-\pi x) = \cos(\pi x)$$

Because of this, we can assume $\omega > 0$.

THEOREM

If $\omega > 0$, the amplitude and period of $y = A\sin(\omega x)$ and $y = A\cos(\omega x)$ are given by

$$\text{Amplitude} = |A| \qquad \text{Period} = T = \frac{2\pi}{\omega} \qquad \textbf{(1)}$$

EXAMPLE 4   Finding the Amplitude and Period of a Sinusoidal Function

Determine the amplitude and period of $y = 5\sin(-4x)$.

Solution   First, we use the fact that the sine function is odd and write $y = 5\sin(-4x)$ as $y = -5\sin(4x)$. Comparing $y = -5\sin(4x)$ to $y = A\sin(\omega x)$, we find that $A = -5$ and $\omega = 4$. From equation (1),

$$\text{Amplitude} = |A| = |-5| = 5 \qquad \text{Period} = T = \frac{2\pi}{\omega} = \frac{2\pi}{4} = \frac{\pi}{2}$$

═══ **Now Work** PROBLEM 23

4 Graph Sinusoidal Functions Using Key Points

So far, we have graphed functions of the form $y = A\sin(\omega x)$ or $y = A\cos(\omega x)$ using transformations. We now introduce another method that can be used to graph these functions.

Figure 60 on page 402 shows one cycle of the graphs of $y = \sin x$ and $y = \cos x$ on the interval $[0, 2\pi]$. Notice that each graph consists of four parts corresponding to the four subintervals:

$$\left[0, \frac{\pi}{2}\right] \qquad \left[\frac{\pi}{2}, \pi\right] \qquad \left[\pi, \frac{3\pi}{2}\right] \qquad \left[\frac{3\pi}{2}, 2\pi\right]$$

Each subinterval is of length $\dfrac{\pi}{2}$ (the period 2π divided by 4, the number of parts), and the endpoints of these intervals, $x = 0$, $x = \dfrac{\pi}{2}$, $x = \pi$, $x = \dfrac{3\pi}{2}$, $x = 2\pi$, give rise to five key points on each graph:

For $y = \sin x$: $(0, 0), \left(\dfrac{\pi}{2}, 1\right), (\pi, 0), \left(\dfrac{3\pi}{2}, -1\right), (2\pi, 0)$

For $y = \cos x$: $(0, 1), \left(\dfrac{\pi}{2}, 0\right), (\pi, -1), \left(\dfrac{3\pi}{2}, 0\right), (2\pi, 1)$

Look again at Figure 60.

Figure 60

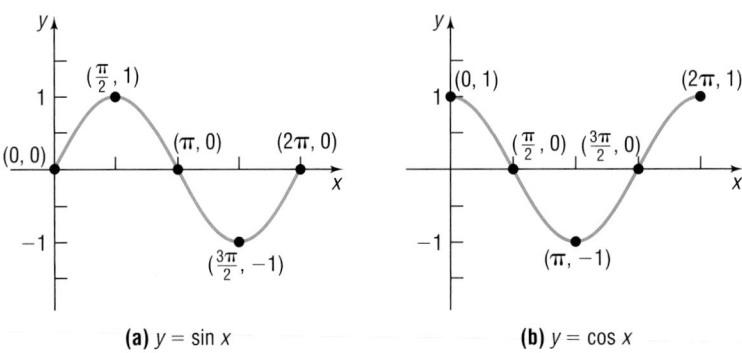

(a) $y = \sin x$ **(b)** $y = \cos x$

Let's look at an example that illustrates how to graph a sinusoidal function using key points.

| EXAMPLE 5 | **How to Graph a Sinusoidal Function Using Key Points** |

Graph $y = 3\sin(4x)$ using key points.

Step-by-Step Solution

STEP 1 Determine the amplitude and period of the sinusoidal function.

Comparing $y = 3\sin(4x)$ to $y = A\sin(\omega x)$, we see that $A = 3$ and $\omega = 4$, so the amplitude is $|A| = 3$ and the period is $\dfrac{2\pi}{\omega} = \dfrac{2\pi}{4} = \dfrac{\pi}{2}$. Because the amplitude is 3, the graph of $y = 3\sin(4x)$ will lie between -3 and 3 on the y-axis. Because the period is $\dfrac{\pi}{2}$, one cycle will begin at $x = 0$ and end at $x = \dfrac{\pi}{2}$.

STEP 2 Divide the interval $\left[0, \dfrac{2\pi}{\omega}\right]$ into four subintervals of the same length.

We divide the interval $\left[0, \dfrac{\pi}{2}\right]$ into four subintervals, each of length $\dfrac{\pi}{2} \div 4 = \dfrac{\pi}{8}$, as follows:

$$\left[0, \dfrac{\pi}{8}\right] \quad \left[\dfrac{\pi}{8}, \dfrac{\pi}{8} + \dfrac{\pi}{8}\right] = \left[\dfrac{\pi}{8}, \dfrac{\pi}{4}\right] \quad \left[\dfrac{\pi}{4}, \dfrac{\pi}{4} + \dfrac{\pi}{8}\right] = \left[\dfrac{\pi}{4}, \dfrac{3\pi}{8}\right] \quad \left[\dfrac{3\pi}{8}, \dfrac{3\pi}{8} + \dfrac{\pi}{8}\right] = \left[\dfrac{3\pi}{8}, \dfrac{\pi}{2}\right]$$

The endpoints of the subintervals are $0, \dfrac{\pi}{8}, \dfrac{\pi}{4}, \dfrac{3\pi}{8}, \dfrac{\pi}{2}$. These values represent the x-coordinates of the five key points on the graph.

STEP 3 Use the endpoints of these subintervals to obtain five key points on the graph.

To obtain the y-coordinates of the five key points of $y = 3\sin(4x)$, we multiply the y-coordinates of the five key points for $y = \sin x$ in Figure 60(a) by $A = 3$. The five key points are

$$(0, 0) \quad \left(\dfrac{\pi}{8}, 3\right) \quad \left(\dfrac{\pi}{4}, 0\right) \quad \left(\dfrac{3\pi}{8}, -3\right) \quad \left(\dfrac{\pi}{2}, 0\right)$$

STEP 4 Plot the five key points and draw a sinusoidal graph to obtain the graph of one cycle. Extend the graph in each direction to make it complete.

We plot the five key points obtained in Step 3 and fill in the graph of the sine curve as shown in Figure 61(a). We extend the graph in each direction to obtain the complete graph shown in Figure 61(b). Notice that additional key points appear every $\dfrac{\pi}{8}$ radian.

Figure 61

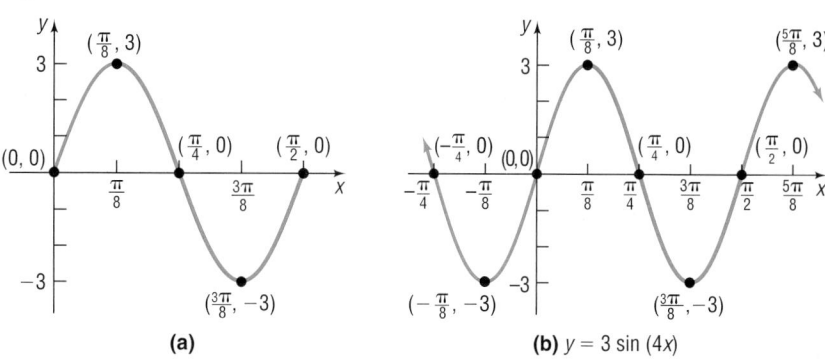

(a)

(b) $y = 3 \sin(4x)$

NOTE In Step 3 of Example 5, we could also obtain the five key points by evaluating $y = 3 \sin(4x)$ at each value of x. ■

✓ **Check:** Graph $y = 3 \sin(4x)$ using transformations. Which graphing method do you prefer?

— **Now Work** PROBLEM 45 USING KEY POINTS

SUMMARY **Steps for Graphing a Sinusoidal Function of the Form $y = A \sin(\omega x)$ or $y = A \cos(\omega x)$ Using Key Points**

STEP 1: Determine the amplitude and period of the sinusoidal function.

STEP 2: Divide the interval $\left[0, \dfrac{2\pi}{\omega}\right]$ into four subintervals of the same length.

STEP 3: Use the endpoints of these subintervals to obtain five key points on the graph.

STEP 4: Plot the five key points with a sinusoidal graph to obtain the graph of one cycle. Extend the graph in each direction to make it complete.

EXAMPLE 6 **Graphing a Sinusoidal Function Using Key Points**

Graph $y = 2 \sin\left(-\dfrac{\pi}{2}x\right)$ using key points.

Solution Since the sine function is odd, we can use the equivalent form:

$$y = -2 \sin\left(\dfrac{\pi}{2}x\right)$$

STEP 1: Comparing $y = -2 \sin\left(\dfrac{\pi}{2}x\right)$ to $y = A \sin(\omega x)$, we find that $A = -2$ and $\omega = \dfrac{\pi}{2}$. The amplitude is $|A| = |-2| = 2$, and the period is $T = \dfrac{2\pi}{\omega} = \dfrac{2\pi}{\dfrac{\pi}{2}} = 4$.

The graph of $y = -2 \sin\left(\dfrac{\pi}{2}x\right)$ will lie between -2 and 2 on the y-axis. One cycle will begin at $x = 0$ and end at $x = 4$.

STEP 2: We divide the interval $[0, 4]$ into four subintervals, each of length $4 \div 4 = 1$. The x-coordinates of the five key points are:

0	$0 + 1 = 1$	$1 + 1 = 2$	$2 + 1 = 3$	$3 + 1 = 4$
1st x-coordinate	2nd x-coordinate	3rd x-coordinate	4th x-coordinate	5th x-coordinate

COMMENT To graph a sinusoidal function of the form $y = A \sin(\omega x)$ or $y = A \cos(\omega x)$ using a graphing utility, we use the amplitude to set $Y_{\min}$ and $Y_{\max}$ and use the period to set $X_{\min}$ and $X_{\max}$. ∎

STEP 3: Since $y = -2 \sin\left(\dfrac{\pi}{2}x\right)$, we multiply the y-coordinates of the five key points in Figure 60(a) by $A = -2$. The five key points on the graph are

$$(0, 0) \quad (1, -2) \quad (2, 0) \quad (3, 2) \quad (4, 0)$$

STEP 4: We plot these five points and fill in the graph of the sine function as shown in Figure 62(a). Extending the graph in each direction, we obtain Figure 62(b).

Figure 62(c) shows the graph using a graphing utility.

Figure 62

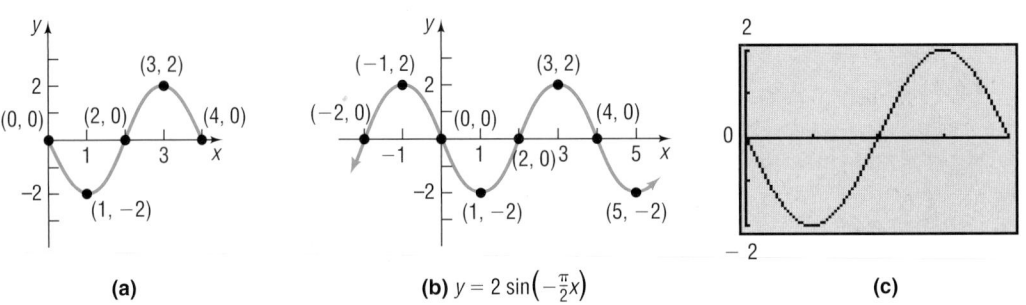

(a)

(b) $y = 2 \sin\left(-\frac{\pi}{2}x\right)$

(c)

✓ **Check:** Graph $y = 2 \sin\left(-\dfrac{\pi}{2}x\right)$ using transformations. Which graphing method do you prefer?

─── **Now Work** PROBLEM 49 USING KEY POINTS

If the function to be graphed is of the form $y = A \sin(\omega x) + B$ [or $y = A \cos(\omega x) + B$], first graph $y = A \sin(\omega x)$ [or $y = A \cos(\omega x)$] and then use a vertical shift.

EXAMPLE 7	**Graphing a Sinusoidal Function Using Key Points**

Graph $y = -4 \cos(\pi x) - 2$ using key points. Use the graph to determine the domain and the range of $y = -4 \cos(\pi x) - 2$.

Solution

We begin by graphing the function $y = -4 \cos(\pi x)$. Comparing $y = -4 \cos(\pi x)$ with $y = A \cos(\omega x)$, we find that $A = -4$ and $\omega = \pi$. The amplitude is $|A| = |-4| = 4$, and the period is $T = \dfrac{2\pi}{\omega} = \dfrac{2\pi}{\pi} = 2$.

The graph of $y = -4 \cos(\pi x)$ will lie between -4 and 4 on the y-axis. One cycle will begin at $x = 0$ and end at $x = 2$.

We divide the interval $[0, 2]$ into four subintervals, each of length $2 \div 4 = \dfrac{1}{2}$. The x-coordinates of the five key points are:

0	$0 + \dfrac{1}{2} = \dfrac{1}{2}$	$\dfrac{1}{2} + \dfrac{1}{2} = 1$	$1 + \dfrac{1}{2} = \dfrac{3}{2}$	$\dfrac{3}{2} + \dfrac{1}{2} = 2$
1st x-coordinate	2nd x-coordinate	3rd x-coordinate	4th x-coordinate	5th x-coordinate

Since $y = -4 \cos(\pi x)$, we multiply the y-coordinates of the five key points of $y = \cos x$ shown in Figure 60(b) by $A = -4$ to obtain the five key points on the graph of $y = -4 \cos(\pi x)$:

$$(0, -4) \quad \left(\frac{1}{2}, 0\right) \quad (1, 4) \quad \left(\frac{3}{2}, 0\right) \quad (2, -4)$$

We plot these five points and fill in the graph of the cosine function as shown in Figure 63(a). Extending the graph in each direction, we obtain Figure 63(b), the graph of $y = -4\cos(\pi x)$.

A vertical shift down 2 units gives the graph of $y = -4\cos(\pi x) - 2$, as shown in Figure 63(c).

Figure 63

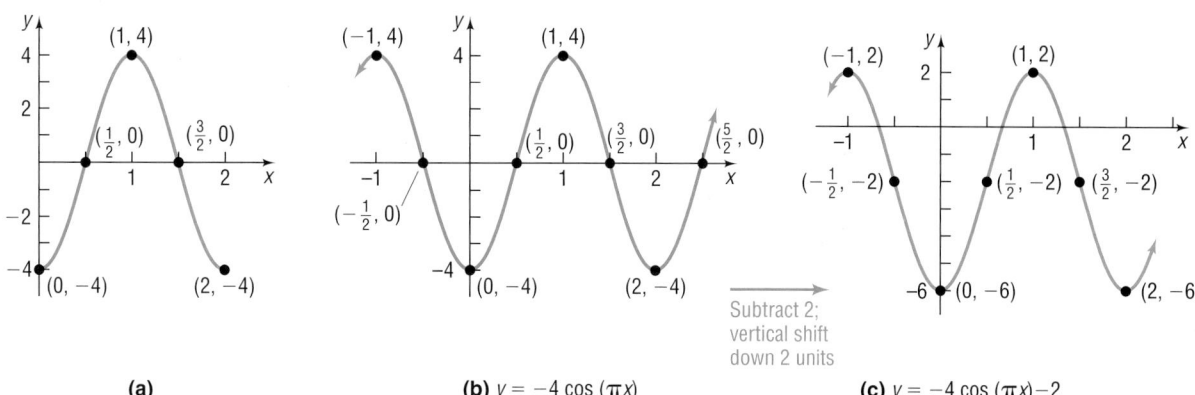

(a)   (b) $y = -4 \cos (\pi x)$ (c) $y = -4 \cos (\pi x) - 2$

The domain of $y = -4\cos(\pi x) - 2$ is the set of all real numbers or $(-\infty, \infty)$. The range of $y = -4\cos(\pi x) - 2$ is $\{y \mid -6 \le y \le 2\}$ or $[-6, 2]$.

━━━━━━━━━ **Now Work** PROBLEM 59

5 Find an Equation for a Sinusoidal Graph

We can also use the ideas of amplitude and period to identify a sinusoidal function when its graph is given.

| EXAMPLE 8 | **Finding an Equation for a Sinusoidal Graph** |

Find an equation for the graph shown in Figure 64.

Figure 64

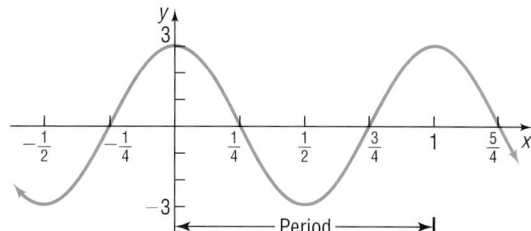

Solution   The graph has the characteristics of a cosine function. Do you see why? The maximum value occurs at $x = 0$. So we view the equation as a cosine function $y = A\cos(\omega x)$ with $A = 3$ and period $T = 1$. Then $\dfrac{2\pi}{\omega} = 1$, so $\omega = 2\pi$. The cosine function whose graph is given in Figure 64 is

$$y = A\cos(\omega x) = 3\cos(2\pi x)$$

✓ Check: Graph $Y_1 = 3\cos(2\pi x)$ and compare the result with Figure 64.

| EXAMPLE 9 | **Finding an Equation for a Sinusoidal Graph** |

Find an equation for the graph shown in Figure 65 on the following page.

Figure 65

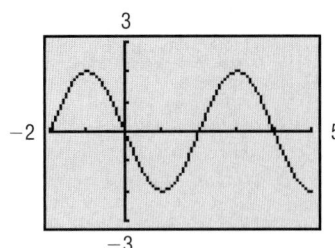

Solution The graph is sinusoidal, with amplitude $|A| = 2$. The period is 4, so $\dfrac{2\pi}{\omega} = 4$ or $\omega = \dfrac{\pi}{2}$. Since the graph passes through the origin, it is easiest to view the equation as a sine function,* but notice that the graph is actually the reflection of a sine function about the x-axis (since the graph is decreasing near the origin). This requires that $A = -2$. The sine function whose graph is given in Figure 65 is

$$y = A \sin(\omega x) = -2 \sin\left(\frac{\pi}{2}x\right)$$

✓ Check: Graph $Y_1 = -2 \sin\left(\dfrac{\pi}{2}x\right)$ and compare the result with Figure 65.

━━━ **Now Work** PROBLEMS 67 AND 71

*The equation could also be viewed as a cosine function with a horizontal shift, but viewing it as a sine function is easier.

6.4 Assess Your Understanding

'Are You Prepared?' *Answers are given at the end of these exercises. If you get a wrong answer, read the pages listed in red.*

1. Use transformations to graph $y = 3x^2$. (pp. 102–104)

2. Use transformations to graph $y = \sqrt{2x}$. (pp. 102–104)

Concepts and Vocabulary

3. The maximum value of $y = \sin x, 0 \le x \le 2\pi$, is _____ and occurs at $x = $ _____.

4. The function $y = A\sin(\omega x)$, $A > 0$, has amplitude 3 and period 2; then $A = $ _____ and $\omega = $ _____.

5. The function $y = 3\cos(6x)$ has amplitude _____ and period _____.

6. **True or False** The graphs of $y = \sin x$ and $y = \cos x$ are identical except for a horizontal shift.

7. **True or False** For $y = 2\sin(\pi x)$, the amplitude is 2 and the period is $\dfrac{\pi}{2}$.

8. **True or False** The graph of the sine function has infinitely many x-intercepts.

Skill Building

In Problems 9–18, if necessary, refer to a graph to answer each question.

9. What is the y-intercept of $y = \sin x$?

10. What is the y-intercept of $y = \cos x$?

11. For what numbers x, $-\pi \le x \le \pi$, is the graph of $y = \sin x$ increasing?

12. For what numbers x, $-\pi \le x \le \pi$, is the graph of $y = \cos x$ decreasing?

13. What is the largest value of $y = \sin x$?

14. What is the smallest value of $y = \cos x$?

15. For what numbers x, $0 \le x \le 2\pi$, does $\sin x = 0$?

16. For what numbers x, $0 \le x \le 2\pi$, does $\cos x = 0$?

17. For what numbers x, $-2\pi \le x \le 2\pi$, does $\sin x = 1$? Where does $\sin x = -1$?

18. For what numbers x, $-2\pi \le x \le 2\pi$, does $\cos x = 1$? Where does $\cos x = -1$?

In Problems 19–28, determine the amplitude and period of each function without graphing.

19. $y = 2 \sin x$

20. $y = 3 \cos x$

21. $y = -4 \cos(2x)$

22. $y = -\sin\left(\dfrac{1}{2}x\right)$

23. $y = 6 \sin(\pi x)$

24. $y = -3 \cos(3x)$

25. $y = -\dfrac{1}{2}\cos\left(\dfrac{3}{2}x\right)$

26. $y = \dfrac{4}{3}\sin\left(\dfrac{2}{3}x\right)$

27. $y = \dfrac{5}{3}\sin\left(-\dfrac{2\pi}{3}x\right)$

28. $y = \dfrac{9}{5}\cos\left(-\dfrac{3\pi}{2}x\right)$

In Problems 29–38, match the given function to one of the graphs (A)–(J).

(A)

(B)

(C)

(D)

(E)

(F)

(G)

(H)

(I)

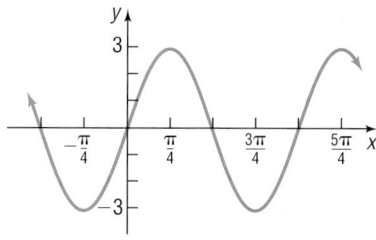

(J)

29. $y = 2 \sin\left(\dfrac{\pi}{2}x\right)$

30. $y = 2 \cos\left(\dfrac{\pi}{2}x\right)$

31. $y = 2 \cos\left(\dfrac{1}{2}x\right)$

32. $y = 3 \cos(2x)$

33. $y = -3 \sin(2x)$

34. $y = 2 \sin\left(\dfrac{1}{2}x\right)$

35. $y = -2 \cos\left(\dfrac{1}{2}x\right)$

36. $y = -2 \cos\left(\dfrac{\pi}{2}x\right)$

37. $y = 3 \sin(2x)$

38. $y = -2 \sin\left(\dfrac{1}{2}x\right)$

In Problems 39–42, match the given function to one of the graphs (A)–(D).

(A)

(B)

(C)

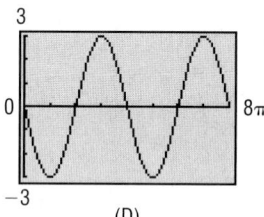

(D)

39. $y = 3 \sin\left(\dfrac{1}{2}x\right)$

40. $y = -3 \sin(2x)$

41. $y = 3 \sin(2x)$

42. $y = -3 \sin\left(\dfrac{1}{2}x\right)$

In Problems 43–66, graph each function. Be sure to label key points and show at least two cycles. Verify the graph using a graphing utility. Use the graph to determine the domain and the range of each function.

43. $y = 4 \cos x$

44. $y = 3 \sin x$

45. $y = -4 \sin x$

46. $y = -3 \cos x$

47. $y = \cos(4x)$

48. $y = \sin(3x)$

49. $y = \sin(-2x)$

50. $y = \cos(-2x)$

51. $y = 2 \sin\left(\dfrac{1}{2} x\right)$

52. $y = 2 \cos\left(\dfrac{1}{4} x\right)$

53. $y = -\dfrac{1}{2} \cos(2x)$

54. $y = -4 \sin\left(\dfrac{1}{8} x\right)$

55. $y = 2 \sin x + 3$

56. $y = 3 \cos x + 2$

57. $y = 5 \cos(\pi x) - 3$

58. $y = 4 \sin\left(\dfrac{\pi}{2} x\right) - 2$

59. $y = -6 \sin\left(\dfrac{\pi}{3} x\right) + 4$

60. $y = -3 \cos\left(\dfrac{\pi}{4} x\right) + 2$

61. $y = 5 - 3 \sin(2x)$

62. $y = 2 - 4 \cos(3x)$

63. $y = \dfrac{5}{3} \sin\left(-\dfrac{2\pi}{3} x\right)$

64. $y = \dfrac{9}{5} \cos\left(-\dfrac{3\pi}{2} x\right)$

65. $y = -\dfrac{3}{2} \cos\left(\dfrac{\pi}{4} x\right) + \dfrac{1}{2}$

66. $y = -\dfrac{1}{2} \sin\left(\dfrac{\pi}{8} x\right) + \dfrac{3}{2}$

In Problems 67–70, write the equation of a sine function that has the given characteristics.

67. Amplitude: 3
Period: π

68. Amplitude: 2
Period: 4π

69. Amplitude: 3
Period: 2

70. Amplitude: 4
Period: 1

In Problems 71–84, find an equation for each graph.

71.

72.

73.

74.

75.

76.

77.

78.

79.

80.

81.

82.

83.

84.

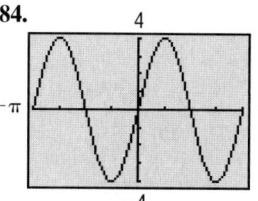

Mixed Practice

In Problems 85–88, find the average rate of change of f from 0 to $\dfrac{\pi}{2}$.

85. $f(x) = \sin x$

86. $f(x) = \cos x$

87. $f(x) = \sin\left(\dfrac{x}{2}\right)$

88. $f(x) = \cos(2x)$

In Problems 89–92, find $(f \circ g)(x)$ and $(g \circ f)(x)$ and graph each of these functions.

89. $f(x) = \sin x$
$g(x) = 4x$

90. $f(x) = \cos x$
$g(x) = \dfrac{1}{2} x$

91. $f(x) = -2x$
$g(x) = \cos x$

92. $f(x) = -3x$
$g(x) = \sin x$

Applications and Extensions

93. Alternating Current (ac) Circuits The current I, in amperes, flowing through an ac (alternating current) circuit at time t in seconds, is

$$I(t) = 220 \sin(60\pi t) \qquad t \geq 0$$

What is the period? What is the amplitude? Graph this function over two periods.

94. Alternating Current (ac) Circuits The current I, in amperes, flowing through an ac (alternating current) circuit at time t in seconds, is

$$I(t) = 120 \sin(30\pi t) \qquad t \geq 0$$

What is the period? What is the amplitude? Graph this function over two periods.

95. Alternating Current (ac) Generators The voltage V, in volts, produced by an ac generator at time t, in seconds, is

$$V(t) = 220 \sin(120\pi t)$$

(a) What is the amplitude? What is the period?
(b) Graph V over two periods, beginning at $t = 0$.
(c) If a resistance of $R = 10$ ohms is present, what is the current I?
[**Hint:** Use Ohm's Law, $V = IR$.]
(d) What is the amplitude and period of the current I?
(e) Graph I over two periods, beginning at $t = 0$.

96. Alternating Current (ac) Generators The voltage V, in volts, produced by an ac generator at time t, in seconds, is

$$V(t) = 120 \sin(120\pi t)$$

(a) What is the amplitude? What is the period?
(b) Graph V over two periods, beginning at $t = 0$.
(c) If a resistance of $R = 20$ ohms is present, what is the current I?
[**Hint:** Use Ohm's Law, $V = IR$.]
(d) What is the amplitude and period of the current I?
(e) Graph I over two periods, beginning at $t = 0$.

97. Alternating Current (ac) Generators The voltage V produced by an ac generator is sinusoidal. As a function of time, the voltage V is

$$V(t) = V_0 \sin(2\pi f t)$$

where f is the **frequency**, the number of complete oscillations (cycles) per second. [In the United States and Canada, f is 60 hertz (Hz).] The **power** P delivered to a resistance R at any time t is defined as

$$P(t) = \dfrac{[V(t)]^2}{R}$$

(a) Show that $P(t) = \dfrac{V_0^2}{R} \sin^2(2\pi f t)$.

(b) The graph of P is shown in the figure. Express P as a sinusoidal function.

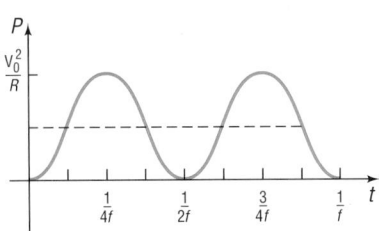

Power in an ac generator

(c) Deduce that

$$\sin^2(2\pi ft) = \frac{1}{2}[1 - \cos(4\pi ft)]$$

98. Bridge Clearance A one-lane highway runs through a tunnel in the shape of one-half a sine curve cycle. The opening is 28 feet wide at road level and is 15 feet tall at its highest point.

15 ft

14 ft

28 ft

(a) Find an equation for the sine curve that fits the opening. Place the origin at the left end of the sine curve.
(b) If the road is 14 feet wide with 7-foot shoulders on each side, what is the height of the tunnel at the edge of the road?

Source: en.wikipedia.org/wiki/Interstate_Highway_standards and Ohio Revised Code

99. Biorhythms In the theory of biorhythms, a sine function of the form

$$P(t) = 50\sin(\omega t) + 50$$

is used to measure the percent P of a person's potential at time t, where t is measured in days and $t = 0$ is the person's birthday. Three characteristics are commonly measured:

Physical potential: period of 23 days

Emotional potential: period of 28 days

Intellectual potential: period of 33 days

(a) Find ω for each characteristic.
(b) Using a graphing utility, graph all three functions on the same screen.
(c) Is there a time t when all three characteristics have 100% potential? When is it?
(d) Suppose that you are 20 years old today ($t = 7305$ days). Describe your physical, emotional, and intellectual potential for the next 30 days.

100. Graph $y = |\cos x|$, $-2\pi \le x \le 2\pi$.

101. Graph $y = |\sin x|$, $-2\pi \le x \le 2\pi$.

Discussion and Writing

102. Explain how you would scale the x-axis and y-axis before graphing $y = 3\cos(\pi x)$.

103. Explain the term *amplitude* as it relates to the graph of a sinusoidal function.

104. Explain how the amplitude and period of a sinusoidal graph are used to establish the scale on each coordinate axis.

105. Find an application in your major field that leads to a sinusoidal graph. Write a paper about your findings.

'Are You Prepared?' Answers

1. Vertical stretch by a factor of 3

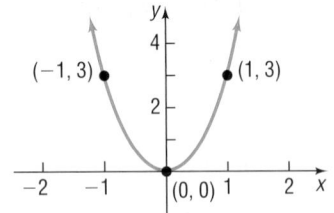

2. Horizontal compression by a factor of $\frac{1}{2}$

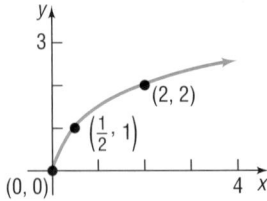

6.5 Graphs of the Tangent, Cotangent, Cosecant, and Secant Functions

PREPARING FOR THIS SECTION *Before getting started, review the following:*

- Vertical Asymptotes (Section 4.2, pp. 194–196)

Now Work the 'Are You Prepared?' problems on page 417.

OBJECTIVES 1 Graph Functions of the Form $y = A\tan(\omega x) + B$ and $y = A\cot(\omega x) + B$ (p. 413)

2 Graph Functions of the Form $y = A\csc(\omega x) + B$ and $y = A\sec(\omega x) + B$ (p. 415)

The Graph of the Tangent Function

Because the tangent function has period π, we only need to determine the graph over some interval of length π. The rest of the graph will consist of repetitions of that graph. Because the tangent function is not defined at $\ldots, -\dfrac{3\pi}{2}, -\dfrac{\pi}{2}, \dfrac{\pi}{2}, \dfrac{3\pi}{2}, \ldots$, we will concentrate on the interval $\left(-\dfrac{\pi}{2}, \dfrac{\pi}{2}\right)$, of length π, and construct Table 8, which lists some points on the graph of $y = \tan x$, $-\dfrac{\pi}{2} < x < \dfrac{\pi}{2}$. We plot the points in the table and connect them with a smooth curve. See Figure 66 for a partial graph of $y = \tan x$, where $-\dfrac{\pi}{3} \le x \le \dfrac{\pi}{3}$.

Table 8

x	$y = \tan x$	(x, y)
$-\dfrac{\pi}{3}$	$-\sqrt{3} \approx -1.73$	$\left(-\dfrac{\pi}{3}, -\sqrt{3}\right)$
$-\dfrac{\pi}{4}$	-1	$\left(-\dfrac{\pi}{4}, -1\right)$
$-\dfrac{\pi}{6}$	$-\dfrac{\sqrt{3}}{3} \approx -0.58$	$\left(-\dfrac{\pi}{6}, -\dfrac{\sqrt{3}}{3}\right)$
0	0	$(0, 0)$
$\dfrac{\pi}{6}$	$\dfrac{\sqrt{3}}{3} \approx 0.58$	$\left(\dfrac{\pi}{6}, \dfrac{\sqrt{3}}{3}\right)$
$\dfrac{\pi}{4}$	1	$\left(\dfrac{\pi}{4}, 1\right)$
$\dfrac{\pi}{3}$	$\sqrt{3} \approx 1.73$	$\left(\dfrac{\pi}{3}, \sqrt{3}\right)$

Figure 66

$y = \tan x$, $-\dfrac{\pi}{3} \le x \le \dfrac{\pi}{3}$

To complete one period of the graph of $y = \tan x$, we need to investigate the behavior of the function as x approaches $-\dfrac{\pi}{2}$ and $\dfrac{\pi}{2}$. We must be careful, though, because $y = \tan x$ is not defined at these numbers. To determine this behavior, we use the identity

$$\tan x = \frac{\sin x}{\cos x}$$

See Table 9. If x is close to $\dfrac{\pi}{2} \approx 1.5708$, but remains less than $\dfrac{\pi}{2}$, then $\sin x$ will be close to 1 and $\cos x$ will be positive and close to 0. (To see this, refer back to the graphs of the sine function and the cosine function.) So the ratio $\dfrac{\sin x}{\cos x}$ will be positive and large. In fact, the closer x gets to $\dfrac{\pi}{2}$, the closer $\sin x$ gets to 1 and $\cos x$ gets to 0, so $\tan x$ approaches $\infty \left(\lim\limits_{x \to \frac{\pi}{2}^-} \tan x = \infty \right)$. In other words, the vertical line $x = \dfrac{\pi}{2}$ is a vertical asymptote to the graph of $y = \tan x$.

Table 9

x	sin x	cos x	y = tan x
$\dfrac{\pi}{3} \approx 1.05$	$\dfrac{\sqrt{3}}{2}$	$\dfrac{1}{2}$	$\sqrt{3} \approx 1.73$
1.5	0.9975	0.0707	14.1
1.57	0.9999	7.96E−4	1255.8
1.5707	0.9999	9.6E−5	10,381
$\dfrac{\pi}{2} \approx 1.5708$	1	0	Undefined

If x is close to $-\dfrac{\pi}{2}$, but remains greater than $-\dfrac{\pi}{2}$, then $\sin x$ will be close to -1 and $\cos x$ will be positive and close to 0. The ratio $\dfrac{\sin x}{\cos x}$ approaches $-\infty \left(\lim\limits_{x \to -\frac{\pi}{2}^+} \tan x = -\infty \right)$. In other words, the vertical line $x = -\dfrac{\pi}{2}$ is also a vertical asymptote to the graph.

With these observations, we can complete one period of the graph. We obtain the complete graph of $y = \tan x$ by repeating this period, as shown in Figure 67.

Figure 68 shows the graph of $y = \tan x$, $-\infty < x < \infty$, using a graphing utility. Notice we used dot mode when graphing $y = \tan x$. Do you know why?

Figure 67
$y = \tan x$, $-\infty < x < \infty$, x not equal to odd multiples of $\dfrac{\pi}{2}$

Figure 68

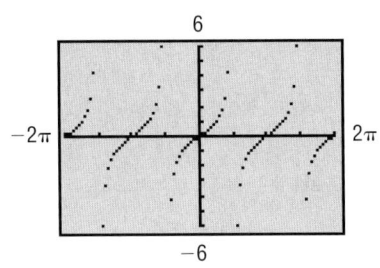

The graph of $y = \tan x$ in Figure 67 illustrates the following properties.

Properties of the Tangent Function

1. The domain is the set of all real numbers, except odd multiples of $\dfrac{\pi}{2}$.
2. The range is the set of all real numbers.
3. The tangent function is an odd function, as the symmetry of the graph with respect to the origin indicates.

4. The tangent function is periodic, with period π.

5. The x-intercepts are $\ldots, -2\pi, -\pi, 0, \pi, 2\pi, 3\pi, \ldots$; the y-intercept is 0.

6. Vertical asymptotes occur at $x = \ldots, -\dfrac{3\pi}{2}, -\dfrac{\pi}{2}, \dfrac{\pi}{2}, \dfrac{3\pi}{2}, \ldots$.

 Now Work PROBLEMS 7 AND 15

1 Graph Functions of the Form $y = A \tan(\omega x) + B$

For tangent functions, there is no concept of amplitude since the range of the tangent function is $(-\infty, \infty)$. The role of A in $y = A \tan(\omega x) + B$ is to provide the magnitude of the vertical stretch. The period of $y = \tan x$ is π, so the period of $y = A \tan(\omega x) + B$ is $\dfrac{\pi}{\omega}$, caused by the horizontal compression of the graph by a factor of $\dfrac{1}{\omega}$. Finally, the presence of B indicates that a vertical shift is required.

EXAMPLE 1	**Graphing Functions of the Form $y = A \tan(\omega x) + B$**

Graph $y = 2 \tan x - 1$. Use the graph to determine the domain and the range of $y = 2 \tan x - 1$.

Solution   Figure 69 shows the steps using transformations.

Figure 69

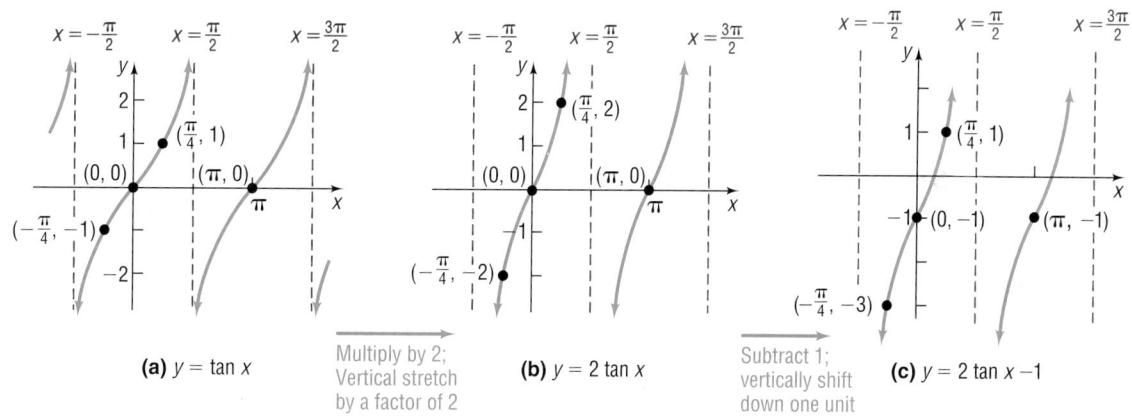

(a) $y = \tan x$
Multiply by 2; Vertical stretch by a factor of 2
(b) $y = 2 \tan x$
Subtract 1; vertically shift down one unit
(c) $y = 2 \tan x - 1$

The domain of $y = 2 \tan x - 1$ is $\left\{x \mid x \neq \dfrac{k\pi}{2}, k \text{ is an odd integer}\right\}$ and the range is the set of all real numbers or $(-\infty, \infty)$.

✓**Check:** Graph $Y_1 = 2 \tan x - 1$ to verify the graph shown in Figure 69(c).

EXAMPLE 2	**Graphing Functions of the Form $y = A \tan(\omega x) + B$**

Graph $y = 3 \tan(2x)$. Use the graph to determine the domain and the range of $y = 3 \tan(2x)$.

Solution   Figure 70 shows the steps using transformations.

Figure 70

(a) $y = \tan x$ Multiply by 3; Vertical stretch by a factor of 3   **(b)** $y = 3 \tan x$ Replace x by $2x$; Horizontal compression by a factor of $\frac{1}{2}$ **(c)** $y = 3 \tan (2x)$

The domain of $y = 3 \tan(2x)$ is $\{x \,|\, x \neq \dfrac{k\pi}{4}, k \text{ is an odd integer}\}$ and the range is the set of all real numbers or $(-\infty, \infty)$.

✓**Check:** Graph $Y_1 = 3 \tan(2x)$ to verify the graph in Figure 70(c).

Notice in Figure 70(c) that the period of $y = 3 \tan(2x)$ is $\dfrac{\pi}{2}$ due to the compression of the original period π by a factor of $\dfrac{1}{2}$. Notice that the asymptotes are $x = -\dfrac{\pi}{4}$, $x = \dfrac{\pi}{4}$, $x = \dfrac{3\pi}{4}$, and so on, also due to the compression.

Table 10

x	$y = \cot x$	(x, y)
$\dfrac{\pi}{6}$	$\sqrt{3}$	$\left(\dfrac{\pi}{6}, \sqrt{3}\right)$
$\dfrac{\pi}{4}$	1	$\left(\dfrac{\pi}{4}, 1\right)$
$\dfrac{\pi}{3}$	$\dfrac{\sqrt{3}}{3}$	$\left(\dfrac{\pi}{3}, \dfrac{\sqrt{3}}{3}\right)$
$\dfrac{\pi}{2}$	0	$\left(\dfrac{\pi}{2}, 0\right)$
$\dfrac{2\pi}{3}$	$-\dfrac{\sqrt{3}}{3}$	$\left(\dfrac{2\pi}{3}, -\dfrac{\sqrt{3}}{3}\right)$
$\dfrac{3\pi}{4}$	-1	$\left(\dfrac{3\pi}{4}, -1\right)$
$\dfrac{5\pi}{6}$	$-\sqrt{3}$	$\left(\dfrac{5\pi}{6}, -\sqrt{3}\right)$

━━ **Now Work** PROBLEM 21

The Graph of the Cotangent Function

We obtain the graph of $y = \cot x$ as we did the graph of $y = \tan x$. The period of $y = \cot x$ is π. Because the cotangent function is not defined for integer multiples of π, we will concentrate on the interval $(0, \pi)$. Table 10 lists some points on the graph of $y = \cot x$, $0 < x < \pi$. As x approaches 0, but remains greater than 0, the value of $\cos x$ will be close to 1 and the value of $\sin x$ will be positive and close to 0. Hence, the ratio $\dfrac{\cos x}{\sin x} = \cot x$ will be positive and large; so as x approaches 0, with $x > 0$, $\cot x$ approaches ∞ ($\lim\limits_{x \to 0^+} \cot x = \infty$). Similarly, as x approaches π, but remains less than π, the value of $\cos x$ will be close to -1, and the value of $\sin x$ will be positive and close to 0. So the ratio $\dfrac{\cos x}{\sin x} = \cot x$ will be negative and will approach $-\infty$ as x approaches π ($\lim\limits_{x \to \pi^-} \cot x = -\infty$). Figure 71 shows the graph.

Figure 71
$y = \cot x$, $-\infty < x < \infty$, x not equal to integer multiples of π, $-\infty < y < \infty$

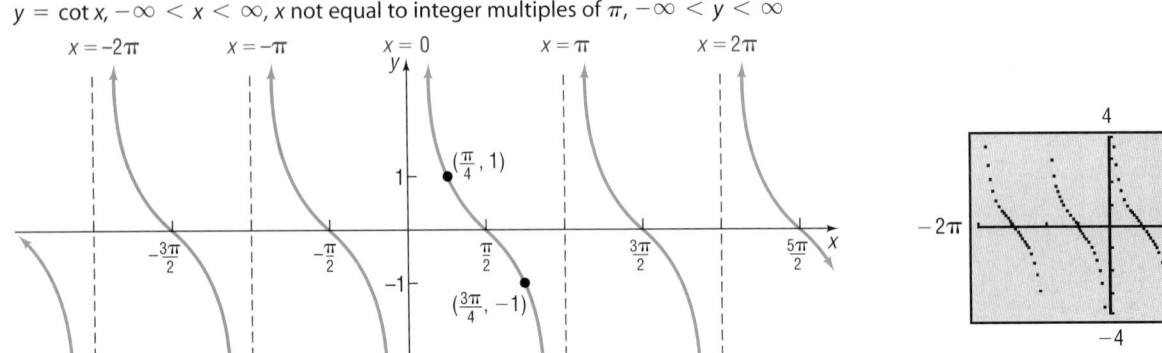

The graph of $y = A\cot(\omega x) + B$ has similar characteristics to those of the tangent function. The cotangent function $y = A\cot(\omega x) + B$ has period $\dfrac{\pi}{\omega}$. The cotangent function has no amplitude. The role of A is to provide the magnitude of the vertical stretch; the presence of B indicates a vertical shift is required.

Now Work PROBLEM 23

The Graph of the Cosecant Function and the Secant Function

The cosecant and secant functions, sometimes referred to as **reciprocal functions,** are graphed by making use of the reciprocal identities

$$\csc x = \frac{1}{\sin x} \quad \text{and} \quad \sec x = \frac{1}{\cos x}$$

For example, the value of the cosecant function $y = \csc x$ at a given number x equals the reciprocal of the corresponding value of the sine function, provided that the value of the sine function is not 0. If the value of $\sin x$ is 0, then x is an integer multiple of π. At such numbers, the cosecant function is not defined. In fact, the graph of the cosecant function has vertical asymptotes at integer multiples of π. Figure 72 shows the graph.

Figure 72

$y = \csc x$, $-\infty < x < \infty$, x not equal to integer multiples of π, $|y| \geq 1$

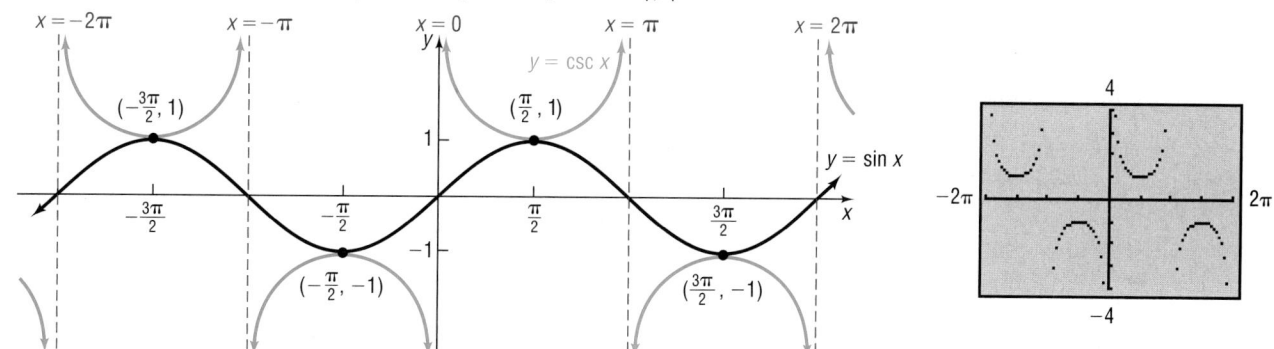

Using the idea of reciprocals, we can similarly obtain the graph of $y = \sec x$. See Figure 73.

Figure 73

$y = \sec x$, $-\infty < x < \infty$, x not equal to odd multiples of $\dfrac{\pi}{2}$, $|y| \geq 1$

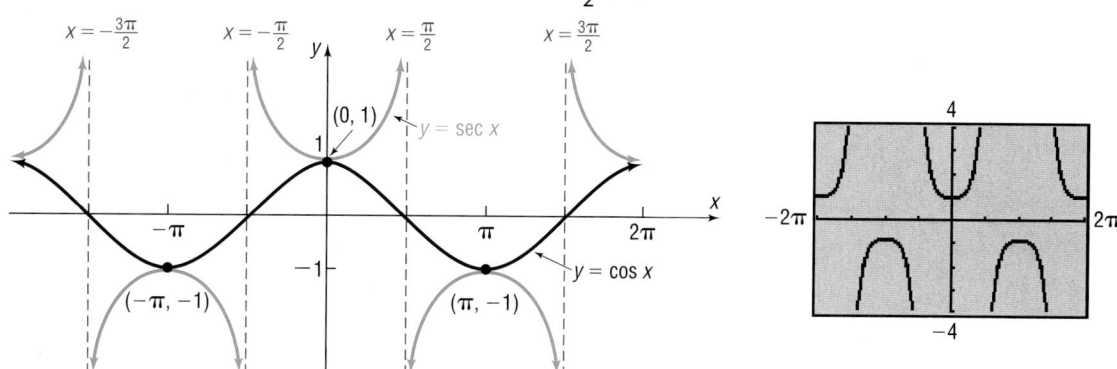

2 Graph Functions of the Form $y = A\csc(\omega x) + B$

The role of A in these functions is to set the range. The range of $y = \csc x$ is $\{y \mid y \leq -1 \text{ or } y \geq 1\}$ or $\{y \mid |y| \geq 1\}$; the range of $y = A\csc x$ is $\{y \mid |y| \geq |A|\}$, due to the vertical stretch of the graph by a factor of $|A|$. Just as with the sine and cosine functions, the period of $y = \csc(\omega x)$ and $y = \sec(\omega x)$ becomes $\dfrac{2\pi}{\omega}$, due to the horizontal compression of the graph by a factor of $\dfrac{1}{\omega}$. The presence of B indicates a vertical shift is required.

We shall graph these functions in two ways: using transformations and using the reciprocal function.

| EXAMPLE 3 | Graphing Functions of the Form $y = A \csc(\omega x) + B$ |

Graph $y = 2 \csc x - 1$. Use the graph to determine the domain and the range of $y = 2 \csc x - 1$.

Solution
Using Transformations

Figure 74 shows the required steps.

Figure 74

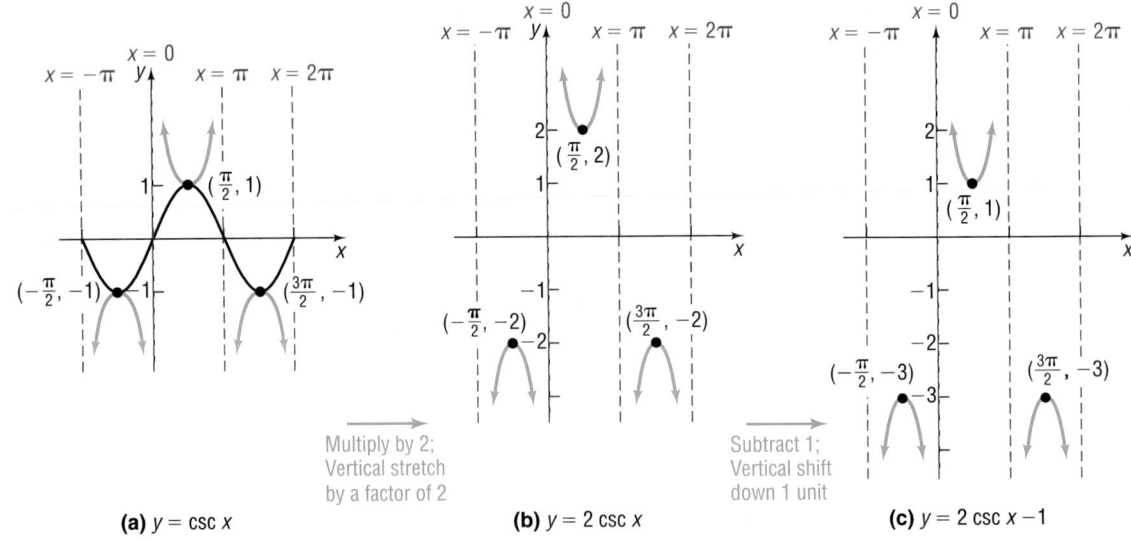

(a) $y = \csc x$ (b) $y = 2 \csc x$ (c) $y = 2 \csc x - 1$

Solution
Using the Reciprocal Function

We graph $y = 2 \csc x - 1$ by first graphing the reciprocal function $y = 2 \sin x - 1$ and then filling in the graph of $y = 2 \csc x - 1$, using the idea of reciprocals. See Figure 75.

Figure 75

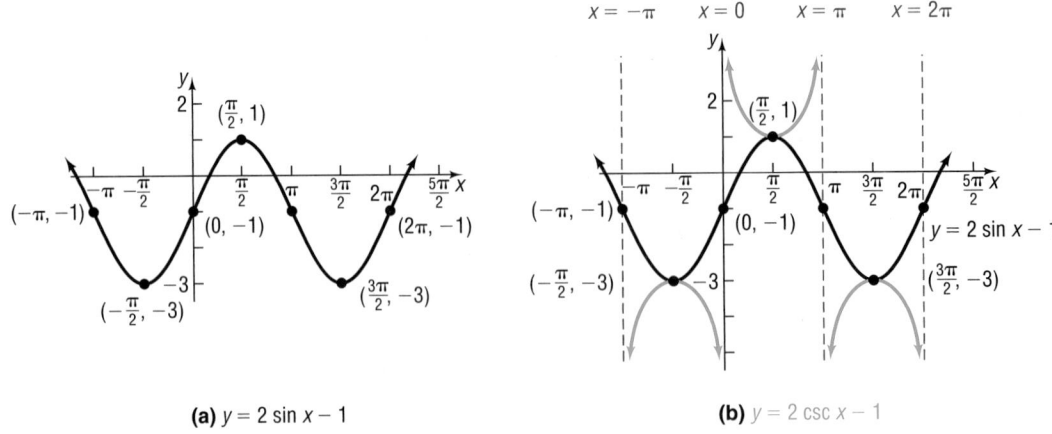

(a) $y = 2 \sin x - 1$ (b) $y = 2 \csc x - 1$

The domain of $y = 2 \csc x - 1$ is $\{x \mid x \neq k\pi, k \text{ is an integer}\}$ and the range is $\{y \mid y \leq -3 \text{ or } y \geq 1\}$, or, using interval notation $(-\infty, -3] \cup [1, \infty)$.

√ Check: Graph $Y_1 = 2 \csc x - 1$ to verify the graph shown in Figure 74 (c) or 75 (b).

━━━━━ **Now Work** PROBLEM 29

6.5 Assess Your Understanding

'Are You Prepared?' *Answers are given at the end of these exercises. If you get a wrong answer, read the pages listed in* red.

1. The graph of $y = \dfrac{3x - 6}{x - 4}$ has a vertical asymptote. What is it?
(pp. 195–196)

2. *True or False* If $x = 3$ is a vertical asymptote of a function R, then $\lim\limits_{x \to 3} |R(x)| = \infty$. (pp. 194–196)

Concepts and Vocabulary

3. The graph of $y = \tan x$ is symmetric with respect to the _____ and has vertical asymptotes at _____.

4. The graph of $y = \sec x$ is symmetric with respect to the _____ and has vertical asymptotes at _____.

5. It is easiest to graph $y = \sec x$ by first sketching the graph of _____.

6. *True or False* The graphs of $y = \tan x$, $y = \cot x$, $y = \sec x$, and $y = \csc x$ each have infinitely many vertical asymptotes.

Skill Building

In Problems 7–16, if necessary, refer to the graphs to answer each question.

7. What is the y-intercept of $y = \tan x$?

8. What is the y-intercept of $y = \cot x$?

9. What is the y-intercept of $y = \sec x$?

10. What is the y-intercept of $y = \csc x$?

11. For what numbers x, $-2\pi \le x \le 2\pi$, does $\sec x = 1$? For what numbers x does $\sec x = -1$?

12. For what numbers x, $-2\pi \le x \le 2\pi$, does $\csc x = 1$? For what numbers x does $\csc x = -1$?

13. For what numbers x, $-2\pi \le x \le 2\pi$, does the graph of $y = \sec x$ have vertical asymptotes?

14. For what numbers x, $-2\pi \le x \le 2\pi$, does the graph of $y = \csc x$ have vertical asymptotes?

15. For what numbers x, $-2\pi \le x \le 2\pi$, does the graph of $y = \tan x$ have vertical asymptotes?

16. For what numbers x, $-2\pi \le x \le 2\pi$, does the graph of $y = \cot x$ have vertical asymptotes?

In Problems 17–40, graph each function. Be sure to label key points and show at least two cycles. Verify the graph using a graphing utility. Use the graph to determine the domain and the range of each function.

17. $y = 3 \tan x$

18. $y = -2 \tan x$

19. $y = 4 \cot x$

20. $y = -3 \cot x$

21. $y = \tan\left(\dfrac{\pi}{2}x\right)$

22. $y = \tan\left(\dfrac{1}{2}x\right)$

23. $y = \cot\left(\dfrac{1}{4}x\right)$

24. $y = \cot\left(\dfrac{\pi}{4}x\right)$

25. $y = 2 \sec x$

26. $y = \dfrac{1}{2} \csc x$

27. $y = -3 \csc x$

28. $y = -4 \sec x$

29. $y = 4 \sec\left(\dfrac{1}{2}x\right)$

30. $y = \dfrac{1}{2} \csc(2x)$

31. $y = -2 \csc(\pi x)$

32. $y = -3 \sec\left(\dfrac{\pi}{2}x\right)$

33. $y = \tan\left(\dfrac{1}{4}x\right) + 1$

34. $y = 2 \cot x - 1$

35. $y = \sec\left(\dfrac{2\pi}{3}x\right) + 2$

36. $y = \csc\left(\dfrac{3\pi}{2}x\right)$

37. $y = \dfrac{1}{2} \tan\left(\dfrac{1}{4}x\right) - 2$

38. $y = 3 \cot\left(\dfrac{1}{2}x\right) - 2$

39. $y = 2 \csc\left(\dfrac{1}{3}x\right) - 1$

40. $y = 3 \sec\left(\dfrac{1}{4}x\right) + 1$

Mixed Practice

In Problems 41–44, find the average rate of change of f from 0 to $\dfrac{\pi}{6}$.

41. $f(x) = \tan x$

42. $f(x) = \sec x$

43. $f(x) = \tan(2x)$

44. $f(x) = \sec(2x)$

In Problems 45–48, find $(f \circ g)(x)$ and $(g \circ f)(x)$ and graph each of these functions.

45. $f(x) = \tan x$
$\quad g(x) = 4x$

46. $f(x) = 2 \sec x$
$\quad g(x) = \dfrac{1}{2}x$

47. $f(x) = -2x$
$\quad g(x) = \cot x$

48. $f(x) = \dfrac{1}{2}x$
$\quad g(x) = 2 \csc x$

Applications and Extensions

49. Carrying a Ladder around a Corner Two hallways, one of width 3 feet, the other of width 4 feet, meet at a right angle. See the illustration.

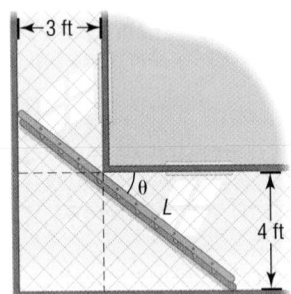

(a) Show that the length L of the line segment shown as a function of the angle θ is

$$L(\theta) = 3 \sec \theta + 4 \csc \theta$$

(b) Graph $L = L(\theta), 0 < \theta < \dfrac{\pi}{2}$.

(c) For what value of θ is L the least?

(d) What is the length of the longest ladder that can be carried around the corner? Why is this also the least value of L?

50. A Rotating Beacon Suppose that a fire truck is parked in front of a building as shown in the figure.

The beacon light on top of the fire truck is located 10 feet from the wall and has a light on each side. If the beacon light rotates 1 revolution every 2 seconds, then a model for determining the distance d, in feet, that the beacon of light is from point A on the wall after t seconds is given by

$$d(t) = |10 \tan(\pi t)|$$

(a) Graph $d(t) = |10 \tan(\pi t)|$ for $0 \le t \le 2$.

(b) For what values of t is the function undefined? Explain what this means in terms of the beam of light on the wall.

(c) Fill in the following table.

t	0	0.1	0.2	0.3	0.4
$d(t) = 10 \tan(\pi t)$					

(d) Compute $\dfrac{d(0.1) - d(0)}{0.1 - 0}, \dfrac{d(0.2) - d(0.1)}{0.2 - 0.1}$, and so on, for each consecutive value of t. These are called **first differences.**

(e) Interpret the first differences found in part (d). What is happening to the speed of the beam of light as d increases?

51. Exploration Graph

$$y = \tan x \quad \text{and} \quad y = -\cot\left(x + \frac{\pi}{2}\right)$$

Do you think that $\tan x = -\cot\left(x + \dfrac{\pi}{2}\right)$?

'Are You Prepared?' Answers

1. $x = 4$ **2.** True

6.6 Phase Shift; Sinusoidal Curve Fitting

OBJECTIVES   **1** Graph Sinusoidal Functions of the Form $y = A \sin(\omega x - \phi) + B$ (p. 419)

2 Build Sinusoidal Models from Data (p. 423)

1 Graph Sinusoidal Functions of the Form $y = A \sin(\omega x - \phi) + B$

Figure 76
One cycle of
$y = A \sin(\omega x), A > 0, \omega > 0$

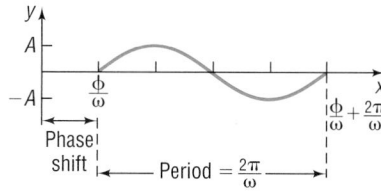

We have seen that the graph of $y = A \sin(\omega x)$, $\omega > 0$, has amplitude $|A|$ and period $T = \dfrac{2\pi}{\omega}$. One cycle can be drawn as x varies from 0 to $\dfrac{2\pi}{\omega}$ or, equivalently, as ωx varies from 0 to 2π. See Figure 76.

We now want to discuss the graph of

$$y = A \sin(\omega x - \phi)$$

which may also be written as

$$y = A \sin\left[\omega\left(x - \frac{\phi}{\omega}\right)\right]$$

where $\omega > 0$ and ϕ (the Greek letter phi) are real numbers. The graph will be a sine curve with amplitude $|A|$. As $\omega x - \phi$ varies from 0 to 2π, one period will be traced out. This period will begin when

$$\omega x - \phi = 0 \quad \text{or} \quad x = \frac{\phi}{\omega}$$

and will end when

$$\omega x - \phi = 2\pi \quad \text{or} \quad x = \frac{\phi}{\omega} + \frac{2\pi}{\omega}$$

See Figure 77.

NOTE We can also find the beginning and end of the period by solving the inequality:

$$0 \le \omega x - \phi \le 2\pi$$
$$\phi \le \omega x \le 2\pi + \phi$$
$$\frac{\phi}{\omega} \le x \le \frac{2\pi}{\omega} + \frac{\phi}{\omega} \quad ■$$

Figure 77
One cycle of
$y = A \sin(\omega x - \phi), A > 0, \omega > 0, \phi > 0$

We see that the graph of $y = A \sin(\omega x - \phi) = A \sin\left[\omega\left(x - \dfrac{\phi}{\omega}\right)\right]$ is the same as the graph of $y = A \sin(\omega x)$, except that it has been shifted $\dfrac{\phi}{\omega}$ units (to the right if $\phi > 0$ and to the left if $\phi < 0$). This number $\dfrac{\phi}{\omega}$ is called the **phase shift** of the graph of $y = A \sin(\omega x - \phi)$.

For the graphs of $y = A \sin(\omega x - \phi)$ or $y = A \cos(\omega x - \phi)$, $\omega > 0$,

$$\text{Amplitude} = |A| \qquad \text{Period} = T = \frac{2\pi}{\omega} \qquad \text{Phase shift} = \frac{\phi}{\omega}$$

The phase shift is to the left if $\phi < 0$ and to the right if $\phi > 0$.

EXAMPLE 1

Finding the Amplitude, Period, and Phase Shift of a Sinusoidal Function and Graphing It

Find the amplitude, period, and phase shift of $y = 3 \sin(2x - \pi)$ and graph the function.

Solution

We will use the four steps used to graph sinusoidal functions of the form $y = A \sin(\omega x)$ or $y = A \cos(\omega x)$ given on page 403.

STEP 1: Comparing $\quad y = 3 \sin(2x - \pi) = 3 \sin\left[2\left(x - \dfrac{\pi}{2}\right)\right]$

to

$$y = A \sin(\omega x - \phi) = A \sin\left[\omega\left(x - \dfrac{\phi}{\omega}\right)\right]$$

we find that $A = 3$, $\omega = 2$, and $\phi = \pi$. The graph is a sine curve with amplitude $|A| = 3$, period $T = \dfrac{2\pi}{\omega} = \dfrac{2\pi}{2} = \pi$, and phase shift $= \dfrac{\phi}{\omega} = \dfrac{\pi}{2}$.

NOTE We also can find the interval defining one cycle by solving the inequality

$$0 \le 2x - \pi \le 2\pi$$

Then

$$\pi \le 2x \le 3\pi$$

$$\dfrac{\pi}{2} \le x \le \dfrac{3\pi}{2}$$ ∎

STEP 2: The graph of $y = 3 \sin(2x - \pi)$ will lie between -3 and 3 on the y-axis. One cycle will begin at $x = \dfrac{\phi}{\omega} = \dfrac{\pi}{2}$ and end at $x = \dfrac{\phi}{\omega} + \dfrac{2\pi}{\omega} = \dfrac{\pi}{2} + \pi = \dfrac{3\pi}{2}$.

To find the five key points, we divide the interval $\left[\dfrac{\pi}{2}, \dfrac{3\pi}{2}\right]$ into four subintervals, each of length $\pi \div 4 = \dfrac{\pi}{4}$, by finding the following values of x:

$$\underset{\text{1st x-coordinate}}{\dfrac{\pi}{2}} \qquad \underset{\text{2nd x-coordinate}}{\dfrac{\pi}{2} + \dfrac{\pi}{4} = \dfrac{3\pi}{4}} \qquad \underset{\text{3rd x-coordinate}}{\dfrac{3\pi}{4} + \dfrac{\pi}{4} = \pi} \qquad \underset{\text{4th x-coordinate}}{\pi + \dfrac{\pi}{4} = \dfrac{5\pi}{4}} \qquad \underset{\text{5th x-coordinate}}{\dfrac{5\pi}{4} + \dfrac{\pi}{4} = \dfrac{3\pi}{2}}$$

STEP 3: Use these values of x to determine the five key points on the graph:

$$\left(\dfrac{\pi}{2}, 0\right) \quad \left(\dfrac{3\pi}{4}, 3\right) \quad (\pi, 0) \quad \left(\dfrac{5\pi}{4}, -3\right) \quad \left(\dfrac{3\pi}{2}, 0\right)$$

STEP 4: We plot these five points and fill in the graph of the sine function as shown in Figure 78(a). Extending the graph in each direction, we obtain Figure 78(b).

Figure 78

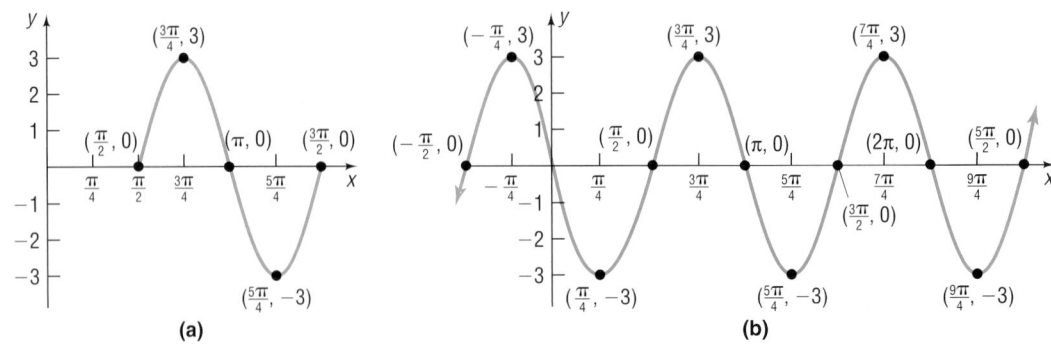

(a)

(b)

The graph of $y = 3 \sin(2x - \pi) = 3 \sin\left[2\left(x - \dfrac{\pi}{2}\right)\right]$ may also be obtained using transformations. See Figure 79.

Figure 79

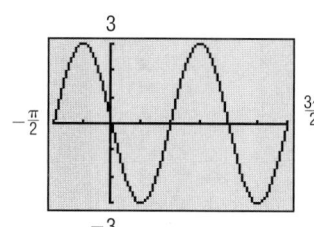

Multiply by 3;
Vertical stretch
by a factor of 3

Replace x by $2x$;
Horizontal compression
by a factor of $\frac{1}{2}$

Replace x by $x - \frac{\pi}{2}$;
Shift right
$\frac{\pi}{2}$ units

(a) $y = \sin x$ **(b)** $y = 3 \sin x$ **(c)** $y = 3 \sin(2x)$ **(d)** $y = 3 \sin\left[2\left(x - \frac{\pi}{2}\right)\right]$
$= 3 \sin(2x - \pi)$

Figure 80

✓ **Check:** Figure 80 shows the graph of $Y_1 = 3 \sin(2x - \pi)$ using a graphing utility.

To graph a sinusoidal function of the form $y = A \sin(\omega x - \phi) + B$, we first graph the function $y = A \sin(\omega x - \phi)$ and then apply a vertical shift.

EXAMPLE 2   **Finding the Amplitude, Period, and Phase Shift of a Sinusoidal Function and Graphing It**

Find the amplitude, period, and phase shift of $y = 2 \cos(4x + 3\pi) + 1$ and graph the function.

Solution   **STEP 1:** We begin by graphing $y = 2 \cos(4x + 3\pi)$. Comparing

$$y = 2 \cos(4x + 3\pi) = 2 \cos\left[4\left(x + \frac{3\pi}{4}\right)\right]$$

to

$$y = A \cos(\omega x - \phi) = A \cos\left[\omega\left(x - \frac{\phi}{\omega}\right)\right]$$

we see that $A = 2$, $\omega = 4$, and $\phi = -3\pi$. The graph is a cosine curve with amplitude $|A| = 2$, period $T = \dfrac{2\pi}{\omega} = \dfrac{2\pi}{4} = \dfrac{\pi}{2}$, and phase shift $= \dfrac{\phi}{\omega} = -\dfrac{3\pi}{4}$.

NOTE We can also find the interval defining one cycle by solving the inequality

$$0 \le 4x + 3\pi \le 2\pi$$

Then

$$-3\pi \le 4x \le -\pi$$

$$-\frac{3\pi}{4} \le x \le -\frac{\pi}{4}$$ ■

STEP 2: The graph of $y = 2 \cos(4x + 3\pi)$ will lie between -2 and 2 on the y-axis. One cycle will begin at $x = \dfrac{\phi}{\omega} = -\dfrac{3\pi}{4}$ and end at $x = \dfrac{\phi}{\omega} + \dfrac{2\pi}{\omega} = -\dfrac{3\pi}{4} + \dfrac{\pi}{2} = -\dfrac{\pi}{4}$. To find the five key points, we divide the interval $\left[-\dfrac{3\pi}{4}, -\dfrac{\pi}{4}\right]$ into four subintervals, each of the length $\dfrac{\pi}{2} \div 4 = \dfrac{\pi}{8}$, by finding the following values.

$$-\frac{3\pi}{4} \qquad -\frac{3\pi}{4} + \frac{\pi}{8} = -\frac{5\pi}{8} \qquad -\frac{5\pi}{8} + \frac{\pi}{8} = -\frac{\pi}{2} \qquad -\frac{\pi}{2} + \frac{\pi}{8} = -\frac{3\pi}{8} \qquad -\frac{3\pi}{8} + \frac{\pi}{8} = -\frac{\pi}{4}$$

1st x-coordinate   2nd x-coordinate   3rd x-coordinate   4th x-coordinate   5th x-coordinate

STEP 3: The five key points on the graph of $y = 2\cos(4x + 3\pi)$ are

$$\left(-\frac{3\pi}{4}, 2\right) \quad \left(-\frac{5\pi}{8}, 0\right) \quad \left(-\frac{\pi}{2}, -2\right) \quad \left(-\frac{3\pi}{8}, 0\right) \quad \left(-\frac{\pi}{4}, 2\right)$$

STEP 4: We plot these five points and fill in the graph of the cosine function as shown in Figure 81(a). Extending the graph in each direction, we obtain Figure 81(b), the graph of $y = 2\cos(4x + 3\pi)$.

STEP 5: A vertical shift up 1 unit gives the final graph. See Figure 81(c).

Figure 81

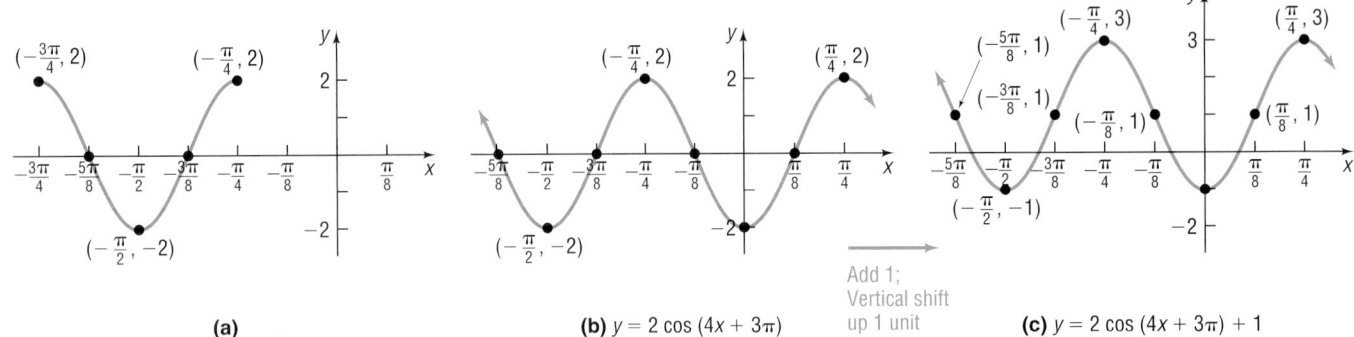

(a)

(b) $y = 2\cos(4x + 3\pi)$

Add 1;
Vertical shift
up 1 unit

(c) $y = 2\cos(4x + 3\pi) + 1$

The graph of $y = 2\cos(4x + 3\pi) + 1 = 2\cos\left[4\left(x + \frac{3\pi}{4}\right)\right] + 1$ may also be obtained using transformations. See Figure 82.

Figure 82

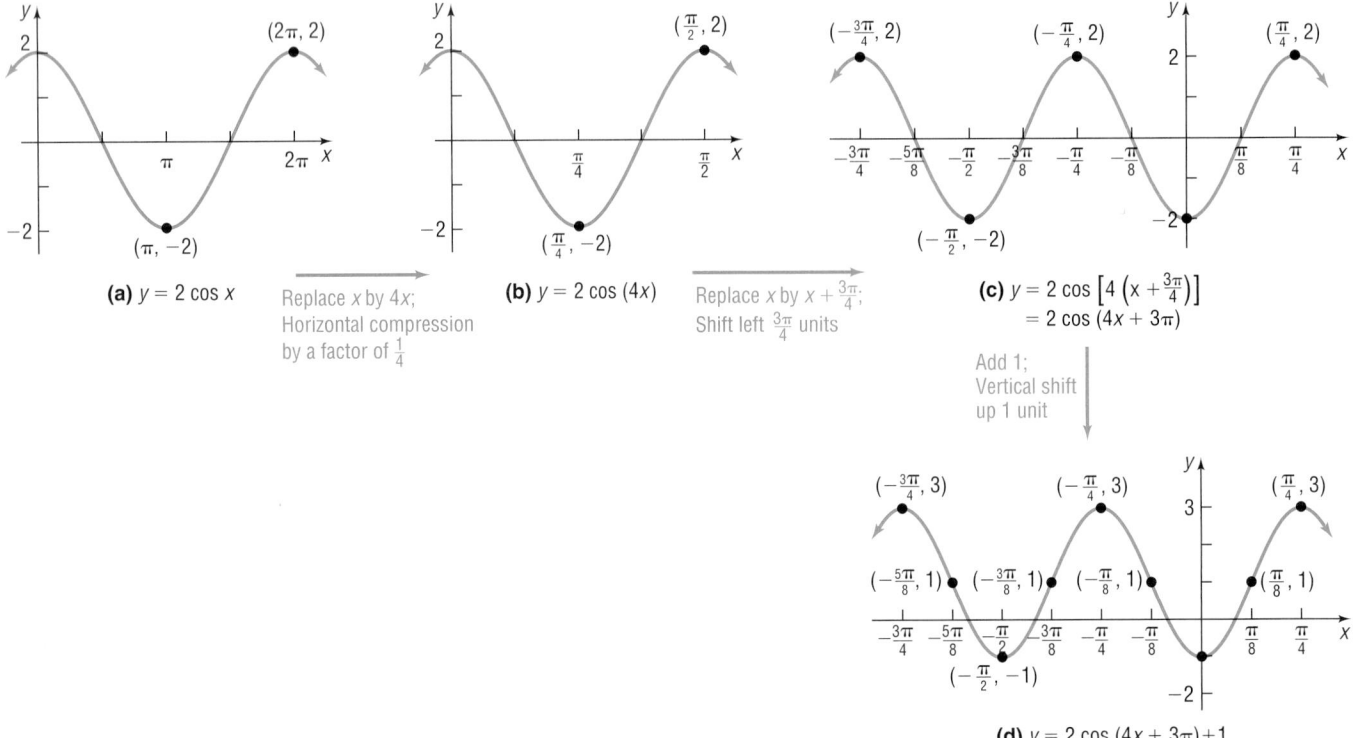

(a) $y = 2\cos x$

Replace x by $4x$;
Horizontal compression
by a factor of $\frac{1}{4}$

(b) $y = 2\cos(4x)$

Replace x by $x + \frac{3\pi}{4}$;
Shift left $\frac{3\pi}{4}$ units

(c) $y = 2\cos\left[4\left(x + \frac{3\pi}{4}\right)\right]$
$= 2\cos(4x + 3\pi)$

Add 1;
Vertical shift
up 1 unit

(d) $y = 2\cos(4x + 3\pi) + 1$

✓ **Check:** Graph $Y_1 = 2\cos(4x + 3\pi) + 1$ to verify the graph in Figure 81(c) or Figure 82(d).

Now Work PROBLEM 3

SUMMARY   Steps for Graphing Sinusoidal Functions $y = A\sin(\omega x - \phi) + B$
or $y = A\cos(\omega x - \phi) + B$

STEP 1: Determine the amplitude $|A|$ and period $T = \dfrac{2\pi}{\omega}$.

STEP 2: Determine the starting point of one cycle of the graph, $\dfrac{\phi}{\omega}$. Determine the ending point of one cycle of

the graph, $\dfrac{\phi}{\omega} + \dfrac{2\pi}{\omega}$. Divide the interval $\left[\dfrac{\phi}{\omega}, \dfrac{\phi}{\omega} + \dfrac{2\pi}{\omega}\right]$ into four subintervals, each of length $\dfrac{2\pi}{\omega} \div 4$.

STEP 3: Use the endpoints of the subintervals to find the five key points on the graph.

STEP 4: Plot the five key points with a sinusoidal graph to obtain one cycle of the graph. Extend the graph in each direction to make it complete.

STEP 5: If $B \neq 0$, apply a vertical shift.

2 Build Sinusoidal Models from Data

Scatter diagrams of data sometimes take the form of a sinusoidal function. Let's look at an example.

The data given in Table 11 represent the average monthly temperatures in Denver, Colorado. Since the data represent *average* monthly temperatures collected over many years, the data will not vary much from year to year and so will essentially repeat each year. In other words, the data are periodic. Figure 83 shows the scatter diagram of these data repeated over 2 years, where $x = 1$ represents January, $x = 2$ represents February, and so on.

Table 11

Month, x	Average Monthly Temperature, °F
January, 1	29.7
February, 2	33.4
March, 3	39.0
April, 4	48.2
May, 5	57.2
June, 6	66.9
July, 7	73.5
August, 8	71.4
September, 9	62.3
October, 10	51.4
November, 11	39.0
December, 12	31.0

Source: U.S. National Oceanic and Atmospheric Administration

Figure 83

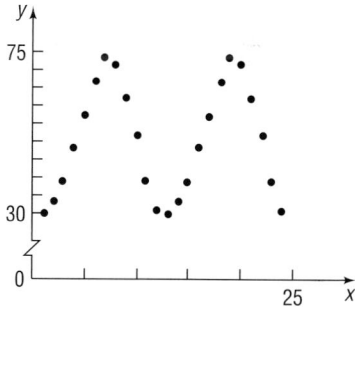

Notice that the scatter diagram looks like the graph of a sinusoidal function. We choose to fit the data to a sine function of the form

$$y = A\sin(\omega x - \phi) + B$$

where A, B, ω, and ϕ are constants.

| EXAMPLE 3 | Finding a Sinusoidal Function from Temperature Data |

Find a sine function that models the data in Table 11.

Solution   We begin with a scatter diagram of the data for 1 year. See Figure 84. The data will be fitted to a sine function of the form

$$y = A \sin(\omega x - \phi) + B$$

Figure 84

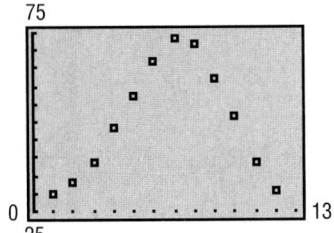

STEP 1: To find the amplitude A, we compute

$$\text{Amplitude} = \frac{\text{largest data value} - \text{smallest data value}}{2}$$

$$= \frac{73.5 - 29.7}{2} = 21.9$$

To see the remaining steps in this process, we superimpose the graph of the function $y = 21.9 \sin x$, where x represents months, on the scatter diagram. Figure 85 shows the two graphs. To fit the data, the graph needs to be shifted vertically, shifted horizontally, and stretched horizontally.

Figure 85

STEP 2: We determine the vertical shift by finding the average of the highest and lowest data values.

$$\text{Vertical shift} = \frac{73.5 + 29.7}{2} = 51.6$$

Now we superimpose the graph of $y = 21.9 \sin x + 51.6$ on the scatter diagram. See Figure 86.

We see that the graph needs to be shifted horizontally and stretched horizontally.

Figure 86

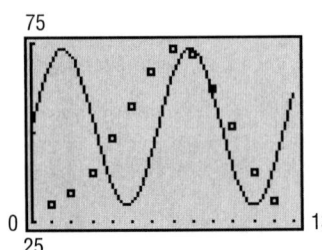

STEP 3: It is easier to find the horizontal stretch factor first. Since the temperatures repeat every 12 months, the period of the function is $T = 12$. Since $T = \frac{2\pi}{\omega} = 12$, we find

$$\omega = \frac{2\pi}{12} = \frac{\pi}{6}$$

Now we superimpose the graph of $y = 21.9 \sin\left(\frac{\pi}{6}x\right) + 51.6$ on the scatter diagram. See Figure 87. We see that the graph still needs to be shifted horizontally.

Figure 87

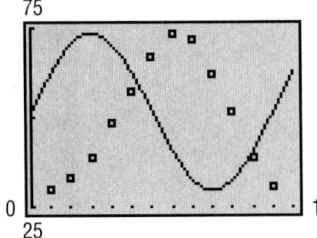

STEP 4: To determine the horizontal shift, we use the period $T = 12$ and divide the interval $[0, 12]$ into four subintervals of length $12 \div 4 = 3$:

$$[0, 3] \quad [3, 6] \quad [6, 9] \quad [9, 12]$$

The sine curve is increasing on the interval $(0, 3)$ and is decreasing on the interval $(3, 9)$, so a local maximum occurs at $x = 3$. The data indicate that a maximum occurs at $x = 7$ (corresponding to July's temperature), so we must shift the graph of the function 4 units to the right by replacing x by $x - 4$. Doing this, we obtain

$$y = 21.9 \sin\left(\frac{\pi}{6}(x - 4)\right) + 51.6$$

Multiplying out, we find that a sine function of the form $y = A \sin(\omega x - \phi) + B$ that fits the data is

$$y = 21.9 \sin\left(\frac{\pi}{6}x - \frac{2\pi}{3}\right) + 51.6$$

Figure 88

The graph of $y = 21.9 \sin\left(\dfrac{\pi}{6}x - \dfrac{2\pi}{3}\right) + 51.6$ and the scatter diagram of the data are shown in Figure 88.

The steps to fit a sine function

$$y = A \sin(\omega x - \phi) + B$$

to sinusoidal data follow:

Steps for Fitting a Sine Function $y = A \sin(\omega x - \phi) + B$ to Data

STEP 1: Determine A, the amplitude of the function.

$$\text{Amplitude} = \frac{\text{largest data value} - \text{smallest data value}}{2}$$

STEP 2: Determine B, the vertical shift of the function.

$$\text{Vertical shift} = \frac{\text{largest data value} + \text{smallest data value}}{2}$$

STEP 3: Determine ω. Since the period T, the time it takes for the data to repeat, is $T = \dfrac{2\pi}{\omega}$, we have

$$\omega = \frac{2\pi}{T}$$

STEP 4: Determine the horizontal shift of the function by using the period of the data. Divide the period into four subintervals of equal length. Determine the x-coordinate for the maximum of the sine function and the x-coordinate for the maximum value of the data. Use this information to determine the value of the phase shift, $\dfrac{\phi}{\omega}$.

Now Work   PROBLEM 29(a)–(c)

Let's look at another example. Since the number of hours of sunlight in a day cycles annually, the number of hours of sunlight in a day for a given location can be modeled by a sinusoidal function.

The longest day of the year (in terms of hours of sunlight) occurs on the day of the summer solstice. For locations in the northern hemisphere, the summer solstice is the time when the sun is farthest north. In 2007, the summer solstice occurred on June 21 (the 172nd day of the year) at 2:06 PM EDT. The shortest day of the year occurs on the day of the winter solstice. The winter solstice is the time when the Sun is farthest south (again, for locations in the northern hemisphere). In 2007, the winter solstice occurred on December 22 (the 356th day of the year) at 1:08 AM (EST).

| EXAMPLE 4 | Finding a Sinusoidal Function for Hours of Daylight |

According to the *Old Farmer's Almanac,* the number of hours of sunlight in Boston on the summer solstice is 15.30 and the number of hours of sunlight on the winter solstice is 9.08.

(a) Find a sinusoidal function of the form $y = A \sin(\omega x - \phi) + B$ that models the data.

(b) Use the function found in part (a) to predict the number of hours of sunlight on April 1, the 91st day of the year.

(c) Draw a graph of the function found in part (a).

(d) Look up the number of hours of sunlight for April 1 in the *Old Farmer's Almanac* and compare it to the results found in part (b).

Source: The *Old Farmer's Almanac,* www.almanac.com/rise

Solution (a) **STEP 1:** Amplitude $= \dfrac{\text{largest data value} - \text{smallest data value}}{2}$

$$= \dfrac{15.30 - 9.08}{2} = 3.11$$

STEP 2: Vertical shift $= \dfrac{\text{largest data value} + \text{smallest data value}}{2}$

$$= \dfrac{15.30 + 9.08}{2} = 12.19$$

STEP 3: The data repeat every 365 days. Since $T = \dfrac{2\pi}{\omega} = 365$, we find

$$\omega = \dfrac{2\pi}{365}$$

So far we have $y = 3.11 \sin\left(\dfrac{2\pi}{365}x - \phi\right) + 12.19$.

STEP 4: To determine the horizontal shift, we use the period $T = 365$ and divide the interval $[0, 365]$ into four subintervals of length $365 \div 4 = 91.25$:

$$[0, 91.25] \quad [91.25, 182.5] \quad [182.5, 273.75] \quad [273.75, 365]$$

The sine curve is increasing on the interval $(0, 91.25)$ and is decreasing on the interval $(91.25, 273.75)$, so a local maximum occurs at $x = 91.25$. Since the maximum occurs on the summer solstice at $x = 172$, we must shift the graph of the function $172 - 91.25 = 80.75$ units to the right by replacing x by $x - 80.75$. Doing this, we obtain

$$y = 3.11 \sin\left(\dfrac{2\pi}{365}(x - 80.75)\right) + 12.19$$

Multiplying out, we find that a sine function of the form $y = A \sin(\omega x - \phi) + B$ that models the data is

$$y = 3.11 \sin\left(\dfrac{2\pi}{365}x - \dfrac{323\pi}{730}\right) + 12.19$$

(b) To predict the number of hours of daylight on April 1, we let $x = 91$ in the function found in part (a) and obtain

$$y = 3.11 \sin\left(\dfrac{2\pi}{365} \cdot 91 - \dfrac{323}{730}\pi\right) + 12.19$$

$$\approx 12.74$$

So we predict that there will be about 12.74 hours $= 12$ hours, 44 minutes of sunlight on April 1 in Boston.

(c) The graph of the function found in part (a) is given in Figure 89.

(d) According to the *Old Farmer's Almanac,* there will be 12 hours 43 minutes of sunlight on April 1 in Boston.

Figure 89

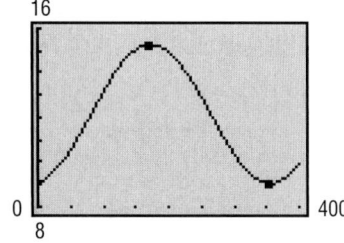

Now Work PROBLEM 35

Certain graphing utilities (such as a TI-83, TI-84 Plus, and TI-86) have the capability of finding the sine function of best fit for sinusoidal data. At least four data points are required for this process.

EXAMPLE 5	Finding the Sine Function of Best Fit

Use a graphing utility to find the sine function of best fit that models the data in Table 11. Graph this function with the scatter diagram of the data.

Solution Enter the data from Table 11 and execute the SINe REGression program. The result is shown in Figure 90.

The output that the utility provides shows the equation

$$y = a \sin(bx + c) + d$$

The sinusoidal function of best fit is

$$y = 21.15 \sin(0.55x - 2.35) + 51.19$$

where x represents the month and y represents the average temperature.

Figure 91 shows the graph of the sinusoidal function of best fit on the scatter diagram.

Figure 90

Figure 91

— **Now Work** PROBLEMS 29(d) AND (e)

6.6 Assess Your Understanding

Concepts and Vocabulary

1. For the graph of $y = A \sin(\omega x - \phi)$, the number $\dfrac{\phi}{\omega}$ is called the _____.

2. *True or False* Only two data points are required by a graphing utility to find the sine function of best fit.

Skill Building

In Problems 3–14, find the amplitude, period, and phase shift of each function. Graph each function. Be sure to label key points. Show at least two periods. Verify your graph using a graphing utility.

3. $y = 4 \sin(2x - \pi)$

4. $y = 3 \sin(3x - \pi)$

5. $y = 2 \cos\left(3x + \dfrac{\pi}{2}\right)$

6. $y = 3 \cos(2x + \pi)$

7. $y = -3 \sin\left(2x + \dfrac{\pi}{2}\right)$

8. $y = -2 \cos\left(2x - \dfrac{\pi}{2}\right)$

9. $y = 4 \sin(\pi x + 2) - 5$

10. $y = 2 \cos(2\pi x + 4) + 4$

11. $y = 3 \cos(\pi x - 2) + 5$

12. $y = 2 \cos(2\pi x - 4) - 1$

13. $y = -3 \sin\left(-2x + \dfrac{\pi}{2}\right)$

14. $y = -3 \cos\left(-2x + \dfrac{\pi}{2}\right)$

In Problems 15–18, write the equation of a sine function that has the given characteristics.

15. Amplitude: 2
 Period: π
 Phase shift: $\dfrac{1}{2}$

16. Amplitude: 3
 Period: $\dfrac{\pi}{2}$
 Phase shift: 2

17. Amplitude: 3
 Period: 3π
 Phase shift: $-\dfrac{1}{3}$

18. Amplitude: 2
 Period: π
 Phase shift: -2

Mixed Practice

In Problems 19–26, apply the methods of this and the previous section to graph each function. Be sure to label key points and show at least two periods. Verify your graph using a graphing utility.

19. $y = 2 \tan(4x - \pi)$ **20.** $y = \dfrac{1}{2} \cot(2x - \pi)$ **21.** $y = 3 \csc\left(2x - \dfrac{\pi}{4}\right)$ **22.** $y = \dfrac{1}{2} \sec(3x - \pi)$

23. $y = -\cot\left(2x + \dfrac{\pi}{2}\right)$ **24.** $y = -\tan\left(3x + \dfrac{\pi}{2}\right)$ **25.** $y = -\sec(2\pi x + \pi)$ **26.** $y = -\csc\left(-\dfrac{1}{2}\pi x + \dfrac{\pi}{4}\right)$

Applications and Extensions

27. Alternating Current (ac) Circuits The current I, in amperes, flowing through an ac (alternating current) circuit at time t, in seconds, is

$$I(t) = 120 \sin\left(30\pi t - \frac{\pi}{3}\right) \quad t \geq 0$$

What is the period? What is the amplitude? What is the phase shift? Graph this function over two periods.

28. Alternating Current (ac) Circuits The current I, in amperes, flowing through an ac (alternating current) circuit at time t, in seconds, is

$$I(t) = 220 \sin\left(60\pi t - \frac{\pi}{6}\right) \quad t \geq 0$$

What is the period? What is the amplitude? What is the phase shift? Graph this function over two periods.

29. Monthly Temperature The following data represent the average monthly temperatures for Juneau, Alaska.

Month, x	Average Monthly Temperature, °F
January, 1	24.2
February, 2	28.4
March, 3	32.7
April, 4	39.7
May, 5	47.0
June, 6	53.0
July, 7	56.0
August, 8	55.0
September, 9	49.4
October, 10	42.2
November, 11	32.0
December, 12	27.1

Source: U.S. National Oceanic and Atmospheric Administration

(a) Draw a scatter diagram of the data for one period.
(b) Find a sinusoidal function of the form
$y = A \sin(\omega x - \phi) + B$ that models the data.
(c) Draw the sinusoidal function found in part (b) on the scatter diagram.
(d) Use a graphing utility to find the sinusoidal function of best fit.
(e) Draw the sinusoidal function of best fit on a scatter diagram of the data.

30. Monthly Temperature The following data represent the average monthly temperatures for Washington, D.C.
(a) Draw a scatter diagram of the data for one period.

(b) Find a sinusoidal function of the form
$y = A \sin(\omega x - \phi) + B$ that models the data.
(c) Draw the sinusoidal function found in part (b) on the scatter diagram.
(d) Use a graphing utility to find the sinusoidal function of best fit.
(e) Graph the sinusoidal function of best fit on a scatter diagram of the data.

Month, x	Average Monthly Temperature, °F
January, 1	34.6
February, 2	37.5
March, 3	47.2
April, 4	56.5
May, 5	66.4
June, 6	75.6
July, 7	80.0
August, 8	78.5
September, 9	71.3
October, 10	59.7
November, 11	49.8
December, 12	39.4

Source: U.S. National Oceanic and Atmospheric Administration

31. Monthly Temperature The following data represent the average monthly temperatures for Indianapolis, Indiana.

Month, x	Average Monthly Temperature, °F
January, 1	25.5
February, 2	29.6
March, 3	41.4
April, 4	52.4
May, 5	62.8
June, 6	71.9
July, 7	75.4
August, 8	73.2
September, 9	66.6
October, 10	54.7
November, 11	43.0
December, 12	30.9

Source: U.S. National Oceanic and Atmospheric Administration

(a) Draw a scatter diagram of the data for one period.
(b) Find a sinusoidal function of the form
   $y = A \sin(\omega x - \phi) + B$ that models the data.
(c) Draw the sinusoidal function found in part (b) on the scatter diagram.
(d) Use a graphing utility to find the sinusoidal function of best fit.
(e) Graph the sinusoidal function of best fit on a scatter diagram of the data.

32. Monthly Temperature   The following data represent the average monthly temperatures for Baltimore, Maryland.
(a) Draw a scatter diagram of the data for one period.
(b) Find a sinusoidal function of the form
   $y = A \sin(\omega x - \phi) + B$ that models the data.
(c) Draw the sinusoidal function found in part (b) on the scatter diagram.
(d) Use a graphing utility to find the sinusoidal function of best fit.
(e) Graph the sinusoidal function of best fit on a scatter diagram of the data.

Month, x	Average Monthly Temperature, °F
January, 1	31.8
February, 2	34.8
March, 3	44.1
April, 4	53.4
May, 5	63.4
June, 6	72.5
July, 7	77.0
August, 8	75.6
September, 9	68.5
October, 10	56.6
November, 11	46.8
December, 12	36.7

Source: U.S. National Oceanic and Atmospheric Administration

33. Tides   Suppose that the length of time between consecutive high tides is approximately 12.5 hours. According to the National Oceanic and Atmospheric Administration, on Saturday, August 7, 2007, in Savannah, Georgia, high tide occurred at 3:38 AM (3.6333 hours) and low tide occurred at 10:08 AM (10.1333 hours). Water heights are measured as the amounts above or below the mean lower low water. The height of the water at high tide was 8.2 feet, and the height of the water at low tide was −0.6 foot.
(a) Approximately when will the next high tide occur?
(b) Find a sinusoidal function of the form
   $y = A \sin(\omega x - \phi) + B$ that models the data.
(c) Draw a graph of the function found in part (b).
(d) Use the function found in part (b) to predict the height of the water at the next high tide.

34. Tides   Suppose that the length of time between consecutive high tides is approximately 12.5 hours. According to the National Oceanic and Atmospheric Administration, on Saturday, August 7, 2007, in Juneau, Alaska, high tide occurred at

8:11 AM (8.1833 hours) and low tide occurred at 2:14 PM (14.2333 hours). Water heights are measured as the amounts above or below the mean lower low water. The height of the water at high tide was 13.2 feet, and the height of the water at low tide was 2.2 feet.
(a) Approximately when will the next high tide occur?
(b) Find a sinusoidal function of the form
   $y = A \sin(\omega x - \phi) + B$ that models the data.
(c) Draw a graph of the function found in part (b).
(d) Use the function found in part (b) to predict the height of the water at the next high tide.

35. Hours of Daylight   According to the *Old Farmer's Almanac*, in Miami, Florida, the number of hours of sunlight on the summer solstice of 2007 was 13.75, and the number of hours of sunlight on the winter solstice was 10.55.
(a) Find a sinusoidal function of the form
   $y = A \sin(\omega x - \phi) + B$ that models the data.
(b) Use the function found in part (a) to predict the number of hours of sunlight on April 1, the 91st day of the year.
(c) Draw a graph of the function found in part (a).
(d) Look up the number of hours of sunlight for April 1 in the *Old Farmer's Almanac*, and compare the actual hours of daylight to the results found in part (c).

36. Hours of Daylight   According to the *Old Farmer's Almanac*, in Detroit, Michigan, the number of hours of sunlight on the summer solstice of 2007 was 15.30, and the number of hours of sunlight on the winter solstice was 9.10.
(a) Find a sinusoidal function of the form
   $y = A \sin(\omega x - \phi) + B$ that models the data.
(b) Use the function found in part (a) to predict the number of hours of sunlight on April 1, the 91st day of the year.
(c) Draw a graph of the function found in part (a).
(d) Look up the number of hours of sunlight for April 1 in the *Old Farmer's Almanac*, and compare the actual hours of daylight to the results found in part (c).

37. Hours of Daylight   According to the *Old Farmer's Almanac*, in Anchorage, Alaska, the number of hours of sunlight on the summer solstice of 2007 was 19.42 and the number of hours of sunlight on the winter solstice was 5.48.
(a) Find a sinusoidal function of the form
   $y = A \sin(\omega x - \phi) + B$ that models the data.
(b) Use the function found in part (a) to predict the number of hours of sunlight on April 1, the 91st day of the year.
(c) Draw a graph of the function found in part (a).
(d) Look up the number of hours of sunlight for April 1 in the *Old Farmer's Almanac*, and compare the actual hours of daylight to the results found in part (c).

38. Hours of Daylight   According to the *Old Farmer's Almanac*, in Honolulu, Hawaii, the number of hours of sunlight on the summer solstice of 2007 was 13.43 and the number of hours of sunlight on the winter solstice was 10.85.
(a) Find a sinusoidal function of the form
   $y = A \sin(\omega x - \phi) + B$ that models the data.
(b) Use the function found in part (a) to predict the number of hours of sunlight on April 1, the 91st day of the year.
(c) Draw a graph of the function found in part (a).
(d) Look up the number of hours of sunlight for April 1 in the *Old Farmer's Almanac*, and compare the actual hours of daylight to the results found in part (c).

Discussion and Writing

39. Explain how the amplitude and period of a sinusoidal graph are used to establish the scale on each coordinate axis.

40. Find an application in your major field that leads to a sinusoidal graph. Write a paper about your findings.

CHAPTER REVIEW

Things to Know

Definitions

Angle in standard position (p. 352) — Vertex is at the origin; initial side is along the positive x-axis.

1 Degree ($1°$) (p. 353) — $1° = \dfrac{1}{360}$ revolution

1 Radian (p. 355) — The measure of a central angle of a circle whose rays subtend an arc whose length is the radius of the circle

Trigonometric functions (pp. 366–368) — $P = (x, y)$ is the point on the unit circle corresponding to $\theta = t$ radians.

$$\sin t = \sin \theta = y \qquad \cos t = \cos \theta = x \qquad \tan t = \tan \theta = \dfrac{y}{x} \quad x \neq 0$$

$$\csc t = \csc \theta = \dfrac{1}{y} \quad y \neq 0 \qquad \sec t = \sec \theta = \dfrac{1}{x} \quad x \neq 0 \qquad \cot t = \cot \theta = \dfrac{x}{y} \quad y \neq 0$$

Trigonometric functions using a circle of radius r (p. 377) — For an angle θ in standard position $P = (x, y)$ is the point on the terminal side of θ that is also on the circle $x^2 + y^2 = r^2$.

$$\sin \theta = \dfrac{y}{r} \qquad \cos \theta = \dfrac{x}{r} \qquad \tan \theta = \dfrac{y}{x} \quad x \neq 0$$

$$\csc \theta = \dfrac{r}{y} \quad y \neq 0 \qquad \sec \theta = \dfrac{r}{x} \quad x \neq 0 \qquad \cot \theta = \dfrac{x}{y} \quad y \neq 0$$

Periodic function (p. 384) — $f(\theta + p) = f(\theta)$, for all θ, $p > 0$, where the smallest such p is the fundamental period

Formulas

1 revolution $= 360°$ (p. 354) $\qquad 1° = \dfrac{\pi}{180}$ radians (p. 357) $\qquad$ 1 radian $= \dfrac{180}{\pi}$ degrees (p. 357)
$\qquad\qquad = 2\pi$ radians (p. 357)

$s = r\theta$ (p. 356) — θ is measured in radians; s is the length of arc subtended by the central angle θ of the circle of radius r.

$A = \dfrac{1}{2}r^2\theta$ (p. 359) — A is the area of the sector of a circle of radius r formed by a central angle of θ radians.

$v = r\omega$ (p. 360) — v is the linear speed along the circle of radius r; ω is the angular speed (measured in radians per unit time).

Table of Values (pp. 370 and 373)

θ (Radians)	θ (Degrees)	$\sin \theta$	$\cos \theta$	$\tan \theta$	$\csc \theta$	$\sec \theta$	$\cot \theta$
0	0°	0	1	0	Not defined	1	Not defined
$\dfrac{\pi}{6}$	30°	$\dfrac{1}{2}$	$\dfrac{\sqrt{3}}{2}$	$\dfrac{\sqrt{3}}{3}$	2	$\dfrac{2\sqrt{3}}{3}$	$\sqrt{3}$
$\dfrac{\pi}{4}$	45°	$\dfrac{\sqrt{2}}{2}$	$\dfrac{\sqrt{2}}{2}$	1	$\sqrt{2}$	$\sqrt{2}$	1
$\dfrac{\pi}{3}$	60°	$\dfrac{\sqrt{3}}{2}$	$\dfrac{1}{2}$	$\sqrt{3}$	$\dfrac{2\sqrt{3}}{3}$	2	$\dfrac{\sqrt{3}}{3}$
$\dfrac{\pi}{2}$	90°	1	0	Not defined	1	Not defined	0
π	180°	0	−1	0	Not defined	−1	Not defined
$\dfrac{3\pi}{2}$	270°	−1	0	Not defined	−1	Not defined	0

The Unit Circle (p. 374–375)

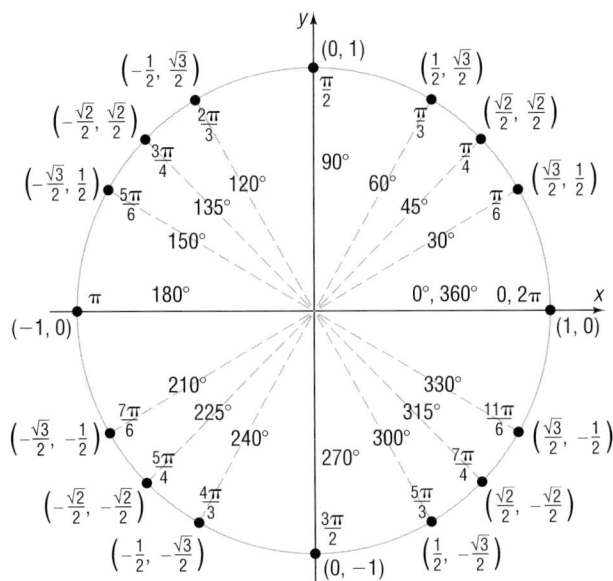

Fundamental identities (p. 388)

$$\tan \theta = \frac{\sin \theta}{\cos \theta} \qquad \cot \theta = \frac{\cos \theta}{\sin \theta}$$

$$\csc \theta = \frac{1}{\sin \theta} \qquad \sec \theta = \frac{1}{\cos \theta} \qquad \cot \theta = \frac{1}{\tan \theta}$$

$$\sin^2 \theta + \cos^2 \theta = 1 \qquad \tan^2 \theta + 1 = \sec^2 \theta \qquad \cot^2 \theta + 1 = \csc^2 \theta$$

Properties of the trigonometric functions

$y = \sin x$ Domain: $-\infty < x < \infty$

(p. 396)   Range: $-1 \le y \le 1$

      Periodic: period $= 2\pi \,(360°)$

      Odd function

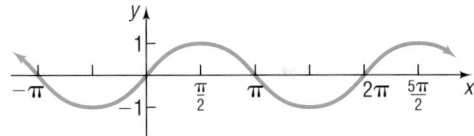

$y = \cos x$ Domain: $-\infty < x < \infty$

(p. 398)   Range: $-1 \le y \le 1$

      Periodic: period $= 2\pi \,(360°)$

      Even function

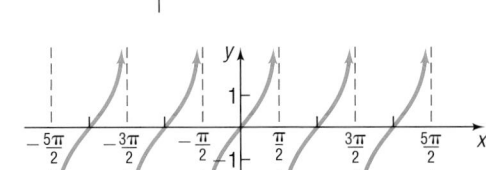

$y = \tan x$ Domain: $-\infty < x < \infty$, except odd integer multiples of $\dfrac{\pi}{2}\,(90°)$

(pp. 412–413)   Range: $-\infty < y < \infty$

      Periodic: period $= \pi \,(180°)$

      Odd function

      Vertical asymptotes at odd integer multiples of $\dfrac{\pi}{2}$

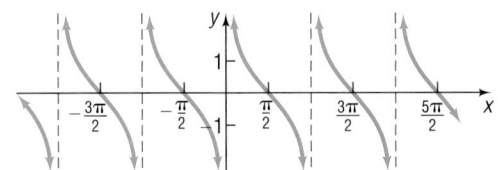

$y = \cot x$ Domain: $-\infty < x < \infty$, except integer multiples of $\pi \,(180°)$

(p. 414)   Range: $-\infty < y < \infty$

      Periodic: period $= \pi \,(180°)$

      Odd function

      Vertical asymptotes at integer multiples of π

$y = \csc x$ (p. 415)	Domain: $-\infty < x < \infty$, except integer multiples of π (180°) Range: $\lvert y \rvert \geq 1$ Periodic: period $= 2\pi$ (360°) Odd function Vertical asymptotes at integer multiples of π	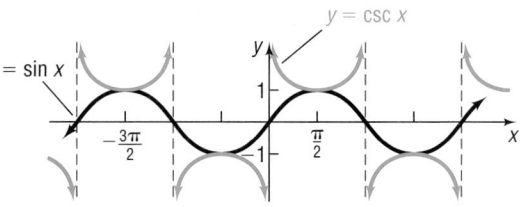
$y = \sec x$ (p. 415)	Domain: $-\infty < x < \infty$, except odd integer multiples of $\dfrac{\pi}{2}$ (90°) Range: $\lvert y \rvert \geq 1$ Periodic: period $= 2\pi$ (360°) Even function Vertical asymptotes at odd integer multiples of $\dfrac{\pi}{2}$	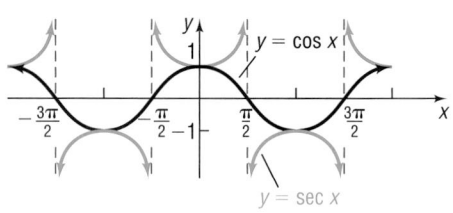

Sinusoidal graphs

$y = A \sin(\omega x) + B, \quad \omega > 0$ Period $= \dfrac{2\pi}{\omega}$ (pp. 401, 419)

$y = A \cos(\omega x) + B, \quad \omega > 0$ Amplitude $= \lvert A \rvert$ (pp. 401, 419)

$y = A \sin(\omega x - \phi) + B = A \sin\left[\omega\left(x - \dfrac{\phi}{\omega}\right)\right] + B$ Phase shift $= \dfrac{\phi}{\omega}$ (p. 419)

$y = A \cos(\omega x - \phi) + B = A \cos\left[\omega\left(x - \dfrac{\phi}{\omega}\right)\right] + B$

Objectives

Section		You should be able to:	Example(s)	Review Exercises
6.1	1	Convert between decimals and degrees, minutes, seconds forms for angles (p. 354)	2	86
	2	Find the arc length of a circle (p. 356)	3	87, 88
	3	Convert from degrees to radians and from radians to degrees (p. 356)	4–6	1–8
	4	Find the area of a sector of a circle (p. 359)	7	87
	5	Find the linear speed of an object traveling in circular motion (p. 360)	8	89–92
6.2	1	Find the exact values of the trigonometric functions using a point on the unit circle (p. 367)	1	83, 97
	2	Find the exact values of the trigonometric functions of quadrantal angles (p. 368)	2, 3	10, 17, 18, 20, 97
	3	Find the exact values of the trigonometric functions of $\dfrac{\pi}{4} = 45°$ (p. 370)	4, 5	9, 11, 13, 15, 16
	4	Find the exact values of the trigonometric functions of $\dfrac{\pi}{6} = 30°$ and $\dfrac{\pi}{3} = 60°$ (p. 371)	6–8	9–15
	5	Find the exact values of the trigonometric functions for integer multiples of $\dfrac{\pi}{6} = 30°$, $\dfrac{\pi}{4} = 45°$, and $\dfrac{\pi}{3} = 60°$ (p. 374)	9, 10	13–16, 19, 97
	6	Use a calculator to approximate the value of a trigonometric function (p. 375)	11	79, 80
	7	Use circle of radius r to evaluate the trigonometric functions (p. 376)	12	84
6.3	1	Determine the domain and the range of the trigonometric functions (p. 382)	pp. 382–384	85
	2	Determine the period of the trigonometric functions (p. 384)	1	85
	3	Determine the signs of the trigonometric functions in a given quadrant (p. 386)	2	81, 82

Section		You should be able to:	Example(s)	Review Exercises
	4	Find the values of the trigonometric functions using fundamental identities (p. 386)	3, 4	21–30
	5	Find the exact values of the trigonometric functions of an angle given one of the functions and the quadrant of the angle (p. 389)	5, 6	31–46
	6	Use even–odd properties to find the exact values of the trigonometric functions (p. 391)	7	27–30
6.4	1	Graph functions of the form $y = A \sin(\omega x)$ using transformations (p. 397)	1, 2	47
	2	Graph functions of the form $y = A \cos(\omega x)$ using transformations (p. 398)	3	48
	3	Determine the amplitude and period of sinusoidal functions (p. 400)	4	63–68
	4	Graph sinusoidal functions using key points (p. 401)	5–7	47, 48, 67, 68, 93
	5	Find an equation for a sinusoidal graph (p. 405)	8, 9	75–78
6.5	1	Graph functions of the form $y = A \tan(\omega x) + B$ and $y = A \cot(\omega x) + B$ (p. 413)	1, 2	53, 54, 56
	2	Graph functions of the form $y = A \csc(\omega x) + B$ and $y = A \sec(\omega x) + B$ (p. 415)	3	57
6.6	1	Graph sinusoidal functions of the form $y = A \sin(\omega x - \phi) + B$ (p. 419)	1, 2	49, 50, 59, 60, 69–74, 94
	2	Build sinusoidal models from data (p. 423)	3	95, 96

Review Exercises

In Problems 1–4, convert each angle in degrees to radians. Express your answer as a multiple of π.

1. $135°$ **2.** $210°$ **3.** $18°$ **4.** $15°$

In Problems 5–8, convert each angle in radians to degrees.

5. $\dfrac{3\pi}{4}$ **6.** $\dfrac{2\pi}{3}$ **7.** $-\dfrac{5\pi}{2}$ **8.** $-\dfrac{3\pi}{2}$

In Problems 9–30, find the exact value of each expression. Do not use a calculator.

9. $\tan \dfrac{\pi}{4} - \sin \dfrac{\pi}{6}$

10. $\cos \dfrac{\pi}{3} + \sin \dfrac{\pi}{2}$

11. $3 \sin 45° - 4 \tan \dfrac{\pi}{6}$

12. $4 \cos 60° + 3 \tan \dfrac{\pi}{3}$

13. $6 \cos \dfrac{3\pi}{4} + 2 \tan\left(-\dfrac{\pi}{3}\right)$

14. $3 \sin \dfrac{2\pi}{3} - 4 \cos \dfrac{5\pi}{2}$

15. $\sec\left(-\dfrac{\pi}{3}\right) - \cot\left(-\dfrac{5\pi}{4}\right)$

16. $4 \csc \dfrac{3\pi}{4} - \cot\left(-\dfrac{\pi}{4}\right)$

17. $\tan \pi + \sin \pi$

18. $\cos \dfrac{\pi}{2} - \csc\left(-\dfrac{\pi}{2}\right)$

19. $\cos 540° - \tan(-405°)$

20. $\sin 270° + \cos(-180°)$

21. $\sin^2 20° + \dfrac{1}{\sec^2 20°}$

22. $\dfrac{1}{\cos^2 40°} - \dfrac{1}{\cot^2 40°}$

23. $\sec 50° \cos 50°$

24. $\tan 10° \cot 10°$

25. $\dfrac{\sin 50°}{\cos 40°}$

26. $\dfrac{\tan 20°}{\cot 70°}$

27. $\dfrac{\sin(-40°)}{\cos 50°}$

28. $\tan(-20°) \cot 20°$

29. $\sin 400° \sec(-50°)$

30. $\cot 200° \cot(-70°)$

In Problems 31–46, find the exact value of each of the remaining trigonometric functions.

31. $\sin \theta = \dfrac{4}{5}$, θ is acute

32. $\tan \theta = \dfrac{1}{4}$, θ is acute

33. $\tan \theta = \dfrac{12}{5}$, $\sin \theta < 0$

34. $\cot \theta = \dfrac{12}{5}$, $\cos \theta < 0$

35. $\sec \theta = -\dfrac{5}{4}$, $\tan \theta < 0$

36. $\csc \theta = -\dfrac{5}{3}$, $\cot \theta < 0$

37. $\sin \theta = \dfrac{12}{13}$, θ in quadrant II

38. $\cos \theta = -\dfrac{3}{5}$, θ in quadrant III

39. $\sin \theta = -\dfrac{5}{13}$, $\dfrac{3\pi}{2} < \theta < 2\pi$

40. $\cos \theta = \dfrac{12}{13}$, $\dfrac{3\pi}{2} < \theta < 2\pi$

41. $\tan \theta = \dfrac{1}{3}$, $180° < \theta < 270°$

42. $\tan \theta = -\dfrac{2}{3}$, $90° < \theta < 180°$

43. $\sec \theta = 3$, $\dfrac{3\pi}{2} < \theta < 2\pi$

44. $\csc \theta = -4$, $\pi < \theta < \dfrac{3\pi}{2}$

45. $\cot \theta = -2$, $\dfrac{\pi}{2} < \theta < \pi$

46. $\tan \theta = -2$, $\dfrac{3\pi}{2} < \theta < 2\pi$

In Problems 47–62, graph each function. Each graph should contain at least two periods. Verify the graph using a graphing utility. Use the graph to determine the domain and the range of each function.

47. $y = 2 \sin(4x)$

48. $y = -3 \cos(2x)$

49. $y = -2 \cos\left(x + \dfrac{\pi}{2}\right)$

50. $y = 3 \sin(x - \pi)$

51. $y = \tan(x + \pi)$

52. $y = -\tan\left(x - \dfrac{\pi}{2}\right)$

53. $y = -2 \tan(3x)$

54. $y = 4 \tan(2x)$

55. $y = \cot\left(x + \dfrac{\pi}{4}\right)$

56. $y = -4 \cot(2x)$

57. $y = 4 \sec(2x)$

58. $y = \csc\left(x + \dfrac{\pi}{4}\right)$

59. $y = 4 \sin(2x + 4) - 2$

60. $y = 3 \cos(4x + 2) + 1$

61. $y = 4 \tan\left(\dfrac{x}{2} + \dfrac{\pi}{4}\right)$

62. $y = 5 \cot\left(\dfrac{x}{3} - \dfrac{\pi}{4}\right)$

In Problems 63–66, determine the amplitude and period of each function without graphing.

63. $y = 4 \cos x$

64. $y = \sin(2x)$

65. $y = -8 \sin\left(\dfrac{\pi}{2}x\right)$

66. $y = -2 \cos(3\pi x)$

In Problems 67–74, find the amplitude, period, and phase shift of each function. Graph each function. Show at least two periods. Verify the graph using a graphing utility.

67. $y = 4 \sin(3x)$

68. $y = 2 \cos\left(\dfrac{1}{3}x\right)$

69. $y = 2 \sin(2x - \pi)$

70. $y = -\cos\left(\dfrac{1}{2}x + \dfrac{\pi}{2}\right)$

71. $y = \dfrac{1}{2} \sin\left(\dfrac{3}{2}x - \pi\right)$

72. $y = \dfrac{3}{2} \cos(6x + 3\pi)$

73. $y = -\dfrac{2}{3} \cos(\pi x - 6)$

74. $y = -7 \sin\left(\dfrac{\pi}{3}x - \dfrac{4}{3}\right)$

In Problems 75–78, find a function whose graph is given.

75.

76.

77.

78.

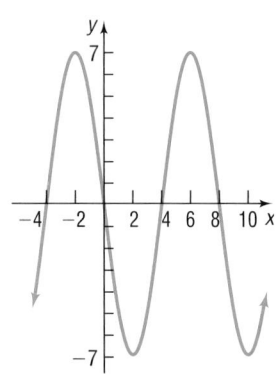

79. Use a calculator to approximate $\sin \dfrac{\pi}{8}$. Round the answer to two decimal places.

80. Use a calculator to approximate $\sec 10°$. Round the answer to two decimal places.

81. Determine the signs of the six trigonometric functions of an angle θ whose terminal side is in quadrant III.

82. Name the quadrant θ lies in if $\cos \theta > 0$ and $\tan \theta < 0$.

83. Find the exact values of the six trigonometric functions of t if $P = \left(-\dfrac{1}{3}, \dfrac{2\sqrt{2}}{3}\right)$ is the point on the unit circle that corresponds to t.

84. Find the exact value of $\sin t$, $\cos t$, and $\tan t$ if $P = (-2, 5)$ is the point on the circle that corresponds to t.

85. What is the domain and the range of the secant function? What is the period?

86. (a) Convert the angle $32°20'35''$ to a decimal in degrees. Round the answer to two decimal places.
(b) Convert the angle $63.18°$ to D°M′S″ form. Express the answer to the nearest second.

87. Find the length of the arc subtended by a central angle of $30°$ on a circle of radius 2 feet. What is the area of the sector?

88. The minute hand of a clock is 8 inches long. How far does the tip of the minute hand move in 30 minutes? How far does it move in 20 minutes?

89. Angular Speed of a Race Car A race car is driven around a circular track at a constant speed of 180 miles per hour. If the diameter of the track is $\frac{1}{2}$ mile, what is the angular speed of the car? Express your answer in revolutions per hour (which is equivalent to laps per hour).

90. Merry-Go-Rounds A neighborhood carnival has a merry-go-round whose radius is 25 feet. If the time for one revolution is 30 seconds, how fast is the merry-go-round going?

91. Lighthouse Beacons The Montauk Point Lighthouse on Long Island has dual beams (two light sources opposite each other). Ships at sea observe a blinking light every 5 seconds. What rotation speed is required to do this?

92. Spin Balancing Tires The radius of each wheel of a car is 16 inches. At how many revolutions per minute should a spin balancer be set to balance the tires at a speed of 90 miles per hour? Is the setting different for a wheel of radius 14 inches? If so, what is this setting?

93. Alternating Voltage The electromotive force E, in volts, in a certain ac (alternating circuit) circuit obeys the function

$$E(t) = 120 \sin(120\pi t), \qquad t \geq 0$$

where t is measured in seconds.
(a) What is the maximum value of E?
(b) What is the period?
(c) Graph this function over two periods.

94. Alternating Current The current I, in amperes, flowing through an ac (alternating current) circuit at time t is

$$I(t) = 220 \sin\left(30\pi t + \frac{\pi}{6}\right), \qquad t \geq 0$$

(a) What is the period?
(b) What is the amplitude?
(c) What is the phase shift?
(d) Graph this function over two periods.

95. Monthly Temperature The following data represent the average monthly temperatures for Phoenix, Arizona.

Month, m	Average Monthly Temperature, T
January, 1	51
February, 2	55
March, 3	63
April, 4	67
May, 5	77
June, 6	86
July, 7	90
August, 8	90
September, 9	84
October, 10	71
November, 11	59
December, 12	52

SOURCE: U.S. National Oceanic and Atmospheric Administration

(a) Draw a scatter diagram of the data for one period.
(b) Find a sinusoidal function of the form
$y = A \sin(\omega x - \phi) + B$ that fits the data.
(c) Draw the sinusoidal function found in part (b) on the scatter diagram.
(d) Use a graphing utility to find the sinusoidal function of best fit.
(e) Graph the sinusoidal function of best fit on the scatter diagram.

96. Hours of Daylight According to the *Old Farmer's Almanac*, in Las Vegas, Nevada, the number of hours of sunlight on the summer solstice is 14.63 and the number of hours of sunlight on the winter solstice is 9.72.
(a) Find a sinusoidal function of the form
$y = A \sin(\omega x - \phi) + B$ that fits the data.
(b) Use the function found in part (a) to predict the number of hours of sunlight on April 1, the 91st day of the year.
(c) Draw a graph of the function found in part (a).
(d) Look up the number of hours of sunlight for April 1 in the *Old Farmer's Almanac* and compare the actual hours of daylight to the results found in part (c).

97. Unit Circle On the unit circle below, fill in the missing angles (in radians) and the corresponding terminal points P of each angle.

CHAPTER TEST

In Problems 1–3, convert each angle in degrees to radians. Express your answer as a multiple of π.

1. $260°$ **2.** $-400°$ **3.** $13°$

In Problems 4–6 convert each angle in radians to degrees.

4. $-\dfrac{\pi}{8}$ **5.** $\dfrac{9\pi}{2}$ **6.** $\dfrac{3\pi}{4}$

In Problems 7–12, find the exact value of each expression.

7. $\sin \dfrac{\pi}{6}$ **8.** $\cos\left(-\dfrac{5\pi}{4}\right) - \cos\dfrac{3\pi}{4}$

9. $\cos(-120°)$ **10.** $\tan 330°$

11. $\sin\dfrac{\pi}{2} - \tan\dfrac{19\pi}{4}$ **12.** $2\sin^2 60° - 3\cos 45°$

In Problems 13–16, use a calculator to evaluate each expression. Round your answer to three decimal places.

13. $\sin 17°$ **14.** $\cos\dfrac{2\pi}{5}$ **15.** $\sec 229°$ **16.** $\cot\dfrac{28\pi}{9}$

17. Fill in each table entry with the sign of each function.

	$\sin\theta$	$\cos\theta$	$\tan\theta$	$\sec\theta$	$\csc\theta$	$\cot\theta$
θ in QI						
θ in QII						
θ in QIII						
θ in QIV						

18. If $f(x) = \sin x$ and $f(a) = \dfrac{3}{5}$, find $f(-a)$.

In Problems 19–21 find the value of the remaining five trigonometric functions of θ.

19. $\sin\theta = \dfrac{5}{7}$, θ in quadrant II **20.** $\cos\theta = \dfrac{2}{3}$, $\dfrac{3\pi}{2} < \theta < 2\pi$

21. $\tan\theta = -\dfrac{12}{5}$, $\dfrac{\pi}{2} < \theta < \pi$

In Problems 22–24, the point (x, y) is on the terminal side of angle θ in standard position. Find the exact value of the given trigonometric function.

22. $(2, 7)$, $\sin\theta$ **23.** $(-5, 11)$, $\cos\theta$

24. $(6, -3)$, $\tan\theta$

In Problems 25 and 26, graph the function.

25. $y = 2\sin\left(\dfrac{x}{3} - \dfrac{\pi}{6}\right)$ **26.** $y = \tan\left(-x + \dfrac{\pi}{4}\right) + 2$

27. Write an equation for a sinusoidal graph with the following properties:

$$A = -3 \qquad \text{period} = \dfrac{2\pi}{3} \qquad \text{phase shift} = -\dfrac{\pi}{4}$$

28. Logan has a garden in the shape of a sector of a circle; the outer rim of the garden is 25 feet long and the central angle of the sector is 50°. She wants to add a 3-foot wide walk to the outer rim; how many square feet of paving blocks will she need to build the walk?

29. Hungarian Adrian Annus won the gold medal for the hammer throw at the 2004 Olympics in Athens with a winning distance of 83.19 meters.* The event consists of swinging a 16-pound weight attached to a wire 190 centimeters long—in a circle and then releasing it. Assuming his release is at a 45° angle to the ground, the hammer will travel a distance of $\dfrac{v_0^2}{g}$ meters, where $g = 9.8$ meters/second² and v_0 is the linear speed of the hammer when released. At what rate (rpm) was he swinging the hammer upon release?

* Annus was stripped of his medal after refusing to cooperate with postmedal drug testing.

CUMULATIVE REVIEW

1. Find the real solutions, if any, of the equation $2x^2 + x - 1 = 0$.

2. Find an equation for the line with slope -3 containing the point $(-2, 5)$.

3. Find an equation for a circle of radius 4 and center at the point $(0, -2)$.

4. Discuss the equation $2x - 3y = 12$. Graph it.

5. Discuss the equation $x^2 + y^2 - 2x + 4y - 4 = 0$. Graph it.

6. Use transformations to graph the function $y = (x - 3)^2 + 2$.

7. Sketch a graph of each of the following functions. Label at least three points on each graph.
 (a) $y = x^2$ (b) $y = x^3$ (c) $y = e^x$
 (d) $y = \ln x$ (e) $y = \sin x$ (f) $y = \tan x$

8. Find the inverse function of $f(x) = 3x - 2$.

9. Find the exact value of $(\sin 14°)^2 + (\cos 14°)^2 - 3$.

10. Graph $y = 3\sin(2x)$.

11. Find the exact value of $\tan\dfrac{\pi}{4} - 3\cos\dfrac{\pi}{6} + \csc\dfrac{\pi}{6}$.

12. Find an exponential function for the following graph. Express your answer in the form $y = Ab^x$.

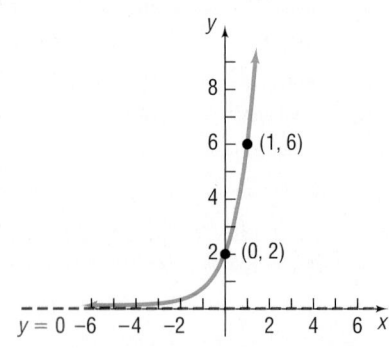

13. Find a sinusoidal function for the following graph.

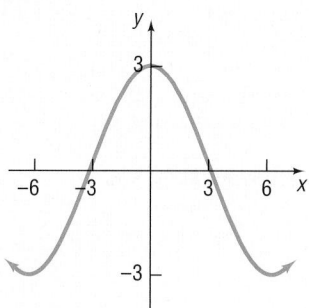

14. (a) Find a linear function that contains the points $(-2, 3)$ and $(1, -6)$. What is the slope? What are the intercepts of the function? Graph the function. Be sure to label the intercepts.

(b) Find a quadratic function that contains the point $(-2, 3)$ with vertex $(1, -6)$. What are the intercepts of the function? Graph the function.

(c) Show that there is no exponential function of the form $f(x) = ae^x$ that contains the points $(-2, 3)$ and $(1, -6)$.

15. (a) Find a polynomial function of degree 3 whose y-intercept is 5 and whose x-intercepts are $-2, 3,$ and 5. Graph the function.

(b) Find a rational function whose y-intercept is 5 and whose x-intercepts are $-2, 3,$ and 5 that has the line $x = 2$ as a vertical asymptote. Graph the function.

CHAPTER PROJECTS

I. **Tides** The given table is a partial tide table for November 2006 for the Sabine Bank Lighthouse, a shoal located offshore from Texas where the Sabine River empties into the Gulf of Mexico.

1. On November 15, when was the tide high? This is called *high tide*. On November 19, when was the tide low? This is called *low tide*. Most days will have two high tides and two low tides.

2. Why do you think there is a negative height for the low tide on November 20? What is the height measured against?

3. On your graphing utility, draw a scatter diagram for the data in the table. Let t (time, in hours) be the independent variable, with $t = 0$ being 12:00 AM on November 14, $t = 24$ being 12:00 AM on November 15, and so on. Let h be the height in feet. Remember that there are 60 minutes in an hour. Also, make sure your graphing utility is in radian mode.

4. What shape does the data take? What is the period of the data? What is the amplitude? Is the amplitude constant? Explain.

5. Find a sine curve that models the data. Is there a vertical shift? Is there a phase shift?

6. Using your graphing utility, find the sinusoidal function of best fit. How does this model compare to the model from part 5?

7. Using the model found in part (5) and the sinusoidal equation of best fit found in part (6), predict the high tides and the low tides on November 21.

8. Looking at the times of day that the low tides occur, what do you think causes the low tides to vary so much each day? Explain. Does this seem to have the same type of effect on the high tides? Explain.

	Low Tide		Low Tide		High Tide		High Tide		Sun/Moon Phase	
Nov	**Time**	**Ht (ft)**	**Time**	**Ht (ft)**	**Time**	**Ht (ft)**	**Time**	**Ht (ft)**	**Sunrise/set**	**Moonrise/set**
14	6:26a	2.0	4:38p	1.4	9:29a	2.2	11:14p	2.8	6:40a/5:20p	1:05a/2:02p
15	6:22a	1.6	5:34p	1.8	11:18a	2.4	11:15p	2.6	6:41a/5:20p	1:58a/2:27p
16	6:28a	1.2	6:25p	2.0	12:37p	2.6	11:16p	2.6	6:41a/5:19p	2:50a/2:52p
17	6:40a	0.8	7:12p	2.4	1:38p	2.8	11:16p	2.6	6:42a/5:19p	3:43a/3:19p
18	6:56a	0.4	7:57p	2.6	2:27p	3.0	11:14p	2.8	6:43a/5:19p	4:38a/3:47p
19	7:17a	0.0	8:38p	2.6	3:10p	3.2	11:05p	2.8	6:44a/5:18p	5:35a/4:20p
20	7:43a	−0.2			3:52p	3.4			6:45a/5:18p	6:34a/4:57p

[**Note:** a, AM; p, PM.]

Sources: National Oceanic and Atmospheric Administration (http://tidesandcurrents.noaa.gov) and U.S. Naval Observatory (http://aa.usno.navy.mil)

The following projects are available on the Instructor's Resource Center (IRC):

II. **Project at Motorola** *Digital Transmission over the Air*   Learn how Motorola Corporation transmits digital sequences by modulating the phase of the carrier waves.

III. **Identifying Mountain Peaks in Hawaii**   The visibility of a mountain is affected by its altitude, distance from the viewer, and the curvature of Earth's surface. Trigonometry can be used to determine whether a distant object can be seen.

IV. **CBL Experiment**   Technology is used to model and study the effects of damping on sound waves.

Analytic Trigonometry

7

In an Instant, the Land Merged with the Sea

John Lancaster and Peter S. Goodman—Washington Post Foreign Service—Sunday, January 2, 2005—Although the tsunami would have been barely perceptible to passengers on a ship at sea, it rolled outward from the fault zone at about 420 miles per hour, roughly the speed of a commercial jetliner. Even at that speed, however, the surge took about two hours to travel to the Indian mainland.

The tsunami hit coastal areas in different ways. In some places, the first event was the recession of water; in others, it was a flood. The difference was determined at the origin of the tsunami: Along the fault line, the sea floor rose in some places and fell in others. Some coastal areas felt the effect of the sinking first and saw the water recede before it returned, often with a vengeance; elsewhere, the opposite happened. Places farther from the origin of the tsunami, such as Sri Lanka, experienced more waves than did closer areas, such as Sumatra.

As the tsunami approached shallower water near land, its behavior began to change. Its velocity slowed and the distance between its crests, known as wavelength, shortened. The stored energy in the wave was partly transformed into an increase in wave height. What happened next varied widely according to local bottom contours. In some areas, the tsunami broke like a massive beach wave; in others, it caused a sudden, rapid increase in sea level, like water pouring over the edge of a tub.

"The ocean turns into a river," explained Steven N. Ward, a geophysicist and tsunami expert at the University of California at Santa Cruz. "It comes in for about 10 minutes, and it flows back out for 10 minutes. You can't duck under it, you can't stand up in it, and you can't outrun it."

Source: Excerpt from "In an Instant, the Land Merged with the Sea," by John Lancaster and Peter S. Goodman. Washington Post, *January 2, 2005, p. A1.* © 2005, The Washington Post. Reprinted with Permission.

—*See Chapter Project I*—

A Look Back

In Chapter 5, we defined inverse functions and developed their properties, particularly the relationship between the domain and range of a function and its inverse. We learned that the graphs of a function and its inverse are symmetric with respect to the line $y = x$.

We continued in Chapter 5 by defining the exponential function and the inverse of the exponential function, the logarithmic function. In Chapter 6, we defined the six trigonometric functions and looked at their properties.

A Look Ahead

In the first two sections of this chapter, we define the six inverse trigonometric functions and investigate their properties. In Sections 7.3 through 7.6 of this chapter, we continue the derivation of identities. These identities play an important role in calculus, the physical and life sciences, and economics, where they are used to simplify complicated expressions. The last two sections of this chapter deal with equations that contain trigonometric functions.

Outline

7.1 The Inverse Sine, Cosine, and Tangent Functions

7.2 The Inverse Trigonometric Functions (Continued)

7.3 Trigonometric Identities

7.4 Sum and Difference Formulas

7.5 Double-angle and Half-angle Formulas

7.6 Product-to-Sum and Sum-to-Product Formulas

7.7 Trigonometric Equations (I)

7.8 Trigonometric Equations (II)

Chapter Review

Chapter Test

Cumulative Review

Chapter Projects

439

7.1 The Inverse Sine, Cosine, and Tangent Functions

PREPARING FOR THIS SECTION *Before getting started, review the following:*

- Inverse Functions (Section 5.2, pp. 255–265)
- Values of the Trigonometric Functions (Section 6.2, pp. 365–377)
- Properties of the Sine, Cosine, and Tangent Functions (Section 6.3, pp. 382–392)
- Graphs of the Sine, Cosine, and Tangent Functions (Section 6.4, pp. 395–399, and Section 6.5, pp. 411–415)

Now Work the 'Are You Prepared?' problems on page 450.

OBJECTIVES 1 Find the Exact Value of an Inverse Sine, Cosine, or Tangent Function (p. 441)
2 Find an Approximate Value of an Inverse Sine Function (p. 443)
3 Use Properties of Inverse Functions to Find Exact Values of Certain Composite Functions (p. 443)
4 Find the Inverse Function of a Trigonometric Function (p. 449)
5 Solve Equations Involving Inverse Trigonometric Functions (p. 450)

In Section 5.2 we discussed inverse functions, and we noted that if a function is one-to-one it will have an inverse function. We also observed that if a function is not one-to-one it may be possible to restrict its domain in some suitable manner so that the restricted function is one-to-one. For example, the function $y = x^2$ is not one-to-one; however, if we restrict the domain to $x \geq 0$, the function is one-to-one.

Other properties of a one-to-one function f and its inverse function f^{-1} that we discussed in Section 5.2 are summarized next.

1. $f^{-1}(f(x)) = x$ for every x in the domain of f and $f(f^{-1}(x)) = x$ for every x in the domain of f^{-1}.
2. Domain of f = range of f^{-1} and range of f = domain of f^{-1}.
3. The graph of f and the graph of f^{-1} are symmetric with respect to the line $y = x$.
4. If a function $y = f(x)$ has an inverse function, the implicit equation of the inverse function is $x = f(y)$. If we solve this equation for y, we obtain the explicit equation $y = f^{-1}(x)$.

The Inverse Sine Function

In Figure 1, we show the graph of $y = \sin x$. Because every horizontal line $y = b$, where b is between -1 and 1, intersects the graph of $y = \sin x$ infinitely many times, it follows from the horizontal-line test that the function $y = \sin x$ is not one-to-one.

Figure 1
$y = \sin x, -\infty < x < \infty, -1 \leq y \leq 1$

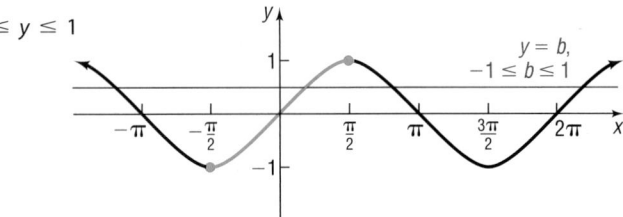

Figure 2
$y = \sin x, -\dfrac{\pi}{2} \leq x \leq \dfrac{\pi}{2}, -1 \leq y \leq 1$

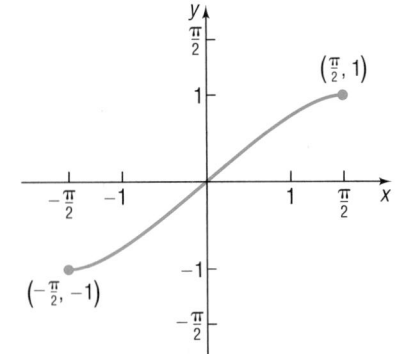

However, if we restrict the domain of $y = \sin x$ to the interval $\left[-\dfrac{\pi}{2}, \dfrac{\pi}{2}\right]$, the restricted function

$$y = \sin x \qquad -\dfrac{\pi}{2} \leq x \leq \dfrac{\pi}{2}$$

is one-to-one and so will have an inverse function.* See Figure 2.

*Although there are many other ways to restrict the domain and obtain a one-to-one function, mathematicians have agreed to use the interval $\left[-\dfrac{\pi}{2}, \dfrac{\pi}{2}\right]$ to define the inverse of $y = \sin x$.

An equation for the inverse of $y = f(x) = \sin x$ is obtained by interchanging x and y. The implicit form of the inverse function is $x = \sin y, -\dfrac{\pi}{2} \le y \le \dfrac{\pi}{2}$. The explicit form is called the **inverse sine** of x and is symbolized by $y = f^{-1}(x) = \sin^{-1} x$.

DEFINITION

> $$y = \sin^{-1} x \quad \text{means} \quad x = \sin y$$
> $$\text{where} \quad -1 \le x \le 1 \quad \text{and} \quad -\frac{\pi}{2} \le y \le \frac{\pi}{2} \qquad \textbf{(1)}$$

NOTE Remember, the domain of a function f equals the range of its inverse, f^{-1}, and the range of a function f equals the domain of its inverse, f^{-1}. Because the restricted domain of the sine function is $\left[-\dfrac{\pi}{2}, \dfrac{\pi}{2} \right]$, the range of the inverse sine function is $\left[-\dfrac{\pi}{2}, \dfrac{\pi}{2} \right]$; because the range of the sine function is $[-1, 1]$, the domain of the inverse sine function is $[-1, 1]$. ∎

Because $y = \sin^{-1} x$ means $x = \sin y$, we read $y = \sin^{-1} x$ as "y is the angle or real number whose sine equals x." Alternatively, we can say that "y is the inverse sine of x." Be careful about the notation used. The superscript -1 that appears in $y = \sin^{-1} x$ is not an exponent, but is reminiscent of the symbolism f^{-1} used to denote the inverse function of f. (To avoid this notation, some books use the notation $y = \text{Arcsin } x$ instead of $y = \sin^{-1} x$.)

The inverse of a function f receives as input an element from the range of f and returns as output an element in the domain of f. The restricted sine function, $y = f(x) = \sin x$, receives as input an angle or real number x in the interval $\left[-\dfrac{\pi}{2}, \dfrac{\pi}{2} \right]$ and outputs a real number in the interval $[-1, 1]$. Therefore, the inverse sine function $y = \sin^{-1} x$ receives as input a real number in the interval $[-1, 1]$ or $-1 \le x \le 1$, its domain, and outputs an angle or real number in the interval $\left[-\dfrac{\pi}{2}, \dfrac{\pi}{2} \right]$ or $-\dfrac{\pi}{2} \le y \le \dfrac{\pi}{2}$, its range.

The graph of the inverse sine function can be obtained by reflecting the restricted portion of the graph of $y = f(x) = \sin x$ about the line $y = x$, as shown in Figure 3(a). Figure 3(b) shows the graph using a graphing utility.

Figure 3

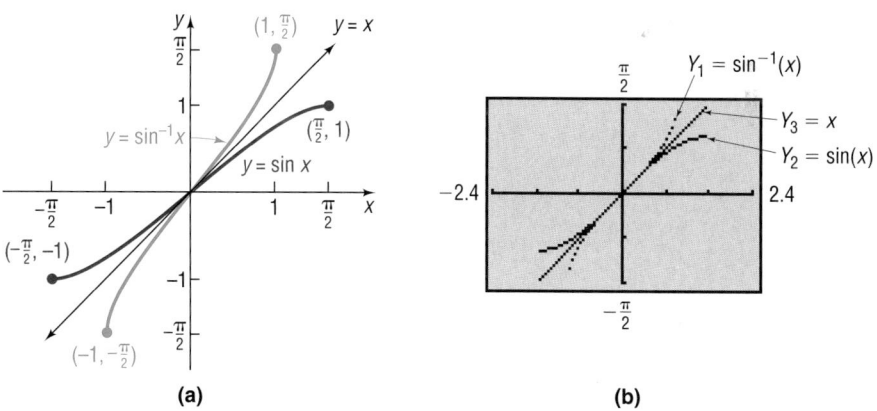

      (a)   (b)

1 Find the Exact Value of an Inverse Sine Function

For some numbers x, it is possible to find the exact value of $y = \sin^{-1} x$.

EXAMPLE 1   **Finding the Exact Value of an Inverse Sine Function**

Find the exact value of: $\sin^{-1} 1$

Solution   Let $\theta = \sin^{-1} 1$. We seek the angle $\theta, -\dfrac{\pi}{2} \le \theta \le \dfrac{\pi}{2}$, whose sine equals 1.

$$\theta = \sin^{-1} 1 \qquad -\frac{\pi}{2} \le \theta \le \frac{\pi}{2}$$
$$\sin \theta = 1 \qquad -\frac{\pi}{2} \le \theta \le \frac{\pi}{2} \quad \text{By definition of } y = \sin^{-1} x$$

Now look at Table 1 and Figure 4.

Table 1

θ	$-\dfrac{\pi}{2}$	$-\dfrac{\pi}{3}$	$-\dfrac{\pi}{4}$	$-\dfrac{\pi}{6}$	0	$\dfrac{\pi}{6}$	$\dfrac{\pi}{4}$	$\dfrac{\pi}{3}$	$\dfrac{\pi}{2}$
$\sin\theta$	-1	$-\dfrac{\sqrt{3}}{2}$	$-\dfrac{\sqrt{2}}{2}$	$-\dfrac{1}{2}$	0	$\dfrac{1}{2}$	$\dfrac{\sqrt{2}}{2}$	$\dfrac{\sqrt{3}}{2}$	1

Figure 4

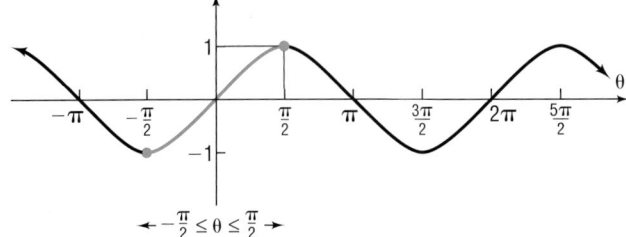

We see that the only angle θ within the interval $\left[-\dfrac{\pi}{2}, \dfrac{\pi}{2}\right]$ whose sine is 1 is $\dfrac{\pi}{2}$. (Note that $\sin\dfrac{5\pi}{2}$ also equals 1, but $\dfrac{5\pi}{2}$ lies outside the interval $\left[-\dfrac{\pi}{2}, \dfrac{\pi}{2}\right]$ and hence is not admissible.) So, since $\sin\dfrac{\pi}{2} = 1$ and $\dfrac{\pi}{2}$ is in $\left[-\dfrac{\pi}{2}, \dfrac{\pi}{2}\right]$, we conclude that

$$\sin^{-1} 1 = \dfrac{\pi}{2}$$

Now Work PROBLEM 13

EXAMPLE 2 | **Finding the Exact Value of an Inverse Sine Function**

Find the exact value of: $\sin^{-1}\left(-\dfrac{1}{2}\right)$

Solution Let $\theta = \sin^{-1}\left(-\dfrac{1}{2}\right)$. We seek the angle θ, $-\dfrac{\pi}{2} \le \theta \le \dfrac{\pi}{2}$, whose sine equals $-\dfrac{1}{2}$.

$$\theta = \sin^{-1}\left(-\dfrac{1}{2}\right) \qquad -\dfrac{\pi}{2} \le \theta \le \dfrac{\pi}{2}$$

$$\sin\theta = -\dfrac{1}{2} \qquad -\dfrac{\pi}{2} \le \theta \le \dfrac{\pi}{2}$$

(Refer to Table 1 and Figure 4, if necessary.) The only angle within the interval $\left[-\dfrac{\pi}{2}, \dfrac{\pi}{2}\right]$ whose sine is $-\dfrac{1}{2}$ is $-\dfrac{\pi}{6}$. So, since $\sin\left(-\dfrac{\pi}{6}\right) = -\dfrac{1}{2}$ and $-\dfrac{\pi}{6}$ is in the interval $\left[-\dfrac{\pi}{2}, \dfrac{\pi}{2}\right]$, we conclude that

$$\sin^{-1}\left(-\dfrac{1}{2}\right) = -\dfrac{\pi}{6}$$

Now Work PROBLEM 19

2 Find an Approximate Value of an Inverse Sine Function

For most numbers x, the value $y = \sin^{-1} x$ must be approximated.

EXAMPLE 3 | **Finding an Approximate Value of an Inverse Sine Function**

Find an approximate value of:

(a) $\sin^{-1} \dfrac{1}{3}$ (b) $\sin^{-1}\left(-\dfrac{1}{4}\right)$

Express the answer in radians rounded to two decimal places.

Solution   Because we want the angle measured in radians, we first set the mode to radians.

(a) Figure 5(a) shows the solution using a TI-84 Plus graphing calculator.

Figure 5a

We have $\sin^{-1} \dfrac{1}{3} = 0.34$, rounded to two decimal places.

(b) Figure 5(b) shows the solution using a TI-84 Plus graphing calculator.

Figure 5b

We have $\sin^{-1}\left(-\dfrac{1}{4}\right) = -0.25$, rounded to two decimal places.

Now Work PROBLEM 25

3 Use Properties of Inverse Functions to Find Exact Values of Certain Composite Functions

When we discussed functions and their inverses in Section 5.2, we found that $f^{-1}(f(x)) = x$ for all x in the domain of f and $f(f^{-1}(x)) = x$ for all x in the domain of f^{-1}. In terms of the sine function and its inverse, these properties are of the form

$$f^{-1}(f(x)) = \sin^{-1}(\sin x) = x \qquad \text{where } -\frac{\pi}{2} \le x \le \frac{\pi}{2} \qquad \textbf{(2a)}$$

$$f(f^{-1}(x)) = \sin(\sin^{-1} x) = x \qquad \text{where } -1 \le x \le 1 \qquad \textbf{(2b)}$$

EXAMPLE 4 | **Finding the Exact Value of Certain Composite Functions**

Find the exact value of each of the following composite functions:

(a) $\sin^{-1}\left(\sin \dfrac{\pi}{8}\right)$ (b) $\sin^{-1}\left(\sin \dfrac{5\pi}{8}\right)$

Solution   (a) The composite function $\sin^{-1}\left(\sin \dfrac{\pi}{8}\right)$ follows the form of equation (2a).

Because $\dfrac{\pi}{8}$ is in the interval $\left[-\dfrac{\pi}{2}, \dfrac{\pi}{2}\right]$, we can use (2a). Then

$$\sin^{-1}\left(\sin \frac{\pi}{8}\right) = \frac{\pi}{8}$$

Figure 6

Figure 6 shows the calculation using a graphing calculator.

(b) The composite function $\sin^{-1}\left(\sin\dfrac{5\pi}{8}\right)$ follows the form of equation (2a), but $\dfrac{5\pi}{8}$ is not in the interval $\left[-\dfrac{\pi}{2}, \dfrac{\pi}{2}\right]$. To use (2a) we need to find an angle θ in the interval $\left[-\dfrac{\pi}{2}, \dfrac{\pi}{2}\right]$ for which $\sin\theta = \sin\dfrac{5\pi}{8}$. Then, using (2a), $\sin^{-1}\left(\sin\dfrac{5\pi}{8}\right) = \sin^{-1}(\sin\theta) = \theta$, and we are finished.

Look at Figure 7. We see that $\sin\dfrac{5\pi}{8} = y = \sin\dfrac{3\pi}{8}$. Since $\dfrac{3\pi}{8}$ is in the interval $\left[-\dfrac{\pi}{2}, \dfrac{\pi}{2}\right]$, we have

$$\sin^{-1}\left(\sin\dfrac{5\pi}{8}\right) = \sin^{-1}\left(\sin\dfrac{3\pi}{8}\right) = \dfrac{3\pi}{8}$$

Apply (2a).

Figure 7

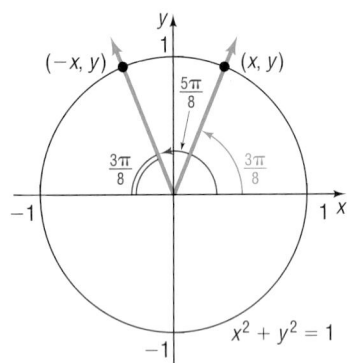

We can verify the results using a graphing calculator. Figure 8(a) shows that $\sin^{-1}\left(\sin\dfrac{5\pi}{8}\right) \neq \dfrac{5\pi}{8}$. In Figure 8(b), we see that

$$\sin^{-1}\left(\sin\dfrac{5\pi}{8}\right) = \sin^{-1}\left(\sin\dfrac{3\pi}{8}\right) = \dfrac{3\pi}{8}$$

Figure 8

(a)

(b)

━━━━ **Now Work** PROBLEM 41

| EXAMPLE 5 | **Finding the Exact Value of Certain Composite Functions** |

Find the exact value, if any, of each composite function.

(a) $\sin(\sin^{-1}0.8)$ (b) $\sin(\sin^{-1}1.8)$

Solution

(a) The composite function $\sin(\sin^{-1}0.8)$ follows the form of equation (2b) and 0.8 is in the interval $[-1, 1]$. So we use (2b):

$$\sin(\sin^{-1}0.8) = 0.8$$

Figure 9

Figure 9 verifies the result.

(b) The composite function $\sin(\sin^{-1}1.8)$ follows the form of equation (2b), but 1.8 is not in the domain of the inverse sine function. This composite function is not defined. See Figure 10. Can you explain why the error occurs?

Figure 10

━━━━ **Now Work** PROBLEM 45

The Inverse Cosine Function

In Figure 11 we show the graph of $y = \cos x$. Because every horizontal line $y = b$, where b is between -1 and 1, intersects the graph of $y = \cos x$ infinitely many times, it follows that the cosine function is not one-to-one.

Figure 11
$y = \cos x, -\infty < x < \infty, -1 \le y \le 1.$

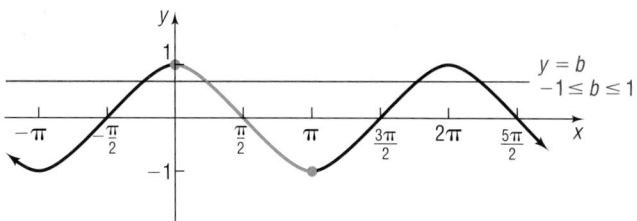

Figure 12
$y = \cos x, 0 \le x \le \pi, -1 \le y \le 1$

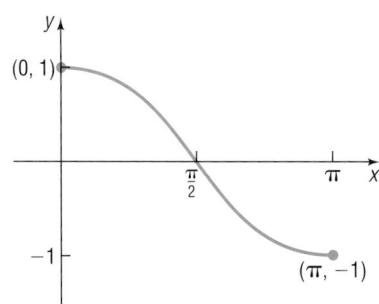

However, if we restrict the domain of $y = \cos x$ to the interval $[0, \pi]$, the restricted function

$$y = \cos x \qquad 0 \le x \le \pi$$

is one-to-one and hence will have an inverse function.* See Figure 12.

An equation for the inverse of $y = f(x) = \cos x$ is obtained by interchanging x and y. The implicit form of the inverse function is $x = \cos y, 0 \le y \le \pi$. The explicit form is called the **inverse cosine** of x and is symbolized by $y = f^{-1}(x) = \cos^{-1} x$ (or by $y = \text{Arccos } x$).

DEFINITION

> $$y = \cos^{-1} x \quad \text{means} \quad x = \cos y$$
> $$\text{where} \quad -1 \le x \le 1 \quad \text{and} \quad 0 \le y \le \pi$$
> **(3)**

Here y is the angle whose cosine is x. Because the range of the cosine function, $y = \cos x$, is $-1 \le y \le 1$, the domain of the inverse function $y = \cos^{-1} x$ is $-1 \le x \le 1$. Because the restricted domain of the cosine function, $y = \cos x$, is $0 \le x \le \pi$, the range of the inverse function $y = \cos^{-1} x$ is $0 \le y \le \pi$.

The graph of $y = \cos^{-1} x$ can be obtained by reflecting the restricted portion of the graph of $y = \cos x$ about the line $y = x$, as shown in Figure 13.

Figure 13
$y = \cos^{-1} x, -1 \le x \le 1, 0 \le y \le \pi$

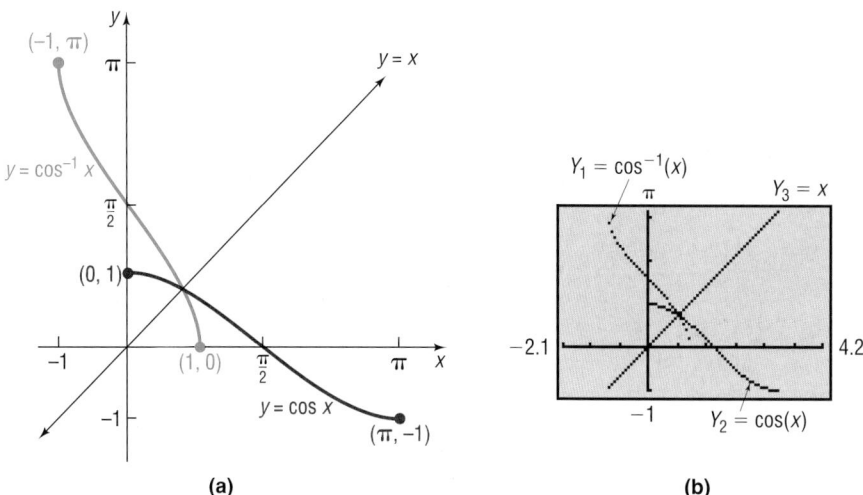

(a)

(b)

*This is the generally accepted restriction to define the inverse cosine function.

| EXAMPLE 6 | Finding the Exact Value of an Inverse Cosine Function |

Find the exact value of: $\cos^{-1} 0$

Solution Let $\theta = \cos^{-1} 0$. We seek the angle $\theta, 0 \le \theta \le \pi$, whose cosine equals 0.

$$\theta = \cos^{-1} 0 \qquad 0 \le \theta \le \pi$$
$$\cos \theta = 0 \qquad 0 \le \theta \le \pi$$

Look at Table 2 and Figure 14.

Table 2

θ	$\cos \theta$
0	1
$\dfrac{\pi}{6}$	$\dfrac{\sqrt{3}}{2}$
$\dfrac{\pi}{4}$	$\dfrac{\sqrt{2}}{2}$
$\dfrac{\pi}{3}$	$\dfrac{1}{2}$
$\dfrac{\pi}{2}$	0
$\dfrac{2\pi}{3}$	$-\dfrac{1}{2}$
$\dfrac{3\pi}{4}$	$-\dfrac{\sqrt{2}}{2}$
$\dfrac{5\pi}{6}$	$-\dfrac{\sqrt{3}}{2}$
π	-1

Figure 14

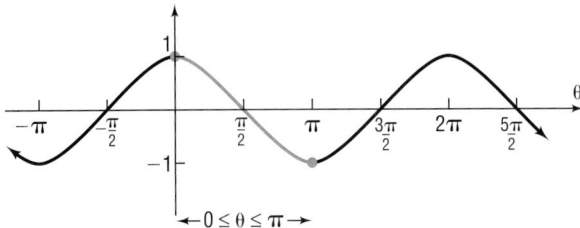

We see that the only angle θ within the interval $[0, \pi]$ whose cosine is 0 is $\dfrac{\pi}{2}$. [Note that $\cos \dfrac{3\pi}{2}$ and $\cos\left(-\dfrac{\pi}{2}\right)$ also equal 0, but they lie outside the interval $[0, \pi]$ and hence are not admissible.] Since $\cos \dfrac{\pi}{2} = 0$ and $\dfrac{\pi}{2}$ is in the interval $[0, \pi]$, we conclude that

$$\cos^{-1} 0 = \frac{\pi}{2}$$

| EXAMPLE 7 | Finding the Exact Value of an Inverse Cosine Function |

Find the exact value of: $\cos^{-1}\left(-\dfrac{\sqrt{2}}{2}\right)$

Solution Let $\theta = \cos^{-1}\left(-\dfrac{\sqrt{2}}{2}\right)$. We seek the angle $\theta, 0 \le \theta \le \pi$, whose cosine equals $-\dfrac{\sqrt{2}}{2}$.

$$\theta = \cos^{-1}\left(-\frac{\sqrt{2}}{2}\right) \qquad 0 \le \theta \le \pi$$
$$\cos \theta = -\frac{\sqrt{2}}{2} \qquad 0 \le \theta \le \pi$$

Look at Table 2 and Figure 15.

Figure 15

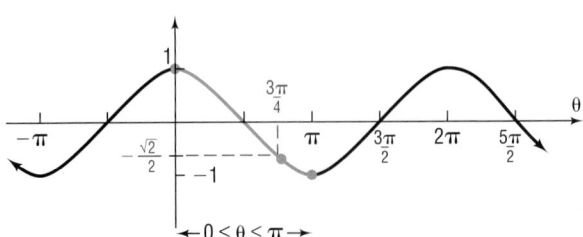

We see that the only angle θ within the interval $[0, \pi]$ whose cosine is $-\dfrac{\sqrt{2}}{2}$ is $\dfrac{3\pi}{4}$. So, since $\cos \dfrac{3\pi}{4} = -\dfrac{\sqrt{2}}{2}$ and $\dfrac{3\pi}{4}$ is in the interval $[0, \pi]$, we conclude that

$$\cos^{-1}\left(-\frac{\sqrt{2}}{2}\right) = \frac{3\pi}{4}$$

➤ **Now Work** PROBLEM 23

For the cosine function and its inverse, the following properties hold:

$$f^{-1}(f(x)) = \cos^{-1}(\cos x) = x \qquad \text{where } 0 \le x \le \pi \qquad \textbf{(4a)}$$
$$f(f^{-1}(x)) = \cos(\cos^{-1} x) = x \qquad \text{where } -1 \le x \le 1 \qquad \textbf{(4b)}$$

EXAMPLE 8

Using Properties of Inverse Functions to Find the Exact Value of Certain Composite Functions

Find the exact value of:

(a) $\cos^{-1}\left(\cos \dfrac{\pi}{12}\right)$ (b) $\cos[\cos^{-1}(-0.4)]$ (c) $\cos^{-1}\left[\cos\left(-\dfrac{2\pi}{3}\right)\right]$ (d) $\cos(\cos^{-1}\pi)$

Solution

(a) $\cos^{-1}\left(\cos \dfrac{\pi}{12}\right) = \dfrac{\pi}{12}$ $\dfrac{\pi}{12}$ is in the interval $[0, \pi]$; use Property (4a).

(b) $\cos[\cos^{-1}(-0.4)] = -0.4$ -0.4 is in the interval $[-1, 1]$; use Property (4b).

(c) The angle $-\dfrac{2\pi}{3}$ is not in the interval $[0, \pi]$, so we cannot use (4a). However, because the cosine function is even, $\cos\left(-\dfrac{2\pi}{3}\right) = \cos \dfrac{2\pi}{3}$. Since $\dfrac{2\pi}{3}$ is in the interval $[0, \pi]$, we have

$$\cos^{-1}\left[\cos\left(-\frac{2\pi}{3}\right)\right] = \cos^{-1}\left(\cos \frac{2\pi}{3}\right) = \frac{2\pi}{3} \quad \frac{2\pi}{3} \text{ is in the interval } [0, \pi]; \text{ apply (4a).}$$

(d) Because π is not in the interval $[-1, 1]$, the domain of the inverse cosine function, $\cos^{-1}\pi$ is not defined. This means the composite function $\cos(\cos^{-1}\pi)$ is also not defined.

➤ **Now Work** PROBLEMS 37 AND 49

The Inverse Tangent Function

In Figure 16 on page 448 we show the graph of $y = \tan x$. Because every horizontal line intersects the graph infinitely many times, it follows that the tangent function is not one-to-one.

However, if we restrict the domain of $y = \tan x$ to the interval $\left(-\dfrac{\pi}{2}, \dfrac{\pi}{2}\right)$, the restricted function

$$y = \tan x \qquad -\frac{\pi}{2} < x < \frac{\pi}{2}$$

is one-to-one and hence has an inverse function.* See Figure 17.

*This is the generally accepted restriction.

Figure 16

$y = \tan x, -\infty < x < \infty, x$ not equal to odd multiples of $\dfrac{\pi}{2}, -\infty < y < \infty$

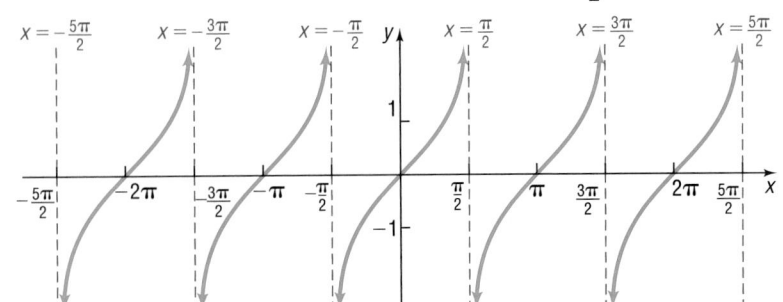

Figure 17

$y = \tan x, -\dfrac{\pi}{2} < x < \dfrac{\pi}{2}, -\infty < y < \infty$

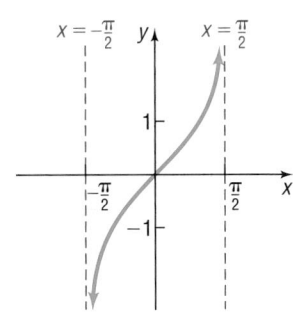

An equation for the inverse of $y = f(x) = \tan x$ is obtained by interchanging x and y. The implicit form of the inverse function is $x = \tan y, -\dfrac{\pi}{2} < y < \dfrac{\pi}{2}$. The explicit form is called the **inverse tangent** of x and is symbolized by $y = f^{-1}(x) = \tan^{-1} x$ (or by $y = \text{Arctan}\, x$).

DEFINITION

$$y = \tan^{-1} x \quad \text{means} \quad x = \tan y$$
$$\text{where} \quad -\infty < x < \infty \quad \text{and} \quad -\frac{\pi}{2} < y < \frac{\pi}{2} \tag{5}$$

Here y is the angle whose tangent is x. The domain of the function $y = \tan^{-1} x$ is $-\infty < x < \infty$, and its range is $-\dfrac{\pi}{2} < y < \dfrac{\pi}{2}$. The graph of $y = \tan^{-1} x$ can be obtained by reflecting the restricted portion of the graph of $y = \tan x$ about the line $y = x$, as shown in Figure 18.

Figure 18

$y = \tan^{-1} x,$

$-\infty < x < \infty,$

$-\dfrac{\pi}{2} < y < \dfrac{\pi}{2}$

(a)

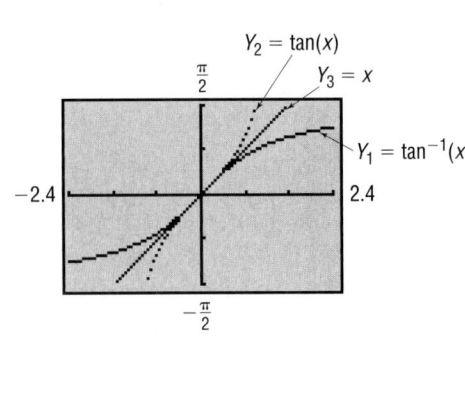

(b)

EXAMPLE 9   **Finding the Exact Value of an Inverse Tangent Function**

Find the exact value of:

(a) $\tan^{-1} 1$

(b) $\tan^{-1}\left(-\sqrt{3}\right)$

Solution   (a) Let $\theta = \tan^{-1} 1$. We seek the angle θ, $-\dfrac{\pi}{2} < \theta < \dfrac{\pi}{2}$, whose tangent equals 1.

$$\theta = \tan^{-1} 1 \qquad -\dfrac{\pi}{2} < \theta < \dfrac{\pi}{2}$$

$$\tan \theta = 1 \qquad -\dfrac{\pi}{2} < \theta < \dfrac{\pi}{2}$$

Table 3

θ	$\tan \theta$
$-\dfrac{\pi}{2}$	Undefined
$-\dfrac{\pi}{3}$	$-\sqrt{3}$
$-\dfrac{\pi}{4}$	-1
$-\dfrac{\pi}{6}$	$-\dfrac{\sqrt{3}}{3}$
0	0
$\dfrac{\pi}{6}$	$\dfrac{\sqrt{3}}{3}$
$\dfrac{\pi}{4}$	1
$\dfrac{\pi}{3}$	$\sqrt{3}$
$\dfrac{\pi}{2}$	Undefined

Look at Table 3. The only angle θ within the interval $\left(-\dfrac{\pi}{2}, \dfrac{\pi}{2}\right)$ whose tangent is 1 is $\dfrac{\pi}{4}$. Since $\tan \dfrac{\pi}{4} = 1$ and $\dfrac{\pi}{4}$ is in the interval $\left(-\dfrac{\pi}{2}, \dfrac{\pi}{2}\right)$, we conclude that

$$\tan^{-1} 1 = \dfrac{\pi}{4}$$

(b) Let $\theta = \tan^{-1}\left(-\sqrt{3}\right)$. We seek the angle θ, $-\dfrac{\pi}{2} < \theta < \dfrac{\pi}{2}$, whose tangent equals $-\sqrt{3}$.

$$\theta = \tan^{-1}\left(-\sqrt{3}\right) \qquad -\dfrac{\pi}{2} < \theta < \dfrac{\pi}{2}$$

$$\tan \theta = -\sqrt{3} \qquad -\dfrac{\pi}{2} < \theta < \dfrac{\pi}{2}$$

Look at Table 3. The only angle θ within the interval $\left(-\dfrac{\pi}{2}, \dfrac{\pi}{2}\right)$ whose tangent is $-\sqrt{3}$ is $-\dfrac{\pi}{3}$. Since $\tan\left(-\dfrac{\pi}{3}\right) = -\sqrt{3}$ and $-\dfrac{\pi}{3}$ is in the interval $\left(-\dfrac{\pi}{2}, \dfrac{\pi}{2}\right)$, we conclude that

$$\tan^{-1}\left(-\sqrt{3}\right) = -\dfrac{\pi}{3}$$

Now Work PROBLEM 17

For the tangent function and its inverse, the following properties hold:

$$f^{-1}(f(x)) = \tan^{-1}(\tan x) = x \qquad \text{where } -\dfrac{\pi}{2} < x < \dfrac{\pi}{2}$$

$$f(f^{-1}(x)) = \tan(\tan^{-1} x) = x \qquad \text{where } -\infty < x < \infty$$

Now Work PROBLEM 43

4 Find the Inverse Function of a Trigonometric Function

EXAMPLE 10   **Finding the Inverse Function of a Trigonometric Function**

Find the inverse function f^{-1} of $f(x) = 2 \sin x - 1$. State the domain and the range of f and f^{-1}.

Solution   We follow the steps on page 263 for finding the inverse function.

$$y = 2 \sin x - 1$$
$$x = 2 \sin y - 1 \qquad \text{Interchange } x \text{ and } y.$$
$$x + 1 = 2 \sin y \qquad \text{Proceed to solve for } y.$$
$$\sin y = \dfrac{x + 1}{2}$$
$$y = \sin^{-1} \dfrac{x + 1}{2} \qquad \text{Apply the definition (1).}$$

The inverse function is $f^{-1}(x) = \sin^{-1} \dfrac{x + 1}{2}$.

The domain of $f(x) = 2 \sin x - 1$ is the set of all real numbers. Therefore, the range of f^{-1} is the set of all real numbers.

The graph of $f(x) = 2 \sin x - 1$ can be obtained by vertically stretching $y = \sin x$ by a factor of 2 and then shifting the resulting graph down 1 unit. So the range of $f(x) = 2 \sin x - 1$ is $[-3, 1]$. Therefore, the domain of f^{-1} is $[-3, 1]$.

We could also find the domain of f^{-1} by noting that the argument of the inverse sine function is $\dfrac{x+1}{2}$ and that it must lie in the interval $[-1, 1]$. That is,

$$-1 \le \frac{x+1}{2} \le 1$$

$$-2 \le x + 1 \le 2 \quad \text{Multiply each part by 2.}$$

$$-3 \le x \le 1 \quad \text{Add } -1 \text{ to each part.}$$

The domain of f^{-1} is $\{x \mid -3 \le x \le 1\}$.

━━━━━ **Now Work** PROBLEM 55

5 Solve Equations Involving Inverse Trigonometric Functions

Equations that contain inverse trigonometric functions are called **inverse trigonometric equations.**

EXAMPLE 11

Solving an Equation Involving an Inverse Trigonometric Function

Solve the equation: $3 \sin^{-1} x = \pi$

Solution

To solve an equation involving a single inverse trigonometric function, first isolate the inverse trigonometric function.

$$3 \sin^{-1} x = \pi$$

$$\sin^{-1} x = \frac{\pi}{3} \qquad \text{Divide both sides by 3.}$$

$$x = \sin \frac{\pi}{3} \quad y = \sin^{-1} x \text{ means } x = \sin y.$$

$$x = \frac{\sqrt{3}}{2}$$

The solution set is $\left\{ \dfrac{\sqrt{3}}{2} \right\}$.

━━━━━ **Now Work** PROBLEM 61

7.1 Assess Your Understanding

'Are You Prepared?' *Answers are given at the end of these exercises. If you get a wrong answer, read the pages listed in red.*

1. What is the domain and the range of $y = \sin x$? (pp. 382–384)

2. A suitable restriction on the domain of the function $f(x) = (x - 1)^2$ to make it one-to-one would be _____. (pp. 257–258, 264)

3. If the domain of a one-to-one function is $[3, \infty)$, the range of its inverse is _____. (pp. 258–259)

4. True or False   The graph of $y = \cos x$ is decreasing on the interval $[0, \pi]$. (p. 398)

5. $\tan \dfrac{\pi}{4} = $ _____; $\sin \dfrac{\pi}{3} = $ _____ (pp. 370–374)

6. $\sin\left(-\dfrac{\pi}{6}\right) = $ _____; $\cos \pi = $ _____ (pp. 369–375)

Concepts and Vocabulary

7. $y = \sin^{-1} x$ means _____,

   where $-1 \le x \le 1$ and $-\dfrac{\pi}{2} \le y \le \dfrac{\pi}{2}$.

8. The value of $\sin^{-1}\left[\sin \dfrac{\pi}{2}\right]$ is _____.

9. $\cos^{-1}\left[\cos\dfrac{\pi}{5}\right] =$ _____.

11. True or False $\sin(\sin^{-1} 0) = 0$ and $\cos(\cos^{-1} 0) = 0$.

12. True or False $y = \tan^{-1} x$ means $x = \tan y$, where $-\infty < x < \infty$ and $-\dfrac{\pi}{2} < y < \dfrac{\pi}{2}$.

10. True or False   The domain of $y = \sin^{-1} x$ is $-\dfrac{\pi}{2} \le x \le \dfrac{\pi}{2}$.

Skill Building

In Problems 13–24, find the exact value of each expression.

13. $\sin^{-1} 0$

14. $\cos^{-1} 1$

15. $\sin^{-1}(-1)$

16. $\cos^{-1}(-1)$

17. $\tan^{-1} 0$

18. $\tan^{-1}(-1)$

19. $\sin^{-1}\dfrac{\sqrt{2}}{2}$

20. $\tan^{-1}\dfrac{\sqrt{3}}{3}$

21. $\tan^{-1}\sqrt{3}$

22. $\sin^{-1}\left(-\dfrac{\sqrt{3}}{2}\right)$

23. $\cos^{-1}\left(-\dfrac{\sqrt{3}}{2}\right)$

24. $\sin^{-1}\left(-\dfrac{\sqrt{2}}{2}\right)$

In Problems 25–36, use a calculator to find the value of each expression rounded to two decimal places.

25. $\sin^{-1} 0.1$

26. $\cos^{-1} 0.6$

27. $\tan^{-1} 5$

28. $\tan^{-1} 0.2$

29. $\cos^{-1}\dfrac{7}{8}$

30. $\sin^{-1}\dfrac{1}{8}$

31. $\tan^{-1}(-0.4)$

32. $\tan^{-1}(-3)$

33. $\sin^{-1}(-0.12)$

34. $\cos^{-1}(-0.44)$

35. $\cos^{-1}\dfrac{\sqrt{2}}{3}$

36. $\sin^{-1}\dfrac{\sqrt{3}}{5}$

In Problems 37–44, find the exact value of each expression. Do not use a calculator.

37. $\cos^{-1}\left(\cos\dfrac{4\pi}{5}\right)$

38. $\sin^{-1}\left[\sin\left(-\dfrac{\pi}{10}\right)\right]$

39. $\tan^{-1}\left[\tan\left(-\dfrac{3\pi}{8}\right)\right]$

40. $\sin^{-1}\left[\sin\left(-\dfrac{3\pi}{7}\right)\right]$

41. $\sin^{-1}\left(\sin\dfrac{9\pi}{8}\right)$

42. $\cos^{-1}\left[\cos\left(-\dfrac{5\pi}{3}\right)\right]$

43. $\tan^{-1}\left(\tan\dfrac{4\pi}{5}\right)$

44. $\tan^{-1}\left[\tan\left(-\dfrac{2\pi}{3}\right)\right]$

In Problems 45–52, find the exact value, if any, of each composite function. If there is no value, say it is "not defined." Do not use a calculator.

45. $\sin\left(\sin^{-1}\dfrac{1}{4}\right)$

46. $\cos\left[\cos^{-1}\left(-\dfrac{2}{3}\right)\right]$

47. $\tan\left(\tan^{-1} 4\right)$

48. $\tan\left[\tan^{-1}(-2)\right]$

49. $\cos\left(\cos^{-1} 1.2\right)$

50. $\sin\left[\sin^{-1}(-2)\right]$

51. $\tan\left(\tan^{-1}\pi\right)$

52. $\sin\left[\sin^{-1}(-1.5)\right]$

In Problems 53–60, find the inverse function f^{-1} of each function f. State the domain and the range of f and f^{-1}.

53. $f(x) = 5\sin x + 2$

54. $f(x) = 2\tan x - 3$

55. $f(x) = -2\cos(3x)$

56. $f(x) = 3\sin(2x)$

57. $f(x) = -\tan(x + 1) - 3$

58. $f(x) = \cos(x + 2) + 1$

59. $f(x) = 3\sin(2x + 1)$

60. $f(x) = 2\cos(3x + 2)$

In Problems 61–68, find the exact solution of each equation.

61. $4\sin^{-1}(x) = \pi$

62. $2\cos^{-1} x = \pi$

63. $3\cos^{-1}(2x) = 2\pi$

64. $-6\sin^{-1}(3x) = \pi$

65. $3\tan^{-1} x = \pi$

66. $-4\tan^{-1} x = \pi$

67. $4\cos^{-1} x - 2\pi = 2\cos^{-1} x$

68. $5\sin^{-1} x - 2\pi = 2\sin^{-1} x - 3\pi$

Applications and Extensions

In Problems 69–74, use the following discussion. The formula

$$D = 24\left[1 - \dfrac{\cos^{-1}(\tan i \tan \theta)}{\pi}\right]$$

can be used to approximate the number of hours of daylight D when the declination of the Sun is $i°$ at a location $\theta°$ north latitude for any date between the vernal equinox and autumnal equinox. The declination of the Sun is defined as the angle i between the equatorial plane and any ray of light from the Sun. The latitude of

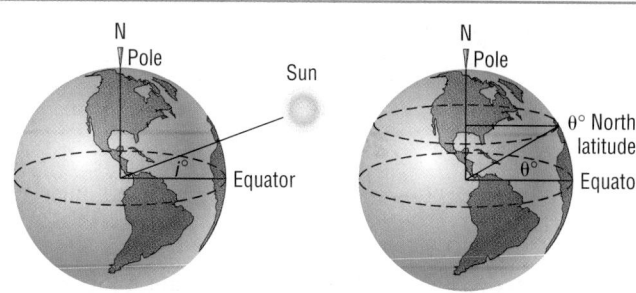

a location is the angle θ between the Equator and the location on the surface of Earth, with the vertex of the angle located at the center of Earth. See the figure. To use the formula, $\cos^{-1}(\tan i \tan \theta)$ *must be expressed in radians.*

69. Approximate the number of hours of daylight in Houston, Texas (29°45′ north latitude), for the following dates:
    (a) Summer solstice ($i = 23.5°$)
    (b) Vernal equinox ($i = 0°$)
    (c) July 4 ($i = 22°48′$)

70. Approximate the number of hours of daylight in New York, New York (40°45′ north latitude), for the following dates:
    (a) Summer solstice ($i = 23.5°$)
    (b) Vernal equinox ($i = 0°$)
    (c) July 4 ($i = 22°48′$)

71. Approximate the number of hours of daylight in Honolulu, Hawaii (21°18′ north latitude), for the following dates:
    (a) Summer solstice ($i = 23.5°$)
    (b) Vernal equinox ($i = 0°$)
    (c) July 4 ($i = 22°48′$)

72. Approximate the number of hours of daylight in Anchorage, Alaska (61°10′ north latitude), for the following dates:
    (a) Summer solstice ($i = 23.5°$)
    (b) Vernal equinox ($i = 0°$)
    (c) July 4 ($i = 22°48′$)

73. Approximate the number of hours of daylight at the Equator (0° north latitude) for the following dates:
    (a) Summer solstice ($i = 23.5°$)
    (b) Vernal equinox ($i = 0°$)
    (c) July 4 ($i = 22°48′$)
    (d) What do you conclude about the number of hours of daylight throughout the year for a location at the Equator?

74. Approximate the number of hours of daylight for any location that is 66°30′ north latitude for the following dates:
    (a) Summer solstice ($i = 23.5°$)
    (b) Vernal equinox ($i = 0°$)
    (c) July 4 ($i = 22°48′$)
    (d) The number of hours of daylight on the winter solstice may be found by computing the number of hours of daylight on the summer solstice and subtracting this result from 24 hours, due to the symmetry of the orbital path of Earth around the Sun. Compute the number of hours of daylight for this location on the winter solstice. What do you conclude about daylight for a location at 66°30′ north latitude?

75. **Being the First to See the Rising Sun** Cadillac Mountain, elevation 1530 feet, is located in Acadia National Park, Maine, and is the highest peak on the east coast of the United States. It is said that a person standing on the summit will be the first person in the United States to see the rays of the rising Sun. How much sooner would a person atop Cadillac Mountain see the first rays than a person standing below at sea level?

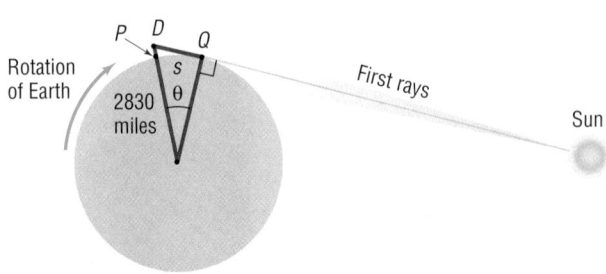

   [**Hint:** Consult the figure. When the person at *D* sees the first rays of the Sun, the person at *P* does not. The person at

P sees the first rays of the Sun only after Earth has rotated so that *P* is at location *Q*. Compute the length of the arc subtended by the central angle θ. Then use the fact that, at the latitude of Cadillac Mountain, in 24 hours a length of $2\pi(2830) \approx 17{,}781.4$ miles is subtended, and find the time that it takes to subtend this length.]

76. **Movie Theater Screens** Suppose that a movie theater has a screen that is 28 feet tall. When you sit down, the bottom of the screen is 6 feet above your eye level. The angle formed by drawing a line from your eye to the bottom of the screen and from your eye to the top of the screen is called the **viewing angle**. In the figure, θ is the viewing angle. Suppose that you sit *x* feet from the screen. The viewing angle θ is given by the function

$$\theta(x) = \tan^{-1}\left(\frac{34}{x}\right) - \tan^{-1}\left(\frac{6}{x}\right)$$

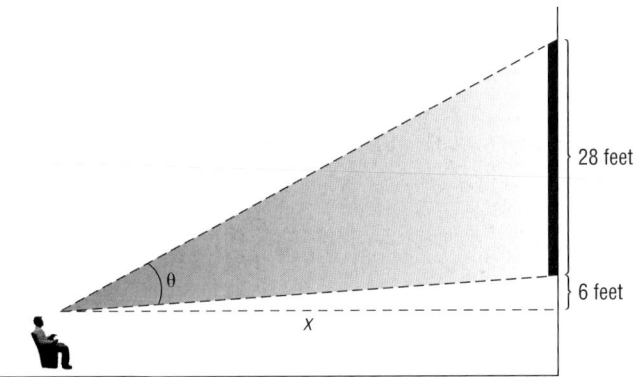

    (a) What is your viewing angle if you sit 10 feet from the screen? 15 feet? 20 feet?
    (b) If there is 5 feet between the screen and the first row of seats and there is 3 feet between each row, which row results in the largest viewing angle?
    (c) Using a graphing utility, graph

$$\theta(x) = \tan^{-1}\left(\frac{34}{x}\right) - \tan^{-1}\left(\frac{6}{x}\right)$$

    What value of *x* results in the largest viewing angle?

77. **Area under a Curve** The area under the graph of $y = \frac{1}{1 + x^2}$ and above the *x*-axis between $x = a$ and $x = b$ is given by

$$\tan^{-1} b - \tan^{-1} a$$

See the figure.

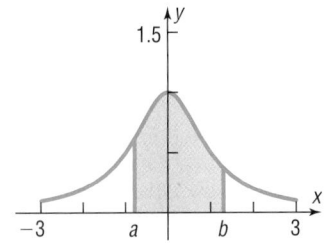

(a) Find the exact area under the graph of $y = \dfrac{1}{1 + x^2}$ and above the x-axis between $x = 0$ and $x = \sqrt{3}$.

(b) Find the exact area under the graph of $y = \dfrac{1}{1 + x^2}$ and above the x-axis between $x = -\dfrac{\sqrt{3}}{3}$ and $x = 1$.

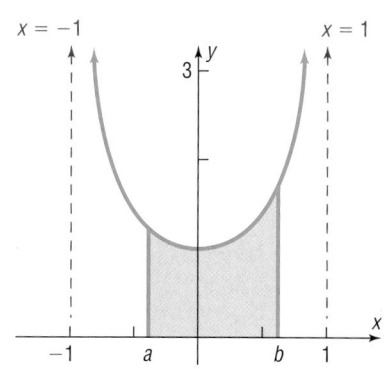

△ **78. Area under a Curve** The area under the graph of

$y = \dfrac{1}{\sqrt{1 - x^2}}$ and above the x-axis between $x = a$ and $x = b$ is given by

$$\sin^{-1} b - \sin^{-1} a$$

See the figure.

(a) Find the exact area under the graph of $y = \dfrac{1}{\sqrt{1 - x^2}}$ and above the x-axis between $x = 0$ and $x = \dfrac{\sqrt{3}}{2}$.

(b) Find the exact area under the graph of $y = \dfrac{1}{\sqrt{1 - x^2}}$ and above the x-axis between $x = -\dfrac{1}{2}$ and $x = \dfrac{1}{2}$.

Problems 79 and 80 require the following discussion:
The shortest distance between two points on Earth's surface can be determined from the latitude and longitude of the two locations. For example, if location 1 has (lat, lon) = (α_1, β_1) and location 2 has (lat, lon) = (α_2, β_2), the shortest distance between the two locations is approximately

$$d = \frac{2\pi}{360} r \cos^{-1}[(\cos \alpha_1 \cos \beta_1 \cos \alpha_2 \cos \beta_2) + (\cos \alpha_1 \sin \beta_1 \cos \alpha_2 \sin \beta_2) + (\sin \alpha_1 \sin \alpha_2)]$$

where $r = $ radius of Earth ≈ 3960 miles and the inverse cosine function is expressed in radians. Also N latitude and E longitude are positive angles while S latitude and W longitude are negative angles.

Source: www.infoplease.com

City	Latitude	Longitude
Chicago, IL	41°50′N	87°37′W
Honolulu, HI	21°18′N	157°50′W
Melbourne, Australia	37°47′S	144°58′E

79. Shortest Distance from Chicago to Honolulu Find the shortest distance from Chicago, latitude 41°50′N, longitude 87°37′W to Honolulu, latitude 21°18′N, longitude 157°50′W. Round your answer to the nearest mile.

80. Shortest Distance from Honolulu to Melbourne, Australia Find the shortest distance from Honolulu to Melbourne, Australia, latitude 37°47′S, longitude 144°58′E. Round your answer to the nearest mile.

'Are You Prepared?' Answers

1. Domain: the set of all real numbers; range: $-1 \le y \le 1$

2. Two answers are possible: $x \le 1$ or $x \ge 1$

3. $[3, \infty)$

4. True

5. $1; \dfrac{\sqrt{3}}{2}$

6. $-\dfrac{1}{2}; -1$

7.2 The Inverse Trigonometric Functions (Continued)

PREPARING FOR THIS SECTION *Before getting started, review the following concepts:*

- Finding Exact Values Given the Value of a Trigonometric Function and the Quadrant of the Angle (Section 6.3, pp. 389–391)
- Graphs of the Secant, Cosecant, and Cotangent Functions (Section 6.5, pp. 414–417)
- Domain and Range of the Secant, Cosecant, and Cotangent Functions (Section 6.3, pp. 382–384)

Now Work the 'Are You Prepared?' problems on page 457.

OBJECTIVES 1 Find the Exact Value of Expressions Involving the Inverse Sine, Cosine, and Tangent Functions (p. 454)

2 Know the Definitions of the Inverse Secant, Cosecant, and Cotangent Functions (p. 455)

3 Use a Calculator to Evaluate $\sec^{-1} x$, $\csc^{-1} x$, and $\cot^{-1} x$ (p. 456)

4 Write a Trigonometric Expression as an Algebraic Expression (p. 456)

1 Find the Exact Value of Expressions Involving the Inverse Sine, Cosine, and Tangent Functions

EXAMPLE 1	Finding the Exact Value of Expressions Involving Inverse Trigonometric Functions

Figure 19

$\tan \theta = \dfrac{1}{2}$

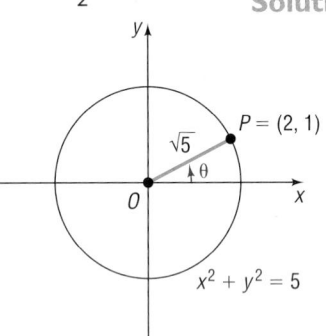

Find the exact value of: $\sin\left(\tan^{-1}\dfrac{1}{2}\right)$

Solution Let $\theta = \tan^{-1}\dfrac{1}{2}$. Then $\tan \theta = \dfrac{1}{2}$, where $-\dfrac{\pi}{2} < \theta < \dfrac{\pi}{2}$. We seek $\sin \theta$. Because $\tan \theta > 0$, it follows that $0 < \theta < \dfrac{\pi}{2}$, so θ lies in quadrant I. Since $\tan \theta = \dfrac{1}{2} = \dfrac{y}{x}$, we let $x = 2$ and $y = 1$. Since $r = d(O, P) = \sqrt{2^2 + 1^2} = \sqrt{5}$, the point $P = (x, y) = (2, 1)$ is on the circle $x^2 + y^2 = 5$. See Figure 19. Then, with $x = 2$, $y = 1$, and $r = \sqrt{5}$, we have

$$\sin\left(\tan^{-1}\dfrac{1}{2}\right) = \sin \theta = \dfrac{1}{\sqrt{5}} = \dfrac{\sqrt{5}}{5}$$

$\uparrow$
$\sin \theta = \dfrac{y}{r}$

EXAMPLE 2	Finding the Exact Value of Expressions Involving Inverse Trigonometric Functions

Find the exact value of: $\cos\left[\sin^{-1}\left(-\dfrac{1}{3}\right)\right]$

Figure 20

$\sin \theta = -\dfrac{1}{3}$

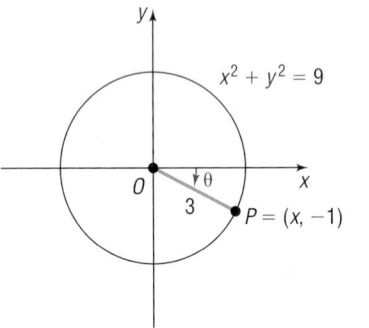

Solution Let $\theta = \sin^{-1}\left(-\dfrac{1}{3}\right)$. Then $\sin \theta = -\dfrac{1}{3}$ and $-\dfrac{\pi}{2} \le \theta \le \dfrac{\pi}{2}$. We seek $\cos \theta$. Because $\sin \theta < 0$, it follows that $-\dfrac{\pi}{2} \le \theta < 0$, so θ lies in quadrant IV. Since $\sin \theta = \dfrac{-1}{3} = \dfrac{y}{r}$, we let $y = -1$ and $r = 3$. The point $P = (x, y) = (x, -1)$, $x > 0$, is on a circle of radius 3, $x^2 + y^2 = 9$. See Figure 20. Then

$$\begin{aligned} x^2 + y^2 &= 9 \\ x^2 + (-1)^2 &= 9 \qquad y = -1 \\ x^2 &= 8 \\ x &= 2\sqrt{2} \qquad x > 0 \end{aligned}$$

Then we have $x = 2\sqrt{2}$, $y = -1$, and $r = 3$, so

$$\cos\left[\sin^{-1}\left(-\dfrac{1}{3}\right)\right] = \cos \theta = \dfrac{2\sqrt{2}}{3}$$

$\uparrow$
$\cos \theta = \dfrac{x}{r}$

EXAMPLE 3	Finding the Exact Value of Expressions Involving Inverse Trigonometric Functions

Find the exact value of: $\tan\left[\cos^{-1}\left(-\dfrac{1}{3}\right)\right]$

Solution Let $\theta = \cos^{-1}\left(-\dfrac{1}{3}\right)$. Then $\cos \theta = -\dfrac{1}{3}$ and $0 \le \theta \le \pi$. We seek $\tan \theta$. Because $\cos \theta < 0$, it follows that $\dfrac{\pi}{2} < \theta \le \pi$, so θ lies in quadrant II. Since $\cos \theta = \dfrac{-1}{3} = \dfrac{x}{r}$, we let $x = -1$ and $r = 3$. The point $P = (x, y) = (-1, y)$, $y > 0$, is on a circle of radius $r = 3$, $x^2 + y^2 = 9$. See Figure 21. Then

$$\begin{aligned} x^2 + y^2 &= 9 \\ (-1)^2 + y^2 &= 9 \qquad x = -1 \end{aligned}$$

Figure 21

$$\cos\theta = -\frac{1}{3}$$

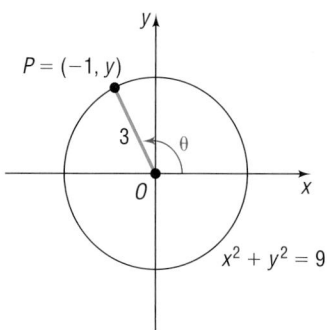

$$y^2 = 8$$
$$y = 2\sqrt{2} \qquad y > 0$$

Then, we have $x = -1$, $y = 2\sqrt{2}$, and $r = 3$, so

$$\tan\left[\cos^{-1}\left(-\frac{1}{3}\right)\right] = \tan\theta = \frac{2\sqrt{2}}{-1} = -2\sqrt{2}$$

$$\uparrow \; {\scriptstyle \tan\theta = \frac{y}{x}}$$

Now Work PROBLEMS 9 AND 27

2 Know the Definitions of the Inverse Secant, Cosecant, and Cotangent Functions

The inverse secant, inverse cosecant, and inverse cotangent functions are defined as follows:

DEFINITION

> $$y = \sec^{-1} x \quad \text{means} \quad x = \sec y \qquad (1)$$
> $$\text{where} \quad |x| \ge 1 \quad \text{and} \quad 0 \le y \le \pi, \quad y \ne \frac{\pi}{2}{}^*$$
>
> $$y = \csc^{-1} x \quad \text{means} \quad x = \csc y \qquad (2)$$
> $$\text{where} \quad |x| \ge 1 \quad \text{and} \quad -\frac{\pi}{2} \le y \le \frac{\pi}{2}, \quad y \ne 0^\dagger$$
>
> $$y = \cot^{-1} x \quad \text{means} \quad x = \cot y \qquad (3)$$
> $$\text{where} \quad -\infty < x < \infty \quad \text{and} \quad 0 < y < \pi$$

You are encouraged to review the graphs of the cotangent, cosecant, and secant functions in Figures 71, 72, and 73 in Section 6.5 to help you to see the basis for these definitions.

EXAMPLE 4

Finding the Exact Value of an Inverse Cosecant Function

Find the exact value of: $\csc^{-1} 2$

Solution

Let $\theta = \csc^{-1} 2$. We seek the angle θ, $-\dfrac{\pi}{2} \le \theta \le \dfrac{\pi}{2}$, $\theta \ne 0$, whose cosecant equals 2 $\left(\text{or, equivalently, whose sine equals } \dfrac{1}{2}\right)$.

$$\theta = \csc^{-1} 2 \qquad -\frac{\pi}{2} \le \theta \le \frac{\pi}{2}, \quad \theta \ne 0$$
$$\csc\theta = 2 \qquad -\frac{\pi}{2} \le \theta \le \frac{\pi}{2}, \quad \theta \ne 0 \quad {\scriptstyle \sin\theta = \frac{1}{2}}$$

The only angle θ in the interval $-\dfrac{\pi}{2} \le \theta \le \dfrac{\pi}{2}$, $\theta \ne 0$, whose cosecant is 2 $\left[\sin\theta = \dfrac{1}{2}\right]$ is $\dfrac{\pi}{6}$, so $\csc^{-1} 2 = \dfrac{\pi}{6}$.

Now Work PROBLEM 39

*Most books use this definition. A few use the restriction $0 \le y < \dfrac{\pi}{2}$, $\pi \le y < \dfrac{3\pi}{2}$.

†Most books use this definition. A few use the restriction $-\pi < y \le -\dfrac{\pi}{2}$, $0 < y \le \dfrac{\pi}{2}$.

3 Use a Calculator to Evaluate $\sec^{-1} x$, $\csc^{-1} x$, and $\cot^{-1} x$

Most calculators do not have keys for evaluating the inverse cotangent, cosecant, and secant functions. The easiest way to evaluate them is to convert to an inverse trigonometric function whose range is the same as the one to be evaluated. In this regard, notice that $y = \cot^{-1} x$ and $y = \sec^{-1} x$, except where undefined, each have the same range as $y = \cos^{-1} x$; $y = \csc^{-1} x$, except where undefined, has the same range as $y = \sin^{-1} x$.

NOTE Remember, the range of $y = \sin^{-1}x$ is $\left[-\dfrac{\pi}{2}, \dfrac{\pi}{2} \right]$; the range of $y = \cos^{-1}x$ is $[0, \pi]$. ∎

EXAMPLE 5   **Approximating the Value of Inverse Trigonometric Functions**

Use a calculator to approximate each expression in radians rounded to two decimal places.

(a) $\sec^{-1} 3$ (b) $\csc^{-1}(-4)$ (c) $\cot^{-1} \dfrac{1}{2}$ (d) $\cot^{-1}(-2)$

Solution   First, set your calculator to radian mode.

(a) Let $\theta = \sec^{-1} 3$. Then $\sec \theta = 3$ and $0 \le \theta \le \pi, \theta \ne \dfrac{\pi}{2}$. We seek $\cos \theta$ because $y = \cos^{-1}x$ has the same range as $y = \sec^{-1}x$, except where undefined. Since $\sec \theta = \dfrac{1}{\cos \theta} = 3$, we have $\cos \theta = \dfrac{1}{3}$. Then $\theta = \cos^{-1} \dfrac{1}{3}$ and

$$\sec^{-1} 3 = \theta = \cos^{-1} \dfrac{1}{3} \underset{\underset{\text{Use a calculator.}}{\uparrow}}{\approx} 1.23$$

Figure 22
$\cot \theta = \dfrac{1}{2}, 0 < \theta < \pi$

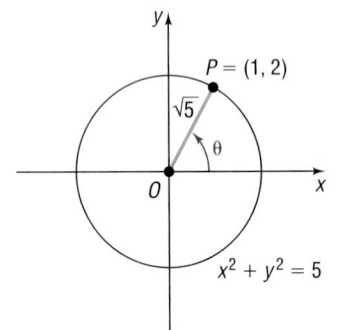

(b) Let $\theta = \csc^{-1}(-4)$. Then $\csc \theta = -4, -\dfrac{\pi}{2} \le \theta \le \dfrac{\pi}{2}, \theta \ne 0$. We seek $\sin \theta$ because $y = \sin^{-1}x$ has the same range as $y = \csc^{-1}x$, except where undefined. Since $\csc \theta = \dfrac{1}{\sin \theta} = -4$, we have $\sin \theta = -\dfrac{1}{4}$. Then $\theta = \sin^{-1}\left(-\dfrac{1}{4} \right)$, and

$$\csc^{-1}(-4) = \theta = \sin^{-1}\left(-\dfrac{1}{4} \right) \approx -0.25$$

(c) We proceed as before. Let $\theta = \cot^{-1} \dfrac{1}{2}$. Then $\cot \theta = \dfrac{1}{2}, 0 < \theta < \pi$. From these facts we know that θ lies in quadrant I. We seek $\cos \theta$ because $y = \cos^{-1}x$ has the same range as $y = \cot^{-1}x$, except where undefined. To find $\cos \theta$, we use Figure 22. Then $\cos \theta = \dfrac{1}{\sqrt{5}}, 0 < \theta < \dfrac{\pi}{2}, \theta = \cos^{-1}\left(\dfrac{1}{\sqrt{5}} \right)$, and

$$\cot^{-1} \dfrac{1}{2} = \theta = \cos^{-1}\left(\dfrac{1}{\sqrt{5}} \right) \approx 1.11$$

Figure 23
$\cot \theta = -2, 0 < \theta < \pi$

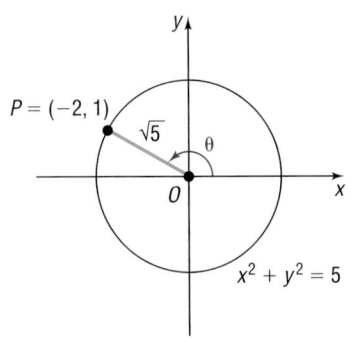

(d) Let $\theta = \cot^{-1}(-2)$. Then $\cot \theta = -2, 0 < \theta < \pi$. From these facts we know that θ lies in quadrant II. We seek $\cos \theta$. To find it, we use Figure 23. Then $\cos \theta = -\dfrac{2}{\sqrt{5}}, \dfrac{\pi}{2} < \theta < \pi, \theta = \cos^{-1}\left(-\dfrac{2}{\sqrt{5}} \right)$, and

$$\cot^{-1}(-2) = \theta = \cos^{-1}\left(-\dfrac{2}{\sqrt{5}} \right) \approx 2.68$$

➤ **Now Work** PROBLEM 45

4 Write a Trigonometric Expression as an Algebraic Expression

EXAMPLE 6   **Writing a Trigonometric Expression as an Algebraic Expression**

Write $\sin(\tan^{-1}u)$ as an algebraic expression containing u.

Solution   Let $\theta = \tan^{-1}u$ so that $\tan\theta = u, -\dfrac{\pi}{2} < \theta < \dfrac{\pi}{2}, -\infty < u < \infty$. As a result, we know that $\sec\theta > 0$. Then

$$\sin(\tan^{-1}u) = \sin\theta = \sin\theta \cdot \frac{\cos\theta}{\cos\theta} = \tan\theta\cos\theta = \frac{\tan\theta}{\sec\theta} = \frac{\tan\theta}{\sqrt{1+\tan^2\theta}} = \frac{u}{\sqrt{1+u^2}}$$

$$\underset{\substack{\uparrow \\ \text{Multiply by 1:} \frac{\cos\theta}{\cos\theta}.}}{} \qquad \underset{\substack{\uparrow \\ \frac{\sin\theta}{\cos\theta}=\tan\theta \quad \sec^2\theta=1+\tan^2\theta}}{} \qquad \underset{\substack{\uparrow \\ \sec\theta>0}}{}$$

■

Now Work PROBLEM 57

7.2 Assess Your Understanding

'Are You Prepared?' *Answers are given at the end of these exercises. If you get a wrong answer, read the pages listed in red.*

1. What is the domain and the range of $y = \sec x$? (pp. 382–384)

2. True or False   The graph of $y = \sec x$ is increasing on the interval $\left[0, \dfrac{\pi}{2}\right)$ and on the interval $\left(\dfrac{\pi}{2}, \pi\right]$. (p. 415)

3. If $\cot\theta = -2$ and $0 < \theta < \pi$, then $\cos\theta = $ _____. (pp. 389–391)

Concepts and Vocabulary

4. $y = \sec^{-1}x$ means _____, where $|x|$ _____ and _____ $\leq y \leq$ _____, $y \neq \dfrac{\pi}{2}$.

5. $\cos(\tan^{-1}1) = $ ____.

6. True or False   It is impossible to obtain exact values for the inverse secant function.

7. True or False $\csc^{-1}0.5$ is not defined.

8. True or False   The domain of the inverse cotangent function is the set of real numbers.

Skill Building

In Problems 9–36, find the exact value of each expression.

9. $\cos\left(\sin^{-1}\dfrac{\sqrt{2}}{2}\right)$

10. $\sin\left(\cos^{-1}\dfrac{1}{2}\right)$

11. $\tan\left[\cos^{-1}\left(-\dfrac{\sqrt{3}}{2}\right)\right]$

12. $\tan\left[\sin^{-1}\left(-\dfrac{1}{2}\right)\right]$

13. $\sec\left(\cos^{-1}\dfrac{1}{2}\right)$

14. $\cot\left[\sin^{-1}\left(-\dfrac{1}{2}\right)\right]$

15. $\csc(\tan^{-1}1)$

16. $\sec\left(\tan^{-1}\sqrt{3}\right)$

17. $\sin[\tan^{-1}(-1)]$

18. $\cos\left[\sin^{-1}\left(-\dfrac{\sqrt{3}}{2}\right)\right]$

19. $\sec\left[\sin^{-1}\left(-\dfrac{1}{2}\right)\right]$

20. $\csc\left[\cos^{-1}\left(-\dfrac{\sqrt{3}}{2}\right)\right]$

21. $\cos^{-1}\left(\cos\dfrac{5\pi}{4}\right)$

22. $\tan^{-1}\left(\tan\dfrac{2\pi}{3}\right)$

23. $\sin^{-1}\left[\sin\left(-\dfrac{7\pi}{6}\right)\right]$

24. $\cos^{-1}\left[\cos\left(-\dfrac{\pi}{3}\right)\right]$

25. $\tan\left(\sin^{-1}\dfrac{1}{3}\right)$

26. $\tan\left(\cos^{-1}\dfrac{1}{3}\right)$

27. $\sec\left(\tan^{-1}\dfrac{1}{2}\right)$

28. $\cos\left(\sin^{-1}\dfrac{\sqrt{2}}{3}\right)$

29. $\cot\left[\sin^{-1}\left(-\dfrac{\sqrt{2}}{3}\right)\right]$

30. $\csc[\tan^{-1}(-2)]$

31. $\sin[\tan^{-1}(-3)]$

32. $\cot\left[\cos^{-1}\left(-\dfrac{\sqrt{3}}{3}\right)\right]$

33. $\sec\left(\sin^{-1}\dfrac{2\sqrt{5}}{5}\right)$

34. $\csc\left(\tan^{-1}\dfrac{1}{2}\right)$

35. $\sin^{-1}\left(\cos\dfrac{3\pi}{4}\right)$

36. $\cos^{-1}\left(\sin\dfrac{7\pi}{6}\right)$

In Problems 37–44, find the exact value of each expression.

37. $\cot^{-1}\sqrt{3}$

38. $\cot^{-1}1$

39. $\csc^{-1}(-1)$

40. $\csc^{-1}\sqrt{2}$

41. $\sec^{-1}\dfrac{2\sqrt{3}}{3}$

42. $\sec^{-1}(-2)$

43. $\cot^{-1}\left(-\dfrac{\sqrt{3}}{3}\right)$

44. $\csc^{-1}\left(-\dfrac{2\sqrt{3}}{3}\right)$

In Problems 45–56, use a calculator to find the value of each expression rounded to two decimal places.

45. $\sec^{-1}4$

46. $\csc^{-1}5$

47. $\cot^{-1}2$

48. $\sec^{-1}(-3)$

49. $\csc^{-1}(-3)$

50. $\cot^{-1}\left(-\dfrac{1}{2}\right)$

51. $\cot^{-1}\left(-\sqrt{5}\right)$

52. $\cot^{-1}(-8.1)$

53. $\csc^{-1}\left(-\dfrac{3}{2}\right)$

54. $\sec^{-1}\left(-\dfrac{4}{3}\right)$

55. $\cot^{-1}\left(-\dfrac{3}{2}\right)$

56. $\cot^{-1}\left(-\sqrt{10}\right)$

In Problems 57–66, write each trigonometric expression as an algebraic expression in u.

57. $\cos(\tan^{-1}u)$ **58.** $\sin(\cos^{-1}u)$ **59.** $\tan(\sin^{-1}u)$ **60.** $\tan(\cos^{-1}u)$ **61.** $\sin(\sec^{-1}u)$

62. $\sin(\cot^{-1}u)$ **63.** $\cos(\csc^{-1}u)$ **64.** $\cos(\sec^{-1}u)$ **65.** $\tan(\cot^{-1}u)$ **66.** $\tan(\sec^{-1}u)$

Mixed Practice

In Problems 67–78, $f(x) = \sin x$, $g(x) = \cos x$, and $h(x) = \tan x$. Find the exact value of each composite function.

67. $g\left(f^{-1}\left(\dfrac{12}{13}\right)\right)$ **68.** $f\left(g^{-1}\left(\dfrac{5}{13}\right)\right)$ **69.** $g^{-1}\left(f\left(\dfrac{7\pi}{4}\right)\right)$ **70.** $f^{-1}\left(g\left(\dfrac{5\pi}{6}\right)\right)$

71. $h\left(f^{-1}\left(-\dfrac{3}{5}\right)\right)$ **72.** $h\left(g^{-1}\left(-\dfrac{4}{5}\right)\right)$ **73.** $g\left(h^{-1}\left(\dfrac{12}{5}\right)\right)$ **74.** $f\left(h^{-1}\left(\dfrac{5}{12}\right)\right)$

75. $g^{-1}\left(f\left(-\dfrac{4\pi}{3}\right)\right)$ **76.** $g^{-1}\left(f\left(-\dfrac{5\pi}{6}\right)\right)$ **77.** $h\left(g^{-1}\left(-\dfrac{1}{4}\right)\right)$ **78.** $h\left(f^{-1}\left(-\dfrac{2}{5}\right)\right)$

Applications and Extensions

Problems 79 and 80 require the following discussion: When granular materials are allowed to fall freely, they form conical (cone-shaped) piles. The naturally occurring angle of slope, measured from the horizontal, at which the loose material comes to rest is called the angle of repose *and varies for different materials. The angle of repose θ is related to the height h and base radius r of the conical pile by the equation $\theta = \cot^{-1}\dfrac{r}{h}$. See the illustration.*

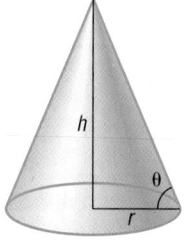

79. Angle of Repose: Deicing Salt Because of potential transportation issues (for example, frozen waterways), the deicing salt used by highway departments in the Midwest must be ordered early and stored for future use. When deicing salt is stored in a pile 14 feet high, the diameter of the base of the pile is 45 feet.
(a) Find the angle of repose for deicing salt.
(b) What is the base diameter of a pile that is 17 feet high?
(c) What is the height of a pile that has a base diameter of approximately 122 feet?

Source: *Salt Institute, The Salt Storage Handbook,* 2006

80. Angle of Repose: Bunker Sand The steepness of sand bunkers on a golf course is affected by the angle of repose of the sand (a larger angle of repose allows for steeper bunkers). A freestanding pile of loose sand from a United States Golf Association (USGA) bunker had a height of 4 feet and a base diameter of approximately 6.68 feet.
(a) Find the angle of repose for USGA bunker sand.
(b) What is the height of such a pile if the diameter of the base is 8 feet?
(c) A 6-foot high pile of loose Tour Grade 50/50 sand has a base diameter of approximately 8.44 feet. Which type of sand (USGA or Tour Grade 50/50) would be better suited for steep bunkers?

Source: 2004 *Annual Report, Purdue University Turfgrass Science Program*

81. Artillery A projectile fired into the first quadrant from the origin of a coordinate system will pass through the point (x, y) at time t according to the relationship $\cot\theta = \dfrac{2x}{2y + gt^2}$ where θ = the angle of elevation of the launcher and g = the acceleration due to gravity = 32.2 feet/second². An artilleryman is firing at an enemy bunker located 2450 feet up the side of a hill that is 6175 feet away. He fires a round, and exactly 2.27 seconds later he scores a direct hit.
(a) What angle of elevation did he use?

(b) If the angle of elevation is also given by $\sec\theta = \dfrac{v_0 t}{x}$, where v_0 is the muzzle velocity of the weapon, find the muzzle velocity of the artillery piece he used.

Source: *www.egwald.com/geometry/projectile3d.php*

82. Using a graphing utility, graph $y = \cot^{-1}x$.
83. Using a graphing utility, graph $y = \sec^{-1}x$.
84. Using a graphing utility, graph $y = \csc^{-1}x$.

Discussion and Writing

85. Explain in your own words how you would use your calculator to find the value of $\cot^{-1}10$.

86. Consult three books on calculus and write down the definition in each of $y = \sec^{-1}x$ and $y = \csc^{-1}x$. Compare these with the definitions given in this book.

'Are You Prepared?' Answers

1. Domain: $\left\{x \,\middle|\, x \neq \text{odd integer multiples of } \dfrac{\pi}{2}\right\}$; range: $\{y \leq -1 \text{ or } y \geq 1\}$ **2.** True   **3.** $\dfrac{-2\sqrt{5}}{5}$

7.3 Trigonometric Identities

PREPARING FOR THIS SECTION   *Before getting started, review the following:*

- Fundamental Identities (Section 6.3, p. 388)
- Even–Odd Properties (Section 6.3, p. 391)

Now Work the 'Are You Prepared?' problems on page 463.

OBJECTIVES   **1** Use Algebra to Simplify Trigonometric Expressions (p. 460)

   2 Establish Identities (p. 461)

We saw in the previous chapter that the trigonometric functions lend themselves to a wide variety of identities. Before establishing some additional identities, let's review the definition of an *identity*.

DEFINITION   Two functions f and g are said to be **identically equal** if

$$f(x) = g(x)$$

for every value of x for which both functions are defined. Such an equation is referred to as an **identity.** An equation that is not an identity is called a **conditional equation.**

For example, the following are identities:

$$(x + 1)^2 = x^2 + 2x + 1 \qquad \sin^2 x + \cos^2 x = 1 \qquad \csc x = \frac{1}{\sin x}$$

The following are conditional equations:

$2x + 5 = 0$ True only if $x = -\dfrac{5}{2}$

$\sin x = 0$ True only if $x = k\pi$, k an integer

$\sin x = \cos x$ True only if $x = \dfrac{\pi}{4} + 2k\pi$ or $x = \dfrac{5\pi}{4} + 2k\pi$, k an integer

The following summarizes the trigonometric identities that we have established thus far.

Quotient Identities

$$\tan \theta = \frac{\sin \theta}{\cos \theta} \qquad \cot \theta = \frac{\cos \theta}{\sin \theta}$$

Reciprocal Identities

$$\csc \theta = \frac{1}{\sin \theta} \qquad \sec \theta = \frac{1}{\cos \theta} \qquad \cot \theta = \frac{1}{\tan \theta}$$

Pythagorean Identities

$$\sin^2 \theta + \cos^2 \theta = 1 \qquad \tan^2 \theta + 1 = \sec^2 \theta$$
$$\cot^2 \theta + 1 = \csc^2 \theta$$

Even–Odd Identities

$$\sin(-\theta) = -\sin \theta \qquad \cos(-\theta) = \cos \theta \qquad \tan(-\theta) = -\tan \theta$$
$$\csc(-\theta) = -\csc \theta \qquad \sec(-\theta) = \sec \theta \qquad \cot(-\theta) = -\cot \theta$$

This list of identities comprises what we shall refer to as the **basic trigonometric identities.** These identities should not merely be memorized, but should be *known* (just as you know your name rather than have it memorized). In fact, minor variations of a basic identity are often used. For example, we might want to use

$$\sin^2 \theta = 1 - \cos^2 \theta \quad \text{or} \quad \cos^2 \theta = 1 - \sin^2 \theta$$

instead of $\sin^2 \theta + \cos^2 \theta = 1$. For this reason, among others, you need to know these relationships and be very comfortable with variations of them.

1 Use Algebra to Simplify Trigonometric Expressions

The ability to use algebra to manipulate trigonometric expressions is a key skill that one must have to establish identities. Some of the techniques used in establishing identities are multiplying by a "well-chosen 1," writing a trigonometric expression over a common denominator, rewriting a trigonometric expression in terms of sine and cosine only, and factoring.

| EXAMPLE 1 | **Using Algebraic Techniques to Simplify Trigonometric Expressions** |

(a) Simplify $\dfrac{\cot \theta}{\csc \theta}$ by rewriting each trigonometric function in terms of sine and cosine functions.

(b) Show that $\dfrac{\cos \theta}{1 + \sin \theta} = \dfrac{1 - \sin \theta}{\cos \theta}$ by multiplying the numerator and denominator by $1 - \sin \theta$.

(c) Simplify $\dfrac{1 + \sin u}{\sin u} + \dfrac{\cot u - \cos u}{\cos u}$ by rewriting the expression over a common denominator.

(d) Simplify $\dfrac{\sin^2 v - 1}{\tan v \sin v - \tan v}$ by factoring.

Solution

(a) $\dfrac{\cot \theta}{\csc \theta} = \dfrac{\dfrac{\cos \theta}{\sin \theta}}{\dfrac{1}{\sin \theta}} = \dfrac{\cos \theta}{\sin \theta} \cdot \dfrac{\sin \theta}{1} = \cos \theta$

(b) $\dfrac{\cos \theta}{1 + \sin \theta} = \dfrac{\cos \theta}{1 + \sin \theta} \cdot \dfrac{1 - \sin \theta}{1 - \sin \theta} = \dfrac{\cos \theta(1 - \sin \theta)}{1 - \sin^2 \theta}$

$\uparrow$ Multiply by a well-chosen 1: $\dfrac{1 - \sin \theta}{1 - \sin \theta}$.

$= \dfrac{\cos \theta(1 - \sin \theta)}{\cos^2 \theta} = \dfrac{1 - \sin \theta}{\cos \theta}$

(c) $\dfrac{1 + \sin u}{\sin u} + \dfrac{\cot u - \cos u}{\cos u} = \dfrac{1 + \sin u}{\sin u} \cdot \dfrac{\cos u}{\cos u} + \dfrac{\cot u - \cos u}{\cos u} \cdot \dfrac{\sin u}{\sin u}$

$= \dfrac{\cos u + \sin u \cos u + \cot u \sin u - \cos u \sin u}{\sin u \cos u} = \dfrac{\cos u + \dfrac{\cos u}{\sin u} \cdot \sin u}{\sin u \cos u}$

$\uparrow \cot u = \dfrac{\cos u}{\sin u}$

$= \dfrac{\cos u + \cos u}{\sin u \cos u} = \dfrac{2 \cos u}{\sin u \cos u} = \dfrac{2}{\sin u}$

(d) $\dfrac{\sin^2 v - 1}{\tan v \sin v - \tan v} = \dfrac{(\sin v + 1)(\sin v - 1)}{\tan v(\sin v - 1)} = \dfrac{\sin v + 1}{\tan v}$

Now Work PROBLEMS 9, 11, AND 13

2 Establish Identities

In the examples that follow, the directions will read "Establish the identity. . . . " As you will see, this is accomplished by starting with one side of the given equation (usually the one containing the more complicated expression) and, using appropriate basic identities and algebraic manipulations, arriving at the other side. The selection of appropriate basic identities to obtain the desired result is learned only through experience and lots of practice.

| EXAMPLE 2 | **Establishing an Identity** |

Establish the identity: $\csc \theta \cdot \tan \theta = \sec \theta$

Solution

NOTE A graphing utility can be used to provide evidence of an identity. For example, if we graph $Y_1 = \csc x \cdot \tan x$ and $Y_2 = \sec x$, the graphs appear to be the same. This provides evidence that $Y_1 = Y_2$. However, it does not prove their equality. A graphing utility *cannot* be used to establish an identity—identities must be established algebraically. ∎

We start with the left side, because it contains the more complicated expression, and apply a reciprocal identity and a quotient identity.

$$\csc \theta \cdot \tan \theta = \frac{1}{\sin \theta} \cdot \frac{\sin \theta}{\cos \theta} = \frac{1}{\cos \theta} = \sec \theta$$

Having arrived at the right side, the identity is established.

▬▬▬ **Now Work** PROBLEM 19

| EXAMPLE 3 | **Establishing an Identity** |

Establish the identity: $\sin^2(-\theta) + \cos^2(-\theta) = 1$

Solution

We begin with the left side and, because the arguments are $-\theta$, apply Even–Odd Identities.

$$\sin^2(-\theta) + \cos^2(-\theta) = [\sin(-\theta)]^2 + [\cos(-\theta)]^2$$
$$= (-\sin \theta)^2 + (\cos \theta)^2 \qquad \text{Even–Odd Identities}$$
$$= (\sin \theta)^2 + (\cos \theta)^2$$
$$= 1 \qquad \text{Pythagorean Identity}$$

| EXAMPLE 4 | **Establishing an Identity** |

Establish the identity: $\dfrac{\sin^2(-\theta) - \cos^2(-\theta)}{\sin(-\theta) - \cos(-\theta)} = \cos \theta - \sin \theta$

Solution

We begin with two observations: The left side contains the more complicated expression. Also, the left side contains expressions with the argument $-\theta$, whereas the right side contains expressions with the argument θ. We decide, therefore, to start with the left side and apply Even–Odd Identities.

$$\frac{\sin^2(-\theta) - \cos^2(-\theta)}{\sin(-\theta) - \cos(-\theta)} = \frac{[\sin(-\theta)]^2 - [\cos(-\theta)]^2}{\sin(-\theta) - \cos(-\theta)}$$

$$= \frac{(-\sin \theta)^2 - (\cos \theta)^2}{-\sin \theta - \cos \theta} \qquad \text{Even–Odd Identities}$$

$$= \frac{(\sin \theta)^2 - (\cos \theta)^2}{-\sin \theta - \cos \theta} \qquad \text{Simplify.}$$

$$= \frac{(\sin \theta - \cos \theta)(\sin \theta + \cos \theta)}{-(\sin \theta + \cos \theta)} \qquad \text{Factor.}$$

$$= \frac{\sin \theta - \cos \theta}{-1} = -(\sin \theta - \cos \theta) = -\sin \theta + \cos \theta$$

$$= \cos \theta - \sin \theta \qquad \text{Cancel and simplify.}$$

| EXAMPLE 5 | Establishing an Identity |

Establish the identity: $\dfrac{1 + \tan u}{1 + \cot u} = \tan u$

Solution

$$\dfrac{1 + \tan u}{1 + \cot u} = \dfrac{1 + \tan u}{1 + \dfrac{1}{\tan u}} = \dfrac{1 + \tan u}{\dfrac{\tan u + 1}{\tan u}}$$

$$= \dfrac{\tan u(1 + \tan u)}{\tan u + 1} = \tan u$$

---- **Now Work** PROBLEMS 23 AND 27

When sums or differences of quotients appear, it is usually best to rewrite them as a single quotient, especially if the other side of the identity consists of only one term.

| EXAMPLE 6 | Establishing an Identity |

Establish the identity: $\dfrac{\sin \theta}{1 + \cos \theta} + \dfrac{1 + \cos \theta}{\sin \theta} = 2 \csc \theta$

Solution

The left side is more complicated, so we start with it and proceed to add.

$$\dfrac{\sin \theta}{1 + \cos \theta} + \dfrac{1 + \cos \theta}{\sin \theta} = \dfrac{\sin^2 \theta + (1 + \cos \theta)^2}{(1 + \cos \theta)(\sin \theta)} \qquad \text{Add the quotients.}$$

$$= \dfrac{\sin^2 \theta + 1 + 2 \cos \theta + \cos^2 \theta}{(1 + \cos \theta)(\sin \theta)} \qquad \text{Remove parentheses in the numerator.}$$

$$= \dfrac{(\sin^2 \theta + \cos^2 \theta) + 1 + 2 \cos \theta}{(1 + \cos \theta)(\sin \theta)} \qquad \text{Regroup.}$$

$$= \dfrac{2 + 2 \cos \theta}{(1 + \cos \theta)(\sin \theta)} \qquad \text{Pythagorean Identity}$$

$$= \dfrac{2(1 + \cos \theta)}{(1 + \cos \theta)(\sin \theta)} \qquad \text{Factor and cancel.}$$

$$= \dfrac{2}{\sin \theta}$$

$$= 2 \csc \theta \qquad \text{Reciprocal Identity}$$

---- **Now Work** PROBLEM 49

Sometimes it helps to write one side in terms of sine and cosine functions only.

| EXAMPLE 7 | Establishing an Identity |

Establish the identity: $\dfrac{\tan v + \cot v}{\sec v \csc v} = 1$

Solution

$$\frac{\tan v + \cot v}{\sec v \csc v} = \frac{\dfrac{\sin v}{\cos v} + \dfrac{\cos v}{\sin v}}{\dfrac{1}{\cos v} \cdot \dfrac{1}{\sin v}} = \frac{\dfrac{\sin^2 v + \cos^2 v}{\cos v \sin v}}{\dfrac{1}{\cos v \sin v}}$$

$\uparrow$ *Change to sines and cosines.* $\uparrow$ *Add the quotients in the numerator.*

$$= \frac{1}{\cos v \sin v} \cdot \frac{\cos v \sin v}{1} = 1$$

$\uparrow$ *Divide the quotients;*
$\sin^2 v + \cos^2 v = 1.$

──── **Now Work** PROBLEM 69

Sometimes, multiplying the numerator and denominator by an appropriate factor will result in a simplification.

EXAMPLE 8	**Establishing an Identity**

Establish the identity: $\dfrac{1 - \sin \theta}{\cos \theta} = \dfrac{\cos \theta}{1 + \sin \theta}$

Solution

We start with the left side and multiply the numerator and the denominator by $1 + \sin \theta$. (Alternatively, we could multiply the numerator and denominator of the right side by $1 - \sin \theta$.)

$$\frac{1 - \sin \theta}{\cos \theta} = \frac{1 - \sin \theta}{\cos \theta} \cdot \frac{1 + \sin \theta}{1 + \sin \theta}$$
Multiply the numerator and denominator by $1 + \sin \theta$.

$$= \frac{1 - \sin^2 \theta}{\cos \theta (1 + \sin \theta)}$$

$$= \frac{\cos^2 \theta}{\cos \theta (1 + \sin \theta)}$$
$1 - \sin^2 \theta = \cos^2 \theta$

$$= \frac{\cos \theta}{1 + \sin \theta}$$
Cancel.

──── **Now Work** PROBLEM 53

Although a lot of practice is the only real way to learn how to establish identities, the following guidelines should prove helpful.

WARNING Be careful not to handle identities to be established as if they were conditional equations. You *cannot* establish an identity by such methods as adding the same expression to each side and obtaining a true statement. This practice is not allowed, because the original statement is precisely the one that you are trying to establish. You do not know until it has been established that it is, in fact, true. ■

Guidelines for Establishing Identities

1. It is almost always preferable to start with the side containing the more complicated expression.
2. Rewrite sums or differences of quotients as a single quotient.
3. Sometimes rewriting one side in terms of sine and cosine functions only will help.
4. Always keep your goal in mind. As you manipulate one side of the expression, you must keep in mind the form of the expression on the other side.

7.3 Assess Your Understanding

'Are You Prepared?' *Answers are given at the end of these exercises. If you get a wrong answer, read the pages listed in red.*

1. True or False $\sin^2 \theta = 1 - \cos^2 \theta$. (p. 388)

2. True or False $\sin(-\theta) + \cos(-\theta) = \cos \theta - \sin \theta$. (p. 391)

Concepts and Vocabulary

3. Suppose that f and g are two functions with the same domain. If $f(x) = g(x)$ for every x in the domain, the equation is called a(n) _____. Otherwise, it is called a(n) _____ equation.

4. $\tan^2 \theta - \sec^2 \theta = $ _____.

5. $\cos(-\theta) - \cos \theta = $ _____.

6. True or False $\sin(-\theta) + \sin \theta = 0$ for any value of θ.

7. True or False In establishing an identity, it is often easiest to just multiply both sides by a well-chosen nonzero expression involving the variable.

8. True or False $\tan \theta \cdot \cos \theta = \sin \theta$ for any $\theta \neq (2k + 1)\dfrac{\pi}{2}$.

Skill Building

In Problems 9–18, simplify each trigonometric expression by following the indicated direction.

9. Rewrite in terms of sine and cosine functions: $\tan \theta \cdot \csc \theta$

10. Rewrite in terms of sine and cosine functions: $\cot \theta \cdot \sec \theta$

11. Multiply $\dfrac{\cos \theta}{1 - \sin \theta}$ by $\dfrac{1 + \sin \theta}{1 + \sin \theta}$.

12. Multiply $\dfrac{\sin \theta}{1 + \cos \theta}$ by $\dfrac{1 - \cos \theta}{1 - \cos \theta}$.

13. Rewrite over a common denominator:

$$\frac{\sin \theta + \cos \theta}{\cos \theta} + \frac{\cos \theta - \sin \theta}{\sin \theta}$$

14. Rewrite over a common denominator:

$$\frac{1}{1 - \cos v} + \frac{1}{1 + \cos v}$$

15. Multiply and simplify: $\dfrac{(\sin \theta + \cos \theta)(\sin \theta + \cos \theta) - 1}{\sin \theta \cos \theta}$

16. Multiply and simplify: $\dfrac{(\tan \theta + 1)(\tan \theta + 1) - \sec^2 \theta}{\tan \theta}$

17. Factor and simplify: $\dfrac{3 \sin^2 \theta + 4 \sin \theta + 1}{\sin^2 \theta + 2 \sin \theta + 1}$

18. Factor and simplify: $\dfrac{\cos^2 \theta - 1}{\cos^2 \theta - \cos \theta}$

In Problems 19–98, establish each identity.

19. $\csc \theta \cdot \cos \theta = \cot \theta$

20. $\sec \theta \cdot \sin \theta = \tan \theta$

21. $1 + \tan^2(-\theta) = \sec^2 \theta$

22. $1 + \cot^2(-\theta) = \csc^2 \theta$

23. $\cos \theta(\tan \theta + \cot \theta) = \csc \theta$

24. $\sin \theta(\cot \theta + \tan \theta) = \sec \theta$

25. $\tan u \cot u - \cos^2 u = \sin^2 u$

26. $\sin u \csc u - \cos^2 u = \sin^2 u$

27. $(\sec \theta - 1)(\sec \theta + 1) = \tan^2 \theta$

28. $(\csc \theta - 1)(\csc \theta + 1) = \cot^2 \theta$

29. $(\sec \theta + \tan \theta)(\sec \theta - \tan \theta) = 1$

30. $(\csc \theta + \cot \theta)(\csc \theta - \cot \theta) = 1$

31. $\cos^2 \theta(1 + \tan^2 \theta) = 1$

32. $(1 - \cos^2 \theta)(1 + \cot^2 \theta) = 1$

33. $(\sin \theta + \cos \theta)^2 + (\sin \theta - \cos \theta)^2 = 2$

34. $\tan^2 \theta \cos^2 \theta + \cot^2 \theta \sin^2 \theta = 1$

35. $\sec^4 \theta - \sec^2 \theta = \tan^4 \theta + \tan^2 \theta$

36. $\csc^4 \theta - \csc^2 \theta = \cot^4 \theta + \cot^2 \theta$

37. $\sec u - \tan u = \dfrac{\cos u}{1 + \sin u}$

38. $\csc u - \cot u = \dfrac{\sin u}{1 + \cos u}$

39. $3 \sin^2 \theta + 4 \cos^2 \theta = 3 + \cos^2 \theta$

40. $9 \sec^2 \theta - 5 \tan^2 \theta = 5 + 4 \sec^2 \theta$

41. $1 - \dfrac{\cos^2 \theta}{1 + \sin \theta} = \sin \theta$

42. $1 - \dfrac{\sin^2 \theta}{1 - \cos \theta} = -\cos \theta$

43. $\dfrac{1 + \tan v}{1 - \tan v} = \dfrac{\cot v + 1}{\cot v - 1}$

44. $\dfrac{\csc v - 1}{\csc v + 1} = \dfrac{1 - \sin v}{1 + \sin v}$

45. $\dfrac{\sec \theta}{\csc \theta} + \dfrac{\sin \theta}{\cos \theta} = 2 \tan \theta$

46. $\dfrac{\csc \theta - 1}{\cot \theta} = \dfrac{\cot \theta}{\csc \theta + 1}$

47. $\dfrac{1 + \sin \theta}{1 - \sin \theta} = \dfrac{\csc \theta + 1}{\csc \theta - 1}$

48. $\dfrac{\cos \theta + 1}{\cos \theta - 1} = \dfrac{1 + \sec \theta}{1 - \sec \theta}$

49. $\dfrac{1 - \sin v}{\cos v} + \dfrac{\cos v}{1 - \sin v} = 2 \sec v$

50. $\dfrac{\cos v}{1 + \sin v} + \dfrac{1 + \sin v}{\cos v} = 2 \sec v$

51. $\dfrac{\sin \theta}{\sin \theta - \cos \theta} = \dfrac{1}{1 - \cot \theta}$

52. $1 - \dfrac{\sin^2 \theta}{1 + \cos \theta} = \cos \theta$

53. $\dfrac{1 - \sin \theta}{1 + \sin \theta} = (\sec \theta - \tan \theta)^2$

54. $\dfrac{1 - \cos \theta}{1 + \cos \theta} = (\csc \theta - \cot \theta)^2$

55. $\dfrac{\cos \theta}{1 - \tan \theta} + \dfrac{\sin \theta}{1 - \cot \theta} = \sin \theta + \cos \theta$

56. $\dfrac{\cot \theta}{1 - \tan \theta} + \dfrac{\tan \theta}{1 - \cot \theta} = 1 + \tan \theta + \cot \theta$

57. $\tan \theta + \dfrac{\cos \theta}{1 + \sin \theta} = \sec \theta$

58. $\dfrac{\sin \theta \cos \theta}{\cos^2 \theta - \sin^2 \theta} = \dfrac{\tan \theta}{1 - \tan^2 \theta}$

59. $\dfrac{\tan \theta + \sec \theta - 1}{\tan \theta - \sec \theta + 1} = \tan \theta + \sec \theta$

60. $\dfrac{\sin \theta - \cos \theta + 1}{\sin \theta + \cos \theta - 1} = \dfrac{\sin \theta + 1}{\cos \theta}$

61. $\dfrac{\tan \theta - \cot \theta}{\tan \theta + \cot \theta} = \sin^2 \theta - \cos^2 \theta$

62. $\dfrac{\sec \theta - \cos \theta}{\sec \theta + \cos \theta} = \dfrac{\sin^2 \theta}{1 + \cos^2 \theta}$

63. $\dfrac{\tan u - \cot u}{\tan u + \cot u} + 1 = 2 \sin^2 u$

64. $\dfrac{\tan u - \cot u}{\tan u + \cot u} + 2 \cos^2 u = 1$

65. $\dfrac{\sec \theta + \tan \theta}{\cot \theta + \cos \theta} = \tan \theta \sec \theta$

66. $\dfrac{\sec \theta}{1 + \sec \theta} = \dfrac{1 - \cos \theta}{\sin^2 \theta}$

67. $\dfrac{1 - \tan^2 \theta}{1 + \tan^2 \theta} + 1 = 2 \cos^2 \theta$

68. $\dfrac{1 - \cot^2 \theta}{1 + \cot^2 \theta} + 2 \cos^2 \theta = 1$

69. $\dfrac{\sec \theta - \csc \theta}{\sec \theta \csc \theta} = \sin \theta - \cos \theta$

70. $\dfrac{\sin^2 \theta - \tan \theta}{\cos^2 \theta - \cot \theta} = \tan^2 \theta$

71. $\sec \theta - \cos \theta = \sin \theta \tan \theta$

72. $\tan \theta + \cot \theta = \sec \theta \csc \theta$

73. $\dfrac{1}{1 - \sin \theta} + \dfrac{1}{1 + \sin \theta} = 2 \sec^2 \theta$

74. $\dfrac{1 + \sin \theta}{1 - \sin \theta} - \dfrac{1 - \sin \theta}{1 + \sin \theta} = 4 \tan \theta \sec \theta$

75. $\dfrac{\sec \theta}{1 - \sin \theta} = \dfrac{1 + \sin \theta}{\cos^3 \theta}$

76. $\dfrac{1 + \sin \theta}{1 - \sin \theta} = (\sec \theta + \tan \theta)^2$

77. $\dfrac{(\sec v - \tan v)^2 + 1}{\csc v (\sec v - \tan v)} = 2 \tan v$

78. $\dfrac{\sec^2 v - \tan^2 v + \tan v}{\sec v} = \sin v + \cos v$

79. $\dfrac{\sin \theta + \cos \theta}{\cos \theta} - \dfrac{\sin \theta - \cos \theta}{\sin \theta} = \sec \theta \csc \theta$

80. $\dfrac{\sin \theta + \cos \theta}{\sin \theta} - \dfrac{\cos \theta - \sin \theta}{\cos \theta} = \sec \theta \csc \theta$

81. $\dfrac{\sin^3 \theta + \cos^3 \theta}{\sin \theta + \cos \theta} = 1 - \sin \theta \cos \theta$

82. $\dfrac{\sin^3 \theta + \cos^3 \theta}{1 - 2 \cos^2 \theta} = \dfrac{\sec \theta - \sin \theta}{\tan \theta - 1}$

83. $\dfrac{\cos^2 \theta - \sin^2 \theta}{1 - \tan^2 \theta} = \cos^2 \theta$

84. $\dfrac{\cos \theta + \sin \theta - \sin^3 \theta}{\sin \theta} = \cot \theta + \cos^2 \theta$

85. $\dfrac{(2 \cos^2 \theta - 1)^2}{\cos^4 \theta - \sin^4 \theta} = 1 - 2 \sin^2 \theta$

86. $\dfrac{1 - 2 \cos^2 \theta}{\sin \theta \cos \theta} = \tan \theta - \cot \theta$

87. $\dfrac{1 + \sin \theta + \cos \theta}{1 + \sin \theta - \cos \theta} = \dfrac{1 + \cos \theta}{\sin \theta}$

88. $\dfrac{1 + \cos \theta + \sin \theta}{1 + \cos \theta - \sin \theta} = \sec \theta + \tan \theta$

89. $(a \sin \theta + b \cos \theta)^2 + (a \cos \theta - b \sin \theta)^2 = a^2 + b^2$

90. $(2a \sin \theta \cos \theta)^2 + a^2 (\cos^2 \theta - \sin^2 \theta)^2 = a^2$

91. $\dfrac{\tan \alpha + \tan \beta}{\cot \alpha + \cot \beta} = \tan \alpha \tan \beta$

92. $(\tan \alpha + \tan \beta)(1 - \cot \alpha \cot \beta) + (\cot \alpha + \cot \beta)(1 - \tan \alpha \tan \beta) = 0$

93. $(\sin \alpha + \cos \beta)^2 + (\cos \beta + \sin \alpha)(\cos \beta - \sin \alpha) = 2 \cos \beta (\sin \alpha + \cos \beta)$

94. $(\sin \alpha - \cos \beta)^2 + (\cos \beta + \sin \alpha)(\cos \beta - \sin \alpha) = -2 \cos \beta (\sin \alpha - \cos \beta)$

95. $\ln |\sec \theta| = -\ln |\cos \theta|$

96. $\ln |\tan \theta| = \ln |\sin \theta| - \ln |\cos \theta|$

97. $\ln |1 + \cos \theta| + \ln |1 - \cos \theta| = 2 \ln |\sin \theta|$

98. $\ln |\sec \theta + \tan \theta| + \ln |\sec \theta - \tan \theta| = 0$

In Problems 99–102, show that the functions f and g are identically equal.

99. $f(x) = \sin x \cdot \tan x, \quad g(x) = \sec x - \cos x$

100. $f(x) = \cos x \cdot \cot x, \quad g(x) = \csc x - \sin x$

101. $f(\theta) = \dfrac{1 - \sin \theta}{\cos \theta} - \dfrac{\cos \theta}{1 + \sin \theta}, \quad g(\theta) = 0$

102. $f(\theta) = \tan \theta + \sec \theta, \quad g(\theta) = \dfrac{\cos \theta}{1 - \sin \theta}$

Applications and Extensions

103. Searchlights A searchlight at the grand opening of a new car dealership casts a spot of light on a wall located 75 meters from the searchlight. The acceleration $\ddot{r}$ of the spot of light is found to be $\ddot{r} = 1200 \sec \theta (2 \sec^2 \theta - 1)$. Show that this is equivalent to $\ddot{r} = 1200 \left(\dfrac{1 + \sin^2 \theta}{\cos^3 \theta} \right)$.

Source: Adapted from Hibbeler, *Engineering Mechanics: Dynamics*, 10th ed. © 2004.

104. Optical Measurement Optical methods of measurement often rely on the interference of two light waves. If two light waves, identical except for a phase lag, are mixed together, the resulting intensity, or irradiance, is given by

$$I_t = 4A^2 \frac{(\csc \theta - 1)(\sec \theta + \tan \theta)}{\csc \theta \sec \theta}.$$ Show that this is equivalent to $I_t = (2A \cos \theta)^2$.

Source: *Experimental Techniques*, July/August 2002.

Discussion and Writing

105. Write a few paragraphs outlining your strategy for establishing identities.

106. Write down the three Pythagorean Identities.

107. Why do you think it is usually preferable to start with the side containing the more complicated expression when establishing an identity?

108. Make up an identity that is not a Fundamental Identity.

'Are You Prepared?' Answers

1. True   **2.** True

7.4 Sum and Difference Formulas

PREPARING FOR THIS SECTION *Before getting started, review the following:*

- Distance Formula (Section 1.1, pp. 4–6)
- Values of the Trigonometric Functions (Section 6.2, pp. 365–377)
- Finding Exact Values Given the Value of a Trigonometric Function and the Quadrant of the Angle (Section 6.3, pp. 389–391)

✎ **Now Work** the 'Are You Prepared?' problems on page 473.

OBJECTIVES 1 Use Sum and Difference Formulas to Find Exact Values (p. 467)
2 Use Sum and Difference Formulas to Establish Identities (p. 468)
3 Use Sum and Difference Formulas Involving Inverse Trigonometric Functions (p. 472)

In this section, we continue our derivation of trigonometric identities by obtaining formulas that involve the sum or difference of two angles, such as $\cos(\alpha + \beta)$, $\cos(\alpha - \beta)$, or $\sin(\alpha + \beta)$. These formulas are referred to as the **sum and difference formulas**. We begin with the formulas for $\cos(\alpha + \beta)$ and $\cos(\alpha - \beta)$.

THEOREM

Sum and Difference Formulas for the Cosine Function

$$\cos(\alpha + \beta) = \cos \alpha \cos \beta - \sin \alpha \sin \beta \qquad \textbf{(1)}$$
$$\cos(\alpha - \beta) = \cos \alpha \cos \beta + \sin \alpha \sin \beta \qquad \textbf{(2)}$$

In Words
Formula (1) states that the cosine of the sum of two angles equals the cosine of the first angle times the cosine of the second angle minus the sine of the first angle times the sine of the second angle.

Proof We will prove formula (2) first. Although this formula is true for all numbers α and β, we shall assume in our proof that $0 < \beta < \alpha < 2\pi$. We begin with the unit circle and place the angles α and β in standard position, as shown in Figure 24(a). The point P_1 lies on the terminal side of β, so its coordinates are $(\cos \beta, \sin \beta)$; and the point P_2 lies on the terminal side of α, so its coordinates are $(\cos \alpha, \sin \alpha)$.

Now place the angle $\alpha - \beta$ in standard position, as shown in Figure 24(b). The point A has coordinates $(1, 0)$, and the point P_3 is on the terminal side of the angle $\alpha - \beta$, so its coordinates are $(\cos(\alpha - \beta), \sin(\alpha - \beta))$.

Figure 24

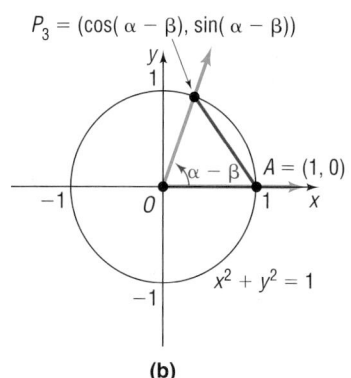

(a)   (b)

Looking at triangle OP_1P_2 in Figure 24(a) and triangle OAP_3 in Figure 24(b), we see that these triangles are congruent. (Do you see why? We have SAS: two sides and the included angle, $\alpha - \beta$, are equal.) As a result, the unknown side of each triangle must be equal; that is,

$$d(A, P_3) = d(P_1, P_2)$$

Using the distance formula, we find that

$$\sqrt{[\cos(\alpha - \beta) - 1]^2 + [\sin(\alpha - \beta) - 0]^2} = \sqrt{(\cos \alpha - \cos \beta)^2 + (\sin \alpha - \sin \beta)^2} \qquad d(A, P_3) = d(P_1, P_2)$$

$$[\cos(\alpha - \beta) - 1]^2 + \sin^2(\alpha - \beta) = (\cos \alpha - \cos \beta)^2 + (\sin \alpha - \sin \beta)^2 \qquad \text{Square both sides.}$$

$$\cos^2(\alpha - \beta) - 2\cos(\alpha - \beta) + 1 + \sin^2(\alpha - \beta) = \cos^2 \alpha - 2\cos \alpha \cos \beta + \cos^2 \beta \qquad \text{Multiply out the squared terms.}$$
$$+ \sin^2 \alpha - 2\sin \alpha \sin \beta + \sin^2 \beta$$

$$2 - 2\cos(\alpha - \beta) = 2 - 2\cos \alpha \cos \beta - 2\sin \alpha \sin \beta \qquad \text{Apply a Pythagorean Identity (3 times).}$$

$$-2\cos(\alpha - \beta) = -2\cos \alpha \cos \beta - 2\sin \alpha \sin \beta \qquad \text{Subtract 2 from each side.}$$

$$\cos(\alpha - \beta) = \cos \alpha \cos \beta + \sin \alpha \sin \beta \qquad \text{Divide each side by } -2.$$

This is formula (2).   ∎

The proof of formula (1) follows from formula (2) and the Even–Odd Identities. We use the fact that $\alpha + \beta = \alpha - (-\beta)$. Then

$$\cos(\alpha + \beta) = \cos[\alpha - (-\beta)]$$
$$= \cos \alpha \cos(-\beta) + \sin \alpha \sin(-\beta) \qquad \text{Use formula (2).}$$
$$= \cos \alpha \cos \beta - \sin \alpha \sin \beta \qquad \text{Even–Odd Identities}$$

1 Use Sum and Difference Formulas to Find Exact Values

One use of formulas (1) and (2) is to obtain the exact value of the cosine of an angle that can be expressed as the sum or difference of angles whose sine and cosine are known exactly.

| EXAMPLE 1 | **Using the Sum Formula to Find Exact Values** |

Find the exact value of cos 75°.

Solution   Since $75° = 45° + 30°$, we use formula (1) to obtain

$$\cos 75° = \cos(45° + 30°) = \cos 45°\cos 30° - \sin 45°\sin 30°$$
$$\uparrow$$
$$\text{Formula (1)}$$

$$= \frac{\sqrt{2}}{2} \cdot \frac{\sqrt{3}}{2} - \frac{\sqrt{2}}{2} \cdot \frac{1}{2} = \frac{1}{4}(\sqrt{6} - \sqrt{2})$$

EXAMPLE 2 | **Using the Difference Formula to Find Exact Values**

Find the exact value of $\cos\dfrac{\pi}{12}$.

Solution

$$\cos\frac{\pi}{12} = \cos\left(\frac{3\pi}{12} - \frac{2\pi}{12}\right) = \cos\left(\frac{\pi}{4} - \frac{\pi}{6}\right)$$

$$= \cos\frac{\pi}{4}\cos\frac{\pi}{6} + \sin\frac{\pi}{4}\sin\frac{\pi}{6} \qquad \textit{Use formula (2).}$$

$$= \frac{\sqrt{2}}{2}\cdot\frac{\sqrt{3}}{2} + \frac{\sqrt{2}}{2}\cdot\frac{1}{2} = \frac{1}{4}\left(\sqrt{6} + \sqrt{2}\right)$$

━━━━▶ **Now Work** PROBLEM 11

2 Use Sum and Difference Formulas to Establish Identities

Another use of formulas (1) and (2) is to establish other identities. Two important identities are given next.

Seeing the Concept

Graph $Y_1 = \cos\left(\dfrac{\pi}{2} - \theta\right)$ and $Y_2 = \sin\theta$ on the same screen. Does this demonstrate the result 3(a)? How would you demonstrate the result 3(b)?

$$\cos\left(\frac{\pi}{2} - \theta\right) = \sin\theta \qquad \textbf{(3a)}$$

$$\sin\left(\frac{\pi}{2} - \theta\right) = \cos\theta \qquad \textbf{(3b)}$$

Proof To prove formula (3a), we use the formula for $\cos(\alpha - \beta)$ with $\alpha = \dfrac{\pi}{2}$ and $\beta = \theta$.

$$\cos\left(\frac{\pi}{2} - \theta\right) = \cos\frac{\pi}{2}\cos\theta + \sin\frac{\pi}{2}\sin\theta$$

$$= 0\cdot\cos\theta + 1\cdot\sin\theta$$

$$= \sin\theta$$

To prove formula (3b), we make use of the identity (3a) just established.

$$\sin\left(\frac{\pi}{2} - \theta\right) = \cos\left[\frac{\pi}{2} - \left(\frac{\pi}{2} - \theta\right)\right] = \cos\theta$$

$$\underset{\textit{Use (3a)}}{\uparrow}$$

■

Formulas (3a) and (3b) should look familiar. They are the basis for the theorem stated in Chapter 6: Cofunctions of complementary angles are equal. Also, since

$$\cos\left(\frac{\pi}{2} - \theta\right) = \cos\left[-\left(\theta - \frac{\pi}{2}\right)\right] = \cos\left(\theta - \frac{\pi}{2}\right)$$

$$\underset{\textit{Even property of cosine}}{\uparrow}$$

and since

$$\cos\left(\frac{\pi}{2} - \theta\right) = \sin\theta$$

$$\underset{\textit{3(a)}}{\uparrow}$$

it follows that $\cos\left(\theta - \dfrac{\pi}{2}\right) = \sin\theta$. The graphs of $y = \cos\left(\theta - \dfrac{\pi}{2}\right)$ and $y = \sin\theta$ are identical.

Having established the identities in formulas (3a) and (3b), we now can derive the sum and difference formulas for $\sin(\alpha + \beta)$ and $\sin(\alpha - \beta)$.

Proof $\sin(\alpha + \beta) = \cos\left[\dfrac{\pi}{2} - (\alpha + \beta)\right]$ Formula (3a)

$$= \cos\left[\left(\dfrac{\pi}{2} - \alpha\right) - \beta\right]$$

$$= \cos\left(\dfrac{\pi}{2} - \alpha\right)\cos\beta + \sin\left(\dfrac{\pi}{2} - \alpha\right)\sin\beta \quad \text{Formula (2)}$$

$$= \sin\alpha\cos\beta + \cos\alpha\sin\beta \quad \text{Formulas (3a) and (3b)}$$

$$\sin(\alpha - \beta) = \sin[\alpha + (-\beta)]$$

$$= \sin\alpha\cos(-\beta) + \cos\alpha\sin(-\beta) \quad \text{Use the sum formula for the sine just obtained.}$$

$$= \sin\alpha\cos\beta + \cos\alpha(-\sin\beta) \quad \text{Even–Odd Identities}$$

$$= \sin\alpha\cos\beta - \cos\alpha\sin\beta \qquad\qquad \blacksquare$$

> **In Words**
> Formula (4) states that the sine of the sum of two angles equals the sine of the first angle times the cosine of the second angle plus the cosine of the first angle times the sine of the second angle.

THEOREM   **Sum and Difference Formulas for the Sine Function**

$$\sin(\alpha + \beta) = \sin\alpha\cos\beta + \cos\alpha\sin\beta \qquad\qquad \textbf{(4)}$$

$$\sin(\alpha - \beta) = \sin\alpha\cos\beta - \cos\alpha\sin\beta \qquad\qquad \textbf{(5)}$$

EXAMPLE 3   **Using the Sum Formula to Find Exact Values**

Find the exact value of $\sin\dfrac{7\pi}{12}$.

Solution $\sin\dfrac{7\pi}{12} = \sin\left(\dfrac{3\pi}{12} + \dfrac{4\pi}{12}\right) = \sin\left(\dfrac{\pi}{4} + \dfrac{\pi}{3}\right)$

$$= \sin\dfrac{\pi}{4}\cos\dfrac{\pi}{3} + \cos\dfrac{\pi}{4}\sin\dfrac{\pi}{3} \qquad \text{Formula (4)}$$

$$= \dfrac{\sqrt{2}}{2}\cdot\dfrac{1}{2} + \dfrac{\sqrt{2}}{2}\cdot\dfrac{\sqrt{3}}{2} = \dfrac{1}{4}\left(\sqrt{2} + \sqrt{6}\right)$$

Now Work PROBLEM 17

EXAMPLE 4   **Using the Difference Formula to Find Exact Values**

Find the exact value of $\sin 80° \cos 20° - \cos 80° \sin 20°$.

Solution   The form of the expression $\sin 80° \cos 20° - \cos 80° \sin 20°$ is that of the right side of formula (5) for $\sin(\alpha - \beta)$ with $\alpha = 80°$ and $\beta = 20°$. That is,

$$\sin 80° \cos 20° - \cos 80° \sin 20° = \sin(80° - 20°) = \sin 60° = \dfrac{\sqrt{3}}{2}$$

Now Work PROBLEMS 23 AND 27

EXAMPLE 5   **Finding Exact Values**

If it is known that $\sin\alpha = \dfrac{4}{5}$, $\dfrac{\pi}{2} < \alpha < \pi$, and that $\sin\beta = -\dfrac{2}{\sqrt{5}} = -\dfrac{2\sqrt{5}}{5}$, $\pi < \beta < \dfrac{3\pi}{2}$, find the exact value of

(a) $\cos\alpha$ (b) $\cos\beta$ (c) $\cos(\alpha + \beta)$ (d) $\sin(\alpha + \beta)$

Solution

Figure 25

$\sin \alpha = \dfrac{4}{5}, \dfrac{\pi}{2} < \alpha < \pi$

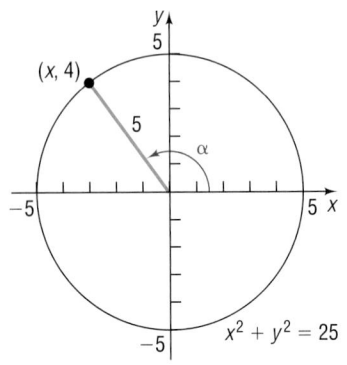

(a) Since $\sin \alpha = \dfrac{4}{5} = \dfrac{y}{r}$ and $\dfrac{\pi}{2} < \alpha < \pi$, we let $y = 4$ and $r = 5$ and place α in quadrant II. The point $P = (x, y) = (x, 4)$, $x < 0$, is on a circle of radius 5, that is, $x^2 + y^2 = 25$. See Figure 25. Then

$$x^2 + y^2 = 25$$
$$x^2 + 16 = 25 \qquad \qquad {\scriptstyle y = 4}$$
$$x^2 = 25 - 16 = 9$$
$$x = -3 \qquad \qquad {\scriptstyle x < 0}$$

Then

$$\cos \alpha = \frac{x}{r} = -\frac{3}{5}$$

Alternatively, we can find $\cos \alpha$ using identities, as follows:

$$\cos \alpha = -\sqrt{1 - \sin^2 \alpha} = -\sqrt{1 - \frac{16}{25}} = -\sqrt{\frac{9}{25}} = -\frac{3}{5}$$

$\uparrow$
α in quadrant II,
$\cos \alpha < 0$

(b) Since $\sin \beta = \dfrac{-2}{\sqrt{5}} = \dfrac{y}{r}$ and $\pi < \beta < \dfrac{3\pi}{2}$, we let $y = -2$ and $r = \sqrt{5}$ and place β in quadrant III. The point $P = (x, y) = (x, -2)$, $x < 0$, is on a circle of radius $\sqrt{5}$, that is, $x^2 + y^2 = 5$. See Figure 26. Then,

$$x^2 + y^2 = 5$$
$$x^2 + 4 = 5 \qquad {\scriptstyle y = -2}$$
$$x^2 = 1$$
$$x = -1 \qquad {\scriptstyle x < 0}$$

Figure 26

$\sin \beta = \dfrac{-2}{\sqrt{5}}, \pi < \beta < \dfrac{3\pi}{2}$

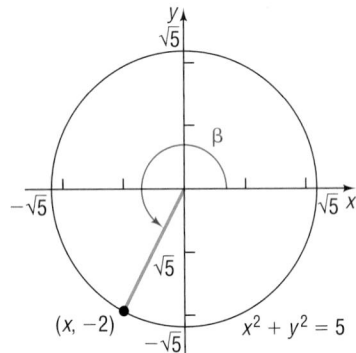

Then

$$\cos \beta = \frac{x}{r} = \frac{-1}{\sqrt{5}} = -\frac{\sqrt{5}}{5}$$

Alternatively, we can find $\cos \beta$ using identities, as follows:

$$\cos \beta = -\sqrt{1 - \sin^2 \beta} = -\sqrt{1 - \frac{4}{5}} = -\sqrt{\frac{1}{5}} = -\frac{\sqrt{5}}{5}$$

(c) Using the results found in parts (a) and (b) and formula (1), we have

$$\cos(\alpha + \beta) = \cos \alpha \cos \beta - \sin \alpha \sin \beta$$

$$= -\frac{3}{5}\left(-\frac{\sqrt{5}}{5}\right) - \frac{4}{5}\left(-\frac{2\sqrt{5}}{5}\right) = \frac{11\sqrt{5}}{25}$$

(d) $\sin(\alpha + \beta) = \sin \alpha \cos \beta + \cos \alpha \sin \beta$

$$= \frac{4}{5}\left(-\frac{\sqrt{5}}{5}\right) + \left(-\frac{3}{5}\right)\left(-\frac{2\sqrt{5}}{5}\right) = \frac{2\sqrt{5}}{25}$$

$\rule{2cm}{0pt}$ **Now Work** PROBLEMS 31(a), (b), AND (c)

| EXAMPLE 6 | **Establishing an Identity** |

Establish the identity: $\dfrac{\cos(\alpha - \beta)}{\sin \alpha \sin \beta} = \cot \alpha \cot \beta + 1$

Solution

$$\frac{\cos(\alpha - \beta)}{\sin \alpha \sin \beta} = \frac{\cos \alpha \cos \beta + \sin \alpha \sin \beta}{\sin \alpha \sin \beta}$$

$$= \frac{\cos \alpha \cos \beta}{\sin \alpha \sin \beta} + \frac{\sin \alpha \sin \beta}{\sin \alpha \sin \beta}$$

$$= \frac{\cos \alpha}{\sin \alpha} \cdot \frac{\cos \beta}{\sin \beta} + 1$$

$$= \cot \alpha \cot \beta + 1$$

Now Work PROBLEMS 45 AND 57

We use the identity $\tan \theta = \dfrac{\sin \theta}{\cos \theta}$ and the sum formulas for $\sin(\alpha + \beta)$ and $\cos(\alpha + \beta)$ to derive a formula for $\tan(\alpha + \beta)$.

Proof $\quad \tan(\alpha + \beta) = \dfrac{\sin(\alpha + \beta)}{\cos(\alpha + \beta)} = \dfrac{\sin \alpha \cos \beta + \cos \alpha \sin \beta}{\cos \alpha \cos \beta - \sin \alpha \sin \beta}$

Now we divide the numerator and denominator by $\cos \alpha \cos \beta$.

$$\tan(\alpha + \beta) = \frac{\dfrac{\sin \alpha \cos \beta + \cos \alpha \sin \beta}{\cos \alpha \cos \beta}}{\dfrac{\cos \alpha \cos \beta - \sin \alpha \sin \beta}{\cos \alpha \cos \beta}} = \frac{\dfrac{\sin \alpha \cos \beta}{\cos \alpha \cos \beta} + \dfrac{\cos \alpha \sin \beta}{\cos \alpha \cos \beta}}{\dfrac{\cos \alpha \cos \beta}{\cos \alpha \cos \beta} - \dfrac{\sin \alpha \sin \beta}{\cos \alpha \cos \beta}}$$

$$= \frac{\dfrac{\sin \alpha}{\cos \alpha} + \dfrac{\sin \beta}{\cos \beta}}{1 - \dfrac{\sin \alpha}{\cos \alpha} \cdot \dfrac{\sin \beta}{\cos \beta}} = \frac{\tan \alpha + \tan \beta}{1 - \tan \alpha \tan \beta}$$

Proof We use the sum formula for $\tan(\alpha + \beta)$ and Even–Odd Properties to get the difference formula.

$$\tan(\alpha - \beta) = \tan[\alpha + (-\beta)] = \frac{\tan \alpha + \tan(-\beta)}{1 - \tan \alpha \tan(-\beta)} = \frac{\tan \alpha - \tan \beta}{1 + \tan \alpha \tan \beta} \quad\blacksquare$$

We have proved the following results:

THEOREM

Sum and Difference Formulas for the Tangent Function

$$\tan(\alpha + \beta) = \frac{\tan \alpha + \tan \beta}{1 - \tan \alpha \tan \beta} \tag{6}$$

$$\tan(\alpha - \beta) = \frac{\tan \alpha - \tan \beta}{1 + \tan \alpha \tan \beta} \tag{7}$$

In Words
Formula (6) states that the tangent of the sum of two angles equals the tangent of the first angle plus the tangent of the second angle, all divided by 1 minus their product.

Now Work PROBLEM 31(d)

EXAMPLE 7 | **Establishing an Identity**

Prove the identity: $\tan(\theta + \pi) = \tan \theta$

Solution $\quad \tan(\theta + \pi) = \dfrac{\tan \theta + \tan \pi}{1 - \tan \theta \tan \pi} = \dfrac{\tan \theta + 0}{1 - \tan \theta \cdot 0} = \tan \theta$

The result obtained in Example 7 verifies that the tangent function is periodic with period π, a fact that we discussed earlier.

| EXAMPLE 8 | Establishing an Identity |

Prove the identity: $\tan\left(\theta + \dfrac{\pi}{2}\right) = -\cot\theta$

Solution

We cannot use formula (6), since $\tan\dfrac{\pi}{2}$ is not defined. Instead, we proceed as follows:

WARNING Be careful when using formulas (6) and (7). These formulas can be used only for angles α and β for which $\tan\alpha$ and $\tan\beta$ are defined, that is, all angles except odd integer multiples of $\dfrac{\pi}{2}$. ∎

$$\tan\left(\theta + \frac{\pi}{2}\right) = \frac{\sin\left(\theta + \dfrac{\pi}{2}\right)}{\cos\left(\theta + \dfrac{\pi}{2}\right)} = \frac{\sin\theta\cos\dfrac{\pi}{2} + \cos\theta\sin\dfrac{\pi}{2}}{\cos\theta\cos\dfrac{\pi}{2} - \sin\theta\sin\dfrac{\pi}{2}}$$

$$= \frac{(\sin\theta)(0) + (\cos\theta)(1)}{(\cos\theta)(0) - (\sin\theta)(1)} = \frac{\cos\theta}{-\sin\theta} = -\cot\theta$$

3 Use Sum and Difference Formulas Involving Inverse Trigonometric Functions

| EXAMPLE 9 | Finding the Exact Value of an Expression Involving Inverse Trigonometric Functions |

Find the exact value of: $\sin\left(\cos^{-1}\dfrac{1}{2} + \sin^{-1}\dfrac{3}{5}\right)$

Solution

We seek the sine of the sum of two angles, $\alpha = \cos^{-1}\dfrac{1}{2}$ and $\beta = \sin^{-1}\dfrac{3}{5}$. Then

$$\cos\alpha = \frac{1}{2} \quad 0 \le \alpha \le \pi \quad \text{and} \quad \sin\beta = \frac{3}{5} \quad -\frac{\pi}{2} \le \beta \le \frac{\pi}{2}$$

NOTE In Example 9, we could also find $\sin\alpha$ by using $\cos\alpha = \dfrac{1}{2} = \dfrac{x}{r}$, so $x = 1$ and $r = 2$. Then $b = \sqrt{3}$ and $\sin\alpha = \dfrac{y}{r} = \dfrac{\sqrt{3}}{2}$. We could find $\cos\beta$ in a similar fashion. ∎

We use Pythagorean Identities to obtain $\sin\alpha$ and $\cos\beta$. Since $\sin\alpha \ge 0$ and $\cos\beta \ge 0$ (do you know why?), we find

$$\sin\alpha = \sqrt{1 - \cos^2\alpha} = \sqrt{1 - \frac{1}{4}} = \sqrt{\frac{3}{4}} = \frac{\sqrt{3}}{2}$$

$$\cos\beta = \sqrt{1 - \sin^2\beta} = \sqrt{1 - \frac{9}{25}} = \sqrt{\frac{16}{25}} = \frac{4}{5}$$

As a result,

$$\sin\left(\cos^{-1}\frac{1}{2} + \sin^{-1}\frac{3}{5}\right) = \sin(\alpha + \beta) = \sin\alpha\cos\beta + \cos\alpha\sin\beta$$

$$= \frac{\sqrt{3}}{2}\cdot\frac{4}{5} + \frac{1}{2}\cdot\frac{3}{5} = \frac{4\sqrt{3} + 3}{10}$$

➡ **Now Work** PROBLEM 73

| EXAMPLE 10 | Writing a Trigonometric Expression as an Algebraic Expression |

Write $\sin(\sin^{-1}u + \cos^{-1}v)$ as an algebraic expression containing u and v (that is, without any trigonometric functions). Give the restrictions on u and v.

Solution

First, for $\sin^{-1}u$, we have $-1 \le u \le 1$ and for $\cos^{-1}v$, we have $-1 \le v \le 1$. Now let $\alpha = \sin^{-1}u$ and $\beta = \cos^{-1}v$. Then

$$\sin\alpha = u \quad -\frac{\pi}{2} \le \alpha \le \frac{\pi}{2} \quad -1 \le u \le 1$$

$$\cos\beta = v \quad 0 \le \beta \le \pi \quad -1 \le v \le 1$$

Since $-\dfrac{\pi}{2} \le \alpha \le \dfrac{\pi}{2}$, we know that $\cos \alpha \ge 0$. As a result,

$$\cos \alpha = \sqrt{1 - \sin^2 \alpha} = \sqrt{1 - u^2}$$

Similarly, since $0 \le \beta \le \pi$, we know that $\sin \beta \ge 0$. Then

$$\sin \beta = \sqrt{1 - \cos^2 \beta} = \sqrt{1 - v^2}$$

As a result,

$$\sin(\sin^{-1} u + \cos^{-1} v) = \sin(\alpha + \beta) = \sin \alpha \cos \beta + \cos \alpha \sin \beta$$

$$= uv + \sqrt{1 - u^2}\,\sqrt{1 - v^2}$$

Now Work PROBLEM 83

SUMMARY   Sum and Difference Formulas

$$\cos(\alpha + \beta) = \cos \alpha \cos \beta - \sin \alpha \sin \beta \qquad \cos(\alpha - \beta) = \cos \alpha \cos \beta + \sin \alpha \sin \beta$$

$$\sin(\alpha + \beta) = \sin \alpha \cos \beta + \cos \alpha \sin \beta \qquad \sin(\alpha - \beta) = \sin \alpha \cos \beta - \cos \alpha \sin \beta$$

$$\tan(\alpha + \beta) = \frac{\tan \alpha + \tan \beta}{1 - \tan \alpha \tan \beta} \qquad \tan(\alpha - \beta) = \frac{\tan \alpha - \tan \beta}{1 + \tan \alpha \tan \beta}$$

7.4 Assess Your Understanding

'Are You Prepared?' *Answers are given at the end of these exercises. If you get a wrong answer, read the pages listed in red.*

1. The distance d from the point $(2, -3)$ to the point $(5, 1)$ is _____. (pp. 4–6)

2. If $\sin \theta = \dfrac{4}{5}$ and θ is in quadrant II, then $\cos \theta =$ _____. (pp. 389–391)

3. (a) $\sin \dfrac{\pi}{4} \cdot \cos \dfrac{\pi}{3} =$ _____. (pp. 370–374)

(b) $\tan \dfrac{\pi}{4} - \sin \dfrac{\pi}{6} =$ _____. (pp. 370–374)

Concepts and Vocabulary

4. $\cos(\alpha + \beta) = \cos \alpha \cos \beta$ _____ $\sin \alpha \sin \beta$

5. $\sin(\alpha - \beta) = \sin \alpha \cos \beta$ _____ $\cos \alpha \sin \beta$

6. True or False $\sin(\alpha + \beta) = \sin \alpha + \sin \beta + 2 \sin \alpha \sin \beta$

7. True or False $\tan 75° = \tan 30° + \tan 45°$

8. True or False $\cos\left(\dfrac{\pi}{2} - \theta\right) = \cos \theta$

Skill Building

In Problems 9–20, find the exact value of each expression.

9. $\sin \dfrac{5\pi}{12}$

10. $\sin \dfrac{\pi}{12}$

11. $\cos \dfrac{7\pi}{12}$

12. $\tan \dfrac{7\pi}{12}$

13. $\cos 165°$

14. $\sin 105°$

15. $\tan 15°$

16. $\tan 195°$

17. $\sin \dfrac{17\pi}{12}$

18. $\tan \dfrac{19\pi}{12}$

19. $\sec\left(-\dfrac{\pi}{12}\right)$

20. $\cot\left(-\dfrac{5\pi}{12}\right)$

In Problems 21–30, find the exact value of each expression.

21. $\sin 20° \cos 10° + \cos 20° \sin 10°$

22. $\sin 20° \cos 80° - \cos 20° \sin 80°$

23. $\cos 70° \cos 20° - \sin 70° \sin 20°$

24. $\cos 40° \cos 10° + \sin 40° \sin 10°$

25. $\dfrac{\tan 20° + \tan 25°}{1 - \tan 20° \tan 25°}$

26. $\dfrac{\tan 40° - \tan 10°}{1 + \tan 40° \tan 10°}$

27. $\sin \dfrac{\pi}{12} \cos \dfrac{7\pi}{12} - \cos \dfrac{\pi}{12} \sin \dfrac{7\pi}{12}$

28. $\cos \dfrac{5\pi}{12} \cos \dfrac{7\pi}{12} - \sin \dfrac{5\pi}{12} \sin \dfrac{7\pi}{12}$

29. $\cos \dfrac{\pi}{12} \cos \dfrac{5\pi}{12} + \sin \dfrac{5\pi}{12} \sin \dfrac{\pi}{12}$

30. $\sin \dfrac{\pi}{18} \cos \dfrac{5\pi}{18} + \cos \dfrac{\pi}{18} \sin \dfrac{5\pi}{18}$

In Problems 31–36, find the exact value of each of the following under the given conditions:

(a) $\sin(\alpha + \beta)$ (b) $\cos(\alpha + \beta)$ (c) $\sin(\alpha - \beta)$ (d) $\tan(\alpha - \beta)$

31. $\sin \alpha = \dfrac{3}{5}, 0 < \alpha < \dfrac{\pi}{2}; \quad \cos \beta = \dfrac{2\sqrt{5}}{5}, -\dfrac{\pi}{2} < \beta < 0$

32. $\cos \alpha = \dfrac{\sqrt{5}}{5}, 0 < \alpha < \dfrac{\pi}{2}; \quad \sin \beta = -\dfrac{4}{5}, -\dfrac{\pi}{2} < \beta < 0$

33. $\tan \alpha = -\dfrac{4}{3}, \dfrac{\pi}{2} < \alpha < \pi; \quad \cos \beta = \dfrac{1}{2}, 0 < \beta < \dfrac{\pi}{2}$

34. $\tan \alpha = \dfrac{5}{12}, \pi < \alpha < \dfrac{3\pi}{2}; \quad \sin \beta = -\dfrac{1}{2}, \pi < \beta < \dfrac{3\pi}{2}$

35. $\sin \alpha = \dfrac{5}{13}, -\dfrac{3\pi}{2} < \alpha < -\pi; \quad \tan \beta = -\sqrt{3}, \dfrac{\pi}{2} < \beta < \pi$

36. $\cos \alpha = \dfrac{1}{2}, -\dfrac{\pi}{2} < \alpha < 0; \quad \sin \beta = \dfrac{1}{3}, 0 < \beta < \dfrac{\pi}{2}$

37. If $\sin \theta = \dfrac{1}{3}, \theta$ in quadrant II, find the exact value of:

(a) $\cos \theta$ (b) $\sin\left(\theta + \dfrac{\pi}{6}\right)$

(c) $\cos\left(\theta - \dfrac{\pi}{3}\right)$ (d) $\tan\left(\theta + \dfrac{\pi}{4}\right)$

38. If $\cos \theta = \dfrac{1}{4}, \theta$ in quadrant IV, find the exact value of:

(a) $\sin \theta$ (b) $\sin\left(\theta - \dfrac{\pi}{6}\right)$

(c) $\cos\left(\theta + \dfrac{\pi}{3}\right)$ (d) $\tan\left(\theta - \dfrac{\pi}{4}\right)$

In Problems 39–44, use the figures to evaluate each function if $f(x) = \sin x$, $g(x) = \cos x$, and $h(x) = \tan x$.

39. $f(\alpha + \beta)$ **40.** $g(\alpha + \beta)$ **41.** $g(\alpha - \beta)$

42. $f(\alpha - \beta)$ **43.** $h(\alpha + \beta)$ **44.** $h(\alpha - \beta)$

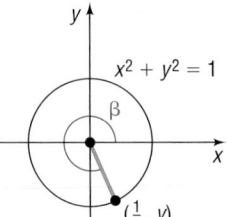

In Problems 45–70, establish each identity.

45. $\sin\left(\dfrac{\pi}{2} + \theta\right) = \cos \theta$

46. $\cos\left(\dfrac{\pi}{2} + \theta\right) = -\sin \theta$

47. $\sin(\pi - \theta) = \sin \theta$

48. $\cos(\pi - \theta) = -\cos \theta$

49. $\sin(\pi + \theta) = -\sin \theta$

50. $\cos(\pi + \theta) = -\cos \theta$

51. $\tan(\pi - \theta) = -\tan \theta$

52. $\tan(2\pi - \theta) = -\tan \theta$

53. $\sin\left(\dfrac{3\pi}{2} + \theta\right) = -\cos \theta$

54. $\cos\left(\dfrac{3\pi}{2} + \theta\right) = \sin \theta$

55. $\sin(\alpha + \beta) + \sin(\alpha - \beta) = 2 \sin \alpha \cos \beta$

56. $\cos(\alpha + \beta) + \cos(\alpha - \beta) = 2 \cos \alpha \cos \beta$

57. $\dfrac{\sin(\alpha + \beta)}{\sin \alpha \cos \beta} = 1 + \cot \alpha \tan \beta$

58. $\dfrac{\sin(\alpha + \beta)}{\cos \alpha \cos \beta} = \tan \alpha + \tan \beta$

59. $\dfrac{\cos(\alpha + \beta)}{\cos \alpha \cos \beta} = 1 - \tan \alpha \tan \beta$

60. $\dfrac{\cos(\alpha - \beta)}{\sin \alpha \cos \beta} = \cot \alpha + \tan \beta$

61. $\dfrac{\sin(\alpha + \beta)}{\sin(\alpha - \beta)} = \dfrac{\tan \alpha + \tan \beta}{\tan \alpha - \tan \beta}$

62. $\dfrac{\cos(\alpha + \beta)}{\cos(\alpha - \beta)} = \dfrac{1 - \tan \alpha \tan \beta}{1 + \tan \alpha \tan \beta}$

63. $\cot(\alpha + \beta) = \dfrac{\cot \alpha \cot \beta - 1}{\cot \beta + \cot \alpha}$

64. $\cot(\alpha - \beta) = \dfrac{\cot \alpha \cot \beta + 1}{\cot \beta - \cot \alpha}$

65. $\sec(\alpha + \beta) = \dfrac{\csc \alpha \csc \beta}{\cot \alpha \cot \beta - 1}$

66. $\sec(\alpha - \beta) = \dfrac{\sec \alpha \sec \beta}{1 + \tan \alpha \tan \beta}$

67. $\sin(\alpha - \beta) \sin(\alpha + \beta) = \sin^2 \alpha - \sin^2 \beta$

68. $\cos(\alpha - \beta) \cos(\alpha + \beta) = \cos^2 \alpha - \sin^2 \beta$

69. $\sin(\theta + k\pi) = (-1)^k \sin \theta, k$ any integer

70. $\cos(\theta + k\pi) = (-1)^k \cos \theta, k$ any integer

In Problems 71–82, find the exact value of each expression.

71. $\sin\left(\sin^{-1}\dfrac{1}{2} + \cos^{-1}0\right)$

72. $\sin\left(\sin^{-1}\dfrac{\sqrt{3}}{2} + \cos^{-1}1\right)$

73. $\sin\left[\sin^{-1}\dfrac{3}{5} - \cos^{-1}\left(-\dfrac{4}{5}\right)\right]$

74. $\sin\left[\sin^{-1}\left(-\dfrac{4}{5}\right) - \tan^{-1}\dfrac{3}{4}\right]$

75. $\cos\left(\tan^{-1}\dfrac{4}{3} + \cos^{-1}\dfrac{5}{13}\right)$

76. $\cos\left[\tan^{-1}\dfrac{5}{12} - \sin^{-1}\left(-\dfrac{3}{5}\right)\right]$

77. $\cos\left(\sin^{-1}\dfrac{5}{13} - \tan^{-1}\dfrac{3}{4}\right)$

78. $\cos\left(\tan^{-1}\dfrac{4}{3} + \cos^{-1}\dfrac{12}{13}\right)$

79. $\tan\left(\sin^{-1}\dfrac{3}{5} + \dfrac{\pi}{6}\right)$

80. $\tan\left(\dfrac{\pi}{4} - \cos^{-1}\dfrac{3}{5}\right)$

81. $\tan\left(\sin^{-1}\dfrac{4}{5} + \cos^{-1}1\right)$

82. $\tan\left(\cos^{-1}\dfrac{4}{5} + \sin^{-1}1\right)$

In Problems 83–88, write each trigonometric expression as an algebraic expression containing u and v. Give the restrictions required on u and v.

83. $\cos(\cos^{-1} u + \sin^{-1} v)$

84. $\sin(\sin^{-1} u - \cos^{-1} v)$

85. $\sin(\tan^{-1} u - \sin^{-1} v)$

86. $\cos(\tan^{-1} u + \tan^{-1} v)$

87. $\tan(\sin^{-1} u - \cos^{-1} v)$

88. $\sec(\tan^{-1} u + \cos^{-1} v)$

Applications and Extensions

89. Show that $\sin^{-1} v + \cos^{-1} v = \dfrac{\pi}{2}$.

90. Show that $\tan^{-1} v + \cot^{-1} v = \dfrac{\pi}{2}$.

91. Show that $\tan^{-1}\left(\dfrac{1}{v}\right) = \dfrac{\pi}{2} - \tan^{-1} v$, if $v > 0$.

92. Show that $\cot^{-1} e^{v} = \tan^{-1} e^{-v}$.

93. Show that $\sin(\sin^{-1} v + \cos^{-1} v) = 1$.

94. Show that $\cos(\sin^{-1} v + \cos^{-1} v) = 0$.

95. Calculus Show that the difference quotient for $f(x) = \sin x$ is given by

$$\frac{f(x + h) - f(x)}{h} = \frac{\sin(x + h) - \sin x}{h}$$

$$= \cos x \cdot \frac{\sin h}{h} - \sin x \cdot \frac{1 - \cos h}{h}$$

96. Calculus Show that the difference quotient for $f(x) = \cos x$ is given by

$$\frac{f(x + h) - f(x)}{h} = \frac{\cos(x + h) - \cos x}{h}$$

$$= -\sin x \cdot \frac{\sin h}{h} - \cos x \cdot \frac{1 - \cos h}{h}$$

97. One, Two, Three

(a) Show that $\tan(\tan^{-1} 1 + \tan^{-1} 2 + \tan^{-1} 3) = 0$.

(b) Conclude from part (a) that

$$\tan^{-1} 1 + \tan^{-1} 2 + \tan^{-1} 3 = \pi$$

Source: *College Mathematics Journal*, Vol. 37, No. 3, May 2006

98. Electric Power In an alternating current (ac) circuit, the instantaneous power p at time t is given by

$$p(t) = V_m I_m \cos \phi \sin^2(\omega t) - V_m I_m \sin \phi \sin(\omega t) \cos(\omega t)$$

Show that this is equivalent to

$$p(t) = V_m I_m \sin(\omega t) \sin(\omega t - \phi)$$

Source: *HyperPhysics, hosted by Georgia State University*

99. Geometry: Angle Between Two Lines Let L_1 and L_2 denote two nonvertical intersecting lines, and let θ denote the acute angle between L_1 and L_2 (see the figure). Show that

$$\tan \theta = \frac{m_2 - m_1}{1 + m_1 m_2}$$

where m_1 and m_2 are the slopes of L_1 and L_2, respectively.

[**Hint:** Use the facts that $\tan \theta_1 = m_1$ and $\tan \theta_2 = m_2$.]

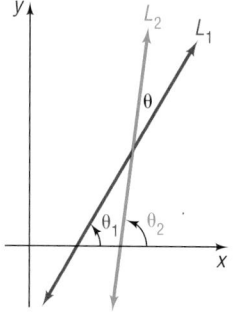

100. If $\alpha + \beta + \gamma = 180°$ and

$$\cot \theta = \cot \alpha + \cot \beta + \cot \gamma, \quad 0 < \theta < 90°$$

show that

$$\sin^3 \theta = \sin(\alpha - \theta) \sin(\beta - \theta) \sin(\gamma - \theta)$$

101. If $\tan \alpha = x + 1$ and $\tan \beta = x - 1$, show that

$$2 \cot(\alpha - \beta) = x^2$$

Discussion and Writing

102. Discuss the following derivation:

$$\tan\left(\theta + \frac{\pi}{2}\right) = \frac{\tan \theta + \tan \dfrac{\pi}{2}}{1 - \tan \theta \tan \dfrac{\pi}{2}} = \frac{\dfrac{\tan \theta}{\tan \dfrac{\pi}{2}} + 1}{\dfrac{1}{\tan \dfrac{\pi}{2}} - \tan \theta} = \frac{0 + 1}{0 - \tan \theta} = \frac{1}{-\tan \theta} = -\cot \theta$$

Can you justify each step?

103. Explain why formula (7) cannot be used to show that

$$\tan\left(\frac{\pi}{2} - \theta\right) = \cot \theta$$

Establish this identity by using formulas (3a) and (3b).

'Are You Prepared?' Answers

1. 5   **2.** $-\dfrac{3}{5}$ **3.** (a) $\dfrac{\sqrt{2}}{4}$ (b) $\dfrac{1}{2}$

7.5 Double-angle and Half-angle Formulas

OBJECTIVES **1** Use Double-angle Formulas to Find Exact Values (p. 476)
2 Use Double-angle Formulas to Establish Identities (p. 477)
3 Use Half-angle Formulas to Find Exact Values (p. 479)

In this section we derive formulas for $\sin(2\theta)$, $\cos(2\theta)$, $\sin\left(\dfrac{1}{2}\theta\right)$, and $\cos\left(\dfrac{1}{2}\theta\right)$ in terms of $\sin\theta$ and $\cos\theta$. They are derived using the sum formulas.

In the sum formulas for $\sin(\alpha + \beta)$ and $\cos(\alpha + \beta)$, let $\alpha = \beta = \theta$. Then

$$\sin(\alpha + \beta) = \sin\alpha\cos\beta + \cos\alpha\sin\beta$$
$$\sin(\theta + \theta) = \sin\theta\cos\theta + \cos\theta\sin\theta$$
$$\sin(2\theta) = 2\sin\theta\cos\theta$$

and

$$\cos(\alpha + \beta) = \cos\alpha\cos\beta - \sin\alpha\sin\beta$$
$$\cos(\theta + \theta) = \cos\theta\cos\theta - \sin\theta\sin\theta$$
$$\cos(2\theta) = \cos^2\theta - \sin^2\theta$$

An application of the Pythagorean Identity $\sin^2\theta + \cos^2\theta = 1$ results in two other ways to express $\cos(2\theta)$.

$$\cos(2\theta) = \cos^2\theta - \sin^2\theta = (1 - \sin^2\theta) - \sin^2\theta = 1 - 2\sin^2\theta$$

and

$$\cos(2\theta) = \cos^2\theta - \sin^2\theta = \cos^2\theta - (1 - \cos^2\theta) = 2\cos^2\theta - 1$$

We have established the following **Double-angle Formulas:**

THEOREM **Double-angle Formulas**

$\sin(2\theta) = 2\sin\theta\cos\theta$	**(1)**
$\cos(2\theta) = \cos^2\theta - \sin^2\theta$	**(2)**
$\cos(2\theta) = 1 - 2\sin^2\theta$	**(3)**
$\cos(2\theta) = 2\cos^2\theta - 1$	**(4)**

1 Use Double-angle Formulas to Find Exact Values

EXAMPLE 1 **Finding Exact Values Using the Double-angle Formula**

If $\sin\theta = \dfrac{3}{5}$, $\dfrac{\pi}{2} < \theta < \pi$, find the exact value of:

(a) $\sin(2\theta)$ (b) $\cos(2\theta)$

Solution (a) Because $\sin(2\theta) = 2\sin\theta\cos\theta$ and we already know that $\sin\theta = \dfrac{3}{5}$, we only need to find $\cos\theta$. Since $\sin\theta = \dfrac{3}{5} = \dfrac{y}{r}$, $\dfrac{\pi}{2} < \theta < \pi$, we let $y = 3$ and $r = 5$

Figure 27

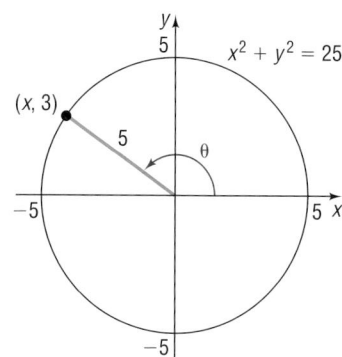

and place θ in quadrant II. The point $P = (x, y) = (x, 3), x < 0$, is on a circle of radius 5, that is, $x^2 + y^2 = 25$. See Figure 27. Then

$$x^2 + y^2 = 25$$
$$x^2 + 9 = 25 \qquad\qquad y = 3$$
$$x^2 = 25 - 9 = 16$$
$$x = -4 \qquad\qquad x < 0$$

We find that $\cos \theta = \dfrac{x}{r} = \dfrac{-4}{5}$. Now we use formula (1) to obtain

$$\sin(2\theta) = 2 \sin \theta \cos \theta = 2\left(\frac{3}{5}\right)\left(-\frac{4}{5}\right) = -\frac{24}{25}$$

(b) Because we are given $\sin \theta = \dfrac{3}{5}$, it is easiest to use formula (3) to get $\cos(2\theta)$.

$$\cos(2\theta) = 1 - 2 \sin^2 \theta = 1 - 2\left(\frac{9}{25}\right) = 1 - \frac{18}{25} = \frac{7}{25}$$

WARNING In finding $\cos(2\theta)$ in Example 1(b), we chose to use a version of the Double-angle Formula, formula (3). Note that we are unable to use the Pythagorean Identity $\cos(2\theta) = \pm\sqrt{1 - \sin^2(2\theta)}$, with $\sin(2\theta) = -\dfrac{24}{25}$, because we have no way of knowing which sign to choose. ∎

──── **Now Work** PROBLEMS 7(a) AND (b)

2 Use Double-angle Formulas to Establish Identities

EXAMPLE 2 **Establishing Identities**

(a) Develop a formula for $\tan(2\theta)$ in terms of $\tan \theta$.
(b) Develop a formula for $\sin(3\theta)$ in terms of $\sin \theta$ and $\cos \theta$.

Solution (a) In the sum formula for $\tan(\alpha + \beta)$, let $\alpha = \beta = \theta$. Then

$$\tan(\alpha + \beta) = \frac{\tan \alpha + \tan \beta}{1 - \tan \alpha \tan \beta}$$

$$\tan(\theta + \theta) = \frac{\tan \theta + \tan \theta}{1 - \tan \theta \tan \theta}$$

$$\boxed{\tan(2\theta) = \frac{2 \tan \theta}{1 - \tan^2 \theta}} \qquad\qquad \textbf{(5)}$$

(b) To get a formula for $\sin(3\theta)$, we use the sum formula and write 3θ as $2\theta + \theta$.

$$\sin(3\theta) = \sin(2\theta + \theta) = \sin(2\theta) \cos \theta + \cos(2\theta) \sin \theta$$

Now use the Double-angle Formulas to get

$$\sin(3\theta) = (2 \sin \theta \cos \theta)(\cos \theta) + (\cos^2 \theta - \sin^2 \theta)(\sin \theta)$$
$$= 2 \sin \theta \cos^2 \theta + \sin \theta \cos^2 \theta - \sin^3 \theta$$
$$= 3 \sin \theta \cos^2 \theta - \sin^3 \theta$$

The formula obtained in Example 2(b) can also be written as

$$\sin(3\theta) = 3 \sin \theta \cos^2 \theta - \sin^3 \theta = 3 \sin \theta(1 - \sin^2 \theta) - \sin^3 \theta$$
$$= 3 \sin \theta - 4 \sin^3 \theta$$

That is, $\sin(3\theta)$ is a third-degree polynomial in the variable $\sin\theta$. In fact, $\sin(n\theta)$, n a positive odd integer, can always be written as a polynomial of degree n in the variable $\sin\theta$.*

Now Work PROBLEM 65

By rearranging the Double-angle Formulas (3) and (4), we obtain other formulas that we will use later in this section.

We begin with formula (3) and proceed to solve for $\sin^2\theta$.

$$\cos(2\theta) = 1 - 2\sin^2\theta$$

$$2\sin^2\theta = 1 - \cos(2\theta)$$

$$\sin^2\theta = \frac{1 - \cos(2\theta)}{2} \qquad (6)$$

Similarly, using formula (4), we proceed to solve for $\cos^2\theta$.

$$\cos(2\theta) = 2\cos^2\theta - 1$$

$$2\cos^2\theta = 1 + \cos(2\theta)$$

$$\cos^2\theta = \frac{1 + \cos(2\theta)}{2} \qquad (7)$$

Formulas (6) and (7) can be used to develop a formula for $\tan^2\theta$.

$$\tan^2\theta = \frac{\sin^2\theta}{\cos^2\theta} = \frac{\dfrac{1 - \cos(2\theta)}{2}}{\dfrac{1 + \cos(2\theta)}{2}}$$

$$\tan^2\theta = \frac{1 - \cos(2\theta)}{1 + \cos(2\theta)} \qquad (8)$$

Formulas (6) through (8) do not have to be memorized since their derivations are so straightforward.

 Formulas (6) and (7) are important in calculus. The next example illustrates a problem that arises in calculus requiring the use of formula (7).

| EXAMPLE 3 | **Establishing an Identity** |

Write an equivalent expression for $\cos^4\theta$ that does not involve any powers of sine or cosine greater than 1.

Solution　　　The idea here is to apply formula (7) twice.

$$\cos^4\theta = (\cos^2\theta)^2 = \left(\frac{1 + \cos(2\theta)}{2}\right)^2 \qquad \text{Formula (7)}$$

$$= \frac{1}{4}[1 + 2\cos(2\theta) + \cos^2(2\theta)]$$

*Because of the work done by P. L. Chebyshëv, these polynomials are sometimes called *Chebyshëv polynomials.*

$$= \frac{1}{4} + \frac{1}{2}\cos(2\theta) + \frac{1}{4}\cos^2(2\theta)$$

$$= \frac{1}{4} + \frac{1}{2}\cos(2\theta) + \frac{1}{4}\left\{\frac{1 + \cos[2(2\theta)]}{2}\right\} \quad \text{Formula (7)}$$

$$= \frac{1}{4} + \frac{1}{2}\cos(2\theta) + \frac{1}{8}[1 + \cos(4\theta)]$$

$$= \frac{3}{8} + \frac{1}{2}\cos(2\theta) + \frac{1}{8}\cos(4\theta)$$

Now Work PROBLEM 41

Identities, such as the Double-angle Formulas, can sometimes be used to rewrite expressions in a more suitable form. Let's look at an example.

| EXAMPLE 4 | **Projectile Motion** |

Figure 28

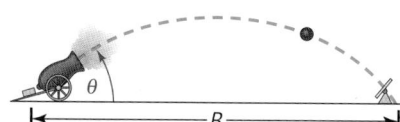

An object is propelled upward at an angle θ to the horizontal with an initial velocity of v_0 feet per second. See Figure 28. If air resistance is ignored, the **range** R, the horizontal distance that the object travels, is given by the function

$$R(\theta) = \frac{1}{16}v_0^2 \sin\theta \cos\theta$$

(a) Show that $R(\theta) = \frac{1}{32}v_0^2 \sin(2\theta)$.

(b) Find the angle θ for which R is a maximum.

Solution

(a) We rewrite the given expression for the range using the Double-angle Formula $\sin(2\theta) = 2\sin\theta\cos\theta$. Then

$$R(\theta) = \frac{1}{16}v_0^2 \sin\theta\cos\theta = \frac{1}{16}v_0^2 \frac{2\sin\theta\cos\theta}{2} = \frac{1}{32}v_0^2 \sin(2\theta)$$

(b) In this form, the largest value for the range R can be found. For a fixed initial speed v_0, the angle θ of inclination to the horizontal determines the value of R. Since the largest value of a sine function is 1, occurring when the argument 2θ is 90°, it follows that for maximum R we must have

$$2\theta = 90°$$
$$\theta = 45°$$

An inclination to the horizontal of 45° results in the maximum range.

---

3 Use Half-angle Formulas to Find Exact Values

Another important use of formulas (6) through (8) is to prove the *Half-angle Formulas*. In formulas (6) through (8), let $\theta = \dfrac{\alpha}{2}$. Then

$$\sin^2\frac{\alpha}{2} = \frac{1 - \cos\alpha}{2} \qquad \cos^2\frac{\alpha}{2} = \frac{1 + \cos\alpha}{2} \qquad \tan^2\frac{\alpha}{2} = \frac{1 - \cos\alpha}{1 + \cos\alpha} \qquad (9)$$

COMMENT The identities in box (9) will prove useful in integral calculus.

If we solve for the trigonometric functions on the left sides of equations (9), we obtain the Half-angle Formulas.

THEOREM   **Half-angle Formulas**

$$\sin \frac{\alpha}{2} = \pm \sqrt{\frac{1 - \cos \alpha}{2}} \tag{10a}$$

$$\cos \frac{\alpha}{2} = \pm \sqrt{\frac{1 + \cos \alpha}{2}} \tag{10b}$$

$$\tan \frac{\alpha}{2} = \pm \sqrt{\frac{1 - \cos \alpha}{1 + \cos \alpha}} \tag{10c}$$

where the + or − sign is determined by the quadrant of the angle $\dfrac{\alpha}{2}$.

EXAMPLE 5   **Finding Exact Values Using Half-angle Formulas**

Use a Half-angle Formula to find the exact value of:

(a) $\cos 15°$ (b) $\sin(-15°)$

Solution   (a) Because $15° = \dfrac{30°}{2}$, we can use the Half-angle Formula for $\cos \dfrac{\alpha}{2}$ with $\alpha = 30°$.
Also, because $15°$ is in quadrant I, $\cos 15° > 0$, we choose the + sign in using formula (10b):

$$\cos 15° = \cos \frac{30°}{2} = \sqrt{\frac{1 + \cos 30°}{2}}$$

$$= \sqrt{\frac{1 + \sqrt{3}/2}{2}} = \sqrt{\frac{2 + \sqrt{3}}{4}} = \frac{\sqrt{2 + \sqrt{3}}}{2}$$

(b) We use the fact that $\sin(-15°) = -\sin 15°$ and then apply formula (10a).

$$\sin(-15°) = -\sin \frac{30°}{2} = -\sqrt{\frac{1 - \cos 30°}{2}}$$

$$= -\sqrt{\frac{1 - \sqrt{3}/2}{2}} = -\sqrt{\frac{2 - \sqrt{3}}{4}} = -\frac{\sqrt{2 - \sqrt{3}}}{2}$$

It is interesting to compare the answer found in Example 5(a) with the answer to Example 2 of Section 7.4. There we calculated

$$\cos \frac{\pi}{12} = \cos 15° = \frac{1}{4}\left(\sqrt{6} + \sqrt{2}\right)$$

Based on this and the result of Example 5(a), we conclude that

$$\frac{1}{4}\left(\sqrt{6} + \sqrt{2}\right) \quad \text{and} \quad \frac{\sqrt{2 + \sqrt{3}}}{2}$$

are equal. (Since each expression is positive, you can verify this equality by squaring each expression.) Two very different looking, yet correct, answers can be obtained, depending on the approach taken to solve a problem.

✏️ **Now Work** PROBLEM 19

$$= \frac{1}{4} + \frac{1}{2}\cos(2\theta) + \frac{1}{4}\cos^2(2\theta)$$

$$= \frac{1}{4} + \frac{1}{2}\cos(2\theta) + \frac{1}{4}\left\{\frac{1 + \cos[2(2\theta)]}{2}\right\} \qquad \text{Formula (7)}$$

$$= \frac{1}{4} + \frac{1}{2}\cos(2\theta) + \frac{1}{8}[1 + \cos(4\theta)]$$

$$= \frac{3}{8} + \frac{1}{2}\cos(2\theta) + \frac{1}{8}\cos(4\theta)$$

Now Work PROBLEM 41

Identities, such as the Double-angle Formulas, can sometimes be used to rewrite expressions in a more suitable form. Let's look at an example.

| EXAMPLE 4 | **Projectile Motion** |

Figure 28

An object is propelled upward at an angle θ to the horizontal with an initial velocity of v_0 feet per second. See Figure 28. If air resistance is ignored, the **range** R, the horizontal distance that the object travels, is given by the function

$$R(\theta) = \frac{1}{16}v_0^2 \sin\theta \cos\theta$$

(a) Show that $R(\theta) = \frac{1}{32}v_0^2 \sin(2\theta)$.

(b) Find the angle θ for which R is a maximum.

Solution
(a) We rewrite the given expression for the range using the Double-angle Formula $\sin(2\theta) = 2\sin\theta\cos\theta$. Then

$$R(\theta) = \frac{1}{16}v_0^2 \sin\theta \cos\theta = \frac{1}{16}v_0^2 \frac{2\sin\theta\cos\theta}{2} = \frac{1}{32}v_0^2 \sin(2\theta)$$

(b) In this form, the largest value for the range R can be found. For a fixed initial speed v_0, the angle θ of inclination to the horizontal determines the value of R. Since the largest value of a sine function is 1, occurring when the argument 2θ is $90°$, it follows that for maximum R we must have

$$2\theta = 90°$$
$$\theta = 45°$$

An inclination to the horizontal of $45°$ results in the maximum range.

---

3 Use Half-angle Formulas to Find Exact Values

Another important use of formulas (6) through (8) is to prove the *Half-angle Formulas*. In formulas (6) through (8), let $\theta = \frac{\alpha}{2}$. Then

$$\boxed{\sin^2\frac{\alpha}{2} = \frac{1 - \cos\alpha}{2} \qquad \cos^2\frac{\alpha}{2} = \frac{1 + \cos\alpha}{2} \qquad \tan^2\frac{\alpha}{2} = \frac{1 - \cos\alpha}{1 + \cos\alpha}} \qquad (9)$$

COMMENT The identities in box (9) will prove useful in integral calculus.

If we solve for the trigonometric functions on the left sides of equations (9), we obtain the Half-angle Formulas.

THEOREM   **Half-angle Formulas**

$$\sin \frac{\alpha}{2} = \pm \sqrt{\frac{1 - \cos \alpha}{2}} \qquad \text{(10a)}$$

$$\cos \frac{\alpha}{2} = \pm \sqrt{\frac{1 + \cos \alpha}{2}} \qquad \text{(10b)}$$

$$\tan \frac{\alpha}{2} = \pm \sqrt{\frac{1 - \cos \alpha}{1 + \cos \alpha}} \qquad \text{(10c)}$$

where the + or − sign is determined by the quadrant of the angle $\dfrac{\alpha}{2}$.

EXAMPLE 5   **Finding Exact Values Using Half-angle Formulas**

Use a Half-angle Formula to find the exact value of:

(a) $\cos 15°$ (b) $\sin(-15°)$

Solution   (a) Because $15° = \dfrac{30°}{2}$, we can use the Half-angle Formula for $\cos \dfrac{\alpha}{2}$ with $\alpha = 30°$.

Also, because $15°$ is in quadrant I, $\cos 15° > 0$, we choose the + sign in using formula (10b):

$$\cos 15° = \cos \frac{30°}{2} = \sqrt{\frac{1 + \cos 30°}{2}}$$

$$= \sqrt{\frac{1 + \sqrt{3}/2}{2}} = \sqrt{\frac{2 + \sqrt{3}}{4}} = \frac{\sqrt{2 + \sqrt{3}}}{2}$$

(b) We use the fact that $\sin(-15°) = -\sin 15°$ and then apply formula (10a).

$$\sin(-15°) = -\sin \frac{30°}{2} = -\sqrt{\frac{1 - \cos 30°}{2}}$$

$$= -\sqrt{\frac{1 - \sqrt{3}/2}{2}} = -\sqrt{\frac{2 - \sqrt{3}}{4}} = -\frac{\sqrt{2 - \sqrt{3}}}{2}$$

It is interesting to compare the answer found in Example 5(a) with the answer to Example 2 of Section 7.4. There we calculated

$$\cos \frac{\pi}{12} = \cos 15° = \frac{1}{4}\left(\sqrt{6} + \sqrt{2}\right)$$

Based on this and the result of Example 5(a), we conclude that

$$\frac{1}{4}\left(\sqrt{6} + \sqrt{2}\right) \quad \text{and} \quad \frac{\sqrt{2 + \sqrt{3}}}{2}$$

are equal. (Since each expression is positive, you can verify this equality by squaring each expression.) Two very different looking, yet correct, answers can be obtained, depending on the approach taken to solve a problem.

   Now Work PROBLEM 19

| EXAMPLE 6 | Finding Exact Values Using Half-angle Formulas |

If $\cos \alpha = -\dfrac{3}{5}$, $\pi < \alpha < \dfrac{3\pi}{2}$, find the exact value of:

(a) $\sin \dfrac{\alpha}{2}$ (b) $\cos \dfrac{\alpha}{2}$ (c) $\tan \dfrac{\alpha}{2}$

Solution First, we observe that if $\pi < \alpha < \dfrac{3\pi}{2}$ then $\dfrac{\pi}{2} < \dfrac{\alpha}{2} < \dfrac{3\pi}{4}$. As a result, $\dfrac{\alpha}{2}$ lies in quadrant II.

(a) Because $\dfrac{\alpha}{2}$ lies in quadrant II, $\sin \dfrac{\alpha}{2} > 0$, so we use the $+$ sign in formula (10a) to get

$$\sin \frac{\alpha}{2} = \sqrt{\frac{1 - \cos \alpha}{2}} = \sqrt{\frac{1 - \left(-\dfrac{3}{5}\right)}{2}}$$

$$= \sqrt{\frac{\dfrac{8}{5}}{2}} = \sqrt{\frac{4}{5}} = \frac{2}{\sqrt{5}} = \frac{2\sqrt{5}}{5}$$

(b) Because $\dfrac{\alpha}{2}$ lies in quadrant II, $\cos \dfrac{\alpha}{2} < 0$, so we use the $-$ sign in formula (10b) to get

$$\cos \frac{\alpha}{2} = -\sqrt{\frac{1 + \cos \alpha}{2}} = -\sqrt{\frac{1 + \left(-\dfrac{3}{5}\right)}{2}}$$

$$= -\sqrt{\frac{\dfrac{2}{5}}{2}} = -\frac{1}{\sqrt{5}} = -\frac{\sqrt{5}}{5}$$

(c) Because $\dfrac{\alpha}{2}$ lies in quadrant II, $\tan \dfrac{\alpha}{2} < 0$, so we use the $-$ sign in formula (10c) to get

$$\tan \frac{\alpha}{2} = -\sqrt{\frac{1 - \cos \alpha}{1 + \cos \alpha}} = -\sqrt{\frac{1 - \left(-\dfrac{3}{5}\right)}{1 + \left(-\dfrac{3}{5}\right)}} = -\sqrt{\frac{\dfrac{8}{5}}{\dfrac{2}{5}}} = -2$$

Another way to solve Example 6(c) is to use the solutions found in parts (a) and (b).

$$\tan \frac{\alpha}{2} = \frac{\sin \dfrac{\alpha}{2}}{\cos \dfrac{\alpha}{2}} = \frac{\dfrac{2\sqrt{5}}{5}}{-\dfrac{\sqrt{5}}{5}} = -2$$

Now Work PROBLEMS 7(c) AND (d)

There is a formula for $\tan \dfrac{\alpha}{2}$ that does not contain $+$ and $-$ signs, making it more useful than Formula 10(c). To derive it, we use the formulas

$$1 - \cos \alpha = 2 \sin^2 \frac{\alpha}{2} \quad \text{Formula (9)}$$

and

$$\sin \alpha = \sin\left[2\left(\frac{\alpha}{2}\right)\right] = 2 \sin \frac{\alpha}{2} \cos \frac{\alpha}{2} \qquad \text{Double-angle Formula}$$

Then

$$\frac{1 - \cos \alpha}{\sin \alpha} = \frac{2 \sin^2 \frac{\alpha}{2}}{2 \sin \frac{\alpha}{2} \cos \frac{\alpha}{2}} = \frac{\sin \frac{\alpha}{2}}{\cos \frac{\alpha}{2}} = \tan \frac{\alpha}{2}$$

Since it also can be shown that

$$\frac{1 - \cos \alpha}{\sin \alpha} = \frac{\sin \alpha}{1 + \cos \alpha}$$

we have the following two Half-angle Formulas:

Half-angle Formulas for tan $\dfrac{\alpha}{2}$

$$\tan \frac{\alpha}{2} = \frac{1 - \cos \alpha}{\sin \alpha} = \frac{\sin \alpha}{1 + \cos \alpha} \qquad \textbf{(11)}$$

With this formula, the solution to Example 6(c) can be obtained as follows:

$$\cos \alpha = -\frac{3}{5} \qquad \pi < \alpha < \frac{3\pi}{2}$$

$$\sin \alpha = -\sqrt{1 - \cos^2 \alpha} = -\sqrt{1 - \frac{9}{25}} = -\sqrt{\frac{16}{25}} = -\frac{4}{5}$$

Then, by equation (11),

$$\tan \frac{\alpha}{2} = \frac{1 - \cos \alpha}{\sin \alpha} = \frac{1 - \left(-\dfrac{3}{5}\right)}{-\dfrac{4}{5}} = \frac{\dfrac{8}{5}}{-\dfrac{4}{5}} = -2$$

7.5 Assess Your Understanding

Concepts and Vocabulary

1. $\cos(2\theta) = \cos^2 \theta - \underline{\quad} = \underline{\quad} - 1 = 1 - \underline{\quad}$.

2. $\sin^2 \dfrac{\theta}{2} = \dfrac{\underline{\quad}}{2}$.

3. $\tan \dfrac{\theta}{2} = \dfrac{1 - \cos \theta}{\underline{\quad}}$.

4. True or False $\cos(2\theta)$ has three equivalent forms:
$$\cos^2 \theta - \sin^2 \theta, \quad 1 - 2 \sin^2 \theta, \quad 2 \cos^2 \theta - 1$$

5. True or False $\sin(2\theta)$ has two equivalent forms:
$$2 \sin \theta \cos \theta \quad \text{and} \quad \sin^2 \theta - \cos^2 \theta$$

6. True or False $\tan(2\theta) + \tan(2\theta) = \tan(4\theta)$

Skill Building

In Problems 7–18, use the information given about the angle θ, $0 \le \theta < 2\pi$, to find the exact value of

(a) $\sin(2\theta)$ (b) $\cos(2\theta)$ (c) $\sin \dfrac{\theta}{2}$ (d) $\cos \dfrac{\theta}{2}$

7. $\sin \theta = \dfrac{3}{5}$ $0 < \theta < \dfrac{\pi}{2}$

8. $\cos \theta = \dfrac{3}{5}$ $0 < \theta < \dfrac{\pi}{2}$

9. $\tan \theta = \dfrac{4}{3}$ $\pi < \theta < \dfrac{3\pi}{2}$

10. $\tan \theta = \dfrac{1}{2}$ $\pi < \theta < \dfrac{3\pi}{2}$

11. $\cos \theta = -\dfrac{\sqrt{6}}{3}$ $\dfrac{\pi}{2} < \theta < \pi$

12. $\sin \theta = -\dfrac{\sqrt{3}}{3}$ $\dfrac{3\pi}{2} < \theta < 2\pi$

13. $\sec\theta = 3 \quad \sin\theta > 0$

14. $\csc\theta = -\sqrt{5} \quad \cos\theta < 0$

15. $\cot\theta = -2 \quad \sec\theta < 0$

16. $\sec\theta = 2 \quad \csc\theta < 0$

17. $\tan\theta = -3 \quad \sin\theta < 0$

18. $\cot\theta = 3 \quad \cos\theta < 0$

In Problems 19–28, use the Half-angle Formulas to find the exact value of each expression.

19. $\sin 22.5°$

20. $\cos 22.5°$

21. $\tan\dfrac{7\pi}{8}$

22. $\tan\dfrac{9\pi}{8}$

23. $\cos 165°$

24. $\sin 195°$

25. $\sec\dfrac{15\pi}{8}$

26. $\csc\dfrac{7\pi}{8}$

27. $\sin\left(-\dfrac{\pi}{8}\right)$

28. $\cos\left(-\dfrac{3\pi}{8}\right)$

In Problems 29–40, use the figures to evaluate each function given that $f(x) = \sin x$, $g(x) = \cos x$, and $h(x) = \tan x$.

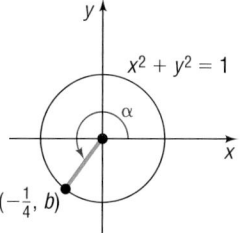

29. $f(2\theta)$

30. $g(2\theta)$

31. $g\left(\dfrac{\theta}{2}\right)$

32. $f\left(\dfrac{\theta}{2}\right)$

33. $h(2\theta)$

34. $h\left(\dfrac{\theta}{2}\right)$

35. $g(2\alpha)$

36. $f(2\alpha)$

37. $f\left(\dfrac{\alpha}{2}\right)$

38. $g\left(\dfrac{\alpha}{2}\right)$

39. $h\left(\dfrac{\alpha}{2}\right)$

40. $h(2\alpha)$

41. Show that $\sin^4\theta = \dfrac{3}{8} - \dfrac{1}{2}\cos(2\theta) + \dfrac{1}{8}\cos(4\theta)$.

42. Show that $\sin(4\theta) = (\cos\theta)(4\sin\theta - 8\sin^3\theta)$.

43. Develop a formula for $\cos(3\theta)$ as a third-degree polynomial in the variable $\cos\theta$.

44. Develop a formula for $\cos(4\theta)$ as a fourth-degree polynomial in the variable $\cos\theta$.

45. Find an expression for $\sin(5\theta)$ as a fifth-degree polynomial in the variable $\sin\theta$.

46. Find an expression for $\cos(5\theta)$ as a fifth-degree polynomial in the variable $\cos\theta$.

In Problems 47–68, establish each identity.

47. $\cos^4\theta - \sin^4\theta = \cos(2\theta)$

48. $\dfrac{\cot\theta - \tan\theta}{\cot\theta + \tan\theta} = \cos(2\theta)$

49. $\cot(2\theta) = \dfrac{\cot^2\theta - 1}{2\cot\theta}$

50. $\cot(2\theta) = \dfrac{1}{2}(\cot\theta - \tan\theta)$

51. $\sec(2\theta) = \dfrac{\sec^2\theta}{2 - \sec^2\theta}$

52. $\csc(2\theta) = \dfrac{1}{2}\sec\theta\csc\theta$

53. $\cos^2(2u) - \sin^2(2u) = \cos(4u)$

54. $(4\sin u\cos u)(1 - 2\sin^2 u) = \sin(4u)$

55. $\dfrac{\cos(2\theta)}{1 + \sin(2\theta)} = \dfrac{\cot\theta - 1}{\cot\theta + 1}$

56. $\sin^2\theta\cos^2\theta = \dfrac{1}{8}[1 - \cos(4\theta)]$

57. $\sec^2\dfrac{\theta}{2} = \dfrac{2}{1 + \cos\theta}$

58. $\csc^2\dfrac{\theta}{2} = \dfrac{2}{1 - \cos\theta}$

59. $\cot^2\dfrac{v}{2} = \dfrac{\sec v + 1}{\sec v - 1}$

60. $\tan\dfrac{v}{2} = \csc v - \cot v$

61. $\cos\theta = \dfrac{1 - \tan^2\dfrac{\theta}{2}}{1 + \tan^2\dfrac{\theta}{2}}$

62. $1 - \dfrac{1}{2}\sin(2\theta) = \dfrac{\sin^3\theta + \cos^3\theta}{\sin\theta + \cos\theta}$

63. $\dfrac{\sin(3\theta)}{\sin\theta} - \dfrac{\cos(3\theta)}{\cos\theta} = 2$

64. $\dfrac{\cos\theta + \sin\theta}{\cos\theta - \sin\theta} - \dfrac{\cos\theta - \sin\theta}{\cos\theta + \sin\theta} = 2\tan(2\theta)$

65. $\tan(3\theta) = \dfrac{3\tan\theta - \tan^3\theta}{1 - 3\tan^2\theta}$

66. $\tan\theta + \tan(\theta + 120°) + \tan(\theta + 240°) = 3\tan(3\theta)$

67. $\ln|\sin\theta| = \dfrac{1}{2}(\ln|1 - \cos(2\theta)| - \ln 2)$

68. $\ln|\cos\theta| = \dfrac{1}{2}(\ln|1 + \cos(2\theta)| - \ln 2)$

Mixed Practice

In Problems 69–80, find the exact value of each expression.

69. $\sin\left(2\sin^{-1}\frac{1}{2}\right)$

70. $\sin\left[2\sin^{-1}\frac{\sqrt{3}}{2}\right]$

71. $\cos\left(2\sin^{-1}\frac{3}{5}\right)$

72. $\cos\left(2\cos^{-1}\frac{4}{5}\right)$

73. $\tan\left[2\cos^{-1}\left(-\frac{3}{5}\right)\right]$

74. $\tan\left(2\tan^{-1}\frac{3}{4}\right)$

75. $\sin\left(2\cos^{-1}\frac{4}{5}\right)$

76. $\cos\left[2\tan^{-1}\left(-\frac{4}{3}\right)\right]$

77. $\sin^{2}\left(\frac{1}{2}\cos^{-1}\frac{3}{5}\right)$

78. $\cos^{2}\left(\frac{1}{2}\sin^{-1}\frac{3}{5}\right)$

79. $\sec\left(2\tan^{-1}\frac{3}{4}\right)$

80. $\csc\left[2\sin^{-1}\left(-\frac{3}{5}\right)\right]$

Applications and Extensions

81. Laser Projection In a laser projection system, the **optical** or **scanning angle** θ is related to the throw distance D from the scanner to the screen and the projected image width W by the equation

$$D = \frac{\frac{1}{2}W}{\csc\theta - \cot\theta}$$

(a) Show that the projected image width is given by

$$W = 2D\tan\frac{\theta}{2}$$

(b) Find the optical angle if the throw distance is 15 feet and the projected image width is 6.5 feet.

Source: *Pangolin Laser Systems, Inc.*

82. Product of Inertia The **product of inertia** for an area about inclined axes is given by the formula

$$I_{uv} = I_{x}\sin\theta\cos\theta - I_{y}\sin\theta\cos\theta + I_{xy}(\cos^{2}\theta - \sin^{2}\theta)$$

Show that this is equivalent to

$$I_{uv} = \frac{I_{x} - I_{y}}{2}\sin(2\theta) + I_{xy}\cos(2\theta)$$

Source: Adapted from Hibbeler, *Engineering Mechanics: Statics*, 10th ed., Prentice Hall © 2004.

83. Projectile Motion An object is propelled upward at an angle θ, $45° < \theta < 90°$, to the horizontal with an initial velocity of v_{0} feet per second from the base of a plane that makes an angle of $45°$ with the horizontal. See the illustration. If air resistance is ignored, the distance R that it travels up the inclined plane is given by the function

$$R(\theta) = \frac{v_{0}^{2}\sqrt{2}}{16}\cos\theta(\sin\theta - \cos\theta)$$

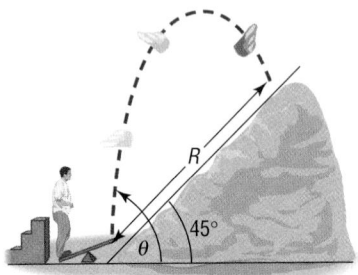

(a) Show that

$$R(\theta) = \frac{v_{0}^{2}\sqrt{2}}{32}[\sin(2\theta) - \cos(2\theta) - 1]$$

(b) Graph $R = R(\theta)$. (Use $v_{0} = 32$ feet per second.)
(c) What value of θ makes R the largest? (Use $v_{0} = 32$ feet per second.)

84. Sawtooth Curve An oscilloscope often displays a sawtooth curve. This curve can be approximated by sinusoidal curves of varying periods and amplitudes. A first approximation to the sawtooth curve is given by

$$y = \frac{1}{2}\sin(2\pi x) + \frac{1}{4}\sin(4\pi x)$$

Show that $y = \sin(2\pi x)\cos^{2}(\pi x)$.

85. Area of an Isosceles Triangle Show that the area A of an isosceles triangle whose equal sides are of length s and θ is the angle between them is

$$A = \frac{1}{2}s^{2}\sin\theta$$

[Hint: See the illustration. The height h bisects the angle θ and is the perpendicular bisector of the base.]

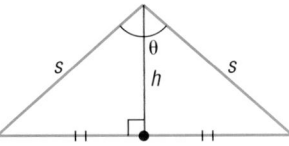

86. Geometry A rectangle is inscribed in a semicircle of radius 1. See the illustration.

(a) Express the area A of the rectangle as a function of the angle θ shown in the illustration.
(b) Show that $A(\theta) = \sin(2\theta)$.
(c) Find the angle θ that results in the largest area A.
(d) Find the dimensions of this largest rectangle.

87. If $x = 2\tan\theta$, express $\sin(2\theta)$ as a function of x.

88. If $x = 2\tan\theta$, express $\cos(2\theta)$ as a function of x.

89. Find the value of the number C:
$$\frac{1}{2}\sin^2 x + C = -\frac{1}{4}\cos(2x)$$

90. Find the value of the number C:
$$\frac{1}{2}\cos^2 x + C = \frac{1}{4}\cos(2x)$$

91. If $z = \tan\dfrac{\alpha}{2}$, show that $\sin\alpha = \dfrac{2z}{1 + z^2}$.

92. If $z = \tan\dfrac{\alpha}{2}$, show that $\cos\alpha = \dfrac{1 - z^2}{1 + z^2}$.

93. Graph $f(x) = \sin^2 x = \dfrac{1 - \cos(2x)}{2}$ for $0 \le x \le 2\pi$ by using transformations.

94. Repeat Problem 93 for $g(x) = \cos^2 x$.

95. Use the fact that
$$\cos\frac{\pi}{12} = \frac{1}{4}\left(\sqrt{6} + \sqrt{2}\right)$$
to find $\sin\dfrac{\pi}{24}$ and $\cos\dfrac{\pi}{24}$.

96. Show that
$$\cos\frac{\pi}{8} = \frac{\sqrt{2 + \sqrt{2}}}{2}$$
and use it to find $\sin\dfrac{\pi}{16}$ and $\cos\dfrac{\pi}{16}$.

97. Show that
$$\sin^3\theta + \sin^3(\theta + 120°) + \sin^3(\theta + 240°) = -\frac{3}{4}\sin(3\theta)$$

98. If $\tan\theta = a\tan\dfrac{\theta}{3}$, express $\tan\dfrac{\theta}{3}$ in terms of a.

Discussion and Writing

99. Research Chebyshëv polynomials. Write a report on your findings.

7.6 Product-to-Sum and Sum-to-Product Formulas

OBJECTIVES **1** Express Products as Sums (p. 485)
2 Express Sums as Products (p. 486)

1 Express Products as Sums

Sum and difference formulas can be used to derive formulas for writing the products of sines and/or cosines as sums or differences. These identities are usually called the **Product-to-Sum Formulas.**

THEOREM   **Product-to-Sum Formulas**

$$\sin\alpha\sin\beta = \frac{1}{2}[\cos(\alpha - \beta) - \cos(\alpha + \beta)] \qquad \textbf{(1)}$$

$$\cos\alpha\cos\beta = \frac{1}{2}[\cos(\alpha - \beta) + \cos(\alpha + \beta)] \qquad \textbf{(2)}$$

$$\sin\alpha\cos\beta = \frac{1}{2}[\sin(\alpha + \beta) + \sin(\alpha - \beta)] \qquad \textbf{(3)}$$

These formulas do not have to be memorized. Instead, you should remember how they are derived. Then, when you want to use them, either look them up or derive them, as needed.

To derive formulas (1) and (2), write down the sum and difference formulas for the cosine:

$$\cos(\alpha - \beta) = \cos\alpha\cos\beta + \sin\alpha\sin\beta \qquad \textbf{(4)}$$
$$\cos(\alpha + \beta) = \cos\alpha\cos\beta - \sin\alpha\sin\beta \qquad \textbf{(5)}$$

Subtract equation (5) from equation (4) to get

$$\cos(\alpha - \beta) - \cos(\alpha + \beta) = 2\sin\alpha\sin\beta$$

from which

$$\sin\alpha\sin\beta = \frac{1}{2}[\cos(\alpha - \beta) - \cos(\alpha + \beta)]$$

Now add equations (4) and (5) to get

$$\cos(\alpha - \beta) + \cos(\alpha + \beta) = 2 \cos \alpha \cos \beta$$

from which

$$\cos \alpha \cos \beta = \frac{1}{2}[\cos(\alpha - \beta) + \cos(\alpha + \beta)]$$

To derive Product-to-Sum Formula (3), use the sum and difference formulas for sine in a similar way. (You are asked to do this in Problem 43.)

EXAMPLE 1	**Expressing Products as Sums**

Express each of the following products as a sum containing only sines or only cosines.

(a) $\sin(6\theta) \sin(4\theta)$ (b) $\cos(3\theta) \cos \theta$ (c) $\sin(3\theta) \cos(5\theta)$

Solution   (a) We use formula (1) to get

$$\sin(6\theta) \sin(4\theta) = \frac{1}{2}[\cos(6\theta - 4\theta) - \cos(6\theta + 4\theta)]$$

$$= \frac{1}{2}[\cos(2\theta) - \cos(10\theta)]$$

(b) We use formula (2) to get

$$\cos(3\theta) \cos \theta = \frac{1}{2}[\cos(3\theta - \theta) + \cos(3\theta + \theta)]$$

$$= \frac{1}{2}[\cos(2\theta) + \cos(4\theta)]$$

(c) We use formula (3) to get

$$\sin(3\theta) \cos(5\theta) = \frac{1}{2}[\sin(3\theta + 5\theta) + \sin(3\theta - 5\theta)]$$

$$= \frac{1}{2}[\sin(8\theta) + \sin(-2\theta)] = \frac{1}{2}[\sin(8\theta) - \sin(2\theta)]$$

━━━━━ **Now Work** PROBLEM 1

2 Express Sums as Products

The **Sum-to-Product Formulas** are given next.

THEOREM   **Sum-to-Product Formulas**

$$\sin \alpha + \sin \beta = 2 \sin \frac{\alpha + \beta}{2} \cos \frac{\alpha - \beta}{2} \qquad (6)$$

$$\sin \alpha - \sin \beta = 2 \sin \frac{\alpha - \beta}{2} \cos \frac{\alpha + \beta}{2} \qquad (7)$$

$$\cos \alpha + \cos \beta = 2 \cos \frac{\alpha + \beta}{2} \cos \frac{\alpha - \beta}{2} \qquad (8)$$

$$\cos \alpha - \cos \beta = -2 \sin \frac{\alpha + \beta}{2} \sin \frac{\alpha - \beta}{2} \qquad (9)$$

We will derive formula (6) and leave the derivations of formulas (7) through (9) as exercises (see Problems 44 through 46).

Proof

$$2 \sin \frac{\alpha + \beta}{2} \cos \frac{\alpha - \beta}{2} \underset{\uparrow}{=} 2 \cdot \frac{1}{2} \left[\sin\left(\frac{\alpha + \beta}{2} + \frac{\alpha - \beta}{2} \right) + \sin\left(\frac{\alpha + \beta}{2} - \frac{\alpha - \beta}{2} \right) \right]$$

Product-to-Sum Formula (3)

$$= \sin \frac{2\alpha}{2} + \sin \frac{2\beta}{2} = \sin \alpha + \sin \beta \qquad ■$$

EXAMPLE 2	**Expressing Sums (or Differences) as a Product**

Express each sum or difference as a product of sines and/or cosines.

(a) $\sin(5\theta) - \sin(3\theta)$ (b) $\cos(3\theta) + \cos(2\theta)$

Solution (a) We use formula (7) to get

$$\sin(5\theta) - \sin(3\theta) = 2 \sin \frac{5\theta - 3\theta}{2} \cos \frac{5\theta + 3\theta}{2}$$

$$= 2 \sin \theta \cos(4\theta)$$

(b) $\cos(3\theta) + \cos(2\theta) = 2 \cos \frac{3\theta + 2\theta}{2} \cos \frac{3\theta - 2\theta}{2}$ Formula (8)

$$= 2 \cos \frac{5\theta}{2} \cos \frac{\theta}{2}$$

Now Work   PROBLEM 11

7.6 Assess Your Understanding

Skill Building

In Problems 1–10, express each product as a sum containing only sines or only cosines.

1. $\sin(4\theta) \sin(2\theta)$ **2.** $\cos(4\theta) \cos(2\theta)$ **3.** $\sin(4\theta) \cos(2\theta)$ **4.** $\sin(3\theta) \sin(5\theta)$ **5.** $\cos(3\theta) \cos(5\theta)$

6. $\sin(4\theta) \cos(6\theta)$ **7.** $\sin \theta \sin(2\theta)$ **8.** $\cos(3\theta) \cos(4\theta)$ **9.** $\sin \frac{3\theta}{2} \cos \frac{\theta}{2}$ **10.** $\sin \frac{\theta}{2} \cos \frac{5\theta}{2}$

In Problems 11–18, express each sum or difference as a product of sines and/or cosines.

11. $\sin(4\theta) - \sin(2\theta)$ **12.** $\sin(4\theta) + \sin(2\theta)$ **13.** $\cos(2\theta) + \cos(4\theta)$ **14.** $\cos(5\theta) - \cos(3\theta)$

15. $\sin \theta + \sin(3\theta)$ **16.** $\cos \theta + \cos(3\theta)$ **17.** $\cos \frac{\theta}{2} - \cos \frac{3\theta}{2}$ **18.** $\sin \frac{\theta}{2} - \sin \frac{3\theta}{2}$

In Problems 19–36, establish each identity.

19. $\dfrac{\sin \theta + \sin(3\theta)}{2 \sin(2\theta)} = \cos \theta$ **20.** $\dfrac{\cos \theta + \cos(3\theta)}{2 \cos(2\theta)} = \cos \theta$ **21.** $\dfrac{\sin(4\theta) + \sin(2\theta)}{\cos(4\theta) + \cos(2\theta)} = \tan(3\theta)$

22. $\dfrac{\cos \theta - \cos(3\theta)}{\sin(3\theta) - \sin \theta} = \tan(2\theta)$ **23.** $\dfrac{\cos \theta - \cos(3\theta)}{\sin \theta + \sin(3\theta)} = \tan \theta$ **24.** $\dfrac{\cos \theta - \cos(5\theta)}{\sin \theta + \sin(5\theta)} = \tan(2\theta)$

25. $\sin \theta [\sin \theta + \sin(3\theta)] = \cos \theta [\cos \theta - \cos(3\theta)]$ **26.** $\sin \theta [\sin(3\theta) + \sin(5\theta)] = \cos \theta [\cos(3\theta) - \cos(5\theta)]$

27. $\dfrac{\sin(4\theta) + \sin(8\theta)}{\cos(4\theta) + \cos(8\theta)} = \tan(6\theta)$ **28.** $\dfrac{\sin(4\theta) - \sin(8\theta)}{\cos(4\theta) - \cos(8\theta)} = -\cot(6\theta)$

29. $\dfrac{\sin(4\theta) + \sin(8\theta)}{\sin(4\theta) - \sin(8\theta)} = -\dfrac{\tan(6\theta)}{\tan(2\theta)}$ **30.** $\dfrac{\cos(4\theta) - \cos(8\theta)}{\cos(4\theta) + \cos(8\theta)} = \tan(2\theta) \tan(6\theta)$

31. $\dfrac{\sin \alpha + \sin \beta}{\sin \alpha - \sin \beta} = \tan \dfrac{\alpha + \beta}{2} \cot \dfrac{\alpha - \beta}{2}$ **32.** $\dfrac{\cos \alpha + \cos \beta}{\cos \alpha - \cos \beta} = -\cot \dfrac{\alpha + \beta}{2} \cot \dfrac{\alpha - \beta}{2}$

33. $\dfrac{\sin \alpha + \sin \beta}{\cos \alpha + \cos \beta} = \tan \dfrac{\alpha + \beta}{2}$

34. $\dfrac{\sin \alpha - \sin \beta}{\cos \alpha - \cos \beta} = -\cot \dfrac{\alpha + \beta}{2}$

35. $1 + \cos(2\theta) + \cos(4\theta) + \cos(6\theta) = 4\cos\theta\cos(2\theta)\cos(3\theta)$

36. $1 - \cos(2\theta) + \cos(4\theta) - \cos(6\theta) = 4\sin\theta\cos(2\theta)\sin(3\theta)$

Applications and Extensions

37. Touch-Tone Phones On a Touch-Tone phone, each button produces a unique sound. The sound produced is the sum of two tones, given by

$$y = \sin(2\pi lt) \quad \text{and} \quad y = \sin(2\pi ht)$$

where l and h are the low and high frequencies (cycles per second) shown on the illustration. For example, if you touch 7, the low frequency is $l = 852$ cycles per second and the high frequency is $h = 1209$ cycles per second. The sound emitted by touching 7 is

$$y = \sin[2\pi(852)t] + \sin[2\pi(1209)t]$$

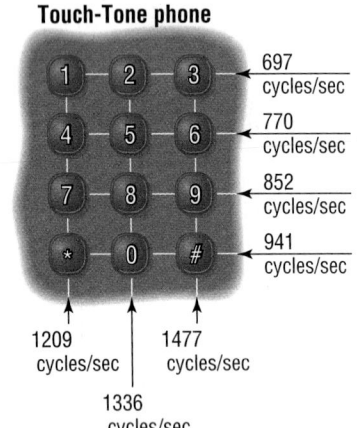

Touch-Tone phone

697 cycles/sec

770 cycles/sec

852 cycles/sec

941 cycles/sec

1209 cycles/sec   1477 cycles/sec

1336 cycles/sec

(a) Write this sound as a product of sines and/or cosines.
(b) Determine the maximum value of y.
(c) Graph the sound emitted by touching 7.

38. Touch-Tone Phones
(a) Write the sound emitted by touching the # key as a product of sines and/or cosines.
(b) Determine the maximum value of y.
(c) Graph the sound emitted by touching the # key.

39. Moment of Inertia The moment of inertia I of an object is a measure of how easy it is to rotate the object about some fixed point. In engineering mechanics, it is sometimes necessary to compute moments of inertia with respect to a set of rotated axes. These moments are given by the equations

$$I_u = I_x \cos^2 \theta + I_y \sin^2 \theta - 2I_{xy} \sin \theta \cos \theta$$

$$I_v = I_x \sin^2 \theta + I_y \cos^2 \theta + 2I_{xy} \sin \theta \cos \theta$$

Use Product-to-Sum Formulas to show that

$$I_u = \frac{I_x + I_y}{2} + \frac{I_x - I_y}{2}\cos(2\theta) - I_{xy}\sin(2\theta)$$

and

$$I_v = \frac{I_x + I_y}{2} - \frac{I_x - I_y}{2}\cos(2\theta) + I_{xy}\sin(2\theta)$$

Source: Adapted from Hibbeler, *Engineering Mechanics: Statics*, 10th ed., Prentice Hall © 2004.

40. Projectile Motion The range R of a projectile propelled downward from the top of an inclined plane at an angle θ to the inclined plane is given by

$$R(\theta) = \frac{2v_0^2 \sin\theta\cos(\theta - \phi)}{g\cos^2\phi}$$

where v_0 is the initial velocity of the projectile, ϕ is the angle the plane makes with respect to the horizontal, and g is acceleration due to gravity.

(a) Show that for fixed v_0 and ϕ the maximum range down the incline is given by $R_{\max} = \dfrac{v_0^2}{g(1 - \sin\phi)}$.

(b) Determine the maximum range if the projectile has an initial velocity of 50 meters/second, the angle of the plane is $\phi = 35°$, and $g = 9.8$ meters/second^2.

41. If $\alpha + \beta + \gamma = \pi$, show that

$$\sin(2\alpha) + \sin(2\beta) + \sin(2\gamma) = 4\sin\alpha\sin\beta\sin\gamma$$

42. If $\alpha + \beta + \gamma = \pi$, show that

$$\tan\alpha + \tan\beta + \tan\gamma = \tan\alpha\tan\beta\tan\gamma$$

43. Derive formula (3).

44. Derive formula (7).

45. Derive formula (8).

46. Derive formula (9).

7.7 Trigonometric Equations (I)

PREPARING FOR THIS SECTION *Before getting started, review the following:*

- Solving Equations (Appendix A, Section A.6, pp. A46–A57)
- Values of the Trigonometric Functions (Section 6.2, pp. 368–376)

Now Work the 'Are You Prepared?' problems on page 492.

OBJECTIVE 1 Solve Equations Involving a Single Trigonometric Function (p. 489)

1 Solve Equations Involving a Single Trigonometric Function

The previous four sections of this chapter were devoted to trigonometric identities, that is, equations involving trigonometric functions that are satisfied by every value in the domain of the variable. In the remaining two sections, we discuss **trigonometric equations**, that is, equations involving trigonometric functions that are satisfied only by some values of the variable (or, possibly, are not satisfied by any values of the variable). The values that satisfy the equation are called **solutions** of the equation.

EXAMPLE 1   **Checking Whether a Given Number Is a Solution of a Trigonometric Equation**

Determine whether $\theta = \dfrac{\pi}{4}$ is a solution of the equation $2\sin\theta - 1 = 0$. Is $\theta = \dfrac{\pi}{6}$ a solution?

Solution   Replace θ by $\dfrac{\pi}{4}$ in the given equation. The result is

$$2\sin\frac{\pi}{4} - 1 = 2 \cdot \frac{\sqrt{2}}{2} - 1 = \sqrt{2} - 1 \neq 0$$

We conclude that $\dfrac{\pi}{4}$ is not a solution.

Next replace θ by $\dfrac{\pi}{6}$ in the equation. The result is

$$2\sin\frac{\pi}{6} - 1 = 2 \cdot \frac{1}{2} - 1 = 1 - 1 = 0$$

We conclude that $\dfrac{\pi}{6}$ is a solution of the given equation.

The equation given in Example 1 has other solutions besides $\theta = \dfrac{\pi}{6}$. For example, $\theta = \dfrac{5\pi}{6}$ is also a solution, as is $\theta = \dfrac{13\pi}{6}$. (You should check this for yourself.) In fact, the equation has an infinite number of solutions due to the periodicity of the sine function, as can be seen in Figure 29, which shows the graph of $Y_1 = 2\sin x - 1$. Each x-intercept represents a solution of the equation $2\sin x - 1 = 0$.

Figure 29

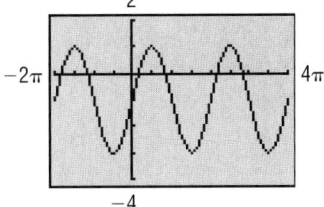

Unless the domain of the variable is restricted, we need to find *all* the solutions of a trigonometric equation. As the next example illustrates, finding all the solutions can be accomplished by first finding solutions over an interval whose length equals the period of the function and then adding multiples of that period to the solutions found. Let's look at some examples.

EXAMPLE 2   **Finding All the Solutions of a Trigonometric Equation**

Solve the equation: $\cos\theta = \dfrac{1}{2}$

Give a general formula for all the solutions. List eight of the solutions.

Solution

Figure 30

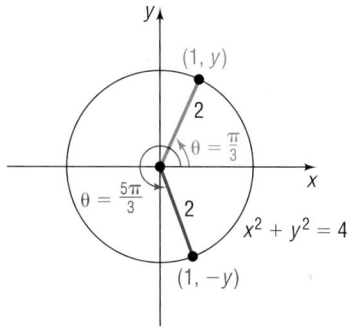

The period of the cosine function is 2π. In the interval $[0, 2\pi)$, there are two angles θ for which $\cos\theta = \dfrac{1}{2}$: $\theta = \dfrac{\pi}{3}$ and $\theta = \dfrac{5\pi}{3}$. See Figure 30. Because the cosine function has period 2π, all the solutions of $\cos\theta = \dfrac{1}{2}$ may be given by the general formula

$$\theta = \frac{\pi}{3} + 2k\pi \quad \text{or} \quad \theta = \frac{5\pi}{3} + 2k\pi \quad \text{k any integer}$$

Eight of the solutions are

$$\underbrace{-\frac{5\pi}{3},\ -\frac{\pi}{3}}_{k=-1},\ \underbrace{\frac{\pi}{3},\ \frac{5\pi}{3}}_{k=0},\ \underbrace{\frac{7\pi}{3},\ \frac{11\pi}{3}}_{k=1},\ \underbrace{\frac{13\pi}{3},\ \frac{17\pi}{3}}_{k=2}$$

Figure 31

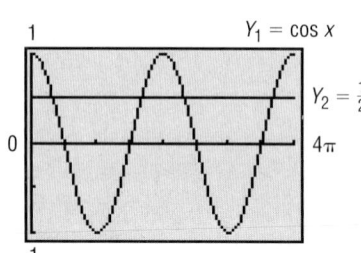

✔ **Check:** We can verify the solutions by graphing $Y_1 = \cos x$ and $Y_2 = \dfrac{1}{2}$ to determine where the graphs intersect. (Be sure to graph in radian mode.) See Figure 31. The graph of Y_1 intersects the graph of Y_2 at $x = 1.05 \left(\approx \dfrac{\pi}{3}\right)$, $5.24 \left(\approx \dfrac{5\pi}{3}\right)$, $7.33 \left(\approx \dfrac{7\pi}{3}\right)$, and $11.52 \left(\approx \dfrac{11\pi}{3}\right)$, rounded to two decimal places.

◾

✏ **Now Work PROBLEM 31**

In most of our work, we shall be interested only in finding solutions of trigonometric equations for $0 \leq \theta < 2\pi$.

EXAMPLE 3	**Solving a Linear Trigonometric Equation**

Solve the equation: $2\sin\theta + \sqrt{3} = 0, \quad 0 \leq \theta < 2\pi$

Solution We solve the equation for $\sin\theta$.

$$2\sin\theta + \sqrt{3} = 0$$
$$2\sin\theta = -\sqrt{3} \quad \text{Subtract } \sqrt{3} \text{ from both sides.}$$
$$\sin\theta = -\frac{\sqrt{3}}{2} \quad \text{Divide both sides by 2.}$$

In the interval $[0, 2\pi)$, there are two angles θ for which $\sin\theta = -\dfrac{\sqrt{3}}{2}$: $\theta = \dfrac{4\pi}{3}$ and $\theta = \dfrac{5\pi}{3}$. The solution set is $\left\{\dfrac{4\pi}{3}, \dfrac{5\pi}{3}\right\}$.

◾

✏ **Now Work PROBLEM 7**

When the argument of the trigonometric function in an equation is a multiple of θ, the general formula must be used to solve the equation.

EXAMPLE 4	**Solving a Trigonometric Equation**

Solve the equation: $\sin(2\theta) = \dfrac{1}{2}, \quad 0 \leq \theta < 2\pi$

Solution In the interval $[0, 2\pi)$, the sine function has a value $\frac{1}{2}$ at $\frac{\pi}{6}$ and $\frac{5\pi}{6}$. See Figure 32. Since the period of the sine function is 2π and the argument is 2θ in the equation $\sin(2\theta) = \frac{1}{2}$, we write the general formula that gives all the solutions.

Figure 32

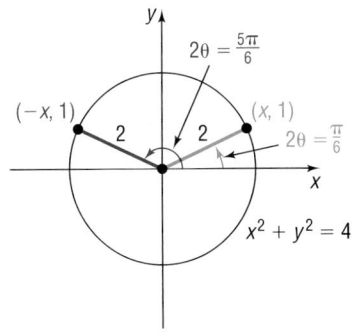

$$2\theta = \frac{\pi}{6} + 2k\pi \quad \text{or} \quad 2\theta = \frac{5\pi}{6} + 2k\pi \quad \textit{k any integer}$$

$$\theta = \frac{\pi}{12} + k\pi \quad \text{or} \quad \theta = \frac{5\pi}{12} + k\pi \quad \textit{Divide by 2.}$$

Then

$$\theta = \frac{\pi}{12} + (-1)\pi = \frac{-11\pi}{12} \quad \textit{k = -1} \qquad \theta = \frac{5\pi}{12} + (-1)\pi = \frac{-7\pi}{12}$$

$$\theta = \frac{\pi}{12} + (0)\pi = \frac{\pi}{12} \quad \textit{k = 0} \qquad \theta = \frac{5\pi}{12} + (0)\pi = \frac{5\pi}{12}$$

$$\theta = \frac{\pi}{12} + (1)\pi = \frac{13\pi}{12} \quad \textit{k = 1} \qquad \theta = \frac{5\pi}{12} + (1)\pi = \frac{17\pi}{12}$$

$$\theta = \frac{\pi}{12} + (2)\pi = \frac{25\pi}{12} \quad \textit{k = 2} \qquad \theta = \frac{5\pi}{12} + (2)\pi = \frac{29\pi}{12}$$

In the interval $[0, 2\pi)$, the solutions of $\sin(2\theta) = \frac{1}{2}$ are $\theta = \frac{\pi}{12}, \theta = \frac{5\pi}{12}, \theta = \frac{13\pi}{12}$, and $\theta = \frac{17\pi}{12}$. The solution set is $\left\{ \frac{\pi}{12}, \frac{5\pi}{12}, \frac{13\pi}{12}, \frac{17\pi}{12} \right\}$.

✓**Check:** Verify these solutions by graphing $Y_1 = \sin(2x)$ and $Y_2 = \frac{1}{2}$ for $0 \le x \le 2\pi$.

WARNING In solving a trigonometric equation for θ, $0 \le \theta < 2\pi$, in which the argument is not θ (as in Example 4), you must write down all the solutions first and then list those that are in the interval $[0, 2\pi)$. Otherwise, solutions may be lost. For example, in solving $\sin(2\theta) = \frac{1}{2}$, if you write the solutions $2\theta = \frac{\pi}{6}$ and $2\theta = \frac{5\pi}{6}$, you will find only $\theta = \frac{\pi}{12}$ and $\theta = \frac{5\pi}{12}$ and miss the other solutions. ∎

▬▬▬ **Now Work** PROBLEM 13

EXAMPLE 5 | **Solving a Trigonometric Equation**

Solve the equation: $\tan\left(\theta - \frac{\pi}{2}\right) = 1, \quad 0 \le \theta < 2\pi$

Solution The period of the tangent function is π. In the interval $[0, \pi)$, the tangent function has the value 1 when the argument is $\frac{\pi}{4}$. Because the argument is $\theta - \frac{\pi}{2}$ in the given equation, we write the general formula that gives all the solutions.

$$\theta - \frac{\pi}{2} = \frac{\pi}{4} + k\pi \quad \textit{k any integer}$$

$$\theta = \frac{3\pi}{4} + k\pi$$

In the interval $[0, 2\pi)$, $\theta = \frac{3\pi}{4}$ and $\theta = \frac{3\pi}{4} + \pi = \frac{7\pi}{4}$ are the only solutions. The solution set is $\left\{ \frac{3\pi}{4}, \frac{7\pi}{4} \right\}$.

The next example illustrates how to solve trigonometric equations using a calculator.

> | EXAMPLE 6 | **Solving a Trigonometric Equation with a Calculator**

Use a calculator to solve the equation $\sin \theta = 0.3, 0 \le \theta < 2\pi$. Express any solutions in radians, rounded to two decimal places.

Solution

Figure 33

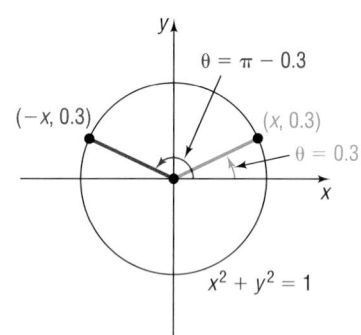

To solve $\sin \theta = 0.3$ on a calculator, first set the mode to radians. Then use the $\boxed{\sin^{-1}}$ key to obtain

$$\theta = \sin^{-1}(0.3) \approx 0.3046927$$

Rounded to two decimal places, $\theta = \sin^{-1}(0.3) = 0.30$ radian. Because of the definition of $y = \sin^{-1} x$, the angle θ that we obtain is the angle $-\dfrac{\pi}{2} \le \theta \le \dfrac{\pi}{2}$ for which $\sin \theta = 0.3$. Another angle for which $\sin \theta = 0.3$ is $\pi - 0.30$. See Figure 33. The angle $\pi - 0.30$ is the angle in quadrant II, where $\sin \theta = 0.3$. The solutions for $\sin \theta = 0.3, 0 \le \theta < 2\pi$, are

$$\theta = 0.30 \text{ radian} \quad \text{and} \quad \theta = \pi - 0.30 \approx 2.84 \text{ radians}$$

The solution set is $\{0.30, 2.84\}$.

WARNING Example 6 illustrates that caution must be exercised when solving trigonometric equations on a calculator. Remember that the calculator supplies an angle only within the restrictions of the definition of the inverse trigonometric function. To find the remaining solutions, you must identify other quadrants, if any, in which a solution may be located. ∎

➡ **Now Work** PROBLEM 41

7.7 Assess Your Understanding

'Are You Prepared?' *Answers are given at the end of these exercises. If you get a wrong answer, read the pages listed in red.*

1. Solve: $3x - 5 = -x + 1$ (pp. A47–A49)

2. $\sin\left(\dfrac{\pi}{4}\right) = $ _____; $\cos\left(\dfrac{8\pi}{3}\right) = $ _____ (pp. 370–371 and 374–375)

Concepts and Vocabulary

3. Two solutions of the equation $\sin \theta = \dfrac{1}{2}$ are _____ and _____.

4. All the solutions of the equation $\sin \theta = \dfrac{1}{2}$ are _____.

5. True or False   Most trigonometric equations have unique solutions.

6. True or False   The equation $\sin \theta = 2$ has a real solution that can be found using a calculator.

Skill Building

In Problems 7–30, solve each equation on the interval $0 \le \theta < 2\pi$.

7. $2 \sin \theta + 3 = 2$

8. $1 - \cos \theta = \dfrac{1}{2}$

9. $4 \cos^2 \theta = 1$

10. $\tan^2 \theta = \dfrac{1}{3}$

11. $2 \sin^2 \theta - 1 = 0$

12. $4 \cos^2 \theta - 3 = 0$

13. $\sin(3\theta) = -1$

14. $\tan\dfrac{\theta}{2} = \sqrt{3}$

15. $\cos(2\theta) = -\dfrac{1}{2}$

16. $\tan(2\theta) = -1$

17. $\sec\dfrac{3\theta}{2} = -2$

18. $\cot\dfrac{2\theta}{3} = -\sqrt{3}$

19. $2 \sin \theta + 1 = 0$

20. $\cos \theta + 1 = 0$

21. $\tan \theta + 1 = 0$

22. $\sqrt{3} \cot \theta + 1 = 0$

23. $4 \sec \theta + 6 = -2$

24. $5 \csc \theta - 3 = 2$

25. $3\sqrt{2} \cos \theta + 2 = -1$

26. $4 \sin \theta + 3\sqrt{3} = \sqrt{3}$

27. $\cos\left(2\theta - \dfrac{\pi}{2}\right) = -1$

28. $\sin\left(3\theta + \dfrac{\pi}{18}\right) = 1$

29. $\tan\left(\dfrac{\theta}{2} + \dfrac{\pi}{3}\right) = 1$

30. $\cos\left(\dfrac{\theta}{3} - \dfrac{\pi}{4}\right) = \dfrac{1}{2}$

In Problems 31–40, solve each equation. Give a general formula for all the solutions. List six solutions.

31. $\sin \theta = \dfrac{1}{2}$ **32.** $\tan \theta = 1$ **33.** $\tan \theta = -\dfrac{\sqrt{3}}{3}$ **34.** $\cos \theta = -\dfrac{\sqrt{3}}{2}$ **35.** $\cos \theta = 0$

36. $\sin \theta = \dfrac{\sqrt{2}}{2}$ **37.** $\cos(2\theta) = -\dfrac{1}{2}$ **38.** $\sin(2\theta) = -1$ **39.** $\sin \dfrac{\theta}{2} = -\dfrac{\sqrt{3}}{2}$ **40.** $\tan \dfrac{\theta}{2} = -1$

In Problems 41–52, use a calculator to solve each equation on the interval $0 \le \theta < 2\pi$. Round answers to two decimal places.

41. $\sin \theta = 0.4$ **42.** $\cos \theta = 0.6$ **43.** $\tan \theta = 5$ **44.** $\cot \theta = 2$

45. $\cos \theta = -0.9$ **46.** $\sin \theta = -0.2$ **47.** $\sec \theta = -4$ **48.** $\csc \theta = -3$

49. $5 \tan \theta + 9 = 0$ **50.** $4 \cot \theta = -5$ **51.** $3 \sin \theta - 2 = 0$ **52.** $4 \cos \theta + 3 = 0$

Mixed Practice

53. What are the zeros of $f(x) = 4 \sin^2 x - 3$ on the interval $[0, 2\pi]$?

54. What are the zeros of $f(x) = 2 \cos(3x) + 1$ on the interval $[0, \pi]$?

55. $f(x) = 3 \sin x$.
  (a) Find the zeros of f on the interval $[-2\pi, 4\pi]$.
  (b) Graph $f(x) = 3 \sin x$ on the interval $[-2\pi, 4\pi]$.
  (c) Solve $f(x) = \dfrac{3}{2}$ on the interval $[-2\pi, 4\pi]$. What points are on the graph of f? Label these points on the graph drawn in part (b).
  (d) Use the graph drawn in part (b) along with the results of part (c) to determine the values of x such that $f(x) > \dfrac{3}{2}$ on the interval $[-2\pi, 4\pi]$.

56. $f(x) = 2 \cos x$.
  (a) Find the zeros of f on the interval $[-2\pi, 4\pi]$.
  (b) Graph $f(x) = 2 \cos x$ on the interval $[-2\pi, 4\pi]$.
  (c) Solve $f(x) = -\sqrt{3}$ on the interval $[-2\pi, 4\pi]$. What points are on the graph of f? Label these points on the graph drawn in part (b).
  (d) Use the graph drawn in part (b) along with the results of part (c) to determine the values of x such that $f(x) < -\sqrt{3}$ on the interval $[-2\pi, 4\pi]$.

57. $f(x) = 4 \tan x$.
  (a) Solve $f(x) = -4$.
  (b) For what values of x is $f(x) < -4$ on the interval $\left(-\dfrac{\pi}{2}, \dfrac{\pi}{2}\right)$?

58. $f(x) = \cot x$.
  (a) Solve $f(x) = -\sqrt{3}$.
  (b) For what values of x is $f(x) > -\sqrt{3}$ on the interval $(0, \pi)$?

59. (a) Graph $f(x) = 3 \sin(2x) + 2$ and $g(x) = \dfrac{7}{2}$ on the same Cartesian plane for the interval $[0, \pi]$.
  (b) Solve $f(x) = g(x)$ on the interval $[0, \pi]$ and label the points of intersection on the graph drawn in part (b).
  (c) Solve $f(x) > g(x)$ on the interval $[0, \pi]$.
  (d) Shade the region bounded by $f(x) = 3 \sin(2x) + 2$ and $g(x) = \dfrac{7}{2}$ between the two points found in part (b) on the graph drawn in part (a).

60. (a) Graph $f(x) = 2 \cos \dfrac{x}{2} + 3$ and $g(x) = 4$ on the same Cartesian plane for the interval $[0, 4\pi]$.
  (b) Solve $f(x) = g(x)$ on the interval $[0, 4\pi]$ and label the points of intersection on the graph drawn in part (b).
  (c) Solve $f(x) < g(x)$ on the interval $[0, 4\pi]$.
  (d) Shade the region bounded by $f(x) = 2 \cos \dfrac{x}{2} + 3$ and $g(x) = 4$ between the two points found in part (b) on the graph drawn in part (a).

61. (a) Graph $f(x) = -4 \cos x$ and $g(x) = 2 \cos x + 3$ on the same Cartesian plane for the interval $[0, 2\pi]$.
  (b) Solve $f(x) = g(x)$ on the interval $[0, 2\pi]$ and label the points of intersection on the graph drawn in part (b).
  (c) Solve $f(x) > g(x)$ on the interval $[0, 2\pi]$.
  (d) Shade the region bounded by $f(x) = -4 \cos x$ and $g(x) = 2 \cos x + 3$ between the two points found in part (b) on the graph drawn in part (a).

62. (a) Graph $f(x) = 2 \sin x$ and $g(x) = -2 \sin x + 2$ on the same Cartesian plane for the interval $[0, 2\pi]$.
  (b) Solve $f(x) = g(x)$ on the interval $[0, 2\pi]$ and label the points of intersection on the graph drawn in part (b).
  (c) Solve $f(x) > g(x)$ on the interval $[0, 2\pi]$.
  (d) Shade the region bounded by $f(x) = 2 \sin x$ and $g(x) = -2 \sin x + 2$ between the two points found in part (b) on the graph drawn in part (a).

Applications and Extensions

63. Blood Pressure Blood pressure is a way of measuring the amount of force exerted on the walls of blood vessels. It is measured using two numbers: systolic (as the heart beats) blood pressure and diastolic (as the heart rests) blood pressure. Blood pressures vary substantially from person to person, but a typical blood pressure is 120/80, which means the systolic blood pressure is 120 mm Hg and the diastolic blood pressure is 80 mmHg. Assuming that a person's heart beats 70 times per minute, the blood pressure of an individual P after t seconds can be modeled by the function

$$P(t) = 100 + 20 \sin\left(\dfrac{7\pi}{3} t\right)$$

(a) In the interval $[0, 1]$, determine the times at which the blood pressure is 100 mmHg.

(b) In the interval $[0, 1]$, determine the times at which the blood pressure is 120 mmHg.
(c) In the interval $[0, 1]$, determine the times at which the blood pressures is between 100 and 105 mmHg.

64. The Ferris Wheel In 1893, George Ferris engineered the Ferris Wheel. It was 250 feet in diameter. If the wheel makes 1 revolution every 40 seconds, then the function

$$h(t) = 125 \sin\left(0.157t - \frac{\pi}{2}\right) + 125$$

represents the height h, in feet, of a seat on the wheel as a function of time t, where t is measured in seconds. The ride begins when $t = 0$.
(a) During the first 40 seconds of the ride, at what time t is an individual on the Ferris Wheel exactly 125 feet above the ground?
(b) During the first 80 seconds of the ride, at what time t is an individual on the Ferris Wheel exactly 250 feet above the ground?
(c) During the first 40 seconds of the ride, over what interval of time t is an individual on the Ferris Wheel more than 125 feet above the ground?

65. Holding Pattern An airplane is asked to stay within a holding pattern near Chicago's O'Hare International Airport. The function $d(x) = 70 \sin(0.65x) + 150$ represents the distance d, in miles, that the airplane is from the airport at time x, in minutes.
(a) When the plane enters the holding pattern, $x = 0$, how far is it from O'Hare?
(b) During the first 20 minutes after the plane enters the holding pattern, at what time x is the plane exactly 100 miles from the airport?
(c) During the first 20 minutes after the plane enters the holding pattern, at what time x is the plane more than 100 miles from the airport?
(d) While the plane is in the holding pattern, will it ever be within 70 miles of the airport? Why?

66. Projectile Motion A golfer hits a golf ball with an initial velocity of 100 miles per hour. The range R of the ball as a function of the angle θ to the horizontal is given by $R(\theta) = 672 \sin(2\theta)$, where R is measured in feet.
(a) At what angle θ should the ball be hit if the golfer wants the ball to travel 450 feet (150 yards)?
(b) At what angle θ should the ball be hit if the golfer wants the ball to travel 540 feet (180 yards)?
(c) At what angle θ should the ball be hit if the golfer wants the ball to travel at least 480 feet (160 yards)?
(d) Can the golfer hit the ball 720 feet (240 yards)?

 The following discussion of Snell's Law of Refraction* (named after Willebrord Snell, 1580–1626) is needed for Problems 67–73. Light, sound, and other waves travel at different speeds, depending on the media (air, water, wood, and so on) through which they pass. Suppose that light travels from a point A in one medium, where its speed is v_1, to a point B in another medium, where its speed is v_2. Refer to the figure, where the angle θ_1 is called the angle of incidence *and the angle θ_2 is the* angle of refraction. *Snell's Law, which can be proved using calculus, states that*

$$\frac{\sin \theta_1}{\sin \theta_2} = \frac{v_1}{v_2}$$

The ratio $\dfrac{v_1}{v_2}$ is called the index of refraction. *Some values are given in the following table.*

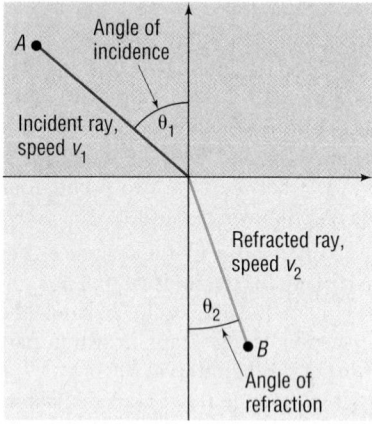

Some Indexes of Refraction	
Medium	**Index of Refraction**[†]
Water	1.33
Ethyl alcohol (20°C)	1.36
Carbon disulfide	1.63
Air (1 atm and 0°C)	1.00029
Diamond	2.42
Fused quartz	1.46
Glass, crown	1.52
Glass, dense flint	1.66
Sodium chloride	1.54

67. The index of refraction of light in passing from a vacuum into water is 1.33. If the angle of incidence is 40°, determine the angle of refraction.

68. The index of refraction of light in passing from a vacuum into dense flint glass is 1.66. If the angle of incidence is 50°, determine the angle of refraction.

69. Ptolemy, who lived in the city of Alexandria in Egypt during the second century AD, gave the measured values in the following table for the angle of incidence θ_1 and the angle of refraction θ_2 for a light beam passing from air into water. Do these values agree with Snell's Law? If so, what index of refraction results? (These data are of interest as the oldest recorded physical measurements.)[†]

θ_1	θ_2	θ_1	θ_2
10°	8°	50°	35°0'
20°	15°30'	60°	40°30'
30°	22°30'	70°	45°30'
40°	29°0'	80°	50°0'

---

*Because this law was also deduced by René Descartes in France, it is also known as Descartes's Law.

[†]For light of wavelength 589 nanometers, measured with respect to a vacuum. The index with respect to air is negligibly different in most cases.

70. Bending Light   The speed of yellow sodium light (wavelength, 589 nanometers) in a certain liquid is measured to be 1.92×10^8 meters per second. What is the index of refraction of this liquid, with respect to air, for sodium light?*
[**Hint:** The speed of light in air is approximately 2.998×10^8 meters per second.]

71. Bending Light   A beam of light with a wavelength of 589 nanometers traveling in air makes an angle of incidence of $40°$ on a slab of transparent material, and the refracted beam makes an angle of refraction of $26°$. Find the index of refraction of the material.*

72. Bending Light   A light ray with a wavelength of 589 nanometers (produced by a sodium lamp) traveling through air makes an angle of incidence of $30°$ on a smooth, flat slab of crown glass. Find the angle of refraction.*

73. A light beam passes through a thick slab of material whose index of refraction is n_2. Show that the emerging beam is parallel to the incident beam.*

74. Brewster's Law   If the angle of incidence and the angle of refraction are complementary angles, the angle of incidence is referred to as the Brewster angle θ_B. The Brewster angle is related to the index of refractions of the two media, n_1 and n_2, by the equation $n_1 \sin \theta_B = n_2 \cos \theta_B$, where n_1 is the index of refraction of the incident medium and n_2 is the index of refraction of the refractive medium. Determine the Brewster angle for a light beam traveling through water (at $20°C$) that makes an angle of incidence with a smooth, flat slab of crown glass.

*Adapted from Halliday and Resnick, *Fundamentals of Physics*, 7th ed., 2005, John Wiley & Sons.

Discussion and Writing

75. Explain in your own words how you would use your calculator to solve the equation $\cos x = -0.6, 0 \le x < 2\pi$. How would you modify your approach to solve the equation $\cot x = 5, 0 < x < 2\pi$?

'Are You Prepared?' Answers

1. $\left\{\dfrac{3}{2}\right\}$ **2.** $\dfrac{\sqrt{2}}{2}; -\dfrac{1}{2}$

7.8 Trigonometric Equations (II)

PREPARING FOR THIS SECTION   *Before getting started, review the following:*

- Solving Quadratic Equations by Factoring (Appendix A, Section A.6, pp. A50–A51)
- The Quadratic Formula (Appendix A, Section A.6, pp. A53–A55)

- Solving Equations Quadratic in Form (Appendix A, Section A.6, pp. A55–A56)
- Using a Graphing Utility to Solve Equations (Section 1.3, pp. 26–28)

Now Work the 'Are You Prepared?' problems on page 500.

OBJECTIVES   **1** Solve Trigonometric Equations Quadratic in Form (p. 495)
    2 Solve Trigonometric Equations Using Identities (p. 496)
    3 Solve Trigonometric Equations Linear in Sine and Cosine (p. 498)
    4 Solve Trigonometric Equations Using a Graphing Utility (p. 500)

1 Solve Trigonometric Equations Quadratic in Form

In this section we continue our study of trigonometric equations. Many trigonometric equations can be solved by applying techniques that we already know, such as applying the quadratic formula (if the equation is a second-degree polynomial) or factoring.

EXAMPLE 1   **Solving a Trigonometric Equation Quadratic in Form**

Solve the equation: $2 \sin^2 \theta - 3 \sin \theta + 1 = 0, \quad 0 \le \theta < 2\pi$

Solution   This equation is a quadratic equation (in $\sin \theta$) that can be factored.

$$2 \sin^2 \theta - 3 \sin \theta + 1 = 0 \quad 2x^2 - 3x + 1 = 0, \quad x = \sin \theta$$
$$(2 \sin \theta - 1)(\sin \theta - 1) = 0 \quad (2x - 1)(x - 1) = 0$$

$$2 \sin \theta - 1 = 0 \quad \text{or} \quad \sin \theta - 1 = 0 \quad \text{Use the Zero-Product Property.}$$

$$\sin \theta = \frac{1}{2} \quad \text{or} \quad \sin \theta = 1$$

Solving each equation in the interval $[0, 2\pi)$, we obtain

$$\theta = \frac{\pi}{6} \qquad \theta = \frac{5\pi}{6} \qquad \theta = \frac{\pi}{2}$$

The solution set is $\left\{ \dfrac{\pi}{6}, \dfrac{5\pi}{6}, \dfrac{\pi}{2} \right\}$.

 ━━━━━━ **Now Work** PROBLEM 7

2 Solve Trigonometric Equations Using Identities

When a trigonometric equation contains more than one trigonometric function, identities sometimes can be used to obtain an equivalent equation that contains only one trigonometric function.

EXAMPLE 2	**Solving a Trigonometric Equation Using Identities**

Solve the equation: $\quad 3 \cos \theta + 3 = 2 \sin^2 \theta, \quad 0 \le \theta < 2\pi$

Solution   The equation in its present form contains a sine and a cosine. However, a form of the Pythagorean Identity can be used to transform the equation into an equivalent expression containing only cosines.

$$3 \cos \theta + 3 = 2 \sin^2 \theta$$
$$3 \cos \theta + 3 = 2(1 - \cos^2 \theta) \qquad \sin^2 \theta = 1 - \cos^2 \theta$$
$$3 \cos \theta + 3 = 2 - 2 \cos^2 \theta$$
$$2 \cos^2 \theta + 3 \cos \theta + 1 = 0 \qquad\qquad \text{Quadratic in } \cos \theta$$
$$(2 \cos \theta + 1)(\cos \theta + 1) = 0 \qquad\qquad \text{Factor.}$$
$$2 \cos \theta + 1 = 0 \quad \text{or} \quad \cos \theta + 1 = 0 \quad \text{Use the Zero-Product Property.}$$
$$\cos \theta = -\frac{1}{2} \quad \text{or} \qquad \cos \theta = -1$$

Solving each equation in the interval $[0, 2\pi)$, we obtain

$$\theta = \frac{2\pi}{3} \qquad \theta = \frac{4\pi}{3} \qquad \theta = \pi$$

The solution set is $\left\{ \dfrac{2\pi}{3}, \pi, \dfrac{4\pi}{3} \right\}$.

✓**Check:** Graph $Y_1 = 3 \cos x + 3$ and $Y_2 = 2 \sin^2 x, 0 \le x \le 2\pi$, and approximate the points of intersection.

When a trigonometric equation contains trigonometric functions with different arguments, identities can sometimes be used to obtain an equivalent equation with the same argument.

EXAMPLE 3	**Solving a Trigonometric Equation Using Identities**

Solve the equation: $\quad \cos(2\theta) + 3 = 5 \cos \theta, \quad 0 \le \theta < 2\pi$

Solution   First, we observe that the given equation contains two cosine functions, but with different arguments, θ and 2θ. We use the Double-angle Formula $\cos(2\theta) = 2 \cos^2 \theta - 1$ to obtain an equivalent equation containing only $\cos \theta$.

$$\cos(2\theta) + 3 = 5 \cos \theta$$
$$(2 \cos^2 \theta - 1) + 3 = 5 \cos \theta \qquad \cos(2\theta) = 2 \cos^2 \theta - 1$$
$$2 \cos^2 \theta - 5 \cos \theta + 2 = 0 \qquad\qquad \text{Place in standard form.}$$

$$(\cos\theta - 2)(2\cos\theta - 1) = 0 \quad \text{Factor.}$$

$$\cos\theta = 2 \quad \text{or} \quad \cos\theta = \frac{1}{2} \quad \text{Solve by using the Zero-Product property.}$$

For any angle θ, $-1 \le \cos\theta \le 1$; therefore, the equation $\cos\theta = 2$ has no solution. The solutions of $\cos\theta = \frac{1}{2}$, $0 \le \theta < 2\pi$, are

$$\theta = \frac{\pi}{3} \qquad \theta = \frac{5\pi}{3}$$

The solution set is $\left\{ \frac{\pi}{3}, \frac{5\pi}{3} \right\}$.

✓ **Check:** Graph $Y_1 = \cos(2x) + 3$ and $Y_2 = 5\cos x$, $0 \le x \le 2\pi$, and approximate the points of intersection.

━━━ **Now Work** PROBLEM 23

| EXAMPLE 4 | **Solving a Trigonometric Equation Using Identities** |

Solve the equation: $\cos^2\theta + \sin\theta = 2$, $0 \le \theta < 2\pi$

Solution

This equation involves two trigonometric functions, sine and cosine. We use a form of the Pythagorean Identity, $\sin^2\theta + \cos^2\theta = 1$, to rewrite the equation in terms of $\sin\theta$.

$$\cos^2\theta + \sin\theta = 2$$
$$(1 - \sin^2\theta) + \sin\theta = 2 \quad \cos^2\theta = 1 - \sin^2\theta$$
$$\sin^2\theta - \sin\theta + 1 = 0$$

This is a quadratic equation in $\sin\theta$. The discriminant is $b^2 - 4ac = (-1)^2 - 4\cdot 1\cdot 1 = -3 < 0$. Therefore, the equation has no real solution. The solution set is the empty set, $\varnothing$.

✓ **Check:** Graph $Y_1 = \cos^2 x + \sin x$ and $Y_2 = 2$. See Figure 34. The two graphs never intersect, so the equation $Y_1 = Y_2$ has no real solution.

Figure 34

| EXAMPLE 5 | **Solving a Trigonometric Equation Using Identities** |

Solve the equation: $\sin\theta\cos\theta = -\frac{1}{2}$, $0 \le \theta < 2\pi$

Solution

The left side of the given equation is in the form of the Double-angle Formula $2\sin\theta\cos\theta = \sin(2\theta)$, except for a factor of 2. We multiply each side by 2.

$$\sin\theta\cos\theta = -\frac{1}{2}$$
$$2\sin\theta\cos\theta = -1 \quad \text{Multiply each side by 2.}$$
$$\sin(2\theta) = -1 \quad \text{Double-angle Formula}$$

The argument here is 2θ. So we need to write all the solutions of this equation and then list those that are in the interval $[0, 2\pi)$. Because $\sin\left(\dfrac{3\pi}{2} + 2\pi k\right) = -1$ for any integer k, we have

$$2\theta = \frac{3\pi}{2} + 2k\pi \quad \text{\small{k any integer}}$$

$$\theta = \frac{3\pi}{4} + k\pi$$

$$\theta = \frac{3\pi}{4} + (-1)\pi = -\frac{\pi}{4}, \quad \theta = \frac{3\pi}{4} + (0)\pi = \frac{3\pi}{4}, \quad \theta = \frac{3\pi}{4} + (1)\pi = \frac{7\pi}{4}, \quad \theta = \frac{3\pi}{4} + (2)\pi = \frac{11\pi}{4}$$

$$\uparrow \qquad\qquad\qquad \uparrow \qquad\qquad\qquad \uparrow \qquad\qquad\qquad \uparrow$$

$$\text{\small{$k = -1$}} \qquad\qquad \text{\small{$k = 0$}} \qquad\qquad \text{\small{$k = 1$}} \qquad\qquad \text{\small{$k = 2$}}$$

The solutions in the interval $[0, 2\pi)$ are

$$\theta = \frac{3\pi}{4} \qquad \theta = \frac{7\pi}{4}$$

The solution set is $\left\{ \dfrac{3\pi}{4}, \dfrac{7\pi}{4} \right\}$.

3 Solve Trigonometric Equations Linear in Sine and Cosine

Sometimes it is necessary to square both sides of an equation to obtain expressions that allow the use of identities. Remember, squaring both sides of an equation may introduce extraneous solutions. As a result, apparent solutions must be checked.

| EXAMPLE 6 | **Solving a Trigonometric Equation Linear in Sine and Cosine** |

Solve the equation: $\sin\theta + \cos\theta = 1, \quad 0 \le \theta < 2\pi$

Solution A Attempts to use available identities do not lead to equations that are easy to solve. (Try it yourself.) Given the form of this equation, we decide to square each side.

$$\sin\theta + \cos\theta = 1$$
$$(\sin\theta + \cos\theta)^2 = 1 \quad \text{\small{Square each side.}}$$
$$\sin^2\theta + 2\sin\theta\cos\theta + \cos^2\theta = 1 \quad \text{\small{Remove parentheses.}}$$
$$2\sin\theta\cos\theta = 0 \quad \text{\small{$\sin^2\theta + \cos^2\theta = 1$}}$$
$$\sin\theta\cos\theta = 0$$

Setting each factor equal to zero, we obtain

$$\sin\theta = 0 \quad \text{or} \quad \cos\theta = 0$$

The apparent solutions are

$$\theta = 0 \qquad \theta = \pi \qquad \theta = \frac{\pi}{2} \qquad \theta = \frac{3\pi}{2}$$

Because we squared both sides of the original equation, we must check these apparent solutions to see if any are extraneous.

$$\theta = 0: \quad \sin 0 + \cos 0 = 0 + 1 = 1 \qquad \text{\small{A solution}}$$
$$\theta = \pi: \quad \sin\pi + \cos\pi = 0 + (-1) = -1 \qquad \text{\small{Not a solution}}$$
$$\theta = \frac{\pi}{2}: \quad \sin\frac{\pi}{2} + \cos\frac{\pi}{2} = 1 + 0 = 1 \qquad \text{\small{A solution}}$$
$$\theta = \frac{3\pi}{2}: \quad \sin\frac{3\pi}{2} + \cos\frac{3\pi}{2} = -1 + 0 = -1 \qquad \text{\small{Not a solution}}$$

The values $\theta = \pi$ and $\theta = \dfrac{3\pi}{2}$ are extraneous. The solution set is $\left\{ 0, \dfrac{\pi}{2} \right\}$.

Solution B   We start with the equation

$$\sin \theta + \cos \theta = 1$$

and divide each side by $\sqrt{2}$. (The reason for this choice will become apparent shortly.) Then

$$\frac{1}{\sqrt{2}} \sin \theta + \frac{1}{\sqrt{2}} \cos \theta = \frac{1}{\sqrt{2}}$$

The left side now resembles the formula for the sine of the sum of two angles, one of which is θ. The other angle is unknown (call it ϕ.) Then

$$\sin(\theta + \phi) = \sin \theta \cos \phi + \cos \theta \sin \phi = \frac{1}{\sqrt{2}} = \frac{\sqrt{2}}{2} \qquad \textbf{(1)}$$

where

$$\cos \phi = \frac{1}{\sqrt{2}} = \frac{\sqrt{2}}{2}, \qquad \sin \phi = \frac{1}{\sqrt{2}} = \frac{\sqrt{2}}{2}, \qquad 0 \le \phi < 2\pi$$

The angle ϕ is therefore $\dfrac{\pi}{4}$. As a result, equation (1) becomes

$$\sin\left(\theta + \frac{\pi}{4}\right) = \frac{\sqrt{2}}{2}$$

Figure 35

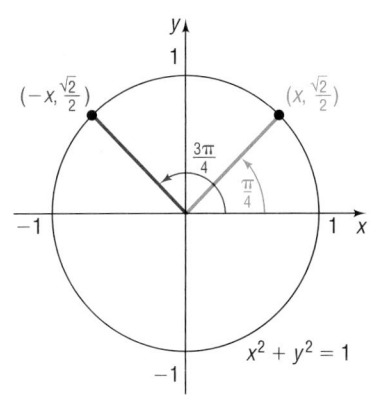

In the interval $[0, 2\pi)$, there are two angles whose sine is $\dfrac{\sqrt{2}}{2}$: $\dfrac{\pi}{4}$ and $\dfrac{3\pi}{4}$. See Figure 35. As a result,

$$\theta + \frac{\pi}{4} = \frac{\pi}{4} \quad \text{or} \quad \theta + \frac{\pi}{4} = \frac{3\pi}{4}$$

$$\theta = 0 \quad \text{or} \quad \theta = \frac{\pi}{2}$$

The solution set is $\left\{0, \dfrac{\pi}{2}\right\}$.

This second method of solution can be used to solve any linear equation in the variables $\sin \theta$ and $\cos \theta$. Let's look at an example.

EXAMPLE 7   **Solving a Trigonometric Equation Linear in $\sin \theta$ and $\cos \theta$**

Solve:

$$a \sin \theta + b \cos \theta = c \qquad \textbf{(2)}$$

where a, b, and c are constants and either $a \ne 0$ or $b \ne 0$.

Solution   We divide each side of equation (2) by $\sqrt{a^2 + b^2}$. Then

$$\frac{a}{\sqrt{a^2 + b^2}} \sin \theta + \frac{b}{\sqrt{a^2 + b^2}} \cos \theta = \frac{c}{\sqrt{a^2 + b^2}} \qquad \textbf{(3)}$$

There is a unique angle ϕ, $0 \le \phi < 2\pi$, for which

Figure 36

$$\cos \phi = \frac{a}{\sqrt{a^2 + b^2}} \quad \text{and} \quad \sin \phi = \frac{b}{\sqrt{a^2 + b^2}} \qquad \textbf{(4)}$$

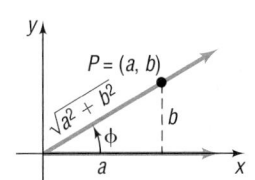

Figure 36 shows the situation for $a > 0$ and $b > 0$. Equation (3) may be written as

$$\sin \theta \cos \phi + \cos \theta \sin \phi = \frac{c}{\sqrt{a^2 + b^2}}$$

or, equivalently,

$$\sin(\theta + \phi) = \frac{c}{\sqrt{a^2 + b^2}} \qquad \textbf{(5)}$$

where ϕ satisfies the equations in (4).

If $|c| > \sqrt{a^2 + b^2}$, then $\sin(\theta + \phi) > 1$ or $\sin(\theta + \phi) < -1$, and equation (5) has no solution.

If $|c| \le \sqrt{a^2 + b^2}$, then all the solutions of equation (5) are

$$\theta + \phi = \sin^{-1}\frac{c}{\sqrt{a^2 + b^2}} + 2k\pi \quad \text{or} \quad \theta + \phi = \pi - \sin^{-1}\frac{c}{\sqrt{a^2 + b^2}} + 2k\pi$$

Because the angle ϕ is determined by the equations in (4), these provide the solutions to equation (2).

➤ **Now Work** PROBLEM 41

4 Solve Trigonometric Equations Using a Graphing Utility

The techniques introduced in this section apply only to certain types of trigonometric equations. Solutions for other types are usually studied in calculus, using numerical methods. In the next example, we show how a graphing utility may be used to obtain solutions.

EXAMPLE 8 **Solving Trigonometric Equations Using a Graphing Utility**

Solve: $5 \sin x + x = 3$

Express the solution(s) rounded to two decimal places.

Solution This type of trigonometric equation cannot be solved by previous methods. A graphing utility, though, can be used here. The solution(s) of this equation is the same as the points of intersection of the graphs of $Y_1 = 5 \sin x + x$ and $Y_2 = 3$. See Figure 37.

There are three points of intersection; the x-coordinates are the solutions that we seek. Using INTERSECT, we find

$$x = 0.52 \qquad x = 3.18 \qquad x = 5.71$$

The solution set is $\{0.52, 3.18, 5.71\}$.

Figure 37

➤ **Now Work** PROBLEM 47

7.8 Assess Your Understanding

'Are You Prepared?' *Answers are given at the end of these exercises. If you get a wrong answer, read the pages listed in red.*

1. Find the real solutions of $4x^2 - x - 5 = 0$. (pp. A50–A51)

2. Find the real solutions of $x^2 - x - 1 = 0$. (pp. A53–A55)

3. Find the real solutions of $(2x - 1)^2 - 3(2x - 1) - 4 = 0$. (pp. A55–A56)

4. Use a graphing utility to solve $5x^3 - 2 = x - x^2$. Round answers to two decimal places. (pp. 26–27)

Skill Building

In Problems 5–46, solve each equation on the interval $0 \le \theta < 2\pi$. Verify your results using a graphing utility.

5. $2\cos^2\theta + \cos\theta = 0$

6. $\sin^2\theta - 1 = 0$

7. $2\sin^2\theta - \sin\theta - 1 = 0$

8. $2\cos^2\theta + \cos\theta - 1 = 0$

9. $(\tan\theta - 1)(\sec\theta - 1) = 0$

10. $(\cot\theta + 1)\left(\csc\theta - \dfrac{1}{2}\right) = 0$

11. $\sin^2\theta - \cos^2\theta = 1 + \cos\theta$

12. $\cos^2\theta - \sin^2\theta + \sin\theta = 0$

13. $\sin^2\theta = 6(\cos\theta + 1)$

14. $2\sin^2\theta = 3(1 - \cos\theta)$

15. $\cos(2\theta) + 6\sin^2\theta = 4$

16. $\cos(2\theta) = 2 - 2\sin^2\theta$

17. $\cos\theta = \sin\theta$

18. $\cos\theta + \sin\theta = 0$

19. $\tan\theta = 2\sin\theta$

20. $\sin(2\theta) = \cos\theta$

21. $\sin\theta = \csc\theta$

22. $\tan\theta = \cot\theta$

23. $\cos(2\theta) = \cos\theta$

24. $\sin(2\theta)\sin\theta = \cos\theta$

25. $\sin(2\theta) + \sin(4\theta) = 0$

26. $\cos(2\theta) + \cos(4\theta) = 0$

27. $\cos(4\theta) - \cos(6\theta) = 0$

28. $\sin(4\theta) - \sin(6\theta) = 0$

29. $1 + \sin\theta = 2\cos^2\theta$

30. $\sin^2\theta = 2\cos\theta + 2$

31. $2\sin^2\theta - 5\sin\theta + 3 = 0$

32. $2\cos^2\theta - 7\cos\theta - 4 = 0$

33. $3(1 - \cos\theta) = \sin^2\theta$

34. $4(1 + \sin\theta) = \cos^2\theta$

35. $\tan^2\theta = \dfrac{3}{2}\sec\theta$

36. $\csc^2\theta = \cot\theta + 1$

37. $3 - \sin\theta = \cos(2\theta)$

38. $\cos(2\theta) + 5\cos\theta + 3 = 0$

39. $\sec^2\theta + \tan\theta = 0$

40. $\sec\theta = \tan\theta + \cot\theta$

41. $\sin\theta - \sqrt{3}\cos\theta = 1$

42. $\sqrt{3}\sin\theta + \cos\theta = 1$

43. $\tan(2\theta) + 2\sin\theta = 0$

44. $\tan(2\theta) + 2\cos\theta = 0$

45. $\sin\theta + \cos\theta = \sqrt{2}$

46. $\sin\theta + \cos\theta = -\sqrt{2}$

In Problems 47–58, use a graphing utility to solve each equation. Express the solution(s) rounded to two decimal places.

47. $x + 5\cos x = 0$

48. $x - 4\sin x = 0$

49. $22x - 17\sin x = 3$

50. $19x + 8\cos x = 2$

51. $\sin x + \cos x = x$

52. $\sin x - \cos x = x$

53. $x^2 - 2\cos x = 0$

54. $x^2 + 3\sin x = 0$

55. $x^2 - 2\sin(2x) = 3x$

56. $x^2 = x + 3\cos(2x)$

57. $6\sin x - e^x = 2, \quad x > 0$

58. $4\cos(3x) - e^x = 1, \quad x > 0$

Mixed Practice

In Problems 59–64, find the real zeros of each trigonometric function on the interval $0 \le x < 2\pi$.

59. $f(x) = 4\cos^2 x - 1$

60. $f(x) = 4\sin^2 x - 3$

61. $f(x) = \sin(2x) - \sin x$

62. $f(x) = \cos(2x) + \cos x$

63. $f(x) = \sin^2 x + 2\cos x + 2$

64. $f(x) = \cos(2x) + \sin^2 x$

Applications and Extensions

65. Constructing a Rain Gutter A rain gutter is to be constructed of aluminum sheets 12 inches wide. After marking off a length of 4 inches from each edge, this length is bent up at an angle θ. See the illustration. The area A of the opening as a function of θ is given by

$$A(\theta) = 16\sin\theta(\cos\theta + 1) \quad 0° < \theta < 90°$$

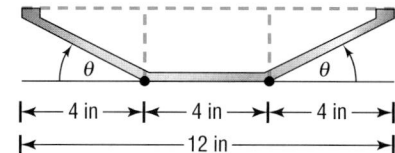

|← 4 in →|← 4 in →|← 4 in →|
|← 12 in →|

⚠ (a) In calculus, you will be asked to find the angle θ that maximizes A by solving the equation

$$\cos(2\theta) + \cos\theta = 0, \quad 0° < \theta < 90°$$

Solve this equation for θ by using the Double-angle Formula.

(b) Solve the equation in part (a) for θ by writing the sum of the two cosines as a product.

(c) What is the maximum area A of the opening?

(d) Graph $A = A(\theta), 0° \le \theta \le 90°$, and find the angle θ that maximizes the area A. Also find the maximum area. Compare the results to the answers found earlier.

66. Projectile Motion An object is propelled upward at an angle θ, $45° < \theta < 90°$, to the horizontal with an initial velocity of v_0 feet per second from the base of an inclined plane that makes an angle of $45°$ with the horizontal. See the illustration. If air resistance is ignored, the distance R that the object travels up the inclined plane is given by

$$R(\theta) = \frac{v_0^2 \sqrt{2}}{32}[\sin(2\theta) - \cos(2\theta) - 1]$$

$\triangle$ (a) In calculus, you will be asked to find the angle θ that maximizes R by solving the equation

$$\sin(2\theta) + \cos(2\theta) = 0$$

Solve this equation for θ using the method of Example 7.
(b) Solve this equation for θ by dividing each side by $\cos(2\theta)$.
(c) What is the maximum distance R if $v_0 = 32$ feet per second?
(d) Graph $R = R(\theta), 45° \le \theta \le 90°$, and find the angle θ that maximizes the distance R. Also find the maximum distance. Use $v_0 = 32$ feet per second. Compare the results with the answers found earlier.

67. Heat Transfer In the study of heat transfer, the equation $x + \tan x = 0$ occurs. Graph $Y_1 = -x$ and $Y_2 = \tan x$ for $x \ge 0$. Conclude that there are an infinite number of points of intersection of these two graphs. Now find the first two positive solutions of $x + \tan x = 0$ rounded to two decimal places.

68. Carrying a Ladder Around a Corner Two hallways, one of width 3 feet, the other of width 4 feet, meet at a right angle. See the illustration.

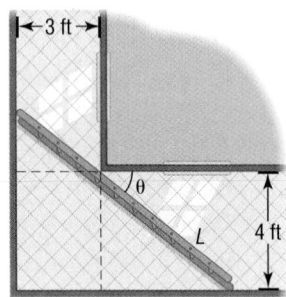

(a) Show that the length L as a function of θ is

$$L(\theta) = 4 \csc \theta + 3 \sec \theta$$

$\triangle$ (b) In calculus, you will be asked to find the length of the longest ladder that can turn the corner by solving the equation

$$3 \sec \theta \tan \theta - 4 \csc \theta \cot \theta = 0, \quad 0° < \theta < 90°$$

Solve this equation for θ.

(c) What is the length of the longest ladder that can be carried around the corner?
(d) Graph $L = L(\theta), 0° \le \theta \le 90°$, and find the angle θ that minimizes the length L.
(e) Compare the result with the one found in part (b). Explain why the two answers are the same.

69. Projectile Motion The horizontal distance that a projectile will travel in the air (ignoring air resistance) is given by the equation

$$R(\theta) = \frac{v_0^2 \sin(2\theta)}{g}$$

where v_0 is the initial velocity of the projectile, θ is the angle of elevation, and g is acceleration due to gravity (9.8 meters per second squared).
(a) If you can throw a baseball with an initial speed of 34.8 meters per second, at what angle of elevation θ should you direct the throw so that the ball travels a distance of 107 meters before striking the ground?
(b) Determine the maximum distance that you can throw the ball.
(c) Graph $R = R(\theta)$, with $v_0 = 34.8$ meters per second.
(d) Verify the results obtained in parts (a) and (b) using a graphing utility.

70. Projectile Motion Refer to Problem 69.
(a) If you can throw a baseball with an initial speed of 40 meters per second, at what angle of elevation θ should you direct the throw so that the ball travels a distance of 110 meters before striking the ground?
(b) Determine the maximum distance that you can throw the ball.
(c) Graph $R = R(\theta)$, with $v_0 = 40$ meters per second.
(d) Verify the results obtained in parts (a) and (b) using a graphing utility.

'Are You Prepared?' Answers

1. $\left\{ -1, \dfrac{5}{4} \right\}$ 2. $\left\{ \dfrac{1 - \sqrt{5}}{2}, \dfrac{1 + \sqrt{5}}{2} \right\}$ 3. $\left\{ 0, \dfrac{5}{2} \right\}$ 4. $\{0.76\}$

CHAPTER REVIEW

Things to Know

Definitions of the six inverse trigonometric functions

$y = \sin^{-1} x$ means $x = \sin y$ where $-1 \le x \le 1, \quad -\dfrac{\pi}{2} \le y \le \dfrac{\pi}{2}$ (p. 441)

$y = \cos^{-1} x$ means $x = \cos y$ where $-1 \le x \le 1, \quad 0 \le y \le \pi$ (p. 445)

$y = \tan^{-1} x$ means $x = \tan y$ where $-\infty < x < \infty, \quad -\dfrac{\pi}{2} < y < \dfrac{\pi}{2}$ (p. 448)

$y = \sec^{-1} x$ means $x = \sec y$ where $|x| \ge 1, \quad 0 \le y \le \pi, \quad y \ne \dfrac{\pi}{2}$ (p. 455)

$y = \csc^{-1} x$ means $x = \csc y$ where $|x| \ge 1, \quad -\dfrac{\pi}{2} \le y \le \dfrac{\pi}{2}, \quad y \ne 0$ (p. 455)

$y = \cot^{-1} x$ means $x = \cot y$ where $-\infty < x < \infty, \quad 0 < y < \pi$ (p. 455)

Sum and difference formulas (pp. 466, 469, and 471)

$$\cos(\alpha + \beta) = \cos\alpha\cos\beta - \sin\alpha\sin\beta \qquad \cos(\alpha - \beta) = \cos\alpha\cos\beta + \sin\alpha\sin\beta$$

$$\sin(\alpha + \beta) = \sin\alpha\cos\beta + \cos\alpha\sin\beta \qquad \sin(\alpha - \beta) = \sin\alpha\cos\beta - \cos\alpha\sin\beta$$

$$\tan(\alpha + \beta) = \frac{\tan\alpha + \tan\beta}{1 - \tan\alpha\tan\beta} \qquad \tan(\alpha - \beta) = \frac{\tan\alpha - \tan\beta}{1 + \tan\alpha\tan\beta}$$

Double-angle Formulas (pp. 476 and 477)

$$\sin(2\theta) = 2\sin\theta\cos\theta \qquad \cos(2\theta) = \cos^2\theta - \sin^2\theta \qquad \tan(2\theta) = \frac{2\tan\theta}{1 - \tan^2\theta}$$

$$\cos(2\theta) = 2\cos^2\theta - 1 \qquad \cos(2\theta) = 1 - 2\sin^2\theta$$

Half-angle Formulas (pp. 479, 480, and 482)

$$\sin^2\frac{\alpha}{2} = \frac{1 - \cos\alpha}{2} \qquad \cos^2\frac{\alpha}{2} = \frac{1 + \cos\alpha}{2} \qquad \tan^2\frac{\alpha}{2} = \frac{1 - \cos\alpha}{1 + \cos\alpha}$$

$$\sin\frac{\alpha}{2} = \pm\sqrt{\frac{1 - \cos\alpha}{2}} \qquad \cos\frac{\alpha}{2} = \pm\sqrt{\frac{1 + \cos\alpha}{2}} \qquad \tan\frac{\alpha}{2} = \pm\sqrt{\frac{1 - \cos\alpha}{1 + \cos\alpha}} = \frac{1 - \cos\alpha}{\sin\alpha} = \frac{\sin\alpha}{1 + \cos\alpha}$$

where the + or − is determined by the quadrant of $\dfrac{\alpha}{2}$.

Product-to-Sum Formulas (p. 485)

$$\sin\alpha\sin\beta = \frac{1}{2}[\cos(\alpha - \beta) - \cos(\alpha + \beta)]$$

$$\cos\alpha\cos\beta = \frac{1}{2}[\cos(\alpha - \beta) + \cos(\alpha + \beta)]$$

$$\sin\alpha\cos\beta = \frac{1}{2}[\sin(\alpha + \beta) + \sin(\alpha - \beta)]$$

Sum-to-Product Formulas (p. 486)

$$\sin\alpha + \sin\beta = 2\sin\frac{\alpha + \beta}{2}\cos\frac{\alpha - \beta}{2} \qquad \sin\alpha - \sin\beta = 2\sin\frac{\alpha - \beta}{2}\cos\frac{\alpha + \beta}{2}$$

$$\cos\alpha + \cos\beta = 2\cos\frac{\alpha + \beta}{2}\cos\frac{\alpha - \beta}{2} \qquad \cos\alpha - \cos\beta = -2\sin\frac{\alpha + \beta}{2}\sin\frac{\alpha - \beta}{2}$$

Objectives

Section		You should be able to ...	Example(s)	Review Exercises
7.1	1	Find the exact value of an inverse sine, cosine, or tangent function (p. 441)	1, 2, 6, 7, 9	1–6
	2	Find an approximate value of an inverse sine function (p. 443)	3	121–124
	3	Use properties of inverse functions to find exact values of certain composite functions (p. 443)	4, 5, 8	9–20
	4	Find the inverse function of a trigonometric function (p. 449)	10	33–36
	5	Solve equations involving inverse trigonometric functions (p. 450)	11	133, 134
7.2	1	Find the exact value of expressions involving the inverse sine, cosine, and tangent functions (p. 454)	1–3	21–32
	2	Know the definitions of the inverse secant, cosecant, and cotangent functions (p. 455)	4	7, 8, 29, 30
	3	Use a calculator to evaluate $\sec^{-1}x$, $\csc^{-1}x$, and $\cot^{-1}x$ (p. 456)	5	125, 126
	4	Write a trigonometric expression as an algebraic expression (p. 456)	6	37–40
7.3	1	Use algebra to simplify trigonometric expressions (p. 460)	1	41–72
	2	Establish identities (p. 461)	2–8	41–58
7.4	1	Use sum and difference formulas to find exact values (p. 467)	1, 2	73–80, 81–90(a)–(d), 135
	2	Use sum and difference formulas to establish identities (p. 468)	3–8	59–62
	3	Use sum and difference formulas involving inverse trigonometric functions (p. 472)	9, 10	91–94

7.5	1	Use double-angle formulas to find exact values (p. 476)	1	81–90(e), (f), 95, 96
	2	Use double-angle formulas to establish identities (p. 477)	2–4	65–67
	3	Use half-angle formulas to find exact values (p. 479)	5, 6	81–90(g), (h), 135
7.6	1	Express products as sums (p. 485)	1	68
	2	Express sums as products (p. 486)	2	69–72
7.7	1	Solve equations involving a single trigonometric function (p. 489)	1–6	97–106
7.8	1	Solve trigonometric equations quadratic in form (p. 495)	1	113, 114
	2	Solve trigonometric equations using identities (p. 496)	2–5	97–112, 115–118
	3	Solve trigonometric equations linear in sine and cosine (p. 498)	6, 7	119, 120
	4	Solve trigonometric equations using a graphing utility (p. 500)	8	127–132

Review Exercises

In Problems 1–8, find the exact value of each expression. Do not use a calculator.

1. $\sin^{-1} 1$ **2.** $\cos^{-1} 0$ **3.** $\tan^{-1} 1$ **4.** $\sin^{-1}\left(-\dfrac{1}{2}\right)$

5. $\cos^{-1}\left(-\dfrac{\sqrt{3}}{2}\right)$ **6.** $\tan^{-1}\left(-\sqrt{3}\right)$ **7.** $\sec^{-1}\sqrt{2}$ **8.** $\cot^{-1}(-1)$

In Problems 9–32, find the exact value, if any, of each composite function. If there is no value, say it is "not defined." Do not use a calculator.

9. $\sin^{-1}\left(\sin\dfrac{3\pi}{8}\right)$ **10.** $\cos^{-1}\left(\cos\dfrac{3\pi}{4}\right)$ **11.** $\tan^{-1}\left(\tan\dfrac{2\pi}{3}\right)$ **12.** $\sin^{-1}\left[\sin\left(-\dfrac{\pi}{8}\right)\right]$

13. $\cos^{-1}\left(\cos\dfrac{15\pi}{7}\right)$ **14.** $\sin^{-1}\left[\sin\left(-\dfrac{8\pi}{9}\right)\right]$ **15.** $\sin(\sin^{-1} 0.9)$ **16.** $\cos(\cos^{-1} 0.6)$

17. $\cos[\cos^{-1}(-0.3)]$ **18.** $\tan[\tan^{-1} 5]$ **19.** $\cos[\cos^{-1}(-1.6)]$ **20.** $\sin(\sin^{-1} 1.6)$

21. $\sin^{-1}\left(\cos\dfrac{2\pi}{3}\right)$ **22.** $\cos^{-1}\left(\tan\dfrac{3\pi}{4}\right)$ **23.** $\tan^{-1}\left(\tan\dfrac{7\pi}{4}\right)$ **24.** $\cos^{-1}\left(\cos\dfrac{7\pi}{6}\right)$

25. $\tan\left[\sin^{-1}\left(-\dfrac{\sqrt{3}}{2}\right)\right]$ **26.** $\tan\left[\cos^{-1}\left(-\dfrac{1}{2}\right)\right]$ **27.** $\sec\left(\tan^{-1}\dfrac{\sqrt{3}}{3}\right)$ **28.** $\csc\left(\sin^{-1}\dfrac{\sqrt{3}}{2}\right)$

29. $\sin\left(\cot^{-1}\dfrac{3}{4}\right)$ **30.** $\cos\left(\csc^{-1}\dfrac{5}{3}\right)$ **31.** $\tan\left[\sin^{-1}\left(-\dfrac{4}{5}\right)\right]$ **32.** $\tan\left[\cos^{-1}\left(-\dfrac{3}{5}\right)\right]$

In Problems 33–36, find the inverse function f^{-1} of each function f. State the domain and the range of f^{-1} and f.

33. $f(x) = 2\sin(3x)$ **34.** $f(x) = \tan(2x + 3) - 1$ **35.** $f(x) = -\cos x + 3$ **36.** $f(x) = 2\sin(-x + 1)$

In Problems 37–40, write each trigonometric expression as an algebraic expression in u.

37. $\cos(\sin^{-1} u)$ **38.** $\cos(\csc^{-1} u)$ **39.** $\sin(\csc^{-1} u)$ **40.** $\tan(\csc^{-1} u)$

In Problems 41–72, establish each identity.

41. $\tan\theta\cot\theta - \sin^2\theta = \cos^2\theta$ **42.** $\sin\theta\csc\theta - \sin^2\theta = \cos^2\theta$ **43.** $\sin^2\theta(1 + \cot^2\theta) = 1$

44. $(1 - \sin^2\theta)(1 + \tan^2\theta) = 1$ **45.** $5\cos^2\theta + 3\sin^2\theta = 3 + 2\cos^2\theta$ **46.** $4\sin^2\theta + 2\cos^2\theta = 4 - 2\cos^2\theta$

47. $\dfrac{1 - \cos\theta}{\sin\theta} + \dfrac{\sin\theta}{1 - \cos\theta} = 2\csc\theta$ **48.** $\dfrac{\sin\theta}{1 + \cos\theta} + \dfrac{1 + \cos\theta}{\sin\theta} = 2\csc\theta$ **49.** $\dfrac{\cos\theta}{\cos\theta - \sin\theta} = \dfrac{1}{1 - \tan\theta}$

50. $1 - \dfrac{\sin^2\theta}{1 + \cos\theta} = \cos\theta$ **51.** $\dfrac{\csc\theta}{1 + \csc\theta} = \dfrac{1 - \sin\theta}{\cos^2\theta}$ **52.** $\dfrac{1 + \sec\theta}{\sec\theta} = \dfrac{\sin^2\theta}{1 - \cos\theta}$

53. $\csc\theta - \sin\theta = \cos\theta\cot\theta$ **54.** $\dfrac{\csc\theta}{1 - \cos\theta} = \dfrac{1 + \cos\theta}{\sin^3\theta}$ **55.** $\dfrac{1 - \sin\theta}{\sec\theta} = \dfrac{\cos^3\theta}{1 + \sin\theta}$

56. $\dfrac{1 - \cos\theta}{1 + \cos\theta} = (\csc\theta - \cot\theta)^2$ **57.** $\dfrac{1 - 2\sin^2\theta}{\sin\theta\cos\theta} = \cot\theta - \tan\theta$ **58.** $\dfrac{(2\sin^2\theta - 1)^2}{\sin^4\theta - \cos^4\theta} = 1 - 2\cos^2\theta$

59. $\dfrac{\cos(\alpha + \beta)}{\cos\alpha\sin\beta} = \cot\beta - \tan\alpha$ **60.** $\dfrac{\sin(\alpha - \beta)}{\sin\alpha\cos\beta} = 1 - \cot\alpha\tan\beta$ **61.** $\dfrac{\cos(\alpha - \beta)}{\cos\alpha\cos\beta} = 1 + \tan\alpha\tan\beta$

62. $\dfrac{\cos(\alpha + \beta)}{\sin\alpha\cos\beta} = \cot\alpha - \tan\beta$ **63.** $(1 + \cos\theta)\tan\dfrac{\theta}{2} = \sin\theta$ **64.** $\sin\theta\tan\dfrac{\theta}{2} = 1 - \cos\theta$

65. $2 \cot \theta \cot(2\theta) = \cot^2 \theta - 1$

66. $2 \sin(2\theta)(1 - 2 \sin^2 \theta) = \sin(4\theta)$

67. $1 - 8 \sin^2 \theta \cos^2 \theta = \cos(4\theta)$

68. $\dfrac{\sin(3\theta) \cos \theta - \sin \theta \cos(3\theta)}{\sin(2\theta)} = 1$

69. $\dfrac{\sin(2\theta) + \sin(4\theta)}{\cos(2\theta) + \cos(4\theta)} = \tan(3\theta)$

70. $\dfrac{\sin(2\theta) + \sin(4\theta)}{\sin(2\theta) - \sin(4\theta)} + \dfrac{\tan(3\theta)}{\tan \theta} = 0$

71. $\dfrac{\cos(2\theta) - \cos(4\theta)}{\cos(2\theta) + \cos(4\theta)} - \tan \theta \tan(3\theta) = 0$

72. $\cos(2\theta) - \cos(10\theta) = \tan(4\theta)[\sin(2\theta) + \sin(10\theta)]$

In Problems 73–80, find the exact value of each expression.

73. $\sin 165°$

74. $\tan 105°$

75. $\cos \dfrac{5\pi}{12}$

76. $\sin\left(-\dfrac{\pi}{12}\right)$

77. $\cos 80° \cos 20° + \sin 80° \sin 20°$

78. $\sin 70° \cos 40° - \cos 70° \sin 40°$

79. $\tan \dfrac{\pi}{8}$

80. $\sin \dfrac{5\pi}{8}$

In Problems 81–90, use the information given about the angles α and β to find the exact value of:

(a) $\sin(\alpha + \beta)$ (b) $\cos(\alpha + \beta)$ (c) $\sin(\alpha - \beta)$ (d) $\tan(\alpha + \beta)$

(e) $\sin(2\alpha)$ (f) $\cos(2\beta)$ (g) $\sin \dfrac{\beta}{2}$ (h) $\cos \dfrac{\alpha}{2}$

81. $\sin \alpha = \dfrac{4}{5}, 0 < \alpha < \dfrac{\pi}{2}; \sin \beta = \dfrac{5}{13}, \dfrac{\pi}{2} < \beta < \pi$

82. $\cos \alpha = \dfrac{4}{5}, 0 < \alpha < \dfrac{\pi}{2}; \cos \beta = \dfrac{5}{13}, -\dfrac{\pi}{2} < \beta < 0$

83. $\sin \alpha = -\dfrac{3}{5}, \pi < \alpha < \dfrac{3\pi}{2}; \cos \beta = \dfrac{12}{13}, \dfrac{3\pi}{2} < \beta < 2\pi$

84. $\sin \alpha = -\dfrac{4}{5}, -\dfrac{\pi}{2} < \alpha < 0; \cos \beta = -\dfrac{5}{13}, \dfrac{\pi}{2} < \beta < \pi$

85. $\tan \alpha = \dfrac{3}{4}, \pi < \alpha < \dfrac{3\pi}{2}; \tan \beta = \dfrac{12}{5}, 0 < \beta < \dfrac{\pi}{2}$

86. $\tan \alpha = -\dfrac{4}{3}, \dfrac{\pi}{2} < \alpha < \pi; \cot \beta = \dfrac{12}{5}, \pi < \beta < \dfrac{3\pi}{2}$

87. $\sec \alpha = 2, -\dfrac{\pi}{2} < \alpha < 0; \sec \beta = 3, \dfrac{3\pi}{2} < \beta < 2\pi$

88. $\csc \alpha = 2, \dfrac{\pi}{2} < \alpha < \pi; \sec \beta = -3, \dfrac{\pi}{2} < \beta < \pi$

89. $\sin \alpha = -\dfrac{2}{3}, \pi < \alpha < \dfrac{3\pi}{2}; \cos \beta = -\dfrac{2}{3}, \pi < \beta < \dfrac{3\pi}{2}$

90. $\tan \alpha = -2, \dfrac{\pi}{2} < \alpha < \pi; \cot \beta = -2, \dfrac{\pi}{2} < \beta < \pi$

In Problems 91–96, find the exact value of each expression.

91. $\cos\left(\sin^{-1}\dfrac{3}{5} - \cos^{-1}\dfrac{1}{2}\right)$

92. $\sin\left(\cos^{-1}\dfrac{5}{13} - \cos^{-1}\dfrac{4}{5}\right)$

93. $\tan\left[\sin^{-1}\left(-\dfrac{1}{2}\right) - \tan^{-1}\dfrac{3}{4}\right]$

94. $\cos\left[\tan^{-1}(-1) + \cos^{-1}\left(-\dfrac{4}{5}\right)\right]$

95. $\sin\left[2 \cos^{-1}\left(-\dfrac{3}{5}\right)\right]$

96. $\cos\left(2 \tan^{-1}\dfrac{4}{3}\right)$

In Problems 97–120, solve each equation on the interval $0 \le \theta < 2\pi$. Verify your results using a graphing utility.

97. $\cos \theta = \dfrac{1}{2}$

98. $\sin \theta = -\dfrac{\sqrt{3}}{2}$

99. $2 \cos \theta + \sqrt{2} = 0$

100. $\tan \theta + \sqrt{3} = 0$

101. $\sin(2\theta) + 1 = 0$

102. $\cos(2\theta) = 0$

103. $\tan(2\theta) = 0$

104. $\sin(3\theta) = 1$

105. $\sec^2 \theta = 4$

106. $\csc^2 \theta = 1$

107. $\sin \theta = \tan \theta$

108. $\cos \theta = \sec \theta$

109. $\sin \theta + \sin(2\theta) = 0$

110. $\cos(2\theta) = \sin \theta$

111. $\sin(2\theta) - \cos \theta - 2 \sin \theta + 1 = 0$

112. $\sin(2\theta) - \sin \theta - 2 \cos \theta + 1 = 0$

113. $2 \sin^2 \theta - 3 \sin \theta + 1 = 0$

114. $2 \cos^2 \theta + \cos \theta - 1 = 0$

115. $4 \sin^2 \theta = 1 + 4 \cos \theta$

116. $8 - 12 \sin^2 \theta = 4 \cos^2 \theta$

117. $\sin(2\theta) = \sqrt{2} \cos \theta$

118. $1 + \sqrt{3} \cos \theta + \cos(2\theta) = 0$

119. $\sin \theta - \cos \theta = 1$

120. $\sin \theta - \sqrt{3} \cos \theta = 2$

In Problems 121–126, use a calculator to find an approximate value for each expression, rounded to two decimal places.

121. $\sin^{-1} 0.7$

122. $\cos^{-1} \dfrac{4}{5}$

123. $\tan^{-1}(-2)$

124. $\cos^{-1}(-0.2)$

125. $\sec^{-1} 3$

126. $\cot^{-1}(-4)$

In Problems 127–132, use a graphing utility to solve each equation on the interval $0 \le x < 2\pi$. Approximate any solutions rounded to two decimal places.

127. $2x = 5 \cos x$

128. $2x = 5 \sin x$

129. $2 \sin x + 3 \cos x = 4x$

130. $3 \cos x + x = \sin x$

131. $\sin x = \ln x$

132. $\sin x = e^{-x}$

In Problems 133 and 134, find the exact solution of each equation.

133. $-3 \sin^{-1} x = \pi$

134. $2 \cos^{-1} x + \pi = 4 \cos^{-1} x$

135. Use a Half-angle Formula to find the exact value of $\sin 15°$. Then use a difference formula to find the exact value of $\sin 15°$. Show that the answers found are the same.

136. If you are given the value of $\cos \theta$ and want the exact value of $\cos(2\theta)$, what form of the Double-angle Formula for $\cos(2\theta)$ is most efficient to use?

CHAPTER TEST

In Problems 1–6, find the exact value of each expression. Express angles in radians.

1. $\sec^{-1}\left(\dfrac{2}{\sqrt{3}}\right)$

2. $\sin^{-1}\left(-\dfrac{\sqrt{2}}{2}\right)$

3. $\sin^{-1}\left(\sin\dfrac{11\pi}{5}\right)$

4. $\tan\left(\tan^{-1}\dfrac{7}{3}\right)$

5. $\cot\left(\csc^{-1}\sqrt{10}\right)$

6. $\sec\left(\cos^{-1}\left(-\dfrac{3}{4}\right)\right)$

In Problems 7–10, use a calculator to evaluate each expression. Express angles in radians rounded to two decimal places.

7. $\sin^{-1}0.382$

8. $\sec^{-1}1.4$

9. $\tan^{-1}3$

10. $\cot^{-1}5$

In Problems 11–16 establish each identity.

11. $\dfrac{\csc\theta + \cot\theta}{\sec\theta + \tan\theta} = \dfrac{\sec\theta - \tan\theta}{\csc\theta - \cot\theta}$

12. $\sin\theta\tan\theta + \cos\theta = \sec\theta$

13. $\tan\theta + \cot\theta = 2\csc(2\theta)$

14. $\dfrac{\sin(\alpha + \beta)}{\tan\alpha + \tan\beta} = \cos\alpha\cos\beta$

15. $\sin(3\theta) = 3\sin\theta - 4\sin^3\theta$

16. $\dfrac{\tan\theta - \cot\theta}{\tan\theta + \cot\theta} = 1 - 2\cos^2\theta$

In Problems 17–24 use sum, difference, product, or half-angle formulas to find the exact value of each expression.

17. $\cos 15°$

18. $\tan 75°$

19. $\sin\left(\dfrac{1}{2}\cos^{-1}\dfrac{3}{5}\right)$

20. $\tan\left(2\sin^{-1}\dfrac{6}{11}\right)$

21. $\cos\left(\sin^{-1}\dfrac{2}{3} + \tan^{-1}\dfrac{3}{2}\right)$

22. $\sin 75°\cos 15°$

23. $\sin 75° + \sin 15°$

24. $\cos 65°\cos 20° + \sin 65°\sin 20°$

In Problems 25–29, solve each equation on $0 \le \theta < 2\pi$.

25. $4\sin^2\theta - 3 = 0$

26. $-3\cos\left(\dfrac{\pi}{2} - \theta\right) = \tan\theta$

27. $\cos^2\theta + 2\sin\theta\cos\theta - \sin^2\theta = 0$

28. $\sin(\theta + 1) = \cos\theta$

29. $4\sin^2\theta + 7\sin\theta = 2$

30. Stage 16 of the 2004 Tour de France was a time trial from Bourg d'Oisans to L'Alpe d'Huez. The average grade (slope as a percent) for most of the 15-kilometer mountainous trek was 7.9%. What was the change in elevation from the beginning to the end of the route?

CUMULATIVE REVIEW

1. Find the real solutions, if any, of the equation $3x^2 + x - 1 = 0$.

2. Find an equation for the line containing the points $(-2, 5)$ and $(4, -1)$. What is the distance between these points? What is their midpoint?

3. Test the equation $3x + y^2 = 9$ for symmetry with respect to the *x*-axis, *y*-axis, and origin. List the intercepts.

4. Use transformations to graph the equation $y = |x - 3| + 2$.

5. Use transformations to graph the equation $y = 3e^x - 2$.

6. Use transformations to graph the equation
$$y = \cos\left(x - \dfrac{\pi}{2}\right) - 1.$$

7. Sketch a graph of each of the following functions. Label at least three points on each graph. Name the inverse function of each and show its graph.
(a) $y = x^3$
(b) $y = e^x$
(c) $y = \sin x, \quad -\dfrac{\pi}{2} \le x \le \dfrac{\pi}{2}$
(d) $y = \cos x, \quad 0 \le x \le \pi$

8. If $\sin\theta = -\dfrac{1}{3}$ and $\pi < \theta < \dfrac{3\pi}{2}$, find the exact value of:
(a) $\cos\theta$
(b) $\tan\theta$
(c) $\sin(2\theta)$
(d) $\cos(2\theta)$
(e) $\sin\left(\dfrac{1}{2}\theta\right)$
(f) $\cos\left(\dfrac{1}{2}\theta\right)$

9. Find the exact value of $\cos(\tan^{-1}2)$.

10. If $\sin\alpha = \dfrac{1}{3}, \dfrac{\pi}{2} < \alpha < \pi$, and $\cos\beta = -\dfrac{1}{3}, \pi < \beta < \dfrac{3\pi}{2}$, find the exact value of:
(a) $\cos\alpha$
(b) $\sin\beta$
(c) $\cos(2\alpha)$
(d) $\cos(\alpha + \beta)$
(e) $\sin\dfrac{\beta}{2}$

11. For the function
$$f(x) = 2x^5 - x^4 - 4x^3 + 2x^2 + 2x - 1:$$
(a) Find the real zeros and their multiplicity.
(b) Find the intercepts.
(c) Find the power function that the graph of *f* resembles for large $|x|$.
(d) Graph *f* using a graphing utility.
(e) Approximate the turning points, if any exist.
(f) Use the information obtained in parts (a)–(e) to sketch a graph of *f* by hand.
(g) Identify the intervals on which *f* is increasing, decreasing, or constant.

12. If $f(x) = 2x^2 + 3x + 1$ and $g(x) = x^2 + 3x + 2$, solve:
(a) $f(x) = 0$
(b) $f(x) = g(x)$
(c) $f(x) > 0$
(d) $f(x) \ge g(x)$

CHAPTER PROJECTS

I. **Waves** A stretched string that is attached at both ends, pulled in a direction perpendicular to the string, and released has motion that is described as wave motion. If we assume no friction and a length such that there are no "echoes" (that is, the wave does not bounce back), the transverse motion (motion perpendicular to the string) can be modeled by the equation

$$y = y_m \sin(kx - \omega t)$$

where y_m is the amplitude measured in meters and k and ω are constants. The height of the wave depends on the distance x from one endpoint of the string and on the time t, so a typical wave has horizontal and vertical motion over time.

(a) What is the amplitude of the wave

$$y = 0.00421 \sin(68.3x - 2.68t)?$$

(b) The value of ω is the angular frequency measured in radians per second. What is the angular frequency of the wave given in part (a)?

(c) The frequency f is the number of vibrations per second (hertz) made by the wave as it passes a certain point. Its value is found using the formula $f = \dfrac{\omega}{2\pi}$. What is the frequency of the wave given in part (a)?

(d) The wavelength, λ, of a wave is the shortest distance at which the wave pattern repeats itself for a constant t. Thus, $\lambda = \dfrac{2\pi}{k}$. What is the wavelength of the wave given in part (a)?

(e) Graph the height of the string a distance $x = 1$ meter from an endpoint.

(f) If two waves travel simultaneously along the same stretched string, the vertical displacement of the string when both waves act is $y = y_1 + y_2$, where y_1 is the vertical displacement of the first wave and y_2 is the vertical displacement of the second wave. This result is called the Principle of Superposition and was analyzed by the French mathematician Jean Baptiste Fourier (1768–1830). When two waves travel along the same string, one wave will differ from the other wave by a phase constant ϕ. That is,

$$y_1 = y_m \sin(kx - \omega t)$$
$$y_2 = y_m \sin(kx - \omega t + \phi)$$

assuming that each wave has the same amplitude. Write $y_1 + y_2$ as a product using the Sum-to-Product Formulas.

(g) Suppose that two waves are moving in the same direction along a stretched string. The amplitude of each wave is 0.0045 meter, and the phase difference between them is 2.5 radians. The wavelength, λ, of each wave is 0.09 meter, and the frequency, f, is 2.3 hertz. Find y_1, y_2, and $y_1 + y_2$.

(h) Using a graphing utility, graph y_1, y_2, and $y_1 + y_2$ on the same viewing window.

(i) Redo parts (g) and (h) with the phase difference between the waves being 0.4 radian.

(j) What effect does the phase difference have on the amplitude of $y_1 + y_2$?

The following projects are available on the Instructor's Resource Center (IRC):

II. **Project at Motorola** Sending Pictures Wirelessly The electronic transmission of pictures is made practical by image compression, mathematical methods that greatly reduce the number of bits of data used to compose the picture.

III. **Calculus of Differences** Finding consecutive difference quotients is called finding finite differences and is used to analyze the graph of an unknown function.

Applications of Trigonometric Functions

8

From Lewis and Clark to Landsat

For $140, you can buy a handheld Global Positioning System receiver that will gauge your latitude and longitude to within a couple of meters. But in 1804, when Meriwether Lewis and William Clark ventured across the Louisiana Territory, a state of the art positioning system consisted of an octant, a pocket chronometer, and a surveyor's compass.

But somehow, Clark—the cartographer in the group—made do. When San Francisco map collector David Rumsey took his copy of Lewis and Clark's published map of their journey, scanned it into a computer, and matched landmarks such as river junctions against corresponding features on today's maps, he found that it took only a slight amount of digital stretching and twisting to make Clark's map conform to modern coordinates. In fact, Rumsey was able to combine Clark's depiction of his party's route to the Pacific with pages from government atlases from the 1870s and 1970s and photos from NASA Landsat satellites, creating a digital composite that documents not only a historic adventure, but also the history of mapmaking itself.

Source: Wade Roush, "From Lewis and Clark to Landsat: David Rumsey's Digital Maps Marry Past and Present," *Technology Review*, 108, no. 7 (July 2005): 26–27.

—See Chapter Project I—

A Look Back

In Chapter 6 we defined the six trigonometric functions using the unit circle and then extended this definition to include general angles. In particular, we learned to evaluate the trigonometric functions. We also learned how to graph sinusoidal functions. In Chapter 7, we defined the inverse trigonometric functions and solved equations involving the trigonometric functions.

A Look Ahead

In this chapter, we define the trigonometric functions using right triangles and then use the trigonometric functions to solve applied problems. The first four sections deal with applications involving right triangles and *oblique triangles*, triangles that do not have a right angle. To solve problems involving oblique triangles, we will develop the Law of Sines and the Law of Cosines. We will also develop formulas for finding the area of a triangle.

The final section deals with applications of sinusoidal functions involving simple harmonic motion and damped motion.

Outline

8.1 Right Triangle Trigonometry; Applications
8.2 The Law of Sines
8.3 The Law of Cosines
8.4 Area of a Triangle
8.5 Simple Harmonic Motion; Damped Motion; Combining Waves
    Chapter Review
    Chapter Test
    Cumulative Review
    Chapter Projects

8.1 Right Triangle Trigonometry; Applications

PREPARING FOR THIS SECTION *Before getting started, review the following:*

- Pythagorean Theorem (Appendix A, Section A.2, pp. A14–A15)
- Trigonometric Equations (I) (Section 7.7, pp. 488–492)

Now Work the 'Are You Prepared?' problems on page 517.

OBJECTIVES **1** Find the Value of Trigonometric Functions of Acute Angles Using Right Triangles (p. 510)

   2 Use the Complementary Angle Theorem (p. 512)

   3 Solve Right Triangles (p. 512)

   4 Solve Applied Problems (p. 513)

1 Find the Value of Trigonometric Functions of Acute Angles Using Right Triangles

A triangle in which one angle is a right angle (90°) is called a **right triangle.** Recall that the side opposite the right angle is called the **hypotenuse,** and the remaining two sides are called the **legs** of the triangle. In Figure 1(a), we have labeled the hypotenuse as c to indicate that its length is c units, and, in a like manner, we have labeled the legs as a and b. Because the triangle is a right triangle, the Pythagorean Theorem tells us that

$$a^2 + b^2 = c^2$$

In Figure 1(a), we also show the angle θ. The angle θ is an **acute angle:** that is, $0° < \theta < 90°$ for θ measured in degrees and $0 < \theta < \dfrac{\pi}{2}$ for θ measured in radians.

Place θ in standard position, as shown in Figure 1(b). Then the coordinates of the point P are (a, b). Also, P is a point on the terminal side of θ that is on the circle $x^2 + y^2 = c^2$. (Do you see why?)

Figure 1

(a)

(b)

Now use the theorem on page 377 with a circle of radius c, $x^2 + y^2 = c^2$. By referring to the lengths of the sides of the triangle by the names hypotenuse (c), opposite (b), and adjacent (a), as indicated in Figure 2, we can express the trigonometric functions of θ as ratios of the sides of a right triangle.

Figure 2

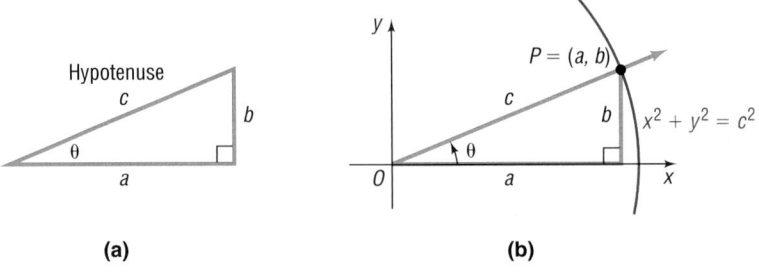

$$\sin \theta = \frac{\text{Opposite}}{\text{Hypotenuse}} = \frac{b}{c} \qquad \csc \theta = \frac{\text{Hypotenuse}}{\text{Opposite}} = \frac{c}{b}$$

$$\cos \theta = \frac{\text{Adjacent}}{\text{Hypotenuse}} = \frac{a}{c} \qquad \sec \theta = \frac{\text{Hypotenuse}}{\text{Adjacent}} = \frac{c}{a} \qquad \textbf{(1)}$$

$$\tan \theta = \frac{\text{Opposite}}{\text{Adjacent}} = \frac{b}{a} \qquad \cot \theta = \frac{\text{Adjacent}}{\text{Opposite}} = \frac{a}{b}$$

Notice that each trigonometric function of the acute angle θ is positive.

| EXAMPLE 1 | **Finding the Value of Trigonometric Functions from a Right Triangle** |

Find the exact value of the six trigonometric functions of the angle θ in Figure 3.

Solution   We see in Figure 3 that the two given sides of the triangle are

$$c = \text{Hypotenuse} = 5, \quad a = \text{Adjacent} = 3$$

Figure 3

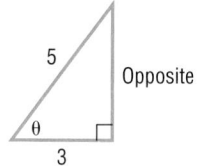

To find the length of the opposite side, we use the Pythagorean Theorem.

$$(\text{Adjacent})^2 + (\text{Opposite})^2 = (\text{Hypotenuse})^2$$
$$3^2 + (\text{Opposite})^2 = 5^2$$
$$(\text{Opposite})^2 = 25 - 9 = 16$$
$$\text{Opposite} = 4$$

Now that we know the lengths of the three sides, we use the ratios in equations (1) to find the value of each of the six trigonometric functions.

$$\sin \theta = \frac{\text{Opposite}}{\text{Hypotenuse}} = \frac{4}{5} \quad \cos \theta = \frac{\text{Adjacent}}{\text{Hypotenuse}} = \frac{3}{5} \quad \tan \theta = \frac{\text{Opposite}}{\text{Adjacent}} = \frac{4}{3}$$

$$\csc \theta = \frac{\text{Hypotenuse}}{\text{Opposite}} = \frac{5}{4} \quad \sec \theta = \frac{\text{Hypotenuse}}{\text{Adjacent}} = \frac{5}{3} \quad \cot \theta = \frac{\text{Adjacent}}{\text{Opposite}} = \frac{3}{4}$$

━━━━━ **Now Work** PROBLEM 9

The values of the trigonometric functions of an acute angle are ratios of the lengths of the sides of a right triangle. This way of viewing the trigonometric functions leads to many applications and, in fact, was the point of view used by early mathematicians (before calculus) in studying the subject of trigonometry. We look at one such application next.

| EXAMPLE 2 | **Constructing a Rain Gutter** |

A rain gutter is to be constructed of aluminum sheets 12 inches wide. See Figure 4(a). After marking off a length of 4 inches from each edge, this length is bent up at an angle θ. See Figure 4(b).

(a) Express the area A of the opening as a function of θ.
   [**Hint:** Let b denote the vertical height of the bend.]
(b) Graph $A = A(\theta)$. Find the angle θ that makes A largest. (This bend will allow the most water to flow through the gutter.)

Figure 4

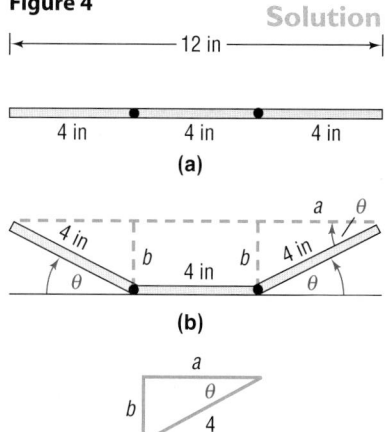

Solution   (a) Look again at Figure 4(b). The area A of the opening is the sum of the areas of two congruent right triangles and one rectangle. Look at Figure 4(c), which shows one of the triangles in Figure 4(b) redrawn. We see that

$$\cos \theta = \frac{a}{4} \quad \text{so} \quad a = 4 \cos \theta \qquad \sin \theta = \frac{b}{4} \quad \text{so} \quad b = 4 \sin \theta$$

The area of the triangle is

$$\text{area} = \frac{1}{2}(\text{base})(\text{height}) = \frac{1}{2}ab = \frac{1}{2}(4 \cos \theta)(4 \sin \theta) = 8 \sin \theta \cos \theta$$

So the area of the two congruent triangles is $16 \sin \theta \cos \theta$.
     The rectangle has length 4 and height b, so its area is

$$4b = 4(4 \sin \theta) = 16 \sin \theta$$

Figure 5

The area A of the opening is

$$A = \text{area of the two triangles} + \text{area of the rectangle}$$
$$A(\theta) = 16 \sin \theta \cos \theta + 16 \sin \theta = 16 \sin \theta (\cos \theta + 1)$$

(b) Figure 5 shows the graph of $A = A(\theta)$. Using MAXIMUM, the angle θ that makes A largest is $60°$.

2 Use the Complementary Angle Theorem

Two acute angles are called **complementary** if their sum is a right angle. Because the sum of the angles of any triangle is $180°$, it follows that, for a right triangle, the two acute angles are complementary.

Refer now to Figure 6. We have labeled the angle opposite side b as B and the angle opposite side a as A. Notice that side b is adjacent to angle A and side a is adjacent to angle B. As a result,

Figure 6

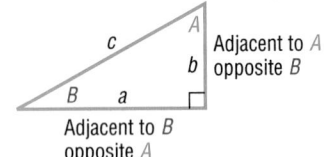

$$\sin B = \frac{b}{c} = \cos A \qquad \cos B = \frac{a}{c} = \sin A \qquad \tan B = \frac{b}{a} = \cot A$$

$$\csc B = \frac{c}{b} = \sec A \qquad \sec B = \frac{c}{a} = \csc A \qquad \cot B = \frac{a}{b} = \tan A \qquad \textbf{(2)}$$

Because of these relationships, the functions sine and cosine, tangent and cotangent, and secant and cosecant are called **cofunctions** of each other. The identities (2) may be expressed in words as follows:

THEOREM

Complementary Angle Theorem

Cofunctions of complementary angles are equal.

Examples of this theorem are given next:

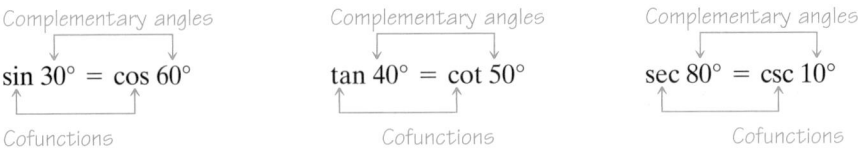

EXAMPLE 3

Using the Complementary Angle Theorem

(a) $\sin 62° = \cos(90° - 62°) = \cos 28°$

(b) $\tan \dfrac{\pi}{12} = \cot\left(\dfrac{\pi}{2} - \dfrac{\pi}{12}\right) = \cot \dfrac{5\pi}{12}$

(c) $\sin^2 40° + \sin^2 50° = \sin^2 40° + \cos^2 40° = 1$

$\qquad\qquad\qquad \uparrow$

$\qquad\qquad \sin 50° = \cos 40°$

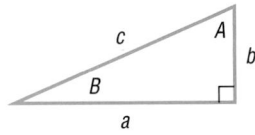 **Now Work** PROBLEM 19

3 Solve Right Triangles

Figure 7

In the discussion that follows, we will always label a right triangle so that side a is opposite angle A, side b is opposite angle B, and side c is the hypotenuse, as shown in Figure 7. **To solve a right triangle** means to find the missing lengths of its sides and the measurements of its angles. We shall follow the practice of expressing the lengths of the sides rounded to two decimal places and expressing angles in degrees rounded to one decimal place. (Be sure that your calculator is in degree mode.)

To solve a right triangle, we need to know one of the acute angles A or B and a side, or else two sides. Then we make use of the Pythagorean Theorem and the fact that the sum of the angles of a triangle is 180°. The sum of the angles A and B in a right triangle is therefore 90°.

THEOREM

For the right triangle shown in Figure 7, we have

$$c^2 = a^2 + b^2 \qquad A + B = 90°$$

| EXAMPLE 4 | **Solving a Right Triangle** |

Use Figure 8. If $b = 2$ and $A = 40°$, find a, c, and B.

Solution

Since $A = 40°$ and $A + B = 90°$, we find that $B = 50°$. To find the sides a and c, we use the facts that

$$\tan 40° = \frac{a}{2} \quad \text{and} \quad \cos 40° = \frac{2}{c}$$

Now solve for a and c.

$$a = 2 \tan 40° \approx 1.68 \quad \text{and} \quad c = \frac{2}{\cos 40°} \approx 2.61$$

Figure 8

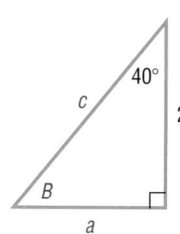

━━━▶ **Now Work** PROBLEM 29

| EXAMPLE 5 | **Solving a Right Triangle** |

Use Figure 9. If $a = 3$ and $b = 2$, find c, A, and B.

Figure 9

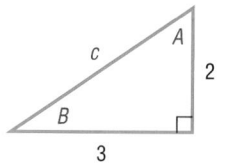

Solution

Since $a = 3$ and $b = 2$, then, by the Pythagorean Theorem, we have

$$c^2 = a^2 + b^2 = 3^2 + 2^2 = 9 + 4 = 13$$
$$c = \sqrt{13} \approx 3.61$$

To find angle A, we use the fact that

$$\tan A = \frac{3}{2} \quad \text{so} \quad A = \tan^{-1} \frac{3}{2}$$

NOTE To avoid round-off errors when using a calculator, we will store unrounded values in memory for use in subsequent calculations. ∎

Set the mode on your calculator to degrees. Then, rounded to one decimal place, we find that $A = 56.3°$. Since $A + B = 90°$, we find that $B = 33.7°$.

━━━▶ **Now Work** PROBLEM 39

4 Solve Applied Problems*

In addition to developing models using right triangles, we can use right triangle trigonometry to measure heights and distances that are either awkward or impossible to measure by ordinary means. When using right triangles to solve these problems, pay attention to the known measures. This will indicate what trigonometric function to use. For example, if we know the measure of an angle and the length of the side adjacent to the angle, and wish to find the length of the opposite side, we would use the tangent function. Do you know why?

---

*In applied problems, it is important that answers be reported with both justifiable accuracy and appropriate significant figures. In this chapter we shall assume that the problem data are accurate to the number of significant digits, resulting in sides being rounded to two decimal places and angles being rounded to one decimal place.

| EXAMPLE 6 | Finding the Width of a River |

A surveyor can measure the width of a river by setting up a transit* at a point C on one side of the river and taking a sighting of a point A on the other side. Refer to Figure 10. After turning through an angle of $90°$ at C, the surveyor walks a distance of 200 meters to point B. Using the transit at B, the angle θ is measured and found to be $20°$. What is the width of the river rounded to the nearest meter?

Figure 10

Solution   We seek the length of side b. We know a and θ. So we use the fact that b is opposite θ and a is adjacent to θ and write

$$\tan \theta = \frac{b}{a}$$

which leads to

$$\tan 20° = \frac{b}{200}$$

$$b = 200 \tan 20° \approx 72.79 \text{ meters}$$

The width of the river is 73 meters, rounded to the nearest meter.

━━━━━ **Now Work** PROBLEM 49

| EXAMPLE 7 | Finding the Inclination of a Mountain Trail |

A straight trail leads from the Alpine Hotel, elevation 8000 feet, to a scenic overlook, elevation 11,100 feet. The length of the trail is 14,100 feet. What is the inclination (grade) of the trail? That is, what is the angle B in Figure 11?

Solution   As we can see in Figure 11, we know the length of the side opposite angle B and the length of the hypotenuse. The angle B obeys the equation

$$\sin B = \frac{3100}{14,100}$$

Figure 11

Using a calculator,

$$B = \sin^{-1} \frac{3100}{14,100} \approx 12.7°$$

The inclination (grade) of the trail is approximately $12.7°$.

━━━━━ **Now Work** PROBLEM 55

Vertical heights can sometimes be measured using either the *angle of elevation* or the *angle of depression*. If a person is looking up at an object, the acute angle measured from the horizontal to a line of sight to the object is called the **angle of elevation**. See Figure 12(a).

---

* An instrument used in surveying to measure angles.

Figure 12

(a)   (b)

If a person is standing on a cliff looking down at an object, the acute angle made by the line of sight to the object and the horizontal is called the **angle of depression.** See Figure 12(b).

EXAMPLE 8 | **Finding the Height of a Cloud**

Meteorologists find the height of a cloud using an instrument called a **ceilometer.** A ceilometer consists of a **light projector** that directs a vertical light beam up to the cloud base and a **light detector** that scans the cloud to detect the light beam. See Figure 13(a). On December 1, 2006, at Midway Airport in Chicago, a ceilometer was employed to find the height of the cloud cover. It was set up with its light detector 300 feet from its light projector. If the angle of elevation from the light detector to the base of the cloud is 75°, what is the height of the cloud cover?

Figure 13

(a)   (b)

Solution | Figure 13(b) illustrates the situation. To find the height h, we use the fact that $\tan 75° = \dfrac{h}{300}$, so

$$h = 300 \tan 75° \approx 1120 \text{ feet}$$

The ceiling (height to the base of the cloud cover) is approximately 1120 feet.

--- **Now Work** PROBLEM 51

The idea behind Example 8 can also be used to find the height of an object with a base that is not accessible to the horizontal.

EXAMPLE 9 | **Finding the Height of a Statue on a Building**

Adorning the top of the Board of Trade building in Chicago is a statue of Ceres, the Roman goddess of wheat. From street level, two observations are taken 400 feet from the center of the building. The angle of elevation to the base of the statue is found to be 55.1° and the angle of elevation to the top of the statue is 56.5°. See Figure 14(a). What is the height of the statue?

Figure 14

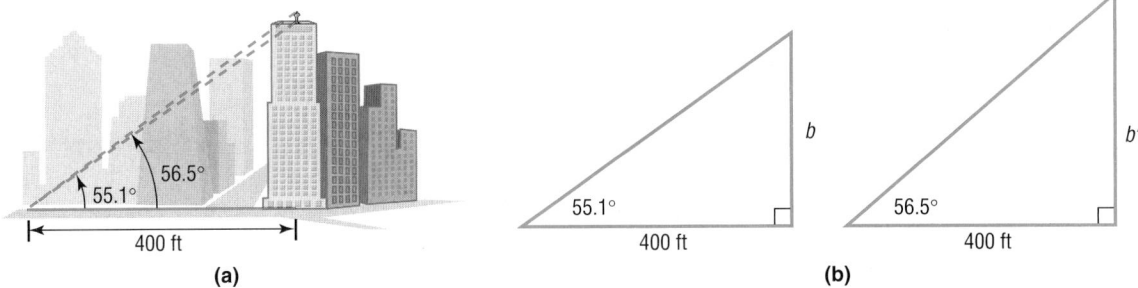

(a)

(b)

Solution   Figure 14(b) shows two triangles that replicate Figure 14(a). The height of the statue of Ceres will be $b' - b$. To find b and b', we refer to Figure 14(b).

$$\tan 55.1° = \frac{b}{400} \qquad\qquad \tan 56.5° = \frac{b'}{400}$$

$$b = 400 \tan 55.1° \approx 573.39 \qquad\qquad b' = 400 \tan 56.5° \approx 604.33$$

The height of the statue is approximately $604.33 - 573.39 = 30.94$ feet ≈ 31 feet.

 Now Work PROBLEM 71

EXAMPLE 10 | **The Gibb's Hill Lighthouse, Southampton, Bermuda**

In operation since 1846, the Gibb's Hill Lighthouse stands 117 feet high on a hill 245 feet high, so its beam of light is 362 feet above sea level. A brochure states that the light can be seen on the horizon about 26 miles from the lighthouse. Verify the accuracy of this statement.

Solution   Figure 15 illustrates the situation. The central angle θ, positioned at the center of Earth, radius 3960 miles, obeys the equation

Figure 15

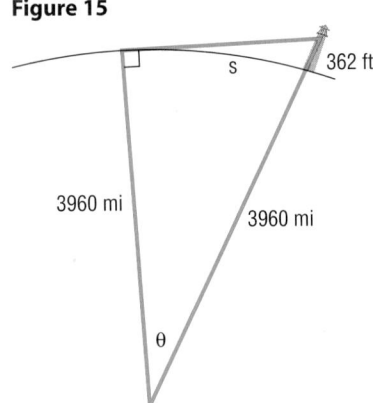

$$\cos \theta = \frac{3960}{3960 + \dfrac{362}{5280}} \approx 0.999982687 \quad \text{1 mile = 5280 feet}$$

Solving for θ, we find

$$\theta \approx 0.33715° \approx 20.23'$$

The brochure does not indicate whether the distance is measured in nautical miles or statute miles. Let's calculate both distances.

     The distance s in nautical miles (refer to Problem 114, p. 364) is the measure of the angle θ in minutes, so $s \approx 20.23$ nautical miles.

     The distance s in statute miles is given by the formula $s = r\theta$, where θ is measured in radians. Then, since

$$\theta \approx 20.23' \approx 0.33715° \approx 0.00588 \text{ radian}$$
$$\uparrow \qquad\qquad\quad \uparrow$$
$$1' = \frac{1°}{60} \qquad 1° = \frac{\pi}{180} \text{ radian}$$

Figure 16

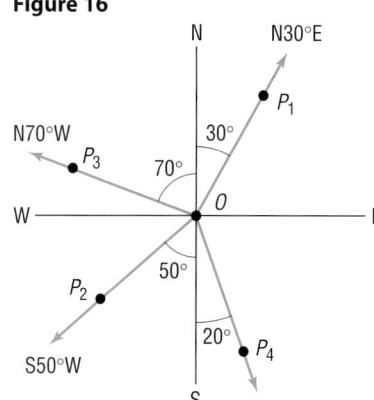

we find that

$$s = r\theta \approx (3960)(0.00588) \approx 23.3 \text{ miles}$$

In either case, it would seem that the brochure overstated the distance somewhat. ∎

In navigation and surveying, the **direction** or **bearing** from a point O to a point P equals the acute angle θ between the ray OP and the vertical line through O, the north–south line.

Figure 16 illustrates some bearings. Notice that the bearing from O to P_1 is denoted by the symbolism N30°E, indicating that the bearing is 30° east of north. In writing the bearing from O to P, the direction north or south always appears first, followed by an acute angle, followed by east or west. In Figure 16, the bearing from O to P_2 is S50°W, and from O to P_3 it is N70°W.

EXAMPLE 11	Finding the Bearing of an Object

In Figure 16, what is the bearing from O to an object at P_4?

Solution   The acute angle between the ray OP_4 and the north–south line through O is given as 20°. The bearing from O to P_4 is S20°E.

∎

EXAMPLE 12	Finding the Bearing of an Airplane

A Boeing 777 aircraft takes off from O'Hare Airport on runway 2 LEFT, which has a bearing of N20°E.* After flying for 1 mile, the pilot of the aircraft requests permission to turn 90° and head toward the northwest. The request is granted. After the plane goes 2 miles in this direction, what bearing should the control tower use to locate the aircraft?

Figure 17

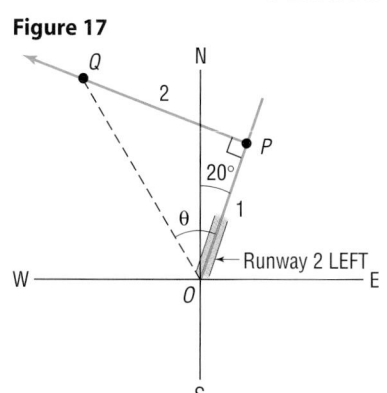

Solution   Figure 17 illustrates the situation. After flying 1 mile from the airport O (the control tower), the aircraft is at P. After turning 90° toward the northwest and flying 2 miles, the aircraft is at the point Q. In triangle OPQ, the angle θ obeys the equation

$$\tan \theta = \frac{2}{1} = 2 \quad \text{so} \quad \theta = \tan^{-1} 2 \approx 63.4°$$

The acute angle between north and the ray OQ is $63.4° - 20° = 43.4°$. The bearing of the aircraft from O to Q is N43.4°W.

∎

━━━ **Now Work** PROBLEM 63

* In air navigation, the term **azimuth** denotes the positive angle measured clockwise from the north (N) to a ray OP. In Figure 16, the azimuth from O to P_1 is 30°; the azimuth from O to P_2 is 230°; the azimuth from O to P_3 is 290°. In naming runways, the units digit is left off the azimuth. Runway 2 LEFT means the left runway with a direction of azimuth 20° (bearing N20°E). Runway 23 is the runway with azimuth 230° and bearing S50°W.

8.1 Assess Your Understanding

'Are You Prepared?'   *Answers are given at the end of these exercises. If you get a wrong answer, read the pages listed in red.*

1. In a right triangle, if the length of the hypotenuse is 5 and the length of one of the other sides is 3, what is the length of the third side? (pp. A14–A15)

2. If θ is an acute angle, solve the equation $\tan \theta = \frac{1}{2}$. Express your answer in degrees, rounded to one decimal place. (pp. 488–492)

3. If θ is an acute angle, solve the equation $\sin \theta = \frac{1}{2}$. (pp. 488–492)

Concepts and Vocabulary

4. *True or False* $\sin 52° = \cos 48°$.

5. *True or False* In a right triangle, one of the angles is 90° and the sum of the other two angles is 90°.

6. When you look up at an object, the acute angle measured from the horizontal to a line-of-sight observation of the object is called the _____ _____ _____.

7. *True or False* In a right triangle, if two sides are known, we can solve the triangle.

8. *True or False* In a right triangle, if we know the two acute angles, we can solve the triangle.

Skill Building

In Problems 9–18, find the exact value of the six trigonometric functions of the angle θ in each figure.

9.

10.

11.

12.

13.

14.

15.

16.

17.

18.

In Problems 19–28, find the exact value of each expression. Do not use a calculator.

19. $\sin 38° - \cos 52°$

20. $\tan 12° - \cot 78°$

21. $\dfrac{\cos 10°}{\sin 80°}$

22. $\dfrac{\cos 40°}{\sin 50°}$

23. $1 - \cos^2 20° - \cos^2 70°$

24. $1 + \tan^2 5° - \csc^2 85°$

25. $\tan 20° - \dfrac{\cos 70°}{\cos 20°}$

26. $\cot 40° - \dfrac{\sin 50°}{\sin 40°}$

27. $\cos 35° \sin 55° + \sin 35° \cos 55°$

28. $\sec 35° \csc 55° - \tan 35° \cot 55°$

In Problems 29–42, use the right triangle shown below. Then, using the given information, solve the triangle.

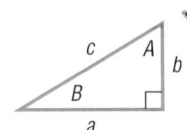

29. $b = 5$, $B = 20°$; find a, c, and A

30. $b = 4$, $B = 10°$; find a, c, and A

31. $a = 6$, $B = 40°$; find b, c, and A

32. $a = 7$, $B = 50°$; find b, c, and A

33. $b = 4$, $A = 10°$; find a, c, and B

34. $b = 6$, $A = 20°$; find a, c, and B

35. $a = 5$, $A = 25°$; find b, c, and B

36. $a = 6$, $A = 40°$; find b, c, and B

37. $c = 9$, $B = 20°$; find b, a, and A

38. $c = 10$, $A = 40°$; find b, a, and B

39. $a = 5$, $b = 3$; find c, A, and B

40. $a = 2$, $b = 8$; find c, A, and B

41. $a = 2$, $c = 5$; find b, A, and B

42. $b = 4$, $c = 6$; find a, A, and B

Applications and Extensions

43. Geometry The hypotenuse of a right triangle is 5 inches. If one leg is 2 inches, find the degree measure of each angle.

44. Geometry The hypotenuse of a right triangle is 3 feet. If one leg is 1 foot, find the degree measure of each angle.

45. Geometry A right triangle has a hypotenuse of length 8 inches. If one angle is 35°, find the length of each leg.

46. Geometry A right triangle has a hypotenuse of length 10 centimeters. If one angle is 40°, find the length of each leg.

47. Geometry A right triangle contains a 25° angle.
(a) If one leg is of length 5 inches, what is the length of the hypotenuse?
(b) There are two answers. How is this possible?

48. Geometry A right triangle contains an angle of $\dfrac{\pi}{8}$ radian.
(a) If one leg is of length 3 meters, what is the length of the hypotenuse?
(b) There are two answers. How is this possible?

49. Finding the Width of a Gorge Find the distance from A to C across the gorge illustrated in the figure.

50. Finding the Distance across a Pond Find the distance from *A* to *C* across the pond illustrated in the figure.

51. The Eiffel Tower The tallest tower built before the era of television masts, the Eiffel Tower was completed on March 31, 1889. Find the height of the Eiffel Tower (before a television mast was added to the top) using the information given in the illustration.

52. Finding the Distance of a Ship from Shore A person in a small boat, offshore from a vertical cliff known to be 100 feet in height, takes a sighting of the top of the cliff. If the angle of elevation is found to be 25°, how far offshore is the boat?

53. Finding the Distance to a Plateau Suppose that you are headed toward a plateau 50 meters high. If the angle of elevation to the top of the plateau is 20°, how far are you from the base of the plateau?

54. Finding the Reach of a Ladder A 22-foot extension ladder leaning against a building makes a 70° angle with the ground. How far up the building does the ladder touch?

55. Finding the Angle of Elevation of the Sun At 10 AM on April 26, 2007, a building 300 feet high casts a shadow 50 feet long. What is the angle of elevation of the Sun?

56. Directing a Laser Beam A laser beam is to be directed through a small hole in the center of a circle of radius 10 feet. The origin of the beam is 35 feet from the circle (see the figure). At what angle of elevation should the beam be aimed to ensure that it goes through the hole?

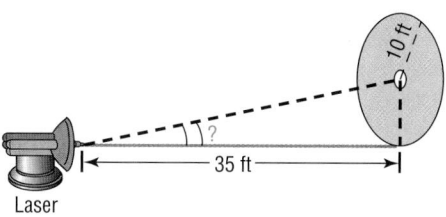

57. Finding the Speed of a Truck A state trooper is hidden 30 feet from a highway. One second after a truck passes, the angle θ between the highway and the line of observation from the patrol car to the truck is measured. See the illustration.

(a) If the angle measures 15°, how fast is the truck traveling? Express the answer in feet per second and in miles per hour.

(b) If the angle measures 20°, how fast is the truck traveling? Express the answer in feet per second and in miles per hour.

(c) If the speed limit is 55 miles per hour and a speeding ticket is issued for speeds of 5 miles per hour or more over the limit, for what angles should the trooper issue a ticket?

58. Security A security camera in a neighborhood bank is mounted on a wall 9 feet above the floor. What angle of depression should be used if the camera is to be directed to a spot 6 feet above the floor and 12 feet from the wall?

59. Parallax One method of measuring the distance from Earth to a star is the parallax method. The idea behind computing this distance is to measure the angle formed between the Earth and the star at two different points in time. Typically, the measurements are taken so that the side opposite the angle is as large as possible. Therefore, the optimal approach is to measure the angle when Earth is on opposite sides of the Sun, as shown in the figure.

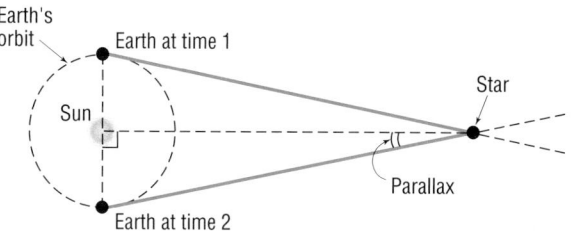

(a) Proxima Centauri is 4.22 light-years from Earth. If 1 light-year is about 5.9 trillion miles, how many miles is Proxima Centauri from Earth?

(b) The mean distance from Earth to the Sun is 93,000,000 miles. What is the parallax of Proxima Centauri?

60. Parallax See Problem 59. 61 Cygni, sometimes called Bessel's Star (after Friedrich Bessel, who measured the distance from Earth to the star in 1838), is a star in the constellation Cygnus.

(a) 61 Cygni is 11.14 light-years from Earth. If 1 light-year is about 5.9 trillion miles, how many miles is 61 Cygni from Earth?

(b) The mean distance from Earth to the Sun is 93,000,000 miles. What is the parallax of 61 Cygni?

61. Washington Monument   The angle of elevation of the Sun is 35.1° at the instant the shadow cast by the Washington Monument is 789 feet long. Use this information to calculate the height of the monument.

62. Finding the Length of a Mountain Trail   A straight trail with an inclination of 17° leads from a hotel at an elevation of 9000 feet to a mountain lake at an elevation of 11,200 feet. What is the length of the trail?

63. Finding the Bearing of an Aircraft   A DC-9 aircraft leaves Midway Airport from runway 4 RIGHT, whose bearing is N40°E. After flying for $\frac{1}{2}$ mile, the pilot requests permission to turn 90° and head toward the southeast. The permission is granted. After the airplane goes 1 mile in this direction, what bearing should the control tower use to locate the aircraft?

64. Finding the Bearing of a Ship   A ship leaves the port of Miami with a bearing of S80°E and a speed of 15 knots. After 1 hour, the ship turns 90° toward the south. After 2 hours, maintaining the same speed, what is the bearing to the ship from port?

65. Niagara Falls Incline Railway   Situated between Portage Road and the Niagara Parkway directly across from the Canadian Horseshoe Falls, the Falls Incline Railway is a funicular that carries passengers up an embankment to Table Rock Observation Point. If the length of the track is 51.8 meters and the angle of inclination is 36°2′, determine the height of the embankment.

Source: www.niagaraparks.com

66. Sears Tower   The Sears Tower in Chicago is the third tallest building in the world and is topped by a high antenna. A surveyor on the ground makes the following measurement:

1. The angle of elevation from his position to the top of the building is 34°.
2. The distance from his position to the top of the building is 2593 feet.
3. The distance from his position to the top of the antenna is 2743 feet.
   (a) How far away from the (base of the) building is the surveyor located?
   (b) How tall is the building?
   (c) What is the angle of elevation from the surveyor to the top of the antenna?
   (d) How tall is the antenna?

Source: www.infoplease.com/ce6/us/A0844218.html

67. Constructing a Highway   A highway whose primary directions are north–south is being constructed along the west coast of Florida. Near Naples, a bay obstructs the straight path of the road. Since the cost of a bridge is prohibitive, engineers decide to go around the bay. The illustration shows the path that they decide on and the measurements taken. What is the length of highway needed to go around the bay?

68. Photography   A camera is mounted on a tripod 4 feet high at a distance of 10 feet from George, who is 6 feet tall. See the illustration. If the camera lens has angles of depression and elevation of 20°, will George's feet and head be seen by the lens? If not, how far back will the camera need to be moved to include George's feet and head?

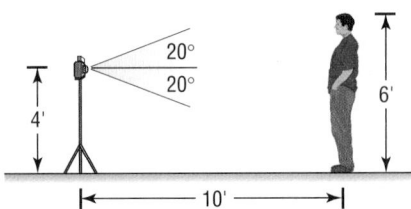

69. Finding the Distance between Two Objects   A blimp, suspended in the air at a height of 500 feet, lies directly over a line from Soldier Field to the Adler Planetarium on Lake Michigan (see the figure). If the angle of depression from the blimp to the stadium is 32° and from the blimp to the planetarium is 23°, find the distance between Soldier Field and the Adler Planetarium.

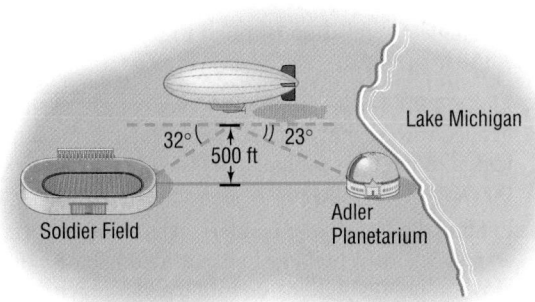

70. Hot-Air Balloon   While taking a ride in a hot-air balloon in Napa Valley, Francisco wonders how high he is. To find out, he chooses a landmark that is to the east of the balloon and measures the angle of depression to be 54°. A few minutes later, after traveling 100 feet east, the angle of depression to the same landmark is determined to be 61°. Use this information to determine the height of the balloon.

71. Mt. Rushmore   To measure the height of Lincoln's caricature on Mt. Rushmore, two sightings 800 feet from the base of the mountain are taken. If the angle of elevation to the bottom of Lincoln's face is 32° and the angle of elevation to the top is 35°, what is the height of Lincoln's face?

72. The CN Tower The CN Tower, located in Toronto, Canada, is the tallest structure in the world. While visiting Toronto, a tourist wondered what the height of the tower above the top of the Sky Pod is. While standing 4000 feet from the tower, she measured the angle to the top of the Sky Pod to be 20.1°. At this same distance, the angle of elevation to the top of the tower was found to be 24.4°. Use this information to determine the height of the tower above the Sky Pod.

73. Chicago Skyscrapers The angle of inclination from the base of the John Hancock Center to the top of the main structure of the Sears Tower is approximately 10.3°. If the main structure of the Sears Tower is 1451 feet tall, how far apart are the two skyscrapers? Assume the bases of the two buildings are at the same elevation.

Source: www.emporis.com

74. Estimating the Width of the Mississippi River A tourist at the top of the Gateway Arch (height, 630 feet) in St. Louis, Missouri observes a boat moored on the Illinois side of the Mississippi River 2070 feet directly across from the Arch. She also observes a boat moored on the Missouri side directly across from the first boat (see diagram). Given that $B = \cot^{-1}\dfrac{67}{55}$, estimate the width of the Mississippi River at the St. Louis riverfront.

Source: U.S. Army Corps of Engineers

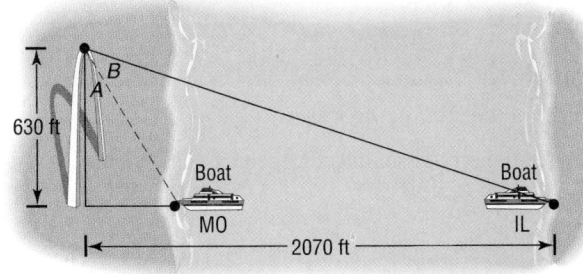

75. Finding the Pitch of a Roof A carpenter is preparing to put a roof on a garage that is 20 feet by 40 feet by 20 feet. A steel support beam 46 feet in length is positioned in the center of the garage. To support the roof, another beam will be attached to the top of the center beam (see the figure). At what angle of elevation is the new beam? In other words, what is the pitch of the roof?

76. Shooting Free Throws in Basketball The eyes of a basketball player are 6 feet above the floor. The player is at the free-throw line, which is 15 feet from the center of the basket rim (see the figure). What is the angle of elevation from the player's eyes to the center of the rim?

[**Hint:** The rim is 10 feet above the floor.]

77. Geometry Find the value of the angle θ in degrees rounded to the nearest tenth of a degree.

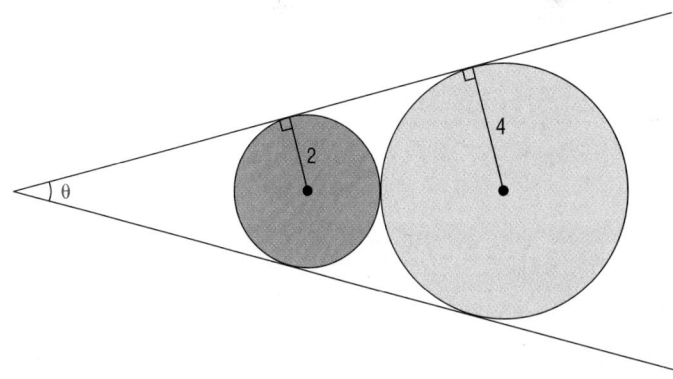

78. Surveillance Satellites A surveillance satellite circles Earth at a height of h miles above the surface. Suppose that d is the distance, in miles, on the surface of Earth that can be observed from the satellite. See the illustration on page 522.
(a) Find an equation that relates the central angle θ to the height h.
(b) Find an equation that relates the observable distance d and θ.
(c) Find an equation that relates d and h.
(d) If d is to be 2500 miles, how high must the satellite orbit above Earth?

(e) If the satellite orbits at a height of 300 miles, what distance *d* on the surface can be observed?

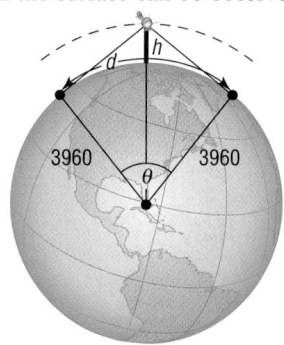

79. Calculating Pool Shots   A pool player located at **X** wants to shoot the white ball off the top cushion and hit the red ball dead center. He knows from physics that the white ball will come off a cushion at the same angle as it hits a cushion. Where on the top cushion should he hit the white ball?

80. The Freedom Tower   The Freedom Tower is to be the centerpiece of the rebuilding of the World Trade Center in New York City. The tower will be 1776 feet tall (not including a broadcast antenna). The angle of elevation from the base of an office building to the top of the tower is 34°. The angle of elevation from the helipad on the roof of the office building to the top of the tower is 20°.

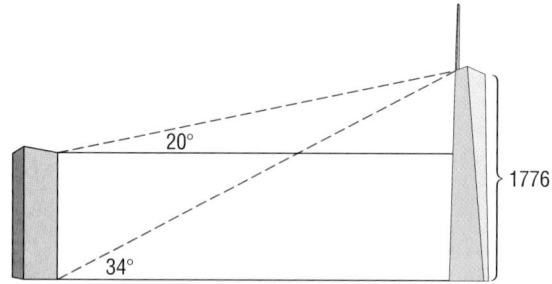

(a) How far away is the office building from the Freedom Tower? Assume the side of the tower is vertical. Round to the nearest foot.
(b) How tall is the office building? Round to the nearest foot.

Discussion and Writing

81. Explain how you would measure the width of the Grand Canyon from a point on its ridge.

82. Explain how you would measure the height of a TV tower that is on the roof of a tall building.

83. The Gibb's Hill Lighthouse. Southampton, Bermuda   In operation since 1846, the Gibb's Hill Lighthouse stands

117 feet high on a hill 245 feet high, so its beam of light is 362 feet above sea level. A brochure states that ships 40 miles away can see the light and planes flying at 10,000 feet can see it 120 miles away. Verify the accuracy of these statements. What assumption did the brochure make about the height of the ship?

'Are You Prepared?' Answers

1. 4   **2.** 26.6°   **3.** 30°

8.2 The Law of Sines

PREPARING FOR THIS SECTION   *Before getting started, review the following:*

- Trigonometric Equations (I) (Section 7.7, pp. 488–492)
- Difference Formula for the Sine Function (Section 7.4, p. 469)
- Geometry Essentials (Appendix A, Section A.2, pp. A14–A19)

Now Work the 'Are You Prepared?' problems on page 529.

OBJECTIVES   1 Solve SAA or ASA Triangles (p. 524)
2 Solve SSA Triangles (p. 525)
3 Solve Applied Problems (p. 527)

If none of the angles of a triangle is a right angle, the triangle is called **oblique.** An oblique triangle will have either three acute angles or two acute angles and one obtuse angle (an angle between 90° and 180°). See Figure 18.

Figure 18

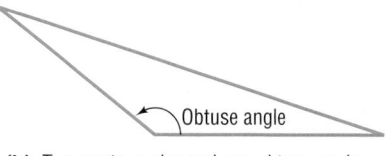

(a) All angles are acute   **(b)** Two acute angles and one obtuse angle

Figure 19

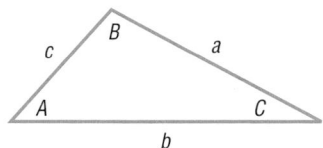

In the discussion that follows, we will always label an oblique triangle so that side a is opposite angle A, side b is opposite angle B, and side c is opposite angle C, as shown in Figure 19.

To **solve an oblique triangle** means to find the lengths of its sides and the measurements of its angles. To do this, we shall need to know the length of one side* along with (i) two angles; (ii) one angle and one other side; or (iii) the other two sides. There are four possibilities to consider:

Case 1: One side and two angles are known (ASA or SAA).
Case 2: Two sides and the angle opposite one of them are known (SSA).
Case 3: Two sides and the included angle are known (SAS).
Case 4: Three sides are known (SSS).

Figure 20 illustrates the four cases.

Figure 20

        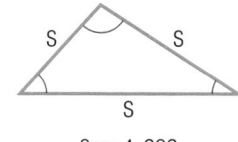

Case 1: ASA   Case 1: SAA   Case 2: SSA   Case 3: SAS   Case 4: SSS

WARNING Oblique triangles cannot be solved using the methods of Section 8.1. Do you know why? ■

The **Law of Sines** is used to solve triangles for which Case 1 or 2 holds. Cases 3 and 4 are considered when we study the Law of Cosines in the next section.

THEOREM

Law of Sines

For a triangle with sides a, b, c and opposite angles A, B, C, respectively,

$$\frac{\sin A}{a} = \frac{\sin B}{b} = \frac{\sin C}{c} \qquad \textbf{(1)}$$

A proof of the Law of Sines is given at the end of this section. The Law of Sines actually consists of three equalities:

$$\frac{\sin A}{a} = \frac{\sin B}{b} \qquad \frac{\sin A}{a} = \frac{\sin C}{c} \qquad \frac{\sin B}{b} = \frac{\sin C}{c}$$

Formula (1) is a compact way to write these three equations.

In applying the Law of Sines to solve triangles, we use the fact that the sum of the angles of any triangle equals 180°; that is,

$$A + B + C = 180° \qquad \textbf{(2)}$$

*The reason we need to know the length of one side is that, if we only know the angles, this will result in a family of *similar triangles*.

1 Solve SAA or ASA Triangles

Our first two examples show how to solve a triangle when one side and two angles are known (Case 1: SAA or ASA).

| EXAMPLE 1 | **Using the Law of Sines to Solve an SAA Triangle** |

Solve the triangle: $A = 40°$, $B = 60°$, $a = 4$

Solution

Figure 21

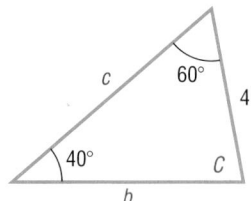

Figure 21 shows the triangle that we want to solve. The third angle C is found using equation (2).

$$A + B + C = 180°$$
$$40° + 60° + C = 180°$$
$$C = 80°$$

Now we use the Law of Sines (twice) to find the unknown sides b and c.

$$\frac{\sin A}{a} = \frac{\sin B}{b} \qquad \frac{\sin A}{a} = \frac{\sin C}{c}$$

Because $a = 4$, $A = 40°$, $B = 60°$, and $C = 80°$, we have

$$\frac{\sin 40°}{4} = \frac{\sin 60°}{b} \qquad \frac{\sin 40°}{4} = \frac{\sin 80°}{c}$$

NOTE Although not a check, we can verify the reasonableness of our answer by determining if the longest side is opposite the largest angle and the shortest side is opposite the smallest angle. ∎

Solving for b and c, we find that

$$b = \frac{4 \sin 60°}{\sin 40°} \approx 5.39 \qquad c = \frac{4 \sin 80°}{\sin 40°} \approx 6.13$$

Notice in Example 1 that we found b and c by working with the given side a. This is better than finding b first and working with a rounded value of b to find c.

Now Work PROBLEM 9

| EXAMPLE 2 | **Using the Law of Sines to Solve an ASA Triangle** |

Solve the triangle: $A = 35°$, $B = 15°$, $c = 5$

Solution

Figure 22

Figure 22 illustrates the triangle that we want to solve. Because we know two angles ($A = 35°$ and $B = 15°$), we find the third angle using equation (2).

$$A + B + C = 180°$$
$$35° + 15° + C = 180°$$
$$C = 130°$$

Now we know the three angles and one side ($c = 5$) of the triangle. To find the remaining two sides a and b, we use the Law of Sines (twice).

$$\frac{\sin A}{a} = \frac{\sin C}{c} \qquad \frac{\sin B}{b} = \frac{\sin C}{c}$$

$$\frac{\sin 35°}{a} = \frac{\sin 130°}{5} \qquad \frac{\sin 15°}{b} = \frac{\sin 130°}{5}$$

$$a = \frac{5 \sin 35°}{\sin 130°} \approx 3.74 \qquad b = \frac{5 \sin 15°}{\sin 130°} \approx 1.69$$

Now Work PROBLEM 23

2 Solve SSA Triangles

Figure 23

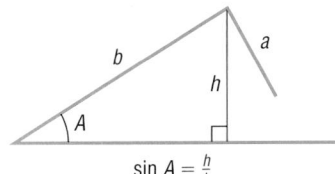

$$\sin A = \frac{h}{b}$$

Case 2 (SSA), which applies to triangles for which two sides and the angle opposite one of them are known, is referred to as the **ambiguous case,** because the known information may result in one triangle, two triangles, or no triangle at all. Suppose that we are given sides a and b and angle A, as illustrated in Figure 23. The key to determining the possible triangles, if any, that may be formed from the given information lies primarily with the relative size of side a, the height h, and the fact that $h = b \sin A$.

No Triangle If $a < h = b \sin A$, then side a is not sufficiently long to form a triangle. See Figure 24.

One Right Triangle If $a = h = b \sin A$, then side a is just long enough to form a right triangle. See Figure 25.

Figure 24
$a < h = b \sin A$

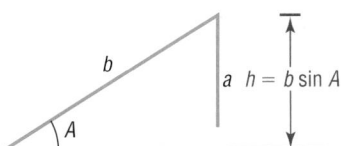

Figure 25
$a = h = b \sin A$

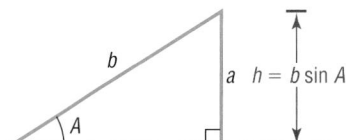

Two Triangles If $h = b \sin A < a$, and $a < b$, two distinct triangles can be formed from the given information. See Figure 26.

One Triangle If $a \geq b$, only one triangle can be formed. See Figure 27.

Figure 26
$b \sin A < a$ and $a < b$

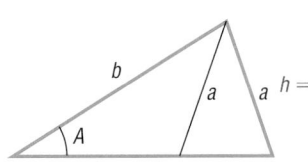

Figure 27
$a \geq b$

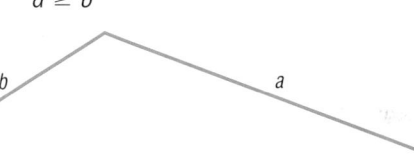

Fortunately, we do not have to rely on an illustration or complicated relationships to draw the correct conclusion in the ambiguous case. The Law of Sines will lead us to the correct determination. Let's see how.

EXAMPLE 3

Using the Law of Sines to Solve an SSA Triangle (One Solution)

Solve the triangle: $a = 3, b = 2, A = 40°$

Solution

See Figure 28(a). Because we know an angle ($A = 40°$), the side opposite the known angle ($a = 3$), and the side opposite angle B ($b = 2$), we use the Law of Sines to find the angle B.

Figure 28(a)

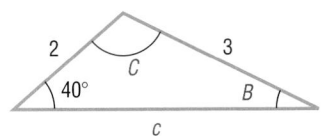

$$\frac{\sin A}{a} = \frac{\sin B}{b}$$

Then

$$\frac{\sin 40°}{3} = \frac{\sin B}{2}$$

$$\sin B = \frac{2 \sin 40°}{3} \approx 0.43$$

NOTE Here we computed B_1 by determining the value of $\sin^{-1}\!\left(\dfrac{2 \sin 40°}{3}\right)$.

If you use the rounded value and evaluate $\sin^{-1}(0.43)$, you will obtain a slightly different result. ∎

There are two angles B, $0° < B < 180°$, for which $\sin B \approx 0.43$.

$$B_1 \approx 25.4° \quad \text{and} \quad B_2 \approx 180° - 25.4° = 154.6°$$

The second possibility, $B_2 \approx 154.6°$, is ruled out, because $A = 40°$, making $A + B_2 \approx 194.6° > 180°$. Now, using $B_1 \approx 25.4°$, we find that

$$C = 180° - A - B_1 \approx 180° - 40° - 25.4° = 114.6°$$

The third side c may now be determined using the Law of Sines.

$$\frac{\sin A}{a} = \frac{\sin C}{c}$$

Figure 28(b)

$$\frac{\sin 40°}{3} = \frac{\sin 114.6°}{c}$$

$$c = \frac{3 \sin 114.6°}{\sin 40°} \approx 4.24$$

Figure 28(b) illustrates the solved triangle.

EXAMPLE 4 **Using the Law of Sines to Solve an SSA Triangle (Two Solutions)**

Solve the triangle: $a = 6, b = 8, A = 35°$

Solution See Figure 29(a). Because $a = 6$, $b = 8$, and $A = 35°$ are known, we use the Law of Sines to find the angle B.

Figure 29(a)

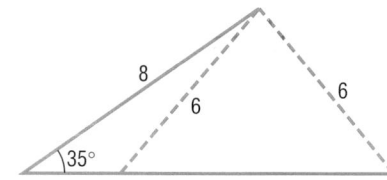

$$\frac{\sin A}{a} = \frac{\sin B}{b}$$

Then

$$\frac{\sin 35°}{6} = \frac{\sin B}{8}$$

$$\sin B = \frac{8 \sin 35°}{6} \approx 0.76$$

$$B_1 \approx 49.9° \quad \text{or} \quad B_2 \approx 180° - 49.9° = 130.1°$$

For both choices of B, we have $A + B < 180°$. There are two triangles, one containing the angle $B_1 \approx 49.9°$ and the other containing the angle $B_2 \approx 130.1°$. The third angle C is either

$$C_1 = 180° - A - B_1 \approx 95.1° \quad \text{or} \quad C_2 = 180° - A - B_2 \approx 14.9°$$
$$\qquad\qquad \uparrow \qquad\qquad\qquad\qquad\qquad\qquad\qquad\qquad \uparrow$$
$$\qquad\qquad A = 35° \qquad\qquad\qquad\qquad\qquad\qquad\qquad A = 35°$$
$$\qquad\qquad B_1 = 49.9° \qquad\qquad\qquad\qquad\qquad\qquad B_2 = 130.1°$$

The third side c obeys the Law of Sines, so we have

Figure 29(b)

$$\frac{\sin A}{a} = \frac{\sin C_1}{c_1} \qquad\qquad \frac{\sin A}{a} = \frac{\sin C_2}{c_2}$$

$$\frac{\sin 35°}{6} = \frac{\sin 95.1°}{c_1} \qquad\qquad \frac{\sin 35°}{6} = \frac{\sin 14.9°}{c_2}$$

$$c_1 = \frac{6 \sin 95.1°}{\sin 35°} \approx 10.42 \qquad c_2 = \frac{6 \sin 14.9°}{\sin 35°} \approx 2.69$$

The two solved triangles are illustrated in Figure 29(b).

EXAMPLE 5 **Using the Law of Sines to Solve a SSA Triangle (No Solution)**

Solve the triangle: $a = 2, c = 1, C = 50°$

Solution   Because $a = 2$, $c = 1$, and $C = 50°$ are known, we use the Law of Sines to find the angle A.

$$\frac{\sin A}{a} = \frac{\sin C}{c}$$

$$\frac{\sin A}{2} = \frac{\sin 50°}{1}$$

$$\sin A = 2 \sin 50° \approx 1.53$$

Since there is no angle A for which $\sin A > 1$, there can be no triangle with the given measurements. Figure 30 illustrates the measurements given. Notice that, no matter how we attempt to position side c, it will never touch side b to form a triangle.

Figure 30

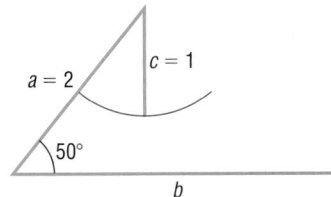

$c = 1$

$a = 2$

$50°$

b

Now Work PROBLEMS 25 AND 31

3 Solve Applied Problems

The Law of Sines is particularly useful for solving certain applied problems.

EXAMPLE 6   **Finding the Height of a Mountain**

To measure the height of a mountain, a surveyor takes two sightings of the peak at a distance 900 meters apart on a direct line to the mountain.* See Figure 31(a). The first observation results in an angle of elevation of $47°$, and the second results in an angle of elevation of $35°$. If the transit is 2 meters high, what is the height h of the mountain?

Figure 31

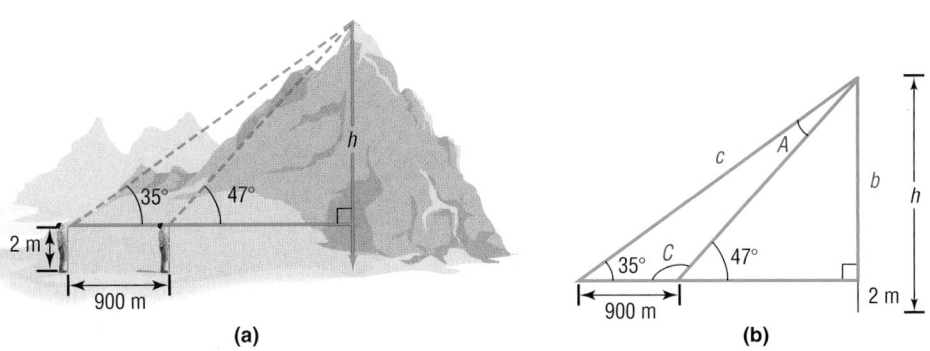

(a)   (b)

Solution   Figure 31(b) shows the triangles that replicate the illustration in Figure 31(a). Since $C + 47° = 180°$, we find that $C = 133°$. Also, since $A + C + 35° = 180°$, we find that $A = 180° - 35° - C = 145° - 133° = 12°$. We use the Law of Sines to find c.

$$\frac{\sin A}{a} = \frac{\sin C}{c} \quad \text{A = 12°, C = 133°, a = 900}$$

$$c = \frac{900 \sin 133°}{\sin 12°} \approx 3165.86$$

Using the larger right triangle, we have

$$\sin 35° = \frac{b}{c} \quad \text{c = 3165.86}$$

$$b = 3165.86 \sin 35° \approx 1815.86 \approx 1816 \text{ meters}$$

The height of the peak from ground level is approximately $1816 + 2 = 1818$ meters.

Now Work PROBLEM 39

*For simplicity, we assume that these sightings are at the same level.

| EXAMPLE 7 | Rescue at Sea |

Coast Guard Station Zulu is located 120 miles due west of Station X-ray. A ship at sea sends an SOS call that is received by each station. The call to Station Zulu indicates that the bearing of the ship from Zulu is N40°E (40° east of north). The call to Station X-ray indicates that the bearing of the ship from X-ray is N30°W (30° west of north).

(a) How far is each station from the ship?

(b) If a helicopter capable of flying 200 miles per hour is dispatched from the nearest station to the ship, how long will it take to reach the ship?

Solution   (a) Figure 32 illustrates the situation. The angle C is found to be

$$C = 180° - 50° - 60° = 70°$$

The Law of Sines can now be used to find the two distances a and b that we seek.

$$\frac{\sin 50°}{a} = \frac{\sin 70°}{120}$$

$$a = \frac{120 \sin 50°}{\sin 70°} \approx 97.82 \text{ miles}$$

$$\frac{\sin 60°}{b} = \frac{\sin 70°}{120}$$

$$b = \frac{120 \sin 60°}{\sin 70°} \approx 110.59 \text{ miles}$$

Figure 32

Station Zulu is about 111 miles from the ship, and Station X-ray is about 98 miles from the ship.

(b) The time t needed for the helicopter to reach the ship from Station X-ray is found by using the formula

$$(\text{Rate}, r)(\text{Time}, t) = \text{Distance}, a$$

Then

$$t = \frac{a}{r} = \frac{97.82}{200} \approx 0.49 \text{ hour} \approx 29 \text{ minutes}$$

It will take about 29 minutes for the helicopter to reach the ship.

━━━━━➤ **Now Work** PROBLEM **37**

Proof of the Law of Sines   To prove the Law of Sines, we construct an altitude of length h from one of the vertices of a triangle. Figure 33(a) shows h for a triangle with three acute angles, and Figure 33(b) shows h for a triangle with an obtuse angle. In each case, the altitude is drawn from the vertex at B. Using either illustration, we have

Figure 33

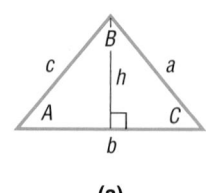

(a)

(b)

$$\sin C = \frac{h}{a}$$

from which

$$h = a \sin C \qquad (3)$$

From Figure 33(a), it also follows that

$$\sin A = \frac{h}{c}$$

from which

$$h = c \sin A \qquad (4)$$

From Figure 33(b), it follows that

$$\sin(180° - A) = \sin A = \frac{h}{c}$$

$$\uparrow$$

$$\sin(180° - A) = \sin 180° \cos A - \cos 180° \sin A = \sin A$$

which again gives

$$h = c \sin A$$

So, whether the triangle has three acute angles or has two acute angles and one obtuse angle, equations (3) and (4) hold. As a result, we may equate the expressions for h in equations (3) and (4) to get

$$a \sin C = c \sin A$$

from which

Figure 34

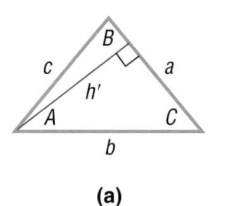

(a)

(b)

$$\frac{\sin A}{a} = \frac{\sin C}{c} \qquad \textbf{(5)}$$

In a similar manner, by constructing the altitude h' from the vertex of angle A as shown in Figure 34, we can show that

$$\sin B = \frac{h'}{c} \quad \text{and} \quad \sin C = \frac{h'}{b}$$

Equating the expressions for h', we find that

$$h' = c \sin B = b \sin C$$

from which

$$\frac{\sin B}{b} = \frac{\sin C}{c} \qquad \textbf{(6)}$$

When equations (5) and (6) are combined, we have equation (1), the Law of Sines. ∎

8.2 Assess Your Understanding

'Are You Prepared?' *Answers are given at the end of these exercises. If you get a wrong answer, read the pages listed in red.*

1. The difference formula for the sine function is $\sin(A - B) =$ _____. (p. 469)

2. If θ is an acute angle, solve the equation $\cos \theta = \dfrac{\sqrt{3}}{2}$.
(pp. 488–492)

3. The two triangles shown are similar. Find the missing length. (pp. A16–A19)

Concepts and Vocabulary

4. If none of the angles of a triangle is a right angle, the triangle is called _____.

5. For a triangle with sides a, b, c and opposite angles A, B, C, the Law of Sines states that _____.

6. *True or False* An oblique triangle in which two sides and an angle are given always results in at least one triangle.

7. *True or False* The sum of the angles of any triangle equals 180°.

8. *True or False* The ambiguous case refers to the fact that, when two sides and the angle opposite one of them are given, sometimes the Law of Sines cannot be used.

Skill Building

In Problems 9–16, solve each triangle.

9.

10.

11.

12.

13.

14.

15.

16.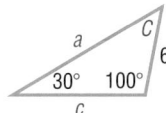

In Problems 17–24, solve each triangle.

17. $A = 40°$, $B = 20°$, $a = 2$

18. $A = 50°$, $C = 20°$, $a = 3$

19. $B = 70°$, $C = 10°$, $b = 5$

20. $A = 70°$, $B = 60°$, $c = 4$

21. $A = 110°$, $C = 30°$, $c = 3$

22. $B = 10°$, $C = 100°$, $b = 2$

23. $A = 40°$, $B = 40°$, $c = 2$

24. $B = 20°$, $C = 70°$, $a = 1$

In Problems 25–36, two sides and an angle are given. Determine whether the given information results in one triangle, two triangles, or no triangle at all. Solve any triangle(s) that results.

25. $a = 3$, $b = 2$, $A = 50°$

26. $b = 4$, $c = 3$, $B = 40°$

27. $b = 5$, $c = 3$, $B = 100°$

28. $a = 2$, $c = 1$, $A = 120°$

29. $a = 4$, $b = 5$, $A = 60°$

30. $b = 2$, $c = 3$, $B = 40°$

31. $b = 4$, $c = 6$, $B = 20°$

32. $a = 3$, $b = 7$, $A = 70°$

33. $a = 2$, $c = 1$, $C = 100°$

34. $b = 4$, $c = 5$, $B = 95°$

35. $a = 2$, $c = 1$, $C = 25°$

36. $b = 4$, $c = 5$, $B = 40°$

Applications and Extensions

37. Rescue at Sea Coast Guard Station Able is located 150 miles due south of Station Baker. A ship at sea sends an SOS call that is received by each station. The call to Station Able indicates that the ship is located N55°E; the call to Station Baker indicates that the ship is located S60°E.
   (a) How far is each station from the ship?
   (b) If a helicopter capable of flying 200 miles per hour is dispatched from the station nearest the ship, how long will it take to reach the ship?

38. Distance to the Moon At exactly the same time, Tom and Alice measured the angle of elevation to the moon while standing exactly 300 km apart. The angle of elevation to the moon for Tom was 49.8974° and the angle of elevation to the moon for Alice was 49.9312°. See the figure. To the nearest 1000 km, how far was the moon from Earth when the measurement was obtained?

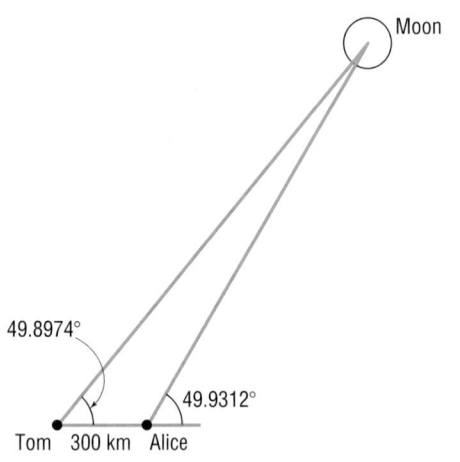

39. Finding the Length of a Ski Lift Consult the figure. To find the length of the span of a proposed ski lift from P to Q, a surveyor measures $\angle DPQ$ to be 25° and then walks off a distance of 1000 feet to R and measures $\angle PRQ$ to be 15°. What is the distance from P to Q?

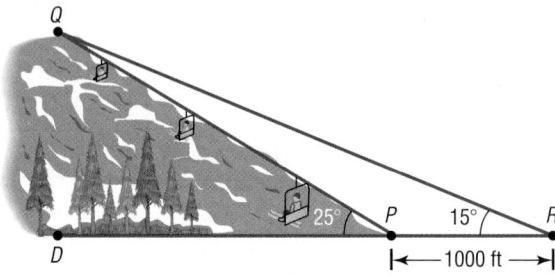

40. Finding the Height of a Mountain Use the illustration in Problem 39 to find the height QD of the mountain.

41. Finding the Height of an Airplane An aircraft is spotted by two observers who are 1000 feet apart. As the airplane passes over the line joining them, each observer takes a sighting of the angle of elevation to the plane, as indicated in the figure. How high is the airplane?

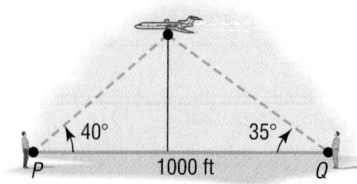

42. Finding the Height of the Bridge over the Royal Gorge The highest bridge in the world is the bridge over the Royal Gorge of the Arkansas River in Colorado. Sightings to the same point at water level directly under the bridge are taken from each side of the 880-foot-long bridge, as indicated in the figure. How high is the bridge?

Source: Guinness Book of World Records

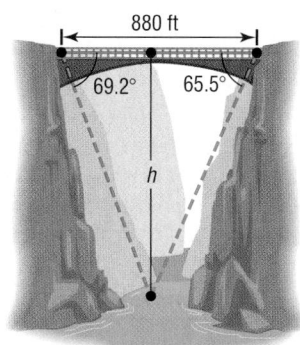

43. Landscaping Pat needs to determine the height of a tree before cutting it down to be sure that it will not fall on a nearby fence. The angle of elevation of the tree from one position on a flat path from the tree is 30°, and from a second position 40 feet farther along this path it is 20°. What is the height of the tree?

44. Construction A loading ramp 10 feet long that makes an angle of 18° with the horizontal is to be replaced by one that makes an angle of 12° with the horizontal. How long is the new ramp?

45. Commercial Navigation Adam must fly home to St. Louis from a business meeting in Oklahoma City. One flight option flies directly to St. Louis, a distance of about 461.1 miles. A second flight option flies first to Kansas City and then connects to St. Louis. The bearing from Oklahoma City to Kansas City is N29.6°E, and the bearing from Oklahoma City to St. Louis is N57.7°E. The bearing from St. Louis to Oklahoma City is S62.1°W, and the bearing from St. Louis to Kansas City is N79.4°W. How many more frequent flyer miles will Adam receive if he takes the connecting flight rather than the direct flight?

Source: www.landings.com

46. Time Lost due to a Navigation Error In attempting to fly from city P to city Q, an aircraft followed a course that was 10° in error, as indicated in the figure. After flying a distance of 50 miles, the pilot corrected the course by turning at point R and flying 70 miles farther. If the constant speed of the

aircraft was 250 miles per hour, how much time was lost due to the error?

47. Finding the Lean of the Leaning Tower of Pisa The famous Leaning Tower of Pisa was originally 184.5 feet high.* At a distance of 123 feet from the base of the tower, the angle of elevation to the top of the tower is found to be 60°. Find $\angle RPQ$ indicated in the figure. Also, find the perpendicular distance from R to PQ.

48. Crankshafts on Cars On a certain automobile, the crankshaft is 3 inches long and the connecting rod is 9 inches long (see the figure). At the time when $\angle OPQ$ is 15°, how far is the piston (P) from the center (O) of the crankshaft?

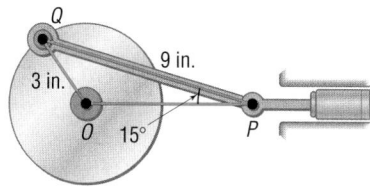

49. Constructing a Highway U.S. 41, a highway whose primary directions are north–south, is being constructed along the west coast of Florida. Near Naples, a bay obstructs the straight

---

*On February 27, 1964, the government of Italy requested aid in preventing the tower from toppling. A multinational task force of engineers, mathematicians, and historians was assigned and met on the Azores islands to discuss stabilization methods. After over two decades of work on the subject, the tower was closed to the public in January 1990. During the time that the tower was closed, the bells were removed to relieve some weight, and cables were cinched around the third level and anchored several hundred meters away. Apartments and houses in the path of the tower were vacated for safety concerns. After a decade of corrective reconstruction and stabilization efforts, the tower was reopened to the public on December 15, 2001. Many methods were proposed to stabilize the tower, including the addition of 800 metric tons of lead counterweights to the raised end of the base. The final solution to correcting the lean was to remove 38 cubic meters of soil from underneath the raised end. The tower has been declared stable for at least another 300 years.

Source: http://en.wikipedia.org/wiki/Leaning_Tower_of_Pisa, page last modified June 28, 2006

path of the road. Since the cost of a bridge is prohibitive, engineers decide to go around the bay. The illustration shows the path that they decide on and the measurements taken. What is the length of highway needed to go around the bay?

50. Calculating Distances at Sea   The navigator of a ship at sea spots two lighthouses that she knows to be 3 miles apart along a straight seashore. She determines that the angles formed between two line-of-sight observations of the lighthouses and the line from the ship directly to shore are 15° and 35°. See the illustration.
(a) How far is the ship from lighthouse *P*?
(b) How far is the ship from lighthouse *Q*?
(c) How far is the ship from shore?

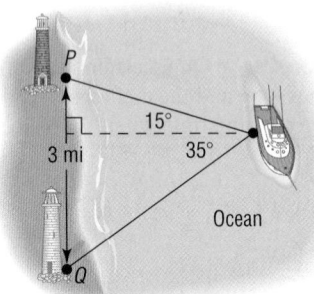

51. Designing an Awning   An awning that covers a sliding glass door that is 88 inches tall forms an angle of 50° with the wall. The purpose of the awning is to prevent sunlight from entering the house when the angle of elevation of the Sun is more than 65°. See the figure. Find the length *L* of the awning.

52. Finding Distances   A forest ranger is walking on a path inclined at 5° to the horizontal directly toward a 100-foot-tall fire observation tower. The angle of elevation from the path to the top of the tower is 40°. How far is the ranger from the tower at this time?

53. Great Pyramid of Cheops   One of the original Seven Wonders of the World, the Great Pyramid of Cheops was built about 2580 BC. Its original height was 480 feet 11 inches, but owing to the loss of its topmost stones, it is now shorter. Find the current height of the Great Pyramid using the information given in the illustration.

Source: Guinness Book of World Records

54. Determining the Height of an Aircraft   Two sensors are spaced 700 feet apart along the approach to a small airport. When an aircraft is nearing the airport, the angle of elevation from the first sensor to the aircraft is 20°, and from the second sensor to the aircraft it is 15°. Determine how high the aircraft is at this time.

55. Mercury   The distance from the Sun to Earth is approximately 149,600,000 kilometers (km). The distance from the Sun to Mercury is approximately 57,910,000 km. The **elongation angle** α is the angle formed between the line of sight from Earth to the Sun and the line of sight from Earth to Mercury. See the figure. Suppose that the elongation angle for Mercury is 15°. Use this information to find the possible distances between Earth and Mercury.

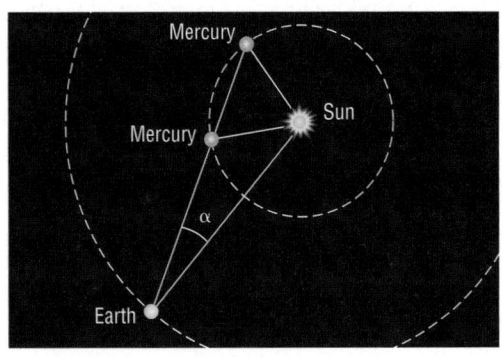

56. Venus The distance from the Sun to Earth is approximately 149,600,000 km. The distance from the Sun to Venus is approximately 108,200,000 km. The elongation angle α is the angle formed between the line of sight from Earth to the Sun and the line of sight from Earth to Venus. Suppose that the elongation angle for Venus is 10°. Use this information to find the possible distances between Earth and Venus.

57. The Original Ferris Wheel George Washington Gale Ferris, Jr., designed the original Ferris wheel for the 1893 World's Columbian Exposition in Chicago, Illinois. The wheel had 36 equally spaced cars each the size of a school bus. The distance between adjacent cars was approximately 22 feet. Determine the diameter of the wheel to the nearest foot.

Source: Carnegie Library of Pittsburgh, www.clpgh.org

58. Mollweide's Formula For any triangle, Mollweide's Formula (named after Karl Mollweide, 1774–1825) states that

$$\frac{a + b}{c} = \frac{\cos\left[\frac{1}{2}(A - B)\right]}{\sin\left(\frac{1}{2}C\right)}$$

Derive it.

[**Hint:** Use the Law of Sines and then a Sum-to-Product Formula. Notice that this formula involves all six parts of a triangle. As a result, it is sometimes used to check the solution of a triangle.]

59. Mollweide's Formula Another form of Mollweide's Formula is

$$\frac{a - b}{c} = \frac{\sin\left[\frac{1}{2}(A - B)\right]}{\cos\left(\frac{1}{2}C\right)}$$

Derive it.

60. For any triangle, derive the formula

$$a = b \cos C + c \cos B$$

[**Hint:** Use the fact that $\sin A = \sin(180° - B - C)$.]

61. Law of Tangents For any triangle, derive the Law of Tangents.

$$\frac{a - b}{a + b} = \frac{\tan\left[\frac{1}{2}(A - B)\right]}{\tan\left[\frac{1}{2}(A + B)\right]}$$

[**Hint:** Use Mollweide's Formula.]

62. Circumscribing a Triangle Show that

$$\frac{\sin A}{a} = \frac{\sin B}{b} = \frac{\sin C}{c} = \frac{1}{2r}$$

where r is the radius of the circle circumscribing the triangle PQR whose sides are $a, b,$ and c, as shown in the figure.

[**Hint:** Draw the diameter PP'. Then $B = \angle PQR = \angle PP'R$, and angle $\angle PRP' = 90°$.]

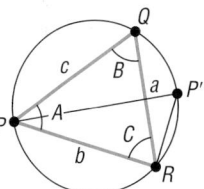

Discussion and Writing

63. Make up three problems involving oblique triangles. One should result in one triangle, the second in two triangles, and the third in no triangle.

64. What do you do first if you are asked to solve a triangle and are given one side and two angles?

65. What do you do first if you are asked to solve a triangle and are given two sides and the angle opposite one of them?

'Are You Prepared?' Answers

1. $\sin A \cos B - \cos A \sin B$ **2.** 30°   **3.** $\dfrac{15}{2}$

8.3 The Law of Cosines

PREPARING FOR THIS SECTION *Before getting started, review the following:*

- Trigonometric Equations (I) (Section 7.7, pp. 488–492)
- Distance Formula (Section 1.1, p. 5)

Now Work the 'Are You Prepared?' problems on page 537.

OBJECTIVES   **1** Solve SAS Triangles (p. 534)

               2 Solve SSS Triangles (p. 535)

               3 Solve Applied Problems (p. 536)

In the previous section, we used the Law of Sines to solve Case 1 (SAA or ASA) and Case 2 (SSA) of an oblique triangle. In this section, we derive the Law of Cosines and use it to solve the remaining cases, 3 and 4.

Case 3: Two sides and the included angle are known (SAS).
Case 4: Three sides are known (SSS).

THEOREM

Law of Cosines

For a triangle with sides a, b, c and opposite angles A, B, C, respectively,

$$c^2 = a^2 + b^2 - 2ab \cos C \quad \quad (1)$$
$$b^2 = a^2 + c^2 - 2ac \cos B \quad \quad (2)$$
$$a^2 = b^2 + c^2 - 2bc \cos A \quad \quad (3)$$

Figure 35

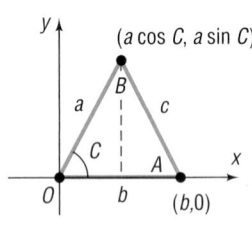

(a) Angle C is acute

(b) Angle C is obtuse

Proof We will prove only formula (1) here. Formulas (2) and (3) may be proved using the same argument.

We begin by strategically placing a triangle on a rectangular coordinate system so that the vertex of angle C is at the origin and side b lies along the positive x-axis. Regardless of whether C is acute, as in Figure 35(a), or obtuse, as in Figure 35(b), the vertex of angle B has coordinates $(a \cos C, a \sin C)$. The vertex of angle A has coordinates $(b, 0)$.

We can now use the distance formula to compute c^2.

$$c^2 = (b - a \cos C)^2 + (0 - a \sin C)^2$$
$$= b^2 - 2ab \cos C + a^2 \cos^2 C + a^2 \sin^2 C$$
$$= b^2 - 2ab \cos C + a^2(\cos^2 C + \sin^2 C)$$
$$= a^2 + b^2 - 2ab \cos C \quad \blacksquare$$

Each of formulas (1), (2), and (3) may be stated in words as follows:

THEOREM

Law of Cosines

The square of one side of a triangle equals the sum of the squares of the other two sides minus twice their product times the cosine of their included angle.

Observe that if the triangle is a right triangle (so that, say, $C = 90°$), formula (1) becomes the familiar Pythagorean Theorem: $c^2 = a^2 + b^2$. The Pythagorean Theorem is a special case of the Law of Cosines!

1 Solve SAS Triangles

Let's see how to use the Law of Cosines to solve Case 3 (SAS), which applies to triangles for which two sides and the included angle are known.

EXAMPLE 1 | Using the Law of Cosines to Solve an SAS Triangle

Solve the triangle: $a = 2$, $b = 3$, $C = 60°$

Solution See Figure 36. Because we know two sides, a and b, and the included angle, $C = 60°$, the Law of Cosines makes it easy to find the third side, c.

Figure 36

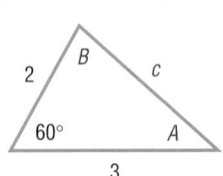

$$c^2 = a^2 + b^2 - 2ab \cos C$$
$$= 2^2 + 3^2 - 2 \cdot 2 \cdot 3 \cdot \cos 60° \quad a = 2, b = 3, C = 60°$$
$$= 13 - \left(12 \cdot \frac{1}{2}\right) = 7$$
$$c = \sqrt{7}$$

Side c is of length $\sqrt{7}$. To find the angles A and B, we may use either the Law of Sines or the Law of Cosines. It is preferable to use the Law of Cosines, since it will lead to an equation with one solution. Using the Law of Sines would lead to an equation with two solutions that would need to be checked to determine which solution fits the given data. We choose to use formulas (2) and (3) of the Law of Cosines to find A and B.

For A:

$$a^2 = b^2 + c^2 - 2bc \cos A$$

$$2bc \cos A = b^2 + c^2 - a^2$$

$$\cos A = \frac{b^2 + c^2 - a^2}{2bc} = \frac{9 + 7 - 4}{2 \cdot 3\sqrt{7}} = \frac{12}{6\sqrt{7}} = \frac{2\sqrt{7}}{7}$$

$$A = \cos^{-1}\frac{2\sqrt{7}}{7} \approx 40.9°$$

For B:

$$b^2 = a^2 + c^2 - 2ac \cos B$$

$$\cos B = \frac{a^2 + c^2 - b^2}{2ac} = \frac{4 + 7 - 9}{4\sqrt{7}} = \frac{2}{4\sqrt{7}} = \frac{\sqrt{7}}{14}$$

$$B = \cos^{-1}\frac{\sqrt{7}}{14} \approx 79.1°$$

Notice that $A + B + C = 40.9° + 79.1° + 60° = 180°$, as required.

━━━➤ **Now Work** PROBLEM 9

2 Solve SSS Triangles

The next example illustrates how the Law of Cosines is used when three sides of a triangle are known, Case 4 (SSS).

| EXAMPLE 2 | **Using the Law of Cosines to Solve an SSS Triangle** |

Solve the triangle: $a = 4, b = 3, c = 6$

Solution See Figure 37. To find the angles A, B, and C, we proceed as we did in the latter part of the solution to Example 1.

For A:

$$\cos A = \frac{b^2 + c^2 - a^2}{2bc} = \frac{9 + 36 - 16}{2 \cdot 3 \cdot 6} = \frac{29}{36}$$

$$A = \cos^{-1}\frac{29}{36} \approx 36.3°$$

For B:

$$\cos B = \frac{a^2 + c^2 - b^2}{2ac} = \frac{16 + 36 - 9}{2 \cdot 4 \cdot 6} = \frac{43}{48}$$

$$B = \cos^{-1}\frac{43}{48} \approx 26.4°$$

Figure 37

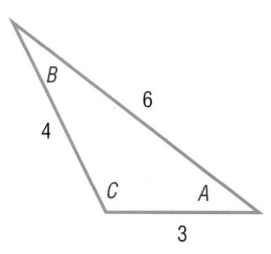

Since we know A and B,

$$C = 180° - A - B \approx 180° - 36.3° - 26.4° = 117.3°$$

━━━➤ **Now Work** PROBLEM 15

3 Solve Applied Problems

| EXAMPLE 3 | Correcting a Navigational Error |

A motorized sailboat leaves Naples, Florida, bound for Key West, 150 miles away. Maintaining a constant speed of 15 miles per hour, but encountering heavy crosswinds and strong currents, the crew finds, after 4 hours, that the sailboat is off course by 20°.

(a) How far is the sailboat from Key West at this time?
(b) Through what angle should the sailboat turn to correct its course?
(c) How much time has been added to the trip because of this? (Assume that the speed remains at 15 miles per hour.)

Solution   See Figure 38. With a speed of 15 miles per hour, the sailboat has gone 60 miles after 4 hours. We seek the distance x of the sailboat from Key West. We also seek the angle θ that the sailboat should turn through to correct its course.

(a) To find x, we use the Law of Cosines, since we know two sides and the included angle.

$$x^2 = 150^2 + 60^2 - 2(150)(60) \cos 20° \approx 9186.53$$

$$x \approx 95.8$$

Figure 38

The sailboat is about 96 miles from Key West.

(b) We now know three sides of the triangle, so we can use the Law of Cosines again to find the angle A opposite the side of length 150 miles.

$$150^2 = 96^2 + 60^2 - 2(96)(60) \cos A$$

$$9684 = -11{,}520 \cos A$$

$$\cos A \approx -0.8406$$

$$A \approx 147.2°$$

The sailboat should turn through an angle of

$$\theta = 180° - A \approx 180° - 147.2° = 32.8°$$

The sailboat should turn through an angle of about 33° to correct its course.

(c) The total length of the trip is now $60 + 96 = 156$ miles. The extra 6 miles will only require about 0.4 hour or 24 minutes more if the speed of 15 miles per hour is maintained.

━━━━ **Now Work** PROBLEM 45

Historical Feature

The Law of Sines was known vaguely long before it was explicitly stated by Nasir Eddin (about AD 1250). Ptolemy (about AD 150) was aware of it in a form using a chord function instead of the sine function. But it was first clearly stated in Europe by Regiomontanus, writing in 1464.

The Law of Cosines appears first in Euclid's *Elements* (Book II), but in a well-disguised form in which squares built on the sides of triangles are added and a rectangle representing the cosine term is subtracted. It was thus known to all mathematicians because of their familiarity with Euclid's work. An early modern form of the Law of Cosines, that for finding the angle when the sides are known, was stated by François Viète (in 1593).

The Law of Tangents (see Problem 61 of Exercise 8.2) has become obsolete. In the past it was used in place of the Law of Cosines, because the Law of Cosines was very inconvenient for calculation with logarithms or slide rules. Mixing of addition and multiplication is now very easy on a calculator, however, and the Law of Tangents has been shelved along with the slide rule.

8.3 Assess Your Understanding

'Are You Prepared?' *Answers are given at the end of these exercises. If you get a wrong answer, read the pages listed in red.*

1. Write the formula for the distance d from $P_1 = (x_1, y_1)$ to $P_2 = (x_2, y_2)$. (p. 5)

2. If θ is an acute angle, solve the equation $\cos \theta = \dfrac{\sqrt{2}}{2}$. (pp. 488–492)

Concepts and Vocabulary

3. If three sides of a triangle are given, the Law of _____ is used to solve the triangle.

4. If one side and two angles of a triangle are given, the Law of _____ is used to solve the triangle.

5. If two sides and the included angle of a triangle are given, the Law of _____ is used to solve the triangle.

6. *True or False* Given only the three sides of a triangle, there is insufficient information to solve the triangle.

7. *True or False* Given two sides and the included angle, the first thing to do to solve the triangle is to use the Law of Sines.

8. *True or False* A special case of the Law of Cosines is the Pythagorean Theorem.

Skill Building

In Problems 9–16, solve each triangle.

9.

10.

11.

12.

13.

14.

15.

16.
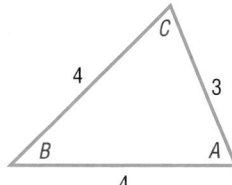

In Problems 17–32, solve each triangle.

17. $a = 3$, $b = 4$, $C = 40°$

18. $a = 2$, $c = 1$, $B = 10°$

19. $b = 1$, $c = 3$, $A = 80°$

20. $a = 6$, $b = 4$, $C = 60°$

21. $a = 3$, $c = 2$, $B = 110°$

22. $b = 4$, $c = 1$, $A = 120°$

23. $a = 2$, $b = 2$, $C = 50°$

24. $a = 3$, $c = 2$, $B = 90°$

25. $a = 12$, $b = 13$, $c = 5$

26. $a = 4$, $b = 5$, $c = 3$

27. $a = 2$, $b = 2$, $c = 2$

28. $a = 3$, $b = 3$, $c = 2$

29. $a = 5$, $b = 8$, $c = 9$

30. $a = 4$, $b = 3$, $c = 6$

31. $a = 10$, $b = 8$, $c = 5$

32. $a = 9$, $b = 7$, $c = 10$

Mixed Practice

In Problems 33–42, solve each triangle using either the Law of Sines or the Law of Cosines.

33. $B = 20°$, $C = 75°$, $b = 5$

34. $A = 50°$, $B = 55°$, $c = 9$

35. $a = 6$, $b = 8$, $c = 9$

36. $a = 14$, $b = 7$, $A = 85°$

37. $B = 35°$, $C = 65°$, $a = 15$

38. $a = 4$, $c = 5$, $B = 55°$

39. $A = 10°$, $a = 3$, $b = 10$

40. $A = 65°$, $B = 72°$, $b = 7$

41. $b = 5$, $c = 12$, $A = 60°$

42. $a = 10$, $b = 10$, $c = 15$

Applications and Extensions

43. Distance to the Green A golfer hits an errant tee shot that lands in the rough. A marker in the center of the fairway is 150 yards from the center of the green. While standing on the marker and facing the green, the golfer turns 110° toward his ball. He then paces off 35 yards to his ball. See the figure. How far is the ball from the center of the green?

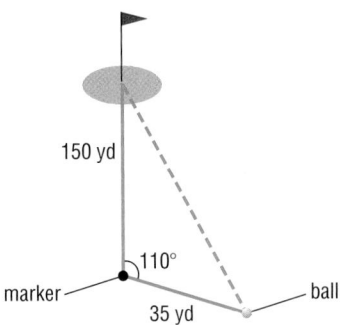

44. Navigation An airplane flies due north from Ft. Myers to Sarasota, a distance of 150 miles, and then turns through an angle of 50° and flies to Orlando, a distance of 100 miles. See the figure.
(a) How far is it directly from Ft. Myers to Orlando?
(b) What bearing should the pilot use to fly directly from Ft. Myers to Orlando?

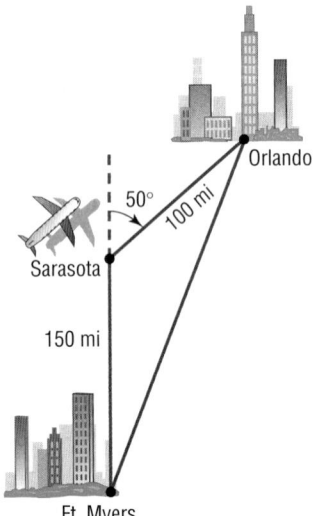

45. Avoiding a Tropical Storm A cruise ship maintains an average speed of 15 knots in going from San Juan, Puerto Rico, to Barbados, West Indies, a distance of 600 nautical miles. To avoid a tropical storm, the captain heads out of San Juan in a direction of 20° off a direct heading to Barbados. The captain maintains the 15-knot speed for 10 hours, after which time the path to Barbados becomes clear of storms.

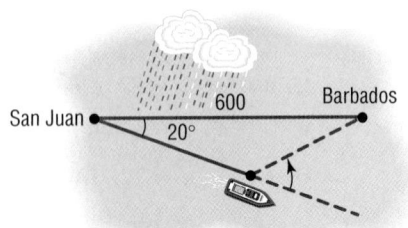

(a) Through what angle should the captain turn to head directly to Barbados?
(b) Once the turn is made, how long will it be before the ship reaches Barbados if the same 15-knot speed is maintained?

46. Revising a Flight Plan In attempting to fly from Chicago to Louisville, a distance of 330 miles, a pilot inadvertently took a course that was 10° in error, as indicated in the figure.
(a) If the aircraft maintains an average speed of 220 miles per hour and if the error in direction is discovered after 15 minutes, through what angle should the pilot turn to head toward Louisville?
(b) What new average speed should the pilot maintain so that the total time of the trip is 90 minutes?

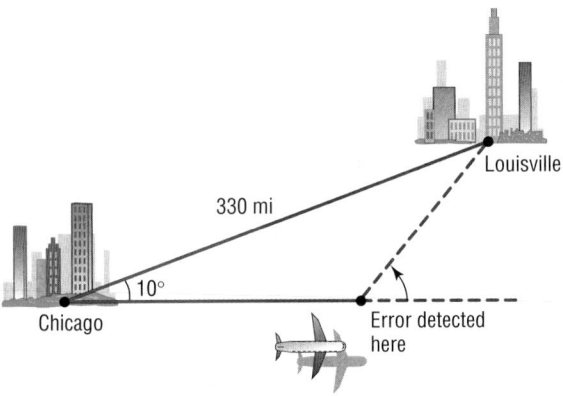

47. Major League Baseball Field A Major League baseball diamond is actually a square 90 feet on a side. The pitching rubber is located 60.5 feet from home plate on a line joining home plate and second base.
(a) How far is it from the pitching rubber to first base?
(b) How far is it from the pitching rubber to second base?
(c) If a pitcher faces home plate, through what angle does he need to turn to face first base?

48. Little League Baseball Field According to Little League baseball official regulations, the diamond is a square 60 feet on a side. The pitching rubber is located 46 feet from home plate on a line joining home plate and second base.
(a) How far is it from the pitching rubber to first base?
(b) How far is it from the pitching rubber to second base?
(c) If a pitcher faces home plate, through what angle does he need to turn to face first base?

49. Finding the Length of a Guy Wire The height of a radio tower is 500 feet, and the ground on one side of the tower slopes upward at an angle of 10° (see the figure).

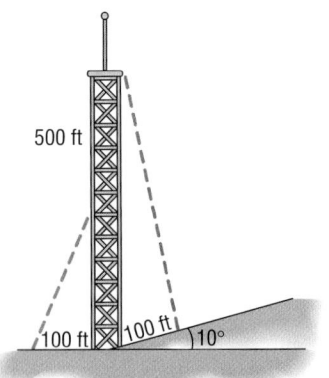

(a) How long should a guy wire be if it is to connect to the top of the tower and be secured at a point on the sloped side 100 feet from the base of the tower?

(b) How long should a second guy wire be if it is to connect to the middle of the tower and be secured at a point 100 feet from the base on the flat side?

50. **Finding the Length of a Guy Wire**   A radio tower 500 feet high is located on the side of a hill with an inclination to the horizontal of 5°. See the figure. How long should two guy wires be if they are to connect to the top of the tower and be secured at two points 100 feet directly above and directly below the base of the tower?

51. **Wrigley Field, Home of the Chicago Cubs**   The distance from home plate to the fence in dead center in Wrigley Field is 400 feet (see the figure). How far is it from the fence in dead center to third base?

52. **Little League Baseball**   The distance from home plate to the fence in dead center at the Oak Lawn Little League field is 280 feet. How far is it from the fence in dead center to third base?

[**Hint:** The distance between the bases in Little League is 60 feet.]

53. **Building a Swing Set**   Clint is building a wooden swing set for his children. Each supporting end of the swing set is to be an A-frame constructed with two 10-foot-long 4 by 4s joined at a 45° angle. To prevent the swing set from tipping over, Clint wants to secure the base of each A-frame to concrete footings. How far apart should the footings for each A-frame be?

54. **Rods and Pistons**   Rod OA rotates about the fixed point O so that point A travels on a circle of radius r. Connected to point A is another rod AB of length $L > 2r$, and point B is connected to a piston. See the figure. Show that the distance x between point O and point B is given by

$$x = r \cos \theta + \sqrt{r^2 \cos^2 \theta + L^2 - r^2}$$

where θ is the angle of rotation of rod OA.

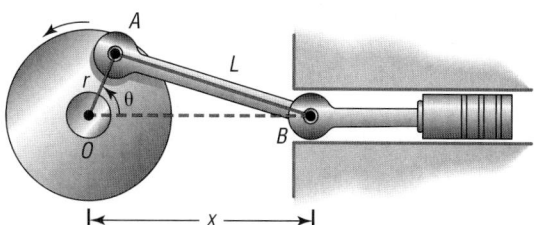

55. **Geometry**   Show that the length d of a chord of a circle of radius r is given by the formula

$$d = 2r \sin \frac{\theta}{2}$$

where θ is the central angle formed by the radii to the ends of the chord. See the figure. Use this result to derive the fact that $\sin \theta < \theta$, where $\theta > 0$ is measured in radians.

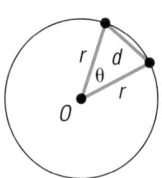

56. For any triangle, show that

$$\cos \frac{C}{2} = \sqrt{\frac{s(s - c)}{ab}}$$

where $s = \frac{1}{2}(a + b + c)$.

[**Hint:** Use a Half-angle Formula and the Law of Cosines.]

57. For any triangle show that

$$\sin \frac{C}{2} = \sqrt{\frac{(s - a)(s - b)}{ab}}$$

where $s = \frac{1}{2}(a + b + c)$.

58. Use the Law of Cosines to prove the identity

$$\frac{\cos A}{a} + \frac{\cos B}{b} + \frac{\cos C}{c} = \frac{a^2 + b^2 + c^2}{2abc}$$

Discussion and Writing

59. What do you do first if you are asked to solve a triangle and are given two sides and the included angle?

60. What do you do first if you are asked to solve a triangle and are given three sides?

61. Make up an applied problem that requires using the Law of Cosines.

62. Write down your strategy for solving an oblique triangle.

'Are You Prepared?' Answers

1. $d = \sqrt{(x_2 - x_1)^2 + (y_2 - y_1)^2}$ 2. $\theta = 45°$

8.4 Area of a Triangle

PREPARING FOR THIS SECTION   *Before getting started, review the following:*

- Geometry Essentials (Appendix A, Section A.2, pp. A15–A16)

Now Work the 'Are You Prepared?' problems on page 542.

OBJECTIVES   **1** Find the Area of SAS Triangles (p. 540)

                      2 Find the Area of SSS Triangles (p. 541)

In this section, we will derive several formulas for calculating the area of a triangle. The most familiar of these is the following:

THEOREM   The area K of a triangle is

$$K = \frac{1}{2}bh \qquad (1)$$

where b is the base and h is an altitude drawn to that base.

Proof   The derivation of this formula is rather easy once a rectangle of base b and height h is constructed around the triangle. See Figures 39 and 40.

    Triangles 1 and 2 in Figure 40 are equal in area, as are triangles 3 and 4. Consequently, the area of the triangle with base b and altitude h is exactly half the area of the rectangle, which is bh.

Figure 39

Figure 40

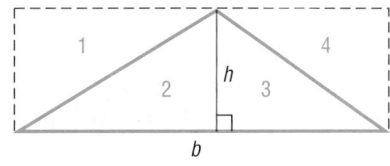

1 Find the Area of SAS Triangles

Figure 41

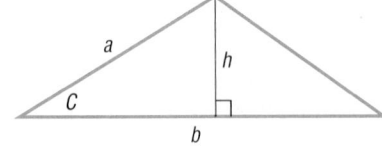

If the base b and altitude h to that base are known, then we can find the area of such a triangle using formula (1). Usually, though, the information required to use formula (1) is not given. Suppose, for example, that we know two sides a and b and the included angle C. See Figure 41. Then the altitude h can be found by noting that

$$\frac{h}{a} = \sin C$$

so that

$$h = a \sin C$$

Using this fact in formula (1) produces

$$K = \frac{1}{2}bh = \frac{1}{2}b(a \sin C) = \frac{1}{2}ab \sin C$$

We now have the formula

$$K = \frac{1}{2}ab \sin C \qquad (2)$$

By dropping altitudes from the other two vertices of the triangle, we obtain the following corresponding formulas:

$$K = \frac{1}{2}bc \sin A \qquad\qquad (3)$$

$$K = \frac{1}{2}ac \sin B \qquad\qquad (4)$$

It is easiest to remember these formulas using the following wording:

THEOREM

The area K of a triangle equals one-half the product of two of its sides times the sine of their included angle.

| EXAMPLE 1 | **Finding the Area of an SAS Triangle** |

Find the area K of the triangle for which $a = 8, b = 6$, and $C = 30°$.

Solution See Figure 42. We use formula (2) to get

$$K = \frac{1}{2}ab \sin C = \frac{1}{2} \cdot 8 \cdot 6 \cdot \sin 30° = 12 \text{ square units}$$

Figure 42

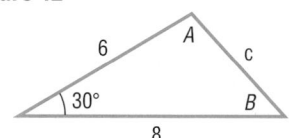

Now Work PROBLEM 5

2 Find the Area of SSS Triangles

If the three sides of a triangle are known, another formula, called **Heron's Formula** (named after Heron of Alexandria), can be used to find the area of a triangle.

THEOREM

Heron's Formula

The area K of a triangle with sides $a, b,$ and c is

$$K = \sqrt{s(s - a)(s - b)(s - c)} \qquad\qquad (5)$$

where $s = \frac{1}{2}(a + b + c)$.

A proof of Heron's Formula is given at the end of this section.

| EXAMPLE 2 | **Finding the Area of an SSS Triangle** |

Find the area of a triangle whose sides are 4, 5, and 7.

Solution We let $a = 4, b = 5,$ and $c = 7$. Then

$$s = \frac{1}{2}(a + b + c) = \frac{1}{2}(4 + 5 + 7) = 8$$

Heron's Formula then gives the area K as

$$K = \sqrt{s(s - a)(s - b)(s - c)} = \sqrt{8 \cdot 4 \cdot 3 \cdot 1} = \sqrt{96} = 4\sqrt{6} \text{ square units}$$

Now Work PROBLEM 11

Proof of Heron's Formula The proof that we shall give uses the Law of Cosines and is quite different from the proof given by Heron.

From the Law of Cosines,

$$c^2 = a^2 + b^2 - 2ab \cos C$$

and the Half-angle Formula

$$\cos^2 \frac{C}{2} = \frac{1 + \cos C}{2}$$

we find that

$$\cos^2 \frac{C}{2} = \frac{1 + \cos C}{2} = \frac{1 + \dfrac{a^2 + b^2 - c^2}{2ab}}{2}$$

$$= \frac{a^2 + 2ab + b^2 - c^2}{4ab} = \frac{(a+b)^2 - c^2}{4ab}$$

$$= \underset{\underset{\text{Factor}}{\uparrow}}{\frac{(a + b - c)(a + b + c)}{4ab}} = \underset{\underset{\substack{a+b-c=a+b+c-2c \\ =2s-2c=2(s-c)}}{\uparrow}}{\frac{2(s - c) \cdot 2s}{4ab}} = \frac{s(s - c)}{ab} \qquad \textbf{(6)}$$

Similarly, using $\sin^2 \dfrac{C}{2} = \dfrac{1 - \cos C}{2}$, we find that

$$\sin^2 \frac{C}{2} = \frac{(s - a)(s - b)}{ab} \qquad \textbf{(7)}$$

Now we use formula (2) for the area.

$$K = \frac{1}{2} ab \sin C$$

$$= \frac{1}{2} ab \cdot 2 \sin \frac{C}{2} \cos \frac{C}{2} \qquad \sin C = \sin\left[2\left(\frac{C}{2}\right)\right] = 2 \sin \frac{C}{2} \cos \frac{C}{2}$$

$$= ab \sqrt{\frac{(s - a)(s - b)}{ab}} \sqrt{\frac{s(s - c)}{ab}} \qquad \text{Use equations (6) and (7).}$$

$$= \sqrt{s(s - a)(s - b)(s - c)} \qquad \blacksquare$$

Historical Feature

Heron's Formula (also known as *Hero's Formula*) is due to Heron of Alexandria (first century AD), who had, besides his mathematical talents, a good deal of engineering skills. In various temples his mechanical devices produced effects that seemed supernatural, and visitors presumably were thus influenced to generosity. Heron's book *Metrica*, on making such devices, has survived and was discovered in 1896 in the city of Constantinople.

Heron's Formulas for the area of a triangle caused some mild discomfort in Greek mathematics, because a product with two factors was an area, while one with three factors was a volume, but four factors seemed contradictory in Heron's time.

8.4 Assess Your Understanding

'Are You Prepared?' *Answer is given at the end of these exercises. If you get the wrong answer, read the page listed in red.*

1. The area of a triangle whose base is b and whose height is h is _____ (p. A15)

Concepts and Vocabulary

2. If three sides of a triangle are given, _____ Formula is used to find the area of the triangle.

3. *True or False* No formula exists for finding the area of a triangle when only three sides are given.

4. *True or False* Given two sides and the included angle, there is a formula that can be used to find the area of the triangle.

Skill Building

In Problems 5–12, find the area of each triangle. Round answers to two decimal places.

5.

6.

7.

8.

9.

10.

11.

12.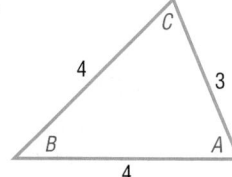

In Problems 13–24, find the area of each triangle. Round answers to two decimal places.

13. $a = 3$, $b = 4$, $C = 40°$

14. $a = 2$, $c = 1$, $B = 10°$

15. $b = 1$, $c = 3$, $A = 80°$

16. $a = 6$, $b = 4$, $C = 60°$

17. $a = 3$, $c = 2$, $B = 110°$

18. $b = 4$, $c = 1$, $A = 120°$

19. $a = 12$, $b = 13$, $c = 5$

20. $a = 4$, $b = 5$, $c = 3$

21. $a = 2$, $b = 2$, $c = 2$

22. $a = 3$, $b = 3$, $c = 2$

23. $a = 5$, $b = 8$, $c = 9$

24. $a = 4$, $b = 3$, $c = 6$

Applications and Extensions

25. Area of an ASA Triangle If two angles and the included side are given, the third angle is easy to find. Use the Law of Sines to show that the area K of a triangle with side a and angles A, B, and C is

$$K = \frac{a^2 \sin B \sin C}{2 \sin A}$$

26. Area of a Triangle Prove the two other forms of the formula given in Problem 25.

$$K = \frac{b^2 \sin A \sin C}{2 \sin B} \quad \text{and} \quad K = \frac{c^2 \sin A \sin B}{2 \sin C}$$

In Problems 27–32, use the results of Problem 25 or 26 to find the area of each triangle. Round answers to two decimal places.

27. $A = 40°$, $B = 20°$, $a = 2$

28. $A = 50°$, $C = 20°$, $a = 3$

29. $B = 70°$, $C = 10°$, $b = 5$

30. $A = 70°$, $B = 60°$, $c = 4$

31. $A = 110°$, $C = 30°$, $c = 3$

32. $B = 10°$, $C = 100°$, $b = 2$

33. Area of a Segment Find the area of the segment (shaded in blue in the figure) of a circle whose radius is 8 feet, formed by a central angle of 70°.

[**Hint:** Subtract the area of the triangle from the area of the sector to obtain the area of the segment.]

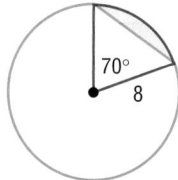

34. Area of a Segment Find the area of the segment of a circle whose radius is 5 inches, formed by a central angle of 40°.

35. Cost of a Triangular Lot The dimensions of a triangular lot are 100 feet by 50 feet by 75 feet. If the price of such land is $3 per square foot, how much does the lot cost?

36. Amount of Material to Make a Tent A cone-shaped tent is made from a circular piece of canvas 24 feet in diameter by removing a sector with central angle 100° and connecting the ends. What is the surface area of the tent?

37. Dimensions of Home Plate The dimensions of home plate at any major league baseball stadium are shown. Find the area of home plate.

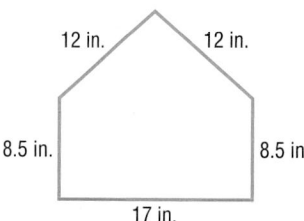

38. Computing Areas Find the area of the shaded region enclosed in a semicircle of diameter 10 inches. The length of the chord PQ is 8 inches.

[**Hint:** Triangle PQR is a right triangle.]

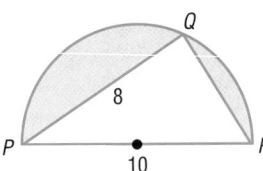

39. Geometry Consult the figure, which shows a circle of radius r with center at O. Find the area K of the shaded region as a function of the central angle θ.

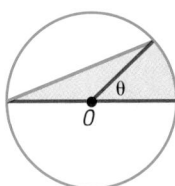

40. Approximating the Area of a Lake To approximate the area of a lake, a surveyor walks around the perimeter of the lake, taking the measurements shown in the illustration. Using this technique, what is the approximate area of the lake?

[**Hint:** Use the Law of Cosines on the three triangles shown and then find the sum of their areas.]

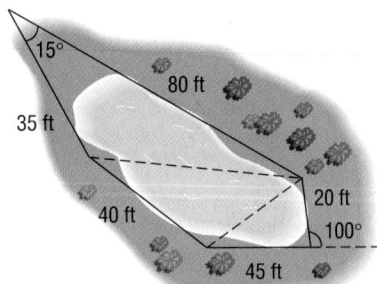

41. The Flatiron Building Completed in 1902 in New York City, the Flatiron Building is triangular shaped and bounded by 22nd Street, Broadway, and 5th Avenue. The building measures approximately 87 feet on the 22nd Street side, 190 feet on the Broadway side, and 173 feet on the 5th Avenue side. Approximate the ground area covered by the building.

Source: Sarah Bradford Landau and Carl W. Condit, *Rise of the New York Skyscraper: 1865–1913.* New Haven, CT: Yale University Press, 1996

42. Bermuda Triangle The Bermuda Triangle is roughly defined by Hamilton, Bermuda; San Juan, Puerto Rico; and Fort Lauderdale, Florida. The distances from Hamilton to Fort Lauderdale, Fort Lauderdale to San Juan, and San Juan to Hamilton are approximately 1028, 1046, and 965 miles respectively. Ignoring the curvature of Earth, approximate the area of the Bermuda Triangle.

Source: www.worldatlas.com

43. Geometry Refer to the figure. If $|OA| = 1$, show that:

(a) Area $\triangle OAC = \dfrac{1}{2}\sin\alpha\cos\alpha$

(b) Area $\triangle OCB = \dfrac{1}{2}|OB|^2\sin\beta\cos\beta$

(c) Area $\triangle OAB = \dfrac{1}{2}|OB|\sin(\alpha + \beta)$

(d) $|OB| = \dfrac{\cos\alpha}{\cos\beta}$

(e) $\sin(\alpha + \beta) = \sin\alpha\cos\beta + \cos\alpha\sin\beta$

[**Hint:** Area $\triangle OAB$ = Area $\triangle OAC$ + Area $\triangle OCB$.]

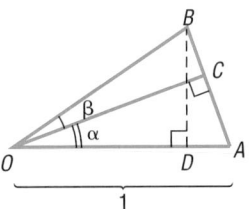

44. Geometry Refer to the figure, in which a unit circle is drawn. The line segment DB is tangent to the circle and θ is acute.

(a) Express the area of $\triangle OBC$ in terms of $\sin\theta$ and $\cos\theta$.
(b) Express the area of $\triangle OBD$ in terms of $\sin\theta$ and $\cos\theta$.
(c) The area of the sector $\overset{\frown}{OBC}$ of the circle is $\dfrac{1}{2}\theta$, where θ is measured in radians. Use the results of parts (a) and (b) and the fact that

$$\text{Area }\triangle OBC < \text{Area }\overset{\frown}{OBC} < \text{Area }\triangle OBD$$

to show that

$$1 < \frac{\theta}{\sin\theta} < \frac{1}{\cos\theta}$$

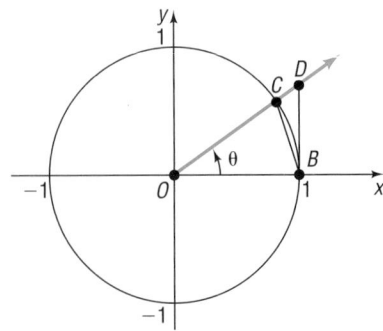

45. The Cow Problem* A cow is tethered to one corner of a square barn, 10 feet by 10 feet, with a rope 100 feet long. What is the maximum grazing area for the cow?

[**Hint:** See the illustration on page 545.]

*Suggested by Professor Teddy Koukounas of Suffolk Community College, who learned of it from an old farmer in Virginia. Solution provided by Professor Kathleen Miranda of SUNY at Old Westbury.

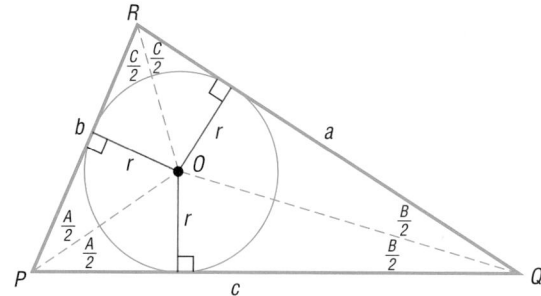

Rope

Barn

10 A_3 A_2

10

A_1

46. Another Cow Problem   If the barn in Problem 45 is rectangular, 10 feet by 20 feet, what is the maximum grazing area for the cow?

47. Perfect Triangles   A *perfect triangle* is one having natural number sides for which the area is numerically equal to the perimeter. Show that the triangles with the given side lengths are perfect.
(a) 9, 10, 17   (b) 6, 25, 29

Source: M.V. Bonsangue, G. E. Gannon, E. Buchman, and N. Gross, "In Search of Perfect Triangles," *Mathematics Teacher,* Vol. 92, No. 1, 1999: 56–61

48. If h_1, h_2, and h_3 are the altitudes dropped from P, Q, and R, respectively, in a triangle (see the figure), show that

$$\frac{1}{h_1} + \frac{1}{h_2} + \frac{1}{h_3} = \frac{s}{K}$$

where K is the area of the triangle and $s = \frac{1}{2}(a + b + c)$.

[Hint: $h_1 = \dfrac{2K}{a}$.**]**

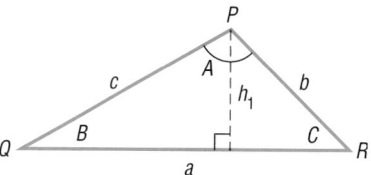

49. Show that a formula for the altitude h from a vertex to the opposite side a of a triangle is

$$h = \frac{a \sin B \sin C}{\sin A}$$

Inscribed Circle   *For Problems 50–53, the lines that bisect each angle of a triangle meet in a single point O, and the perpendicular distance r from O to each side of the triangle is the same. The circle with center at O and radius r is called the **inscribed circle** of the triangle (see the figure).*

R

$\frac{C}{2}$ $\frac{C}{2}$

b r a

r O

r

$\frac{A}{2}$

$\frac{A}{2}$ $\frac{B}{2}$

P c Q $\frac{B}{2}$

50. Apply the formula from Problem 49 to triangle OPQ to show that

$$r = \frac{c \sin \dfrac{A}{2} \sin \dfrac{B}{2}}{\cos \dfrac{C}{2}}$$

51. Use the result of Problem 50 and the result of Problems 56 and 57 in Section 8.3 to show that

$$\cot \frac{C}{2} = \frac{s - c}{r}$$

where $s = \frac{1}{2}(a + b + c)$.

52. Show that

$$\cot \frac{A}{2} + \cot \frac{B}{2} + \cot \frac{C}{2} = \frac{s}{r}$$

53. Show that the area K of triangle PQR is $K = rs$, where $s = \frac{1}{2}(a + b + c)$. Then show that

$$r = \sqrt{\frac{(s - a)(s - b)(s - c)}{s}}$$

Discussion and Writing

54. What do you do first if you are asked to find the area of a triangle and are given two sides and the included angle?

55. What do you do first if you are asked to find the area of a triangle and are given three sides?

'Are You Prepared?' Answer

1. $K = \frac{1}{2}bh$

8.5 Simple Harmonic Motion; Damped Motion; Combining Waves

PREPARING FOR THIS SECTION *Before getting started, review the following:*

• Sinusoidal Graphs (Section 6.4, pp. 399–406)

Now Work the 'Are You Prepared?' problem on page 552.

OBJECTIVES 1 Build a Model for an Object in Simple Harmonic Motion (p. 546)
2 Analyze Simple Harmonic Motion (p. 548)
3 Analyze an Object in Damped Motion (p. 549)
4 Graph the Sum of Two Functions (p. 550)

1 Build a Model for an Object in Simple Harmonic Motion

Many physical phenomena can be described as simple harmonic motion. Radio and television waves, light waves, sound waves, and water waves exhibit motion that is simple harmonic.

The swinging of a pendulum, the vibrations of a tuning fork, and the bobbing of a weight attached to a coiled spring are examples of vibrational motion. In this type of motion, an object swings back and forth over the same path. In Figure 43, the point *B* is the **equilibrium (rest) position** of the vibrating object. The **amplitude** is the distance from the object's rest position to its point of greatest displacement (either point *A* or point *C* in Figure 43). The **period** is the time required to complete one vibration, that is, the time it takes to go from, say, point *A* through *B* to *C* and back to *A*.

Vibrating tuning fork

Simple harmonic motion is a special kind of vibrational motion in which the acceleration *a* of the object is directly proportional to the negative of its displacement *d* from its rest position. That is, $a = -kd$, $k > 0$.

For example, when the mass hanging from the spring in Figure 43 is pulled down from its rest position *B* to the point *C*, the force of the spring tries to restore the mass to its rest position. Assuming that there is no frictional force* to retard the motion, the amplitude will remain constant. The force increases in direct proportion to the distance that the mass is pulled from its rest position. Since the force increases directly, the acceleration of the mass of the object must do likewise, because (by Newton's Second Law of Motion) force is directly proportional to acceleration. As a result, the acceleration of the object varies directly with its displacement, and the motion is an example of simple harmonic motion.

Simple harmonic motion is related to circular motion. To see this relationship, consider a circle of radius *a*, with center at $(0, 0)$. See Figure 44. Suppose that an

Figure 43

Coiled spring

Figure 44

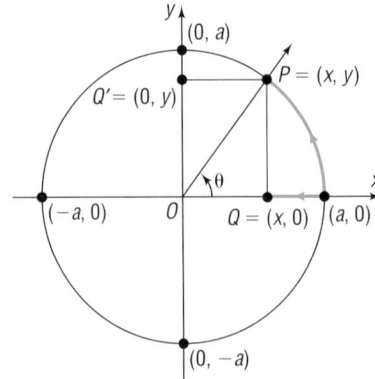

*If friction is present, the amplitude will decrease with time to 0. This type of motion is an example of **damped motion**, which is discussed later in this section.

object initially placed at $(a, 0)$ moves counterclockwise around the circle at a constant angular speed ω. Suppose further that after time t has elapsed the object is at the point $P = (x, y)$ on the circle. The angle θ, in radians, swept out by the ray $\overrightarrow{OP}$ in this time t is

$$\theta = \omega t$$

The coordinates of the point P at time t are

$$x = a \cos \theta = a \cos(\omega t)$$
$$y = a \sin \theta = a \sin(\omega t)$$

Corresponding to each position $P = (x, y)$ of the object moving about the circle, there is the point $Q = (x, 0)$, called the **projection of P on the x-axis.** As P moves around the circle at a constant rate, the point Q moves back and forth between the points $(a, 0)$ and $(-a, 0)$ along the x-axis with a motion that is simple harmonic. Similarly, for each point P there is a point $Q' = (0, y)$, called the **projection of P on the y-axis.** As P moves around the circle, the point Q' moves back and forth between the points $(0, a)$ and $(0, -a)$ on the y-axis with a motion that is simple harmonic. Simple harmonic motion can be described as the projection of constant circular motion on a coordinate axis.

To put it another way, again consider a mass hanging from a spring where the mass is pulled down from its rest position to the point C and then released. See Figure 45(a). The graph shown in Figure 45(b) describes the displacement d of the object from its rest position as a function of time t, assuming that no frictional force is present.

Figure 45

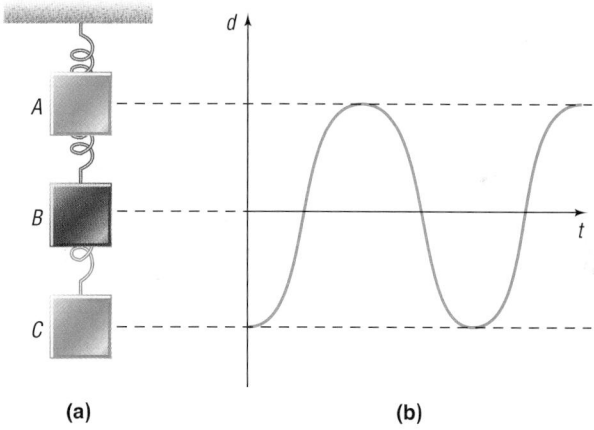

(a)   (b)

THEOREM

Simple Harmonic Motion

An object that moves on a coordinate axis so that the distance d from its rest position at time t is given by either

$$d = a \cos(\omega t) \quad \text{or} \quad d = a \sin(\omega t)$$

where a and $\omega > 0$ are constants, moves with simple harmonic motion. The motion has amplitude $|a|$ and period $\dfrac{2\pi}{\omega}$.

The **frequency** f of an object in simple harmonic motion is the number of oscillations per unit time. Since the period is the time required for one oscillation, it follows that the frequency is the reciprocal of the period; that is,

$$f = \frac{\omega}{2\pi} \qquad \omega > 0$$

EXAMPLE 1   **Build a Model for an Object in Harmonic Motion**

Figure 46

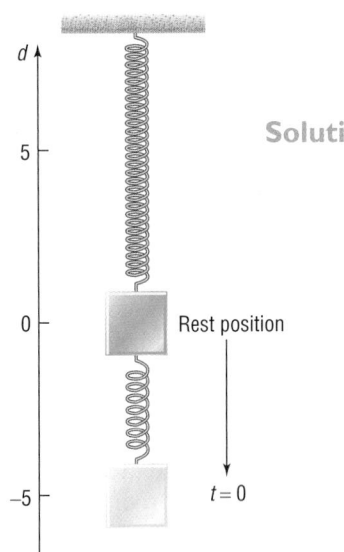

Suppose that an object attached to a coiled spring is pulled down a distance of 5 inches from its rest position and then released. If the time for one oscillation is 3 seconds, develop a model that relates the displacement d of the object from its rest position after time t (in seconds). Assume no friction.

Solution   The motion of the object is simple harmonic. See Figure 46. When the object is released ($t = 0$), the displacement of the object from the rest position is -5 units (since the object was pulled down). Because $d = -5$ when $t = 0$, it is easier to use the cosine function*

$$d = a \cos(\omega t)$$

to describe the motion. Now the amplitude is $|-5| = 5$ and the period is 3, so

$$a = -5 \quad \text{and} \quad \frac{2\pi}{\omega} = \text{period} = 3, \quad \omega = \frac{2\pi}{3}$$

An equation that models the motion of the object is

$$d = -5 \cos\left[\frac{2\pi}{3} t\right]$$

NOTE In the solution to Example 1, we let $a = -5$, since the initial motion is down. If the initial direction were up, we would let $a = 5$.   ∎

━━━━━ **Now Work** PROBLEM 5

2 Analyze Simple Harmonic Motion

EXAMPLE 2   **Analyzing the Motion of an Object**

Suppose that the displacement d (in meters) of an object at time t (in seconds) satisfies the equation

$$d = 10 \sin(5t)$$

(a) Describe the motion of the object.
(b) What is the maximum displacement from its resting position?
(c) What is the time required for one oscillation?
(d) What is the frequency?

Solution   We observe that the given equation is of the form

$$d = a \sin(\omega t) \quad d = 10 \sin(5t)$$

where $a = 10$ and $\omega = 5$.

(a) The motion is simple harmonic.
(b) The maximum displacement of the object from its resting position is the amplitude: $|a| = 10$ meters.
(c) The time required for one oscillation is the period:

$$\text{Period} = \frac{2\pi}{\omega} = \frac{2\pi}{5} \text{ seconds}$$

(d) The frequency is the reciprocal of the period. Thus,

$$\text{Frequency} = f = \frac{5}{2\pi} \text{ oscillations per second}$$

━━━━━ **Now Work** PROBLEM 13

*No phase shift is required if a cosine function is used.

3 Analyze an Object in Damped Motion

Most physical phenomena are affected by friction or other resistive forces. These forces remove energy from a moving system and thereby damp its motion. For example, when a mass hanging from a spring is pulled down a distance a and released, the friction in the spring causes the distance that the mass moves from its at-rest position to decrease over time. As a result, the amplitude of any real oscillating spring or swinging pendulum decreases with time due to air resistance, friction, and so forth. See Figure 47.

Figure 47

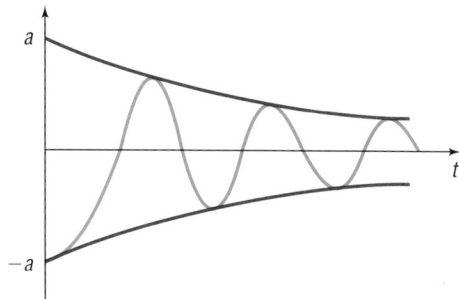

A model that describes this phenomenon maintains a sinusoidal component, but the amplitude of this component will decrease with time to account for the damping effect. In addition, the period of the oscillating component will be affected by the damping. The next result, from physics, describes damped motion.

THEOREM **Damped Motion**

The displacement d of an oscillating object from its at-rest position at time t is given by

$$d(t) = ae^{-bt/(2m)} \cos\left(\sqrt{\omega^2 - \frac{b^2}{4m^2}}\, t \right)$$

where b is the **damping factor** or **damping coefficient** and m is the mass of the oscillating object. Here $|a|$ is the displacement at $t = 0$, and $\dfrac{2\pi}{\omega}$ is the period under simple harmonic motion (no damping).

Notice for $b = 0$ (zero damping) that we have the formula for simple harmonic motion with amplitude $|a|$ and period $\dfrac{2\pi}{\omega}$.

EXAMPLE 3 Analyzing the Motion of a Pendulum with Damped Motion

Figure 48

20 cm

Rest position

Suppose that a simple pendulum with a bob of mass 10 grams and a damping factor of 0.8 gram/second is pulled 20 centimeters from its at-rest position and released. See Figure 48. The period of the pendulum without the damping effect is 4 seconds.

(a) Develop a model that describes the position of the pendulum bob.

(b) Using a graphing utility, graph the function found in part (a).

(c) What is the displacement of the bob at the start of the second oscillation?

(d) What happens to the displacement of the bob as time increases without bound?

Solution (a) We have $m = 10$, $a = 20$, and $b = 0.8$. Since the period of the pendulum under simple harmonic motion is 4 seconds, we have

$$4 = \frac{2\pi}{\omega}$$

$$\omega = \frac{2\pi}{4} = \frac{\pi}{2}$$

Figure 49

Figure 50

Substituting these values into the equation for damped motion, we obtain

$$d(t) = 20e^{-0.8t/2(10)} \cos\left(\sqrt{\left(\frac{\pi}{2}\right)^2 - \frac{0.8^2}{4(10)^2}}\, t\right)$$

$$= 20e^{-0.8t/20} \cos\left(\sqrt{\frac{\pi^2}{4} - \frac{0.64}{400}}\, t\right)$$

(b) See Figure 49 for the graph of $d = d(t)$.

(c) See Figure 50. At the start of the second oscillation the displacement is approximately 17.05 centimeters.

(d) As t increases without bound, $e^{-0.8t/20} \rightarrow 0$, so the displacement of the bob approaches zero. As a result, the pendulum will eventually come to rest.

━━━━ **Now Work** PROBLEM 21

4 Graph the Sum of Two Functions

Many physical and biological applications require the graph of the sum of two functions, such as

$$f(x) = x + \sin x \quad \text{or} \quad g(x) = \sin x + \cos(2x)$$

For example, if two tones are emitted, the sound produced is the sum of the waves produced by the two tones. See Problem 47 for an explanation of Touch-Tone phones.

To graph the sum of two (or more) functions, we can use the method of adding y-coordinates described next.

EXAMPLE 4

Graphing the Sum of Two Functions

Use the method of adding y-coordinates to graph $f(x) = x + \sin x$.

Solution

First, we graph the component functions,

$$y = f_1(x) = x \qquad y = f_2(x) = \sin x$$

in the same coordinate system. See Figure 51(a). Now, select several values of x, say, $x = 0$, $x = \dfrac{\pi}{2}$, $x = \pi$, $x = \dfrac{3\pi}{2}$, and $x = 2\pi$, at which we compute $f(x) = f_1(x) + f_2(x)$. Table 1 shows the computation. We plot these points and connect them to get the graph, as shown in Figure 51(b).

Table 1

x	0	$\dfrac{\pi}{2}$	π	$\dfrac{3\pi}{2}$	2π
$y = f_1(x) = x$	0	$\dfrac{\pi}{2}$	π	$\dfrac{3\pi}{2}$	2π
$y = f_2(x) = \sin x$	0	1	0	-1	0
$f(x) = x + \sin x$	0	$\dfrac{\pi}{2} + 1 \approx 2.57$	π	$\dfrac{3\pi}{2} - 1 \approx 3.71$	2π
Point on graph of f	$(0, 0)$	$\left(\dfrac{\pi}{2}, 2.57\right)$	(π, π)	$\left(\dfrac{3\pi}{2}, 3.71\right)$	$(2\pi, 2\pi)$

Figure 51

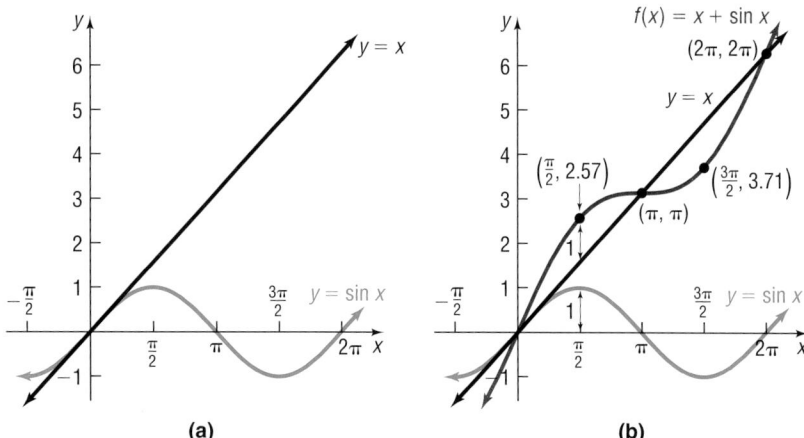

(a)   (b)

In Figure 51(b), notice that the graph of $f(x) = x + \sin x$ intersects the line $y = x$ whenever $\sin x = 0$. Also, notice that the graph of f is not periodic.

✓ **Check:** Graph $Y_1 = x$, $Y_2 = \sin x$, and $Y_3 = x + \sin x$ and compare the result with Figure 51(b). Use INTERSECT to verify that the graphs of Y_1 and Y_3 intersect when $\sin x = 0$.

The next example shows a periodic graph.

EXAMPLE 5

Graphing the Sum of Two Sinusoidal Functions

Use the method of adding y-coordinates to graph

$$f(x) = \sin x + \cos(2x)$$

Solution Table 2 shows the steps for computing several points on the graph of f. Figure 52 illustrates the graphs of the component functions, $y = f_1(x) = \sin x$ and $y = f_2(x) = \cos(2x)$, and the graph of $f(x) = \sin x + \cos(2x)$, which is shown in red.

Table 2

x	$-\dfrac{\pi}{2}$	0	$\dfrac{\pi}{2}$	π	$\dfrac{3\pi}{2}$	2π
$y = f_1(x) = \sin x$	-1	0	1	0	-1	0
$y = f_2(x) = \cos(2x)$	-1	1	-1	1	-1	1
$f(x) = \sin x + \cos(2x)$	-2	1	0	1	-2	1
Point on graph of f	$\left(-\dfrac{\pi}{2}, -2\right)$	$(0, 1)$	$\left(\dfrac{\pi}{2}, 0\right)$	$(\pi, 1)$	$\left(\dfrac{3\pi}{2}, -2\right)$	$(2\pi, 1)$

Figure 52

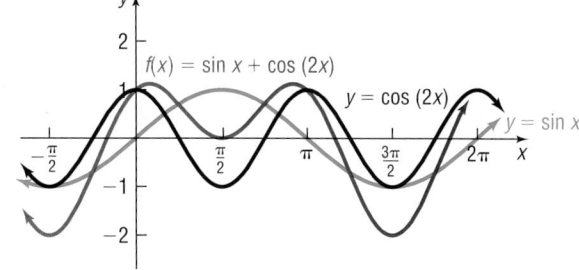

Notice that f is periodic, with period 2π.

✓ **Check:** Graph $Y_1 = \sin x$, $Y_2 = \cos(2x)$, and $Y_3 = \sin x + \cos(2x)$ and compare the result with Figure 52.

Now Work PROBLEM 33

8.5 Assess Your Understanding

'Are You Prepared?' *Answer given at the end of these exercises. If you get a wrong answer, read the pages listed in red.*

1. The amplitude A and period T of $f(x) = 5\sin(4x)$ are _____ and _____. (pp. 400–401)

Concepts and Vocabulary

2. The motion of an object obeys the equation $d = 4\cos(6t)$. Such motion is described as _____ _____. The number 4 is called the _____.

3. When a mass hanging from a spring is pulled down and then released, the motion is called _____ _____ if there is no

frictional force to retard the motion, and the motion is called _____ if there is friction.

4. **True or False** If the distance d of an object from its rest position at time t is given by a sinusoidal graph, the motion of the object is simple harmonic motion.

Skill Building

In Problems 5–8, an object attached to a coiled spring is pulled down a distance a from its rest position and then released. Assuming that the motion is simple harmonic with period T, develop a model that relates the displacement d of the object from its rest position after t seconds. Also assume that the positive direction of the motion is up.

5. $a = 5$; $T = 2$ seconds

6. $a = 10$; $T = 3$ seconds

7. $a = 6$; $T = \pi$ seconds

8. $a = 4$; $T = \dfrac{\pi}{2}$ seconds

9. Rework Problem 5 under the same conditions except that, at time $t = 0$, the object is at its resting position and moving down.

10. Rework Problem 6 under the same conditions except that, at time $t = 0$, the object is at its resting position and moving down.

11. Rework Problem 7 under the same conditions except that, at time $t = 0$, the object is at its resting position and moving down.

12. Rework Problem 8 under the same conditions except that, at time $t = 0$, the object is at its resting position and moving down.

In Problems 13–20, the displacement d (in meters) of an object at time t (in seconds) is given.
   (a) Describe the motion of the object.
   (b) What is the maximum displacement from its resting position?
   (c) What is the time required for one oscillation?
   (d) What is the frequency?

13. $d = 5\sin(3t)$

14. $d = 4\sin(2t)$

15. $d = 6\cos(\pi t)$

16. $d = 5\cos\left(\dfrac{\pi}{2}t\right)$

17. $d = -3\sin\left(\dfrac{1}{2}t\right)$

18. $d = -2\cos(2t)$

19. $d = 6 + 2\cos(2\pi t)$

20. $d = 4 + 3\sin(\pi t)$

In Problems 21–26, an object of mass m (in grams) attached to a coiled spring with damping factor b (in grams per second) is pulled down a distance a (in centimeters) from its rest position and then released. Assume that the positive direction of the motion is up and the period is T (in seconds) under simple harmonic motion.
   (a) Develop a model that relates the distance d of the object from its rest position after t seconds.
   (b) Graph the equation found in part (a) for 5 oscillations using a graphing utility.

21. $m = 25$, $a = 10$, $b = 0.7$, $T = 5$

22. $m = 20$, $a = 15$, $b = 0.75$, $T = 6$

23. $m = 30$, $a = 18$, $b = 0.6$, $T = 4$

24. $m = 15$, $a = 16$, $b = 0.65$, $T = 5$

25. $m = 10$, $a = 5$, $b = 0.8$, $T = 3$

26. $m = 10$, $a = 5$, $b = 0.7$, $T = 3$

In Problems 27–32, the distance d (in meters) of the bob of a pendulum of mass m (in kilograms) from its rest position at time t (in seconds) is given. The bob is released from the left of its rest position, which represents a negative direction.
   (a) Describe the motion of the object. Be sure to give the mass and damping factor.
   (b) What is the initial displacement of the bob? That is, what is the displacement at t = 0?
   (c) Graph the motion using a graphing utility.
   (d) What is the displacement of the bob at the start of the second oscillation?
   (e) What happens to the displacement of the bob as time increases without bound?

27. $d = -20e^{-0.7t/40}\cos\left(\sqrt{\left(\dfrac{2\pi}{5}\right)^2 - \dfrac{0.49}{1600}}\,t\right)$

28. $d = -20e^{-0.8t/40}\cos\left(\sqrt{\left(\dfrac{2\pi}{5}\right)^2 - \dfrac{0.64}{1600}}\,t\right)$

29. $d = -30e^{-0.6t/80}\cos\left(\sqrt{\left(\dfrac{2\pi}{7}\right)^2 - \dfrac{0.36}{6400}}\,t\right)$

30. $d = -30e^{-0.5t/70}\cos\left(\sqrt{\left(\dfrac{\pi}{2}\right)^2 - \dfrac{0.25}{4900}}\,t\right)$

31. $d = -15e^{-0.9t/30}\cos\left(\sqrt{\left(\dfrac{\pi}{3}\right)^2 - \dfrac{0.81}{900}}\,t\right)$

32. $d = -10e^{-0.8t/50}\cos\left(\sqrt{\left(\dfrac{2\pi}{3}\right)^2 - \dfrac{0.64}{2500}}\,t\right)$

In Problems 33–40, use the method of adding y-coordinates to graph each function.

33. $f(x) = x + \cos x$

34. $f(x) = x + \cos(2x)$

35. $f(x) = x - \sin x$

36. $f(x) = x - \cos x$

37. $f(x) = \sin x + \cos x$

38. $f(x) = \sin(2x) + \cos x$

39. $g(x) = \sin x + \sin(2x)$

40. $g(x) = \cos(2x) + \cos x$

Applications and Extensions

41. Loudspeaker A loudspeaker diaphragm is oscillating in simple harmonic motion described by the equation $d = a \cos(\omega t)$ with a frequency of 520 hertz (cycles per second) and a maximum displacement of 0.80 millimeter. Find ω and then determine a model that describes the movement of the diaphragm.

42. Colossus Added to Six Flags St. Louis in 1986, the Colossus is a giant Ferris wheel. Its diameter is 165 feet, it rotates at a rate of about 1.6 revolutions per minute, and the bottom of the wheel is 15 feet above the ground. Determine a model that relates a rider's height above the ground at time t. Assume the passenger begins the ride at the bottom of the wheel.

Source: Six Flags Theme Parks, Inc.

43. Tuning Fork The end of a tuning fork moves in simple harmonic motion described by the equation $d = a \sin(\omega t)$. If a tuning fork for the note A above middle C on an even-tempered scale (A_4, the tone by which an orchestra tunes itself) has a frequency of 440 hertz (cycles per second), find ω. If the maximum displacement of the end of the tuning fork is 0.01 millimeter, determine a model that describes the movement of the tuning fork.

Source: David Lapp. Physics of Music and Musical Instruments. Medford, MA: Tufts University, 2003

44. Tuning Fork The end of a tuning fork moves in simple harmonic motion described by the equation $d = a \sin(\omega t)$. If a tuning fork for the note E above middle C on an even-tempered scale (E_4) has a frequency of approximately 329.63 hertz (cycles per second), find ω. If the maximum displacement of the end of the tuning fork is 0.025 millimeter, determine a model that describes the movement of the tuning fork.

Source: David Lapp. Physics of Music and Musical Instruments. Medford, MA: Tufts University, 2003

45. Charging a Capacitor If a charged capacitor is connected to a coil by closing a switch, energy is transferred to the coil and then back to the capacitor in an oscillatory motion. See the illustration. The voltage V (in volts) across the capacitor will gradually diminish to 0 with time t (in seconds).

(a) Graph the function relating V and t:
$$V(t) = e^{-t/3} \cos(\pi t), \quad 0 \le t \le 3$$

(b) At what times t will the graph of V touch the graph of $y = e^{-t/3}$? When does the graph of V touch the graph of $y = -e^{-t/3}$?

(c) When will the voltage V be between -0.4 and 0.4 volt?

46. The Sawtooth Curve An oscilloscope often displays a *sawtooth curve*. This curve can be approximated by sinusoidal curves of varying periods and amplitudes.

(a) Use a graphing utility to graph the following function, which can be used to approximate the sawtooth curve.
$$f(x) = \frac{1}{2}\sin(2\pi x) + \frac{1}{4}\sin(4\pi x), \quad 0 \le x \le 4$$

(b) A better approximation to the sawtooth curve is given by
$$f(x) = \frac{1}{2}\sin(2\pi x) + \frac{1}{4}\sin(4\pi x) + \frac{1}{8}\sin(8\pi x)$$

Use a graphing utility to graph this function for $0 \le x \le 4$ and compare the result to the graph obtained in part (a).

(c) A third and even better approximation to the sawtooth curve is given by
$$f(x) = \frac{1}{2}\sin(2\pi x) + \frac{1}{4}\sin(4\pi x) + \frac{1}{8}\sin(8\pi x) + \frac{1}{16}\sin(16\pi x)$$

Use a graphing utility to graph this function for $0 \le x \le 4$ and compare the result to the graphs obtained in parts (a) and (b).

(d) What do you think the next approximation to the sawtooth curve is?

47. Touch-Tone Phones On a Touch-Tone phone, each button produces a unique sound. The sound produced is the sum of two tones, given by
$$y = \sin(2\pi l t) \quad \text{and} \quad y = \sin(2\pi h t)$$

where l and h are the low and high frequencies (cycles per second) shown in the illustration. For example, if you touch 7, the low frequency is $l = 852$ cycles per second and the high frequency is $h = 1209$ cycles per second. The sound emitted by touching 7 is
$$y = \sin[2\pi(852)t] + \sin[2\pi(1209)t]$$

Use a graphing utility to graph the sound emitted by touching 7.

Touch-Tone phone

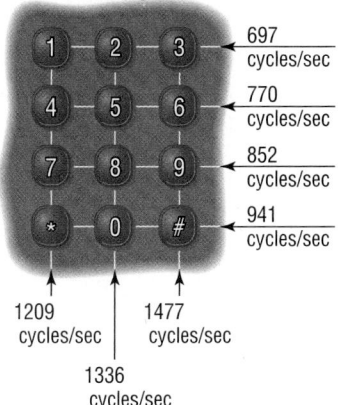

48. Use a graphing utility to graph the sound emitted by the * key on a Touch-Tone phone. See Problem 47.

49. CBL Experiment Pendulum motion is analyzed to estimate simple harmonic motion. A plot is generated with the position of the pendulum over time. The graph is used to find a sinusoidal curve of the form $y = A \cos[B(x - C)] + D$. Determine the amplitude, period, and frequency. (Activity 16, Real-World Math with the CBL System.)

50. CBL Experiment The sound from a tuning fork is collected over time. Determine the amplitude, frequency, and period of the graph. A model of the form $y = A \cos[B(x - C)]$ is fitted to the data. (Activity 23, Real-World Math with the CBL System.)

Discussion and Writing

51. Use a graphing utility to graph the function $f(x) = \dfrac{\sin x}{x}$, $x > 0$. Based on the graph, what do you conjecture about the value of $\dfrac{\sin x}{x}$ for x close to 0?

52. Use a graphing utility to graph $y = x \sin x$, $y = x^2 \sin x$, and $y = x^3 \sin x$ for $x > 0$. What patterns do you observe?

53. Use a graphing utility to graph $y = \dfrac{1}{x} \sin x$, $y = \dfrac{1}{x^2} \sin x$, and $y = \dfrac{1}{x^3} \sin x$ for $x > 0$. What patterns do you observe?

54. How would you explain to a friend what simple harmonic motion is? How would you explain damped motion?

'Are You Prepared?' Answer

1. $A = 5; T = \dfrac{\pi}{2}$

CHAPTER REVIEW

Things to Know

Formulas

Law of Sines (p. 523)	$\dfrac{\sin A}{a} = \dfrac{\sin B}{b} = \dfrac{\sin C}{c}$
Law of Cosines (p. 534)	$c^2 = a^2 + b^2 - 2ab \cos C$ $b^2 = a^2 + c^2 - 2ac \cos B$ $a^2 = b^2 + c^2 - 2bc \cos A$
Area of a triangle (pp. 540–541)	$K = \dfrac{1}{2}bh \quad K = \dfrac{1}{2}ab \sin C \quad K = \dfrac{1}{2}bc \sin A \quad K = \dfrac{1}{2}ac \sin B$ $K = \sqrt{s(s-a)(s-b)(s-c)} \quad$ where $\quad s = \dfrac{1}{2}(a+b+c)$

Objectives

Section		You should be able to . . .	Example(s)	Review Exercises
8.1	1	Find the value of trigonometric functions of acute angles using right triangles (p. 510)	1, 2	1–4, 46
	2	Use the complementary angle theorem (p. 512)	3	5–10
	3	Solve right triangles (p. 512)	4, 5	11–14, 46
	4	Solve applied problems (p. 513)	6–10	47–52, 60–62
8.2	1	Solve SAA or ASA triangles (p. 524)	1, 2	15, 16, 32
	2	Solve SSA triangles (p. 525)	3–5	17–20, 22, 27, 28, 31
	3	Solve applied problems (p. 527)	6, 7	53–55
8.3	1	Solve SAS triangles (p. 534)	1	21, 25, 26, 33, 34
	2	Solve SSS triangles (p. 535)	2	23, 24, 29, 30
	3	Solve applied problems (p. 536)	3	56, 57
8.4	1	Find the area of SAS triangles (p. 540)	1	35–38, 45, 58, 59
	2	Find the area of SSS triangles (p. 541)	2	39–42
8.5	1	Build a model for an object in simple harmonic motion (p. 546)	1	63, 64
	2	Analyze simple harmonic motion (p. 548)	2	65–68
	3	Analyze an object in damped motion (p. 549)	3	69–72
	4	Graph the sum of two functions (p. 550)	4, 5	73, 74

Review Exercises

In Problems 1–4, find the exact value of the six trigonometric functions of the angle θ in each figure.

1.

2.

3.

4.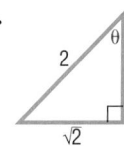

In Problems 5–10, find the exact value of each expression. Do not use a calculator.

5. $\cos 62° - \sin 28°$

6. $\tan 15° - \cot 75°$

7. $\dfrac{\sec 55°}{\csc 35°}$

8. $\dfrac{\tan 40°}{\cot 50°}$

9. $\cos^2 40° + \cos^2 50°$

10. $\tan^2 40° - \csc^2 50°$

In Problems 11–14, solve each triangle.

11.

12.

13.

14.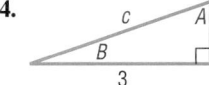

In Problems 15–34, find the remaining angle(s) and side(s) of each triangle, if it (they) exists. If no triangle exists, say "No triangle."

15. $A = 50°, \quad B = 30°, \quad a = 1$

16. $A = 10°, \quad C = 40°, \quad c = 2$

17. $A = 100°, \quad a = 5, \quad c = 2$

18. $a = 2, \quad c = 5, \quad A = 60°$

19. $a = 3, \quad c = 1, \quad C = 110°$

20. $a = 3, \quad c = 1, \quad C = 20°$

21. $a = 3, \quad c = 1, \quad B = 100°$

22. $a = 3, \quad b = 5, \quad B = 80°$

23. $a = 2, \quad b = 3, \quad c = 1$

24. $a = 10, \quad b = 7, \quad c = 8$

25. $a = 1, \quad b = 3, \quad C = 40°$

26. $a = 4, \quad b = 1, \quad C = 100°$

27. $a = 5, \quad b = 3, \quad A = 80°$

28. $a = 2, \quad b = 3, \quad A = 20°$

29. $a = 1, \quad b = \dfrac{1}{2}, \quad c = \dfrac{4}{3}$

30. $a = 3, \quad b = 2, \quad c = 2$

31. $a = 3, \quad A = 10°, \quad b = 4$

32. $a = 4, \quad A = 20°, \quad B = 100°$

33. $c = 5, \quad b = 4, \quad A = 70°$

34. $a = 1, \quad b = 2, \quad C = 60°$

In Problems 35–44, find the area of each triangle.

35. $a = 2, \quad b = 3, \quad C = 40°$

36. $b = 5, \quad c = 5, \quad A = 20°$

37. $b = 4, \quad c = 10, \quad A = 70°$

38. $a = 2, \quad b = 1, \quad C = 100°$

39. $a = 4, \quad b = 3, \quad c = 5$

40. $a = 10, \quad b = 7, \quad c = 8$

41. $a = 4, \quad b = 2, \quad c = 5$

42. $a = 3, \quad b = 2, \quad c = 2$

43. $A = 50°, \quad B = 30°, \quad a = 1$

44. $A = 10°, \quad C = 40°, \quad c = 3$

45. Area of a Segment Find the area of the segment of a circle whose radius is 6 inches formed by a central angle of 50°.

46. Geometry The hypotenuse of a right triangle is 12 feet. If one leg is 8 feet, find the degree measure of each angle.

47. Finding the Width of a River Find the distance from A to C across the river illustrated in the figure.

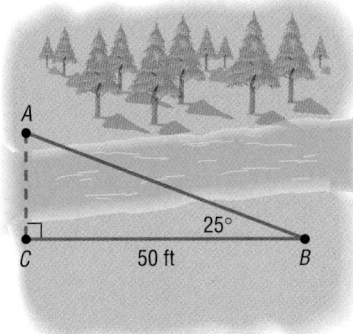

48. Finding the Height of a Building Find the height of the building shown in the figure.

49. Finding the Distance to Shore The Sears Tower in Chicago is 1454 feet tall and is situated about 1 mile inland from the shore of Lake Michigan, as indicated in the figure. An observer in a pleasure boat on the lake directly in front of the Sears Tower looks at the top of the tower and measures the angle of elevation as 5°. How far offshore is the boat?

1454 ft
5°
1 mi
Lake Michigan

50. Measuring the Length of a Lake From a stationary hot-air balloon 500 feet above the ground, two sightings of a lake are made (see the figure). How long is the lake?

500 ft
25°   65°

51. Finding the Speed of a Glider From a glider 200 feet above the ground, two sightings of a stationary object directly in front are taken 1 minute apart (see the figure). What is the speed of the glider?

40°
10°
200 ft

52. Finding the Grade of a Mountain Trail A straight trail with a uniform inclination leads from a hotel, elevation 5000 feet, to a lake in a valley, elevation 4100 feet. The length of the trail is 4100 feet. What is the inclination (grade) of the trail?

53. Finding the Height of a Helicopter Two observers simultaneously measure the angle of elevation of a helicopter. One angle is measured as 25°, the other as 40° (see the figure). If the observers are 100 feet apart and the helicopter lies over the line joining them, how high is the helicopter?

54. Determining Distances at Sea Rebecca, the navigator of a ship at sea, spots two lighthouses that she knows to be 2 miles apart along a straight shoreline. She determines that the angles formed between two line-of-sight observations of the lighthouses and the line from the ship directly to shore are 12° and 30°. See the illustration.
(a) How far is the ship from lighthouse L_1?
(b) How far is the ship from lighthouse L_2?
(c) How far is the ship from shore?

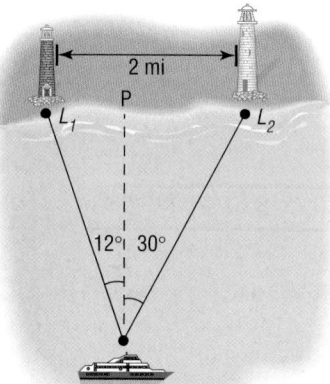

2 mi
P
L_1 L_2
12°   30°

55. Constructing a Highway A highway whose primary directions are north–south is being constructed along the west coast of Florida. Near Naples, a bay obstructs the straight path of the road. Since the cost of a bridge is prohibitive, engineers decide to go around the bay. The illustration shows the path that they decide on and the measurements taken. What is the length of highway needed to go around the bay?

120°
$\frac{1}{4}$ mi
Ocean   3 mi
Clam Bay
$\frac{1}{4}$ mi
115°

56. Correcting a Navigational Error A sailboat leaves St. Thomas bound for an island in the British West Indies, 200 miles away. Maintaining a constant speed of 18 miles per hour, but encountering heavy crosswinds and strong currents, the crew finds after 4 hours that the sailboat is off course by 15°.
(a) How far is the sailboat from the island at this time?
(b) Through what angle should the sailboat turn to correct its course?
(c) How much time has been added to the trip because of this? (Assume that the speed remains at 18 miles per hour.)

British West Indies
St. Thomas   200 mi
15°

57. Surveying Two homes are located on opposite sides of a small hill. See the illustration. To measure the distance between them, a surveyor walks a distance of 50 feet from house P to point R, uses a transit to measure $\angle PRQ$, which is found to be $80°$, and then walks to house Q, a distance of 60 feet. How far apart are the houses?

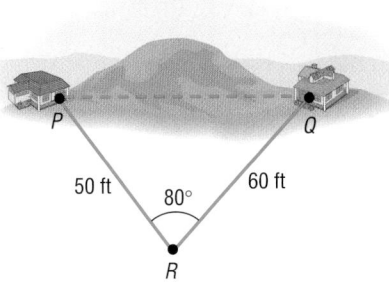

58. Approximating the Area of a Lake To approximate the area of a lake, Cindy walks around the perimeter of the lake, taking the measurements shown in the illustration. Using this technique, what is the approximate area of the lake?

[**Hint:** Use the Law of Cosines on the three triangles shown and then find the sum of their areas.]

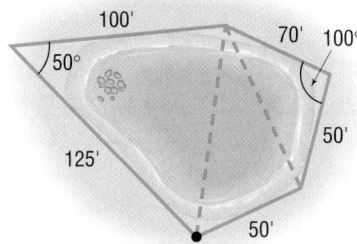

59. Calculating the Cost of Land The irregular parcel of land shown in the figure is being sold for $100 per square foot. What is the cost of this parcel?

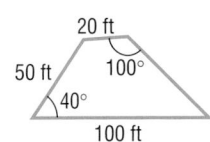

60. Finding the Bearing of a Ship The *Majesty* leaves the Port at Boston for Bermuda with a bearing of S80°E at an average speed of 10 knots. After 1 hour, the ship turns 90° toward the southwest. After 2 hours at an average speed of 20 knots, what is the bearing of the ship from Boston?

61. Drive Wheels of an Engine The drive wheel of an engine is 13 inches in diameter, and the pulley on the rotary pump is 5 inches in diameter. If the shafts of the drive wheel and the pulley are 2 feet apart, what length of belt is required to join them as shown in the figure?

62. Rework Problem 61 if the belt is crossed, as shown in the figure.

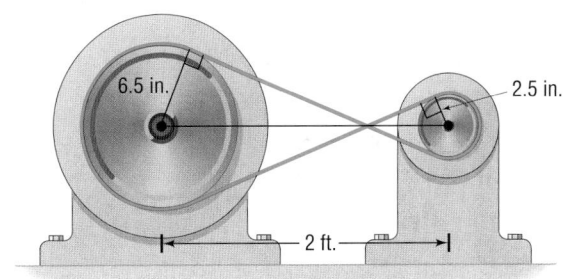

In Problems 63 and 64, an object attached to a coiled spring is pulled down a distance a from its rest position and then released. Assuming that the motion is simple harmonic with period T, develop a model that relates the displacement d of the object from its rest position after t seconds. Also assume that the positive direction of the motion is up.

63. $a = 3$; $T = 4$ seconds

64. $a = 5$; $T = 6$ seconds

In Problems 65–68, the distance d (in feet) that an object travels in time t (in seconds) is given.
(a) Describe the motion of the object.
(b) What is the maximum displacement from its rest position?
(c) What is the time required for one oscillation?
(d) What is the frequency?

65. $d = 6 \sin(2t)$

66. $d = 2 \cos(4t)$

67. $d = -2 \cos(\pi t)$

68. $d = -3 \sin\left[\dfrac{\pi}{2}t\right]$

In Problems 69 and 70, an object of mass m attached to a coiled spring with damping factor b is pulled down a distance a from its rest position and then released. Assume that the positive direction of the motion is up and the period is T under simple harmonic motion.
(a) Develop a model that relates the distance d of the object from its rest position after t seconds.
(b) Graph the equation found in part (a) for 5 oscillations.

69. $m = 40$ grams; $a = 15$ centimeters; $b = 0.75$ gram/second; $T = 5$ seconds

70. $m = 25$ grams; $a = 13$ centimeters; $b = 0.65$ gram/second; $T = 4$ seconds

In Problems 71 and 72, the distance d (in meters) of the bob of a pendulum of mass m (in kilograms) from its rest position at time t (in seconds) is given.
(a) Describe the motion of the object.
(b) What is the initial displacement of the bob? That is, what is the displacement at t = 0?
(c) Graph the motion using a graphing utility.
(d) What is the displacement of the bob at the start of the second oscillation?
(e) What happens to the displacement of the bob as time increases without bound?

71. $d = -15e^{-0.6t/40} \cos\left(\sqrt{\left(\dfrac{2\pi}{5}\right)^2 - \dfrac{0.36}{1600}}\, t\right)$

72. $d = -20e^{-0.5t/60} \cos\left(\sqrt{\left(\dfrac{2\pi}{3}\right)^2 - \dfrac{0.25}{3600}}\, t\right)$

In Problems 73 and 74, graph each function.

73. $y = 2\sin x + \cos(2x), \quad 0 \le x \le 2\pi$

74. $y = 2\cos(2x) + \sin\dfrac{x}{2}, \quad 0 \le x \le 2\pi$

CHAPTER TEST

1. Find the exact value of the six trigonometric functions of the angle θ in the figure.

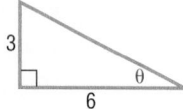

2. Find the exact value of $\sin 40° - \cos 50°$.

In Problems 3–5, use the given information to determine the three remaining parts of each triangle.

3.

4.

5.

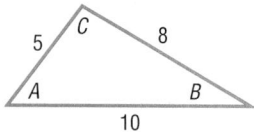

In Problems 6–8, solve each triangle.

6. $A = 55°, \quad C = 20°, \quad a = 4$

7. $a = 3, \quad b = 7, \quad A = 40°$

8. $a = 8, \quad b = 4, \quad C = 70°$

9. Find the area of the triangle described in Problem 8.

10. Find the area of the triangle described in Problem 5.

11. A 12-foot ladder leans against a building. The top of the ladder leans against the wall 10.5 feet from the ground. What is the angle formed by the ground and the ladder?

12. A hot-air balloon is flying at a height of 600 feet and is directly above the Marshall Space Flight Center in Huntsville, Alabama. The pilot of the balloon looks down at the airport that is known to be 5 miles from the Marshall Space Flight Center. What is the angle of depression from the balloon to the airport?

13. Find the area of the shaded region enclosed in a semicircle of diameter 8 centimeters. The length of the chord AB is 6 centimeters.

[**Hint:** Triangle ABC is a right triangle.]

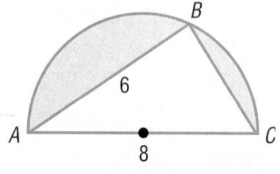

14. Find the area of the quadrilateral shown.

15. Madison wants to swim across Lake William from the fishing lodge (A) to the boat ramp (B), but she wants to know the distance first. Highway 20 goes right past the boat ramp and County Road 3 goes to the lodge. The two roads intersect at point (C), 4.2 miles from the ramp and 3.5 miles from the lodge. Madison uses a transit to measure the angle of intersection of the two roads to be 32°. How far will she need to swim?

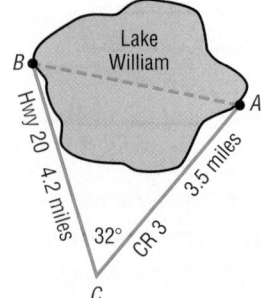

16. Given that $\triangle OAB$ is an isosceles triangle and the shaded sector is a semicircle, find the area of the entire region. Express your answer as a decimal rounded to two places.

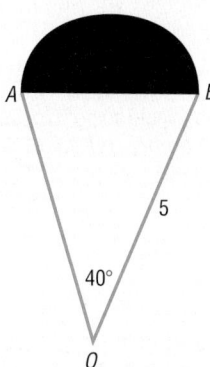

17. The area of the triangle shown below is $54\sqrt{6}$ square units; find the lengths of the sides.

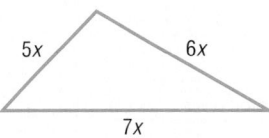

18. Logan is playing on her swing. One full swing (front to back to front) takes 6 seconds and at the peak of her swing she is at an angle of $42°$ with the vertical. If her swing is 5 feet long, and we ignore all resistive forces, develop a model that relates her horizontal displacement (from the rest position) after time t.

CUMULATIVE REVIEW

1. Find the real solutions, if any, of the equation $3x^2 + 1 = 4x$.

2. Find an equation for the circle with center at the point $(-5, 1)$ and radius 3. Graph this circle.

3. Determine the domain of the function
$$f(x) = \sqrt{x^2 - 3x - 4}$$

4. Graph the function $y = 3\sin(\pi x)$.

5. Graph the function $y = -2\cos(2x - \pi)$.

6. If $\tan \theta = -2$ and $\dfrac{3\pi}{2} < \theta < 2\pi$, find the exact value of:

(a) $\sin \theta$ (b) $\cos \theta$ (c) $\sin(2\theta)$

(d) $\cos(2\theta)$ (e) $\sin\left(\dfrac{1}{2}\theta\right)$ (f) $\cos\left(\dfrac{1}{2}\theta\right)$

7. Graph each of the following functions on the interval $[0, 4]$:

(a) $y = e^x$ (b) $y = \sin x$

(c) $y = e^x \sin x$ (d) $y = 2x + \sin x$

8. Sketch the graph of each of the following functions:

(a) $y = x$ (b) $y = x^2$ (c) $y = \sqrt{x}$

(d) $y = x^3$ (e) $y = e^x$ (f) $y = \ln x$

(g) $y = \sin x$ (h) $y = \cos x$ (i) $y = \tan x$

9. Solve the triangle:

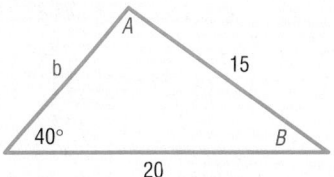

10. In the complex number system, solve the equation
$$3x^5 - 10x^4 + 21x^3 - 42x^2 + 36x - 8 = 0$$

11. Analyze the graph of the rational function
$$R(x) = \frac{2x^2 - 7x - 4}{x^2 + 2x - 15}$$

12. Solve $3^x = 12$. Round your answer to two decimal places.

13. Solve $\log_3(x + 8) + \log_3 x = 2$.

14. Suppose that $f(x) = 4x + 5$ and $g(x) = x^2 + 5x - 24$.

(a) Solve $f(x) = 0$.   (e) Solve $g(x) \le 0$.

(b) Solve $f(x) = 13$.   (f) Graph $y = f(x)$.

(c) Solve $f(x) = g(x)$.   (g) Graph $y = g(x)$.

(d) Solve $f(x) > 0$.

CHAPTER PROJECTS

I. **Spherical Trigonometry** When the distance between two locations on the surface of Earth is small, we can compute the distance in statutory miles. Using this assumption, we can use the Law of Sines and the Law of Cosines to approximate distances and angles. However, if you look at a globe, you notice that Earth is a sphere; so, as the distance between two points on its surface increases, the linear distance is less accurate because of curvature. Under this circumstance, we need to take into account the curvature of Earth when using the Law of Sines and the Law of Cosines.

1. Draw a spherical triangle and label each vertex by A, B, and C. Then connect each vertex by a radius to the center O of the sphere. Now draw tangent lines to the sides a and b of the triangle that go through C. Extend the lines OA and OB to intersect the tangent lines at P and Q, respectively. See the figure. List the plane right triangles. Determine the measures of the central angles.

2. Apply the Law of Cosines to triangles OPQ and CPQ to find two expressions for the length of PQ.

3. Subtract the expressions in part (2) from each other. Solve for the term containing cos *c*.

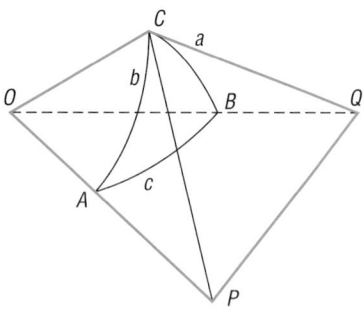

4. Use the Pythagorean Theorem to find another value for $OQ^2 - CQ^2$ and $OP^2 - CP^2$. Now solve for cos *c*.

5. Replacing the ratios in part (4) by the cosines of the sides of the spherical triangle, you should now have the Law of Cosines for spherical triangles:

$$\cos c = \cos a \cos b + \sin a \sin b \cos C$$

Source: For the spherical Law of Cosines; see *Mathematics from the Birth of Numbers* by Jan Gullberg. W. W. Norton & Co., Publishers, 1996, pp. 491–494.

II. The Lewis and Clark Expedition Lewis and Clark followed several rivers in their trek from what is now Great Falls, Montana, to the Pacific coast. First, they went down the Missouri and Jefferson rivers from Great Falls to Lemhi, Idaho. Because the two cities are on different longitudes and different latitudes, we must account for the curvature of Earth when computing the distance that they traveled. Assume that the radius of Earth is 3960 miles.

1. Great Falls is at approximately 47.5°N and 111.3°W. Lemhi is at approximately 45.5°N and 113.5°W. (We will assume

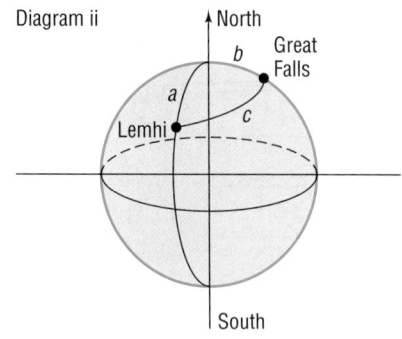

Diagram ii

that the rivers flow straight from Great Falls to Lemhi on the surface of Earth.) This line is called a geodesic line. Apply the Law of Cosines for a spherical triangle to find the angle between Great Falls and Lemhi. (The central angles are found by using the differences in the latitudes and longitudes of the towns. See the diagram.) Then find the length of the arc joining the two towns. (Recall $s = r\theta$.)

2. From Lemhi, they went up the Bitteroot River and the Snake River to what is now Lewiston and Clarkston on the border of Idaho and Washington. Although this is not really a side to a triangle, we will make a side that goes from Lemhi to Lewiston and Clarkston. If Lewiston and Clarkston are at about 46.5°N 117.0°W, find the distance from Lemhi using the Law of Cosines for a spherical triangle and the arc length.

3. How far did the explorers travel just to get that far?

4. Draw a plane triangle connecting the three towns. If the distance from Lewiston to Great Falls is 282 miles and the angle at Great Falls is 42° and the angle at Lewiston is 48.5°, find the distance from Great Falls to Lemhi and from Lemhi to Lewiston. How do these distances compare with the ones computed in parts (1) and (2)?

Source: For Lewis and Clark Expedition: *American Journey: The Quest for Liberty to 1877, Texas Edition.* Prentice Hall, 1992, p. 345.

Source: For map coordinates: *National Geographic Atlas of the World,* published by National Geographic Society, 1981, pp. 74–75.

The following projects are available at the Instructor's Resource Center (IRC):

III. Project at Motorola: *How Can You Build or Analyze a Vibration Profile?* Fourier functions are not only important to analyze vibrations, but they are also what a mathematician would call interesting. Complete the project to see why.

IV. Leaning Tower of Pisa Trigonometry is used to analyze the apparent height and tilt of the Leaning Tower of Pisa.

V. Locating Lost Treasure Clever treasure seekers who know the Law of Sines are able to efficiently find a buried treasure.

VI. Jacob's Field Angles of elevation and the Law of Sines are used to determine the height of the stadium wall and the distance from home plate to the top of the wall.

Polar Coordinates; Vectors

9

How Do Airplanes Fly?

Have you ever watched a big jetliner lumber into position on the runway for takeoff and wonder, "How does that thing ever get off the ground?" You know it's because of the wing that it stays up in the air, but how does it really work?

When air flows around a wing, it creates lift. The way it creates lift is based on the wing's movement through the air and the air pressure created around the wing. An airplane's wing, in varying degrees depending on the type and design of the airplane, is curved over the top of the wing and straighter underneath the wing. As air hits the wing, it is "split in two," with air moving both over and under the wing. Since the top of the wing has more curve than the bottom of the wing, the air moving over the top of the wing has farther to travel, and thus must move faster than the air moving underneath the wing. The air moving over the top of the wing now exerts less air pressure on the wing than the slower-moving air under the wing. Lift is created.

The difference in air pressure is the primary force creating lift on a wing, but one other force exerted on the wing also helps to produce lift. This is the force of deflection. Air moving along the underside of the wing is deflected downward. Remember the Newtonian principle: For every action, there is an equal and opposite reaction. The air that is deflected downward (action) helps to push the wing upward (reaction), producing more lift.

These two natural forces on the wing, pressure and deflection, produce lift. The faster the wing moves through the air, the greater the forces become, and the greater the lift.

Source: Thomas Schueneman. How do airplanes fly? http://meme.essortment.com/howdoairplane_rlmi.htm, accessed August 2006. © 2002 by Pagewise, Inc. Used with permission.

—See Chapter Project I—

A Look Back, A Look Ahead

This chapter is in two parts: Polar Coordinates, Sections 9.1–9.3, and Vectors, Sections 9.4–9.7. They are independent of each other and may be covered in any order.

Sections 9.1–9.3: In Chapter 1 we introduced rectangular coordinates *x* and *y* and discussed the graph of an equation in two variables involving *x* and *y*. In Sections 9.1 and 9.2, we introduce polar coordinates, an alternative to rectangular coordinates, and discuss graphing equations that involve polar coordinates. In Section 5.3, we discussed raising a real number to a real power. In Section 9.3 we extend this idea by raising a complex number to a real power. As it turns out, polar coordinates are useful for the discussion.

Sections 9.4–9.7: We have seen in many chapters that we are often required to solve an equation to obtain a solution to applied problems. In the last four sections of this chapter, we develop the notion of a vector and show how it can be used to model applied problems in physics and engineering.

Outline

9.1 Polar Coordinates
9.2 Polar Equations and Graphs
9.3 The Complex Plane; De Moivre's Theorem
9.4 Vectors
9.5 The Dot Product
9.6 Vectors in Space
9.7 The Cross Product
Chapter Review
Chapter Test
Cumulative Review
Chapter Projects

9.1 Polar Coordinates

PREPARING FOR THIS SECTION *Before getting started, review the following:*

- Rectangular Coordinates (Section 1.1, pp. 2–3)
- Definitions of the Sine and Cosine Functions (Section 6.2, pp. 376–377)
- Inverse Tangent Function (Section 7.1, pp. 447–449)
- Completing the Square (Appendix A, Section A.6, p. A52)

Now Work the 'Are You Prepared?' problems on page 569.

OBJECTIVES 1 Plot Points Using Polar Coordinates (p. 562)

2 Convert from Polar Coordinates to Rectangular Coordinates (p. 564)

3 Convert from Rectangular Coordinates to Polar Coordinates (p. 566)

4 Transform Equations from Polar to Rectangular Form (p. 568)

So far, we have always used a system of rectangular coordinates to plot points in the plane. Now we are ready to describe another system, called *polar coordinates.* As we shall soon see, in many instances polar coordinates offer certain advantages over rectangular coordinates.

In a rectangular coordinate system, you will recall, a point in the plane is represented by an ordered pair of numbers (x, y), where x and y equal the signed distance of the point from the y-axis and x-axis, respectively. In a polar coordinate system, we select a point, called the **pole**, and then a ray with vertex at the pole, called the **polar axis**. See Figure 1. Comparing the rectangular and polar coordinate systems, we see that the origin in rectangular coordinates coincides with the pole in polar coordinates, and the positive x-axis in rectangular coordinates coincides with the polar axis in polar coordinates.

Figure 1

1 Plot Points Using Polar Coordinates

A point P in a polar coordinate system is represented by an ordered pair of numbers (r, θ). If $r > 0$, then r is the distance of the point from the pole; θ is an angle (in degrees or radians) formed by the polar axis and a ray from the pole through the point. We call the ordered pair (r, θ) the **polar coordinates** of the point. See Figure 2.

As an example, suppose that the polar coordinates of a point P are $\left(2, \dfrac{\pi}{4}\right)$. We locate P by first drawing an angle of $\dfrac{\pi}{4}$ radian, placing its vertex at the pole and its initial side along the polar axis. Then we go out a distance of 2 units along the terminal side of the angle to reach the point P. See Figure 3.

Figure 2

Figure 3

In using polar coordinates (r, θ), it is possible for r to be negative. When this happens, instead of the point being on the terminal side of θ, it is on the ray from the pole extending in the direction *opposite* the terminal side of θ at a distance $|r|$ units from the pole. See Figure 4 for an illustration.

For example, to plot the point $\left(-3, \dfrac{2\pi}{3}\right)$, we use the ray in the opposite direction of $\dfrac{2\pi}{3}$ and go out $|-3| = 3$ units along that ray. See Figure 5.

Figure 4   **Figure 5**

 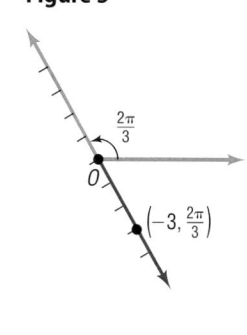

EXAMPLE 1   **Plotting Points Using Polar Coordinates**

Plot the points with the following polar coordinates:

(a) $\left(3, \dfrac{5\pi}{3}\right)$ (b) $\left(2, -\dfrac{\pi}{4}\right)$ (c) $(3, 0)$ (d) $\left(-2, \dfrac{\pi}{4}\right)$

Solution   Figure 6 shows the points.

Figure 6

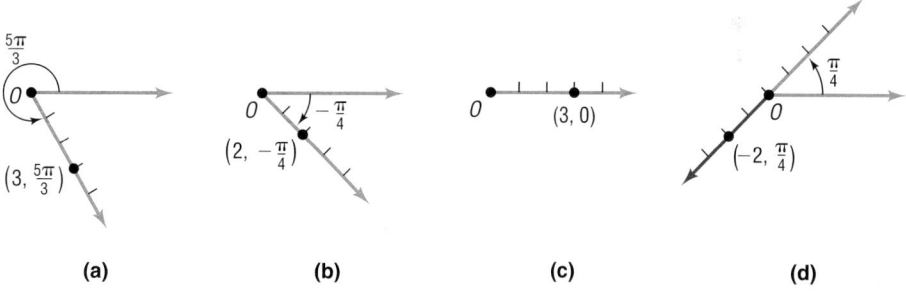

(a)   (b)   (c)   (d)

 Now Work PROBLEMS **11, 19,** AND **27**

Recall that an angle measured counterclockwise is positive and an angle measured clockwise is negative. This convention has some interesting consequences relating to polar coordinates. Let's see what these consequences are.

EXAMPLE 2   **Finding Several Polar Coordinates of a Single Point**

Consider again the point P with polar coordinates $\left(2, \dfrac{\pi}{4}\right)$, as shown in Figure 7(a). Because $\dfrac{\pi}{4}$, $\dfrac{9\pi}{4}$, and $-\dfrac{7\pi}{4}$ all have the same terminal side, we also could have located this point P by using the polar coordinates $\left(2, \dfrac{9\pi}{4}\right)$ or $\left(2, -\dfrac{7\pi}{4}\right)$, as shown in Figures 7(b) and (c). The point $\left(2, \dfrac{\pi}{4}\right)$ can also be represented by the polar coordinates $\left(-2, \dfrac{5\pi}{4}\right)$. See Figure 7(d).

Figure 7

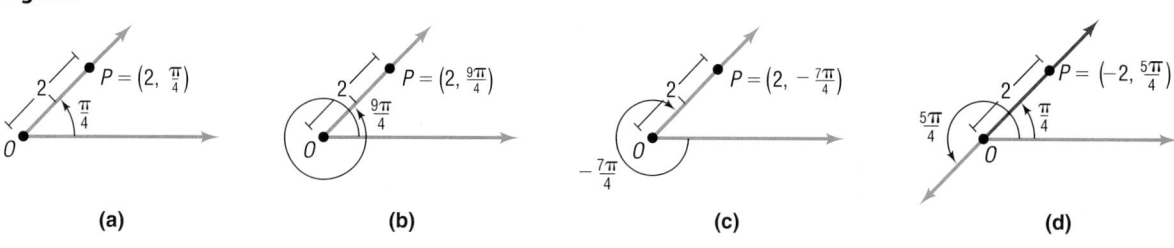

(a)   (b)   (c)   (d)

| EXAMPLE 3 | Finding Other Polar Coordinates of a Given Point |

Plot the point P with polar coordinates $\left(3, \dfrac{\pi}{6}\right)$, and find other polar coordinates (r, θ) of this same point for which:

(a) $r > 0, \quad 2\pi \le \theta < 4\pi$ (b) $r < 0, \quad 0 \le \theta < 2\pi$
(c) $r > 0, \quad -2\pi \le \theta < 0$

Solution   The point $\left(3, \dfrac{\pi}{6}\right)$ is plotted in Figure 8.

Figure 8

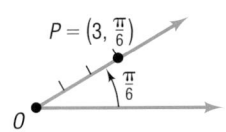

(a) We add 1 revolution (2π radians) to the angle $\dfrac{\pi}{6}$ to get
$P = \left(3, \dfrac{\pi}{6} + 2\pi\right) = \left(3, \dfrac{13\pi}{6}\right)$. See Figure 9.

(b) We add $\dfrac{1}{2}$ revolution (π radians) to the angle $\dfrac{\pi}{6}$ and replace 3 by -3 to get
$P = \left(-3, \dfrac{\pi}{6} + \pi\right) = \left(-3, \dfrac{7\pi}{6}\right)$. See Figure 10.

(c) We subtract 2π from the angle $\dfrac{\pi}{6}$ to get $P = \left(3, \dfrac{\pi}{6} - 2\pi\right) = \left(3, -\dfrac{11\pi}{6}\right)$. See Figure 11.

Figure 9   **Figure 10**   **Figure 11**

          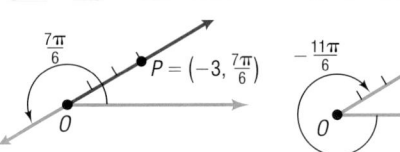

These examples show a major difference between rectangular coordinates and polar coordinates. In the former, each point has exactly one pair of rectangular coordinates; in the latter, a point can have infinitely many pairs of polar coordinates.

SUMMARY   A point with polar coordinates (r, θ) can also be represented by either of the following:

$$(r, \theta + 2\pi k) \quad \text{or} \quad (-r, \theta + \pi + 2\pi k) \qquad k \text{ any integer}$$

The polar coordinates of the pole are $(0, \theta)$, where θ can be any angle.

Now Work   PROBLEM 31

2 Convert from Polar Coordinates to Rectangular Coordinates

Sometimes we need to convert coordinates or equations in rectangular form to polar form, and vice versa. To do this, we recall that the origin in rectangular coordinates is the pole in polar coordinates and that the positive x-axis in rectangular coordinates is the polar axis in polar coordinates.

THEOREM   **Conversion from Polar Coordinates to Rectangular Coordinates**

If P is a point with polar coordinates (r, θ), the rectangular coordinates (x, y) of P are given by

$$x = r \cos \theta \qquad y = r \sin \theta \tag{1}$$

Figure 12

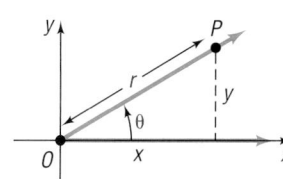

Proof Suppose that P has the polar coordinates (r, θ). We seek the rectangular coordinates (x, y) of P. Refer to Figure 12.

If $r = 0$, then, regardless of θ, the point P is the pole, for which the rectangular coordinates are $(0, 0)$. Formula (1) is valid for $r = 0$.

If $r > 0$, the point P is on the terminal side of θ, and $r = d(O, P) = \sqrt{x^2 + y^2}$. Since

$$\cos \theta = \frac{x}{r} \qquad \sin \theta = \frac{y}{r}$$

we have

$$x = r \cos \theta \qquad y = r \sin \theta$$

If $r < 0$, the point $P = (r, \theta)$ can be represented as $(-r, \pi + \theta)$, where $-r > 0$. Since

$$\cos(\pi + \theta) = -\cos \theta = \frac{x}{-r} \qquad \sin(\pi + \theta) = -\sin \theta = \frac{y}{-r}$$

we have

$$x = r \cos \theta \qquad y = r \sin \theta \qquad \blacksquare$$

EXAMPLE 4

Converting from Polar Coordinates to Rectangular Coordinates

Find the rectangular coordinates of the points with the following polar coordinates:

(a) $\left(6, \dfrac{\pi}{6}\right)$

(b) $\left(-4, -\dfrac{\pi}{4}\right)$

Solution We use formula (1): $x = r \cos \theta$ and $y = r \sin \theta$.

Figure 13

(a)

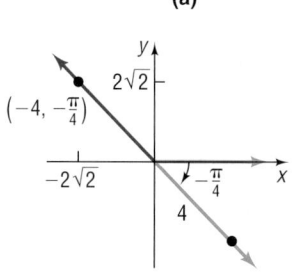

(b)

(a) Figure 13(a) shows $\left(6, \dfrac{\pi}{6}\right)$ plotted. Notice that $\left(6, \dfrac{\pi}{6}\right)$ lies in quadrant I of the rectangular coordinate system. So we expect both the x-coordinate and the y-coordinate to be positive. With $r = 6$ and $\theta = \dfrac{\pi}{6}$, we have

$$x = r \cos \theta = 6 \cos \frac{\pi}{6} = 6 \cdot \frac{\sqrt{3}}{2} = 3\sqrt{3}$$

$$y = r \sin \theta = 6 \sin \frac{\pi}{6} = 6 \cdot \frac{1}{2} = 3$$

The rectangular coordinates of the point $\left(6, \dfrac{\pi}{6}\right)$ are $\left(3\sqrt{3}, 3\right)$, which lies in quadrant I, as expected.

(b) Figure 13(b) shows $\left(-4, -\dfrac{\pi}{4}\right)$ plotted. Notice that $\left(-4, -\dfrac{\pi}{4}\right)$ lies in quadrant II of the rectangular coordinate system. With $r = -4$ and $\theta = -\dfrac{\pi}{4}$, we have

$$x = r \cos \theta = -4 \cos\left(-\frac{\pi}{4}\right) = -4 \cdot \frac{\sqrt{2}}{2} = -2\sqrt{2}$$

$$y = r \sin \theta = -4 \sin\left(-\frac{\pi}{4}\right) = -4\left(-\frac{\sqrt{2}}{2}\right) = 2\sqrt{2}$$

The rectangular coordinates of the point $\left(-4, -\dfrac{\pi}{4}\right)$ are $\left(-2\sqrt{2}, 2\sqrt{2}\right)$, which lies in quadrant II, as expected.

Figure 14

Most calculators have the capability of converting from polar coordinates to rectangular coordinates. Consult your owner's manual for the proper key strokes. Since in most cases this procedure is tedious, you will find that using formula (1) is faster.

Figure 14 verifies the result obtained in Example 4(a) using a TI-84 Plus. Note that the calculator is in radian mode.

═══════ **Now Work** PROBLEMS **39** AND **51**

3 Convert from Rectangular Coordinates to Polar Coordinates

Converting from rectangular coordinates (x, y) to polar coordinates (r, θ) is a little more complicated. Notice that we begin each example by plotting the given rectangular coordinates.

| EXAMPLE 5 | **How to Convert from Rectangular Coordinates to Polar Coordinates with the Point on a Coordinate Axis** |

Find polar coordinates of a point whose rectangular coordinates are $(0, 3)$.

Step-by-Step Solution

STEP 1 Plot the point (x, y) and note the quadrant the point lies in or the coordinate axis the point lies on.

We plot the point $(0, 3)$ in a rectangular coordinate system. See Figure 15. The point lies on the positive y-axis

Figure 15

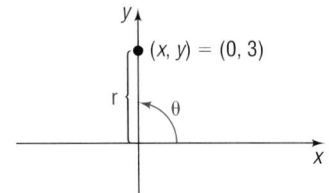

STEP 2 Determine the distance r from the origin to the point.

The point $(0, 3)$ lies on the y-axis a distance of 3 units from the origin (pole), so $r = 3$.

STEP 3 Determine θ.

A ray with vertex at the pole through $(0, 3)$ forms an angle $\theta = \dfrac{\pi}{2}$ with the polar axis.

Polar coordinates for this point can be given by $\left(3, \dfrac{\pi}{2}\right)$. Other possible representations include $\left(-3, -\dfrac{\pi}{2}\right)$ and $\left(3, \dfrac{5\pi}{2}\right)$.

Figure 16

Most graphing calculators have the capability of converting from rectangular coordinates to polar coordinates. Consult your owner's manual for the proper keystrokes. Figure 16 verifies the results obtained in Example 5 using a TI-84 Plus. Note that the calculator is in radian mode.

Figure 17 shows polar coordinates of points that lie on either the x-axis or the y-axis. In each illustration, $a > 0$.

Figure 17

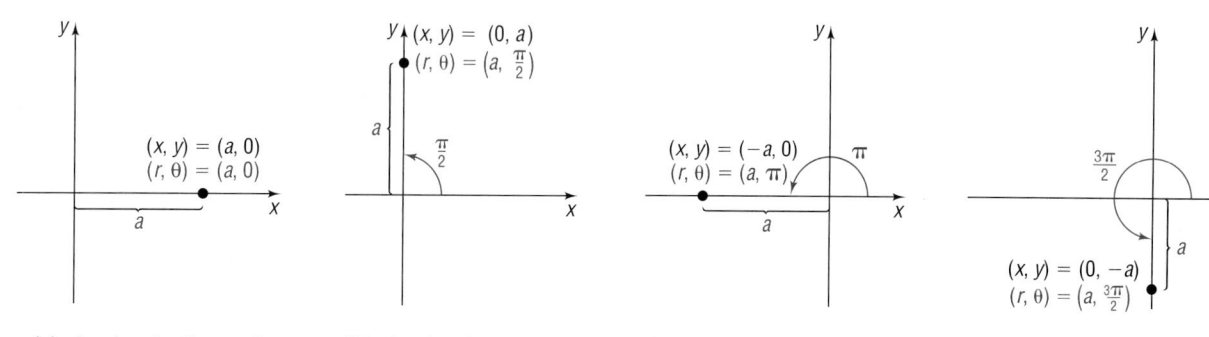

(a) $(x, y) = (a, 0), a > 0$ **(b)** $(x, y) = (0, a), a > 0$ **(c)** $(x, y) = (-a, 0), a > 0$ **(d)** $(x, y) = (0, -a), a > 0$

━━━ **Now Work** PROBLEM 55

| EXAMPLE 6 | **How to Convert from Rectangular Coordinates to Polar Coordinates with the Point in a Quadrant** |

Find the polar coordinates of a point whose rectangular coordinates are $(2, -2)$.

Step-by-Step Solution

STEP 1 Plot the point (x, y) and note the quadrant the point lies in or the coordinate axis the point lies on.

We plot the point $(2, -2)$ in a rectangular coordinate system. See Figure 18. The point lies in quadrant IV.

Figure 18

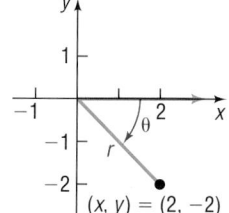

STEP 2 Determine the distance r from the origin to the point using $r = \sqrt{x^2 + y^2}$.

$$r = \sqrt{x^2 + y^2} = \sqrt{(2)^2 + (-2)^2} = \sqrt{8} = 2\sqrt{2}$$

STEP 3 Determine θ.

We find θ by recalling that $\tan\theta = \dfrac{y}{x}$, so $\theta = \tan^{-1}\dfrac{y}{x}$, $-\dfrac{\pi}{2} < \theta < \dfrac{\pi}{2}$. Since $(2, -2)$ lies in quadrant IV, we know that $-\dfrac{\pi}{2} < \theta < 0$. As a result,

$$\theta = \tan^{-1}\frac{y}{x} = \tan^{-1}\left(\frac{-2}{2}\right) = \tan^{-1}(-1) = -\frac{\pi}{4}$$

A set of polar coordinates for the point $(2, -2)$ is $\left(2\sqrt{2}, -\dfrac{\pi}{4}\right)$. Other possible representations include $\left(2\sqrt{2}, \dfrac{7\pi}{4}\right)$ and $\left(-2\sqrt{2}, \dfrac{3\pi}{4}\right)$.

■

| EXAMPLE 7 | **Converting from Rectangular Coordinates to Polar Coordinates** |

Find polar coordinates of a point whose rectangular coordinates are $\left(-1, -\sqrt{3}\right)$.

Solution   **STEP 1:** See Figure 19. The point lies in quadrant III.

STEP 2: The distance r from the origin to the point $\left(-1, -\sqrt{3}\right)$ is

$$r = \sqrt{(-1)^2 + \left(-\sqrt{3}\right)^2} = \sqrt{4} = 2$$

Figure 19

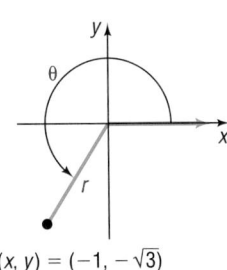

$(x, y) = (-1, -\sqrt{3})$

STEP 3: To find θ, we use $\theta = \tan^{-1}\dfrac{y}{x} = \tan^{-1}\dfrac{-\sqrt{3}}{-1} = \tan^{-1}\sqrt{3}, -\dfrac{\pi}{2} < \theta < \dfrac{\pi}{2}$.

Since the point $\left(-1, -\sqrt{3}\right)$ lies in quadrant III and the inverse tangent function gives an angle in quadrant I, we add π to the result to obtain an angle in quadrant III.

$$\theta = \pi + \tan^{-1}\left(\frac{-\sqrt{3}}{-1}\right) = \pi + \tan^{-1}\sqrt{3} = \pi + \frac{\pi}{3} = \frac{4\pi}{3}$$

A set of polar coordinates for this point is $\left(2, \dfrac{4\pi}{3}\right)$. Other possible representations include $\left(-2, \dfrac{\pi}{3}\right)$ and $\left(2, -\dfrac{2\pi}{3}\right)$.

Figure 20 shows how to find polar coordinates of a point that lies in a quadrant when its rectangular coordinates (x, y) are given.

Figure 20

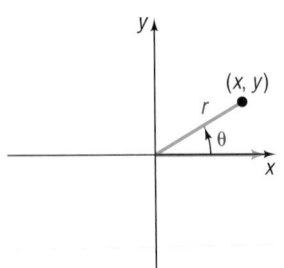

(a) $r = \sqrt{x^2 + y^2}$
$\theta = \tan^{-1}\dfrac{y}{x}$

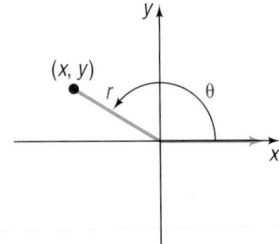

(b) $r = \sqrt{x^2 + y^2}$
$\theta = \pi + \tan^{-1}\dfrac{y}{x}$

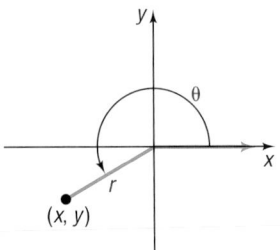

(c) $r = \sqrt{x^2 + y^2}$
$\theta = \pi + \tan^{-1}\dfrac{y}{x}$

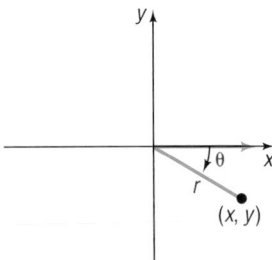

(d) $r = \sqrt{x^2 + y^2}$
$\theta = \tan^{-1}\dfrac{y}{x}$

Based on the preceding discussion, we have the formulas

$$r^2 = x^2 + y^2 \qquad \tan\theta = \frac{y}{x} \qquad \text{if } x \neq 0 \qquad \textbf{(2)}$$

To use formula (2) effectively, follow these steps:

Steps for Converting from Rectangular to Polar Coordinates

STEP 1: Always plot the point (x, y) first, as we did in Examples 5 and 6. Note the quadrant the point lies in or the coordinate axis the point lies on.

STEP 2: If $x = 0$ or $y = 0$, use your illustration to find r. See Figure 17. If $x \neq 0$ and $y \neq 0$, then $r = \sqrt{x^2 + y^2}$.

STEP 3: Find θ. If $x = 0$ or $y = 0$, use your illustration to find θ. See Figure 17. If $x \neq 0$ and $y \neq 0$, note the quadrant in which the point lies.

Quadrant I or IV: $\theta = \tan^{-1}\dfrac{y}{x}$

Quadrant II or III: $\theta = \pi + \tan^{-1}\dfrac{y}{x}$

See Figure 20.

Now Work PROBLEM 59

4 Transform Equations from Polar to Rectangular Form

Formulas (1) and (2) may also be used to transform equations from polar form to rectangular form, and vice versa. Two common techniques for transforming an equation from polar form to rectangular form are the following:

1. Multiplying both sides of the equation by r
2. Squaring both sides of the equation

| EXAMPLE 8 | **Transforming an Equation from Polar to Rectangular Form** |

Transform the equation $r = 6 \cos \theta$ from polar coordinates to rectangular coordinates, and identify the graph.

Solution   If we multiply each side by r, it will be easier to apply formulas (1) and (2).

$$r = 6 \cos \theta$$
$$r^2 = 6r \cos \theta \qquad \text{Multiply each side by } r.$$
$$x^2 + y^2 = 6x \qquad r^2 = x^2 + y^2; x = r \cos \theta$$

This is the equation of a circle, so we proceed to complete the square to obtain the standard form of the equation.

$$x^2 + y^2 = 6x$$
$$(x^2 - 6x) + y^2 = 0 \qquad \text{General form}$$
$$(x^2 - 6x + 9) + y^2 = 9 \qquad \text{Complete the square in } x.$$
$$(x - 3)^2 + y^2 = 9 \qquad \text{Factor.}$$

This is the standard form of the equation of a circle with center $(3, 0)$ and radius 3.

━━━━━ **Now Work** PROBLEM 75

| EXAMPLE 9 | **Transforming an Equation from Rectangular to Polar Form** |

Transform the equation $4xy = 9$ from rectangular coordinates to polar coordinates.

Solution   We use formula (1): $x = r \cos \theta$ and $y = r \sin \theta$.

$$4xy = 9$$
$$4(r \cos \theta)(r \sin \theta) = 9 \qquad x = r \cos \theta, y = r \sin \theta$$
$$4r^2 \cos \theta \sin \theta = 9$$

This is the polar form of the equation. It can be simplified as shown next:

$$2r^2(2 \sin \theta \cos \theta) = 9 \qquad \text{Factor out } 2r^2.$$
$$2r^2 \sin(2\theta) = 9 \qquad \text{Double-angle Formula}$$

━━━━━ **Now Work** PROBLEM 69

9.1 Assess Your Understanding

'Are You Prepared?' *Answers are given at the end of these exercises. If you get a wrong answer, read the pages listed in red.*

1. Plot the point whose rectangular coordinates are $(3, -1)$. What quadrant does the point lie in? (pp. 2–3)
2. To complete the square of $x^2 + 6x$, add ____ . (p. A52)

3. If $P = (a, b)$ is a point on the terminal side of the angle θ at a distance r from the origin, then $\sin \theta =$ ____ . (pp. 376–377)
4. $\tan^{-1}(-1) =$ ____ . (pp. 447–449)

Concepts and Vocabulary

5. In polar coordinates, the origin is called the ____ and the positive x-axis is referred to as the ____ ____ .

6. Another representation in polar coordinates for the point $\left(2, \dfrac{\pi}{3}\right)$ is $\left(\underline{\quad}, \dfrac{4\pi}{3}\right)$.

7. The polar coordinates $\left(-2, \dfrac{\pi}{6}\right)$ are represented in rectangular coordinates by $(\underline{\quad}, \underline{\quad})$.

8. **True or False** The polar coordinates of a point are unique.

9. **True or False** The rectangular coordinates of a point are unique.

10. **True or False** In (r, θ), the number r can be negative.

Skill Building

In Problems 11–18, match each point in polar coordinates with either A, B, C, or D on the graph.

11. $\left(2, -\dfrac{11\pi}{6}\right)$

12. $\left(-2, -\dfrac{\pi}{6}\right)$

13. $\left(-2, \dfrac{\pi}{6}\right)$

14. $\left(2, \dfrac{7\pi}{6}\right)$

15. $\left(2, \dfrac{5\pi}{6}\right)$

16. $\left(-2, \dfrac{5\pi}{6}\right)$

17. $\left(-2, \dfrac{7\pi}{6}\right)$

18. $\left(2, \dfrac{11\pi}{6}\right)$

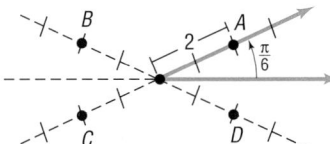

In Problems 19–30, plot each point given in polar coordinates.

19. $(3, 90°)$

20. $(4, 270°)$

21. $(-2, 0)$

22. $(-3, \pi)$

23. $\left(6, \dfrac{\pi}{6}\right)$

24. $\left(5, \dfrac{5\pi}{3}\right)$

25. $(-2, 135°)$

26. $(-3, 120°)$

27. $\left(-1, -\dfrac{\pi}{3}\right)$

28. $\left(-3, -\dfrac{3\pi}{4}\right)$

29. $(-2, -\pi)$

30. $\left(-3, -\dfrac{\pi}{2}\right)$

In Problems 31–38, plot each point given in polar coordinates, and find other polar coordinates (r, θ) of the point for which:

(a) $r > 0$, $-2\pi \le \theta < 0$

(b) $r < 0$, $0 \le \theta < 2\pi$

(c) $r > 0$, $2\pi \le \theta < 4\pi$

31. $\left(5, \dfrac{2\pi}{3}\right)$

32. $\left(4, \dfrac{3\pi}{4}\right)$

33. $(-2, 3\pi)$

34. $(-3, 4\pi)$

35. $\left(1, \dfrac{\pi}{2}\right)$

36. $(2, \pi)$

37. $\left(-3, -\dfrac{\pi}{4}\right)$

38. $\left(-2, -\dfrac{2\pi}{3}\right)$

In Problems 39–54, the polar coordinates of a point are given. Find the rectangular coordinates of each point.

39. $\left(3, \dfrac{\pi}{2}\right)$

40. $\left(4, \dfrac{3\pi}{2}\right)$

41. $(-2, 0)$

42. $(-3, \pi)$

43. $(6, 150°)$

44. $(5, 300°)$

45. $\left(-2, \dfrac{3\pi}{4}\right)$

46. $\left(-2, \dfrac{2\pi}{3}\right)$

47. $\left(-1, -\dfrac{\pi}{3}\right)$

48. $\left(-3, -\dfrac{3\pi}{4}\right)$

49. $(-2, -180°)$

50. $(-3, -90°)$

51. $(7.5, 110°)$

52. $(-3.1, 182°)$

53. $(6.3, 3.8)$

54. $(8.1, 5.2)$

In Problems 55–66, the rectangular coordinates of a point are given. Find polar coordinates for each point.

55. $(3, 0)$

56. $(0, 2)$

57. $(-1, 0)$

58. $(0, -2)$

59. $(1, -1)$

60. $(-3, 3)$

61. $\left(\sqrt{3}, 1\right)$

62. $\left(-2, -2\sqrt{3}\right)$

63. $(1.3, -2.1)$

64. $(-0.8, -2.1)$

65. $(8.3, 4.2)$

66. $(-2.3, 0.2)$

In Problems 67–74, the letters x and y represent rectangular coordinates. Write each equation using polar coordinates (r, θ).

67. $2x^2 + 2y^2 = 3$

68. $x^2 + y^2 = x$

69. $x^2 = 4y$

70. $y^2 = 2x$

71. $2xy = 1$

72. $4x^2y = 1$

73. $x = 4$

74. $y = -3$

In Problems 75–82, the letters r and θ represent polar coordinates. Write each equation using rectangular coordinates (x, y).

75. $r = \cos\theta$

76. $r = \sin\theta + 1$

77. $r^2 = \cos\theta$

78. $r = \sin\theta - \cos\theta$

79. $r = 2$

80. $r = 4$

81. $r = \dfrac{4}{1 - \cos\theta}$

82. $r = \dfrac{3}{3 - \cos\theta}$

Applications and Extensions

83. Chicago In Chicago, the road system is set up like a Cartesian plane, where streets are indicated by the number of blocks they are from Madison Street and State Street. For example, Wrigley Field in Chicago is located at 1060 West Addison, which is 10 blocks west of State Street and 36 blocks north of Madison Street. Treat the intersection of Madison Street and State Street as the origin of a coordinate system, with east being the positive x-axis.

(a) Write the location of Wrigley Field using rectangular coordinates.

(b) Write the location of Wrigley Field using polar coordinates. Use the east direction for the polar axis. Express θ in degrees.

(c) U.S. Cellular Field, home of the White Sox, is located at 35th and Princeton, which is 3 blocks west of State Street and 35 blocks south of Madison. Write the location of U.S. Cellular Field using rectangular coordinates.

(d) Write the location of U.S. Cellular Field using polar coordinates. Use the east direction for the polar axis. Express θ in degrees.

84. Show that the formula for the distance d between two points $P_1 = (r_1, \theta_1)$ and $P_2 = (r_2, \theta_2)$ is

$$d = \sqrt{r_1^2 + r_2^2 - 2r_1 r_2 \cos(\theta_2 - \theta_1)}$$

City of Chicago, Illinois

Discussion and Writing

85. In converting from polar coordinates to rectangular coordinates, what formulas will you use?

86. Explain how you proceed to convert from rectangular coordinates to polar coordinates.

87. Is the street system in your town based on a rectangular coordinate system, a polar coordinate system, or some other system? Explain.

'Are You Prepared?' Answers

1. 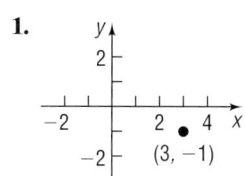 ; quadrant IV   **2.** 9   **3.** $\dfrac{b}{r}$ **4.** $-\dfrac{\pi}{4}$

9.2 Polar Equations and Graphs

PREPARING FOR THIS SECTION *Before getting started, review the following:*

- Symmetry (Section 1.2, pp. 19–21)
- Circles (Section 1.5, pp. 44–48)
- Even–Odd Properties of Trigonometric Functions (Section 6.3, pp. 391–392)
- Difference Formulas for Sine and Cosine (Section 7.4, pp. 466 and 469)
- Value of the Sine and Cosine Functions at Certain Angles (Section 6.2, pp. 368–375)

Now Work the 'Are You Prepared?' problems on page 586.

OBJECTIVES 1 Graph and Identify Polar Equations by Converting to Rectangular Equations (p. 572)

           2 Graph Polar Equations Using a Graphing Utility (p. 573)

           3 Test Polar Equations for Symmetry (p. 577)

           4 Graph Polar Equations by Plotting Points (p. 578)

Just as a rectangular grid may be used to plot points given by rectangular coordinates, as in Figure 21(a), we can use a grid consisting of concentric circles (with centers at the pole) and rays (with vertices at the pole) to plot points given by polar coordinates, as shown in Figure 21(b). We shall use such **polar grids** to graph *polar equations*.

Figure 21

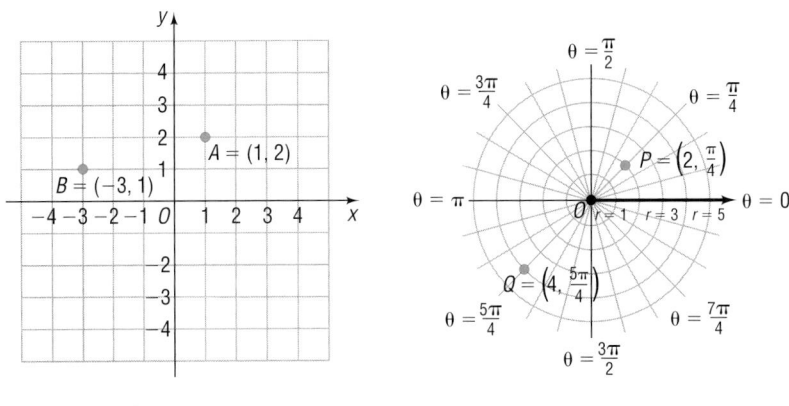

(a) Rectangular grid   (b) Polar grid

DEFINITION   An equation whose variables are polar coordinates is called a **polar equation.**
The **graph of a polar equation** consists of all points whose polar coordinates
satisfy the equation.

1 Graph and Identify Polar Equations by Converting to Rectangular Equations

One method that we can use to graph a polar equation is to convert the equation to
rectangular coordinates. In the discussion that follows, (x, y) represent the rectangular coordinates of a point P, and (r, θ) represent polar coordinates of the point P.

| **EXAMPLE 1** | Identifying and Graphing a Polar Equation (Circle) |

Identify and graph the equation: $r = 3$

Solution   We convert the polar equation to a rectangular equation.

$$r = 3$$
$$r^2 = 9 \quad \text{Square both sides.}$$
$$x^2 + y^2 = 9 \quad r^2 = x^2 + y^2$$

The graph of $r = 3$ is a circle, with center at the pole and radius 3. See Figure 22.

Figure 22
$r = 3$ or $x^2 + y^2 = 9$

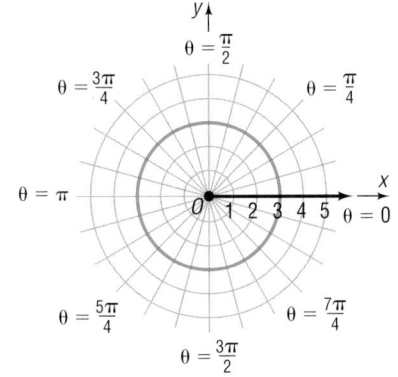

━━━━▶ **Now Work** PROBLEM **13**

| **EXAMPLE 2** | Identifying and Graphing a Polar Equation (Line) |

Identify and graph the equation: $\theta = \dfrac{\pi}{4}$

Solution We convert the polar equation to a rectangular equation.

Figure 23

$\theta = \dfrac{\pi}{4}$ or $y = x$

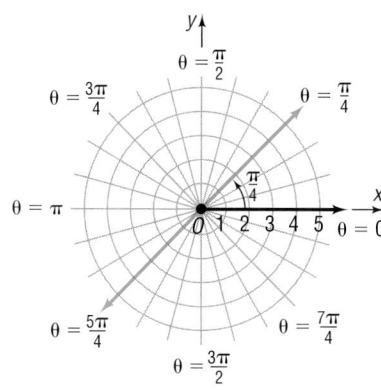

$$\theta = \frac{\pi}{4}$$

$$\tan \theta = \tan \frac{\pi}{4} \quad \text{Take the tangent of both sides.}$$

$$\frac{y}{x} = 1 \qquad \tan \theta = \frac{y}{x}; \tan \frac{\pi}{4} = 1$$

$$y = x$$

The graph of $\theta = \dfrac{\pi}{4}$ is a line passing through the pole making an angle of $\dfrac{\pi}{4}$ with the polar axis. See Figure 23.

Now Work PROBLEM 15

EXAMPLE 3 **Identifying and Graphing a Polar Equation (Horizontal Line)**

Identify and graph the equation: $r \sin \theta = 2$

Solution Since $y = r \sin \theta$, we can write the equation as

$$y = 2$$

We conclude that the graph of $r \sin \theta = 2$ is a horizontal line 2 units above the pole. See Figure 24.

Figure 24
$r \sin \theta = 2$ or $y = 2$

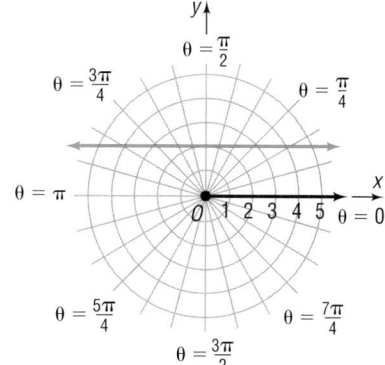

2 Graph Polar Equations Using a Graphing Utility

A second method we can use to graph a polar equation is to graph the equation using a graphing utility.

Most graphing utilities require the following steps to obtain the graph of an equation:

Graphing a Polar Equation Using a Graphing Utility

STEP 1: Solve the equation for r in terms of θ.

STEP 2: Select the viewing window in POLar mode. In addition to setting Xmin, Xmax, Xscl, and so forth, the viewing window in polar mode requires setting minimum and maximum values for θ and an increment setting for θ (θstep). Finally, a square screen and radian measure should be used.

STEP 3: Enter the expression involving θ that you found in Step 1. (Consult your manual for the correct way to enter the expression.)

STEP 4: Press graph.

| EXAMPLE 4 | Graphing a Polar Equation Using a Graphing Utility |

Use a graphing utility to graph the polar equation $r \sin \theta = 2$.

Solution **STEP 1:** We solve the equation for r in terms of θ.

$$r \sin \theta = 2$$

$$r = \frac{2}{\sin \theta}$$

STEP 2: From the polar mode, select a square viewing window. We will use the one given next.

$$\theta\min = 0 \qquad X\min = -9 \qquad Y\min = -6$$
$$\theta\max = 2\pi \qquad X\max = 9 \qquad Y\max = 6$$
$$\theta\text{step} = \frac{\pi}{24} \qquad X\text{scl} = 1 \qquad Y\text{scl} = 1$$

θstep determines the number of points the graphing utility will plot. For example, if θstep is $\dfrac{\pi}{24}$, then the graphing utility will evaluate r at $\theta = 0$ ($\theta\min$), $\dfrac{\pi}{24}, \dfrac{2\pi}{24}, \dfrac{3\pi}{24}$, and so forth, up to 2π ($\theta\max$).

The smaller θstep is the more points the graphing utility will plot. The student is encouraged to experiment with different values for $\theta\min$, $\theta\max$, and θstep to see how the graph is affected.

Figure 25

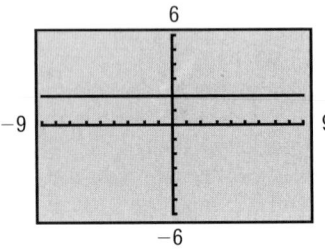

STEP 3: Enter the expression $\dfrac{2}{\sin \theta}$ after the prompt $r =$.

STEP 4: Graph.

The graph is shown in Figure 25.

| EXAMPLE 5 | Identifying and Graphing a Polar Equation (Vertical Line) |

Identify and graph the equation: $r \cos \theta = -3$

Solution Since $x = r \cos \theta$, we can write the equation as

$$x = -3$$

We conclude that the graph of $r \cos \theta = -3$ is a vertical line 3 units to the left of the pole. Figure 26(a) shows the graph drawn by hand. Figure 26(b) shows the graph using a graphing utility with $\theta\min = 0$, $\theta\max = 2\pi$, and $\theta\text{step} = \dfrac{\pi}{24}$.

Figure 26
$r \cos \theta = -3$ or $x = -3$

(a)

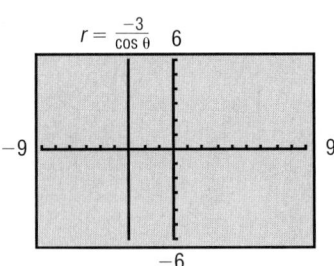

(b)

Based on Examples 3, 4, and 5, we are led to the following results. (The proofs are left as exercises. See Problems 81 and 82.)

THEOREM

Let a be a nonzero real number. Then the graph of the equation

$$r \sin \theta = a$$

is a horizontal line a units above the pole if $a > 0$ and $|a|$ units below the pole if $a < 0$.

The graph of the equation

$$r \cos \theta = a$$

is a vertical line a units to the right of the pole if $a > 0$ and $|a|$ units to the left of the pole if $a < 0$.

⎯ **Now Work** PROBLEM 19

EXAMPLE 6   **Identifying and Graphing a Polar Equation (Circle)**

Identify and graph the equation: $r = 4 \sin \theta$

Solution   To transform the equation to rectangular coordinates, we multiply each side by r.

$$r^2 = 4r \sin \theta$$

Now we use the facts that $r^2 = x^2 + y^2$ and $y = r \sin \theta$. Then

$$x^2 + y^2 = 4y$$

$$x^2 + (y^2 - 4y) = 0$$

$$x^2 + (y^2 - 4y + 4) = 4 \qquad \text{Complete the square in } y.$$

$$x^2 + (y - 2)^2 = 4 \qquad \text{Factor.}$$

This is the standard equation of a circle with center at $(0, 2)$ in rectangular coordinates and radius 2. Figure 27(a) shows the graph drawn by hand. Figure 27(b) shows the graph using a graphing utility with $\theta\min = 0, \theta\max = 2\pi$, and $\theta\text{step} = \dfrac{\pi}{24}$.

Figure 27
$r = 4 \sin \theta$ or $x^2 + (y - 2)^2 = 4$

(a)

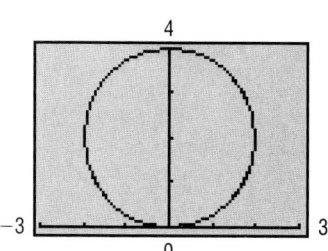

(b)

EXAMPLE 7	**Identifying and Graphing a Polar Equation (Circle)**

Identify and graph the equation: $r = -2 \cos \theta$

Solution We proceed as in Example 6.

$$r^2 = -2r \cos \theta \quad \text{Multiply both sides by } r.$$

$$x^2 + y^2 = -2x \quad r^2 = x^2 + y^2; \quad x = r \cos \theta$$

$$x^2 + 2x + y^2 = 0$$

$$(x^2 + 2x + 1) + y^2 = 1 \quad \text{Complete the square in } x.$$

$$(x + 1)^2 + y^2 = 1 \quad \text{Factor.}$$

This is the standard equation of a circle with center at $(-1, 0)$ in rectangular coordinates and radius 1. Figure 28(a) shows the graph drawn by hand. Figure 28(b) shows the graph using a graphing utility with $\theta\min = 0$, $\theta\max = 2\pi$, and $\theta\text{step} = \dfrac{\pi}{24}$.

Figure 28

$r = -2 \cos \theta$ or $(x + 1)^2 + y^2 = 1$

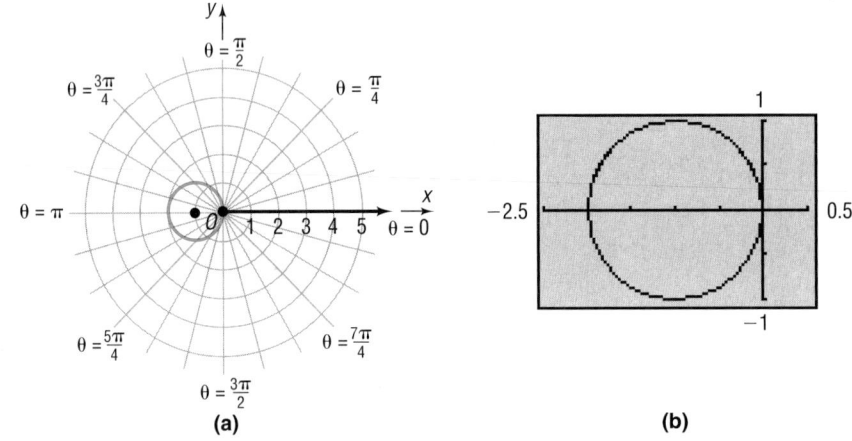

(a)　　　　　(b)

Exploration

Using a square screen, graph $r_1 = \sin \theta$, $r_2 = 2 \sin \theta$, and $r_3 = 3 \sin \theta$. Do you see the pattern? Clear the screen and graph $r_1 = -\sin \theta$, $r_2 = -2 \sin \theta$, and $r_3 = -3 \sin \theta$. Do you see the pattern? Clear the screen and graph $r_1 = \cos \theta$, $r_2 = 2 \cos \theta$, and $r_3 = 3 \cos \theta$. Do you see the pattern? Clear the screen and graph $r_1 = -\cos \theta$, $r_2 = -2 \cos \theta$, and $r_3 = -3 \cos \theta$. Do you see the pattern?

Based on Examples 6 and 7 and the preceding Exploration, we are led to the following results. (The proofs are left as exercises. See Problems 83–86.)

THEOREM Let a be a positive real number. Then

Equation	Description
(a) $r = 2a \sin \theta$	Circle: radius a; center at $(0, a)$ in rectangular coordinates
(b) $r = -2a \sin \theta$	Circle: radius a; center at $(0, -a)$ in rectangular coordinates
(c) $r = 2a \cos \theta$	Circle: radius a; center at $(a, 0)$ in rectangular coordinates
(d) $r = -2a \cos \theta$	Circle: radius a; center at $(-a, 0)$ in rectangular coordinates

Each circle passes through the pole.

Now Work PROBLEM 21

The method of converting a polar equation to an identifiable rectangular equation to obtain the graph is not always helpful, nor is it always necessary. Usually, we set up a table that lists several points on the graph. By checking for symmetry, it may be possible to reduce the number of points needed to draw the graph.

3 Test Polar Equations for Symmetry

In polar coordinates, the points (r, θ) and $(r, -\theta)$ are symmetric with respect to the polar axis (and to the x-axis). See Figure 29(a). The points (r, θ) and $(r, \pi - \theta)$ are symmetric with respect to the line $\theta = \dfrac{\pi}{2}$ (the y-axis). See Figure 29(b). The points (r, θ) and $(-r, \theta)$ are symmetric with respect to the pole (the origin). See Figure 29(c).

Figure 29

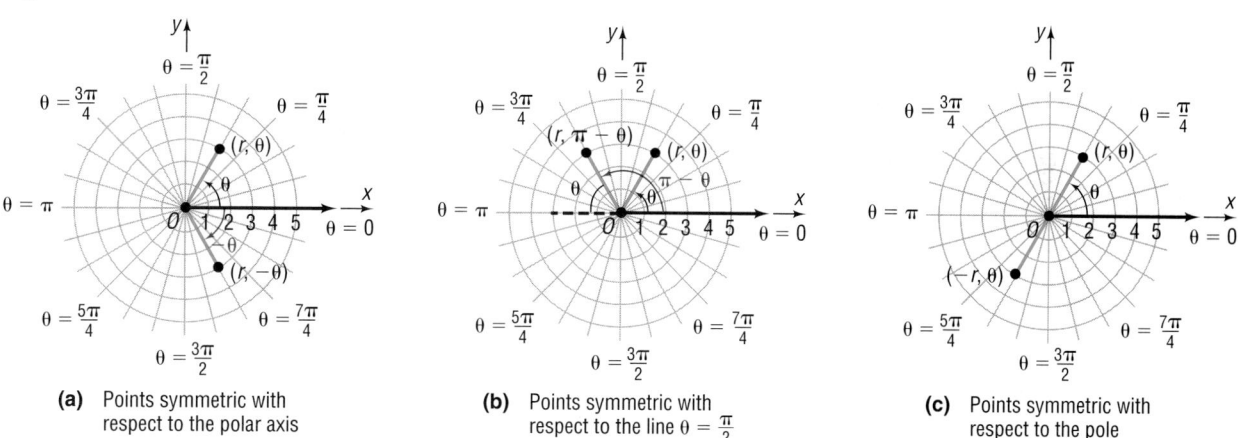

(a) Points symmetric with respect to the polar axis

(b) Points symmetric with respect to the line $\theta = \dfrac{\pi}{2}$

(c) Points symmetric with respect to the pole

The following tests are a consequence of these observations.

THEOREM

Tests for Symmetry

Symmetry with Respect to the Polar Axis (x-Axis)

In a polar equation, replace θ by $-\theta$. If an equivalent equation results, the graph is symmetric with respect to the polar axis.

Symmetry with Respect to the Line $\theta = \dfrac{\pi}{2}$ (y-Axis)

In a polar equation, replace θ by $\pi - \theta$. If an equivalent equation results, the graph is symmetric with respect to the line $\theta = \dfrac{\pi}{2}$.

Symmetry with Respect to the Pole (Origin)

In a polar equation, replace r by $-r$. If an equivalent equation results, the graph is symmetric with respect to the pole.

The three tests for symmetry given here are *sufficient* conditions for symmetry, but they are not *necessary* conditions. That is, an equation may fail these tests and still have a graph that is symmetric with respect to the polar axis, the line $\theta = \dfrac{\pi}{2}$, or the pole. For example, the graph of $r = \sin(2\theta)$ turns out to be symmetric with respect to the polar axis, the line $\theta = \dfrac{\pi}{2}$, and the pole, but all three tests given here fail. See also Problems 87–89.

4 Graph Polar Equations by Plotting Points

> **EXAMPLE 8**   **Graphing a Polar Equation (Cardioid)**
>
> Graph the equation: $r = 1 - \sin \theta$

Solution

We check for symmetry first.

Polar Axis: Replace θ by $-\theta$. The result is

$$r = 1 - \sin(-\theta) = 1 + \sin \theta \quad \text{\small sin}(-\theta) = -\sin \theta$$

The test fails, so the graph may or may not be symmetric with respect to the polar axis.

The Line $\theta = \dfrac{\pi}{2}$:   Replace θ by $\pi - \theta$. The result is

$$r = 1 - \sin(\pi - \theta) = 1 - (\sin \pi \cos \theta - \cos \pi \sin \theta)$$
$$= 1 - [0 \cdot \cos \theta - (-1) \sin \theta] = 1 - \sin \theta$$

The test is satisfied, so the graph is symmetric with respect to the line $\theta = \dfrac{\pi}{2}$.

The Pole: Replace r by $-r$. Then the result is $-r = 1 - \sin \theta$, so $r = -1 + \sin \theta$. The test fails, so the graph may or may not be symmetric with respect to the pole.

Next, we identify points on the graph by assigning values to the angle θ and calculating the corresponding values of r. Due to the symmetry with respect to the line $\theta = \dfrac{\pi}{2}$, we only need to assign values to θ from $-\dfrac{\pi}{2}$ to $\dfrac{\pi}{2}$, as given in Table 1.

Now we plot the points (r, θ) from Table 1 and trace out the graph, beginning at the point $\left(2, -\dfrac{\pi}{2}\right)$ and ending at the point $\left(0, \dfrac{\pi}{2}\right)$. Then we reflect this portion of the graph about the line $\theta = \dfrac{\pi}{2}$ (the y-axis) to obtain the complete graph. Figure 30(a) shows the graph drawn by hand. Figure 30(b) shows the graph using a graphing utility with $\theta\min = 0$, $\theta\max = 2\pi$, and $\theta\text{step} = \dfrac{\pi}{24}$.

Table 1

θ	$r = 1 - \sin \theta$
$-\dfrac{\pi}{2}$	$1 - (-1) = 2$
$-\dfrac{\pi}{3}$	$1 - \left(-\dfrac{\sqrt{3}}{2}\right) \approx 1.87$
$-\dfrac{\pi}{6}$	$1 - \left(-\dfrac{1}{2}\right) = \dfrac{3}{2}$
0	$1 - 0 = 1$
$\dfrac{\pi}{6}$	$1 - \dfrac{1}{2} = \dfrac{1}{2}$
$\dfrac{\pi}{3}$	$1 - \dfrac{\sqrt{3}}{2} \approx 0.13$
$\dfrac{\pi}{2}$	$1 - 1 = 0$

Figure 30

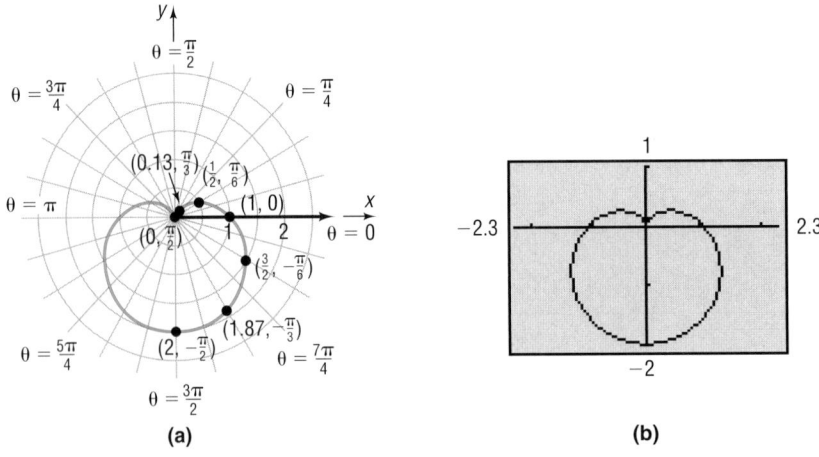

(a)   (b)

Exploration

Graph $r_1 = 1 + \sin \theta$. Clear the screen and graph $r_1 = 1 - \cos \theta$. Clear the screen and graph $r_1 = 1 + \cos \theta$. Do you see a pattern?

The curve in Figure 30 is an example of a *cardioid* (a heart-shaped curve).

DEFINITION

Cardioids are characterized by equations of the form

$$r = a(1 + \cos \theta) \qquad r = a(1 + \sin \theta)$$
$$r = a(1 - \cos \theta) \qquad r = a(1 - \sin \theta)$$

where $a > 0$. The graph of a cardioid passes through the pole.

━━━ **Now Work** PROBLEM 37

EXAMPLE 9

Graphing a Polar Equation (Limaçon without Inner Loop)

Graph the equation: $r = 3 + 2 \cos \theta$

Solution

We check for symmetry first.

Polar Axis: Replace θ by $-\theta$. The result is

$$r = 3 + 2 \cos(-\theta) = 3 + 2 \cos \theta \quad \cos(-\theta) = \cos \theta$$

The test is satisfied, so the graph is symmetric with respect to the polar axis.

The Line $\theta = \dfrac{\pi}{2}$: Replace θ by $\pi - \theta$. The result is

$$r = 3 + 2 \cos(\pi - \theta) = 3 + 2(\cos \pi \cos \theta + \sin \pi \sin \theta)$$
$$= 3 - 2 \cos \theta$$

The test fails, so the graph may or may not be symmetric with respect to the line $\theta = \dfrac{\pi}{2}$.

The Pole: Replace r by $-r$. The test fails, so the graph may or may not be symmetric with respect to the pole.

Next, we identify points on the graph by assigning values to the angle θ and calculating the corresponding values of r. Due to the symmetry with respect to the polar axis, we only need to assign values to θ from 0 to π, as given in Table 2.

Now we plot the points (r, θ) from Table 2 and trace out the graph, beginning at the point $(5, 0)$ and ending at the point $(1, \pi)$. Then we reflect this portion of the graph about the polar axis (the x-axis) to obtain the complete graph. Figure 31(a) shows the graph drawn by hand. Figure 31(b) shows the graph using a graphing utility with $\theta\min = 0$, $\theta\max = 2\pi$, and $\theta\text{step} = \dfrac{\pi}{24}$.

Table 2

θ	$r = 3 + 2 \cos \theta$
0	$3 + 2(1) = 5$
$\dfrac{\pi}{6}$	$3 + 2\left(\dfrac{\sqrt{3}}{2}\right) \approx 4.73$
$\dfrac{\pi}{3}$	$3 + 2\left(\dfrac{1}{2}\right) = 4$
$\dfrac{\pi}{2}$	$3 + 2(0) = 3$
$\dfrac{2\pi}{3}$	$3 + 2\left(-\dfrac{1}{2}\right) = 2$
$\dfrac{5\pi}{6}$	$3 + 2\left(-\dfrac{\sqrt{3}}{2}\right) \approx 1.27$
π	$3 + 2(-1) = 1$

Figure 31

(a)

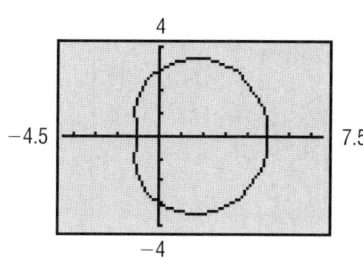

(b)

Exploration

Graph $r_1 = 3 - 2 \cos \theta$. Clear the screen and graph $r_1 = 3 + 2 \sin \theta$. Clear the screen and graph $r_1 = 3 - 2 \sin \theta$. Do you see a pattern?

The curve in Figure 31 is an example of a *limaçon* (the French word for *snail*) *without an inner loop.*

DEFINITION

Limaçons without an inner loop are characterized by equations of the form

$$r = a + b \cos \theta \qquad r = a + b \sin \theta$$
$$r = a - b \cos \theta \qquad r = a - b \sin \theta$$

where $a > 0, b > 0$, and $a > b$. The graph of a limaçon without an inner loop does not pass through the pole.

━━━━▶ **Now Work** PROBLEM 43

EXAMPLE 10   Graphing a Polar Equation (Limaçon with Inner Loop)

Graph the equation: $r = 1 + 2 \cos \theta$

Solution   First, we check for symmetry.

Polar Axis: Replace θ by $-\theta$. The result is

$$r = 1 + 2 \cos(-\theta) = 1 + 2 \cos \theta$$

The test is satisfied, so the graph is symmetric with respect to the polar axis.

The Line $\theta = \dfrac{\pi}{2}$: Replace θ by $\pi - \theta$. The result is

$$r = 1 + 2 \cos(\pi - \theta) = 1 + 2(\cos \pi \cos \theta + \sin \pi \sin \theta)$$
$$= 1 - 2 \cos \theta$$

The test fails, so the graph may or may not be symmetric with respect to the line $\theta = \dfrac{\pi}{2}$.

The Pole: Replace r by $-r$. The test fails, so the graph may or may not be symmetric with respect to the pole.

Next, we identify points on the graph of $r = 1 + 2 \cos \theta$ by assigning values to the angle θ and calculating the corresponding values of r. Due to the symmetry with respect to the polar axis, we only need to assign values to θ from 0 to π, as given in Table 3.

Now we plot the points (r, θ) from Table 3, beginning at $(3, 0)$ and ending at $(-1, \pi)$. See Figure 32(a). Finally, we reflect this portion of the graph about the polar axis (the x-axis) to obtain the complete graph. See Figure 32(b). Figure 32(c) shows the graph using a graphing utility with $\theta\text{min} = 0$, $\theta\text{max} = 2\pi$, and $\theta\text{step} = \dfrac{\pi}{24}$.

Table 3

θ	$r = 1 + 2 \cos \theta$
0	$1 + 2(1) = 3$
$\dfrac{\pi}{6}$	$1 + 2\left(\dfrac{\sqrt{3}}{2}\right) \approx 2.73$
$\dfrac{\pi}{3}$	$1 + 2\left(\dfrac{1}{2}\right) = 2$
$\dfrac{\pi}{2}$	$1 + 2(0) = 1$
$\dfrac{2\pi}{3}$	$1 + 2\left(-\dfrac{1}{2}\right) = 0$
$\dfrac{5\pi}{6}$	$1 + 2\left(-\dfrac{\sqrt{3}}{2}\right) \approx -0.73$
π	$1 + 2(-1) = -1$

Figure 32

(a)

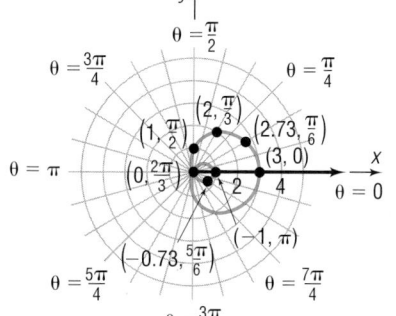

(b) $r = 1 + 2 \cos \theta$

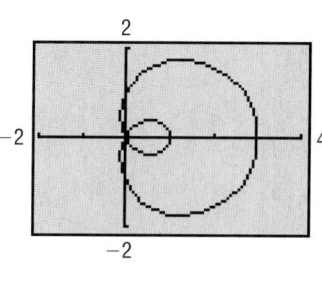

(c)

Exploration

Graph $r_1 = 1 - 2 \cos \theta$. Clear the screen and graph $r_1 = 1 + 2 \sin \theta$. Clear the screen and graph $r_1 = 1 - 2 \sin \theta$. Do you see a pattern?

The curve in Figure 32(b) or 32(c) is an example of a *limaçon with an inner loop*.

DEFINITION

Limaçons with an inner loop are characterized by equations of the form

$$r = a + b \cos \theta \qquad r = a + b \sin \theta$$
$$r = a - b \cos \theta \qquad r = a - b \sin \theta$$

where $a > 0, b > 0$, and $a < b$. The graph of a limaçon with an inner loop will pass through the pole twice.

━━━━ **Now Work** PROBLEM 45

EXAMPLE 11 **Graphing a Polar Equation (Rose)**

Graph the equation: $r = 2 \cos(2\theta)$

Solution We check for symmetry.

Polar Axis: If we replace θ by $-\theta$, the result is

$$r = 2 \cos[2(-\theta)] = 2 \cos(2\theta)$$

The test is satisfied, so the graph is symmetric with respect to the polar axis.

The Line $\theta = \dfrac{\pi}{2}$: If we replace θ by $\pi - \theta$, we obtain

$$r = 2 \cos[2(\pi - \theta)] = 2 \cos(2\pi - 2\theta) = 2 \cos(2\theta)$$

The test is satisfied, so the graph is symmetric with respect to the line $\theta = \dfrac{\pi}{2}$.

The Pole: Since the graph is symmetric with respect to both the polar axis and the line $\theta = \dfrac{\pi}{2}$, it must be symmetric with respect to the pole.

Table 4

θ	$r = 2\cos(2\theta)$
0	$2(1) = 2$
$\dfrac{\pi}{6}$	$2\left(\dfrac{1}{2}\right) = 1$
$\dfrac{\pi}{4}$	$2(0) = 0$
$\dfrac{\pi}{3}$	$2\left(-\dfrac{1}{2}\right) = -1$
$\dfrac{\pi}{2}$	$2(-1) = -2$

Next, we construct Table 4. Due to the symmetry with respect to the polar axis, the line $\theta = \dfrac{\pi}{2}$, and the pole, we consider only values of θ from 0 to $\dfrac{\pi}{2}$.

We plot and connect these points in Figure 33(a). Finally, because of symmetry, we reflect this portion of the graph first about the polar axis (the x-axis) and then about the line $\theta = \dfrac{\pi}{2}$ (the y-axis) to obtain the complete graph. See Figure 33(b). Figure 33(c) shows the graph using a graphing utility with $\theta\min = 0$, $\theta\max = 2\pi$, and $\theta\text{step} = \dfrac{\pi}{24}$.

Figure 33

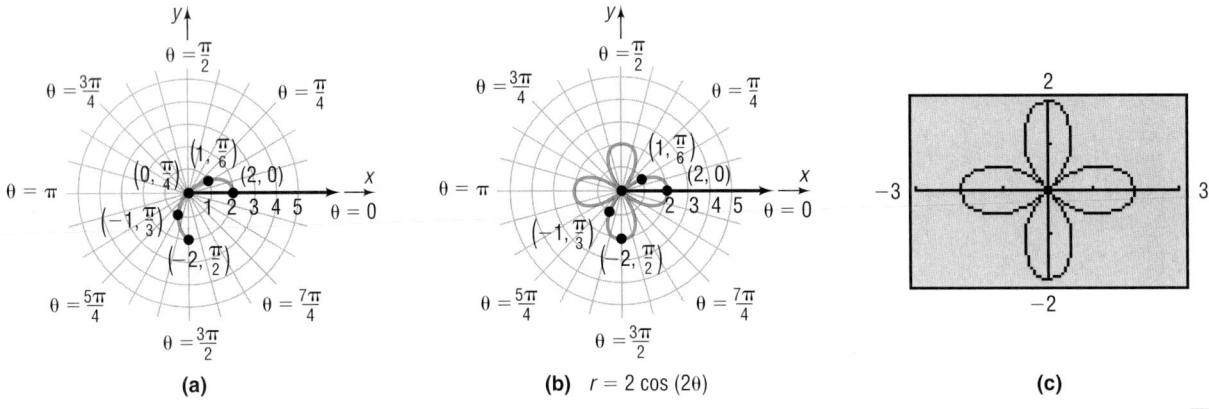

(a)   (b) $r = 2\cos(2\theta)$ (c)

Exploration

Graph $r_1 = 2\cos(4\theta)$; clear the screen and graph $r_1 = 2\cos(6\theta)$. How many petals did each of these graphs have?

   Clear the screen and graph, in order, each on a clear screen, $r_1 = 2\cos(3\theta)$, $r_1 = 2\cos(5\theta)$, and $r_1 = 2\cos(7\theta)$. What do you notice about the number of petals?

The curve in Figure 33(b) or 33(c) is called a *rose* with four petals.

DEFINITION

Rose curves are characterized by equations of the form

$$r = a\cos(n\theta), \qquad r = a\sin(n\theta), \qquad a \neq 0$$

and have graphs that are rose shaped. If $n \neq 0$ is even, the rose has $2n$ petals; if $n \neq \pm 1$ is odd, the rose has n petals.

Now Work PROBLEM 49

EXAMPLE 12   **Graphing a Polar Equation (Lemniscate)**

Graph the equation: $r^2 = 4\sin(2\theta)$

Table 5

θ	$r^2 = 4\sin(2\theta)$	r
0	$4(0) = 0$	0
$\dfrac{\pi}{6}$	$4\left(\dfrac{\sqrt{3}}{2}\right) = 2\sqrt{3}$	± 1.9
$\dfrac{\pi}{4}$	$4(1) = 4$	± 2
$\dfrac{\pi}{3}$	$4\left(\dfrac{\sqrt{3}}{2}\right) = 2\sqrt{3}$	± 1.9
$\dfrac{\pi}{2}$	$4(0) = 0$	0

Solution We leave it to you to verify that the graph is symmetric with respect to the pole. Because of the symmetry with respect to the pole, we only need to consider values of θ between $\theta = 0$ and $\theta = \pi$. Note that there are no points on the graph for $\dfrac{\pi}{2} < \theta < \pi$ (quadrant II), since $\sin(2\theta) < 0$ for such values. Table 5 lists points on the graph for values of $\theta = 0$ through $\theta = \dfrac{\pi}{2}$. The points from Table 5 where $r \geq 0$ are plotted in Figure 34(a). The remaining points on the graph may be obtained by using symmetry. Figure 34(b) shows the final graph drawn by hand. Figure 34(c) shows the graph using a graphing utility with θmin $= 0$, θmax $= 2\pi$, and θstep $= \dfrac{\pi}{24}$.

Figure 34

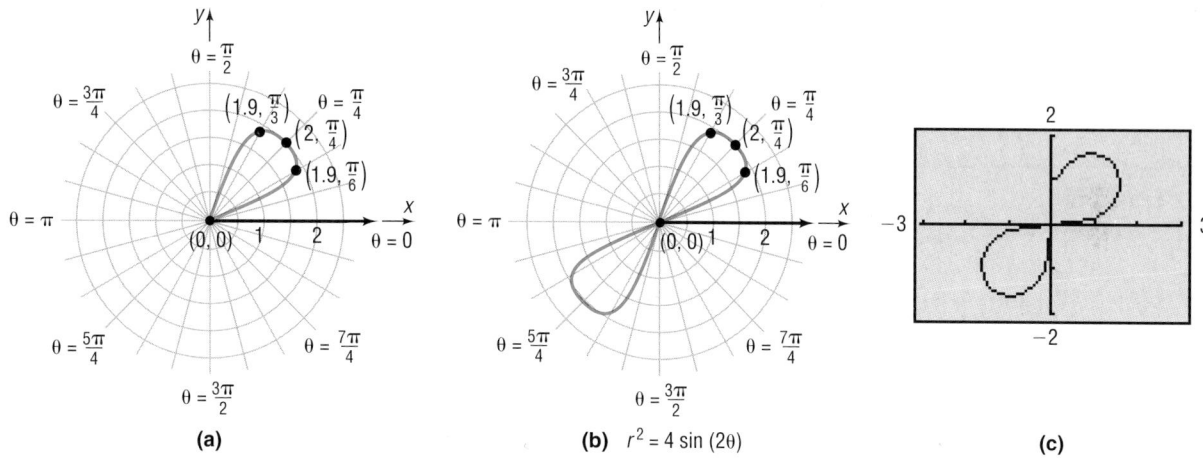

(a)

(b) $r^2 = 4\sin(2\theta)$

(c)

The curve in Figure 34(b) or 34(c) is an example of a *lemniscate* (from the Greek word *ribbon*).

DEFINITION **Lemniscates** are characterized by equations of the form

$$r^2 = a^2\sin(2\theta) \qquad r^2 = a^2\cos(2\theta)$$

where $a \neq 0$, and have graphs that are propeller shaped.

Now Work PROBLEM 53

EXAMPLE 13 **Graphing a Polar Equation (Spiral)**

Graph the equation: $r = e^{\theta/5}$

Solution The tests for symmetry with respect to the pole, the polar axis, and the line $\theta = \dfrac{\pi}{2}$ fail. Furthermore, there is no number θ for which $r = 0$, so the graph does not pass through the pole. We observe that r is positive for all θ, r increases as θ increases, $r \to 0$ as $\theta \to -\infty$, and $r \to \infty$ as $\theta \to \infty$. With the help of a calculator, we obtain the values in Table 6. See Figure 35(a) for the graph drawn by hand. Figure 35(b)

Table 6

θ	$r = e^{\theta/5}$
$-\dfrac{3\pi}{2}$	0.39
$-\pi$	0.53
$-\dfrac{\pi}{2}$	0.73
$-\dfrac{\pi}{4}$	0.85
0	1
$\dfrac{\pi}{4}$	1.17
$\dfrac{\pi}{2}$	1.37
π	1.87
$\dfrac{3\pi}{2}$	2.57
2π	3.51

shows the graph using a graphing utility with $\theta\min = -4\pi$, $\theta\max = 3\pi$, and $\theta\text{step} = \dfrac{\pi}{24}$.

Figure 35
$r = e^{\theta/5}$

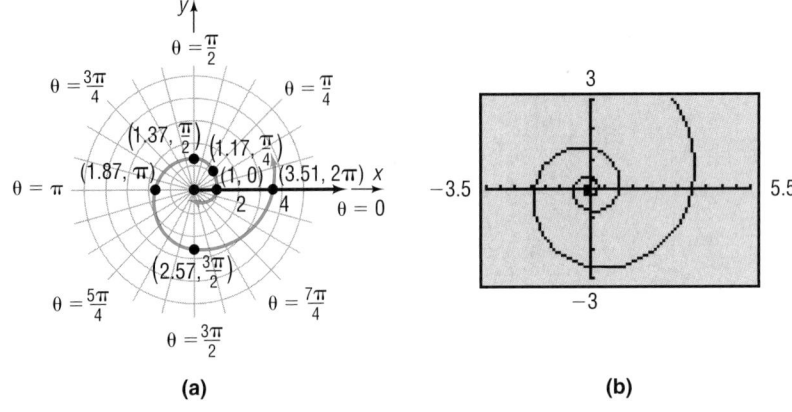

(a)　　　　　　　　　　(b)

The curve in Figure 35 is called a **logarithmic spiral,** since its equation may be written as $\theta = 5 \ln r$ and it spirals infinitely both toward the pole and away from it.

Classification of Polar Equations

The equations of some lines and circles in polar coordinates and their corresponding equations in rectangular coordinates are given in Table 7. Also included are the names and graphs of a few of the more frequently encountered polar equations.

Table 7

Lines			
Description	Line passing through the pole making an angle α with the polar axis	Vertical line	Horizontal line
Rectangular equation	$y = (\tan \alpha)x$	$x = a$	$y = b$
Polar equation	$\theta = \alpha$	$r \cos \theta = a$	$r \sin \theta = b$
Typical graph			

Circles			
Description	Center at the pole, radius a	Passing through the pole, tangent to the line $\theta = \dfrac{\pi}{2}$, center on the polar axis, radius a	Passing through the pole, tangent to the polar axis, center on the line $\theta = \dfrac{\pi}{2}$, radius a
Rectangular equation	$x^2 + y^2 = a^2,\ \ a > 0$	$x^2 + y^2 = \pm 2ax,\ \ a > 0$	$x^2 + y^2 = \pm 2ay,\ \ a > 0$
Polar equation	$r = a,\ \ a > 0$	$r = \pm 2a \cos \theta,\ \ a > 0$	$r = \pm 2a \sin \theta,\ \ a > 0$
Typical graph			

	Other Equations		
Name	Cardioid	Limaçon without inner loop	Limaçon with inner loop
Polar equations	$r = a \pm a \cos \theta, \quad a > 0$	$r = a \pm b \cos \theta, \quad 0 < b < a$	$r = a \pm b \cos \theta, \quad 0 < a < b$
	$r = a \pm a \sin \theta, \quad a > 0$	$r = a \pm b \sin \theta, \quad 0 < b < a$	$r = a \pm b \sin \theta, \quad 0 < a < b$
Typical graph			
Name	Lemniscate	Rose with three petals	Rose with four petals
Polar equations	$r^2 = a^2 \cos(2\theta), \quad a > 0$	$r = a \sin(3\theta), \quad a > 0$	$r = a \sin(2\theta), \quad a > 0$
	$r^2 = a^2 \sin(2\theta), \quad a > 0$	$r = a \cos(3\theta), \quad a > 0$	$r = a \cos(2\theta), \quad a > 0$
Typical graph			

Sketching Quickly

If a polar equation involves only a sine (or cosine) function, you can quickly obtain a sketch of its graph by making use of Table 7, periodicity, and a short table.

EXAMPLE 14   **Sketching the Graph of a Polar Equation Quickly**

Graph the equation: $r = 2 + 2 \sin \theta$

Solution   We recognize the polar equation: Its graph is a cardioid. The period of $\sin \theta$ is 2π, so we form a table using $0 \le \theta \le 2\pi$, compute r, plot the points (r, θ), and sketch the graph of a cardioid as θ varies from 0 to 2π. See Table 8 and Figure 36.

Table 8

θ	$r = 2 + 2 \sin \theta$
0	$2 + 2(0) = 2$
$\dfrac{\pi}{2}$	$2 + 2(1) = 4$
π	$2 + 2(0) = 2$
$\dfrac{3\pi}{2}$	$2 + 2(-1) = 0$
2π	$2 + 2(0) = 2$

Figure 36

 Now Work PROBLEM **37**

⚓ **Calculus Comment**   For those of you who are planning to study calculus, a comment about one important role of polar equations is in order.

In rectangular coordinates, the equation $x^2 + y^2 = 1$, whose graph is the unit circle, is not the graph of a function. In fact, it requires two functions to obtain the graph of the unit circle:

$$y_1 = \sqrt{1 - x^2} \quad \text{Upper semicircle} \qquad y_2 = -\sqrt{1 - x^2} \quad \text{Lower semicircle}$$

In polar coordinates, the equation $r = 1$, whose graph is also the unit circle, does define a function. For each choice of θ, there is only one corresponding value of r, that is, $r = 1$. Since many problems in calculus require the use of functions, the opportunity to express nonfunctions in rectangular coordinates as functions in polar coordinates becomes extremely useful.

Note also that the vertical-line test for functions is valid only for equations in rectangular coordinates.

Historical Feature

Jakob Bernoulli (1654–1705)

Polar coordinates seem to have been invented by Jakob Bernoulli (1654–1705) in about 1691, although, as with most such ideas, earlier traces of the notion exist. Early users of calculus remained committed to rectangular coordinates, and polar coordinates did not become widely used until the early 1800s. Even then, it was mostly geometers who used them for describing odd curves. Finally, about the mid-1800s, applied mathematicians realized the tremendous simplification that polar coordinates make possible in the description of objects with circular or cylindrical symmetry. From then on their use became widespread.

9.2 Assess Your Understanding

'Are You Prepared?' *Answers are given at the end of these exercises. If you get a wrong answer, read the pages listed in* red.

1. If the rectangular coordinates of a point are $(4, -6)$, the point symmetric to it with respect to the origin is _____. (pp. 19–20)

2. The difference formula for cosine is $\cos(A - B) = $ _____. (p. 466)

3. The standard equation of a circle with center at $(-2, 5)$ and radius 3 is _____. (pp. 44–45)

4. Is the sine function even, odd, or neither? (p. 391)

5. $\sin \dfrac{5\pi}{4} = $ _____. (pp. 374–375)

6. $\cos \dfrac{2\pi}{3} = $ _____. (pp. 374–375)

Concepts and Vocabulary

7. An equation whose variables are polar coordinates is called a(n) _____ _____.

8. Using polar coordinates (r, θ), the circle $x^2 + y^2 = 2x$ takes the form _____.

9. A polar equation is symmetric with respect to the pole if an equivalent equation results when r is replaced by _____.

10. **True or False** The tests for symmetry in polar coordinates are necessary, but not sufficient.

11. **True or False** The graph of a cardioid never passes through the pole.

12. **True or False** All polar equations have a symmetric feature.

Skill Building

In Problems 13–28, transform each polar equation to an equation in rectangular coordinates. Then identify and graph the equation. Verify your graph using a graphing utility.

13. $r = 4$

14. $r = 2$

15. $\theta = \dfrac{\pi}{3}$

16. $\theta = -\dfrac{\pi}{4}$

17. $r \sin \theta = 4$

18. $r \cos \theta = 4$

19. $r \cos \theta = -2$

20. $r \sin \theta = -2$

21. $r = 2 \cos \theta$

22. $r = 2 \sin \theta$

23. $r = -4 \sin \theta$

24. $r = -4 \cos \theta$

25. $r \sec \theta = 4$

26. $r \csc \theta = 8$

27. $r \csc \theta = -2$

28. $r \sec \theta = -4$

In Problems 29–36, match each of the graphs (A) through (H) to one of the following polar equations.

29. $r = 2$

30. $\theta = \dfrac{\pi}{4}$

31. $r = 2\cos\theta$

32. $r\cos\theta = 2$

33. $r = 1 + \cos\theta$

34. $r = 2\sin\theta$

35. $\theta = \dfrac{3\pi}{4}$

36. $r\sin\theta = 2$

(A)

(B)

(C)

(D)

(E)

(F)

(G)

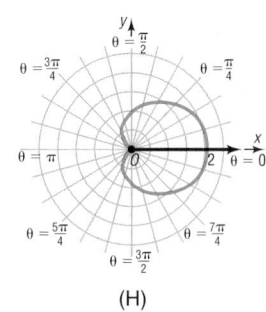

(H)

In Problems 37–60, identify and graph each polar equation. Verify your graph using a graphing utility.

37. $r = 2 + 2\cos\theta$

38. $r = 1 + \sin\theta$

39. $r = 3 - 3\sin\theta$

40. $r = 2 - 2\cos\theta$

41. $r = 2 + \sin\theta$

42. $r = 2 - \cos\theta$

43. $r = 4 - 2\cos\theta$

44. $r = 4 + 2\sin\theta$

45. $r = 1 + 2\sin\theta$

46. $r = 1 - 2\sin\theta$

47. $r = 2 - 3\cos\theta$

48. $r = 2 + 4\cos\theta$

49. $r = 3\cos(2\theta)$

50. $r = 2\sin(3\theta)$

51. $r = 4\sin(5\theta)$

52. $r = 3\cos(4\theta)$

53. $r^2 = 9\cos(2\theta)$

54. $r^2 = \sin(2\theta)$

55. $r = 2^{\theta}$

56. $r = 3^{\theta}$

57. $r = 1 - \cos\theta$

58. $r = 3 + \cos\theta$

59. $r = 1 - 3\cos\theta$

60. $r = 4\cos(3\theta)$

Mixed Practice

In Problems 61–66, graph each pair of polar equations on the same polar grid. Find the polar coordinates of the point(s) of intersection and label the point(s) on the graph.

61. $r = 8\cos\theta$; $r = 2\sec\theta$

62. $r = 8\sin\theta$; $r = 4\csc\theta$

63. $r = \sin\theta$; $r = 1 + \cos\theta$

64. $r = 3$; $r = 2 + 2\cos\theta$

65. $r = 1 + \sin\theta$; $r = 1 + \cos\theta$

66. $r = 1 + \cos\theta$; $r = 3\cos\theta$

Applications and Extensions

In Problems 67–70, the polar equation for each graph is either $r = a + b\cos\theta$ or $r = a + b\sin\theta$, $a > 0$, $b > 0$. Select the correct equation and find the values of a and b.

67.

68.

69.

70.

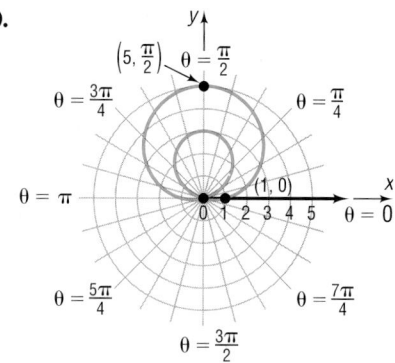

In Problems 71–80, graph each polar equation by hand. Verify your graph using a graphing utility.

71. $r = \dfrac{2}{1 - \cos \theta}$ (parabola)

72. $r = \dfrac{2}{1 - 2 \cos \theta}$ (hyperbola)

73. $r = \dfrac{1}{3 - 2 \cos \theta}$ (ellipse)

74. $r = \dfrac{1}{1 - \cos \theta}$ (parabola)

75. $r = \theta, \quad \theta \geq 0$ (spiral of Archimedes)

76. $r = \dfrac{3}{\theta}$ (reciprocal spiral)

77. $r = \csc \theta - 2, \quad 0 < \theta < \pi$ (conchoid)

78. $r = \sin \theta \tan \theta$ (cissoid)

79. $r = \tan \theta, \quad -\dfrac{\pi}{2} < \theta < \dfrac{\pi}{2}$ (kappa curve)

80. $r = \cos \dfrac{\theta}{2}$

81. Show that the graph of the equation $r \sin \theta = a$ is a horizontal line a units above the pole if $a > 0$ and $|a|$ units below the pole if $a < 0$.

82. Show that the graph of the equation $r \cos \theta = a$ is a vertical line a units to the right of the pole if $a > 0$ and $|a|$ units to the left of the pole if $a < 0$.

83. Show that the graph of the equation $r = 2a \sin \theta, a > 0$, is a circle of radius a with center at $(0, a)$ in rectangular coordinates.

84. Show that the graph of the equation $r = -2a \sin \theta, a > 0$, is a circle of radius a with center at $(0, -a)$ in rectangular coordinates.

85. Show that the graph of the equation $r = 2a \cos \theta, a > 0$, is a circle of radius a with center at $(a, 0)$ in rectangular coordinates.

86. Show that the graph of the equation $r = -2a \cos \theta, a > 0$, is a circle of radius a with center at $(-a, 0)$ in rectangular coordinates.

Discussion and Writing

87. Explain why the following test for symmetry is valid: Replace r by $-r$ and θ by $-\theta$ in a polar equation. If an equivalent equation results, the graph is symmetric with respect to the line $\theta = \dfrac{\pi}{2}$ (y-axis).

   (a) Show that the test on page 577 fails for $r^2 = \cos \theta$, yet this new test works.

   (b) Show that the test on page 577 works for $r^2 = \sin \theta$, yet this new test fails.

88. Develop a new test for symmetry with respect to the pole.

   (a) Find a polar equation for which this new test fails, yet the test on page 577 works.

   (b) Find a polar equation for which the test on page 577 fails, yet the new test works.

89. Write down two different tests for symmetry with respect to the polar axis. Find examples in which one test works and the other fails. Which test do you prefer to use? Justify your answer.

90. The tests for symmetry given on page 577 are sufficient, but not necessary. Explain what this means.

'Are You Prepared?' Answers

1. $(-4, 6)$ **2.** $\cos A \cos B + \sin A \sin B$ **3.** $(x + 2)^2 + (y - 5)^2 = 9$ **4.** Odd   **5.** $-\dfrac{\sqrt{2}}{2}$ **6.** $-\dfrac{1}{2}$

9.3 The Complex Plane; De Moivre's Theorem

PREPARING FOR THIS SECTION *Before getting started, review the following:*

- Complex Numbers (Appendix A, Section A.7, pp. A60–A64)
- Value of the Sine and Cosine Functions at Certain Angles (Section 6.2, pp. 368–375)
- Sum and Difference Formulas for Sine and Cosine (Section 7.4, pp. 466 and 469)

Now Work the 'Are You Prepared?' problems on page 595.

OBJECTIVES 1 Plot Points in the Complex Plane (p. 589)
2 Convert a Complex Number from Rectangular Form to Polar Form (p. 590)
3 Find Products and Quotients of Complex Numbers in Polar Form (p. 591)
4 Use De Moivre's Theorem (p. 592)
5 Find Complex Roots (p. 593)

1 Plot Points in the Complex Plane

Figure 37
Complex plane

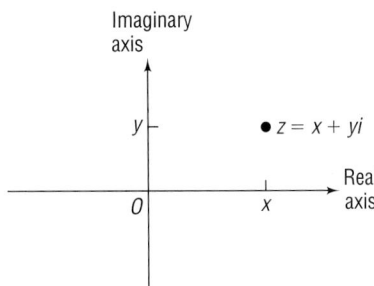

Complex numbers are discussed in Appendix A, Section A.7. In that discussion, we were not prepared to give a geometric interpretation of a complex number. Now we are ready. Although we could give several interpretations, the one that follows is the easiest to understand.

A complex number $z = x + yi$ can be interpreted geometrically as the point (x, y) in the xy-plane. Each point in the plane corresponds to a complex number and, conversely, each complex number corresponds to a point in the plane. We shall refer to the collection of such points as the **complex plane.** The x-axis will be referred to as the **real axis,** because any point that lies on the real axis is of the form $z = x + 0i = x$, a real number. The y-axis is called the **imaginary axis,** because any point that lies on it is of the form $z = 0 + yi = yi$, a pure imaginary number. See Figure 37.

EXAMPLE 1 | **Plotting a Point in the Complex Plane**

Plot the point corresponding to $z = \sqrt{3} - i$ in the complex plane.

Solution The point corresponding to $z = \sqrt{3} - i$ has the rectangular coordinates $(\sqrt{3}, -1)$. The point, located in quadrant IV, is plotted in Figure 38.

Figure 38

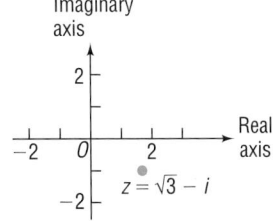

DEFINITION Let $z = x + yi$ be a complex number. The **magnitude** or **modulus** of z, denoted by $|z|$, is defined as the distance from the origin to the point (x, y). That is,

$$|z| = \sqrt{x^2 + y^2} \tag{1}$$

Figure 39

See Figure 39 for an illustration.

This definition for $|z|$ is consistent with the definition for the absolute value of a real number: If $z = x + yi$ is real, then $z = x + 0i$ and

$$|z| = \sqrt{x^2 + 0^2} = \sqrt{x^2} = |x|$$

For this reason, the magnitude of z is sometimes called the **absolute value of z.**

Recall that if $z = x + yi$ then its **conjugate,** denoted by $\bar{z}$, is $\bar{z} = x - yi$. Because $z\bar{z} = x^2 + y^2$, which is a nonnegative real number, it follows from equation (1) that the magnitude of z can be written as

$$|z| = \sqrt{z\bar{z}} \tag{2}$$

2 Convert a Complex Number from Rectangular Form to Polar Form

When a complex number is written in the standard form $z = x + yi$, we say that it is in **rectangular,** or **Cartesian, form,** because (x, y) are the rectangular coordinates of the corresponding point in the complex plane. Suppose that (r, θ) are the polar coordinates of this point. Then

$$x = r \cos \theta, \qquad y = r \sin \theta \tag{3}$$

DEFINITION

If $r \geq 0$ and $0 \leq \theta < 2\pi$, the complex number $z = x + yi$ may be written in **polar form** as

$$z = x + yi = (r \cos \theta) + (r \sin \theta)i = r(\cos \theta + i \sin \theta) \tag{4}$$

Figure 40

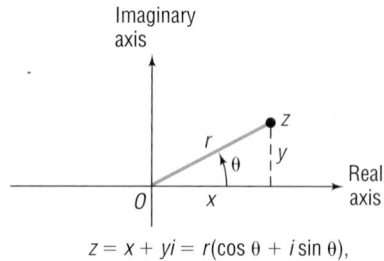

$z = x + yi = r(\cos \theta + i \sin \theta),$
$r \geq 0, 0 \leq \theta < 2\pi$

See Figure 40.

If $z = r(\cos \theta + i \sin \theta)$ is the polar form of a complex number, the angle θ, $0 \leq \theta < 2\pi$, is called the **argument of z.**

Also, because $r \geq 0$, we have $r = \sqrt{x^2 + y^2}$. From equation (1), it follows that the magnitude of $z = r(\cos \theta + i \sin \theta)$ is

$$|z| = r$$

EXAMPLE 2   **Writing a Complex Number in Polar Form**

Write an expression for $z = \sqrt{3} - i$ in polar form.

Solution   The point, located in quadrant IV, is plotted in Figure 38. Because $x = \sqrt{3}$ and $y = -1$, it follows that

$$r = \sqrt{x^2 + y^2} = \sqrt{\left(\sqrt{3}\right)^2 + (-1)^2} = \sqrt{4} = 2$$

So

$$\sin \theta = \frac{y}{r} = \frac{-1}{2}, \qquad \cos \theta = \frac{x}{r} = \frac{\sqrt{3}}{2}, \qquad 0 \leq \theta < 2\pi$$

Then $\theta = \dfrac{11\pi}{6}$ and $r = 2$, so the polar form of $z = \sqrt{3} - i$ is

$$z = r(\cos \theta + i \sin \theta) = 2\left(\cos \frac{11\pi}{6} + i \sin \frac{11\pi}{6}\right)$$

Now Work   PROBLEM 11

EXAMPLE 3 Plotting a Point in the Complex Plane and Converting from Polar to Rectangular Form

Plot the point corresponding to $z = 2(\cos 30° + i \sin 30°)$ in the complex plane, and write an expression for z in rectangular form.

Solution To plot the complex number $z = 2(\cos 30° + i \sin 30°)$, we plot the point whose polar coordinates are $(r, \theta) = (2, 30°)$, as shown in Figure 41. In rectangular form,

Figure 41

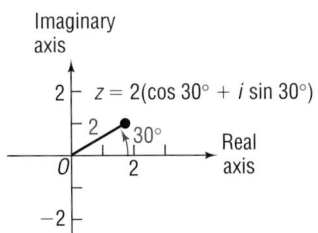

$$z = 2(\cos 30° + i \sin 30°) = 2\left(\frac{\sqrt{3}}{2} + \frac{1}{2}i\right) = \sqrt{3} + i$$

━━━━━ **Now Work** PROBLEM 23

3 Find Products and Quotients of Complex Numbers in Polar Form

The polar form of a complex number provides an alternative method for finding products and quotients of complex numbers.

THEOREM Let $z_1 = r_1(\cos \theta_1 + i \sin \theta_1)$ and $z_2 = r_2(\cos \theta_2 + i \sin \theta_2)$ be two complex numbers. Then

$$z_1 z_2 = r_1 r_2 [\cos(\theta_1 + \theta_2) + i \sin(\theta_1 + \theta_2)] \tag{5}$$

If $z_2 \neq 0$, then

$$\frac{z_1}{z_2} = \frac{r_1}{r_2}[\cos(\theta_1 - \theta_2) + i \sin(\theta_1 - \theta_2)] \tag{6}$$

In Words

The magnitude of a complex number z is r and its argument is θ, so when

$$z = r(\cos \theta + i \sin \theta)$$

the magnitude of the product (quotient) of two complex numbers equals the product (quotient) of their magnitudes; the argument of the product (quotient) of two complex numbers is determined by the sum (difference) of their arguments.

Proof We will prove formula (5). The proof of formula (6) is left as an exercise (see Problem 66).

$$z_1 z_2 = [r_1(\cos \theta_1 + i \sin \theta_1)][r_2(\cos \theta_2 + i \sin \theta_2)]$$
$$= r_1 r_2[(\cos \theta_1 + i \sin \theta_1)(\cos \theta_2 + i \sin \theta_2)]$$
$$= r_1 r_2[(\cos \theta_1 \cos \theta_2 - \sin \theta_1 \sin \theta_2) + i(\sin \theta_1 \cos \theta_2 + \cos \theta_1 \sin \theta_2)]$$
$$= r_1 r_2[\cos(\theta_1 + \theta_2) + i \sin(\theta_1 + \theta_2)] \qquad ∎$$

Let's look at an example of how this theorem can be used.

EXAMPLE 4 Finding Products and Quotients of Complex Numbers in Polar Form

If $z = 3(\cos 20° + i \sin 20°)$ and $w = 5(\cos 100° + i \sin 100°)$, find the following (leave your answers in polar form):

(a) zw (b) $\dfrac{z}{w}$

Solution (a) $zw = [3(\cos 20° + i \sin 20°)][5(\cos 100° + i \sin 100°)]$
$$= (3 \cdot 5)[\cos(20° + 100°) + i \sin(20° + 100°)]$$
$$= 15(\cos 120° + i \sin 120°) \qquad \text{Apply equation (5).}$$

(b) $\dfrac{z}{w} = \dfrac{3(\cos 20° + i \sin 20°)}{5(\cos 100° + i \sin 100°)}$

$= \dfrac{3}{5}[\cos(20° - 100°) + i \sin(20° - 100°)]$ *Apply equation (6).*

$= \dfrac{3}{5}[\cos(-80°) + i \sin(-80°)]$

$= \dfrac{3}{5}(\cos 280° + i \sin 280°)$ *The argument must lie between 0° and 360°.*

━━━━━ **Now Work** PROBLEM 33

4 Use De Moivre's Theorem

De Moivre's Theorem, stated by Abraham De Moivre (1667–1754) in 1730, but already known to many people by 1710, is important for the following reason: The fundamental processes of algebra are the four operations of addition, subtraction, multiplication, and division, together with powers and the extraction of roots. De Moivre's Theorem allows these latter fundamental algebraic operations to be applied to complex numbers.

De Moivre's Theorem, in its most basic form, is a formula for raising a complex number z to the power n, where $n \geq 1$ is a positive integer. Let's see if we can conjecture the form of the result.

Let $z = r(\cos \theta + i \sin \theta)$ be a complex number. Then, based on equation (5), we have

$n = 2$: $z^2 = r^2[\cos(2\theta) + i \sin(2\theta)]$ *Equation (5)*

$n = 3$: $z^3 = z^2 \cdot z$

$\qquad = \{r^2[\cos(2\theta) + i \sin(2\theta)]\}[r(\cos \theta + i \sin \theta)]$

$\qquad = r^3[\cos(3\theta) + i \sin(3\theta)]$ *Equation (5)*

$n = 4$: $z^4 = z^3 \cdot z$

$\qquad = \{r^3[\cos(3\theta) + i \sin(3\theta)]\}[r(\cos \theta + i \sin \theta)]$

$\qquad = r^4[\cos(4\theta) + i \sin(4\theta)]$ *Equation (5)*

Do you see the pattern?

THEOREM

De Moivre's Theorem

If $z = r(\cos \theta + i \sin \theta)$ is a complex number, then

$$z^n = r^n[\cos(n\theta) + i \sin(n\theta)] \tag{7}$$

where $n \geq 1$ is a positive integer.

The proof of De Moivre's Theorem requires mathematical induction (which is not discussed until Section 12.4), so it is omitted here.

Let's look at some examples.

| EXAMPLE 5 | **Using De Moivre's Theorem** |

Write $[2(\cos 20° + i \sin 20°)]^3$ in the standard form $a + bi$.

Solution $[2(\cos 20° + i \sin 20°)]^3 = 2^3[\cos(3 \cdot 20°) + i \sin(3 \cdot 20°)]$ *Apply De Moivre's Theorem.*

$= 8(\cos 60° + i \sin 60°)$

$= 8\left(\dfrac{1}{2} + \dfrac{\sqrt{3}}{2}i\right) = 4 + 4\sqrt{3}i$

━━━━━ **Now Work** PROBLEM 41

EXAMPLE 6 Using De Moivre's Theorem

Write $(1 + i)^5$ in the standard form $a + bi$.

Algebraic Solution

To apply De Moivre's Theorem, we must first write the complex number in polar form. Since the magnitude of $1 + i$ is $\sqrt{1^2 + 1^2} = \sqrt{2}$, we begin by writing

$$1 + i = \sqrt{2}\left(\frac{1}{\sqrt{2}} + \frac{1}{\sqrt{2}}i\right) = \sqrt{2}\left(\cos\frac{\pi}{4} + i\sin\frac{\pi}{4}\right)$$

Now

$$(1 + i)^5 = \left[\sqrt{2}\left(\cos\frac{\pi}{4} + i\sin\frac{\pi}{4}\right)\right]^5$$

$$= (\sqrt{2})^5\left[\cos\left(5\cdot\frac{\pi}{4}\right) + i\sin\left(5\cdot\frac{\pi}{4}\right)\right]$$

$$= 4\sqrt{2}\left(\cos\frac{5\pi}{4} + i\sin\frac{5\pi}{4}\right)$$

$$= 4\sqrt{2}\left[-\frac{1}{\sqrt{2}} + \left(-\frac{1}{\sqrt{2}}\right)i\right] = -4 - 4i$$

Graphing Solution

Using a TI-84 Plus graphing calculator, we obtain the solution shown in Figure 42.

Figure 42

5 Find Complex Roots

Let w be a given complex number, and let $n \geq 2$ denote a positive integer. Any complex number z that satisfies the equation

$$z^n = w$$

is called a **complex nth root** of w. In keeping with previous usage, if $n = 2$, the solutions of the equation $z^2 = w$ are called **complex square roots** of w, and if $n = 3$, the solutions of the equation $z^3 = w$ are called **complex cube roots** of w.

THEOREM **Finding Complex Roots**

Let $w = r(\cos\theta_0 + i\sin\theta_0)$ be a complex number, and let $n \geq 2$ be an integer. If $w \neq 0$, there are n distinct complex roots of w, given by the formula

$$z_k = \sqrt[n]{r}\left[\cos\left(\frac{\theta_0}{n} + \frac{2k\pi}{n}\right) + i\sin\left(\frac{\theta_0}{n} + \frac{2k\pi}{n}\right)\right] \qquad (8)$$

where $k = 0, 1, 2, \ldots, n - 1$.

Proof (Outline) We will not prove this result in its entirety. Instead, we shall show only that each z_k in equation (8) satisfies the equation $z_k^n = w$, proving that each z_k is a complex nth root of w.

$$z_k^n = \left\{\sqrt[n]{r}\left[\cos\left(\frac{\theta_0}{n} + \frac{2k\pi}{n}\right) + i\sin\left(\frac{\theta_0}{n} + \frac{2k\pi}{n}\right)\right]\right\}^n$$

$$= (\sqrt[n]{r})^n\left\{\cos\left[n\left(\frac{\theta_0}{n} + \frac{2k\pi}{n}\right)\right] + i\sin\left[n\left(\frac{\theta_0}{n} + \frac{2k\pi}{n}\right)\right]\right\} \quad \text{Apply De Moivre's Theorem.}$$

$$= r[\cos(\theta_0 + 2k\pi) + i\sin(\theta_0 + 2k\pi)] \quad \text{Simplify.}$$

$$= r(\cos\theta_0 + i\sin\theta_0) = w \quad \text{The Periodic Property}$$

So each z_k, $k = 0, 1, \ldots, n-1$, is a complex nth root of w. To complete the proof, we would need to show that each z_k, $k = 0, 1, \ldots, n-1$, is, in fact, distinct and that there are no complex nth roots of w other than those given by equation (8). ∎

EXAMPLE 7 | **Finding Complex Cube Roots**

Find the complex cube roots of $-1 + \sqrt{3}i$. Leave your answers in polar form, with the argument in degrees.

Solution   First, we express $-1 + \sqrt{3}i$ in polar form using degrees.

$$-1 + \sqrt{3}i = 2\left(-\frac{1}{2} + \frac{\sqrt{3}}{2}i\right) = 2(\cos 120° + i \sin 120°)$$

The three complex cube roots of $-1 + \sqrt{3}i = 2(\cos 120° + i \sin 120°)$ are

$$z_k = \sqrt[3]{2}\left[\cos\left(\frac{120°}{3} + \frac{360°k}{3}\right) + i \sin\left(\frac{120°}{3} + \frac{360°k}{3}\right)\right]$$

$$= \sqrt[3]{2}\left[\cos(40° + 120°k) + i \sin(40° + 120°k)\right] \qquad k = 0, 1, 2$$

So

WARNING Most graphing utilities will only provide the answer z_0 to the calculation $(-1 + \sqrt{3}i) \wedge \left(\frac{1}{3}\right)$. The paragraph following Example 7 explains how to obtain z_1 and z_2 from z_0. ∎

$$z_0 = \sqrt[3]{2}\left[\cos(40° + 120°\cdot 0) + i \sin(40° + 120°\cdot 0)\right] = \sqrt[3]{2}\left(\cos 40° + i \sin 40°\right)$$

$$z_1 = \sqrt[3]{2}\left[\cos(40° + 120°\cdot 1) + i \sin(40° + 120°\cdot 1)\right] = \sqrt[3]{2}\left(\cos 160° + i \sin 160°\right)$$

$$z_2 = \sqrt[3]{2}\left[\cos(40° + 120°\cdot 2) + i \sin(40° + 120°\cdot 2)\right] = \sqrt[3]{2}\left(\cos 280° + i \sin 280°\right)$$

Notice that each of the three complex roots of $-1 + \sqrt{3}i$ has the same magnitude, $\sqrt[3]{2}$. This means that the points corresponding to each cube root lie the same distance from the origin; that is, the three points lie on a circle with center at the origin and radius $\sqrt[3]{2}$. Furthermore, the arguments of these cube roots are 40°, 160°, and 280°, the difference of consecutive pairs being $120° = \dfrac{360°}{3}$. This means that the three points are equally spaced on the circle, as shown in Figure 43. These results are not coincidental. In fact, you are asked to show that these results hold for complex nth roots in Problems 63 through 65.

Figure 43

Historical Feature

John Wallis

The Babylonians, Greeks, and Arabs considered square roots of negative quantities to be impossible and equations with complex solutions to be unsolvable. The first hint that there was some connection between real solutions of equations and complex numbers came when Girolamo Cardano (1501–1576) and Tartaglia (1499–1557) found *real* roots of cubic equations by taking cube roots of *complex* quantities. For centuries thereafter, mathematicians worked with complex numbers without much belief in their actual existence. In 1673, John Wallis appears to have been the first to suggest the graphical representation of complex numbers, a truly significant idea that was not pursued further until about 1800. Several people, including Karl Friedrich Gauss (1777–1855), then rediscovered the idea, and graphical representation helped to establish complex numbers as equal members of the number family. In practical applications, complex numbers have found their greatest uses in the study of alternating current, where they are a commonplace tool, and in the field of subatomic physics.

Historical Problems

1. The quadratic formula will work perfectly well if the coefficients are complex numbers. Solve the following. [**Hint:** The answers are "nice."]

 (a) $z^2 - (2 + 5i)z - 3 + 5i = 0$ **(b)** $z^2 - (1 + i)z - 2 - i = 0$

9.3 Assess Your Understanding

'Are You Prepared?' *Answers are given at the end of these exercises. If you get a wrong answer, read the pages listed in red.*

1. The conjugate of $-4 - 3i$ is _____. (p. A62)

2. The sum formula for the sine function is $\sin(A + B) = $ _____. (p. 469)

3. The sum formula for the cosine function is $\cos(A + B) = $ _____. (p. 466)

4. $\sin 120° = $ _____; $\cos 240° = $ _____. (pp. 374–375)

Concepts and Vocabulary

5. When a complex number z is written in the polar form $z = r(\cos\theta + i\sin\theta)$, the nonnegative number r is the _____ or _____ of z, and the angle $\theta, 0 \le \theta < 2\pi$, is the _____ of z.

6. _____ Theorem can be used to raise a complex number to a power.

7. Every nonzero complex number will have exactly _____ cube roots.

8. **True or False** De Moivre's Theorem is useful for raising a complex number to a positive integer power.

9. **True or False** Using De Moivre's Theorem, the square of a complex number will have two answers.

10. **True or False** The polar form of a complex number is unique.

Skill Building

In Problems 11–22, plot each complex number in the complex plane and write it in polar form. Express the argument in degrees.

11. $1 + i$

12. $-1 + i$

13. $\sqrt{3} - i$

14. $1 - \sqrt{3}i$

15. $-3i$

16. -2

17. $4 - 4i$

18. $9\sqrt{3} + 9i$

19. $3 - 4i$

20. $2 + \sqrt{3}i$

21. $-2 + 3i$

22. $\sqrt{5} - i$

In Problems 23–32, write each complex number in rectangular form.

23. $2(\cos 120° + i \sin 120°)$

24. $3(\cos 210° + i \sin 210°)$

25. $4\left(\cos\dfrac{7\pi}{4} + i \sin\dfrac{7\pi}{4}\right)$

26. $2\left(\cos\dfrac{5\pi}{6} + i \sin\dfrac{5\pi}{6}\right)$

27. $3\left(\cos\dfrac{3\pi}{2} + i \sin\dfrac{3\pi}{2}\right)$

28. $4\left(\cos\dfrac{\pi}{2} + i \sin\dfrac{\pi}{2}\right)$

29. $0.2(\cos 100° + i \sin 100°)$

30. $0.4(\cos 200° + i \sin 200°)$

31. $2\left(\cos\dfrac{\pi}{18} + i \sin\dfrac{\pi}{18}\right)$

32. $3\left(\cos\dfrac{\pi}{10} + i \sin\dfrac{\pi}{10}\right)$

In Problems 33–40, find zw and $\dfrac{z}{w}$. Leave your answers in polar form.

33. $z = 2(\cos 40° + i \sin 40°)$
 $w = 4(\cos 20° + i \sin 20°)$

34. $z = \cos 120° + i \sin 120°$
 $w = \cos 100° + i \sin 100°$

35. $z = 3(\cos 130° + i \sin 130°)$
 $w = 4(\cos 270° + i \sin 270°)$

36. $z = 2(\cos 80° + i \sin 80°)$
    $w = 6(\cos 200° + i \sin 200°)$

37. $z = 2\left(\cos \dfrac{\pi}{8} + i \sin \dfrac{\pi}{8}\right)$
    $w = 2\left(\cos \dfrac{\pi}{10} + i \sin \dfrac{\pi}{10}\right)$

38. $z = 4\left(\cos \dfrac{3\pi}{8} + i \sin \dfrac{3\pi}{8}\right)$
    $w = 2\left(\cos \dfrac{9\pi}{16} + i \sin \dfrac{9\pi}{16}\right)$

39. $z = 2 + 2i$
    $w = \sqrt{3} - i$

40. $z = 1 - i$
    $w = 1 - \sqrt{3}i$

In Problems 41–52, write each expression in the standard form $a + bi$.

41. $[4(\cos 40° + i \sin 40°)]^3$

42. $[3(\cos 80° + i \sin 80°)]^3$

43. $\left[2\left(\cos \dfrac{\pi}{10} + i \sin \dfrac{\pi}{10}\right)\right]^5$

44. $\left[\sqrt{2}\left(\cos \dfrac{5\pi}{16} + i \sin \dfrac{5\pi}{16}\right)\right]^4$

45. $\left[\sqrt{3}(\cos 10° + i \sin 10°)\right]^6$

46. $\left[\dfrac{1}{2}(\cos 72° + i \sin 72°)\right]^5$

47. $\left[\sqrt{5}\left(\cos \dfrac{3\pi}{16} + i \sin \dfrac{3\pi}{16}\right)\right]^4$

48. $\left[\sqrt{3}\left(\cos \dfrac{5\pi}{18} + i \sin \dfrac{5\pi}{18}\right)\right]^6$

49. $(1 - i)^5$

50. $\left(\sqrt{3} - i\right)^6$

51. $\left(\sqrt{2} - i\right)^6$

52. $\left(1 - \sqrt{5}i\right)^8$

In Problems 53–60, find all the complex roots. Leave your answers in polar form with the argument in degrees.

53. The complex cube roots of $1 + i$

54. The complex fourth roots of $\sqrt{3} - i$

55. The complex fourth roots of $4 - 4\sqrt{3}i$

56. The complex cube roots of $-8 - 8i$

57. The complex fourth roots of $-16i$

58. The complex cube roots of -8

59. The complex fifth roots of i

60. The complex fifth roots of $-i$

Applications and Extensions

61. Find the four complex fourth roots of unity (1) and plot them.

62. Find the six complex sixth roots of unity (1) and plot them.

63. Show that each complex nth root of a nonzero complex number w has the same magnitude.

64. Use the result of Problem 63 to draw the conclusion that each complex nth root lies on a circle with center at the origin. What is the radius of this circle?

65. Refer to Problem 64. Show that the complex nth roots of a nonzero complex number w are equally spaced on the circle.

66. Prove formula (6).

67. Mandelbrot Sets
   (a) Consider the expression $a_n = (a_{n-1})^2 + z$, where z is some complex number (called the **seed**) and $a_0 = z$. Compute $a_1 (= a_0^2 + z)$, $a_2 (= a_1^2 + z)$, $a_3 (= a_2^2 + z)$, a_4, a_5, and a_6 for the following seeds: $z_1 = 0.1 - 0.4i$, $z_2 = 0.5 + 0.8i$, $z_3 = -0.9 + 0.7i$, $z_4 = -1.1 + 0.1i$, $z_5 = 0 - 1.3i$, and $z_6 = 1 + 1i$.
   (b) The dark portion of the graph represents the set of all values $z = x + yi$ that are in the Mandelbrot set. Determine which complex numbers in part (a) are in this set by plotting them on the graph. Do the complex

numbers that are not in the Mandelbrot set have any common characteristics regarding the values of a_6 found in part (a)?

   (c) Compute $|z| = \sqrt{x^2 + y^2}$ for each of the complex numbers in part (a). Now compute $|a_6|$ for each of the complex numbers in part (a). For which complex numbers is $|a_6| \le |z|$ and $|z| \le 2$? Conclude that the criterion for a complex number to be in the Mandelbrot set is that $|a_n| \le |z|$ and $|z| \le 2$.

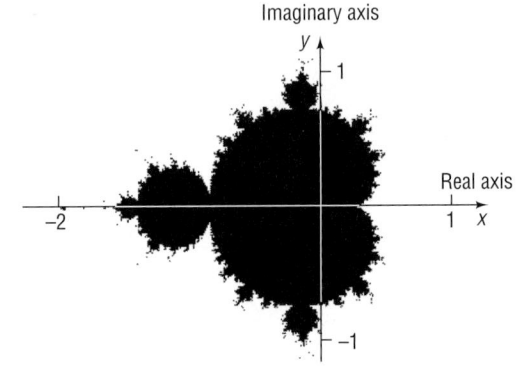

'Are You Prepared?' Answers

1. $-4 + 3i$

2. $\sin A \cos B + \cos A \sin B$

3. $\cos A \cos B - \sin A \sin B$

4. $\dfrac{\sqrt{3}}{2}; -\dfrac{1}{2}$

9.4 Vectors

OBJECTIVES 1 Graph Vectors (p. 599)
2 Find a Position Vector (p. 600)
3 Add and Subtract Vectors Algebraically (p. 601)
4 Find a Scalar Multiple and the Magnitude of a Vector (p. 602)
5 Find a Unit Vector (p. 602)
6 Find a Vector from Its Direction and Magnitude (p. 603)
7 Analyze Objects in Static Equilibrium (p. 604)

Figure 44

In simple terms, a **vector** (derived from the Latin *vehere*, meaning "to carry") is a quantity that has both magnitude and direction. It is customary to represent a vector by using an arrow. The length of the arrow represents the **magnitude** of the vector, and the arrowhead indicates the **direction** of the vector.

Many quantities in physics can be represented by vectors. For example, the velocity of an aircraft can be represented by an arrow that points in the direction of movement; the length of the arrow represents speed. If the aircraft speeds up, we lengthen the arrow; if the aircraft changes direction, we introduce an arrow in the new direction. See Figure 44. Based on this representation, it is not surprising that vectors and *directed line segments* are somehow related.

Geometric Vectors

If P and Q are two distinct points in the xy-plane, there is exactly one line containing both P and Q [Figure 45(a)]. The points on that part of the line that joins P to Q, including P and Q, form what is called the **line segment** $\overline{PQ}$ [Figure 45(b)]. If we order the points so that they proceed from P to Q, we have a **directed line segment** from P to Q, or a **geometric vector,** which we denote by $\overrightarrow{PQ}$. In a directed line segment $\overrightarrow{PQ}$, we call P the **initial point** and Q the **terminal point,** as indicated in Figure 45(c).

Figure 45

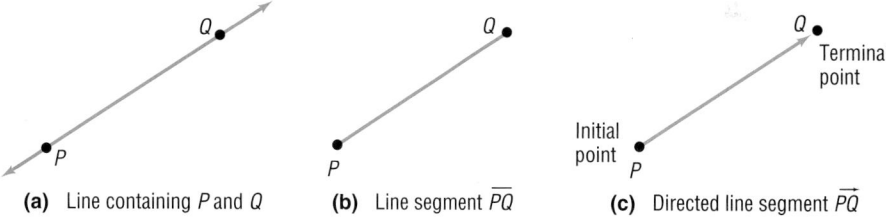

(a) Line containing P and Q **(b)** Line segment $\overline{PQ}$ **(c)** Directed line segment $\overrightarrow{PQ}$

The magnitude of the directed line segment $\overrightarrow{PQ}$ is the distance from the point P to the point Q; that is, it is the length of the line segment. The direction of $\overrightarrow{PQ}$ is from P to Q. If a vector **v*** has the same magnitude and the same direction as the directed line segment $\overrightarrow{PQ}$, we write

$$\mathbf{v} = \overrightarrow{PQ}$$

The vector **v** whose magnitude is 0 is called the **zero vector, 0.** The zero vector is assigned no direction.

Two vectors **v** and **w** are **equal,** written

$$\mathbf{v} = \mathbf{w}$$

if they have the same magnitude and the same direction.

Figure 46

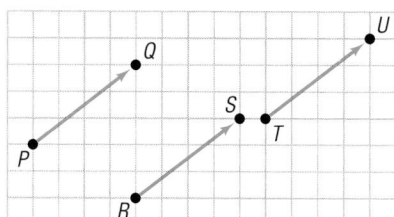

For example, the three vectors shown in Figure 46 have the same magnitude and the same direction, so they are equal, even though they have different initial points

---

*Boldface letters will be used to denote vectors, to distinguish them from numbers. For handwritten work, an arrow is placed over the letter to signify a vector.

and different terminal points. As a result, we find it useful to think of a vector simply as an arrow, keeping in mind that two arrows (vectors) are equal if they have the same direction and the same magnitude (length).

Adding Vectors Geometrically

Figure 47

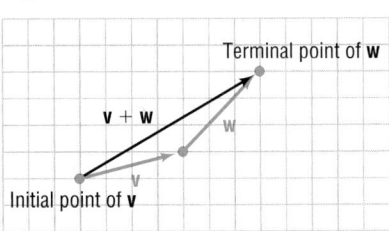

The **sum v + w** of two vectors is defined as follows: We position the vectors **v** and **w** so that the terminal point of **v** coincides with the initial point of **w**, as shown in Figure 47. The vector **v + w** is then the unique vector whose initial point coincides with the initial point of **v** and whose terminal point coincides with the terminal point of **w**.

Vector addition is **commutative.** That is, if **v** and **w** are any two vectors, then

$$\mathbf{v} + \mathbf{w} = \mathbf{w} + \mathbf{v}$$

Figure 48

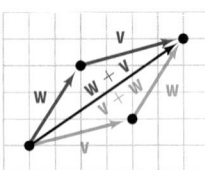

Figure 48 illustrates this fact. (Observe that the commutative property is another way of saying that opposite sides of a parallelogram are equal and parallel.)

Vector addition is also **associative.** That is, if **u**, **v**, and **w** are vectors, then

$$\mathbf{u} + (\mathbf{v} + \mathbf{w}) = (\mathbf{u} + \mathbf{v}) + \mathbf{w}$$

Figure 49
(u + v) + w = u + (v + w)

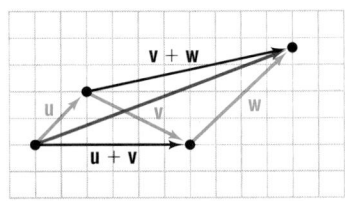

Figure 49 illustrates the associative property for vectors.

The zero vector **0** has the property that

$$\mathbf{v} + \mathbf{0} = \mathbf{0} + \mathbf{v} = \mathbf{v}$$

for any vector **v**.

If **v** is a vector, then −**v** is the vector having the same magnitude as **v**, but whose direction is opposite to **v**, as shown in Figure 50.
Furthermore,

Figure 50

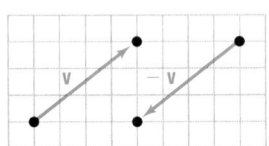

$$\mathbf{v} + (-\mathbf{v}) = \mathbf{0}$$

If **v** and **w** are two vectors, we define the **difference v − w** as

$$\mathbf{v} - \mathbf{w} = \mathbf{v} + (-\mathbf{w})$$

Figure 51

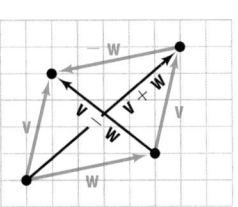

Figure 51 illustrates the relationships among **v**, **w**, **v + w**, and **v − w**.

Multiplying Vectors by Numbers Geometrically

When dealing with vectors, we refer to real numbers as **scalars.** Scalars are quantities that have only magnitude. Examples from physics of scalar quantities are temperature, speed, and time. We now define how to multiply a vector by a scalar.

DEFINITION

If α is a scalar and **v** is a vector, the **scalar multiple** $\alpha\mathbf{v}$ is defined as follows:

1. If $\alpha > 0$, $\alpha\mathbf{v}$ is the vector whose magnitude is α times the magnitude of **v** and whose direction is the same as **v**.
2. If $\alpha < 0$, $\alpha\mathbf{v}$ is the vector whose magnitude is $|\alpha|$ times the magnitude of **v** and whose direction is opposite that of **v**.
3. If $\alpha = 0$ or if **v** = **0**, then $\alpha\mathbf{v}$ = **0**.

Figure 52

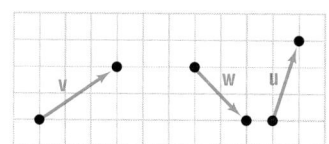

See Figure 52 for some illustrations.

For example, if **a** is the acceleration of an object of mass m due to a force **F** being exerted on it, then, by Newton's second law of motion, $\mathbf{F} = m\mathbf{a}$. Here, $m\mathbf{a}$ is the product of the scalar m and the vector **a**.

Scalar multiples have the following properties:

$$0\mathbf{v} = \mathbf{0} \qquad 1\mathbf{v} = \mathbf{v} \qquad -1\mathbf{v} = -\mathbf{v}$$

$$(\alpha + \beta)\mathbf{v} = \alpha\mathbf{v} + \beta\mathbf{v} \qquad \alpha(\mathbf{v} + \mathbf{w}) = \alpha\mathbf{v} + \alpha\mathbf{w}$$

$$\alpha(\beta\mathbf{v}) = (\alpha\beta)\mathbf{v}$$

1 Graph Vectors

EXAMPLE 1 **Graphing Vectors**

Use the vectors illustrated in Figure 53 to graph each of the following vectors:

(a) $\mathbf{v} - \mathbf{w}$ (b) $2\mathbf{v} + 3\mathbf{w}$ (c) $2\mathbf{v} - \mathbf{w} + \mathbf{u}$

Solution Figure 54 illustrates each graph.

Figure 53

Figure 54

(a) $\mathbf{v} - \mathbf{w}$ (b) $2\mathbf{v} + 3\mathbf{w}$ (c) $2\mathbf{v} - \mathbf{w} + \mathbf{u}$

Now Work PROBLEMS 7 AND 9

Magnitudes of Vectors

If **v** is a vector, we use the symbol $\|\mathbf{v}\|$ to represent the **magnitude** of **v**. Since $\|\mathbf{v}\|$ equals the length of a directed line segment, it follows that $\|\mathbf{v}\|$ has the following properties:

THEOREM **Properties of $\|\mathbf{v}\|$**

If **v** is a vector and if α is a scalar, then

(a) $\|\mathbf{v}\| \geq 0$ (b) $\|\mathbf{v}\| = 0$ if and only if $\mathbf{v} = \mathbf{0}$

(c) $\|-\mathbf{v}\| = \|\mathbf{v}\|$ (d) $\|\alpha\mathbf{v}\| = |\alpha|\|\mathbf{v}\|$

Property (a) is a consequence of the fact that distance is a nonnegative number. Property (b) follows, because the length of the directed line segment $\overrightarrow{PQ}$ is positive unless P and Q are the same point, in which case the length is 0. Property (c) follows because the length of the line segment $\overline{PQ}$ equals the length of the line segment $\overline{QP}$. Property (d) is a direct consequence of the definition of a scalar multiple.

DEFINITION A vector **u** for which $\|\mathbf{u}\| = 1$ is called a **unit vector.**

2 Find a Position Vector

To compute the magnitude and direction of a vector, we need an algebraic way of representing vectors.

DEFINITION

An **algebraic vector v** is represented as

$$\mathbf{v} = \langle a, b \rangle$$

where a and b are real numbers (scalars) called the **components** of the vector **v**.

Figure 55

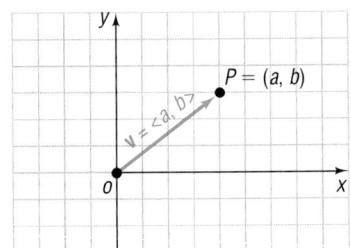

We use a rectangular coordinate system to represent algebraic vectors in the plane. If $\mathbf{v} = \langle a, b \rangle$ is an algebraic vector whose initial point is at the origin, then **v** is called a **position vector.** See Figure 55. Notice that the terminal point of the position vector $\mathbf{v} = \langle a, b \rangle$ is $P = (a, b)$.

The next result states that any vector whose initial point is not at the origin is equal to a unique position vector.

THEOREM

Suppose that **v** is a vector with initial point $P_1 = (x_1, y_1)$, not necessarily the origin, and terminal point $P_2 = (x_2, y_2)$. If $\mathbf{v} = \overrightarrow{P_1P_2}$, then **v** is equal to the position vector

$$\mathbf{v} = \langle x_2 - x_1, y_2 - y_1 \rangle \tag{1}$$

To see why this is true, look at Figure 56.

Figure 56
$\mathbf{v} = \langle a, b \rangle = \langle x_2 - x_1, y_2 - y_1 \rangle$

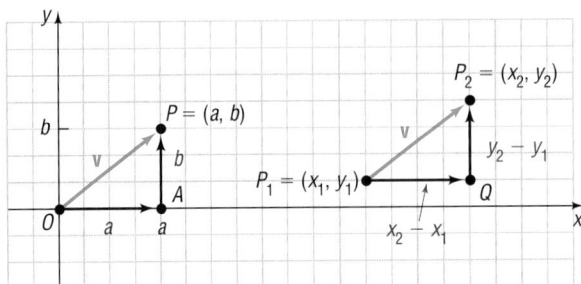

Triangle OPA and triangle P_1P_2Q are congruent. [Do you see why? The line segments have the same magnitude, so $d(O, P) = d(P_1, P_2)$; and they have the same direction, so $\angle POA = \angle P_2P_1Q$. Since the triangles are right triangles, we have angle–side–angle.] It follows that corresponding sides are equal. As a result, $x_2 - x_1 = a$ and $y_2 - y_1 = b$, so **v** may be written as

$$\mathbf{v} = \langle a, b \rangle = \langle x_2 - x_1, y_2 - y_1 \rangle$$

Because of this result, we can replace any algebraic vector by a unique position vector, and vice versa. This flexibility is one of the main reasons for the wide use of vectors.

| EXAMPLE 2 | Finding a Position Vector |

Find the position vector of the vector $\mathbf{v} = \overrightarrow{P_1P_2}$ if $P_1 = (-1, 2)$ and $P_2 = (4, 6)$.

Solution By equation (1), the position vector equal to **v** is

$$\mathbf{v} = \langle 4 - (-1), 6 - 2 \rangle = \langle 5, 4 \rangle$$

See Figure 57.

Figure 57

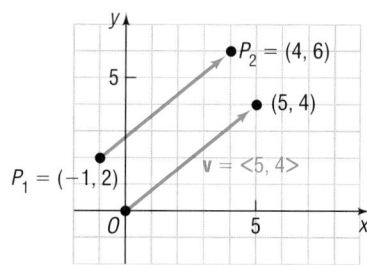

Two position vectors **v** and **w** are equal if and only if the terminal point of **v** is the same as the terminal point of **w**. This leads to the following result:

THEOREM   **Equality of Vectors**

Two vectors **v** and **w** are equal if and only if their corresponding components are equal. That is,

$$\text{If } \mathbf{v} = \langle a_1, b_1 \rangle \quad \text{and} \quad \mathbf{w} = \langle a_2, b_2 \rangle$$

$$\text{then} \quad \mathbf{v} = \mathbf{w} \quad \text{if and only if} \quad a_1 = a_2 \quad \text{and} \quad b_1 = b_2.$$

Figure 58

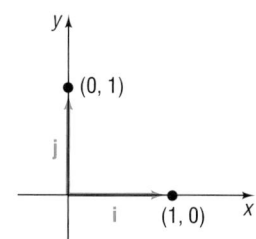

We now present an alternative representation of a vector in the plane that is common in the physical sciences. Let **i** denote the unit vector whose direction is along the positive x-axis; let **j** denote the unit vector whose direction is along the positive y-axis. Then $\mathbf{i} = \langle 1, 0 \rangle$ and $\mathbf{j} = \langle 0, 1 \rangle$, as shown in Figure 58. Any vector $\mathbf{v} = \langle a, b \rangle$ can be written using the unit vectors **i** and **j** as follows:

$$\mathbf{v} = \langle a, b \rangle = a\langle 1, 0 \rangle + b\langle 0, 1 \rangle = a\mathbf{i} + b\mathbf{j}$$

We call a and b the **horizontal** and **vertical components** of **v**, respectively. For example, if $\mathbf{v} = \langle 5, 4 \rangle = 5\mathbf{i} + 4\mathbf{j}$, then 5 is the horizontal component and 4 is the vertical component.

✏️ **Now Work** PROBLEM 27

3 Add and Subtract Vectors Algebraically

We define addition, subtraction, scalar multiple, and magnitude of algebraic vectors in terms of their components.

DEFINITION   Let $\mathbf{v} = a_1\mathbf{i} + b_1\mathbf{j} = \langle a_1, b_1 \rangle$ and $\mathbf{w} = a_2\mathbf{i} + b_2\mathbf{j} = \langle a_2, b_2 \rangle$ be two vectors, and let α be a scalar. Then

$$\mathbf{v} + \mathbf{w} = (a_1 + a_2)\mathbf{i} + (b_1 + b_2)\mathbf{j} = \langle a_1 + a_2, b_1 + b_2 \rangle \tag{2}$$

$$\mathbf{v} - \mathbf{w} = (a_1 - a_2)\mathbf{i} + (b_1 - b_2)\mathbf{j} = \langle a_1 - a_2, b_1 - b_2 \rangle \tag{3}$$

$$\alpha\mathbf{v} = (\alpha a_1)\mathbf{i} + (\alpha b_1)\mathbf{j} = \langle \alpha a_1, \alpha b_1 \rangle \tag{4}$$

$$\|\mathbf{v}\| = \sqrt{a_1^2 + b_1^2} \tag{5}$$

In Words
To add two vectors, add corresponding components. To subtract two vectors, subtract corresponding components.

These definitions are compatible with the geometric definitions given earlier in this section. See Figure 59 on the next page.

Figure 59

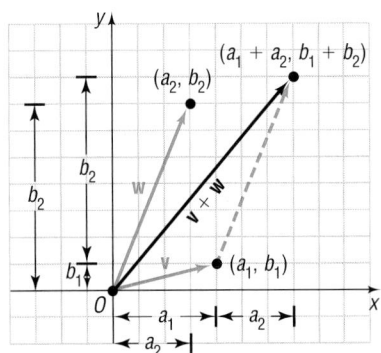

(a)   Illustration of property (2)

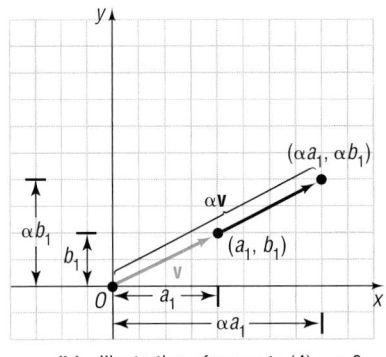

(b)   Illustration of property (4), $\alpha > 0$

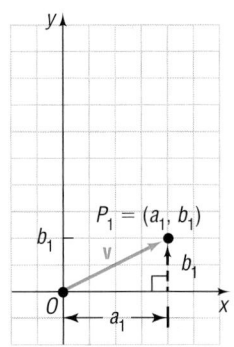

(c)   Illustration of property (5):
$\|\mathbf{v}\| =$ Distance from O to P_1
$\|\mathbf{v}\| = \sqrt{a_1^2 + b_1^2}$

EXAMPLE 3   **Adding and Subtracting Vectors**

If $\mathbf{v} = 2\mathbf{i} + 3\mathbf{j} = \langle 2, 3 \rangle$ and $\mathbf{w} = 3\mathbf{i} - 4\mathbf{j} = \langle 3, -4 \rangle$, find:

(a) $\mathbf{v} + \mathbf{w}$ (b) $\mathbf{v} - \mathbf{w}$

Solution   (a) $\mathbf{v} + \mathbf{w} = (2\mathbf{i} + 3\mathbf{j}) + (3\mathbf{i} - 4\mathbf{j}) = (2 + 3)\mathbf{i} + (3 - 4)\mathbf{j} = 5\mathbf{i} - \mathbf{j}$

or

$\mathbf{v} + \mathbf{w} = \langle 2, 3 \rangle + \langle 3, -4 \rangle = \langle 2 + 3, 3 + (-4) \rangle = \langle 5, -1 \rangle$

(b) $\mathbf{v} - \mathbf{w} = (2\mathbf{i} + 3\mathbf{j}) - (3\mathbf{i} - 4\mathbf{j}) = (2 - 3)\mathbf{i} + [3 - (-4)]\mathbf{j} = -\mathbf{i} + 7\mathbf{j}$

or

$\mathbf{v} - \mathbf{w} = \langle 2, 3 \rangle - \langle 3, -4 \rangle = \langle 2 - 3, 3 - (-4) \rangle = \langle -1, 7 \rangle$

---

4 Find a Scalar Multiple and the Magnitude of a Vector

EXAMPLE 4   **Finding Scalar Multiples and Magnitudes of Vectors**

If $\mathbf{v} = 2\mathbf{i} + 3\mathbf{j} = \langle 2, 3 \rangle$ and $\mathbf{w} = 3\mathbf{i} - 4\mathbf{j} = \langle 3, -4 \rangle$, find:

(a) $3\mathbf{v}$ (b) $2\mathbf{v} - 3\mathbf{w}$ (c) $\|\mathbf{v}\|$

Solution   (a) $3\mathbf{v} = 3(2\mathbf{i} + 3\mathbf{j}) = 6\mathbf{i} + 9\mathbf{j}$

or

$3\mathbf{v} = 3\langle 2, 3 \rangle = \langle 6, 9 \rangle$

(b) $2\mathbf{v} - 3\mathbf{w} = 2(2\mathbf{i} + 3\mathbf{j}) - 3(3\mathbf{i} - 4\mathbf{j}) = 4\mathbf{i} + 6\mathbf{j} - 9\mathbf{i} + 12\mathbf{j}$

$= -5\mathbf{i} + 18\mathbf{j}$

or

$2\mathbf{v} - 3\mathbf{w} = 2\langle 2, 3 \rangle - 3\langle 3, -4 \rangle = \langle 4, 6 \rangle - \langle 9, -12 \rangle$

$= \langle 4 - 9, 6 - (-12) \rangle = \langle -5, 18 \rangle$

(c) $\|\mathbf{v}\| = \|2\mathbf{i} + 3\mathbf{j}\| = \sqrt{2^2 + 3^2} = \sqrt{13}$

Now Work PROBLEMS **33** AND **39**

For the remainder of the section, we will express a vector $\mathbf{v}$ in the form $a\mathbf{i} + b\mathbf{j}$.

5 Find a Unit Vector

Recall that a unit vector $\mathbf{u}$ is a vector for which $\|\mathbf{u}\| = 1$. In many applications, it is useful to be able to find a unit vector $\mathbf{u}$ that has the same direction as a given vector $\mathbf{v}$.

THEOREM   **Unit Vector in the Direction of v**

For any nonzero vector **v**, the vector

$$\mathbf{u} = \frac{\mathbf{v}}{\|\mathbf{v}\|}$$

is a unit vector that has the same direction as **v**.

Proof   Let $\mathbf{v} = a\mathbf{i} + b\mathbf{j}$. Then $\|\mathbf{v}\| = \sqrt{a^2 + b^2}$ and

$$\mathbf{u} = \frac{\mathbf{v}}{\|\mathbf{v}\|} = \frac{a\mathbf{i} + b\mathbf{j}}{\sqrt{a^2 + b^2}} = \frac{a}{\sqrt{a^2 + b^2}}\mathbf{i} + \frac{b}{\sqrt{a^2 + b^2}}\mathbf{j}$$

The vector **u** is in the same direction as **v**, since $\|\mathbf{v}\| > 0$. Furthermore,

$$\|\mathbf{u}\| = \sqrt{\frac{a^2}{a^2 + b^2} + \frac{b^2}{a^2 + b^2}} = \sqrt{\frac{a^2 + b^2}{a^2 + b^2}} = 1$$

That is, **u** is a unit vector in the direction of **v**.   ∎

As a consequence of this theorem, if **u** is a unit vector in the same direction as a vector **v**, then **v** may be expressed as

$$\mathbf{v} = \|\mathbf{v}\|\mathbf{u} \tag{6}$$

This way of expressing a vector is useful in many applications.

EXAMPLE 5   **Finding a Unit Vector**

Find a unit vector in the same direction as $\mathbf{v} = 4\mathbf{i} - 3\mathbf{j}$.

Solution   We find $\|\mathbf{v}\|$ first.

$$\|\mathbf{v}\| = \|4\mathbf{i} - 3\mathbf{j}\| = \sqrt{16 + 9} = 5$$

Now we multiply **v** by the scalar $\dfrac{1}{\|\mathbf{v}\|} = \dfrac{1}{5}$. A unit vector in the same direction as **v** is

$$\frac{\mathbf{v}}{\|\mathbf{v}\|} = \frac{4\mathbf{i} - 3\mathbf{j}}{5} = \frac{4}{5}\mathbf{i} - \frac{3}{5}\mathbf{j}$$

✓**Check:** This vector is, in fact, a unit vector because

$$\left(\frac{4}{5}\right)^2 + \left(-\frac{3}{5}\right)^2 = \frac{16}{25} + \frac{9}{25} = \frac{25}{25} = 1$$

Now Work PROBLEM 49

6 Find a Vector from Its Direction and Magnitude

If a vector represents the speed and direction of an object, it is called a **velocity vector.** If a vector represents the direction and amount of a force acting on an object, it is called a **force vector.** In many applications, a vector is described in terms of its magnitude and direction, rather than in terms of its components. For example, a ball thrown with an initial speed of 25 miles per hour at an angle 30° to the horizontal is a velocity vector.

Suppose that we are given the magnitude $\|\mathbf{v}\|$ of a nonzero vector **v** and the angle α, $0° \leq \alpha < 360°$, between **v** and **i**. To express **v** in terms of $\|\mathbf{v}\|$ and α, we first find the unit vector **u** having the same direction as **v**.

$$\mathbf{u} = \frac{\mathbf{v}}{\|\mathbf{v}\|} \quad \text{or} \quad \mathbf{v} = \|\mathbf{v}\|\mathbf{u} \tag{7}$$

Figure 60

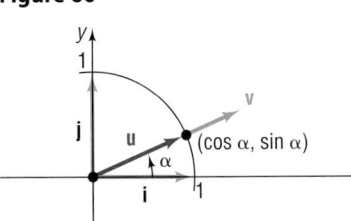

Look at Figure 60. The coordinates of the terminal point of **u** are $(\cos\alpha, \sin\alpha)$. Then $\mathbf{u} = \cos\alpha\mathbf{i} + \sin\alpha\mathbf{j}$ and, from (7),

$$\mathbf{v} = \|\mathbf{v}\|(\cos\alpha\,\mathbf{i} + \sin\alpha\,\mathbf{j}) \qquad (8)$$

where α is the angle between **v** and **i**.

EXAMPLE 6 | **Writing a Vector When Its Magnitude and Direction Are Given**

A ball is thrown with an initial speed of 25 miles per hour in a direction that makes an angle of 30° with the positive x-axis. Express the velocity vector **v** in terms of **i** and **j**. What is the initial speed in the horizontal direction? What is the initial speed in the vertical direction?

Solution The magnitude of **v** is $\|\mathbf{v}\| = 25$ miles per hour, and the angle between the direction of **v** and **i**, the positive x-axis, is $\alpha = 30°$. By equation (8),

Figure 61

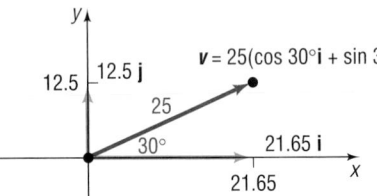

$$\mathbf{v} = \|\mathbf{v}\|(\cos\alpha\mathbf{i} + \sin\alpha\mathbf{j}) = 25(\cos 30°\mathbf{i} + \sin 30°\mathbf{j}) = 25\left(\frac{\sqrt{3}}{2}\mathbf{i} + \frac{1}{2}\mathbf{j}\right) = \frac{25\sqrt{3}}{2}\mathbf{i} + \frac{25}{2}\mathbf{j}$$

The initial speed of the ball in the horizontal direction is the horizontal component of **v**, $\dfrac{25\sqrt{3}}{2} \approx 21.65$ miles per hour. The initial speed in the vertical direction is the vertical component of **v**, $\dfrac{25}{2} = 12.5$ miles per hour. See Figure 61.

Now Work PROBLEM 63

7 Analyze Objects in Static Equilibrium

Figure 62

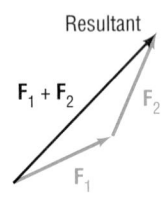

Because forces can be represented by vectors, two forces "combine" the way that vectors "add." If $\mathbf{F}_1$ and $\mathbf{F}_2$ are two forces simultaneously acting on an object, the vector sum $\mathbf{F}_1 + \mathbf{F}_2$ is the **resultant force**. The resultant force produces the same effect on the object as that obtained when the two forces $\mathbf{F}_1$ and $\mathbf{F}_2$ act on the object. See Figure 62. An application of this concept is *static equilibrium*. An object is said to be in **static equilibrium** if (1) the object is at rest and (2) the sum of all forces acting on the object is zero, that is, if the resultant force is 0.

EXAMPLE 7 | **An Object in Static Equilibrium**

Figure 63

A box of supplies that weighs 1200 pounds is suspended by two cables attached to the ceiling, as shown in Figure 63. What are the tensions in the two cables?

Solution We draw a force diagram using the vectors shown in Figure 64. The tensions in the cables are the magnitudes $\|\mathbf{F}_1\|$ and $\|\mathbf{F}_2\|$ of the force vectors $\mathbf{F}_1$ and $\mathbf{F}_2$. The magnitude of the force vector $\mathbf{F}_3$ equals 1200 pounds, the weight of the box. Now write each force vector in terms of the unit vectors **i** and **j**. For $\mathbf{F}_1$ and $\mathbf{F}_2$, we use equation (8). Remember that α is the angle between the vector and the positive x-axis.

Figure 64

$$\mathbf{F}_1 = \|\mathbf{F}_1\|(\cos 150°\mathbf{i} + \sin 150°\mathbf{j}) = \|\mathbf{F}_1\|\left(-\frac{\sqrt{3}}{2}\mathbf{i} + \frac{1}{2}\mathbf{j}\right) = -\frac{\sqrt{3}}{2}\|\mathbf{F}_1\|\mathbf{i} + \frac{1}{2}\|\mathbf{F}_1\|\mathbf{j}$$

$$\mathbf{F}_2 = \|\mathbf{F}_2\|(\cos 45°\mathbf{i} + \sin 45°\mathbf{j}) = \|\mathbf{F}_2\|\left(\frac{\sqrt{2}}{2}\mathbf{i} + \frac{\sqrt{2}}{2}\mathbf{j}\right) = \frac{\sqrt{2}}{2}\|\mathbf{F}_2\|\mathbf{i} + \frac{\sqrt{2}}{2}\|\mathbf{F}_2\|\mathbf{j}$$

$$\mathbf{F}_3 = -1200\mathbf{j}$$

For static equilibrium, the sum of the force vectors must equal zero.

$$\mathbf{F}_1 + \mathbf{F}_2 + \mathbf{F}_3 = -\frac{\sqrt{3}}{2}\|\mathbf{F}_1\|\mathbf{i} + \frac{1}{2}\|\mathbf{F}_1\|\mathbf{j} + \frac{\sqrt{2}}{2}\|\mathbf{F}_2\|\mathbf{i} + \frac{\sqrt{2}}{2}\|\mathbf{F}_2\|\mathbf{j} - 1200\mathbf{j} = \mathbf{0}$$

The **i** component and **j** component will each equal zero. This results in the two equations

$$-\frac{\sqrt{3}}{2}\|\mathbf{F}_1\| + \frac{\sqrt{2}}{2}\|\mathbf{F}_2\| = 0 \qquad (9)$$

$$\frac{1}{2}\|\mathbf{F}_1\| + \frac{\sqrt{2}}{2}\|\mathbf{F}_2\| - 1200 = 0 \qquad (10)$$

We solve equation (9) for $\|\mathbf{F}_2\|$ and obtain

$$\|\mathbf{F}_2\| = \frac{\sqrt{3}}{\sqrt{2}}\|\mathbf{F}_1\| \qquad (11)$$

Substituting into equation (10) and solving for $\|\mathbf{F}_1\|$, we obtain

$$\frac{1}{2}\|\mathbf{F}_1\| + \frac{\sqrt{2}}{2}\left(\frac{\sqrt{3}}{\sqrt{2}}\|\mathbf{F}_1\|\right) - 1200 = 0$$

$$\frac{1}{2}\|\mathbf{F}_1\| + \frac{\sqrt{3}}{2}\|\mathbf{F}_1\| - 1200 = 0$$

$$\frac{1 + \sqrt{3}}{2}\|\mathbf{F}_1\| = 1200$$

$$\|\mathbf{F}_1\| = \frac{2400}{1 + \sqrt{3}} \approx 878.5 \text{ pounds}$$

Substituting this value into equation (11) yields $\|\mathbf{F}_2\|$.

$$\|\mathbf{F}_2\| = \frac{\sqrt{3}}{\sqrt{2}}\|\mathbf{F}_1\| = \frac{\sqrt{3}}{\sqrt{2}} \cdot \frac{2400}{1 + \sqrt{3}} \approx 1075.9 \text{ pounds}$$

The left cable has tension of approximately 878.5 pounds and the right cable has tension of approximately 1075.9 pounds.

━━━━ **Now Work** PROBLEM **67**

Historical Feature

Josiah Gibbs (1839–1903)

The history of vectors is surprisingly complicated for such a natural concept. In the xy-plane, complex numbers do a good job of imitating vectors. About 1840, mathematicians became interested in finding a system that would do for three dimensions what the complex numbers do for two dimensions. Hermann Grassmann (1809–1877), in Germany, and William Rowan Hamilton (1805–1865), in Ireland, both attempted to find solutions.

Hamilton's system was the *quaternions,* which are best thought of as a real number plus a vector, and do for four dimensions what complex numbers do for two dimensions. In this system the order of multiplication matters; that is, **ab ≠ ba.** Also, two products of vectors emerged, the scalar (or dot) product and the vector (or cross) product.

Grassmann's abstract style, although easily read today, was almost impenetrable during the previous century, and only a few of his ideas were appreciated. Among those few were the same scalar and vector products that Hamilton had found.

About 1880, the American physicist Josiah Willard Gibbs (1839–1903) worked out an algebra involving only the simplest concepts: the vectors and the two products. He then added some calculus, and the resulting system was simple, flexible, and well adapted to expressing a large number of physical laws. This system remains in use essentially unchanged. Hamilton's and Grassmann's more extensive systems each gave birth to much interesting mathematics, but little of this mathematics is seen at elementary levels.

9.4 Assess Your Understanding

Concepts and Vocabulary

1. A vector whose magnitude is 1 is called a(n) _____ vector.

2. The product of a vector by a number is called a(n) _____ multiple.

3. If $\mathbf{v} = a\mathbf{i} + b\mathbf{j}$, then a is called the _____ component of $\mathbf{v}$ and b is the _____ component of $\mathbf{v}$.

4. *True or False* Vectors are quantities that have magnitude and direction.

5. *True or False* Force is a physical example of a vector.

6. *True or False* Mass is a physical example of a vector.

Skill Building

In Problems 7–14, use the vectors in the figure at the right to graph each of the following vectors.

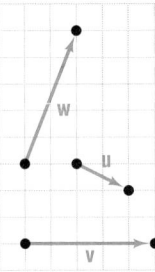

7. $\mathbf{v} + \mathbf{w}$

8. $\mathbf{u} + \mathbf{v}$

9. $3\mathbf{v}$

10. $4\mathbf{w}$

11. $\mathbf{v} - \mathbf{w}$

12. $\mathbf{u} - \mathbf{v}$

13. $3\mathbf{v} + \mathbf{u} - 2\mathbf{w}$

14. $2\mathbf{u} - 3\mathbf{v} + \mathbf{w}$

In Problems 15–22, use the figure at the right. Determine whether the given statement is true or false.

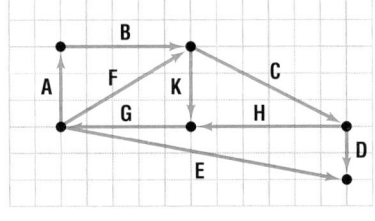

15. $\mathbf{A} + \mathbf{B} = \mathbf{F}$

16. $\mathbf{K} + \mathbf{G} = \mathbf{F}$

17. $\mathbf{C} = \mathbf{D} - \mathbf{E} + \mathbf{F}$

18. $\mathbf{G} + \mathbf{H} + \mathbf{E} = \mathbf{D}$

19. $\mathbf{E} + \mathbf{D} = \mathbf{G} + \mathbf{H}$

20. $\mathbf{H} - \mathbf{C} = \mathbf{G} - \mathbf{F}$

21. $\mathbf{A} + \mathbf{B} + \mathbf{K} + \mathbf{G} = \mathbf{0}$

22. $\mathbf{A} + \mathbf{B} + \mathbf{C} + \mathbf{H} + \mathbf{G} = \mathbf{0}$

23. If $\|\mathbf{v}\| = 4$, what is $\|3\mathbf{v}\|$?

24. If $\|\mathbf{v}\| = 2$, what is $\|-4\mathbf{v}\|$?

In Problems 25–32, the vector $\mathbf{v}$ has initial point P and terminal point Q. Write $\mathbf{v}$ in the form $a\mathbf{i} + b\mathbf{j}$; that is, find its position vector.

25. $P = (0, 0);\ \ Q = (3, 4)$

26. $P = (0, 0);\ \ Q = (-3, -5)$

27. $P = (3, 2);\ \ Q = (5, 6)$

28. $P = (-3, 2);\ \ Q = (6, 5)$

29. $P = (-2, -1);\ \ Q = (6, -2)$

30. $P = (-1, 4);\ \ Q = (6, 2)$

31. $P = (1, 0);\ \ Q = (0, 1)$

32. $P = (1, 1);\ \ Q = (2, 2)$

In Problems 33–38, find $\|\mathbf{v}\|$.

33. $\mathbf{v} = 3\mathbf{i} - 4\mathbf{j}$

34. $\mathbf{v} = -5\mathbf{i} + 12\mathbf{j}$

35. $\mathbf{v} = \mathbf{i} - \mathbf{j}$

36. $\mathbf{v} = -\mathbf{i} - \mathbf{j}$

37. $\mathbf{v} = -2\mathbf{i} + 3\mathbf{j}$

38. $\mathbf{v} = 6\mathbf{i} + 2\mathbf{j}$

In Problems 39–44, find each quantity if $\mathbf{v} = 3\mathbf{i} - 5\mathbf{j}$ and $\mathbf{w} = -2\mathbf{i} + 3\mathbf{j}$.

39. $2\mathbf{v} + 3\mathbf{w}$

40. $3\mathbf{v} - 2\mathbf{w}$

41. $\|\mathbf{v} - \mathbf{w}\|$

42. $\|\mathbf{v} + \mathbf{w}\|$

43. $\|\mathbf{v}\| - \|\mathbf{w}\|$

44. $\|\mathbf{v}\| + \|\mathbf{w}\|$

In Problems 45–50, find the unit vector in the same direction as $\mathbf{v}$.

45. $\mathbf{v} = 5\mathbf{i}$

46. $\mathbf{v} = -3\mathbf{j}$

47. $\mathbf{v} = 3\mathbf{i} - 4\mathbf{j}$

48. $\mathbf{v} = -5\mathbf{i} + 12\mathbf{j}$

49. $\mathbf{v} = \mathbf{i} - \mathbf{j}$

50. $\mathbf{v} = 2\mathbf{i} - \mathbf{j}$

51. Find a vector $\mathbf{v}$ whose magnitude is 4 and whose component in the $\mathbf{i}$ direction is twice the component in the $\mathbf{j}$ direction.

52. Find a vector $\mathbf{v}$ whose magnitude is 3 and whose component in the $\mathbf{i}$ direction is equal to the component in the $\mathbf{j}$ direction.

53. If $\mathbf{v} = 2\mathbf{i} - \mathbf{j}$ and $\mathbf{w} = x\mathbf{i} + 3\mathbf{j}$, find all numbers x for which $\|\mathbf{v} + \mathbf{w}\| = 5$.

54. If $P = (-3, 1)$ and $Q = (x, 4)$, find all numbers x such that the vector represented by $\overrightarrow{PQ}$ has length 5.

In Problems 55–60, write the vector **v** *in the form* a**i** + b**j**, *given its magnitude* ‖**v**‖ *and the angle* α *it makes with the positive x-axis.*

55. ‖**v**‖ = 5, α = 60°

56. ‖**v**‖ = 8, α = 45°

57. ‖**v**‖ = 14, α = 120°

58. ‖**v**‖ = 3, α = 240°

59. ‖**v**‖ = 25, α = 330°

60. ‖**v**‖ = 15, α = 315°

Applications and Extensions

61. Computer Graphics The field of computer graphics utilizes vectors to compute translations of points. For example, if the point $(-3, 2)$ is to be translated by $\mathbf{v} = \langle 5, 2 \rangle$, then the new location will be $\mathbf{u}' = \mathbf{u} + \mathbf{v} = \langle -3, 2 \rangle + \langle 5, 2 \rangle = \langle 2, 4 \rangle$. As illustrated in the figure, the point $(-3, 2)$ is translated to $(2, 4)$ by **v**.

Source: Phil Dadd. Vectors and Matrices: A Primer. www.gamedev.net/reference/articles/article1832.asp

(a) Determine the new coordinates of $(3, -1)$ if it is translated by $\mathbf{v} = \langle -4, 5 \rangle$.

(b) Illustrate this translation graphically.

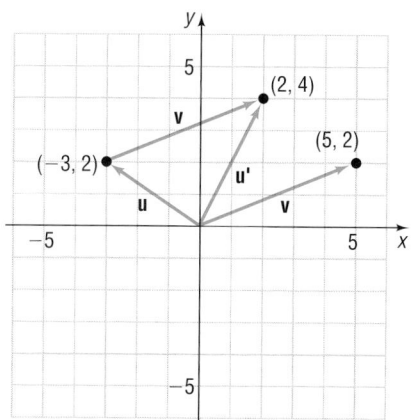

62. Computer Graphics Refer to Problem 61. The points $(-3, 0), (-1, -2), (3, 1)$ and $(1, 3)$ are the vertices of a parallelogram $ABCD$.

(a) Find the new vertices of a parallelogram $A'B'C'D'$ if it is translated by $\mathbf{v} = \langle 3, -2 \rangle$.

(b) Find the new vertices of a parallelogram $A'B'C'D'$ if it is translated by $-\dfrac{1}{2}\mathbf{v}$.

63. Force Vectors A child pulls a wagon with a force of 40 pounds. The handle of the wagon makes an angle of 30° with the ground. Express the force vector **F** in terms of **i** and **j**.

64. Force Vectors A man pushes a wheelbarrow up an incline of 20° with a force of 100 pounds. Express the force vector **F** in terms of **i** and **j**.

65. Resultant Force Two forces of magnitude 40 newtons (N) and 60 N act on an object at angles of 30° and −45° with the positive x-axis, as shown in the figure. Find the direction and magnitude of the resultant force; that is, find $\mathbf{F}_1 + \mathbf{F}_2$.

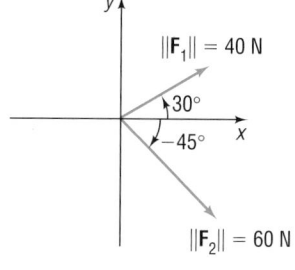

66. Resultant Force Two forces of magnitude 30 newtons (N) and 70 N act on an object at angles of 45° and 120° with the positive x-axis, as shown in the figure. Find the direction and magnitude of the resultant force; that is, find $\mathbf{F}_1 + \mathbf{F}_2$.

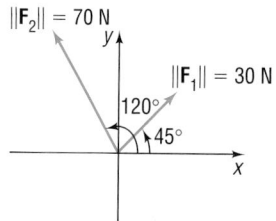

67. Static Equilibrium A weight of 1000 pounds is suspended from two cables as shown in the figure. What are the tensions in the two cables?

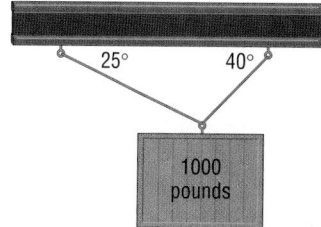

68. Static Equilibrium A weight of 800 pounds is suspended from two cables, as shown in the figure. What are the tensions in the two cables?

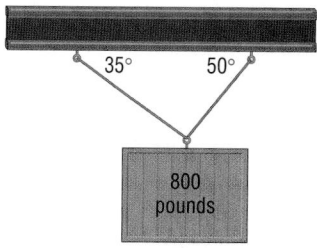

69. Static Equilibrium A tightrope walker located at a certain point deflects the rope as indicated in the figure. If the weight of the tightrope walker is 150 pounds, how much tension is in each part of the rope?

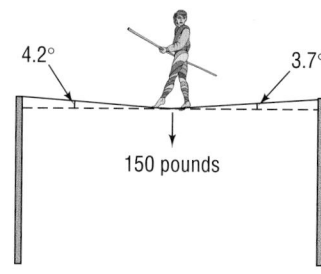

70. Static Equilibrium Repeat Problem 69 if the left angle is 3.8°, the right angle is 2.6°, and the weight of the tightrope walker is 135 pounds.

71. Truck Pull At a county fair truck pull, two pickup trucks are attached to the back end of a monster truck as illustrated in the figure. One of the pickups pulls with a force of 2000 pounds and the other pulls with a force of 3000 pounds with an angle of 45° between them. With how much force must the monster truck pull in order to remain unmoved?
[**Hint:** Find the resultant force of the two trucks.]

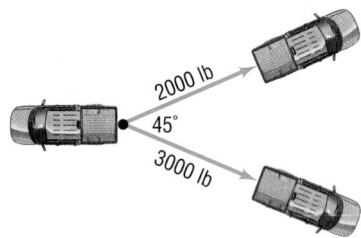

72. Removing a Stump A farmer wishes to remove a stump from a field by pulling it out with his tractor. Having removed many stumps before, he estimates that he will need 6 tons (12,000 pounds) of force to remove the stump. However, his tractor is only capable of pulling with a force of 7000 pounds, so he asks his neighbor to help. His neighbor's tractor can pull with a force of 5500 pounds. They attach the two tractors to the stump with a 40° angle between the forces as shown in the figure.

(a) Assuming the farmer's estimate of a needed 6-ton force is correct, will the farmer be successful in removing the stump? Explain.

(b) Had the farmer arranged the tractors with a 25° angle between the forces, would he have been successful in removing the stump? Explain.

73. Static Equilibrium Show on the following graph the force needed for the object at P to be in static equilibrium.

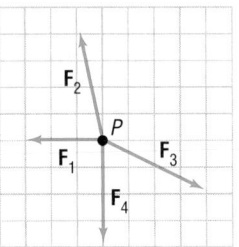

Discussion and Writing

74. Explain in your own words what a vector is. Give an example of a vector.

75. Write a brief paragraph comparing the algebra of complex numbers and the algebra of vectors.

9.5 The Dot Product

PREPARING FOR THIS SECTION   *Before getting started, review the following:*

- Law of Cosines (Section 8.3, p. 534)

Now Work the 'Are You Prepared?' problem on page 614.

OBJECTIVES   **1** Find the Dot Product of Two Vectors (p. 608)
2 Find the Angle between Two Vectors (p. 609)
3 Determine Whether Two Vectors Are Parallel (p. 611)
4 Determine Whether Two Vectors Are Orthogonal (p. 611)
5 Decompose a Vector into Two Orthogonal Vectors (p. 612)
6 Compute Work (p. 613)

1 Find the Dot Product of Two Vectors

The definition for a product of two vectors is somewhat unexpected. However, such a product has meaning in many geometric and physical applications.

DEFINITION   If $\mathbf{v} = a_1\mathbf{i} + b_1\mathbf{j}$ and $\mathbf{w} = a_2\mathbf{i} + b_2\mathbf{j}$ are two vectors, the **dot product** $\mathbf{v} \cdot \mathbf{w}$ is defined as

$$\mathbf{v} \cdot \mathbf{w} = a_1a_2 + b_1b_2 \tag{1}$$

EXAMPLE 1	Finding Dot Products

If $\mathbf{v} = 2\mathbf{i} - 3\mathbf{j}$ and $\mathbf{w} = 5\mathbf{i} + 3\mathbf{j}$, find:

(a) $\mathbf{v} \cdot \mathbf{w}$ (b) $\mathbf{w} \cdot \mathbf{v}$ (c) $\mathbf{v} \cdot \mathbf{v}$

(d) $\mathbf{w} \cdot \mathbf{w}$ (e) $\|\mathbf{v}\|$ (f) $\|\mathbf{w}\|$

Solution

(a) $\mathbf{v} \cdot \mathbf{w} = 2(5) + (-3)3 = 1$ (b) $\mathbf{w} \cdot \mathbf{v} = 5(2) + 3(-3) = 1$

(c) $\mathbf{v} \cdot \mathbf{v} = 2(2) + (-3)(-3) = 13$ (d) $\mathbf{w} \cdot \mathbf{w} = 5(5) + 3(3) = 34$

(e) $\|\mathbf{v}\| = \sqrt{2^2 + (-3)^2} = \sqrt{13}$ (f) $\|\mathbf{w}\| = \sqrt{5^2 + 3^2} = \sqrt{34}$

COMMENT A scalar multiple $\alpha\mathbf{v}$ is a vector. A dot product $\mathbf{u} \cdot \mathbf{v}$ is a scalar (real number). ∎

Since the dot product $\mathbf{v} \cdot \mathbf{w}$ of two vectors $\mathbf{v}$ and $\mathbf{w}$ is a real number (scalar), we sometimes refer to it as the **scalar product.**

The results obtained in Example 1 suggest some general properties.

THEOREM

Properties of the Dot Product

If $\mathbf{u}$, $\mathbf{v}$, and $\mathbf{w}$ are vectors, then

Commutative Property

$$\mathbf{u} \cdot \mathbf{v} = \mathbf{v} \cdot \mathbf{u} \tag{2}$$

Distributive Property

$$\mathbf{u} \cdot (\mathbf{v} + \mathbf{w}) = \mathbf{u} \cdot \mathbf{v} + \mathbf{u} \cdot \mathbf{w} \tag{3}$$

$$\mathbf{v} \cdot \mathbf{v} = \|\mathbf{v}\|^2 \tag{4}$$

$$\mathbf{0} \cdot \mathbf{v} = 0 \tag{5}$$

Proof We will prove properties (2) and (4) here and leave properties (3) and (5) as exercises (see Problems 40 and 41).

To prove property (2), we let $\mathbf{u} = a_1\mathbf{i} + b_1\mathbf{j}$ and $\mathbf{v} = a_2\mathbf{i} + b_2\mathbf{j}$. Then

$$\mathbf{u} \cdot \mathbf{v} = a_1a_2 + b_1b_2 = a_2a_1 + b_2b_1 = \mathbf{v} \cdot \mathbf{u}$$

To prove property (4), we let $\mathbf{v} = a\mathbf{i} + b\mathbf{j}$. Then

$$\mathbf{v} \cdot \mathbf{v} = a^2 + b^2 = \|\mathbf{v}\|^2 \qquad ∎$$

2 Find the Angle between Two Vectors

One use of the dot product is to calculate the angle between two vectors. We proceed as follows.

Let $\mathbf{u}$ and $\mathbf{v}$ be two vectors with the same initial point A. Then the vectors $\mathbf{u}$, $\mathbf{v}$, and $\mathbf{u} - \mathbf{v}$ form a triangle. The angle θ at vertex A of the triangle is the angle between the vectors $\mathbf{u}$ and $\mathbf{v}$. See Figure 65. We wish to find a formula for calculating the angle θ.

The sides of the triangle have lengths $\|\mathbf{v}\|$, $\|\mathbf{u}\|$, and $\|\mathbf{u} - \mathbf{v}\|$, and θ is the included angle between the sides of length $\|\mathbf{v}\|$ and $\|\mathbf{u}\|$. The Law of Cosines (Section 8.3) can be used to find the cosine of the included angle.

$$\|\mathbf{u} - \mathbf{v}\|^2 = \|\mathbf{u}\|^2 + \|\mathbf{v}\|^2 - 2\|\mathbf{u}\|\|\mathbf{v}\| \cos\theta$$

Now we use property (4) to rewrite this equation in terms of dot products.

$$(\mathbf{u} - \mathbf{v}) \cdot (\mathbf{u} - \mathbf{v}) = \mathbf{u} \cdot \mathbf{u} + \mathbf{v} \cdot \mathbf{v} - 2\|\mathbf{u}\|\|\mathbf{v}\| \cos\theta \tag{6}$$

Figure 65

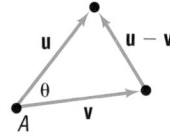

Then we apply the distributive property (3) twice on the left side of (6) to obtain

$$(\mathbf{u} - \mathbf{v}) \cdot (\mathbf{u} - \mathbf{v}) = \mathbf{u} \cdot (\mathbf{u} - \mathbf{v}) - \mathbf{v} \cdot (\mathbf{u} - \mathbf{v})$$

$$= \mathbf{u} \cdot \mathbf{u} - \mathbf{u} \cdot \mathbf{v} - \mathbf{v} \cdot \mathbf{u} + \mathbf{v} \cdot \mathbf{v}$$

$$= \mathbf{u} \cdot \mathbf{u} + \mathbf{v} \cdot \mathbf{v} - 2\,\mathbf{u} \cdot \mathbf{v} \qquad \textbf{(7)}$$

$\uparrow$
Property (2)

Combining equations (6) and (7), we have

$$\mathbf{u} \cdot \mathbf{u} + \mathbf{v} \cdot \mathbf{v} - 2\,\mathbf{u} \cdot \mathbf{v} = \mathbf{u} \cdot \mathbf{u} + \mathbf{v} \cdot \mathbf{v} - 2\,\|\mathbf{u}\|\|\mathbf{v}\|\cos\theta$$

$$\mathbf{u} \cdot \mathbf{v} = \|\mathbf{u}\|\|\mathbf{v}\|\cos\theta$$

We have proved the following result:

THEOREM   **Angle between Vectors**

If **u** and **v** are two nonzero vectors, the angle θ, $0 \le \theta \le \pi$, between **u** and **v** is determined by the formula

$$\cos\theta = \frac{\mathbf{u} \cdot \mathbf{v}}{\|\mathbf{u}\|\|\mathbf{v}\|} \qquad \textbf{(8)}$$

EXAMPLE 2   **Finding the Angle θ between Two Vectors**

Find the angle θ between $\mathbf{u} = 4\mathbf{i} - 3\mathbf{j}$ and $\mathbf{v} = 2\mathbf{i} + 5\mathbf{j}$.

Solution   We compute the quantities $\mathbf{u} \cdot \mathbf{v}$, $\|\mathbf{u}\|$, and $\|\mathbf{v}\|$.

Figure 66

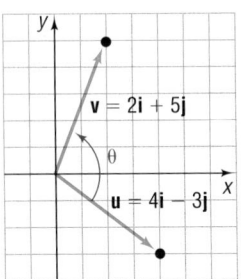

$$\mathbf{u} \cdot \mathbf{v} = 4(2) + (-3)(5) = -7$$

$$\|\mathbf{u}\| = \sqrt{4^2 + (-3)^2} = 5$$

$$\|\mathbf{v}\| = \sqrt{2^2 + 5^2} = \sqrt{29}$$

By formula (8), if θ is the angle between **u** and **v**, then

$$\cos\theta = \frac{\mathbf{u} \cdot \mathbf{v}}{\|\mathbf{u}\|\|\mathbf{v}\|} = \frac{-7}{5\sqrt{29}} \approx -0.26$$

We find that $\theta \approx 105°$. See Figure 66.

Now Work PROBLEMS 7(a) AND (b)

EXAMPLE 3   **Finding the Actual Speed and Direction of an Aircraft**

A Boeing 737 aircraft maintains a constant airspeed of 500 miles per hour in the direction due south. The velocity of the jet stream is 80 miles per hour in a northeasterly direction. Find the actual speed and direction of the aircraft relative to the ground.

Solution   We set up a coordinate system in which north (N) is along the positive y-axis. See Figure 67. Let

$$\mathbf{v}_a = \text{velocity of aircraft relative to the air} = -500\mathbf{j}$$

$$\mathbf{v}_w = \text{velocity of jet stream}$$

$$\mathbf{v}_g = \text{velocity of aircraft relative to ground}$$

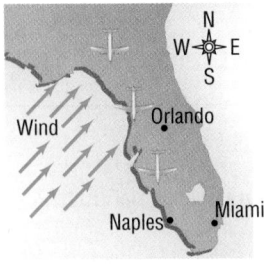

The velocity of the jet stream $\mathbf{v}_w$ has magnitude 80 and direction NE (northeast), so the angle between $\mathbf{v}_w$ and **i** is 45°. We express $\mathbf{v}_w$ in terms of **i** and **j** as

$$\mathbf{v}_w = 80(\cos 45°\mathbf{i} + \sin 45°\mathbf{j}) = 80\left(\frac{\sqrt{2}}{2}\mathbf{i} + \frac{\sqrt{2}}{2}\mathbf{j}\right) = 40\sqrt{2}\,(\mathbf{i} + \mathbf{j})$$

Figure 67

The velocity of the aircraft relative to the ground is

$$\mathbf{v}_g = \mathbf{v}_a + \mathbf{v}_w = -500\mathbf{j} + 40\sqrt{2}\,(\mathbf{i} + \mathbf{j}) = 40\sqrt{2}\,\mathbf{i} + \left(40\sqrt{2} - 500\right)\mathbf{j}$$

The actual speed of the aircraft is

$$\|\mathbf{v}_g\| = \sqrt{\left(40\sqrt{2}\right)^2 + \left(40\sqrt{2} - 500\right)^2} \approx 447 \text{ miles per hour}$$

The angle θ between $\mathbf{v}_g$ and the vector $\mathbf{v}_a = -500\mathbf{j}$ (the velocity of the aircraft relative to the air) is determined by the equation

$$\cos\theta = \frac{\mathbf{v}_g \cdot \mathbf{v}_a}{\|\mathbf{v}_g\|\|\mathbf{v}_a\|} \approx \frac{\left(40\sqrt{2} - 500\right)(-500)}{(447)(500)} \approx 0.9920$$

$$\theta \approx 7.3°$$

The direction of the aircraft relative to the ground is approximately S7.3°E (about 7.3° east of south).

━━━━━━━━━━ **Now Work** PROBLEM 29

3 Determine Whether Two Vectors Are Parallel

Two vectors $\mathbf{v}$ and $\mathbf{w}$ are said to be **parallel** if there is a nonzero scalar α so that $\mathbf{v} = \alpha\mathbf{w}$. In this case, the angle θ between $\mathbf{v}$ and $\mathbf{w}$ is 0 or π.

| EXAMPLE 4 | Determining Whether Vectors Are Parallel |

The vectors $\mathbf{v} = 3\mathbf{i} - \mathbf{j}$ and $\mathbf{w} = 6\mathbf{i} - 2\mathbf{j}$ are parallel, since $\mathbf{v} = \dfrac{1}{2}\mathbf{w}$. Furthermore, since

$$\cos\theta = \frac{\mathbf{v} \cdot \mathbf{w}}{\|\mathbf{v}\|\|\mathbf{w}\|} = \frac{18 + 2}{\sqrt{10}\,\sqrt{40}} = \frac{20}{\sqrt{400}} = 1$$

the angle θ between $\mathbf{v}$ and $\mathbf{w}$ is 0.

4 Determine Whether Two Vectors Are Orthogonal

Figure 68
$\mathbf{v}$ is orthogonal to $\mathbf{w}$.

If the angle θ between two nonzero vectors $\mathbf{v}$ and $\mathbf{w}$ is $\dfrac{\pi}{2}$, the vectors $\mathbf{v}$ and $\mathbf{w}$ are called **orthogonal.*** See Figure 68.

Since $\cos\dfrac{\pi}{2} = 0$, it follows from formula (8) that if $\mathbf{v}$ and $\mathbf{w}$ are orthogonal then $\mathbf{v} \cdot \mathbf{w} = 0$.

On the other hand, if $\mathbf{v} \cdot \mathbf{w} = 0$, then either $\mathbf{v} = 0$ or $\mathbf{w} = 0$ or $\cos\theta = 0$. In the latter case, $\theta = \dfrac{\pi}{2}$, and $\mathbf{v}$ and $\mathbf{w}$ are orthogonal. If $\mathbf{v}$ or $\mathbf{w}$ is the zero vector, then, since the zero vector has no specific direction, we adopt the convention that the zero vector is orthogonal to every vector.

THEOREM

Two vectors $\mathbf{v}$ and $\mathbf{w}$ are orthogonal if and only if

$$\mathbf{v} \cdot \mathbf{w} = 0$$

---

*Orthogonal, perpendicular, and *normal* are all terms that mean "meet at a right angle." It is customary to refer to two vectors as being *orthogonal,* two lines as being *perpendicular,* and a line and a plane or a vector and a plane as being *normal.*

Figure 69

EXAMPLE 5 | **Determining Whether Two Vectors Are Orthogonal**

The vectors

$$\mathbf{v} = 2\mathbf{i} - \mathbf{j} \quad \text{and} \quad \mathbf{w} = 3\mathbf{i} + 6\mathbf{j}$$

are orthogonal, since

$$\mathbf{v} \cdot \mathbf{w} = 6 - 6 = 0$$

See Figure 69.

➤ **Now Work** PROBLEM 7(c)

5 Decompose a Vector into Two Orthogonal Vectors

In many physical applications, it is necessary to find "how much" of a vector is applied in a given direction. Look at Figure 70. The force **F** due to gravity is pulling straight down (toward the center of Earth) on the block. To study the effect of gravity on the block, it is necessary to determine how much of **F** is actually pushing the block down the incline ($\mathbf{F}_1$) and how much is pressing the block against the incline ($\mathbf{F}_2$), at a right angle to the incline. Knowing the **decomposition** of **F** often will allow us to determine when friction (the force holding the block in place on the incline) is overcome and the block will slide down the incline.

Figure 70

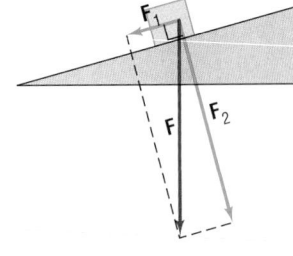

Suppose that **v** and **w** are two nonzero vectors with the same initial point P. We seek to decompose **v** into two vectors: $\mathbf{v}_1$, which is parallel to **w**, and $\mathbf{v}_2$, which is orthogonal to **w**. See Figure 71(a) and (b). The vector $\mathbf{v}_1$ is called the **vector projection of v onto w**.

The vector $\mathbf{v}_1$ is obtained as follows: From the terminal point of **v**, drop a perpendicular to the line containing **w**. The vector $\mathbf{v}_1$ is the vector from P to the foot of this perpendicular. The vector $\mathbf{v}_2$ is given by $\mathbf{v}_2 = \mathbf{v} - \mathbf{v}_1$. Note that $\mathbf{v} = \mathbf{v}_1 + \mathbf{v}_2$, the vector $\mathbf{v}_1$ is parallel to **w**, and the vector $\mathbf{v}_2$ is orthogonal to **w**. This is the decomposition of **v** that we wanted.

Figure 71

(a)

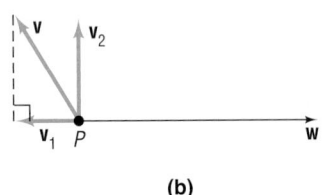

(b)

Now we seek a formula for $\mathbf{v}_1$ that is based on a knowledge of the vectors **v** and **w**. Since $\mathbf{v} = \mathbf{v}_1 + \mathbf{v}_2$, we have

$$\mathbf{v} \cdot \mathbf{w} = (\mathbf{v}_1 + \mathbf{v}_2) \cdot \mathbf{w} = \mathbf{v}_1 \cdot \mathbf{w} + \mathbf{v}_2 \cdot \mathbf{w} \tag{9}$$

Since $\mathbf{v}_2$ is orthogonal to **w**, we have $\mathbf{v}_2 \cdot \mathbf{w} = 0$. Since $\mathbf{v}_1$ is parallel to **w**, we have $\mathbf{v}_1 = \alpha\mathbf{w}$ for some scalar α. Equation (9) can be written as

$$\mathbf{v} \cdot \mathbf{w} = \alpha\mathbf{w} \cdot \mathbf{w} = \alpha\|\mathbf{w}\|^2 \qquad \text{\small $\mathbf{v}_1 = \alpha\mathbf{w}; \mathbf{v}_2 \cdot \mathbf{w} = 0$}$$

$$\alpha = \frac{\mathbf{v} \cdot \mathbf{w}}{\|\mathbf{w}\|^2}$$

Then

$$\mathbf{v}_1 = \alpha\mathbf{w} = \frac{\mathbf{v} \cdot \mathbf{w}}{\|\mathbf{w}\|^2}\mathbf{w}$$

THEOREM

If **v** and **w** are two nonzero vectors, the vector projection of **v** onto **w** is

$$\mathbf{v}_1 = \frac{\mathbf{v} \cdot \mathbf{w}}{\|\mathbf{w}\|^2}\mathbf{w} \tag{10}$$

The decomposition of **v** into $\mathbf{v}_1$ and $\mathbf{v}_2$, where $\mathbf{v}_1$ is parallel to **w** and $\mathbf{v}_2$ is orthogonal to **w**, is

$$\mathbf{v}_1 = \frac{\mathbf{v} \cdot \mathbf{w}}{\|\mathbf{w}\|^2}\mathbf{w} \qquad \mathbf{v}_2 = \mathbf{v} - \mathbf{v}_1 \tag{11}$$

| EXAMPLE 6 | Decomposing a Vector into Two Orthogonal Vectors |

Find the vector projection of $\mathbf{v} = \mathbf{i} + 3\mathbf{j}$ onto $\mathbf{w} = \mathbf{i} + \mathbf{j}$. Decompose $\mathbf{v}$ into two vectors, $\mathbf{v}_1$ and $\mathbf{v}_2$, where $\mathbf{v}_1$ is parallel to $\mathbf{w}$ and $\mathbf{v}_2$ is orthogonal to $\mathbf{w}$.

Solution We use formulas (10) and (11).

Figure 72

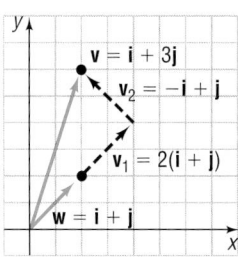

$$\mathbf{v}_1 = \frac{\mathbf{v} \cdot \mathbf{w}}{\|\mathbf{w}\|^2} \mathbf{w} = \frac{1 + 3}{(\sqrt{2})^2} \mathbf{w} = 2\mathbf{w} = 2(\mathbf{i} + \mathbf{j})$$

$$\mathbf{v}_2 = \mathbf{v} - \mathbf{v}_1 = (\mathbf{i} + 3\mathbf{j}) - 2(\mathbf{i} + \mathbf{j}) = -\mathbf{i} + \mathbf{j}$$

See Figure 72.

━━━━ **Now Work** PROBLEM 19

6 Compute Work

In elementary physics, the **work** W done by a constant force $\mathbf{F}$ in moving an object from a point A to a point B is defined as

$$W = (\text{magnitude of force})(\text{distance}) = \|\mathbf{F}\|\|\overrightarrow{AB}\|$$

Figure 73

Work is commonly measured in foot-pounds or in newton-meters (joules).

In this definition, it is assumed that the force $\mathbf{F}$ is applied along the line of motion. If the constant force $\mathbf{F}$ is not along the line of motion, but, instead, is at an angle θ to the direction of the motion, as illustrated in Figure 73, the **work W done by $\mathbf{F}$** in moving an object from A to B is defined as

$$W = \mathbf{F} \cdot \overrightarrow{AB} \qquad\qquad (12)$$

This definition is compatible with the force times distance definition, since

$$W = (\text{amount of force in the direction of } \overrightarrow{AB})(\text{distance})$$

$$= \|\text{projection of } \mathbf{F} \text{ on } AB\|\|\overrightarrow{AB}\| = \underset{\uparrow}{\frac{\mathbf{F} \cdot \overrightarrow{AB}}{\|\overrightarrow{AB}\|^2}} \|\overrightarrow{AB}\|\|\overrightarrow{AB}\| = \mathbf{F} \cdot \overrightarrow{AB}$$

Use formula (10).

| EXAMPLE 7 | Computing Work |

Figure 74(a) shows a girl pulling a wagon with a force of 50 pounds. How much work is done in moving the wagon 100 feet if the handle makes an angle of 30° with the ground?

Figure 74

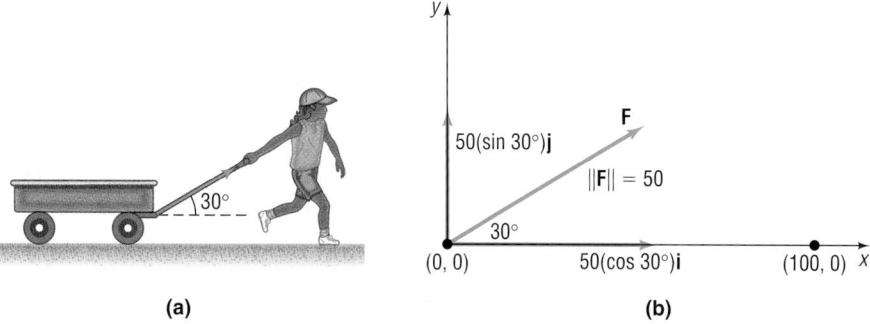

(a)   (b)

Solution We position the vectors in a coordinate system in such a way that the wagon is moved from $(0, 0)$ to $(100, 0)$. The motion is from $A = (0, 0)$ to $B = (100, 0)$, so $\overrightarrow{AB} = 100\mathbf{i}$. The force vector $\mathbf{F}$, as shown in Figure 74(b), is

$$\mathbf{F} = 50(\cos 30°\mathbf{i} + \sin 30°\mathbf{j}) = 50\left(\frac{\sqrt{3}}{2}\mathbf{i} + \frac{1}{2}\mathbf{j}\right) = 25(\sqrt{3}\mathbf{i} + \mathbf{j})$$

By formula (12), the work done is

$$W = \mathbf{F} \cdot \overrightarrow{AB} = 25\left(\sqrt{3}\mathbf{i} + \mathbf{j}\right) \cdot 100\mathbf{i} = 2500\sqrt{3} \text{ foot-pounds}$$

━━━━━ **Now Work** PROBLEM 25

Historical Feature

We stated in an earlier Historical Feature that complex numbers were used as vectors in the plane before the general notion of a vector was clarified. Suppose that we make the correspondence

Vector ↔ Complex number

$$a\mathbf{i} + b\mathbf{j} \leftrightarrow a + bi$$
$$c\mathbf{i} + d\mathbf{j} \leftrightarrow c + di$$

Show that

$$(a\mathbf{i} + b\mathbf{j}) \cdot (c\mathbf{i} + d\mathbf{j}) = \text{real part } [\overline{(a + bi)}(c + di)]$$

This is how the dot product was found originally. The imaginary part is also interesting. It is a determinant (see Section 11.3) and represents the area of the parallelogram whose edges are the vectors. This is close to some of Hermann Grassmann's ideas and is also connected with the scalar triple product of three-dimensional vectors.

9.5 Assess Your Understanding

'Are You Prepared?' *The answer is given at the end of these exercises. If you get the wrong answer, read the page listed in* red.

1. In a triangle with sides a, b, c and angles A, B, C, the Law of Cosines states that _____. (p. 534)

Concepts and Vocabulary

2. If $\mathbf{v} \cdot \mathbf{w} = 0$, then the two vectors $\mathbf{v}$ and $\mathbf{w}$ are _____.

3. If $\mathbf{v} = 3\mathbf{w}$, then the two vectors $\mathbf{v}$ and $\mathbf{w}$ are _____.

4. *True or False* If $\mathbf{v}$ and $\mathbf{w}$ are parallel vectors, then $\mathbf{v} \cdot \mathbf{w} = 0$.

5. *True or False* Given two nonzero vectors $\mathbf{v}$ and $\mathbf{w}$, it is always possible to decompose $\mathbf{v}$ into two vectors, one parallel to $\mathbf{w}$ and the other perpendicular to $\mathbf{w}$.

6. *True or False* Work is a physical example of a vector.

Skill Building

In Problems 7–16, (a) find the dot product $\mathbf{v} \cdot \mathbf{w}$; (b) find the angle between $\mathbf{v}$ and $\mathbf{w}$; (c) state whether the vectors are parallel, orthogonal, or neither.

7. $\mathbf{v} = \mathbf{i} - \mathbf{j}, \quad \mathbf{w} = \mathbf{i} + \mathbf{j}$

8. $\mathbf{v} = \mathbf{i} + \mathbf{j}, \quad \mathbf{w} = -\mathbf{i} + \mathbf{j}$

9. $\mathbf{v} = 2\mathbf{i} + \mathbf{j}, \quad \mathbf{w} = \mathbf{i} - 2\mathbf{j}$

10. $\mathbf{v} = 2\mathbf{i} + 2\mathbf{j}, \quad \mathbf{w} = \mathbf{i} + 2\mathbf{j}$

11. $\mathbf{v} = \sqrt{3}\mathbf{i} - \mathbf{j}, \quad \mathbf{w} = \mathbf{i} + \mathbf{j}$

12. $\mathbf{v} = \mathbf{i} + \sqrt{3}\mathbf{j}, \quad \mathbf{w} = \mathbf{i} - \mathbf{j}$

13. $\mathbf{v} = 3\mathbf{i} + 4\mathbf{j}, \quad \mathbf{w} = -6\mathbf{i} - 8\mathbf{j}$

14. $\mathbf{v} = 3\mathbf{i} - 4\mathbf{j}, \quad \mathbf{w} = 9\mathbf{i} - 12\mathbf{j}$

15. $\mathbf{v} = 4\mathbf{i}, \quad \mathbf{w} = \mathbf{j}$

16. $\mathbf{v} = \mathbf{i}, \quad \mathbf{w} = -3\mathbf{j}$

17. Find a so that the vectors $\mathbf{v} = \mathbf{i} - a\mathbf{j}$ and $\mathbf{w} = 2\mathbf{i} + 3\mathbf{j}$ are orthogonal.

18. Find b so that the vectors $\mathbf{v} = \mathbf{i} + \mathbf{j}$ and $\mathbf{w} = \mathbf{i} + b\mathbf{j}$ are orthogonal.

In Problems 19–24, decompose $\mathbf{v}$ into two vectors $\mathbf{v}_1$ and $\mathbf{v}_2$, where $\mathbf{v}_1$ is parallel to $\mathbf{w}$ and $\mathbf{v}_2$ is orthogonal to $\mathbf{w}$.

19. $\mathbf{v} = 2\mathbf{i} - 3\mathbf{j}, \quad \mathbf{w} = \mathbf{i} - \mathbf{j}$

20. $\mathbf{v} = -3\mathbf{i} + 2\mathbf{j}, \quad \mathbf{w} = 2\mathbf{i} + \mathbf{j}$

21. $\mathbf{v} = \mathbf{i} - \mathbf{j}, \quad \mathbf{w} = -\mathbf{i} - 2\mathbf{j}$

22. $\mathbf{v} = 2\mathbf{i} - \mathbf{j}, \quad \mathbf{w} = \mathbf{i} - 2\mathbf{j}$

23. $\mathbf{v} = 3\mathbf{i} + \mathbf{j}, \quad \mathbf{w} = -2\mathbf{i} - \mathbf{j}$

24. $\mathbf{v} = \mathbf{i} - 3\mathbf{j}, \quad \mathbf{w} = 4\mathbf{i} - \mathbf{j}$

Applications and Extensions

25. **Computing Work** Find the work done by a force of 3 pounds acting in the direction 60° to the horizontal in moving an object 6 feet from $(0, 0)$ to $(6, 0)$.

26. **Computing Work** A wagon is pulled horizontally by exerting a force of 20 pounds on the handle at an angle of 30° with the horizontal. How much work is done in moving the wagon 100 feet?

27. **Solar Energy** The amount of energy collected by a solar panel depends on the intensity of the sun's rays and the area of the panel. Let the vector $\mathbf{I}$ represent the intensity, in watts per square centimeter, having the direction of the sun's rays. Let the vector **A** represent the area, in square centimeters, whose direction is the orientation of a solar panel. See the figure. The total number of watts collected by the panel is given by $W = |\mathbf{I} \cdot \mathbf{A}|$.

Suppose $\mathbf{I} = \langle -0.02, -0.01 \rangle$ and $\mathbf{A} = \langle 300, 400 \rangle$.

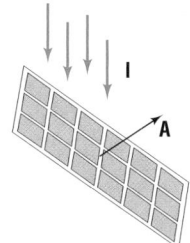

(a) Find $\|\mathbf{I}\|$ and $\|\mathbf{A}\|$ and interpret the meaning of each.
(b) Compute W and interpret its meaning.
(c) If the solar panel is to collect the maximum number of watts, what must be true about **I** and **A**?

28. Rainfall Measurement Let the vector **R** represent the amount of rainfall, in inches, whose direction is the inclination of the rain to a rain gauge. Let the vector **A** represent the area, in square inches, whose direction is the orientation of the opening of the rain gauge. See the figure. The volume of rain collected in the gauge, in cubic inches, is given by $V = |\mathbf{R} \cdot \mathbf{A}|$, even when the rain falls in a slanted direction or the gauge is not perfectly vertical.

Suppose $\mathbf{R} = \langle 0.75, -1.75 \rangle$ and $\mathbf{A} = \langle 0.3, 1 \rangle$.

(a) Find $\|\mathbf{R}\|$ and $\|\mathbf{A}\|$ and interpret the meaning of each.
(b) Compute V and interpret its meaning
(c) If the gauge is to collect the maximum volume of rain, what must be true about **R** and **A**?

29. Finding the Actual Speed and Direction of an Aircraft A Boeing 747 jumbo jet maintains an airspeed of 550 miles per hour in a southwesterly direction. The velocity of the jet stream is a constant 80 miles per hour from the west. Find the actual speed and direction of the aircraft.

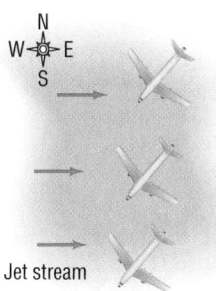

Jet stream

30. Finding the Correct Compass Heading The pilot of an aircraft wishes to head directly east, but is faced with a wind speed of 40 miles per hour from the northwest. If the pilot maintains an airspeed of 250 miles per hour, what compass heading should be maintained to head directly east? What is the actual speed of the aircraft?

31. Correct Direction for Crossing a River A river has a constant current of 3 kilometers per hour. At what angle to a boat dock should a motorboat, capable of maintaining a constant speed of 20 kilometers per hour, be headed in order to reach a point directly opposite the dock? If the river is $\frac{1}{2}$ kilometer wide, how long will it take to cross?

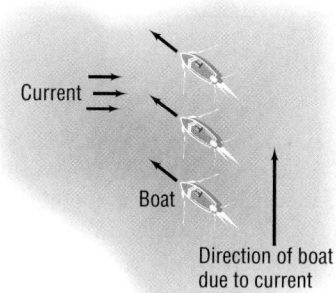

Current

Boat

Direction of boat due to current

32. Crossing a River A small motorboat in still water maintains a speed of 20 miles per hour. In heading directly across a river (that is, perpendicular to the current) whose current is 3 miles per hour, find a vector representing the speed and direction of the motorboat. What is the true speed of the motorboat? What is its direction?

33. Braking Load A Toyota Sienna with a gross weight of 5300 pounds is parked on a street with a slope of 8°. See the figure. Find the force required to keep the Sienna from rolling down the hill. What is the force perpendicular to the hill?

Weight = 5300 pounds

34. Braking Load A Pontiac Bonneville with a gross weight of 4500 pounds is parked on a street with a slope of 10°. Find the force required to keep the Bonneville from rolling down the hill. What is the force perpendicular to the hill?

35. Ground Speed and Direction of an Airplane An airplane has an airspeed of 500 kilometers per hour (km/hr) bearing N45°E. The wind velocity is 60 km/hr in the direction N30°W. Find the resultant vector representing the path of the plane relative to the ground. What is the ground speed of the plane? What is its direction?

36. Ground Speed and Direction of an Airplane An airplane has an airspeed of 600 km/hr bearing S30°E. The wind velocity is 40 km/hr in the direction S45°E. Find the resultant vector representing the path of the plane relative to the ground. What is the ground speed of the plane? What is its direction?

37. Ramp Angle Billy and Timmy are using a ramp to load furniture into a truck. While rolling a 250-pound piano up the ramp, they discover that the truck is too full of other furniture for the piano to fit. Timmy holds the piano in place on the ramp while Billy repositions other items to make room for it in the truck. If the angle of inclination of the ramp is 20°, how many pounds of force must Timmy exert to hold the piano in position?

20°

250 lb

38. Incline Angle   A bulldozer exerts 1000 pounds of force to prevent a 5000-pound boulder from rolling down a hill. Determine the angle of inclination of the hill.

39. Find the acute angle that a constant unit force vector makes with the positive *x*-axis if the work done by the force in moving a particle from $(0, 0)$ to $(4, 0)$ equals 2.

40. Prove the distributive property:

$$\mathbf{u} \cdot (\mathbf{v} + \mathbf{w}) = \mathbf{u} \cdot \mathbf{v} + \mathbf{u} \cdot \mathbf{w}$$

41. Prove property (5), $\mathbf{0} \cdot \mathbf{v} = 0$.

42. If $\mathbf{v}$ is a unit vector and the angle between $\mathbf{v}$ and $\mathbf{i}$ is α, show that $\mathbf{v} = \cos \alpha \mathbf{i} + \sin \alpha \mathbf{j}$.

43. Suppose that $\mathbf{v}$ and $\mathbf{w}$ are unit vectors. If the angle between $\mathbf{v}$ and $\mathbf{i}$ is α and that between $\mathbf{w}$ and $\mathbf{i}$ is β, use the idea of the dot product $\mathbf{v} \cdot \mathbf{w}$ to prove that

$$\cos(\alpha - \beta) = \cos \alpha \cos \beta + \sin \alpha \sin \beta$$

44. Show that the projection of $\mathbf{v}$ onto $\mathbf{i}$ is $(\mathbf{v} \cdot \mathbf{i})\mathbf{i}$. Then show that we can always write a vector $\mathbf{v}$ as

$$\mathbf{v} = (\mathbf{v} \cdot \mathbf{i})\mathbf{i} + (\mathbf{v} \cdot \mathbf{j})\mathbf{j}$$

45. (a) If $\mathbf{u}$ and $\mathbf{v}$ have the same magnitude, show that $\mathbf{u} + \mathbf{v}$ and $\mathbf{u} - \mathbf{v}$ are orthogonal.

(b) Use this to prove that an angle inscribed in a semicircle is a right angle (see the figure).

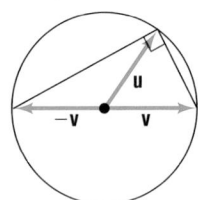

46. Let $\mathbf{v}$ and $\mathbf{w}$ denote two nonzero vectors. Show that the vector $\mathbf{v} - \alpha\mathbf{w}$ is orthogonal to $\mathbf{w}$ if $\alpha = \dfrac{\mathbf{v} \cdot \mathbf{w}}{\|\mathbf{w}\|^2}$.

47. Let $\mathbf{v}$ and $\mathbf{w}$ denote two nonzero vectors. Show that the vectors $\|\mathbf{w}\|\mathbf{v} + \|\mathbf{v}\|\mathbf{w}$ and $\|\mathbf{w}\|\mathbf{v} - \|\mathbf{v}\|\mathbf{w}$ are orthogonal.

48. In the definition of work given in this section, what is the work done if $\mathbf{F}$ is orthogonal to $\overrightarrow{AB}$?

49. Prove the **polarization identity**,

$$\|\mathbf{u} + \mathbf{v}\|^2 - \|\mathbf{u} - \mathbf{v}\|^2 = 4(\mathbf{u} \cdot \mathbf{v})$$

Discussion and Writing

50. Create an application different from any found in the text that requires a dot product.

'Are You Prepared?' Answer

1. $c^2 = a^2 + b^2 - 2ab \cos C$

9.6 Vectors in Space

PREPARING FOR THIS SECTION   *Before getting started, review the following:*

• Distance Formula (Section 1.1, p. 5)

Now Work the 'Are You Prepared?' problem on page 624.

OBJECTIVES   **1** Find the Distance between Two Points in Space (p. 618)
  2 Find Position Vectors in Space (p. 618)
  3 Perform Operations on Vectors (p. 619)
  4 Find the Dot Product (p. 620)
  5 Find the Angle between Two Vectors (p. 621)
  6 Find the Direction Angles of a Vector (p. 621)

Rectangular Coordinates in Space

Figure 75

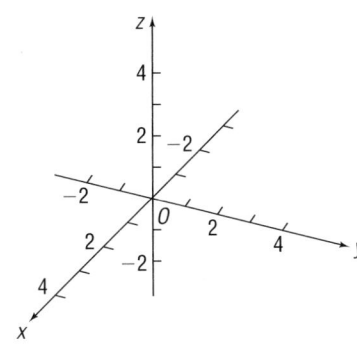

In the plane, each point is associated with an ordered pair of real numbers. In space, each point is associated with an ordered triple of real numbers. Through a fixed point, called the **origin** O, draw three mutually perpendicular lines, the x-axis, the y-axis, and the z-axis. On each of these axes, select an appropriate scale and the positive direction. See Figure 75.

The direction chosen for the positive z-axis in Figure 75 makes the system *right-handed*. This conforms to the *right-hand rule*, which states that, if the index finger of the right hand points in the direction of the positive x-axis and the middle finger points in the direction of the positive y-axis, then the thumb will point in the direction of the positive z-axis. See Figure 76.

We associate with each point P an ordered triple (x, y, z) of real numbers, the **coordinates of P.** For example, the point $(2, 3, 4)$ is located by starting at the origin and moving 2 units along the positive x-axis, 3 units in the direction of the positive y-axis, and 4 units in the direction of the positive z-axis. See Figure 77.

Figure 76

Figure 77

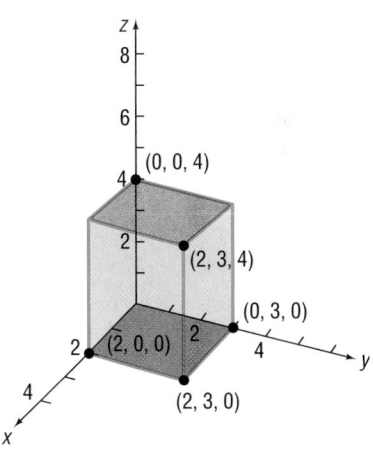

Figure 77 also shows the location of the points $(2, 0, 0)$, $(0, 3, 0)$, $(0, 0, 4)$, and $(2, 3, 0)$. Points of the form $(x, 0, 0)$ lie on the x-axis, while points of the form $(0, y, 0)$ and $(0, 0, z)$ lie on the y-axis and z-axis, respectively. Points of the form $(x, y, 0)$ lie in a plane, called the **xy-plane.** Its equation is $z = 0$. Similarly, points of the form $(x, 0, z)$ lie in the **xz-plane** (equation $y = 0$) and points of the form $(0, y, z)$ lie in the **yz-plane** (equation $x = 0$). See Figure 78(a). By extension of these ideas, all points obeying the equation $z = 3$ will lie in a plane parallel to and 3 units above the xy-plane. The equation $y = 4$ represents a plane parallel to the xz-plane and 4 units to the right of the plane $y = 0$. See Figure 78(b).

Figure 78

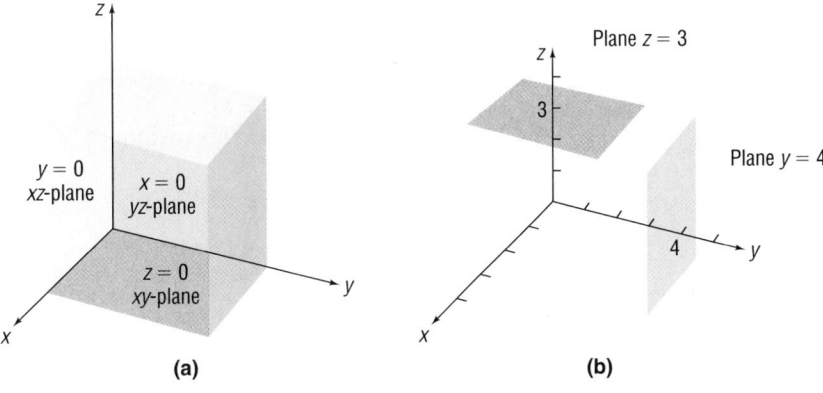

(a)   (b)

Now Work PROBLEM **9**

1 Find the Distance between Two Points in Space

The formula for the distance between two points in space is an extension of the Distance Formula for points in the plane given in Chapter 1.

THEOREM

Distance Formula in Space

If $P_1 = (x_1, y_1, z_1)$ and $P_2 = (x_2, y_2, z_2)$ are two points in space, the distance d from P_1 to P_2 is

$$d = \sqrt{(x_2 - x_1)^2 + (y_2 - y_1)^2 + (z_2 - z_1)^2} \qquad \textbf{(1)}$$

The proof, which we omit, utilizes a double application of the Pythagorean Theorem.

EXAMPLE 1

Using the Distance Formula

Find the distance from $P_1 = (-1, 3, 2)$ to $P_2 = (4, -2, 5)$.

Solution

$$d = \sqrt{[4 - (-1)]^2 + [-2 - 3]^2 + [5 - 2]^2} = \sqrt{25 + 25 + 9} = \sqrt{59}$$

→ **Now Work** PROBLEM 15

2 Find Position Vectors in Space

To represent vectors in space, we introduce the unit vectors **i**, **j**, and **k** whose directions are along the positive x-axis, positive y-axis, and positive z-axis, respectively. If **v** is a vector with initial point at the origin O and terminal point at $P = (a, b, c)$, we can represent **v** in terms of the vectors **i**, **j**, and **k** as

$$\mathbf{v} = a\mathbf{i} + b\mathbf{j} + c\mathbf{k}$$

Figure 79

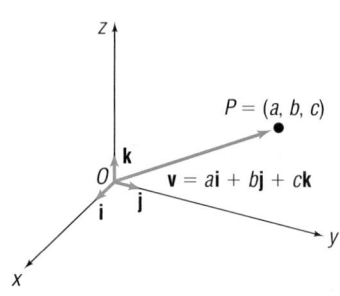

See Figure 79.

The scalars a, b, and c are called the **components** of the vector $\mathbf{v} = a\mathbf{i} + b\mathbf{j} + c\mathbf{k}$, with a being the component in the direction **i**, b the component in the direction **j**, and c the component in the direction **k**.

A vector whose initial point is at the origin is called a **position vector.** The next result states that any vector whose initial point is not at the origin is equal to a unique position vector.

THEOREM

Suppose that **v** is a vector with initial point $P_1 = (x_1, y_1, z_1)$, not necessarily the origin, and terminal point $P_2 = (x_2, y_2, z_2)$. If $\mathbf{v} = \overrightarrow{P_1 P_2}$, then **v** is equal to the position vector

$$\mathbf{v} = (x_2 - x_1)\mathbf{i} + (y_2 - y_1)\mathbf{j} + (z_2 - z_1)\mathbf{k} \qquad \textbf{(2)}$$

Figure 80 illustrates this result.

Figure 80

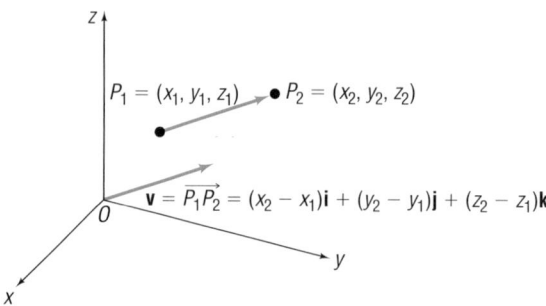

EXAMPLE 2

Finding a Position Vector

Find the position vector of the vector $\mathbf{v} = \overrightarrow{P_1 P_2}$ if $P_1 = (-1, 2, 3)$ and $P_2 = (4, 6, 2)$.

Solution

By equation (2), the position vector equal to $\mathbf{v}$ is

$$\mathbf{v} = [4 - (-1)]\mathbf{i} + (6 - 2)\mathbf{j} + (2 - 3)\mathbf{k} = 5\mathbf{i} + 4\mathbf{j} - \mathbf{k}$$

Now Work PROBLEM 29

3 Perform Operations on Vectors

We can define equality, addition, subtraction, scalar product, and magnitude in terms of the components of a vector.

DEFINITION

Let $\mathbf{v} = a_1\mathbf{i} + b_1\mathbf{j} + c_1\mathbf{k}$ and $\mathbf{w} = a_2\mathbf{i} + b_2\mathbf{j} + c_2\mathbf{k}$ be two vectors, and let α be a scalar. Then

$$\mathbf{v} = \mathbf{w} \quad \text{if and only if} \quad a_1 = a_2, b_1 = b_2, \text{ and } c_1 = c_2$$
$$\mathbf{v} + \mathbf{w} = (a_1 + a_2)\mathbf{i} + (b_1 + b_2)\mathbf{j} + (c_1 + c_2)\mathbf{k}$$
$$\mathbf{v} - \mathbf{w} = (a_1 - a_2)\mathbf{i} + (b_1 - b_2)\mathbf{j} + (c_1 - c_2)\mathbf{k}$$
$$\alpha\mathbf{v} = (\alpha a_1)\mathbf{i} + (\alpha b_1)\mathbf{j} + (\alpha c_1)\mathbf{k}$$
$$\|\mathbf{v}\| = \sqrt{a_1^2 + b_1^2 + c_1^2}$$

These definitions are compatible with the geometric definitions given earlier in Section 9.4.

EXAMPLE 3

Adding and Subtracting Vectors

If $\mathbf{v} = 2\mathbf{i} + 3\mathbf{j} - 2\mathbf{k}$ and $\mathbf{w} = 3\mathbf{i} - 4\mathbf{j} + 5\mathbf{k}$, find:

(a) $\mathbf{v} + \mathbf{w}$ (b) $\mathbf{v} - \mathbf{w}$

Solution

(a) $\mathbf{v} + \mathbf{w} = (2\mathbf{i} + 3\mathbf{j} - 2\mathbf{k}) + (3\mathbf{i} - 4\mathbf{j} + 5\mathbf{k})$
$$= (2 + 3)\mathbf{i} + (3 - 4)\mathbf{j} + (-2 + 5)\mathbf{k}$$
$$= 5\mathbf{i} - \mathbf{j} + 3\mathbf{k}$$

(b) $\mathbf{v} - \mathbf{w} = (2\mathbf{i} + 3\mathbf{j} - 2\mathbf{k}) - (3\mathbf{i} - 4\mathbf{j} + 5\mathbf{k})$
$$= (2 - 3)\mathbf{i} + [3 - (-4)]\mathbf{j} + [-2 - 5]\mathbf{k}$$
$$= -\mathbf{i} + 7\mathbf{j} - 7\mathbf{k}$$

EXAMPLE 4

Finding Scalar Products and Magnitudes

If $\mathbf{v} = 2\mathbf{i} + 3\mathbf{j} - 2\mathbf{k}$ and $\mathbf{w} = 3\mathbf{i} - 4\mathbf{j} + 5\mathbf{k}$, find:

(a) $3\mathbf{v}$ (b) $2\mathbf{v} - 3\mathbf{w}$ (c) $\|\mathbf{v}\|$

Solution

(a) $3\mathbf{v} = 3(2\mathbf{i} + 3\mathbf{j} - 2\mathbf{k}) = 6\mathbf{i} + 9\mathbf{j} - 6\mathbf{k}$

(b) $2\mathbf{v} - 3\mathbf{w} = 2(2\mathbf{i} + 3\mathbf{j} - 2\mathbf{k}) - 3(3\mathbf{i} - 4\mathbf{j} + 5\mathbf{k})$
$$= 4\mathbf{i} + 6\mathbf{j} - 4\mathbf{k} - 9\mathbf{i} + 12\mathbf{j} - 15\mathbf{k} = -5\mathbf{i} + 18\mathbf{j} - 19\mathbf{k}$$

(c) $\|\mathbf{v}\| = \|2\mathbf{i} + 3\mathbf{j} - 2\mathbf{k}\| = \sqrt{2^2 + 3^2 + (-2)^2} = \sqrt{17}$

Now Work PROBLEMS 33 AND 39

Recall that a unit vector **u** is one for which $\|\mathbf{u}\| = 1$. In many applications, it is useful to be able to find a unit vector **u** that has the same direction as a given vector **v**.

THEOREM

Unit Vector in the Direction of v

For any nonzero vector **v**, the vector

$$\mathbf{u} = \frac{\mathbf{v}}{\|\mathbf{v}\|}$$

is a unit vector that has the same direction as **v**.

As a consequence of this theorem, if **u** is a unit vector in the same direction as a vector **v**, then **v** may be expressed as

$$\mathbf{v} = \|\mathbf{v}\|\mathbf{u}$$

EXAMPLE 5   **Finding a Unit Vector**

Find the unit vector in the same direction as $\mathbf{v} = 2\mathbf{i} - 3\mathbf{j} - 6\mathbf{k}$.

Solution   We find $\|\mathbf{v}\|$ first.

$$\|\mathbf{v}\| = \|2\mathbf{i} - 3\mathbf{j} - 6\mathbf{k}\| = \sqrt{4 + 9 + 36} = \sqrt{49} = 7$$

Now we multiply **v** by the scalar $\dfrac{1}{\|\mathbf{v}\|} = \dfrac{1}{7}$. The result is the unit vector

$$\mathbf{u} = \frac{\mathbf{v}}{\|\mathbf{v}\|} = \frac{2\mathbf{i} - 3\mathbf{j} - 6\mathbf{k}}{7} = \frac{2}{7}\mathbf{i} - \frac{3}{7}\mathbf{j} - \frac{6}{7}\mathbf{k}$$

━━━━▶ **Now Work** PROBLEM 47

4 Find the Dot Product

The definition of *dot product* is an extension of the definition given for vectors in the plane.

DEFINITION

If $\mathbf{v} = a_1\mathbf{i} + b_1\mathbf{j} + c_1\mathbf{k}$ and $\mathbf{w} = a_2\mathbf{i} + b_2\mathbf{j} + c_2\mathbf{k}$ are two vectors, the **dot product** $\mathbf{v} \cdot \mathbf{w}$ is defined as

$$\mathbf{v} \cdot \mathbf{w} = a_1a_2 + b_1b_2 + c_1c_2 \tag{3}$$

EXAMPLE 6   **Finding Dot Products**

If $\mathbf{v} = 2\mathbf{i} - 3\mathbf{j} + 6\mathbf{k}$ and $\mathbf{w} = 5\mathbf{i} + 3\mathbf{j} - \mathbf{k}$, find:

(a) $\mathbf{v} \cdot \mathbf{w}$ (b) $\mathbf{w} \cdot \mathbf{v}$ (c) $\mathbf{v} \cdot \mathbf{v}$
(d) $\mathbf{w} \cdot \mathbf{w}$ (e) $\|\mathbf{v}\|$ (f) $\|\mathbf{w}\|$

Solution   (a) $\mathbf{v} \cdot \mathbf{w} = 2(5) + (-3)3 + 6(-1) = -5$

(b) $\mathbf{w} \cdot \mathbf{v} = 5(2) + 3(-3) + (-1)(6) = -5$

(c) $\mathbf{v} \cdot \mathbf{v} = 2(2) + (-3)(-3) + 6(6) = 49$

(d) $\mathbf{w} \cdot \mathbf{w} = 5(5) + 3(3) + (-1)(-1) = 35$

(e) $\|\mathbf{v}\| = \sqrt{2^2 + (-3)^2 + 6^2} = \sqrt{49} = 7$

(f) $\|\mathbf{w}\| = \sqrt{5^2 + 3^2 + (-1)^2} = \sqrt{35}$

The dot product in space has the same properties as the dot product in the plane.

THEOREM   **Properties of the Dot Product**

If **u**, **v**, and **w** are vectors, then

Commutative Property

$$\mathbf{u} \cdot \mathbf{v} = \mathbf{v} \cdot \mathbf{u}$$

Distributive Property

$$\mathbf{u} \cdot (\mathbf{v} + \mathbf{w}) = \mathbf{u} \cdot \mathbf{v} + \mathbf{u} \cdot \mathbf{w}$$

$$\mathbf{v} \cdot \mathbf{v} = \|\mathbf{v}\|^2$$
$$\mathbf{0} \cdot \mathbf{v} = 0$$

5 Find the Angle between Two Vectors

The angle θ between two vectors in space follows the same formula as for two vectors in the plane.

THEOREM   **Angle between Vectors**

If **u** and **v** are two nonzero vectors, the angle $\theta, 0 \le \theta \le \pi$, between **u** and **v** is determined by the formula

$$\cos \theta = \frac{\mathbf{u} \cdot \mathbf{v}}{\|\mathbf{u}\| \, \|\mathbf{v}\|} \qquad (4)$$

EXAMPLE 7   **Finding the Angle θ between Two Vectors**

Find the angle θ between $\mathbf{u} = 2\mathbf{i} - 3\mathbf{j} + 6\mathbf{k}$ and $\mathbf{v} = 2\mathbf{i} + 5\mathbf{j} - \mathbf{k}$.

Solution   We compute the quantities $\mathbf{u} \cdot \mathbf{v}, \|\mathbf{u}\|$, and $\|\mathbf{v}\|$.

$$\mathbf{u} \cdot \mathbf{v} = 2(2) + (-3)(5) + 6(-1) = -17$$
$$\|\mathbf{u}\| = \sqrt{2^2 + (-3)^2 + 6^2} = \sqrt{49} = 7$$
$$\|\mathbf{v}\| = \sqrt{2^2 + 5^2 + (-1)^2} = \sqrt{30}$$

By formula (4), if θ is the angle between **u** and **v**, then

$$\cos \theta = \frac{\mathbf{u} \cdot \mathbf{v}}{\|\mathbf{u}\| \, \|\mathbf{v}\|} = \frac{-17}{7\sqrt{30}} \approx -0.443$$

We find that $\theta \approx 116.3°$.

═══ **Now Work** PROBLEM 51

6 Find the Direction Angles of a Vector

A nonzero vector **v** in space can be described by specifying its magnitude and its three **direction angles** α, β, and γ. These direction angles are defined as

$$\alpha = \text{the angle between } \mathbf{v} \text{ and } \mathbf{i}, \text{ the positive } x\text{-axis}, 0 \le \alpha \le \pi$$

$$\beta = \text{the angle between } \mathbf{v} \text{ and } \mathbf{j}, \text{ the positive } y\text{-axis}, 0 \le \beta \le \pi$$

$$\gamma = \text{the angle between } \mathbf{v} \text{ and } \mathbf{k}, \text{ the positive } z\text{-axis}, 0 \le \gamma \le \pi$$

See Figure 81.

Figure 81

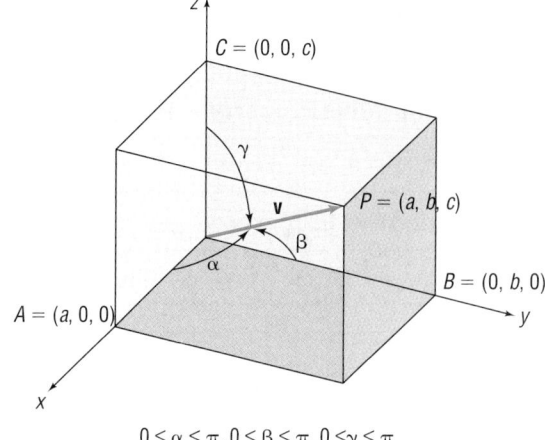

$$0 \leq \alpha \leq \pi, 0 \leq \beta \leq \pi, 0 \leq \gamma \leq \pi$$

Our first goal is to find expressions for α, β, and γ in terms of the components of a vector. Let $\mathbf{v} = a\mathbf{i} + b\mathbf{j} + c\mathbf{k}$ denote a nonzero vector. The angle α between $\mathbf{v}$ and $\mathbf{i}$, the positive x-axis, obeys

$$\cos \alpha = \frac{\mathbf{v} \cdot \mathbf{i}}{\|\mathbf{v}\| \|\mathbf{i}\|} = \frac{a}{\|\mathbf{v}\|}$$

Similarly,

$$\cos \beta = \frac{b}{\|\mathbf{v}\|} \qquad \cos \gamma = \frac{c}{\|\mathbf{v}\|}$$

Since $\|\mathbf{v}\| = \sqrt{a^2 + b^2 + c^2}$, we have the following result:

THEOREM **Direction Angles**

If $\mathbf{v} = a\mathbf{i} + b\mathbf{j} + c\mathbf{k}$ is a nonzero vector in space, the direction angles α, β, and γ obey

$$\cos \alpha = \frac{a}{\sqrt{a^2 + b^2 + c^2}} = \frac{a}{\|\mathbf{v}\|} \qquad \cos \beta = \frac{b}{\sqrt{a^2 + b^2 + c^2}} = \frac{b}{\|\mathbf{v}\|}$$

$$\cos \gamma = \frac{c}{\sqrt{a^2 + b^2 + c^2}} = \frac{c}{\|\mathbf{v}\|} \tag{5}$$

The numbers $\cos \alpha$, $\cos \beta$, and $\cos \gamma$ are called the **direction cosines** of the vector $\mathbf{v}$.

EXAMPLE 8 **Finding the Direction Angles of a Vector**

Find the direction angles of $\mathbf{v} = -3\mathbf{i} + 2\mathbf{j} - 6\mathbf{k}$.

Solution

$$\|\mathbf{v}\| = \sqrt{(-3)^2 + 2^2 + (-6)^2} = \sqrt{49} = 7$$

Using the formulas in equation (5), we have

$$\cos \alpha = \frac{-3}{7} \qquad \cos \beta = \frac{2}{7} \qquad \cos \gamma = \frac{-6}{7}$$

$$\alpha \approx 115.4° \qquad \beta \approx 73.4° \qquad \gamma \approx 149.0°$$

THEOREM

Property of the Direction Cosines

If α, β, and γ are the direction angles of a nonzero vector $\mathbf{v}$ in space, then

$$\cos^2 \alpha + \cos^2 \beta + \cos^2 \gamma = 1 \qquad (6)$$

The proof is a direct consequence of the equations in (5).

Based on equation (6), when two direction cosines are known, the third is determined up to its sign. Knowing two direction cosines is not sufficient to uniquely determine the direction of a vector in space.

EXAMPLE 9

Finding the Direction Angle of a Vector

The vector $\mathbf{v}$ makes an angle of $\alpha = \dfrac{\pi}{3}$ with the positive x-axis, an angle of $\beta = \dfrac{\pi}{3}$ with the positive y-axis, and an acute angle γ with the positive z-axis. Find γ.

Solution

By equation (6), we have

$$\cos^2\left(\frac{\pi}{3}\right) + \cos^2\left(\frac{\pi}{3}\right) + \cos^2 \gamma = 1 \qquad 0 < \gamma < \frac{\pi}{2}$$

$$\left(\frac{1}{2}\right)^2 + \left(\frac{1}{2}\right)^2 + \cos^2 \gamma = 1$$

$$\cos^2 \gamma = \frac{1}{2}$$

$$\cos \gamma = \frac{\sqrt{2}}{2} \quad \text{or} \quad \cos \gamma = -\frac{\sqrt{2}}{2}$$

$$\gamma = \frac{\pi}{4} \quad \text{or} \quad \gamma = \frac{3\pi}{4}$$

Since we are requiring that γ be acute, $\gamma = \dfrac{\pi}{4}$.

The direction cosines of a vector give information about only the direction of the vector; they provide no information about its magnitude. For example, *any* vector parallel to the *xy*-plane and making an angle of $\dfrac{\pi}{4}$ radian with the positive *x*-axis and *y*-axis has direction cosines

$$\cos \alpha = \frac{\sqrt{2}}{2} \qquad \cos \beta = \frac{\sqrt{2}}{2} \qquad \cos \gamma = 0$$

However, if the direction angles *and* the magnitude of a vector are known, the vector is uniquely determined.

EXAMPLE 10

Writing a Vector in Terms of Its Magnitude and Direction Cosines

Show that any nonzero vector $\mathbf{v}$ in space can be written in terms of its magnitude and direction cosines as

$$\mathbf{v} = \|\mathbf{v}\|[(\cos \alpha)\mathbf{i} + (\cos \beta)\mathbf{j} + (\cos \gamma)\mathbf{k}] \qquad (7)$$

Solution

Let $\mathbf{v} = a\mathbf{i} + b\mathbf{j} + c\mathbf{k}$. From the equations in (5), we see that

$$a = \|\mathbf{v}\| \cos \alpha \qquad b = \|\mathbf{v}\| \cos \beta \qquad c = \|\mathbf{v}\| \cos \gamma$$

Substituting, we find that

$$\mathbf{v} = a\mathbf{i} + b\mathbf{j} + c\mathbf{k} = \|\mathbf{v}\|(\cos\alpha)\mathbf{i} + \|\mathbf{v}\|(\cos\beta)\mathbf{j} + \|\mathbf{v}\|(\cos\gamma)\mathbf{k}$$
$$= \|\mathbf{v}\|[(\cos\alpha)\mathbf{i} + (\cos\beta)\mathbf{j} + (\cos\gamma)\mathbf{k}]$$

━━━━━► **Now Work** PROBLEM 59

Example 10 shows that the direction cosines of a vector **v** are also the components of the unit vector in the direction of **v**.

9.6 Assess Your Understanding

'Are You Prepared?' *Answer is given at the end of these exercises. If you get the wrong answer, read the page listed in red.*

1. The distance d from $P_1 = (x_1, y_1)$ to $P_2 = (x_2, y_2)$ is $d =$ _____ (pp. 4–6)

Concepts and Vocabulary

2. In space, points of the form $(x, y, 0)$ lie in a plane called the _____.

3. If $\mathbf{v} = a\mathbf{i} + b\mathbf{j} + c\mathbf{k}$ is a vector in space, the scalars a, b, c are called the _____ of **v**.

4. The sum of the squares of the direction cosines of a vector in space add up to _____.

5. **True or False** In space, the dot product of two vectors is a positive number.

6. **True or False** A vector in space may be described by specifying its magnitude and its direction angles.

Skill Building

In Problems 7–14, describe the set of points (x, y, z) defined by the equation.

7. $y = 0$
8. $x = 0$
9. $z = 2$
10. $y = 3$
11. $x = -4$
12. $z = -3$
13. $x = 1$ and $y = 2$
14. $x = 3$ and $z = 1$

In Problems 15–20, find the distance from P_1 to P_2.

15. $P_1 = (0, 0, 0)$ and $P_2 = (4, 1, 2)$
16. $P_1 = (0, 0, 0)$ and $P_2 = (1, -2, 3)$
17. $P_1 = (-1, 2, -3)$ and $P_2 = (0, -2, 1)$
18. $P_1 = (-2, 2, 3)$ and $P_2 = (4, 0, -3)$
19. $P_1 = (4, -2, -2)$ and $P_2 = (3, 2, 1)$
20. $P_1 = (2, -3, -3)$ and $P_2 = (4, 1, -1)$

In Problems 21–26, opposite vertices of a rectangular box whose edges are parallel to the coordinate axes are given. List the coordinates of the other six vertices of the box.

21. $(0, 0, 0);\quad (2, 1, 3)$
22. $(0, 0, 0);\quad (4, 2, 2)$
23. $(1, 2, 3);\quad (3, 4, 5)$
24. $(5, 6, 1);\quad (3, 8, 2)$
25. $(-1, 0, 2);\quad (4, 2, 5)$
26. $(-2, -3, 0);\quad (-6, 7, 1)$

*In Problems 27–32, the vector **v** has initial point P and terminal point Q. Write **v** in the form $a\mathbf{i} + b\mathbf{j} + c\mathbf{k}$; that is, find its position vector.*

27. $P = (0, 0, 0);\quad Q = (3, 4, -1)$
28. $P = (0, 0, 0);\quad Q = (-3, -5, 4)$
29. $P = (3, 2, -1);\quad Q = (5, 6, 0)$
30. $P = (-3, 2, 0);\quad Q = (6, 5, -1)$
31. $P = (-2, -1, 4);\quad Q = (6, -2, 4)$
32. $P = (-1, 4, -2);\quad Q = (6, 2, 2)$

In Problems 33–38, find $\|\mathbf{v}\|$.

33. $\mathbf{v} = 3\mathbf{i} - 6\mathbf{j} - 2\mathbf{k}$
34. $\mathbf{v} = -6\mathbf{i} + 12\mathbf{j} + 4\mathbf{k}$
35. $\mathbf{v} = \mathbf{i} - \mathbf{j} + \mathbf{k}$
36. $\mathbf{v} = -\mathbf{i} - \mathbf{j} + \mathbf{k}$
37. $\mathbf{v} = -2\mathbf{i} + 3\mathbf{j} - 3\mathbf{k}$
38. $\mathbf{v} = 6\mathbf{i} + 2\mathbf{j} - 2\mathbf{k}$

In Problems 39–44, find each quantity if $\mathbf{v} = 3\mathbf{i} - 5\mathbf{j} + 2\mathbf{k}$ and $\mathbf{w} = -2\mathbf{i} + 3\mathbf{j} - 2\mathbf{k}$.

39. $2\mathbf{v} + 3\mathbf{w}$
40. $3\mathbf{v} - 2\mathbf{w}$
41. $\|\mathbf{v} - \mathbf{w}\|$
42. $\|\mathbf{v} + \mathbf{w}\|$
43. $\|\mathbf{v}\| - \|\mathbf{w}\|$
44. $\|\mathbf{v}\| + \|\mathbf{w}\|$

*In Problems 45–50, find the unit vector in the same direction as **v**.*

45. $\mathbf{v} = 5\mathbf{i}$
46. $\mathbf{v} = -3\mathbf{j}$
47. $\mathbf{v} = 3\mathbf{i} - 6\mathbf{j} - 2\mathbf{k}$
48. $\mathbf{v} = -6\mathbf{i} + 12\mathbf{j} + 4\mathbf{k}$
49. $\mathbf{v} = \mathbf{i} + \mathbf{j} + \mathbf{k}$
50. $\mathbf{v} = 2\mathbf{i} - \mathbf{j} + \mathbf{k}$

*In Problems 51–58, find the dot product $\mathbf{v} \cdot \mathbf{w}$ and the angle between **v** and **w**.*

51. $\mathbf{v} = \mathbf{i} - \mathbf{j},\quad \mathbf{w} = \mathbf{i} + \mathbf{j} + \mathbf{k}$
52. $\mathbf{v} = \mathbf{i} + \mathbf{j},\quad \mathbf{w} = -\mathbf{i} + \mathbf{j} - \mathbf{k}$
53. $\mathbf{v} = 2\mathbf{i} + \mathbf{j} - 3\mathbf{k},\quad \mathbf{w} = \mathbf{i} + 2\mathbf{j} + 2\mathbf{k}$
54. $\mathbf{v} = 2\mathbf{i} + 2\mathbf{j} - \mathbf{k},\quad \mathbf{w} = \mathbf{i} + 2\mathbf{j} + 3\mathbf{k}$

55. $v = 3i - j + 2k$, $w = i + j - k$

56. $v = i + 3j + 2k$, $w = i - j + k$

57. $v = 3i + 4j + k$, $w = 6i + 8j + 2k$

58. $v = 3i - 4j + k$, $w = 6i - 8j + 2k$

In Problems 59–66, find the direction angles of each vector. Write each vector in the form of equation (7).

59. $v = 3i - 6j - 2k$

60. $v = -6i + 12j + 4k$

61. $v = i + j + k$

62. $v = i - j - k$

63. $v = i + j$

64. $v = j + k$

65. $v = 3i - 5j + 2k$

66. $v = 2i + 3j - 4k$

Applications and Extensions

67. Robotic Arm Consider the double-jointed robotic arm shown in the figure. Let the lower arm be modeled by $a = \langle 2, 3, 4 \rangle$, the middle arm be modeled by $b = \langle 1, -1, 3 \rangle$, and the upper arm by $c = \langle 4, -1, -2 \rangle$, where units are in feet.

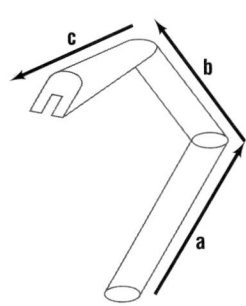

(a) Find a vector **d** that represents the position of the hand.

(b) Determine the distance of the hand from the origin.

68. The Sphere In space, the collection of all points that are the same distance from some fixed point is called a **sphere**. See the illustration. The constant distance is called the **radius**, and the fixed point is the **center** of the sphere. Show that the equation of a sphere with center at (x_0, y_0, z_0) and radius r is

$$(x - x_0)^2 + (y - y_0)^2 + (z - z_0)^2 = r^2$$

[**Hint:** Use the Distance Formula (1).]

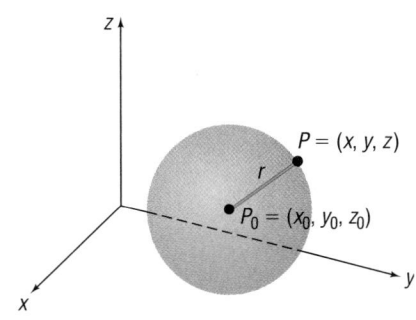

In Problems 69 and 70, find the equation of a sphere with radius r and center P_0.

69. $r = 1$; $P_0 = (3, 1, 1)$

70. $r = 2$; $P_0 = (1, 2, 2)$

In Problems 71–76, find the radius and center of each sphere.
[**Hint:** *Complete the square in each variable.*]

71. $x^2 + y^2 + z^2 + 2x - 2y = 2$

72. $x^2 + y^2 + z^2 + 2x - 2z = -1$

73. $x^2 + y^2 + z^2 - 4x + 4y + 2z = 0$

74. $x^2 + y^2 + z^2 - 4x = 0$

75. $2x^2 + 2y^2 + 2z^2 - 8x + 4z = -1$

76. $3x^2 + 3y^2 + 3z^2 + 6x - 6y = 3$

*The **work** W done by a constant force **F** in moving an object from a point A in space to a point B in space is defined as $W = F \cdot \overrightarrow{AB}$. Use this definition in Problems 77–79.*

77. Work Find the work done by a force of 3 newtons acting in the direction $2i + j + 2k$ in moving an object 2 meters from $(0, 0, 0)$ to $(0, 2, 0)$.

78. Work Find the work done by a force of 1 newton acting in the direction $2i + 2j + k$ in moving an object 3 meters from $(0, 0, 0)$ to $(1, 2, 2)$.

79. Work Find the work done in moving an object along a vector $u = 3i + 2j - 5k$ if the applied force is $F = 2i - j - k$. Use meters for distance and newtons for force.

'Are You Prepared?' Answer

1. $d = \sqrt{(x_2 - x_1)^2 + (y_2 - y_1)^2}$

9.7 The Cross Product

OBJECTIVES
1. Find the Cross Product of Two Vectors (p. 626)
2. Know Algebraic Properties of the Cross Product (p. 627)
3. Know Geometric Properties of the Cross Product (p. 628)
4. Find a Vector Orthogonal to Two Given Vectors (p. 628)
5. Find the Area of a Parallelogram (p. 629)

1 Find the Cross Product of Two Vectors

For vectors in space, and only for vectors in space, a second product of two vectors is defined, called the *cross product*. The cross product of two vectors in space is, in fact, also a vector that has applications in both geometry and physics.

DEFINITION

If $\mathbf{v} = a_1\mathbf{i} + b_1\mathbf{j} + c_1\mathbf{k}$ and $\mathbf{w} = a_2\mathbf{i} + b_2\mathbf{j} + c_2\mathbf{k}$ are two vectors in space, the **cross product $\mathbf{v} \times \mathbf{w}$** is defined as the vector

$$\mathbf{v} \times \mathbf{w} = (b_1c_2 - b_2c_1)\mathbf{i} - (a_1c_2 - a_2c_1)\mathbf{j} + (a_1b_2 - a_2b_1)\mathbf{k} \qquad \textbf{(1)}$$

Notice that the cross product $\mathbf{v} \times \mathbf{w}$ of two vectors is a vector. Because of this, it is sometimes referred to as the **vector product.**

EXAMPLE 1 **Finding Cross Products Using Equation (1)**

If $\mathbf{v} = 2\mathbf{i} + 3\mathbf{j} + 5\mathbf{k}$ and $\mathbf{w} = \mathbf{i} + 2\mathbf{j} + 3\mathbf{k}$, an application of equation (1) gives

$$\begin{aligned}
\mathbf{v} \times \mathbf{w} &= (3 \cdot 3 - 2 \cdot 5)\mathbf{i} - (2 \cdot 3 - 1 \cdot 5)\mathbf{j} + (2 \cdot 2 - 1 \cdot 3)\mathbf{k} \\
&= (9 - 10)\mathbf{i} - (6 - 5)\mathbf{j} + (4 - 3)\mathbf{k} \\
&= -\mathbf{i} - \mathbf{j} + \mathbf{k}
\end{aligned}$$

Determinants* may be used as an aid in computing cross products. A **2 by 2 determinant,** symbolized by

$$\begin{vmatrix} a_1 & b_1 \\ a_2 & b_2 \end{vmatrix}$$

has the value $a_1b_2 - a_2b_1$; that is,

$$\begin{vmatrix} a_1 & b_1 \\ a_2 & b_2 \end{vmatrix} = a_1b_2 - a_2b_1$$

A **3 by 3 determinant** has the value

$$\begin{vmatrix} A & B & C \\ a_1 & b_1 & c_1 \\ a_2 & b_2 & c_2 \end{vmatrix} = \begin{vmatrix} b_1 & c_1 \\ b_2 & c_2 \end{vmatrix} A - \begin{vmatrix} a_1 & c_1 \\ a_2 & c_2 \end{vmatrix} B + \begin{vmatrix} a_1 & b_1 \\ a_2 & b_2 \end{vmatrix} C$$

EXAMPLE 2 **Evaluating Determinants**

(a) $\begin{vmatrix} 2 & 3 \\ 1 & 2 \end{vmatrix} = 2 \cdot 2 - 1 \cdot 3 = 4 - 3 = 1$

(b) $\begin{vmatrix} A & B & C \\ 2 & 3 & 5 \\ 1 & 2 & 3 \end{vmatrix} = \begin{vmatrix} 3 & 5 \\ 2 & 3 \end{vmatrix} A - \begin{vmatrix} 2 & 5 \\ 1 & 3 \end{vmatrix} B + \begin{vmatrix} 2 & 3 \\ 1 & 2 \end{vmatrix} C$

$\qquad\qquad\qquad = (9 - 10)A - (6 - 5)B + (4 - 3)C$

$\qquad\qquad\qquad = -A - B + C$

===== **Now Work** PROBLEM 7

The cross product of the vectors $\mathbf{v} = a_1\mathbf{i} + b_1\mathbf{j} + c_1\mathbf{k}$ and $\mathbf{w} = a_2\mathbf{i} + b_2\mathbf{j} + c_2\mathbf{k}$, that is,

$$\mathbf{v} \times \mathbf{w} = (b_1c_2 - b_2c_1)\mathbf{i} - (a_1c_2 - a_2c_1)\mathbf{j} + (a_1b_2 - a_2b_1)\mathbf{k}$$

---

*Determinants are discussed in detail in Section 11.3.

may be written symbolically using determinants as

$$\mathbf{v} \times \mathbf{w} = \begin{vmatrix} \mathbf{i} & \mathbf{j} & \mathbf{k} \\ a_1 & b_1 & c_1 \\ a_2 & b_2 & c_2 \end{vmatrix} = \begin{vmatrix} b_1 & c_1 \\ b_2 & c_2 \end{vmatrix} \mathbf{i} - \begin{vmatrix} a_1 & c_1 \\ a_2 & c_2 \end{vmatrix} \mathbf{j} + \begin{vmatrix} a_1 & b_1 \\ a_2 & b_2 \end{vmatrix} \mathbf{k}$$

EXAMPLE 3 | **Using Determinants to Find Cross Products**

If $\mathbf{v} = 2\mathbf{i} + 3\mathbf{j} + 5\mathbf{k}$ and $\mathbf{w} = \mathbf{i} + 2\mathbf{j} + 3\mathbf{k}$, find:

(a) $\mathbf{v} \times \mathbf{w}$ (b) $\mathbf{w} \times \mathbf{v}$ (c) $\mathbf{v} \times \mathbf{v}$ (d) $\mathbf{w} \times \mathbf{w}$

Solution   (a) $\mathbf{v} \times \mathbf{w} = \begin{vmatrix} \mathbf{i} & \mathbf{j} & \mathbf{k} \\ 2 & 3 & 5 \\ 1 & 2 & 3 \end{vmatrix} = \begin{vmatrix} 3 & 5 \\ 2 & 3 \end{vmatrix} \mathbf{i} - \begin{vmatrix} 2 & 5 \\ 1 & 3 \end{vmatrix} \mathbf{j} + \begin{vmatrix} 2 & 3 \\ 1 & 2 \end{vmatrix} \mathbf{k} = -\mathbf{i} - \mathbf{j} + \mathbf{k}$

(b) $\mathbf{w} \times \mathbf{v} = \begin{vmatrix} \mathbf{i} & \mathbf{j} & \mathbf{k} \\ 1 & 2 & 3 \\ 2 & 3 & 5 \end{vmatrix} = \begin{vmatrix} 2 & 3 \\ 3 & 5 \end{vmatrix} \mathbf{i} - \begin{vmatrix} 1 & 3 \\ 2 & 5 \end{vmatrix} \mathbf{j} + \begin{vmatrix} 1 & 2 \\ 2 & 3 \end{vmatrix} \mathbf{k} = \mathbf{i} + \mathbf{j} - \mathbf{k}$

(c) $\mathbf{v} \times \mathbf{v} = \begin{vmatrix} \mathbf{i} & \mathbf{j} & \mathbf{k} \\ 2 & 3 & 5 \\ 2 & 3 & 5 \end{vmatrix}$

$= \begin{vmatrix} 3 & 5 \\ 3 & 5 \end{vmatrix} \mathbf{i} - \begin{vmatrix} 2 & 5 \\ 2 & 5 \end{vmatrix} \mathbf{j} + \begin{vmatrix} 2 & 3 \\ 2 & 3 \end{vmatrix} \mathbf{k} = 0\mathbf{i} - 0\mathbf{j} + 0\mathbf{k} = \mathbf{0}$

(d) $\mathbf{w} \times \mathbf{w} = \begin{vmatrix} \mathbf{i} & \mathbf{j} & \mathbf{k} \\ 1 & 2 & 3 \\ 1 & 2 & 3 \end{vmatrix}$

$= \begin{vmatrix} 2 & 3 \\ 2 & 3 \end{vmatrix} \mathbf{i} - \begin{vmatrix} 1 & 3 \\ 1 & 3 \end{vmatrix} \mathbf{j} + \begin{vmatrix} 1 & 2 \\ 1 & 2 \end{vmatrix} \mathbf{k} = 0\mathbf{i} - 0\mathbf{j} + 0\mathbf{k} = \mathbf{0}$

Now Work PROBLEM 15

2 Know Algebraic Properties of the Cross Product

Notice in Examples 3(a) and (b) that $\mathbf{v} \times \mathbf{w}$ and $\mathbf{w} \times \mathbf{v}$ are negatives of one another. From Examples 3(c) and (d), we might conjecture that the cross product of a vector with itself is the zero vector. These and other algebraic properties of the cross product are given next.

THEOREM | **Algebraic Properties of the Cross Product**

If $\mathbf{u}$, $\mathbf{v}$, and $\mathbf{w}$ are vectors in space and if α is a scalar, then

$$\mathbf{u} \times \mathbf{u} = \mathbf{0} \tag{2}$$
$$\mathbf{u} \times \mathbf{v} = -(\mathbf{v} \times \mathbf{u}) \tag{3}$$
$$\alpha(\mathbf{u} \times \mathbf{v}) = (\alpha\mathbf{u}) \times \mathbf{v} = \mathbf{u} \times (\alpha\mathbf{v}) \tag{4}$$
$$\mathbf{u} \times (\mathbf{v} + \mathbf{w}) = (\mathbf{u} \times \mathbf{v}) + (\mathbf{u} \times \mathbf{w}) \tag{5}$$

Proof We will prove properties (2) and (4) here and leave properties (3) and (5) as exercises (see Problems 60 and 61).

To prove property (2), we let $\mathbf{u} = a_1\mathbf{i} + b_1\mathbf{j} + c_1\mathbf{k}$. Then

$$\mathbf{u} \times \mathbf{u} = \begin{vmatrix} \mathbf{i} & \mathbf{j} & \mathbf{k} \\ a_1 & b_1 & c_1 \\ a_1 & b_1 & c_1 \end{vmatrix} = \begin{vmatrix} b_1 & c_1 \\ b_1 & c_1 \end{vmatrix} \mathbf{i} - \begin{vmatrix} a_1 & c_1 \\ a_1 & c_1 \end{vmatrix} \mathbf{j} + \begin{vmatrix} a_1 & b_1 \\ a_1 & b_1 \end{vmatrix} \mathbf{k}$$

$$= 0\mathbf{i} - 0\mathbf{j} + 0\mathbf{k} = \mathbf{0}$$

To prove property (4), we let $\mathbf{u} = a_1\mathbf{i} + b_1\mathbf{j} + c_1\mathbf{k}$ and $\mathbf{v} = a_2\mathbf{i} + b_2\mathbf{j} + c_2\mathbf{k}$. Then

$$\alpha(\mathbf{u} \times \mathbf{v}) = \alpha[(b_1c_2 - b_2c_1)\mathbf{i} - (a_1c_2 - a_2c_1)\mathbf{j} + (a_1b_2 - a_2b_1)\mathbf{k}]$$

$\uparrow$
Apply (1).

$$= \alpha(b_1c_2 - b_2c_1)\mathbf{i} - \alpha(a_1c_2 - a_2c_1)\mathbf{j} + \alpha(a_1b_2 - a_2b_1)\mathbf{k} \qquad \textbf{(6)}$$

Since $\alpha\mathbf{u} = \alpha a_1\mathbf{i} + \alpha b_1\mathbf{j} + \alpha c_1\mathbf{k}$, we have

$$(\alpha\mathbf{u}) \times \mathbf{v} = (\alpha b_1c_2 - b_2\alpha c_1)\mathbf{i} - (\alpha a_1c_2 - a_2\alpha c_1)\mathbf{j} + (\alpha a_1b_2 - a_2\alpha b_1)\mathbf{k}$$

$$= \alpha(b_1c_2 - b_2c_1)\mathbf{i} - \alpha(a_1c_2 - a_2c_1)\mathbf{j} + \alpha(a_1b_2 - a_2b_1)\mathbf{k} \qquad \textbf{(7)}$$

Based on equations (6) and (7), the first part of property (4) follows. The second part can be proved in like fashion. ∎

Now Work PROBLEM 17

3 Know Geometric Properties of the Cross Product

The cross product has several interesting geometric properties.

THEOREM

> **Geometric Properties of the Cross Product**
>
> Let $\mathbf{u}$ and $\mathbf{v}$ be vectors in space.
>
> $\mathbf{u} \times \mathbf{v}$ is orthogonal to both $\mathbf{u}$ and $\mathbf{v}$. $\qquad$ **(8)**
>
> $\|\mathbf{u} \times \mathbf{v}\| = \|\mathbf{u}\|\,\|\mathbf{v}\|\sin\theta,$ $\qquad$ **(9)**
> where θ is the angle between $\mathbf{u}$ and $\mathbf{v}$.
>
> $\|\mathbf{u} \times \mathbf{v}\|$ is the area of the parallelogram $\qquad$ **(10)**
> having $\mathbf{u} \neq \mathbf{0}$ and $\mathbf{v} \neq \mathbf{0}$ as adjacent sides.
>
> $\mathbf{u} \times \mathbf{v} = \mathbf{0}$ if and only if $\mathbf{u}$ and $\mathbf{v}$ are parallel. $\qquad$ **(11)**

Proof of Property (8) Let $\mathbf{u} = a_1\mathbf{i} + b_1\mathbf{j} + c_1\mathbf{k}$ and $\mathbf{v} = a_2\mathbf{i} + b_2\mathbf{j} + c_2\mathbf{k}$. Then

$$\mathbf{u} \times \mathbf{v} = (b_1c_2 - b_2c_1)\mathbf{i} - (a_1c_2 - a_2c_1)\mathbf{j} + (a_1b_2 - a_2b_1)\mathbf{k}$$

Now we compute the dot product $\mathbf{u} \cdot (\mathbf{u} \times \mathbf{v})$.

$$\mathbf{u} \cdot (\mathbf{u} \times \mathbf{v}) = (a_1\mathbf{i} + b_1\mathbf{j} + c_1\mathbf{k}) \cdot [(b_1c_2 - b_2c_1)\mathbf{i} - (a_1c_2 - a_2c_1)\mathbf{j} + (a_1b_2 - a_2b_1)\mathbf{k}]$$

$$= a_1(b_1c_2 - b_2c_1) - b_1(a_1c_2 - a_2c_1) + c_1(a_1b_2 - a_2b_1) = 0$$

Since two vectors are orthogonal if their dot product is zero, it follows that $\mathbf{u}$ and $\mathbf{u} \times \mathbf{v}$ are orthogonal. Similarly, $\mathbf{v} \cdot (\mathbf{u} \times \mathbf{v}) = 0$, so $\mathbf{v}$ and $\mathbf{u} \times \mathbf{v}$ are orthogonal. ∎

Figure 82

4 Find a Vector Orthogonal to Two Given Vectors

As long as the vectors $\mathbf{u}$ and $\mathbf{v}$ are not parallel, they will form a plane in space. See Figure 82. Based on property (8), the vector $\mathbf{u} \times \mathbf{v}$ is normal to this plane. As Figure 82 illustrates, there are essentially (without regard to magnitude) two vectors normal to the plane containing $\mathbf{u}$ and $\mathbf{v}$. It can be shown that the vector $\mathbf{u} \times \mathbf{v}$ is the one determined by the thumb of the right hand when the other fingers of the right hand are cupped so that they point in a direction from $\mathbf{u}$ to $\mathbf{v}$. See Figure 83.*

Figure 83

* This is a consequence of using a right-handed coordinate system.

| EXAMPLE 4 | Finding a Vector Orthogonal to Two Given Vectors |

Find a vector that is orthogonal to $\mathbf{u} = 3\mathbf{i} - 2\mathbf{j} + \mathbf{k}$ and $\mathbf{v} = -\mathbf{i} + 3\mathbf{j} - \mathbf{k}$.

Solution Based on property (8), such a vector is $\mathbf{u} \times \mathbf{v}$.

$$\mathbf{u} \times \mathbf{v} = \begin{vmatrix} \mathbf{i} & \mathbf{j} & \mathbf{k} \\ 3 & -2 & 1 \\ -1 & 3 & -1 \end{vmatrix} = (2 - 3)\mathbf{i} - [-3 - (-1)]\mathbf{j} + (9 - 2)\mathbf{k} = -\mathbf{i} + 2\mathbf{j} + 7\mathbf{k}$$

The vector $-\mathbf{i} + 2\mathbf{j} + 7\mathbf{k}$ is orthogonal to both $\mathbf{u}$ and $\mathbf{v}$.

✓ Check: Two vectors are orthogonal if their dot product is zero.

$$\mathbf{u} \cdot (-\mathbf{i} + 2\mathbf{j} + 7\mathbf{k}) = (3\mathbf{i} - 2\mathbf{j} + \mathbf{k}) \cdot (-\mathbf{i} + 2\mathbf{j} + 7\mathbf{k}) = -3 - 4 + 7 = 0$$
$$\mathbf{v} \cdot (-\mathbf{i} + 2\mathbf{j} + 7\mathbf{k}) = (-\mathbf{i} + 3\mathbf{j} - \mathbf{k}) \cdot (-\mathbf{i} + 2\mathbf{j} + 7\mathbf{k}) = 1 + 6 - 7 = 0$$

━━━ **Now Work** PROBLEM 41

The proof of property (9) is left as an exercise. See Problem 62.

Figure 84

Proof of Property (10) Suppose that $\mathbf{u}$ and $\mathbf{v}$ are adjacent sides of a parallelogram. See Figure 84. Then the lengths of these sides are $\|\mathbf{u}\|$ and $\|\mathbf{v}\|$. If θ is the angle between $\mathbf{u}$ and $\mathbf{v}$, then the height of the parallelogram is $\|\mathbf{v}\| \sin \theta$ and its area is

$$\text{Area of parallelogram} = \text{Base} \times \text{Height} = \|\mathbf{u}\| [\|\mathbf{v}\| \sin \theta] = \|\mathbf{u} \times \mathbf{v}\|$$
$$\underset{\text{Property (9)}}{\uparrow}$$
■

5 Find the Area of a Parallelogram

| EXAMPLE 5 | Finding the Area of a Parallelogram |

Find the area of the parallelogram whose vertices are $P_1 = (0, 0, 0)$, $P_2 = (3, -2, 1)$, $P_3 = (-1, 3, -1)$, and $P_4 = (2, 1, 0)$.

Solution Two adjacent sides of this parallelogram are

$$\mathbf{u} = \overrightarrow{P_1 P_2} = 3\mathbf{i} - 2\mathbf{j} + \mathbf{k} \quad \text{and} \quad \mathbf{v} = \overrightarrow{P_1 P_3} = -\mathbf{i} + 3\mathbf{j} - \mathbf{k}$$

WARNING Not all pairs of vertices give rise to a side. For example, $\overrightarrow{P_1 P_4}$ is a diagonal of the parallelogram since $\overrightarrow{P_1 P_3} + \overrightarrow{P_3 P_4} = \overrightarrow{P_1 P_4}$. Also, $\overrightarrow{P_1 P_3}$ and $\overrightarrow{P_2 P_4}$ are not adjacent sides; they are parallel sides. ■

Since $\mathbf{u} \times \mathbf{v} = -\mathbf{i} + 2\mathbf{j} + 7\mathbf{k}$ (Example 4), the area of the parallelogram is

$$\text{Area of parallelogram} = \|\mathbf{u} \times \mathbf{v}\| = \sqrt{1 + 4 + 49} = \sqrt{54} = 3\sqrt{6} \text{ square units}$$

━━━ **Now Work** PROBLEM 49

Proof of Property (11) The proof requires two parts. If $\mathbf{u}$ and $\mathbf{v}$ are parallel, then there is a scalar α such that $\mathbf{u} = \alpha \mathbf{v}$. Then

$$\mathbf{u} \times \mathbf{v} = (\alpha \mathbf{v}) \times \mathbf{v} = \alpha(\mathbf{v} \times \mathbf{v}) = \mathbf{0}$$
$$\qquad\quad \underset{\text{Property (4)}}{\uparrow} \qquad \underset{\text{Property (2)}}{\uparrow}$$

If $\mathbf{u} \times \mathbf{v} = \mathbf{0}$, then, by property (9), we have

$$\|\mathbf{u} \times \mathbf{v}\| = \|\mathbf{u}\| \, \|\mathbf{v}\| \sin \theta = 0$$

Since $\mathbf{u} \neq \mathbf{0}$ and $\mathbf{v} \neq \mathbf{0}$, we must have $\sin \theta = 0$, so $\theta = 0$ or $\theta = \pi$. In either case, since θ is the angle between $\mathbf{u}$ and $\mathbf{v}$, then $\mathbf{u}$ and $\mathbf{v}$ are parallel. ■

9.7 Assess Your Understanding

Concepts and Vocabulary

1. True or False If **u** and **v** are parallel vectors, then $\mathbf{u} \times \mathbf{v} = \mathbf{0}$.

2. True or False For any vector **v**, $\mathbf{v} \times \mathbf{v} = \mathbf{0}$.

3. True or False If **u** and **v** are vectors, then $\mathbf{u} \times \mathbf{v} + \mathbf{v} \times \mathbf{u} = \mathbf{0}$.

4. True or False $\mathbf{u} \times \mathbf{v}$ is a vector that is parallel to both **u** and **v**.

5. True or False $\|\mathbf{u} \times \mathbf{v}\| = \|\mathbf{u}\|\,\|\mathbf{v}\| \cos \theta$, where θ is the angle between **u** and **v**.

6. True or False The area of the parallelogram having **u** and **v** as adjacent sides is the magnitude of the cross product of **u** and **v**.

Skill Building

In Problems 7–14, find the value of each determinant.

7. $\begin{vmatrix} 3 & 4 \\ 1 & 2 \end{vmatrix}$

8. $\begin{vmatrix} -2 & 5 \\ 2 & -3 \end{vmatrix}$

9. $\begin{vmatrix} 6 & 5 \\ -2 & -1 \end{vmatrix}$

10. $\begin{vmatrix} -4 & 0 \\ 5 & 3 \end{vmatrix}$

11. $\begin{vmatrix} A & B & C \\ 2 & 1 & 4 \\ 1 & 3 & 1 \end{vmatrix}$

12. $\begin{vmatrix} A & B & C \\ 0 & 2 & 4 \\ 3 & 1 & 3 \end{vmatrix}$

13. $\begin{vmatrix} A & B & C \\ -1 & 3 & 5 \\ 5 & 0 & -2 \end{vmatrix}$

14. $\begin{vmatrix} A & B & C \\ 1 & -2 & -3 \\ 0 & 2 & -2 \end{vmatrix}$

In Problems 15–22, find (a) $\mathbf{v} \times \mathbf{w}$, (b) $\mathbf{w} \times \mathbf{v}$, (c) $\mathbf{w} \times \mathbf{w}$, and (d) $\mathbf{v} \times \mathbf{v}$.

15. $\mathbf{v} = 2\mathbf{i} - 3\mathbf{j} + \mathbf{k}$
$\mathbf{w} = 3\mathbf{i} - 2\mathbf{j} - \mathbf{k}$

16. $\mathbf{v} = -\mathbf{i} + 3\mathbf{j} + 2\mathbf{k}$
$\mathbf{w} = 3\mathbf{i} - 2\mathbf{j} - \mathbf{k}$

17. $\mathbf{v} = \mathbf{i} + \mathbf{j}$
$\mathbf{w} = 2\mathbf{i} + \mathbf{j} + \mathbf{k}$

18. $\mathbf{v} = \mathbf{i} - 4\mathbf{j} + 2\mathbf{k}$
$\mathbf{w} = 3\mathbf{i} + 2\mathbf{j} + \mathbf{k}$

19. $\mathbf{v} = 2\mathbf{i} - \mathbf{j} + 2\mathbf{k}$
$\mathbf{w} = \mathbf{j} - \mathbf{k}$

20. $\mathbf{v} = 3\mathbf{i} + \mathbf{j} + 3\mathbf{k}$
$\mathbf{w} = \mathbf{i} - \mathbf{k}$

21. $\mathbf{v} = \mathbf{i} - \mathbf{j} - \mathbf{k}$
$\mathbf{w} = 4\mathbf{i} - 3\mathbf{k}$

22. $\mathbf{v} = 2\mathbf{i} - 3\mathbf{j}$
$\mathbf{w} = 3\mathbf{j} - 2\mathbf{k}$

In Problems 23–44, use the given vectors **u**, **v**, and **w** to find each expression.

$$\mathbf{u} = 2\mathbf{i} - 3\mathbf{j} + \mathbf{k}, \qquad \mathbf{v} = -3\mathbf{i} + 3\mathbf{j} + 2\mathbf{k}, \qquad \mathbf{w} = \mathbf{i} + \mathbf{j} + 3\mathbf{k}$$

23. $\mathbf{u} \times \mathbf{v}$

24. $\mathbf{v} \times \mathbf{w}$

25. $\mathbf{v} \times \mathbf{u}$

26. $\mathbf{w} \times \mathbf{v}$

27. $\mathbf{v} \times \mathbf{v}$

28. $\mathbf{w} \times \mathbf{w}$

29. $(3\mathbf{u}) \times \mathbf{v}$

30. $\mathbf{v} \times (4\mathbf{w})$

31. $\mathbf{u} \times (2\mathbf{v})$

32. $(-3\mathbf{v}) \times \mathbf{w}$

33. $\mathbf{u} \cdot (\mathbf{u} \times \mathbf{v})$

34. $\mathbf{v} \cdot (\mathbf{v} \times \mathbf{w})$

35. $\mathbf{u} \cdot (\mathbf{v} \times \mathbf{w})$

36. $(\mathbf{u} \times \mathbf{v}) \cdot \mathbf{w}$

37. $\mathbf{v} \cdot (\mathbf{u} \times \mathbf{w})$

38. $(\mathbf{v} \times \mathbf{u}) \cdot \mathbf{w}$

39. $\mathbf{u} \times (\mathbf{v} \times \mathbf{v})$

40. $(\mathbf{w} \times \mathbf{w}) \times \mathbf{v}$

41. Find a vector orthogonal to both **u** and **v**.

42. Find a vector orthogonal to both **u** and **w**.

43. Find a vector orthogonal to both **u** and $\mathbf{i} + \mathbf{j}$.

44. Find a vector orthogonal to both **u** and $\mathbf{j} + \mathbf{k}$.

In Problems 45–48, find the area of the parallelogram with one corner at P_1 and adjacent sides $\overrightarrow{P_1P_2}$ and $\overrightarrow{P_1P_3}$.

45. $P_1 = (0, 0, 0)$, $P_2 = (1, 2, 3)$, $P_3 = (-2, 3, 0)$

46. $P_1 = (0, 0, 0)$, $P_2 = (2, 3, 1)$, $P_3 = (-2, 4, 1)$

47. $P_1 = (1, 2, 0)$, $P_2 = (-2, 3, 4)$, $P_3 = (0, -2, 3)$

48. $P_1 = (-2, 0, 2)$, $P_2 = (2, 1, -1)$, $P_3 = (2, -1, 2)$

In Problems 49–52, find the area of the parallelogram with vertices P_1, P_2, P_3, and P_4.

49. $P_1 = (1, 1, 2)$, $P_2 = (1, 2, 3)$, $P_3 = (-2, 3, 0)$,
$P_4 = (-2, 4, 1)$

50. $P_1 = (2, 1, 1)$, $P_2 = (2, 3, 1)$, $P_3 = (-2, 4, 1)$,
$P_4 = (-2, 6, 1)$

51. $P_1 = (1, 2, -1)$, $P_2 = (4, 2, -3)$, $P_3 = (6, -5, 2)$,
$P_4 = (9, -5, 0)$

52. $P_1 = (-1, 1, 1)$, $P_2 = (-1, 2, 2)$, $P_3 = (-3, 4, -5)$,
$P_4 = (-3, 5, -4)$

Applications and Extensions

53. Find a unit vector normal to the plane containing $\mathbf{v} = \mathbf{i} + 3\mathbf{j} - 2\mathbf{k}$ and $\mathbf{w} = -2\mathbf{i} + \mathbf{j} + 3\mathbf{k}$.

54. Find a unit vector normal to the plane containing $\mathbf{v} = 2\mathbf{i} + 3\mathbf{j} - \mathbf{k}$ and $\mathbf{w} = -2\mathbf{i} - 4\mathbf{j} - 3\mathbf{k}$.

55. Volume of a Parallelepiped A **parallelepiped** is a prism whose faces are all parallelograms. Let **A**, **B**, and **C** be the vectors that define the parallelepiped shown in the figure. The volume V of the parallelepiped is given by the formula $V = |(\mathbf{A} \times \mathbf{B}) \cdot \mathbf{C}|$.

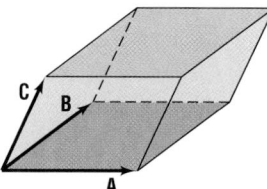

Find the volume of a parallelepiped if the defining vectors are $\mathbf{A} = 3\mathbf{i} - 2\mathbf{j} + 4\mathbf{k}$, $\mathbf{B} = 2\mathbf{i} + \mathbf{j} - 2\mathbf{k}$, and $\mathbf{C} = 3\mathbf{i} - 6\mathbf{j} - 2\mathbf{k}$.

56. Volume of a Parallelepiped Refer to Problems 55. Find the volume of a parallelepiped whose defining vectors are $\mathbf{A} = \langle 1, 0, 6 \rangle$, $\mathbf{B} = \langle 2, 3, -8 \rangle$, and $\mathbf{C} = \langle 8, -5, 6 \rangle$.

57. Prove for vectors **u** and **v** that
$$\|\mathbf{u} \times \mathbf{v}\|^2 = \|\mathbf{u}\|^2\|\mathbf{v}\|^2 - (\mathbf{u} \cdot \mathbf{v})^2$$
[**Hint:** Proceed as in the proof of property (4), computing first the left side and then the right side.]

58. Show that if **u** and **v** are orthogonal then
$$\|\mathbf{u} \times \mathbf{v}\| = \|\mathbf{u}\| \, \|\mathbf{v}\|$$

59. Show that if **u** and **v** are orthogonal unit vectors then $\mathbf{u} \times \mathbf{v}$ is also a unit vector.

60. Prove property (3).

61. Prove property (5).

62. Prove property (9).

[**Hint:** Use the result of Problem 57 and the fact that if θ is the angle between **u** and **v** then $\mathbf{u} \cdot \mathbf{v} = \|\mathbf{u}\| \, \|\mathbf{v}\| \cos \theta$.]

Discussion and Writing

63. If $\mathbf{u} \cdot \mathbf{v} = 0$ and $\mathbf{u} \times \mathbf{v} = \mathbf{0}$, what, if anything, can you conclude about **u** and **v**?

CHAPTER REVIEW

Things to Know

Polar Coordinates (p. 562–568)

Relationship between polar coordinates (r, θ) and rectangular coordinates (x, y) (pp. 564 and 568)

$x = r \cos \theta, \ y = r \sin \theta$

$r^2 = x^2 + y^2, \ \tan \theta = \dfrac{y}{x}, \ x \neq 0$

Polar form of a complex number (p. 590)

If $z = x + yi$, then $z = r(\cos \theta + i \sin \theta)$, where $r = |z| = \sqrt{x^2 + y^2}$, $\sin \theta = \dfrac{y}{r}$, $\cos \theta = \dfrac{x}{r}$, $0 \le \theta < 2\pi$.

De Moivre's Theorem (p. 592)

If $z = r(\cos \theta + i \sin \theta)$, then $z^n = r^n[\cos(n\theta) + i \sin(n\theta)]$, where $n \ge 1$ is a positive integer.

nth root of a complex number $w = r(\cos \theta_0 + i \sin \theta_0)$ (p. 593)

$z_k = \sqrt[n]{r}\left[\cos\left(\dfrac{\theta_0}{n} + \dfrac{2k\pi}{n}\right) + i \sin\left(\dfrac{\theta_0}{n} + \dfrac{2k\pi}{n}\right)\right], \ k = 0, \dots, n-1,$ where $n \ge 2$ is an integer.

Vector (pp. 597–604)

Quantity having magnitude and direction; equivalent to a directed line segment $\overrightarrow{PQ}$

Position vector (pp. 600 and 618)

Vector whose initial point is at the origin

Unit vector (pp. 603 and 620)

Vector whose magnitude is 1

Dot product (pp. 608 and 620)

If $\mathbf{v} = a_1\mathbf{i} + b_1\mathbf{j}$ and $\mathbf{w} = a_2\mathbf{i} + b_2\mathbf{j}$, then $\mathbf{v} \cdot \mathbf{w} = a_1a_2 + b_1b_2$.
If $\mathbf{v} = a_1\mathbf{i} + b_1\mathbf{j} + c_1\mathbf{k}$ and $\mathbf{w} = a_2\mathbf{i} + b_2\mathbf{j} + c_2\mathbf{k}$, then $\mathbf{v} \cdot \mathbf{w} = a_1a_2 + b_1b_2 + c_1c_2$.

Angle θ between two nonzero vectors **u** and **v** (pp. 610 and 621)

$\cos \theta = \dfrac{\mathbf{u} \cdot \mathbf{v}}{\|\mathbf{u}\| \, \|\mathbf{v}\|}$

Direction angles of a vector in space (p. 622–623)

If $\mathbf{v} = a\mathbf{i} + b\mathbf{j} + c\mathbf{k}$, then $\mathbf{v} = \|\mathbf{v}\|[(\cos \alpha)\mathbf{i} + (\cos \beta)\mathbf{j} + (\cos \gamma)\mathbf{k}]$, where $\cos \alpha = \dfrac{a}{\|\mathbf{v}\|}$, $\cos \beta = \dfrac{b}{\|\mathbf{v}\|}$, $\cos \gamma = \dfrac{c}{\|\mathbf{v}\|}$.

Cross product (p. 626)

If $\mathbf{v} = a_1\mathbf{i} + b_1\mathbf{j} + c_1\mathbf{k}$ and $\mathbf{w} = a_2\mathbf{i} + b_2\mathbf{j} + c_2\mathbf{k}$, then $\mathbf{v} \times \mathbf{w} = [b_1c_2 - b_2c_1]\mathbf{i} - [a_1c_2 - a_2c_1]\mathbf{j} + [a_1b_2 - a_2b_1]\mathbf{k}$.

Area of a parallelogram (pp. 628 and 629)

$\|\mathbf{u} \times \mathbf{v}\| = \|\mathbf{u}\| \, \|\mathbf{v}\| \sin \theta$, where θ is the angle between **u** and **v**.

Objectives

Section		You should be able to . . .	Example(s)	Review Exercises
9.1	1	Plot points using polar coordinates (p. 562)	1–3	1–6
	2	Convert from polar coordinates to rectangular coordinates (p. 564)	4	1–6
	3	Convert from rectangular coordinates to polar coordinates (p. 566)	5–7	7–12
	4	Transform equations from polar to rectangular form (p. 568)	8, 9	13(a)–18(a)
9.2	1	Graph and identify polar equations by converting to rectangular equations (p. 572)	1–7	13(b)–18(b)
	2	Graph polar equations using a graphing utility (p. 573)	4–7	19–24
	3	Test polar equations for symmetry (p. 577)	8–11	19–24
	4	Graph polar equations by plotting points (p. 578)	8–13	19–24
9.3	1	Plot points in the complex plane (p. 589)	1	25–28
	2	Convert a complex number from rectangular form to polar form (p. 590)	2, 3	29–34
	3	Find products and quotients of complex numbers in polar form (p. 591)	4	35–40
	4	Use De Moivre's Theorem (p. 592)	5, 6	41–48
	5	Find complex roots (p. 593)	7	49–50
9.4	1	Graph vectors (p. 599)	1	51–54
	2	Find a position vector (p. 600)	2	55–58
	3	Add and subtract vectors algebraically (p. 601)	3	59, 60
	4	Find a scalar multiple and the magnitude of a vector (p. 602)	4	55–58, 61–66
	5	Find a unit vector (p. 602)	5	67, 68
	6	Find a vector from its direction and magnitude (p. 603)	6	69, 70
	7	Analyze objects in static equilibrium (p. 604)	7	111
9.5	1	Find the dot product of two vectors (p. 608)	1	85–88
	2	Find the angle between two vectors (p. 609)	2, 3	85–88, 109, 110, 112
	3	Determine whether two vectors are parallel (p. 611)	4	93–98
	4	Determine whether two vectors are orthogonal (p. 611)	5	93–98
	5	Decompose a vector into two orthogonal vectors (p. 612)	6	99–102
	6	Compute work (p. 613)	7	113
9.6	1	Find the distance between two points in space (p. 618)	1	71, 72
	2	Find position vectors in space (p. 618)	2	73, 74
	3	Perform operations on vectors (p. 619)	3–5	75–80
	4	Find the dot product (p. 620)	6	89–92
	5	Find the angle between two vectors (p. 621)	7	89–92
	6	Find the direction angles of a vector (p. 621)	8–10	103, 104
9.7	1	Find the cross product of two vectors (p. 626)	1–3	81, 82
	2	Know algebraic properties of the cross product (p. 627)	pp. 627–628	107, 108
	3	Know geometric properties of the cross product (p. 628)	p. 628	105, 106
	4	Find a vector orthogonal to two given vectors (p. 628)	4	84
	5	Find the area of a parallelogram (p. 629)	5	105, 106

Review Exercises

In Problems 1–6, plot each point given in polar coordinates, and find its rectangular coordinates.

1. $\left(3, \dfrac{\pi}{6}\right)$ **2.** $\left(4, \dfrac{2\pi}{3}\right)$ **3.** $\left(-2, \dfrac{4\pi}{3}\right)$ **4.** $\left(-1, \dfrac{5\pi}{4}\right)$ **5.** $\left(-3, -\dfrac{\pi}{2}\right)$ **6.** $\left(-4, -\dfrac{\pi}{4}\right)$

In Problems 7–12, the rectangular coordinates of a point are given. Find two pairs of polar coordinates (r, θ) for each point, one with $r > 0$ and the other with $r < 0$. Express θ in radians.

7. $(-3, 3)$ **8.** $(1, -1)$ **9.** $(0, -2)$ **10.** $(2, 0)$ **11.** $(3, 4)$ **12.** $(-5, 12)$

In Problems 13–18, the variables r and θ represent polar coordinates. (a) Write each polar equation as an equation in rectangular coordinates (x, y). (b) Identify the equation and graph it.

13. $r = 2 \sin \theta$

14. $3r = \sin \theta$

15. $r = 5$

16. $\theta = \dfrac{\pi}{4}$

17. $r \cos \theta + 3r \sin \theta = 6$

18. $r^2 + 4r \sin \theta - 8r \cos \theta = 5$

In Problems 19–24, by hand sketch the graph of each polar equation. Be sure to test for symmetry. Verify your graph using a graphing utility.

19. $r = 4 \cos \theta$

20. $r = 3 \sin \theta$

21. $r = 3 - 3 \sin \theta$

22. $r = 2 + \cos \theta$

23. $r = 4 - \cos \theta$

24. $r = 1 - 2 \sin \theta$

In Problems 25–28, write each complex number in polar form. Express each argument in degrees.

25. $-1 - i$

26. $-\sqrt{3} + i$

27. $4 - 3i$

28. $3 - 2i$

In Problems 29–34, write each complex number in the standard form a + bi and plot each in the complex plane.

29. $2(\cos 150° + i \sin 150°)$

30. $3(\cos 60° + i \sin 60°)$

31. $3\left(\cos \dfrac{2\pi}{3} + i \sin \dfrac{2\pi}{3}\right)$

32. $4\left(\cos \dfrac{3\pi}{4} + i \sin \dfrac{3\pi}{4}\right)$

33. $0.1(\cos 350° + i \sin 350°)$

34. $0.5(\cos 160° + i \sin 160°)$

In Problems 35–40, find zw and $\dfrac{z}{w}$. Leave your answers in polar form.

35. $z = \cos 80° + i \sin 80°$
  $w = \cos 50° + i \sin 50°$

36. $z = \cos 205° + i \sin 205°$
  $w = \cos 85° + i \sin 85°$

37. $z = 3\left(\cos \dfrac{9\pi}{5} + i \sin \dfrac{9\pi}{5}\right)$
  $w = 2\left(\cos \dfrac{\pi}{5} + i \sin \dfrac{\pi}{5}\right)$

38. $z = 2\left(\cos \dfrac{5\pi}{3} + i \sin \dfrac{5\pi}{3}\right)$
  $w = 3\left(\cos \dfrac{\pi}{3} + i \sin \dfrac{\pi}{3}\right)$

39. $z = 5(\cos 10° + i \sin 10°)$
  $w = \cos 355° + i \sin 355°$

40. $z = 4(\cos 50° + i \sin 50°)$
  $w = \cos 340° + i \sin 340°$

In Problems 41–48, write each expression in the standard form a + bi.

41. $[3(\cos 20° + i \sin 20°)]^3$

42. $[2(\cos 50° + i \sin 50°)]^3$

43. $\left[\sqrt{2}\left(\cos \dfrac{5\pi}{8} + i \sin \dfrac{5\pi}{8}\right)\right]^4$

44. $\left[2\left(\cos \dfrac{5\pi}{16} + i \sin \dfrac{5\pi}{16}\right)\right]^4$

45. $\left(1 - \sqrt{3}i\right)^6$

46. $(2 - 2i)^8$

47. $(3 + 4i)^4$

48. $(1 - 2i)^4$

49. Find all the complex cube roots of 27.

50. Find all the complex fourth roots of −16.

In Problems 51–54, use the figure to graph each of the following:

51. $\mathbf{u} + \mathbf{v}$

52. $\mathbf{v} + \mathbf{w}$

53. $2\mathbf{u} + 3\mathbf{v}$

54. $5\mathbf{v} - 2\mathbf{w}$

In Problems 55–58, the vector $\mathbf{v}$ is represented by the directed line segment $\overrightarrow{PQ}$. Write $\mathbf{v}$ in the form $a\mathbf{i} + b\mathbf{j}$ and find $\|\mathbf{v}\|$.

55. $P = (1, -2)$; $Q = (3, -6)$

56. $P = (-3, 1)$; $Q = (4, -2)$

57. $P = (0, -2)$; $Q = (-1, 1)$

58. $P = (3, -4)$; $Q = (-2, 0)$

In Problems 59–68, use the vectors $\mathbf{v} = -2\mathbf{i} + \mathbf{j}$ and $\mathbf{w} = 4\mathbf{i} - 3\mathbf{j}$ to find:

59. $\mathbf{v} + \mathbf{w}$

60. $\mathbf{v} - \mathbf{w}$

61. $4\mathbf{v} - 3\mathbf{w}$

62. $-\mathbf{v} + 2\mathbf{w}$

63. $\|\mathbf{v}\|$

64. $\|\mathbf{v} + \mathbf{w}\|$

65. $\|\mathbf{v}\| + \|\mathbf{w}\|$

66. $\|2\mathbf{v}\| - 3\|\mathbf{w}\|$

67. Find a unit vector in the same direction as $\mathbf{v}$.

68. Find a unit vector in the opposite direction of $\mathbf{w}$.

69. Find the vector $\mathbf{v}$ in the xy-plane with magnitude 3 if the angle between $\mathbf{v}$ and $\mathbf{i}$ is 60°.

70. Find the vector $\mathbf{v}$ in the xy-plane with magnitude 5 if the angle between $\mathbf{v}$ and $\mathbf{i}$ is 150°.

71. Find the distance from $P_1 = (1, 3, -2)$ to $P_2 = (4, -2, 1)$.

72. Find the distance from $P_1 = (0, -4, 3)$ to $P_2 = (6, -5, -1)$.

73. A vector **v** has initial point $P = (1, 3, -2)$ and terminal point $Q = (4, -2, 1)$. Write **v** in the form $\mathbf{v} = a\mathbf{i} + b\mathbf{j} + c\mathbf{k}$.

74. A vector **v** has initial point $P = (0, -4, 3)$ and terminal point $Q = (6, -5, -1)$. Write **v** in the form $\mathbf{v} = a\mathbf{i} + b\mathbf{j} + c\mathbf{k}$.

In Problems 75–84, use the vectors $\mathbf{v} = 3\mathbf{i} + \mathbf{j} - 2\mathbf{k}$ and $\mathbf{w} = -3\mathbf{i} + 2\mathbf{j} - \mathbf{k}$ to find each expression.

75. $4\mathbf{v} - 3\mathbf{w}$

76. $-\mathbf{v} + 2\mathbf{w}$

77. $\|\mathbf{v} - \mathbf{w}\|$

78. $\|\mathbf{v} + \mathbf{w}\|$

79. $\|\mathbf{v}\| - \|\mathbf{w}\|$

80. $\|\mathbf{v}\| + \|\mathbf{w}\|$

81. $\mathbf{v} \times \mathbf{w}$

82. $\mathbf{v} \cdot (\mathbf{v} \times \mathbf{w})$

83. Find a unit vector in the same direction as **v** and then in the opposite direction of **v**.

84. Find a unit vector orthogonal to both **v** and **w**.

*In Problems 85–92, find the dot product $\mathbf{v} \cdot \mathbf{w}$ and the angle between **v** and **w**.*

85. $\mathbf{v} = -2\mathbf{i} + \mathbf{j}, \quad \mathbf{w} = 4\mathbf{i} - 3\mathbf{j}$

86. $\mathbf{v} = 3\mathbf{i} - \mathbf{j}, \quad \mathbf{w} = \mathbf{i} + \mathbf{j}$

87. $\mathbf{v} = \mathbf{i} - 3\mathbf{j}, \quad \mathbf{w} = -\mathbf{i} + \mathbf{j}$

88. $\mathbf{v} = \mathbf{i} + 4\mathbf{j}, \quad \mathbf{w} = 3\mathbf{i} - 2\mathbf{j}$

89. $\mathbf{v} = \mathbf{i} + \mathbf{j} + \mathbf{k}, \quad \mathbf{w} = \mathbf{i} - \mathbf{j} + \mathbf{k}$

90. $\mathbf{v} = \mathbf{i} - \mathbf{j} + \mathbf{k}, \quad \mathbf{w} = 2\mathbf{i} + \mathbf{j} + \mathbf{k}$

91. $\mathbf{v} = 4\mathbf{i} - \mathbf{j} + 2\mathbf{k}, \quad \mathbf{w} = \mathbf{i} - 2\mathbf{j} - 3\mathbf{k}$

92. $\mathbf{v} = -\mathbf{i} - 2\mathbf{j} + 3\mathbf{k}, \quad \mathbf{w} = 5\mathbf{i} + \mathbf{j} + \mathbf{k}$

*In Problems 93–98, determine whether **v** and **w** are parallel, orthogonal, or neither.*

93. $\mathbf{v} = 2\mathbf{i} + 3\mathbf{j}; \quad \mathbf{w} = -4\mathbf{i} - 6\mathbf{j}$

94. $\mathbf{v} = -2\mathbf{i} - \mathbf{j}; \quad \mathbf{w} = 2\mathbf{i} + \mathbf{j}$

95. $\mathbf{v} = 3\mathbf{i} - 4\mathbf{j}; \quad \mathbf{w} = -3\mathbf{i} + 4\mathbf{j}$

96. $\mathbf{v} = -2\mathbf{i} + 2\mathbf{j}; \quad \mathbf{w} = -3\mathbf{i} + 2\mathbf{j}$

97. $\mathbf{v} = 3\mathbf{i} - 2\mathbf{j}; \quad \mathbf{w} = 4\mathbf{i} + 6\mathbf{j}$

98. $\mathbf{v} = -4\mathbf{i} + 2\mathbf{j}; \quad \mathbf{w} = 2\mathbf{i} + 4\mathbf{j}$

*In Problems 99–102, decompose **v** into two vectors, one parallel to **w** and the other orthogonal to **w**.*

99. $\mathbf{v} = 2\mathbf{i} + \mathbf{j}; \quad \mathbf{w} = -4\mathbf{i} + 3\mathbf{j}$

100. $\mathbf{v} = -3\mathbf{i} + 2\mathbf{j}; \quad \mathbf{w} = -2\mathbf{i} + \mathbf{j}$

101. $\mathbf{v} = 2\mathbf{i} + 3\mathbf{j}; \quad \mathbf{w} = 3\mathbf{i} + \mathbf{j}$

102. $\mathbf{v} = -\mathbf{i} + 2\mathbf{j}; \quad \mathbf{w} = 3\mathbf{i} - \mathbf{j}$

---

103. Find the direction angles of the vector $\mathbf{v} = 3\mathbf{i} - 4\mathbf{j} + 2\mathbf{k}$.

104. Find the direction angles of the vector $\mathbf{v} = \mathbf{i} - \mathbf{j} + 2\mathbf{k}$.

105. Find the area of the parallelogram with vertices $P_1 = (1, 1, 1)$, $P_2 = (2, 3, 4)$, $P_3 = (6, 5, 2)$, and $P_4 = (7, 7, 5)$.

106. Find the area of the parallelogram with vertices $P_1 = (2, -1, 1)$, $P_2 = (5, 1, 4)$, $P_3 = (0, 1, 1)$, and $P_4 = (3, 3, 4)$.

107. If $\mathbf{u} \times \mathbf{v} = 2\mathbf{i} - 3\mathbf{j} + \mathbf{k}$, what is $\mathbf{v} \times \mathbf{u}$?

108. Suppose that $\mathbf{u} = 3\mathbf{v}$. What is $\mathbf{u} \times \mathbf{v}$?

109. Actual Speed and Direction of a Swimmer A swimmer can maintain a constant speed of 5 miles per hour. If the swimmer heads directly across a river that has a current moving at the rate of 2 miles per hour, what is the actual speed of the swimmer? (See the figure.) If the river is 1 mile wide, how far downstream will the swimmer end up from the point directly across the river from the starting point?

110. Actual Speed and Direction of an Airplane An airplane has an airspeed of 500 kilometers per hour in a northerly direction. The wind velocity is 60 kilometers per hour in a southeasterly direction. Find the actual speed and direction of the plane relative to the ground.

111. Static Equilibrium A weight of 2000 pounds is suspended from two cables, as shown in the figure. What are the tensions in each cable?

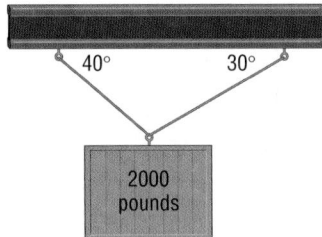

112. Actual Speed and Distance of a Motorboat A small motorboat is moving at a true speed of 11 miles per hour in a southerly direction. The current is known to be from the northeast at 3 miles per hour. What is the speed of the motorboat relative to the water? In what direction does the compass indicate that the boat is headed?

113. Computing Work Find the work done by a force of 5 pounds acting in the direction 60° to the horizontal in moving an object 20 feet from $(0, 0)$ to $(20, 0)$.

CHAPTER TEST

In Problems 1–3, plot each point given in polar coordinates.

1. $\left(2, \dfrac{3\pi}{4}\right)$

2. $\left(3, -\dfrac{\pi}{6}\right)$

3. $\left(-4, \dfrac{\pi}{3}\right)$

4. Convert $\left(2, 2\sqrt{3}\right)$ from rectangular coordinates to polar coordinates (r, θ), where $r > 0$ and $0 \le \theta < 2\pi$.

In Problems 5–7, convert the polar equation to a rectangular equation. Graph the equation.

5. $r = 7$

6. $\tan \theta = 3$

7. $r \sin^2 \theta + 8 \sin \theta = r$

In Problems 8 and 9, test the polar equation for symmetry with respect to the pole, the polar axis, and the line $\theta = \dfrac{\pi}{2}$.

8. $r^2 \cos \theta = 5$

9. $r = 5 \sin \theta \cos^2 \theta$

In Problems 10–12, perform the given operation, where $z = 2(\cos 85° + i \sin 85°)$ and $w = 3(\cos 22° + i \sin 22°)$. Write your answer in polar form.

10. $z \cdot w$

11. $\dfrac{w}{z}$

12. w^5

13. Find all the cube roots of $-8 + 8\sqrt{3}i$. Write all answers in the form $a + bi$ and then plot them in rectangular coordinates.

In Problems 14–18, $P_1 = \left(3\sqrt{2}, 7\sqrt{2}\right)$ and $P_2 = \left(8\sqrt{2}, 2\sqrt{2}\right)$.

14. Find the position vector $\mathbf{v}$ equal to $\overrightarrow{P_1 P_2}$.

15. Find $\|\mathbf{v}\|$.

16. Find the unit vector in the direction of $\mathbf{v}$.

17. Find the angle between $\mathbf{v}$ and $\mathbf{i}$.

18. Decompose $\mathbf{v}$ into its vertical and horizontal components.

In Problems 19–22, $\mathbf{v}_1 = \langle 4, 6 \rangle$, $\mathbf{v}_2 = \langle -3, -6 \rangle$, $\mathbf{v}_3 = \langle -8, 4 \rangle$, and $\mathbf{v}_4 = \langle 10, 15 \rangle$.

19. Find the vector $\mathbf{v}_1 + 2\mathbf{v}_2 - \mathbf{v}_3$.

20. Which two vectors are parallel?

21. Which two vectors are orthogonal?

22. Find the angle between vectors $\mathbf{v}_1$ and $\mathbf{v}_2$.

In Problems 23–25, use the vectors $\mathbf{u} = 2\mathbf{i} - 3\mathbf{j} + \mathbf{k}$ and $\mathbf{v} = -\mathbf{i} + 3\mathbf{j} + 2\mathbf{k}$.

23. Find $\mathbf{u} \times \mathbf{v}$.

24. Find the direction angles for $\mathbf{u}$.

25. Find the area of the parallelogram that has $\mathbf{u}$ and $\mathbf{v}$ as adjacent sides.

26. A 1200-pound chandelier is to be suspended over a large ballroom; the chandelier will be hung on a cable whose ends will be attached to the ceiling, 16 feet apart. The chandelier will be free hanging so that the ends of the cable will make equal angles with the ceiling. If the top of the chandelier is to be 16 feet from the ceiling, what is the minimum tension the cable must be able to endure?

CUMULATIVE REVIEW

1. Find the real solutions, if any, of the equation $e^{x^2 - 9} = 1$.

2. Find an equation for the line containing the origin that makes an angle of $30°$ with the positive x-axis.

3. Find an equation for the circle with center at the point $(0, 1)$ and radius 3. Graph this circle.

4. What is the domain of the function $f(x) = \ln(1 - 2x)$?

5. Test the equation $x^2 + y^3 = 2x^4$ for symmetry with respect to the x-axis, the y-axis, and the origin.

6. Graph the function $y = |\ln x|$.

7. Graph the function $y = |\sin x|$.

8. Graph the function $y = \sin|x|$.

9. Find the exact value of $\sin^{-1}\left(-\dfrac{1}{2}\right)$.

10. Graph the equations $x = 3$ and $y = 4$ on the same set of rectangular coordinates.

11. Graph the equations $r = 2$ and $\theta = \dfrac{\pi}{3}$ on the same set of polar coordinates.

12. What is the amplitude and period of $y = -4\cos(\pi x)$?

CHAPTER PROJECTS

Source: *www.aeromuseum.org/eduHowtoFly.html*

I. **Modeling Aircraft Motion** Four aerodynamic forces act on an airplane in flight: lift, weight, thrust, and drag. While an aircraft is in flight, these four forces continuously battle each other. Weight opposes lift and drag opposes thrust. See the figure. In balanced flight at constant speed, both the lift and weight are equal and the thrust and drag are equal.

1. What will happen to the aircraft if the lift is held constant while the weight is decreased (say from burning off fuel)?

2. What will happen to the aircraft if the lift is decreased while the weight is held constant?

3. What will happen to the aircraft if the thrust is increased while the drag is held constant?

4. What will happen to the aircraft if the drag is increased while the thrust is held constant?

In 1903 the Wright brothers made the first controlled powered flight. The weight of their plane was approximately 700 pounds (lb). Newton's Second Law of motion states that force = mass × acceleration ($F = ma$). If the mass is measured in kilograms (kg) and acceleration in meters per second squared (m/sec^2), then the force will be measured in newtons (N). [**Note:** $1\,N = 1\text{kg} \cdot \text{m/sec}^2$.]

5. If 1 kg = 2.205 lb, convert the weight of the Wright brother's plane to kilograms.

6. If acceleration due to gravity is $a = 9.80$ m/sec^2, determine the force due to weight on the Wright brother's plane.

7. What must be true about the lift force of the Wright brother's plane in order for it to get off the ground?

8. The weight of a fully loaded Cessna 170B is 2200 lb. What lift force is required to get this plane off the ground?

9. The maximum gross weight of a Boeing 747 is 255,000 lb. What lift force is required to get this jet off the ground?

The following projects are available at the Instructor's Resource Center (IRC):

II. **Project at Motorola** *Signal Fades Due to Interference* Complex trigonometric functions are used to assure that a cellphone has optimal reception as the user travels up and down an elevator.

III. **Compound Interest** The effect of continuously compounded interest is analyzed using polar coordinates.

IV. **Complex Equations** Analysis of complex equations illustrates the connections between complex and real equations. At times, using complex equations is more efficient for proving mathematical theorems.

Analytic Geometry

Pluto's Unusual Orbit

Pluto is about 39 times as far from the Sun as Earth is. Its average distance from the Sun is about 3,647,240,000 miles (5,869,660,000 kilometers). Pluto travels around the Sun in an elliptical (oval-shaped) orbit. At some point in its orbit, it comes closer to the Sun than Neptune, the outermost planet. It stays inside Neptune's orbit for about 20 Earth-years. This event occurs every 248 Earth-years, which is about the same number of Earth-years it takes Pluto to travel once around the Sun. Pluto entered Neptune's orbit on January 23, 1979, and remained there until February 11, 1999.

Source: Adapted from: Gulbis, Amanda A. S. "Pluto." World Book Online Reference Center © 2007. By permission of the publisher. http://www.worldbookonline.com.

—See Chapter Project I—

A Look Back

In Chapter 1, we introduced rectangular coordinates and showed how geometry problems can be solved algebraically. We defined a circle geometrically and then used the distance formula and rectangular coordinates to obtain an equation for a circle.

A Look Ahead

In this chapter we give geometric definitions for the conics and use the distance formula and rectangular coordinates to obtain their equations. We will learn that a circle is a conic.

Historically, Apollonius (200 BC) was among the first to study *conics* and discover some of their interesting properties. Today, conics are still studied because of their many uses. *Paraboloids of revolution* (parabolas rotated about their axes of symmetry) are used as signal collectors (the satellite dishes used with radar and dish TV, for example), as solar energy collectors, and as reflectors (telescopes, light projection, and so on). The planets circle the Sun in approximately *elliptical* orbits. Elliptical surfaces can be used to reflect signals such as light and sound from one place to another. A third conic, the *hyperbola,* can be used to determine the location of lightning strikes.

The Greeks used the methods of Euclidean geometry to study conics. However, we shall use the more powerful methods of analytic geometry, bringing to bear both algebra and geometry, for our study of conics.

This chapter concludes with a section on equations of conics in polar coordinates and a section on plane curves and parametric equations.

Outline

10.1 Conics
10.2 The Parabola
10.3 The Ellipse
10.4 The Hyperbola
10.5 Rotation of Axes; General Form of a Conic
10.6 Polar Equations of Conics
10.7 Plane Curves and Parametric Equations
Chapter Review
Chapter Test
Cumulative Review
Chapter Projects

10.1 Conics

OBJECTIVE 1 Know the Names of the Conics (p. 638)

1 Know the Names of the Conics

The word *conic* derives from the word *cone,* which is a geometric figure that can be constructed in the following way: Let *a* and *g* be two distinct lines that intersect at a point *V.* Keep the line *a* fixed. Now rotate the line *g* about *a* while maintaining the same angle between *a* and *g.* The collection of points swept out (generated) by the line *g* is called a **(right circular) cone.** See Figure 1. The fixed line *a* is called the **axis** of the cone; the point *V* is its **vertex;** the lines that pass through *V* and make the same angle with *a* as *g* are **generators** of the cone. Each generator is a line that lies entirely on the cone. The cone consists of two parts, called **nappes,** that intersect at the vertex.

Figure 1

Axis, *a*

Generators

Vertex, *V*

g

    Conics, an abbreviation for **conic sections,** are curves that result from the intersection of a right circular cone and a plane. The conics we shall study arise when the plane does not contain the vertex, as shown in Figure 2. These conics are **circles** when the plane is perpendicular to the axis of the cone and intersects each generator; **ellipses** when the plane is tilted slightly so that it intersects each generator, but intersects only one nappe of the cone; **parabolas** when the plane is tilted farther so that it is parallel to one (and only one) generator and intersects only one nappe of the cone; and **hyperbolas** when the plane intersects both nappes.

    If the plane does contain the vertex, the intersection of the plane and the cone is a point, a line, or a pair of intersecting lines. These are usually called **degenerate conics.**

Figure 2

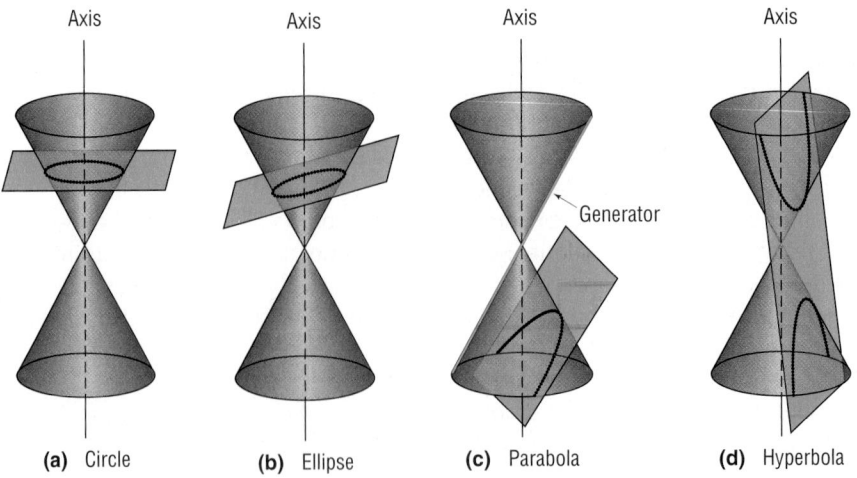

Axis   Axis   Axis   Axis

Generator

(a) Circle   **(b)** Ellipse   **(c)** Parabola   **(d)** Hyperbola

10.2 The Parabola

PREPARING FOR THIS SECTION *Before getting started, review the following:*

- Distance Formula (Section 1.1, p. 5)
- Symmetry (Section 1.2, pp. 19–21)
- Square Root Method (Appendix A, Section A.6, p. A51)

- Completing the Square (Appendix A, Section A.6, pp. A52–A53)
- Graphing Techniques: Transformations (Section 2.5, pp. 100–108)

Now Work the 'Are You Prepared?' problems on page 646.

OBJECTIVES 1 Analyze Parabolas with Vertex at the Origin (p. 639)
2 Analyze Parabolas with Vertex at (h, k) (p. 643)
3 Solve Applied Problems Involving Parabolas (p. 644)

We stated earlier (Section 3.3) that the graph of a quadratic function is a parabola. In this section, we begin with a geometric definition of a parabola and use it to obtain an equation.

DEFINITION

A **parabola** is the collection of all points P in the plane that are the same distance from a fixed point F as they are from a fixed line D. The point F is called the **focus** of the parabola, and the line D is its **directrix.** As a result, a parabola is the set of points P for which

$$d(F, P) = d(P, D) \qquad (1)$$

Figure 3

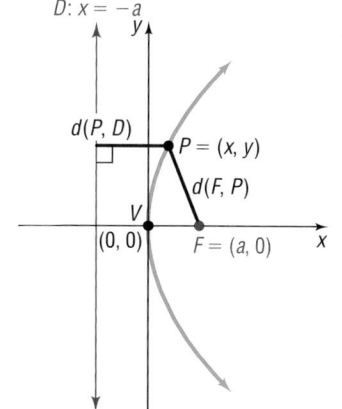

Figure 3 shows a parabola (in blue). The line through the focus F and perpendicular to the directrix D is called the **axis of symmetry** of the parabola. The point of intersection of the parabola with its axis of symmetry is called the **vertex** V.

Because the vertex V lies on the parabola, it must satisfy equation (1): $d(F, V) = d(V, D)$. The vertex is midway between the focus and the directrix. We shall let a equal the distance $d(F, V)$ from F to V. Now we are ready to derive an equation for a parabola. To do this, we use a rectangular system of coordinates positioned so that the vertex V, focus F, and directrix D of the parabola are conveniently located.

1 Analyze Parabolas with Vertex at the Origin

If we choose to locate the vertex V at the origin $(0, 0)$, we can conveniently position the focus F on either the x-axis or the y-axis. First, we consider the case where the focus F is on the positive x-axis, as shown in Figure 4. Because the distance from F to V is a, the coordinates of F will be $(a, 0)$ with $a > 0$. Similarly, because the distance from V to the directrix D is also a and, because D must be perpendicular to the x-axis (since the x-axis is the axis of symmetry), the equation of the directrix D must be $x = -a$.

Now, if $P = (x, y)$ is any point on the parabola, P must obey equation (1):

$$d(F, P) = d(P, D)$$

Figure 4

So we have

$$\sqrt{(x - a)^2 + (y - 0)^2} = |x + a| \qquad \text{Use the Distance Formula.}$$

$$(x - a)^2 + y^2 = (x + a)^2 \qquad \text{Square both sides.}$$

$$x^2 - 2ax + a^2 + y^2 = x^2 + 2ax + a^2 \qquad \text{Remove parentheses.}$$

$$y^2 = 4ax \qquad \text{Simplify.}$$

THEOREM   **Equation of a Parabola: Vertex at (0, 0), Focus at (a, 0), a > 0**

The equation of a parabola with vertex at $(0, 0)$, focus at $(a, 0)$, and directrix $x = -a, a > 0$, is

$$y^2 = 4ax \qquad\qquad (2)$$

EXAMPLE 1	Finding the Equation of a Parabola and Graphing It

Find an equation of the parabola with vertex at $(0, 0)$ and focus at $(3, 0)$. Graph the equation.

Solution   The distance from the vertex $(0, 0)$ to the focus $(3, 0)$ is $a = 3$. Based on equation (2), the equation of this parabola is

$$y^2 = 4ax$$
$$y^2 = 12x \qquad a = 3$$

Figure 5

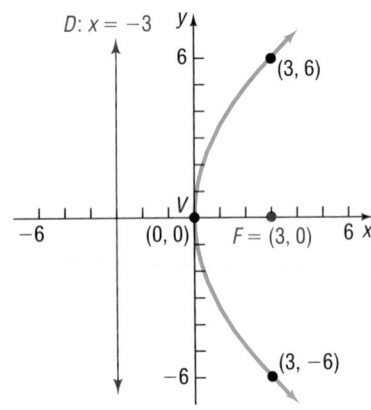

To graph this parabola, it is helpful to plot the points on the graph directly above or below the focus. To locate these two points, we let $x = 3$. Then

$$y^2 = 12x = 12(3) = 36$$
$$y = \pm 6 \qquad\qquad \textit{Solve for y.}$$

The points on the parabola directly above or below the focus are $(3, 6)$ and $(3, -6)$. These points help in graphing the parabola because they determine the "opening." See Figure 5.

In general, the points on a parabola $y^2 = 4ax$ that lie above and below the focus $(a, 0)$ are each at a distance $2a$ from the focus. This follows from the fact that if $x = a$ then $y^2 = 4ax = 4a^2$, so $y = \pm 2a$. The line segment joining these two points is called the **latus rectum;** its length is $4a$.

━━▶ **Now Work** PROBLEM **19**

EXAMPLE 2	Graphing a Parabola Using a Graphing Utility

Graph the parabola $y^2 = 12x$.

Solution   To graph the parabola $y^2 = 12x$, we need to graph the two functions $Y_1 = \sqrt{12x}$ and $Y_2 = -\sqrt{12x}$ on a square screen. Figure 6 shows the graph of $y^2 = 12x$. Notice that the graph fails the vertical line test, so $y^2 = 12x$ is not a function.

Figure 6

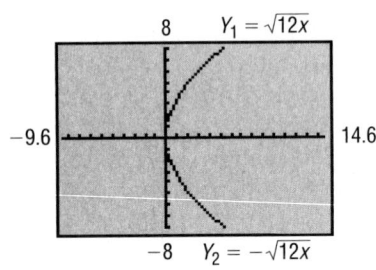

By reversing the steps we used to obtain equation (2), it follows that the graph of an equation of the form of equation (2), $y^2 = 4ax$, is a parabola; its vertex is at $(0, 0)$, its focus is at $(a, 0)$, its directrix is the line $x = -a$, and its axis of symmetry is the x-axis.

For the remainder of this section, the direction **"Analyze the equation"** will mean to find the vertex, focus, and directrix of the parabola and graph it.

EXAMPLE 3	Analyzing the Equation of a Parabola

Analyze the equation: $y^2 = 8x$

Solution   The equation $y^2 = 8x$ is of the form $y^2 = 4ax$, where $4a = 8$, so $a = 2$. Consequently, the graph of the equation is a parabola with vertex at $(0, 0)$ and focus on the positive x-axis at $(2, 0)$. The directrix is the vertical line $x = -2$. The two points defining the latus rectum are obtained by letting $x = 2$. Then $y^2 = 16$, so $y = \pm 4$. See Figure 7(a) for the graph drawn by hand. Figure 7(b) shows the graph obtained using a graphing utility.

Figure 7

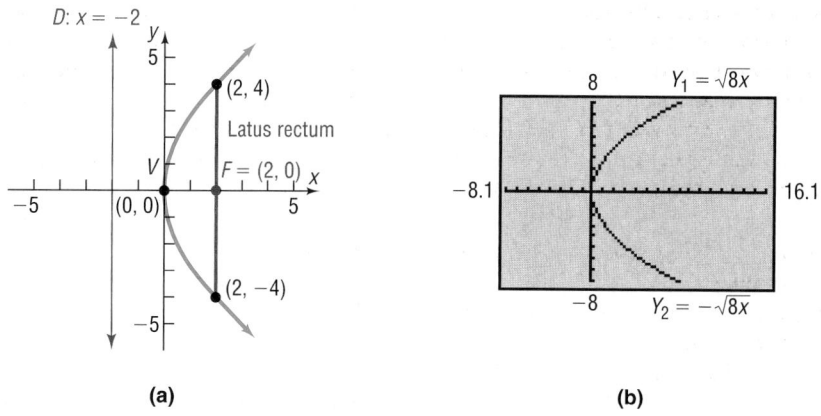

(a)

(b)

Recall that we arrived at equation (2) after placing the focus on the positive x-axis. If the focus is placed on the negative x-axis, positive y-axis, or negative y-axis, a different form of the equation for the parabola results. The four forms of the equation of a parabola with vertex at $(0, 0)$ and focus on a coordinate axis a distance a from $(0, 0)$ are given in Table 1, and their graphs are given in Figure 8. Notice that each graph is symmetric with respect to its axis of symmetry.

Table 1

EQUATIONS OF A PARABOLA VERTEX AT (0,0); FOCUS ON AN AXIS; $a > 0$				
Vertex	**Focus**	**Directrix**	**Equation**	**Description**
$(0, 0)$	$(a, 0)$	$x = -a$	$y^2 = 4ax$	Parabola, axis of symmetry is the x-axis, opens right
$(0, 0)$	$(-a, 0)$	$x = a$	$y^2 = -4ax$	Parabola, axis of symmetry is the x-axis, opens left
$(0, 0)$	$(0, a)$	$y = -a$	$x^2 = 4ay$	Parabola, axis of symmetry is the y-axis, opens up
$(0, 0)$	$(0, -a)$	$y = a$	$x^2 = -4ay$	Parabola, axis of symmetry is the y-axis, opens down

Figure 8

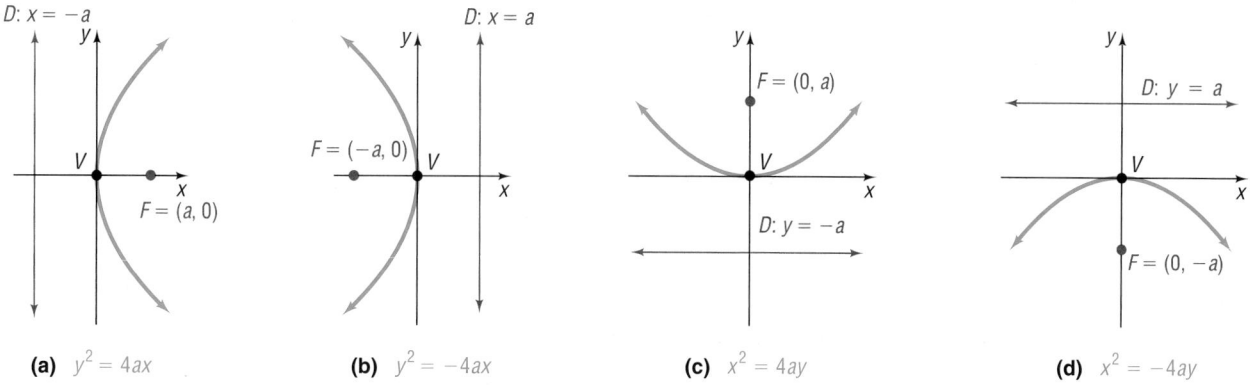

(a) $y^2 = 4ax$

(b) $y^2 = -4ax$

(c) $x^2 = 4ay$

(d) $x^2 = -4ay$

EXAMPLE 4 | Analyzing the Equation of a Parabola

Analyze the equation: $x^2 = -12y$

Solution The equation $x^2 = -12y$ is of the form $x^2 = -4ay$, with $a = 3$. Consequently, the graph of the equation is a parabola with vertex at $(0, 0)$, focus at $(0, -3)$ and directrix the line $y = 3$. The parabola opens down, and its axis of symmetry is the y-axis. To obtain the points defining the latus rectum, let $y = -3$. Then $x^2 = 36$, so $x = \pm 6$. See Figure 9(a) for the graph drawn by hand. Figure 9(b) shows the graph using a graphing utility.

Figure 9

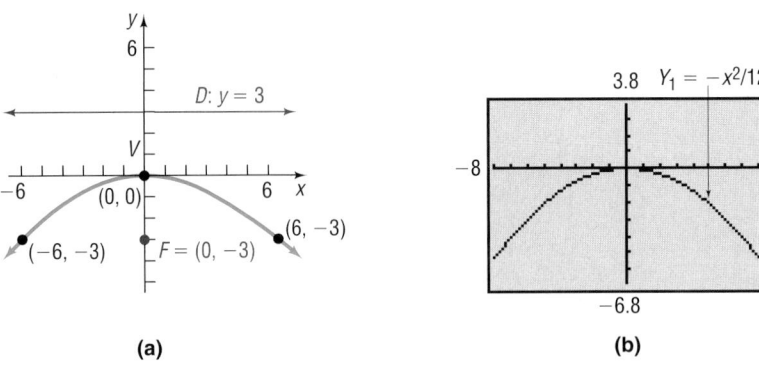

(a)   (b)

━━━ **Now Work** PROBLEM 39

EXAMPLE 5 | **Finding the Equation of a Parabola**

Find the equation of the parabola with focus at $(0, 4)$ and directrix the line $y = -4$. Graph the equation.

Solution

Figure 10

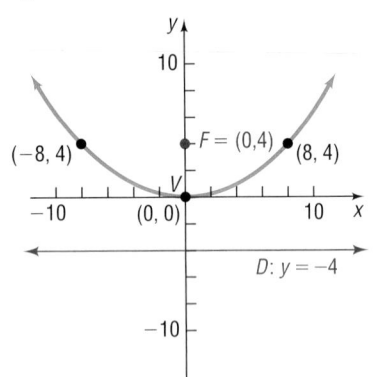

A parabola whose focus is at $(0, 4)$ and whose directrix is the horizontal line $y = -4$ will have its vertex at $(0, 0)$. (Do you see why? The vertex is midway between the focus and the directrix.) Since the focus is on the positive y-axis at $(0, 4)$, the equation of this parabola is of the form $x^2 = 4ay$, with $a = 4$; that is,

$$x^2 = 4ay = 4(4)y = 16y$$
$$\uparrow$$
$$a = 4$$

Letting $y = 4$, we find $x^2 = 64$, so $x = \pm 8$. The points $(8, 4)$ and $(-8, 4)$ determine the latus rectum. Figure 10 shows the graph of $x^2 = 16y$.

✓ **Check:** Verify the graph drawn in Figure 10 by graphing $Y_1 = \dfrac{x^2}{16}$ using a graphing utility.

EXAMPLE 6 | **Finding the Equation of a Parabola**

Find the equation of a parabola with vertex at $(0, 0)$ if its axis of symmetry is the x-axis and its graph contains the point $\left(-\dfrac{1}{2}, 2\right)$. Find its focus and directrix, and graph the equation.

Solution

The vertex is at the origin, the axis of symmetry is the x-axis, and the graph contains a point in the second quadrant, so the parabola opens to the left. We see from Table 1 that the form of the equation is

$$y^2 = -4ax$$

Because the point $\left(-\dfrac{1}{2}, 2\right)$ is on the parabola, the coordinates $x = -\dfrac{1}{2}$, $y = 2$ must satisfy the equation $y^2 = -4ax$. Substituting $x = -\dfrac{1}{2}$ and $y = 2$ into the equation, we find that

$$2^2 = -4a\left(-\dfrac{1}{2}\right) \qquad y^2 = -4ax; x = -\dfrac{1}{2}, y = 2$$

$$a = 2$$

The equation of the parabola is

$$y^2 = -4(2)x = -8x$$

Figure 11

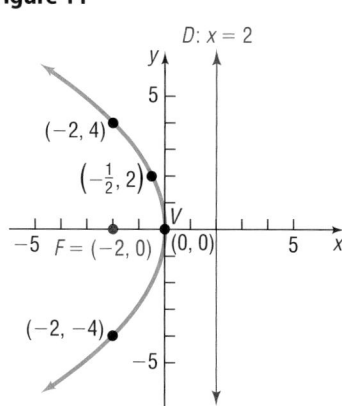

The focus is at $(-2, 0)$ and the directrix is the line $x = 2$. Letting $x = -2$, we find $y^2 = 16$, so $y = \pm 4$. The points $(-2, 4)$ and $(-2, -4)$ define the latus rectum. See Figure 11.

Now Work PROBLEM 27

2 Analyze Parabolas with Vertex at (*h*, *k*)

If a parabola with vertex at the origin and axis of symmetry along a coordinate axis is shifted horizontally *h* units and then vertically *k* units, the result is a parabola with vertex at (h, k) and axis of symmetry parallel to a coordinate axis. The equations of such parabolas have the same forms as those in Table 1, but with *x* replaced by $x - h$ (the horizontal shift) and *y* replaced by $y - k$ (the vertical shift). Table 2 gives the forms of the equations of such parabolas. Figures 12(a)–(d) illustrate the graphs for $h > 0, k > 0$.

Table 2

PARABOLAS WITH VERTEX AT (*h*, *k*); AXIS OF SYMMETRY PARALLEL TO A COORDINATE AXIS; *a* > 0				
Vertex	**Focus**	**Directrix**	**Equation**	**Description**
(h, k)	$(h + a, k)$	$x = h - a$	$(y - k)^2 = 4a(x - h)$	Parabola, axis of symmetry parallel to *x*-axis, opens right
(h, k)	$(h - a, k)$	$x = h + a$	$(y - k)^2 = -4a(x - h)$	Parabola, axis of symmetry parallel to *x*-axis, opens left
(h, k)	$(h, k + a)$	$y = k - a$	$(x - h)^2 = 4a(y - k)$	Parabola, axis of symmetry parallel to *y*-axis, opens up
(h, k)	$(h, k - a)$	$y = k + a$	$(x - h)^2 = -4a(y - k)$	Parabola, axis of symmetry parallel to *y*-axis, opens down

Figure 12

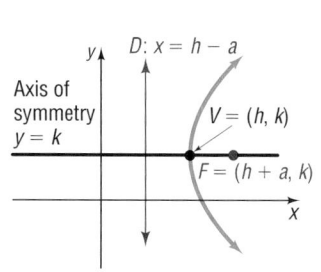

(a) $(y - k)^2 = 4a(x - h)$

(b) $(y - k)^2 = -4a(x - h)$

(c) $(x - h)^2 = 4a(y - k)$

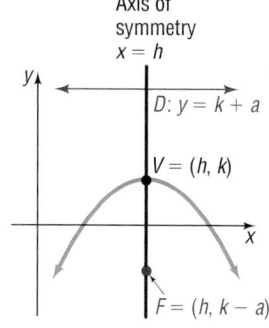

(d) $(x - h)^2 = -4a(y - k)$

EXAMPLE 7 | Finding the Equation of a Parabola, Vertex Not at Origin

Find an equation of the parabola with vertex at $(-2, 3)$ and focus at $(0, 3)$. Graph the equation.

Solution | The vertex $(-2, 3)$ and focus $(0, 3)$ both lie on the horizontal line $y = 3$ (the axis of symmetry). The distance *a* from the vertex $(-2, 3)$ to the focus $(0, 3)$ is $a = 2$. Also, because the focus lies to the right of the vertex, we know that the parabola opens to the right. Consequently, the form of the equation is

$$(y - k)^2 = 4a(x - h)$$

Figure 13

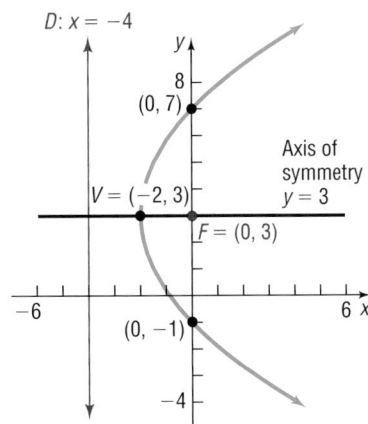

where $(h, k) = (-2, 3)$ and $a = 2$. Therefore, the equation is

$$(y - 3)^2 = 4 \cdot 2[x - (-2)]$$

$$(y - 3)^2 = 8(x + 2)$$

If $x = 0$, then $(y - 3)^2 = 16$. Then $y - 3 = \pm 4$, so $y = -1$ or $y = 7$. The points $(0, -1)$ and $(0, 7)$ define the latus rectum; the line $x = -4$ is the directrix. See Figure 13.

Now Work PROBLEM 29

EXAMPLE 8   **Using a Graphing Utility to Graph a Parabola, Vertex Not at Origin**

Using a graphing utility, graph the equation $(y - 3)^2 = 8(x + 2)$.

Solution   First, we must solve the equation for y.

Figure 14

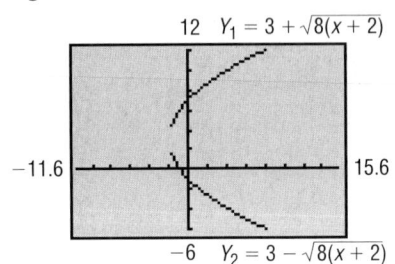

$$(y - 3)^2 = 8(x + 2)$$

$$y - 3 = \pm\sqrt{8(x + 2)} \qquad \text{Use the Square Root Method.}$$

$$y = 3 \pm \sqrt{8(x + 2)} \qquad \text{Add 3 to both sides.}$$

Figure 14 shows the graphs of the equations $Y_1 = 3 + \sqrt{8(x + 2)}$ and $Y_2 = 3 - \sqrt{8(x + 2)}$.

Polynomial equations define parabolas whenever they involve two variables that are quadratic in one variable and linear in the other. To analyze this type of equation, we first complete the square of the variable that is quadratic.

EXAMPLE 9   **Analyzing the Equation of a Parabola**

Analyze the equation: $x^2 + 4x - 4y = 0$

Solution   To analyze the equation $x^2 + 4x - 4y = 0$, we complete the square involving the variable x.

Figure 15

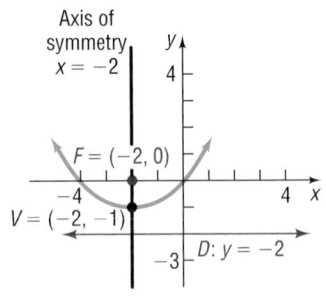

$$x^2 + 4x - 4y = 0$$

$$x^2 + 4x = 4y \qquad \text{Isolate the terms involving } x \text{ on the left side.}$$

$$x^2 + 4x + 4 = 4y + 4 \qquad \text{Complete the square on the left side.}$$

$$(x + 2)^2 = 4(y + 1) \qquad \text{Factor.}$$

This equation is of the form $(x - h)^2 = 4a(y - k)$, with $h = -2, k = -1$, and $a = 1$. The graph is a parabola with vertex at $(h, k) = (-2, -1)$ that opens up. The focus is $a = 1$ unit above the vertex at $(-2, 0)$, and the directrix is the line $y = -2$. See Figure 15.

Now Work PROBLEM 47

3 Solve Applied Problems Involving Parabolas

Parabolas find their way into many applications. For example, as we discussed in Section 3.4, suspension bridges have cables in the shape of a parabola. Another property of parabolas that is used in applications is their reflecting property.

Suppose that a mirror is shaped like a **paraboloid of revolution,** a surface formed by rotating a parabola about its axis of symmetry. If a light (or any other emitting source) is placed at the focus of the parabola, all the rays emanating from the light will reflect off the mirror in lines parallel to the axis of symmetry. This principle is used in the design of searchlights, flashlights, certain automobile headlights, and other such devices. See Figure 16.

Conversely, suppose that rays of light (or other signals) emanate from a distant source so that they are essentially parallel. When these rays strike the surface of a parabolic mirror whose axis of symmetry is parallel to these rays, they are reflected to a single point at the focus. This principle is used in the design of some solar energy devices, satellite dishes, and the mirrors used in some types of telescopes. See Figure 17.

Figure 16
Searchlight

Figure 17
Telescope

EXAMPLE 10 | **Satellite Dish**

A satellite dish is shaped like a paraboloid of revolution. The signals that emanate from a satellite strike the surface of the dish and are reflected to a single point, where the receiver is located. If the dish is 8 feet across at its opening and 3 feet deep at its center, at what position should the receiver be placed? That is, where is the focus?

Solution

Figure 18(a) shows the satellite dish. We draw the parabola used to form the dish on a rectangular coordinate system so that the vertex of the parabola is at the origin and its focus is on the positive y-axis. See Figure 18(b).

Figure 18

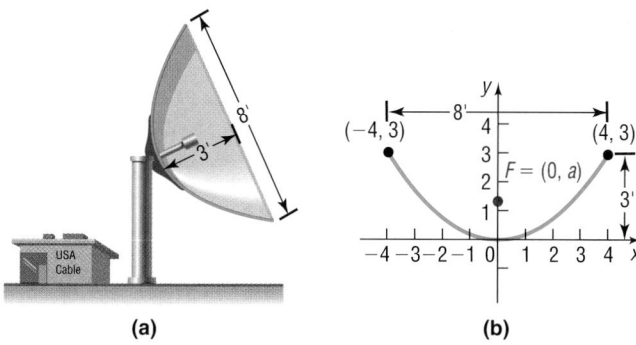

(a)   (b)

The form of the equation of the parabola is

$$x^2 = 4ay$$

and its focus is at $(0, a)$. Since $(4, 3)$ is a point on the graph, we have

$$4^2 = 4a(3) \quad \text{x = 4, y = 3}$$

$$a = \frac{4}{3} \quad \text{Solve for a.}$$

The receiver should be located $1\frac{1}{3}$ feet from the base of the dish, along its axis of symmetry.

Now Work PROBLEM 63

10.2 Assess Your Understanding

'Are You Prepared?' *Answers are given at the end of these exercises. If you get a wrong answer, read the pages listed in red.*

1. The formula for the distance d from $P_1 = (x_1, y_1)$ to $P_2 = (x_2, y_2)$ is $d = $ _____. (p. 5)

2. To complete the square of $x^2 - 4x$, add _____. (p. A52)

3. Use the Square Root Method to find the real solutions of $(x + 4)^2 = 9$. (p. A51)

4. The point that is symmetric with respect to the x-axis to the point $(-2, 5)$ is _____. (pp. 19–20)

5. To graph $y = (x - 3)^2 + 1$, shift the graph of $y = x^2$ to the right _____ units and then _____ 1 unit. (pp. 100–102)

Concepts and Vocabulary

6. A(n) _____ is the collection of all points in the plane such that the distance from each point to a fixed point equals its distance to a fixed line.

7. The surface formed by rotating a parabola about its axis of symmetry is called a _____ _____ _____.

8. **True or False** The vertex of a parabola is a point on the parabola that also is on its axis of symmetry.

9. **True or False** If a light is placed at the focus of a parabola, all the rays reflected off the parabola will be parallel to the axis of symmetry.

10. **True or False** The graph of a quadratic function is a parabola.

Skill Building

In Problems 11–18, the graph of a parabola is given. Match each graph to its equation.

(A) $y^2 = 4x$

(B) $x^2 = 4y$

(C) $y^2 = -4x$

(D) $x^2 = -4y$

(E) $(y - 1)^2 = 4(x - 1)$

(F) $(x + 1)^2 = 4(y + 1)$

(G) $(y - 1)^2 = -4(x - 1)$

(H) $(x + 1)^2 = -4(y + 1)$

11.

12.

13.

14.

15.

16.

17.

18.
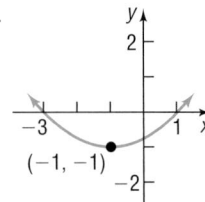

In Problems 19–36, find the equation of the parabola described. Find the two points that define the latus rectum, and graph the equation by hand.

19. Focus at $(4, 0)$; vertex at $(0, 0)$

20. Focus at $(0, 2)$; vertex at $(0, 0)$

21. Focus at $(0, -3)$; vertex at $(0, 0)$

22. Focus at $(-4, 0)$; vertex at $(0, 0)$

23. Focus at $(-2, 0)$; directrix the line $x = 2$

24. Focus at $(0, -1)$; directrix the line $y = 1$

25. Directrix the line $y = -\dfrac{1}{2}$; vertex at $(0, 0)$

26. Directrix the line $x = -\dfrac{1}{2}$; vertex at $(0, 0)$

27. Vertex at $(0, 0)$; axis of symmetry the y-axis; containing the point $(2, 3)$

28. Vertex at $(0, 0)$; axis of symmetry the x-axis; containing the point $(2, 3)$

29. Vertex at $(2, -3)$; focus at $(2, -5)$

30. Vertex at $(4, -2)$; focus at $(6, -2)$

31. Vertex at $(-1, -2)$; focus at $(0, -2)$

32. Vertex at $(3, 0)$; focus at $(3, -2)$

33. Focus at $(-3, 4)$; directrix the line $y = 2$

34. Focus at $(2, 4)$; directrix the line $x = -4$

35. Focus at $(-3, -2)$; directrix the line $x = 1$

36. Focus at $(-4, 4)$; directrix the line $y = -2$

In Problems 37–54, find the vertex, focus, and directrix of each parabola. Graph the equation by hand. Verify your graph using a graphing utility.

37. $x^2 = 4y$

38. $y^2 = 8x$

39. $y^2 = -16x$

40. $x^2 = -4y$

41. $(y - 2)^2 = 8(x + 1)$

42. $(x + 4)^2 = 16(y + 2)$

43. $(x - 3)^2 = -(y + 1)$

44. $(y + 1)^2 = -4(x - 2)$

45. $(y + 3)^2 = 8(x - 2)$

46. $(x - 2)^2 = 4(y - 3)$

47. $y^2 - 4y + 4x + 4 = 0$

48. $x^2 + 6x - 4y + 1 = 0$

49. $x^2 + 8x = 4y - 8$

50. $y^2 - 2y = 8x - 1$

51. $y^2 + 2y - x = 0$

52. $x^2 - 4x = 2y$

53. $x^2 - 4x = y + 4$

54. $y^2 + 12y = -x + 1$

In Problems 55–62, write an equation for each parabola.

55.

56.

57.

58.

59.

60.

61.

62.
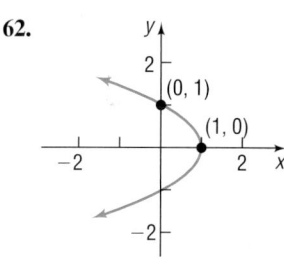

Applications and Extensions

63. Satellite Dish A satellite dish is shaped like a paraboloid of revolution. The signals that emanate from a satellite strike the surface of the dish and are reflected to a single point, where the receiver is located. If the dish is 10 feet across at its opening and 4 feet deep at its center, at what position should the receiver be placed?

64. Constructing a TV Dish A cable TV receiving dish is in the shape of a paraboloid of revolution. Find the location of the receiver, which is placed at the focus, if the dish is 6 feet across at its opening and 2 feet deep.

65. Constructing a Flashlight The reflector of a flashlight is in the shape of a paraboloid of revolution. Its diameter is 4 inches and its depth is 1 inch. How far from the vertex should the light bulb be placed so that the rays will be reflected parallel to the axis?

66. Constructing a Headlight A sealed-beam headlight is in the shape of a paraboloid of revolution. The bulb, which is placed at the focus, is 1 inch from the vertex. If the depth is to be 2 inches, what is the diameter of the headlight at its opening?

67. Suspension Bridge The cables of a suspension bridge are in the shape of a parabola, as shown in the figure. The towers supporting the cable are 600 feet apart and 80 feet high. If

the cables touch the road surface midway between the towers, what is the height of the cable from the road at a point 150 feet from the center of the bridge?

68. Suspension Bridge The cables of a suspension bridge are in the shape of a parabola. The towers supporting the cable are 400 feet apart and 100 feet high. If the cables are at a height of 10 feet midway between the towers, what is the height of the cable at a point 50 feet from the center of the bridge?

69. Searchlight A searchlight is shaped like a paraboloid of revolution. If the light source is located 2 feet from the base along the axis of symmetry and the opening is 5 feet across, how deep should the searchlight be?

70. Searchlight A searchlight is shaped like a paraboloid of revolution. If the light source is located 2 feet from the base along the axis of symmetry and the depth of the searchlight is 4 feet, what should the width of the opening be?

71. Solar Heat A mirror is shaped like a paraboloid of revolution and will be used to concentrate the rays of the sun at its focus, creating a heat source. See the figure. If the mirror is 20 feet across at its opening and is 6 feet deep, where will the heat source be concentrated?

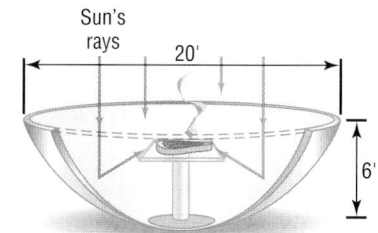

72. Reflecting Telescope A reflecting telescope contains a mirror shaped like a paraboloid of revolution. If the mirror is 4 inches across at its opening and is 3 inches deep, where will the collected light be concentrated?

73. Parabolic Arch Bridge A bridge is built in the shape of a parabolic arch. The bridge has a span of 120 feet and a maximum height of 25 feet. See the illustration. Choose a suitable rectangular coordinate system and find the height of the arch at distances of 10, 30, and 50 feet from the center.

74. Parabolic Arch Bridge A bridge is to be built in the shape of a parabolic arch and is to have a span of 100 feet. The height of the arch a distance of 40 feet from the center is to be 10 feet. Find the height of the arch at its center.

75. Gateway Arch The Gateway Arch in St. Louis is often mistaken to be parabolic is shape. In fact, it is a *catenary*, which has a more complicated formula than a parabola. The Arch is 625 feet high and 598 feet wide at its base.
   (a) Find the equation of a parabola with the same dimensions. Let x equal the horizontal distance from the center of the arc.
   (b) The table gives the height of the Arch at various widths; find the corresponding heights for the parabola found in part (a).

Width (ft)	Height (ft)
567	100
478	312.5
308	525

(c) Do the data support the notion that the Arch is in the shape of a parabola?
Source: Wikipedia, the free encyclopedia

76. Show that an equation of the form

$$Ax^2 + Ey = 0 \qquad A \neq 0, E \neq 0$$

is the equation of a parabola with vertex at $(0, 0)$ and axis of symmetry the y-axis. Find its focus and directrix.

77. Show that an equation of the form

$$Cy^2 + Dx = 0 \qquad C \neq 0, D \neq 0$$

is the equation of a parabola with vertex at $(0, 0)$ and axis of symmetry the x-axis. Find its focus and directrix.

78. Show that the graph of an equation of the form

$$Ax^2 + Dx + Ey + F = 0 \qquad A \neq 0$$

   (a) Is a parabola if $E \neq 0$.
   (b) Is a vertical line if $E = 0$ and $D^2 - 4AF = 0$.
   (c) Is two vertical lines if $E = 0$ and $D^2 - 4AF > 0$.
   (d) Contains no points if $E = 0$ and $D^2 - 4AF < 0$.

79. Show that the graph of an equation of the form

$$Cy^2 + Dx + Ey + F = 0 \qquad C \neq 0$$

   (a) Is a parabola if $D \neq 0$.
   (b) Is a horizontal line if $D = 0$ and $E^2 - 4CF = 0$.
   (c) Is two horizontal lines if $D = 0$ and $E^2 - 4CF > 0$.
   (d) Contains no points if $D = 0$ and $E^2 - 4CF < 0$.

'Are You Prepared?' Answers

1. $d = \sqrt{(x_2 - x_1)^2 + (y_2 - y_1)^2}$ **2.** 4 **3.** $x + 4 = \pm 3; \{-7, -1\}$ **4.** $(-2, -5)$ **5.** 3; up

10.3 The Ellipse

PREPARING FOR THIS SECTION *Before getting started, review the following:*

- Distance Formula (Section 1.1, p. 5)
- Completing the Square (Appendix A, Section A.6, pp. A52–A53)
- Intercepts (Section 1.2, pp. 18–19)
- Symmetry (Section 1.2, pp. 19–21)
- Circles (Section 1.5, pp. 44–48)
- Graphing Techniques: Transformations (Section 2.5, pp. 100–108)

Now Work the 'Are You Prepared?' problems on page 657.

OBJECTIVES **1** Analyze Ellipses with Center at the Origin (p. 649)
2 Analyze Ellipses with Center at (h, k) (p. 653)
3 Solve Applied Problems Involving Ellipses (p. 656)

DEFINITION   An **ellipse** is the set of all points P in the plane the sum of whose distances from two fixed points, called the **foci,** is a constant.

The definition contains within it a physical means for drawing an ellipse. Find a piece of string (the length of this string is the constant referred to in the definition). Then take two thumbtacks (the foci) and stick them into a piece of cardboard so that the distance between them is less than the length of the string. Now attach the ends of the string to the thumbtacks and, using the point of a pencil, pull the string taut. See Figure 19. Keeping the string taut, rotate the pencil around the two thumbtacks. The pencil traces out an ellipse, as shown in Figure 19.

In Figure 19, the foci are labeled F_1 and F_2. The line containing the foci is called the **major axis**. The midpoint of the line segment joining the foci is the **center** of the ellipse. The line through the center and perpendicular to the major axis is the **minor axis**.

The two points of intersection of the ellipse and the major axis are the **vertices,** V_1 and V_2, of the ellipse. The distance from one vertex to the other is the **length of the major axis.** The ellipse is symmetric with respect to its major axis, with respect to its minor axis, and with respect to its center.

Figure 19

Figure 20

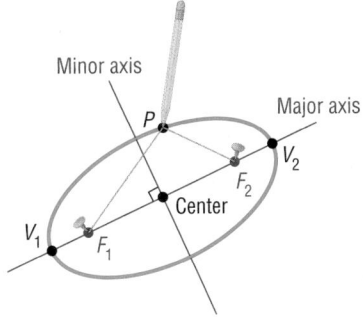

1   Analyze Ellipses with Center at the Origin

With these ideas in mind, we are now ready to find the equation of an ellipse in a rectangular coordinate system. First, we place the center of the ellipse at the origin. Second, we position the ellipse so that its major axis coincides with a coordinate axis. Suppose that the major axis coincides with the x-axis, as shown in Figure 20. If c is the distance from the center to a focus, one focus will be at $F_1 = (-c, 0)$ and the other at $F_2 = (c, 0)$. As we shall see, it is convenient to let $2a$ denote the constant distance referred to in the definition. Then, if $P = (x, y)$ is any point on the ellipse, we have

$$d(F_1, P) + d(F_2, P) = 2a$$ Sum of the distances from P to the foci equals a constant, $2a$.

$$\sqrt{(x + c)^2 + (y - 0)^2} + \sqrt{(x - c)^2 + (y - 0)^2} = 2a$$ Use the Distance Formula.

$$\sqrt{(x + c)^2 + y^2} = 2a - \sqrt{(x - c)^2 + y^2}$$ Isolate one radical.

$$(x + c)^2 + y^2 = 4a^2 - 4a\sqrt{(x - c)^2 + y^2} + (x - c)^2 + y^2$$ Square both sides.

$$x^2 + 2cx + c^2 + y^2 = 4a^2 - 4a\sqrt{(x - c)^2 + y^2} + x^2 - 2cx + c^2 + y^2$$ Remove parentheses.

$$4cx - 4a^2 = -4a\sqrt{(x - c)^2 + y^2}$$ Simplify; isolate the radical.

$$cx - a^2 = -a\sqrt{(x - c)^2 + y^2}$$ Divide each side by 4.

$$(cx - a^2)^2 = a^2[(x - c)^2 + y^2]$$ Square both sides again.

$$c^2x^2 - 2a^2cx + a^4 = a^2(x^2 - 2cx + c^2 + y^2)$$ Remove parentheses.

$$(c^2 - a^2)x^2 - a^2y^2 = a^2c^2 - a^4$$ Rearrange the terms.

$$(a^2 - c^2)x^2 + a^2y^2 = a^2(a^2 - c^2)$$ Multiply each side by -1;   **(1)** factor a^2 on the right side.

To obtain points on the ellipse off the x-axis, it must be that $a > c$. To see why, look again at Figure 20. Then

$$d(F_1, P) + d(F_2, P) > d(F_1, F_2)$$ The sum of the lengths of two sides of a triangle is greater than the length of the third side.

$$2a > 2c$$ $d(F_1, P) + d(F_2, P) = 2a$, $d(F_1, F_2) = 2c$

$$a > c$$

Since $a > c$, we also have $a^2 > c^2$, so $a^2 - c^2 > 0$. Let $b^2 = a^2 - c^2, b > 0$. Then $a > b$ and equation (1) can be written as

$$b^2x^2 + a^2y^2 = a^2b^2$$

$$\frac{x^2}{a^2} + \frac{y^2}{b^2} = 1 \qquad \text{Divide each side by } a^2b^2.$$

As you can verify, this equation is symmetric with respect to the x-axis, y-axis, and origin.

Because the major axis is the x-axis, we find the vertices of this ellipse by letting $y = 0$. The vertices satisfy the equation $\frac{x^2}{a^2} = 1$, the solutions of which are $x = \pm a$. Consequently, the vertices of this ellipse are $V_1 = (-a, 0)$ and $V_2 = (a, 0)$. The y-intercepts of the ellipse, found by letting $x = 0$, have coordinates $(0, -b)$ and $(0, b)$. These four intercepts, $(a, 0)$, $(-a, 0)$, $(0, b)$, and $(0, -b)$, are used to graph the ellipse.

Figure 21

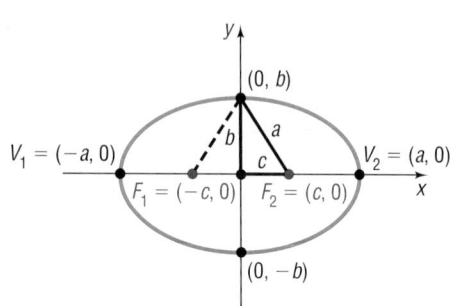

THEOREM

Equation of an Ellipse: Center at (0, 0); Major Axis along the x-Axis

An equation of the ellipse with center at $(0, 0)$, foci at $(-c, 0)$ and $(c, 0)$, and vertices at $(-a, 0)$ and $(a, 0)$ is

$$\frac{x^2}{a^2} + \frac{y^2}{b^2} = 1 \qquad \text{where } a > b > 0 \text{ and } b^2 = a^2 - c^2 \qquad \textbf{(2)}$$

The major axis is the x-axis. See Figure 21.

Notice in Figure 21 the right triangle formed with the points $(0, 0)$, $(c, 0)$, and $(0, b)$. Because $b^2 = a^2 - c^2$ (or $b^2 + c^2 = a^2$), the distance from the focus at $(c, 0)$ to the point $(0, b)$ is a.

This can be seen another way. Look at the two right triangles in Figure 21. They are congruent. Do you see why? Because the sum of the distances from the foci to a point on the ellipse is $2a$, it follows that the distance from $(c, 0)$ to $(0, b)$ is a.

EXAMPLE 1 Finding an Equation of an Ellipse

Find an equation of the ellipse with center at the origin, one focus at $(3, 0)$, and a vertex at $(-4, 0)$. Graph the equation.

Figure 22

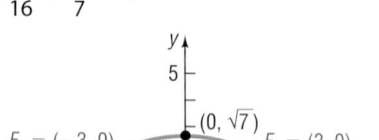

Solution The ellipse has its center at the origin and, since the given focus and vertex lie on the x-axis, the major axis is the x-axis. The distance from the center, $(0, 0)$, to one of the foci, $(3, 0)$, is $c = 3$. The distance from the center, $(0, 0)$, to one of the vertices, $(-4, 0)$, is $a = 4$. Because the center is the origin, the other focus is $(-3, 0)$ and the other vertex is $(4, 0)$. With $a = 4$ and $c = 3$, from equation (2), it follows that

$$b^2 = a^2 - c^2 = 16 - 9 = 7$$

so an equation of the ellipse is

$$\frac{x^2}{16} + \frac{y^2}{7} = 1$$

The y-intercepts are $(0, \pm b) = (0, \pm\sqrt{7})$. Figure 22 shows the graph.

Notice in Figure 22 how we used the intercepts of the equation to graph the ellipse. Following this practice will make it easier for you to obtain an accurate graph of an ellipse when graphing by hand. The intercepts also tell you how to set the initial viewing window when using a graphing utility.

➡ **Now Work** PROBLEM 27

| EXAMPLE 2 | Graphing an Ellipse Using a Graphing Utility |

Use a graphing utility to graph the ellipse $\dfrac{x^2}{16} + \dfrac{y^2}{7} = 1$.

Solution   First, we must solve $\dfrac{x^2}{16} + \dfrac{y^2}{7} = 1$ for y.

Figure 23

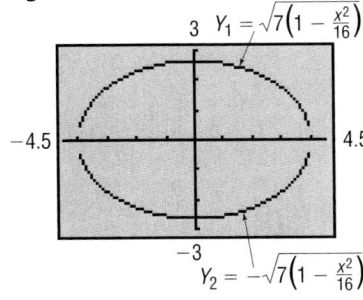

$$\frac{y^2}{7} = 1 - \frac{x^2}{16} \qquad \text{Subtract } \frac{x^2}{16} \text{ from each side.}$$

$$y^2 = 7\left(1 - \frac{x^2}{16}\right) \qquad \text{Multiply both sides by 7.}$$

$$y = \pm\sqrt{7\left(1 - \frac{x^2}{16}\right)} \qquad \text{Apply the Square Root Method.}$$

Figure 23* shows the graphs of $Y_1 = \sqrt{7\left(1 - \dfrac{x^2}{16}\right)}$ and $Y_2 = -\sqrt{7\left(1 - \dfrac{x^2}{16}\right)}$.

Notice in Figure 23 that we used a square screen. As with circles and parabolas, this is done to avoid a distorted view of the graph.

An equation of the form of equation (2), with $a > b$, is the equation of an ellipse with center at the origin, foci on the x-axis at $(-c, 0)$ and $(c, 0)$, where $c^2 = a^2 - b^2$, and major axis along the x-axis.

For the remainder of this section, the direction **"Analyze the equation"** will mean to find the center, major axis, foci, and vertices of the ellipse and graph it.

| EXAMPLE 3 | Analyzing the Equation of an Ellipse |

Analyze the equation: $\dfrac{x^2}{25} + \dfrac{y^2}{9} = 1$

Solution   The given equation is of the form of equation (2), with $a^2 = 25$ and $b^2 = 9$. The equation is that of an ellipse with center $(0, 0)$ and major axis along the x-axis. The vertices are at $(\pm a, 0) = (\pm 5, 0)$. Because $b^2 = a^2 - c^2$, we find that

$$c^2 = a^2 - b^2 = 25 - 9 = 16$$

The foci are at $(\pm c, 0) = (\pm 4, 0)$. The y-intercepts are $(0, \pm b) = (0, \pm 3)$. Figure 24(a) shows the graph drawn by hand. Figure 24(b) shows the graph obtained using a graphing utility.

Figure 24

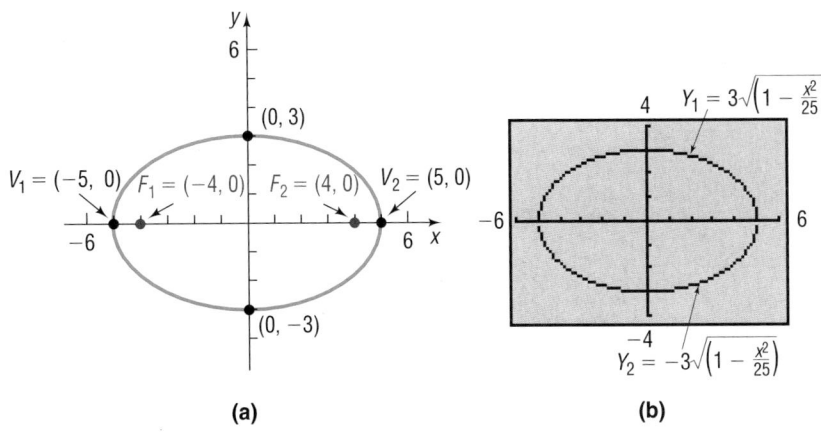

(a)   (b)

Now Work PROBLEM 17

*The initial viewing window selected was $X\min = -4$, $X\max = 4$, $Y\min = -3$, $Y\max = 3$. Then we used the ZOOM-SQUARE option to obtain the window shown.

If the major axis of an ellipse with center at $(0, 0)$ lies on the y-axis, then the foci are at $(0, -c)$ and $(0, c)$. Using the same steps as before, the definition of an ellipse leads to the following result:

THEOREM

Equation of an Ellipse; Center at (0, 0); Major Axis along the y-Axis

An equation of the ellipse with center at $(0, 0)$, foci at $(0, -c)$ and $(0, c)$, and vertices at $(0, -a)$ and $(0, a)$ is

$$\frac{x^2}{b^2} + \frac{y^2}{a^2} = 1 \qquad \text{where } a > b > 0 \text{ and } b^2 = a^2 - c^2 \qquad \textbf{(3)}$$

The major axis is the y-axis.

Figure 25

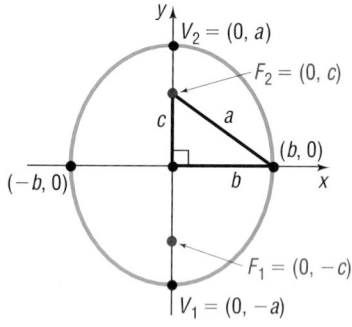

Figure 25 illustrates the graph of such an ellipse. Again, notice the right triangle with the points at $(0, 0)$, $(b, 0)$, and $(0, c)$.

Look closely at equations (2) and (3). Although they may look alike, there is a difference! In equation (2), the larger number, a^2, is in the denominator of the x^2-term, so the major axis of the ellipse is along the x-axis. In equation (3), the larger number, a^2, is in the denominator of the y^2-term, so the major axis is along the y-axis.

EXAMPLE 4

Analyzing the Equation of an Ellipse

Analyze the equation: $9x^2 + y^2 = 9$

Solution

To put the equation in proper form, we divide each side by 9.

$$x^2 + \frac{y^2}{9} = 1$$

The larger number, 9, is in the denominator of the y^2 term so, based on equation (3), this is the equation of an ellipse with center at the origin and major axis along the y-axis. Also, we conclude that $a^2 = 9$, $b^2 = 1$, and $c^2 = a^2 - b^2 = 9 - 1 = 8$. The vertices are at $(0, \pm a) = (0, \pm 3)$, and the foci are at $(0, \pm c) = (0, \pm 2\sqrt{2})$. The x-intercepts are at $(\pm b, 0) = (\pm 1, 0)$. Figure 26(a) shows the graph drawn by hand. Figure 26(b) shows the graph obtained using a graphing utility.

Figure 26

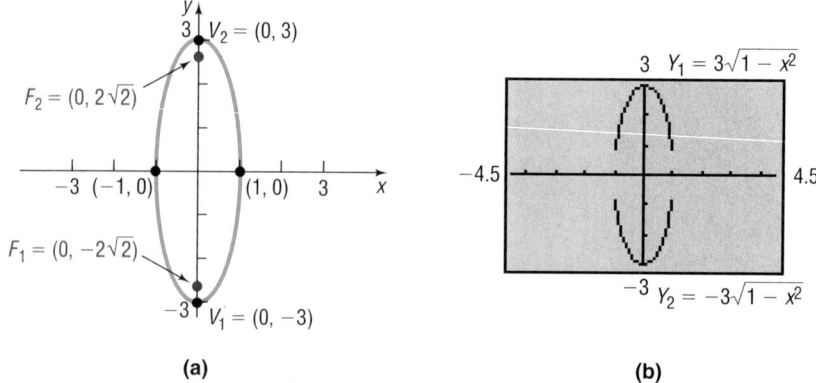

(a)   (b)

Now Work PROBLEM 21

| EXAMPLE 5 | Finding an Equation of an Ellipse |

Find an equation of the ellipse having one focus at $(0, 2)$ and vertices at $(0, -3)$ and $(0, 3)$. Graph the equation by hand.

Solution

Figure 27

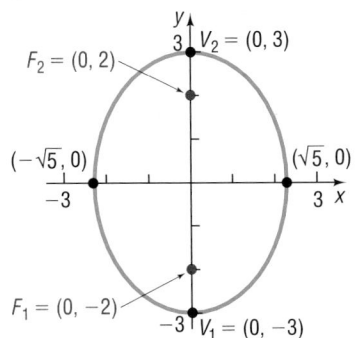

Because the vertices are at $(0, -3)$ and $(0, 3)$, the center of this ellipse is at their midpoint, the origin. The vertices and foci lie on the y-axis, so the major axis lies on the y-axis. The distance from the center, $(0, 0)$, to one of the foci, $(0, 2)$, is $c = 2$. The distance from the center, $(0, 0)$, to one of the vertices, $(0, 3)$, is $a = 3$. So $b^2 = a^2 - c^2 = 9 - 4 = 5$. The form of the equation of this ellipse is given by equation (3).

$$\frac{x^2}{b^2} + \frac{y^2}{a^2} = 1$$

$$\frac{x^2}{5} + \frac{y^2}{9} = 1$$

Figure 27 shows the graph.

━━ **Now Work** PROBLEM 29

The circle may be considered a special kind of ellipse. To see why, let $a = b$ in equation (2) or (3). Then

$$\frac{x^2}{a^2} + \frac{y^2}{a^2} = 1$$

$$x^2 + y^2 = a^2$$

This is the equation of a circle with center at the origin and radius a. The value of c is

$$c^2 = a^2 - b^2 = 0$$

We conclude that the closer the two foci of an ellipse are to the center the more the ellipse will look like a circle.

2 Analyze Ellipses with Center at (h, k)

If an ellipse with center at the origin and major axis coinciding with a coordinate axis is shifted horizontally h units and then vertically k units, the result is an ellipse with center at (h, k) and major axis parallel to a coordinate axis. The equations of such ellipses have the same forms as those given in equations (2) and (3), except that x is replaced by $x - h$ (the horizontal shift) and y is replaced by $y - k$ (the vertical shift). Table 3 gives the forms of the equations of such ellipses and Figure 28 on the next page shows their graphs.

Table 3

ELLIPSES WITH CENTER AT (h, k) AND MAJOR AXIS PARALLEL TO A COORDINATE AXIS				
Center	**Major Axis**	**Foci**	**Vertices**	**Equation**
(h, k)	Parallel to x-axis	$(h + c, k)$	$(h + a, k)$	$\dfrac{(x - h)^2}{a^2} + \dfrac{(y - k)^2}{b^2} = 1,$
		$(h - c, k)$	$(h - a, k)$	$a > b$ and $b^2 = a^2 - c^2$
(h, k)	Parallel to y-axis	$(h, k + c)$	$(h, k + a)$	$\dfrac{(x - h)^2}{b^2} + \dfrac{(y - k)^2}{a^2} = 1,$
		$(h, k - c)$	$(h, k - a)$	$a > b$ and $b^2 = a^2 - c^2$

Figure 28

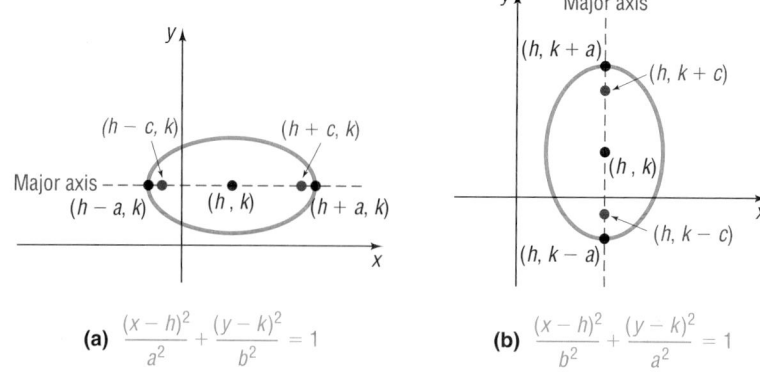

(a) $\dfrac{(x-h)^2}{a^2} + \dfrac{(y-k)^2}{b^2} = 1$

(b) $\dfrac{(x-h)^2}{b^2} + \dfrac{(y-k)^2}{a^2} = 1$

EXAMPLE 6	**Finding an Equation of an Ellipse, Center Not at the Origin**

Find an equation for the ellipse with center at $(2, -3)$, one focus at $(3, -3)$, and one vertex at $(5, -3)$. Graph the equation by hand.

Solution   The center is at $(h, k) = (2, -3)$, so $h = 2$ and $k = -3$. Since the center, focus, and vertex all lie on the line $y = -3$, the major axis is parallel to the x-axis. The distance from the center $(2, -3)$ to a focus $(3, -3)$ is $c = 1$; the distance from the center $(2, -3)$ to a vertex $(5, -3)$ is $a = 3$. Then $b^2 = a^2 - c^2 = 9 - 1 = 8$. The form of the equation is

$$\frac{(x-h)^2}{a^2} + \frac{(y-k)^2}{b^2} = 1 \qquad \text{where } h = 2, k = -3, a = 3, b = 2\sqrt{2}$$

$$\frac{(x-2)^2}{9} + \frac{(y+3)^2}{8} = 1$$

To graph the equation, we use the center $(h, k) = (2, -3)$ to locate the vertices. The major axis is parallel to the x-axis, so the vertices are $a = 3$ units left and right of the center $(2, -3)$. Therefore, the vertices are

$$V_1 = (2 - 3, -3) = (-1, -3) \quad \text{and} \quad V_2 = (2 + 3, -3) = (5, -3)$$

Figure 29

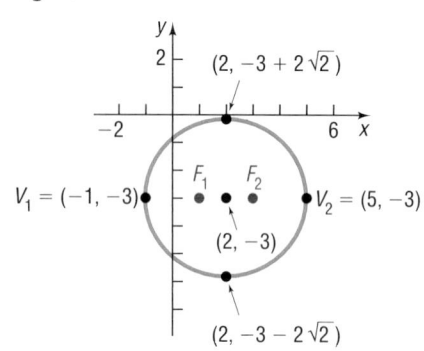

Since $c = 1$ and the major axis is parallel to the x-axis, the foci are 1 unit left and right of the center. Therefore, the foci are

$$F_1 = (2 - 1, -3) = (1, -3) \quad \text{and} \quad F_2 = (2 + 1, -3) = (3, -3)$$

Finally, we use the value of $b = 2\sqrt{2}$ to find the two points above and below the center.

$$\left(2, -3 - 2\sqrt{2}\right) \quad \text{and} \quad \left(2, -3 + 2\sqrt{2}\right)$$

Figure 29 shows the graph.

➤ **Now Work**   PROBLEM 55

EXAMPLE 7	**Using a Graphing Utility to Graph an Ellipse,** **Center Not at the Origin**

Using a graphing utility, graph the ellipse: $\dfrac{(x-2)^2}{9} + \dfrac{(y+3)^2}{8} = 1$

Solution   First, we must solve the equation $\dfrac{(x-2)^2}{9} + \dfrac{(y+3)^2}{8} = 1$ for y.

$$\frac{(y+3)^2}{8} = 1 - \frac{(x-2)^2}{9} \qquad \text{Subtract } \frac{(x-2)^2}{9} \text{ from each side.}$$

$$(y+3)^2 = 8\left[1 - \frac{(x-2)^2}{9}\right] \qquad \text{Multiply each side by 8.}$$

$$y + 3 = \pm\sqrt{8\left[1 - \frac{(x-2)^2}{9}\right]} \qquad \text{Apply the Square Root Method.}$$

$$y = -3 \pm \sqrt{8\left[1 - \frac{(x-2)^2}{9}\right]} \qquad \text{Subtract 3 from each side.}$$

Figure 30 shows the graphs of $Y_1 = -3 + \sqrt{8\left[1 - \dfrac{(x-2)^2}{9}\right]}$ and $Y_2 = -3 - \sqrt{8\left[1 - \dfrac{(x-2)^2}{9}\right]}$.

Figure 30

$$1 \quad Y_1 = -3 + \sqrt{8\left(1 - \frac{(x-2)^2}{9}\right)}$$

-3.3   7.3

$$-6 \quad Y_2 = -3 - \sqrt{8\left(1 - \frac{(x-2)^2}{9}\right)}$$

EXAMPLE 8   **Analyzing the Equation of an Ellipse**

Analyze the equation: $4x^2 + y^2 - 8x + 4y + 4 = 0$

Solution   We proceed to complete the squares in x and in y.

$$4x^2 + y^2 - 8x + 4y + 4 = 0$$

$$4x^2 - 8x + y^2 + 4y = -4 \qquad \text{Group like variables; place the constant on the right side.}$$

$$4(x^2 - 2x) + (y^2 + 4y) = -4 \qquad \text{Factor out 4 from the first two terms.}$$

$$4(x^2 - 2x + 1) + (y^2 + 4y + 4) = -4 + 4 + 4 \qquad \text{Complete each square.}$$

$$4(x-1)^2 + (y+2)^2 = 4 \qquad \text{Factor.}$$

$$(x-1)^2 + \frac{(y+2)^2}{4} = 1 \qquad \text{Divide each side by 4.}$$

This is the equation of an ellipse with center at $(1, -2)$ and major axis parallel to the y-axis. Since $a^2 = 4$ and $b^2 = 1$, we have $c^2 = a^2 - b^2 = 4 - 1 = 3$. The vertices are at $(h, k \pm a) = (1, -2 \pm 2)$ or $(1, 0)$ and $(1, -4)$. The foci are at $(h, k \pm c) = (1, -2 \pm \sqrt{3})$ or $(1, -2 - \sqrt{3})$ and $(1, -2 + \sqrt{3})$. Figure 31(a) shows the graph drawn by hand. Figure 31(b) shows the graph obtained using a graphing utility.

Figure 31

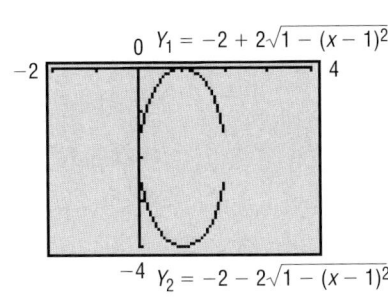

(a)

$$0 \quad Y_1 = -2 + 2\sqrt{1 - (x-1)^2}$$

-2   4

$$-4 \quad Y_2 = -2 - 2\sqrt{1 - (x-1)^2}$$

(b)

Now Work   PROBLEM 47

3 Solve Applied Problems Involving Ellipses

Ellipses are found in many applications in science and engineering. For example, the orbits of the planets around the Sun are elliptical, with the Sun's position at a focus. See Figure 32.

Figure 32

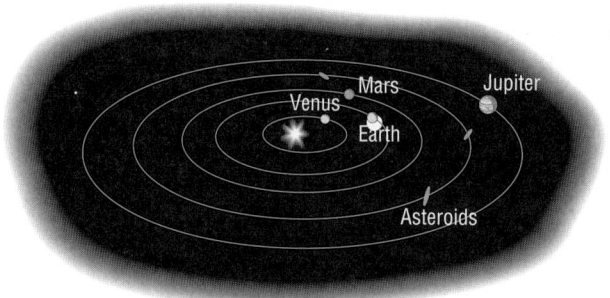

Stone and concrete bridges are often shaped as semielliptical arches. Elliptical gears are used in machinery when a variable rate of motion is required.

Ellipses also have an interesting reflection property. If a source of light (or sound) is placed at one focus, the waves transmitted by the source will reflect off the ellipse and concentrate at the other focus. This is the principle behind *whispering galleries*, which are rooms designed with elliptical ceilings. A person standing at one focus of the ellipse can whisper and be heard by a person standing at the other focus, because all the sound waves that reach the ceiling are reflected to the other person.

| EXAMPLE 9 | A Whispering Gallery |

The whispering gallery in the Museum of Science and Industry in Chicago is 47.3 feet long. The distance from the center of the room to the foci is 20.3 feet. Find an equation that describes the shape of the room. How high is the room at its center?

Source: Chicago Museum of Science and Industry Web site; www.msichicago.org

Solution   We set up a rectangular coordinate system so that the center of the ellipse is at the origin and the major axis is along the *x*-axis. The equation of the ellipse is

$$\frac{x^2}{a^2} + \frac{y^2}{b^2} = 1$$

Since the length of the room is 47.3 feet, the distance from the center of the room to each vertex (the end of the room) will be $\dfrac{47.3}{2} = 23.65$ feet; so $a = 23.65$ feet. The distance from the center of the room to each focus is $c = 20.3$ feet. See Figure 33.

Since $b^2 = a^2 - c^2$, we find $b^2 = 23.65^2 - 20.3^2 = 147.2325$. An equation that describes the shape of the room is given by

$$\frac{x^2}{23.65^2} + \frac{y^2}{147.2325} = 1$$

The height of the room at its center is $b = \sqrt{147.2325} \approx 12.1$ feet.

Figure 33

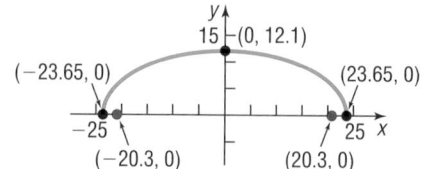

━━ **Now Work** PROBLEM 71

10.3 Assess Your Understanding

'Are You Prepared?' *Answers are given at the end of these exercises. If you get a wrong answer, read the pages listed in red.*

1. The distance d from $P_1 = (2, -5)$ to $P_2 = (4, -2)$ is $d =$ _____. (pp. 4–6)

2. To complete the square of $x^2 - 3x$, add _____. (p. A52)

3. Find the intercepts of the equation $y^2 = 16 - 4x^2$. (pp. 18–19)

4. The point that is symmetric with respect to the y-axis to the point $(-2, 5)$ is _____. (pp. 19–20)

5. To graph $y = (x + 1)^2 - 4$, shift the graph of $y = x^2$ to the (left/right) _____ unit(s) and then (up/down) _____ unit(s). (pp. 100–102)

6. The standard equation of a circle with center at $(2, -3)$ and radius 1 is _____. (pp. 44–45)

Concepts and Vocabulary

7. A(n) _____ is the collection of all points in the plane the sum of whose distances from two fixed points is a constant.

8. For an ellipse, the foci lie on a line called the _____ axis.

9. For the ellipse $\dfrac{x^2}{4} + \dfrac{y^2}{25} = 1$, the vertices are the points _____ and _____.

10. *True or False* The foci, vertices, and center of an ellipse lie on a line called the axis of symmetry.

11. *True or False* If the center of an ellipse is at the origin and the foci lie on the y-axis, the ellipse is symmetric with respect to the x-axis, the y-axis, and the origin.

12. *True or False* A circle is a certain type of ellipse.

Skill Building

In Problems 13–16, the graph of an ellipse is given. Match each graph to its equation.

(A) $\dfrac{x^2}{4} + y^2 = 1$ (B) $x^2 + \dfrac{y^2}{4} = 1$ (C) $\dfrac{x^2}{16} + \dfrac{y^2}{4} = 1$ (D) $\dfrac{x^2}{4} + \dfrac{y^2}{16} = 1$

13.

14.

15.

16.
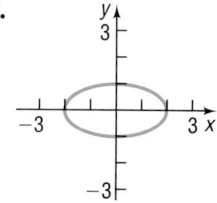

In Problems 17–26, find the vertices and foci of each ellipse. Graph each equation by hand. Verify your graph using a graphing utility.

17. $\dfrac{x^2}{25} + \dfrac{y^2}{4} = 1$

18. $\dfrac{x^2}{9} + \dfrac{y^2}{4} = 1$

19. $\dfrac{x^2}{9} + \dfrac{y^2}{25} = 1$

20. $x^2 + \dfrac{y^2}{16} = 1$

21. $4x^2 + y^2 = 16$

22. $x^2 + 9y^2 = 18$

23. $4y^2 + x^2 = 8$

24. $4y^2 + 9x^2 = 36$

25. $x^2 + y^2 = 16$

26. $x^2 + y^2 = 4$

In Problems 27–38, find an equation for each ellipse. Graph the equation by hand.

27. Center at $(0, 0)$; focus at $(3, 0)$; vertex at $(5, 0)$

28. Center at $(0, 0)$; focus at $(-1, 0)$; vertex at $(3, 0)$

29. Center at $(0, 0)$; focus at $(0, -4)$; vertex at $(0, 5)$

30. Center at $(0, 0)$; focus at $(0, 1)$; vertex at $(0, -2)$

31. Foci at $(\pm 2, 0)$; length of the major axis is 6

32. Foci at $(0, \pm 2)$; length of the major axis is 8

33. Focus at $(-4, 0)$; vertices at $(\pm 5, 0)$

34. Focus at $(0, -4)$; vertices at $(0, \pm 8)$

35. Foci at $(0, \pm 3)$; x-intercepts are ± 2

36. Vertices at $(\pm 4, 0)$; y-intercepts are ± 1

37. Center at $(0, 0)$; vertex at $(0, 4)$; $b = 1$

38. Vertices at $(\pm 5, 0)$; $c = 2$

In Problems 39–42, write an equation for each ellipse.

39.

40.

41.

42.
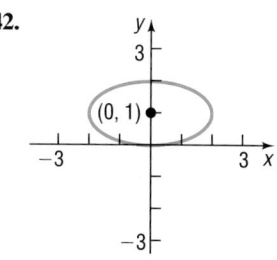

In Problems 43–54, analyze each equation; that is, find the center, foci, and vertices of each ellipse. Graph each equation by hand. Verify your graph using a graphing utility.

43. $\dfrac{(x-3)^2}{4} + \dfrac{(y+1)^2}{9} = 1$

44. $\dfrac{(x+4)^2}{9} + \dfrac{(y+2)^2}{4} = 1$

45. $(x+5)^2 + 4(y-4)^2 = 16$

46. $9(x-3)^2 + (y+2)^2 = 18$

47. $x^2 + 4x + 4y^2 - 8y + 4 = 0$

48. $x^2 + 3y^2 - 12y + 9 = 0$

49. $2x^2 + 3y^2 - 8x + 6y + 5 = 0$

50. $4x^2 + 3y^2 + 8x - 6y = 5$

51. $9x^2 + 4y^2 - 18x + 16y - 11 = 0$

52. $x^2 + 9y^2 + 6x - 18y + 9 = 0$

53. $4x^2 + y^2 + 4y = 0$

54. $9x^2 + y^2 - 18x = 0$

In Problems 55–64, find an equation for each ellipse. Graph the equation by hand.

55. Center at $(2, -2)$; vertex at $(7, -2)$; focus at $(4, -2)$

56. Center at $(-3, 1)$; vertex at $(-3, 3)$; focus at $(-3, 0)$

57. Vertices at $(4, 3)$ and $(4, 9)$; focus at $(4, 8)$

58. Foci at $(1, 2)$ and $(-3, 2)$; vertex at $(-4, 2)$

59. Foci at $(5, 1)$ and $(-1, 1)$; length of the major axis is 8

60. Vertices at $(2, 5)$ and $(2, -1)$; $c = 2$

61. Center at $(1, 2)$; focus at $(4, 2)$; contains the point $(1, 3)$

62. Center at $(1, 2)$; focus at $(1, 4)$; contains the point $(2, 2)$

63. Center at $(1, 2)$; vertex at $(4, 2)$; contains the point $(1, 3)$

64. Center at $(1, 2)$; vertex at $(1, 4)$; contains the point $(2, 2)$

In Problems 65–68, graph each function. Be sure to label all the intercepts.
[Hint: *Notice that each function is half an ellipse.***]**

65. $f(x) = \sqrt{16 - 4x^2}$

66. $f(x) = \sqrt{9 - 9x^2}$

67. $f(x) = -\sqrt{64 - 16x^2}$

68. $f(x) = -\sqrt{4 - 4x^2}$

Applications and Extensions

69. Semielliptical Arch Bridge An arch in the shape of the upper half of an ellipse is used to support a bridge that is to span a river 20 meters wide. The center of the arch is 6 meters above the center of the river. See the figure. Write an equation for the ellipse in which the x-axis coincides with the water level and the y-axis passes through the center of the arch.

70. Semielliptical Arch Bridge The arch of a bridge is a semi-ellipse with a horizontal major axis. The span is 30 feet, and the top of the arch is 10 feet above the major axis. The roadway is horizontal and is 2 feet above the top of the arch. Find the vertical distance from the roadway to the arch at 5-foot intervals along the roadway.

71. Whispering Gallery A hall 100 feet in length is to be designed as a whispering gallery. If the foci are located 25 feet from the center, how high will the ceiling be at the center?

72. Whispering Gallery Jim, standing at one focus of a whispering gallery, is 6 feet from the nearest wall. His friend is standing at the other focus, 100 feet away. What is the length of this whispering gallery? How high is its elliptical ceiling at the center?

73. Semielliptical Arch Bridge A bridge is built in the shape of a semielliptical arch. The bridge has a span of 120 feet and a maximum height of 25 feet. Choose a suitable rectangular coordinate system and find the height of the arch at distances of 10, 30, and 50 feet from the center.

74. Semielliptical Arch Bridge A bridge is to be built in the shape of a semielliptical arch and is to have a span of 100 feet.

The height of the arch, at a distance of 40 feet from the center, is to be 10 feet. Find the height of the arch at its center.

75. Racetrack Design Consult the figure. A racetrack is in the shape of an ellipse, 100 feet long and 50 feet wide. What is the width 10 feet from a vertex?

76. Semielliptical Arch Bridge An arch for a bridge over a highway is in the form of half an ellipse. The top of the arch is 20 feet above the ground level (the major axis). The highway has four lanes, each 12 feet wide; a center safety strip 8 feet wide; and two side strips, each 4 feet wide. What should the span of the bridge be (the length of its major axis) if the height 28 feet from the center is to be 13 feet?

77. Installing a Vent Pipe A homeowner is putting in a fireplace that has a 4-inch-radius vent pipe. He needs to cut an elliptical hole in his roof to accommodate the pipe. If the pitch of his roof is $\dfrac{5}{4}$ (a rise of 5, run of 4), what are the dimensions of the hole?

Source: www.pen.k12.va.us

78. Volume of a Football A football is in the shape of a **prolate spheroid**, which is simply a solid obtained by rotating an ellipse $\left(\dfrac{x^2}{a^2} + \dfrac{y^2}{b^2} = 1 \right)$ about its major axis. An inflated NFL football averages 11.125 inches in length and 28.25 inches in center circumference. If the volume of a prolate spheroid is $\dfrac{4}{3}\pi ab^2$, how much air does the football contain? (Neglect material thickness.)

Source: www.answerbag.com

*In Problems 79–82, use the fact that the orbit of a planet about the Sun is an ellipse, with the Sun at one focus. The **aphelion** of a planet is its greatest distance from the Sun, and the **perihelion** is its shortest distance. The **mean distance** of a planet from the Sun is the length of the semimajor axis of the elliptical orbit. See the illustration.*

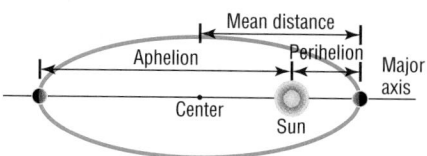

79. Earth The mean distance of Earth from the Sun is 93 million miles. If the aphelion of Earth is 94.5 million miles, what is the perihelion? Write an equation for the orbit of Earth around the Sun.

80. Mars The mean distance of Mars from the Sun is 142 million miles. If the perihelion of Mars is 128.5 million miles, what is the aphelion? Write an equation for the orbit of Mars about the Sun.

81. Jupiter The aphelion of Jupiter is 507 million miles. If the distance from the center of its elliptical orbit to the Sun is 23.2 million miles, what is the perihelion? What is the mean distance? Write an equation for the orbit of Jupiter around the Sun.

82. Pluto The perihelion of Pluto is 4551 million miles, and the distance from the center of its elliptical orbit to the Sun is 897.5 million miles. Find the aphelion of Pluto. What is the mean distance of Pluto from the Sun? Write an equation for the orbit of Pluto about the Sun.

83. Show that an equation of the form
$$Ax^2 + Cy^2 + F = 0 \qquad A \neq 0, C \neq 0, F \neq 0$$
where A and C are of the same sign and F is of opposite sign,
(a) Is the equation of an ellipse with center at $(0, 0)$ if $A \neq C$.
(b) Is the equation of a circle with center $(0, 0)$ if $A = C$.

84. Show that the graph of an equation of the form
$$Ax^2 + Cy^2 + Dx + Ey + F = 0 \qquad A \neq 0, C \neq 0$$
where A and C are of the same sign,
(a) Is an ellipse if $\dfrac{D^2}{4A} + \dfrac{E^2}{4C} - F$ is the same sign as A.
(b) Is a point if $\dfrac{D^2}{4A} + \dfrac{E^2}{4C} - F = 0$.
(c) Contains no points if $\dfrac{D^2}{4A} + \dfrac{E^2}{4C} - F$ is of opposite sign to A.

Discussion and Writing

85. The **eccentricity** e of an ellipse is defined as the number $\dfrac{c}{a}$, where a and c are the numbers given in equation (2). Because $a > c$, it follows that $e < 1$. Write a brief paragraph about the general shape of each of the following ellipses. Be sure to justify your conclusions.
(a) Eccentricity close to 0   (b) Eccentricity = 0.5   (c) Eccentricity close to 1

'Are You Prepared?' Answers

1. $\sqrt{13}$ **2.** $\dfrac{9}{4}$ **3.** $(-2, 0), (2, 0), (0, -4), (0, 4)$ **4.** $(2, 5)$ **5.** left; 1; down: 4   **6.** $(x - 2)^2 + (y + 3)^2 = 1$

10.4 The Hyperbola

PREPARING FOR THIS SECTION   *Before getting started, review the following:*

- Distance Formula (Section 1.1, p. 5)
- Completing the Square (Appendix A, Section A.6, pp. A52–A53)
- Intercepts (Section 1.2, pp. 18–19)
- Symmetry (Section 1.2, pp. 19–21)
- Asymptotes (Section 4.2, pp. 194–199)
- Graphing Techniques: Transformations (Section 2.5, pp. 100–108)
- Square Root Method (Appendix A, Section A.6, p. A51)

Now Work the 'Are You Prepared?' problems on page 670.

OBJECTIVES 1 Analyze Hyperbolas with Center at the Origin (p. 660)
2 Find the Asymptotes of a Hyperbola (p. 665)
3 Analyze Hyperbolas with Center at (h, k) (p. 666)
4 Solve Applied Problems Involving Hyperbolas (p. 668)

DEFINITION   A **hyperbola** is the set of all points P in the plane, the difference of whose distances from two fixed points, called the **foci,** is a constant.

Figure 34

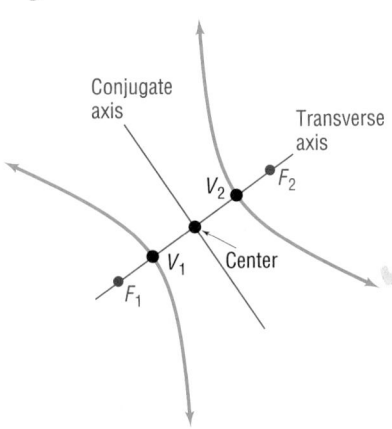

Figure 34 illustrates a hyperbola with foci F_1 and F_2. The line containing the foci is called the **transverse axis.** The midpoint of the line segment joining the foci is the **center** of the hyperbola. The line through the center and perpendicular to the transverse axis is the **conjugate axis.** The hyperbola consists of two separate curves, called **branches,** that are symmetric with respect to the transverse axis, conjugate axis, and center. The two points of intersection of the hyperbola and the transverse axis are the **vertices,** V_1 and V_2, of the hyperbola.

1 Analyze Hyperbolas with Center at the Origin

With these ideas in mind, we are now ready to find the equation of a hyperbola in the rectangular coordinate system. First, we place the center at the origin. Next, we position the hyperbola so that its transverse axis coincides with a coordinate axis. Suppose that the transverse axis coincides with the x-axis, as shown in Figure 35.

If c is the distance from the center to a focus, one focus will be at $F_1 = (-c, 0)$ and the other at $F_2 = (c, 0)$. Now we let the constant difference of the distances from any point $P = (x, y)$ on the hyperbola to the foci F_1 and F_2 be denoted by $\pm 2a$. (If P is on the right branch, the $+$ sign is used; if P is on the left branch, the $-$ sign is used.) The coordinates of P must satisfy the equation

Figure 35
$d(F_1, P) - d(F_2, P) = \pm 2a$

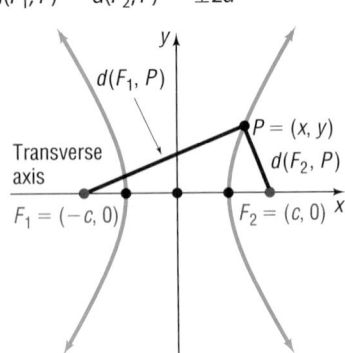

$$d(F_1, P) - d(F_2, P) = \pm 2a \qquad \text{Difference of the distances from } P \text{ to the foci equals } \pm 2a.$$

$$\sqrt{(x + c)^2 + y^2} - \sqrt{(x - c)^2 + y^2} = \pm 2a \qquad \text{Use the Distance Formula.}$$

$$\sqrt{(x + c)^2 + y^2} = \pm 2a + \sqrt{(x - c)^2 + y^2} \qquad \text{Isolate one radical.}$$

$$(x + c)^2 + y^2 = 4a^2 \pm 4a\sqrt{(x - c)^2 + y^2} \qquad \text{Square both sides.}$$
$$+ (x - c)^2 + y^2$$

Next we remove the parentheses by expanding the binomials.

$$x^2 + 2cx + c^2 + y^2 = 4a^2 \pm 4a\sqrt{(x - c)^2 + y^2} + x^2 - 2cx + c^2 + y^2$$

$$4cx - 4a^2 = \pm 4a\sqrt{(x - c)^2 + y^2} \qquad \text{Simplify; isolate the radical.}$$

$$cx - a^2 = \pm a\sqrt{(x - c)^2 + y^2} \qquad \text{Divide each side by 4.}$$

$$(cx - a^2)^2 = a^2[(x - c)^2 + y^2] \qquad \text{Square both sides.}$$

$$c^2x^2 - 2ca^2x + a^4 = a^2(x^2 - 2cx + c^2 + y^2) \qquad \text{Simplify.}$$

$$c^2x^2 + a^4 = a^2x^2 + a^2c^2 + a^2y^2 \qquad \text{Distribute and simplify.}$$

$$(c^2 - a^2)x^2 - a^2y^2 = a^2c^2 - a^4 \qquad \text{Rearrange terms.}$$

$$(c^2 - a^2)x^2 - a^2y^2 = a^2(c^2 - a^2) \qquad \text{Factor } a^2 \text{ on the right side.} \quad \textbf{(1)}$$

To obtain points on the hyperbola off the x-axis, it must be that $a < c$. To see why, look again at Figure 35.

$$d(F_1, P) < d(F_2, P) + d(F_1, F_2) \qquad \text{Use triangle } F_1PF_2.$$

$$d(F_1, P) - d(F_2, P) < d(F_1, F_2)$$

$$2a < 2c \qquad \qquad P \text{ is on the right branch, so}$$
$$\qquad \qquad d(F_1, P) - d(F_2, P) = 2a;$$
$$\qquad \qquad d(F_1, F_2) = 2c.$$

$$a < c$$

Since $a < c$, we also have $a^2 < c^2$, so $c^2 - a^2 > 0$. Let $b^2 = c^2 - a^2, b > 0$. Then equation (1) can be written as

$$b^2 x^2 - a^2 y^2 = a^2 b^2$$

$$\frac{x^2}{a^2} - \frac{y^2}{b^2} = 1 \qquad \textit{Divide each side by } a^2 b^2.$$

To find the vertices of the hyperbola defined by this equation, let $y = 0$. The vertices satisfy the equation $\dfrac{x^2}{a^2} = 1$, the solutions of which are $x = \pm a$. Consequently, the vertices of the hyperbola are $V_1 = (-a, 0)$ and $V_2 = (a, 0)$. Notice that the distance from the center $(0, 0)$ to either vertex is a.

THEOREM

Equation of a Hyperbola: Center at (0, 0); Transverse Axis along the x-Axis

An equation of the hyperbola with center at $(0, 0)$, foci at $(-c, 0)$ and $(c, 0)$, and vertices at $(-a, 0)$ and $(a, 0)$ is

$$\frac{x^2}{a^2} - \frac{y^2}{b^2} = 1 \qquad \text{where } b^2 = c^2 - a^2 \qquad \textbf{(2)}$$

The transverse axis is the x-axis.

Figure 36

$\dfrac{x^2}{a^2} - \dfrac{y^2}{b^2} = 1, \quad b^2 = c^2 - a^2$

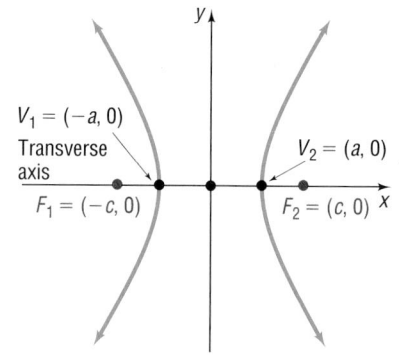

See Figure 36. As you can verify, the hyperbola defined by equation (2) is symmetric with respect to the x-axis, y-axis, and origin. To find the y-intercepts, if any, let $x = 0$ in equation (2). This results in the equation $\dfrac{y^2}{b^2} = -1$, which has no real solution. We conclude that the hyperbola defined by equation (2) has no y-intercepts. In fact, since $\dfrac{x^2}{a^2} - 1 = \dfrac{y^2}{b^2} \geq 0$, it follows that $\dfrac{x^2}{a^2} \geq 1$. There are no points on the graph for $-a < x < a$.

EXAMPLE 1 Finding and Graphing an Equation of a Hyperbola

Find an equation of the hyperbola with center at the origin, one focus at $(3, 0)$, and one vertex at $(-2, 0)$. Graph the equation.

Solution The hyperbola has its center at the origin. Because the focus and vertex lie on the x-axis, the transverse axis coincides with the x-axis. One focus is at $(c, 0) = (3, 0)$, so $c = 3$. One vertex is at $(-a, 0) = (-2, 0)$, so $a = 2$. From equation (2), it follows that $b^2 = c^2 - a^2 = 9 - 4 = 5$, so an equation of the hyperbola is

$$\frac{x^2}{4} - \frac{y^2}{5} = 1$$

To graph a hyperbola, it is helpful to locate and plot other points on the graph. For example, to find the points above and below the foci, we let $x = \pm 3$. Then

$$\frac{x^2}{4} - \frac{y^2}{5} = 1$$

$$\frac{(\pm 3)^2}{4} - \frac{y^2}{5} = 1 \qquad x = \pm 3$$

$$\frac{9}{4} - \frac{y^2}{5} = 1$$

Figure 37

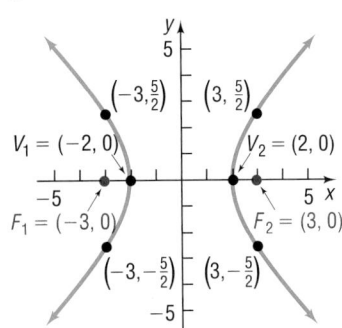

$$\frac{y^2}{5} = \frac{5}{4}$$

$$y^2 = \frac{25}{4}$$

$$y = \pm\frac{5}{2}$$

The points above and below the foci are $\left(\pm3, \frac{5}{2}\right)$ and $\left(\pm3, -\frac{5}{2}\right)$. These points determine the "opening" of the hyperbola. See Figure 37.

Now Work PROBLEM 17

EXAMPLE 2 | **Using a Graphing Utility to Graph a Hyperbola**

Using a graphing utility, graph the hyperbola: $\dfrac{x^2}{4} - \dfrac{y^2}{5} = 1$

Solution

To graph the hyperbola $\dfrac{x^2}{4} - \dfrac{y^2}{5} = 1$, we need to graph the two functions

$Y_1 = \sqrt{5}\sqrt{\dfrac{x^2}{4} - 1}$ and $Y_2 = -\sqrt{5}\sqrt{\dfrac{x^2}{4} - 1}$. As with graphing circles, parabolas, and ellipses on a graphing utility, we use a square screen setting so that the graph is not distorted. Figure 38 shows the graph of the hyperbola.

Figure 38

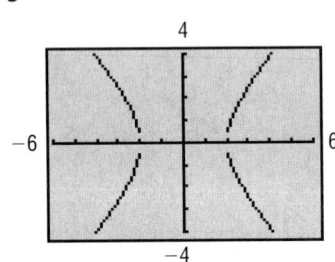

An equation of the form of equation (2) is the equation of a hyperbola with center at the origin, foci on the x-axis at $(-c, 0)$ and $(c, 0)$, where $c^2 = a^2 + b^2$, and transverse axis along the x-axis.

For the next two examples of this section, the direction **"Analyze the equation"** will mean to find the center, transverse axis, vertices, and foci of the hyperbola and graph it.

EXAMPLE 3 | **Analyzing the Equation of a Hyperbola**

Analyze the equation: $\dfrac{x^2}{16} - \dfrac{y^2}{4} = 1$

Solution

The given equation is of the form of equation (2), with $a^2 = 16$ and $b^2 = 4$. The graph of the equation is a hyperbola with center at $(0, 0)$ and transverse axis along the x-axis. Also, we know that $c^2 = a^2 + b^2 = 16 + 4 = 20$. The vertices are at $(\pm a, 0) = (\pm4, 0)$, and the foci are at $(\pm c, 0) = (\pm2\sqrt{5}, 0)$.

To locate the points on the graph above and below the foci, we let $x = \pm2\sqrt{5}$. Then

$$\frac{x^2}{16} - \frac{y^2}{4} = 1$$

$$\frac{\left(\pm2\sqrt{5}\right)^2}{16} - \frac{y^2}{4} = 1 \qquad x = \pm2\sqrt{5}$$

$$\frac{20}{16} - \frac{y^2}{4} = 1$$

$$\frac{5}{4} - \frac{y^2}{4} = 1$$

$$\frac{y^2}{4} = \frac{1}{4}$$

$$y = \pm1$$

The points above and below the foci are $(\pm 2\sqrt{5}, 1)$ and $(\pm 2\sqrt{5}, -1)$. See Figure 39(a) for the graph drawn by hand. Figure 39(b) shows the graph obtained using a graphing utility, where $Y_1 = \sqrt{4\left(\dfrac{x^2}{16} - 1\right)}$ and $Y_2 = -\sqrt{4\left(\dfrac{x^2}{16} - 1\right)}$.

Figure 39

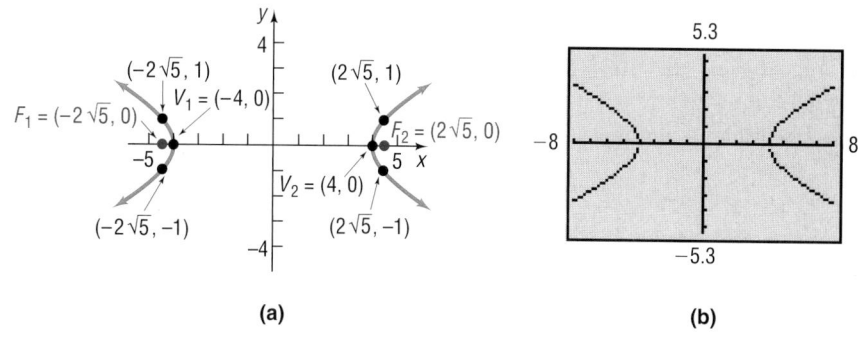

(a)   (b)

The next result gives the form of the equation of a hyperbola with center at the origin and transverse axis along the y-axis.

THEOREM

Equation of a Hyperbola; Center at (0, 0); Transverse Axis along the y-Axis

An equation of the hyperbola with center at $(0, 0)$, foci at $(0, -c)$ and $(0, c)$, and vertices at $(0, -a)$ and $(0, a)$ is

$$\frac{y^2}{a^2} - \frac{x^2}{b^2} = 1 \qquad \text{where } b^2 = c^2 - a^2 \qquad \textbf{(3)}$$

The transverse axis is the y-axis.

Figure 40

$$\frac{y^2}{a^2} - \frac{x^2}{b^2} = 1, b^2 = c^2 - a^2$$

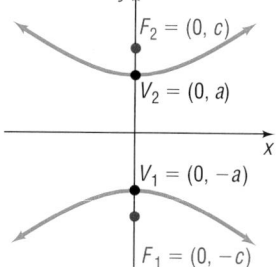

Figure 40 shows the graph of a typical hyperbola defined by equation (3).

An equation of the form of equation (2), $\dfrac{x^2}{a^2} - \dfrac{y^2}{b^2} = 1$, is the equation of a hyperbola with center at the origin, foci on the x-axis at $(-c, 0)$ and $(c, 0)$, where $c^2 = a^2 + b^2$, and transverse axis along the x-axis.

An equation of the form of equation (3), $\dfrac{y^2}{a^2} - \dfrac{x^2}{b^2} = 1$, is the equation of a hyperbola with center at the origin, foci on the y-axis at $(0, -c)$ and $(0, c)$, where $c^2 = a^2 + b^2$, and transverse axis along the y-axis.

Notice the difference in the forms of equations (2) and (3). When the y^2-term is subtracted from the x^2-term, the transverse axis is along the x-axis. When the x^2-term is subtracted from the y^2-term, the transverse axis is along the y-axis.

EXAMPLE 4 | Analyzing the Equation of a Hyperbola

Analyze the equation: $y^2 - 4x^2 = 4$

Solution To put the equation in proper form, we divide each side by 4:

$$\frac{y^2}{4} - x^2 = 1$$

Since the x^2-term is subtracted from the y^2-term, the equation is that of a hyperbola with center at the origin and transverse axis along the y-axis. Also, comparing the above equation to equation (3), we find $a^2 = 4, b^2 = 1$, and $c^2 = a^2 + b^2 = 5$. The vertices are at $(0, \pm a) = (0, \pm 2)$, and the foci are at $(0, \pm c) = (0, \pm\sqrt{5})$.

To locate other points on the graph, we let $x = \pm 2$. Then

$$y^2 - 4x^2 = 4$$

$$y^2 - 4(\pm 2)^2 = 4 \qquad x = \pm 2$$

$$y^2 - 16 = 4$$

$$y^2 = 20$$

$$y = \pm 2\sqrt{5}$$

Four other points on the graph are $(\pm 2, 2\sqrt{5})$ and $(\pm 2, -2\sqrt{5})$. See Figure 41(a) for the graph drawn by hand. Figure 41(b) shows the graph obtained using a graphing utility.

Figure 41

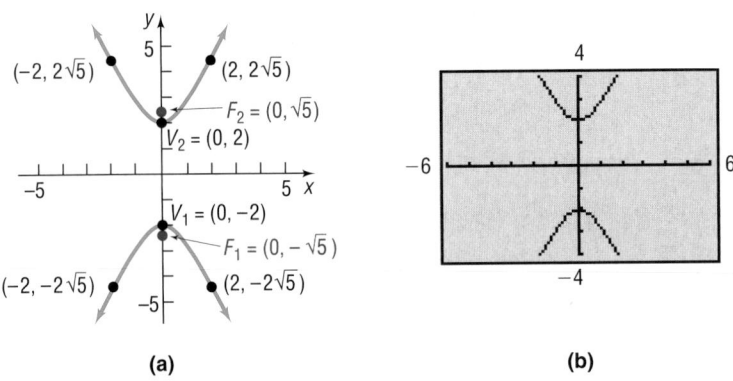

(a)   (b)

EXAMPLE 5	**Finding an Equation of a Hyperbola**

Find an equation of the hyperbola having one vertex at $(0, 2)$ and foci at $(0, -3)$ and $(0, 3)$. Graph the equation.

Solution

Figure 42

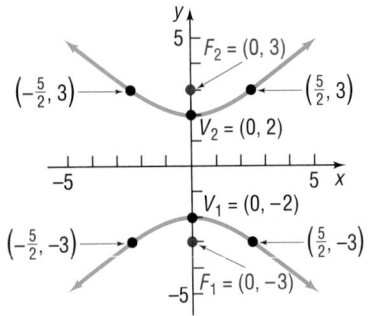

Since the foci are at $(0, -3)$ and $(0, 3)$, the center of the hyperbola, which is at their midpoint, is the origin. Because the foci lie on the y-axis, the transverse axis is along the y-axis. The given information also reveals that $c = 3$, $a = 2$, and $b^2 = c^2 - a^2 = 9 - 4 = 5$. The form of the equation of the hyperbola is given by equation (3):

$$\frac{y^2}{a^2} - \frac{x^2}{b^2} = 1$$

$$\frac{y^2}{4} - \frac{x^2}{5} = 1$$

Let $y = \pm 3$ to obtain points on the graph on either side of the foci. See Figure 42.

Now Work PROBLEM 19

Look at the equations of the hyperbolas in Examples 3 and 5. For the hyperbola in Example 3, $a^2 = 16$ and $b^2 = 4$, so $a > b$; for the hyperbola in Example 5, $a^2 = 4$ and $b^2 = 5$, so $a < b$. We conclude that, for hyperbolas, there are no requirements involving the relative sizes of a and b. Contrast this situation to the case of an ellipse, in which the relative sizes of a and b dictate which axis is the major axis. Hyperbolas have another feature to distinguish them from ellipses and parabolas: Hyperbolas have asymptotes.

2 Find the Asymptotes of a Hyperbola

Recall from Section 4.2 that a horizontal or oblique asymptote of a graph is a line with the property that the distance from the line to points on the graph approaches 0 as $x \to -\infty$ or as $x \to \infty$. The asymptotes provide information about the end behavior of the graph of a hyperbola.

THEOREM

Asymptotes of a Hyperbola

The hyperbola $\dfrac{x^2}{a^2} - \dfrac{y^2}{b^2} = 1$ has the two oblique asymptotes

$$y = \frac{b}{a}x \quad \text{and} \quad y = -\frac{b}{a}x \qquad (4)$$

Proof   We begin by solving for y in the equation of the hyperbola.

$$\frac{x^2}{a^2} - \frac{y^2}{b^2} = 1$$

$$\frac{y^2}{b^2} = \frac{x^2}{a^2} - 1$$

$$y^2 = b^2\left(\frac{x^2}{a^2} - 1\right)$$

Since $x \neq 0$, we can rearrange the right side in the form

$$y^2 = \frac{b^2 x^2}{a^2}\left(1 - \frac{a^2}{x^2}\right)$$

$$y = \pm\frac{bx}{a}\sqrt{1 - \frac{a^2}{x^2}}$$

Now, as $x \to -\infty$ or as $x \to \infty$, the term $\dfrac{a^2}{x^2}$ approaches 0, so the expression under the radical approaches 1. So, as $x \to -\infty$ or as $x \to \infty$, the value of y approaches $\pm\dfrac{bx}{a}$; that is, the graph of the hyperbola approaches the lines

$$y = -\frac{b}{a}x \quad \text{and} \quad y = \frac{b}{a}x$$

These lines are oblique asymptotes of the hyperbola.   ∎

The asymptotes of a hyperbola are not part of the hyperbola, but they do serve as a guide for graphing a hyperbola. For example, suppose that we want to graph the equation

$$\frac{x^2}{a^2} - \frac{y^2}{b^2} = 1$$

We begin by plotting the vertices $(-a, 0)$ and $(a, 0)$. Then we plot the points $(0, -b)$ and $(0, b)$ and use these four points to construct a rectangle, as shown in Figure 43.

The diagonals of this rectangle have slopes $\dfrac{b}{a}$ and $-\dfrac{b}{a}$, and their extensions are the asymptotes $y = \dfrac{b}{a}x$ and $y = -\dfrac{b}{a}x$ of the hyperbola. If we graph the asymptotes, we can use them to establish the "opening" of the hyperbola and avoid plotting other points.

Figure 43

$\dfrac{x^2}{a^2} - \dfrac{y^2}{b^2} = 1$

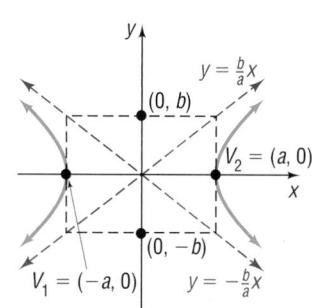

THEOREM

Asymptotes of a Hyperbola

The hyperbola $\dfrac{y^2}{a^2} - \dfrac{x^2}{b^2} = 1$ has the two oblique asymptotes:

$$y = \frac{a}{b}x \quad \text{and} \quad y = -\frac{a}{b}x \qquad \textbf{(5)}$$

You are asked to prove this result in Problem 82.

For the remainder of this section, the direction **"Analyze the equation"** will mean to find the center, transverse axis, vertices, foci, and asymptotes of the hyperbola and graph it.

EXAMPLE 6

Analyzing the Equation of a Hyperbola

Analyze the equation: $9x^2 - 4y^2 = 36$

Solution

Divide each side of the equation by 36 to put the equation in proper form.

$$\frac{x^2}{4} - \frac{y^2}{9} = 1$$

We now proceed to analyze the equation. The center of the hyperbola is the origin. Since the x^2-term is first in the equation, we know that the transverse axis is along the x-axis and the vertices and foci will lie on the x-axis. Using equation (2), we find $a^2 = 4$, $b^2 = 9$, and $c^2 = a^2 + b^2 = 13$. The vertices are $a = 2$ units left and right of the center at $(\pm a, 0) = (\pm 2, 0)$, the foci are $c = \sqrt{13}$ units left and right of the center at $(\pm c, 0) = (\pm\sqrt{13}, 0)$, and the asymptotes have the equations

$$y = \frac{b}{a}x = \frac{3}{2}x \quad \text{and} \quad y = -\frac{b}{a}x = -\frac{3}{2}x$$

To graph the hyperbola by hand, form the rectangle containing the points $(\pm a, 0)$ and $(0, \pm b)$, that is, $(-2, 0)$, $(2, 0)$, $(0, -3)$, and $(0, 3)$. The extensions of the diagonals of this rectangle are the asymptotes. See Figure 44(a) for the graph drawn by hand. Figure 44(b) shows the graph obtained using a graphing utility.

Figure 44

(a)

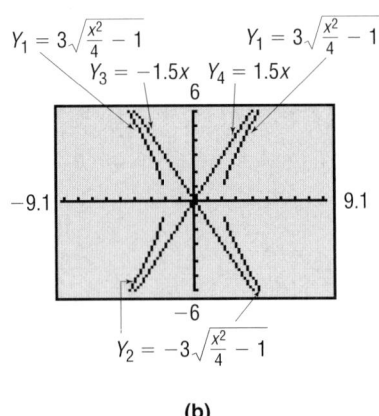

(b)

Seeing the Concept

Refer to Figure 44(b). Create a TABLE using Y_1 and Y_4 with $x = 10, 100, 1000$, and 10,000. Compare the values of Y_1 and Y_4. Repeat for Y_1 and Y_3, Y_2 and Y_3, and Y_2 and Y_4.

Now Work PROBLEM 29

3 Analyze Hyperbolas with Center at (h, k)

If a hyperbola with center at the origin and transverse axis coinciding with a coordinate axis is shifted horizontally h units and then vertically k units, the result is a hyperbola with center at (h, k) and transverse axis parallel to a coordinate axis. The equations of such hyperbolas have the same forms as those given in equations (2) and (3), except that x is replaced by $x - h$ (the horizontal shift) and y is replaced by $y - k$ (the vertical shift). Table 4 gives the forms of the equations of such hyperbolas. See Figure 45 for typical graphs.

Table 4

HYPERBOLAS WITH CENTER AT (h, k) AND TRANSVERSE AXIS PARALLEL TO A COORDINATE AXIS					
Center	Transverse Axis	Foci	Vertices	Equation	Asymptotes
(h, k)	Parallel to the x-axis	$(h \pm c, k)$	$(h \pm a, k)$	$\dfrac{(x - h)^2}{a^2} - \dfrac{(y - k)^2}{b^2} = 1, \quad b^2 = c^2 - a^2$	$y - k = \pm\dfrac{b}{a}(x - h)$
(h, k)	Parallel to the y-axis	$(h, k \pm c)$	$(h, k \pm a)$	$\dfrac{(y - k)^2}{a^2} - \dfrac{(x - h)^2}{b^2} = 1, \quad b^2 = c^2 - a^2$	$y - k = \pm\dfrac{a}{b}(x - h)$

Figure 45

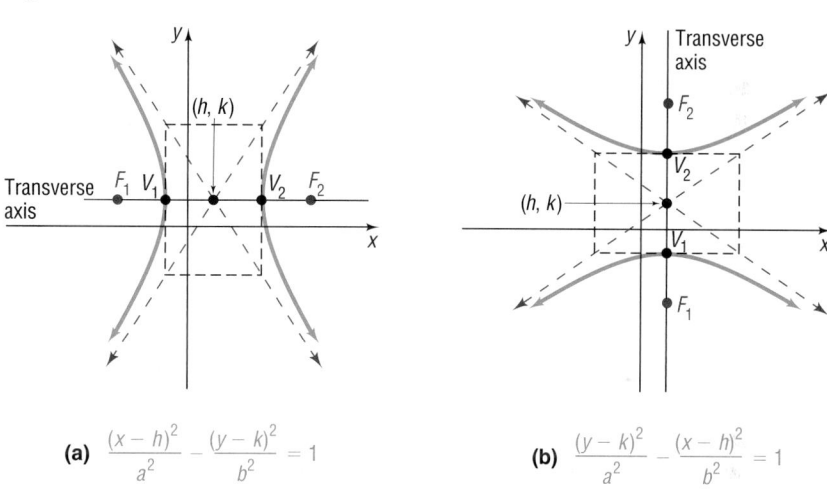

(a) $\dfrac{(x - h)^2}{a^2} - \dfrac{(y - k)^2}{b^2} = 1$

(b) $\dfrac{(y - k)^2}{a^2} - \dfrac{(x - h)^2}{b^2} = 1$

EXAMPLE 7   **Finding an Equation of a Hyperbola, Center Not at the Origin**

Find an equation for the hyperbola with center at $(1, -2)$, one focus at $(4, -2)$, and one vertex at $(3, -2)$. Graph the equation by hand.

Figure 46

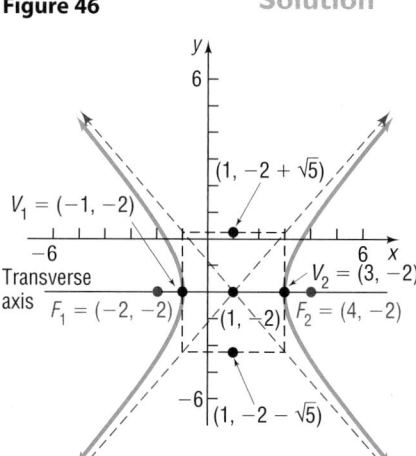

Solution   The center is at $(h, k) = (1, -2)$, so $h = 1$ and $k = -2$. Since the center, focus, and vertex all lie on the line $y = -2$, the transverse axis is parallel to the x-axis. The distance from the center $(1, -2)$ to the focus $(4, -2)$ is $c = 3$; the distance from the center $(1, -2)$ to the vertex $(3, -2)$ is $a = 2$. Thus, $b^2 = c^2 - a^2 = 9 - 4 = 5$. The equation is

$$\frac{(x - h)^2}{a^2} - \frac{(y - k)^2}{b^2} = 1$$

$$\frac{(x - 1)^2}{4} - \frac{(y + 2)^2}{5} = 1$$

See Figure 46.

Now Work   PROBLEM 39

EXAMPLE 8

Analyzing the Equation of a Hyperbola

Analyze the equation: $-x^2 + 4y^2 - 2x - 16y + 11 = 0$

Solution

We complete the squares in x and in y.

$$-x^2 + 4y^2 - 2x - 16y + 11 = 0$$

$$-(x^2 + 2x) + 4(y^2 - 4y) = -11 \qquad \text{Group terms.}$$

$$-(x^2 + 2x + 1) + 4(y^2 - 4y + 4) = -11 - 1 + 16 \qquad \text{Complete each square.}$$

$$-(x + 1)^2 + 4(y - 2)^2 = 4$$

$$(y - 2)^2 - \frac{(x + 1)^2}{4} = 1 \qquad \text{Divide each side by 4.}$$

This is the equation of a hyperbola with center at $(-1, 2)$ and transverse axis parallel to the y-axis. Also, $a^2 = 1$ and $b^2 = 4$, so $c^2 = a^2 + b^2 = 5$. Since the transverse axis is parallel to the y-axis, the vertices and foci are located a and c units above and below the center, respectively. The vertices are at $(h, k \pm a) = (-1, 2 \pm 1)$, or $(-1, 1)$ and $(-1, 3)$. The foci are at $(h, k \pm c) = (-1, 2 \pm \sqrt{5})$. The asymptotes are $y - 2 = \frac{1}{2}(x + 1)$ and $y - 2 = -\frac{1}{2}(x + 1)$. Figure 47(a) shows the graph drawn by hand. Figure 47(b) shows the graph obtained using a graphing utility.

Figure 47

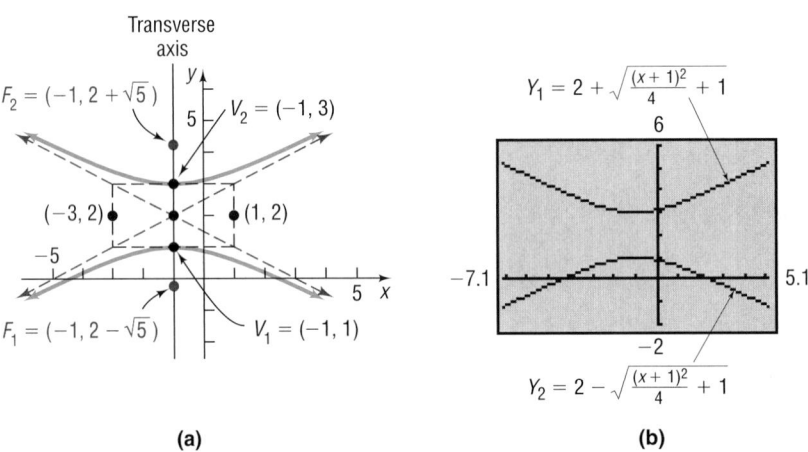

(a)

(b)

━━━━ **Now Work** PROBLEM 53

4 Solve Applied Problems Involving Hyperbolas

Figure 48

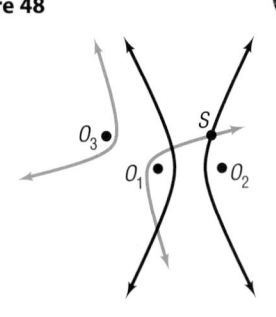

Look at Figure 48. Suppose that three microphones are located at points O_1, O_2, and O_3 (the foci of the two hyperbolas). In addition, suppose that a gun is fired at S and the microphone at O_1 records the gun shot 1 second after the microphone at O_2. Because sound travels at about 1100 feet per second, we conclude that the microphone at O_1 is 1100 feet farther from the gunshot than O_2. We can model this situation by saying that S lies on a branch of a hyperbola with foci at O_1 and O_2. (Do you see why? The difference of the distances from S to O_1 and from S to O_2 is the constant 1100.) If the third microphone at O_3 records the gunshot 2 seconds after O_1, then S will lie on a branch of a second hyperbola with foci at O_1 and O_3. In this case, the constant difference will be 2200. The intersection of the two hyperbolas will identify the location of S.

| EXAMPLE 9 | Lightning Strikes |

Suppose that two people standing 1 mile apart both see a flash of lightning. After a period of time, the person standing at point A hears the thunder. One second later, the person standing at point B hears the thunder. If the person at B is due west of the person at A and the lightning strike is known to occur due north of the person standing at point A, where did the lightning strike?

Solution See Figure 49 in which the ordered pair (x, y) represents the location of the lightning strike. We know that sound travels at 1100 feet per second, so the person at point A is 1100 feet closer to the lightning strike than the person at point B. Since the difference of the distance from (x, y) to A and the distance from (x, y) to B is the constant 1100, the point (x, y) lies on a hyperbola whose foci are at A and B.

Figure 49

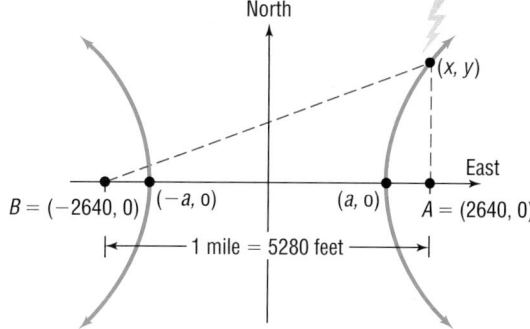

An equation of the hyperbola is

$$\frac{x^2}{a^2} - \frac{y^2}{b^2} = 1$$

where $2a = 1100$, so $a = 550$.

Because the distance between the two people is 1 mile (5280 feet) and each person is at a focus of the hyperbola, we have

$$2c = 5280$$

$$c = \frac{5280}{2} = 2640$$

Since $b^2 = c^2 - a^2 = 2640^2 - 550^2 = 6{,}667{,}100$, the equation of the hyperbola that describes the location of the lightning strike is

$$\frac{x^2}{550^2} - \frac{y^2}{6{,}667{,}100} = 1$$

Refer again to Figure 49. Since the lightning strikes due north of the individual at the point $A = (2640, 0)$, we let $x = 2640$ and solve the resulting equation.

$$\frac{2640^2}{550^2} - \frac{y^2}{6{,}667{,}100} = 1$$

$$-\frac{y^2}{6{,}667{,}100} = -22.04 \qquad \text{Subtract } \frac{2640^2}{550^2} \text{ from both sides.}$$

$$y^2 = 146{,}942{,}884 \qquad \text{Multiply both sides by } -6{,}667{,}100.$$

$$y = 12{,}122 \qquad \begin{array}{l} y > 0 \text{ since the lightning strike} \\ \text{occured in quadrant I.} \end{array}$$

✓ Check: The difference between the distance from $(2640, 12{,}122)$ to the person at the point $B = (-2640, 0)$ and the distance from $(2640, 12{,}122)$ to the person at the point $A = (2640, 0)$ should be 1100. Using the distance formula, we find the difference in the distances is

$$\sqrt{[2640 - (-2640)]^2 + (12{,}122 - 0)^2} - \sqrt{(2640 - 2640)^2 + (12{,}122 - 0)^2} = 1100$$

as required.

The lightning strike is 12,122 feet north of the person standing at point A.

Now Work PROBLEM 73

10.4 Assess Your Understanding

'Are You Prepared?' *Answers are given at the end of these exercises. If you get a wrong answer, read the pages listed in red.*

1. The distance d from $P_1 = (3, -4)$ to $P_2 = (-2, 1)$ is $d = $ _____. (pp. 4–6)

2. To complete the square of $x^2 + 5x$, add _____. (p. A52)

3. Find the intercepts of the equation $y^2 = 9 + 4x^2$. (pp. 18–19)

4. **True or False** The equation $y^2 = 9 + x^2$ is symmetric with respect to the x-axis, the y-axis, and the origin. (pp. 19–21)

5. To graph $y = (x - 5)^3 - 4$, shift the graph of $y = x^3$ to the (left/right) _____ unit(s) and then (up/down) _____ unit(s). (pp. 100–102)

6. Find the vertical asymptotes, if any, and the horizontal or oblique asymptotes, if any, of $y = \dfrac{x^2 - 9}{x^2 - 4}$. (pp. 194–199)

Concepts and Vocabulary

7. A(n) _____ is the collection of points in the plane the difference of whose distances from two fixed points is a constant.

8. For a hyperbola, the foci lie on a line called the _____ _____.

9. The asymptotes of the hyperbola $\dfrac{x^2}{4} - \dfrac{y^2}{9} = 1$ are _____ and _____.

10. **True or False** The foci of a hyperbola lie on a line called the axis of symmetry.

11. **True or False** Hyperbolas always have asymptotes.

12. **True or False** A hyperbola will never intersect its transverse axis.

Skill Building

In Problems 13–16, the graph of a hyperbola is given. Match each graph to its equation.

(A) $\dfrac{x^2}{4} - y^2 = 1$ (B) $x^2 - \dfrac{y^2}{4} = 1$ (C) $\dfrac{y^2}{4} - x^2 = 1$ (D) $y^2 - \dfrac{x^2}{4} = 1$

13.

14.

15.

16.
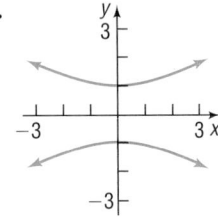

In Problems 17–26, find an equation for the hyperbola described. Graph the equation by hand.

17. Center at $(0, 0)$; focus at $(3, 0)$; vertex at $(1, 0)$

18. Center at $(0, 0)$; focus at $(0, 5)$; vertex at $(0, 3)$

19. Center at $(0, 0)$; focus at $(0, -6)$; vertex at $(0, 4)$

20. Center at $(0, 0)$; focus at $(-3, 0)$; vertex at $(2, 0)$

21. Foci at $(-5, 0)$ and $(5, 0)$; vertex at $(3, 0)$

22. Focus at $(0, 6)$; vertices at $(0, -2)$ and $(0, 2)$

23. Vertices at $(0, -6)$ and $(0, 6)$; asymptote the line $y = 2x$

24. Vertices at $(-4, 0)$ and $(4, 0)$; asymptote the line $y = 2x$

25. Foci at $(-4, 0)$ and $(4, 0)$; asymptote the line $y = -x$

26. Foci at $(0, -2)$ and $(0, 2)$; asymptote the line $y = -x$

In Problems 27–34, find the center, transverse axis, vertices, foci, and asymptotes. Graph each equation by hand. Verify your graph using a graphing utility.

27. $\dfrac{x^2}{25} - \dfrac{y^2}{9} = 1$

28. $\dfrac{y^2}{16} - \dfrac{x^2}{4} = 1$

29. $4x^2 - y^2 = 16$

30. $4y^2 - x^2 = 16$

31. $y^2 - 9x^2 = 9$

32. $x^2 - y^2 = 4$

33. $y^2 - x^2 = 25$

34. $2x^2 - y^2 = 4$

In Problems 35–38, write an equation for each hyperbola.

35.

36.

37.

38.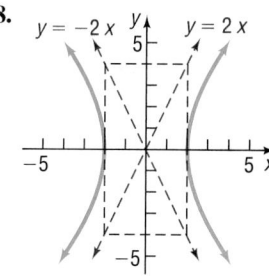

In Problems 39–46, find an equation for the hyperbola described. Graph each equation by hand.

39. Center at $(4, -1)$; focus at $(7, -1)$; vertex at $(6, -1)$

40. Center at $(-3, 1)$; focus at $(-3, 6)$; vertex at $(-3, 4)$

41. Center at $(-3, -4)$; focus at $(-3, -8)$; vertex at $(-3, -2)$

42. Center at $(1, 4)$; focus at $(-2, 4)$; vertex at $(0, 4)$

43. Foci at $(3, 7)$ and $(7, 7)$; vertex at $(6, 7)$

44. Focus at $(-4, 0)$ vertices at $(-4, 4)$ and $(-4, 2)$

45. Vertices at $(-1, -1)$ and $(3, -1)$; asymptote the line $y + 1 = \dfrac{3}{2}(x - 1)$

46. Vertices at $(1, -3)$ and $(1, 1)$; asymptote the line $y + 1 = \dfrac{3}{2}(x - 1)$

In Problems 47–60, find the center, transverse axis, vertices, foci, and asymptotes. Graph each equation by hand. Verify your graph using a graphing utility.

47. $\dfrac{(x - 2)^2}{4} - \dfrac{(y + 3)^2}{9} = 1$

48. $\dfrac{(y + 3)^2}{4} - \dfrac{(x - 2)^2}{9} = 1$

49. $(y - 2)^2 - 4(x + 2)^2 = 4$

50. $(x + 4)^2 - 9(y - 3)^2 = 9$

51. $(x + 1)^2 - (y + 2)^2 = 4$

52. $(y - 3)^2 - (x + 2)^2 = 4$

53. $x^2 - y^2 - 2x - 2y - 1 = 0$

54. $y^2 - x^2 - 4y + 4x - 1 = 0$

55. $y^2 - 4x^2 - 4y - 8x - 4 = 0$

56. $2x^2 - y^2 + 4x + 4y - 4 = 0$

57. $4x^2 - y^2 - 24x - 4y + 16 = 0$

58. $2y^2 - x^2 + 2x + 8y + 3 = 0$

59. $y^2 - 4x^2 - 16x - 2y - 19 = 0$

60. $x^2 - 3y^2 + 8x - 6y + 4 = 0$

In Problems 61–64, graph each function. Be sure to label any intercepts.
[Hint: *Notice that each function is half a hyperbola.*]

61. $f(x) = \sqrt{16 + 4x^2}$

62. $f(x) = -\sqrt{9 + 9x^2}$

63. $f(x) = -\sqrt{-25 + x^2}$

64. $f(x) = \sqrt{-1 + x^2}$

Mixed Practice

In Problems 65–72, analyze each conic section.

65. $\dfrac{(x - 3)^2}{4} - \dfrac{y^2}{25} = 1$

66. $\dfrac{(y + 2)^2}{16} - \dfrac{(x - 2)^2}{4} = 1$

67. $x^2 = 16(y - 3)$

68. $y^2 = -12(x + 1)$

69. $25x^2 + 9y^2 - 250x + 400 = 0$

70. $x^2 + 36y^2 - 2x + 288y + 541 = 0$

71. $x^2 - 6x - 8y - 31 = 0$

72. $9x^2 - y^2 - 18x - 8y - 88 = 0$

Applications and Extensions

73. Fireworks Display   Suppose that two people standing 2 miles apart both see the burst from a fireworks display. After a period of time, the first person standing at point A hears the burst. One second later, the second person standing at point B hears the burst. If the person at point B is due west of the person at point A and if the display is known to occur due north of the person at point A, where did the fireworks display occur?

74. **Lightning Strikes** Suppose that two people standing 1 mile apart both see a flash of lightning. After a period of time, the first person standing at point A hears the thunder. Two seconds later, the second person standing at point B hears the thunder. If the person at point B is due west of the person at point A and if the lightning strike is known to occur due north of the person standing at point A, where did the lightning strike?

75. **Nuclear Power Plant** Some nuclear power plants utilize "natural draft" cooling towers in the shape of a **hyperboloid,** a solid obtained by rotating a hyperbola about its conjugate axis. Suppose such a cooling tower has a base diameter of 400 feet and the diameter at its narrowest point, 360 feet above the ground, is 200 feet. If the diameter at the top of the tower is 300 feet, how tall is the tower?

Source: Bay Area Air Quality Management District

76. **An Explosion** Two recording devices are set 2400 feet apart, with the device at point A to the west of the device at point B. At a point between the devices, 300 feet from point B, a small amount of explosive is detonated. The recording devices record the time until the sound reaches each. How far directly north of point B should a second explosion be done so that the measured time difference recorded by the devices is the same as that for the first detonation?

77. **Rutherford's Experiment** In May 1911, Ernest Rutherford published a paper in *Philosophical Magazine.* In this article, he described the motion of alpha particles as they are shot at a piece of gold foil 0.00004 cm thick. Before conducting this experiment, Rutherford expected that the alpha particles would shoot through the foil just as a bullet would shoot through snow. Instead, a small fraction of the alpha particles bounced off the foil. This led to the conclusion that the nucleus of an atom is dense, while the remainder of the atom is sparse. Only the density of the nucleus could cause the alpha particles to deviate from their path. The figure shows a diagram from Rutherford's paper that indicates that the deflected alpha particles follow the path of one branch of a hyperbola.

(a) Find an equation of the asymptotes under this scenario.
(b) If the vertex of the path of the alpha particles is 10 cm from the center of the hyperbola, find a model that describes the path of the particle.

78. **Hyperbolic Mirrors** Hyperbolas have interesting reflective properties that make them useful for lenses and mirrors. For example, if a ray of light strikes a convex hyperbolic mirror on a line that would (theoretically) pass through its rear focus, it is reflected through the front focus. This property, and that of the parabola, were used to develop the *Cassegrain* telescope in 1672. The focus of the parabolic mirror and the rear focus of the hyperbolic mirror are the same point. The rays are collected by the parabolic mirror, reflected toward the (common) focus, and thus are reflected by the hyperbolic mirror through the opening to its front focus, where the eyepiece is located. If the equation of the hyperbola is $\dfrac{y^2}{9} - \dfrac{x^2}{16} = 1$ and the focal length (distance from the vertex to the focus) of the parabola is 6, find the equation of the parabola.

Source: www.enchantedlearning.com

79. The **eccentricity** e of a hyperbola is defined as the number $\dfrac{c}{a}$, where a and c are the numbers given in equation (2). Because $c > a$, it follows that $e > 1$. Describe the general shape of a hyperbola whose eccentricity is close to 1. What is the shape if e is very large?

80. A hyperbola for which $a = b$ is called an **equilateral hyperbola.** Find the eccentricity e of an equilateral hyperbola.

[**Note:** The eccentricity of a hyperbola is defined in Problem 79.]

81. Two hyperbolas that have the same set of asymptotes are called **conjugate.** Show that the hyperbolas

$$\frac{x^2}{4} - y^2 = 1 \quad \text{and} \quad y^2 - \frac{x^2}{4} = 1$$

are conjugate. Graph each hyperbola on the same set of coordinate axes.

82. Prove that the hyperbola

$$\frac{y^2}{a^2} - \frac{x^2}{b^2} = 1$$

has the two oblique asymptotes

$$y = \frac{a}{b}x \quad \text{and} \quad y = -\frac{a}{b}x$$

83. Show that the graph of an equation of the form

$$Ax^2 + Cy^2 + F = 0 \qquad A \neq 0, C \neq 0, F \neq 0$$

where A and C are of opposite sign, is a hyperbola with center at $(0, 0)$.

84. Show that the graph of an equation of the form

$$Ax^2 + Cy^2 + Dx + Ey + F = 0 \qquad A \neq 0, C \neq 0$$

where A and C are of opposite sign,

(a) is a hyperbola if $\dfrac{D^2}{4A} + \dfrac{E^2}{4C} - F \neq 0$

(b) is two intersecting lines if $\dfrac{D^2}{4A} + \dfrac{E^2}{4C} - F = 0$

'Are You Prepared?' Answers

1. $5\sqrt{2}$ 2. $\dfrac{25}{4}$ 3. $(0, -3), (0, 3)$ 4. True   5. right; 5; down; 4   6. Vertical: $x = -2, x = 2$; horizontal: $y = 1$

10.5 Rotation of Axes; General Form of a Conic

PREPARING FOR THIS SECTION *Before getting started, review the following:*

- Sum Formulas for Sine and Cosine (Section 7.4, pp. 466 and 469)
- Double-angle Formulas for Sine and Cosine (Section 7.5, p. 476)
- Half-angle Formulas for Sine and Cosine (Section 7.5, p. 480)

Now Work the 'Are You Prepared?' problems on page 679.

OBJECTIVES 1 Identify a Conic (p. 673)
2 Use a Rotation of Axes to Transform Equations (p. 674)
3 Analyze an Equation Using a Rotation of Axes (p. 676)
4 Identify Conics without a Rotation of Axes (p. 678)

In this section, we show that the graph of a general second-degree polynomial containing two variables x and y, that is, an equation of the form

$$Ax^2 + Bxy + Cy^2 + Dx + Ey + F = 0 \qquad \textbf{(1)}$$

where A, B, and C are not simultaneously 0, is a conic. We shall not concern ourselves here with the degenerate cases of equation (1), such as $x^2 + y^2 = 0$, whose graph is a single point $(0, 0)$; or $x^2 + 3y^2 + 3 = 0$, whose graph contains no points; or $x^2 - 4y^2 = 0$, whose graph is two lines, $x - 2y = 0$ and $x + 2y = 0$.

We begin with the case where $B = 0$. In this case, the term containing xy is not present, so equation (1) has the form

$$Ax^2 + Cy^2 + Dx + Ey + F = 0$$

where either $A \neq 0$ or $C \neq 0$.

1 Identify a Conic

We have already discussed the procedure for identifying the graph of this kind of equation; we complete the squares of the quadratic expressions in x or y, or both. Once this has been done, the conic can be identified by comparing it to one of the forms studied in Sections 10.2 through 10.4.

In fact, though, we can identify the conic directly from the equation without completing the squares.

THEOREM

Identifying Conics without Completing the Squares

Excluding degenerate cases, the equation

$$Ax^2 + Cy^2 + Dx + Ey + F = 0 \qquad \textbf{(2)}$$

where A and C cannot both equal zero:

(a) Defines a parabola if $AC = 0$.
(b) Defines an ellipse (or a circle) if $AC > 0$.
(c) Defines a hyperbola if $AC < 0$.

Proof

(a) If $AC = 0$, then either $A = 0$ or $C = 0$, but not both, so the form of equation (2) is either

$$Ax^2 + Dx + Ey + F = 0, \qquad A \neq 0$$

or

$$Cy^2 + Dx + Ey + F = 0, \qquad C \neq 0$$

Using the results of Problems 78 and 79 in Exercise 10.2, it follows that, except for the degenerate cases, the equation is a parabola.

(b) If $AC > 0$, then A and C are of the same sign. Using the results of Problem 84 in Exercise 10.3, except for the degenerate cases, the equation is an ellipse if $A \neq C$ or a circle if $A = C$.

(c) If $AC < 0$, then A and C are of opposite sign. Using the results of Problem 84 in Exercise 10.4, except for the degenerate cases, the equation is a hyperbola. ∎

We will not be concerned with the degenerate cases of equation (2). However, in practice, you should be alert to the possibility of degeneracy.

| EXAMPLE 1 | **Identifying a Conic without Completing the Squares** |

Identify each equation without completing the squares.

(a) $3x^2 + 6y^2 + 6x - 12y = 0$ (b) $2x^2 - 3y^2 + 6y + 4 = 0$
(c) $y^2 - 2x + 4 = 0$

Solution

(a) We compare the given equation to equation (2) and conclude that $A = 3$ and $C = 6$. Since $AC = 18 > 0$, the equation is an ellipse.
(b) Here $A = 2$ and $C = -3$, so $AC = -6 < 0$. The equation is a hyperbola.
(c) Here $A = 0$ and $C = 1$, so $AC = 0$. The equation is a parabola.

◾

 Now Work PROBLEM 11

Although we can now identify the type of conic represented by any equation of the form of equation (2) without completing the squares, we will still need to complete the squares if we desire additional information about the conic, such as its graph.

Now we turn our attention to equations of the form of equation (1), where $B \neq 0$. To discuss this case, we first need to investigate a new procedure: *rotation of axes*.

2 Use a Rotation of Axes to Transform Equations

In a **rotation of axes,** the origin remains fixed while the x-axis and y-axis are rotated through an angle θ to a new position; the new positions of the x-axis and the y-axis are denoted by x' and y', respectively, as shown in Figure 50(a).

Now look at Figure 50(b). There the point P has the coordinates (x, y) relative to the xy-plane, while the same point P has coordinates (x', y') relative to the $x'y'$-plane. We seek relationships that will enable us to express x and y in terms of x', y', and θ.

As Figure 50(b) shows, r denotes the distance from the origin O to the point P, and α denotes the angle between the positive x'-axis and the ray from O through P. Then, using the definitions of sine and cosine, we have

$$x' = r \cos \alpha \qquad y' = r \sin \alpha \qquad \textbf{(3)}$$
$$x = r \cos(\theta + \alpha) \qquad y = r \sin(\theta + \alpha) \qquad \textbf{(4)}$$

Figure 50

(a)

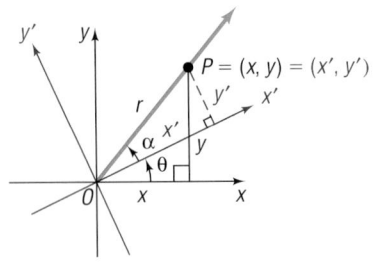

(b)

Now

$$x = r \cos(\theta + \alpha)$$
$$= r(\cos \theta \cos \alpha - \sin \theta \sin \alpha) \qquad \text{Apply the Sum Formula for cosine.}$$
$$= (r \cos \alpha)(\cos \theta) - (r \sin \alpha)(\sin \theta)$$
$$= x' \cos \theta - y' \sin \theta \qquad \text{By equation (3)}$$

Similarly,

$$y = r \sin(\theta + \alpha)$$
$$= r(\sin \theta \cos \alpha + \cos \theta \sin \alpha) \qquad \text{Apply the Sum Formula for sine.}$$
$$= x' \sin \theta + y' \cos \theta \qquad \text{By equation (3)}$$

THEOREM **Rotation Formulas**

If the x- and y-axes are rotated through an angle θ, the coordinates (x, y) of a point P relative to the xy-plane and the coordinates (x', y') of the same point relative to the new x'- and y'-axes are related by the formulas

$$x = x' \cos \theta - y' \sin \theta \qquad y = x' \sin \theta + y' \cos \theta \qquad \textbf{(5)}$$

EXAMPLE 2   **Rotating Axes**

Express the equation $xy = 1$ in terms of new $x'y'$-coordinates by rotating the axes through a 45° angle. Discuss the new equation.

Solution   Let $\theta = 45°$ in equation (5). Then

$$x = x' \cos 45° - y' \sin 45° = x' \frac{\sqrt{2}}{2} - y' \frac{\sqrt{2}}{2} = \frac{\sqrt{2}}{2}(x' - y')$$

$$y = x' \sin 45° + y' \cos 45° = x' \frac{\sqrt{2}}{2} + y' \frac{\sqrt{2}}{2} = \frac{\sqrt{2}}{2}(x' + y')$$

Figure 51

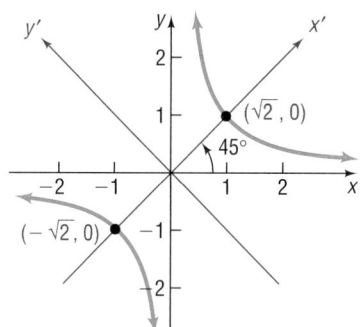

Substituting these expressions for x and y in $xy = 1$ gives

$$\left[\frac{\sqrt{2}}{2}(x' - y') \right]\left[\frac{\sqrt{2}}{2}(x' + y') \right] = 1$$

$$\frac{1}{2}(x'^2 - y'^2) = 1$$

$$\frac{x'^2}{2} - \frac{y'^2}{2} = 1$$

This is the equation of a hyperbola with center at $(0, 0)$ and transverse axis along the x'-axis. The vertices are at $(\pm\sqrt{2}, 0)$ on the x'-axis; the asymptotes are $y' = x'$ and $y' = -x'$ (which correspond to the original x- and y-axes). See Figure 51 for the graph.

As Example 2 illustrates, a rotation of axes through an appropriate angle can transform a second-degree equation in x and y containing an xy-term into one in x' and y' in which no $x'y'$-term appears. In fact, we will show that a rotation of axes through an appropriate angle will transform any equation of the form of equation (1) into an equation in x' and y' without an $x'y'$-term.

To find the formula for choosing an appropriate angle θ through which to rotate the axes, we begin with equation (1),

$$Ax^2 + Bxy + Cy^2 + Dx + Ey + F = 0 \qquad B \neq 0$$

Next we rotate through an angle θ using rotation formulas (5).

$$A(x' \cos \theta - y' \sin \theta)^2 + B(x' \cos \theta - y' \sin \theta)(x' \sin \theta + y' \cos \theta)$$

$$+ C(x' \sin \theta + y' \cos \theta)^2 + D(x' \cos \theta - y' \sin \theta)$$

$$+ E(x' \sin \theta + y' \cos \theta) + F = 0$$

By expanding and collecting like terms, we obtain

$$(A \cos^2 \theta + B \sin \theta \cos \theta + C \sin^2 \theta)x'^2 + [B(\cos^2 \theta - \sin^2 \theta) + 2(C - A)(\sin \theta \cos \theta)]x'y'$$

$$+ (A \sin^2 \theta - B \sin \theta \cos \theta + C \cos^2 \theta)y'^2$$

$$+ (D \cos \theta + E \sin \theta)x'$$

$$+ (-D \sin \theta + E \cos \theta)y' + F = 0 \qquad \textbf{(6)}$$

In equation (6), the coefficient of $x'y'$ is

$$B(\cos^2 \theta - \sin^2 \theta) + 2(C - A)(\sin \theta \cos \theta)$$

Since we want to eliminate the $x'y'$-term, we select an angle θ so that this coefficient is 0.

$$B(\cos^2\theta - \sin^2\theta) + 2(C - A)(\sin\theta\cos\theta) = 0$$

$$B\cos(2\theta) + (C - A)\sin(2\theta) = 0 \qquad \text{Double-angle Formulas}$$

$$B\cos(2\theta) = (A - C)\sin(2\theta)$$

$$\cot(2\theta) = \frac{A - C}{B} \qquad B \neq 0$$

THEOREM

To transform the equation

$$Ax^2 + Bxy + Cy^2 + Dx + Ey + F = 0 \qquad B \neq 0$$

into an equation in x' and y' without an $x'y'$-term, rotate the axes through an angle θ that satisfies the equation

$$\cot(2\theta) = \frac{A - C}{B} \tag{7}$$

Equation (7) has an infinite number of solutions for θ. We shall adopt the convention of choosing the acute angle θ that satisfies (7). Then we have the following two possibilities:

If $\cot(2\theta) \geq 0$, then $0° < 2\theta \leq 90°$, so $0° < \theta \leq 45°$.

If $\cot(2\theta) < 0$, then $90° < 2\theta < 180°$, so $45° < \theta < 90°$.

Each of these results in a counterclockwise rotation of the axes through an acute angle θ.*

WARNING Be careful if you use a calculator to solve equation (7).

1. If $\cot(2\theta) = 0$, then $2\theta = 90°$ and $\theta = 45°$.
2. If $\cot(2\theta) \neq 0$, first find $\cos(2\theta)$. Then use the inverse cosine function key(s) to obtain $2\theta, 0° < 2\theta < 180°$. Finally, divide by 2 to obtain the correct acute angle θ. ∎

3 Analyze an Equation Using a Rotation of Axes

For the remainder of this section, the direction **"Analyze the equation"** will mean to transform the given equation so that it contains no xy-term and to graph the equation.

EXAMPLE 3

Analyzing an Equation Using a Rotation of Axes

Analyze the equation: $x^2 + \sqrt{3}xy + 2y^2 - 10 = 0$

Solution

Since an xy-term is present, we must rotate the axes. Using $A = 1, B = \sqrt{3}$, and $C = 2$ in equation (7), the appropriate acute angle θ through which to rotate the axes satisfies the equation

$$\cot(2\theta) = \frac{A - C}{B} = \frac{-1}{\sqrt{3}} = -\frac{\sqrt{3}}{3} \qquad 0° < 2\theta < 180°$$

---

* Any rotation through an angle θ that satisfies $\cot(2\theta) = \dfrac{A - C}{B}$ will eliminate the $x'y'$-term. However, the final form of the transformed equation may be different (but equivalent), depending on the angle chosen.

Since $\cot(2\theta) = -\dfrac{\sqrt{3}}{3}$, we find $2\theta = 120°$, so $\theta = 60°$. Using $\theta = 60°$ in rotation formulas (5), we find

$$x = x'\cos 60° - y'\sin 60° = \frac{1}{2}x' - \frac{\sqrt{3}}{2}y' = \frac{1}{2}\left(x' - \sqrt{3}y'\right)$$

$$y = x'\sin 60° + y'\cos 60° = \frac{\sqrt{3}}{2}x' + \frac{1}{2}y' = \frac{1}{2}\left(\sqrt{3}x' + y'\right)$$

Substituting these values into the original equation and simplifying, we have

$$x^2 + \sqrt{3}xy + 2y^2 - 10 = 0$$

$$\frac{1}{4}\left(x' - \sqrt{3}y'\right)^2 + \sqrt{3}\left[\frac{1}{2}\left(x' - \sqrt{3}y'\right)\right]\left[\frac{1}{2}\left(\sqrt{3}x' + y'\right)\right] + 2\left[\frac{1}{4}\left(\sqrt{3}x' + y'\right)^2\right] = 10$$

Multiply both sides by 4 and expand to obtain

$$x'^2 - 2\sqrt{3}x'y' + 3y'^2 + \sqrt{3}\left(\sqrt{3}x'^2 - 2x'y' - \sqrt{3}y'^2\right) + 2\left(3x'^2 + 2\sqrt{3}x'y' + y'^2\right) = 40$$

$$10x'^2 + 2y'^2 = 40$$

$$\frac{x'^2}{4} + \frac{y'^2}{20} = 1$$

Figure 52

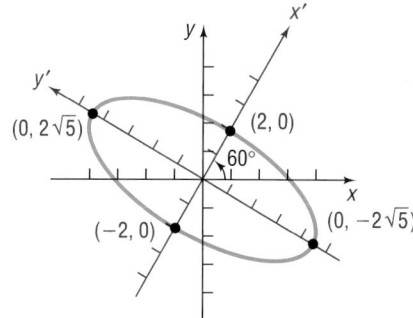

This is the equation of an ellipse with center at $(0,0)$ and major axis along the y'-axis. The vertices are at $(0, \pm 2\sqrt{5})$ on the y'-axis. See Figure 52 for the graph.

To graph the equation $x^2 + \sqrt{3}xy + 2y^2 - 10 = 0$ using a graphing utility, we need to solve the equation for y. Rearranging the terms, we observe that the equation is quadratic in the variable y: $2y^2 + \sqrt{3}xy + (x^2 - 10) = 0$. We can solve the equation for y using the quadratic formula with $a = 2$, $b = \sqrt{3}x$, and $c = x^2 - 10$.

Figure 53

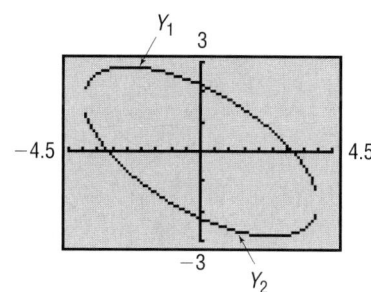

$$Y_1 = \frac{-\sqrt{3}x + \sqrt{\left(\sqrt{3}x\right)^2 - 4(2)(x^2 - 10)}}{2(2)} = \frac{-\sqrt{3}x + \sqrt{-5x^2 + 80}}{4}$$

and

$$Y_2 = \frac{-\sqrt{3}x - \sqrt{\left(\sqrt{3}x\right)^2 - 4(2)(x^2 - 10)}}{2(2)} = \frac{-\sqrt{3}x - \sqrt{-5x^2 + 80}}{4}$$

Figure 53 shows the graph of Y_1 and Y_2.

Now Work PROBLEM 31

In Example 3, the acute angle θ through which to rotate the axes was easy to find because of the numbers that we used in the given equation. In general, the equation $\cot(2\theta) = \dfrac{A - C}{B}$ will not have such a "nice" solution. As the next example shows, we can still find the appropriate rotation formulas without using a calculator approximation by applying Half-angle Formulas.

EXAMPLE 4 **Analyzing an Equation Using a Rotation of Axes**

Analyze the equation: $4x^2 - 4xy + y^2 + 5\sqrt{5}x + 5 = 0$

Solution Letting $A = 4$, $B = -4$, and $C = 1$ in equation (7), the appropriate angle θ through which to rotate the axes satisfies

$$\cot(2\theta) = \frac{A - C}{B} = \frac{3}{-4} = -\frac{3}{4}$$

To use rotation formulas (5), we need to know the values of $\sin\theta$ and $\cos\theta$. Since we seek an acute angle θ, we know that $\sin\theta > 0$ and $\cos\theta > 0$. We use the Half-angle Formulas in the form

$$\sin\theta = \sqrt{\frac{1 - \cos(2\theta)}{2}} \qquad \cos\theta = \sqrt{\frac{1 + \cos(2\theta)}{2}}$$

Now we need to find the value of $\cos(2\theta)$. Since $\cot(2\theta) = -\frac{3}{4}$, then $90° < 2\theta < 180°$ (Do you know why?), so $\cos(2\theta) = -\frac{3}{5}$. Then

$$\sin\theta = \sqrt{\frac{1 - \cos(2\theta)}{2}} = \sqrt{\frac{1 - \left(-\frac{3}{5}\right)}{2}} = \sqrt{\frac{4}{5}} = \frac{2}{\sqrt{5}} = \frac{2\sqrt{5}}{5}$$

$$\cos\theta = \sqrt{\frac{1 + \cos(2\theta)}{2}} = \sqrt{\frac{1 + \left(-\frac{3}{5}\right)}{2}} = \sqrt{\frac{1}{5}} = \frac{1}{\sqrt{5}} = \frac{\sqrt{5}}{5}$$

With these values, the rotation formulas (5) are

$$x = \frac{\sqrt{5}}{5}x' - \frac{2\sqrt{5}}{5}y' = \frac{\sqrt{5}}{5}(x' - 2y')$$

$$y = \frac{2\sqrt{5}}{5}x' + \frac{\sqrt{5}}{5}y' = \frac{\sqrt{5}}{5}(2x' + y')$$

Substituting these values in the original equation and simplifying, we obtain

$$4x^2 - 4xy + y^2 + 5\sqrt{5}x + 5 = 0$$

$$4\left[\frac{\sqrt{5}}{5}(x' - 2y')\right]^2 - 4\left[\frac{\sqrt{5}}{5}(x' - 2y')\right]\left[\frac{\sqrt{5}}{5}(2x' + y')\right]$$

$$+ \left[\frac{\sqrt{5}}{5}(2x' + y')\right]^2 + 5\sqrt{5}\left[\frac{\sqrt{5}}{5}(x' - 2y')\right] = -5$$

Multiply both sides by 5 and expand to obtain

$$4(x'^2 - 4x'y' + 4y'^2) - 4(2x'^2 - 3x'y' - 2y'^2)$$

$$+ 4x'^2 + 4x'y' + y'^2 + 25(x' - 2y') = -25$$

$$25y'^2 - 50y' + 25x' = -25 \qquad \text{Combine like terms.}$$

$$y'^2 - 2y' + x' = -1 \qquad \text{Divide by 25.}$$

$$y'^2 - 2y' + 1 = -x' \qquad \text{Complete the square in } y'.$$

$$(y' - 1)^2 = -x'$$

Figure 54

This is the equation of a parabola with vertex at $(0, 1)$ in the $x'y'$-plane. The axis of symmetry is parallel to the x'-axis. Using a calculator to solve $\sin\theta = \frac{2\sqrt{5}}{5}$, we find that $\theta \approx 63.4°$. See Figure 54 for the graph.

<hr>

─ **Now Work** PROBLEM 37

4 Identify Conics without a Rotation of Axes

Suppose that we are required only to identify (rather than analyze) an equation of the form

$$Ax^2 + Bxy + Cy^2 + Dx + Ey + F = 0 \qquad B \neq 0 \qquad \textbf{(8)}$$

If we apply the rotation formulas (5) to this equation, we obtain an equation of the form

$$A'x'^2 + B'x'y' + C'y'^2 + D'x' + E'y' + F' = 0 \qquad (9)$$

where A', B', C', D', E', and F' can be expressed in terms of A, B, C, D, E, F and the angle θ of rotation (see Problem 53). It can be shown that the value of $B^2 - 4AC$ in equation (8) and the value of $B'^2 - 4A'C'$ in equation (9) are equal no matter what angle θ of rotation is chosen (see Problem 55). In particular, if the angle θ of rotation satisfies equation (7), then $B' = 0$ in equation (9), and $B^2 - 4AC = -4A'C'$. Since equation (9) then has the form of equation (2),

$$A'x'^2 + C'y'^2 + D'x' + E'y' + F' = 0$$

we can identify it without completing the squares, as we did in the beginning of this section. In fact, now we can identify the conic described by any equation of the form of equation (8) without a rotation of axes.

THEOREM

Identifying Conics without a Rotation of Axes

Except for degenerate cases, the equation

$$Ax^2 + Bxy + Cy^2 + Dx + Ey + F = 0$$

(a) Defines a parabola if $B^2 - 4AC = 0$.
(b) Defines an ellipse (or a circle) if $B^2 - 4AC < 0$.
(c) Defines a hyperbola if $B^2 - 4AC > 0$.

You are asked to prove this theorem in Problem 56.

EXAMPLE 5 | **Identifying a Conic without a Rotation of Axes**

Identify the equation: $8x^2 - 12xy + 17y^2 - 4\sqrt{5}x - 2\sqrt{5}y - 15 = 0$

Solution   Here $A = 8$, $B = -12$, and $C = 17$, so $B^2 - 4AC = -400$. Since $B^2 - 4AC < 0$, the equation defines an ellipse.

── **Now Work** PROBLEM 43

10.5 Assess Your Understanding

'Are You Prepared?' *Answers are given at the end of these exercises. If you get a wrong answer, read the pages listed in red.*

1. The sum formula for the sine function is $\sin(A + B) = $ _____. (p. 469)

2. The Double-angle Formula for the sine function is $\sin(2\theta) = $ _____. (p. 476)

3. If θ is acute, the Half-angle Formula for the sine function is $\sin\dfrac{\theta}{2} = $ _____. (p. 480)

4. If θ is acute, the Half-angle Formula for the cosine function is $\cos\dfrac{\theta}{2} = $ _____. (p. 480)

Concepts and Vocabulary

5. To transform the equation
$$Ax^2 + Bxy + Cy^2 + Dx + Ey + F = 0, \qquad B \neq 0$$
into one in x' and y' without an $x'y'$-term, rotate the axes through an acute angle θ that satisfies the equation _____.

6. Identify the conic: $x^2 - 2y^2 - x - y - 18 = 0$ _____.

7. Identify the conic: $x^2 + 2xy + 3y^2 - 2x + 4y + 10 = 0$ _____.

8. **True or False** The equation $ax^2 + 6y^2 - 12y = 0$ defines an ellipse if $a > 0$.

9. **True or False** The equation $3x^2 + bxy + 12y^2 = 10$ defines a parabola if $b = -12$.

10. **True or False** To eliminate the xy-term from the equation $x^2 - 2xy + y^2 - 2x + 3y + 5 = 0$, rotate the axes through an angle θ, where $\cot\theta = B^2 - 4AC$.

Skill Building

In Problems 11–20, identify each equation without completing the squares.

11. $x^2 + 4x + y + 3 = 0$

12. $2y^2 - 3y + 3x = 0$

13. $6x^2 + 3y^2 - 12x + 6y = 0$

14. $2x^2 + y^2 - 8x + 4y + 2 = 0$

15. $3x^2 - 2y^2 + 6x + 4 = 0$

16. $4x^2 - 3y^2 - 8x + 6y + 1 = 0$

17. $2y^2 - x^2 - y + x = 0$

18. $y^2 - 8x^2 - 2x - y = 0$

19. $x^2 + y^2 - 8x + 4y = 0$

20. $2x^2 + 2y^2 - 8x + 8y = 0$

In Problems 21–30, determine the appropriate rotation formulas to use so that the new equation contains no xy-term.

21. $x^2 + 4xy + y^2 - 3 = 0$

22. $x^2 - 4xy + y^2 - 3 = 0$

23. $5x^2 + 6xy + 5y^2 - 8 = 0$

24. $3x^2 - 10xy + 3y^2 - 32 = 0$

25. $13x^2 - 6\sqrt{3}xy + 7y^2 - 16 = 0$

26. $11x^2 + 10\sqrt{3}xy + y^2 - 4 = 0$

27. $4x^2 - 4xy + y^2 - 8\sqrt{5}x - 16\sqrt{5}y = 0$

28. $x^2 + 4xy + 4y^2 + 5\sqrt{5}y + 5 = 0$

29. $25x^2 - 36xy + 40y^2 - 12\sqrt{13}x - 8\sqrt{13}y = 0$

30. $34x^2 - 24xy + 41y^2 - 25 = 0$

In Problems 31–42, rotate the axes so that the new equation contains no xy-term. Analyze and graph the new equation. Refer to Problems 21–30 for Problems 31–40. Verify your graph using a graphing utility.

31. $x^2 + 4xy + y^2 - 3 = 0$

32. $x^2 - 4xy + y^2 - 3 = 0$

33. $5x^2 + 6xy + 5y^2 - 8 = 0$

34. $3x^2 - 10xy + 3y^2 - 32 = 0$

35. $13x^2 - 6\sqrt{3}xy + 7y^2 - 16 = 0$

36. $11x^2 + 10\sqrt{3}xy + y^2 - 4 = 0$

37. $4x^2 - 4xy + y^2 - 8\sqrt{5}x - 16\sqrt{5}y = 0$

38. $x^2 + 4xy + 4y^2 + 5\sqrt{5}y + 5 = 0$

39. $25x^2 - 36xy + 40y^2 - 12\sqrt{13}x - 8\sqrt{13}y = 0$

40. $34x^2 - 24xy + 41y^2 - 25 = 0$

41. $16x^2 + 24xy + 9y^2 - 130x + 90y = 0$

42. $16x^2 + 24xy + 9y^2 - 60x + 80y = 0$

In Problems 43–52, identify each equation without applying a rotation of axes.

43. $x^2 + 3xy - 2y^2 + 3x + 2y + 5 = 0$

44. $2x^2 - 3xy + 4y^2 + 2x + 3y - 5 = 0$

45. $x^2 - 7xy + 3y^2 - y - 10 = 0$

46. $2x^2 - 3xy + 2y^2 - 4x - 2 = 0$

47. $9x^2 + 12xy + 4y^2 - x - y = 0$

48. $10x^2 + 12xy + 4y^2 - x - y + 10 = 0$

49. $10x^2 - 12xy + 4y^2 - x - y - 10 = 0$

50. $4x^2 + 12xy + 9y^2 - x - y = 0$

51. $3x^2 - 2xy + y^2 + 4x + 2y - 1 = 0$

52. $3x^2 + 2xy + y^2 + 4x - 2y + 10 = 0$

Applications and Extensions

In Problems 53–56, apply the rotation formulas (5) to

$$Ax^2 + Bxy + Cy^2 + Dx + Ey + F = 0$$

to obtain the equation

$$A'x'^2 + B'x'y' + C'y'^2 + D'x' + E'y' + F' = 0$$

53. Express $A', B', C', D', E',$ and F' in terms of $A, B, C, D, E, F,$ and the angle θ of rotation.

   [**Hint:** Refer to equation (6).]

54. Show that $A + C = A' + C'$, and thus show that $A + C$ is **invariant;** that is, its value does not change under a rotation of axes.

55. Refer to Problem 54. Show that $B^2 - 4AC$ is invariant.

56. Prove that, except for degenerate cases, the equation

$$Ax^2 + Bxy + Cy^2 + Dx + Ey + F = 0$$

   (a) Defines a parabola if $B^2 - 4AC = 0$.
   (b) Defines an ellipse (or a circle) if $B^2 - 4AC < 0$.
   (c) Defines a hyperbola if $B^2 - 4AC > 0$.

57. Use rotation formulas (5) to show that distance is invariant under a rotation of axes. That is, show that the distance from $P_1 = (x_1, y_1)$ to $P_2 = (x_2, y_2)$ in the xy-plane equals the distance from $P_1 = (x_1', y_1')$ to $P_2 = (x_2', y_2')$ in the x'y'-plane.

58. Show that the graph of the equation $x^{1/2} + y^{1/2} = a^{1/2}$ is part of the graph of a parabola.

Discussion and Writing

59. Formulate a strategy for discussing and graphing an equation of the form

$$Ax^2 + Cy^2 + Dx + Ey + F = 0$$

60. How does your strategy change if the equation is of the following form?

$$Ax^2 + Bxy + Cy^2 + Dx + Ey + F = 0$$

'Are You Prepared?' Answers

1. $\sin A \cos B + \cos A \sin B$ **2.** $2 \sin \theta \cos \theta$ **3.** $\sqrt{\dfrac{1 - \cos \theta}{2}}$ **4.** $\sqrt{\dfrac{1 + \cos \theta}{2}}$

10.6 Polar Equations of Conics

PREPARING FOR THIS SECTION *Before getting started, review the following:*

- Polar Coordinates (Section 9.1, pp. 562–569)

Now Work the 'Are You Prepared?' problems on page 685.

OBJECTIVES 1 Analyze and Graph Polar Equations of Conics (p. 681)
2 Convert the Polar Equation of a Conic to a Rectangular Equation (p. 685)

1 Analyze and Graph Polar Equations of Conics

In Sections 10.2 through 10.4, we gave separate definitions for the parabola, ellipse, and hyperbola based on geometric properties and the distance formula. In this section, we present an alternative definition that simultaneously defines all these conics. As we shall see, this approach is well suited to polar coordinate representation. (Refer to Section 9.1.)

DEFINITION
Let D denote a fixed line called the **directrix;** let F denote a fixed point called the **focus,** which is not on D; and let e be a fixed positive number called the **eccentricity.** A **conic** is the set of points P in the plane such that the ratio of the distance from F to P to the distance from D to P equals e. That is, a conic is the collection of points P for which

$$\frac{d(F, P)}{d(D, P)} = e \qquad \textbf{(1)}$$

If $e = 1$, the conic is a **parabola.**
If $e < 1$, the conic is an **ellipse.**
If $e > 1$, the conic is a **hyperbola.**

Observe that if $e = 1$ the definition of a parabola in equation (1) is exactly the same as the definition used earlier in Section 10.2.

In the case of an ellipse, the **major axis** is a line through the focus perpendicular to the directrix. In the case of a hyperbola, the **transverse axis** is a line through the focus perpendicular to the directrix. For both an ellipse and a hyperbola, the eccentricity e satisfies

$$e = \frac{c}{a} \qquad \textbf{(2)}$$

Figure 55

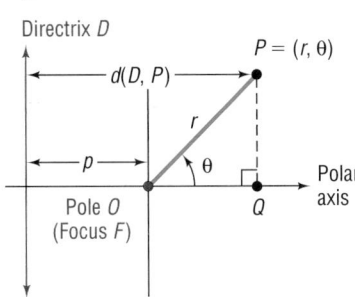

where c is the distance from the center to the focus and a is the distance from the center to a vertex.

Just as we did earlier using rectangular coordinates, we derive equations for the conics in polar coordinates by choosing a convenient position for the focus F and the directrix D. The focus F is positioned at the pole, and the directrix D is either parallel or perpendicular to the polar axis.

Suppose that we start with the directrix D perpendicular to the polar axis at a distance p units to the left of the pole (the focus F). See Figure 55.

If $P = (r, \theta)$ is any point on the conic, then, by equation (1),

$$\frac{d(F, P)}{d(D, P)} = e \quad \text{or} \quad d(F, P) = e \cdot d(D, P) \tag{3}$$

Now we use the point Q obtained by dropping the perpendicular from P to the polar axis to calculate $d(D, P)$.

$$d(D, P) = p + d(O, Q) = p + r \cos \theta$$

Using this expression and the fact that $d(F, P) = d(O, P) = r$ in equation (3), we get

$$d(F, P) = e \cdot d(D, P)$$
$$r = e(p + r \cos \theta)$$
$$r = ep + er \cos \theta$$
$$r - er \cos \theta = ep$$
$$r(1 - e \cos \theta) = ep$$
$$r = \frac{ep}{1 - e \cos \theta}$$

THEOREM

Polar Equation of a Conic; Focus at the Pole; Directrix Perpendicular to the Polar Axis a Distance p to the Left of the Pole

The polar equation of a conic with focus at the pole and directrix perpendicular to the polar axis at a distance p to the left of the pole is

$$r = \frac{ep}{1 - e \cos \theta} \tag{4}$$

where e is the eccentricity of the conic.

EXAMPLE 1   **Analyzing and Graphing the Polar Equation of a Conic**

Analyze and graph the equation: $r = \dfrac{4}{2 - \cos \theta}$

Solution   The given equation is not quite in the form of equation (4), since the first term in the denominator is 2 instead of 1. We divide the numerator and denominator by 2 to obtain

$$r = \frac{2}{1 - \frac{1}{2}\cos \theta} \qquad r = \frac{ep}{1 - e \cos \theta}$$

This equation is in the form of equation (4), with

$$e = \frac{1}{2} \quad \text{and} \quad ep = 2$$

Then

$$\frac{1}{2}p = 2, \quad \text{so} \quad p = 4$$

We conclude that the conic is an ellipse, since $e = \dfrac{1}{2} < 1$. One focus is at the pole, and the directrix is perpendicular to the polar axis, a distance of $p = 4$ units to the left of the pole. It follows that the major axis is along the polar axis. To find the vertices, we let $\theta = 0$ and $\theta = \pi$. The vertices of the ellipse are $(4, 0)$ and $\left(\dfrac{4}{3}, \pi\right)$. The midpoint of the vertices, $\left(\dfrac{4}{3}, 0\right)$ in polar coordinates, is the center of the ellipse.

Figure 56

(a)

(b)

[Do you see why? The vertices $(4, 0)$ and $\left(\dfrac{4}{3}, \pi\right)$ in polar coordinates are $(4, 0)$ and $\left(-\dfrac{4}{3}, 0\right)$ in rectangular coordinates. The midpoint in rectangular coordinates is $\left(\dfrac{4}{3}, 0\right)$, which is also $\left(\dfrac{4}{3}, 0\right)$ in polar coordinates.] Then $a =$ distance from the center to a vertex $= \dfrac{8}{3}$. Using $a = \dfrac{8}{3}$ and $e = \dfrac{1}{2}$ in equation (2), $e = \dfrac{c}{a}$, we find $c = ae = \dfrac{4}{3}$. Finally, using $a = \dfrac{8}{3}$ and $c = \dfrac{4}{3}$ in $b^2 = a^2 - c^2$, we have

$$b^2 = a^2 - c^2 = \frac{64}{9} - \frac{16}{9} = \frac{48}{9}$$

$$b = \frac{4\sqrt{3}}{3}$$

Figure 56(a) shows the graph drawn by hand.

Figure 56(b) shows the graph of the equation obtained using a graphing utility in POLar mode with $\theta\min = 0$, $\theta\max = 2\pi$, and $\theta\text{step} = \dfrac{\pi}{24}$.

Exploration

Graph $r_1 = \dfrac{4}{2 + \cos\theta}$ and compare the result with Figure 56. What do you conclude? Clear the screen and graph $r_1 = \dfrac{4}{2 - \sin\theta}$ and then $r_1 = \dfrac{4}{2 + \sin\theta}$. Compare each of these graphs with Figure 56. What do you conclude?

Now Work   PROBLEM 11

Equation (4) was obtained under the assumption that the directrix was perpendicular to the polar axis at a distance p units to the left of the pole. A similar derivation (see Problem 43), in which the directrix is perpendicular to the polar axis at a distance p units to the right of the pole, results in the equation

$$r = \frac{ep}{1 + e \cos\theta}$$

In Problems 44 and 45, you are asked to derive the polar equations of conics with focus at the pole and directrix parallel to the polar axis. Table 5 summarizes the polar equations of conics.

Table 5

POLAR EQUATIONS OF CONICS (FOCUS AT THE POLE, ECCENTRICITY e)	
Equation	**Description**
(a) $r = \dfrac{ep}{1 - e \cos\theta}$	Directrix is perpendicular to the polar axis at a distance p units to the left of the pole.
(b) $r = \dfrac{ep}{1 + e \cos\theta}$	Directrix is perpendicular to the polar axis at a distance p units to the right of the pole.
(c) $r = \dfrac{ep}{1 + e \sin\theta}$	Directrix is parallel to the polar axis at a distance p units above the pole.
(d) $r = \dfrac{ep}{1 - e \sin\theta}$	Directrix is parallel to the polar axis at a distance p units below the pole.

Eccentricity

If $e = 1$, the conic is a parabola; the axis of symmetry is perpendicular to the directrix.

If $e < 1$, the conic is an ellipse; the major axis is perpendicular to the directrix.

If $e > 1$, the conic is a hyperbola; the transverse axis is perpendicular to the directrix.

| EXAMPLE 2 | Analyzing and Graphing the Polar Equation of a Conic |

Analyze and graph the equation: $r = \dfrac{6}{3 + 3\sin\theta}$

Solution

To place the equation in proper form, we divide the numerator and denominator by 3 to get

$$r = \frac{2}{1 + \sin\theta}$$

Referring to Table 5, we conclude that this equation is in the form of equation (c) with

$$e = 1 \quad \text{and} \quad ep = 2$$

$$p = 2 \quad \scriptstyle e = 1$$

The conic is a parabola with focus at the pole. The directrix is parallel to the polar axis at a distance 2 units above the pole; the axis of symmetry is perpendicular to the polar axis. The vertex of the parabola is at $\left(1, \dfrac{\pi}{2}\right)$. (Do you see why?) See Figure 57(a) for the graph drawn by hand. Notice that we plotted two additional points, $(2, 0)$ and $(2, \pi)$, to assist in graphing.

Figure 57(b) shows the graph of the equation using a graphing utility in POLar mode with $\theta\min = 0$, $\theta\max = 2\pi$, and $\theta\text{step} = \dfrac{\pi}{24}$.

Figure 57

(a)

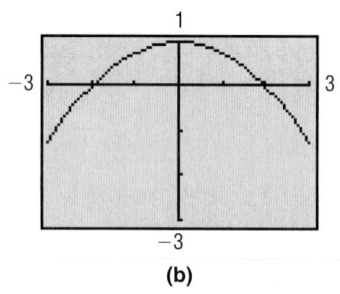

(b)

━━━ **Now Work** PROBLEM 13

| EXAMPLE 3 | Analyzing and Graphing the Polar Equation of a Conic |

Analyze and graph the equation: $r = \dfrac{3}{1 + 3\cos\theta}$

Solution

This equation is in the form of equation (b) in Table 5. We conclude that

$$e = 3 \quad \text{and} \quad ep = 3$$

$$p = 1 \quad \scriptstyle e = 3$$

This is the equation of a hyperbola with a focus at the pole. The directrix is perpendicular to the polar axis, 1 unit to the right of the pole. The transverse axis is along the polar axis. To find the vertices, we let $\theta = 0$ and $\theta = \pi$. The vertices are $\left(\dfrac{3}{4}, 0\right)$ and $\left(-\dfrac{3}{2}, \pi\right)$. The center, which is at the midpoint of $\left(\dfrac{3}{4}, 0\right)$ and $\left(-\dfrac{3}{2}, \pi\right)$, is $\left(\dfrac{9}{8}, 0\right)$. Then c = distance from the center to a focus = $\dfrac{9}{8}$. Since $e = 3$, it follows from equation (2), $e = \dfrac{c}{a}$, that $a = \dfrac{3}{8}$. Finally, using $a = \dfrac{3}{8}$ and $c = \dfrac{9}{8}$ in $b^2 = c^2 - a^2$, we find

$$b^2 = c^2 - a^2 = \frac{81}{64} - \frac{9}{64} = \frac{72}{64} = \frac{9}{8}$$

$$b = \frac{3}{2\sqrt{2}} = \frac{3\sqrt{2}}{4}$$

Figure 58(a) shows the graph drawn by hand. Notice that we plotted two additional points, $\left(3, \dfrac{\pi}{2}\right)$ and $\left(3, \dfrac{3\pi}{2}\right)$, on the left branch and used symmetry to obtain the right branch. The asymptotes of this hyperbola were found in the usual way by constructing the rectangle shown.

Figures 58(b) and (c) show the graph of the equation using a graphing utility in POLar mode with $\theta\text{min} = 0$, $\theta\text{max} = 2\pi$, and $\theta\text{step} = \dfrac{\pi}{24}$, using both dot mode and connected mode. Notice the extraneous asymptotes in connected mode.

Figure 58

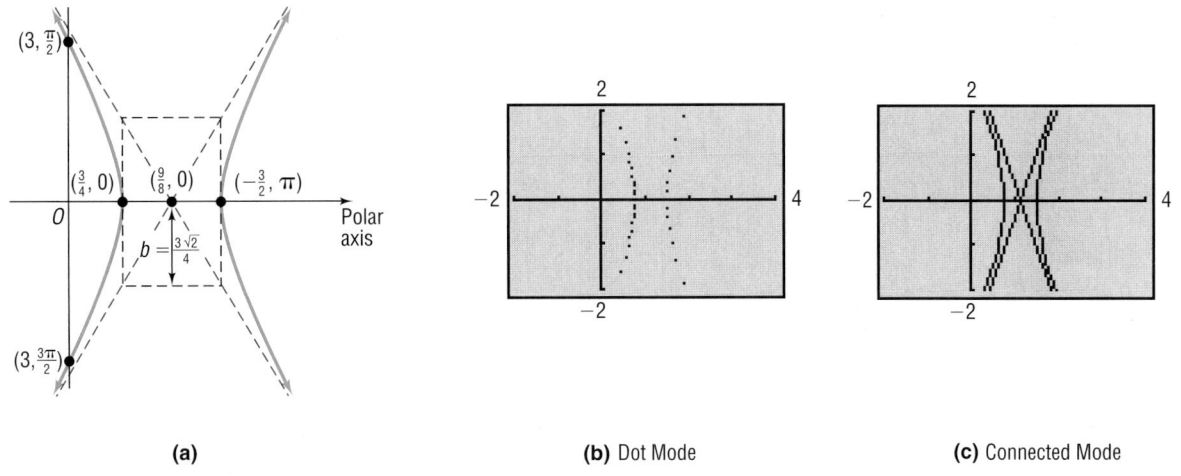

(a) (b) Dot Mode (c) Connected Mode

Now Work PROBLEM 17

2 Convert the Polar Equation of a Conic to a Rectangular Equation

EXAMPLE 4

Converting a Polar Equation to a Rectangular Equation

Convert the polar equation

$$r = \frac{1}{3 - 3\cos\theta}$$

to a rectangular equation.

Solution The strategy here is first to rearrange the equation and square each side before using the transformation equations.

$$r = \frac{1}{3 - 3\cos\theta}$$

$$3r - 3r\cos\theta = 1$$

$$3r = 1 + 3r\cos\theta \qquad \textit{Rearrange the equation.}$$

$$9r^2 = (1 + 3r\cos\theta)^2 \qquad \textit{Square each side.}$$

$$9(x^2 + y^2) = (1 + 3x)^2 \qquad \textit{x}^2 + y^2 = r^2; x = r\cos\theta$$

$$9x^2 + 9y^2 = 9x^2 + 6x + 1$$

$$9y^2 = 6x + 1$$

This is the equation of a parabola in rectangular coordinates.

Now Work PROBLEM 25

10.6 Assess Your Understanding

'Are You Prepared?' *Answers are given at the end of these exercises. If you get a wrong answer, read the pages listed in red.*

1. If (x, y) are the rectangular coordinates of a point P and (r, θ) are its polar coordinates, then $x =$ _____ and $y =$ _____. (p. 564)

2. Transform the equation $r = 6\cos\theta$ from polar coordinates to rectangular coordinates. (pp. 568–569)

Concepts and Vocabulary

3. The polar equation $r = \dfrac{8}{4 - 2 \sin \theta}$ is a conic whose eccentricity is _____. It is a(n) _____ whose directrix is _____ to the polar axis at a distance _____ units _____ of the pole.

4. The eccentricity e of a parabola is _____, of an ellipse it is _____, and of a hyperbola it is _____.

5. *True or False* If (r, θ) are polar coordinates, the equation $r = \dfrac{2}{2 + 3 \sin \theta}$ defines a hyperbola.

6. *True or False* The eccentricity of any parabola is 1.

Skill Building

In Problems 7–12, identify the conic that each polar equation represents. Also, give the position of the directrix.

7. $r = \dfrac{1}{1 + \cos \theta}$

8. $r = \dfrac{3}{1 - \sin \theta}$

9. $r = \dfrac{4}{2 - 3 \sin \theta}$

10. $r = \dfrac{2}{1 + 2 \cos \theta}$

11. $r = \dfrac{3}{4 - 2 \cos \theta}$

12. $r = \dfrac{6}{8 + 2 \sin \theta}$

In Problems 13–24, analyze each equation and graph it by hand. Verify your graph using a graphing utility.

13. $r = \dfrac{1}{1 + \cos \theta}$

14. $r = \dfrac{3}{1 - \sin \theta}$

15. $r = \dfrac{8}{4 + 3 \sin \theta}$

16. $r = \dfrac{10}{5 + 4 \cos \theta}$

17. $r = \dfrac{9}{3 - 6 \cos \theta}$

18. $r = \dfrac{12}{4 + 8 \sin \theta}$

19. $r = \dfrac{8}{2 - \sin \theta}$

20. $r = \dfrac{8}{2 + 4 \cos \theta}$

21. $r(3 - 2 \sin \theta) = 6$

22. $r(2 - \cos \theta) = 2$

23. $r = \dfrac{6 \sec \theta}{2 \sec \theta - 1}$

24. $r = \dfrac{3 \csc \theta}{\csc \theta - 1}$

In Problems 25–36, convert each polar equation to a rectangular equation.

25. $r = \dfrac{1}{1 + \cos \theta}$

26. $r = \dfrac{3}{1 - \sin \theta}$

27. $r = \dfrac{8}{4 + 3 \sin \theta}$

28. $r = \dfrac{10}{5 + 4 \cos \theta}$

29. $r = \dfrac{9}{3 - 6 \cos \theta}$

30. $r = \dfrac{12}{4 + 8 \sin \theta}$

31. $r = \dfrac{8}{2 - \sin \theta}$

32. $r = \dfrac{8}{2 + 4 \cos \theta}$

33. $r(3 - 2 \sin \theta) = 6$

34. $r(2 - \cos \theta) = 2$

35. $r = \dfrac{6 \sec \theta}{2 \sec \theta - 1}$

36. $r = \dfrac{3 \csc \theta}{\csc \theta - 1}$

In Problems 37–42, find a polar equation for each conic. For each, a focus is at the pole.

37. $e = 1$; directrix is parallel to the polar axis 1 unit above the pole.

38. $e = 1$; directrix is parallel to the polar axis 2 units below the pole.

39. $e = \dfrac{4}{5}$; directrix is perpendicular to the polar axis 3 units to the left of the pole.

40. $e = \dfrac{2}{3}$; directrix is parallel to the polar axis 3 units above the pole.

41. $e = 6$; directrix is parallel to the polar axis 2 units below the pole.

42. $e = 5$; directrix is perpendicular to the polar axis 5 units to the right of the pole.

Applications and Extensions

43. Derive equation (b) in Table 5:
$$r = \dfrac{ep}{1 + e \cos \theta}$$

44. Derive equation (c) in Table 5:
$$r = \dfrac{ep}{1 + e \sin \theta}$$

45. Derive equation (d) in Table 5:
$$r = \dfrac{ep}{1 - e \sin \theta}$$

46. Orbit of Mercury The planet Mercury travels around the Sun in an elliptical orbit given approximately by
$$r = \dfrac{(3.442)10^7}{1 - 0.206 \cos \theta}$$

where r is measured in miles and the Sun is at the pole. Find the distance from Mercury to the Sun at *aphelion* (greatest distance from the Sun) and at *perihelion* (shortest distance from the Sun). See the figure. Use the aphelion and perihelion to graph the orbit of Mercury using a graphing utility.

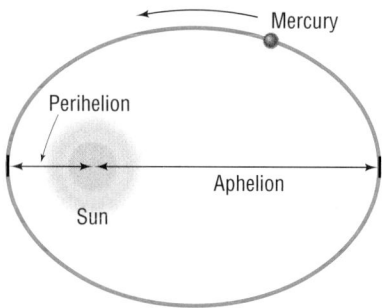

'Are You Prepared?' Answers

1. $r \cos \theta$; $r \sin \theta$

2. $x^2 + y^2 = 6x$ or $(x - 3)^2 + y^2 = 9$

10.7   Plane Curves and Parametric Equations

PREPARING FOR THIS SECTION   *Before getting started, review the following:*

- Amplitude and Period of Sinusoidal Graphs (Section 6.4, pp. 400–401)

Now Work the 'Are You Prepared?' problem on page 697.

OBJECTIVES   1   Graph Parametric Equations by Hand (p. 687)
2   Graph Parametric Equations Using a Graphing Utility (p. 688)
3   Find a Rectangular Equation for a Curve Defined Parametrically (p. 689)
4   Use Time as a Parameter in Parametric Equations (p. 691)
5   Find Parametric Equations for Curves Defined by Rectangular Equations (p. 694)

Equations of the form $y = f(x)$, where f is a function, have graphs that are intersected no more than once by any vertical line. The graphs of many of the conics and certain other, more complicated, graphs do not have this characteristic. Yet each graph, like the graph of a function, is a collection of points (x, y) in the xy-plane; that is, each is a *plane curve*. In this section, we discuss another way of representing such graphs.

Let $x = f(t)$ and $y = g(t)$, where f and g are two functions whose common domain is some interval I. The collection of points defined by

$$(x, y) = (f(t), g(t))$$

is called a **plane curve.** The equations

$$x = f(t) \qquad y = g(t)$$

where t is in I, are called **parametric equations** of the curve. The variable t is called a **parameter.**

1   Graph Parametric Equations by Hand

Parametric equations are particularly useful in describing movement along a curve. Suppose that a curve is defined by the parametric equations

$$x = f(t), \qquad y = g(t), \qquad a \le t \le b$$

Figure 59

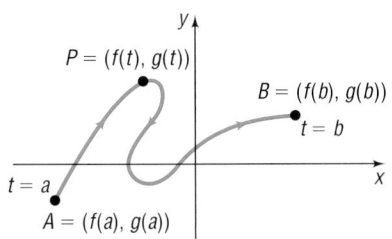

where f and g are each defined over the interval $a \le t \le b$. For a given value of t, we can find the value of $x = f(t)$ and $y = g(t)$, obtaining a point (x, y) on the curve. In fact, as t varies over the interval from $t = a$ to $t = b$, successive values of t give rise to a directed movement along the curve; that is, the curve is traced out in a certain direction by the corresponding succession of points (x, y). See Figure 59. The arrows show the direction, or **orientation,** along the curve as t varies from a to b.

EXAMPLE 1   Graphing a Curve Defined by Parametric Equations

Graph the curve defined by the parametric equations

$$x = 3t^2, \qquad y = 2t, \qquad -2 \le t \le 2$$

Solution   For each number t, $-2 \le t \le 2$, there corresponds a number x and a number y. For example, when $t = -2$, then $x = 3(-2)^2 = 12$ and $y = 2(-2) = -4$. When $t = 0$, then $x = 0$ and $y = 0$. We can set up a table listing various choices of the parameter t and the corresponding values for x and y, as shown in Table 6. Plotting these points and connecting them with a smooth curve leads to Figure 60. The arrows in Figure 60 are used to indicate the orientation.

Table 6

t	x	y	(x, y)
−2	12	−4	(12, −4)
−1	3	−2	(3, −2)
0	0	0	(0, 0)
1	3	2	(3, 2)
2	12	4	(12, 4)

Figure 60

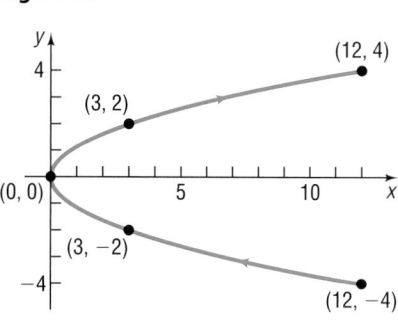

2 Graph Parametric Equations Using a Graphing Utility

Most graphing utilities have the capability of graphing parametric equations. The following steps are usually required to obtain the graph of parametric equations. Check your owner's manual to see how yours works.

Graphing Parametric Equations Using a Graphing Utility

STEP 1: Set the mode to PARametric, Enter $x(t)$ and $y(t)$.
STEP 2: Select the viewing window. In addition to setting Xmin, Xmax, Xscl, and so on, the viewing window in parametric mode requires setting minimum and maximum values for the parameter t and an increment setting for t(Tstep).
STEP 3: Graph.

EXAMPLE 2

Graphing a Curve Defined by Parametric Equations Using a Graphing Utility

Graph the curve defined by the parametric equations

$$x = 3t^2, \qquad y = 2t, \qquad -2 \le t \le 2 \qquad \textbf{(1)}$$

Solution

STEP 1: Enter the equations $x(t) = 3t^2$, $y(t) = 2t$ with the graphing utility in PARametric mode.
STEP 2: Select the viewing window. The interval I is $-2 \le t \le 2$, so we select the following square viewing window:

$$T\text{min} = -2 \qquad X\text{min} = 0 \qquad Y\text{min} = -5$$
$$T\text{max} = 2 \qquad X\text{max} = 15 \qquad Y\text{max} = 5$$
$$T\text{step} = 0.1 \qquad X\text{scl} = 1 \qquad Y\text{scl} = 1$$

We choose Tmin $= -2$ and Tmax $= 2$ because $-2 \le t \le 2$. Finally, the choice for Tstep will determine the number of points the graphing utility will plot. For example, with Tstep at 0.1, the graphing utility will evaluate x and y at $t = -2, -1.9, -1.8$, and so on. The smaller the Tstep, the more points the graphing utility will plot. The reader is encouraged to experiment with different values of Tstep to see how the graph is affected.
STEP 3: Graph. Notice the direction the graph is drawn in. This direction shows the orientation of the curve. See Figure 61.

Figure 61

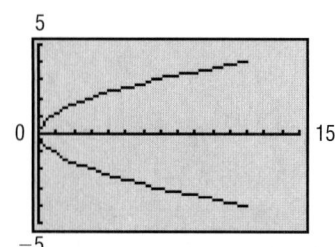

3 Find a Rectangular Equation for a Curve Defined Parametrically

The curve given in Examples 1 and 2 should be familiar. To identify it accurately, we
find the corresponding rectangular equation by eliminating the parameter t from
the parametric equations given in Example 1:

$$x = 3t^2, \qquad y = 2t, \qquad -2 \leq t \leq 2$$

Noting that we can easily solve for t in $y = 2t$, obtaining $t = \dfrac{y}{2}$, we substitute this
expression in the other equation.

$$x = 3t^2 = 3\left(\frac{y}{2}\right)^2 = \frac{3y^2}{4}$$
$$\uparrow$$
$$t = \frac{y}{2}$$

This equation, $x = \dfrac{3y^2}{4}$, is the equation of a parabola with vertex at $(0, 0)$ and axis
of symmetry along the x-axis.

Note that the parameterized curve defined by equation (1) and shown in
Figure 60 (or 61) is only a part of the parabola $x = \dfrac{3y^2}{4}$. The graph of the rectangular
equation obtained by eliminating the parameter will, in general, contain more points
than the original parameterized curve. Care must therefore be taken when a parameterized curve is sketched by hand after eliminating the parameter. Even so, the
process of eliminating the parameter t of a parameterized curve to identify it accurately is sometimes a better approach than plotting points. However, the elimination process sometimes requires a little ingenuity.

EXAMPLE 3 **Finding the Rectangular Equation of a Curve Defined Parametrically**

Find the rectangular equation of the curve whose parametric equations are

$$x = a \cos t, \qquad y = a \sin t, \qquad -\infty < t < \infty$$

where $a > 0$ is a constant. By hand, graph this curve, indicating its orientation.

Solution The presence of sines and cosines in the parametric equations suggests that we use a Pythagorean Identity. In fact, since

$$\cos t = \frac{x}{a} \qquad \sin t = \frac{y}{a}$$

we find that

$$\cos^2 t + \sin^2 t = 1$$

$$\left(\frac{x}{a}\right)^2 + \left(\frac{y}{a}\right)^2 = 1$$

$$x^2 + y^2 = a^2$$

Figure 62

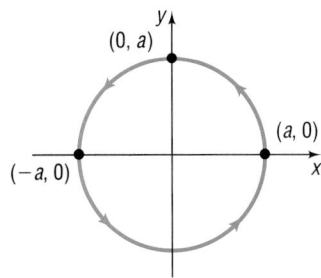

The curve is a circle with center at $(0, 0)$ and radius a. As the parameter t increases, say from $t = 0$ [the point $(a, 0)$] to $t = \dfrac{\pi}{2}$ [the point $(0, a)$] to $t = \pi$ [the point $(-a, 0)$], we see that the corresponding points are traced in a counterclockwise direction around the circle. The orientation is as indicated in Figure 62.

Now Work PROBLEMS 7 AND 19

Let's analyze the curve in Example 3 further. The domain of each parametric equation is $-\infty < t < \infty$. Thus, the graph in Figure 62 is actually being repeated each time that t increases by 2π.

If we wanted the curve to consist of exactly 1 revolution in the counterclockwise direction, we could write

$$x = a \cos t, \qquad y = a \sin t, \qquad 0 \le t \le 2\pi$$

This curve starts at $t = 0$ [the point $(a, 0)$] and, proceeding counterclockwise around the circle, ends at $t = 2\pi$ [also the point $(a, 0)$].

If we wanted the curve to consist of exactly three revolutions in the counterclockwise direction, we could write

$$x = a \cos t, \qquad y = a \sin t, \qquad -2\pi \le t \le 4\pi$$

or

$$x = a \cos t, \qquad y = a \sin t, \qquad 0 \le t \le 6\pi$$

or

$$x = a \cos t, \qquad y = a \sin t, \qquad 2\pi \le t \le 8\pi$$

EXAMPLE 4 | **Describing Parametric Equations**

Find rectangular equations for the following curves defined by parametric equations. Graph each curve.

(a) $x = a \cos t, \quad y = a \sin t, \quad 0 \le t \le \pi, \quad a > 0$

(b) $x = -a \sin t, \quad y = -a \cos t, \quad 0 \le t \le \pi, \quad a > 0$

Solution (a) We eliminate the parameter t using a Pythagorean Identity.

$$\cos^2 t + \sin^2 t = 1$$

$$\left(\frac{x}{a}\right)^2 + \left(\frac{y}{a}\right)^2 = 1$$

$$x^2 + y^2 = a^2$$

The curve defined by these parametric equations is a circle, with radius a and center at $(0, 0)$. The circle begins at the point $(a, 0)$, $t = 0$; passes through the point $(0, a)$, $t = \dfrac{\pi}{2}$; and ends at the point $(-a, 0)$, $t = \pi$.

Figure 63

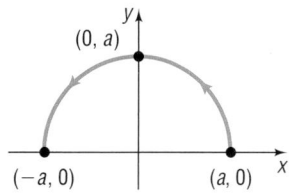

The parametric equations define an upper semicircle of radius a with a counterclockwise orientation. See Figure 63. The rectangular equation is

$$y = \sqrt{a^2 - x^2} \qquad -a \le x \le a$$

(b) We eliminate the parameter t using a Pythagorean Identity.

$$\sin^2 t + \cos^2 t = 1$$

$$\left(\frac{x}{-a}\right)^2 + \left(\frac{y}{-a}\right)^2 = 1$$

$$x^2 + y^2 = a^2$$

Figure 64

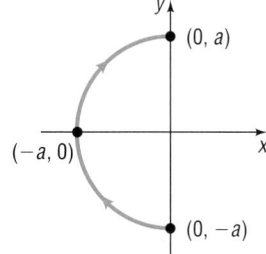

The curve defined by these parametric equations is a circle, with radius a and center at $(0, 0)$. The circle begins at the point $(0, -a), t = 0$; passes through the point $(-a, 0), t = \dfrac{\pi}{2}$; and ends at the point $(0, a), t = \pi$. The parametric equations define a left semicircle of radius a with a clockwise orientation. See Figure 64. The rectangular equation is

$$x = -\sqrt{a^2 - y^2} \qquad -a \le y \le a$$

Seeing the Concept

Graph $\quad x = \cos t, y = \sin t \quad$ for $0 \le t \le 2\pi$. Compare to Figure 62.
Graph $\quad x = \cos t, y = \sin t \quad$ for $0 \le t \le \pi$. Compare to Figure 63.
Graph $\quad x = -\sin t, y = -\cos t \quad$ for $0 \le t \le \pi$. Compare to Figure 64.

Example 4 illustrates the versatility of parametric equations for replacing complicated rectangular equations, while providing additional information about orientation. These characteristics make parametric equations very useful in applications, such as projectile motion.

4 Use Time as a Parameter in Parametric Equations

If we think of the parameter t as time, then the parametric equations $x = f(t)$ and $y = g(t)$ of a curve C specify how the x- and y-coordinates of a moving point vary with time.

For example, we can use parametric equations to model the motion of an object, sometimes referred to as **curvilinear motion.** Using parametric equations, we can specify not only where the object travels, that is, its location (x, y), but also when it gets there, that is, the time t.

When an object is propelled upward at an inclination θ to the horizontal with initial speed v_0, the resulting motion is called **projectile motion.** See Figure 65(a).

In calculus it is shown that the parametric equations of the path of a projectile fired at an inclination θ to the horizontal, with an initial speed v_0, from a height h above the horizontal are

$$x = (v_0 \cos \theta)t \qquad y = -\frac{1}{2}gt^2 + (v_0 \sin \theta)t + h \qquad \textbf{(2)}$$

where t is the time and g is the constant acceleration due to gravity (approximately 32 ft/sec/sec or 9.8 m/sec/sec). See Figure 65(b).

Figure 65

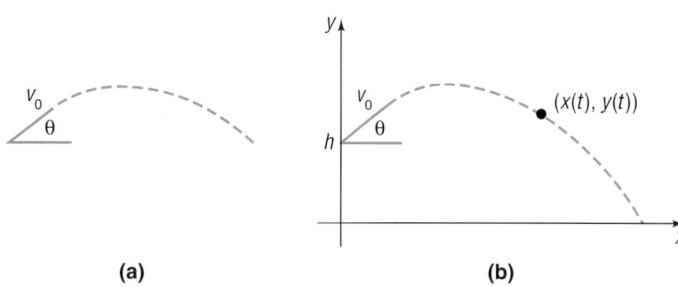

(a)   (b)

| EXAMPLE 5 | Projectile Motion |

Figure 66

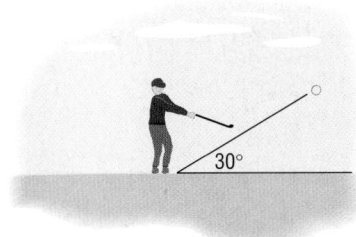

Suppose that Jim hit a golf ball with an initial velocity of 150 feet per second at an angle of 30° to the horizontal. See Figure 66.

(a) Find parametric equations that describe the position of the ball as a function of time.

(b) How long is the golf ball in the air?

(c) When is the ball at its maximum height? Determine the maximum height of the ball.

(d) Determine the distance that the ball traveled.

(e) Using a graphing utility, simulate the motion of the golf ball by simultaneously graphing the equations found in part (a).

Solution

(a) We have $v_0 = 150$ ft/sec, $\theta = 30°$, $h = 0$ (the ball is on the ground), and $g = 32$ (since the units are in feet and seconds). Substituting these values into equations (2), we find that

$$x = (v_0 \cos \theta)t = (150 \cos 30°)t = 75\sqrt{3}\,t$$

$$y = -\frac{1}{2}gt^2 + (v_0 \sin \theta)t + h = -\frac{1}{2}(32)t^2 + (150 \sin 30°)t + 0$$

$$= -16t^2 + 75t$$

(b) To determine the length of time that the ball is in the air, we solve the equation $y = 0$.

$$-16t^2 + 75t = 0$$

$$t(-16t + 75) = 0$$

$$t = 0 \text{ sec} \quad \text{or} \quad t = \frac{75}{16} = 4.6875 \text{ sec}$$

The ball will strike the ground after 4.6875 seconds.

(c) Notice that the height y of the ball is a quadratic function of t, so the maximum height of the ball can be found by determining the vertex of $y = -16t^2 + 75t$. The value of t at the vertex is

$$t = \frac{-b}{2a} = \frac{-75}{-32} = 2.34375 \text{ sec}$$

The ball is at its maximum height after 2.34375 seconds. The maximum height of the ball is found by evaluating the function y at $t = 2.34375$ seconds.

$$\text{Maximum height} = -16(2.34375)^2 + (75)2.34375 \approx 87.89 \text{ feet}$$

Figure 67

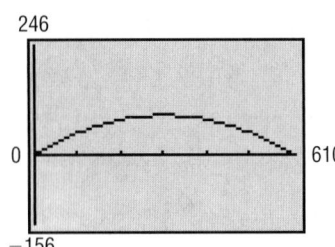

(d) Since the ball is in the air for 4.6875 seconds, the horizontal distance that the ball travels is

$$x = \left(75\sqrt{3}\right)4.6875 \approx 608.92 \text{ feet}$$

(e) We enter the equations from part (a) into a graphing utility with $T\text{min} = 0$, $T\text{max} = 4.7$, and $T\text{step} = 0.1$. We use ZOOM-SQUARE to avoid any distortion to the angle of elevation. See Figure 67.

∎

Exploration

Simulate the motion of a ball thrown straight up with an initial speed of 100 feet per second from a height of 5 feet above the ground. Use PARametric mode with $T\text{min} = 0$, $T\text{max} = 6.5$, $T\text{step} = 0.1$, $X\text{min} = 0$, $X\text{max} = 5$, $Y\text{min} = 0$, and $Y\text{max} = 180$. What happens to the speed with which the graph is drawn as the ball goes up and then comes back down? How do you interpret this physically? Repeat the experiment using other values for $T\text{step}$. How does this affect the experiment?

[**Hint:** In the projectile motion equations, let $\theta = 90°$, $v_0 = 100$, $h = 5$, and $g = 32$. We use $x = 3$ instead of $x = 0$ to see the vertical motion better.]

Result   See Figure 68. In Figure 68(a) the ball is going up. In Figure 68(b) the ball is near its highest point. Finally, in Figure 68(c) the ball is coming back down.

Figure 68

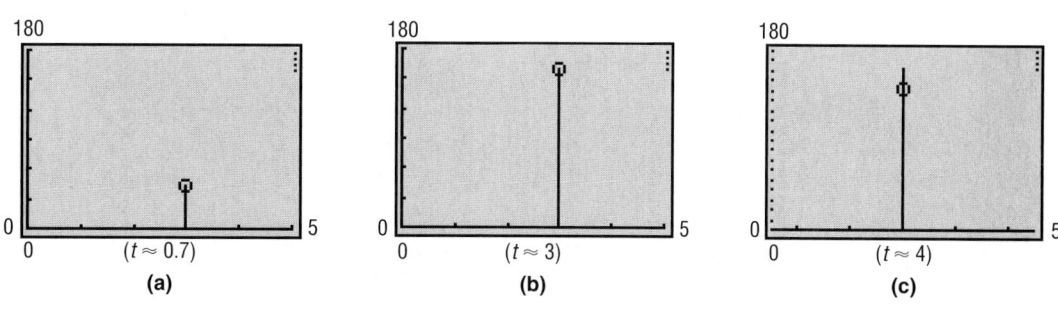

(a)   ($t \approx 0.7$)   (b)   ($t \approx 3$)   (c)   ($t \approx 4$)

Notice that, as the ball goes up, its speed decreases, until at the highest point it is zero. Then the speed increases as the ball comes back down.

Now Work   PROBLEM 49

A graphing utility can be used to simulate other kinds of motion as well. Let's work again Example 5 from Appendix A, Section A.8.

EXAMPLE 6   **Simulating Motion**

Tanya, who is a long distance runner, runs at an average speed of 8 miles per hour. Two hours after Tanya leaves your house, you leave in your Honda and follow the same route. If your average speed is 40 miles per hour, how long will it be before you catch up to Tanya? See Figure 69. Use a simulation of the two motions to verify the answer.

Figure 69

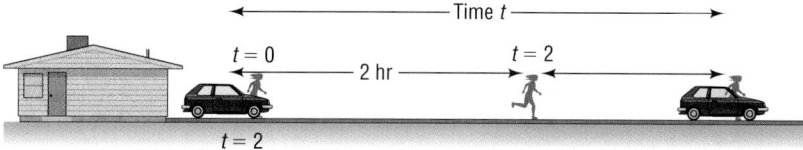

Solution   We begin with two sets of parametric equations: one to describe Tanya's motion, the other to describe the motion of the Honda. We choose time $t = 0$ to be when Tanya leaves the house. If we choose $y_1 = 2$ as Tanya's path, then we can use $y_2 = 4$ as the parallel path of the Honda. The horizontal distances traversed in time t (Distance = Rate × Time) are

$$\text{Tanya:} \quad x_1 = 8t \qquad \text{Honda:} \quad x_2 = 40(t - 2)$$

The Honda catches up to Tanya when $x_1 = x_2$.

$$8t = 40(t - 2)$$
$$8t = 40t - 80$$
$$-32t = -80$$
$$t = \frac{-80}{-32} = 2.5$$

The Honda catches up to Tanya 2.5 hours after Tanya leaves the house.
In PARametric mode with Tstep $= 0.01$, we simultaneously graph

$$\text{Tanya:} \quad x_1 = 8t \qquad \text{Honda:} \quad x_2 = 40(t - 2)$$
$$y_1 = 2 \qquad\qquad\qquad y_2 = 4$$

for $0 \leq t \leq 3$.

Figure 70 shows the relative position of Tanya and the Honda for $t = 0, t = 2, t = 2.25, t = 2.5,$ and $t = 2.75.$

Figure 70

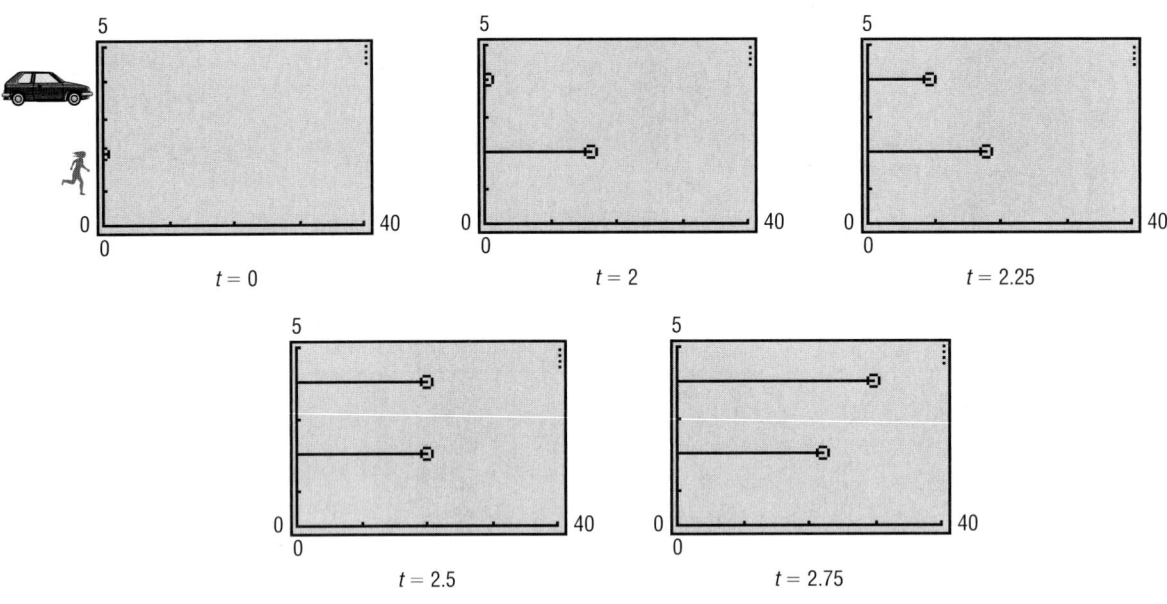

$t = 0$ $t = 2$ $t = 2.25$

$t = 2.5$ $t = 2.75$

5 Find Parametric Equations for Curves Defined by Rectangular Equations

We now take up the question of how to find parametric equations of a given curve.

If a curve is defined by the equation $y = f(x)$, where f is a function, one way of finding parametric equations is to let $x = t$. Then $y = f(t)$ and

$$x = t, \quad y = f(t), \quad t \text{ in the domain of } f$$

are parametric equations of the curve.

| EXAMPLE 7 | Finding Parametric Equations for a Curve Defined by a Rectangular Equation |

Find two different parametric equations for the equation $y = x^2 - 4.$

Solution   For the first parametric equation, let $x = t$. Then the parametric equations are

$$x = t, \quad y = t^2 - 4, \quad -\infty < t < \infty$$

A second parametric equation is found by letting $x = t^3$. Then the parametric equations become

$$x = t^3, \quad y = t^6 - 4, \quad -\infty < t < \infty$$

Care must be taken when using the second approach in Example 7, since the substitution for x must be a function that allows x to take on all the values stipulated by the domain of f. For example, letting $x = t^2$ so that $y = t^4 - 4$ does not result in equivalent parametric equations for $y = x^2 - 4$, since only points for which $x \geq 0$ are obtained; yet the domain of $y = x^2 - 4$ is $\{x \mid x \text{ is any real number}\}$.

━━━━━━ **Now Work** PROBLEM 33

| EXAMPLE 8 | **Finding Parametric Equations for an Object in Motion** |

Find parametric equations for the ellipse

$$x^2 + \frac{y^2}{9} = 1$$

where the parameter t is time (in seconds) and

(a) The motion around the ellipse is clockwise, begins at the point $(0, 3)$, and requires 1 second for a complete revolution.

(b) The motion around the ellipse is counterclockwise, begins at the point $(1, 0)$, and requires 2 seconds for a complete revolution.

Figure 71

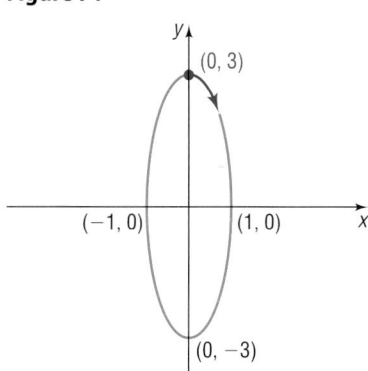

Solution (a) See Figure 71. Since the motion begins at the point $(0, 3)$, we want $x = 0$ and $y = 3$ when $t = 0$. Furthermore, since the given equation is an ellipse, we begin by letting

$$x = \sin(\omega t) \qquad \frac{y}{3} = \cos(\omega t)$$

for some constant ω. These parametric equations satisfy the equation of the ellipse. Furthermore, with this choice, when $t = 0$, we have $x = 0$ and $y = 3$.

For the motion to be clockwise, the motion will have to begin with the value of x increasing and y decreasing as t increases. This requires that $\omega > 0$. [Do you know why? If $\omega > 0$, then $x = \sin(\omega t)$ is increasing when $t > 0$ is near zero and $y = 3 \cos(\omega t)$ is decreasing when $t > 0$ is near zero.] See the red part of the graph in Figure 71.

Finally, since 1 revolution requires 1 second, the period $\dfrac{2\pi}{\omega} = 1$, so $\omega = 2\pi$.

Parametric equations that satisfy the conditions stipulated are

$$x = \sin(2\pi t), \qquad y = 3 \cos(2\pi t), \qquad 0 \le t \le 1 \qquad \textbf{(3)}$$

Figure 72

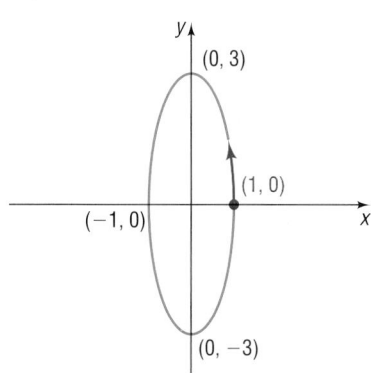

(b) See Figure 72. Since the motion begins at the point $(1, 0)$, we want $x = 1$ and $y = 0$ when $t = 0$. The given equation is an ellipse, so we begin by letting

$$x = \cos(\omega t) \qquad \frac{y}{3} = \sin(\omega t)$$

for some constant ω. These parametric equations satisfy the equation of the ellipse. Furthermore, with this choice, when $t = 0$, we have $x = 1$ and $y = 0$.

For the motion to be counterclockwise, the motion will have to begin with the value of x decreasing and y increasing as t increases. This requires that $\omega > 0$. [Do you know why?] Finally, since 1 revolution requires 2 seconds, the period is $\dfrac{2\pi}{\omega} = 2$, so $\omega = \pi$. The parametric equations that satisfy the conditions stipulated are

$$x = \cos(\pi t), \qquad y = 3 \sin(\pi t), \qquad 0 \le t \le 2 \qquad \textbf{(4)}$$

Either equation (3) or (4) can serve as a parametric equation for the ellipse $x^2 + \dfrac{y^2}{9} = 1$ given in Example 8. The direction of the motion, the beginning point, and the time for 1 revolution serve to help us arrive at a particular parametric representation.

━━➤ **Now Work** PROBLEM **39**

The Cycloid

Suppose that a circle of radius a rolls along a horizontal line without slipping. As the circle rolls along the line, a point P on the circle will trace out a curve called a **cycloid** (see Figure 73). We now seek parametric equations* for a cycloid.

Figure 73

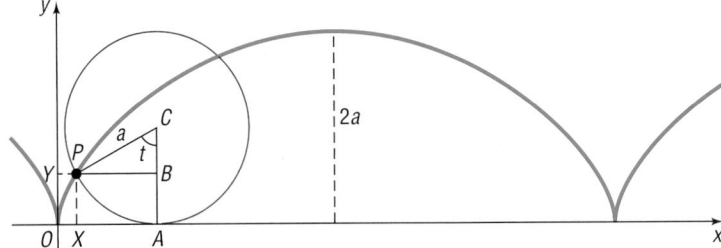

We begin with a circle of radius a and take the fixed line on which the circle rolls as the x-axis. Let the origin be one of the points at which the point P comes in contact with the x-axis. Figure 73 illustrates the position of this point P after the circle has rolled somewhat. The angle t (in radians) measures the angle through which the circle has rolled.

Since we require no slippage, it follows that

$$\text{Arc } AP = d(O, A)$$

The length of the arc AP is given by $s = r\theta$, where $r = a$ and $\theta = t$ radians. Then

$$at = d(O, A) \quad \text{\scriptsize $s = r\theta$, where $r = a$ and $\theta = t$}$$

The x-coordinate of the point P is

$$d(O, X) = d(O, A) - d(X, A) = at - a\sin t = a(t - \sin t)$$

The y-coordinate of the point P is equal to

$$d(O, Y) = d(A, C) - d(B, C) = a - a\cos t = a(1 - \cos t)$$

The parametric equations of the cycloid are

$$\boxed{x = a(t - \sin t) \qquad y = a(1 - \cos t) \tag{5}}$$

Exploration

Graph $\quad x = t - \sin t, y = 1 - \cos t,$

$0 \leq t \leq 3\pi$, using your graphing utility

with Tstep $= \dfrac{\pi}{36}$ and a square screen.

Compare your results with Figure 73.

Applications to Mechanics

If a is negative in equation (5), we obtain an inverted cycloid, as shown in Figure 74(a). The inverted cycloid occurs as a result of some remarkable applications in the field of mechanics. We shall mention two of them: the *brachistochrone* and the *tautochrone*.†

Figure 74

(a) Inverted cycloid   **(b)** Curve of quickest descent   **(c)** All reach Q at the same time

*Any attempt to derive the rectangular equation of a cycloid would soon demonstrate how complicated the task is.

†In Greek, *brachistochrone* means "the shortest time" and *tautochrone* means "equal time."

The **brachistochrone** is the curve of quickest descent. If a particle is constrained to follow some path from one point A to a lower point B (not on the same vertical line) and is acted on only by gravity, the time needed to make the descent is least if the path is an inverted cycloid. See Figure 74(b). This remarkable discovery, which is attributed to many famous mathematicians (including Johann Bernoulli and Blaise Pascal), was a significant step in creating the branch of mathematics known as the *calculus of variations.*

To define the **tautochrone,** let Q be the lowest point on an inverted cycloid. If several particles placed at various positions on an inverted cycloid simultaneously begin to slide down the cycloid, they will reach the point Q at the same time, as indicated in Figure 74(c). The tautochrone property of the cycloid was used by Christiaan Huygens (1629–1695), the Dutch mathematician, physicist, and astronomer, to construct a pendulum clock with a bob that swings along a cycloid (see Figure 75). In Huygen's clock, the bob was made to swing along a cycloid by suspending the bob on a thin wire constrained by two plates shaped like cycloids. In a clock of this design, the period of the pendulum is independent of its amplitude.

Figure 75

Cycloid   Cycloid

Cycloid

10.7 Assess Your Understanding

'Are You Prepared?' *Answers are given at the end of this exercise. If you get a wrong answer, read the page listed in red.*

1. The function $f(x) = 3\sin(4x)$ has amplitude _____ and period _____. (p. 401)

Concepts and Vocabulary

2. Let $x = f(t)$ and $y = g(t)$, where f and g are two functions whose common domain is some interval I. The collection of points defined by $(x, y) = (f(t), g(t))$ is called a(n) _____ _____. The variable t is called a(n) _____.

3. The parametric equations $x = 2\sin t, y = 3\cos t$ define a(n) _____.

4. If a circle rolls along a horizontal line without slippage, a point P on the circle will trace out a curve called a(n) _____.

5. **True or False** Parametric equations defining a curve are unique.

6. **True or False** Curves defined using parametric equations have an orientation.

Skill Building

In Problems 7–26, graph the curve whose parametric equations are given and show its orientation. Find the rectangular equation of each curve. Verify your graph using a graphing utility.

7. $x = 3t + 2$, $y = t + 1$; $0 \le t \le 4$

8. $x = t - 3$, $y = 2t + 4$; $0 \le t \le 2$

9. $x = t + 2$, $y = \sqrt{t}$; $t \ge 0$

10. $x = \sqrt{2t}$, $y = 4t$; $t \ge 0$

11. $x = t^2 + 4$, $y = t^2 - 4$; $-\infty < t < \infty$

12. $x = \sqrt{t} + 4$, $y = \sqrt{t} - 4$; $t \ge 0$

13. $x = 3t^2$, $y = t + 1$; $-\infty < t < \infty$

14. $x = 2t - 4$, $y = 4t^2$; $-\infty < t < \infty$

15. $x = 2e^t$, $y = 1 + e^t$; $t \ge 0$

16. $x = e^t$, $y = e^{-t}$; $t \ge 0$

17. $x = \sqrt{t}$, $y = t^{3/2}$; $t \ge 0$

18. $x = t^{3/2} + 1$, $y = \sqrt{t}$; $t \ge 0$

19. $x = 2\cos t$, $y = 3\sin t$; $0 \le t \le 2\pi$

20. $x = 2\cos t$, $y = 3\sin t$; $0 \le t \le \pi$

21. $x = 2\cos t$, $y = 3\sin t$; $-\pi \le t \le 0$

22. $x = 2\cos t$, $y = \sin t$; $0 \le t \le \dfrac{\pi}{2}$

23. $x = \sec t$, $y = \tan t$; $0 \le t \le \dfrac{\pi}{4}$

24. $x = \csc t$, $y = \cot t$; $\dfrac{\pi}{4} \le t \le \dfrac{\pi}{2}$

25. $x = \sin^2 t$, $y = \cos^2 t$; $0 \le t \le 2\pi$

26. $x = t^2$, $y = \ln t$; $t > 0$

In Problems 27–34, find two different parametric equations for each rectangular equation.

27. $y = 4x - 1$

28. $y = -8x + 3$

29. $y = x^2 + 1$

30. $y = -2x^2 + 1$

31. $y = x^3$

32. $y = x^4 + 1$

33. $x = y^{3/2}$

34. $x = \sqrt{y}$

In Problems 35–38, find parametric equations that define the curve shown.

35.

36.

37.

38.
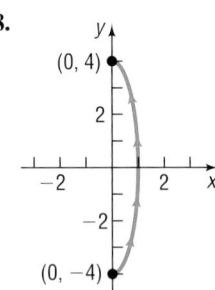

In Problems 39–42, find parametric equations for an object that moves along the ellipse $\dfrac{x^2}{4} + \dfrac{y^2}{9} = 1$ with the motion described.

39. The motion begins at $(2, 0)$, is clockwise, and requires 2 seconds for a complete revolution.

40. The motion begins at $(0, 3)$, is counterclockwise, and requires 1 second for a complete revolution.

41. The motion begins at $(0, 3)$, is clockwise, and requires 1 second for a complete revolution.

42. The motion begins at $(2, 0)$, is counterclockwise, and requires 3 seconds for a complete revolution.

In Problems 43 and 44, the parametric equations of four curves are given. Graph each of them, indicating the orientation.

43. C_1: $x = t$, $y = t^2$; $-4 \le t \le 4$
C_2: $x = \cos t$, $y = 1 - \sin^2 t$; $0 \le t \le \pi$
C_3: $x = e^t$, $y = e^{2t}$; $0 \le t \le \ln 4$
C_4: $x = \sqrt{t}$, $y = t$; $0 \le t \le 16$

44. C_1: $x = t$, $y = \sqrt{1 - t^2}$; $-1 \le t \le 1$
C_2: $x = \sin t$, $y = \cos t$; $0 \le t \le 2\pi$
C_3: $x = \cos t$, $y = \sin t$; $0 \le t \le 2\pi$
C_4: $x = \sqrt{1 - t^2}$, $y = t$; $-1 \le t \le 1$

In Problems 45–48, use a graphing utility to graph the curve defined by the given parametric equations.

45. $x = t \sin t$, $y = t \cos t$, $t > 0$

46. $x = \sin t + \cos t$, $y = \sin t - \cos t$

47. $x = 4 \sin t - 2 \sin(2t)$
$y = 4 \cos t - 2 \cos(2t)$

48. $x = 4 \sin t + 2 \sin(2t)$
$y = 4 \cos t + 2 \cos(2t)$

Applications and Extensions

49. Projectile Motion Bob throws a ball straight up with an initial speed of 50 feet per second from a height of 6 feet.
(a) Find parametric equations that model the motion of the ball as a function of time.
(b) How long is the ball in the air?
(c) When is the ball at its maximum height? Determine the maximum height of the ball.
(d) Simulate the motion of the ball by graphing the equations found in part (a).

50. Projectile Motion Alice throws a ball straight up with an initial speed of 40 feet per second from a height of 5 feet.
(a) Find parametric equations that model the motion of the ball as a function of time.
(b) How long is the ball in the air?
(c) When is the ball at its maximum height? Determine the maximum height of the ball.
(d) Simulate the motion of the ball by graphing the equations found in part (a).

51. Catching a Train Bill's train leaves at 8:06 AM and accelerates at the rate of 2 meters per second per second. Bill, who can run 5 meters per second, arrives at the train station 5 seconds after the train has left and runs for the train.
(a) Find parametric equations that model the motions of the train and Bill as a function of time.

[**Hint:** The position s at time t of an object having acceleration a is $s = \dfrac{1}{2}at^2$.]

(b) Determine algebraically whether Bill will catch the train. If so, when?
(c) Simulate the motion of the train and Bill by simultaneously graphing the equations found in part (a).

52. Catching a Bus Jodi's bus leaves at 5:30 PM and accelerates at the rate of 3 meters per second per second. Jodi, who can run 5 meters per second, arrives at the bus station 2 seconds after the bus has left and runs for the bus.
(a) Find parametric equations that model the motions of the bus and Jodi as a function of time.

[**Hint:** The position s at time t of an object having acceleration a is $s = \dfrac{1}{2}at^2$.]

(b) Determine algebraically whether Jodi will catch the bus. If so, when?
(c) Simulate the motion of the bus and Jodi by simultaneously graphing the equations found in part (a).

53. Projectile Motion Ichiro throws a baseball with an initial speed of 145 feet per second at an angle of $20°$ to the horizontal. The ball leaves Ichiro's hand at a height of 5 feet.
(a) Find parametric equations that model the position of the ball as a function of time.
(b) How long is the ball in the air?
(c) Determine the horizontal distance that the ball traveled.
(d) When is the ball at its maximum height? Determine the maximum height of the ball.
(e) Using a graphing utility, simultaneously graph the equations found in part (a).

54. Projectile Motion Barry Bonds hit a baseball with an initial speed of 125 feet per second at an angle of 40° to the horizontal. The ball was hit at a height of 3 feet off the ground.
(a) Find parametric equations that model the position of the ball as a function of time.
(b) How long is the ball in the air?
(c) Determine the horizontal distance that the ball traveled.
(d) When is the ball at its maximum height? Determine the maximum height of the ball.
(e) Using a graphing utility, simultaneously graph the equations found in part (a).

55. Projectile Motion Suppose that Adam hits a golf ball off a cliff 300 meters high with an initial speed of 40 meters per second at an angle of 45° to the horizontal.
(a) Find parametric equations that model the position of the ball as a function of time.
(b) How long is the ball in the air?
(c) Determine the horizontal distance that the ball traveled.
(d) When is the ball at its maximum height? Determine the maximum height of the ball.
(e) Using a graphing utility, simultaneously graph the equations found in part (a).

56. Projectile Motion Suppose that Karla hits a golf ball off a cliff 300 meters high with an initial speed of 40 meters per second at an angle of 45° to the horizontal on the Moon (gravity on the Moon is one-sixth of that on Earth).
(a) Find parametric equations that model the position of the ball as a function of time.
(b) How long is the ball in the air?
(c) Determine the horizontal distance that the ball traveled.
(d) When is the ball at its maximum height? Determine the maximum height of the ball.
(e) Using a graphing utility, simultaneously graph the equations found in part (a).

57. Uniform Motion A Toyota Camry (traveling east at 40 mph) and a Chevy Impala (traveling north at 30 mph) are heading toward the same intersection. The Camry is 5 miles from the intersection when the Impala is 4 miles from the intersection. See the figure.

(a) Find parametric equations that model the motion of the Camry and Impala.
(b) Find a formula for the distance between the cars as a function of time.
(c) Graph the function in part (b) using a graphing utility.
(d) What is the minimum distance between the cars? When are the cars closest?
(e) Simulate the motion of the cars by simultaneously graphing the equations found in part (a).

58. Uniform Motion A Cessna (heading south at 120 mph) and a Boeing 747 (heading west at 600 mph) are flying toward the same point at the same altitude. The Cessna is 100 miles from the point where the flight patterns intersect, and the 747 is 550 miles from this intersection point. See the figure.

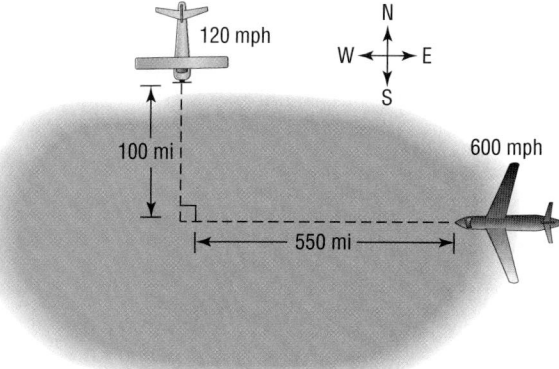

(a) Find parametric equations that model the motion of the Cessna and the 747.
(b) Find a formula for the distance between the planes as a function of time.
(c) Graph the function in part (b) using a graphing utility.
(d) What is the minimum distance between the planes? When are the planes closest?
(e) Simulate the motion of the planes by simultaneously graphing the equations found in part (a).

59. The Green Monster The left field wall at Fenway Park is 310 feet from home plate; the wall itself (affectionately named the Green Monster) is 37 feet high. A batted ball must clear the wall to be a home run. Suppose a ball leaves the bat 3 feet off the ground, at an angle of 45°. Use $g = 32$ feet per second^2 as the acceleration due to gravity and ignore any air resistance.
(a) Find parametric equations that model the position of the ball as a function of time.
(b) What is the maximum height of the ball if it leaves the bat with a speed of 90 miles per hour? Give your answer in feet.
(c) How far is the ball from home plate at its maximum height? Give your answer in feet.
(d) If the ball is hit straight down the left field wall, will it clear the Green Monster? If it does, by how much does it clear the wall?

Source: The Boston Red Sox

60. Projectile Motion The position of a projectile fired with an initial velocity v_0 feet per second and at an angle θ to the horizontal at the end of t seconds is given by the parametric equations

$$x = (v_0 \cos \theta)t \qquad y = (v_0 \sin \theta)t - 16t^2$$

See the illustration.

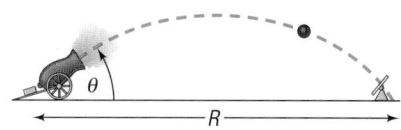

(a) Obtain the rectangular equation of the trajectory and identify the curve.

(b) Show that the projectile hits the ground $(y = 0)$ when

$$t = \frac{1}{16} v_0 \sin \theta.$$

(c) How far has the projectile traveled (horizontally) when it strikes the ground? In other words, find the range R.

(d) Find the time t when $x = y$. Then find the horizontal distance x and the vertical distance y traveled by the projectile in this time. Then compute $\sqrt{x^2 + y^2}$. This is the distance R, the range, that the projectile travels up a plane inclined at $45°$ to the horizontal $(x = y)$. See the following illustration. (See also Problem 83 in Section 7.5.)

61. Show that the parametric equations for a line passing through the points (x_1, y_1) and (x_2, y_2) are

$$x = (x_2 - x_1)t + x_1$$

$$y = (y_2 - y_1)t + y_1, \quad -\infty < t < \infty$$

What is the orientation of this line?

62. Hypocycloid The hypocycloid is a curve defined by the parametric equations

$$x(t) = \cos^3 t, \quad y(t) = \sin^3 t, \quad 0 \le t \le 2\pi$$

(a) Graph the hypocycloid using a graphing utility.
(b) Find rectangular equations of the hypocycloid.

Discussion and Writing

63. In Problem 62, we graphed the hypocycloid. Now graph the rectangular equations of the hypocycloid. Did you obtain a complete graph? If not, experiment until you do.

64. Look up the curves called *hypocycloid* and *epicycloid*. Write a report on what you find. Be sure to draw comparisons with the cycloid.

'Are You Prepared?' Answers

1. $3; \dfrac{\pi}{2}$

CHAPTER REVIEW

Things to Know

Equations

Parabola (pp. 639–644)	See Tables 1 and 2 (pp. 641 and 643).
Ellipse (pp. 648–655)	See Table 3 (p. 653).
Hyperbola (pp. 659–668)	See Table 4 (p. 667).
General equation of a conic (p. 679)	$Ax^2 + Bxy + Cy^2 + Dx + Ey + F = 0$ Parabola if $B^2 - 4AC = 0$
	Ellipse (or circle) if $B^2 - 4AC < 0$
	Hyperbola if $B^2 - 4AC > 0$
Polar equations of a conic with focus at the pole (pp. 681–685)	See Table 5 (p. 683).
Parametric equations of a curve (p. 687)	$x = f(t), y = g(t), t$ is the parameter

Definitions

Parabola (p. 639)	Set of points P in the plane for which $d(F, P) = d(P, D)$, where F is the focus and D is the directrix
Ellipse (p. 649)	Set of points P in the plane, the sum of whose distances from two fixed points (the foci) is a constant
Hyperbola (p. 659)	Set of points P in the plane, the difference of whose distances from two fixed points (the foci) is a constant
Conic in polar coordinates (p. 681)	$\dfrac{d(F, P)}{d(P, D)} = e$ Parabola if $e = 1$
	Ellipse if $e < 1$
	Hyperbola if $e > 1$

Formulas

Rotation formulas (p. 675)	$x = x' \cos \theta - y' \sin \theta$
	$y = x' \sin \theta + y' \cos \theta$
Angle θ of rotation that eliminates the $x'y'$-term (p. 676)	$\cot(2\theta) = \dfrac{A - C}{B}, \quad 0° < \theta < 90°$

Objectives

Section	You should be able to . . .	Example(s)	Review Exercises
10.1	**1** Know the names of the conics (p. 638)		1–32
10.2	**1** Analyze parabolas with vertex at the origin (p. 639)	1–6	1, 2, 21, 24
	2 Analyze parabolas with vertex at (h, k) (p. 643)	7–9	7, 11, 12, 17, 18, 27, 30
	3 Solve applied problems involving parabolas (p. 644)	10	77, 78
10.3	**1** Analyze ellipses with center at the origin (p. 649)	1–5	5, 6, 10, 22, 25
	2 Analyze ellipses with center at (h, k) (p. 653)	6–8	14–16, 19, 28, 31
	3 Solve applied problems involving ellipses (p. 656)	9	79, 80
10.4	**1** Analyze hyperbolas with center at the origin (p. 660)	1–5	3, 4, 8, 9, 23, 26
	2 Find the asymptotes of a hyperbola (p. 665)	6	3, 4, 8, 9
	3 Analyze hyperbolas with center at (h, k) (p. 666)	7, 8	13, 20, 29, 32–36
	4 Solve applied problems involving hyperbolas (p. 668)	9	81
10.5	**1** Identify a conic (p. 673)	1	37–40
	2 Use a rotation of axes to transform equations (p. 674)	2	47–52
	3 Analyze an equation using a rotation of axes (p. 676)	3, 4	47–52
	4 Identify conics without a rotation of axes (p. 678)	5	41–46
10.6	**1** Analyze and graph polar equations of conics (p. 681)	1–3	53–58
	2 Convert the polar equation of a conic to a rectangular equation (p. 685)	4	59–62
10.7	**1** Graph parametric equations by hand (p. 687)	1	63–68
	2 Graph parametric equations using a graphing utility (p. 688)	2	63–68
	3 Find a rectangular equation for a curve defined parametrically (p. 689)	3, 4	63–68
	4 Use time as a parameter in parametric equations (p. 691)	5, 6	82, 83
	5 Find parametric equations for curves defined by rectangular equations (p. 694)	7, 8	69–72

Review Exercises

In Problems 1–20, identify each equation. If it is a parabola, give its vertex, focus, and directrix; if it is an ellipse, give its center, vertices, and foci; if it is a hyperbola, give its center, vertices, foci, and asymptotes.

1. $y^2 = -16x$ **2.** $16x^2 = y$ **3.** $\dfrac{x^2}{25} - y^2 = 1$ **4.** $\dfrac{y^2}{25} - x^2 = 1$

5. $\dfrac{y^2}{25} + \dfrac{x^2}{16} = 1$ **6.** $\dfrac{x^2}{9} + \dfrac{y^2}{16} = 1$ **7.** $x^2 + 4y = 4$ **8.** $3y^2 - x^2 = 9$

9. $4x^2 - y^2 = 8$ **10.** $9x^2 + 4y^2 = 36$ **11.** $x^2 - 4x = 2y$ **12.** $2y^2 - 4y = x - 2$

13. $y^2 - 4y - 4x^2 + 8x = 4$ **14.** $4x^2 + y^2 + 8x - 4y + 4 = 0$ **15.** $4x^2 + 9y^2 - 16x - 18y = 11$

16. $4x^2 + 9y^2 - 16x + 18y = 11$ **17.** $4x^2 - 16x + 16y + 32 = 0$ **18.** $4y^2 + 3x - 16y + 19 = 0$

19. $9x^2 + 4y^2 - 18x + 8y = 23$ **20.** $x^2 - y^2 - 2x - 2y = 1$

In Problems 21–36, find an equation of the conic described. Graph the equation by hand.

21. Parabola;   focus at $(-2, 0)$;   directrix the line $x = 2$

22. Ellipse;   center at $(0, 0)$;   focus at $(0, 3)$;   vertex at $(0, 5)$

23. Hyperbola;   center at $(0,0)$;   focus at $(0,4)$;   vertex at $(0, -2)$

24. Parabola;   vertex at $(0, 0)$;   directrix the line $y = -3$

25. Ellipse;   foci at $(-3, 0)$ and $(3, 0)$;   vertex at $(4, 0)$

26. Hyperbola;   vertices at $(-2, 0)$ and $(2, 0)$;   focus at $(4, 0)$

27. Parabola;   vertex at $(2, -3)$;   focus at $(2, -4)$

28. Ellipse;   center at $(-1, 2)$;   focus at $(0, 2)$;   vertex at $(2, 2)$

29. Hyperbola;   center at $(-2, -3)$;   focus at $(-4, -3)$;   vertex at $(-3, -3)$

30. Parabola;   focus at $(3, 6)$;   directrix the line $y = 8$

31. Ellipse;   foci at $(-4, 2)$ and $(-4, 8)$;   vertex at $(-4, 10)$

32. Hyperbola;   vertices at $(-3, 3)$ and $(5, 3)$;   focus at $(7, 3)$

33. Center at $(-1, 2)$; $a = 3$; $c = 4$; transverse axis parallel to the x-axis

34. Center at $(4, -2)$; $a = 1$; $c = 4$; transverse axis parallel to the y-axis

35. Vertices at $(0, 1)$ and $(6, 1)$; asymptote the line $3y + 2x = 9$

36. Vertices at $(4, 0)$ and $(4, 4)$; asymptote the line $y + 2x = 10$

In Problems 37–46, identify each conic without completing the squares and without applying a rotation of axes.

37. $y^2 + 4x + 3y - 8 = 0$

38. $2x^2 - y + 8x = 0$

39. $x^2 + 2y^2 + 4x - 8y + 2 = 0$

40. $x^2 - 8y^2 - x - 2y = 0$

41. $9x^2 - 12xy + 4y^2 + 8x + 12y = 0$

42. $4x^2 + 4xy + y^2 - 8\sqrt{5}x + 16\sqrt{5}y = 0$

43. $4x^2 + 10xy + 4y^2 - 9 = 0$

44. $4x^2 - 10xy + 4y^2 - 9 = 0$

45. $x^2 - 2xy + 3y^2 + 2x + 4y - 1 = 0$

46. $4x^2 + 12xy - 10y^2 + x + y - 10 = 0$

In Problems 47–52, rotate the axes so that the new equation contains no xy-term. Analyze and graph the new equation.

47. $2x^2 + 5xy + 2y^2 - \dfrac{9}{2} = 0$

48. $2x^2 - 5xy + 2y^2 - \dfrac{9}{2} = 0$

49. $6x^2 + 4xy + 9y^2 - 20 = 0$

50. $x^2 + 4xy + 4y^2 + 16\sqrt{5}x - 8\sqrt{5}y = 0$

51. $4x^2 - 12xy + 9y^2 + 12x + 8y = 0$

52. $9x^2 - 24xy + 16y^2 + 80x + 60y = 0$

In Problems 53–58, identify the conic that each polar equation represents and graph it by hand. Verify your graph using a graphing utility.

53. $r = \dfrac{4}{1 - \cos\theta}$

54. $r = \dfrac{6}{1 + \sin\theta}$

55. $r = \dfrac{6}{2 - \sin\theta}$

56. $r = \dfrac{2}{3 + 2\cos\theta}$

57. $r = \dfrac{8}{4 + 8\cos\theta}$

58. $r = \dfrac{10}{5 + 20\sin\theta}$

In Problems 59–62, convert each polar equation to a rectangular equation.

59. $r = \dfrac{4}{1 - \cos\theta}$

60. $r = \dfrac{6}{2 - \sin\theta}$

61. $r = \dfrac{8}{4 + 8\cos\theta}$

62. $r = \dfrac{2}{3 + 2\cos\theta}$

In Problems 63–68, by hand, graph the curve whose parametric equations are given and show its orientation. Find the rectangular equation of each curve. Verify your graph using a graphing utility.

63. $x = 4t - 2, \quad y = 1 - t; \quad -\infty < t < \infty$

64. $x = 2t^2 + 6, \quad y = 5 - t; \quad -\infty < t < \infty$

65. $x = 3\sin t, \quad y = 4\cos t + 2; \quad 0 \le t \le 2\pi$

66. $x = \ln t, \quad y = t^3; \quad t > 0$

67. $x = \sec^2 t, \quad y = \tan^2 t; \quad 0 \le t \le \dfrac{\pi}{4}$

68. $x = t^{\frac{3}{2}}, \quad y = 2t + 4; \quad t \ge 0$

In Problems 69 and 70, find two different parametric equations for each rectangular equation.

69. $y = -2x + 4$

70. $y = 2x^2 - 8$

In Problems 71 and 72, find parametric equations for an object that moves along the ellipse $\dfrac{x^2}{16} + \dfrac{y^2}{9} = 1$ with the motion described.

71. The motion begins at $(4, 0)$, is counterclockwise, and requires 4 seconds for a complete revolution.

72. The motion begins at $(0, 3)$, is clockwise, and requires 5 seconds for a complete revolution.

---

73. Find an equation of the hyperbola whose foci are the vertices of the ellipse $4x^2 + 9y^2 = 36$ and whose vertices are the foci of this ellipse.

74. Find an equation of the ellipse whose foci are the vertices of the hyperbola $x^2 - 4y^2 = 16$ and whose vertices are the foci of this hyperbola.

75. Describe the collection of points in a plane so that the distance from each point to the point $(3, 0)$ is three-fourths of its distance from the line $x = \dfrac{16}{3}$.

76. Describe the collection of points in a plane so that the distance from each point to the point $(5, 0)$ is five-fourths of its distance from the line $x = \dfrac{16}{5}$.

77. Searchlight A searchlight is shaped like a paraboloid of revolution. If a light source is located 1 foot from the vertex

along the axis of symmetry and the opening is 2 feet across, how deep should the mirror be in order to reflect the light rays parallel to the axis of symmetry?

78. Parabolic Arch Bridge A bridge is built in the shape of a parabolic arch. The bridge has a span of 60 feet and a maximum height of 20 feet. Find the height of the arch at distances of 5, 10, and 20 feet from the center.

79. Semielliptical Arch Bridge A bridge is built in the shape of a semielliptical arch. The bridge has a span of 60 feet and a maximum height of 20 feet. Find the height of the arch at distances of 5, 10, and 20 feet from the center.

80. Whispering Gallery The figure shows the specifications for an elliptical ceiling in a hall designed to be a whispering gallery. Where are the foci located in the hall?

(a) Find parametric equations that model the motion of the train and Mary as a function of time.

[**Hint:** The position s at time t of an object having acceleration a is $s = \dfrac{1}{2}at^2$.]

(b) Determine algebraically whether Mary will catch the train. If so, when?

(c) Simulate the motions of the train and Mary by simultaneously graphing the equations found in part (a).

81. **Calibrating Instruments** In a test of their recording devices, a team of seismologists positioned two of the devices 2000 feet apart, with the device at point A to the west of the device at point B. At a point between the devices and 200 feet from point B, a small amount of explosive was detonated and a note made of the time at which the sound reached each device. A second explosion is to be carried out at a point directly north of point B. How far north should the site of the second explosion be chosen so that the measured time difference recorded by the devices for the second detonation is the same as that recorded for the first detonation?

82. **Uniform Motion** Mary's train leaves at 7:15 AM and accelerates at the rate of 3 meters per second per second. Mary, who can run 6 meters per second, arrives at the train station 2 seconds after the train has left.

83. **Projectile Motion** Drew Brees throws a football with an initial speed of 80 feet per second at an angle of $35°$ to the horizontal. The ball leaves Brees's hand at a height of 6 feet.

(a) Find parametric equations that model the position of the ball as a function of time.

(b) How long is the ball in the air?

(c) When is the ball at its maximum height? Determine the maximum height of the ball.

(d) Determine the horizontal distance that the ball travels.

(e) Using a graphing utility, simultaneously graph the equations found in part (a).

84. Formulate a strategy for discussing and graphing an equation of the form

$$Ax^2 + Bxy + Cy^2 + Dx + Ey + F = 0$$

CHAPTER TEST

In Problems 1–3, identify each equation. If it is a parabola, give its vertex, focus, and directrix; if an ellipse, give its center, vertices, and foci; if a hyperbola, give its center, vertices, foci, and asymptotes.

1. $\dfrac{(x+1)^2}{4} - \dfrac{y^2}{9} = 1$

2. $8y = (x-1)^2 - 4$

3. $2x^2 + 3y^2 + 4x - 6y = 13$

In Problems 4–6, find an equation of the conic described; graph the equation by hand.

4. Parabola: focus $(-1, 4.5)$, vertex $(-1, 3)$

5. Ellipse: center $(0, 0)$, vertex $(0, -4)$, focus $(0, 3)$

6. Hyperbola: center $(2, 2)$, vertex $(2, 4)$, contains the point $\left(2 + \sqrt{10}, 5\right)$

In Problems 7–9, identify each conic without completing the square or rotating axes.

7. $2x^2 + 5xy + 3y^2 + 3x - 7 = 0$

8. $3x^2 - xy + 2y^2 + 3y + 1 = 0$

9. $x^2 - 6xy + 9y^2 + 2x - 3y - 2 = 0$

10. Given the equation $41x^2 - 24xy + 34y^2 - 25 = 0$, rotate the axes so that there is no xy-term. Analyze and graph the new equation.

11. Identify the conic represented by the polar equation $r = \dfrac{3}{1 - 2\cos\theta}$. Find the rectangular equation.

12. Graph the curve whose parametric equations are given and show its orientation. Find the rectangular equation for the curve.

$$x = 3t - 2, \quad y = 1 - \sqrt{t}, \quad 0 \le t \le 9$$

13. A parabolic reflector (paraboloid of revolution) is used by TV crews at football games to pick up the referee's announcements, quarterback signals, and so on. A microphone is placed at the focus of the parabola. If a certain reflector is 4 feet wide and 1.5 feet deep, where should the microphone be placed?

CUMULATIVE REVIEW

1. For $f(x) = -3x^2 + 5x - 2$, find

$$\frac{f(x+h) - f(x)}{h} \qquad h \ne 0$$

2. In the complex number system, solve the equation

$$9x^4 + 33x^3 - 71x^2 - 57x - 10 = 0$$

3. For what numbers x is $6 - x \ge x^2$?

4. (a) Find the domain and range of $y = 3^x + 2$.

(b) Find the inverse of $y = 3^x + 2$ and state its domain and range.

5. $f(x) = \log_4(x - 2)$

(a) Solve $f(x) = 2$.

(b) Solve $f(x) \le 2$.

6. Find an equation for each of the following graphs:

(a) Line:

(b) Circle:

(c) Ellipse:

(d) Parabola:

(e) Hyperbola:

(f) Exponential:

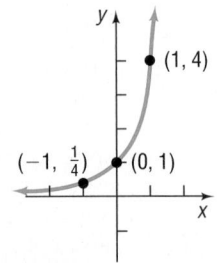

7. Find all the solutions of the equation $\sin(2\theta) = 0.5$.

8. Find a polar equation for the line containing the origin that makes an angle of $30°$ with the positive x-axis.

9. Find a polar equation for the circle with center at the point $(0, 4)$ and radius 4. Graph this circle.

10. What is the domain of the function $f(x) = \dfrac{3}{\sin x + \cos x}$?

11. Solve the equation $\cot(2\theta) = 1$, where $0° < \theta < 90°$.

12. Find the rectangular equation of the curve

$$x = 5 \tan t, \quad y = 5 \sec^2 t, \quad -\frac{\pi}{2} < t < \frac{\pi}{2}$$

CHAPTER PROJECTS

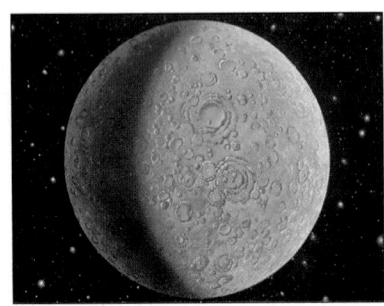

I. The Orbits of Neptune and Pluto The orbit of a planet about the Sun is an ellipse, with the Sun at one focus. The **aphelion** of a planet is its greatest distance from the Sun and the **perihelion** is its shortest distance. The **mean distance** of a planet from the Sun is the length of the semimajor axis of the elliptical orbit. See the illustration.

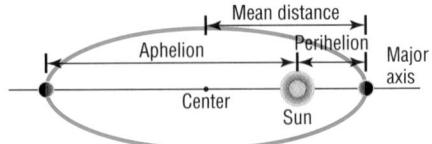

1. The aphelion of Neptune is 4532.2×10^6 kilometers (km) and its perihelion is 4458.0×10^6 km. Find a model for the orbit of Neptune around the Sun.

2. The aphelion of Pluto* is 7381.2×10^6 km and its perihelion is 4445.8×10^6 km. Find a model for the orbit of Pluto around the Sun.

3. Graph the orbits of Pluto and Neptune on a graphing utility. Knowing that the orbits of the planets intersect, what is wrong with the graphs you obtained?

4. The graphs of the orbits drawn in part 3 have the same center, but their foci lie in different locations. To see an accurate representation, the location of the Sun (a focus) needs to be the same for both graphs. This can be accomplished by shifting Pluto's orbit to the left. The shift amount is equal to Pluto's distance from the center (in the graph in part 3) to the Sun minus Neptune's distance from the center to the Sun. Find the new model representing the orbit of Pluto.

5. Graph the equation for the orbit of Pluto found in part 4 along with the equation of the orbit of Neptune. Do you see that Pluto's orbit is sometimes inside Neptune's?

6. Find the point(s) of intersection of the two orbits.

7. Do you think two planets will ever collide?

The following projects can be found on the Instructor's Resource Center (IRC):

II. Project at Motorola *Distorted Deployable Space Reflector Antennas* An engineer designs an antenna that will deploy in space to collect sunlight.

III. Constructing a Bridge over the East River The size of ships using a river and fluctuations in water height due to tides or flooding must be considered when designing a bridge that will cross a major waterway.

IV. Systems of Parametric Equations Choosing an approach to use when solving a system of equations depends on the form of the system and on the domains of the equations.

*Pluto's status was reduced to a dwarf planet in September 2006.

Systems of Equations and Inequalities

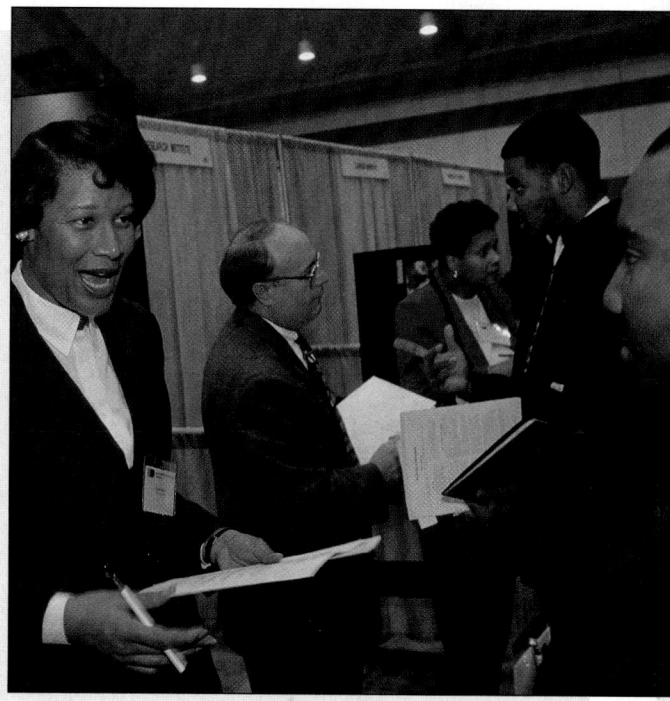

Economic Outcomes

Annual Earnings of Young Adults

For both males and females, earnings increase with education: full-time workers with at least a bachelor's degree have higher median earnings than those with less education. For example, in 2003, male college graduates earned 93 percent more than male high school completers. Females with a bachelor's or higher degree earned 91 percent more than female high school completers. Males and females who dropped out of high school earned 37 and 39 percent less, respectively, than male and female high school completers.

The median earnings of young adults who have at least a bachelor's degree declined in the 1970s relative to their counterparts who were high school completers, before increasing between 1980 and 2003. Males with a bachelor's degree or higher had earnings 19 percent higher than male high school completers in 1980 and had earnings 93 percent higher in 2003. Among females, those with at least a bachelor's degree had earnings 34 percent higher than female high school completers in 1980, compared with earnings 91 percent higher in 2003.

—See Chapter Project I—

A Look Back

In Chapters 1–5 and 7, we solved various kinds of equations and inequalities involving a single variable.

A Look Ahead

In this chapter we take up the problem of solving equations and inequalities containing two or more variables. There are various ways to solve such problems.

The *method of substitution* for solving equations in several unknowns goes back to ancient times.

The *method of elimination*, although it had existed for centuries, was put into systematic order by Karl Friedrich Gauss (1777–1855) and by Camille Jordan (1838–1922).

The theory of *matrices* was developed in 1857 by Arthur Cayley (1821–1895), although only later were matrices used as we use them in this chapter. Matrices have become a very flexible instrument, useful in almost all areas of mathematics.

The method of *determinants* was invented by Takakazu Seki Kôwa (1642–1708) in 1683 in Japan and by Gottfried Wilhelm von Leibniz (1646–1716) in 1693 in Germany. *Cramer's Rule* is named after Gabriel Cramer (1704–1752) of Switzerland, who popularized the use of determinants for solving linear systems.

Section 11.5, on *partial fraction decomposition*, provides an application of systems of equations. This particular application is one that is used in integral calculus.

Section 11.8 introduces *linear programming*, a modern application of linear inequalities. This topic is particularly useful for students interested in operations research.

Outline

11.1 Systems of Linear Equations: Substitution and Elimination

11.2 Systems of Linear Equations: Matrices

11.3 Systems of Linear Equations: Determinants

11.4 Matrix Algebra

11.5 Partial Fraction Decomposition

11.6 Systems of Nonlinear Equations

11.7 Systems of Inequalities

11.8 Linear Programming
  Chapter Review
  Chapter Test
  Cumulative Review
  Chapter Projects

11.1 Systems of Linear Equations: Substitution and Elimination

PREPARING FOR THIS SECTION *Before getting started, review the following:*

- Linear Equations (Appendix A, Section A.6, pp. A47–A49)
- Lines (Section 1.4, pp. 29–40)

Now Work the 'Are You Prepared?' problems on page 716.

OBJECTIVES 1 Solve Systems of Equations by Substitution (p. 708)
2 Solve Systems of Equations by Elimination (p. 710)
3 Identify Inconsistent Systems of Equations Containing Two Variables (p. 711)
4 Express the Solution of a System of Dependent Equations Containing Two Variables (p. 712)
5 Solve Systems of Three Equations Containing Three Variables (p. 712)
6 Identify Inconsistent Systems of Equations Containing Three Variables (p. 714)
7 Express the Solution of a System of Dependent Equations Containing Three Variables (p. 715)

We begin with an example.

EXAMPLE 1 **Movie Theater Ticket Sales**

A movie theater sells tickets for $8.00 each, with seniors receiving a discount of $2.00. One evening the theater took in $3580 in revenue. If x represents the number of tickets sold at $8.00 and y the number of tickets sold at the discounted price of $6.00, write an equation that relates these variables.

Solution Each nondiscounted ticket brings in $8.00, so x tickets will bring in $8x$ dollars. Similarly, y discounted tickets bring in $6y$ dollars. Since the total brought in is $3580, we must have

$$8x + 6y = 3580$$

In Example 1, suppose that we also know that 525 tickets were sold that evening. Then we have another equation relating the variables x and y:

$$x + y = 525$$

The two equations

$$8x + 6y = 3580$$
$$x + y = 525$$

form a *system* of equations.

In general, a **system of equations** is a collection of two or more equations, each containing one or more variables. Example 2 gives some illustrations of systems of equations.

EXAMPLE 2 **Examples of Systems of Equations**

(a) $\begin{cases} 2x + y = 5 & (1) \\ -4x + 6y = -2 & (2) \end{cases}$ Two equations containing two variables, x and y

(b) $\begin{cases} x + y^2 = 5 & (1) \\ 2x + y = 4 & (2) \end{cases}$ Two equations containing two variables, x and y

(c) $\begin{cases} x + y + z = 6 & (1) \quad \textit{Three equations containing three variables, x, y, and z} \\ 3x - 2y + 4z = 9 & (2) \\ x - y - z = 0 & (3) \end{cases}$

(d) $\begin{cases} x + y + z = 5 & (1) \quad \textit{Two equations containing three variables, x, y, and z} \\ x - y = 2 & (2) \end{cases}$

(e) $\begin{cases} x + y + z = 6 & (1) \quad \textit{Four equations containing three variables, x, y, and z} \\ 2x + 2z = 4 & (2) \\ y + z = 2 & (3) \\ x = 4 & (4) \end{cases}$

We use a brace, as shown, to remind us that we are dealing with a system of equations. We also will find it convenient to number each equation in the system.

A **solution** of a system of equations consists of values for the variables that are solutions of each equation of the system. To **solve** a system of equations means to find all solutions of the system.

For example, $x = 2$, $y = 1$ is a solution of the system in Example 2(a), because

$$\begin{cases} 2x + y = 5 & (1) \\ -4x + 6y = -2 & (2) \end{cases} \qquad \begin{cases} 2(2) + 1 = 4 + 1 = 5 \\ -4(2) + 6(1) = -8 + 6 = -2 \end{cases}$$

We may also write this solution as the ordered pair $(2, 1)$.

A solution of the system in Example 2(b) is $x = 1$, $y = 2$, because

$$\begin{cases} x + y^2 = 5 & (1) \\ 2x + y = 4 & (2) \end{cases} \qquad \begin{cases} 1 + 2^2 = 1 + 4 = 5 \\ 2(1) + 2 = 2 + 2 = 4 \end{cases}$$

Another solution of the system in Example 2(b) is $x = \dfrac{11}{4}$, $y = -\dfrac{3}{2}$, which you can check for yourself.

A solution of the system in Example 2(c) is $x = 3$, $y = 2$, $z = 1$, because

$$\begin{cases} x + y + z = 6 & (1) \\ 3x - 2y + 4z = 9 & (2) \\ x - y - z = 0 & (3) \end{cases} \qquad \begin{cases} 3 + 2 + 1 = 6 & (1) \\ 3(3) - 2(2) + 4(1) = 9 - 4 + 4 = 9 & (2) \\ 3 - 2 - 1 = 0 & (3) \end{cases}$$

We may also write this solution as the ordered triplet $(3, 2, 1)$.

Note that $x = 3$, $y = 3$, $z = 0$ is not a solution of the system in Example 2(c).

$$\begin{cases} x + y + z = 6 & (1) \\ 3x - 2y + 4z = 9 & (2) \\ x - y - z = 0 & (3) \end{cases} \qquad \begin{cases} 3 + 3 + 0 = 6 & (1) \\ 3(3) - 2(3) + 4(0) = 3 \neq 9 & (2) \\ 3 - 3 - 0 = 0 & (3) \end{cases}$$

Although $x = 3$, $y = 3$, and $z = 0$ satisfy equations (1) and (3), they do not satisfy equation (2). Any solution of the system must satisfy *each* equation of the system.

⟜▸ **Now Work** PROBLEM 9

When a system of equations has at least one solution, it is said to be **consistent;** otherwise, it is called **inconsistent.**

An equation in n variables is said to be **linear** if it is equivalent to an equation of the form

$$a_1 x_1 + a_2 x_2 + \cdots + a_n x_n = b$$

where $x_1, x_2, \ldots, x_n$ are n distinct variables, $a_1, a_2, \ldots, a_n, b$ are constants, and at least one of the a's is not 0.

Some examples of linear equations are

$$2x + 3y = 2 \qquad 5x - 2y + 3z = 10 \qquad 8x + 8y - 2z + 5w = 0$$

If each equation in a system of equations is linear, we have a **system of linear equations.** The systems in Examples 2(a), (c), (d), and (e) are linear, whereas the system in Example 2(b) is nonlinear. In this chapter we shall solve linear systems in Sections 11.1 to 11.3. We discuss nonlinear systems in Section 11.6.

We begin by discussing a system of two linear equations containing two variables. We can view the problem of solving such a system as a geometry problem. The graph of each equation in such a system is a line. So a system of two linear equations containing two variables represents a pair of lines. The lines either (1) intersect or (2) are parallel or (3) are **coincident** (that is, identical).

1. If the lines intersect, the system of equations has one solution, given by the point of intersection. The system is **consistent** and the equations are **independent.** See Figure 1(a).

2. If the lines are parallel, the system of equations has no solution, because the lines never intersect. The system is **inconsistent.** See Figure 1(b).

3. If the lines are coincident, the system of equations has infinitely many solutions, represented by the totality of points on the line. The system is **consistent** and the equations are **dependent.** See Figure 1(c).

Figure 1

(a) Intersecting lines; system has one solution

(b) Parallel lines; system has no solution

(c) Coincident lines; system has infinitely many solutions

EXAMPLE 3   **Solving a System of Linear Equations Using a Graphing Utility**

Solve: $\begin{cases} 2x + y = 5 & (1) \\ -4x + 6y = 12 & (2) \end{cases}$

Solution

First, we solve each equation for y. This is equivalent to writing each equation in slope–intercept form. Equation (1) in slope–intercept form is $Y_1 = -2x + 5$. Equation (2) in slope–intercept form is $Y_2 = \dfrac{2}{3}x + 2$. Figure 2 shows the graphs using a graphing utility. From the graph in Figure 2, we see that the lines intersect, so the system is consistent and the equations are independent. Using INTERSECT, we obtain the solution $(1.125, 2.75)$.

Figure 2

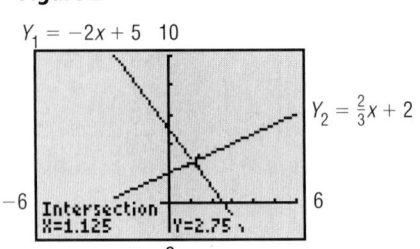

1 Solve Systems of Equations by Substitution

Sometimes to obtain exact solutions, we must use algebraic methods. A number of methods are available to us for solving systems of linear equations algebraically. In this section, we introduce two methods: *substitution* and *elimination*. We illustrate the **method of substitution** by solving the system given in Example 3.

EXAMPLE 4   **How to Solve a System of Linear Equations by Substitution**

Solve: $\begin{cases} 2x + y = 5 & (1) \\ -4x + 6y = 12 & (2) \end{cases}$

Step-by-Step Solution

STEP 1 Pick one of the equations and solve for one of the variables in terms of the remaining variable(s).

We solve equation (1) for y.

$$2x + y = 5 \qquad \text{Equation (1)}$$
$$y = -2x + 5 \qquad \text{Subtract } 2x \text{ from each side of (1).}$$

STEP 2 Substitute the result into the remaining equation(s).

We substitute $-2x + 5$ for y in equation (2). The result is an equation containing just the variable x, which we can solve.

$$-4x + 6y = 12 \qquad \text{Equation (2)}$$
$$-4x + 6(-2x + 5) = 12 \qquad \text{Substitute } -2x + 5 \text{ for } y \text{ in (2).}$$

STEP 3 If one equation in one variable results, solve this equation. Otherwise, repeat Steps 1 and 2 until a single equation with one variable remains.

$$-4x - 12x + 30 = 12 \qquad \text{Distribute.}$$
$$-16x + 30 = 12 \qquad \text{Combine like terms.}$$
$$-16x = -18 \qquad \text{Subtract 30 from both sides.}$$
$$x = \frac{-18}{-16} \qquad \text{Divide both sides by } -16.$$
$$= \frac{9}{8} \qquad \text{Simplify.}$$

STEP 4 Find the values of the remaining variables by back-substitution.

Because we know that $x = \frac{9}{8}$, we can find the value of y by **back-substitution,** that is, by substituting $\frac{9}{8}$ for x in one of the original equations. Equation (1) seems easier to work with, so we will back-substitute into equation (1).

$$2x + y = 5 \qquad \text{Equation (1)}$$
$$2\left(\frac{9}{8}\right) + y = 5 \qquad \text{Substitute } x = \frac{9}{8} \text{ into equation (1).}$$
$$\frac{9}{4} + y = 5 \qquad \text{Simplify.}$$
$$y = 5 - \frac{9}{4} \qquad \text{Subtract } \frac{9}{4} \text{ from both sides.}$$
$$= \frac{11}{4} \qquad 5 - \frac{9}{4} = \frac{20}{4} - \frac{9}{4} = \frac{11}{4}$$

STEP 5 Check the solution found.

We have $x = \frac{9}{8}$ and $y = \frac{11}{4}$. We verify that both equations are satisfied (true) for these values.

$$\begin{cases} 2x + y = 5: & 2\left(\dfrac{9}{8}\right) + \dfrac{11}{4} = \dfrac{9}{4} + \dfrac{11}{4} = \dfrac{20}{4} = 5 \\[3mm] -4x + 6y = 12: & -4\left(\dfrac{9}{8}\right) + 6\left(\dfrac{11}{4}\right) = -\dfrac{9}{2} + \dfrac{33}{2} = \dfrac{24}{2} = 12 \end{cases}$$

The solution of the system is $x = \frac{9}{8} = 1.125$ and $y = \frac{11}{4} = 2.75$. We can also write the solution as the ordered pair $\left(\frac{9}{8}, \frac{11}{4}\right)$.

> **Now Use Substitution to Work** PROBLEM 19

2 Solve Systems of Equations by Elimination

A second method for solving a system of linear equations is the *method of elimination*. This method is usually preferred over substitution if substitution leads to fractions or if the system contains more than two variables. Elimination also provides the necessary motivation for solving systems using matrices (the subject of Section 11.2).

The idea behind the **method of elimination** is to replace the original system of equations by an equivalent system so that adding two of the equations eliminates a variable. The rules for obtaining equivalent equations are the same as those studied earlier. However, we may also interchange any two equations of the system and/or replace any equation in the system by the sum (or difference) of that equation and a nonzero multiple of any other equation in the system.

> **In Words**
>
> When using elimination, we want to get the coefficients of one of the variables to be negatives of one another.

Rules for Obtaining an Equivalent System of Equations

1. Interchange any two equations of the system.

2. Multiply (or divide) each side of an equation by the same nonzero constant.

3. Replace any equation in the system by the sum (or difference) of that equation and a nonzero multiple of any other equation in the system.

An example will give you the idea. As you work through the example, pay particular attention to the pattern being followed.

EXAMPLE 5   **How to Solve a System of Linear Equations by Elimination**

Solve: $\begin{cases} 2x + 3y = 1 & (1) \\ -x + y = -3 & (2) \end{cases}$

Step-by-Step Solution

STEP 1 Multiply both sides of one or both equations by a nonzero constant so that the coefficients of one of the variables are additive inverses.

We will multiply both sides of equation (2) by 2 so that the coefficients of x in the two equations are additive inverses.

$$\begin{cases} 2x + 3y = 1 & (1) \\ -x + y = -3 & (2) \end{cases}$$

$$\begin{cases} 2x + 3y = 1 & (1) \\ 2(-x + y) = 2(-3) & (2) \end{cases}$$

$$\begin{cases} 2x + 3y = 1 & (1) \\ -2x + 2y = -6 & (2) \end{cases}$$

STEP 2 Add the equations to eliminate the variable. Solve the resulting equation for the remaining unknown.

$$\begin{cases} 2x + 3y = 1 & (1) \\ -2x + 2y = -6 & (2) \end{cases}$$

$$5y = -5 \quad \text{Add equations (1) and (2).}$$

$$y = -1 \quad \text{Divide both sides by 5.}$$

STEP 3 Back-substitute the value of the variable found in Step 2 into one of the original equations to find the value of the remaining variable.

We back-substitute $y = -1$ into equation (1) and solve for x.

$$2x + 3y = 1 \quad \text{Equation (1)}$$

$$2x + 3(-1) = 1 \quad \text{Substitute } y = -1 \text{ into equation (1).}$$

$$2x - 3 = 1 \quad \text{Simplify.}$$

$$2x = 4 \quad \text{Add 3 to both sides.}$$

$$x = 2 \quad \text{Divide both sides by 2.}$$

STEP 4 Check the solution found.   We leave the check to you.

The solution of the system is $x = 2$ and $y = -1$. We can also write the solution as the ordered pair $(2, -1)$.

Now Use Elimination to Work **PROBLEM 19**

| EXAMPLE 6 | Movie Theater Ticket Sales |

A movie theater sells tickets for $8.00 each, with seniors receiving a discount of $2.00. One evening the theater sold 525 tickets and took in $3580 in revenue. How many of each type of ticket were sold?

Solution If x represents the number of tickets sold at $8.00 and y the number of tickets sold at the discounted price of $6.00, then the given information results in the system of equations

$$\begin{cases} 8x + 6y = 3580 & (1) \\ x + y = 525 & (2) \end{cases}$$

We use the method of elimination. First, multiply the second equation by -6, and then add the equations.

$$\begin{cases} 8x + 6y = 3580 \\ -6x - 6y = -3150 \end{cases}$$
$$2x = 430 \quad \text{Add the equations.}$$
$$x = 215$$

Since $x + y = 525$, then $y = 525 - x = 525 - 215 = 310$. So 215 nondiscounted tickets and 310 senior discount tickets were sold.

3 Identify Inconsistent Systems of Equations Containing Two Variables

The previous examples dealt with consistent systems of equations that had a single solution. The next two examples deal with two other possibilities that may occur, the first being a system that has no solution.

| EXAMPLE 7 | An Inconsistent System of Linear Equations |

Solve: $\begin{cases} 2x + y = 5 & (1) \\ 4x + 2y = 8 & (2) \end{cases}$

Solution We choose to use the method of substitution and solve equation (1) for y.

$$2x + y = 5 \qquad (1)$$
$$y = -2x + 5 \quad \text{Subtract 2x from each side.}$$

Now substitute $-2x + 5$ for y in equation (2) and solve for x.

$$4x + 2y = 8 \qquad (2)$$
$$4x + 2(-2x + 5) = 8 \quad \text{Substitute } y = -2x + 5 \text{ in (2).}$$
$$4x - 4x + 10 = 8 \quad \text{Remove parentheses.}$$
$$0 = -2 \quad \text{Subtract 10 from both sides.}$$

This statement is false. We conclude that the system has no solution and is therefore inconsistent.

Figure 3

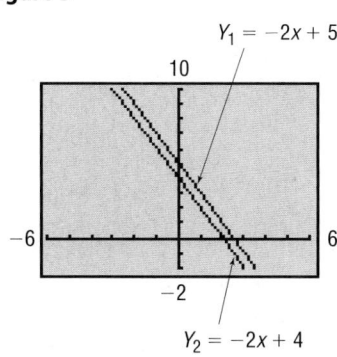

$Y_1 = -2x + 5$

$Y_2 = -2x + 4$

Figure 3 illustrates the pair of lines whose equations form the system in Example 7. Notice that the graphs of the two equations are lines, each with slope -2;

one has a y-intercept of 5, the other a y-intercept of 4. The lines are parallel and have no point of intersection. This geometric statement is equivalent to the algebraic statement that the system has no solution.

4 Express the Solution of a System of Dependent Equations Containing Two Variables

EXAMPLE 8 | **Solving a System of Dependent Equations**

Solve: $\begin{cases} 2x + y = 4 & (1) \\ -6x - 3y = -12 & (2) \end{cases}$

Solution We choose to use the method of elimination.

$$\begin{cases} 2x + y = 4 & (1) \\ -6x - 3y = -12 & (2) \end{cases}$$

$$\begin{cases} 6x + 3y = 12 & (1) \quad \text{Multiply each side of equation (1) by 3.} \\ -6x - 3y = -12 & (2) \end{cases}$$

$$\begin{cases} 6x + 3y = 12 & (1) \\ 0 = 0 & (2) \quad \text{Replace equation (2) by the sum of equations (1) and (2).} \end{cases}$$

The original system is equivalent to a system containing one equation, so the equations are dependent. This means that any values of x and y which satisfy $6x + 3y = 12$ or, equivalently, $2x + y = 4$ are solutions. For example, $x = 2, y = 0; x = 0, y = 4; x = -2, y = 8; x = 4, y = -4;$ and so on, are solutions. There are, in fact, infinitely many values of x and y for which $2x + y = 4$, so the original system has infinitely many solutions. We will write the solution of the original system either as

$$y = -2x + 4 \quad \text{where } x \text{ can be any real number}$$

or as

$$x = -\frac{1}{2}y + 2 \quad \text{where } y \text{ can be any real number.}$$

We can also express the solution as $\{(x, y)\mid y = -2x + 4, x \text{ is any real number}\}$ or as $\{(x, y)\mid x = -\frac{1}{2}y + 2, y \text{ is any real number}\}$.

Figure 4

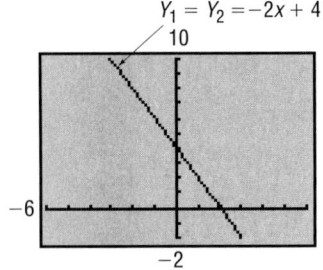

$Y_1 = Y_2 = -2x + 4$

Figure 4 illustrates the situation presented in Example 8. Notice that the graphs of the two equations are lines, each with slope -2 and each with y-intercept 4. The lines are coincident. Notice also that equation (2) in the original system is -3 times equation (1), indicating that the two equations are dependent.

For the system in Example 8, we can write down some of the infinite number of solutions by assigning values to x and then finding $y = -2x + 4$.

If $x = -2$, then $y = -2(-2) + 4 = 8$.

If $x = 0$, then $y = 4$.

If $x = 2$, then $y = 0$.

The ordered pairs $(-2, 8)$, $(0, 4)$, and $(2, 0)$ are three of the points on the line in Figure 4.

Now Work PROBLEMS 25 AND 29

5 Solve Systems of Three Equations Containing Three Variables

Just as with a system of two linear equations containing two variables, a system of three linear equations containing three variables has either (1) exactly one solution (a consistent system with independent equations), or (2) no solution (an inconsistent system), or (3) infinitely many solutions (a consistent system with dependent equations).

We can view the problem of solving a system of three linear equations containing three variables as a geometry problem. The graph of each equation in such a system is a plane in space. A system of three linear equations containing three variables represents three planes in space. Figure 5 illustrates some of the possibilities.

Figure 5

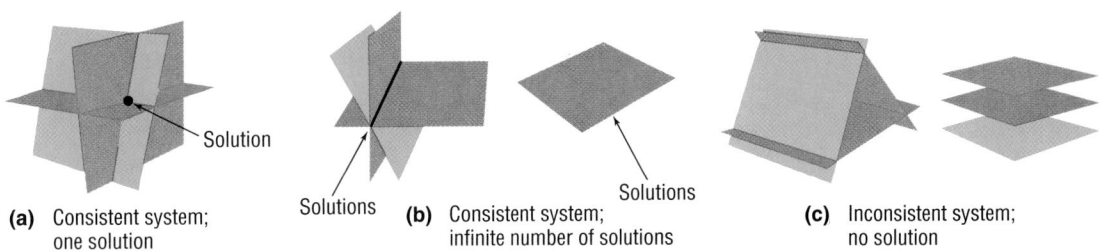

(a) Consistent system; one solution

Solutions

Solutions

(b) Consistent system; infinite number of solutions

(c) Inconsistent system; no solution

Recall that a **solution** to a system of equations consists of values for the variables that are solutions of each equation of the system. For example, $x = 3$, $y = -1$, $z = -5$ or, using ordered triplets, $(3, -1, -5)$ is a solution to the system of equations

$$\begin{cases} x + y + z = -3 \quad (1) \\ 2x - 3y + 6z = -21 \quad (2) \\ -3x + 5y = -14 \quad (3) \end{cases} \quad \begin{aligned} 3 + (-1) + (-5) &= -3 \\ 2(3) - 3(-1) + 6(-5) &= 6 + 3 - 30 = -21 \\ -3(3) + 5(-1) &= -9 - 5 = -14 \end{aligned}$$

because these values of the variables are solutions of each equation.

Typically, when solving a system of three linear equations containing three variables, we use the method of elimination. Recall that the idea behind the method of elimination is to form equivalent equations so that adding two of the equations eliminates a variable.

Let's see how elimination works on a system of three equations containing three variables.

EXAMPLE 9 | **Solving a System of Three Linear Equations with Three Variables**

Use the method of elimination to solve the system of equations.

$$\begin{cases} x + y - z = -1 \quad (1) \\ 4x - 3y + 2z = 16 \quad (2) \\ 2x - 2y - 3z = 5 \quad (3) \end{cases}$$

Solution For a system of three equations, we attempt to eliminate one variable at a time, using pairs of equations until an equation with a single variable remains. Our strategy for solving this system will be to use equation (1) to eliminate the variable x from equations (2) and (3). We can then treat the new equations (2) and (3) as a system with two unknowns. Alternatively, we could use equation (1) to eliminate either y or z from equations (2) and (3). Try one of these approaches for yourself.

We begin by multiplying each side of equation (1) by -4 and adding the result to equation (2). (Do you see why? The coefficients of x are now negatives of one another.) We also multiply equation (1) by -2 and add the result to equation (3). Notice that these two procedures result in the elimination of the variable x from equations (2) and (3).

$$\begin{aligned} x + y - z &= -1 \;(1) \quad \text{Multiply by } -4 \\ 4x - 3y + 2z &= 16 \;(2) \end{aligned}$$

$$\begin{aligned} -4x - 4y + 4z &= 4 \;(1) \\ 4x - 3y + 2z &= 16 \;(2) \\ \hline -7y + 6z &= 20 \quad \text{Add.} \end{aligned}$$

$$\begin{aligned} x + y - z &= -1 \;(1) \quad \text{Multiply by } -2 \\ 2x - 2y - 3z &= 5 \;(3) \end{aligned}$$

$$\begin{aligned} -2x - 2y + 2z &= 2 \;(1) \\ 2x - 2y - 3z &= 5 \;(3) \\ \hline -4y - z &= 7 \quad \text{Add.} \end{aligned}$$

$$\begin{cases} x + y - z = -1 \;(1) \\ -7y + 6z = 20 \;(2) \\ -4y - z = 7 \;(3) \end{cases}$$

We now concentrate on the new equations (2) and (3), treating them as a system of two equations containing two variables. It is easiest to eliminate z. We multiply each side of equation (3) by 6 and add equations (2) and (3). The result is the new equation (3).

$$-7y + 6z = 20 \quad (2)$$
$$-4y - z = 7 \quad (3) \quad \text{Multiply by 6} \qquad \begin{aligned} -7y + 6z &= 20 \quad (2) \\ -24y - 6z &= 42 \quad (3) \\ \hline -31y &= 62 \quad \text{Add.} \end{aligned} \qquad \longrightarrow \qquad \begin{cases} x + y - z = -1 \quad (1) \\ \quad -7y + 6z = 20 \quad (2) \\ \quad -31y = 62 \quad (3) \end{cases}$$

We now solve equation (3) for y by dividing both sides of the equation by -31.

$$\begin{cases} x + y - z = -1 \quad (1) \\ \quad -7y + 6z = 20 \quad (2) \\ \quad\quad y = -2 \quad (3) \end{cases}$$

Back-substitute $y = -2$ in equation (2) and solve for z.

$$\begin{aligned} -7y + 6z &= 20 \quad (2) \\ -7(-2) + 6z &= 20 \quad \text{Substitute } y = -2 \text{ in (2).} \\ 6z &= 6 \quad \text{Subtract 14 from both sides of the equation.} \\ z &= 1 \quad \text{Divide both sides of the equation by 6.} \end{aligned}$$

Finally, we back-substitute $y = -2$ and $z = 1$ in equation (1) and solve for x.

$$\begin{aligned} x + y - z &= -1 \quad (1) \\ x + (-2) - 1 &= -1 \quad \text{Substitute } y = -2 \text{ and } z = 1 \text{ in (1).} \\ x - 3 &= -1 \quad \text{Simplify.} \\ x &= 2 \quad \text{Add 3 to both sides.} \end{aligned}$$

The solution of the original system is $x = 2$, $y = -2$, $z = 1$ or, using ordered triplets, $(2, -2, 1)$. You should check this solution.

Look back over the solution given in Example 9. Note the pattern of removing one of the variables from two of the equations, followed by solving this system of two equations and two unknowns. Although which variables to remove is your choice, the methodology remains the same for all systems.

━━━━━━━ **Now Work** PROBLEM 43

6 Identify Inconsistent Systems of Equations Containing Three Variables

| EXAMPLE 10 | **An Inconsistent System of Linear Equations** |

Solve: $\begin{cases} 2x + y - z = -2 \quad (1) \\ x + 2y - z = -9 \quad (2) \\ x - 4y + z = 1 \quad (3) \end{cases}$

Solution Our strategy is the same as in Example 9. However, in this system, it seems easiest to eliminate the variable z first. Do you see why?

Multiply each side of equation (1) by -1 and add the result to equation (2). Also, add equations (2) and (3).

$$\begin{aligned} -2x - y + z &= 2 \quad (1) \quad \text{Multiply by } -1. \\ x + 2y - z &= -9 \quad (2) \\ \hline -x + y &= -7 \quad \text{Add.} \end{aligned}$$

$$\begin{aligned} x + 2y - z &= -9 \quad (2) \\ x - 4y + z &= 1 \quad (3) \\ \hline 2x - 2y &= -8 \quad \text{Add.} \end{aligned}$$

$$\begin{cases} 2x + y - z = -2 \quad (1) \\ -x + y = -7 \quad (2) \\ 2x - 2y = -8 \quad (3) \end{cases}$$

We now concentrate on the new equations (2) and (3), treating them as a system of two equations containing two variables. Multiply each side of equation (2) by 2 and add the result to equation (3).

$$\begin{aligned} -x + y &= -7 \ (2) \quad \text{Multiply by 2.} \\ 2x - 2y &= -8 \ (3) \end{aligned} \qquad \begin{aligned} -2x + 2y &= -14 \ (2) \\ \underline{2x - 2y} &= -8 \ (3) \\ 0 &= -22 \ \text{Add.} \end{aligned} \longrightarrow \begin{cases} 2x + y - z = -2 \ (1) \\ -x + y \qquad = -7 \ (2) \\ \qquad 0 = -22 \ (3) \end{cases}$$

Equation (3) has no solution so the system is inconsistent.

---

7 Express the Solution of a System of Dependent Equations Containing Three Variables

| **EXAMPLE 11** | **Solving a System of Dependent Equations** |

$$\text{Solve:} \quad \begin{cases} x - 2y - z = 8 \ (1) \\ 2x - 3y + z = 23 \ (2) \\ 4x - 5y + 5z = 53 \ (3) \end{cases}$$

Solution Our plan is to eliminate x from equations (2) and (3). Multiply each side of equation (1) by -2 and add the result to equation (2). Also, multiply each side of equation (1) by -4 and add the result to equation (3).

$$\begin{aligned} x - 2y - z &= 8 \ (1) \quad \text{Multiply by } -2. \\ 2x - 3y + z &= 23 \ (2) \end{aligned} \qquad \begin{aligned} -2x + 4y + 2z &= -16 \ (1) \\ \underline{2x - 3y + z} &= 23 \ (2) \\ y + 3z &= 7 \ \text{Add.} \end{aligned}$$

$$\begin{aligned} x - 2y - z &= 8 \ (1) \quad \text{Multiply by } -4. \\ 4x - 5y + 5z &= 53 \ (3) \end{aligned} \qquad \begin{aligned} -4x + 8y + 4z &= -32 \ (1) \\ \underline{4x - 5y + 5z} &= 53 \ (2) \\ 3y + 9z &= 21 \ \text{Add.} \end{aligned}$$

$$\begin{cases} x - 2y - z = 8 \ (1) \\ y + 3z = 7 \ (2) \\ 3y + 9z = 21 \ (3) \end{cases}$$

Treat equations (2) and (3) as a system of two equations containing two variables, and eliminate the variable y by multiplying both sides of equation (2) by -3 and adding the result to equation (3).

$$\begin{aligned} y + 3z &= 7 \quad \text{Multiply by } -3. \\ 3y + 9z &= 21 \end{aligned} \qquad \begin{aligned} -3y - 9z &= -21 \\ \underline{3y + 9z} &= 21 \ \text{Add.} \\ 0 &= 0 \end{aligned} \qquad \begin{cases} x - 2y - z = 8 \ (1) \\ y + 3z = 7 \ (2) \\ 0 = 0 \ (3) \end{cases}$$

The original system is equivalent to a system containing two equations, so the equations are dependent and the system has infinitely many solutions. If we solve equation (2) for y, we can express y in terms of z as $y = -3z + 7$. Substitute this expression into equation (1) to determine x in terms of z.

$$\begin{aligned} x - 2y - z &= 8 & (1) \\ x - 2(-3z + 7) - z &= 8 & \text{Substitute } y = -3z + 7 \text{ in (1).} \\ x + 6z - 14 - z &= 8 & \text{Remove parentheses.} \\ x + 5z &= 22 & \text{Combine like terms.} \\ x &= -5z + 22 & \text{Solve for x.} \end{aligned}$$

We will write the solution to the system as

$$\begin{cases} x = -5z + 22 \\ y = -3z + 7 \end{cases} \quad \text{where } z \text{ can be any real number.}$$

This way of writing the solution makes it easier to find specific solutions of the system. To find specific solutions, choose any value of z and use the equations

$x = -5z + 22$ and $y = -3z + 7$ to determine x and y. For example, if $z = 0$, then $x = 22$ and $y = 7$, and if $z = 1$, then $x = 17$ and $y = 4$.

Using ordered triplets, the solution is

$$\{(x, y, z) \mid x = -5z + 22, y = -3z + 7, z \text{ is any real number}\}$$

> **Now Work** PROBLEM 45

Two distinct points in the Cartesian plane determine a unique line. Given three noncollinear points, we can find the (unique) quadratic function whose graph contains these three points.

EXAMPLE 12 | **Curve Fitting**

Find real numbers a, b, and c so that the graph of the quadratic function $y = ax^2 + bx + c$ contains the points $(-1, -4)$, $(1, 6)$, and $(3, 0)$.

Solution

We require that the three points satisfy the equation $y = ax^2 + bx + c$.

For the point $(-1, -4)$ we have: $-4 = a(-1)^2 + b(-1) + c$ $-4 = a - b + c$
For the point $(1, 6)$ we have: $6 = a(1)^2 + b(1) + c$ $6 = a + b + c$
For the point $(3, 0)$ we have: $0 = a(3)^2 + b(3) + c$ $0 = 9a + 3b + c$

We wish to determine a, b, and c so that each equation is satisfied. That is, we want to solve the following system of three equations containing three variables:

$$\begin{cases} a - b + c = -4 & (1) \\ a + b + c = 6 & (2) \\ 9a + 3b + c = 0 & (3) \end{cases}$$

Figure 6

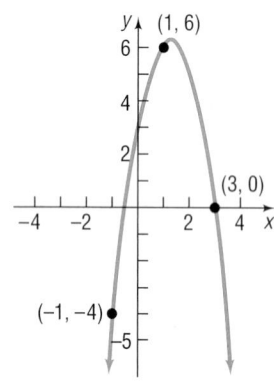

Solving this system of equations, we obtain $a = -2$, $b = 5$, and $c = 3$. So the quadratic function whose graph contains the points $(-1, -4)$, $(1, 6)$, and $(3, 0)$ is

$$y = -2x^2 + 5x + 3 \qquad {\scriptstyle y = ax^2 + bx + c, \quad a = -2, b = 5, c = 3}$$

Figure 6 shows the graph of the function along with the three points.

> **Now Work** PROBLEM 69

11.1 Assess Your Understanding

'Are You Prepared?' *Answers are given at the end of these exercises. If you get a wrong answer, read the pages listed in red.*

1. Solve the equation: $3x + 4 = 8 - x$. (pp. A47–A49)

2. (a) Graph the line: $3x + 4y = 12$.
   (b) What is the slope of a line parallel to this line? (pp. 35–38)

Concepts and Vocabulary

3. If a system of equations has no solution, it is said to be _____.

4. If a system of equations has one or more solutions, the system is said to be _____.

5. *True or False* A system of two linear equations containing two variables always has at least one solution.

6. *True or False* A solution of a system of equations consists of values for the variables that are solutions of each equation of the system.

Skill Building

In Problems 7–16, verify that the values of the variables listed are solutions of the system of equations.

7. $\begin{cases} 2x - y = 5 \\ 5x + 2y = 8 \end{cases}$
$x = 2, y = -1; (2, -1)$

8. $\begin{cases} 3x + 2y = 2 \\ x - 7y = -30 \end{cases}$
$x = -2, y = 4; (-2, 4)$

9. $\begin{cases} 3x - 4y = 4 \\ \dfrac{1}{2}x - 3y = -\dfrac{1}{2} \end{cases}$
$x = 2, y = \dfrac{1}{2}; \left(2, \dfrac{1}{2}\right)$

10. $\begin{cases} 2x + \dfrac{1}{2}y = 0 \\ 3x - 4y = -\dfrac{19}{2} \end{cases}$
$x = -\dfrac{1}{2}, y = 2; \left(-\dfrac{1}{2}, 2\right)$

11. $\begin{cases} x - y = 3 \\ \dfrac{1}{2}x + y = 3 \end{cases}$
$x = 4, y = 1; (4, 1)$

12. $\begin{cases} x - y = 3 \\ -3x + y = 1 \end{cases}$
$x = -2, y = -5; (-2, -5)$

13. $\begin{cases} 3x + 3y + 2z = 4 \\ x - y - z = 0 \\ 2y - 3z = -8 \end{cases}$
$x = 1, y = -1, z = 2;$
$(1, -1, 2)$

14. $\begin{cases} 4x - z = 7 \\ 8x + 5y - z = 0 \\ -x - y + 5z = 6 \end{cases}$
$x = 2, y = -3, z = 1;$
$(2, -3, 1)$

15. $\begin{cases} 3x + 3y + 2z = 4 \\ x - 3y + z = 10 \\ 5x - 2y - 3z = 8 \end{cases}$
$x = 2, y = -2, z = 2; (2, -2, 2)$

16. $\begin{cases} 4x - 5z = 6 \\ 5y - z = -17 \\ -x - 6y + 5z = 24 \end{cases}$
$x = 4, y = -3, z = 2; (4, -3, 2)$

In Problems 17–54, solve each system of equations. If the system has no solution, say that it is inconsistent.

17. $\begin{cases} x + y = 8 \\ x - y = 4 \end{cases}$

18. $\begin{cases} x + 2y = -7 \\ x + y = -3 \end{cases}$

19. $\begin{cases} 5x - y = 21 \\ 2x + 3y = -12 \end{cases}$

20. $\begin{cases} x + 3y = 5 \\ 2x - 3y = -8 \end{cases}$

21. $\begin{cases} 3x = 24 \\ x + 2y = 0 \end{cases}$

22. $\begin{cases} 4x + 5y = -3 \\ -2y = -8 \end{cases}$

23. $\begin{cases} 3x - 6y = 2 \\ 5x + 4y = 1 \end{cases}$

24. $\begin{cases} 2x + 4y = \dfrac{2}{3} \\ 3x - 5y = -10 \end{cases}$

25. $\begin{cases} 2x + y = 1 \\ 4x + 2y = 3 \end{cases}$

26. $\begin{cases} x - y = 5 \\ -3x + 3y = 2 \end{cases}$

27. $\begin{cases} 2x - y = 0 \\ 4x + 2y = 12 \end{cases}$

28. $\begin{cases} 3x + 3y = -1 \\ 4x + y = \dfrac{8}{3} \end{cases}$

29. $\begin{cases} x + 2y = 4 \\ 2x + 4y = 8 \end{cases}$

30. $\begin{cases} 3x - y = 7 \\ 9x - 3y = 21 \end{cases}$

31. $\begin{cases} 2x - 3y = -1 \\ 10x + y = 11 \end{cases}$

32. $\begin{cases} 3x - 2y = 0 \\ 5x + 10y = 4 \end{cases}$

33. $\begin{cases} 2x + 3y = 6 \\ x - y = \dfrac{1}{2} \end{cases}$

34. $\begin{cases} \dfrac{1}{2}x + y = -2 \\ x - 2y = 8 \end{cases}$

35. $\begin{cases} \dfrac{1}{2}x + \dfrac{1}{3}y = 3 \\ \dfrac{1}{4}x - \dfrac{2}{3}y = -1 \end{cases}$

36. $\begin{cases} \dfrac{1}{3}x - \dfrac{3}{2}y = -5 \\ \dfrac{3}{4}x + \dfrac{1}{3}y = 11 \end{cases}$

37. $\begin{cases} 3x - 5y = 3 \\ 15x + 5y = 21 \end{cases}$

38. $\begin{cases} 2x - y = -1 \\ x + \dfrac{1}{2}y = \dfrac{3}{2} \end{cases}$

39. $\begin{cases} \dfrac{1}{x} + \dfrac{1}{y} = 8 \\ \dfrac{3}{x} - \dfrac{5}{y} = 0 \end{cases}$

40. $\begin{cases} \dfrac{4}{x} - \dfrac{3}{y} = 0 \\ \dfrac{6}{x} + \dfrac{3}{2y} = 2 \end{cases}$

[**Hint:** Let $u = \dfrac{1}{x}$ and $v = \dfrac{1}{y}$, and solve for u and v. Then $x = \dfrac{1}{u}$ and $y = \dfrac{1}{v}$.]

41. $\begin{cases} x - y = 6 \\ 2x - 3z = 16 \\ 2y + z = 4 \end{cases}$

42. $\begin{cases} 2x + y = -4 \\ -2y + 4z = 0 \\ 3x - 2z = -11 \end{cases}$

43. $\begin{cases} x - 2y + 3z = 7 \\ 2x + y + z = 4 \\ -3x + 2y - 2z = -10 \end{cases}$

44. $\begin{cases} 2x + y - 3z = 0 \\ -2x + 2y + z = -7 \\ 3x - 4y - 3z = 7 \end{cases}$

45. $\begin{cases} x - y - z = 1 \\ 2x + 3y + z = 2 \\ 3x + 2y = 0 \end{cases}$

46. $\begin{cases} 2x - 3y - z = 0 \\ -x + 2y + z = 5 \\ 3x - 4y - z = 1 \end{cases}$

47. $\begin{cases} x - y - z = 1 \\ -x + 2y - 3z = -4 \\ 3x - 2y - 7z = 0 \end{cases}$

48. $\begin{cases} 2x - 3y - z = 0 \\ 3x + 2y + 2z = 2 \\ x + 5y + 3z = 2 \end{cases}$

49. $\begin{cases} 2x - 2y + 3z = 6 \\ 4x - 3y + 2z = 0 \\ -2x + 3y - 7z = 1 \end{cases}$ **50.** $\begin{cases} 3x - 2y + 2z = 6 \\ 7x - 3y + 2z = -1 \\ 2x - 3y + 4z = 0 \end{cases}$ **51.** $\begin{cases} x + y - z = 6 \\ 3x - 2y + z = -5 \\ x + 3y - 2z = 14 \end{cases}$ **52.** $\begin{cases} x - y + z = -4 \\ 2x - 3y + 4z = -15 \\ 5x + y - 2z = 12 \end{cases}$

53. $\begin{cases} x + 2y - z = -3 \\ 2x - 4y + z = -7 \\ -2x + 2y - 3z = 4 \end{cases}$ **54.** $\begin{cases} x + 4y - 3z = -8 \\ 3x - y + 3z = 12 \\ x + y + 6z = 1 \end{cases}$

Applications and Extensions

55. The perimeter of a rectangular floor is 90 feet. Find the dimensions of the floor if the length is twice the width.

56. The length of fence required to enclose a rectangular field is 3000 meters. What are the dimensions of the field if it is known that the difference between its length and width is 50 meters?

57. Orbital Launches In 2005 there was a total of 55 commercial and noncommercial orbital launches worldwide. In addition, the number of noncommercial orbital launches was one more than twice the number of commercial orbital launches. Determine the number of commercial and noncommercial orbital launches in 2005.

Source: Federal Aviation Administration

58. Movie Theater Tickets A movie theater charges $9.00 for adults and $7.00 for senior citizens. On a day when 325 people paid an admission, the total receipts were $2495. How many who paid were adults? How many were seniors?

59. Mixing Nuts A store sells cashews for $5.00 per pound and peanuts for $1.50 per pound. The manager decides to mix 30 pounds of peanuts with some cashews and sell the mixture for $3.00 per pound. How many pounds of cashews should be mixed with the peanuts so that the mixture will produce the same revenue as would selling the nuts separately?

60. Financial Planning A recently retired couple needs $12,000 per year to supplement their Social Security. They have $150,000 to invest to obtain this income. They have decided on two investment options: AA bonds yielding 10% per annum and a Bank Certificate yielding 5%.

(a) How much should be invested in each to realize exactly $12,000?

(b) If, after 2 years, the couple requires $14,000 per year in income, how should they reallocate their investment to achieve the new amount?

61. Computing Wind Speed With a tail wind, a small Piper aircraft can fly 600 miles in 3 hours. Against this same wind, the Piper can fly the same distance in 4 hours. Find the average wind speed and the average airspeed of the Piper.

62. Computing Wind Speed The average airspeed of a single-engine aircraft is 150 miles per hour. If the aircraft flew the same distance in 2 hours with the wind as it flew in 3 hours against the wind, what was the wind speed?

63. Restaurant Management A restaurant manager wants to purchase 200 sets of dishes. One design costs $25 per set, while another costs $45 per set. If she only has $7400 to spend, how many of each design should be ordered?

64. Cost of Fast Food One group of people purchased 10 hot dogs and 5 soft drinks at a cost of $35.00. A second bought 7 hot dogs and 4 soft drinks at a cost of $25.25. What is the cost of a single hot dog? A single soft drink?

We paid $35.00.
How much is one hot dog?
How much is one soda?

We paid $25.25.
How much is one hot dog?
How much is one soda?

65. Computing a Refund The grocery store we use does not mark prices on its goods. My wife went to this store, bought three 1-pound packages of bacon and two cartons of eggs, and paid a total of $13.45. Not knowing that she went to the store, I also went to the same store, purchased two 1-pound packages of bacon and three cartons of eggs, and paid a total of $11.45. Now we want to return two 1-pound packages of bacon and two cartons of eggs. How much will be refunded?

66. Finding the Current of a Stream Pamela requires 3 hours to swim 15 miles downstream on the Illinois River. The return trip upstream takes 5 hours. Find Pamela's average speed in still water. How fast is the current? (Assume that Pamela's speed is the same in each direction.)

67. Pharmacy A doctor's prescription calls for a daily intake containing 40 milligrams (mg) of vitamin C and 30 mg of vitamin D. Your pharmacy stocks two liquids that can be used: one contains 20% vitamin C and 30% vitamin D, the other 40% vitamin C and 20% vitamin D. How many milligrams of each compound should be mixed to fill the prescription?

68. Pharmacy A doctor's prescription calls for the creation of pills that contain 12 units of vitamin B_{12} and 12 units of vitamin E. Your pharmacy stocks two powders that can be used to make these pills: one contains 20% vitamin B_{12} and 30% vitamin E, the other 40% vitamin B_{12} and 20% vitamin E. How many units of each powder should be mixed in each pill?

69. Curve Fitting Find real numbers a, b, and c so that the graph of the function $y = ax^2 + bx + c$ contains the points $(-1, 4)$, $(2, 3)$, and $(0, 1)$.

70. Curve Fitting Find real numbers a, b, and c so that the graph of the function $y = ax^2 + bx + c$ contains the points $(-1, -2)$, $(1, -4)$, and $(2, 4)$.

71. IS–LM Model in Economics In economics, the IS curve is a linear equation that represents all combinations of income Y and interest rates r that maintain an equilibrium in the market for goods in the economy. The LM curve is a linear equation that represents all combinations of income Y and interest rates r that maintain an equilibrium in the market for money in the economy. In an economy, suppose the equilibrium level of income (in millions of dollars) and interest rates satisfy the system of equations

$$\begin{cases} 0.06Y - 5000r = 240 \\ 0.06Y + 6000r = 900 \end{cases}$$

Find the equilibrium level of income and interest rates.

72. IS–LM Model in Economics In economics, the IS curve is a linear equation that represents all combinations of income Y and interest rates r that maintain an equilibrium in the market for goods in the economy. The LM curve is a linear equation that represents all combinations of income Y and interest rates r that maintain an equilibrium in the market for money in the economy. In an economy, suppose the equilibrium level of income (in millions of dollars) and interest rates satisfy the system of equations

$$\begin{cases} 0.05Y - 1000r = 10 \\ 0.05Y + 800r = 100 \end{cases}$$

Find the equilibrium level of income and interest rates.

73. Electricity: Kirchhoff's Rules An application of Kirchhoff's Rules to the circuit shown results in the following system of equations:

$$\begin{cases} I_2 = I_1 + I_3 \\ 5 - 3I_1 - 5I_2 = 0 \\ 10 - 5I_2 - 7I_3 = 0 \end{cases}$$

Find the currents I_1, I_2, and I_3.

Source: Physics for Scientists & Engineers, 3rd ed., by Serway. © 1990 Brooks/Cole, a division of Thomson Learning.

74. Electricity: Kirchhoff's Rules An application of Kirchhoff's Rules to the circuit shown results in the following system of equations:

$$\begin{cases} I_3 = I_1 + I_2 \\ 8 = 4I_3 + 6I_2 \\ 8I_1 = 4 + 6I_2 \end{cases}$$

Find the currents I_1, I_2, and I_3.

Source: Physics for Scientists & Engineers, 3rd ed., by Serway. © 1990 Brooks/Cole, a division of Thomson Learning.

75. Theater Revenues A Broadway theater has 500 seats, divided into orchestra, main, and balcony seating. Orchestra seats sell for $50, main seats for $35, and balcony seats for $25. If all the seats are sold, the gross revenue to the theater is $17,100. If all the main and balcony seats are sold, but only half the orchestra seats are sold, the gross revenue is $14,600. How many are there of each kind of seat?

76. Theater Revenues A movie theater charges $8.00 for adults, $4.50 for children, and $6.00 for senior citizens. One day the theater sold 405 tickets and collected $2320 in receipts. Twice as many children's tickets were sold as adult tickets. How many adults, children, and senior citizens went to the theater that day?

77. Nutrition A dietitian wishes a patient to have a meal that has 66 grams (g) of protein, 94.5 g of carbohydrates, and 910 milligrams (mg) of calcium. The hospital food service tells the dietitian that the dinner for today is chicken, corn, and 2% milk. Each serving of chicken has 30 g of protein, 35 g of carbohydrates, and 200 mg of calcium. Each serving of corn has 3 g of protein, 16 g of carbohydrates, and 10 mg of calcium. Each glass of 2% milk has 9 g of protein, 13 g of carbohydrates, and 300 mg of calcium. How many servings of each food should the dietitian provide for the patient?

78. Investments Kelly has $20,000 to invest. As her financial planner, you recommend that she diversify into three investments: Treasury bills that yield 5% simple interest, Treasury bonds that yield 7% simple interest, and corporate bonds that yield 10% simple interest. Kelly wishes to earn $1390 per year in income. Also, Kelly wants her investment in Treasury bills to be $3000 more than her investment in corporate bonds. How much money should Kelly place in each investment?

79. Prices of Fast Food One group of customers bought 8 deluxe hamburgers, 6 orders of large fries, and 6 large colas for $26.10. A second group ordered 10 deluxe hamburgers, 6 large fries, and 8 large colas and paid $31.60. Is there sufficient information to determine the price of each food item? If not, construct a table showing the various possibilities. Assume that the hamburgers cost between $1.75 and $2.25, the fries between $0.75 and $1.00, and the colas between $0.60 and $0.90.

80. Prices of Fast Food Use the information given in Problem 79. Suppose that a third group purchased 3 deluxe hamburgers, 2 large fries, and 4 large colas for $10.95. Now is there sufficient information to determine the price of each food item? If so, determine each price.

Find the currents I_1, I_2, and I_3.

81. Painting a House Three painters, Beth, Bill, and Edie, working together, can paint the exterior of a home in 10 hours (hr). Bill and Edie together have painted a similar house in 15 hr. One day, all three worked on this same kind of house for 4 hr, after which Edie left. Beth and Bill required 8 more hr to finish. Assuming no gain or loss in efficiency, how long should it take each person to complete such a job alone?

Discussion and Writing

82. Make up a system of three linear equations containing three variables that has:
(a) No solution
(b) Exactly one solution
(c) Infinitely many solutions
Give the three systems to a friend to solve and critique.

83. Write a brief paragraph outlining your strategy for solving a system of two linear equations containing two variables.

84. Do you prefer the method of substitution or the method of elimination for solving a system of two linear equations containing two variables? Give reasons.

'Are You Prepared?' Answers

1. $\{1\}$ **2. (a)**

y-axis graph with line through points $(0, 3)$ and $(4, 0)$

(b) $-\dfrac{3}{4}$

11.2 Systems of Linear Equations: Matrices

OBJECTIVES **1** Write the Augmented Matrix of a System of Linear Equations (p. 721)
2 Write the System of Equations from the Augmented Matrix (p. 722)
3 Perform Row Operations on a Matrix (p. 722)
4 Solve a System of Linear Equations Using Matrices (p. 724)

The systematic approach of the method of elimination for solving a system of linear equations provides another method of solution that involves a simplified notation.

Consider the following system of linear equations:

$$\begin{cases} x + 4y = 14 \\ 3x - 2y = 0 \end{cases}$$

If we choose not to write the symbols used for the variables, we can represent this system as

$$\begin{bmatrix} 1 & 4 & | & 14 \\ 3 & -2 & | & 0 \end{bmatrix}$$

where it is understood that the first column represents the coefficients of the variable x, the second column the coefficients of y, and the third column the constants on the right side of the equal signs. The vertical line serves as a reminder of the equal signs. The large square brackets are used to denote a *matrix* in algebra.

DEFINITION A **matrix** is defined as a rectangular array of numbers,

$$
\begin{array}{ccccccc}
 & \text{Column 1} & \text{Column 2} & & \text{Column } j & & \text{Column } n \\
\text{Row 1} & a_{11} & a_{12} & \cdots & a_{1j} & \cdots & a_{1n} \\
\text{Row 2} & a_{21} & a_{22} & \cdots & a_{2j} & \cdots & a_{2n} \\
\vdots & \vdots & \vdots & & \vdots & & \vdots \\
\text{Row } i & a_{i1} & a_{i2} & \cdots & a_{ij} & \cdots & a_{in} \\
\vdots & \vdots & \vdots & & \vdots & & \vdots \\
\text{Row } m & a_{m1} & a_{m2} & \cdots & a_{mj} & \cdots & a_{mn}
\end{array}
\tag{1}
$$

Each number a_{ij} of the matrix has two indexes: the **row index** i and the **column index** j. The matrix shown in display (1) has m rows and n columns. The numbers a_{ij} are usually referred to as the **entries** of the matrix. For example, a_{23} refers to the entry in the second row, third column.

1 Write the Augmented Matrix of a System of Linear Equations

Now we will use matrix notation to represent a system of linear equations. The matrix used to represent a system of linear equations is called an **augmented matrix.** In writing the augmented matrix of a system, the variables of each equation must be on the left side of the equal sign and the constants on the right side. A variable that does not appear in an equation has a coefficient of 0.

EXAMPLE 1 **Writing the Augmented Matrix of a System of Linear Equations**

Write the augmented matrix of each system of equations.

(a) $\begin{cases} 3x - 4y = -6 & (1) \\ 2x - 3y = -5 & (2) \end{cases}$

(b) $\begin{cases} 2x - y + z = 0 & (1) \\ x + z - 1 = 0 & (2) \\ x + 2y - 8 = 0 & (3) \end{cases}$

Solution (a) The augmented matrix is

$$
\begin{bmatrix} 3 & -4 & | & -6 \\ 2 & -3 & | & -5 \end{bmatrix}
$$

(b) Care must be taken that the system be written so that the coefficients of all variables are present (if any variable is missing, its coefficient is 0). Also, all constants must be to the right of the equal sign. We need to rearrange the given system as follows:

$$
\begin{cases} 2x - y + z = 0 & (1) \\ x + z - 1 = 0 & (2) \\ x + 2y - 8 = 0 & (3) \end{cases}
$$

$$
\begin{cases} 2x - y + z = 0 & (1) \\ x + 0 \cdot y + z = 1 & (2) \\ x + 2y + 0 \cdot z = 8 & (3) \end{cases}
$$

The augmented matrix is

$$
\begin{bmatrix} 2 & -1 & 1 & | & 0 \\ 1 & 0 & 1 & | & 1 \\ 1 & 2 & 0 & | & 8 \end{bmatrix}
$$

If we do not include the constants to the right of the equal sign, that is, to the right of the vertical bar in the augmented matrix of a system of equations, the resulting matrix is called the **coefficient matrix** of the system. For the systems discussed in Example 1, the coefficient matrices are

$$\begin{bmatrix} 3 & -4 \\ 2 & -3 \end{bmatrix} \text{ and } \begin{bmatrix} 2 & -1 & 1 \\ 1 & 0 & 1 \\ 1 & 2 & 0 \end{bmatrix}$$

━━━━━➤ **Now Work** PROBLEM 7

2 Write the System of Equations from the Augmented Matrix

EXAMPLE 2

Writing the System of Linear Equations from the Augmented Matrix

Write the system of linear equations corresponding to each augmented matrix.

(a) $\begin{bmatrix} 5 & 2 & | & 13 \\ -3 & 1 & | & -10 \end{bmatrix}$
(b) $\begin{bmatrix} 3 & -1 & -1 & | & 7 \\ 2 & 0 & 2 & | & 8 \\ 0 & 1 & 1 & | & 0 \end{bmatrix}$

Solution

(a) The matrix has two rows and so represents a system of two equations. The two columns to the left of the vertical bar indicate that the system has two variables. If x and y are used to denote these variables, the system of equations is

$$\begin{cases} 5x + 2y = 13 & (1) \\ -3x + y = -10 & (2) \end{cases}$$

(b) Since the augmented matrix has three rows, it represents a system of three equations. Since there are three columns to the left of the vertical bar, the system contains three variables. If $x, y,$ and z are the three variables, the system of equations is

$$\begin{cases} 3x - y - z = 7 & (1) \\ 2x + 2z = 8 & (2) \\ y + z = 0 & (3) \end{cases}$$

━━━ ■

3 Perform Row Operations on a Matrix

Row operations on a matrix are used to solve systems of equations when the system is written as an augmented matrix. There are three basic row operations.

Row Operations

1. Interchange any two rows.
2. Replace a row by a nonzero multiple of that row.
3. Replace a row by the sum of that row and a constant nonzero multiple of some other row.

These three row operations correspond to the three rules given earlier for obtaining an equivalent system of equations. When a row operation is performed on a matrix, the resulting matrix represents a system of equations equivalent to the system represented by the original matrix.

For example, consider the augmented matrix

$$\begin{bmatrix} 1 & 2 & | & 3 \\ 4 & -1 & | & 2 \end{bmatrix}$$

Suppose that we want to apply a row operation to this matrix that results in a matrix whose entry in row 2, column 1 is a 0. The row operation to use is

> Multiply each entry in row 1 by -4 and add the result to the corresponding entries in row 2.

(2)

If we use R_2 to represent the new entries in row 2 and r_1 and r_2 to represent the original entries in rows 1 and 2, respectively, we can represent the row operation in statement (2) by

$$R_2 = -4r_1 + r_2$$

Then

$$\begin{bmatrix} 1 & 2 & | & 3 \\ 4 & -1 & | & 2 \end{bmatrix} \xrightarrow[R_2 = -4r_1 + r_2]{} \begin{bmatrix} 1 & 2 & | & 3 \\ -4(1)+4 & -4(2)+(-1) & | & -4(3)+2 \end{bmatrix} = \begin{bmatrix} 1 & 2 & | & 3 \\ 0 & -9 & | & -10 \end{bmatrix}$$

As desired, we now have the entry 0 in row 2, column 1.

EXAMPLE 3   **Applying a Row Operation to an Augmented Matrix**

Apply the row operation $R_2 = -3r_1 + r_2$ to the augmented matrix

$$\begin{bmatrix} 1 & -2 & | & 2 \\ 3 & -5 & | & 9 \end{bmatrix}$$

Solution   The row operation $R_2 = -3r_1 + r_2$ tells us that the entries in row 2 are to be replaced by the entries obtained after multiplying each entry in row 1 by -3 and adding the result to the corresponding entries in row 2.

$$\begin{bmatrix} 1 & -2 & | & 2 \\ 3 & -5 & | & 9 \end{bmatrix} \xrightarrow[R_2 = -3r_1 + r_2]{} \begin{bmatrix} 1 & -2 & | & 2 \\ -3(1)+3 & (-3)(-2)+(-5) & | & -3(2)+9 \end{bmatrix} = \begin{bmatrix} 1 & -2 & | & 2 \\ 0 & 1 & | & 3 \end{bmatrix}$$

Now Work PROBLEM 17

EXAMPLE 4   **Finding a Particular Row Operation**

Find a row operation that will result in the augmented matrix

$$\begin{bmatrix} 1 & -2 & | & 2 \\ 0 & 1 & | & 3 \end{bmatrix}$$

having a 0 in row 1, column 2.

Solution   We want a 0 in row 1, column 2. Because there is a 1 in row 2, column 2, this result can be accomplished by multiplying row 2 by 2 and adding the result to row 1. That is, we apply the row operation $R_1 = 2r_2 + r_1$.

$$\begin{bmatrix} 1 & -2 & | & 2 \\ 0 & 1 & | & 3 \end{bmatrix} \xrightarrow[R_1 = 2r_2 + r_1]{} \begin{bmatrix} 2(0)+1 & 2(1)+(-2) & | & 2(3)+2 \\ 0 & 1 & | & 3 \end{bmatrix} = \begin{bmatrix} 1 & 0 & | & 8 \\ 0 & 1 & | & 3 \end{bmatrix}$$

A word about the notation that we have introduced. A row operation such as $R_1 = 2r_2 + r_1$ changes the entries in row 1. Note also that for this type of row operation we change the entries in a given row by multiplying the entries in some other row by an appropriate nonzero number and adding the results to the original entries of the row to be changed.

4 Solve a System of Linear Equations Using Matrices

To solve a system of linear equations using matrices, we use row operations on the augmented matrix of the system to obtain a matrix that is in *row echelon form*.

DEFINITION

A matrix is in **row echelon form** when the following conditions are met:

1. The entry in row 1, column 1 is a 1, and only 0's appear below it.
2. The first nonzero entry in each row after the first row is a 1, only 0's appear below it, and the 1 appears to the right of the first nonzero entry in any row above.
3. Any rows that contain all 0's to the left of the vertical bar appear at the bottom.

For example, for a system of three equations containing three variables with a unique solution, the augmented matrix is in row echelon form if it is of the form

$$\begin{bmatrix} 1 & a & b & | & d \\ 0 & 1 & c & | & e \\ 0 & 0 & 1 & | & f \end{bmatrix}$$

where a, b, c, d, e, and f are real numbers. The last row of this augmented matrix states that $z = f$. We can then determine the value of y using back-substitution with $z = f$, since row 2 represents the equation $y + cz = e$. Finally, x is determined using back-substitution again.

Two advantages of solving a system of equations by writing the augmented matrix in row echelon form are the following:

1. The process is algorithmic; that is, it consists of repetitive steps that can be programmed on a computer.
2. The process works on any system of linear equations, no matter how many equations or variables are present.

The next example shows how to write a matrix in row echelon form.

| EXAMPLE 5 | How to Solve a System of Linear Equations Using Matrices |

Solve: $\begin{cases} 2x + 2y & = 6 \quad (1) \\ x + y + z = 1 \quad (2) \\ 3x + 4y - z = 13 \quad (3) \end{cases}$

Step-by-Step Solution

STEP 1 Write the augmented matrix that represents the system.

We write the augmented matrix of the system.

$$\begin{bmatrix} 2 & 2 & 0 & | & 6 \\ 1 & 1 & 1 & | & 1 \\ 3 & 4 & -1 & | & 13 \end{bmatrix}$$

STEP 2 Perform row operations that result in the entry in row 1, column 1 becoming 1.

To get a 1 in row 1, column 1, we interchange rows 1 and 2. [Note that this is equivalent to interchanging equations (1) and (2) of the system.]

$$\begin{bmatrix} 1 & 1 & 1 & | & 1 \\ 2 & 2 & 0 & | & 6 \\ 3 & 4 & -1 & | & 13 \end{bmatrix}$$

STEP 3 Perform row operations that leave the entry in row 1, column 1 a 1, while causing the entries in column 1 below row 1 to become 0's.

Next, we want a 0 in row 2, column 1 and a 0 in row 3, column 1. We use the row operations $R_2 = -2r_1 + r_2$ and $R_3 = -3r_1 + r_3$ to accomplish this. Notice that row 1 is unchanged using these row operations. Also, do you see that performing these row operations simultaneously is the same as doing one followed by the other?

$$\begin{bmatrix} 1 & 1 & 1 & | & 1 \\ 2 & 2 & 0 & | & 6 \\ 3 & 4 & -1 & | & 13 \end{bmatrix} \rightarrow \begin{bmatrix} 1 & 1 & 1 & | & 1 \\ 0 & 0 & -2 & | & 4 \\ 0 & 1 & -4 & | & 10 \end{bmatrix}$$

$$R_2 = -2r_1 + r_2$$
$$R_3 = -3r_1 + r_3$$

STEP 4 Perform row operations that result in the entry in row 2, column 2 becoming 1 with 0's below it.

We want the entry in row 2, column 2 to be 1. We also want to have a 0 below the 1 in row 2, column 2. Interchanging rows 2 and 3 will accomplish both goals.

$$\begin{bmatrix} 1 & 1 & 1 & | & 1 \\ 0 & 0 & -2 & | & 4 \\ 0 & 1 & -4 & | & 10 \end{bmatrix} \rightarrow \begin{bmatrix} 1 & 1 & 1 & | & 1 \\ 0 & 1 & -4 & | & 10 \\ 0 & 0 & -2 & | & 4 \end{bmatrix}$$

STEP 5 Repeat Step 4, placing a 1 in row 3, column 3.

To obtain a 1 in row 3, column 3, we use the row operation $R_3 = -\dfrac{1}{2}r_3$. The result is

$$\begin{bmatrix} 1 & 1 & 1 & | & 1 \\ 0 & 1 & -4 & | & 10 \\ 0 & 0 & -2 & | & 4 \end{bmatrix} \rightarrow \begin{bmatrix} 1 & 1 & 1 & | & 1 \\ 0 & 1 & -4 & | & 10 \\ 0 & 0 & 1 & | & -2 \end{bmatrix}$$

$$R_3 = -\dfrac{1}{2}r_3$$

STEP 6 The matrix is the row echelon form of the augmented matrix. Use back-substitution to solve the original system.

The third row of the augmented matrix represents the equation $z = -2$. Using $z = -2$, we back-substitute into the equation $y - 4z = 10$ (from the second row) and obtain

$$\begin{aligned} y - 4z &= 10 \\ y - 4(-2) &= 10 \quad z = -2 \\ y &= 2 \quad \text{Solve for } y. \end{aligned}$$

Finally, we back-substitute $y = 2$ and $z = -2$ into the equation $x + y + z = 1$ (from the first row) and obtain

$$\begin{aligned} x + y + z &= 1 \\ x + 2 + (-2) &= 1 \quad y = 2, z = -2 \\ x &= 1 \quad \text{Solve for } x. \end{aligned}$$

The solution of the system is $x = 1$, $y = 2$, $z = -2$ or, using ordered triplets, $(1, 2, -2)$.

The steps that we used to solve the system of linear equations in Example 5 can be summarized as follows:

Matrix Method for Solving a System of Linear Equations (Row Echelon Form)

STEP 1: Write the augmented matrix that represents the system.

STEP 2: Perform row operations that place the entry 1 in row 1, column 1.

STEP 3: Perform row operations that leave the entry 1 in row 1, column 1 unchanged, while causing 0's to appear below it in column 1.

STEP 4: Perform row operations that place the entry 1 in row 2, column 2, but leave the entries in columns to the left unchanged. If it is impossible to place a 1 in row 2, column 2, proceed to place a 1 in row 2, column 3. Once a 1 is in place, perform row operations to place 0's below it. (Place any rows that contain only 0's on the left side of the vertical bar, at the bottom of the matrix.)

(continued)

In Words

To obtain an augmented matrix in row echelon form:

- Add rows, exchange rows, or multiply the row by a nonzero constant.
- Work from top to bottom and left to right.
- Get 1's in the main diagonal with 0's below the 1's.
- Once the entry in row 1, column 1 is 1 with 0's below it, we do not use row 1 in our row operations. Once the entries in row 1, column 1 and row 2, column 2 are 1 with 0's below, we do not use rows 1 or 2 in our row operations (and so on).

STEP 5: Now repeat Step 4, placing a 1 in the next row, but one column to the right. Continue until the bottom row or the vertical bar is reached.

STEP 6: The matrix that results is the row echelon form of the augmented matrix. Analyze the system of equations corresponding to it to solve the original system.

In the next example, we solve a system of linear equations using these steps. In addition, we solve the system using a graphing utility.

EXAMPLE 6 | **Solving a System of Linear Equations Using Matrices (Row Echelon Form)**

Solve: $\begin{cases} x - y + z = 8 & (1) \\ 2x + 3y - z = -2 & (2) \\ 3x - 2y - 9z = 9 & (3) \end{cases}$

Algebraic Solution

STEP 1: The augmented matrix of the system is

$$\begin{bmatrix} 1 & -1 & 1 & | & 8 \\ 2 & 3 & -1 & | & -2 \\ 3 & -2 & -9 & | & 9 \end{bmatrix}$$

STEP 2: Because the entry 1 is already present in row 1, column 1, we can go to step 3.

STEP 3: Perform the row operations $R_2 = -2r_1 + r_2$ and $R_3 = -3r_1 + r_3$. Each of these leaves the entry 1 in row 1, column 1 unchanged, while causing 0's to appear under it.

$$\begin{bmatrix} 1 & -1 & 1 & | & 8 \\ 2 & 3 & -1 & | & -2 \\ 3 & -2 & -9 & | & 9 \end{bmatrix} \rightarrow \begin{bmatrix} 1 & -1 & 1 & | & 8 \\ 0 & 5 & -3 & | & -18 \\ 0 & 1 & -12 & | & -15 \end{bmatrix}$$
$$\uparrow$$
$$R_2 = -2r_1 + r_2$$
$$R_3 = -3r_1 + r_3$$

STEP 4: The easiest way to obtain the entry 1 in row 2, column 2 without altering column 1 is to interchange rows 2 and 3 (another way would be to multiply row 2 by $\frac{1}{5}$, but this introduces fractions).

$$\begin{bmatrix} 1 & -1 & 1 & | & 8 \\ 0 & 1 & -12 & | & -15 \\ 0 & 5 & -3 & | & -18 \end{bmatrix}$$

To get a 0 under the 1 in row 2, column 2, perform the row operation $R_3 = -5r_2 + r_3$.

$$\begin{bmatrix} 1 & -1 & 1 & | & 8 \\ 0 & 1 & -12 & | & -15 \\ 0 & 5 & -3 & | & -18 \end{bmatrix} \rightarrow \begin{bmatrix} 1 & -1 & 1 & | & 8 \\ 0 & 1 & -12 & | & -15 \\ 0 & 0 & 57 & | & 57 \end{bmatrix}$$
$$\uparrow$$
$$R_3 = -5r_2 + r_3$$

STEP 5: Continuing, we obtain a 1 in row 3, column 3 by using $R_3 = \frac{1}{57}r_3$.

$$\begin{bmatrix} 1 & -1 & 1 & | & 8 \\ 0 & 1 & -12 & | & -15 \\ 0 & 0 & 57 & | & 57 \end{bmatrix} \rightarrow \begin{bmatrix} 1 & -1 & 1 & | & 8 \\ 0 & 1 & -12 & | & -15 \\ 0 & 0 & 1 & | & 1 \end{bmatrix}$$
$$\uparrow$$
$$R_3 = \frac{1}{57}r_3$$

Graphing Solution

The augmented matrix of the system is

$$\begin{bmatrix} 1 & -1 & 1 & | & 8 \\ 2 & 3 & -1 & | & -2 \\ 3 & -2 & -9 & | & 9 \end{bmatrix}$$

We enter this matrix into our graphing utility and name it A. See Figure 7(a). Using the REF (Row Echelon Form) command on matrix A, we obtain the results shown in Figure 7(b). Since the entire matrix does not fit on the screen, we need to scroll right to see the rest of it. See Figure 7(c).

Figure 7

(a)

(b)

(c)

STEP 6: The matrix on the right is the row echelon form of the augmented matrix. The system of equations represented by the matrix in row echelon form is

$$\begin{cases} x - y + z = 8 & (1) \\ y - 12z = -15 & (2) \\ z = 1 & (3) \end{cases}$$

Using $z = 1$, we back-substitute to get

$$\begin{cases} x - y + 1 = 8 & (1) \\ y - 12(1) = -15 & (2) \end{cases} \longrightarrow \begin{cases} x - y = 7 & (1) \\ y = -3 & (2) \end{cases}$$

Simplify.

We get $y = -3$, and back-substituting into $x - y = 7$, we find that $x = 4$. The solution of the system is $x = 4$, $y = -3$, $z = 1$ or, using ordered triplets, $(4, -3, 1)$.

The system of equations represented by the matrix in row echelon form is

$$\begin{cases} x - \frac{2}{3}y - 3z = 3 & (1) \\ y + \frac{15}{13}z = -\frac{24}{13} & (2) \\ z = 1 & (3) \end{cases}$$

Using $z = 1$, we back-substitute to get

$$\begin{cases} x - \frac{2}{3}y - 3(1) = 3 & (1) \\ y + \frac{15}{13}(1) = -\frac{24}{13} & (2) \end{cases}$$

$$\begin{cases} x - \frac{2}{3}y = 6 & (1) \\ y = -\frac{39}{13} = -3 & (2) \end{cases}$$

From the second equation we find that $y = -3$. Back-substituting $y = -3$ into $x - \frac{2}{3}y = 6$, we find that $x = 4$. The solution of the system is $x = 4$, $y = -3$, $z = 1$ or, using ordered triplets, $(4, -3, 1)$.

Notice that the row echelon form of the augmented matrix in the graphing solution differs from the row echelon form in the algebraic solution, yet both matrices provide the same solution! This is because the two solutions used different row operations to obtain the row echelon form. In all likelihood, the two solutions parted ways in Step 4 of the algebraic solution, where we avoided introducing fractions by interchanging rows 2 and 3.

Sometimes it is advantageous to write a matrix in **reduced row echelon form.** In this form, row operations are used to obtain entries that are 0 above (as well as below) the leading 1 in a row. For example, the row echelon form obtained in the algebraic solution to Example 6 is

$$\begin{bmatrix} 1 & -1 & 1 & | & 8 \\ 0 & 1 & -12 & | & -15 \\ 0 & 0 & 1 & | & 1 \end{bmatrix}$$

To write this matrix in reduced row echelon form, we proceed as follows:

$$\begin{bmatrix} 1 & -1 & 1 & | & 8 \\ 0 & 1 & -12 & | & -15 \\ 0 & 0 & 1 & | & 1 \end{bmatrix} \rightarrow \begin{bmatrix} 1 & 0 & -11 & | & -7 \\ 0 & 1 & -12 & | & -15 \\ 0 & 0 & 1 & | & 1 \end{bmatrix} \rightarrow \begin{bmatrix} 1 & 0 & 0 & | & 4 \\ 0 & 1 & 0 & | & -3 \\ 0 & 0 & 1 & | & 1 \end{bmatrix}$$

$$R_1 = r_2 + r_1 \qquad R_1 = 11r_3 + r_1$$
$$R_2 = 12r_3 + r_2$$

The matrix is now written in reduced row echelon form. The advantage of writing the matrix in this form is that the solution to the system, $x = 4$, $y = -3$, $z = 1$, is readily found, without the need to back-substitute. Another advantage will be seen in Section 11.4, where the inverse of a matrix is discussed. The methodology used to write a matrix in reduced row echelon form is called **Gauss–Jordan elimination.**

Most graphing utilities also have the ability to put a matrix in reduced row echelon form. Figure 8 shows the reduced row echelon form of the augmented matrix from Example 6 using the RREF command on a TI-84 Plus graphing calculator.

Figure 8

For the remaining examples in this section, we will only provide algebraic solutions to the systems. The reader is encouraged to verify the results using a graphing utility.

Now Work PROBLEMS 37 AND 47

The matrix method for solving a system of linear equations also identifies systems that have infinitely many solutions and systems that are inconsistent. Let's see how.

EXAMPLE 7 | **Solving a Dependent System of Linear Equations Using Matrices**

Solve: $\begin{cases} 6x - y - z = 4 & (1) \\ -12x + 2y + 2z = -8 & (2) \\ 5x + y - z = 3 & (3) \end{cases}$

Solution
We start with the augmented matrix of the system and proceed to obtain a 1 in row 1, column 1 with 0's below.

$$\begin{bmatrix} 6 & -1 & -1 & | & 4 \\ -12 & 2 & 2 & | & -8 \\ 5 & 1 & -1 & | & 3 \end{bmatrix} \rightarrow \begin{bmatrix} 1 & -2 & 0 & | & 1 \\ -12 & 2 & 2 & | & -8 \\ 5 & 1 & -1 & | & 3 \end{bmatrix} \rightarrow \begin{bmatrix} 1 & -2 & 0 & | & 1 \\ 0 & -22 & 2 & | & 4 \\ 0 & 11 & -1 & | & -2 \end{bmatrix}$$

$$\underset{R_1 = -1r_3 + r_1}{\uparrow} \qquad \underset{\substack{R_2 = 12r_1 + r_2 \\ R_3 = -5r_1 + r_3}}{\uparrow}$$

Obtaining a 1 in row 2, column 2 without altering column 1 can be accomplished by $R_2 = -\dfrac{1}{22}r_2$ or by $R_3 = \dfrac{1}{11}r_3$ and interchanging rows 2 and 3 or by $R_2 = \dfrac{23}{11}r_3 + r_2$. We shall use the first of these.

$$\begin{bmatrix} 1 & -2 & 0 & | & 1 \\ 0 & -22 & 2 & | & 4 \\ 0 & 11 & -1 & | & -2 \end{bmatrix} \rightarrow \begin{bmatrix} 1 & -2 & 0 & | & 1 \\ 0 & 1 & -\dfrac{1}{11} & | & -\dfrac{2}{11} \\ 0 & 11 & -1 & | & -2 \end{bmatrix} \rightarrow \begin{bmatrix} 1 & -2 & 0 & | & 1 \\ 0 & 1 & -\dfrac{1}{11} & | & -\dfrac{2}{11} \\ 0 & 0 & 0 & | & 0 \end{bmatrix}$$

$$\underset{R_2 = -\frac{1}{22}r_2}{\uparrow} \qquad\qquad \underset{R_3 = -11r_2 + r_3}{\uparrow}$$

This matrix is in row echelon form. Because the bottom row consists entirely of 0's, the system actually consists of only two equations.

$$\begin{cases} x - 2y = 1 & (1) \\ y - \dfrac{1}{11}z = -\dfrac{2}{11} & (2) \end{cases}$$

To make it easier to write down some of the solutions, we express both x and y in terms of z.

From the second equation, $y = \dfrac{1}{11}z - \dfrac{2}{11}$. Now back-substitute this solution for y into the first equation to get

$$x = 2y + 1 = 2\left(\dfrac{1}{11}z - \dfrac{2}{11}\right) + 1 = \dfrac{2}{11}z + \dfrac{7}{11}$$

The original system is equivalent to the system

$$\begin{cases} x = \dfrac{2}{11}z + \dfrac{7}{11} & (1) \\ y = \dfrac{1}{11}z - \dfrac{2}{11} & (2) \end{cases} \qquad \text{where } z \text{ can be any real number.}$$

Let's look at the situation. The original system of three equations is equivalent to a system containing two equations. This means that any values of x, y, z that satisfy both

$$x = \frac{2}{11}z + \frac{7}{11} \quad \text{and} \quad y = \frac{1}{11}z - \frac{2}{11}$$

will be solutions. For example, $z = 0, x = \frac{7}{11}, y = -\frac{2}{11}; z = 1, x = \frac{9}{11}, y = -\frac{1}{11};$ and $z = -1, x = \frac{5}{11}, y = -\frac{3}{11}$ are some of the solutions of the original system. There are, in fact, infinitely many values of $x, y,$ and z for which the two equations are satisfied. That is, the original system has infinitely many solutions. We will write the solution of the original system as

$$\begin{cases} x = \dfrac{2}{11}z + \dfrac{7}{11} \\ y = \dfrac{1}{11}z - \dfrac{2}{11} \end{cases} \quad \text{where } z \text{ can be any real number}$$

or, using ordered triplets, as

$$\left\{ (x, y, z) \,\middle|\, x = \frac{2}{11}z + \frac{7}{11}, y = \frac{1}{11}z - \frac{2}{11}, z \text{ any real number} \right\}.$$

We can also find the solution by writing the augmented matrix in reduced row echelon form. Starting with the row echelon form, we have

$$\begin{bmatrix} 1 & -2 & 0 & \bigg| & 1 \\ 0 & 1 & -\dfrac{1}{11} & \bigg| & -\dfrac{2}{11} \\ 0 & 0 & 0 & \bigg| & 0 \end{bmatrix} \underset{\underset{R_1 = 2r_2 + r_1}{\uparrow}}{\rightarrow} \begin{bmatrix} 1 & 0 & -\dfrac{2}{11} & \bigg| & \dfrac{7}{11} \\ 0 & 1 & -\dfrac{1}{11} & \bigg| & -\dfrac{2}{11} \\ 0 & 0 & 0 & \bigg| & 0 \end{bmatrix}$$

The matrix on the right is in reduced row echelon form. The corresponding system of equations is

$$\begin{cases} x - \dfrac{2}{11}z = \dfrac{7}{11} & (1) \\ y - \dfrac{1}{11}z = -\dfrac{2}{11} & (2) \end{cases} \quad \text{where } z \text{ can be any real number}$$

or, equivalently,

$$\begin{cases} x = \dfrac{2}{11}z + \dfrac{7}{11} \\ y = \dfrac{1}{11}z - \dfrac{2}{11} \end{cases} \quad \text{where } z \text{ can be any real number}$$

Now Work PROBLEM 53

EXAMPLE 8	**Solving an Inconsistent System of Linear Equations Using Matrices**

Solve: $\begin{cases} x + y + z = 6 \\ 2x - y - z = 3 \\ x + 2y + 2z = 0 \end{cases}$

Solution   We proceed as follows, beginning with the augmented matrix.

$$\begin{bmatrix} 1 & 1 & 1 & | & 6 \\ 2 & -1 & -1 & | & 3 \\ 1 & 2 & 2 & | & 0 \end{bmatrix} \rightarrow \begin{bmatrix} 1 & 1 & 1 & | & 6 \\ 0 & -3 & -3 & | & -9 \\ 0 & 1 & 1 & | & -6 \end{bmatrix} \rightarrow \begin{bmatrix} 1 & 1 & 1 & | & 6 \\ 0 & 1 & 1 & | & -6 \\ 0 & -3 & -3 & | & -9 \end{bmatrix} \rightarrow \begin{bmatrix} 1 & 1 & 1 & | & 6 \\ 0 & 1 & 1 & | & -6 \\ 0 & 0 & 0 & | & -27 \end{bmatrix}$$

$$R_2 = -2r_1 + r_2 \qquad \text{Interchange rows 2 and 3.} \qquad R_3 = 3r_2 + r_3$$
$$R_3 = -1r_1 + r_3$$

This matrix is in row echelon form. The bottom row is equivalent to the equation

$$0x + 0y + 0z = -27$$

which has no solution. The original system is inconsistent.

═══════ **Now Work** PROBLEM 27

The matrix method is especially effective for systems of equations for which the number of equations and the number of variables are unequal. Here, too, such a system is either inconsistent or consistent. If it is consistent, it will have either exactly one solution or infinitely many solutions.

Let's look at a system of four equations containing three variables.

EXAMPLE 9   **Solving a System of Linear Equations Using Matrices**

$$\text{Solve:} \begin{cases} x - 2y + z = 0 & (1) \\ 2x + 2y - 3z = -3 & (2) \\ y - z = -1 & (3) \\ -x + 4y + 2z = 13 & (4) \end{cases}$$

Solution   We proceed as follows, beginning with the augmented matrix.

$$\begin{bmatrix} 1 & -2 & 1 & | & 0 \\ 2 & 2 & -3 & | & -3 \\ 0 & 1 & -1 & | & -1 \\ -1 & 4 & 2 & | & 13 \end{bmatrix} \rightarrow \begin{bmatrix} 1 & -2 & 1 & | & 0 \\ 0 & 6 & -5 & | & -3 \\ 0 & 1 & -1 & | & -1 \\ 0 & 2 & 3 & | & 13 \end{bmatrix} \rightarrow \begin{bmatrix} 1 & -2 & 1 & | & 0 \\ 0 & 1 & -1 & | & -1 \\ 0 & 6 & -5 & | & -3 \\ 0 & 2 & 3 & | & 13 \end{bmatrix}$$

$$R_2 = -2r_1 + r_2 \qquad \text{Interchange rows 2 and 3.}$$
$$R_4 = r_1 + r_4$$

$$\rightarrow \begin{bmatrix} 1 & -2 & 1 & | & 0 \\ 0 & 1 & -1 & | & -1 \\ 0 & 0 & 1 & | & 3 \\ 0 & 0 & 5 & | & 15 \end{bmatrix} \rightarrow \begin{bmatrix} 1 & -2 & 1 & | & 0 \\ 0 & 1 & -1 & | & -1 \\ 0 & 0 & 1 & | & 3 \\ 0 & 0 & 0 & | & 0 \end{bmatrix}$$

$$R_3 = -6r_2 + r_3 \qquad R_4 = -5r_3 + r_4$$
$$R_4 = -2r_2 + r_4$$

We could stop here, since the matrix is in row echelon form, and back-substitute $z = 3$ to find x and y. Or we can continue and obtain the reduced row echelon form.

$$\begin{bmatrix} 1 & -2 & 1 & | & 0 \\ 0 & 1 & -1 & | & -1 \\ 0 & 0 & 1 & | & 3 \\ 0 & 0 & 0 & | & 0 \end{bmatrix} \rightarrow \begin{bmatrix} 1 & 0 & -1 & | & -2 \\ 0 & 1 & -1 & | & -1 \\ 0 & 0 & 1 & | & 3 \\ 0 & 0 & 0 & | & 0 \end{bmatrix} \rightarrow \begin{bmatrix} 1 & 0 & 0 & | & 1 \\ 0 & 1 & 0 & | & 2 \\ 0 & 0 & 1 & | & 3 \\ 0 & 0 & 0 & | & 0 \end{bmatrix}$$

$$R_1 = 2r_2 + r_1 \qquad R_1 = r_3 + r_1$$
$$R_2 = r_3 + r_2$$

The matrix is now in reduced row echelon form, and we can see that the solution is $x = 1$, $y = 2$, $z = 3$, or using ordered triplets, $(1, 2, 3)$.

═══════ **Now Work** PROBLEM 69

| EXAMPLE 10 | Penalties in the 2006 Fifa World Cup |

Italy and France combined for a total of 46 penalties during the 2006 Fifa World Cup. The penalties were a combination of fouls, yellow cards (cautions), and red cards (expulsions). There was one less red card than half the number of yellow cards and one more foul than 8 times the total number of cards. How many of each type of penalty were there during the match?

Source: fifaworldcup.com

Solution
Let f, y, and r represent the number of fouls, yellow cards, and red cards, respectively. There was a total of 46 penalties, which is found by adding the number of fouls, yellow cards, and red cards. The first equation is $f + y + r = 46$. There was one less red card than half the number of yellow cards, so the number of red cards equals $\frac{1}{2}$ the number of yellow cards, minus 1. This statement leads to the second equation: $r = \frac{1}{2}y - 1$. We also know that there was one more foul than 8 times the total number of cards, so the number of fouls equals 1 plus the product of 8 and the sum of the number of yellow cards and the number of red cards. This statement gives the third equation: $f = 1 + 8(y + r)$.

Putting each equation in standard form, we have the following system of equations:

$$\begin{cases} f + y + r = 46 & (1) \\ -\frac{1}{2}y + r = -1 & (2) \\ f - 8y - 8r = 1 & (3) \end{cases}$$

We begin with the augmented matrix and proceed as follows:

$$\begin{bmatrix} 1 & 1 & 1 & | & 46 \\ 0 & -\frac{1}{2} & 1 & | & -1 \\ 1 & -8 & -8 & | & 1 \end{bmatrix} \rightarrow \begin{bmatrix} 1 & 1 & 1 & | & 46 \\ 0 & -\frac{1}{2} & 1 & | & -1 \\ 0 & -9 & -9 & | & -45 \end{bmatrix} \rightarrow \begin{bmatrix} 1 & 1 & 1 & | & 46 \\ 0 & 1 & -2 & | & 2 \\ 0 & -9 & -9 & | & -45 \end{bmatrix}$$

$$R_3 = -r_1 + r_3 \qquad\qquad R_2 = -2r_2$$

$$\rightarrow \begin{bmatrix} 1 & 1 & 1 & | & 46 \\ 0 & 1 & -2 & | & 2 \\ 0 & 0 & -27 & | & -27 \end{bmatrix} \rightarrow \begin{bmatrix} 1 & 1 & 1 & | & 46 \\ 0 & 1 & -2 & | & 2 \\ 0 & 0 & 1 & | & 1 \end{bmatrix}$$

$$R_3 = 9r_2 + r_3 \qquad\qquad R_3 = -\frac{1}{27}r_3$$

The matrix is now in echelon form. The final matrix represents the system

$$\begin{cases} f + y + r = 46 & (1) \\ y - 2r = 2 & (2) \\ r = 1 & (3) \end{cases}$$

From equation (3), we determine that 1 red card was given. Back-substitute $r = 1$ into equation (2) to find that $y = 4$, so 4 yellow cards were given. Back-substitute these values into equation (1) and to find that $f = 41$, so 41 fouls were called.

11.2 Assess Your Understanding

Concepts and Vocabulary

1. An m by n rectangular array of numbers is called a(n) _____.

2. The matrix used to represent a system of linear equations is called a(n) _____ matrix.

3. *True or False* The augmented matrix of a system of two equations containing three variables has two rows and four columns.

4. *True or False* The matrix $\begin{bmatrix} 1 & 3 & | & -2 \\ 0 & 1 & | & 5 \\ 0 & 0 & | & 0 \end{bmatrix}$ is in row echelon form.

Skill Building

In Problems 5–16, write the augmented matrix of the given system of equations.

5. $\begin{cases} x - 5y = 5 \\ 4x + 3y = 6 \end{cases}$

6. $\begin{cases} 3x + 4y = 7 \\ 4x - 2y = 5 \end{cases}$

7. $\begin{cases} 2x + 3y - 6 = 0 \\ 4x - 6y + 2 = 0 \end{cases}$

8. $\begin{cases} 9x - y = 0 \\ 3x - y - 4 = 0 \end{cases}$

9. $\begin{cases} 0.01x - 0.03y = 0.06 \\ 0.13x + 0.10y = 0.20 \end{cases}$

10. $\begin{cases} \dfrac{4}{3}x - \dfrac{3}{2}y = \dfrac{3}{4} \\ -\dfrac{1}{4}x + \dfrac{1}{3}y = \dfrac{2}{3} \end{cases}$

11. $\begin{cases} x - y + z = 10 \\ 3x + 3y = 5 \\ x + y + 2z = 2 \end{cases}$

12. $\begin{cases} 5x - y - z = 0 \\ x + y = 5 \\ 2x - 3z = 2 \end{cases}$

13. $\begin{cases} x + y - z = 2 \\ 3x - 2y = 2 \\ 5x + 3y - z = 1 \end{cases}$

14. $\begin{cases} 2x + 3y - 4z = 0 \\ x - 5z + 2 = 0 \\ x + 2y - 3z = -2 \end{cases}$

15. $\begin{cases} x - y - z = 10 \\ 2x + y + 2z = -1 \\ -3x + 4y = 5 \\ 4x - 5y + z = 0 \end{cases}$

16. $\begin{cases} x - y + 2z - w = 5 \\ x + 3y - 4z + 2w = 2 \\ 3x - y - 5z - w = -1 \end{cases}$

In Problems 17–24, write the system of equations corresponding to each augmented matrix. Then perform each row operation on the given augmented matrix.

17. $\begin{bmatrix} 1 & -3 & | & -2 \\ 2 & -5 & | & 5 \end{bmatrix}$ $R_2 = -2r_1 + r_2$

18. $\begin{bmatrix} 1 & -3 & | & -3 \\ 2 & -5 & | & -4 \end{bmatrix}$ $R_2 = -2r_1 + r_2$

19. $\begin{bmatrix} 1 & -3 & 4 & | & 3 \\ 3 & -5 & 6 & | & 6 \\ -5 & 3 & 4 & | & 6 \end{bmatrix}$ (a) $R_2 = -3r_1 + r_2$ (b) $R_3 = 5r_1 + r_3$

20. $\begin{bmatrix} 1 & -3 & 3 & | & -5 \\ -4 & -5 & -3 & | & -5 \\ -3 & -2 & 4 & | & 6 \end{bmatrix}$ (a) $R_2 = 4r_1 + r_2$ (b) $R_3 = 3r_1 + r_3$

21. $\begin{bmatrix} 1 & -3 & 2 & | & -6 \\ 2 & -5 & 3 & | & -4 \\ -3 & -6 & 4 & | & 6 \end{bmatrix}$ (a) $R_2 = -2r_1 + r_2$ (b) $R_3 = 3r_1 + r_3$

22. $\begin{bmatrix} 1 & -3 & -4 & | & -6 \\ 6 & -5 & 6 & | & -6 \\ -1 & 1 & 4 & | & 6 \end{bmatrix}$ (a) $R_2 = -6r_1 + r_2$ (b) $R_3 = r_1 + r_3$

23. $\begin{bmatrix} 5 & -3 & 1 & | & -2 \\ 2 & -5 & 6 & | & -2 \\ -4 & 1 & 4 & | & 6 \end{bmatrix}$ (a) $R_1 = -2r_2 + r_1$ (b) $R_1 = r_3 + r_1$

24. $\begin{bmatrix} 4 & -3 & -1 & | & 2 \\ 3 & -5 & 2 & | & 6 \\ -3 & -6 & 4 & | & 6 \end{bmatrix}$ (a) $R_1 = -r_2 + r_1$ (b) $R_1 = r_3 + r_1$

In Problems 25–36, the reduced row echelon form of a system of linear equations is given. Write the system of equations corresponding to the given matrix. Use x, y; or x, y, z; or x_1, x_2, x_3, x_4 as variables. Determine whether the system is consistent or inconsistent. If it is consistent, give the solution.

25. $\begin{bmatrix} 1 & 0 & | & 5 \\ 0 & 1 & | & -1 \end{bmatrix}$

26. $\begin{bmatrix} 1 & 0 & | & -4 \\ 0 & 1 & | & 0 \end{bmatrix}$

27. $\begin{bmatrix} 1 & 0 & 0 & | & 1 \\ 0 & 1 & 0 & | & 2 \\ 0 & 0 & 0 & | & 3 \end{bmatrix}$

28. $\begin{bmatrix} 1 & 0 & 0 & | & 0 \\ 0 & 1 & 0 & | & 0 \\ 0 & 0 & 0 & | & 2 \end{bmatrix}$

29. $\begin{bmatrix} 1 & 0 & 2 & | & -1 \\ 0 & 1 & -4 & | & -2 \\ 0 & 0 & 0 & | & 0 \end{bmatrix}$

30. $\begin{bmatrix} 1 & 0 & 4 & | & 4 \\ 0 & 1 & 3 & | & 2 \\ 0 & 0 & 0 & | & 0 \end{bmatrix}$

31. $\begin{bmatrix} 1 & 0 & 0 & 0 & | & 1 \\ 0 & 1 & 0 & 1 & | & 2 \\ 0 & 0 & 1 & 2 & | & 3 \end{bmatrix}$

32. $\begin{bmatrix} 1 & 0 & 0 & 0 & | & 1 \\ 0 & 1 & 0 & 2 & | & 2 \\ 0 & 0 & 1 & 3 & | & 0 \end{bmatrix}$

33. $\begin{bmatrix} 1 & 0 & 0 & 4 & | & 2 \\ 0 & 1 & 1 & 3 & | & 3 \\ 0 & 0 & 0 & 0 & | & 0 \end{bmatrix}$

34. $\begin{bmatrix} 1 & 0 & 0 & 0 & | & 1 \\ 0 & 1 & 0 & 0 & | & 2 \\ 0 & 0 & 1 & 2 & | & 3 \end{bmatrix}$

35. $\begin{bmatrix} 1 & 0 & 0 & 1 & | & -2 \\ 0 & 1 & 0 & 2 & | & 2 \\ 0 & 0 & 1 & -1 & | & 0 \\ 0 & 0 & 0 & 0 & | & 0 \end{bmatrix}$

36. $\begin{bmatrix} 1 & 0 & 0 & 0 & | & 1 \\ 0 & 1 & 0 & 0 & | & 2 \\ 0 & 0 & 1 & 0 & | & 3 \\ 0 & 0 & 0 & 1 & | & 0 \end{bmatrix}$

In Problems 37–72, solve each system of equations using matrices (row operations). If the system has no solution, say that it is inconsistent.

37. $\begin{cases} x + y = 8 \\ x - y = 4 \end{cases}$

38. $\begin{cases} x + 2y = 5 \\ x + y = 3 \end{cases}$

39. $\begin{cases} 2x - 4y = -2 \\ 3x + 2y = 3 \end{cases}$

40. $\begin{cases} 3x + 3y = 3 \\ 4x + 2y = \dfrac{8}{3} \end{cases}$

41. $\begin{cases} x + 2y = 4 \\ 2x + 4y = 8 \end{cases}$

42. $\begin{cases} 3x - y = 7 \\ 9x - 3y = 21 \end{cases}$

43. $\begin{cases} 2x + 3y = 6 \\ x - y = \dfrac{1}{2} \end{cases}$

44. $\begin{cases} \dfrac{1}{2}x + y = -2 \\ x - 2y = 8 \end{cases}$

45. $\begin{cases} 3x - 5y = 3 \\ 15x + 5y = 21 \end{cases}$

46. $\begin{cases} 2x - y = -1 \\ x + \dfrac{1}{2}y = \dfrac{3}{2} \end{cases}$

47. $\begin{cases} x - y = 6 \\ 2x - 3z = 16 \\ 2y + z = 4 \end{cases}$

48. $\begin{cases} 2x + y = -4 \\ -2y + 4z = 0 \\ 3x - 2z = -11 \end{cases}$

49. $\begin{cases} x - 2y + 3z = 7 \\ 2x + y + z = 4 \\ -3x + 2y - 2z = -10 \end{cases}$

50. $\begin{cases} 2x + y - 3z = 0 \\ -2x + 2y + z = -7 \\ 3x - 4y - 3z = 7 \end{cases}$

51. $\begin{cases} 2x - 2y - 2z = 2 \\ 2x + 3y + z = 2 \\ 3x + 2y = 0 \end{cases}$

52. $\begin{cases} 2x - 3y - z = 0 \\ -x + 2y + z = 5 \\ 3x - 4y - z = 1 \end{cases}$

53. $\begin{cases} -x + y + z = -1 \\ -x + 2y - 3z = -4 \\ 3x - 2y - 7z = 0 \end{cases}$

54. $\begin{cases} 2x - 3y - z = 0 \\ 3x + 2y + 2z = 2 \\ x + 5y + 3z = 2 \end{cases}$

55. $\begin{cases} 2x - 2y + 3z = 6 \\ 4x - 3y + 2z = 0 \\ -2x + 3y - 7z = 1 \end{cases}$

56. $\begin{cases} 3x - 2y + 2z = 6 \\ 7x - 3y + 2z = -1 \\ 2x - 3y + 4z = 0 \end{cases}$

57. $\begin{cases} x + y - z = 6 \\ 3x - 2y + z = -5 \\ x + 3y - 2z = 14 \end{cases}$

58. $\begin{cases} x - y + z = -4 \\ 2x - 3y + 4z = -15 \\ 5x + y - 2z = 12 \end{cases}$

59. $\begin{cases} x + 2y - z = -3 \\ 2x - 4y + z = -7 \\ -2x + 2y - 3z = 4 \end{cases}$

60. $\begin{cases} x + 4y - 3z = -8 \\ 3x - y + 3z = 12 \\ x + y + 6z = 1 \end{cases}$

61. $\begin{cases} 3x + y - z = \dfrac{2}{3} \\ 2x - y + z = 1 \\ 4x + 2y = \dfrac{8}{3} \end{cases}$

62. $\begin{cases} x + y = 1 \\ 2x - y + z = 1 \\ x + 2y + z = \dfrac{8}{3} \end{cases}$

63. $\begin{cases} x + y + z + w = 4 \\ 2x - y + z = 0 \\ 3x + 2y + z - w = 6 \\ x - 2y - 2z + 2w = -1 \end{cases}$

64. $\begin{cases} x + y + z + w = 4 \\ -x + 2y + z = 0 \\ 2x + 3y + z - w = 6 \\ -2x + y - 2z + 2w = -1 \end{cases}$

65. $\begin{cases} x + 2y + z = 1 \\ 2x - y + 2z = 2 \\ 3x + y + 3z = 3 \end{cases}$

66. $\begin{cases} x + 2y - z = 3 \\ 2x - y + 2z = 6 \\ x - 3y + 3z = 4 \end{cases}$

67. $\begin{cases} x - y + z = 5 \\ 3x + 2y - 2z = 0 \end{cases}$

68. $\begin{cases} 2x + y - z = 4 \\ -x + y + 3z = 1 \end{cases}$

69. $\begin{cases} 2x + 3y - z = 3 \\ x - y - z = 0 \\ -x + y + z = 0 \\ x + y + 3z = 5 \end{cases}$

70. $\begin{cases} x - 3y + z = 1 \\ 2x - y - 4z = 0 \\ x - 3y + 2z = 1 \\ x - 2y = 5 \end{cases}$

71. $\begin{cases} 4x + y + z - w = 4 \\ x - y + 2z + 3w = 3 \end{cases}$

72. $\begin{cases} -4x + y = 5 \\ 2x - y + z - w = 5 \\ z + w = 4 \end{cases}$

Applications and Extensions

73. Curve Fitting Find the function $y = ax^2 + bx + c$ whose graph contains the points $(1, 2)$, $(-2, -7)$, and $(2, -3)$.

74. Curve Fitting Find the function $y = ax^2 + bx + c$ whose graph contains the points $(1, -1)$, $(3, -1)$, and $(-2, 14)$.

75. Curve Fitting Find the function $f(x) = ax^3 + bx^2 + cx + d$ for which $f(-3) = -112, f(-1) = -2, f(1) = 4$, and $f(2) = 13$.

76. Curve Fitting Find the function $f(x) = ax^3 + bx^2 + cx + d$ for which $f(-2) = -10, f(-1) = 3, f(1) = 5$, and $f(3) = 15$.

77. Nutrition A dietitian at Palos Community Hospital wants a patient to have a meal that has 78 grams (g) of protein, 59 g of carbohydrates, and 75 milligrams (mg) of vitamin A. The hospital food service tells the dietitian that the dinner for today is salmon steak, baked eggs, and acorn squash. Each serving of salmon steak has 30 g of protein, 20 g of carbohydrates, and 2 mg of vitamin A. Each serving of baked eggs contains 15 g of protein, 2 g of carbohydrates, and 20 mg of vitamin A. Each serving of acorn squash contains 3 g of protein, 25 g of carbohydrates, and 32 mg of vitamin A. How many servings of each food should the dietitian provide for the patient?

78. Nutrition A dietitian at General Hospital wants a patient to have a meal that has 47 grams (g) of protein, 58 g of carbohydrates, and 630 milligrams (mg) of calcium. The hospital food service tells the dietitian that the dinner for today is pork chops, corn on the cob, and 2% milk. Each serving of pork chops has 23 g of protein, 0 g of carbohydrates, and 10 mg of calcium. Each serving of corn on the cob contains 3 g of protein, 16 g of carbohydrates, and 10 mg of calcium. Each glass of 2% milk contains 9 g of protein, 13 g of carbohydrates, and 300 mg of calcium. How many servings of each food should the dietitian provide for the patient?

79. Financial Planning Carletta has $10,000 to invest. As her financial consultant, you recommend that she invest in Treasury bills that yield 6%, Treasury bonds that yield 7%, and corporate bonds that yield 8%. Carletta wants to have an annual income of $680, and the amount invested in corporate bonds must be half that invested in Treasury bills. Find the amount in each investment.

80. Landscaping A landscape company is hired to plant trees in three new subdivisions. The company charges the developer for each tree planted, an hourly rate to plant the trees, and a fixed delivery charge. In one subdivision it took 166 labor hours to plant 250 trees for a cost of $7520. In a second subdivision it took 124 labor hours to plant 200 trees for a cost of $5945. In the final subdivision it took 200 labor hours to plant 300 trees for a cost of $8985. Determine the cost for each tree, the hourly labor charge, and the fixed delivery charge.

Sources: gurney.com; www.bx.org

81. Production To manufacture an automobile requires painting, drying, and polishing. Epsilon Motor Company produces three types of cars: the Delta, the Beta, and the Sigma. Each Delta requires 10 hours (hr) for painting, 3 hr for drying, and 2 hr for polishing. A Beta requires 16 hr for painting, 5 hr for drying, and 3 hr for polishing, and a Sigma requires 8 hr for painting, 2 hr for drying, and 1 hr for polishing. If the company has 240 hr for painting, 69 hr for drying, and 41 hr for polishing per month, how many of each type of car are produced?

82. Production A Florida juice company completes the preparation of its products by sterilizing, filling, and labeling bottles. Each case of orange juice requires 9 minutes (min) for sterilizing, 6 min for filling, and 1 min for labeling. Each case of grapefruit juice requires 10 min for sterilizing, 4 min for filling, and 2 min for labeling. Each case of tomato juice requires 12 min for sterilizing, 4 min for filling, and 1 min for labeling. If the company runs the sterilizing machine for 398 min, the filling machine for 164 min, and the labeling machine for 58 min, how many cases of each type of juice are prepared?

83. Electricity: Kirchhoff's Rules An application of Kirchhoff's Rules to the circuit shown results in the following system of equations:

$$\begin{cases} -4 + 8 - 2I_2 = 0 \\ \quad\quad 8 = 5I_4 + I_1 \\ \quad\quad 4 = 3I_3 + I_1 \\ \quad I_3 + I_4 = I_1 \end{cases}$$

Find the currents I_1, I_2, I_3, and I_4.

Source: Based on Raymond Serway, *Physics,* 3rd ed. (Philadelphia: Saunders, 1990), Prob. 34, p. 790.

84. Electricity: Kirchhoff's Rules An application of Kirchhoff's Rules to the circuit shown results in the following system of equations:

$$\begin{cases} \quad\quad\quad\quad I_1 = I_3 + I_2 \\ 24 - 6I_1 - 3I_3 = 0 \\ 12 + 24 - 6I_1 - 6I_2 = 0 \end{cases}$$

Find the currents I_1, I_2, and I_3.

Source: Ibid., Prob. 38, p. 791.

85. Financial Planning Three retired couples each require an additional annual income of $2000 per year. As their financial consultant, you recommend that they invest some money in Treasury bills that yield 7%, some money in corporate bonds that yield 9%, and some money in junk bonds that yield 11%. Prepare a table for each couple showing the various ways that their goals can be achieved:
(a) If the first couple has $20,000 to invest.
(b) If the second couple has $25,000 to invest.
(c) If the third couple has $30,000 to invest.
(d) What advice would you give each couple regarding the amount to invest and the choices available?

[**Hint:** Higher yields generally carry more risk.]

86. Financial Planning A young couple has $25,000 to invest. As their financial consultant, you recommend that they invest some money in Treasury bills that yield 7%, some money in corporate bonds that yield 9%, and some money in junk bonds that yield 11%. Prepare a table showing the various ways that this couple can achieve the following goals:
(a) $1500 per year in income
(b) $2000 per year in income
(c) $2500 per year in income

(d) What advice would you give this couple regarding the income that they require and the choices available?

[**Hint:** Higher yields generally carry more risk.]

87. Pharmacy A doctor's prescription calls for a daily intake of a supplement containing 40 milligrams (mg) of vitamin C and 30 mg of vitamin D. Your pharmacy stocks three supplements that can be used: one contains 20% vitamin C and 30% vitamin D; a second, 40% vitamin C and 20% vitamin D; and a third, 30% vitamin C and 50% vitamin D. Create a table showing the possible combinations that could be used to fill the prescription.

88. Pharmacy A doctor's prescription calls for the creation of pills that contain 12 units of vitamin B_{12} and 12 units of vitamin E. Your pharmacy stocks three powders that can be used to make these pills: one contains 20% vitamin B_{12} and 30% vitamin E; a second, 40% vitamin B_{12} and 20% vitamin E; and a third, 30% vitamin B_{12} and 40% vitamin E. Create a table showing the possible combinations of each powder that could be mixed in each pill.

Discussion and Writing

89. Write a brief paragraph or two that outlines your strategy for solving a system of linear equations using matrices.

90. When solving a system of linear equations using matrices, do you prefer to place the augmented matrix in row echelon form or in reduced row echelon form? Give reasons for your choice.

91. Make up a system of three linear equations containing three variables that has:
(a) No solution
(b) Exactly one solution
(c) Infinitely many solutions
Give the three systems to a friend to solve and critique.

11.3 Systems of Linear Equations: Determinants

OBJECTIVES 1 Evaluate 2 by 2 Determinants (p. 736)

2 Use Cramer's Rule to Solve a System of Two Equations Containing Two Variables (p. 736)

3 Evaluate 3 by 3 Determinants (p. 739)

4 Use Cramer's Rule to Solve a System of Three Equations Containing Three Variables (p. 741)

5 Know Properties of Determinants (p. 742)

In the preceding section, we described a method of using matrices to solve a system of linear equations. This section deals with yet another method for solving systems of linear equations; however, it can be used only when the number of equations equals the number of variables. Although the method will work for any system (provided that the number of equations equals the number of variables), it is most often used for systems of two equations containing two variables or three equations containing three variables. This method, called *Cramer's Rule,* is based on the concept of a *determinant.*

1 Evaluate 2 by 2 Determinants

DEFINITION

If a, b, c, and d are four real numbers, the symbol

$$D = \begin{vmatrix} a & b \\ c & d \end{vmatrix}$$

is called a **2 by 2 determinant.** Its value is the number $ad - bc$; that is,

$$D = \begin{vmatrix} a & b \\ c & d \end{vmatrix} = ad - bc \qquad (1)$$

The following device may be helpful for remembering the value of a 2 by 2 determinant:

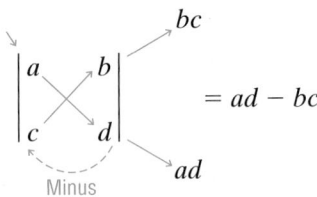

EXAMPLE 1   Evaluating a 2 × 2 Determinant

Evaluate: $\begin{vmatrix} 3 & -2 \\ 6 & 1 \end{vmatrix}$

Algebraic Solution

$\begin{vmatrix} 3 & -2 \\ 6 & 1 \end{vmatrix} = (3)(1) - (6)(-2)$

$= 3 - (-12)$

$= 15$

Graphing Solution

First, we enter the matrix whose entries are those of the determinant into the graphing utility and name it A. Using the determinant command, we obtain the result shown in Figure 9.

Figure 9

Now Work PROBLEM 7

2 Use Cramer's Rule to Solve a System of Two Equations Containing Two Variables

Let's now see the role that a 2 by 2 determinant plays in the solution of a system of two equations containing two variables. Consider the system

$$\begin{cases} ax + by = s & \text{(1)} \\ cx + dy = t & \text{(2)} \end{cases} \qquad (2)$$

We shall use the method of elimination to solve this system.

Provided $d \neq 0$ and $b \neq 0$, this system is equivalent to the system

$$\begin{cases} adx + bdy = sd & \text{(1)} \quad \text{Multiply by } d. \\ bcx + bdy = tb & \text{(2)} \quad \text{Multiply by } b. \end{cases}$$

Subtract the second equation from the first equation and obtain

$$\begin{cases} (ad - bc)x + 0 \cdot y = sd - tb & (1) \\ bcx + bdy = tb & (2) \end{cases}$$

Now the first equation can be rewritten using determinant notation.

$$\begin{vmatrix} a & b \\ c & d \end{vmatrix} x = \begin{vmatrix} s & b \\ t & d \end{vmatrix}$$

If $D = \begin{vmatrix} a & b \\ c & d \end{vmatrix} = ad - bc \neq 0$, we can solve for x to get

$$x = \frac{\begin{vmatrix} s & b \\ t & d \end{vmatrix}}{\begin{vmatrix} a & b \\ c & d \end{vmatrix}} = \frac{\begin{vmatrix} s & b \\ t & d \end{vmatrix}}{D} \qquad (3)$$

Return now to the original system (2). Provided that $a \neq 0$ and $c \neq 0$, the system is equivalent to

$$\begin{cases} acx + bcy = cs & (1) \quad \text{Multiply by } c. \\ acx + ady = at & (2) \quad \text{Multiply by } a. \end{cases}$$

Subtract the first equation from the second equation and obtain

$$\begin{cases} acx + \quad bcy \quad = \quad cs & (1) \\ 0 \cdot x + (ad - bc)y = at - cs & (2) \end{cases}$$

The second equation can now be rewritten using determinant notation.

$$\begin{vmatrix} a & b \\ c & d \end{vmatrix} y = \begin{vmatrix} a & s \\ c & t \end{vmatrix}$$

If $D = \begin{vmatrix} a & b \\ c & d \end{vmatrix} = ad - bc \neq 0$, we can solve for y to get

$$y = \frac{\begin{vmatrix} a & s \\ c & t \end{vmatrix}}{\begin{vmatrix} a & b \\ c & d \end{vmatrix}} = \frac{\begin{vmatrix} a & s \\ c & t \end{vmatrix}}{D} \qquad (4)$$

Equations (3) and (4) lead us to the following result, called **Cramer's Rule.**

THEOREM

Cramer's Rule for Two Equations Containing Two Variables

The solution to the system of equations

$$\begin{cases} ax + by = s & (1) \\ cx + dy = t & (2) \end{cases} \qquad (5)$$

is given by

$$x = \frac{\begin{vmatrix} s & b \\ t & d \end{vmatrix}}{\begin{vmatrix} a & b \\ c & d \end{vmatrix}} \qquad y = \frac{\begin{vmatrix} a & s \\ c & t \end{vmatrix}}{\begin{vmatrix} a & b \\ c & d \end{vmatrix}} \qquad (6)$$

provided that

$$D = \begin{vmatrix} a & b \\ c & d \end{vmatrix} = ad - bc \neq 0$$

In the derivation given for Cramer's Rule above, we assumed that none of the numbers $a, b, c,$ and d was 0. In Problem 61 you will be asked to complete the proof under the less stringent condition that $D = ad - bc \neq 0$.

Now look carefully at the pattern in Cramer's Rule. The denominator in the solution (6) is the determinant of the coefficients of the variables.

$$\begin{cases} ax + by = s \\ cx + dy = t \end{cases} \qquad D = \begin{vmatrix} a & b \\ c & d \end{vmatrix}$$

In the solution for x, the numerator is the determinant, denoted by D_x, formed by replacing the entries in the first column (the coefficients of x) of D by the constants on the right side of the equal sign.

$$D_x = \begin{vmatrix} s & b \\ t & d \end{vmatrix}$$

In the solution for y, the numerator is the determinant, denoted by D_y, formed by replacing the entries in the second column (the coefficients in y) of D by the constants on the right side of the equal sign.

$$D_y = \begin{vmatrix} a & s \\ c & t \end{vmatrix}$$

Cramer's Rule then states that, if $D \neq 0$,

$$x = \frac{D_x}{D} \qquad y = \frac{D_y}{D} \tag{7}$$

| EXAMPLE 2 | **Solving a System of Linear Equations Using Determinants** |

Use Cramer's Rule, if applicable, to solve the system

$$\begin{cases} 3x - 2y = 4 & (1) \\ 6x + y = 13 & (2) \end{cases}$$

Algebraic Solution

The determinant D of the coefficients of the variables is

$$D = \begin{vmatrix} 3 & -2 \\ 6 & 1 \end{vmatrix} = (3)(1) - (6)(-2) = 15$$

Because $D \neq 0$, Cramer's Rule (7) can be used.

$$x = \frac{D_x}{D} = \frac{\begin{vmatrix} 4 & -2 \\ 13 & 1 \end{vmatrix}}{15} \qquad y = \frac{D_y}{D} = \frac{\begin{vmatrix} 3 & 4 \\ 6 & 13 \end{vmatrix}}{15}$$

$$= \frac{(4)(1) - (13)(-2)}{15} \qquad = \frac{(3)(13) - (6)(4)}{15}$$

$$= \frac{30}{15} \qquad = \frac{15}{15}$$

$$= 2 \qquad = 1$$

Graphing Solution

We enter the coefficient matrix into our graphing utility. Call it A and evaluate $\det[A]$. Since $\det[A] \neq 0$, we can use Cramer's Rule. We enter the matrices D_x and D_y into our graphing utility and call them B and C, respectively. Finally, we find x by calculating $\dfrac{\det[B]}{\det[A]}$ and y by calculating $\dfrac{\det[C]}{\det[A]}$. The results are shown in Figure 10.

Figure 10

```
det [A]
                15
det [B]/det [A]
                 2
det [C]/det [A]
                 1
```

The solution is $x = 2, y = 1$ or, using ordered pairs, $(2, 1)$.

In attempting to use Cramer's Rule, if the determinant D of the coefficients of the variables is found to equal 0 (so that Cramer's Rule is not applicable), then the system either is inconsistent or has infinitely many solutions.

Now Work PROBLEM 15

3 Evaluate 3 by 3 Determinants

To use Cramer's Rule to solve a system of three equations containing three variables, we need to define a 3 by 3 determinant.

A **3 by 3 determinant** is symbolized by

$$\begin{vmatrix} a_{11} & a_{12} & a_{13} \\ a_{21} & a_{22} & a_{23} \\ a_{31} & a_{32} & a_{33} \end{vmatrix} \tag{8}$$

in which $a_{11}, a_{12}, \ldots,$ are real numbers.

As with matrices, we use a double subscript to identify an entry by indicating its row and column numbers. For example, the entry a_{23} is in row 2, column 3.

The value of a 3 by 3 determinant may be defined in terms of 2 by 2 determinants by the following formula:

Minus   Plus

$$\begin{vmatrix} a_{11} & a_{12} & a_{13} \\ a_{21} & a_{22} & a_{23} \\ a_{31} & a_{32} & a_{33} \end{vmatrix} = a_{11}\begin{vmatrix} a_{22} & a_{23} \\ a_{32} & a_{33} \end{vmatrix} - a_{12}\begin{vmatrix} a_{21} & a_{23} \\ a_{31} & a_{33} \end{vmatrix} + a_{13}\begin{vmatrix} a_{21} & a_{22} \\ a_{31} & a_{32} \end{vmatrix} \tag{9}$$

2 by 2 determinant left after removing the row and column containing a_{11}

2 by 2 determinant left after removing the row and column containing a_{12}

2 by 2 determinant left after removing the row and column containing a_{13}

The 2 by 2 determinants shown in formula (9) are called **minors** of the 3 by 3 determinant. For an n by n determinant, the **minor** M_{ij} of entry a_{ij} is the determinant resulting from removing the ith row and jth column.

EXAMPLE 3

Finding Minors of a 3 by 3 Determinant

For the determinant $A = \begin{vmatrix} 2 & -1 & 3 \\ -2 & 5 & 1 \\ 0 & 6 & -9 \end{vmatrix}$, find: (a) M_{12}　　(b) M_{23}

Solution

(a) M_{12} is the determinant that results from removing the first row and second column from A.

$$A = \begin{vmatrix} 2 & -1 & 3 \\ -2 & 5 & 1 \\ 0 & 6 & -9 \end{vmatrix} \qquad M_{12} = \begin{vmatrix} -2 & 1 \\ 0 & -9 \end{vmatrix} = (-2)(-9) - (0)(1) = 18$$

(b) M_{23} is the determinant that results from removing the second row and third column from A.

$$A = \begin{vmatrix} 2 & -1 & 3 \\ -2 & 5 & 1 \\ 0 & 6 & -9 \end{vmatrix} \qquad M_{23} = \begin{vmatrix} 2 & -1 \\ 0 & 6 \end{vmatrix} = (2)(6) - (0)(-1) = 12$$

Referring back to formula (9), we see that each element a_{ij} is multiplied by its minor, but sometimes this term is added and other times, subtracted. To determine whether to add or subtract a term, we must consider the *cofactor*.

DEFINITION

For an n by n determinant A, the **cofactor** of entry a_{ij}, denoted by A_{ij}, is given by

$$A_{ij} = (-1)^{i+j} M_{ij}$$

where M_{ij} is the minor of entry a_{ij}.

The exponent of $(-1)^{i+j}$ is the sum of the row and column of the entry a_{ij}, so if $i + j$ is even, $(-1)^{i+j}$ will equal 1, and if $i + j$ is odd, $(-1)^{i+j}$ will equal -1.

To find the value of a determinant, multiply each entry in any row or column by its cofactor and sum the results. This process is referred to as **expanding across a row or column.** For example, the value of the 3 by 3 determinant in formula (9) was found by expanding across row 1.

If we choose to expand down column 2, we obtain

$$\begin{vmatrix} a_{11} & a_{12} & a_{13} \\ a_{21} & a_{22} & a_{23} \\ a_{31} & a_{32} & a_{33} \end{vmatrix} = (-1)^{1+2} a_{12} \begin{vmatrix} a_{21} & a_{23} \\ a_{31} & a_{33} \end{vmatrix} + (-1)^{2+2} a_{22} \begin{vmatrix} a_{11} & a_{13} \\ a_{31} & a_{33} \end{vmatrix} + (-1)^{3+2} a_{32} \begin{vmatrix} a_{11} & a_{13} \\ a_{21} & a_{23} \end{vmatrix}$$

Expand down column 2.

If we choose to expand across row 3, we obtain

$$\begin{vmatrix} a_{11} & a_{12} & a_{13} \\ a_{21} & a_{22} & a_{23} \\ a_{31} & a_{32} & a_{33} \end{vmatrix} = (-1)^{3+1} a_{31} \begin{vmatrix} a_{12} & a_{13} \\ a_{22} & a_{23} \end{vmatrix} + (-1)^{3+2} a_{32} \begin{vmatrix} a_{11} & a_{13} \\ a_{21} & a_{23} \end{vmatrix} + (-1)^{3+3} a_{33} \begin{vmatrix} a_{11} & a_{12} \\ a_{21} & a_{22} \end{vmatrix}$$

Expand across row 3.

It can be shown that the value of a determinant does not depend on the choice of the row or column used in the expansion. However, expanding across a row or column that has an element equal to 0 reduces the amount of work needed to compute the value of the determinant.

EXAMPLE 4 Evaluating a 3 × 3 Determinant

Find the value of the 3 by 3 determinant: $\begin{vmatrix} 3 & 0 & -1 \\ 4 & 6 & 2 \\ 8 & -2 & 3 \end{vmatrix}$

Solution Because of the 0, it is easiest to expand across row 1 or down row 2. We choose to expand across row 1.

$$\begin{vmatrix} 3 & 0 & -1 \\ 4 & 6 & 2 \\ 8 & -2 & 3 \end{vmatrix} = (-1)^{1+1} \cdot 3 \cdot \begin{vmatrix} 6 & 2 \\ -2 & 3 \end{vmatrix} + (-1)^{1+2} \cdot 0 \cdot \begin{vmatrix} 4 & 2 \\ 8 & 3 \end{vmatrix} + (-1)^{1+3} \cdot (-1) \cdot \begin{vmatrix} 4 & 6 \\ 8 & -2 \end{vmatrix}$$

$$= 3(18 - (-4)) - 0 + (-1)(-8 - 48)$$
$$= 3(22) + (-1)(-56)$$
$$= 66 + 56 = 122$$

✓ **Check:** Use a graphing utility to verify the result.

Now Work PROBLEM 11

4 Use Cramer's Rule to Solve a System of Three Equations Containing Three Variables

Consider the following system of three equations containing three variables.

$$\begin{cases} a_{11}x + a_{12}y + a_{13}z = c_1 \\ a_{21}x + a_{22}y + a_{23}z = c_2 \\ a_{31}x + a_{32}y + a_{33}z = c_3 \end{cases} \tag{10}$$

It can be shown that if the determinant D of the coefficients of the variables is not 0, that is, if

$$D = \begin{vmatrix} a_{11} & a_{12} & a_{13} \\ a_{21} & a_{22} & a_{23} \\ a_{31} & a_{32} & a_{33} \end{vmatrix} \neq 0$$

the unique solution of system (10) is given by

THEOREM

Cramer's Rule for Three Equations Containing Three Variables

$$x = \frac{D_x}{D} \qquad y = \frac{D_y}{D} \qquad z = \frac{D_z}{D}$$

where

$$D_x = \begin{vmatrix} c_1 & a_{12} & a_{13} \\ c_2 & a_{22} & a_{23} \\ c_3 & a_{32} & a_{33} \end{vmatrix} \qquad D_y = \begin{vmatrix} a_{11} & c_1 & a_{13} \\ a_{21} & c_2 & a_{23} \\ a_{31} & c_3 & a_{33} \end{vmatrix} \qquad D_z = \begin{vmatrix} a_{11} & a_{12} & c_1 \\ a_{21} & a_{22} & c_2 \\ a_{31} & a_{32} & c_3 \end{vmatrix}$$

Do you see the similarity of this pattern and the pattern observed earlier for a system of two equations containing two variables?

EXAMPLE 5

Using Cramer's Rule

Use Cramer's Rule, if applicable, to solve the following system:

$$\begin{cases} 2x + y - z = 3 & (1) \\ -x + 2y + 4z = -3 & (2) \\ x - 2y - 3z = 4 & (3) \end{cases}$$

Solution   The value of the determinant D of the coefficients of the variables is

$$D = \begin{vmatrix} 2 & 1 & -1 \\ -1 & 2 & 4 \\ 1 & -2 & -3 \end{vmatrix} = (-1)^{1+1} \cdot 2 \cdot \begin{vmatrix} 2 & 4 \\ -2 & -3 \end{vmatrix} + (-1)^{1+2} \cdot 1 \cdot \begin{vmatrix} -1 & 4 \\ 1 & -3 \end{vmatrix} + (-1)^{1+3}(-1) \begin{vmatrix} -1 & 2 \\ 1 & -2 \end{vmatrix}$$

$$= 2(2) - 1(-1) + (-1)(0)$$
$$= 4 + 1 = 5$$

Because $D \neq 0$, we proceed to find the values of $D_x, D_y,$ and D_z.

$$D_x = \begin{vmatrix} 3 & 1 & -1 \\ -3 & 2 & 4 \\ 4 & -2 & -3 \end{vmatrix} = (-1)^{1+1} \cdot 3 \cdot \begin{vmatrix} 2 & 4 \\ -2 & -3 \end{vmatrix} + (-1)^{1+2} \cdot 1 \cdot \begin{vmatrix} -3 & 4 \\ 4 & -3 \end{vmatrix} + (-1)^{1+3}(-1) \begin{vmatrix} -3 & 2 \\ 4 & -2 \end{vmatrix}$$

$$= 3(2) - 1(-7) + (-1)(-2) = 15$$

$$D_y = \begin{vmatrix} 2 & 3 & -1 \\ -1 & -3 & 4 \\ 1 & 4 & -3 \end{vmatrix} = (-1)^{1+1} \cdot 2 \cdot \begin{vmatrix} -3 & 4 \\ 4 & -3 \end{vmatrix} + (-1)^{1+2} \cdot 3 \cdot \begin{vmatrix} -1 & 4 \\ 1 & -3 \end{vmatrix} + (-1)^{1+3}(-1)\begin{vmatrix} -1 & -3 \\ 1 & 4 \end{vmatrix}$$

$$= 2(-7) - 3(-1) + (-1)(-1) = -10$$

$$D_z = \begin{vmatrix} 2 & 1 & 3 \\ -1 & 2 & -3 \\ 1 & -2 & 4 \end{vmatrix} = (-1)^{1+1} \cdot 2 \cdot \begin{vmatrix} 2 & -3 \\ -2 & 4 \end{vmatrix} + (-1)^{1+2} \cdot 1 \cdot \begin{vmatrix} -1 & -3 \\ 1 & 4 \end{vmatrix} + (-1)^{1+3} \cdot 3 \cdot \begin{vmatrix} -1 & 2 \\ 1 & -2 \end{vmatrix}$$

$$= 2(2) - 1(-1) + 3(0) = 5$$

As a result,

$$x = \frac{D_x}{D} = \frac{15}{5} = 3 \qquad y = \frac{D_y}{D} = \frac{-10}{5} = -2 \qquad z = \frac{D_z}{D} = \frac{5}{5} = 1$$

The solution is $x = 3$, $y = -2$, $z = 1$, or, using ordered triplets, $(3, -2, 1)$.

We already know that Cramer's Rule does not apply when the determinant of the coefficients on the variables, D, is 0. But can we learn anything about the system other than it is not a consistent and independent system if $D = 0$? The answer is yes!

Cramer's Rule with Inconsistent or Dependent Systems

- If $D = 0$ and at least one of the determinants D_x, D_y, or D_z is different from 0, then the system is inconsistent and the solution set is $\varnothing$ or { }.
- If $D = 0$ and all the determinants D_x, D_y, and D_z equal 0, then the system is consistent and dependent so that there are infinitely many solutions. The system must be solved using row reduction techniques.

Now Work PROBLEM 33

5 Know Properties of Determinants

Determinants have several properties that are sometimes helpful for obtaining their value. We list some of them here.

THEOREM
The value of a determinant changes sign if any two rows (or any two columns) are interchanged. **(11)**

Proof for 2 by 2 Determinants

$$\begin{vmatrix} a & b \\ c & d \end{vmatrix} = ad - bc \quad \text{and} \quad \begin{vmatrix} c & d \\ a & b \end{vmatrix} = bc - ad = -(ad - bc) \qquad \blacksquare$$

EXAMPLE 6 Demonstrating Theorem (11)

$$\begin{vmatrix} 3 & 4 \\ 1 & 2 \end{vmatrix} = 6 - 4 = 2 \qquad \begin{vmatrix} 1 & 2 \\ 3 & 4 \end{vmatrix} = 4 - 6 = -2$$

THEOREM
If all the entries in any row (or any column) equal 0, the value of the determinant is 0. **(12)**

Proof Expand across the row (or down the column) containing the 0's. $\blacksquare$

THEOREM
If any two rows (or any two columns) of a determinant have corresponding entries that are equal, the value of the determinant is 0. **(13)**

You are asked to prove this result for a 3 by 3 determinant in which the entries in column 1 equal the entries in column 3 in Problem 64.

| EXAMPLE 7 | **Demonstrating Theorem (13)** |

$$\begin{vmatrix} 1 & 2 & 3 \\ 1 & 2 & 3 \\ 4 & 5 & 6 \end{vmatrix} = (-1)^{1+1} \cdot 1 \cdot \begin{vmatrix} 2 & 3 \\ 5 & 6 \end{vmatrix} + (-1)^{1+2} \cdot 2 \cdot \begin{vmatrix} 1 & 3 \\ 4 & 6 \end{vmatrix} + (-1)^{1+3} \cdot 3 \cdot \begin{vmatrix} 1 & 2 \\ 4 & 5 \end{vmatrix}$$

$$= 1(-3) - 2(-6) + 3(-3) = -3 + 12 - 9 = 0$$

THEOREM   If any row (or any column) of a determinant is multiplied by a nonzero number k, the value of the determinant is also changed by a factor of k.   **(14)**

You are asked to prove this result for a 3 by 3 determinant using row 2 in Problem 63.

| EXAMPLE 8 | **Demonstrating Theorem (14)** |

$$\begin{vmatrix} 1 & 2 \\ 4 & 6 \end{vmatrix} = 6 - 8 = -2$$

$$\begin{vmatrix} k & 2k \\ 4 & 6 \end{vmatrix} = 6k - 8k = -2k = k(-2) = k\begin{vmatrix} 1 & 2 \\ 4 & 6 \end{vmatrix}$$

THEOREM   If the entries of any row (or any column) of a determinant are multiplied by a nonzero number k and the result is added to the corresponding entries of another row (or column), the value of the determinant remains unchanged.   **(15)**

In Problem 65, you are asked to prove this result for a 3 by 3 determinant using rows 1 and 2.

| EXAMPLE 9 | **Demonstrating Theorem (15)** |

$$\begin{vmatrix} 3 & 4 \\ 5 & 2 \end{vmatrix} = -14 \qquad \begin{vmatrix} 3 & 4 \\ 5 & 2 \end{vmatrix} \rightarrow \begin{vmatrix} -7 & 0 \\ 5 & 2 \end{vmatrix} = -14$$

Multiply row 2 by -2 and add to row 1.

11.3 Assess Your Understanding

Concepts and Vocabulary

1. Cramer's Rule uses _____ to solve a system of linear equations.

2. $D = \begin{vmatrix} a & b \\ c & d \end{vmatrix} = $ _____

3. *True or False*   A 3 by 3 determinant can never equal 0.

4. *True or False*   The value of a determinant remains unchanged if any two rows or any two columns are interchanged.

Skill Building

In Problems 5–14, find the value of each determinant by hand. Verify your results using a graphing utility.

5. $\begin{vmatrix} 3 & 1 \\ 4 & 2 \end{vmatrix}$

6. $\begin{vmatrix} 6 & 1 \\ 5 & 2 \end{vmatrix}$

7. $\begin{vmatrix} 6 & 4 \\ -1 & 3 \end{vmatrix}$

8. $\begin{vmatrix} 8 & -3 \\ 4 & 2 \end{vmatrix}$

9. $\begin{vmatrix} -3 & -1 \\ 4 & 2 \end{vmatrix}$

10. $\begin{vmatrix} -4 & 2 \\ -5 & 3 \end{vmatrix}$

11. $\begin{vmatrix} 3 & 4 & 2 \\ 1 & -1 & 5 \\ 1 & 2 & -2 \end{vmatrix}$

12. $\begin{vmatrix} 1 & 3 & -2 \\ 6 & 1 & -5 \\ 8 & 2 & 3 \end{vmatrix}$

13. $\begin{vmatrix} 4 & -1 & 2 \\ 6 & -1 & 0 \\ 1 & -3 & 4 \end{vmatrix}$

14. $\begin{vmatrix} 3 & -9 & 4 \\ 1 & 4 & 0 \\ 8 & -3 & 1 \end{vmatrix}$

In Problems 15–42, solve each system of equations using Cramer's Rule if it is applicable. If Cramer's Rule is not applicable, say so.

15. $\begin{cases} x + y = 8 \\ x - y = 4 \end{cases}$

16. $\begin{cases} x + 2y = 5 \\ x - y = 3 \end{cases}$

17. $\begin{cases} 5x - y = 13 \\ 2x + 3y = 12 \end{cases}$

18. $\begin{cases} x + 3y = 5 \\ 2x - 3y = -8 \end{cases}$

19. $\begin{cases} 3x = 24 \\ x + 2y = 0 \end{cases}$

20. $\begin{cases} 4x + 5y = -3 \\ -2y = -4 \end{cases}$

21. $\begin{cases} 3x - 6y = 24 \\ 5x + 4y = 12 \end{cases}$

22. $\begin{cases} 2x + 4y = 16 \\ 3x - 5y = -9 \end{cases}$

23. $\begin{cases} 3x - 2y = 4 \\ 6x - 4y = 0 \end{cases}$

24. $\begin{cases} -x + 2y = 5 \\ 4x - 8y = 6 \end{cases}$

25. $\begin{cases} 2x - 4y = -2 \\ 3x + 2y = 3 \end{cases}$

26. $\begin{cases} 3x + 3y = 3 \\ 4x + 2y = \dfrac{8}{3} \end{cases}$

27. $\begin{cases} 2x - 3y = -1 \\ 10x + 10y = 5 \end{cases}$

28. $\begin{cases} 3x - 2y = 0 \\ 5x + 10y = 4 \end{cases}$

29. $\begin{cases} 2x + 3y = 6 \\ x - y = \dfrac{1}{2} \end{cases}$

30. $\begin{cases} \dfrac{1}{2}x + y = -2 \\ x - 2y = 8 \end{cases}$

31. $\begin{cases} 3x - 5y = 3 \\ 15x + 5y = 21 \end{cases}$

32. $\begin{cases} 2x - y = -1 \\ x + \dfrac{1}{2}y = \dfrac{3}{2} \end{cases}$

33. $\begin{cases} x + y - z = 6 \\ 3x - 2y + z = -5 \\ x + 3y - 2z = 14 \end{cases}$

34. $\begin{cases} x - y + z = -4 \\ 2x - 3y + 4z = -15 \\ 5x + y - 2z = 12 \end{cases}$

35. $\begin{cases} x + 2y - z = -3 \\ 2x - 4y + z = -7 \\ -2x + 2y - 3z = 4 \end{cases}$

36. $\begin{cases} x + 4y - 3z = -8 \\ 3x - y + 3z = 12 \\ x + y + 6z = 1 \end{cases}$

37. $\begin{cases} x - 2y + 3z = 1 \\ 3x + y - 2z = 0 \\ 2x - 4y + 6z = 2 \end{cases}$

38. $\begin{cases} x - y + 2z = 5 \\ 3x + 2y = 4 \\ -2x + 2y - 4z = -10 \end{cases}$

39. $\begin{cases} x + 2y - z = 0 \\ 2x - 4y + z = 0 \\ -2x + 2y - 3z = 0 \end{cases}$

40. $\begin{cases} x + 4y - 3z = 0 \\ 3x - y + 3z = 0 \\ x + y + 6z = 0 \end{cases}$

41. $\begin{cases} x - 2y + 3z = 0 \\ 3x + y - 2z = 0 \\ 2x - 4y + 6z = 0 \end{cases}$

42. $\begin{cases} x - y + 2z = 0 \\ 3x + 2y = 0 \\ -2x + 2y - 4z = 0 \end{cases}$

In Problems 43–50, use properties of determinants to find the value of each determinant if it is known that

$$\begin{vmatrix} x & y & z \\ u & v & w \\ 1 & 2 & 3 \end{vmatrix} = 4$$

43. $\begin{vmatrix} 1 & 2 & 3 \\ u & v & w \\ x & y & z \end{vmatrix}$

44. $\begin{vmatrix} x & y & z \\ u & v & w \\ 2 & 4 & 6 \end{vmatrix}$

45. $\begin{vmatrix} x & y & z \\ -3 & -6 & -9 \\ u & v & w \end{vmatrix}$

46. $\begin{vmatrix} 1 & 2 & 3 \\ x - u & y - v & z - w \\ u & v & w \end{vmatrix}$

47. $\begin{vmatrix} 1 & 2 & 3 \\ x - 3 & y - 6 & z - 9 \\ 2u & 2v & 2w \end{vmatrix}$

48. $\begin{vmatrix} x & y & z - x \\ u & v & w - u \\ 1 & 2 & 2 \end{vmatrix}$

49. $\begin{vmatrix} 1 & 2 & 3 \\ 2x & 2y & 2z \\ u - 1 & v - 2 & w - 3 \end{vmatrix}$

50. $\begin{vmatrix} x + 3 & y + 6 & z + 9 \\ 3u - 1 & 3v - 2 & 3w - 3 \\ 1 & 2 & 3 \end{vmatrix}$

Mixed Practice

In Problems 51–56, solve for x.

51. $\begin{vmatrix} x & x \\ 4 & 3 \end{vmatrix} = 5$

52. $\begin{vmatrix} x & 1 \\ 3 & x \end{vmatrix} = -2$

53. $\begin{vmatrix} x & 1 & 1 \\ 4 & 3 & 2 \\ -1 & 2 & 5 \end{vmatrix} = 2$

54. $\begin{vmatrix} 3 & 2 & 4 \\ 1 & x & 5 \\ 0 & 1 & -2 \end{vmatrix} = 0$

55. $\begin{vmatrix} x & 2 & 3 \\ 1 & x & 0 \\ 6 & 1 & -2 \end{vmatrix} = 7$

56. $\begin{vmatrix} x & 1 & 2 \\ 1 & x & 3 \\ 0 & 1 & 2 \end{vmatrix} = -4x$

Applications and Extensions

57. Geometry: Equation of a Line An equation of the line containing the two points (x_1, y_1) and (x_2, y_2) may be expressed as the determinant

$$\begin{vmatrix} x & y & 1 \\ x_1 & y_1 & 1 \\ x_2 & y_2 & 1 \end{vmatrix} = 0$$

Prove this result by expanding the determinant and comparing the result to the two-point form of the equation of a line.

58. Geometry: Collinear Points Using the result obtained in Problem 57, show that three distinct points (x_1, y_1), (x_2, y_2), and (x_3, y_3) are collinear (lie on the same line) if and only if

$$\begin{vmatrix} x_1 & y_1 & 1 \\ x_2 & y_2 & 1 \\ x_3 & y_3 & 1 \end{vmatrix} = 0$$

59. Geometry: Area of a Triangle A triangle has vertices $(x_1, y_1), (x_2, y_2)$, and (x_3, y_3). Show that the area of the triangle is given by the absolute value of D, where

$$D = \frac{1}{2} \begin{vmatrix} x_1 & x_2 & x_3 \\ y_1 & y_2 & y_3 \\ 1 & 1 & 1 \end{vmatrix}.$$ Use this formula to find the area of a triangle with vertices $(2, 3), (5, 2)$, and $(6, 5)$.

60. Show that $\begin{vmatrix} x^2 & x & 1 \\ y^2 & y & 1 \\ z^2 & z & 1 \end{vmatrix} = (y - z)(x - y)(x - z)$.

61. Complete the proof of Cramer's Rule for two equations containing two variables.

  [**Hint:** In system (5), page 737, if $a = 0$, then $b \neq 0$ and $c \neq 0$, since $D = -bc \neq 0$. Now show that equation (6) provides a solution of the system when $a = 0$. Then three cases remain: $b = 0$, $c = 0$, and $d = 0$.]

62. Interchange columns 1 and 3 of a 3 by 3 determinant. Show that the value of the new determinant is -1 times the value of the original determinant.

63. Multiply each entry in row 2 of a 3 by 3 determinant by the number $k, k \neq 0$. Show that the value of the new determinant is k times the value of the original determinant.

64. Prove that a 3 by 3 determinant in which the entries in column 1 equal those in column 3 has the value 0.

65. Prove that, if row 2 of a 3 by 3 determinant is multiplied by $k, k \neq 0$, and the result is added to the entries in row 1, there is no change in the value of the determinant.

11.4 Matrix Algebra

OBJECTIVES 1 Find the Sum and Difference of Two Matrices (p. 746)
  2 Find Scalar Multiples of a Matrix (p. 748)
  3 Find the Product of Two Matrices (p. 749)
  4 Find the Inverse of a Matrix (p. 754)
  5 Solve a System of Linear Equations Using an Inverse Matrix (p. 757)

In Section 11.2, we defined a matrix as a rectangular array of real numbers and used an augmented matrix to represent a system of linear equations. There is, however, a branch of mathematics, called **linear algebra,** that deals with matrices in such a way that an algebra of matrices is permitted. In this section, we provide a survey of how this **matrix algebra** is developed.

Before getting started, we restate the definition of a matrix.

DEFINITION A **matrix** is defined as a rectangular array of numbers:

$$\begin{array}{c} \\ \text{Row 1} \\ \text{Row 2} \\ \vdots \\ \text{Row } i \\ \vdots \\ \text{Row } m \end{array} \overset{\displaystyle \text{Column 1} \quad \text{Column 2} \quad\;\; \text{Column } j \quad\;\; \text{Column } n}{\begin{bmatrix} a_{11} & a_{12} & \cdots & a_{1j} & \cdots & a_{1n} \\ a_{21} & a_{22} & \cdots & a_{2j} & \cdots & a_{2n} \\ \vdots & \vdots & & \vdots & & \vdots \\ a_{i1} & a_{i2} & \cdots & a_{ij} & \cdots & a_{in} \\ \vdots & \vdots & & \vdots & & \vdots \\ a_{m1} & a_{m2} & \cdots & a_{mj} & \cdots & a_{mn} \end{bmatrix}}$$

Each number a_{ij} of the matrix has two indexes: the **row index** i and the **column index** j. The matrix shown here has m rows and n columns. The numbers a_{ij} are usually referred to as the **entries** of the matrix. For example, a_{23} refers to the entry in the second row, third column.

Let's begin with an example that illustrates how matrices can be used to conveniently represent an array of information.

EXAMPLE 1 | **Arranging Data in a Matrix**

In a survey of 900 people, the following information was obtained:

200 males	Thought federal defense spending was too high
150 males	Thought federal defense spending was too low
45 males	Had no opinion
315 females	Thought federal defense spending was too high
125 females	Thought federal defense spending was too low
65 females	Had no opinion

We can arrange these data in a rectangular array as follows:

	Too High	Too Low	No Opinion
Male	200	150	45
Female	315	125	65

or as the matrix

$$\begin{bmatrix} 200 & 150 & 45 \\ 315 & 125 & 65 \end{bmatrix}$$

This matrix has two rows (representing male and female) and three columns (representing "too high," "too low," and "no opinion").

The matrix we developed in Example 1 has 2 rows and 3 columns. In general, a matrix with m rows and n columns is called an **m by n matrix.** The matrix we developed in Example 1 is a 2 by 3 matrix and contains $2 \cdot 3 = 6$ entries. An m by n matrix will contain $m \cdot n$ entries.

If an m by n matrix has the same number of rows as columns, that is, if $m = n$, the matrix is referred to as a **square matrix.**

EXAMPLE 2 | **Examples of Matrices**

(a) $\begin{bmatrix} 5 & 0 \\ -6 & 1 \end{bmatrix}$ A 2 by 2 square matrix (b) $\begin{bmatrix} 1 & 0 & 3 \end{bmatrix}$ A 1 by 3 matrix

(c) $\begin{bmatrix} 6 & -2 & 4 \\ 4 & 3 & 5 \\ 8 & 0 & 1 \end{bmatrix}$ A 3 by 3 square matrix

---

1 Find the Sum and Difference of Two Matrices

We begin our discussion of matrix algebra by first defining what is meant by two matrices being equal and then defining the operations of addition and subtraction. It is important to note that these definitions require each matrix to have the same number of rows *and* the same number of columns as a condition for equality and for addition and subtraction.

We usually represent matrices by capital letters, such as A, B, and C.

DEFINITION Two matrices A and B are said to be **equal**, written as

$$A = B$$

provided that A and B have the same number of rows and the same number of columns and each entry a_{ij} in A is equal to the corresponding entry b_{ij} in B.

For example,

$$\begin{bmatrix} 2 & 1 \\ 0.5 & -1 \end{bmatrix} = \begin{bmatrix} \sqrt{4} & 1 \\ \dfrac{1}{2} & -1 \end{bmatrix} \quad \text{and} \quad \begin{bmatrix} 3 & 2 & 1 \\ 0 & 1 & -2 \end{bmatrix} = \begin{bmatrix} \sqrt{9} & \sqrt{4} & 1 \\ 0 & 1 & \sqrt[3]{-8} \end{bmatrix}$$

$$\begin{bmatrix} 4 & 1 \\ 6 & 1 \end{bmatrix} \neq \begin{bmatrix} 4 & 0 \\ 6 & 1 \end{bmatrix} \qquad \textit{Because the entries in row 1, column 2 are not equal}$$

$$\begin{bmatrix} 4 & 1 & 2 \\ 6 & 1 & 2 \end{bmatrix} \neq \begin{bmatrix} 4 & 1 & 2 & 3 \\ 6 & 1 & 2 & 4 \end{bmatrix} \qquad \textit{Because the matrix on the left has 3 columns and the matrix on the right has 4 columns}$$

Suppose that A and B represent two m by n matrices. We define their **sum** $A + B$ to be the m by n matrix formed by adding the corresponding entries a_{ij} of A and b_{ij} of B. The **difference $A - B$** is defined as the m by n matrix formed by subtracting the entries b_{ij} in B from the corresponding entries a_{ij} in A. Addition and subtraction of matrices are allowed only for matrices having the same number m of rows and the same number n of columns. For example, a 2 by 3 matrix and a 2 by 4 matrix cannot be added or subtracted.

Graphing utilities make the sometimes tedious process of matrix algebra easy. Let's compare how a graphing utility adds and subtracts matrices with doing it algebraically.

EXAMPLE 3 **Adding and Subtracting Matrices**

Suppose that

$$A = \begin{bmatrix} 2 & 4 & 8 & -3 \\ 0 & 1 & 2 & 3 \end{bmatrix} \quad \text{and} \quad B = \begin{bmatrix} -3 & 4 & 0 & 1 \\ 6 & 8 & 2 & 0 \end{bmatrix}$$

Find: (a) $A + B$ (b) $A - B$

Algebraic Solution

(a) $A + B = \begin{bmatrix} 2 & 4 & 8 & -3 \\ 0 & 1 & 2 & 3 \end{bmatrix} + \begin{bmatrix} -3 & 4 & 0 & 1 \\ 6 & 8 & 2 & 0 \end{bmatrix}$

$= \begin{bmatrix} 2 + (-3) & 4 + 4 & 8 + 0 & -3 + 1 \\ 0 + 6 & 1 + 8 & 2 + 2 & 3 + 0 \end{bmatrix}$ *Add corresponding entries.*

$= \begin{bmatrix} -1 & 8 & 8 & -2 \\ 6 & 9 & 4 & 3 \end{bmatrix}$

(b) $A - B = \begin{bmatrix} 2 & 4 & 8 & -3 \\ 0 & 1 & 2 & 3 \end{bmatrix} - \begin{bmatrix} -3 & 4 & 0 & 1 \\ 6 & 8 & 2 & 0 \end{bmatrix}$

$= \begin{bmatrix} 2 - (-3) & 4 - 4 & 8 - 0 & -3 - 1 \\ 0 - 6 & 1 - 8 & 2 - 2 & 3 - 0 \end{bmatrix}$ *Subtract corresponding entries.*

$= \begin{bmatrix} 5 & 0 & 8 & -4 \\ -6 & -7 & 0 & 3 \end{bmatrix}$

Graphing Solution

Enter the matrices into a graphing utility. Name them $[A]$ and $[B]$. Figure 11 shows the results of adding and subtracting $[A]$ and $[B]$.

Figure 11

```
[A]+[B]
      [[-1  8  8  -2]
       [6   9  4   3]]
[A]-[B]
      [[5   0  8  -4]
       [-6 -7  0   3]]
```

Now Work PROBLEM 7

Many of the algebraic properties of sums of real numbers are also true for sums of matrices. Suppose that A, B, and C are m by n matrices. Then matrix addition is **commutative.** That is,

Commutative Property of Matrix Addition

$$A + B = B + A$$

Matrix addition is also **associative.** That is,

Associative Property of Matrix Addition

$$(A + B) + C = A + (B + C)$$

Although we shall not prove these results, the proofs, as the following example illustrates, are based on the commutative and associative properties for real numbers.

EXAMPLE 4 Demonstrating the Commutative Property

$$\begin{bmatrix} 2 & 3 & -1 \\ 4 & 0 & 7 \end{bmatrix} + \begin{bmatrix} -1 & 2 & 1 \\ 5 & -3 & 4 \end{bmatrix} = \begin{bmatrix} 2 + (-1) & 3 + 2 & -1 + 1 \\ 4 + 5 & 0 + (-3) & 7 + 4 \end{bmatrix}$$

$$= \begin{bmatrix} -1 + 2 & 2 + 3 & 1 + (-1) \\ 5 + 4 & -3 + 0 & 4 + 7 \end{bmatrix}$$

$$= \begin{bmatrix} -1 & 2 & 1 \\ 5 & -3 & 4 \end{bmatrix} + \begin{bmatrix} 2 & 3 & -1 \\ 4 & 0 & 7 \end{bmatrix}$$

■

A matrix whose entries are all equal to 0 is called a **zero matrix.** Each of the following matrices is a zero matrix.

$$\begin{bmatrix} 0 & 0 \\ 0 & 0 \end{bmatrix} \quad \text{2 by 2 square zero matrix} \qquad \begin{bmatrix} 0 & 0 & 0 \\ 0 & 0 & 0 \end{bmatrix} \quad \text{2 by 3 zero matrix} \qquad \begin{bmatrix} 0 & 0 & 0 \end{bmatrix} \quad \text{1 by 3 zero matrix}$$

Zero matrices have properties similar to the real number 0. If A is an m by n matrix and 0 is an m by n zero matrix, then

$$A + 0 = A$$

In other words, the zero matrix is the additive identity in matrix algebra.

2 Find Scalar Multiples of a Matrix

We can also multiply a matrix by a real number. If k is a real number and A is an m by n matrix, the matrix kA is the m by n matrix formed by multiplying each entry a_{ij} in A by k. The number k is sometimes referred to as a **scalar,** and the matrix kA is called a **scalar multiple** of A.

EXAMPLE 5 Operations Using Matrices

Suppose that

$$A = \begin{bmatrix} 3 & 1 & 5 \\ -2 & 0 & 6 \end{bmatrix} \qquad B = \begin{bmatrix} 4 & 1 & 0 \\ 8 & 1 & -3 \end{bmatrix} \qquad C = \begin{bmatrix} 9 & 0 \\ -3 & 6 \end{bmatrix}$$

Find: (a) $4A$ (b) $\dfrac{1}{3}C$ (c) $3A - 2B$

Algebraic Solution

(a) $4A = 4\begin{bmatrix} 3 & 1 & 5 \\ -2 & 0 & 6 \end{bmatrix} = \begin{bmatrix} 4\cdot3 & 4\cdot1 & 4\cdot5 \\ 4(-2) & 4\cdot0 & 4\cdot6 \end{bmatrix} = \begin{bmatrix} 12 & 4 & 20 \\ -8 & 0 & 24 \end{bmatrix}$

(b) $\dfrac{1}{3}C = \dfrac{1}{3}\begin{bmatrix} 9 & 0 \\ -3 & 6 \end{bmatrix} = \begin{bmatrix} \dfrac{1}{3}\cdot9 & \dfrac{1}{3}\cdot0 \\ \dfrac{1}{3}(-3) & \dfrac{1}{3}\cdot6 \end{bmatrix} = \begin{bmatrix} 3 & 0 \\ -1 & 2 \end{bmatrix}$

(c) $3A - 2B = 3\begin{bmatrix} 3 & 1 & 5 \\ -2 & 0 & 6 \end{bmatrix} - 2\begin{bmatrix} 4 & 1 & 0 \\ 8 & 1 & -3 \end{bmatrix}$

$= \begin{bmatrix} 3\cdot3 & 3\cdot1 & 3\cdot5 \\ 3(-2) & 3\cdot0 & 3\cdot6 \end{bmatrix} - \begin{bmatrix} 2\cdot4 & 2\cdot1 & 2\cdot0 \\ 2\cdot8 & 2\cdot1 & 2(-3) \end{bmatrix}$

$= \begin{bmatrix} 9 & 3 & 15 \\ -6 & 0 & 18 \end{bmatrix} - \begin{bmatrix} 8 & 2 & 0 \\ 16 & 2 & -6 \end{bmatrix}$

$= \begin{bmatrix} 9-8 & 3-2 & 15-0 \\ -6-16 & 0-2 & 18-(-6) \end{bmatrix}$

$= \begin{bmatrix} 1 & 1 & 15 \\ -22 & -2 & 24 \end{bmatrix}$

Graphing Solution

Enter the matrices $[A], [B]$, and $[C]$ into a graphing utility. Figure 12 shows the required computations.

Figure 12

(a)

(b)

(c)

Now Work PROBLEM 11

We list next some of the algebraic properties of scalar multiplication. Let h and k be real numbers, and let A and B be m by n matrices. Then

Properties of Scalar Multiplication

$$k(hA) = (kh)A$$

$$(k + h)A = kA + hA$$

$$k(A + B) = kA + kB$$

3 Find the Product of Two Matrices

Unlike the straightforward definition for adding two matrices, the definition for multiplying two matrices is not what we might expect. In preparation for this definition, we need the following definitions:

DEFINITION

A **row vector** R is a 1 by n matrix

$$R = [r_1 \quad r_2 \quad \cdots \quad r_n]$$

A **column vector** C is an n by 1 matrix

$$C = \begin{bmatrix} c_1 \\ c_2 \\ \vdots \\ c_n \end{bmatrix}$$

The **product** RC of R times C is defined as the number

$$RC = [r_1 \quad r_2 \cdots r_n] \begin{bmatrix} c_1 \\ c_2 \\ \vdots \\ c_n \end{bmatrix} = r_1 c_1 + r_2 c_2 + \cdots + r_n c_n$$

Notice that a row vector and a column vector can be multiplied only if they contain the same number of entries.

EXAMPLE 6

The Product of a Row Vector by a Column Vector

If $R = [3 \quad -5 \quad 2]$ and $C = \begin{bmatrix} 3 \\ 4 \\ -5 \end{bmatrix}$, then

$$RC = [3 \quad -5 \quad 2] \begin{bmatrix} 3 \\ 4 \\ -5 \end{bmatrix} = 3 \cdot 3 + (-5)4 + 2(-5) = 9 - 20 - 10 = -21$$

Let's look at an application of the product of a row vector by a column vector.

EXAMPLE 7

Using Matrices to Compute Revenue

A clothing store sells men's shirts for \$40, silk ties for \$20, and wool suits for \$400. Last month, the store had sales consisting of 100 shirts, 200 ties, and 50 suits. What was the total revenue due to these sales?

Solution

We set up a row vector R to represent the prices of each item and a column vector C to represent the corresponding number of items sold. Then

$$\begin{array}{cc} \text{Prices} & \text{Number} \\ \text{Shirts Ties Suits} & \text{sold} \end{array}$$

$$R = [40 \quad 20 \quad 400] \qquad C = \begin{bmatrix} 100 \\ 200 \\ 50 \end{bmatrix} \begin{array}{l} \text{Shirts} \\ \text{Ties} \\ \text{Suits} \end{array}$$

The total revenue obtained is the product RC. That is,

$$RC = [40 \; 20 \; 400] \begin{bmatrix} 100 \\ 200 \\ 50 \end{bmatrix}$$

$$= \underbrace{40 \cdot 100}_{\text{Shirt revenue}} + \underbrace{20 \cdot 200}_{\text{Tie revenue}} + \underbrace{400 \cdot 50}_{\text{Suit revenue}} = \underbrace{\$28,000}_{\text{Total revenue}}$$

The definition for multiplying two matrices is based on the definition of a row vector times a column vector.

DEFINITION

Let A denote an m by r matrix and let B denote an r by n matrix. The **product** AB is defined as the m by n matrix whose entry in row i, column j is the product of the ith row of A and the jth column of B.

The definition of the product AB of two matrices A and B, in this order, requires that the number of columns of A equal the number of rows of B; otherwise, no product is defined.

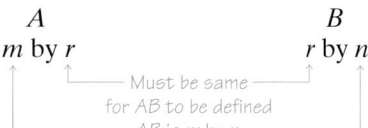

$$A \atop m \text{ by } r \qquad\qquad B \atop r \text{ by } n$$

Must be same for AB to be defined
AB is m by n.

In Words

To find the product AB, the number of columns in A must equal the number of rows in B.

An example will help to clarify the definition.

EXAMPLE 8 **Multiplying Two Matrices**

Find the product AB if

$$A = \begin{bmatrix} 2 & 4 & -1 \\ 5 & 8 & 0 \end{bmatrix} \quad \text{and} \quad B = \begin{bmatrix} 2 & 5 & 1 & 4 \\ 4 & 8 & 0 & 6 \\ -3 & 1 & -2 & -1 \end{bmatrix}$$

Solution

First, we note that A is 2 by 3 and B is 3 by 4. The number of columns in A equals the number of rows in B, so the product AB is defined and will be a 2 by 4 matrix.

Algebraic Solution

Suppose that we want the entry in row 2, column 3 of AB. To find it, we find the product of the row vector from row 2 of A and the column vector from column 3 of B.

Column 3 of B

Row 2 of A
$$[5 \quad 8 \quad 0] \begin{bmatrix} 1 \\ 0 \\ -2 \end{bmatrix} = 5 \cdot 1 + 8 \cdot 0 + 0(-2) = 5$$

So far we have

Column 3

$$AB = \begin{bmatrix} \_\_ & \_\_ & \overset{\downarrow}{5} & \_\_ \end{bmatrix} \leftarrow \text{Row 2}$$

Now, to find the entry in row 1, column 4 of AB, we find the product of row 1 of A and column 4 of B.

Column 4 of B

Row 1 of A
$$[2 \quad 4 \quad -1] \begin{bmatrix} 4 \\ 6 \\ -1 \end{bmatrix} = 2 \cdot 4 + 4 \cdot 6 + (-1)(-1) = 33$$

Graphing Solution

Enter the matrices A and B into a graphing utility. Figure 13 shows the product AB.

Figure 13

Continuing in this fashion, we find AB.

$$AB = \begin{bmatrix} 2 & 4 & -1 \\ 5 & 8 & 0 \end{bmatrix} \begin{bmatrix} 2 & 5 & 1 & 4 \\ 4 & 8 & 0 & 6 \\ -3 & 1 & -2 & -1 \end{bmatrix}$$

$$= \begin{bmatrix} \text{Row 1 of } A & \text{Row 1 of } A & \text{Row 1 of } A & \text{Row 1 of } A \\ \text{times} & \text{times} & \text{times} & \text{times} \\ \text{column 1 of } B & \text{column 2 of } B & \text{column 3 of } B & \text{column 4 of } B \\ & & & \\ \text{Row 2 of } A & \text{Row 2 of } A & \text{Row 2 of } A & \text{Row 2 of } A \\ \text{times} & \text{times} & \text{times} & \text{times} \\ \text{column 1 of } B & \text{column 2 of } B & \text{column 3 of } B & \text{column 4 of } B \end{bmatrix}$$

$$= \begin{bmatrix} 2\cdot2 + 4\cdot4 + (-1)(-3) & 2\cdot5 + 4\cdot8 + (-1)1 & 2\cdot1 + 4\cdot0 + (-1)(-2) & 33 \text{ (from earlier)} \\ 5\cdot2 + 8\cdot4 + 0(-3) & 5\cdot5 + 8\cdot8 + 0\cdot1 & 5 \text{ (from earlier)} & 5\cdot4 + 8\cdot6 + 0(-1) \end{bmatrix}$$

$$= \begin{bmatrix} 23 & 41 & 4 & 33 \\ 42 & 89 & 5 & 68 \end{bmatrix}$$

Now Work PROBLEM 23

Notice that for the matrices given in Example 8 the product BA is not defined, because B is 3 by 4 and A is 2 by 3. Try calculating BA on a graphing utility. What do you notice?

Another result that can occur when multiplying two matrices is illustrated in the next example.*

EXAMPLE 9 **Multiplying Two Matrices**

If

$$A = \begin{bmatrix} 2 & 1 & 3 \\ 1 & -1 & 0 \end{bmatrix} \quad \text{and} \quad B = \begin{bmatrix} 1 & 0 \\ 2 & 1 \\ 3 & 2 \end{bmatrix}$$

find: (a) AB (b) BA

Solution (a) $AB = \begin{bmatrix} 2 & 1 & 3 \\ 1 & -1 & 0 \end{bmatrix} \begin{bmatrix} 1 & 0 \\ 2 & 1 \\ 3 & 2 \end{bmatrix} = \begin{bmatrix} 13 & 7 \\ -1 & -1 \end{bmatrix}$

 2 by 3 3 by 2 2 by 2

(b) $BA = \begin{bmatrix} 1 & 0 \\ 2 & 1 \\ 3 & 2 \end{bmatrix} \begin{bmatrix} 2 & 1 & 3 \\ 1 & -1 & 0 \end{bmatrix} = \begin{bmatrix} 2 & 1 & 3 \\ 5 & 1 & 6 \\ 8 & 1 & 9 \end{bmatrix}$

 3 by 2 2 by 3 3 by 3

Notice in Example 9 that AB is 2 by 2 and BA is 3 by 3. It is possible for both AB and BA to be defined, yet be unequal. In fact, even if A and B are both n by n matrices so that AB and BA are each defined and n by n, AB and BA will usually be unequal.

*For most of the examples that follow, we will multiply matrices algebraically. You should verify each result using a graphing utility.

EXAMPLE 10   Multiplying Two Square Matrices

If

$$A = \begin{bmatrix} 2 & 1 \\ 0 & 4 \end{bmatrix} \quad \text{and} \quad B = \begin{bmatrix} -3 & 1 \\ 1 & 2 \end{bmatrix}$$

find: (a) AB (b) BA

Solution   (a) $AB = \begin{bmatrix} 2 & 1 \\ 0 & 4 \end{bmatrix} \begin{bmatrix} -3 & 1 \\ 1 & 2 \end{bmatrix} = \begin{bmatrix} -5 & 4 \\ 4 & 8 \end{bmatrix}$

(b) $BA = \begin{bmatrix} -3 & 1 \\ 1 & 2 \end{bmatrix} \begin{bmatrix} 2 & 1 \\ 0 & 4 \end{bmatrix} = \begin{bmatrix} -6 & 1 \\ 2 & 9 \end{bmatrix}$

The preceding examples demonstrate that an important property of real numbers, the commutative property of multiplication, is not shared by matrices. In general:

THEOREM   Matrix multiplication is not commutative.

Now Work PROBLEMS 13 AND 15

Next we give two of the properties of real numbers that are shared by matrices. Assuming that each product and sum is defined, we have the following:

Associative Property of Matrix Multiplication

$$A(BC) = (AB)C$$

Distributive Property

$$A(B + C) = AB + AC$$

For an n by n square matrix, the entries located in row i, column i, $1 \le i \le n$, are called the **diagonal entries** or **the main diagonal.** An n by n square matrix whose diagonal entries are 1's, while all other entries are 0's, is called the **identity matrix I_n.** For example,

$$I_2 = \begin{bmatrix} 1 & 0 \\ 0 & 1 \end{bmatrix} \qquad I_3 = \begin{bmatrix} 1 & 0 & 0 \\ 0 & 1 & 0 \\ 0 & 0 & 1 \end{bmatrix}$$

and so on.

EXAMPLE 11   Multiplication with an Identity Matrix

Let

$$A = \begin{bmatrix} -1 & 2 & 0 \\ 0 & 1 & 3 \end{bmatrix} \quad \text{and} \quad B = \begin{bmatrix} 3 & 2 \\ 4 & 6 \\ 5 & 2 \end{bmatrix}$$

Find: (a) AI_3 (b) I_2A (c) BI_2

Solution (a) $AI_3 = \begin{bmatrix} -1 & 2 & 0 \\ 0 & 1 & 3 \end{bmatrix} \begin{bmatrix} 1 & 0 & 0 \\ 0 & 1 & 0 \\ 0 & 0 & 1 \end{bmatrix} = \begin{bmatrix} -1 & 2 & 0 \\ 0 & 1 & 3 \end{bmatrix} = A$

(b) $I_2 A = \begin{bmatrix} 1 & 0 \\ 0 & 1 \end{bmatrix} \begin{bmatrix} -1 & 2 & 0 \\ 0 & 1 & 3 \end{bmatrix} = \begin{bmatrix} -1 & 2 & 0 \\ 0 & 1 & 3 \end{bmatrix} = A$

(c) $BI_2 = \begin{bmatrix} 3 & 2 \\ 4 & 6 \\ 5 & 2 \end{bmatrix} \begin{bmatrix} 1 & 0 \\ 0 & 1 \end{bmatrix} = \begin{bmatrix} 3 & 2 \\ 4 & 6 \\ 5 & 2 \end{bmatrix} = B$

Example 11 demonstrates the following property:

Identity Property

If A is an m by n matrix, then

$$I_m A = A \quad \text{and} \quad AI_n = A$$

If A is an n by n square matrix,

$$AI_n = I_n A = A$$

An identity matrix has properties similar to those of the real number 1. In other words, the identity matrix is a multiplicative identity in matrix algebra.

4 Find the Inverse of a Matrix

DEFINITION Let A be a square n by n matrix. If there exists an n by n matrix A^{-1}, read "A inverse," for which

$$AA^{-1} = A^{-1}A = I_n$$

then A^{-1} is called the **inverse** of the matrix A.

> **Note**
> If the determinant of A is zero, A is singular. (Refer to Section 11.3.)

As we shall soon see, not every square matrix has an inverse. When a matrix A does have an inverse A^{-1}, then A is said to be **nonsingular.** If a matrix A has no inverse, it is called **singular.**

EXAMPLE 12 **Multiplying a Matrix by Its Inverse**

Show that the inverse of

$$A = \begin{bmatrix} 3 & 1 \\ 2 & 1 \end{bmatrix} \quad \text{is} \quad A^{-1} = \begin{bmatrix} 1 & -1 \\ -2 & 3 \end{bmatrix}$$

Solution We need to show that $AA^{-1} = A^{-1}A = I_2$.

$$AA^{-1} = \begin{bmatrix} 3 & 1 \\ 2 & 1 \end{bmatrix} \begin{bmatrix} 1 & -1 \\ -2 & 3 \end{bmatrix} = \begin{bmatrix} 1 & 0 \\ 0 & 1 \end{bmatrix} = I_2$$

$$A^{-1}A = \begin{bmatrix} 1 & -1 \\ -2 & 3 \end{bmatrix} \begin{bmatrix} 3 & 1 \\ 2 & 1 \end{bmatrix} = \begin{bmatrix} 1 & 0 \\ 0 & 1 \end{bmatrix} = I_2$$

We now show one way to find the inverse of

$$A = \begin{bmatrix} 3 & 1 \\ 2 & 1 \end{bmatrix}$$

Suppose that A^{-1} is given by

$$A^{-1} = \begin{bmatrix} x & y \\ z & w \end{bmatrix} \qquad \textbf{(1)}$$

where x, y, z, and w are four variables. Based on the definition of an inverse, if A has an inverse,

$$AA^{-1} = I_2$$

$$\begin{bmatrix} 3 & 1 \\ 2 & 1 \end{bmatrix}\begin{bmatrix} x & y \\ z & w \end{bmatrix} = \begin{bmatrix} 1 & 0 \\ 0 & 1 \end{bmatrix}$$

$$\begin{bmatrix} 3x + z & 3y + w \\ 2x + z & 2y + w \end{bmatrix} = \begin{bmatrix} 1 & 0 \\ 0 & 1 \end{bmatrix}$$

Because corresponding entries must be equal, it follows that this matrix equation is equivalent to two systems of linear equations.

$$\begin{cases} 3x + z = 1 \\ 2x + z = 0 \end{cases} \qquad \begin{cases} 3y + w = 0 \\ 2y + w = 1 \end{cases}$$

The augmented matrix of each system is

$$\begin{bmatrix} 3 & 1 & \big| & 1 \\ 2 & 1 & \big| & 0 \end{bmatrix} \qquad \begin{bmatrix} 3 & 1 & \big| & 0 \\ 2 & 1 & \big| & 1 \end{bmatrix} \qquad \textbf{(2)}$$

The usual procedure would be to transform each augmented matrix into reduced row echelon form. Notice, though, that the left sides of the augmented matrices are equal, so the same row operations (see Section 11.2) can be used to reduce each one. We find it more efficient to combine the two augmented matrices (2) into a single matrix, as shown next, and then transform it into reduced row echelon form.

$$\begin{bmatrix} 3 & 1 & \big| & 1 & 0 \\ 2 & 1 & \big| & 0 & 1 \end{bmatrix}$$

We attempt to transform the left side into an identity matrix.

$$\begin{bmatrix} 3 & 1 & \big| & 1 & 0 \\ 2 & 1 & \big| & 0 & 1 \end{bmatrix} \underset{\underset{R_1 = -1r_2 + r_1}{\uparrow}}{\rightarrow} \begin{bmatrix} 1 & 0 & \big| & 1 & -1 \\ 2 & 1 & \big| & 0 & 1 \end{bmatrix}$$

$$\underset{\underset{R_2 = -2r_1 + r_2}{\uparrow}}{\rightarrow} \begin{bmatrix} 1 & 0 & \big| & 1 & -1 \\ 0 & 1 & \big| & -2 & 3 \end{bmatrix} \qquad \textbf{(3)}$$

Matrix (3) is in reduced row echelon form.

Now we reverse the earlier step of combining the two augmented matrices in (2) and write the single matrix (3) as two augmented matrices.

$$\begin{bmatrix} 1 & 0 & \big| & 1 \\ 0 & 1 & \big| & -2 \end{bmatrix} \text{ and } \begin{bmatrix} 1 & 0 & \big| & -1 \\ 0 & 1 & \big| & 3 \end{bmatrix}$$

We conclude from these matrices that $x = 1$, $z = -2$, and $y = -1$, $w = 3$. Substituting these values into matrix (1), we find that

$$A^{-1} = \begin{bmatrix} 1 & -1 \\ -2 & 3 \end{bmatrix}$$

Notice in display (3) that the 2 by 2 matrix to the right of the vertical bar is, in fact, the inverse of A. Also notice that the identity matrix I_2 is the matrix that appears to the left of the vertical bar. These observations and the procedures followed above will work in general.

Procedure for Finding the Inverse of a Nonsingular Matrix

To find the inverse of an n by n nonsingular matrix A, proceed as follows:

STEP 1: Form the matrix $[A|I_n]$.

STEP 2: Transform the matrix $[A|I_n]$ into reduced row echelon form.

STEP 3: The reduced row echelon form of $[A|I_n]$ will contain the identity matrix I_n on the left of the vertical bar; the n by n matrix on the right of the vertical bar is the inverse of A.

In other words, if A is nonsingular, we begin with the matrix $[A|I_n]$ and, after transforming it into reduced row echelon form, we end up with the matrix $[I_n|A^{-1}]$. Let's look at another example.

EXAMPLE 13 **Finding the Inverse of a Matrix**

The matrix

$$A = \begin{bmatrix} 1 & 1 & 0 \\ -1 & 3 & 4 \\ 0 & 4 & 3 \end{bmatrix}$$

is nonsingular. Find its inverse.

Algebraic Solution

First, we form the matrix

$$[A|I_3] = \begin{bmatrix} 1 & 1 & 0 & | & 1 & 0 & 0 \\ -1 & 3 & 4 & | & 0 & 1 & 0 \\ 0 & 4 & 3 & | & 0 & 0 & 1 \end{bmatrix}$$

Next, we use row operations to transform $[A|I_3]$ into reduced row echelon form.

$$\begin{bmatrix} 1 & 1 & 0 & | & 1 & 0 & 0 \\ -1 & 3 & 4 & | & 0 & 1 & 0 \\ 0 & 4 & 3 & | & 0 & 0 & 1 \end{bmatrix} \rightarrow \begin{bmatrix} 1 & 1 & 0 & | & 1 & 0 & 0 \\ 0 & 4 & 4 & | & 1 & 1 & 0 \\ 0 & 4 & 3 & | & 0 & 0 & 1 \end{bmatrix} \rightarrow \begin{bmatrix} 1 & 1 & 0 & | & 1 & 0 & 0 \\ 0 & 1 & 1 & | & \frac{1}{4} & \frac{1}{4} & 0 \\ 0 & 4 & 3 & | & 0 & 0 & 1 \end{bmatrix}$$

$$\uparrow R_2 = r_1 + r_2 \qquad\qquad \uparrow R_2 = \frac{1}{4}r_2$$

$$\rightarrow \begin{bmatrix} 1 & 0 & -1 & | & \frac{3}{4} & -\frac{1}{4} & 0 \\ 0 & 1 & 1 & | & \frac{1}{4} & \frac{1}{4} & 0 \\ 0 & 0 & -1 & | & -1 & -1 & 1 \end{bmatrix} \rightarrow \begin{bmatrix} 1 & 0 & -1 & | & \frac{3}{4} & -\frac{1}{4} & 0 \\ 0 & 1 & 1 & | & \frac{1}{4} & \frac{1}{4} & 0 \\ 0 & 0 & 1 & | & 1 & 1 & -1 \end{bmatrix}$$

$$\uparrow \begin{array}{l} R_1 = -1r_2 + r_1 \\ R_3 = -4r_2 + r_3 \end{array} \qquad\qquad \uparrow R_3 = -1r_3$$

$$\rightarrow \begin{bmatrix} 1 & 0 & 0 & | & \frac{7}{4} & \frac{3}{4} & -1 \\ 0 & 1 & 0 & | & -\frac{3}{4} & -\frac{3}{4} & 1 \\ 0 & 0 & 1 & | & 1 & 1 & -1 \end{bmatrix}$$

$$\uparrow \begin{array}{l} R_1 = r_3 + r_1 \\ R_2 = -1r_3 + r_2 \end{array}$$

Graphing Solution

Enter the matrix A into a graphing utility. Figure 14 shows A^{-1}.

Figure 14

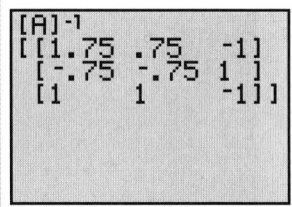

The matrix $[A|I_3]$ is now in reduced row echelon form, and the identity matrix I_3 is on the left of the vertical bar. The inverse of A is

$$A^{-1} = \begin{bmatrix} \dfrac{7}{4} & \dfrac{3}{4} & -1 \\ -\dfrac{3}{4} & -\dfrac{3}{4} & 1 \\ 1 & 1 & -1 \end{bmatrix}$$

You can (and should) verify that this is the correct inverse by showing that

$$AA^{-1} = A^{-1}A = I_3.$$

━━━━━━━▶ **Now Work** PROBLEM 31

If transforming the matrix $[A|I_n]$ into reduced row echelon form does not result in the identity matrix I_n to the left of the vertical bar, then A is singular and has no inverse. The next example demonstrates such a matrix.

EXAMPLE 14   **Showing That a Matrix Has No Inverse**

Show that the matrix $A = \begin{bmatrix} 4 & 6 \\ 2 & 3 \end{bmatrix}$ has no inverse.

Algebraic Solution

Proceeding as in Example 13, we form the matrix

$$[A|I_2] = \begin{bmatrix} 4 & 6 & | & 1 & 0 \\ 2 & 3 & | & 0 & 1 \end{bmatrix}$$

Then we use row operations to transform $[A|I_2]$ into reduced row echelon form.

$$[A|I_2] = \begin{bmatrix} 4 & 6 & | & 1 & 0 \\ 2 & 3 & | & 0 & 1 \end{bmatrix} \rightarrow \begin{bmatrix} 1 & \dfrac{3}{2} & | & \dfrac{1}{4} & 0 \\ 2 & 3 & | & 0 & 1 \end{bmatrix} \rightarrow \begin{bmatrix} 1 & \dfrac{3}{2} & | & \dfrac{1}{4} & 0 \\ 0 & 0 & | & -\dfrac{1}{2} & 1 \end{bmatrix}$$

$$\uparrow \qquad\qquad\qquad\qquad \uparrow$$
$$R_1 = \dfrac{1}{4}r_1 \qquad\qquad\qquad R_2 = -2r_1 + r_2$$

The matrix $[A|I_2]$ is sufficiently reduced for us to see that the identity matrix cannot appear to the left of the vertical bar. We conclude that A is singular and so has no inverse.

Graphing Solution

Enter the matrix A. Figure 15 shows the result when we try to find its inverse. The ERRor comes about because A is singular.

Figure 15

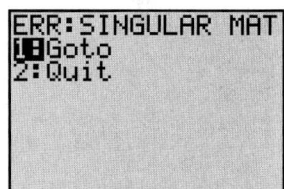

```
ERR:SINGULAR MAT
1▮Goto
2:Quit
```

Seeing the Concept

Compute the determinant of A in Example 14 using a graphing utility. What is the result? Are you surprised?

━━━━━━━▶ **Now Work** PROBLEM 59

---

5 Solve a System of Linear Equations Using an Inverse Matrix

Inverse matrices can be used to solve systems of equations in which the number of equations is the same as the number of variables.

EXAMPLE 15 | Using the Inverse Matrix to Solve a System of Linear Equations

Solve the system of equations: $\begin{cases} x + y = 3 \\ -x + 3y + 4z = -3 \\ 4y + 3z = 2 \end{cases}$

Solution If we let

$$A = \begin{bmatrix} 1 & 1 & 0 \\ -1 & 3 & 4 \\ 0 & 4 & 3 \end{bmatrix} \qquad X = \begin{bmatrix} x \\ y \\ z \end{bmatrix} \qquad B = \begin{bmatrix} 3 \\ -3 \\ 2 \end{bmatrix}$$

then the original system of equations can be written compactly as the matrix equation

$$AX = B \tag{4}$$

We know from Example 13 that the matrix A has the inverse A^{-1}, so we multiply each side of equation (4) by A^{-1}.

$$AX = B$$
$$A^{-1}(AX) = A^{-1}B \quad \text{Multiply both sides by } A^{-1}.$$
$$(A^{-1}A)X = A^{-1}B \quad \text{Associative property of multiplication}$$
$$I_3 X = A^{-1}B \quad \text{Definition of an inverse matrix}$$
$$X = A^{-1}B \quad \text{Property of the identity matrix} \tag{5}$$

Now we use (5) to find $X = \begin{bmatrix} x \\ y \\ z \end{bmatrix}$. This can be done either algebraically or with a graphing utility.

Algebraic Solution

$$X = \begin{bmatrix} x \\ y \\ z \end{bmatrix} = A^{-1}B = \begin{bmatrix} \frac{7}{4} & \frac{3}{4} & -1 \\ -\frac{3}{4} & -\frac{3}{4} & 1 \\ 1 & 1 & -1 \end{bmatrix} \begin{bmatrix} 3 \\ -3 \\ 2 \end{bmatrix} = \begin{bmatrix} 1 \\ 2 \\ -2 \end{bmatrix}$$

$\uparrow$
Example 13

Graphing Solution

Enter the matrices A and B into a graphing utility. Figure 16 shows the solution to the system of equations.

Figure 16

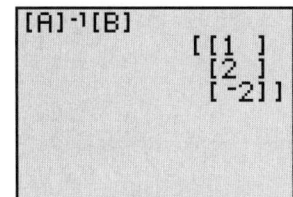

```
[A]⁻¹[B]
            [[1 ]
             [2 ]
             [-2]]
```

So $x = 1$, $y = 2$, $z = -2$, or, using ordered triplets, $(1, 2, -2)$.

The method used in Example 15 to solve a system of equations is particularly useful when it is necessary to solve several systems of equations in which the constants appearing to the right of the equal signs change, while the coefficients of the variables on the left side remain the same. See Problems 39–58 for some illustrations. Be careful; this method can only be used if the inverse exists. If it does not exist, row reduction must be used since the system is either inconsistent or dependent.

Now Work PROBLEM 43

Historical Feature

Arthur Cayley (1821–1895)

Matrices were invented in 1857 by Arthur Cayley (1821–1895) as a way of efficiently computing the result of substituting one linear system into another (see Historical Problem 3). The resulting system had incredible richness, in the sense that a wide variety of mathematical systems could be mimicked by the matrices. Cayley and his friend James J. Sylvester (1814–1897) spent much of the rest of their lives elaborating the theory. The torch was then passed to Georg Frobenius (1849–1917), whose deep investigations established a central place for matrices in modern mathematics. In 1924, rather to the surprise of physicists, it was found that matrices (with complex numbers in them) were exactly the right tool for describing the behavior of atomic systems. Today, matrices are used in a wide variety of applications.

Historical Problems

1. *Matrices and Complex Numbers* Frobenius emphasized in his research how matrices could be used to mimic other mathematical systems. Here, we mimic the behavior of complex numbers using matrices. Mathematicians call such a relationship an *isomorphism*.

$$\text{Complex number} \longleftrightarrow \text{Matrix}$$
$$a + bi \longleftrightarrow \begin{bmatrix} a & b \\ -b & a \end{bmatrix}$$

Note that the complex number can be read off the top line of the matrix. Thus,

$$2 + 3i \longleftrightarrow \begin{bmatrix} 2 & 3 \\ -3 & 2 \end{bmatrix} \quad \text{and} \quad \begin{bmatrix} 4 & -2 \\ 2 & 4 \end{bmatrix} \longleftrightarrow 4 - 2i$$

   (a) Find the matrices corresponding to $2 - 5i$ and $1 + 3i$.
   (b) Multiply the two matrices.
   (c) Find the corresponding complex number for the matrix found in part (b).
   (d) Multiply $2 - 5i$ and $1 + 3i$. The result should be the same as that found in part (c).

   The process also works for addition and subtraction. Try it for yourself.

2. Compute $(a + bi)(a - bi)$ using matrices. Interpret the result.

3. *Cayley's Definition of Matrix Multiplication* Cayley invented matrix multiplication to simplify the following problem:

$$\begin{cases} u = ar + bs \\ v = cr + ds \end{cases} \quad \begin{cases} x = ku + lv \\ y = mu + nv \end{cases}$$

   (a) Find x and y in terms of r and s by substituting u and v from the first system of equations into the second system of equations.
   (b) Use the result of part (a) to find the 2 by 2 matrix A in

$$\begin{bmatrix} x \\ y \end{bmatrix} = A \begin{bmatrix} r \\ s \end{bmatrix}$$

   (c) Now look at the following way to do it. Write the equations in matrix form.

$$\begin{bmatrix} u \\ v \end{bmatrix} = \begin{bmatrix} a & b \\ c & d \end{bmatrix} \begin{bmatrix} r \\ s \end{bmatrix} \qquad \begin{bmatrix} x \\ y \end{bmatrix} = \begin{bmatrix} k & l \\ m & n \end{bmatrix} \begin{bmatrix} u \\ v \end{bmatrix}$$

   So

$$\begin{bmatrix} x \\ y \end{bmatrix} = \begin{bmatrix} k & l \\ m & n \end{bmatrix} \begin{bmatrix} a & b \\ c & d \end{bmatrix} \begin{bmatrix} r \\ s \end{bmatrix}$$

   Do you see how Cayley defined matrix multiplication?

11.4 Assess Your Understanding

Concepts and Vocabulary

1. A matrix B, for which $AB = I_n$, the identity matrix, is called the _____ of A.

2. A matrix that has the same number of rows as columns is called a(n) _____ matrix.

3. In the algebra of matrices, the matrix that has properties similar to the number 1 is called the _____ matrix.

4. *True or False* Every square matrix has an inverse.

5. *True or False* Matrix multiplication is commutative.

6. *True or False* Any pair of matrices can be multiplied.

Skill Building

In Problems 7–22, use the following matrices to compute the given expression. Verify your result using a graphing utility.

$$A = \begin{bmatrix} 0 & 3 & -5 \\ 1 & 2 & 6 \end{bmatrix} \qquad B = \begin{bmatrix} 4 & 1 & 0 \\ -2 & 3 & -2 \end{bmatrix} \qquad C = \begin{bmatrix} 4 & 1 \\ 6 & 2 \\ -2 & 3 \end{bmatrix}$$

7. $A + B$

8. $A - B$

9. $4A$

10. $-3B$

11. $3A - 2B$

12. $2A + 4B$

13. AC

14. BC

15. CA **16.** CB **17.** $C(A + B)$ **18.** $(A + B)C$

19. $AC - 3I_2$ **20.** $CA + 5I_3$ **21.** $CA - CB$ **22.** $AC + BC$

In Problems 23–28, find the product. Verify your result using a graphing utility.

23. $\begin{bmatrix} 2 & -2 \\ 1 & 0 \end{bmatrix}\begin{bmatrix} 2 & 1 & 4 & 6 \\ 3 & -1 & 3 & 2 \end{bmatrix}$

24. $\begin{bmatrix} 4 & 1 \\ 2 & 1 \end{bmatrix}\begin{bmatrix} -6 & 6 & 1 & 0 \\ 2 & 5 & 4 & -1 \end{bmatrix}$

25. $\begin{bmatrix} 1 & 2 & 3 \\ 0 & -1 & 4 \end{bmatrix}\begin{bmatrix} 1 & 2 \\ -1 & 0 \\ 2 & 4 \end{bmatrix}$

26. $\begin{bmatrix} 1 & -1 \\ -3 & 2 \\ 0 & 5 \end{bmatrix}\begin{bmatrix} 2 & 8 & -1 \\ 3 & 6 & 0 \end{bmatrix}$

27. $\begin{bmatrix} 1 & 0 & 1 \\ 2 & 4 & 1 \\ 3 & 6 & 1 \end{bmatrix}\begin{bmatrix} 1 & 3 \\ 6 & 2 \\ 8 & -1 \end{bmatrix}$

28. $\begin{bmatrix} 4 & -2 & 3 \\ 0 & 1 & 2 \\ -1 & 0 & 1 \end{bmatrix}\begin{bmatrix} 2 & 6 \\ 1 & -1 \\ 0 & 2 \end{bmatrix}$

In Problems 29–38, each matrix is nonsingular. Find the inverse of each matrix. Verify your answer using a graphing utility (when possible).

29. $\begin{bmatrix} 2 & 1 \\ 1 & 1 \end{bmatrix}$

30. $\begin{bmatrix} 3 & -1 \\ -2 & 1 \end{bmatrix}$

31. $\begin{bmatrix} 6 & 5 \\ 2 & 2 \end{bmatrix}$

32. $\begin{bmatrix} -4 & 1 \\ 6 & -2 \end{bmatrix}$

33. $\begin{bmatrix} 2 & 1 \\ a & a \end{bmatrix} \quad a \neq 0$

34. $\begin{bmatrix} b & 3 \\ b & 2 \end{bmatrix} \quad b \neq 0$

35. $\begin{bmatrix} 1 & -1 & 1 \\ 0 & -2 & 1 \\ -2 & -3 & 0 \end{bmatrix}$

36. $\begin{bmatrix} 1 & 0 & 2 \\ -1 & 2 & 3 \\ 1 & -1 & 0 \end{bmatrix}$

37. $\begin{bmatrix} 1 & 1 & 1 \\ 3 & 2 & -1 \\ 3 & 1 & 2 \end{bmatrix}$

38. $\begin{bmatrix} 3 & 3 & 1 \\ 1 & 2 & 1 \\ 2 & -1 & 1 \end{bmatrix}$

In Problems 39–58, use the inverses found in Problems 29–38 to solve each system of equations.

39. $\begin{cases} 2x + y = 8 \\ x + y = 5 \end{cases}$

40. $\begin{cases} 3x - y = 8 \\ -2x + y = 4 \end{cases}$

41. $\begin{cases} 2x + y = 0 \\ x + y = 5 \end{cases}$

42. $\begin{cases} 3x - y = 4 \\ -2x + y = 5 \end{cases}$

43. $\begin{cases} 6x + 5y = 7 \\ 2x + 2y = 2 \end{cases}$

44. $\begin{cases} -4x + y = 0 \\ 6x - 2y = 14 \end{cases}$

45. $\begin{cases} 6x + 5y = 13 \\ 2x + 2y = 5 \end{cases}$

46. $\begin{cases} -4x + y = 5 \\ 6x - 2y = -9 \end{cases}$

47. $\begin{cases} 2x + y = -3 \\ ax + ay = -a \end{cases} \quad a \neq 0$

48. $\begin{cases} bx + 3y = 2b + 3 \\ bx + 2y = 2b + 2 \end{cases} \quad b \neq 0$

49. $\begin{cases} 2x + y = \dfrac{7}{a} \\ ax + ay = 5 \end{cases} \quad a \neq 0$

50. $\begin{cases} bx + 3y = 14 \\ bx + 2y = 10 \end{cases} \quad b \neq 0$

51. $\begin{cases} x - y + z = 0 \\ -2y + z = -1 \\ -2x - 3y = -5 \end{cases}$

52. $\begin{cases} x + 2z = 6 \\ -x + 2y + 3z = -5 \\ x - y = 6 \end{cases}$

53. $\begin{cases} x - y + z = 2 \\ -2y + z = 2 \\ -2x - 3y = \dfrac{1}{2} \end{cases}$

54. $\begin{cases} x + 2z = 2 \\ -x + 2y + 3z = -\dfrac{3}{2} \\ x - y = 2 \end{cases}$

55. $\begin{cases} x + y + z = 9 \\ 3x + 2y - z = 8 \\ 3x + y + 2z = 1 \end{cases}$

56. $\begin{cases} 3x + 3y + z = 8 \\ x + 2y + z = 5 \\ 2x - y + z = 4 \end{cases}$

57. $\begin{cases} x + y + z = 2 \\ 3x + 2y - z = \dfrac{7}{3} \\ 3x + y + 2z = \dfrac{10}{3} \end{cases}$

58. $\begin{cases} 3x + 3y + z = 1 \\ x + 2y + z = 0 \\ 2x - y + z = 4 \end{cases}$

In Problems 59–64, show that each matrix has no inverse. Verify your result using a graphing utility.

59. $\begin{bmatrix} 4 & 2 \\ 2 & 1 \end{bmatrix}$

60. $\begin{bmatrix} -3 & \dfrac{1}{2} \\ 6 & -1 \end{bmatrix}$

61. $\begin{bmatrix} 15 & 3 \\ 10 & 2 \end{bmatrix}$

62. $\begin{bmatrix} -3 & 0 \\ 4 & 0 \end{bmatrix}$

63. $\begin{bmatrix} -3 & 1 & -1 \\ 1 & -4 & -7 \\ 1 & 2 & 5 \end{bmatrix}$

64. $\begin{bmatrix} 1 & 1 & -3 \\ 2 & -4 & 1 \\ -5 & 7 & 1 \end{bmatrix}$

In Problems 65–68, use a graphing utility to find the inverse, if it exists, of each matrix. Round answers to two decimal places.

65. $\begin{bmatrix} 25 & 61 & -12 \\ 18 & -2 & 4 \\ 8 & 35 & 21 \end{bmatrix}$
66. $\begin{bmatrix} 18 & -3 & 4 \\ 6 & -20 & 14 \\ 10 & 25 & -15 \end{bmatrix}$
67. $\begin{bmatrix} 44 & 21 & 18 & 6 \\ -2 & 10 & 15 & 5 \\ 21 & 12 & -12 & 4 \\ -8 & -16 & 4 & 9 \end{bmatrix}$
68. $\begin{bmatrix} 16 & 22 & -3 & 5 \\ 21 & -17 & 4 & 8 \\ 2 & 8 & 27 & 20 \\ 5 & 15 & -3 & -10 \end{bmatrix}$

In Problems 69–72, use the idea behind Example 15 with a graphing utility to solve the following systems of equations. Round answers to two decimal places.

69. $\begin{cases} 25x + 61y - 12z = 10 \\ 18x - 12y + 7y = -9 \\ 3x + 4y - z = 12 \end{cases}$
70. $\begin{cases} 25x + 61y - 12z = 15 \\ 18x - 12y + 7z = -3 \\ 3x + 4y - z = 12 \end{cases}$
71. $\begin{cases} 25x + 61y - 12z = 21 \\ 18x - 12y + 7z = 7 \\ 3x + 4y - z = -2 \end{cases}$
72. $\begin{cases} 25x + 61y - 12z = 25 \\ 18x - 12y + 7z = 10 \\ 3x + 4y - z = -4 \end{cases}$

Mixed Practice

In Problems 73–80, algebraically solve each system of equations using any method you wish.

73. $\begin{cases} 2x + 3y = 11 \\ 5x + 7y = 24 \end{cases}$
74. $\begin{cases} 2x + 8y = -8 \\ x + 7y = -13 \end{cases}$
75. $\begin{cases} x - 2y + 4z = 2 \\ -3x + 5y - 2z = 17 \\ 4x - 3y = -22 \end{cases}$
76. $\begin{cases} 2x + 3y - z = -2 \\ 4x + 3z = 6 \\ 6y - 2z = 2 \end{cases}$

77. $\begin{cases} 5x - y + 4z = 2 \\ -x + 5y - 4z = 3 \\ 7x + 13y - 4z = 17 \end{cases}$
78. $\begin{cases} 3x + 2y - z = 2 \\ 2x + y + 6z = -7 \\ 2x + 2y - 14z = 17 \end{cases}$
79. $\begin{cases} 2x - 3y + z = 4 \\ -3x + 2y - z = -3 \\ -5y + z = 6 \end{cases}$
80. $\begin{cases} -4x + 3y + 2z = 6 \\ 3x + y - z = -2 \\ x + 9y + z = 6 \end{cases}$

Applications and Extensions

81. College Tuition Nikki and Joe take classes at a community college, LCCC, and a local university, SIUE. The number of credit hours taken and the cost per credit hour (2006–2007 academic year, tuition only) are as follows:

	LCCC	SIUE
Nikki	6	9
Joe	3	12

Cost per Credit Hour	
LCCC	$71.00
SIUE	$158.60

(a) Write a matrix A for the credit hours taken by each student and a matrix B for the cost per credit hour.
(b) Compute AB and interpret the results.
Sources: www.lc.edu, www.siue.edu

82. School Loan Interest Jamal and Stephanie each have school loans issued from the same two banks. The amounts borrowed and the monthly interest rates are given next (interest is compounded monthly):

	Lender 1	Lender 2
Jamal	$4000	$3000
Stephanie	$2500	$3800

Monthly Interest Rate	
Lender 1	0.011 (1.1%)
Lender 2	0.006 (0.6%)

(a) Write a matrix A for the amounts borrowed by each student and a matrix B for the monthly interest rates.
(b) Compute AB and interpret the results.

(c) Let $C = \begin{bmatrix} 1 \\ 1 \end{bmatrix}$. Compute $A(C + B)$ and interpret the results.

83. Computing the Cost of Production The Acme Steel Company is a producer of stainless steel and aluminum containers. On a certain day, the following stainless steel containers were manufactured: 500 with 10-gallon (gal) capacity, 350 with 5-gal capacity, and 400 with 1-gal capacity. On the same day, the following aluminum containers were manufactured: 700 with 10-gal capacity, 500 with 5-gal capacity, and 850 with 1-gal capacity.
(a) Find a 2 by 3 matrix representing these data. Find a 3 by 2 matrix to represent the same data.
(b) If the amount of material used in the 10-gal containers is 15 pounds (lb), the amount used in the 5-gal containers is 8 lb, and the amount used in the 1-gal containers is 3 lb, find a 3 by 1 matrix representing the amount of material used.
(c) Multiply the 2 by 3 matrix found in part (a) and the 3 by 1 matrix found in part (b) to get a 2 by 1 matrix showing the day's usage of material.
(d) If stainless steel costs Acme $0.10 lb and aluminum costs $0.05 lb, find a 1 by 2 matrix representing cost.
(e) Multiply the matrices found in parts (c) and (d) to determine the total cost of the day's production.

84. Computing Profit Rizza Ford has two locations, one in the city and the other in the suburbs. In January, the city location sold 400 subcompacts, 250 intermediate-size cars, and 50 SUVs; in February, it sold 350 subcompacts, 100 intermediates, and 30 SUVs. At the suburban location in January, 450 subcompacts, 200 intermediates, and 140 SUVs were sold.

In February, the suburban location sold 350 subcompacts, 300 intermediates, and 100 SUVs.

(a) Find 2 by 3 matrices that summarize the sales data for each location for January and February (one matrix for each month).

(b) Use matrix addition to obtain total sales for the 2-month period.

(c) The profit on each kind of car is $100 per subcompact, $150 per intermediate, and $200 per SUV. Find a 3 by 1 matrix representing this profit.

(d) Multiply the matrices found in parts (b) and (c) to get a 2 by 1 matrix showing the profit at each location.

85. Cryptography One method of encryption is to use a matrix to encrypt the message and then use the corresponding inverse matrix to decode the message. The encrypted matrix, E, is obtained by multiplying the message matrix, M, by a key matrix, K. The original message can be retrieved by multiplying the encrypted matrix by the inverse of the key matrix. That is, $E = M \cdot K$ and $M = E \cdot K^{-1}$.

(a) Given the key matrix $K = \begin{bmatrix} 2 & 1 & 1 \\ 1 & 1 & 0 \\ 1 & 1 & 1 \end{bmatrix}$, find its inverse, K^{-1}. [**Note:** This key matrix is known as the Q_2^3 Fibonacci encryption matrix.]

(b) Use your result from part (a) to decode the encrypted matrix $E = \begin{bmatrix} 47 & 34 & 33 \\ 44 & 36 & 27 \\ 47 & 41 & 20 \end{bmatrix}$.

(c) Each entry in your result for part (b) represents the position of a letter in the English alphabet ($A = 1$, $B = 2$, $C = 3$, and so on). What is the original message?
Source: goldenmuseum.com

86. Economic Mobility The relative income of a child (low, medium, or high) generally depends on the relative income of the child's parents. The matrix P, given by

Parent's Income

$$P = \begin{matrix} & \begin{matrix} L & M & H \end{matrix} & \\ \begin{bmatrix} 0.4 & 0.2 & 0.1 \\ 0.5 & 0.6 & 0.5 \\ 0.1 & 0.2 & 0.4 \end{bmatrix} & \begin{matrix} L \\ M \\ H \end{matrix} & \text{Child's income} \end{matrix}$$

is called a *left stochastic transition matrix*. For example, the entry $P_{21} = 0.5$ means that 50% of the children of low relative income parents will transition to the medium level of income. The diagonal entry P_{ii} represents the percent of children who remain in the same income level as their parents. Assuming the transition matrix is valid from one generation to the next, compute and interpret P^2.
Source: Understanding Mobility in America, April 2006

87. Consider the 2 by 2 square matrix

$$A = \begin{bmatrix} a & b \\ c & d \end{bmatrix}$$

If $D = ad - bc \neq 0$, show that A is nonsingular and that

$$A^{-1} = \frac{1}{D} \begin{bmatrix} d & -b \\ -c & a \end{bmatrix}$$

Discussion and Writing

88. Create a situation different from any found in the text that can be represented by a matrix.

11.5 Partial Fraction Decomposition

PREPARING FOR THIS SECTION *Before getting started, review the following:*

- Identity (Appendix A, Section A.6, p. A46)
- Proper and Improper Rational Functions (Section 4.2, pp. 196–197)

- Factoring Polynomials (Appendix A, Section A.3, pp. A28–A29)
- Complex Zeros; Fundamental Theorem of Algebra (Section 4.6, p. 234)

Now Work the 'Are You Prepared?' problems on page 769.

OBJECTIVES 1 Decompose $\dfrac{P}{Q}$, Where Q Has Only Nonrepeated Linear Factors (p. 763)

2 Decompose $\dfrac{P}{Q}$, Where Q Has Repeated Linear Factors (p. 765)

3 Decompose $\dfrac{P}{Q}$, Where Q Has a Nonrepeated Irreducible Quadratic Factor (p. 767)

4 Decompose $\dfrac{P}{Q}$, Where Q Has a Repeated Irreducible Quadratic Factor (p. 768)

Consider the problem of adding two rational expressions:

$$\frac{3}{x+4} \quad \text{and} \quad \frac{2}{x-3}$$

The result is

$$\frac{3}{x+4} + \frac{2}{x-3} = \frac{3(x-3) + 2(x+4)}{(x+4)(x-3)} = \frac{5x-1}{x^2+x-12}$$

The reverse procedure, of starting with the rational expression $\dfrac{5x-1}{x^2+x-12}$ and writing it as the sum (or difference) of the two simpler fractions $\dfrac{3}{x+4}$ and $\dfrac{2}{x-3}$, is referred to as **partial fraction decomposition,** and the two simpler fractions are called **partial fractions.** Decomposing a rational expression into a sum of partial fractions is important in solving certain types of calculus problems. This section presents a systematic way to decompose rational expressions.

We begin by recalling that a rational expression is the ratio of two polynomials, say, P and $Q \neq 0$. We assume that P and Q have no common factors. Recall also that a rational expression $\dfrac{P}{Q}$ is called **proper** if the degree of the polynomial in the numerator is less than the degree of the polynomial in the denominator. Otherwise, the rational expression is termed **improper.**

Because any improper rational expression can be reduced by long division to a mixed form consisting of the sum of a polynomial and a proper rational expression, we shall restrict the discussion that follows to proper rational expressions.

The partial fraction decomposition of the rational expression $\dfrac{P}{Q}$ depends on the factors of the denominator Q. Recall from Section 4.6 that any polynomial whose coefficients are real numbers can be factored (over the real numbers) into products of linear and/or irreducible quadratic factors. This means that the denominator Q of the rational expression $\dfrac{P}{Q}$ will contain only factors of one or both of the following types:

1. *Linear factors* of the form $x - a$, where a is a real number.
2. *Irreducible quadratic factors* of the form $ax^2 + bx + c$, where a, b, and c are real numbers, $a \neq 0$, and $b^2 - 4ac < 0$ (which guarantees that $ax^2 + bx + c$ cannot be written as the product of two linear factors with real coefficients).

As it turns out, there are four cases to be examined. We begin with the case for which Q has only nonrepeated linear factors.

1 Decompose $\dfrac{P}{Q}$, Where Q Has Only Nonrepeated Linear Factors

Case 1:   Q has only nonrepeated linear factors.

Under the assumption that Q has only nonrepeated linear factors, the polynomial Q has the form

$$Q(x) = (x - a_1)(x - a_2) \cdot \cdots \cdot (x - a_n)$$

where none of the numbers $a_1, a_2, \ldots, a_n$ is equal. In this case, the partial fraction decomposition of $\dfrac{P}{Q}$ is of the form

$$\frac{P(x)}{Q(x)} = \frac{A_1}{x - a_1} + \frac{A_2}{x - a_2} + \cdots + \frac{A_n}{x - a_n} \tag{1}$$

where the numbers $A_1, A_2, \ldots, A_n$ are to be determined.

We show how to find these numbers in the example that follows.

EXAMPLE 1 | **Nonrepeated Linear Factors**

Write the partial fraction decomposition of $\dfrac{x}{x^2 - 5x + 6}$.

Solution First, we factor the denominator,

$$x^2 - 5x + 6 = (x - 2)(x - 3)$$

and conclude that the denominator contains only nonrepeated linear factors. Then we decompose the rational expression according to equation (1):

$$\frac{x}{x^2 - 5x + 6} = \frac{A}{x - 2} + \frac{B}{x - 3} \tag{2}$$

where A and B are to be determined. To find A and B, we clear the fractions by multiplying each side by $(x - 2)(x - 3) = x^2 - 5x + 6$. The result is

$$x = A(x - 3) + B(x - 2) \tag{3}$$

or

$$x = (A + B)x + (-3A - 2B)$$

This equation is an identity in x. We equate the coefficients of like powers of x to get

$$\begin{cases} 1 = A + B & \text{Equate coefficients of } x: 1x = (A + B)x. \\ 0 = -3A - 2B & \text{Equate the constants: } 0 = -3A - 2B. \end{cases}$$

This system of two equations containing two variables, A and B, can be solved using whatever method you wish. Solving it, we get

$$A = -2 \qquad B = 3$$

From equation (2), the partial fraction decomposition is

$$\frac{x}{x^2 - 5x + 6} = \frac{-2}{x - 2} + \frac{3}{x - 3}$$

✓ **Check:** The decomposition can be checked by adding the rational expressions.

$$\frac{-2}{x - 2} + \frac{3}{x - 3} = \frac{-2(x - 3) + 3(x - 2)}{(x - 2)(x - 3)} = \frac{x}{(x - 2)(x - 3)}$$

$$= \frac{x}{x^2 - 5x + 6}$$

The numbers to be found in the partial fraction decomposition can sometimes be found more readily by using suitable choices for x (which may include complex numbers) in the identity obtained after fractions have been cleared. In Example 1, the identity after clearing fractions is equation (3):

$$x = A(x - 3) + B(x - 2)$$

If we let $x = 2$ in this expression, the term containing B drops out, leaving $2 = A(-1)$, or $A = -2$. Similarly, if we let $x = 3$, the term containing A drops out, leaving $3 = B$. As before, $A = -2$ and $B = 3$.

━━━ **Now Work** PROBLEM 13

2 Decompose $\dfrac{P}{Q}$, Where Q Has Repeated Linear Factors

Case 2: Q has repeated linear factors.

If the polynomial Q has a repeated linear factor, say $(x - a)^n, n \geq 2$ an integer, then, in the partial fraction decomposition of $\dfrac{P}{Q}$, we allow for the terms

$$\frac{A_1}{x - a} + \frac{A_2}{(x - a)^2} + \cdots + \frac{A_n}{(x - a)^n}$$

where the numbers $A_1, A_2, \ldots, A_n$ are to be determined.

| EXAMPLE 2 | **Repeated Linear Factors** |

Write the partial fraction decomposition of $\dfrac{x + 2}{x^3 - 2x^2 + x}$.

Solution First, we factor the denominator,

$$x^3 - 2x^2 + x = x(x^2 - 2x + 1) = x(x - 1)^2$$

and find that the denominator has the nonrepeated linear factor x and the repeated linear factor $(x - 1)^2$. By Case 1, we must allow for the term $\dfrac{A}{x}$ in the decomposition; and by Case 2 we must allow for the terms $\dfrac{B}{x - 1} + \dfrac{C}{(x - 1)^2}$ in the decomposition.
We write

$$\frac{x + 2}{x^3 - 2x^2 + x} = \frac{A}{x} + \frac{B}{x - 1} + \frac{C}{(x - 1)^2} \tag{4}$$

Again, we clear fractions by multiplying each side by $x^3 - 2x^2 + x = x(x - 1)^2$. The result is the identity

$$x + 2 = A(x - 1)^2 + Bx(x - 1) + Cx \tag{5}$$

If we let $x = 0$ in this expression, the terms containing B and C drop out, leaving $2 = A(-1)^2$, or $A = 2$. Similarly, if we let $x = 1$, the terms containing A and B drop out, leaving $3 = C$. Then equation (5) becomes

$$x + 2 = 2(x - 1)^2 + Bx(x - 1) + 3x$$

Now let $x = 2$ (any choice other than 0 or 1 will work as well). The result is

$$4 = 2(1)^2 + B(2)(1) + 3(2)$$

$$4 = 2 + 2B + 6$$

$$2B = -4$$

$$B = -2$$

We have $A = 2$, $B = -2$, and $C = 3$.
From equation (4), the partial fraction decomposition is

$$\frac{x + 2}{x^3 - 2x^2 + x} = \frac{2}{x} + \frac{-2}{x - 1} + \frac{3}{(x - 1)^2}$$

| EXAMPLE 3 | **Repeated Linear Factors** |

Write the partial fraction decomposition of $\dfrac{x^3 - 8}{x^2(x - 1)^3}$.

Solution   The denominator contains the repeated linear factor x^2 and the repeated linear factor $(x - 1)^3$. The partial fraction decomposition takes the form

$$\frac{x^3 - 8}{x^2(x - 1)^3} = \frac{A}{x} + \frac{B}{x^2} + \frac{C}{x - 1} + \frac{D}{(x - 1)^2} + \frac{E}{(x - 1)^3} \quad \textbf{(6)}$$

As before, we clear fractions and obtain the identity

$$x^3 - 8 = Ax(x - 1)^3 + B(x - 1)^3 + Cx^2(x - 1)^2 + Dx^2(x - 1) + Ex^2 \quad \textbf{(7)}$$

Let $x = 0$. (Do you see why this choice was made?) Then

$$-8 = B(-1)$$

$$B = 8$$

Now let $x = 1$ in equation (7). Then

$$-7 = E$$

Use $B = 8$ and $E = -7$ in equation (7) and collect like terms.

$$x^3 - 8 = Ax(x - 1)^3 + 8(x - 1)^3$$
$$+ Cx^2(x - 1)^2 + Dx^2(x - 1) - 7x^2$$
$$x^3 - 8 - 8(x^3 - 3x^2 + 3x - 1) + 7x^2 = Ax(x - 1)^3 + Cx^2(x - 1)^2 + Dx^2(x - 1)$$
$$-7x^3 + 31x^2 - 24x = x(x - 1)[A(x - 1)^2 + Cx(x - 1) + Dx]$$
$$x(x - 1)(-7x + 24) = x(x - 1)[A(x - 1)^2 + Cx(x - 1) + Dx]$$
$$-7x + 24 = A(x - 1)^2 + Cx(x - 1) + Dx \quad \textbf{(8)}$$

We now work with equation (8). Let $x = 0$. Then

$$24 = A$$

Now let $x = 1$ in equation (8). Then

$$17 = D$$

Use $A = 24$ and $D = 17$ in equation (8).

$$-7x + 24 = 24(x - 1)^2 + Cx(x - 1) + 17x$$

Now let $x = 2$ and simplify.

$$-14 + 24 = 24 + C(2) + 34$$

$$-48 = 2C$$

$$-24 = C$$

We now know all the numbers A, B, C, D, and E, so, from equation (6), we have the decomposition

$$\frac{x^3 - 8}{x^2(x - 1)^3} = \frac{24}{x} + \frac{8}{x^2} + \frac{-24}{x - 1} + \frac{17}{(x - 1)^2} + \frac{-7}{(x - 1)^3}$$

━━━━━ **Now Work Example 3 by solving the system of five equations containing five variables that the expansion of equation (7) leads to.**

━━━━━ **Now Work** PROBLEM 19

The final two cases involve irreducible quadratic factors. A quadratic factor is irreducible if it cannot be factored into linear factors with real coefficients. A quadratic expression $ax^2 + bx + c$ is irreducible whenever $b^2 - 4ac < 0$. For example, $x^2 + x + 1$ and $x^2 + 4$ are irreducible.

3 Decompose $\dfrac{P}{Q}$, Where Q Has a Nonrepeated Irreducible Quadratic Factor

Case 3: Q contains a nonrepeated irreducible quadratic factor

If Q contains a nonrepeated irreducible quadratic factor of the form $ax^2 + bx + c$, then, in the partial fraction decomposition of $\dfrac{P}{Q}$, allow for the term

$$\frac{Ax + B}{ax^2 + bx + c}$$

where the numbers A and B are to be determined.

EXAMPLE 4   Nonrepeated Irreducible Quadratic Factor

Write the partial fraction decomposition of $\dfrac{3x - 5}{x^3 - 1}$.

Solution   We factor the denominator,

$$x^3 - 1 = (x - 1)(x^2 + x + 1)$$

and find that it has a nonrepeated linear factor $x - 1$ and a nonrepeated irreducible quadratic factor $x^2 + x + 1$. We allow for the term $\dfrac{A}{x - 1}$ by Case 1, and we allow for the term $\dfrac{Bx + C}{x^2 + x + 1}$ by Case 3. We write

$$\frac{3x - 5}{x^3 - 1} = \frac{A}{x - 1} + \frac{Bx + C}{x^2 + x + 1} \tag{9}$$

We clear fractions by multiplying each side of equation (9) by $x^3 - 1 = (x - 1)(x^2 + x + 1)$ to obtain the identity

$$3x - 5 = A(x^2 + x + 1) + (Bx + C)(x - 1) \qquad \textbf{(10)}$$

Expand the identity in (10) to obtain

$$3x - 5 = (A + B)x^2 + (A - B + C)x + (A - C)$$

This identity leads to the system of equations

$$\begin{cases} A + B & = & 0 \quad \text{(1)} \\ A - B + C & = & 3 \quad \text{(2)} \\ A \quad\;\; - C & = & -5 \quad \text{(3)} \end{cases}$$

The solution of this system is $A = -\dfrac{2}{3}, B = \dfrac{2}{3}, C = \dfrac{13}{3}$. Then from equation (9), we see that

$$\frac{3x - 5}{x^3 - 1} = \frac{-\dfrac{2}{3}}{x - 1} + \frac{\dfrac{2}{3}x + \dfrac{13}{3}}{x^2 + x + 1}$$

Now Work Example 4 using equation (10) and assigning values to x.

Now Work PROBLEM 21

4 Decompose $\dfrac{P}{Q}$, Where Q Has a Repeated Irreducible Quadratic Factor

Case 4: Q contains a repeated irreducible quadratic factor.

If the polynomial Q contains a repeated irreducible quadratic factor $(ax^2 + bx + c)^n, n \geq 2, n$ an integer, then, in the partial fraction decomposition of $\dfrac{P}{Q}$, allow for the terms

$$\frac{A_1 x + B_1}{ax^2 + bx + c} + \frac{A_2 x + B_2}{(ax^2 + bx + c)^2} + \cdots + \frac{A_n x + B_n}{(ax^2 + bx + c)^n}$$

where the numbers $A_1, B_1, A_2, B_2, \ldots, A_n, B_n$ are to be determined.

EXAMPLE 5 | **Repeated Irreducible Quadratic Factor**

Write the partial fraction decomposition of $\dfrac{x^3 + x^2}{(x^2 + 4)^2}$.

Solution | The denominator contains the repeated irreducible quadratic factor $(x^2 + 4)^2$, so we write

$$\frac{x^3 + x^2}{(x^2 + 4)^2} = \frac{Ax + B}{x^2 + 4} + \frac{Cx + D}{(x^2 + 4)^2} \qquad \textbf{(11)}$$

We clear fractions to obtain

$$x^3 + x^2 = (Ax + B)(x^2 + 4) + Cx + D$$

Collecting like terms yields the identity

$$x^3 + x^2 = Ax^3 + Bx^2 + (4A + C)x + 4B + D$$

| EXAMPLE 4 | Solving a System of Nonlinear Equations |

$$\text{Solve:} \begin{cases} x^2 + x + y^2 - 3y + 2 = 0 & \text{(1)} \\ x + 1 + \dfrac{y^2 - y}{x} = 0 & \text{(2)} \end{cases}$$

Algebraic Solution Using Elimination

Since it is not straightforward how to graph the equations in the system, we proceed directly to use the method of elimination.

First, we multiply equation (2) by x to eliminate the fraction. The result is an equivalent system because x cannot be 0. [Look at equation (2) to see why.]

$$\begin{cases} x^2 + x + y^2 - 3y + 2 = 0 & \text{(1)} \\ x^2 + x + y^2 - y = 0 & \text{(2)} \end{cases}$$

Now subtract equation (2) from equation (1) to eliminate x. The result is

$$-2y + 2 = 0$$
$$y = 1 \quad \text{Solve for } y.$$

To find x, we back-substitute $y = 1$ in equation (1):

$x^2 + x + y^2 - 3y + 2 = 0$ Equation (1)

$x^2 + x + 1 - 3 + 2 = 0$ Substitute 1 for y in (1).

$x^2 + x = 0$ Simplify.

$x(x + 1) = 0$ Factor.

$x = 0 \quad \text{or} \quad x = -1$ Apply the Zero-Product Property.

Because x cannot be 0, the value $x = 0$ is extraneous, and we discard it.

✓ **Check:** We now check $x = -1$, $y = 1$:

$$\begin{cases} (-1)^2 + (-1) + 1^2 - 3(1) + 2 = 1 - 1 + 1 - 3 + 2 = 0 & \text{(1)} \\ -1 + 1 + \dfrac{1^2 - 1}{-1} = 0 + \dfrac{0}{-1} = 0 & \text{(2)} \end{cases}$$

The solution is $x = -1$, $y = 1$. The point of intersection of the graphs of the equations is $(-1, 1)$.

Graphing Solution

First, we multiply equation (2) by x to eliminate the fraction. The result is an equivalent system because x cannot be 0 [look at equation (2) to see why]:

$$\begin{cases} x^2 + x + y^2 - 3y + 2 = 0 & \text{(1)} \\ x^2 + x + y^2 - y = 0 & \text{(2)} \end{cases}$$

We need to solve each equation for y. First, we solve equation (1) for y:

$x^2 + x + y^2 - 3y + 2 = 0$ Equation (1)

$y^2 - 3y = -x^2 - x - 2$ Rearrange so that terms involving y are on left side.

$y^2 - 3y + \dfrac{9}{4} = -x^2 - x - 2 + \dfrac{9}{4}$ Complete the square involving y.

$\left(y - \dfrac{3}{2}\right)^2 = -x^2 - x + \dfrac{1}{4}$ Factor and simplify.

$y - \dfrac{3}{2} = \pm\sqrt{-x^2 - x + \dfrac{1}{4}}$ Square Root Method

$y = \dfrac{3}{2} \pm \sqrt{-x^2 - x + \dfrac{1}{4}}$ Solve for y.

Now we solve equation (2) for y:

$x^2 + x + y^2 - y = 0$ Equation (2)

$y^2 - y = -x^2 - x$ Rearrange so that terms involving y are on left side.

$y^2 - y + \dfrac{1}{4} = -x^2 - x + \dfrac{1}{4}$ Complete the square involving y.

$\left(y - \dfrac{1}{2}\right)^2 = -x^2 - x + \dfrac{1}{4}$ Factor.

$y - \dfrac{1}{2} = \pm\sqrt{-x^2 - x + \dfrac{1}{4}}$ Square Root Method

$y = \dfrac{1}{2} \pm \sqrt{-x^2 - x + \dfrac{1}{4}}$ Solve for y.

Now graph each equation using a graphing utility. See Figure 23.

Using INTERSECT, the points of intersection are $(-1, 1)$ and $(0, 1)$. Since $x \neq 0$ [look back at the original equation (2)], the graph of Y_3 has a hole at the point $(0, 1)$ and Y_4 has a hole at $(0, 0)$. The value $x = 0$ is extraneous, and we discard it. The only solution is $x = -1$ and $y = 1$.

Figure 23

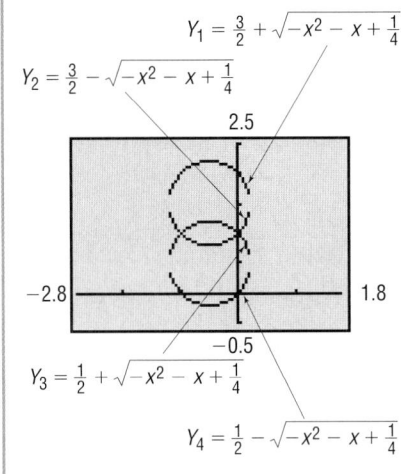

$$Y_1 = \tfrac{3}{2} + \sqrt{-x^2 - x + \tfrac{1}{4}}$$

$$Y_2 = \tfrac{3}{2} - \sqrt{-x^2 - x + \tfrac{1}{4}}$$

$$Y_3 = \tfrac{1}{2} + \sqrt{-x^2 - x + \tfrac{1}{4}}$$

$$Y_4 = \tfrac{1}{2} - \sqrt{-x^2 - x + \tfrac{1}{4}}$$

In Problem 55 you are asked to graph the equations given in Example 4 by hand. Be sure to show holes in the graph of equation (2) at $x = 0$.

Now Work PROBLEMS 29 AND 49

EXAMPLE 5 | **Solving a System of Nonlinear Equations**

Solve: $\begin{cases} 3xy - 2y^2 = -2 & (1) \\ 9x^2 + 4y^2 = 10 & (2) \end{cases}$

Algebraic Solution

We multiply equation (1) by 2 and add the result to equation (2) to eliminate the y^2 terms.

$$\begin{cases} 6xy - 4y^2 = -4 & (1) \\ 9x^2 + 4y^2 = 10 & (2) \end{cases}$$
$$\overline{9x^2 + 6xy = 6} \quad \text{Add.}$$
$$3x^2 + 2xy = 2 \quad \text{Divide each side by 3.}$$

Since $x \neq 0$ (do you see why?), we can solve for y in this equation to get

$$y = \frac{2 - 3x^2}{2x} \qquad x \neq 0 \quad (3)$$

Now substitute for y in equation (2) of the system.

$$9x^2 + 4y^2 = 10 \qquad \text{Equation (2)}$$

$$9x^2 + 4\left(\frac{2 - 3x^2}{2x}\right)^2 = 10 \qquad \text{Substitute } y = \frac{2 - 3x^2}{2x} \text{ in (2).}$$

$$9x^2 + \frac{4 - 12x^2 + 9x^4}{x^2} = 10$$

$$9x^4 + 4 - 12x^2 + 9x^4 = 10x^2 \qquad \text{Multiply both sides by } x^2.$$

$$18x^4 - 22x^2 + 4 = 0 \qquad \text{Subtract } 10x^2 \text{ from both sides.}$$

$$9x^4 - 11x^2 + 2 = 0 \qquad \text{Divide both sides by 2.}$$

Graphing Solution

To graph $3xy - 2y^2 = -2$, we need to solve for y. In this instance, it is easier to view the equation as a quadratic equation in the variable y.

$$3xy - 2y^2 = -2$$

$$2y^2 - 3xy - 2 = 0 \qquad \text{Place in standard form.}$$

$$y = \frac{-(-3x) \pm \sqrt{(-3x)^2 - 4(2)(-2)}}{2(2)}$$

Use the quadratic formula with $a = 2$, $b = -3x$, $c = -2$.

$$y = \frac{3x \pm \sqrt{9x^2 + 16}}{4} \qquad \text{Simplify.}$$

Using a graphing utility, we graph

$$Y_1 = \frac{3x + \sqrt{9x^2 + 16}}{4} \quad \text{and} \quad Y_2 = \frac{3x - \sqrt{9x^2 + 16}}{4}.$$

From equation (2), we graph $Y_3 = \dfrac{\sqrt{10 - 9x^2}}{2}$ and

$$Y_4 = \frac{-\sqrt{10 - 9x^2}}{2}. \text{ See Figure 24.}$$

This quadratic equation (in x^2) can be factored:

$$(9x^2 - 2)(x^2 - 1) = 0$$

$$9x^2 - 2 = 0 \quad \text{or} \quad x^2 - 1 = 0$$

$$x^2 = \frac{2}{9} \qquad\qquad x^2 = 1$$

$$x = \pm\sqrt{\frac{2}{9}} = \pm\frac{\sqrt{2}}{3} \qquad x = \pm 1$$

To find y, we use equation (3):

If $x = \dfrac{\sqrt{2}}{3}$: $\quad y = \dfrac{2 - 3x^2}{2x} = \dfrac{2 - \dfrac{2}{3}}{2\left(\dfrac{\sqrt{2}}{3}\right)} = \dfrac{4}{2\sqrt{2}} = \sqrt{2}$

If $x = -\dfrac{\sqrt{2}}{3}$: $\quad y = \dfrac{2 - 3x^2}{2x} = \dfrac{2 - \dfrac{2}{3}}{2\left(-\dfrac{\sqrt{2}}{3}\right)} = \dfrac{4}{-2\sqrt{2}} = -\sqrt{2}$

If $x = 1$: $\quad y = \dfrac{2 - 3x^2}{2x} = \dfrac{2 - 3(1)^2}{2} = -\dfrac{1}{2}$

If $x = -1$: $\quad y = \dfrac{2 - 3x^2}{2x} = \dfrac{2 - 3(-1)^2}{-2} = \dfrac{1}{2}$

The system has four solutions: $\left(\dfrac{\sqrt{2}}{3}, \sqrt{2}\right), \left(-\dfrac{\sqrt{2}}{3}, -\sqrt{2}\right),$ $\left(1, -\dfrac{1}{2}\right),$ and $\left(-1, \dfrac{1}{2}\right).$ Check them for yourself.

Figure 24

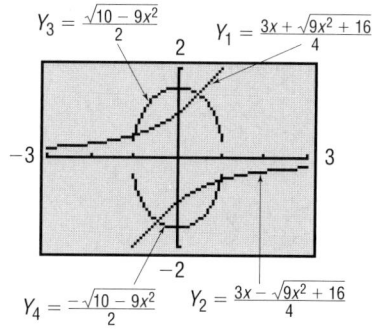

$Y_3 = \dfrac{\sqrt{10 - 9x^2}}{2}$ $\qquad Y_1 = \dfrac{3x + \sqrt{9x^2 + 16}}{4}$

$Y_4 = \dfrac{-\sqrt{10 - 9x^2}}{2}$ $\qquad Y_2 = \dfrac{3x - \sqrt{9x^2 + 16}}{4}$

Using INTERSECT, the solutions to the system of equations are $(-1, 0.5), (0.47, 1.41), (1, -0.5),$ and $(-0.47, -1.41)$, each rounded to two decimal places.

Now Work PROBLEM 47

The next example illustrates an imaginative solution to a system of nonlinear equations.

EXAMPLE 6 **Running a Long-distance Race**

In a 50-mile race, the winner crosses the finish line 1 mile ahead of the second-place runner and 4 miles ahead of the third-place runner. Assuming that each runner maintains a constant speed throughout the race, by how many miles does the second-place runner beat the third-place runner?

|◄——— 3 miles ———►|◄— 1 mile —►|

Solution Let v_1, v_2, and v_3 denote the speeds of the first-, second-, and third-place runners, respectively. Let t_1 and t_2 denote the times (in hours) required for the first-place runner and second-place runner to finish the race. Then we have the system of equations

$$\begin{cases} 50 = v_1 t_1 & \text{(1) First-place runner goes 50 miles in } t_1 \text{ hours.} \\ 49 = v_2 t_1 & \text{(2) Second-place runner goes 49 miles in } t_1 \text{ hours.} \\ 46 = v_3 t_1 & \text{(3) Third-place runner goes 46 miles in } t_1 \text{ hours.} \\ 50 = v_2 t_2 & \text{(4) Second-place runner goes 50 miles in } t_2 \text{ hours.} \end{cases}$$

We seek the distance d of the third-place runner from the finish at time t_2. At time t_2, the third-place runner has gone a distance of $v_3 t_2$ miles, so the distance d remaining is $50 - v_3 t_2$. Now

$$d = 50 - v_3 t_2$$

$$= 50 - v_3 \left(t_1 \cdot \frac{t_2}{t_1} \right)$$

$$= 50 - (v_3 t_1) \cdot \frac{t_2}{t_1}$$

$$= 50 - 46 \cdot \frac{\dfrac{50}{v_2}}{\dfrac{50}{v_1}} \qquad \left\{ \begin{array}{l} \text{From (3), } v_3 t_1 = 46 \\[2mm] \text{From (4), } t_2 = \dfrac{50}{v_2} \\[2mm] \text{From (1), } t_1 = \dfrac{50}{v_1} \end{array} \right.$$

$$= 50 - 46 \cdot \frac{v_1}{v_2}$$

$$= 50 - 46 \cdot \frac{50}{49} \qquad \text{From the quotient of (1) and (2)}$$

$$\approx 3.06 \text{ miles}$$

The second place runner beats the third place runner by approximately 3.06 miles.

Historical Feature

In the beginning of this section, we said that imagination and experience are important in solving systems of nonlinear equations. Indeed, these kinds of problems lead into some of the deepest and most difficult parts of modern mathematics. Look again at the graphs in Examples 1 and 2 of this section (Figures 17 and 19). We see that Example 1 has two solutions, and Example 2 has four solutions. We might conjecture that the number of solutions is equal to the product of the degrees of the equations involved. This conjecture was indeed made by Etienne Bezout (1730–1783), but working out the details took about 150 years. It turns out that, to arrive at the correct number of intersections, we must count not only the complex number intersections, but also those intersections that, in a certain sense, lie at infinity. For example, a parabola and a line lying on the axis of the parabola intersect at the vertex and at infinity. This topic is part of the study of algebraic geometry.

Historical Problem

A papyrus dating back to 1950 BC contains the following problem: "A given surface area of 100 units of area shall be represented as the sum of two squares whose sides are to each other as $1 : \frac{3}{4}$." Solve for the sides by solving the system of equations

$$\begin{cases} x^2 + y^2 = 100 \\ x = \dfrac{3}{4} y \end{cases}$$

11.6 Assess Your Understanding

'Are You Prepared?'

Answers are given at the end of these exercises. If you get a wrong answer, read the pages listed in red.

1. Graph the equation: $y = 3x + 2$ (pp. 34–36)

2. Graph the equation: $y + 4 = x^2$ (pp. 639–643)

3. Graph the equation: $y^2 = x^2 - 1$ (pp. 659–664)

4. Graph the equation: $x^2 + 4y^2 = 4$ (pp. 648–653)

Skill Building

In Problems 5–24, graph each equation of the system by hand. Then solve the system to find the points of intersection.

5. $\begin{cases} y = x^2 + 1 \\ y = x + 1 \end{cases}$

6. $\begin{cases} y = x^2 + 1 \\ y = 4x + 1 \end{cases}$

7. $\begin{cases} y = \sqrt{36 - x^2} \\ y = 8 - x \end{cases}$

8. $\begin{cases} y = \sqrt{4 - x^2} \\ y = 2x + 4 \end{cases}$

9. $\begin{cases} y = \sqrt{x} \\ y = 2 - x \end{cases}$

10. $\begin{cases} y = \sqrt{x} \\ y = 6 - x \end{cases}$

11. $\begin{cases} x = 2y \\ x = y^2 - 2y \end{cases}$

12. $\begin{cases} y = x - 1 \\ y = x^2 - 6x + 9 \end{cases}$

13. $\begin{cases} x^2 + y^2 = 4 \\ x^2 + 2x + y^2 = 0 \end{cases}$

14. $\begin{cases} x^2 + y^2 = 8 \\ x^2 + y^2 + 4y = 0 \end{cases}$

15. $\begin{cases} y = 3x - 5 \\ x^2 + y^2 = 5 \end{cases}$

16. $\begin{cases} x^2 + y^2 = 10 \\ y = x + 2 \end{cases}$

17. $\begin{cases} x^2 + y^2 = 4 \\ y^2 - x = 4 \end{cases}$

18. $\begin{cases} x^2 + y^2 = 16 \\ x^2 - 2y = 8 \end{cases}$

19. $\begin{cases} xy = 4 \\ x^2 + y^2 = 8 \end{cases}$

20. $\begin{cases} x^2 = y \\ xy = 1 \end{cases}$

21. $\begin{cases} x^2 + y^2 = 4 \\ y = x^2 - 9 \end{cases}$

22. $\begin{cases} xy = 1 \\ y = 2x + 1 \end{cases}$

23. $\begin{cases} y = x^2 - 4 \\ y = 6x - 13 \end{cases}$

24. $\begin{cases} x^2 + y^2 = 10 \\ xy = 3 \end{cases}$

In Problems 25–54, solve each system. Use any method you wish.

25. $\begin{cases} 2x^2 + y^2 = 18 \\ xy = 4 \end{cases}$

26. $\begin{cases} x^2 - y^2 = 21 \\ x + y = 7 \end{cases}$

27. $\begin{cases} y = 2x + 1 \\ 2x^2 + y^2 = 1 \end{cases}$

28. $\begin{cases} x^2 - 4y^2 = 16 \\ 2y - x = 2 \end{cases}$

29. $\begin{cases} x + y + 1 = 0 \\ x^2 + y^2 + 6y - x = -5 \end{cases}$

30. $\begin{cases} 2x^2 - xy + y^2 = 8 \\ xy = 4 \end{cases}$

31. $\begin{cases} 4x^2 - 3xy + 9y^2 = 15 \\ 2x + 3y = 5 \end{cases}$

32. $\begin{cases} 2y^2 - 3xy + 6y + 2x + 4 = 0 \\ 2x - 3y + 4 = 0 \end{cases}$

33. $\begin{cases} x^2 - 4y^2 + 7 = 0 \\ 3x^2 + y^2 = 31 \end{cases}$

34. $\begin{cases} 3x^2 - 2y^2 + 5 = 0 \\ 2x^2 - y^2 + 2 = 0 \end{cases}$

35. $\begin{cases} 7x^2 - 3y^2 + 5 = 0 \\ 3x^2 + 5y^2 = 12 \end{cases}$

36. $\begin{cases} x^2 - 3y^2 + 1 = 0 \\ 2x^2 - 7y^2 + 5 = 0 \end{cases}$

37. $\begin{cases} x^2 + 2xy = 10 \\ 3x^2 - xy = 2 \end{cases}$

38. $\begin{cases} 5xy + 13y^2 + 36 = 0 \\ xy + 7y^2 = 6 \end{cases}$

39. $\begin{cases} 2x^2 + y^2 = 2 \\ x^2 - 2y^2 + 8 = 0 \end{cases}$

40. $\begin{cases} y^2 - x^2 + 4 = 0 \\ 2x^2 + 3y^2 = 6 \end{cases}$

41. $\begin{cases} x^2 + 2y^2 = 16 \\ 4x^2 - y^2 = 24 \end{cases}$

42. $\begin{cases} 4x^2 + 3y^2 = 4 \\ 2x^2 - 6y^2 = -3 \end{cases}$

43. $\begin{cases} \dfrac{5}{x^2} - \dfrac{2}{y^2} + 3 = 0 \\ \dfrac{3}{x^2} + \dfrac{1}{y^2} = 7 \end{cases}$

44. $\begin{cases} \dfrac{2}{x^2} - \dfrac{3}{y^2} + 1 = 0 \\ \dfrac{6}{x^2} - \dfrac{7}{y^2} + 2 = 0 \end{cases}$

45. $\begin{cases} \dfrac{1}{x^4} + \dfrac{6}{y^4} = 6 \\ \dfrac{2}{x^4} - \dfrac{2}{y^4} = 19 \end{cases}$

46. $\begin{cases} \dfrac{1}{x^4} - \dfrac{1}{y^4} = 1 \\ \dfrac{1}{x^4} + \dfrac{1}{y^4} = 4 \end{cases}$

47. $\begin{cases} x^2 - 3xy + 2y^2 = 0 \\ x^2 + xy = 6 \end{cases}$

48. $\begin{cases} x^2 - xy - 2y^2 = 0 \\ xy + x + 6 = 0 \end{cases}$

49. $\begin{cases} y^2 + y + x^2 - x - 2 = 0 \\ y + 1 + \dfrac{x - 2}{y} = 0 \end{cases}$

50. $\begin{cases} x^3 - 2x^2 + y^2 + 3y - 4 = 0 \\ x - 2 + \dfrac{y^2 - y}{x^2} = 0 \end{cases}$

51. $\begin{cases} \log_x y = 3 \\ \log_x(4y) = 5 \end{cases}$

52. $\begin{cases} \log_x(2y) = 3 \\ \log_x(4y) = 2 \end{cases}$

53. $\begin{cases} \ln x = 4 \ln y \\ \log_3 x = 2 + 2 \log_3 y \end{cases}$

54. $\begin{cases} \ln x = 5 \ln y \\ \log_2 x = 3 + 2 \log_2 y \end{cases}$

55. Graph the equations given in Example 4.

56. Graph the equations given in Problem 49.

In Problems 57–64, use a graphing utility to solve each system of equations. Express the solution(s) rounded to two decimal places.

57. $\begin{cases} y = x^{2/3} \\ y = e^{-x} \end{cases}$

58. $\begin{cases} y = x^{3/2} \\ y = e^{-x} \end{cases}$

59. $\begin{cases} x^2 + y^3 = 2 \\ x^3 y = 4 \end{cases}$

60. $\begin{cases} x^3 + y^2 = 2 \\ x^2 y = 4 \end{cases}$

61. $\begin{cases} x^4 + y^4 = 12 \\ xy^2 = 2 \end{cases}$

62. $\begin{cases} x^4 + y^4 = 6 \\ xy = 1 \end{cases}$

63. $\begin{cases} xy = 2 \\ y = \ln x \end{cases}$

64. $\begin{cases} x^2 + y^2 = 4 \\ y = \ln x \end{cases}$

Mixed Practice

In Problems 65–70, graph each equation and find the point(s) of intersection, if any.

65. The line $x + 2y = 0$ and
the circle $(x - 1)^2 + (y - 1)^2 = 5$

66. The line $x + 2y + 6 = 0$ and
the circle $(x + 1)^2 + (y + 1)^2 = 5$

67. The circle $(x - 1)^2 + (y + 2)^2 = 4$ and
the parabola $y^2 + 4y - x + 1 = 0$

68. The circle $(x + 2)^2 + (y - 1)^2 = 4$ and
the parabola $y^2 - 2y - x - 5 = 0$

69. $y = \dfrac{4}{x - 3}$ and the circle $x^2 - 6x + y^2 + 1 = 0$

70. $y = \dfrac{4}{x + 2}$ and the circle $x^2 + 4x + y^2 - 4 = 0$

Applications and Extensions

71. The difference of two numbers is 2 and the sum of their squares is 10. Find the numbers.

72. The sum of two numbers is 7 and the difference of their squares is 21. Find the numbers.

73. The product of two numbers is 4 and the sum of their squares is 8. Find the numbers.

74. The product of two numbers is 10 and the difference of their squares is 21. Find the numbers.

75. The difference of two numbers is the same as their product, and the sum of their reciprocals is 5. Find the numbers.

76. The sum of two numbers is the same as their product, and the difference of their reciprocals is 3. Find the numbers.

77. The ratio of a to b is $\dfrac{2}{3}$. The sum of a and b is 10. What is the ratio of $a + b$ to $b - a$?

78. The ratio of a to b is $4 : 3$. The sum of a and b is 14. What is the ratio of $a - b$ to $a + b$?

79. Geometry The perimeter of a rectangle is 16 inches and its area is 15 square inches. What are its dimensions?

80. Geometry An area of 52 square feet is to be enclosed by two squares whose sides are in the ratio of $2 : 3$. Find the sides of the squares.

81. Geometry Two circles have circumferences that add up to 12π centimeters and areas that add up to 20π square centimeters. Find the radius of each circle.

82. Geometry The altitude of an isosceles triangle drawn to its base is 3 centimeters, and its perimeter is 18 centimeters. Find the length of its base.

83. The Tortoise and the Hare In a 21-meter race between a tortoise and a hare, the tortoise leaves 9 minutes before the hare. The hare, by running at an average speed of 0.5 meter per hour faster than the tortoise, crosses the finish line 3 minutes before the tortoise. What are the average speeds of the tortoise and the hare?

84. Running a Race In a 1-mile race, the winner crosses the finish line 10 feet ahead of the second-place runner and 20 feet ahead of the third-place runner. Assuming that each runner maintains a constant speed throughout the race, by how many feet does the second-place runner beat the third-place runner?

85. Constructing a Box A rectangular piece of cardboard, whose area is 216 square centimeters, is made into an open box by cutting a 2-centimeter square from each corner and turning up the sides. See the figure. If the box is to have a volume of 224 cubic centimeters, what size cardboard should you start with?

86. Constructing a Cylindrical Tube A rectangular piece of cardboard, whose area is 216 square centimeters, is made into a cylindrical tube by joining together two sides of the rectangle. See the figure. If the tube is to have a volume of 224 cubic centimeters, what size cardboard should you start with?

87. Fencing A farmer has 300 feet of fence available to enclose a 4500-square-foot region in the shape of adjoining squares, with sides of length x and y. See the figure. Find x and y.

88. Bending Wire A wire 60 feet long is cut into two pieces. Is it possible to bend one piece into the shape of a square and the other into the shape of a circle so that the total area enclosed by the two pieces is 100 square feet? If this is possible, find the length of the side of the square and the radius of the circle.

89. Geometry Find formulas for the length l and width w of a rectangle in terms of its area A and perimeter P.

90. Geometry Find formulas for the base b and one of the equal sides l of an isosceles triangle in terms of its altitude h and perimeter P.

91. Descartes's Method of Equal Roots Descartes's method for finding tangents depends on the idea that, for many graphs,

the tangent line at a given point is the *unique* line that intersects the graph at that point only. We will apply his method to find an equation of the tangent line to the parabola $y = x^2$ at the point $(2, 4)$. See the figure.

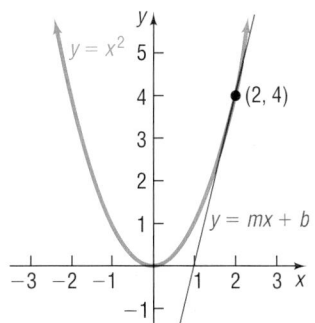

First, we know that the equation of the tangent line must be in the form $y = mx + b$. Using the fact that the point $(2, 4)$ is on the line, we can solve for b in terms of m and get the equation $y = mx + (4 - 2m)$. Now we want $(2, 4)$ to be the *unique* solution to the system

$$\begin{cases} y = x^2 \\ y = mx + 4 - 2m \end{cases}$$

From this system, we get $x^2 - mx + (2m - 4) = 0$. By using the quadratic formula, we get

$$x = \frac{m \pm \sqrt{m^2 - 4(2m - 4)}}{2}$$

To obtain a unique solution for x, the two roots must be equal; in other words, the discriminant $m^2 - 4(2m - 4)$ must be 0. Complete the work to get m, and write an equation of the tangent line.

In Problems 92–98, use Descartes's method from Problem 91 to find the equation of the line tangent to each graph at the given point.

92. $x^2 + y^2 = 10$; at $(1, 3)$

93. $y = x^2 + 2$; at $(1, 3)$

94. $x^2 + y = 5$; at $(-2, 1)$

95. $2x^2 + 3y^2 = 14$; at $(1, 2)$

96. $3x^2 + y^2 = 7$; at $(-1, 2)$

97. $x^2 - y^2 = 3$; at $(2, 1)$

98. $2y^2 - x^2 = 14$; at $(2, 3)$

99. If r_1 and r_2 are two solutions of a quadratic equation $ax^2 + bx + c = 0$, it can be shown that

$$r_1 + r_2 = -\frac{b}{a} \quad \text{and} \quad r_1 r_2 = \frac{c}{a}$$

Solve this system of equations for r_1 and r_2.

Discussion and Writing

100. A circle and a line intersect at most twice. A circle and a parabola intersect at most four times. Deduce that a circle and the graph of a polynomial of degree 3 intersect at most six times. What do you conjecture about a polynomial of degree 4? What about a polynomial of degree n? Can you explain your conclusions using an algebraic argument?

101. Suppose that you are the manager of a sheet metal shop. A customer asks you to manufacture 10,000 boxes, each box being open on top. The boxes are required to have a square

base and a 9-cubic-foot capacity. You construct the boxes by cutting out a square from each corner of a square piece of sheet metal and folding along the edges.

(a) What are the dimensions of the square to be cut if the area of the square piece of sheet metal is 100 square feet?

(b) Could you make the box using a smaller piece of sheet metal? Make a list of the dimensions of the box for various pieces of sheet metal.

'Are You Prepared?' Answers

1.

2.

3.
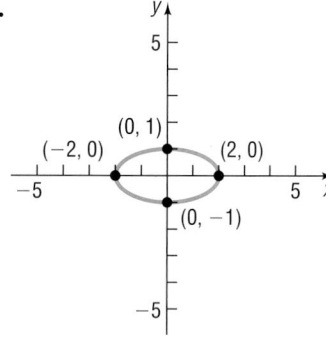

4.

11.7 Systems of Inequalities

PREPARING FOR THIS SECTION   *Before getting started, review the following:*

- Solving Linear Inequalities (Appendix A, Section A.9, pp. A81–A84)
- Lines (Section 1.4, pp. 29–40)
- Circles (Section 1.5, pp. 44–48)
- Graphing Techniques: Transformations (Section 2.5, pp. 100–108)

Now Work the 'Are You Prepared?' problems on page 786.

OBJECTIVES   **1** Graph an Inequality by Hand (p. 780)
   2 Graph an Inequality Using a Graphing Utility (p. 782)
   3 Graph a System of Inequalities (p. 783)

In Appendix A, Section A.9, we discussed inequalities in one variable. In this section, we discuss inequalities in two variables.

EXAMPLE 1   **Examples of Inequalities in Two Variables**

(a) $3x + y \le 6$ (b) $x^2 + y^2 < 4$ (c) $y^2 > x$

---

1 Graph an Inequality by Hand

An inequality in two variables x and y is **satisfied** by an ordered pair (a, b) if, when x is replaced by a and y by b, a true statement results. The **graph of an inequality in two variables** x and y consists of all points (x, y) whose coordinates satisfy the inequality.
    Let's look at an example.

EXAMPLE 2   **Graphing an Inequality by Hand**

Graph the linear inequality: $3x + y \le 6$

Solution   We begin by graphing the equation

$$3x + y = 6$$

formed by replacing (for now) the $\le$ symbol with an $=$ sign. The graph of the equation is a line. See Figure 25(a). This line is part of the graph of the inequality that we seek because the inequality is nonstrict. (Do you see why? We are seeking points for which $3x + y$ is less than *or equal to* 6.)

Figure 25

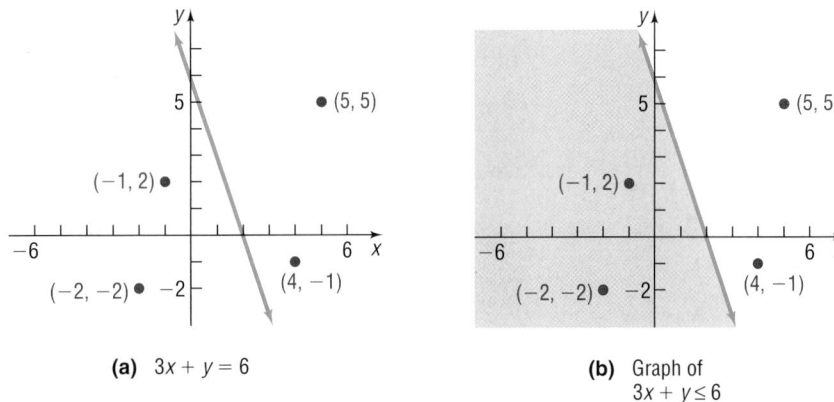

(a) $3x + y = 6$

(b) Graph of $3x + y \le 6$

Now let's test a few randomly selected points to see whether they belong to the graph of the inequality.

	$3x + y \le 6$	Conclusion
$(4, -1)$	$3(4) + (-1) = 11 > 6$	Does not belong to the graph
$(5, 5)$	$3(5) + 5 = 20 > 6$	Does not belong to the graph
$(-1, 2)$	$3(-1) + 2 = -1 \le 6$	Belongs to the graph
$(-2, -2)$	$3(-2) + (-2) = -8 \le 6$	Belongs to the graph

Look again at Figure 25(a). Notice that the two points that belong to the graph both lie on the same side of the line, and the two points that do not belong to the graph lie on the opposite side. As it turns out, this is always the case. The graph we seek consists of all points that lie on the same side of the line as $(-1, 2)$ and $(-2, -2)$ and is shown as the shaded region in Figure 25(b).

━━━━ **Now Work** PROBLEM **15** BY HAND

The graph of any inequality in two variables may be obtained in a like way. The steps to follow are given next.

Steps for Graphing an Inequality by Hand

NOTE The strict inequalities are $<$ and $>$. The nonstrict inequalities are $\le$ and $\ge$. ∎

STEP 1: Replace the inequality symbol by an equal sign and graph the resulting equation. If the inequality is strict, use dashes; if it is nonstrict, use a solid mark. This graph separates the xy-plane into two or more regions.

STEP 2: In each region, select a test point P.

(a) If the coordinates of P satisfy the inequality, so do all the points in that region. Indicate this by shading the region.

(b) If the coordinates of P do not satisfy the inequality, none of the points in that region do.

EXAMPLE 3	Graphing an Inequality by Hand

Graph: $x^2 + y^2 \le 4$

Figure 26

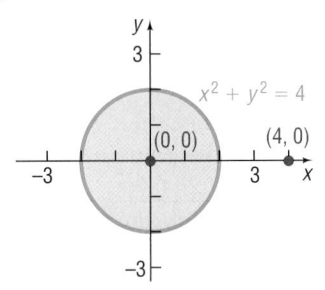

Solution

STEP 1: We graph the equation $x^2 + y^2 = 4$, a circle of radius 2, center at the origin. A solid circle will be used because the inequality is not strict.

STEP 2: We use two test points, one inside the circle, the other outside.

Inside $(0, 0)$: $x^2 + y^2 = 0^2 + 0^2 = 0 \le 4$ *Belongs to the graph*

Outside $(4, 0)$: $x^2 + y^2 = 4^2 + 0^2 = 16 > 4$ *Does not belong to the graph*

All the points inside and on the circle satisfy the inequality. See Figure 26.

━━━━ **Now Work** PROBLEM **17**

Figure 27

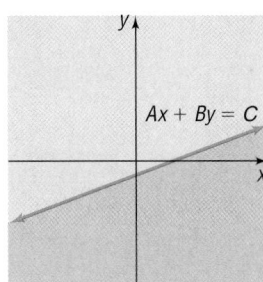

Ax + By = C

Linear Inequalities

Linear inequalities are inequalities in one of the forms

$$Ax + By < C \qquad Ax + By > C \qquad Ax + By \leq C \qquad Ax + By \geq C$$

where A and B are not both zero.

The graph of the corresponding equation of a linear inequality is a line that separates the xy-plane into two regions, called **half-planes.** See Figure 27.

As shown, $Ax + By = C$ is the equation of the boundary line and it divides the plane into two half-planes: one for which $Ax + By < C$ and the other for which $Ax + By > C$. Because of this, for linear inequalities, only one test point is required.

EXAMPLE 4   Graphing Linear Inequalities by Hand

Graph: (a) $y < 2$ (b) $y \geq 2x$

Solution   (a) The graph of the equation $y = 2$ is a dashed horizontal line and so is not part of the graph of the inequality. Since $(0, 0)$ satisfies the inequality, the graph consists of the half-plane below the line $y = 2$. See Figure 28.

(b) The graph of the equation $y = 2x$ is a solid line and so is part of the graph of the inequality. Using $(3, 0)$ as a test point, we find it does not satisfy the inequality $[0 < 2 \cdot 3]$. Points in the half-plane on the opposite side of $(3, 0)$ satisfy the inequality. See Figure 29.

Figure 28

Figure 29

↗ **Now Work** PROBLEM **13** BY HAND

2 Graph an Inequality Using a Graphing Utility

Graphing utilities can also be used to graph inequalities. The steps to follow are given next.

Steps for Graphing an Inequality Using a Graphing Utility

STEP 1: Replace the inequality symbol by an equal sign and graph the resulting equation. This graph separates the xy-plane into two or more regions.

STEP 2: Select a test point P in each region.

(a) Use a graphing utility to determine if the test point P satisfies the inequality. If the test point satisfies the inequality, then so do all the points in this region. Indicate this by using the graphing utility to shade the region.

(b) If the coordinates of P do not satisfy the inequality, then none of the points in that region do.

EXAMPLE 5	Graphing an Inequality Using a Graphing Utility

Use a graphing utility to graph $3x + y \le 6$.

Solution

STEP 1: We begin by graphing the equation $3x + y = 6$ ($Y_1 = -3x + 6$). See Figure 30.

STEP 2: Select a test point in one of the regions and determine whether it satisfies the inequality. To test the point $(-1, 2)$, for example, enter $3(-1) + 2 \le 6$. See Figure 31(a). The 1 that appears indicates that the statement entered (the inequality) is true. When the point $(5, 5)$ is tested, a 0 appears, indicating that the statement entered is false. So $(-1, 2)$ is part of the graph of the inequality and $(5, 5)$ is not. We shade the region containing the point $(-1, 2)$, that is, the region below Y_1. Figure 31(b) shows the graph of the inequality on a TI-84 Plus.

Figure 30

Figure 31

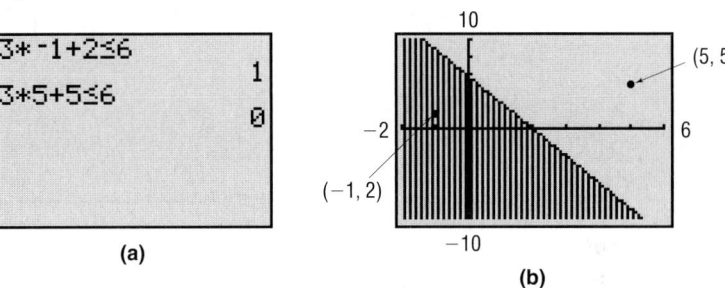

(a)

(b)

━━━━━ **Now Work** PROBLEM **15** USING A GRAPHING UTILITY

3 Graph a System of Inequalities

The **graph of a system of inequalities** in two variables x and y is the set of all points (x, y) that simultaneously satisfy *each* inequality in the system. The graph of a system of inequalities can be obtained by graphing each inequality individually and then determining where, if at all, they intersect.

EXAMPLE 6	Graphing a System of Linear Inequalities by Hand

Graph the system: $\begin{cases} x + y \ge 2 \\ 2x - y \le 4 \end{cases}$

Solution

We begin by graphing the lines $x + y = 2$ and $2x - y = 4$ using solid lines since the inequalities are nonstrict. We use the test point $(0, 0)$ on each inequality. For example, $(0, 0)$ does not satisfy $x + y \ge 2$, so we shade above the line $x + y = 2$. See Figure 32(a). Also, $(0, 0)$ does satisfy $2x - y \le 4$, so we shade above the line $2x - y = 4$. See Figure 32(b). The intersection of the shaded regions gives us the result presented in Figure 32(c).

Figure 32

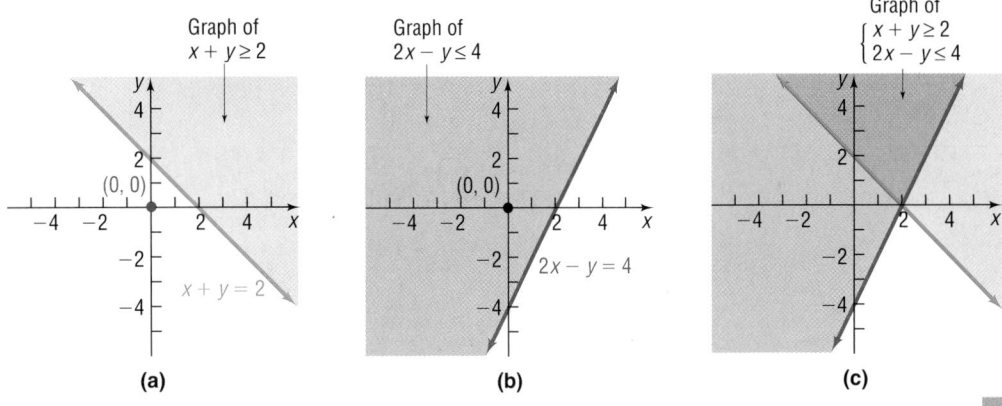

(a)

(b)

(c)

EXAMPLE 7	Graphing a System of Linear Inequalities Using a Graphing Utility

Graph the system: $\begin{cases} x + y \geq 2 \\ 2x - y \leq 4 \end{cases}$

Solution First, we graph the lines $x + y = 2$ ($Y_1 = -x + 2$) and $2x - y = 4$ ($Y_2 = 2x - 4$). See Figure 33.

Notice that the graphs divide the viewing window into four regions. We select a test point for each region and determine whether the point makes *both* inequalities true. We choose to test $(0, 0)$, $(2, 3)$, $(4, 0)$, and $(2, -2)$. Figure 34(a) shows that $(2, 3)$ makes both inequalities true. We obtain the graph shown in Figure 34(b).

Figure 33

Figure 34

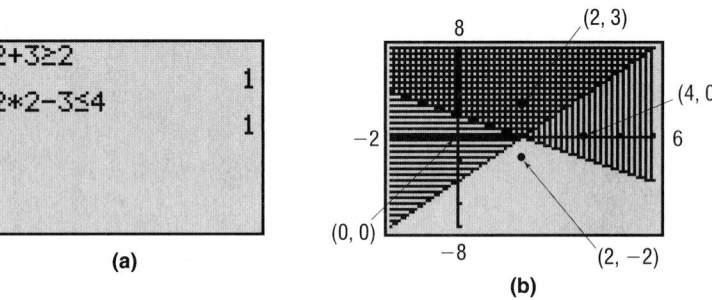

(a)

(b)

Rather than testing four points, we could test just point $(0, 0)$ on each inequality. For example, $(0, 0)$ does not satisfy $x + y \geq 2$, so we shade above the line $x + y = 2$. In addition, $(0, 0)$ does satisfy $2x - y \leq 4$, so we shade above the line $2x - y = 4$. The intersection of the shaded regions gives us the result presented in Figure 34(b).

━━━━━ **Now Work** PROBLEM 23

EXAMPLE 8	Graphing a System of Linear Inequalities by Hand

Graph the system: $\begin{cases} x + y \leq 2 \\ x + y \geq 0 \end{cases}$

Solution See Figure 35. The overlapping purple-shaded region between the two boundary lines is the graph of the system.

Figure 35 $x + y = 0$ $x + y = 2$

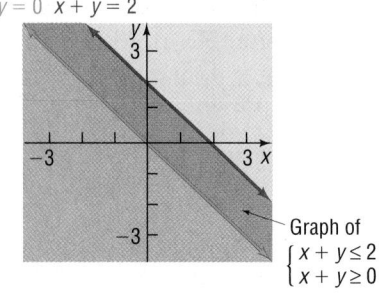

Graph of
$\begin{cases} x + y \leq 2 \\ x + y \geq 0 \end{cases}$

━━━━━ **Now Work** PROBLEM 29

EXAMPLE 9	Graphing a System of Linear Inequalities by Hand

Graph the systems:

(a) $\begin{cases} 2x - y \geq 0 \\ 2x - y \geq 2 \end{cases}$ (b) $\begin{cases} x + 2y \leq 2 \\ x + 2y \geq 6 \end{cases}$

Solution (a) See Figure 36. The overlapping purple-shaded region is the graph of the system. Note that the graph of the system is identical to the graph of the single inequality $2x - y \geq 2$.

(b) See Figure 37. Because no overlapping region results, there are no points in the xy-plane that simultaneously satisfy each inequality. The system has no solution.

Figure 36

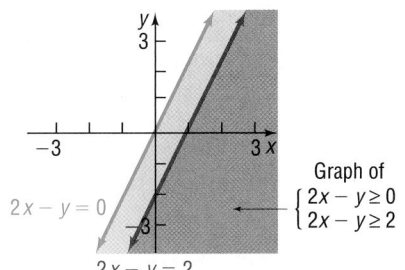

Graph of
$\begin{cases} 2x - y \geq 0 \\ 2x - y \geq 2 \end{cases}$

$2x - y = 0$

$2x - y = 2$

Figure 37

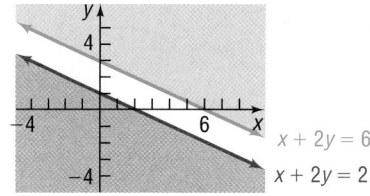

$x + 2y = 6$

$x + 2y = 2$

EXAMPLE 10   **Graphing a System of Nonlinear Inequalities by Hand**

Graph the region below the graph of $x + y = 2$ and above the graph of $y = x^2 - 4$ by graphing the system:

$$\begin{cases} y \geq x^2 - 4 \\ x + y \leq 2 \end{cases}$$

Label all points of intersection.

Figure 38

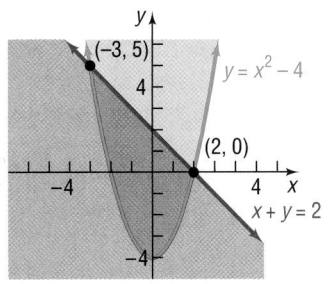

Solution   Figure 38 shows the graph of the region above the graph of the parabola $y = x^2 - 4$ and below the graph of the line $x + y = 2$. The points of intersection are found by solving the system of equations

$$\begin{cases} y = x^2 - 4 \\ x + y = 2 \end{cases}$$

Using substitution, we find

$$x + (x^2 - 4) = 2$$
$$x^2 + x - 6 = 0$$
$$(x + 3)(x - 2) = 0$$
$$x = -3 \quad \text{or} \quad x = 2$$

The two points of intersection are $(-3, 5)$ and $(2, 0)$.

Now Work   PROBLEM 37

EXAMPLE 11   **Graphing a System of Four Linear Inequalities by Hand**

Graph the system: $\begin{cases} x + y \geq 3 \\ 2x + y \geq 4 \\ x \geq 0 \\ y \geq 0 \end{cases}$

Figure 39

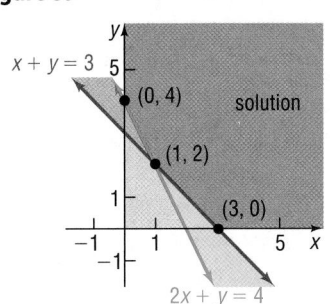

$x + y = 3$

$2x + y = 4$

Solution   See Figure 39. The two inequalities $x \geq 0$ and $y \geq 0$ require the graph of the system to be in quadrant I, which is shaded light gray. We concentrate on the remaining two inequalities. The intersection of the graphs of these two inequalities and quadrant I is shown in dark purple.

| EXAMPLE 12 | Financial Planning |

A retired couple can invest up to $25,000. As their financial adviser, you recommend that they place at least $15,000 in Treasury bills yielding 6% and at most $5000 in corporate bonds yielding 9%.

(a) Using x to denote the amount of money invested in Treasury bills and y the amount invested in corporate bonds, write a system of linear inequalities that describes the possible amounts of each investment. We shall assume that x and y are in thousands of dollars.

(b) Graph the system.

Solution
(a) The system of linear inequalities is

$$\begin{cases} x \geq 0 & \text{x and y are nonnegative variables since they represent} \\ y \geq 0 & \text{money invested in thousands of dollars.} \\ x + y \leq 25 & \text{The total of the two investments, $x + y$, cannot} \\ & \text{exceed \$25,000.} \\ x \geq 15 & \text{At least \$15,000 in Treasury bills} \\ y \leq 5 & \text{At most \$5000 in corporate bonds} \end{cases}$$

(b) See the shaded region in Figure 40. Note that the inequalities $x \geq 0$ and $y \geq 0$ require that the graph of the system be in quadrant I.

Figure 40

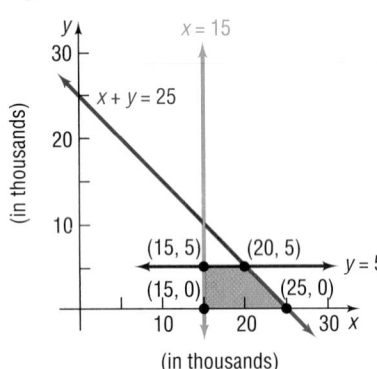

The graph of the system of linear inequalities in Figure 40 is said to be **bounded,** because it can be contained within some circle of sufficiently large radius. A graph that cannot be contained in any circle is said to be **unbounded.** For example, the graph of the system of linear inequalities in Figure 39 is unbounded, since it extends indefinitely in the positive x and positive y directions.

Notice in Figures 39 and 40 that those points belonging to the graph that are also points of intersection of boundary lines have been plotted. Such points are referred to as **vertices** or **corner points** of the graph. The system graphed in Figure 39 has three corner points: $(0, 4)$, $(1, 2)$, and $(3, 0)$. The system graphed in Figure 40 has four corner points: $(15, 0)$, $(25, 0)$, $(20, 5)$, and $(15, 5)$.

These ideas will be used in the next section in developing a method for solving linear programming problems, an important application of linear inequalities.

Now Work PROBLEM 45

11.7 Assess Your Understanding

'Are You Prepared?' *Answers are given at the end of these exercises. If you get a wrong answer, read the pages listed in red.*

1. Solve the inequality: $3x + 4 < 8 - x$ (pp. A81–A82)
2. Graph the equation: $3x - 2y = 6$ (pp. 35–37)
3. Graph the equation: $x^2 + y^2 = 9$ (pp. 44–46)
4. Graph the equation: $y = x^2 + 4$ (pp. 100–102)

5. **True or False** The lines $2x + y = 4$ and $4x + 2y = 0$ are parallel. (pp. 37–38)
6. The graph of $y = (x - 2)^2$ may be obtained by shifting the graph of _____ to the (left/right) a distance of _____ units. (pp. 100–102)

Concepts and Vocabulary

7. An inequality in two variables x and y is _____ by an ordered pair (a, b) if, when x is replaced by a and y by b, a true statement results.
8. The graph of a linear inequality is called a(n) _____.

9. **True or False** The graph of a linear inequality is a line.
10. **True or False** The graph of a system of linear inequalities is sometimes unbounded.

Skill Building

In Problems 11–22, graph each inequality by hand.

11. $y \geq 0$
12. $x \geq 0$
13. $x \geq 4$
14. $y \leq 2$

15. $2x + y \geq 6$
16. $3x + 2y \leq 6$
17. $x^2 + y^2 > 1$
18. $x^2 + y^2 \leq 9$

19. $y \leq x^2 - 1$
20. $y > x^2 + 2$
21. $xy \geq 4$
22. $xy \leq 1$

In Problems 23–34, graph each system of linear inequalities by hand. Verify your graph using a graphing utility.

23. $\begin{cases} x + y \leq 2 \\ 2x + y \geq 4 \end{cases}$
24. $\begin{cases} 3x - y \geq 6 \\ x + 2y \leq 2 \end{cases}$
25. $\begin{cases} 2x - y \leq 4 \\ 3x + 2y \geq -6 \end{cases}$
26. $\begin{cases} 4x - 5y \leq 0 \\ 2x - y \geq 2 \end{cases}$

27. $\begin{cases} 2x - 3y \leq 0 \\ 3x + 2y \leq 6 \end{cases}$
28. $\begin{cases} 4x - y \geq 2 \\ x + 2y \geq 2 \end{cases}$
29. $\begin{cases} x - 2y \leq 6 \\ 2x - 4y \geq 0 \end{cases}$
30. $\begin{cases} x + 4y \leq 8 \\ x + 4y \geq 4 \end{cases}$

31. $\begin{cases} 2x + y \geq -2 \\ 2x + y \geq 2 \end{cases}$
32. $\begin{cases} x - 4y \leq 4 \\ x - 4y \geq 0 \end{cases}$
33. $\begin{cases} 2x + 3y \geq 6 \\ 2x + 3y \leq 0 \end{cases}$
34. $\begin{cases} 2x + y \geq 0 \\ 2x + y \geq 2 \end{cases}$

In Problems 35–42, graph each system of inequalities by hand.

35. $\begin{cases} x^2 + y^2 \leq 9 \\ x + y \geq 3 \end{cases}$
36. $\begin{cases} x^2 + y^2 \geq 9 \\ x + y \leq 3 \end{cases}$
37. $\begin{cases} y \geq x^2 - 4 \\ y \leq x - 2 \end{cases}$
38. $\begin{cases} y^2 \leq x \\ y \geq x \end{cases}$

39. $\begin{cases} x^2 + y^2 \leq 16 \\ y \geq x^2 - 4 \end{cases}$
40. $\begin{cases} x^2 + y^2 \leq 25 \\ y \leq x^2 - 5 \end{cases}$
41. $\begin{cases} xy \geq 4 \\ y \geq x^2 + 1 \end{cases}$
42. $\begin{cases} y + x^2 \leq 1 \\ y \geq x^2 - 1 \end{cases}$

In Problems 43–52, graph each system of linear inequalities by hand. Tell whether the graph is bounded or unbounded, and label the corner points.

43. $\begin{cases} x \geq 0 \\ y \geq 0 \\ 2x + y \leq 6 \\ x + 2y \leq 6 \end{cases}$
44. $\begin{cases} x \geq 0 \\ y \geq 0 \\ x + y \geq 4 \\ 2x + 3y \geq 6 \end{cases}$
45. $\begin{cases} x \geq 0 \\ y \geq 0 \\ x + y \geq 2 \\ 2x + y \geq 4 \end{cases}$
46. $\begin{cases} x \geq 0 \\ y \geq 0 \\ 3x + y \leq 6 \\ 2x + y \leq 2 \end{cases}$

47. $\begin{cases} x \geq 0 \\ y \geq 0 \\ x + y \geq 2 \\ 2x + 3y \leq 12 \\ 3x + y \leq 12 \end{cases}$
48. $\begin{cases} x \geq 0 \\ y \geq 0 \\ x + y \geq 2 \\ x + y \leq 10 \\ 2x + y \leq 3 \end{cases}$
49. $\begin{cases} x \geq 0 \\ y \geq 0 \\ x + y \geq 2 \\ x + y \leq 8 \\ 2x + y \leq 10 \end{cases}$
50. $\begin{cases} x \geq 0 \\ y \geq 0 \\ x + y \geq 2 \\ x + y \leq 8 \\ x + 2y \geq 1 \end{cases}$

51. $\begin{cases} x \geq 0 \\ y \geq 0 \\ x + 2y \geq 1 \\ x + 2y \leq 10 \end{cases}$
52. $\begin{cases} x \geq 0 \\ y \geq 0 \\ x + 2y \geq 1 \\ x + 2y \leq 10 \\ x + y \geq 2 \\ x + y \leq 8 \end{cases}$

In Problems 53–56, write a system of linear inequalities that has the given graph.

53.

54.

55.

56.

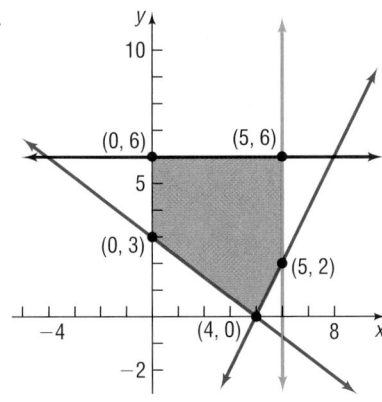

Applications and Extensions

57. Financial Planning A retired couple has up to $50,000 to invest. As their financial adviser, you recommend that they place at least $35,000 in Treasury bills yielding 7% and at most $10,000 in corporate bonds yielding 10%.
   (a) Using x to denote the amount of money invested in Treasury bills and y the amount invested in corporate bonds, write a system of linear inequalities that describes the possible amounts of each investment.
   (b) Graph the system and label the corner points.

58. Manufacturing Trucks Mike's Toy Truck Company manufacturers two models of toy trucks, a standard model and a deluxe model. Each standard model requires 2 hours (hr) for painting and 3 hrs for detail work; each deluxe model requires 3 hrs for painting and 4 hrs for detail work. Two painters and three detail workers are employed by the company, and each works 40 hrs per week.
   (a) Using x to denote the number of standard model trucks and y to denote the number of deluxe model trucks, write a system of linear inequalities that describes the possible number of each model of truck that can be manufactured in a week.
   (b) Graph the system and label the corner points.

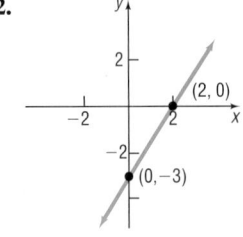

59. Blending Coffee Bill's Coffee House, a store that specializes in coffee, has available 75 pounds (lb) of A grade coffee and 120 lb of B grade coffee. These will be blended into 1-lb packages as follows: An economy blend that contains 4 ounces (oz) of A grade coffee and 12 oz of B grade coffee and a superior blend that contains 8 oz of A grade coffee and 8 oz of B grade coffee.
   (a) Using x to denote the number of packages of the economy blend and y to denote the number of packages of the superior blend, write a system of linear inequalities that describes the possible number of packages of each kind of blend.
   (b) Graph the system and label the corner points.

60. Mixed Nuts Nola's Nuts, a store that specializes in selling nuts, has available 90 pounds (lb) of cashews and 120 lb of peanuts. These are to be mixed in 12-ounce (oz) packages as follows: a lower-priced package containing 8 oz of peanuts and 4 oz of cashews and a quality package containing 6 oz of peanuts and 6 oz of cashews.
   (a) Use x to denote the number of lower-priced packages and use y to denote the number of quality packages. Write a system of linear inequalities that describes the possible number of each kind of package.
   (b) Graph the system and label the corner points.

61. Transporting Goods A small truck can carry no more than 1600 pounds (lb) of cargo nor more than 150 cubic (ft^3) of cargo. A printer weighs 20 lb and occupies 3 ft^3 of space. A microwave oven weighs 30 lb and occupies 2 ft^3 of space.
   (a) Using x to represent the number of microwave ovens and y to represent the number of printers, write a system of linear inequalities that describes the number of ovens and printers that can be hauled by the truck.
   (b) Graph the system and label the corner points.

'Are You Prepared?' Answers

1. $\{x \mid x < 1\}$ or $(-\infty, 1)$

2.

3.

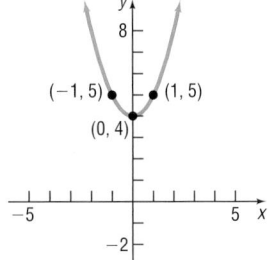

4.

5. True

6. $y = x^2$; right; 2

11.8 Linear Programming

> **OBJECTIVES** **1** Set up a Linear Programming Problem (p. 789)
>
> **2** Solve a Linear Programming Problem (p. 790)

Historically, linear programming evolved as a technique for solving problems involving resource allocation of goods and materials for the U.S. Air Force during World War II. Today, linear programming techniques are used to solve a wide variety of problems, such as optimizing airline scheduling and establishing telephone lines. Although most practical linear programming problems involve systems of several hundred linear inequalities containing several hundred variables, we will limit our discussion to problems containing only two variables, because we can solve such problems using graphing techniques.*

1 Set up a Linear Programming Problem

We begin by returning to Example 12 of the previous section.

EXAMPLE 1 | **Financial Planning**

A retired couple has up to $25,000 to invest. As their financial adviser, you recommend that they place at least $15,000 in Treasury bills yielding 6% and at most $5000 in corporate bonds yielding 9%. How much money should be placed in each investment so that income is maximized?

Solution The problem is typical of a *linear programming problem.* The problem requires that a certain linear expression, the income, be maximized. If I represents income, x the amount invested in Treasury bills at 6%, and y the amount invested in corporate bonds at 9%, then

$$I = 0.06x + 0.09y$$

We shall assume, as before, that I, x, and y are in thousands of dollars.

The linear expression $I = 0.06x + 0.09y$ is called the **objective function.** Furthermore, the problem requires that the maximum income be achieved under certain conditions or **constraints,** each of which is a linear inequality involving the variables. (See Example 12 in Section 11.7.) The linear programming problem given in Example 1 may be restated as

$$\text{Maximize} \quad I = 0.06x + 0.09y$$

subject to the conditions that

$$x \geq 0, \quad y \geq 0$$
$$x + y \leq 25$$
$$x \geq 15$$
$$y \leq 5$$

In general, every linear programming problem has two components:

1. A linear objective function that is to be maximized or minimized

2. A collection of linear inequalities that must be satisfied simultaneously

---

*The **simplex method** is a way to solve linear programming problems involving many inequalities and variables. This method was developed by George Dantzig in 1946 and is particularly well suited for computerization. In 1984, Narendra Karmarkar of Bell Laboratories discovered a way of solving large linear programming problems that improves on the simplex method.

DEFINITION

A **linear programming problem** in two variables x and y consists of maximizing (or minimizing) a linear objective function

$$z = Ax + By \qquad A \text{ and } B \text{ are real numbers, not both } 0$$

subject to certain conditions, or constraints, expressible as linear inequalities in x and y.

2 Solve a Linear Programming Problem

To maximize (or minimize) the quantity $z = Ax + By$, we need to identify points (x, y) that make the expression for z the largest (or smallest) possible. But not all points (x, y) are eligible; only those that also satisfy each linear inequality (constraint) can be used. We refer to each point (x, y) that satisfies the system of linear inequalities (the constraints) as a **feasible point.** In a linear programming problem, we seek the feasible point(s) that maximizes (or minimizes) the objective function.

Let's look again at the linear programming problem in Example 1.

EXAMPLE 2

Analyzing a Linear Programming Problem

Consider the linear programming problem

$$\text{Maximize} \qquad I = 0.06x + 0.09y$$

subject to the conditions that

$$x \geq 0$$
$$y \geq 0$$
$$x + y \leq 25$$
$$x \geq 15$$
$$y \leq 5$$

Graph the constraints. Then graph the objective function for $I = 0, 0.9, 1.35, 1.65,$ and 1.8.

Solution

Figure 41 shows the graph of the constraints. We superimpose on this graph the graph of the objective function for the given values of I.

For $I = 0$, the objective function is the line $0 = 0.06x + 0.09y$.
For $I = 0.9$, the objective function is the line $0.9 = 0.06x + 0.09y$.
For $I = 1.35$, the objective function is the line $1.35 = 0.06x + 0.09y$.
For $I = 1.65$, the objective function is the line $1.65 = 0.06x + 0.09y$.
For $I = 1.8$, the objective function is the line $1.8 = 0.06x + 0.09y$.

Figure 41

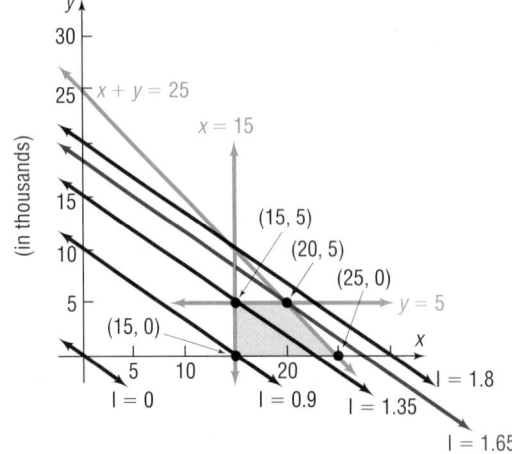

DEFINITION

A **solution** to a linear programming problem consists of a feasible point that maximizes (or minimizes) the objective function, together with the corresponding value of the objective function.

One condition for a linear programming problem in two variables to have a solution is that the graph of the feasible points be bounded. (Refer to page 786.)

If none of the feasible points maximizes (or minimizes) the objective function or if there are no feasible points, the linear programming problem has no solution.

Consider the linear programming problem stated in Example 2, and look again at Figure 41. The feasible points are the points that lie in the shaded region. For example, $(20, 3)$ is a feasible point, as are $(15, 5)$, $(20, 5)$, $(18, 4)$, and so on. To find the solution of the problem requires that we find a feasible point (x, y) that makes $I = 0.06x + 0.09y$ as large as possible. Notice that as I increases in value from $I = 0$ to $I = 0.9$ to $I = 1.35$ to $I = 1.65$ to $I = 1.8$ we obtain a collection of parallel lines. Further, notice that the largest value of I that can be obtained using feasible points is $I = 1.65$, which corresponds to the line $1.65 = 0.06x + 0.09y$. Any larger value of I results in a line that does not pass through any feasible points. Finally, notice that the feasible point that yields $I = 1.65$ is the point $(20, 5)$, a corner point. These observations form the basis of the following result, which we state without proof.

THEOREM

Location of the Solution of a Linear Programming Problem

If a linear programming problem has a solution, it is located at a corner point of the graph of the feasible points.

If a linear programming problem has multiple solutions, at least one of them is located at a corner point of the graph of the feasible points.

In either case, the corresponding value of the objective function is unique.

We shall not consider here linear programming problems that have no solution. As a result, we can outline the procedure for solving a linear programming problem as follows:

Procedure for Solving a Linear Programming Problem

STEP 1: Write an expression for the quantity to be maximized (or minimized). This expression is the objective function.

STEP 2: Write all the constraints as a system of linear inequalities and graph the system.

STEP 3: List the corner points of the graph of the feasible points.

STEP 4: List the corresponding values of the objective function at each corner point. The largest (or smallest) of these is the solution.

EXAMPLE 3 | **Solving a Minimum Linear Programming Problem**

Minimize the expression

$$z = 2x + 3y$$

subject to the constraints

$$y \leq 5 \qquad x \leq 6 \qquad x + y \geq 2 \qquad x \geq 0 \qquad y \geq 0$$

Solution

STEP 1: The objective function is $z = 2x + 3y$.

STEP 2: We seek the smallest value of z that can occur if x and y are solutions of the system of linear inequalities

$$\begin{cases} y \leq 5 \\ x \leq 6 \\ x + y \geq 2 \\ x \geq 0 \\ y \geq 0 \end{cases}$$

STEP 3: The graph of this system (the set of feasible points) is shown as the shaded region in Figure 42. We have also plotted the corner points.

STEP 4: Table 1 lists the corner points and the corresponding values of the objective function. From the table, we can see that the minimum value of z is 4, and it occurs at the point $(2, 0)$.

Figure 42

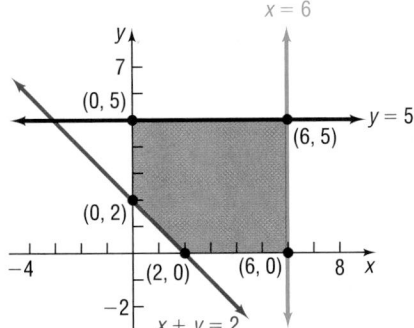

Table 1

Corner Point (x, y)	Value of the Objective Function $z = 2x + 3y$
$(0, 2)$	$z = 2(0) + 3(2) = 6$
$(0, 5)$	$z = 2(0) + 3(5) = 15$
$(6, 5)$	$z = 2(6) + 3(5) = 27$
$(6, 0)$	$z = 2(6) + 3(0) = 12$
$(2, 0)$	$z = 2(2) + 3(0) = 4$

- **Now Work** PROBLEMS 5 AND 11

EXAMPLE 4	**Maximizing Profit**

At the end of every month, after filling orders for its regular customers, a coffee company has some pure Colombian coffee and some special-blend coffee remaining. The practice of the company has been to package a mixture of the two coffees into 1-pound (lb) packages as follows: a low-grade mixture containing 4 ounces (oz) of Colombian coffee and 12 oz of special-blend coffee and a high-grade mixture containing 8 oz of Colombian and 8 oz of special-blend coffee. A profit of \$0.30 per package is made on the low-grade mixture, whereas a profit of \$0.40 per package is made on the high-grade mixture. This month, 120 lb of special-blend coffee and 100 lb of pure Colombian coffee remain. How many packages of each mixture should be prepared to achieve a maximum profit? Assume that all packages prepared can be sold.

Solution   **STEP 1:** We begin by assigning symbols for the two variables.

x = Number of packages of the low-grade mixture

y = Number of packages of the high-grade mixture

If P denotes the profit, then

$$P = \$0.30x + \$0.40y$$

This expression is the objective function.

STEP 2: We seek to maximize P subject to certain constraints on x and y. Because x and y represent numbers of packages, the only meaningful values for x and y are nonnegative integers. So we have the two constraints

$$x \geq 0 \qquad y \geq 0 \quad \text{Nonnegative constraints}$$

We also have only so much of each type of coffee available. For example, the total amount of Colombian coffee used in the two mixtures cannot exceed 100 lb, or 1600 oz. Because we use 4 oz in each low-grade package and 8 oz in each high-grade package, we are led to the constraint

$$4x + 8y \leq 1600 \quad \text{Colombian coffee constraint}$$

Similarly, the supply of 120 lb, or 1920 oz, of special-blend coffee leads to the constraint

$$12x + 8y \leq 1920 \quad \text{Special-blend coffee constraint}$$

The linear programming problem may be stated as

$$\text{Maximize} \qquad P = 0.3x + 0.4y$$

subject to the constraints

$$x \geq 0 \qquad y \geq 0 \qquad 4x + 8y \leq 1600 \qquad 12x + 8y \leq 1920$$

STEP 3: The graph of the constraints (the feasible points) is illustrated in Figure 43. We list the corner points and evaluate the objective function at each.

STEP 4: In Table 2, we can see that the maximum profit, $84, is achieved with 40 packages of the low-grade mixture and 180 packages of the high-grade mixture.

Figure 43

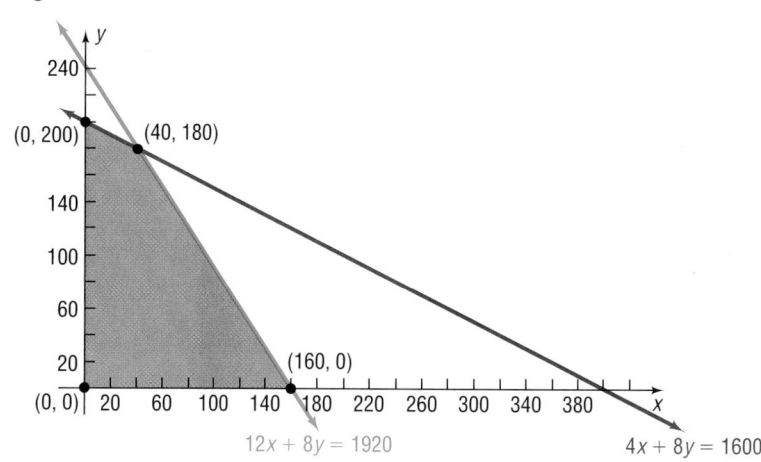

$12x + 8y = 1920$

$4x + 8y = 1600$

Table 2

Corner Point (x, y)	Value of Profit $P = 0.3x + 0.4y$
(0, 0)	$P = 0$
(0, 200)	$P = 0.3(0) + 0.4(200) = \$80$
(40, 180)	$P = 0.3(40) + 0.4(180) = \$84$
(160, 0)	$P = 0.3(160) + 0.4(0) = \$48$

─ **Now Work** PROBLEM 19

11.8 Assess Your Understanding

Concepts and Vocabulary

1. A linear programming problem requires that a linear expression, called the _____ _____, be maximized or minimized.

2. **True or False** If a linear programming problem has a solution, it is located at a corner point of the graph of the feasible points.

Skill Building

In Problems 3–8, find the maximum and minimum value of the given objective function of a linear programming problem. The figure illustrates the graph of the feasible points.

3. $z = x + y$

4. $z = 2x + 3y$

5. $z = x + 10y$

6. $z = 10x + y$

7. $z = 5x + 7y$

8. $z = 7x + 5y$

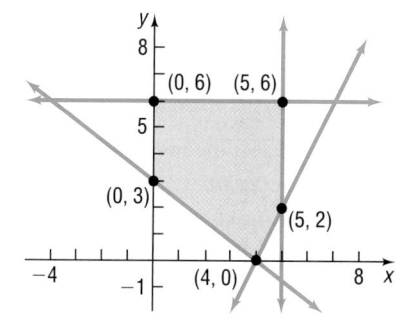

In Problems 9–18, solve each linear programming problem.

9. Maximize $z = 2x + y$ subject to $x \geq 0$, $y \geq 0$, $x + y \leq 6$, $x + y \geq 1$

10. Maximize $z = x + 3y$ subject to $x \geq 0$, $y \geq 0$, $x + y \geq 3$, $x \leq 5$, $y \leq 7$

11. Minimize $z = 2x + 5y$ subject to $x \geq 0$, $y \geq 0$, $x + y \geq 2$, $x \leq 5$, $y \leq 3$

12. Minimize $z = 3x + 4y$ subject to $x \geq 0$, $y \geq 0$, $2x + 3y \geq 6$, $x + y \leq 8$

13. Maximize $z = 3x + 5y$ subject to $x \geq 0$, $y \geq 0$, $x + y \geq 2$, $2x + 3y \leq 12$, $3x + 2y \leq 12$

14. Maximize $z = 5x + 3y$ subject to $x \geq 0$, $y \geq 0$, $x + y \geq 2$, $x + y \leq 8$, $2x + y \leq 10$

15. Minimize $z = 5x + 4y$ subject to $x \geq 0$, $y \geq 0$, $x + y \geq 2$, $2x + 3y \leq 12$, $3x + y \leq 12$

16. Minimize $z = 2x + 3y$ subject to $x \geq 0$, $y \geq 0$, $x + y \geq 3$, $x + y \leq 9$, $x + 3y \geq 6$

17. Maximize $z = 5x + 2y$ subject to $x \geq 0$, $y \geq 0$, $x + y \leq 10$, $2x + y \geq 10$, $x + 2y \geq 10$

18. Maximize $z = 2x + 4y$ subject to $x \geq 0$, $y \geq 0$, $2x + y \geq 4$, $x + y \leq 9$

Applications and Extensions

19. Maximizing Profit A manufacturer of skis produces two types: downhill and cross-country. Use the following table to determine how many of each kind of ski should be produced to achieve a maximum profit. What is the maximum profit? What would the maximum profit be if the time available for manufacturing is increased to 48 hours?

	Downhill	Cross-country	Time Available
Manufacturing time per ski	2 hours	1 hour	40 hours
Finishing time per ski	1 hour	1 hour	32 hours
Profit per ski	$70	$50	

20. Farm Management A farmer has 70 acres of land available for planting either soybeans or wheat. The cost of preparing the soil, the workdays required, and the expected profit per acre planted for each type of crop are given in the following table:

	Soybeans	Wheat
Preparation cost per acre	$60	$30
Workdays required per acre	3	4
Profit per acre	$180	$100

The farmer cannot spend more than $1800 in preparation costs nor use more than a total of 120 workdays. How many acres of each crop should be planted to maximize the profit? What is the maximum profit? What is the maximum profit if the farmer is willing to spend no more than $2400 on preparation?

21. Banquet Seating A banquet hall offers two types of tables for rent: 6-person rectangular tables at a cost of $28 each and 10-person round tables at a cost of $52 each. Kathleen would like to rent the hall for a wedding banquet and needs tables for 250 people. The room can have a maximum of 35 tables and the hall only has 15 rectangular tables available. How many of each type of table should be rented to minimize cost and what is the minimum cost?

Source: facilities.princeton.edu

22. Spring Break The student activities department of a community college plans to rent buses and vans for a spring-break trip. Each bus has 40 regular seats and 1 handicapped seat; each van has 8 regular seats and 3 handicapped seats. The rental cost is $350 for each van and $975 for each bus. If 320 regular and 36 handicapped seats are required for the trip, how many vehicles of each type should be rented to minimize cost?

Source: www.busrates.com

23. Return on Investment An investment broker is instructed by her client to invest up to $20,000, some in a junk bond yielding 9% per annum and some in Treasury bills yielding 7% per annum. The client wants to invest at least $8000 in T-bills and no more than $12,000 in the junk bond.

(a) How much should the broker recommend that the client place in each investment to maximize income if the client insists that the amount invested in T-bills must equal or exceed the amount placed in junk bonds?

(b) How much should the broker recommend that the client place in each investment to maximize income if the client insists that the amount invested in T-bills must not exceed the amount placed in junk bonds?

24. Production Scheduling In a factory, machine 1 produces 8-inch (in.) pliers at the rate of 60 units per hour (hr) and 6-in. pliers at the rate of 70 units/hr. Machine 2 produces 8-in. pliers at the rate of 40 units/hr and 6-in. pliers at the rate of 20 units/hr. It costs $50/hr to operate machine 1, and machine 2 costs $30/hr to operate. The production schedule requires that at least 240 units of 8-in. pliers and at least 140 units of 6-in. pliers be produced during each 10-hr day. Which combination of machines will cost the least money to operate?

25. Managing a Meat Market A meat market combines ground beef and ground pork in a single package for meat loaf. The ground beef is 75% lean (75% beef, 25% fat) and costs the market $0.75 per pound (lb). The ground pork is 60% lean and costs the market $0.45/lb. The meat loaf must be at least 70% lean. If the market wants to use at least 50 lb of its available pork, but no more than 200 lb of its available ground beef, how much ground beef should be mixed with ground pork so that the cost is minimized?

26. Ice Cream The Mom and Pop Ice Cream Company makes two kinds of chocolate ice cream: regular and premium. The properties of 1 gallon (gal) of each type are shown in the table:

	Regular	Premium
Flavoring	24 oz	20 oz
Milk-fat products	12 oz	20 oz
Shipping weight	5 lbs	6 lbs
Profit	$0.75	$0.90

In addition, current commitments require the company to make at least 1 gal of premium for every 4 gal of regular. Each day, the company has available 725 pounds (lb) of flavoring and 425 lb of milk-fat products. If the company can ship no more than 3000 lb of product per day, how many gallons of each type should be produced daily to maximize profit?

Source: www.scitoys.com/ingredients/ice_cream.html

27. Maximizing Profit on Ice Skates A factory manufactures two kinds of ice skates: racing skates and figure skates. The racing skates require 6 work-hours in the fabrication department, whereas the figure skates require 4 work-hours there. The racing skates require 1 work-hour in the finishing department, whereas the figure skates require 2 work-hours there. The fabricating department has available at most 120 work-hours per day, and the finishing department has no more than 40 work-hours per day available. If the profit on each racing skate is $10 and the profit on each figure skate is $12, how many of each should be manufactured each day to maximize profit? (Assume that all skates made are sold.)

28. **Financial Planning** A retired couple has up to $50,000 to place in fixed-income securities. Their financial adviser suggests two securities to them: one is an AAA bond that yields 8% per annum; the other is a certificate of deposit (CD) that yields 4%. After careful consideration of the alternatives, the couple decides to place at most $20,000 in the AAA bond and at least $15,000 in the CD. They also instruct the financial adviser to place at least as much in the CD as in the AAA bond. How should the financial adviser proceed to maximize the return on their investment?

29. **Product Design** An entrepreneur is having a design group produce at least six samples of a new kind of fastener that he wants to market. It costs $9.00 to produce each metal fastener and $4.00 to produce each plastic fastener. He wants to have at least two of each version of the fastener and needs to have all the samples 24 hours (hr) from now. It takes 4 hr to produce each metal sample and 2 hr to produce each plastic sample. To minimize the cost of the samples, how many of each kind should the entrepreneur order? What will be the cost of the samples?

30. **Animal Nutrition** Kevin's dog Amadeus likes two kinds of canned dog food. Gourmet Dog costs 40 cents a can and has 20 units of a vitamin complex; the calorie content is 75 calories. Chow Hound costs 32 cents a can and has 35 units of vitamins and 50 calories. Kevin likes Amadeus to have at least 1175 units of vitamins a month and at least 2375 calories during the same time period. Kevin has space to store only 60 cans of dog food at a time. How much of each kind of dog food should Kevin buy each month to minimize his cost?

31. **Airline Revenue** An airline has two classes of service: first class and coach. Management's experience has been that each aircraft should have at least 8 but no more than 16 first-class seats and at least 80 but not more than 120 coach seats.
    (a) If management decides that the ratio of first class to coach seats should never exceed 1:12, with how many of each type of seat should an aircraft be configured to maximize revenue?
    (b) If management decides that the ratio of first class to coach seats should never exceed 1:8, with how many of each type of seat should an aircraft be configured to maximize revenue?
    (c) If you were management, what would you do?
    [**Hint:** Assume that the airline charges $C for a coach seat and $F for a first-class seat; $C > 0, F > C$.]

Discussion and Writing

32. Explain in your own words what a linear programming problem is and how it can be solved.

CHAPTER REVIEW

Things to Know

Systems of equations (pp. 706–716)

Systems with no solutions are inconsistent.   Systems with a solution are consistent.

Consistent systems of linear equations have either a unique solution (independent) or an infinite number of solutions (dependent).

Matrix (p. 721)   Rectangular array of numbers, called entries

Augmented matrix (p. 721)

Row operations (p. 722)

Row echelon form (p. 724)

Determinants and Cramer's Rule (pp. 736, 737, 739 and 741)

Matrix (p. 745)

m by n matrix (p. 746)	Matrix with m rows and n columns
Identity matrix I_n (p. 753)	An n by n square matrix whose diagonal entries are 1's, while all other entries are 0's
Inverse of a matrix (p. 754)	A^{-1} is the inverse of A if $AA^{-1} = A^{-1}A = I_n$.
Nonsingular matrix (p. 754)	A square matrix that has an inverse

Linear programming problem (p. 790)

Maximize (or minimize) a linear objective function, $z = Ax + By$, subject to certain conditions, or constraints, expressible as linear inequalities in x and y. A feasible point (x, y) is a point that satisfies the constraints (linear inequalities) of a linear programming problem.

Location of solution (p. 791)

If a linear programming problem has a solution, it is located at a corner point of the graph of the feasible points. If a linear programming problem has multiple solutions, at least one of them is located at a corner point of the graph of the feasible points. In either case, the corresponding value of the objective function is unique.

Objectives

Section		You should be able to . . .	Example(s)	Review Exercises
11.1	1	Solve systems of equations by substitution (p. 708)	4	1–14, 101, 102, 105–107
	2	Solve systems of equations by elimination (p. 710)	5, 6	1–14, 101, 102, 105–107
	3	Identify inconsistent systems of equations containing two variables (p. 711)	7	9, 10, 13, 98
	4	Express the solution of a system of dependent equations containing two variables (p. 712)	8	14, 97
	5	Solve systems of three equations containing three variables (p. 712)	9	15–18, 99, 100, 103
	6	Identify inconsistent systems of equations containing three variables (p. 714)	10	18
	7	Express the solution of a system of dependent equations containing three variables (p. 715)	11	17
11.2	1	Write the augmented matrix of a system of linear equations (p. 721)	1	35–44
	2	Write the system of equations from the augmented matrix (p. 722)	2	19, 20
	3	Perform row operations on a matrix (p. 722)	3, 4	35–44
	4	Solve a system of linear equations using matrices (p. 724)	5–10	35–44
11.3	1	Evaluate 2 by 2 determinants (p. 736)	1	45, 46
	2	Use Cramer's Rule to solve a system of two equations containing two variables (p. 736)	2	51–54
	3	Evaluate 3 by 3 determinants (p. 739)	4	47–50
	4	Use Cramer's Rule to solve a system of three equations containing three variables (p. 741)	5	55, 56
	5	Know properties of determinants (p. 742)	6–9	57, 58
11.4	1	Find the sum and difference of two matrices (p. 746)	3, 4	21, 22
	2	Find scalar multiples of a matrix (p. 748)	5	23, 24
	3	Find the product of two matrices (p. 749)	6–11	25–28
	4	Find the inverse of a matrix (p. 754)	12–14	29–34
	5	Solve a system of linear equations using an inverse matrix (p. 757)	15	35–44
11.5	1	Decompose $\dfrac{P}{Q}$, where Q has only nonrepeated linear factors (p. 763)	1	59, 60
	2	Decompose $\dfrac{P}{Q}$, where Q has repeated linear factors (p. 765)	2, 3	61, 62
	3	Decompose $\dfrac{P}{Q}$, where Q has a nonrepeated irreducible quadratic factor (p. 767)	4	63, 64, 67, 68
	4	Decompose $\dfrac{P}{Q}$, where Q has a repeated irreducible quadratic factor (p. 768)	5	65, 66
11.6	1	Solve a system of nonlinear equations using substitution (p. 770)	1, 3	69–78
	2	Solve a system of nonlinear equations using elimination (p. 771)	2, 4	69–78
11.7	1	Graph an inequality by hand (p. 780)	2–4	79–82
	2	Graph an inequality using a graphing utility (p. 782)	5	79–82
	3	Graph a system of inequalities (p. 783)	6–12	83–92, 104
11.8	1	Set up a linear programming problem (p. 789)	1	108, 109
	2	Solve a linear programming problem (p. 790)	2–4	93–96, 108, 109

Review Exercises

In Problems 1–18, solve each system of equations using the method of substitution or the method of elimination. If the system has no solution, say that it is inconsistent.

1. $\begin{cases} 2x - y = 5 \\ 5x + 2y = 8 \end{cases}$

2. $\begin{cases} 2x + 3y = 2 \\ 7x - y = 3 \end{cases}$

3. $\begin{cases} 3x - 4y = 4 \\ x - 3y = \dfrac{1}{2} \end{cases}$

4. $\begin{cases} 2x + y = 0 \\ 5x - 4y = -\dfrac{13}{2} \end{cases}$

5. $\begin{cases} x - 2y - 4 = 0 \\ 3x + 2y - 4 = 0 \end{cases}$

6. $\begin{cases} x - 3y + 5 = 0 \\ 2x + 3y - 5 = 0 \end{cases}$

7. $\begin{cases} y = 2x - 5 \\ x = 3y + 4 \end{cases}$

8. $\begin{cases} x = 5y + 2 \\ y = 5x + 2 \end{cases}$

9. $\begin{cases} x - 3y + 4 = 0 \\ \dfrac{1}{2}x - \dfrac{3}{2}y + \dfrac{4}{3} = 0 \end{cases}$

10. $\begin{cases} x + \dfrac{1}{4}y = 2 \\ y + 4x + 2 = 0 \end{cases}$

11. $\begin{cases} 2x + 3y - 13 = 0 \\ 3x - 2y = 0 \end{cases}$

12. $\begin{cases} 4x + 5y = 21 \\ 5x + 6y = 42 \end{cases}$

13. $\begin{cases} 3x - 2y = 8 \\ x - \dfrac{2}{3}y = 12 \end{cases}$

14. $\begin{cases} 2x + 5y = 10 \\ 4x + 10y = 20 \end{cases}$

15. $\begin{cases} x + 2y - z = 6 \\ 2x - y + 3z = -13 \\ 3x - 2y + 3z = -16 \end{cases}$

16. $\begin{cases} x + 5y - z = 2 \\ 2x + y + z = 7 \\ x - y + 2z = 11 \end{cases}$

17. $\begin{cases} 2x - 4y + z = -15 \\ x + 2y - 4z = 27 \\ 5x - 6y - 2z = -3 \end{cases}$

18. $\begin{cases} x - 4y + 3z = 15 \\ -3x + y - 5z = -5 \\ -7x - 5y - 9z = 10 \end{cases}$

In Problems 19 and 20, write the system of equations corresponding to the given augmented matrix.

19. $\begin{bmatrix} 3 & 2 & | & 8 \\ 1 & 4 & | & -1 \end{bmatrix}$

20. $\begin{bmatrix} 1 & 2 & 5 & | & -2 \\ 5 & 0 & -3 & | & 8 \\ 2 & -1 & 0 & | & 0 \end{bmatrix}$

In Problems 21–28, use the following matrices to compute each expression. Verify your results using a graphing utility.

$$A = \begin{bmatrix} 1 & 0 \\ 2 & 4 \\ -1 & 2 \end{bmatrix} \quad B = \begin{bmatrix} 4 & -3 & 0 \\ 1 & 1 & -2 \end{bmatrix} \quad C = \begin{bmatrix} 3 & -4 \\ 1 & 5 \\ 5 & 2 \end{bmatrix}$$

21. $A + C$

22. $A - C$

23. $6A$

24. $-4B$

25. AB

26. BA

27. CB

28. BC

In Problems 29–34, find the inverse, if there is one, of each matrix. If there is not an inverse, say that the matrix is singular. Verify your results using a graphing utility.

29. $\begin{bmatrix} 4 & 6 \\ 1 & 3 \end{bmatrix}$

30. $\begin{bmatrix} -3 & 2 \\ 1 & -2 \end{bmatrix}$

31. $\begin{bmatrix} 1 & 3 & 3 \\ 1 & 2 & 1 \\ 1 & -1 & 2 \end{bmatrix}$

32. $\begin{bmatrix} 3 & 1 & 2 \\ 3 & 2 & -1 \\ 1 & 1 & 1 \end{bmatrix}$

33. $\begin{bmatrix} 4 & -8 \\ -1 & 2 \end{bmatrix}$

34. $\begin{bmatrix} -3 & 1 \\ -6 & 2 \end{bmatrix}$

In Problems 35–44, solve each system of equations using matrices. If the system has no solution, say that it is inconsistent.

35. $\begin{cases} 3x - 2y = 1 \\ 10x + 10y = 5 \end{cases}$

36. $\begin{cases} 3x + 2y = 6 \\ x - y = -\dfrac{1}{2} \end{cases}$

37. $\begin{cases} 5x - 6y - 3z = 6 \\ 4x - 7y - 2z = -3 \\ 3x + y - 7z = 1 \end{cases}$

38. $\begin{cases} 2x + y + z = 5 \\ 4x - y - 3z = 1 \\ 8x + y - z = 5 \end{cases}$

39. $\begin{cases} x - 2z = 1 \\ 2x + 3y = -3 \\ 4x - 3y - 4z = 3 \end{cases}$

40. $\begin{cases} x + 2y - z = 2 \\ 2x - 2y + z = -1 \\ 6x + 4y + 3z = 5 \end{cases}$

41. $\begin{cases} x - y + z = 0 \\ x - y - 5z - 6 = 0 \\ 2x - 2y + z - 1 = 0 \end{cases}$

42. $\begin{cases} 4x - 3y + 5z = 0 \\ 2x + 4y - 3z = 0 \\ 6x + 2y + z = 0 \end{cases}$

43. $\begin{cases} x - y - z - t = 1 \\ 2x + y - z + 2t = 3 \\ x - 2y - 2z - 3t = 0 \\ 3x - 4y + z + 5t = -3 \end{cases}$

44. $\begin{cases} x - 3y + 3z - t = 4 \\ x + 2y - z = -3 \\ x + 3z + 2t = 3 \\ x + y + 5z = 6 \end{cases}$

In Problems 45–50, find the value of each determinant. Verify your results using a graphing utility.

45. $\begin{vmatrix} 3 & 4 \\ 1 & 3 \end{vmatrix}$

46. $\begin{vmatrix} -4 & 0 \\ 1 & 3 \end{vmatrix}$

47. $\begin{vmatrix} 1 & 4 & 0 \\ -1 & 2 & 6 \\ 4 & 1 & 3 \end{vmatrix}$

48. $\begin{vmatrix} 2 & 3 & 10 \\ 0 & 1 & 5 \\ -1 & 2 & 3 \end{vmatrix}$

49. $\begin{vmatrix} 2 & 1 & -3 \\ 5 & 0 & 1 \\ 2 & 6 & 0 \end{vmatrix}$

50. $\begin{vmatrix} -2 & 1 & 0 \\ 1 & 2 & 3 \\ -1 & 4 & 2 \end{vmatrix}$

In Problems 51–56, use Cramer's Rule, if applicable, to solve each system.

51. $\begin{cases} x - 2y = 4 \\ 3x + 2y = 4 \end{cases}$

52. $\begin{cases} x - 3y = -5 \\ 2x + 3y = 5 \end{cases}$

53. $\begin{cases} 2x + 3y - 13 = 0 \\ 3x - 2y = 0 \end{cases}$

54. $\begin{cases} 3x - 4y - 12 = 0 \\ 5x + 2y + 6 = 0 \end{cases}$

55. $\begin{cases} x + 2y - z = 6 \\ 2x - y + 3z = -13 \\ 3x - 2y + 3z = -16 \end{cases}$

56. $\begin{cases} x - y + z = 8 \\ 2x + 3y - z = -2 \\ 3x - y - 9z = 9 \end{cases}$

In Problems 57 and 58, use properties of determinants to find the value of each determinant if it is known that $\begin{vmatrix} x & y \\ a & b \end{vmatrix} = 8.$

57. $\begin{vmatrix} 2x & y \\ 2a & b \end{vmatrix}$

58. $\begin{vmatrix} y & x \\ b & a \end{vmatrix}$

In Problems 59–68, write the partial fraction decomposition of each rational expression.

59. $\dfrac{6}{x(x-4)}$

60. $\dfrac{x}{(x+2)(x-3)}$

61. $\dfrac{x-4}{x^2(x-1)}$

62. $\dfrac{2x-6}{(x-2)^2(x-1)}$

63. $\dfrac{x}{(x^2+9)(x+1)}$

64. $\dfrac{3x}{(x-2)(x^2+1)}$

65. $\dfrac{x^3}{(x^2+4)^2}$

66. $\dfrac{x^3+1}{(x^2+16)^2}$

67. $\dfrac{x^2}{(x^2+1)(x^2-1)}$

68. $\dfrac{4}{(x^2+4)(x^2-1)}$

In Problems 69–78, solve each system of equations.

69. $\begin{cases} 2x + y + 3 = 0 \\ x^2 + y^2 = 5 \end{cases}$

70. $\begin{cases} x^2 + y^2 = 16 \\ 2x - y^2 = -8 \end{cases}$

71. $\begin{cases} 2xy + y^2 = 10 \\ 3y^2 - xy = 2 \end{cases}$

72. $\begin{cases} 3x^2 - y^2 = 1 \\ 7x^2 - 2y^2 - 5 = 0 \end{cases}$

73. $\begin{cases} x^2 + y^2 = 6y \\ x^2 = 3y \end{cases}$

74. $\begin{cases} 2x^2 + y^2 = 9 \\ x^2 + y^2 = 9 \end{cases}$

75. $\begin{cases} 3x^2 + 4xy + 5y^2 = 8 \\ x^2 + 3xy + 2y^2 = 0 \end{cases}$

76. $\begin{cases} 3x^2 + 2xy - 2y^2 = 6 \\ xy - 2y^2 + 4 = 0 \end{cases}$

77. $\begin{cases} x^2 - 3x + y^2 + y = -2 \\ \dfrac{x^2 - x}{y} + y + 1 = 0 \end{cases}$

78. $\begin{cases} x^2 + x + y^2 = y + 2 \\ x + 1 = \dfrac{2 - y}{x} \end{cases}$

In Problems 79–82 graph each inequality by hand.

79. $3x + 4y \le 12$

80. $2x - 3y \ge 6$

81. $y \le x^2$

82. $x \ge y^2$

In Problems 83–88, graph each system of inequalities by hand. Tell whether the graph is bounded or unbounded, and label the corner points.

83. $\begin{cases} -2x + y \le 2 \\ x + y \ge 2 \end{cases}$

84. $\begin{cases} x - 2y \le 6 \\ 2x + y \ge 2 \end{cases}$

85. $\begin{cases} x \ge 0 \\ y \ge 0 \\ x + y \le 4 \\ 2x + 3y \le 6 \end{cases}$

86. $\begin{cases} x \ge 0 \\ y \ge 0 \\ 3x + y \ge 6 \\ 2x + y \ge 2 \end{cases}$

87. $\begin{cases} x \ge 0 \\ y \ge 0 \\ 2x + y \le 8 \\ x + 2y \ge 2 \end{cases}$

88. $\begin{cases} x \ge 0 \\ y \ge 0 \\ 3x + y \le 9 \\ 2x + 3y \ge 6 \end{cases}$

In Problems 89–92, graph each system of inequalities by hand.

89. $\begin{cases} x^2 + y^2 \le 16 \\ x + y \ge 2 \end{cases}$

90. $\begin{cases} y^2 \le x - 1 \\ x - y \le 3 \end{cases}$

91. $\begin{cases} y \le x^2 \\ xy \le 4 \end{cases}$

92. $\begin{cases} x^2 + y^2 \ge 1 \\ x^2 + y^2 \le 4 \end{cases}$

In Problems 93–96, solve each linear programming problem.

93. Maximize $z = 3x + 4y$ subject to $x \ge 0, y \ge 0, 3x + 2y \ge 6, x + y \le 8$

94. Maximize $z = 2x + 4y$ subject to $x \ge 0, y \ge 0, x + y \le 6, x \ge 2$

95. Minimize $z = 3x + 5y$ subject to $x \ge 0, y \ge 0, x + y \ge 1, 3x + 2y \le 12, x + 3y \le 12$

96. Minimize $z = 3x + y$ subject to $x \ge 0, y \ge 0, x \le 8, y \le 6, 2x + y \ge 4$

---

97. Find A so that the system of equations has infinitely many solutions.

$$\begin{cases} 2x + 5y = 5 \\ 4x + 10y = A \end{cases}$$

98. Find A so that the system in Problem 97 is inconsistent.

99. Curve Fitting Find the quadratic function $y = ax^2 + bx + c$ that passes through the three points $(0, 1), (1, 0)$, and $(-2, 1)$.

100. Curve Fitting Find the general equation of the circle that passes through the three points $(0, 1), (1, 0)$, and $(-2, 1)$.

[**Hint:** The general equation of a circle is $x^2 + y^2 + Dx + Ey + F = 0$.]

101. Blending Coffee A coffee distributor is blending a new coffee that will cost $6.90 per pound. It will consist of a blend of $6.00 per pound coffee and $9.00 per pound coffee. What amounts of each type of coffee should be mixed to achieve the desired blend?

[**Hint:** Assume that the weight of the blended coffee is 100 pounds.]

$6.00/lb $6.90/lb $9.00/lb

102. Farming A 1000-acre farm in Illinois is used to grow corn and soybeans. The cost per acre for raising corn is $65, and the cost per acre for soybeans is $45. If $54,325 has been budgeted for costs and all the acreage is to be used, how many acres should be allocated for each crop?

103. Cookie Orders A cookie company makes three kinds of cookies, oatmeal raisin, chocolate chip, and shortbread, packaged in small, medium, and large boxes. The small box contains 1 dozen oatmeal raisin and 1 dozen chocolate chip; the medium box has 2 dozen oatmeal raisin, 1 dozen chocolate chip, and 1 dozen shortbread; the large box contains 2 dozen oatmeal raisin, 2 dozen chocolate chip, and 3 dozen shortbread. If you require exactly 15 dozen oatmeal raisin, 10 dozen chocolate chip, and 11 dozen shortbread, how many of each size box should you buy?

104. Mixed Nuts A store that specializes in selling nuts has available 72 pounds (lb) of cashews and 120 lb of peanuts. These are to be mixed in 12-ounce (oz) packages as follows: a lower-priced package containing 8 oz of peanuts and 4 oz of cashews and a quality package containing 6 oz of peanuts and 6 oz of cashews.
(a) Use x to denote the number of lower-priced packages and use y to denote the number of quality packages. Write a system of linear inequalities that describes the possible number of each kind of package.
(b) Graph the system and label the corner points.

105. Determining the Speed of the Current of the Aguarico River On a recent trip to the Cuyabeno Wildlife Reserve in the Amazon region of Ecuador, Mike took a 100-kilometer trip by speedboat down the Aguarico River from Chiritza to the Flotel Orellana. As Mike watched the Amazon unfold, he wondered how fast the speedboat was going and how fast the current of the white-water Aguarico River was. Mike timed the trip downstream at 2.5 hours and the return trip at 3 hours. What were the two speeds?

106. Finding the Speed of the Jet Stream On a flight between Midway Airport in Chicago and Ft. Lauderdale, Florida, a Boeing 737 jet maintains an airspeed of 475 miles per hour. If the trip from Chicago to Ft. Lauderdale takes 2 hours, 30 minutes and the return flight takes 2 hours, 50 minutes, what is the speed of the jet stream? (Assume that the speed of the jet stream remains constant at the various altitudes of the plane and that the plane flies with the jet stream one way and against it the other way.)

107. Constant Rate Jobs If Bruce and Bryce work together for 1 hour and 20 minutes, they will finish a certain job. If Bryce and Marty work together for 1 hour and 36 minutes, the same job can be finished. If Marty and Bruce work together, they can complete this job in 2 hours and 40 minutes. How long will it take each of them working alone to finish the job?

108. Maximizing Profit on Figurines A factory manufactures two kinds of ceramic figurines: a dancing girl and a mermaid. Each requires three processes: molding, painting, and glazing. The daily labor available for molding is no more than 90 work-hours, labor available for painting does not exceed 120 work-hours, and labor available for glazing is no more than 60 work-hours. The dancing girl requires 3 work-hours for molding, 6 work-hours for painting, and 2 work-hours for glazing. The mermaid requires 3 work-hours for molding, 4 work-hours for painting, and 3 work-hours for glazing. If the profit on each figurine is $25 for dancing girls and $30 for mermaids, how many of each should be produced each day to maximize profit? If management decides to produce the number of each figurine that maximizes profit, determine which of these processes has work-hours assigned to it that are not used.

109. Minimizing Production Cost A factory produces gasoline engines and diesel engines. Each week the factory is obligated to deliver at least 20 gasoline engines and at least 15 diesel engines. Due to physical limitations, however, the factory cannot make more than 60 gasoline engines nor more than 40 diesel engines in any given week. Finally, to prevent layoffs, a total of at least 50 engines must be produced. If gasoline engines cost $450 each to produce and diesel engines cost $550 each to produce, how many of each should be produced per week to minimize the cost? What is the excess capacity of the factory; that is, how many of each kind of engine is being produced in excess of the number that the factory is obligated to deliver?

110. Describe four ways of solving a system of three linear equations containing three variables. Which method do you prefer? Why?

CHAPTER TEST

In Problems 1–4, solve each system of equations using the method of substitution or the method of elimination. If the system has no solution, say that it is inconsistent.

1. $\begin{cases} -2x + y = -7 \\ 4x + 3y = 9 \end{cases}$

2. $\begin{cases} \dfrac{1}{3}x - 2y = 1 \\ 5x - 30y = 18 \end{cases}$

3. $\begin{cases} x - y + 2z = 5 \\ 3x + 4y - z = -2 \\ 5x + 2y + 3z = 8 \end{cases}$

4. $\begin{cases} 3x + 2y - 8z = -3 \\ -x - \dfrac{2}{3}y + z = 1 \\ 6x - 3y + 15z = 8 \end{cases}$

5. Write the augmented matrix corresponding to the system of equations: $\begin{cases} 4x - 5y + z = 0 \\ -2x - y + 6 = -19 \\ x + 5y - 5z = 10 \end{cases}$

6. Write the system of equations corresponding to the augmented matrix: $\begin{bmatrix} 3 & 2 & 4 & | & -6 \\ 1 & 0 & 8 & | & 2 \\ -2 & 1 & 3 & | & -11 \end{bmatrix}$

In Problems 7–10, use the given matrices to compute each expression.

$$A = \begin{bmatrix} 1 & -1 \\ 0 & -4 \\ 3 & 2 \end{bmatrix} \quad B = \begin{bmatrix} 1 & -2 & 5 \\ 0 & 3 & 1 \end{bmatrix} \quad C = \begin{bmatrix} 4 & 6 \\ 1 & -3 \\ -1 & 8 \end{bmatrix}$$

7. $2A + C$
8. $A - 3C$
9. AC
10. BA

In Problems 11 and 12, find the inverse of each nonsingular matrix.

11. $A = \begin{bmatrix} 3 & 2 \\ 5 & 4 \end{bmatrix}$

12. $B = \begin{bmatrix} 1 & -1 & 1 \\ 2 & 5 & -1 \\ 2 & 3 & 0 \end{bmatrix}$

In Problems 13–16, solve each system of equations using matrices. If the system has no solution, say that it is inconsistent.

13. $\begin{cases} 6x + 3y = 12 \\ 2x - y = -2 \end{cases}$

14. $\begin{cases} x + \dfrac{1}{4}y = 7 \\ 8x + 2y = 56 \end{cases}$

15. $\begin{cases} x + 2y + 4z = -3 \\ 2x + 7y + 15z = -12 \\ 4x + 7y + 13z = -10 \end{cases}$

16. $\begin{cases} 2x + 2y - 3z = 5 \\ x - y + 2z = 8 \\ 3x + 5y - 8z = -2 \end{cases}$

In Problems 17 and 18, find the value of each determinant.

17. $\begin{vmatrix} -2 & 5 \\ 3 & 7 \end{vmatrix}$

18. $\begin{vmatrix} 2 & -4 & 6 \\ 1 & 4 & 0 \\ -1 & 2 & -4 \end{vmatrix}$

In Problems 19 and 20, use Cramer's Rule, if possible, to solve each system.

19. $\begin{cases} 4x + 3y = -23 \\ 3x - 5y = 19 \end{cases}$

20. $\begin{cases} 4x - 3y + 2z = 15 \\ -2x + y - 3z = -15 \\ 5x - 5y + 2z = 18 \end{cases}$

In Problems 21 and 22, solve each system of equations.

21. $\begin{cases} 3x^2 + y^2 = 12 \\ y^2 = 9x \end{cases}$

22. $\begin{cases} 2y^2 - 3x^2 = 5 \\ y - x = 1 \end{cases}$

23. Graph the system of inequalities: $\begin{cases} x^2 + y^2 \le 100 \\ 4x - 3y \ge 0 \end{cases}$

In Problems 24 and 25, write the partial fraction decomposition of each rational expression.

24. $\dfrac{3x + 7}{(x + 3)^2}$

25. $\dfrac{4x^2 - 3}{x(x^2 + 3)^2}$

26. Graph the system of inequalities by hand. Tell whether the graph is bounded or unbounded, and label all corner points.

$$\begin{cases} x \ge 0 \\ y \ge 0 \\ x + 2y \ge 8 \\ 2x - 3y \ge 2 \end{cases}$$

27. Maximize $z = 5x + 8y$ subject to $x \ge 0$, $2x + y \le 8$, and $x - 3y \le -3$.

28. Megan went clothes shopping and bought 2 pairs of flare jeans, 2 camisoles, and 4 T-shirts for $90.00. At the same store, Paige bought one pair of flare jeans and 3 T-shirts for $42.50, while Kara bought 1 pair of flare jeans, 3 camisoles, and 2 T-shirts for $62.00. Determine the price of each clothing item.

CUMULATIVE REVIEW

In Problems 1–6, solve each equation.

1. $2x^2 - x = 0$

2. $\sqrt{3x + 1} = 4$

3. $2x^3 - 3x^2 - 8x - 3 = 0$

4. $3^x = 9^{x+1}$

5. $\log_3(x - 1) + \log_3(2x + 1) = 2$

6. $3^x = e$

7. Determine whether the function $g(x) = \dfrac{2x^3}{x^4 + 1}$ is even, odd, or neither. Is the graph of g symmetric with respect to the x-axis, y-axis, or origin?

8. Find the center and radius of the circle $x^2 + y^2 - 2x + 4y - 11 = 0$. Graph the circle.

9. Graph $f(x) = 3^{x-2} + 1$ using transformations. What is the domain, range, and horizontal asymptote of f?

10. The function $f(x) = \dfrac{5}{x + 2}$ is one-to-one. Find f^{-1}. Find the domain and the range of f and the domain and the range of f^{-1}.

11. Graph each equation.

   (a) $y = 3x + 6$ (b) $x^2 + y^2 = 4$

   (c) $y = x^3$ (d) $y = \dfrac{1}{x}$

   (e) $y = \sqrt{x}$ (f) $y = e^x$

   (g) $y = \ln x$ (h) $2x^2 + 5y^2 = 1$

   (i) $x^2 - 3y^2 = 1$ (j) $x^2 - 2x - 4y + 1 = 0$

   (k) $y = \sin x$ (l) $y = 3\sin(2x)$

12. $f(x) = x^3 - 3x + 5$

   (a) Using a graphing utility, graph f and approximate the zero(s) of f.

   (b) Using a graphing utility, approximate the local maxima and local minima.

   (c) Determine the intervals on which f is increasing.

13. Solve: $2\sin^2 x = 3\cos x$

CHAPTER PROJECTS

I. **Markov Chains** A **Markov chain** (or process) is one in which future outcomes are determined by a current state. Future outcomes are based on probabilities. The probability of moving to a certain state depends only on the state previously occupied and does not vary with time. An example of a Markov chain is the maximum education achieved by children based on the highest education attained by their parents, where the states are (1) earned college degree, (2) high school diploma only, (3) elementary school only. If p_{ij} is the probability of moving from state i to state j, the **transition matrix** is the $m \times m$ matrix

$$P = \begin{bmatrix} p_{11} & p_{12} & \cdots & p_{1m} \\ \vdots & \vdots & & \vdots \\ p_{m1} & p_{m2} & \cdots & p_{mm} \end{bmatrix}$$

The table represents the probabilities of the highest educational level of children based on the highest educational level of their parents. For example, the table shows that the probability p_{21} is 40% that parents with a high-school education (row 2) will have children with a college education (column 1).

Highest Educational Level of Parents	Maximum Education That Children Achieve		
	College	High School	Elementary
College	80%	18%	2%
High school	40%	50%	10%
Elementary	20%	60%	20%

1. Convert the percentages to decimals.

2. What is the transition matrix?

3. Sum across the rows. What do you notice? Why do you think that you obtained this result?

4. If P is the transition matrix of a Markov chain, the (i, j)th entry of P^n (nth power of P) gives the probability of passing from state i to state j in n stages. What is the probability that a grandchild of a college graduate is a college graduate?

5. What is the probability that the grandchild of a high school graduate finishes college?

6. The row vector $v^{(0)} = [0.277 \quad 0.575 \quad 0.148]$ represents the proportion of the U.S. population 25 years or older that has college, high school, and elementary school, respectively, as the highest educational level in 2004.* In a Markov chain the probability distribution $v^{(k)}$ after k stages is $v^{(k)} = v^{(0)}P^k$, where P^k is the kth power of the transition matrix. What will be the distribution of highest educational attainment of the grandchildren of the current population?

7. Calculate $P^3, P^4, P^5, \dots$. Continue until the matrix does not change. This is called the long-run distribution. What is the long-run distribution of highest educational attainment of the population?

Source: U.S. Census Bureau.

The following projects are available at the Instructor's Resource Center (IRC):

II. **Project at Motorola: *Error Control Coding*** The high-powered engineering needed to assure that wireless communications are transmitted correctly is analyzed using matrices to control coding errors.

III. **Using Matrices to Find the Line of Best Fit** Have you wondered how our calculators get a line of best fit? See how to find the line by solving a matrix equation.

IV. **CBL Experiment** Simulate two people walking toward each other at a constant rate. Then solve the resulting system of equations to determine when and where they will meet.

Sequences; Induction; the Binomial Theorem

12

The Future of the World Population

New York, 24 February—World population is expected to increase by 2.6 billion over the next 45 years, from 6.5 billion today to 9.1 billion in 2050. Almost all growth will take place in the less developed regions, where today's 5.3 billion population is expected to swell to 7.8 billion in 2050. By contrast, the population of the more developed regions will remain mostly unchanged, at 1.2 billion.

Future population growth is highly dependent on the path that future fertility takes. In the medium variant, fertility declines from 2.6 children per woman today to slightly over 2 children per woman in 2050. If fertility were to remain about half a child above the levels projected in the medium variant, world population would reach 10.6 billion by 2050. A fertility path half a child below the medium would lead to a population of 7.7 billion by mid-century. That is, at the world level, continued population growth until 2050 is inevitable even if the decline of fertility accelerates.

Because of its low and declining rate of population growth, the population of developed countries as a whole is expected to remain virtually unchanged between 2005 and 2050, at about 1.2 billion. In contrast, the population of the 50 least developed countries is projected to more than double, passing from 0.8 billion in 2005 to 1.7 billion in 2050. Growth in the rest of the developing world is also projected to be robust, though less rapid, with its population rising from 4.5 billion to 6.1 billion between 2005 and 2050.

Source: U.N. Press Release POP/918, February 24, 2005

—See Chapter Project I—

A Look Back, A Look Ahead

This chapter may be divided into three independent parts: Sections 12.1–12.3, Section 12.4, and Section 12.5.

In Chapter 2, we defined a function and its domain, which was usually some set of real numbers. In Sections 12.1–12.3, we discuss a sequence, which is a function whose domain is the set of positive integers.

Throughout this text, where it seemed appropriate, we have given proofs of many of the results. In Section 12.4, a technique for proving theorems involving natural numbers is discussed.

In Appendix A, Section A.3, there are formulas for expanding $(x + a)^2$ and $(x + a)^3$. In Section 12.5, we discuss the Binomial Theorem, a formula for the expansion of $(x + a)^n$, where n is any positive integer.

The topics introduced in this chapter are covered in more detail in courses titled *Discrete Mathematics*. Applications of these topics can be found in the fields of computer science, engineering, business and economics, the social sciences, and the physical and biological sciences.

Outline

12.1 Sequences
12.2 Arithmetic Sequences
12.3 Geometric Sequences; Geometric Series
12.4 Mathematical Induction
12.5 The Binomial Theorem
Chapter Review
Chapter Test
Cumulative Review
Chapter Projects

12.1 Sequences

PREPARING FOR THIS SECTION *Before getting started, review the following concepts:*

- Functions (Section 2.1, pp. 56–64)
- Compound Interest (Section 5.7, pp. 313–318)

Now Work the 'Are You Prepared?' problems on page 813.

OBJECTIVES **1** Write the First Several Terms of a Sequence (p. 804)
  2 Write the Terms of a Sequence Defined by a Recursive Formula (p. 807)
  3 Use Summation Notation (p. 808)
  4 Find the Sum of a Sequence Algebraically and Using a Graphing Utility (p. 809)
  5 Solve Annuity and Amortization Problems (p. 811)

DEFINITION A **sequence** is a function whose domain is the set of positive integers.

Because a sequence is a function, it will have a graph. In Figure 1(a), we show the graph of the function $f(x) = \dfrac{1}{x}, x > 0$. If all the points on this graph were removed except those whose x-coordinates are positive integers, that is, if all points were removed except $(1, 1), \left(2, \dfrac{1}{2}\right), \left(3, \dfrac{1}{3}\right)$, and so on, the remaining points would be the graph of the sequence $f(n) = \dfrac{1}{n}$, as shown in Figure 1(b). Notice that we use n to represent the independent variable in a sequence. This serves to remind us that n is a positive integer.

Figure 1

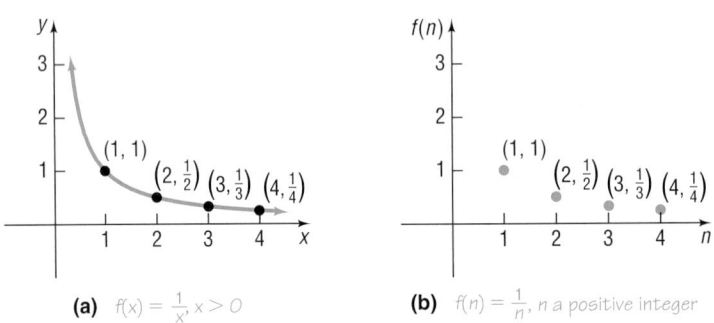

(a) $f(x) = \frac{1}{x}, x > 0$ **(b)** $f(n) = \frac{1}{n}, n$ a positive integer

1 Write the First Several Terms of a Sequence

A sequence is usually represented by listing its values in order. For example, the sequence whose graph is given in Figure 1(b) might be represented as

$$f(1), f(2), f(3), f(4), \dots \quad \text{or} \quad 1, \frac{1}{2}, \frac{1}{3}, \frac{1}{4}, \dots$$

The list never ends, as the ellipsis indicates. The numbers in this ordered list are called the **terms** of the sequence.

In dealing with sequences, we usually use subscripted letters, such as a_1, to represent the first term, a_2 for the second term, a_3 for the third term, and so on. For the sequence $f(n) = \dfrac{1}{n}$, we write

$$a_1 = f(1) = 1, \quad a_2 = f(2) = \frac{1}{2}, \quad a_3 = f(3) = \frac{1}{3}, \quad a_4 = f(4) = \frac{1}{4}, \dots, \quad a_n = f(n) = \frac{1}{n}, \dots$$

In other words, we usually do not use the traditional function notation $f(n)$ for sequences. For this particular sequence, we have a rule for the nth term, which is $a_n = \dfrac{1}{n}$, so it is easy to find any term of the sequence.

When a formula for the nth term (sometimes called the **general term**) of a sequence is known, rather than write out the terms of the sequence, we usually represent the entire sequence by placing braces around the formula for the nth term.

For example, the sequence whose nth term is $b_n = \left(\dfrac{1}{2}\right)^n$ may be represented as

$$\{b_n\} = \left\{\left(\frac{1}{2}\right)^n\right\}$$

or by

$$b_1 = \frac{1}{2}, \quad b_2 = \frac{1}{4}, \quad b_3 = \frac{1}{8}, \dots, \quad b_n = \left(\frac{1}{2}\right)^n, \dots$$

EXAMPLE 1	Writing the First Several Terms of a Sequence

Write down the first six terms of the following sequence and graph it.

$$\{a_n\} = \left\{\frac{n-1}{n}\right\}$$

Algebraic Solution

The first six terms of the sequence are

$$a_1 = \frac{1-1}{1} = 0, \quad a_2 = \frac{1}{2}, \quad a_3 = \frac{2}{3},$$

$$a_4 = \frac{3}{4}, \quad a_5 = \frac{4}{5}, \quad a_6 = \frac{5}{6}$$

See Figure 2 for the graph.

Figure 2

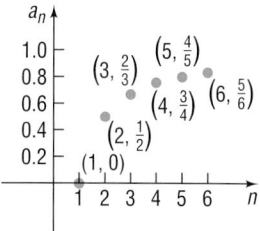

Graphing Solution

Figure 3 shows the sequence generated on a TI-84 Plus graphing calculator. We can see the first few terms of the sequence on the screen. You need to press the right arrow key to scroll right to see the remaining terms of the sequence.

Figure 3

We could also obtain the terms of the sequence using the TABLE feature. First, put the graphing utility in SEQuence mode. Press $Y=$ and enter the formula for the sequence into the graphing utility. See Figure 4. Set up the table with TblStart $= 1$ and ΔTbl $= 1$. See Table 1. Finally, we can graph the sequence. See Figure 5. Notice that the first term of the sequence is not visible since it lies on the x-axis. TRACEing the graph will allow you to determine the terms of the sequence.

Figure 4

Table 1

Figure 5

✏️═══ **Now Work** PROBLEM 19

We will usually provide solutions done by hand. The reader is encouraged to verify solutions using a graphing utility.

| EXAMPLE 2 | **Writing the First Several Terms of a Sequence** |

Write down the first six terms of the following sequence and graph it.

$$\{b_n\} = \left\{(-1)^{n+1}\left(\frac{2}{n}\right)\right\}$$

Figure 6

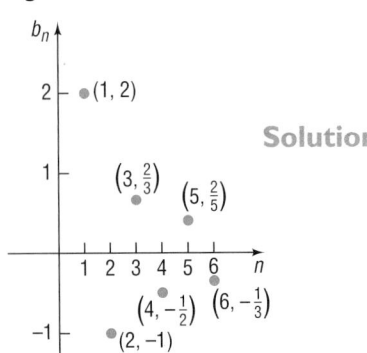

Solution   The first six terms of the sequence are

$$b_1 = 2, \quad b_2 = -1, \quad b_3 = \frac{2}{3}, \quad b_4 = -\frac{1}{2}, \quad b_5 = \frac{2}{5}, \quad b_6 = -\frac{1}{3}$$

See Figure 6 for the graph.

Notice in the sequence $\{b_n\}$ in Example 2 that the signs of the terms **alternate.** When this occurs, we use factors such as $(-1)^{n+1}$, which equals 1 if n is odd and -1 if n is even, or $(-1)^n$, which equals -1 if n is odd and 1 if n is even.

| EXAMPLE 3 | **Writing the First Several Terms of a Sequence** |

Write down the first six terms of the following sequence and graph it.

$$\{c_n\} = \begin{cases} n & \text{if } n \text{ is even} \\ \dfrac{1}{n} & \text{if } n \text{ is odd} \end{cases}$$

Figure 7

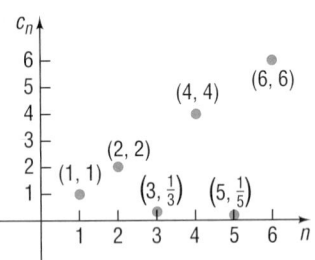

Solution   The first six terms of the sequence are

$$c_1 = 1, \quad c_2 = 2, \quad c_3 = \frac{1}{3}, \quad c_4 = 4, \quad c_5 = \frac{1}{5}, \quad c_6 = 6$$

See Figure 7 for the graph.

━━━ **Now Work**   PROBLEM 21

Sometimes a sequence is indicated by an observed pattern in the first few terms that makes it possible to infer the makeup of the nth term. In the example that follows, a sufficient number of terms of the sequence is given so that a natural choice for the nth term is suggested.

| EXAMPLE 4 | **Determining a Sequence from a Pattern** |

(a) $e, \dfrac{e^2}{2}, \dfrac{e^3}{3}, \dfrac{e^4}{4}, \ldots$ $a_n = \dfrac{e^n}{n}$

(b) $1, \dfrac{1}{3}, \dfrac{1}{9}, \dfrac{1}{27}, \ldots$ $b_n = \dfrac{1}{3^{n-1}}$

(c) $1, 3, 5, 7, \ldots$ $c_n = 2n - 1$

(d) $1, 4, 9, 16, 25, \ldots$ $d_n = n^2$

(e) $1, -\dfrac{1}{2}, \dfrac{1}{3}, -\dfrac{1}{4}, \dfrac{1}{5}, \ldots$ $e_n = (-1)^{n+1}\left(\dfrac{1}{n}\right)$

━━━ **Now Work**   PROBLEM 29

The Factorial Symbol

DEFINITION   If $n \geq 0$ is an integer, the **factorial symbol** $n!$ is defined as follows:

$$0! = 1 \qquad 1! = 1$$
$$n! = n(n-1) \cdot \cdots \cdot 3 \cdot 2 \cdot 1 \qquad \text{if } n \geq 2$$

In other words, we usually do not use the traditional function notation $f(n)$ for sequences. For this particular sequence, we have a rule for the nth term, which is $a_n = \dfrac{1}{n}$, so it is easy to find any term of the sequence.

When a formula for the nth term (sometimes called the **general term**) of a sequence is known, rather than write out the terms of the sequence, we usually represent the entire sequence by placing braces around the formula for the nth term.

For example, the sequence whose nth term is $b_n = \left(\dfrac{1}{2}\right)^n$ may be represented as

$$\{b_n\} = \left\{\left(\dfrac{1}{2}\right)^n\right\}$$

or by

$$b_1 = \dfrac{1}{2}, \quad b_2 = \dfrac{1}{4}, \quad b_3 = \dfrac{1}{8}, \dots, \quad b_n = \left(\dfrac{1}{2}\right)^n, \dots$$

EXAMPLE 1	Writing the First Several Terms of a Sequence

Write down the first six terms of the following sequence and graph it.

$$\{a_n\} = \left\{\dfrac{n-1}{n}\right\}$$

Algebraic Solution

The first six terms of the sequence are

$$a_1 = \dfrac{1-1}{1} = 0, \quad a_2 = \dfrac{1}{2}, \quad a_3 = \dfrac{2}{3},$$

$$a_4 = \dfrac{3}{4}, \quad a_5 = \dfrac{4}{5}, \quad a_6 = \dfrac{5}{6}$$

See Figure 2 for the graph.

Figure 2

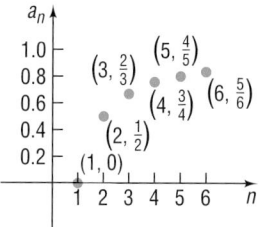

Graphing Solution

Figure 3 shows the sequence generated on a TI-84 Plus graphing calculator. We can see the first few terms of the sequence on the screen. You need to press the right arrow key to scroll right to see the remaining terms of the sequence.

We could also obtain the terms of the sequence using the TABLE feature. First, put the graphing utility in SEQuence mode. Press $Y=$ and enter the formula for the sequence into the graphing utility. See Figure 4. Set up the table with TblStart $= 1$ and ΔTbl $= 1$. See Table 1. Finally, we can graph the sequence. See Figure 5. Notice that the first term of the sequence is not visible since it lies on the x-axis. TRACEing the graph will allow you to determine the terms of the sequence.

Figure 3

Figure 4   **Table 1**   **Figure 5**

Now Work PROBLEM 19

We will usually provide solutions done by hand. The reader is encouraged to verify solutions using a graphing utility.

| EXAMPLE 2 | **Writing the First Several Terms of a Sequence** |

Write down the first six terms of the following sequence and graph it.

$$\{b_n\} = \left\{ (-1)^{n+1}\left(\frac{2}{n}\right) \right\}$$

Figure 6

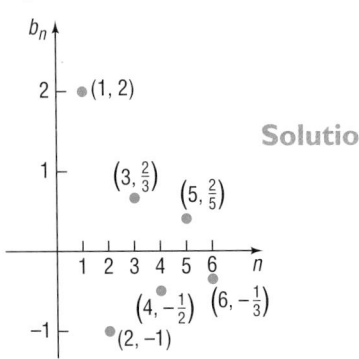

Solution   The first six terms of the sequence are

$$b_1 = 2, \quad b_2 = -1, \quad b_3 = \frac{2}{3}, \quad b_4 = -\frac{1}{2}, \quad b_5 = \frac{2}{5}, \quad b_6 = -\frac{1}{3}$$

See Figure 6 for the graph.

Notice in the sequence $\{b_n\}$ in Example 2 that the signs of the terms **alternate.** When this occurs, we use factors such as $(-1)^{n+1}$, which equals 1 if n is odd and -1 if n is even, or $(-1)^n$, which equals -1 if n is odd and 1 if n is even.

| EXAMPLE 3 | **Writing the First Several Terms of a Sequence** |

Write down the first six terms of the following sequence and graph it.

$$\{c_n\} = \begin{cases} n & \text{if } n \text{ is even} \\ \dfrac{1}{n} & \text{if } n \text{ is odd} \end{cases}$$

Figure 7

Solution   The first six terms of the sequence are

$$c_1 = 1, \quad c_2 = 2, \quad c_3 = \frac{1}{3}, \quad c_4 = 4, \quad c_5 = \frac{1}{5}, \quad c_6 = 6$$

See Figure 7 for the graph.

Figure 7 shows points: $(1, 1)$, $(2, 2)$, $\left(3, \frac{1}{3}\right)$, $(4, 4)$, $\left(5, \frac{1}{5}\right)$, $(6, 6)$

━━━ **Now Work**   PROBLEM 21

Sometimes a sequence is indicated by an observed pattern in the first few terms that makes it possible to infer the makeup of the nth term. In the example that follows, a sufficient number of terms of the sequence is given so that a natural choice for the nth term is suggested.

| EXAMPLE 4 | **Determining a Sequence from a Pattern** |

(a) $e, \dfrac{e^2}{2}, \dfrac{e^3}{3}, \dfrac{e^4}{4}, \ldots$ $a_n = \dfrac{e^n}{n}$

(b) $1, \dfrac{1}{3}, \dfrac{1}{9}, \dfrac{1}{27}, \ldots$ $b_n = \dfrac{1}{3^{n-1}}$

(c) $1, 3, 5, 7, \ldots$ $c_n = 2n - 1$

(d) $1, 4, 9, 16, 25, \ldots$ $d_n = n^2$

(e) $1, -\dfrac{1}{2}, \dfrac{1}{3}, -\dfrac{1}{4}, \dfrac{1}{5}, \ldots$ $e_n = (-1)^{n+1}\left(\dfrac{1}{n}\right)$

━━━ **Now Work**   PROBLEM 29

The Factorial Symbol

DEFINITION   If $n \geq 0$ is an integer, the **factorial symbol $n!$** is defined as follows:

$$0! = 1 \qquad 1! = 1$$
$$n! = n(n - 1) \cdot \cdots \cdot 3 \cdot 2 \cdot 1 \qquad \text{if } n \geq 2$$

Table 2

n	n!
0	1
1	1
2	2
3	6
4	24
5	120
6	720

For example, $2! = 2 \cdot 1 = 2$, $3! = 3 \cdot 2 \cdot 1 = 6$, $4! = 4 \cdot 3 \cdot 2 \cdot 1 = 24$, and so on. Table 2 lists the values of $n!$ for $0 \le n \le 6$.

Because

$$n! = \underbrace{n(n-1)(n-2) \cdot \ldots \cdot 3 \cdot 2 \cdot 1}_{(n-1)!}$$

we can use the formula

$$n! = n(n-1)!$$

to find successive factorials. For example, because $6! = 720$, we have

$$7! = 7 \cdot 6! = 7(720) = 5040$$

and

$$8! = 8 \cdot 7! = 8(5040) = 40{,}320$$

NOTE Your calculator has a factorial key. Use it to see how fast factorials increase in value. Find the value of 69!. What happens when you try to find 70!? In fact, 70! is larger than 10^{100} (a *googol*), larger than most calculators can display. ∎

— **Now Work**   PROBLEM 13

2 Write the Terms of a Sequence Defined by a Recursive Formula

A second way of defining a sequence is to assign a value to the first (or the first few) term(s) and specify the nth term by a formula or equation that involves one or more of the terms preceding it. Sequences defined this way are said to be defined **recursively,** and the rule or formula is called a **recursive formula.**

EXAMPLE 5	Writing the Terms of a Recursively Defined Sequence

Write down the first five terms of the following recursively defined sequence.

$$s_1 = 1, \qquad s_n = n s_{n-1}$$

Algebraic Solution

The first term is given as $s_1 = 1$. To get the second term, we use $n = 2$ in the formula $s_n = n s_{n-1}$ to get $s_2 = 2 s_1 = 2 \cdot 1 = 2$. To get the third term, we use $n = 3$ in the formula to get $s_3 = 3 s_2 = 3 \cdot 2 = 6$. To get a new term requires that we know the value of the preceding term. The first five terms are

$$s_1 = 1$$
$$s_2 = 2 \cdot 1 = 2$$
$$s_3 = 3 \cdot 2 = 6$$
$$s_4 = 4 \cdot 6 = 24$$
$$s_5 = 5 \cdot 24 = 120$$

Do you recognize this sequence? $s_n = n!$.

Graphing Solution

First, put the graphing utility into SEQuence mode. Press $Y =$ and enter the recursive formula into the graphing utility. See Figure 8(a). Next, set up the viewing window to generate the desired sequence. Finally, graph the recursive relation and use TRACE to determine the terms in the sequence. See Figure 8(b). For example, we see that the fourth term of the sequence is 24. Table 3 also shows the terms of the sequence.

Figure 8

(a)

Table 3

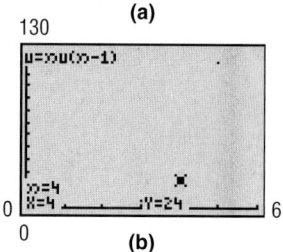

(b)

| EXAMPLE 6 | Writing the Terms of a Recursively Defined Sequence |

Write down the first five terms of the following recursively defined sequence.

$$u_1 = 1, \qquad u_2 = 1, \qquad u_{n+2} = u_n + u_{n+1}$$

Solution We are given the first two terms. To get the third term requires that we know each of the previous two terms. That is,

$$u_1 = 1$$
$$u_2 = 1$$
$$u_3 = u_1 + u_2 = 1 + 1 = 2$$
$$u_4 = u_2 + u_3 = 1 + 2 = 3$$
$$u_5 = u_3 + u_4 = 2 + 3 = 5$$

The sequence defined in Example 6 is called the **Fibonacci sequence,** and the terms of this sequence are called **Fibonacci numbers.** These numbers appear in a wide variety of applications (see Problems 91–94).

➤ **Now Work** PROBLEMS 37 AND 45

3 Use Summation Notation

It is often important to be able to find the sum of the first n terms of a sequence $\{a_n\}$, that is,

$$a_1 + a_2 + a_3 + \cdots + a_n$$

Rather than write down all these terms, we introduce a more concise way to express the sum, called **summation notation.** Using summation notation, we would write the sum as

$$a_1 + a_2 + a_3 + \cdots + a_n = \sum_{k=1}^{n} a_k$$

The symbol Σ (the Greek letter sigma, which is an S in our alphabet) is an instruction to sum, or add up, the terms. The integer k is called the **index** of the sum; it tells you where to start the sum and where to end it. The expression

$$\sum_{k=1}^{n} a_k$$

is an instruction to add the terms a_k of the sequence $\{a_n\}$ starting with $k = 1$ and ending with $k = n$. We read the expression as "the sum of a_k from $k = 1$ to $k = n$."

| EXAMPLE 7 | Expanding Summation Notation |

Write out each sum.

(a) $\sum_{k=1}^{10} \dfrac{1}{k}$

(b) $\sum_{k=1}^{n} k!$

Solution (a) $\sum_{k=1}^{10} \dfrac{1}{k} = 1 + \dfrac{1}{2} + \dfrac{1}{3} + \cdots + \dfrac{1}{10}$

(b) $\sum_{k=1}^{n} k! = 1! + 2! + \cdots + n!$

| EXAMPLE 8 | Writing a Sum in Summation Notation |

Express each sum using summation notation.

(a) $1^2 + 2^2 + 3^2 + \cdots + 9^2$

(b) $1 + \dfrac{1}{2} + \dfrac{1}{4} + \dfrac{1}{8} + \cdots + \dfrac{1}{2^{n-1}}$

Solution (a) The sum $1^2 + 2^2 + 3^2 + \cdots + 9^2$ has 9 terms, each of the form k^2, and starts at $k = 1$ and ends at $k = 9$:

$$1^2 + 2^2 + 3^2 + \cdots + 9^2 = \sum_{k=1}^{9} k^2$$

(b) The sum

$$1 + \frac{1}{2} + \frac{1}{4} + \frac{1}{8} + \cdots + \frac{1}{2^{n-1}}$$

has n terms, each of the form $\dfrac{1}{2^{k-1}}$, and starts at $k = 1$ and ends at $k = n$:

$$1 + \frac{1}{2} + \frac{1}{4} + \frac{1}{8} + \cdots + \frac{1}{2^{n-1}} = \sum_{k=1}^{n} \frac{1}{2^{k-1}}$$

The index of summation need not always begin at 1 or end at n; for example, we could have expressed the sum in Example 8(b) as

$$\sum_{k=0}^{n-1} \frac{1}{2^k} = 1 + \frac{1}{2} + \frac{1}{4} + \cdots + \frac{1}{2^{n-1}}$$

Letters other than k may be used as the index. For example,

$$\sum_{j=1}^{n} j! \quad \text{and} \quad \sum_{i=1}^{n} i!$$

each represent the same sum as the one given in Example 7(b).

━━━ **Now Work** PROBLEMS 53 AND 63

4 Find the Sum of a Sequence Algebraically and Using a Graphing Utility

Next we list some properties of sequences using summation notation. These properties are useful for adding the terms of a sequence algebraically.

THEOREM

Properties of Sequences

If $\{a_n\}$ and $\{b_n\}$ are two sequences and c is a real number, then:

$$\sum_{k=1}^{n} (ca_k) = ca_1 + ca_2 + \cdots + ca_n = c(a_1 + a_2 + \cdots + a_n) = c \sum_{k=1}^{n} a_k \quad \textbf{(1)}$$

$$\sum_{k=1}^{n} (a_k + b_k) = \sum_{k=1}^{n} a_k + \sum_{k=1}^{n} b_k \quad \textbf{(2)}$$

$$\sum_{k=1}^{n} (a_k - b_k) = \sum_{k=1}^{n} a_k - \sum_{k=1}^{n} b_k \quad \textbf{(3)}$$

$$\sum_{k=j+1}^{n} a_k = \sum_{k=1}^{n} a_k - \sum_{k=1}^{j} a_k, \quad \text{where } 0 < j < n \quad \textbf{(4)}$$

The proof of property (1) follows from the distributive property of real numbers. The proofs of properties 2 and 3 are based on the commutative and associative properties of real numbers. Property (4) states that the sum from $j + 1$ to n equals the sum from 1 to n minus the sum from 1 to j. It can be helpful to employ this property when the index of summation begins at a number larger than 1.

Next we give some formulas for finding the sums of certain sequences.

THEOREM **Formulas for Sums of Sequences**

$$\sum_{k=1}^{n} c = \underbrace{c + c + \cdots + c}_{n \text{ terms}} = cn \qquad c \text{ is a real number} \qquad \textbf{(5)}$$

$$\sum_{k=1}^{n} k = 1 + 2 + 3 + \cdots + n = \frac{n(n+1)}{2} \qquad \textbf{(6)}$$

$$\sum_{k=1}^{n} k^2 = 1^2 + 2^2 + 3^2 + \cdots + n^2 = \frac{n(n+1)(2n+1)}{6} \qquad \textbf{(7)}$$

$$\sum_{k=1}^{n} k^3 = 1^3 + 2^3 + 3^3 + \cdots + n^3 = \left[\frac{n(n+1)}{2}\right]^2 \qquad \textbf{(8)}$$

The proof of formula (5) follows from the definition of summation notation. You are asked to prove formula (6) in Problem 102. The proofs of formulas (7) and (8) require mathematical induction, which is discussed in Section 12.4.

Notice the difference between formulas (5) and (6). In (5), the constant c is being summed from 1 to n, while in (6) the index of summation k is being summed from 1 to n.

EXAMPLE 9 **Finding the Sum of a Sequence**

Find the sum of each sequence.

(a) $\displaystyle\sum_{k=1}^{5} (3k)$ (b) $\displaystyle\sum_{k=1}^{10} (k^3 + 1)$

(c) $\displaystyle\sum_{k=1}^{24} (k^2 - 7k + 2)$ (d) $\displaystyle\sum_{k=6}^{20} (4k^2)$

Algebraic Solution

(a) $\displaystyle\sum_{k=1}^{5} (3k) = 3\sum_{k=1}^{5} k$ Property (1)

$\qquad = 3\left(\dfrac{5(5+1)}{2}\right)$ Formula (6)

$\qquad = 3(15)$

$\qquad = 45$

(b) $\displaystyle\sum_{k=1}^{10} (k^3 + 1) = \sum_{k=1}^{10} k^3 + \sum_{k=1}^{10} 1$ Property (2)

$\qquad = \left(\dfrac{10(10+1)}{2}\right)^2 + 1(10)$ Formulas (8) and (5)

$\qquad = 3025 + 10$

$\qquad = 3035$

Graphing Solution

(a) Figure 9 shows the solution using a TI-84 Plus graphing calculator. So $\displaystyle\sum_{k=1}^{5} (3k) = 45$.

Figure 9

```
sum(seq(3n,n,1,5
,1))
              45
```

(b) Figure 10 shows the solution using a TI-84 Plus graphing calculator.

So $\displaystyle\sum_{k=1}^{10} (k^3 + 1) = 3035$.

Figure 10

```
sum(seq(n^3+1,n,
1,10,1))
            3035
```

(c) $\displaystyle\sum_{k=1}^{24}(k^2 - 7k + 2) = \sum_{k=1}^{24}k^2 - \sum_{k=1}^{24}(7k) + \sum_{k=1}^{24}2$ Properties (2) and (3)

$\displaystyle = \sum_{k=1}^{24}k^2 - 7\sum_{k=1}^{24}k + \sum_{k=1}^{24}2$ Property (1)

$\displaystyle = \frac{24(24+1)(2\cdot24+1)}{6} - 7\left(\frac{24(24+1)}{2}\right) + 2(24)$ Formulas (7), (6), (5)

$= 4900 - 2100 + 48$

$= 2848$

(d) Notice that the index of summation starts at 6. We use property (4) as follows:

$$\sum_{k=6}^{20}(4k^2) = 4\sum_{k=6}^{20}k^2 = 4\left[\sum_{k=1}^{20}k^2 - \sum_{k=1}^{5}k^2\right] = 4\left[\frac{20(21)(41)}{6} - \frac{5(6)(11)}{6}\right]$$

        ↑   ↑   ↑

   Property (1)   Property (4)   Formula (7)

$$= 4[2870 - 55] = 11{,}260$$

(c) Figure 11 shows the solution using a TI-84 Plus graphing calculator.

Figure 11

```
sum(seq(n²−7n+2,
n,1,24,1))
              2848
```

(d) Figure 12 shows the solution using a TI-84 Plus graphing calculator.

Figure 12

```
sum(seq(4n²,n,6,
20,1))
             11260
```

— **Now Work** PROBLEM 75

5 Solve Annuity and Amortization Problems

In Section 5.7 we developed the compound interest formula, which gives the future value when a fixed amount of money is deposited in an account that pays interest compounded periodically. Often, though, money is invested in small amounts at periodic intervals. An **annuity** is a sequence of equal periodic deposits. The periodic deposits may be made annually, quarterly, monthly, or daily.

When deposits are made at the same time that the interest is credited, the annuity is called **ordinary**. We will only deal with ordinary annuities here. The **amount of an annuity** is the sum of all deposits made plus all interest paid.

Suppose that the initial amount deposited in an annuity is $\$M$, the periodic deposit is $\$P$, and the per annum rate of interest is $r\%$ (expressed as a decimal) compounded N times per year. The periodic deposit is made at the same time that the interest is credited, so N deposits are made per year. The amount A_n of the annuity after n deposits will equal A_{n-1}, the amount of the annuity after $n - 1$ deposits, plus the interest earned on this amount, plus P, the periodic deposit. That is,

$$A_n = A_{n-1} + \frac{r}{N}A_{n-1} + P = \left(1 + \frac{r}{N}\right)A_{n-1} + P$$

     ↑   ↑   ↑   ↑

   Amount   Amount   Interest   Periodic

   after   in previous   earned   deposit

  n deposits   period

We have established the following result:

THEOREM   **Annuity Formula**

If $A_0 = M$ represents the initial amount deposited in an annuity that earns $r\%$ per annum compounded N times per year, and if P is the periodic deposit made at each payment period, then the amount A_n of the annuity after n deposits is given by the recursive sequence

$$A_0 = M, \qquad A_n = \left(1 + \frac{r}{N}\right)A_{n-1} + P, \qquad n \geq 1 \qquad \textbf{(9)}$$

Formula (9) may be explained as follows: the money in the account initially, A_0, is M; the money in the account after $n - 1$ payments, A_{n-1}, earns interest $\dfrac{r}{N}$ during the nth period; so when the periodic payment of P dollars is added, the amount after n payments, A_n, is obtained.

EXAMPLE 10 **Saving for Spring Break**

A trip to Cancun during spring break will cost $450 and full payment is due March 2. To have the money, a student, on September 1, deposits $100 in a savings account that pays 4% per annum compounded monthly. On the first of each month, the student deposits $50 in this account.

(a) Find a recursive sequence that explains how much is in the account after n months.

(b) Use the TABLE feature to list the amounts of the annuity for the first 6 months.

(c) After the deposit on March 1 is made, is there enough in the account to pay for the Cancun trip?

(d) If the student deposits $60 each month, will there be enough for the trip after the March 1 deposit?

Solution (a) The initial amount deposited in the account is $A_0 = \$100$. The monthly deposit is $P = \$50$, and the per annum rate of interest is $r = 0.04$ compounded $N = 12$ times per year. The amount A_n in the account after n monthly deposits is given by the recursive sequence

$$A_0 = 100, \qquad A_n = \left(1 + \frac{r}{N}\right)A_{n-1} + P = \left(1 + \frac{0.04}{12}\right)A_{n-1} + 50$$

Table 4

n	$u(n)$
0	100
1	150.33
2	200.83
3	251.5
4	302.34
5	353.35
6	404.53

$u(n) \text{B}(1+.04/12)...$

(b) In SEQuence mode on a TI-84 Plus, enter the sequence $\{A_n\}$ and create Table 4. On September 1 ($n = 0$), there is $100 in the account. After the first payment on October 1, the value of the account is $150.33. After the second payment on November 1, the value of the account is $200.83. After the third payment on December 1, the value of the account is $251.50, and so on.

(c) On March 1 ($n = 6$), there is only $404.53, not enough to pay for the trip to Cancun.

(d) If the periodic deposit, P, is $60, then on March 1, there is $465.03 in the account, enough for the trip. See Table 5.

Table 5

n	$u(n)$
0	100
1	160.33
2	220.87
3	281.6
4	342.54
5	403.68
6	465.03

$u(n) \text{B}(1+.04/12)...$

Recursive sequences can also be used to compute information about loans. When equal periodic payments are made to pay off a loan, the loan is said to be **amortized.**

THEOREM **Amortization Formula**

If B is borrowed at an interest rate of $r\%$ (expressed as a decimal) per annum compounded monthly, the balance A_n due after n monthly payments of P is given by the recursive sequence

$$A_0 = B, \qquad A_n = \left(1 + \frac{r}{12}\right)A_{n-1} - P, \qquad n \geq 1 \qquad \textbf{(10)}$$

Formula (10) may be explained as follows: The initial loan balance is B. The balance due A_n after n payments will equal the balance due previously, A_{n-1}, plus the interest charged on that amount, reduced by the periodic payment P.

| EXAMPLE 11 | Mortgage Payments |

Table 6

John and Wanda borrowed $180,000 at 7% per annum compounded monthly for 30 years to purchase a home. Their monthly payment is determined to be $1197.54.

(a) Find a recursive formula that represents their balance after each payment of $1197.54 has been made.

(b) Determine their balance after the first payment is made.

(c) When will their balance be below $170,000?

Solution

(a) We use formula (10) with $A_0 = 180,000$, $r = 0.07$, and $P = \$1197.54$. Then

Table 7

$$A_0 = 180,000 \qquad A_n = \left(1 + \frac{0.07}{12}\right)A_{n-1} - 1197.54$$

(b) In SEQuence mode on a TI-84 Plus, enter the sequence $\{A_n\}$ and create Table 6. After the first payment is made, the balance is $A_1 = \$179,852$.

(c) Scroll down until the balance is below $170,000. See Table 7. After the fifty-eighth payment is made ($n = 58$), or 4 years, 10 months, the balance is below $170,000.

Now Work PROBLEM 83

12.1 Assess Your Understanding

'Are You Prepared?' *Answers are given at the end of these exercises. If you get a wrong answer, read the pages listed in red.*

1. For the function $f(x) = \dfrac{x-1}{x}$, find $f(2)$ and $f(3)$. (pp. 60–62)

2. *True or False* A function is a relation between two sets D and R so that each element x in the first set D is related to exactly one element y in the second set R. (pp. 56–60)

3. If $1000 is invested at 4% per annum compounded semiannually, how much is in the account after 2 years? (pp. 313–317)

4. How much do you need to invest now at 5% per annum compounded monthly so that in 1 year you will have $10,000? (p. 318)

Concepts and Vocabulary

5. A(n) _____ is a function whose domain is the set of positive integers.

6. For the sequence $\{s_n\} = \{4n - 1\}$, the first term is $s_1 = $ _____ and the fourth term is $s_4 = $ _____.

7. $\displaystyle\sum_{k=1}^{4} (2k) = $ _____.

8. *True or False* Sequences are sometimes defined recursively.

9. *True or False* A sequence is a function.

10. *True or False* $\displaystyle\sum_{k=1}^{2} k = 3$

Skill Building

In Problems 11–16, evaluate each factorial expression. Verify your results using a graphing utility.

11. 10!

12. 9!

13. $\dfrac{9!}{6!}$

14. $\dfrac{12!}{10!}$

15. $\dfrac{3! \, 7!}{4!}$

16. $\dfrac{5! \, 8!}{3!}$

In Problems 17–28, write down the first five terms of each sequence. Verify your results using a graphing utility.

17. $\{s_n\} = \{n\}$

18. $\{s_n\} = \{n^2 + 1\}$

19. $\{a_n\} = \left\{\dfrac{n}{n+2}\right\}$

20. $\{b_n\} = \left\{\dfrac{2n+1}{2n}\right\}$

21. $\{c_n\} = \{(-1)^{n+1} n^2\}$

22. $\{d_n\} = \left\{(-1)^{n-1}\left(\dfrac{n}{2n-1}\right)\right\}$

23. $\{s_n\} = \left\{\dfrac{2^n}{3^n + 1}\right\}$

24. $\{s_n\} = \left\{\left(\dfrac{4}{3}\right)^n\right\}$

25. $\{t_n\} = \left\{\dfrac{(-1)^n}{(n+1)(n+2)}\right\}$

26. $\{a_n\} = \left\{\dfrac{3^n}{n}\right\}$

27. $\{b_n\} = \left\{\dfrac{n}{e^n}\right\}$

28. $\{c_n\} = \left\{\dfrac{n^2}{2^n}\right\}$

In Problems 29–36, the given pattern continues. Write down the nth term of a sequence $\{a_n\}$ suggested by the pattern.

29. $\dfrac{1}{2}, \dfrac{2}{3}, \dfrac{3}{4}, \dfrac{4}{5}, \dots$

30. $\dfrac{1}{1 \cdot 2}, \dfrac{1}{2 \cdot 3}, \dfrac{1}{3 \cdot 4}, \dfrac{1}{4 \cdot 5}, \dots$

31. $1, \dfrac{1}{2}, \dfrac{1}{4}, \dfrac{1}{8}, \dots$

32. $\dfrac{2}{3}, \dfrac{4}{9}, \dfrac{8}{27}, \dfrac{16}{81}, \dots$

33. $1, -1, 1, -1, 1, -1, \dots$

34. $1, \dfrac{1}{2}, 3, \dfrac{1}{4}, 5, \dfrac{1}{6}, 7, \dfrac{1}{8}, \dots$

35. $1, -2, 3, -4, 5, -6, \dots$

36. $2, -4, 6, -8, 10, \dots$

In Problems 37–50, a sequence is defined recursively. Write down the first five terms. Verify your results using a graphing utility, when possible.

37. $a_1 = 2; \quad a_n = 3 + a_{n-1}$

38. $a_1 = 3; \quad a_n = 4 - a_{n-1}$

39. $a_1 = -2; \quad a_n = n + a_{n-1}$

40. $a_1 = 1; \quad a_n = n - a_{n-1}$

41. $a_1 = 5; \quad a_n = 2a_{n-1}$

42. $a_1 = 2; \quad a_n = -a_{n-1}$

43. $a_1 = 3; \quad a_n = \dfrac{a_{n-1}}{n}$

44. $a_1 = -2; \quad a_n = n + 3a_{n-1}$

45. $a_1 = 1; \quad a_2 = 2; \quad a_n = a_{n-1} \cdot a_{n-2}$

46. $a_1 = -1; \quad a_2 = 1; \quad a_n = a_{n-2} + na_{n-1}$

47. $a_1 = A; \quad a_n = a_{n-1} + d$

48. $a_1 = A; \quad a_n = ra_{n-1}, \quad r \neq 0$

49. $a_1 = \sqrt{2}; \quad a_n = \sqrt{2 + a_{n-1}}$

50. $a_1 = \sqrt{2}; \quad a_n = \sqrt{\dfrac{a_{n-1}}{2}}$

In Problems 51–60, write out each sum.

51. $\displaystyle\sum_{k=1}^{n} (k + 2)$

52. $\displaystyle\sum_{k=1}^{n} (2k + 1)$

53. $\displaystyle\sum_{k=1}^{n} \dfrac{k^2}{2}$

54. $\displaystyle\sum_{k=1}^{n} (k + 1)^2$

55. $\displaystyle\sum_{k=0}^{n} \dfrac{1}{3^k}$

56. $\displaystyle\sum_{k=0}^{n} \left(\dfrac{3}{2}\right)^k$

57. $\displaystyle\sum_{k=0}^{n-1} \dfrac{1}{3^{k+1}}$

58. $\displaystyle\sum_{k=0}^{n-1} (2k + 1)$

59. $\displaystyle\sum_{k=2}^{n} (-1)^k \ln k$

60. $\displaystyle\sum_{k=3}^{n} (-1)^{k+1} 2^k$

In Problems 61–70, express each sum using summation notation.

61. $1 + 2 + 3 + \cdots + 20$

62. $1^3 + 2^3 + 3^3 + \cdots + 8^3$

63. $\dfrac{1}{2} + \dfrac{2}{3} + \dfrac{3}{4} + \cdots + \dfrac{13}{13 + 1}$

64. $1 + 3 + 5 + 7 + \cdots + [2(12) - 1]$

65. $1 - \dfrac{1}{3} + \dfrac{1}{9} - \dfrac{1}{27} + \cdots + (-1)^6 \left(\dfrac{1}{3^6}\right)$

66. $\dfrac{2}{3} - \dfrac{4}{9} + \dfrac{8}{27} - \cdots + (-1)^{12} \left(\dfrac{2}{3}\right)^{11}$

67. $3 + \dfrac{3^2}{2} + \dfrac{3^3}{3} + \cdots + \dfrac{3^n}{n}$

68. $\dfrac{1}{e} + \dfrac{2}{e^2} + \dfrac{3}{e^3} + \cdots + \dfrac{n}{e^n}$

69. $a + (a + d) + (a + 2d) + \cdots + (a + nd)$

70. $a + ar + ar^2 + \cdots + ar^{n-1}$

In Problems 71–82, find the sum of each sequence. Verify your results using a graphing utility.

71. $\displaystyle\sum_{k=1}^{40} 5$

72. $\displaystyle\sum_{k=1}^{50} 8$

73. $\displaystyle\sum_{k=1}^{40} k$

74. $\displaystyle\sum_{k=1}^{24} (-k)$

75. $\displaystyle\sum_{k=1}^{20} (5k + 3)$

76. $\displaystyle\sum_{k=1}^{26} (3k - 7)$

77. $\displaystyle\sum_{k=1}^{16} (k^2 + 4)$

78. $\displaystyle\sum_{k=0}^{14} (k^2 - 4)$

79. $\displaystyle\sum_{k=10}^{60} (2k)$

80. $\displaystyle\sum_{k=8}^{40} (-3k)$

81. $\displaystyle\sum_{k=5}^{20} k^3$

82. $\displaystyle\sum_{k=4}^{24} k^3$

Applications and Extensions

83. Credit Card Debt John has a balance of $3000 on his Discover card that charges 1% interest per month on any unpaid balance. John can afford to pay $100 toward the balance each month. His balance each month after making a $100 payment is given by the recursively defined sequence

$$B_0 = \$3000, \qquad B_n = 1.01B_{n-1} - 100$$

    (a) Determine John's balance after making the first payment. That is, determine B_1.

(b) Using a graphing utility, determine when John's balance will be below $2000. How many payments of $100 have been made?

(c) Using a graphing utility, determine when John will pay off the balance. What is the total of all the payments?

(d) What was John's interest expense?

84. Car Loans Phil bought a car by taking out a loan for $18,500 at 0.5% interest per month. Phil's normal monthly payment is $434.47 per month, but he decides that he can afford to pay

$100 extra toward the balance each month. His balance each month is given by the recursively defined sequence

$$B_0 = \$18{,}500, \qquad B_n = 1.005B_{n-1} - 534.47$$

(a) Determine Phil's balance after making the first payment. That is, determine B_1.
(b) Using a graphing utility, determine when Phil's balance will be below $10,000. How many payments of $534.47 have been made?
(c) Using a graphing utility, determine when Phil will pay off the balance. What is the total of all the payments?
(d) What was Phil's interest expense?

85. **Trout Population** A pond currently has 2000 trout in it. A fish hatchery decides to add an additional 20 trout each month. In addition, it is known that the trout population is growing 3% per month. The size of the population after n months is given by the recursively defined sequence

$$p_0 = 2000, \qquad p_n = 1.03p_{n-1} + 20$$

(a) How many trout are in the pond at the end of the second month? That is, what is p_2?
(b) Using a graphing utility, determine how long it will be before the trout population reaches 5000.

86. **Environmental Control** The Environmental Protection Agency (EPA) determines that Maple Lake has 250 tons of pollutants as a result of industrial waste and that 10% of the pollutant present is neutralized by solar oxidation every year. The EPA imposes new pollution control laws that result in 15 tons of new pollutant entering the lake each year. The amount of pollutant in the lake at the end of each year is given by the recursively defined sequence

$$p_0 = 250, \qquad p_n = 0.9p_{n-1} + 15$$

(a) Determine the amount of pollutant in the lake at the end of the second year. That is, determine p_2.
(b) Using a graphing utility, provide pollutant amounts for the next 20 years.
(c) What is the equilibrium level of pollution in Maple Lake? That is, what is $\lim\limits_{n \to \infty} p_n$?

87. **Roth IRA** On January 1, 1999, Bob decided to place $500 at the end of each quarter into a Roth Individual Retirement Account.
(a) Find a recursive formula that represents Bob's balance at the end of each quarter if the rate of return is assumed to be 8% per annum compounded quarterly.
(b) How long will it be before the value of the account exceeds $100,000?
(c) What will be the value of the account in 25 years when Bob retires?

88. **Education IRA** On January 1, 1999, John's parents decided to place $45 at the end of each month into an Education IRA.
(a) Find a recursive formula that represents the balance at the end of each month if the rate of return is assumed to be 6% per annum compounded monthly.
(b) How long will it be before the value of the account exceeds $4000?
(c) What will be the value of the account in 16 years when John goes to college?

89. **Home Loan** Bill and Laura borrowed $150,000 at 6% per annum compounded monthly for 30 years to purchase a home. Their monthly payment is determined to be $899.33.
(a) Find a recursive formula for their balance after each monthly payment has been made.

(b) Determine Bill and Laura's balance after the first payment.
(c) Using a graphing utility, create a table showing Bill and Laura's balance after each monthly payment.
(d) Using a graphing utility, determine when Bill and Laura's balance will be below $140,000.
(e) Using a graphing utility, determine when Bill and Laura will pay off the balance.
(f) Determine Bill and Laura's interest expense when the loan is paid.
(g) Suppose that Bill and Laura decide to pay an additional $100 each month on their loan. Answer parts (a) to (f) under this scenario.
(h) Is it worthwhile for Bill and Laura to pay the additional $100? Explain.

90. **Home Loan** Jodi and Jeff borrowed $120,000 at 6.5% per annum compounded monthly for 30 years to purchase a home. Their monthly payment is determined to be $758.48.
(a) Find a recursive formula for their balance after each monthly payment has been made.
(b) Determine Jodi and Jeff's balance after the first payment.
(c) Using a graphing utility, create a table showing Jodi and Jeff's balance after each monthly payment.
(d) Using a graphing utility, determine when Jodi and Jeff's balance will be below $100,000.
(e) Using a graphing utility, determine when Jodi and Jeff will pay off the balance.
(f) Determine Jodi and Jeff's interest expense when the loan is paid.
(g) Suppose that Jodi and Jeff decide to pay an additional $100 each month on their loan. Answer parts (a) to (f) under this scenario.
(h) Is it worthwhile for Jodi and Jeff to pay the additional $100? Explain.

91. **Growth of a Rabbit Colony** A colony of rabbits begins with one pair of mature rabbits, which will produce a pair of offspring (one male, one female) each month. Assume that all rabbits mature in 1 month and produce a pair of offspring (one male, one female) after 2 months. If no rabbits ever die, how many pairs of mature rabbits are there after 7 months?

[**Hint:** The Fibonacci sequence models this colony. Do you see why?]

1 mature pair

1 mature pair

2 mature pairs

3 mature pairs

92. **Fibonacci Sequence** Let

$$u_n = \frac{\left(1 + \sqrt{5}\right)^n - \left(1 - \sqrt{5}\right)^n}{2^n \sqrt{5}}$$

define the nth term of a sequence.
(a) Show that $u_1 = 1$ and $u_2 = 1$.
(b) Show that $u_{n+2} = u_{n+1} + u_n$.
(c) Draw the conclusion that $\{u_n\}$ is the Fibonacci sequence.

93. Pascal's Triangle Divide the triangular array shown (called Pascal's triangle) using diagonal lines as indicated. Find the sum of the numbers in each of these diagonal rows. Do you recognize this sequence?

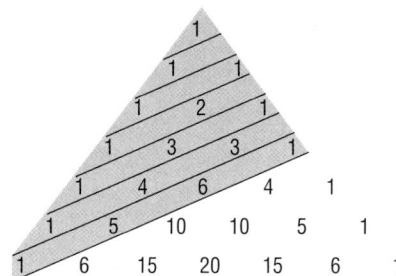

94. Fibonacci Sequence Use the result of Problem 92 to do the following problems:
(a) Write the first 10 terms of the Fibonacci sequence.
(b) Compute the ratio $\dfrac{u_{n+1}}{u_n}$ for the first 10 terms.
(c) As n gets large, what number does the ratio approach? This number is referred to as the **golden ratio.** Rectangles whose sides are in this ratio were considered pleasing to the eye by the Greeks. For example, the facade of the Parthenon was constructed using the golden ratio.
(d) Compute the ratio $\dfrac{u_n}{u_{n+1}}$ for the first 10 terms.
(e) As n gets large, what number does the ratio approach? This number is also referred to as the **conjugate golden ratio.** This ratio is believed to have been used in the construction of the Great Pyramid in Egypt. The ratio equals the sum of the areas of the four face triangles divided by the total surface area of the Great Pyramid.

95. Approximating $f(x) = e^x$ In calculus, it can be shown that

$$f(x) = e^x = \sum_{k=0}^{\infty} \frac{x^k}{k!}$$

We can approximate the value of $f(x) = e^x$ for any x using the following sum:

$$f(x) = e^x \approx \sum_{k=0}^{n} \frac{x^k}{k!}$$

for some n.
(a) Approximate $f(1.3)$ with $n = 4$
(b) Approximate $f(1.3)$ with $n = 7$.
(c) Use a calculator to approximate $f(1.3)$.
(d) Using trial and error along with a graphing utility's SEQuence mode, determine the value of n required to approximate $f(1.3)$ correct to eight decimal places.

96. Approximating $f(x) = e^x$ Refer to Problem 95.
(a) Approximate $f(-2.4)$ with $n = 3$.

(b) Approximate $f(-2.4)$ with $n = 6$.
(c) Use a calculator to approximate $f(-2.4)$.
(d) Using trial and error along with a graphing utility's SEQuence mode, determine the value of n required to approximate $f(-2.4)$ correct to eight decimal places.

97. Bode's Law In 1772, Johann Bode published the following formula for predicting the mean distances, in astronomical units (AU), of the planets from the sun:

$$a_1 = 0.4, \qquad \{a_n\} = \{0.4 + 0.3 \cdot 2^{n-2}\}, n \geq 2$$

where n is the number of the planet from the sun.
(a) Determine the first eight terms of this sequence.
(b) At the time of Bode's publication, the known planets were Mercury (0.39 AU), Venus (0.72 AU), Earth (1 AU), Mars (1.52 AU), Jupiter (5.20 AU), and Saturn (9.54 AU). How do the actual distances compare to the terms of the sequence?
(c) The planet Uranus was discovered in 1781 and the asteroid Ceres was discovered in 1801. The mean orbital distances from the sun to Uranus and Ceres* are 19.2 AU and 2.77 AU, respectively. How well do these values fit within the sequence?
(d) Determine the ninth and tenth terms of Bode's sequence.
(e) The planets Neptune and Pluto* were discovered in 1846 and 1930, respectively. Their mean orbital distances from the sun are 30.07 AU and 39.44 AU, respectively. How do these actual distances compare to the terms of the sequence?
(f) On July 29, 2005, NASA announced the discovery of a tenth planet ($n = 11$), which has temporarily been named 2003 UB313* until a permanent name is decided on. Use Bode's Law to predict the mean orbital distance of 2003 UB313 from the sun. Its actual mean distance is not yet known, but 2003 UB313 is currently about 97 astronomical units from the sun.

Source: NASA.

Computing Square Roots *A method for approximating $\sqrt{p}$ can be traced back to the Babylonians. The formula is given by the recursively defined sequence*

$$a_0 = k \qquad a_n = \frac{1}{2}\left(a_{n-1} + \frac{p}{a_{n-1}}\right)$$

where k is an initial guess as to the value of the square root. Use this recursive formula to approximate the following square roots by finding a_5. Compare this result to the value provided by your calculator.

98. $\sqrt{5}$

99. $\sqrt{8}$

100. $\sqrt{21}$

101. $\sqrt{89}$

*Ceres, Pluto, and 2003 UB313 are now referred to as dwarf planets.

102. Show that

$$1 + 2 + \cdots + (n - 1) + n = \frac{n(n + 1)}{2}$$

[**Hint:** Let

$$S = 1 + 2 + \cdots + (n - 1) + n$$
$$S = n + (n - 1) + (n - 2) + \cdots + 1$$

Add these equations. Then

$$2S = [1 + n] + [2 + (n - 1)] + \cdots + [n + 1]$$

$\underbrace{\qquad\qquad\qquad\qquad\qquad\qquad}_{n \text{ terms in brackets}}$

Now complete the derivation.]

Discussion and Writing

103. Investigate various applications that lead to the Fibonacci sequence, such as art, architecture, or financial markets. Write an essay on these applications.

'Are You Prepared?' Answers

1. $f(2) = \frac{1}{2}; f(3) = \frac{2}{3}$ **2.** True   **3.** $1082.43   **4.** $9513.28

12.2 Arithmetic Sequences

> **OBJECTIVES**   **1** Determine If a Sequence Is Arithmetic (p. 817)
>   **2** Find a Formula for an Arithmetic Sequence (p. 818)
>   **3** Find the Sum of an Arithmetic Sequence (p. 819)

1 Determine If a Sequence Is Arithmetic

When the difference between successive terms of a sequence is always the same number, the sequence is called **arithmetic**.

DEFINITION

An **arithmetic sequence*** may be defined recursively as $a_1 = a$, $a_n - a_{n-1} = d$, or as

$$a_1 = a, \qquad a_n = a_{n-1} + d \qquad \qquad \text{(1)}$$

where $a_1 = a$ and d are real numbers. The number a is the first term, and the number d is called the **common difference**.

The terms of an arithmetic sequence with first term a_1 and common difference d follow the pattern

$$a_1, \quad a_1 + d, \quad a_1 + 2d, \quad a_1 + 3d, \ldots$$

EXAMPLE 1

Determining If a Sequence Is Arithmetic

The sequence

$$4, \quad 6, \quad 8, \quad 10, \ldots$$

is arithmetic since the difference of successive terms is 2. The first term is $a_1 = 4$, and the common difference is $d = 2$.

*Sometimes called an **arithmetic progression**.

EXAMPLE 2	Determining If a Sequence Is Arithmetic

Show that the following sequence is arithmetic. Find the first term and the common difference.

$$\{s_n\} = \{3n + 5\}$$

Solution The first term is $s_1 = 3 \cdot 1 + 5 = 8$. The nth term and the $(n-1)$st term of the sequence $\{s_n\}$ are

$$s_n = 3n + 5 \quad \text{and} \quad s_{n-1} = 3(n-1) + 5 = 3n + 2$$

Their difference d is

$$d = s_n - s_{n-1} = (3n + 5) - (3n + 2) = 5 - 2 = 3$$

Since the difference of any two successive terms is the constant 3, the sequence is arithmetic and the common difference is 3.

EXAMPLE 3	Determining If a Sequence Is Arithmetic

Show that the sequence $\{t_n\} = \{4 - n\}$ is arithmetic. Find the first term and the common difference.

Solution The first term is $t_1 = 4 - 1 = 3$. The nth term and the $(n-1)$st term are

$$t_n = 4 - n \quad \text{and} \quad t_{n-1} = 4 - (n-1) = 5 - n$$

Their difference d is

$$d = t_n - t_{n-1} = (4 - n) - (5 - n) = 4 - 5 = -1$$

Since the difference of any two successive terms is the constant -1; $\{t_n\}$ is an arithmetic sequence whose common difference is -1.

  Now Work PROBLEM 5

2 Find a Formula for an Arithmetic Sequence

Suppose that a is the first term of an arithmetic sequence whose common difference is d. We seek a formula for the nth term, a_n. To see the pattern, we write down the first few terms.

$$a_1 = a$$
$$a_2 = a_1 + d = a_1 + 1 \cdot d$$
$$a_3 = a_2 + d = (a_1 + d) + d = a_1 + 2 \cdot d$$
$$a_4 = a_3 + d = (a_1 + 2 \cdot d) + d = a_1 + 3 \cdot d$$
$$a_5 = a_4 + d = (a_1 + 3 \cdot d) + d = a_1 + 4 \cdot d$$
$$\vdots$$
$$a_n = a_{n-1} + d = [a_1 + (n-2)d] + d = a_1 + (n-1)d$$

We are led to the following result:

THEOREM **nth Term of an Arithmetic Sequence**

For an arithmetic sequence $\{a_n\}$ whose first term is a_1 and whose common difference is d, the nth term is determined by the formula

$$a_n = a_1 + (n-1)d \tag{2}$$

EXAMPLE 4 | **Finding a Particular Term of an Arithmetic Sequence**

Find the forty-first term of the arithmetic sequence: $\quad 2, 6, 10, 14, 18, \ldots$

Solution | The first term of this arithmetic sequence is $a_1 = 2$, and the common difference is $d = 4$. By formula (2), the nth term is

$$a_n = 2 + (n - 1)4 \quad {\scriptstyle a_n = a_1 + (n - 1)d; \; a_1 = 2, \; d = 4}$$

$$= 4n - 2$$

The forty-first term is

$$a_{41} = 4(41) - 2 = 162$$

EXAMPLE 5 | **Finding a Recursive Formula for an Arithmetic Sequence**

The eighth term of an arithmetic sequence is 75, and the twentieth term is 39.

(a) Find the first term and the common difference.
(b) Give a recursive formula for the sequence.
(c) What is the nth term of the sequence?

Solution | (a) By formula (2), we know that $a_n = a_1 + (n - 1)d$. As a result,

$$\begin{cases} a_8 = a_1 + 7d = 75 \\ a_{20} = a_1 + 19d = 39 \end{cases}$$

This is a system of two linear equations containing two variables, a_1 and d, which we can solve by elimination. Subtracting the second equation from the first, we get

$$-12d = 36$$

$$d = -3$$

With $d = -3$, we use $a_1 + 7d = 75$ and find that $a_1 = 75 - 7d = 75 - 7(-3) = 96$. The first term is $a_1 = 96$, and the common difference is $d = -3$.

(b) Using formula (1), a recursive formula for this sequence is

$$a_1 = 96, \qquad a_n = a_{n-1} - 3$$

(c) Using formula (2), a formula for the nth term of the sequence $\{a_n\}$ is

$$a_n = a_1 + (n - 1)d = 96 + (n - 1)(-3) = 99 - 3n$$

Exploration

Graph the recursive formula from Example 5, $a_1 = 96$, $a_n = a_{n-1} - 3$, using a graphing utility. Conclude that the graph of the recursive formula behaves like the graph of a linear function. How is d, the common difference, related to m, the slope of a line?

✏️━━━➤ **Now Work** PROBLEMS 21 AND 27

3 Find the Sum of an Arithmetic Sequence

The next result gives two formulas for finding the sum of the first n terms of an arithmetic sequence.

THEOREM | **Sum of the First n Terms of an Arithmetic Sequence**

Let $\{a_n\}$ be an arithmetic sequence with first term a_1 and common difference d. The sum S_n of the first n terms of $\{a_n\}$ may be found in two ways:

$$S_n = a_1 + a_2 + a_3 + \cdots + a_n$$

$$= \sum_{k=1}^{n} [a_1 + (k - 1)d] = \frac{n}{2}[2a_1 + (n - 1)d] \tag{3}$$

$$S_n = a_1 + a_2 + a_3 + \cdots + a_n$$

$$= \sum_{k=1}^{n} [a_1 + (k - 1)d] = \frac{n}{2}(a_1 + a_n) \tag{4}$$

Proof

$$S_n = a_1 + a_2 + a_3 + \cdots + a_n \qquad \text{Sum of first } n \text{ terms}$$
$$= a_1 + (a_1 + d) + (a_1 + 2d) + \cdots + [a_1 + (n-1)d] \qquad \text{Formula (2)}$$
$$= \underbrace{(a_1 + a_1 + \cdots + a_1)}_{n \text{ terms}} + [d + 2d + \cdots + (n-1)d] \qquad \text{Rearrange terms}$$
$$= na_1 + d[1 + 2 + \cdots + (n-1)]$$
$$= na_1 + d\left[\frac{(n-1)n}{2}\right] \qquad \text{Formula 6, Section 12.1}$$
$$= na_1 + \frac{n}{2}(n-1)d$$
$$= \frac{n}{2}[2a_1 + (n-1)d] \qquad \text{Factor out } \frac{n}{2}; \text{ this is Formula (3).}$$
$$= \frac{n}{2}[a_1 + a_1 + (n-1)d]$$
$$= \frac{n}{2}(a_1 + a_n) \qquad \text{Use Formula (2); this is Formula (4).} \qquad \blacksquare$$

There are two ways to find the sum of the first n terms of an arithmetic sequence. Notice that formula (3) involves the first term and common difference, whereas formula (4) involves the first term and the nth term. Use whichever form is easier.

EXAMPLE 6	**Finding the Sum of an Arithmetic Sequence**

Find the sum S_n of the first n terms of the sequence $\{a_n\} = \{3n + 5\}$; that is, find

$$8 + 11 + 14 + \cdots + (3n + 5) = \sum_{k=1}^{n} (3k + 5)$$

Solution   The sequence $\{a_n\} = \{3n + 5\}$ is an arithmetic sequence with first term $a_1 = 8$ and the nth term $a_n = 3n + 5$. To find the sum S_n, we use formula (4).

$$S_n = \sum_{k=1}^{n} (3k + 5) = \frac{n}{2}[8 + (3n + 5)] = \frac{n}{2}(3n + 13)$$
$$\uparrow$$
$$S_n = \frac{n}{2}(a_1 + a_n)$$

Now Work PROBLEM 35

EXAMPLE 7	**Finding the Sum of an Arithmetic Sequence**

Find the sum: $60 + 64 + 68 + 72 + \cdots + 120$

Solution   This is the sum S_n of an arithmetic sequence $\{a_n\}$ whose first term is $a_1 = 60$ and whose common difference is $d = 4$. The nth term is $a_n = 120$. We use formula (2) to find n.

$$a_n = a_1 + (n-1)d \qquad \text{Formula (2)}$$
$$120 = 60 + (n-1) \cdot 4 \qquad a_n = 120, a_1 = 60, d = 4$$
$$60 = 4(n-1) \qquad \text{Simplify.}$$
$$15 = n - 1 \qquad \text{Divide both sides by 4.}$$
$$n = 16 \qquad \text{Solve for } n.$$

NOTE We can use a graphing utility to verify the results of Example 7 using $\{a_n\} = \{60 + 4(n-1)\}$ and summing the first $n = 16$ terms of the sequence. See Example 9 in Section 12.1. $\blacksquare$

Now we use formula (4) to find the sum S_{16}.

$$60 + 64 + 68 + \cdots + 120 = S_{16} = \frac{16}{2}(60 + 120) = 1440$$

$$\uparrow$$

$$S_n = \frac{n}{2}(a_1 + a_n)$$

═══► **Now Work** PROBLEM 39

| EXAMPLE 8 | **Creating a Floor Design** |

A ceramic tile floor is designed in the shape of a trapezoid 20 feet wide at the base and 10 feet wide at the top. See Figure 13. The tiles, 12 inches by 12 inches, are to be placed so that each successive row contains one less tile than the preceding row. How many tiles will be required?

Figure 13

Solution The bottom row requires 20 tiles and the top row, 10 tiles. Since each successive row requires one less tile, the total number of tiles required is

$$S = 20 + 19 + 18 + \cdots + 11 + 10$$

This is the sum of an arithmetic sequence; the common difference is -1. The number of terms to be added is $n = 11$, with the first term $a_1 = 20$ and the last term $a_{11} = 10$. The sum S is

$$S = \frac{n}{2}(a_1 + a_{11}) = \frac{11}{2}(20 + 10) = 165$$

In all, 165 tiles will be required.

12.2 Assess Your Understanding

Concepts and Vocabulary

1. In a(n) _____ sequence, the difference between successive terms is a constant.

2. *True or False* In an arithmetic sequence the sum of the first and last terms equals twice the sum of all the terms.

Skill Building

In Problems 3–12, show that each sequence is arithmetic. Find the common difference and write out the first four terms.

3. $\{s_n\} = \{n + 4\}$ **4.** $\{s_n\} = \{n - 5\}$ ＼**5.** $\{a_n\} = \{2n - 5\}$ **6.** $\{b_n\} = \{3n + 1\}$ **7.** $\{c_n\} = \{6 - 2n\}$

8. $\{a_n\} = \{4 - 2n\}$ **9.** $\{t_n\} = \left\{\dfrac{1}{2} - \dfrac{1}{3}n\right\}$ **10.** $\{t_n\} = \left\{\dfrac{2}{3} + \dfrac{n}{4}\right\}$ **11.** $\{s_n\} = \{\ln 3^n\}$ **12.** $\{s_n\} = \{e^{\ln n}\}$

In Problems 13–20, find the nth term of the arithmetic sequence $\{a_n\}$ whose initial term a_1 and common difference d are given. What is the fifty-first term?

13. $a_1 = 2;\quad d = 3$ **14.** $a_1 = -2;\quad d = 4$ **15.** $a_1 = 5;\quad d = -3$ **16.** $a_1 = 6;\quad d = -2$

17. $a_1 = 0;\quad d = \dfrac{1}{2}$ **18.** $a_1 = 1;\quad d = -\dfrac{1}{3}$ **19.** $a_1 = \sqrt{2};\quad d = \sqrt{2}$ **20.** $a_1 = 0;\quad d = \pi$

In Problems 21–26, find the indicated term in each arithmetic sequence.

21. 100th term of 2, 4, 6, …

22. 80th term of −1, 1, 3, …

23. 90th term of 1, −2, −5, …

24. 80th term of 5, 0, −5, …

25. 80th term of $2, \dfrac{5}{2}, 3, \dfrac{7}{2}, \ldots$

26. 70th term of $2\sqrt{5}, 4\sqrt{5}, 6\sqrt{5}, \ldots$

In Problems 27–34, find the first term and the common difference of the arithmetic sequence described. Give a recursive formula for the sequence. Find a formula for the nth term.

27. 8th term is 8;   20th term is 44

28. 4th term is 3;   20th term is 35

29. 9th term is −5;   15th term is 31

30. 8th term is 4;   18th term is −96

31. 15th term is 0;   40th term is −50

32. 5th term is −2;   13th term is 30

33. 14th term is −1;   18th term is −9

34. 12th term is 4;   18th term is 28

In Problems 35–52, find each sum. Verify the results using a graphing utility, when possible.

35. $1 + 3 + 5 + \cdots + (2n - 1)$

36. $2 + 4 + 6 + \cdots + 2n$

37. $7 + 12 + 17 + \cdots + (2 + 5n)$

38. $-1 + 3 + 7 + \cdots + (4n - 5)$

39. $2 + 4 + 6 + \cdots + 70$

40. $1 + 3 + 5 + \cdots + 59$

41. $5 + 9 + 13 + \cdots + 49$

42. $2 + 5 + 8 + \cdots + 41$

43. $73 + 78 + 83 + 88 + \cdots + 558$

44. $7 + 1 - 5 - 11 - \cdots - 299$

45. $4 + 4.5 + 5 + 5.5 + \cdots + 100$

46. $8 + 8\dfrac{1}{4} + 8\dfrac{1}{2} + 8\dfrac{3}{4} + 9 + \cdots + 50$

47. $\displaystyle\sum_{n=1}^{80} (2n - 5)$

48. $\displaystyle\sum_{n=1}^{90} (3 - 2n)$

49. $\displaystyle\sum_{n=1}^{100} \left(6 - \dfrac{1}{2}n\right)$

50. $\displaystyle\sum_{n=1}^{80} \left(\dfrac{1}{3}n + \dfrac{1}{2}\right)$

51. The sum of the first 120 terms of the sequence 14, 16, 18, 20, …

52. The sum of the first 46 terms of the sequence 2, −1, −4, −7, …

Applications and Extensions

53. Find x so that $x + 3$, $2x + 1$, and $5x + 2$ are consecutive terms of an arithmetic sequence.

54. Find x so that $2x$, $3x + 2$, and $5x + 3$ are consecutive terms of an arithmetic sequence.

55. How many terms must be added in an arithmetic sequence whose first term is 11 and whose common difference is 3 to obtain a sum of 1092?

56. How many terms must be added in an arithmetic sequence whose first term is 78 and whose common difference is −4 to obtain a sum of 702?

57. Drury Lane Theater The Drury Lane Theater has 25 seats in the first row and 30 rows in all. Each successive row contains one additional seat. How many seats are in the theater?

58. Football Stadium The corner section of a football stadium has 15 seats in the first row and 40 rows in all. Each successive row contains two additional seats. How many seats are in this section?

59. Creating a Mosaic A mosaic is designed in the shape of an equilateral triangle, 20 feet on each side. Each tile in the

mosaic is in the shape of an equilateral triangle, 12 inches to a side. The tiles are to alternate in color as shown in the illustration. How many tiles of each color will be required?

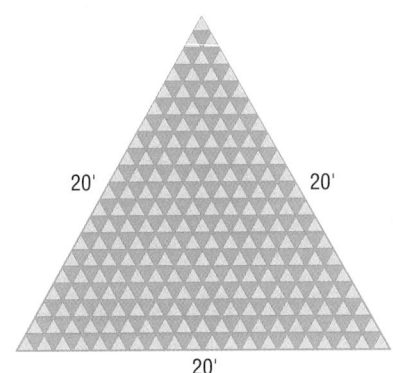

60. Constructing a Brick Staircase A brick staircase has a total of 30 steps. The bottom step requires 100 bricks. Each successive step requires two less bricks than the prior step.
(a) How many bricks are required for the top step?
(b) How many bricks are required to build the staircase?

61. Cooling Air As a parcel of air rises (for example, as it is pushed over a mountain), it cools at the *dry adiabatic lapse rate* of 5.5°F per 1000 feet until it reaches its dew point. If the ground temperature is 67°F, write a formula for the sequence of temperatures, $\{T_n\}$, of a parcel of air that has risen n thousand feet. What is the temperature of a parcel of air if it has risen 5000 feet?

Source: National Aeronautics and Space Administration

62. Citrus Ladders Ladders used by fruit pickers are typically tapered with a wide bottom for stability and a narrow top for ease of picking. Suppose the bottom rung of such a ladder is 49 inches wide and the top rung is 24 inches wide. How many rungs does the ladder have if each rung is 2.5 inches shorter than the one below it? How much material would be needed to make the rungs for the ladder described?

Source: www.stokesladders.com

63. Seats in an Amphitheater An outdoor amphitheater has 35 seats in the first row, 37 in the second row, 39 in the third row, and so on. There are 27 rows altogether. How many seats are in the amphitheater?

64. Stadium Construction How many rows are in the corner section of a stadium containing 2040 seats if the first row has 10 seats and each successive row has 4 additional seats?

65. Salary Suppose that you just received a job offer with a starting salary of $35,000 per year and a guaranteed raise of $1400 per year. How many years will it take before your aggregate salary is $280,000?

[**Hint:** Your aggregate salary after 2 years is $35,000 + ($35,000 + $1400).]

Discussion and Writing

66. Make up an arithmetic sequence. Give it to a friend and ask for its twentieth term.

67. Describe the similarities and differences between arithmetic sequences and linear functions.

12.3 Geometric Sequences; Geometric Series

OBJECTIVES **1** Determine If a Sequence Is Geometric (p. 823)
2 Find a Formula for a Geometric Sequence (p. 824)
3 Find the Sum of a Geometric Sequence (p. 825)
4 Determine Whether a Geometric Series Converges or Diverges (p. 827)

1 Determine If a Sequence Is Geometric

When the ratio of successive terms of a sequence is always the same nonzero number, the sequence is called **geometric.**

DEFINITION A **geometric sequence*** may be defined recursively as $a_1 = a$, $\dfrac{a_n}{a_{n-1}} = r$, or as

$$a_1 = a, \qquad a_n = ra_{n-1} \qquad \qquad \textbf{(1)}$$

where $a_1 = a$ and $r \neq 0$ are real numbers. The number a_1 is the first term, and the nonzero number r is called the **common ratio.**

The terms of a geometric sequence with first term a_1 and common ratio r follow the pattern

$$a_1, \quad a_1r, \quad a_1r^2, \quad a_1r^3, \ldots$$

EXAMPLE 1 Determining If a Sequence Is Geometric

The sequence

$$2, \ 6, \ 18, \ 54, \ 162, \ldots$$

is geometric since the ratio of successive terms is 3: $\dfrac{6}{2} = \dfrac{18}{6} = \dfrac{54}{18} = \cdots = 3$. The first term is $a_1 = 2$, and the common ratio is 3.

*Sometimes called a **geometric progression.**

| EXAMPLE 2 | **Determining If a Sequence Is Geometric** |

Show that the following sequence is geometric.

$$\{s_n\} = \{2^{-n}\}$$

Find the first term and the common ratio.

Solution The first term is $s_1 = 2^{-1} = \dfrac{1}{2}$. The nth term and the $(n-1)$st term of the sequence $\{s_n\}$ are

$$s_n = 2^{-n} \quad \text{and} \quad s_{n-1} = 2^{-(n-1)}$$

Their ratio is

$$\frac{s_n}{s_{n-1}} = \frac{2^{-n}}{2^{-(n-1)}} = 2^{-n+(n-1)} = 2^{-1} = \frac{1}{2}$$

Because the ratio of successive terms is the nonzero constant $\dfrac{1}{2}$, the sequence $\{s_n\}$ is geometric with common ratio $\dfrac{1}{2}$.

| EXAMPLE 3 | **Determining If a Sequence Is Geometric** |

Show that the following sequence is geometric.

$$\{t_n\} = \{4^n\}$$

Find the first term and the common ratio.

Solution The first term is $t_1 = 4^1 = 4$. The nth term and the $(n-1)$st term are

$$t_n = 4^n \quad \text{and} \quad t_{n-1} = 4^{n-1}$$

Their ratio is

$$\frac{t_n}{t_{n-1}} = \frac{4^n}{4^{n-1}} = 4^{n-(n-1)} = 4$$

The sequence, $\{t_n\}$, is a geometric sequence with common ratio 4.

$\longrightarrow$ **Now Work** PROBLEM 9

2 Find a Formula for a Geometric Sequence

Suppose that a_1 is the first term of a geometric sequence with common ratio $r \neq 0$. We seek a formula for the nth term a_n. To see the pattern, we write down the first few terms:

$$a_1 = a_1 \cdot 1 = a_1 r^0$$
$$a_2 = r a_1 = a_1 r^1$$
$$a_3 = r a_2 = r(a_1 r) = a_1 r^2$$
$$a_4 = r a_3 = r(a_1 r^2) = a_1 r^3$$
$$a_5 = r a_4 = r(a_1 r^3) = a_1 r^4$$
$$\vdots$$
$$a_n = r a_{n-1} = r(a_1 r^{n-2}) = a_1 r^{n-1}$$

We are led to the following result:

THEOREM

nth Term of a Geometric Sequence

For a geometric sequence $\{a_n\}$ whose first term is a_1 and whose common ratio is r, the nth term is determined by the formula

$$a_n = a_1 r^{n-1} \qquad r \neq 0 \tag{2}$$

EXAMPLE 4

Finding a Particular Term of a Geometric Sequence

(a) Find the nth term of the geometric sequence: $10, 9, \dfrac{81}{10}, \dfrac{729}{100}, \ldots$

(b) Find the ninth term of this sequence.

(c) Find a recursive formula for this sequence.

Solution

(a) The first term of this geometric sequence is $a_1 = 10$ and the common ratio is $\dfrac{9}{10}$. (Use $\dfrac{9}{10}$ or $\dfrac{\frac{81}{10}}{9} = \dfrac{9}{10}$ or any two successive terms.) Then, by formula (2), the nth term is

$$a_n = 10\left(\frac{9}{10}\right)^{n-1} \qquad a_n = a_1 r^{n-1}; \ a_1 = 10, r = \frac{9}{10}$$

(b) The ninth term is

$$a_9 = 10\left(\frac{9}{10}\right)^{9-1} = 10\left(\frac{9}{10}\right)^{8} \approx 4.3046721$$

(c) The first term in the sequence is 10, and the common ratio is $r = \dfrac{9}{10}$. Using formula (1), the recursive formula is $a_1 = 10$, $a_n = \dfrac{9}{10} a_{n-1}$.

Exploration

Use a graphing utility to find the ninth term of the sequence given in Example 4. Use it to find the twentieth and fiftieth terms. Now use a graphing utility to graph the recursive formula found in Example 4(c). Conclude that the graph of the recursive formula behaves like the graph of an exponential function. How is r, the common ratio, related to a, the base of the exponential function $y = a^x$?

🖊️ **Now Work** PROBLEMS **17, 25,** AND **33**

---

3 Find the Sum of a Geometric Sequence

The next result gives us a formula for finding the sum of the first n terms of a geometric sequence.

THEOREM

Sum of the First n Terms of a Geometric Sequence

Let $\{a_n\}$ be a geometric sequence with first term a_1 and common ratio r, where $r \neq 0$, $r \neq 1$. The sum S_n of the first n terms of $\{a_n\}$ is

$$S_n = a_1 + a_1 r + a_1 r^2 + \cdots + a_1 r^{n-1} = \sum_{k=1}^{n} a_1 r^{k-1}$$

$$= a_1 \cdot \frac{1 - r^n}{1 - r} \qquad r \neq 0, 1 \tag{3}$$

Proof The sum S_n of the first n terms of $\{a_n\} = \{a_1 r^{n-1}\}$ is

$$S_n = a_1 + a_1 r + \cdots + a_1 r^{n-1} \tag{4}$$

Multiply each side by r to obtain

$$rS_n = a_1r + a_1r^2 + \cdots + a_1r^n \qquad \qquad \text{(5)}$$

Now, subtract (5) from (4). The result is

$$S_n - rS_n = a_1 - a_1r^n$$
$$(1 - r)S_n = a_1(1 - r^n)$$

Since $r \neq 1$, we can solve for S_n.

$$S_n = a_1 \cdot \frac{1 - r^n}{1 - r} \qquad \qquad \blacksquare$$

| EXAMPLE 5 | Finding the Sum of the First n Terms of a Geometric Sequence |

Find the sum S_n of the first n terms of the sequence $\left\{\left(\dfrac{1}{2}\right)^n\right\}$; that is, find

$$\frac{1}{2} + \frac{1}{4} + \frac{1}{8} + \cdots + \left(\frac{1}{2}\right)^n = \sum_{k=1}^{n} \frac{1}{2}\left(\frac{1}{2}\right)^{k-1}$$

Solution The sequence $\left\{\left(\dfrac{1}{2}\right)^n\right\}$ is a geometric sequence with $a_1 = \dfrac{1}{2}$ and $r = \dfrac{1}{2}$. So we use formula (3) to get

$$S_n = \sum_{k=1}^{n} \frac{1}{2}\left(\frac{1}{2}\right)^{k-1} = \frac{1}{2} + \frac{1}{4} + \frac{1}{8} + \cdots + \left(\frac{1}{2}\right)^n$$

$$= \frac{1}{2}\left[\frac{1 - \left(\dfrac{1}{2}\right)^n}{1 - \dfrac{1}{2}}\right] \qquad \text{Formula (3); } a_1 = \frac{1}{2}, r = \frac{1}{2}$$

$$= \frac{1}{2}\left[\frac{1 - \left(\dfrac{1}{2}\right)^n}{\dfrac{1}{2}}\right]$$

$$= 1 - \left(\frac{1}{2}\right)^n$$

 Now Work PROBLEM 39

| EXAMPLE 6 | Using a Graphing Utility to Find the Sum of a Geometric Sequence |

Use a graphing utility to find the sum of the first 15 terms of the sequence $\left\{\left(\dfrac{1}{3}\right)^n\right\}$; that is, find

$$\frac{1}{3} + \frac{1}{9} + \frac{1}{27} + \cdots + \left(\frac{1}{3}\right)^{15} = \sum_{k=1}^{15} \frac{1}{3}\left(\frac{1}{3}\right)^{k-1}$$

Figure 14

```
sum(seq((1/3)^n,
n,1,15,1))
        .4999999652
```

Solution Figure 14 shows the result obtained using a TI-84 Plus graphing calculator. The sum of the first 15 terms of the sequence $\left\{\left(\dfrac{1}{3}\right)^n\right\}$ is 0.4999999652.

Now Work PROBLEM 45

4 Determine Whether a Geometric Series Converges or Diverges

DEFINITION

An infinite sum of the form

$$a_1 + a_1r + a_1r^2 + \cdots + a_1r^{n-1} + \cdots$$

with first term a_1 and common ratio r, is called an **infinite geometric series** and is denoted by

$$\sum_{k=1}^{\infty} a_1 r^{k-1}$$

Based on formula (3), the sum S_n of the first n terms of a geometric series is

$$S_n = a_1 \cdot \frac{1 - r^n}{1 - r} = \frac{a_1}{1 - r} - \frac{a_1 r^n}{1 - r} \qquad (6)$$

NOTE In calculus, we use limit notation and write

$$L = \lim_{n \to \infty} S_n = \lim_{n \to \infty} \sum_{k=1}^{n} a_1 r^{k-1}$$
$$= \sum_{k=1}^{\infty} a_1 r^{k-1} \qquad \blacksquare$$

If this finite sum S_n approaches a number L as $n \to \infty$, we say the infinite geometric series $\sum_{k=1}^{\infty} a_1 r^{k-1}$ **converges.** We call L the **sum of the infinite geometric series,** and we write

$$L = \sum_{k=1}^{\infty} a_1 r^{k-1}$$

If a series does not converge, it is called a **divergent series.**

THEOREM

Convergence of an Infinite Geometric Series

If $|r| < 1$, the infinite geometric series $\sum_{k=1}^{\infty} a_1 r^{k-1}$ converges. Its sum is

$$\sum_{k=1}^{\infty} a_1 r^{k-1} = \frac{a_1}{1 - r} \qquad (7)$$

Intuitive Proof Since $|r| < 1$, it follows that $|r^n|$ approaches 0 as $n \to \infty$. Then, based on formula (6), the term $\dfrac{a_1 r^n}{1 - r}$ approaches 0, so the sum S_n approaches $\dfrac{a_1}{1 - r}$ as $n \to \infty$. $\blacksquare$

EXAMPLE 7

Determining whether a Geometric Series Converges or Diverges

Determine if the geometric series

$$\sum_{k=1}^{\infty} 2\left(\frac{2}{3}\right)^{k-1} = 2 + \frac{4}{3} + \frac{8}{9} + \cdots$$

converges or diverges. If it converges, find its sum.

Solution   Comparing $\displaystyle\sum_{k=1}^{\infty} 2\left(\frac{2}{3}\right)^{k-1}$ to $\displaystyle\sum_{k=1}^{\infty} a_1 r^{k-1}$, we see that the first term is $a_1 = 2$, and the

common ratio is $r = \dfrac{2}{3}$. Since $|r| < 1$, the series converges. We use formula (7) to find its sum:

$$\sum_{k=1}^{\infty} 2\left(\frac{2}{3}\right)^{k-1} = 2 + \frac{4}{3} + \frac{8}{9} + \cdots = \frac{2}{1 - \dfrac{2}{3}} = 6$$

> **Now Work** PROBLEM 51

EXAMPLE 8   **Repeating Decimals**

Show that the repeating decimal $0.999\ldots$ equals 1.

Solution   The decimal $0.999\ldots = 0.9 + 0.09 + 0.009 + \cdots = \dfrac{9}{10} + \dfrac{9}{100} + \dfrac{9}{1000} + \cdots$ is an

infinite geometric series. We will write it in the form $\displaystyle\sum_{k=1}^{\infty} a_1 r^{k-1}$ so that we can use formula (7).

$$0.999\ldots = \frac{9}{10} + \frac{9}{100} + \frac{9}{1000} + \cdots = \sum_{k=1}^{\infty} \frac{9}{10^k} = \sum_{k=1}^{\infty} \frac{9}{10 \cdot 10^{k-1}} = \sum_{k=1}^{\infty} \frac{9}{10}\left(\frac{1}{10}\right)^{k-1}$$

Now we can compare this series to $\displaystyle\sum_{k=1}^{\infty} a_1 r^{k-1}$ and conclude that $a_1 = \dfrac{9}{10}$ and $r = \dfrac{1}{10}$.

Since $|r| < 1$, the series converges and its sum is

$$0.999\ldots = \frac{\dfrac{9}{10}}{1 - \dfrac{1}{10}} = \frac{\dfrac{9}{10}}{\dfrac{9}{10}} = 1$$

The repeating decimal $0.999\ldots$ equals 1.

EXAMPLE 9   **Pendulum Swings**

Initially, a pendulum swings through an arc of 18 inches. See Figure 15. On each successive swing, the length of the arc is 0.98 of the previous length.

Figure 15

18"

(a) What is the length of the arc of the 10th swing?
(b) On which swing is the length of the arc first less than 12 inches?
(c) After 15 swings, what total distance will the pendulum have swung?
(d) When it stops, what total distance will the pendulum have swung?

Solution   (a) The length of the first swing is 18 inches.

The length of the second swing is $0.98(18)$ inches.

The length of the third swing is $0.98(0.98)(18) = 0.98^2(18)$ inches.

The length of the arc of the 10th swing is

$$(0.98)^9(18) \approx 15.007 \text{ inches}$$

(b) The length of the arc of the nth swing is $(0.98)^{n-1}(18)$. For this to be exactly 12 inches requires that

$$(0.98)^{n-1}(18) = 12$$

$$(0.98)^{n-1} = \frac{12}{18} = \frac{2}{3} \qquad \text{Divide both sides by 18.}$$

$$n - 1 = \log_{0.98}\left(\frac{2}{3}\right) \qquad \text{Express as a logarithm.}$$

$$n = 1 + \frac{\ln\left(\dfrac{2}{3}\right)}{\ln 0.98} \approx 1 + 20.07 = 21.07 \qquad \begin{array}{l}\text{Solve for } n; \text{ use the Change}\\ \text{of Base Formula.}\end{array}$$

The length of the arc of the pendulum exceeds 12 inches on the 21st swing and is first less than 12 inches on the 22nd swing.

(c) After 15 swings, the pendulum will have swung the following total distance L:

$$L = 18 + \underset{\text{1st}}{\underbrace{}}\,0.98(18) + \underset{\text{2nd}}{\underbrace{}}(0.98)^2(18) + \underset{\text{3rd}}{\underbrace{}}(0.98)^3(18) + \cdots + \underset{\text{4th}}{}\;\;(0.98)^{14}(18)$$

$$L = 18 + 0.98(18) + (0.98)^2(18) + (0.98)^3(18) + \cdots + (0.98)^{14}(18)$$

This is the sum of a geometric sequence. The common ratio is 0.98; the first term is 18. The sum has 15 terms, so

$$L = 18 \cdot \frac{1 - 0.98^{15}}{1 - 0.98} \approx 18(13.07) \approx 235.3 \text{ inches}$$

The pendulum will have swung through 235.3 inches after 15 swings.

(d) When the pendulum stops, it will have swung the following total distance T:

$$T = 18 + 0.98(18) + (0.98)^2(18) + (0.98)^3(18) + \cdots$$

This is the sum of an infinite geometric series. The common ratio is $r = 0.98$; the first term is $a_1 = 18$. Since $|r| < 1$, the series converges. Its sum is

$$T = \frac{a_1}{1 - r} = \frac{18}{1 - 0.98} = 900$$

The pendulum will have swung a total of 900 inches when it finally stops.

Now Work PROBLEM 85

Historical Feature

Fibonacci

Sequences are among the oldest objects of mathematical investigation, having been studied for over 3500 years. After the initial steps, however, little progress was made until about 1600.

Arithmetic and geometric sequences appear in the Rhind papyrus, a mathematical text containing 85 problems copied around 1650 BC by the Egyptian scribe Ahmes from an earlier work (see Historical Problem 1). Fibonacci (AD 1220) wrote about problems similar to those found in the Rhind papyrus, leading one to suspect that Fibonacci may have had material available that is now lost. This material would have been in the non-Euclidean Greek tradition of Heron (about AD 75) and Diophantus (about AD 250). One problem, again modified slightly, is still with us in the familiar puzzle rhyme "As I was going to St. Ives ..." (see Historical Problem 2).

The Rhind papyrus indicates that the Egyptians knew how to add up the terms of an arithmetic or geometric sequence, as did the Babylonians. The rule for summing up a geometric sequence is found in Euclid's *Elements* (Book IX, 35, 36), where, like all Euclid's algebra, it is presented in a geometric form.

Investigations of other kinds of sequences began in the 1500s, when algebra became sufficiently developed to handle the more complicated problems. The development of calculus in the 1600s added a powerful new tool, especially for finding the sum of infinite series, and the subject continues to flourish today.

Historical Problems

1. *Arithmetic sequence problem from the Rhind papyrus (statement modified slightly for clarity)* One hundred loaves of bread are to be divided among five people so that the amounts that they receive form an arithmetic sequence. The first two together receive one-seventh of what the last three receive. How many loaves does each receive?

   [*Partial answer:* First person receives $1\frac{2}{3}$ loaves.]

2. The following old English children's rhyme resembles one of the Rhind papyrus problems.

   > As I was going to St. Ives
   > I met a man with seven wives

   Each wife had seven sacks
   Each sack had seven cats
   Each cat had seven kits [kittens]
   Kits, cats, sacks, wives
   How many were going to St. Ives?

   (a) Assuming that the speaker and the cat fanciers met by traveling in opposite directions, what is the answer?

   (b) How many kittens are being transported?

   (c) Kits, cats, sacks, wives; how many?

12.3 Assess Your Understanding

Concepts and Vocabulary

1. In a(n) _____ sequence the ratio of successive terms is a constant.

2. If $|r| < 1$, the sum of the geometric series $\sum_{k=1}^{\infty} ar^{k-1}$ is _____.

3. If a series does not converge, it is called a _____ _____.

4. *True or False* A geometric sequence may be defined recursively.

5. *True or False* In a geometric sequence the common ratio is always a positive number.

6. *True or False* For a geometric sequence with first term a_1 and common ratio r, where $r \neq 0, r \neq 1$, the sum of the first n terms is $S_n = a_1 \cdot \dfrac{1 - r^n}{1 - r}$.

Skill Building

In Problems 7–16, show that each sequence is geometric. Then find the common ratio and write out the first four terms.

7. $\{s_n\} = \{3^n\}$

8. $\{s_n\} = \{(-5)^n\}$

9. $\{a_n\} = \left\{-3\left(\dfrac{1}{2}\right)^n\right\}$

10. $\{b_n\} = \left\{\left(\dfrac{5}{2}\right)^n\right\}$

11. $\{c_n\} = \left\{\dfrac{2^{n-1}}{4}\right\}$

12. $\{d_n\} = \left\{\dfrac{3^n}{9}\right\}$

13. $\{e_n\} = \{2^{n/3}\}$

14. $\{f_n\} = \{3^{2n}\}$

15. $\{t_n\} = \left\{\dfrac{3^{n-1}}{2^n}\right\}$

16. $\{u_n\} = \left\{\dfrac{2^n}{3^{n-1}}\right\}$

In Problems 17–24, find the fifth term and the nth term of the geometric sequence whose initial term a_1 and common ratio r are given.

17. $a_1 = 2;\ \ r = 3$

18. $a_1 = -2;\ \ r = 4$

19. $a_1 = 5;\ \ r = -1$

20. $a_1 = 6;\ \ r = -2$

21. $a_1 = 0;\ \ r = \dfrac{1}{2}$

22. $a_1 = 1;\ \ r = -\dfrac{1}{3}$

23. $a_1 = \sqrt{2};\ \ r = \sqrt{2}$

24. $a_1 = 0;\ \ r = \dfrac{1}{\pi}$

In Problems 25–30, find the indicated term of each geometric sequence.

25. 7th term of $1, \dfrac{1}{2}, \dfrac{1}{4}, \ldots$

26. 8th term of $1, 3, 9, \ldots$

27. 9th term of $1, -1, 1, \ldots$

28. 10th term of $-1, 2, -4, \ldots$

29. 8th term of $0.4, 0.04, 0.004, \ldots$

30. 7th term of $0.1, 1.0, 10.0, \ldots$

In Problems 31–38, find the nth term a_n of each geometric sequence. When given, r is the common ratio.

31. $7, 14, 28, 56, \ldots$

32. $5, 10, 20, 40, \ldots$

33. $-3, 1, -\dfrac{1}{3}, \dfrac{1}{9}, \ldots$

34. $4, 1, \dfrac{1}{4}, \dfrac{1}{16}, \ldots$

35. $a_6 = 243;\ \ r = -3$

36. $a_2 = 7;\ \ r = \dfrac{1}{3}$

37. $a_2 = 7;\ \ a_4 = 1575$

38. $a_3 = \dfrac{1}{3};\ \ a_6 = \dfrac{1}{81}$

In Problems 39–44, find each sum.

39. $\dfrac{1}{4} + \dfrac{2}{4} + \dfrac{2^2}{4} + \dfrac{2^3}{4} + \cdots + \dfrac{2^{n-1}}{4}$

40. $\dfrac{3}{9} + \dfrac{3^2}{9} + \dfrac{3^3}{9} + \cdots + \dfrac{3^n}{9}$

41. $\sum_{k=1}^{n} \left(\dfrac{2}{3}\right)^k$

42. $\sum_{k=1}^{n} 4 \cdot 3^{k-1}$

43. $-1 - 2 - 4 - 8 - \cdots - (2^{n-1})$

44. $2 + \dfrac{6}{5} + \dfrac{18}{25} + \cdots + 2\left(\dfrac{3}{5}\right)^{n-1}$

For Problems 45–50, use a graphing utility to find the sum of each geometric sequence.

45. $\dfrac{1}{4} + \dfrac{2}{4} + \dfrac{2^2}{4} + \dfrac{2^3}{4} + \cdots + \dfrac{2^{14}}{4}$

46. $\dfrac{3}{9} + \dfrac{3^2}{9} + \dfrac{3^3}{9} + \cdots + \dfrac{3^{15}}{9}$

47. $\displaystyle\sum_{n=1}^{15} \left(\dfrac{2}{3}\right)^n$

48. $\displaystyle\sum_{n=1}^{15} 4 \cdot 3^{n-1}$

49. $-1 - 2 - 4 - 8 - \cdots - 2^{14}$

50. $2 + \dfrac{6}{5} + \dfrac{18}{25} + \cdots + 2\left(\dfrac{3}{5}\right)^{15}$

In Problems 51–66, determine whether each infinite geometric series converges or diverges. If it converges, find its sum.

51. $1 + \dfrac{1}{3} + \dfrac{1}{9} + \cdots$

52. $2 + \dfrac{4}{3} + \dfrac{8}{9} + \cdots$

53. $8 + 4 + 2 + \cdots$

54. $6 + 2 + \dfrac{2}{3} + \cdots$

55. $2 - \dfrac{1}{2} + \dfrac{1}{8} - \dfrac{1}{32} + \cdots$

56. $1 - \dfrac{3}{4} + \dfrac{9}{16} - \dfrac{27}{64} + \cdots$

57. $8 + 12 + 18 + 27 + \cdots$

58. $9 + 12 + 16 + \dfrac{64}{3} + \cdots$

59. $\displaystyle\sum_{k=1}^{\infty} 5\left(\dfrac{1}{4}\right)^{k-1}$

60. $\displaystyle\sum_{k=1}^{\infty} 8\left(\dfrac{1}{3}\right)^{k-1}$

61. $\displaystyle\sum_{k=1}^{\infty} \dfrac{1}{2} 3^{k-1}$

62. $\displaystyle\sum_{k=1}^{\infty} 3\left(\dfrac{3}{2}\right)^{k-1}$

63. $\displaystyle\sum_{k=1}^{\infty} 6\left(-\dfrac{2}{3}\right)^{k-1}$

64. $\displaystyle\sum_{k=1}^{\infty} 4\left(-\dfrac{1}{2}\right)^{k-1}$

65. $\displaystyle\sum_{k=1}^{\infty} 3\left(\dfrac{2}{3}\right)^{k}$

66. $\displaystyle\sum_{k=1}^{\infty} 2\left(\dfrac{3}{4}\right)^{k}$

Mixed Practice

In Problems 67–80, determine whether the given sequence is arithmetic, geometric, or neither. If the sequence is arithmetic, find the common difference; if it is geometric, find the common ratio. If the sequence is arithmetic or geometric, find the sum of the first 50 terms.

67. $\{n + 2\}$

68. $\{2n - 5\}$

69. $\{4n^2\}$

70. $\{5n^2 + 1\}$

71. $\left\{3 - \dfrac{2}{3}n\right\}$

72. $\left\{8 - \dfrac{3}{4}n\right\}$

73. $1, 3, 6, 10, \ldots$

74. $2, 4, 6, 8, \ldots$

75. $\left\{\left(\dfrac{2}{3}\right)^n\right\}$

76. $\left\{\left(\dfrac{5}{4}\right)^n\right\}$

77. $-1, 2, -4, 8, \ldots$

78. $1, 1, 2, 3, 5, 8, \ldots$

79. $\{3^{n/2}\}$

80. $\{(-1)^n\}$

Applications and Extensions

81. Find x so that x, $x + 2$, and $x + 3$ are consecutive terms of a geometric sequence.

82. Find x so that $x - 1$, x, and $x + 2$ are consecutive terms of a geometric sequence.

83. Salary Increases Suppose that you have just been hired at an annual salary of $18,000 and expect to receive annual increases of 5%. What will your salary be when you begin your fifth year?

84. Equipment Depreciation A new piece of equipment cost a company $15,000. Each year, for tax purposes, the company depreciates the value by 15%. What value should the company give the equipment after 5 years?

85. Pendulum Swings Initially, a pendulum swings through an arc of 2 feet. On each successive swing, the length of the arc is 0.9 of the previous length.
  (a) What is the length of the arc of the 10th swing?
  (b) On which swing is the length of the arc first less than 1 foot?
  (c) After 15 swings, what total length will the pendulum have swung?
  (d) When it stops, what total length will the pendulum have swung?

86. Bouncing Balls A ball is dropped from a height of 30 feet. Each time it strikes the ground, it bounces up to 0.8 of the previous height.

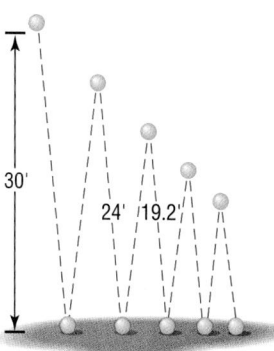

  (a) What height will the ball bounce up to after it strikes the ground for the third time?
  (b) How high will it bounce after it strikes the ground for the nth time?
  (c) How many times does the ball need to strike the ground before its bounce is less than 6 inches?
  (d) What total distance does the ball travel before it stops bouncing?

87. Grains of Wheat on a Chess Board In an old fable, a commoner who had saved the king's life was told he could ask the king for any just reward. Being a shrewd man, the commoner said, "A simple wish, sire. Place one grain of wheat on the first square of a chessboard, two grains on the second square, four grains on the third square, continuing until you have filled the board. This is all I seek." Compute the total number of grains needed to do this to see why the request, seemingly simple, could not be granted. (A chessboard consists of $8 \times 8 = 64$ squares.)

88. Look at the figure. What fraction of the square is eventually shaded if the indicated shading process continues indefinitely?

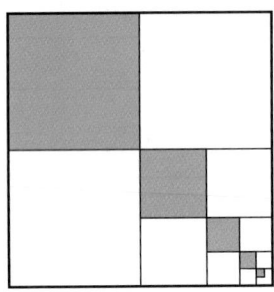

89. Multiplier Suppose that, throughout the U.S. economy, individuals spend 90% of every additional dollar that they earn. Economists would say that an individual's **marginal propensity to consume** is 0.90. For example, if Jane earns an additional dollar, she will spend $0.9(1) = \$0.90$ of it. The individual that earns \$0.90 (from Jane) will spend 90% of it

or \$0.81. This process of spending continues and results in an infinite geometric series as follows:

$$1, 0.90, 0.90^2, 0.90^3, 0.90^4, \ldots$$

The sum of this infinite geometric series is called the **multiplier.** What is the multiplier if individuals spend 90% of every additional dollar that they earn?

90. Multiplier Refer to Problem 91. Suppose that the marginal propensity to consume throughout the U.S. economy is 0.95. What is the multiplier for the U.S. economy?

91. Stock Price One method of pricing a stock is to discount the stream of future dividends of the stock. Suppose that a stock pays P per year in dividends and, historically, the dividend has been increased $i\%$ per year. If you desire an annual rate of return of $r\%$, this method of pricing a stock states that the price that you should pay is the present value of an infinite stream of payments:

$$\text{Price} = P + P\frac{1+i}{1+r} + P\left(\frac{1+i}{1+r}\right)^2 + P\left(\frac{1+i}{1+r}\right)^3 + \cdots$$

The price of the stock is the sum of an infinite geometric series. Suppose that a stock pays an annual dividend of \$4.00 and, historically, the dividend has been increased 3% per year. You desire an annual rate of return of 9%. What is the most you should pay for the stock?

92. Stock Price Refer to Problem 91. Suppose that a stock pays an annual dividend of \$2.50 and, historically, the dividend has increased 4% per year. You desire an annual rate of return of 11%. What is the most that you should pay for the stock?

93. A Rich Man's Promise A rich man promises to give you \$1000 on September 1, 2007. Each day thereafter he will give you $\frac{9}{10}$ of what he gave you the previous day. What is the first date on which the amount you receive is less than 1¢? How much have you received when this happens?

Discussion and Writing

94. Critical Thinking You are interviewing for a job and receive two offers:

    A: \$20,000 to start, with guaranteed annual increases of 6% for the first 5 years

    B: \$22,000 to start, with guaranteed annual increases of 3% for the first 5 years

Which offer is best if your goal is to be making as much as possible after 5 years? Which is best if your goal is to make as much money as possible over the contract (5 years)?

95. Critical Thinking Which of the following choices, A or B, results in more money?

    A: To receive \$1000 on day 1, \$999 on day 2, \$998 on day 3, with the process to end after 1000 days

    B: To receive \$1 on day 1, \$2 on day 2, \$4 on day 3, for 19 days

96. Critical Thinking You have just signed a 7-year professional football league contract with a beginning salary of \$2,000,000 per year. Management gives you the following options with regard to your salary over the 7 years.

1. A bonus of \$100,000 each year

2. An annual increase of 4.5% per year beginning after 1 year

3. An annual increase of \$95,000 per year beginning after 1 year

Which option provides the most money over the 7-year period? Which the least? Which would you choose? Why?

97. Critical Thinking Suppose you were offered a job in which you would work 8 hours per day for 5 workdays per week for 1 month at hard manual labor. Your pay the first day would be 1 penny. On the second day your pay would be two pennies; the third day 4 pennies. Your pay would double on each successive workday. There are 22 workdays in the month. There will be no sick days. If you miss a day of work, there is no pay or pay increase. How much do you get paid if you work all 22 days? How much do you get paid for the 22nd workday? What risks do you run if you take this job offer? Would you take the job?

98. Can a sequence be both arithmetic and geometric? Give reasons for your answer.

99. Make up a geometric sequence. Give it to a friend and ask for its 20th term.

100. Make up two infinite geometric series, one that has a sum and one that does not. Give them to a friend and ask for the sum of each series.

101. Describe the similarities and differences between geometric sequences and exponential functions.

12.4 Mathematical Induction

> **OBJECTIVE** 1 Prove Statements Using Mathematical Induction (p. 833)

1 Prove Statements Using Mathematical Induction

Mathematical induction is a method for proving that statements involving natural numbers are true for all natural numbers.*

For example, the statement "$2n$ is always an even integer" can be proved for all natural numbers n by using mathematical induction. Also, the statement "the sum of the first n positive odd integers equals n^2," that is,

$$1 + 3 + 5 + \cdots + (2n - 1) = n^2 \qquad \textbf{(1)}$$

can be proved for all natural numbers n by using mathematical induction.

Before stating the method of mathematical induction, let's try to gain a sense of the power of the method. We shall use the statement in equation (1) for this purpose by restating it for various values of $n = 1, 2, 3, \ldots$.

$n = 1$	The sum of the first positive odd integer is 1^2; $1 = 1^2$.
$n = 2$	The sum of the first 2 positive odd integers is 2^2; $1 + 3 = 4 = 2^2$.
$n = 3$	The sum of the first 3 positive odd integers is 3^2; $1 + 3 + 5 = 9 = 3^2$.
$n = 4$	The sum of the first 4 positive odd integers is 4^2; $1 + 3 + 5 + 7 = 16 = 4^2$.

Although from this pattern we might conjecture that statement (1) is true for any choice of n, can we really be sure that it does not fail for some choice of n? The method of proof by mathematical induction will, in fact, prove that the statement is true for all n.

THEOREM

The Principle of Mathematical Induction

Suppose that the following two conditions are satisfied with regard to a statement about natural numbers:

CONDITION I:	The statement is true for the natural number 1.
CONDITION II:	If the statement is true for some natural number k, it is also true for the next natural number $k + 1$.

Then the statement is true for all natural numbers.

We shall not prove this principle. However, we can provide a physical interpretation that will help us to see why the principle works. Think of a collection of natural numbers obeying a statement as a collection of infinitely many dominoes. See Figure 16.

Figure 16

Now, suppose that we are told two facts:

1. The first domino is pushed over.
2. If one domino falls over, say the kth domino, so will the next one, the $(k + 1)$st domino.

---

* Recall that the natural numbers are the numbers 1, 2, 3, 4, ... In other words, the terms *natural numbers* and *positive integers* are synonymous.

Is it safe to conclude that *all* the dominoes fall over? The answer is yes, because if the first one falls (Condition I), the second one does also (by Condition II); and if the second one falls, so does the third (by Condition II); and so on.

Now let's prove some statements about natural numbers using mathematical induction.

EXAMPLE 1	**Using Mathematical Induction**

Show that the following statement is true for all natural numbers n.

$$1 + 3 + 5 + \cdots + (2n - 1) = n^2 \qquad \textbf{(2)}$$

Solution   We need to show first that statement (2) holds for $n = 1$. Because $1 = 1^2$, statement (2) is true for $n = 1$. Condition I holds.

Next, we need to show that Condition II holds. Suppose that we know for some k that

$$1 + 3 + \cdots + (2k - 1) = k^2 \qquad \textbf{(3)}$$

We wish to show that, based on equation (3), statement (2) holds for $k + 1$. We look at the sum of the first $k + 1$ positive odd integers to determine whether this sum equals $(k + 1)^2$.

$$1 + 3 + \cdots + (2k - 1) + [2(k + 1) - 1] = \underbrace{[1 + 3 + \cdots + (2k - 1)]}_{= \ k^2 \ \text{by equation (3)}} + (2k + 1)$$

$$= k^2 + (2k + 1)$$
$$= k^2 + 2k + 1 = (k + 1)^2$$

Conditions I and II are satisfied; by the Principle of Mathematical Induction, statement (2) is true for all natural numbers n.

EXAMPLE 2	**Using Mathematical Induction**

Show that the following statement is true for all natural numbers n.

$$2^n > n$$

Solution   First, we show that the statement $2^n > n$ holds when $n = 1$. Because $2^1 = 2 > 1$, the inequality is true for $n = 1$. Condition I holds.

Next, we assume, for some natural number k, that $2^k > k$. We wish to show that the formula holds for $k + 1$; that is, we wish to show that $2^{k+1} > k + 1$. Now

$$2^{k+1} = 2 \cdot 2^k \underset{\substack{\uparrow \\ \text{We know that} \\ 2^k > k.}}{>} 2 \cdot k = k + k \underset{\substack{\uparrow \\ k \geq 1}}{\geq} k + 1$$

If $2^k > k$, then $2^{k+1} > k + 1$, so Condition II of the Principle of Mathematical Induction is satisfied. The statement $2^n > n$ is true for all natural numbers n.

EXAMPLE 3	**Using Mathematical Induction**

Show that the following formula is true for all natural numbers n.

$$1 + 2 + 3 + \cdots + n = \frac{n(n + 1)}{2} \qquad \textbf{(4)}$$

This display in Figure 18 is called the **Pascal triangle,** named after Blaise Pascal (1623–1662), a French mathematician.

The Pascal triangle has 1's down the sides. To get any other entry, add the two nearest entries in the row above it. The shaded triangles in Figure 18 illustrate this feature of the Pascal triangle. Based on this feature, the row corresponding to $n = 6$ is found as follows:

$$n = 5 \rightarrow \quad 1 \quad 5 \quad 10 \quad 10 \quad 5 \quad 1$$
$$n = 6 \rightarrow \quad 1 \quad 6 \quad 15 \quad 20 \quad 15 \quad 6 \quad 1$$

Later we shall prove that this addition always works (see the theorem on page 841).

Although the Pascal triangle provides an interesting and organized display of the symbol $\binom{n}{j}$, in practice it is not all that helpful. For example, if you wanted to know the value of $\binom{12}{5}$, you would need to produce 13 rows of the triangle before seeing the answer. It is much faster to use the definition (1).

2 Use the Binomial Theorem

Now we are ready to state the **Binomial Theorem.**

THEOREM

Binomial Theorem

Let x and a be real numbers. For any positive integer n, we have

$$(x + a)^n = \binom{n}{0}x^n + \binom{n}{1}ax^{n-1} + \cdots + \binom{n}{j}a^j x^{n-j} + \cdots + \binom{n}{n}a^n$$

$$= \sum_{j=0}^{n} \binom{n}{j}x^{n-j}a^j \tag{2}$$

Now you know why we needed to introduce the symbol $\binom{n}{j}$; these symbols are the numerical coefficients that appear in the expansion of $(x + a)^n$. Because of this, the symbol $\binom{n}{j}$ is called a **binomial coefficient.**

EXAMPLE 2   **Expanding a Binomial**

Use the Binomial Theorem to expand $(x + 2)^5$.

Solution   In the Binomial Theorem, let $a = 2$ and $n = 5$. Then

$$(x + 2)^5 = \binom{5}{0}x^5 + \binom{5}{1}2x^4 + \binom{5}{2}2^2x^3 + \binom{5}{3}2^3x^2 + \binom{5}{4}2^4x + \binom{5}{5}2^5$$

↑
Use equation (2).

$$= 1 \cdot x^5 + 5 \cdot 2x^4 + 10 \cdot 4x^3 + 10 \cdot 8x^2 + 5 \cdot 16x + 1 \cdot 32$$

↑
Use row $n = 5$ of the Pascal triangle or formula (1) for $\binom{n}{j}$.

$$= x^5 + 10x^4 + 40x^3 + 80x^2 + 80x + 32$$

EXAMPLE 3	**Expanding a Binomial**

Expand $(2y - 3)^4$ using the Binomial Theorem.

Solution First, we rewrite the expression $(2y - 3)^4$ as $[2y + (-3)]^4$. Now we use the Binomial Theorem with $n = 4$, $x = 2y$, and $a = -3$.

$$[2y + (-3)]^4 = \binom{4}{0}(2y)^4 + \binom{4}{1}(-3)(2y)^3 + \binom{4}{2}(-3)^2(2y)^2$$
$$+ \binom{4}{3}(-3)^3(2y) + \binom{4}{4}(-3)^4$$
$$= 1 \cdot 16y^4 + 4(-3)8y^3 + 6 \cdot 9 \cdot 4y^2 + 4(-27)2y + 1 \cdot 81$$
↑

Use row $n = 4$ of the Pascal triangle or formula (1) for $\binom{n}{j}$.

$$= 16y^4 - 96y^3 + 216y^2 - 216y + 81$$

In this expansion, note that the signs alternate due to the fact that $a = -3 < 0$.

Now Work PROBLEM 21

EXAMPLE 4	**Finding a Particular Coefficient in a Binomial Expansion**

Find the coefficient of y^8 in the expansion of $(2y + 3)^{10}$.

Solution We write out the expansion using the Binomial Theorem.

$$(2y + 3)^{10} = \binom{10}{0}(2y)^{10} + \binom{10}{1}(2y)^9(3)^1 + \binom{10}{2}(2y)^8(3)^2 + \binom{10}{3}(2y)^7(3)^3$$
$$+ \binom{10}{4}(2y)^6(3)^4 + \cdots + \binom{10}{9}(2y)(3)^9 + \binom{10}{10}(3)^{10}$$

From the third term in the expansion, the coefficient of y^8 is

$$\binom{10}{2}(2)^8(3)^2 = \frac{10!}{2! \, 8!} \cdot 2^8 \cdot 9 = \frac{10 \cdot 9 \cdot 8!}{2 \cdot 8!} \cdot 2^8 \cdot 9 = 103,680$$

As this solution demonstrates, we can use the Binomial Theorem to find a particular term in an expansion without writing the entire expansion.

Based on the expansion of $(x + a)^n$, the term containing x^j is

$$\boxed{\binom{n}{n - j}a^{n-j}x^j} \qquad \textbf{(3)}$$

For example, we can solve Example 4 by using formula (3) with $n = 10$, $a = 3$, $x = 2y$, and $j = 8$. Then the term containing y^8 is

$$\binom{10}{10 - 8}3^{10-8}(2y)^8 = \binom{10}{2} \cdot 3^2 \cdot 2^8 \cdot y^8 = \frac{10!}{2! \, 8!} \cdot 9 \cdot 2^8 y^8$$
$$= \frac{10 \cdot 9 \cdot 8!}{2 \cdot 8!} \cdot 9 \cdot 2^8 y^8 = 103,680 y^8$$

EXAMPLE 5	Finding a Particular Term in a Binomial Expansion

Find the sixth term in the expansion of $(x + 2)^9$.

Solution A   We expand using the Binomial Theorem until the sixth term is reached.

$$(x + 2)^9 = \binom{9}{0}x^9 + \binom{9}{1}x^8 \cdot 2 + \binom{9}{2}x^7 \cdot 2^2 + \binom{9}{3}x^6 \cdot 2^3 + \binom{9}{4}x^5 \cdot 2^4$$

$$+ \binom{9}{5}x^4 \cdot 2^5 + \cdots$$

The sixth term is

$$\binom{9}{5}x^4 \cdot 2^5 = \frac{9!}{5! \, 4!} \cdot x^4 \cdot 32 = 4032x^4$$

Solution B   The sixth term in the expansion of $(x + 2)^9$, which has 10 terms total, contains x^4. (Do you see why?) By formula (3), the sixth term is

$$\binom{9}{9 - 4}2^{9-4}x^4 = \binom{9}{5}2^5x^4 = \frac{9!}{5! \, 4!} \cdot 32x^4 = 4032x^4$$

━━━━━ **Now Work**   PROBLEMS 29 AND 35

Next we show that the *triangular addition* feature of the Pascal triangle illustrated in Figure 18 always works.

THEOREM	If n and j are integers with $1 \le j \le n$, then

$$\binom{n}{j - 1} + \binom{n}{j} = \binom{n + 1}{j} \qquad \textbf{(4)}$$

Proof

$$\binom{n}{j - 1} + \binom{n}{j} = \frac{n!}{(j - 1)![n - (j - 1)]!} + \frac{n!}{j!(n - j)!}$$

$$= \frac{n!}{(j - 1)!(n - j + 1)!} + \frac{n!}{j!(n - j)!}$$

$$= \frac{jn!}{j(j - 1)!(n - j + 1)!} + \frac{(n - j + 1)n!}{j!(n - j + 1)(n - j)!} \qquad \text{Multiply the first term by } \frac{j}{j} \text{ and}$$

$$\text{the second term by } \frac{n - j + 1}{n - j + 1}.$$

$$= \frac{jn!}{j!(n - j + 1)!} + \frac{(n - j + 1)n!}{j!(n - j + 1)!} \qquad \text{Now the denominators are equal.}$$

$$= \frac{jn! + (n - j + 1)n!}{j!(n - j + 1)!}$$

$$= \frac{n!(j + n - j + 1)}{j!(n - j + 1)!}$$

$$= \frac{n!(n + 1)}{j!(n - j + 1)!} = \frac{(n + 1)!}{j![(n + 1) - j]!} = \binom{n + 1}{j}$$ ■

Historical Feature

*Omar Khayyám
(1050–1123)*

The case $n = 2$ of the Binomial Theorem, $(a + b)^2$, was known to Euclid in 300 BC, but the general law seems to have been discovered by the Persian mathematician and astronomer Omar Khayyám (1050–1123), who is also well known as the author of the *Rubáiyát*, a collection of four-line poems making observations on the human condition. Omar Khayyám did not state the Binomial Theorem explicitly, but he claimed to have a method for extracting third, fourth, fifth roots, and so on. A little study shows that one must know the Binomial Theorem to create such a method.

The heart of the Binomial Theorem is the formula for the numerical coefficients, and, as we saw, they can be written in a symmetric triangular form. The Pascal triangle appears first in the books of Yang Hui (about 1270) and Chu Shih-chieh (1303). Pascal's name is attached to the triangle because of the many applications he made of it, especially to counting and probability. In establishing these results, he was one of the earliest users of mathematical induction.

Many people worked on the proof of the Binomial Theorem, which was finally completed for all n (including complex numbers) by Niels Abel (1802–1829).

12.5 Assess Your Understanding

Concepts and Vocabulary

1. The _____ _____ is a triangular display of the binomial coefficients.

2. $\dbinom{6}{2} = $ ____

3. *True or False* $\dbinom{n}{j} = \dfrac{j!}{(n - j)!\, n!}$

4. The _____ _____ can be used to expand expressions like $(2x + 3)^6$.

Skill Building

In Problems 5–16, evaluate each expression.

5. $\dbinom{5}{3}$

6. $\dbinom{7}{3}$

7. $\dbinom{7}{5}$

8. $\dbinom{9}{7}$

9. $\dbinom{50}{49}$

10. $\dbinom{100}{98}$

11. $\dbinom{1000}{1000}$

12. $\dbinom{1000}{0}$

13. $\dbinom{55}{23}$

14. $\dbinom{60}{20}$

15. $\dbinom{47}{25}$

16. $\dbinom{37}{19}$

In Problems 17–28, expand each expression using the Binomial Theorem.

17. $(x + 1)^5$

18. $(x - 1)^5$

19. $(x - 2)^6$

20. $(x + 3)^5$

21. $(3x + 1)^4$

22. $(2x + 3)^5$

23. $(x^2 + y^2)^5$

24. $(x^2 - y^2)^6$

25. $\left(\sqrt{x} + \sqrt{2}\right)^6$

26. $\left(\sqrt{x} - \sqrt{3}\right)^4$

27. $(ax + by)^5$

28. $(ax - by)^4$

In Problems 29–42, use the Binomial Theorem to find the indicated coefficient or term.

29. The coefficient of x^6 in the expansion of $(x + 3)^{10}$

30. The coefficient of x^3 in the expansion of $(x - 3)^{10}$

31. The coefficient of x^7 in the expansion of $(2x - 1)^{12}$

32. The coefficient of x^3 in the expansion of $(2x + 1)^{12}$

33. The coefficient of x^7 in the expansion of $(2x + 3)^9$

34. The coefficient of x^2 in the expansion of $(2x - 3)^9$

35. The fifth term in the expansion of $(x + 3)^7$

36. The third term in the expansion of $(x - 3)^7$

37. The third term in the expansion of $(3x - 2)^9$

38. The sixth term in the expansion of $(3x + 2)^8$

39. The coefficient of x^0 in the expansion of $\left(x^2 + \dfrac{1}{x}\right)^{12}$

40. The coefficient of x^0 in the expansion of $\left(x - \dfrac{1}{x^2}\right)^9$

41. The coefficient of x^4 in the expansion of $\left(x - \dfrac{2}{\sqrt{x}}\right)^{10}$

42. The coefficient of x^2 in the expansion of $\left(\sqrt{x} + \dfrac{3}{\sqrt{x}}\right)^8$

Applications and Extensions

43. Use the Binomial Theorem to find the numerical value of $(1.001)^5$ correct to five decimal places.
    [**Hint:** $(1.001)^5 = (1 + 10^{-3})^5$]

44. Use the Binomial Theorem to find the numerical value of $(0.998)^6$ correct to five decimal places.

45. Show that $\dbinom{n}{n-1} = n$ and $\dbinom{n}{n} = 1$.

46. Show that if n and j are integers with $0 \le j \le n$ then

$$\binom{n}{j} = \binom{n}{n-j}$$

Conclude that the Pascal triangle is symmetric with respect to a vertical line drawn from the topmost entry.

47. If n is a positive integer, show that

$$\binom{n}{0} + \binom{n}{1} + \cdots + \binom{n}{n} = 2^n$$

[**Hint:** $2^n = (1 + 1)^n$; now use the Binomial Theorem.]

48. If n is a positive integer, show that

$$\binom{n}{0} - \binom{n}{1} + \binom{n}{2} - \cdots + (-1)^n \binom{n}{n} = 0$$

49. $\dbinom{5}{0}\left(\dfrac{1}{4}\right)^5 + \dbinom{5}{1}\left(\dfrac{1}{4}\right)^4\left(\dfrac{3}{4}\right) + \dbinom{5}{2}\left(\dfrac{1}{4}\right)^3\left(\dfrac{3}{4}\right)^2$

$+ \dbinom{5}{3}\left(\dfrac{1}{4}\right)^2\left(\dfrac{3}{4}\right)^3 + \dbinom{5}{4}\left(\dfrac{1}{4}\right)\left(\dfrac{3}{4}\right)^4 + \dbinom{5}{5}\left(\dfrac{3}{4}\right)^5 = ?$

50. **Stirling's Formula** An approximation for $n!$, when n is large, is given by

$$n! \approx \sqrt{2n\pi}\left(\dfrac{n}{e}\right)^n\left(1 + \dfrac{1}{12n - 1}\right)$$

Calculate 12!, 20!, and 25! on your calculator. Then use Stirling's formula to approximate 12!, 20!, and 25!.

CHAPTER REVIEW

Things to Know

Sequence (p. 804)	A function whose domain is the set of positive integers.
Factorials (p. 806)	$0! = 1, 1! = 1, n! = n(n-1) \cdot \cdots \cdot 3 \cdot 2 \cdot 1$ if $n \ge 2$ is an integer
Arithmetic sequence (pp. 817 and 818)	$a_1 = a,\ a_n = a_{n-1} + d$, where $a_1 = a =$ first term, $d =$ common difference $a_n = a_1 + (n-1)d$
Sum of the first n terms of an arithmetic sequence (p. 819)	$S_n = \dfrac{n}{2}[2a_1 + (n-1)d] = \dfrac{n}{2}(a_1 + a_n)$
Geometric sequence (pp. 823 and 825)	$a_1 = a,\ a_n = ra_{n-1}$, where $a_1 = a =$ first term, $r =$ common ratio $a_n = a_1 r^{n-1},\ r \ne 0$
Sum of the first n terms of a geometric sequence (p. 825)	$S_n = a_1 \dfrac{1 - r^n}{1 - r},\ r \ne 0, 1$
Infinite geometric series (p. 827)	$a_1 + a_1 r + \cdots + a_1 r^{n-1} + \cdots = \displaystyle\sum_{k=1}^{\infty} a_1 r^{k-1}$
Sum of a convergent infinite geometric series (p. 827)	If $|r| < 1,\ \displaystyle\sum_{k=1}^{\infty} a_1 r^{k-1} = \dfrac{a_1}{1 - r}$
Principle of Mathematical Induction (p. 833)	Suppose the following two conditions are satisfied. Condition I: The statement is true for the natural number 1. Condition II: If the statement is true for some natural number k, it is also true for $k + 1$. Then the statement is true for all natural numbers.

Binomial coefficient (p. 837)

$$\binom{n}{j} = \frac{n!}{j!(n-j)!}$$

Pascal triangle (pp. 838–839)

See Figure 18.

Binomial Theorem (p. 839)

$$(x + a)^n = \binom{n}{0}x^n + \binom{n}{1}ax^{n-1} + \cdots + \binom{n}{j}a^j x^{n-j} + \cdots + \binom{n}{n}a^n = \sum_{j=0}^{n}\binom{n}{j}x^{n-j}a^j$$

Objectives

Section	You should be able to . . .	Example(s)	Review Exercises
12.1	**1** Write the first several terms of a sequence (p. 804)	1–4	1–4
	2 Write the terms of a sequence defined by a recursive formula (p. 807)	5, 6	5–8
	3 Use summation notation (p. 808)	7, 8	9–12
	4 Find the sum of a sequence algebraically and using a graphing utility (p. 809)	9	25, 26
	5 Solve annuity and amortization problems (p. 811)	10, 11	68, 69
12.2	**1** Determine if a sequence is arithmetic (p. 817)	1–3	13–24
	2 Find a formula for an arithmetic sequence (p. 818)	4, 5	31, 32, 35, 37–40, 65
	3 Find the sum of an arithmetic sequence (p. 819)	6–8	13, 14, 19, 20, 27, 28, 66
12.3	**1** Determine if a sequence is geometric (p. 823)	1–3	13–24
	2 Find a formula for a geometric sequence (p. 824)	4	22, 33, 34, 36, 70
	3 Find the sum of a geometric sequence (p. 825)	5, 6	17, 18, 21, 22, 29, 30, 67(a)–(c), 70
	4 Determine whether a geometric series converges or diverges (p. 827)	7, 8	41–48, 67(d)
12.4	**1** Prove statements using mathematical induction (p. 833)	1–4	49–54
12.5	**1** Evaluate $\binom{n}{j}$ (p. 837)	1	55, 56
	2 Use the Binomial Theorem (p. 839)	2–5	57–64

Review Exercises

In Problems 1–8, write down the first five terms of each sequence. Verify your results using a graphing utility.

1. $\{a_n\} = \left\{(-1)^n\left(\dfrac{n+3}{n+2}\right)\right\}$ **2.** $\{b_n\} = \{(-1)^{n+1}(2n+3)\}$ **3.** $\{c_n\} = \left\{\dfrac{2^n}{n^2}\right\}$ **4.** $\{d_n\} = \left\{\dfrac{e^n}{n}\right\}$

5. $a_1 = 3;\quad a_n = \dfrac{2}{3}a_{n-1}$ **6.** $a_1 = 4;\quad a_n = -\dfrac{1}{4}a_{n-1}$ **7.** $a_1 = 2;\quad a_n = 2 - a_{n-1}$ **8.** $a_1 = -3;\quad a_n = 4 + a_{n-1}$

In Problems 9 and 10, write out and evaluate each sum.

9. $\displaystyle\sum_{k=1}^{4}(4k+2)$ **10.** $\displaystyle\sum_{k=1}^{3}(3-k^2)$

In Problems 11 and 12, express each sum using summation notation.

11. $1 - \dfrac{1}{2} + \dfrac{1}{3} - \dfrac{1}{4} + \cdots + \dfrac{1}{13}$ **12.** $2 + \dfrac{2^2}{3} + \dfrac{2^3}{3^2} + \cdots + \dfrac{2^{n+1}}{3^n}$

In Problems 13–24, determine whether the given sequence is arithmetic, geometric, or neither. If the sequence is arithmetic, find the common difference and the sum of the first n terms. If the sequence is geometric, find the common ratio and the sum of the first n terms.

13. $\{a_n\} = \{n + 5\}$ **14.** $\{b_n\} = \{4n + 3\}$ **15.** $\{c_n\} = \{2n^3\}$ **16.** $\{d_n\} = \{2n^2 - 1\}$

17. $\{s_n\} = \{2^{3n}\}$ **18.** $\{u_n\} = \{3^{2n}\}$ **19.** $0, 4, 8, 12, \ldots$ **20.** $1, -3, -7, -11, \ldots$

21. $3, \dfrac{3}{2}, \dfrac{3}{4}, \dfrac{3}{8}, \dfrac{3}{16}, \ldots$ **22.** $5, -\dfrac{5}{3}, \dfrac{5}{9}, -\dfrac{5}{27}, \dfrac{5}{81}, \ldots$ **23.** $\dfrac{2}{3}, \dfrac{3}{4}, \dfrac{4}{5}, \dfrac{5}{6}, \ldots$ **24.** $\dfrac{3}{2}, \dfrac{5}{4}, \dfrac{7}{6}, \dfrac{9}{8}, \dfrac{11}{10}, \ldots$

In Problems 25–30, find each sum. Verify your result using a graphing utility.

25. $\displaystyle\sum_{k=1}^{50}(3k)$

26. $\displaystyle\sum_{k=1}^{30}k^2$

27. $\displaystyle\sum_{k=1}^{30}(3k-9)$

28. $\displaystyle\sum_{k=1}^{40}(-2k+8)$

29. $\displaystyle\sum_{k=1}^{7}\left(\frac{1}{3}\right)^k$

30. $\displaystyle\sum_{k=1}^{10}(-2)^k$

In Problems 31–36, find the indicated term in each sequence. [**Hint:** Find the general term first.]

31. 9th term of $3, 7, 11, 15, \ldots$

32. 8th term of $1, -1, -3, -5, \ldots$

33. 11th term of $1, \dfrac{1}{10}, \dfrac{1}{100}, \ldots$

34. 11th term of $1, 2, 4, 8, \ldots$

35. 9th term of $\sqrt{2}, 2\sqrt{2}, 3\sqrt{2}, \ldots$

36. 9th term of $\sqrt{2}, 2, 2^{3/2}, \ldots$

In Problems 37–40, find a general formula for each arithmetic sequence.

37. 7th term is 31; 20th term is 96

38. 8th term is -20; 17th term is -47

39. 10th term is 0; 18th term is 8

40. 12th term is 30; 22nd term is 50

In Problems 41–48, determine whether each infinite geometric series converges or diverges. If it converges, find its sum.

41. $3 + 1 + \dfrac{1}{3} + \dfrac{1}{9} + \cdots$

42. $2 + 1 + \dfrac{1}{2} + \dfrac{1}{4} + \cdots$

43. $2 - 1 + \dfrac{1}{2} - \dfrac{1}{4} + \cdots$

44. $6 - 4 + \dfrac{8}{3} - \dfrac{16}{9} + \cdots$

45. $\dfrac{1}{2} + \dfrac{3}{4} + \dfrac{9}{8} + \cdots$

46. $\displaystyle\sum_{k=1}^{\infty}5\cdot\left(-\frac{5}{4}\right)^{k-1}$

47. $\displaystyle\sum_{k=1}^{\infty}4\left(\frac{1}{2}\right)^{k-1}$

48. $\displaystyle\sum_{k=1}^{\infty}3\left(-\frac{3}{4}\right)^{k-1}$

In Problems 49–54, use the Principle of Mathematical Induction to show that the given statement is true for all natural numbers.

49. $3 + 6 + 9 + \cdots + 3n = \dfrac{3n}{2}(n+1)$

50. $2 + 6 + 10 + \cdots + (4n-2) = 2n^2$

51. $2 + 6 + 18 + \cdots + 2\cdot3^{n-1} = 3^n - 1$

52. $3 + 6 + 12 + \cdots + 3\cdot2^{n-1} = 3(2^n - 1)$

53. $1^2 + 4^2 + 7^2 + \cdots + (3n-2)^2 = \dfrac{1}{2}n(6n^2 - 3n - 1)$

54. $1\cdot3 + 2\cdot4 + 3\cdot5 + \cdots + n(n+2) = \dfrac{n}{6}(n+1)(2n+7)$

In Problems 55 and 56, evaluate each binomial coefficient.

55. $\dbinom{5}{2}$

56. $\dbinom{8}{6}$

In Problems 57–60, expand each expression using the Binomial Theorem.

57. $(x+2)^5$

58. $(x-3)^4$

59. $(2x+3)^5$

60. $(3x-4)^4$

---

61. Find the coefficient of x^7 in the expansion of $(x+2)^9$.

62. Find the coefficient of x^3 in the expansion of $(x-3)^8$.

63. Find the coefficient of x^2 in the expansion of $(2x+1)^7$.

64. Find the coefficient of x^6 in the expansion of $(2x+1)^8$.

65. Constructing a Brick Staircase A brick staircase has a total of 25 steps. The bottom step requires 80 bricks. Each successive step requires three less bricks than the prior step.

    (a) How many bricks are required for the top step?

    (b) How many bricks are required to build the staircase?

66. Creating a Floor Design A mosaic tile floor is designed in the shape of a trapezoid 30 feet wide at the base and 15 feet wide at the top. The tiles, 12 inches by 12 inches, are to be placed so that each successive row contains one less tile than the row below. How many tiles will be required?

67. Bouncing Balls A ball is dropped from a height of 20 feet. Each time it strikes the ground, it bounces up to three-quarters of the previous height.

    (a) What height will the ball bounce up to after it strikes the ground for the third time?

(b) How high will it bounce after it strikes the ground for the *n*th time?

(c) How many times does the ball need to strike the ground before its bounce is less than 6 inches?

(d) What total distance does the ball travel before it stops bouncing?

68. Home Loan Mike and Yola borrowed $190,000 at 6.75% per annum compounded monthly for 30 years to purchase a home. Their monthly payment is determined to be $1232.34.

(a) Find a recursive formula for the balance after each monthly payment has been made.

(b) Determine the balance after the first payment.

(c) Using a graphing utility, create a table showing the balance after each monthly payment.

(d) Using a graphing utility, determine when the balance will be below $100,000.

(e) Using a graphing utility, determine when Mike and Yola will pay off the balance.

(f) Determine their interest expense when the loan is paid.

(g) Suppose that Mike and Yola decide to pay an additional $100 each month on the loan. Answer parts (a) to (f) under this scenario.

69. Credit Card Debt Beth just charged $5000 on a VISA card that charges 1.5% interest per month on any unpaid balance. She can afford to pay $100 toward the balance each month. Her balance at the beginning of each month after making a $100 payment is given by the recursively defined sequence

$$b_1 = \$5000, \quad b_n = 1.015b_{n-1} - 100$$

(a) Determine Beth's balance after making the first payment; that is, determine b_2, the balance at the beginning of the second month.

(b) Using a graphing utility, graph the recursively defined sequence.

(c) Using a graphing utility, determine when Beth's balance will be below $4000. How many payments of $100 will have been made?

(d) Using a graphing utility, determine the number of payments it will take until Beth pays off the balance. What is the total of all the payments?

(e) What was Beth's interest expense?

70. Salary Increases Your friend has just been hired at an annual salary of $20,000. If she expects to receive annual increases of 4%, what will be her salary as she begins her fifth year?

CHAPTER TEST

In Problems 1 and 2, write down the first five terms of each sequence.

1. $\{s_n\} = \left\{\dfrac{n^2 - 1}{n + 8}\right\}$ **2.** $a_1 = 4, a_n = 3a_{n-1} + 2$

5. Write the following sum using summation notation.

$$-\frac{2}{5} + \frac{3}{6} - \frac{4}{7} + \cdots + \frac{11}{14}$$

In Problems 3 and 4, write out each sum. Evaluate each sum.

3. $\displaystyle\sum_{k=1}^{3} (-1)^{k+1}\left(\frac{k + 1}{k^2}\right)$ **4.** $\displaystyle\sum_{k=1}^{4}\left[\left(\frac{2}{3}\right)^k - k\right]$

In Problems 6–11, determine whether the given sequence is arithmetic, geometric, or neither. If the sequence is arithmetic, find the common difference and the sum of the first n terms. If the sequence is geometric, find the common ratio and the sum of the first n terms.

6. $6, 12, 36, 144, \ldots$

7. $\left\{-\dfrac{1}{2} \cdot 4^n\right\}$

8. $-2, -10, -18, -26, \ldots$

9. $\left\{-\dfrac{n}{2} + 7\right\}$

10. $25, 10, 4, \dfrac{8}{5}, \ldots$

11. $\left\{\dfrac{2n - 3}{2n + 1}\right\}$

12. Determine whether the infinite geometric series

$$256 - 64 + 16 - 4 + \cdots$$

converges or diverges. If it converges, find its sum.

13. Expand $(3m + 2)^5$ using the Binomial Theorem.

14. Use the Principle of Mathematical Induction to show that the given statement is true for all natural numbers.

$$\left(1 + \frac{1}{1}\right)\left(1 + \frac{1}{2}\right)\left(1 + \frac{1}{3}\right)\cdots\left(1 + \frac{1}{n}\right) = n + 1$$

15. A 2004 Dodge Durango sold for $31,000. If the vehicle loses 15% of its value each year, how much will it be worth after 10 years?

16. A weight lifter begins his routine by benching 100 pounds and increases the weight by 30 pounds for each set. If he does 10 repetitions in each set, what is the total weight lifted after 5 sets?

CUMULATIVE REVIEW

1. Find all the solutions, real and complex, of the equation
$$|x^2| = 9$$

2. (a) Graph the circle $x^2 + y^2 = 100$ and the parabola $y = 3x^2$.

   (b) Solve the system of equations: $\begin{cases} x^2 + y^2 = 100 \\ \qquad y = 3x^2 \end{cases}$

   (c) Where do the circle and the parabola intersect?

3. Solve the equation $2e^x = 5$.

4. Find an equation of the line with slope 5 and x-intercept 2.

5. Find the standard equation of the circle whose center is the point $(-1, 2)$ if $(3, 5)$ is a point on the circle.

6. $f(x) = \dfrac{3x}{x - 2}$, $g(x) = 2x + 1$

   Find:
   (a) $(f \circ g)(2)$ (b) $(g \circ f)(4)$ (c) $(f \circ g)(x)$
   (d) The domain of $(f \circ g)(x)$
   (e) $(g \circ f)(x)$ (f) The domain of $(g \circ f)(x)$

(g) The function g^{-1} and its domain

(h) The function f^{-1} and its domain

7. Find the equation of an ellipse with center at the origin, a focus at $(0, 3)$, and a vertex at $(0, 4)$.

8. Find the equation of a parabola with vertex at $(-1, 2)$ and focus at $(-1, 3)$.

9. Find the polar equation of a circle with center at $(0, 4)$ that passes through the pole. What is the rectangular equation?

10. Solve the equation
$$2 \sin^2 x - \sin x - 3 = 0, \quad 0 \le x < 2\pi$$

11. Find the exact value of $\cos^{-1}(-0.5)$.

12. If $\sin \theta = \dfrac{1}{4}$ and θ is in the second quadrant, find:

   (a) $\cos \theta$ (b) $\tan \theta$
   (c) $\sin(2\theta)$ (d) $\cos(2\theta)$
   (e) $\sin\left(\dfrac{1}{2}\theta\right)$

CHAPTER PROJECTS

I. Population Growth The size of the population of the United States essentially depends on its current population, the birth and death rates of the population, and immigration. Suppose that b represents the birth rate of the U.S. population and d represents its death rate. Then $r = b - d$ represents the growth rate of the population, where r varies from year to year. The U.S. population after n years can be modeled using the recursive function

$$p_n = (1 + r)p_{n-1} + I$$

where I represents net immigration into the United States.

1. Using data from the National Center for Health Statistics *www.fedstats.gov*, determine the birth and death rates for all races for the most recent year that data are available. Birth rates are given as the number of live births per 1000

population, while death rates are given as the number of deaths per 100,000 population. Each must be computed as the number of births (deaths) per individual. For example, in 2000, the birth rate was 14.7 per 1000 and the death rate was 873.1 per 100,000, so $b = \dfrac{14.7}{1000} = 0.0147$, while $d = \dfrac{873.1}{100,000} = 0.008731$.

Next, using data from the Immigration and Naturalization Service *www.fedstats.gov*, determine the net immigration to the United States for the same year used to obtain b and d in Problem 1.

2. Determine the value of r, the growth rate of the population.

3. Find a recursive formula for the population of the United States.

4. Use the recursive formula to predict the population of the United States in the following year. In other words, if data are available up to the year 2005, predict the U.S. population in 2006.

5. Compare your prediction to actual data.

6. Repeat Problems 1–5 for Uganda using the CIA World Factbook at *www.cia.gov/cia/publications/factbook/index.html* (in 2000, the birth rate was 48.04 per 1000 and the death rate was 18.44 per 1000).

7. Do your results for the United States (a developed country) and Uganda (a developing country) seem in line with the article in the chapter opener? Explain.

8. Do you think the recursive formula found in Problem 3 will be useful in predicting future populations? Why or why not?

The following projects are available at the Instructor's Resource Center (IRC):

II. **Project at Motorola** ***Digital Wireless Communication*** Cell phones take speech and change it into digital code using only zeros and ones. See how the code length can be modeled using a mathematical sequence.

III. **Economics** Economists use the current price of a good and a recursive model to predict future consumer demand and to determine future production.

IV. **Standardized Tests** Many tests of intelligence, aptitude, and achievement contain questions asking for the terms of a mathematical sequence.

Counting and Probability

13

Deal or No Deal

By LYNN ELBER, AP Television Writer—LOS ANGELES—The promise of an easy million bucks, a stage crowded with sexy models and the smoothly calibrated charm of host **Howie Mandel** made "Deal or No Deal" an unexpected hit in television's December dead zone. Based on a series that debuted in Holland in 2002 and became an international hit, "Deal or No Deal" is about luck and playing the odds. Contestants are faced with 26 briefcases held by 26 models, each case with a hidden value ranging from a penny to the top prize that will escalate by week's end to $3 million. As the game progresses and cases are eliminated, a contestant weighs the chance of snaring a big prize against lesser but still tempting offers made by the show's "bank," represented by an anonymous, silhouetted figure.

Source: Adapted from *Lynn Elber, "'Deal or No Deal' back with bigger prizes," Associated Press, February 24, 2006. © 2006 Associated Press.*

—See Chapter Project I—

A Look Back

We first introduced sets in Appendix A, Section A.1. We have been using sets to represent solutions of equations and inequalities and to represent the domain and range of functions.

A Look Ahead

Here we discuss methods for counting the number of elements in a set and the role of sets in probability.

Outline

13.1 Counting
13.2 Permutations and Combinations
13.3 Probability
Chapter Review
Chapter Test
Cumulative Review
Chapter Projects

13.1 Counting

PREPARING FOR THIS SECTION *Before getting started, review the following:*

- Sets (Appendix A, Section A.1, pp. A1–A3)

Now Work the 'Are You Prepared?' problems on page 854.

OBJECTIVES 1 Find All the Subsets of a Set (p. 850)
2 Count the Number of Elements in a Set (p. 850)
3 Solve Counting Problems Using the Multiplication Principle (p. 852)

Counting plays a major role in many diverse areas, such as probability, statistics, and computer science; counting techniques are a part of a branch of mathematics called **combinatorics.**

1 Find All the Subsets of a Set

We begin by reviewing the ways that two sets can be compared.

If two sets A and B have precisely the same elements, we say that A and B are **equal** and write $A = B$.

If each element of a set A is also an element of a set B, we say that A is a **subset** of B and write $A \subseteq B$.

If $A \subseteq B$ and $A \neq B$, we say that A is a **proper subset** of B and write $A \subset B$.

If $A \subseteq B$, every element in set A is also in set B, but B may or may not have additional elements. If $A \subset B$, every element in A is also in B, and B has at least one element not found in A.

Finally, we agree that the empty set is a subset of every set; that is,

$$\varnothing \subseteq A \qquad \text{for any set } A$$

EXAMPLE 1	**Finding All the Subsets of a Set**

Write down all the subsets of the set $\{a, b, c\}$.

Solution To organize our work, we write down all the subsets with no elements, then those with one element, then those with two elements, and finally those with three elements. These will give us all the subsets. Do you see why?

0 Elements	**1 Element**	**2 Elements**	**3 Elements**
$\varnothing$	$\{a\}, \{b\}, \{c\}$	$\{a, b\}, \{b, c\}, \{a, c\}$	$\{a, b, c\}$

Now Work PROBLEM 7

2 Count the Number of Elements in a Set

As you count the number of students in a classroom or the number of pennies in your pocket, what you are really doing is matching, on a one-to-one basis, each object to be counted with the set of counting numbers, $1, 2, 3, \ldots, n$, for some number n. If a set A matched up in this fashion with the set $\{a, b, \ldots, z\}$, you would conclude that there are 26 elements in the set A. We use the notation $n(A) = 26$ to indicate that there are 26 elements in the set A.

Because the empty set has no elements, we write

$$n(\varnothing) = 0$$

In Words
We use the notation $n(A)$ to mean the number of elements in set A.

If the number of elements in a set is a nonnegative integer, we say that the set is **finite.** Otherwise, it is **infinite.** We shall concern ourselves only with finite sets.

Look again at Example 1. A set with 3 elements has $2^3 = 8$ subsets. This result can be generalized.

If A is a set with n elements, A has 2^n subsets.

For example, the set $\{a, b, c, d, e\}$ has $2^5 = 32$ subsets.

| EXAMPLE 2 | **Analyzing Survey Data** |

In a survey of 100 college students, 35 were registered in College Algebra, 52 were registered in Computer Science I, and 18 were registered in both courses.

(a) How many students were registered in College Algebra or Computer Science I?
(b) How many were registered in neither course?

Solution (a) First, let A = set of students in College Algebra

B = set of students in Computer Science I

Then the given information tells us that

$$n(A) = 35 \qquad n(B) = 52 \qquad n(A \cap B) = 18$$

Refer to Figure 1. Since $n(A \cap B) = 18$, we know that the common part of the circles representing set A and set B has 18 elements. In addition, we know that the remaining portion of the circle representing set A will have $35 - 18 = 17$ elements. Similarly, we know that the remaining portion of the circle representing set B has $52 - 18 = 34$ elements. We conclude that $17 + 18 + 34 = 69$ students were registered in College Algebra or Computer Science I.

(b) Since 100 students were surveyed, it follows that $100 - 69 = 31$ were registered in neither course.

Figure 1

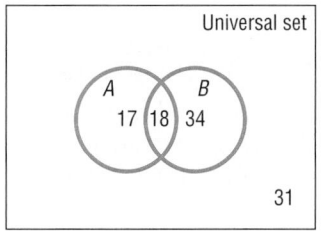

Now Work PROBLEMS 15 AND 25

The solution to Example 2 contains the basis for a general counting formula. If we count the elements in each of two sets A and B, we necessarily count twice any elements that are in both A and B, that is, those elements in $A \cap B$. To count correctly the elements that are in A or B, that is, to find $n(A \cup B)$, we need to subtract those in $A \cap B$ from $n(A) + n(B)$.

THEOREM **Counting Formula**

If A and B are finite sets,

$$n(A \cup B) = n(A) + n(B) - n(A \cap B) \tag{1}$$

Refer back to Example 2. Using (1), we have

$$n(A \cup B) = n(A) + n(B) - n(A \cap B)$$
$$= 35 + 52 - 18$$
$$= 69$$

There are 69 students registered in College Algebra or Computer Science I.

A special case of the counting formula (1) occurs if A and B have no elements in common. In this case, $A \cap B = \varnothing$, so $n(A \cap B) = 0$.

THEOREM **Addition Principle of Counting**

If two sets A and B have no elements in common, that is,

$$\text{if } A \cap B = \varnothing, \text{ then } n(A \cup B) = n(A) + n(B) \tag{2}$$

We can generalize formula (2).

THEOREM

General Addition Principle of Counting

If, for n sets $A_1, A_2, \ldots, A_n$, no two have elements in common,

$$n(A_1 \cup A_2 \cup \cdots \cup A_n) = n(A_1) + n(A_2) + \cdots + n(A_n) \qquad \textbf{(3)}$$

EXAMPLE 3

Counting

In the year 2004, U.S. universities awarded 42,155 doctoral degrees. Table 1 lists the number of doctorates conferred by broad fields of study.

Table 1

Broad Field of Study	Number of Doctorates
Physical sciences	6049
Engineering	5776
Life sciences	8819
Social sciences	6795
Humanities	5467
Education	6635
Professional/other fields	2614

Source: NSF/NIH/USED/NEH/USDA/NASA, *2004 Survey of Earned Doctorates*

(a) How many doctorates were awarded by U.S. universities in physical sciences or life sciences?

(b) How many doctorates were awarded by U.S. universities in physical sciences, life sciences, or engineering?

Solution

Let A represent the set of physical science doctorates, B represent the set of life science doctorates, and C represent the set of engineering doctorates. No two of the sets A, B, and C have elements in common since a single degree cannot be classified into more than one broad field of study. Then

$$n(A) = 6049 \quad n(B) = 8819 \quad n(C) = 5776$$

(a) Using formula (2), we have

$$n(A \cup B) = n(A) + n(B) = 6049 + 8819 = 14{,}868$$

There were 14,868 doctorates awarded in physical sciences or life sciences.

(b) Using formula (3), we have

$$n(A \cup B \cup C) = n(A) + n(B) + n(C) = 6049 + 8819 + 5776 = 20{,}644$$

There were 20,644 doctorates awarded in physical sciences, life sciences, or engineering.

━━━ **Now Work** PROBLEM 29

3 Solve Counting Problems Using the Multiplication Principle

We begin with an example that illustrates the multiplication principle.

| EXAMPLE 4 | Counting the Number of Possible Meals |

The fixed-price dinner at Mabenka Restaurant provides the following choices:

Appetizer: soup or salad
Entree: baked chicken, broiled beef patty, baby beef liver, or roast beef au jus
Dessert: ice cream or cheese cake

How many different meals can be ordered?

Solution   Ordering such a meal requires three separate decisions:

| **Choose an Appetizer** | **Choose an Entree** | **Choose a Dessert** |
| 2 choices | 4 choices | 2 choices |

Look at the **tree diagram** in Figure 2. We see that, for each choice of appetizer, there are 4 choices of entrees. And for each of these $2 \cdot 4 = 8$ choices, there are 2 choices for dessert. A total of

$$2 \cdot 4 \cdot 2 = 16$$

different meals can be ordered.

Figure 2

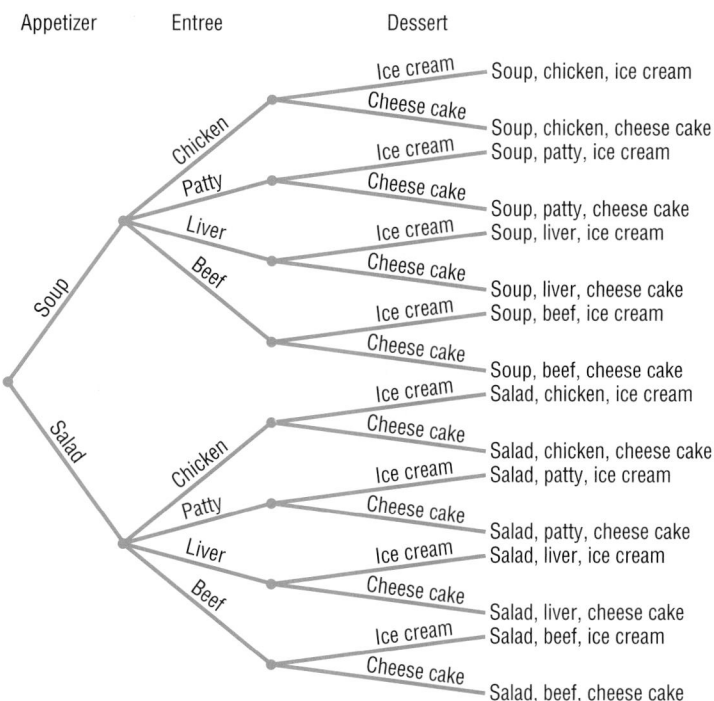

Example 4 demonstrates a general principle of counting.

THEOREM   **Multiplication Principle of Counting**

If a task consists of a sequence of choices in which there are p selections for the first choice, q selections for the second choice, r selections for the third choice, and so on, the task of making these selections can be done in

$$p \cdot q \cdot r \cdot \cdots$$

different ways.

| EXAMPLE 5 | Forming Codes |

How many two-symbol code words can be formed if the first symbol is an upper-case letter and the second symbol is a digit?

Solution　It sometimes helps to begin by listing some of the possibilities. The code consists of an uppercase letter followed by a digit, so some possibilities are A1, A2, B3, X0, and so on. The task consists of making two selections: the first selection requires choosing an uppercase letter (26 choices), and the second task requires choosing a digit (10 choices). By the Multiplication Principle, there are

$$26 \cdot 10 = 260$$

different codewords of the type described.

Now Work PROBLEM 21

13.1 Assess Your Understanding

'Are You Prepared?' *Answers are given at the end of these exercises. If you get a wrong answer, read the pages listed in red.*

1. The _____ of A and B consists of all elements in either A or B or both. (p. A2)

2. The _____ of A with B consists of all elements in both A and B. (p. A2)

3. **True or False** The intersection of two sets is always a sub-set of their union. (pp. A2–A3)

4. **True or False** If A is a set, the complement of A is the set of all the elements in the universal set that are not in A. (p. A2)

Concepts and Vocabulary

5. The Counting Formula states that if A and B are two finite sets then $n(A \cup B) =$ _____.

6. **True or False** The Multiplication Principle states that if A and B are two finite sets then $n(A \cup B) = n(A) \cdot n(B)$.

Skill Building

7. Write down all the subsets of $\{a, b, c, d\}$.

8. Write down all the subsets of $\{a, b, c, d, e\}$.

9. If $n(A) = 15$, $n(B) = 20$, and $n(A \cap B) = 10$, find $n(A \cup B)$.

10. If $n(A) = 30$, $n(B) = 40$, and $n(A \cup B) = 45$, find $n(A \cap B)$.

11. If $n(A \cup B) = 50$, $n(A \cap B) = 10$, and $n(B) = 20$, find $n(A)$.

12. If $n(A \cup B) = 60$, $n(A \cap B) = 40$, and $n(A) = n(B)$, find $n(A)$.

In Problems 13–20, use the information given in the figure.

13. How many are in set A?

14. How many are in set B?

15. How many are in A or B?

16. How many are in A and B?

17. How many are in A but not C?

18. How many are not in A?

19. How many are in A and B and C?

20. How many are in A or B or C?

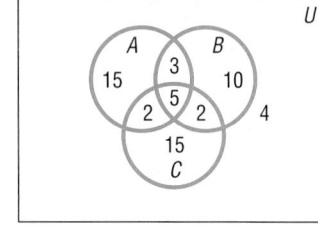

Applications and Extensions

21. **Shirts and Ties** A man has 5 shirts and 3 ties. How many different shirt and tie arrangements can he wear?

22. **Blouses and Skirts** A woman has 5 blouses and 8 skirts. How many different outfits can she wear?

23. **Four-digit Numbers** How many four-digit numbers can be formed using the digits 0, 1, 2, 3, 4, 5, 6, 7, 8, and 9 if the first digit cannot be 0? Repeated digits are allowed.

24. **Five-digit Numbers** How many five-digit numbers can be formed using the digits 0, 1, 2, 3, 4, 5, 6, 7, 8, and 9 if the first digit cannot be 0 or 1? Repeated digits are allowed.

25. **Analyzing Survey Data** In a consumer survey of 500 people, 200 indicated that they would be buying a major appliance within the next month, 150 indicated that they would buy a car, and 25 said that they would purchase both a major appliance and a car. How many will purchase neither? How many will purchase only a car?

26. **Analyzing Survey Data** In a student survey, 200 indicated that they would attend Summer Session I and 150 indicated Summer Session II. If 75 students plan to attend both summer sessions and 275 indicated that they would attend neither session, how many students participated in the survey?

27. Analyzing Survey Data In a survey of 100 investors in the stock market,

    50 owned shares in IBM

    40 owned shares in AT&T

    45 owned shares in GE

    20 owned shares in both IBM and GE

    15 owned shares in both AT&T and GE

    20 owned shares in both IBM and AT&T

    5 owned shares in all three

(a) How many of the investors surveyed did not have shares in any of the three companies?

(b) How many owned just IBM shares?

(c) How many owned just GE shares?

(d) How many owned neither IBM nor GE?

(e) How many owned either IBM or AT&T but no GE?

28. Classifying Blood Types Human blood is classified as either Rh+ or Rh−. Blood is also classified by type: A, if it contains an A antigen but not a B antigen; B, if it contains a B antigen but not an A antigen; AB, if it contains both A and B antigens; and O, if it contains neither antigen. Draw a Venn diagram illustrating the various blood types. Based on this classification, how many different kinds of blood are there?

29. Demographics The following data represent the marital status of males 18 years old and older in 2005.

(a) Determine the number of males 18 years old and older who are widowed or divorced.

(b) Determine the number of males 18 years old and older who are married, widowed, or divorced.

Marital Status	Number (in thousands)
Married	63,318
Widowed	2,723
Divorced	9,200
Never married	29,608

Source: Current Population Survey

30. Demographics The following data represent the marital status of females 18 years old and older in 2005.

Marital Status	Number (in thousands)
Married	63,971
Widowed	11,105
Divorced	12,932
Never married	24,318

Source: Current Population Survey

(a) Determine the number of females 18 years old and older who are widowed or divorced.

(b) Determine the number of females 18 years old and older who are married, widowed, or divorced.

31. Stock Portfolios As a financial planner, you are asked to select one stock each from the following groups: 8 Dow stocks, 15 NASDAQ stocks, and 4 global stocks. How many different portfolios are possible?

Discussion and Writing

32. Make up a problem different from any found in the text that requires the addition principle of counting to solve. Give it to a friend to solve and critique.

33. Investigate the notion of counting as it relates to infinite sets. Write an essay on your findings.

'Are You Prepared?' Answers

1. union   **2.** intersection   **3.** True   **4.** True

13.2 Permutations and Combinations

PREPARING FOR THIS SECTION *Before getting started, review the following:*

- Factorial (Section 12.1, pp. 806–807).

Now Work the 'Are You Prepared?' problems on page 861.

OBJECTIVES **1** Solve Counting Problems Using Permutations Involving *n* Distinct Objects (p. 855)

    2 Solve Counting Problems Using Combinations (p. 858)

    3 Solve Counting Problems Using Permutations Involving *n* Nondistinct Objects (p. 860)

1 Solve Counting Problems Using Permutations Involving *n* Distinct Objects

We begin with a definition.

DEFINITION A **permutation** is an ordered arrangement of *r* objects chosen from *n* objects.

We discuss three types of permutations:

1. The *n* objects are distinct (different), and repetition is allowed in the selection of *r* of them. [Distinct, with repetition]
2. The *n* objects are distinct (different), and repetition is not allowed in the selection of *r* of them, where $r \leq n$. [Distinct, without repetition]
3. The *n* objects are not distinct, and we use all of them in the arrangement. [Not distinct]

We take up the first two types here and deal with the third type at the end of this section.

The first type of permutation is handled using the Multiplication Principle.

| EXAMPLE 1 | **Counting Airport Codes [Permutation: Distinct, with Repetition]** |

The International Airline Transportation Association (IATA) assigns three-letter codes to represent airport locations. For example, the airport code for Ft. Lauderdale, Florida, is FLL. Notice that repetition is allowed in forming this code. How many airport codes are possible?

Solution We are choosing 3 letters from 26 letters and arranging them in order where a letter may be repeated. This is an example of a permutation with repetition in which 3 objects are chosen from 26 distinct objects.

The task of counting the number of such arrangements consists of making three selections. Each selection requires choosing a letter of the alphabet (26 choices). By the Multiplication Principle, there are

$$26 \cdot 26 \cdot 26 = 26^3 = 17{,}576$$

possible airport codes.

The solution given to Example 1 can be generalized.

THEOREM **Permutations: Distinct Objects with Repetition**

The number of ordered arrangements of *r* objects chosen from *n* objects, in which the *n* objects are distinct and repetition is allowed, is n^r.

  Now Work PROBLEM 33

We begin the discussion of permutations in which the objects are distinct and repetition is not allowed with an example.

| EXAMPLE 2 | **Forming Codes [Permutation: Distinct, without Repetition]** |

Suppose that we wish to establish a three-letter code using any of the 26 uppercase letters of the alphabet, but we require that no letter be used more than once. How many different three-letter codes are there?

Solution Some of the possibilities are ABC, ABD, ABZ, ACB, CBA, and so on. The task consists of making three selections. The first selection requires choosing from 26 letters. Because no letter can be used more than once, the second selection requires choosing from 25 letters. The third selection requires choosing from 24 letters. (Do you see why?) By the Multiplication Principle, there are

$$26 \cdot 25 \cdot 24 = 15{,}600$$

different three-letter codes with no letter repeated.

For the second type of permutation, we introduce the following notation.

The notation **P(n, r)** represents the number of ordered arrangements of r objects chosen from n distinct objects, where $r \leq n$ and repetition is not allowed.

For example, the question posed in Example 2 asks for the number of ways that the 26 letters of the alphabet can be arranged in order using three nonrepeated letters. The answer is

$$P(26, 3) = 26 \cdot 25 \cdot 24 = 15,600$$

EXAMPLE 3	**Lining Up People**

In how many ways can 5 people be lined up?

Solution The 5 people are distinct. Once a person is in line, that person will not be repeated elsewhere in the line; and, in lining up people, order is important. We have a permutation of 5 objects taken 5 at a time. We can line up 5 people in

$$P(5, 5) = \underbrace{5 \cdot 4 \cdot 3 \cdot 2 \cdot 1}_{5 \text{ factors}} = 120 \text{ ways}$$

Now Work PROBLEM 35

To arrive at a formula for $P(n, r)$, we note that the task of obtaining an ordered arrangement of n objects in which only $r \leq n$ of them are used, without repeating any of them, requires making r selections. For the first selection, there are n choices; for the second selection, there are $n - 1$ choices; for the third selection, there are $n - 2$ choices; ...; for the rth selection, there are $n - (r - 1)$ choices. By the Multiplication Principle, we have

$$
\begin{array}{ccccc}
\text{1st} & \text{2nd} & \text{3rd} & & r\text{th} \\
\end{array}
$$
$$P(n, r) = n \cdot (n - 1) \cdot (n - 2) \cdot \cdots \cdot [n - (r - 1)]$$
$$= n \cdot (n - 1) \cdot (n - 2) \cdot \cdots \cdot (n - r + 1)$$

This formula for $P(n, r)$ can be compactly written using factorial notation.*

$$P(n, r) = n \cdot (n - 1) \cdot (n - 2) \cdot \cdots \cdot (n - r + 1)$$
$$= n \cdot (n - 1) \cdot (n - 2) \cdot \cdots \cdot (n - r + 1) \cdot \frac{(n - r) \cdot \cdots \cdot 3 \cdot 2 \cdot 1}{(n - r) \cdot \cdots \cdot 3 \cdot 2 \cdot 1} = \frac{n!}{(n - r)!}$$

THEOREM **Permutations of r Objects Chosen from n Distinct Objects without Repetition**

The number of arrangements of n objects using $r \leq n$ of them, in which

1. the n objects are distinct,
2. once an object is used it cannot be repeated, and
3. order is important,

is given by the formula

$$P(n, r) = \frac{n!}{(n - r)!} \qquad \qquad (1)$$

---

*Recall that $0! = 1$, $1! = 1$, $2! = 2 \cdot 1, \ldots, n! = n(n - 1) \cdot \cdots \cdot 3 \cdot 2 \cdot 1$.

EXAMPLE 4	Computing Permutations

Evaluate: (a) $P(7, 3)$ (b) $P(6, 1)$ (c) $P(52, 5)$

Solution   We shall work parts (a) and (b) in two ways.

(a) $P(7, 3) = \underbrace{7 \cdot 6 \cdot 5}_{3 \text{ factors}} = 210$

or

$$P(7, 3) = \frac{7!}{(7 - 3)!} = \frac{7!}{4!} = \frac{7 \cdot 6 \cdot 5 \cdot 4!}{4!} = 210$$

(b) $P(6, 1) = \underbrace{6}_{1 \text{ factor}} = 6$

or

$$P(6, 1) = \frac{6!}{(6 - 1)!} = \frac{6!}{5!} = \frac{6 \cdot 5!}{5!} = 6$$

(c) Figure 3 shows the solution using a TI-84 Plus graphing calculator. So

$$P(52, 5) = 311{,}875{,}200$$

Figure 3

⟝━━━━ **Now Work** PROBLEM 7

EXAMPLE 5	The Birthday Problem

All we know about Shannon, Patrick, and Ryan is that they have different birthdays. If we listed all the possible ways this could occur, how many would there be? Assume that there are 365 days in a year.

Solution   This is an example of a permutation in which 3 birthdays are selected from a possible 365 days, and no birthday may repeat itself. The number of ways that this can occur is

$$P(365, 3) = \frac{365!}{(365 - 3)!} = \frac{365 \cdot 364 \cdot 363 \cdot 362!}{362!} = 365 \cdot 364 \cdot 363 = 48{,}228{,}180$$

There are 48,228,180 ways for three people to have different birthdays.

⟝━━━━ **Now Work** PROBLEM 47

2 Solve Counting Problems Using Combinations

In a permutation, order is important. For example, the arrangements ABC, CAB, BAC, ... are considered different arrangements of the letters A, B, and C. In many situations, though, order is unimportant. For example, in the card game of poker, the order in which the cards are received does not matter; it is the *combination* of the cards that matters.

DEFINITION   A **combination** is an arrangement, without regard to order, of r objects selected from n distinct objects without repetition, where $r \le n$. The notation $C(n, r)$ represents the number of combinations of n distinct objects using r of them.

EXAMPLE 6	Listing Combinations

List all the combinations of the 4 objects a, b, c, d taken 2 at a time. What is $C(4, 2)$?

Solution   One combination of a, b, c, d taken 2 at a time is

$$ab$$

We exclude *ba* from the list because order is not important in a combination (this means that we do not distinguish *ab* from *ba*). The list of all combinations of *a*, *b*, *c*, *d* taken 2 at a time is

$$ab, \quad ac, \quad ad, \quad bc, \quad bd, \quad cd$$

so

$$C(4, 2) = 6$$

We can find a formula for $C(n, r)$ by noting that the only difference between a permutation of type 2 (distinct, without repetition) and a combination is that we disregard order in combinations. To determine $C(n, r)$, we need only eliminate from the formula for $P(n, r)$ the number of permutations that were rearrangements of a given set of *r* objects. This can be determined from the formula for $P(n, r)$ by calculating $P(r, r) = r!$. So, if we divide $P(n, r)$ by $r!$, we will have the desired formula for $C(n, r)$:

$$C(n, r) = \frac{P(n, r)}{r!} = \frac{\dfrac{n!}{(n-r)!}}{r!} = \frac{n!}{(n-r)!\, r!}$$

↑
Use formula (1).

We have proved the following result:

THEOREM

Number of Combinations of *n* Distinct Objects Taken *r* at a Time

The number of arrangements of *n* objects using $r \leq n$ of them, in which

1. the *n* objects are distinct,
2. once an object is used, it cannot be repeated, and
3. order is not important,

is given by the formula

$$C(n, r) = \frac{n!}{(n-r)!\, r!} \tag{2}$$

Based on formula (2), we discover that the symbol $C(n, r)$ and the symbol $\dbinom{n}{r}$ for the binomial coefficients are, in fact, the same. The Pascal triangle (see Section 12.5) can be used to find the value of $C(n, r)$. However, because it is more practical and convenient, we will use formula (2) instead.

EXAMPLE 7 **Using Formula (2)**

Use formula (2) to find the value of each expression.

(a) $C(3, 1)$ (b) $C(6, 3)$ (c) $C(n, n)$ (d) $C(n, 0)$ (e) $C(52, 5)$

Solution (a) $C(3, 1) = \dfrac{3!}{(3-1)!\,1!} = \dfrac{3!}{2!1!} = \dfrac{3 \cdot 2 \cdot 1}{2 \cdot 1 \cdot 1} = 3$

(b) $C(6, 3) = \dfrac{6!}{(6-3)!3!} = \dfrac{6 \cdot 5 \cdot 4 \cdot 3!}{3! \, 3!} = \dfrac{6 \cdot 5 \cdot 4}{6} = 20$

(c) $C(n, n) = \dfrac{n!}{(n-n)!n!} = \dfrac{n!}{0!\,n!} = \dfrac{1}{1} = 1$

Figure 4

(d) $C(n, 0) = \dfrac{n!}{(n - 0)!0!} = \dfrac{n!}{n!0!} = \dfrac{1}{1} = 1$

(e) Figure 4 shows the solution using a TI-84 Plus graphing calculator. So

$$C(52, 5) = 2{,}598{,}960$$

━━━━━ **Now Work** PROBLEM 15

EXAMPLE 8	**Forming Committees**

How many different committees of 3 people can be formed from a pool of 7 people?

Solution The 7 people are distinct. More important, though, is the observation that the order of being selected for a committee is not significant. The problem asks for the number of combinations of 7 objects taken 3 at a time.

$$C(7, 3) = \frac{7!}{4!3!} = \frac{7 \cdot 6 \cdot 5 \cdot 4!}{4!3!} = \frac{7 \cdot 6 \cdot 5}{6} = 35$$

Thirty-five different committees can be formed.

EXAMPLE 9	**Forming Committees**

In how many ways can a committee consisting of 2 faculty members and 3 students be formed if 6 faculty members and 10 students are eligible to serve on the committee?

Solution The problem can be separated into two parts: the number of ways that the faculty members can be chosen, $C(6, 2)$, and the number of ways that the student members can be chosen, $C(10, 3)$. By the Multiplication Principle, the committee can be formed in

$$C(6, 2) \cdot C(10, 3) = \frac{6!}{4!2!} \cdot \frac{10!}{7!3!} = \frac{6 \cdot 5 \cdot 4!}{4!2!} \cdot \frac{10 \cdot 9 \cdot 8 \cdot 7!}{7!3!}$$

$$= \frac{30}{2} \cdot \frac{720}{6} = 1800 \text{ ways}$$

━━━━━ **Now Work** PROBLEM 49

3 Solve Counting Problems Using Permutations Involving *n* Nondistinct Objects

We begin with an example.

EXAMPLE 10	**Forming Different Words**

How many different words (real or imaginary) can be formed using all the letters in the word REARRANGE?

Solution Each word formed will have 9 letters: 3 R's, 2 A's, 2 E's, 1 N, and 1 G. To construct each word, we need to fill in 9 positions with the 9 letters:

$$\underline{1}\ \underline{2}\ \underline{3}\ \underline{4}\ \underline{5}\ \underline{6}\ \underline{7}\ \underline{8}\ \underline{9}$$

The process of forming a word consists of five tasks:

Task 1: Choose the positions for the 3 R's.
Task 2: Choose the positions for the 2 A's.
Task 3: Choose the positions for the 2 E's.

Task 4: Choose the position for the 1 N.

Task 5: Choose the position for the 1 G.

Because the order in which the R's is selected does not matter (since they are not distinct), task 1 can be done in $C(9, 3)$ ways. There then remain 6 positions to be filled, so Task 2 can be done in $C(6, 2)$ ways. There remain 4 positions to be filled, so Task 3 can be done in $C(4, 2)$ ways. There remain 2 positions to be filled, so Task 4 can be done in $C(2, 1)$ ways. The last position can be filled in $C(1, 1)$ way. Using the Multiplication Principle, the number of possible words that can be formed is

$$C(9, 3) \cdot C(6, 2) \cdot C(4, 2) \cdot C(2, 1) \cdot C(1, 1) = \frac{9!}{6! \, 3!} \cdot \frac{6!}{4! \, 2!} \cdot \frac{4!}{2! \, 2!} \cdot \frac{2!}{1! \, 1!} \cdot \frac{1!}{0! \, 1!}$$

$$= \frac{9!}{3! \cdot 2! \cdot 2! \cdot 1! \cdot 1!} = 15{,}120$$

15,120 possible words can be formed.

The form of the expression before the answer to Example 10 is suggestive of a general result. Had the letters in REARRANGE each been different, there would have been $P(9, 9) = 9!$ possible words formed. This is the numerator of the answer. The presence of 3 R's, 2 A's, and 2 E's reduces the number of different words, as the entries in the denominator illustrate. We are led to the following result:

THEOREM **Permutations Involving n Objects That Are Not Distinct**

The number of permutations of n objects of which n_1 are of one kind, n_2 are of a second kind, ..., and n_k are of a kth kind is given by

$$\frac{n!}{n_1! \cdot n_2! \cdot \cdots \cdot n_k!} \tag{3}$$

where $n = n_1 + n_2 + \cdots + n_k$.

EXAMPLE 11 **Arranging Flags**

How many different vertical arrangements are there of 8 flags if 4 are white, 3 are blue, and 1 is red?

Solution We seek the number of permutations of 8 objects, of which 4 are of one kind, 3 are of a second kind, and 1 is of a third kind. Using formula (3), we find that there are

$$\frac{8!}{4! \cdot 3! \cdot 1!} = \frac{8 \cdot 7 \cdot 6 \cdot 5 \cdot 4!}{4! \cdot 3! \cdot 1!} = 280 \text{ different arrangements}$$

Now Work PROBLEM 51

13.2 Assess Your Understanding

'Are You Prepared?' *Answers are given at the end of these exercises. If you get a wrong answer, read the pages listed in* red.

1. $0! = $ _____; $1! = $ _____. (p. 806)

2. *True or False* $n! = \dfrac{(n + 1)!}{n}$. (pp. 806–807)

Concepts and Vocabulary

3. A(n) _____ is an ordered arrangement of r objects chosen from n objects.

4. A(n) _____ is an arrangement of r objects chosen from n distinct objects, without repetition and without regard to order.

5. *True or False* In a combination problem, order is not important.

6. *True or False* In some permutation problems, once an object is used, it cannot be repeated.

Skill Building

In Problems 7–14, find the value of each permutation. Verify your results using a graphing utility.

7. $P(6, 2)$ **8.** $P(7, 2)$ **9.** $P(4, 4)$ **10.** $P(8, 8)$

11. $P(7, 0)$ **12.** $P(9, 0)$ **13.** $P(8, 4)$ **14.** $P(8, 3)$

In Problems 15–22, find the value of each combination. Verify your results using a graphing utility.

15. $C(8, 2)$ **16.** $C(8, 6)$ **17.** $C(7, 4)$ **18.** $C(6, 2)$

19. $C(15, 15)$ **20.** $C(18, 1)$ **21.** $C(26, 13)$ **22.** $C(18, 9)$

Applications and Extensions

23. List all the ordered arrangements of 5 objects a, b, c, d, and e choosing 3 at a time without repetition. What is $P(5, 3)$?

24. List all the ordered arrangements of 5 objects a, b, c, d, and e choosing 2 at a time without repetition. What is $P(5, 2)$?

25. List all the ordered arrangements of 4 objects 1, 2, 3, and 4 choosing 3 at a time without repetition. What is $P(4, 3)$?

26. List all the ordered arrangements of 6 objects 1, 2, 3, 4, 5, and 6 choosing 3 at a time without repetition. What is $P(6, 3)$?

27. List all the combinations of 5 objects a, b, c, d, and e taken 3 at a time. What is $C(5, 3)$?

28. List all the combinations of 5 objects a, b, c, d, and e taken 2 at a time. What is $C(5, 2)$?

29. List all the combinations of 4 objects 1, 2, 3, and 4 taken 3 at a time. What is $C(4, 3)$?

30. List all the combinations of 6 objects 1, 2, 3, 4, 5, and 6 taken 3 at a time. What is $C(6, 3)$?

31. Forming Codes How many two-letter codes can be formed using the letters A, B, C, and D? Repeated letters are allowed.

32. Forming Codes How many two-letter codes can be formed using the letters A, B, C, D, and E? Repeated letters are allowed.

33. Forming Numbers How many three-digit numbers can be formed using the digits 0 and 1? Repeated digits are allowed.

34. Forming Numbers How many three-digit numbers can be formed using the digits 0, 1, 2, 3, 4, 5, 6, 7, 8, and 9? Repeated digits are allowed.

35. Lining Up People In how many ways can 4 people be lined up?

36. Stacking Boxes In how many ways can 5 different boxes be stacked?

37. Forming Codes How many different three-letter codes are there if only the letters A, B, C, D, and E can be used and no letter can be used more than once?

38. Forming Codes How many different four-letter codes are there if only the letters A, B, C, D, E, and F can be used and no letter can be used more than once?

39. Stocks on the NYSE Companies whose stocks are listed on the New York Stock Exchange (NYSE) have their company name represented by either 1, 2, or 3 letters (repetition of letters is allowed). What is the maximum number of companies that can be listed on the NYSE?

40. Stocks on the NASDAQ Companies whose stocks are listed on the NASDAQ stock exchange have their company name represented by either 4 or 5 letters (repetition of letters is allowed). What is the maximum number of companies that can be listed on the NASDAQ?

41. Establishing Committees In how many ways can a committee of 4 students be formed from a pool of 7 students?

42. Establishing Committees In how many ways can a committee of 3 professors be formed from a department having 8 professors?

43. Possible Answers on a True/False Test How many arrangements of answers are possible for a true/false test with 10 questions?

44. Possible Answers on a Multiple-choice Test How many arrangements of answers are possible in a multiple-choice test with 5 questions, each of which has 4 possible answers?

45. Arranging Books Five different mathematics books are to be arranged on a student's desk. How many arrangements are possible?

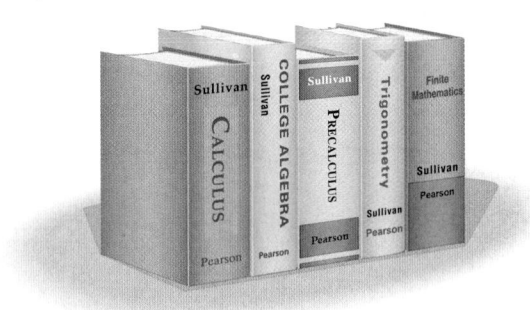

46. Forming License Plate Numbers How many different license plate numbers can be made using 2 letters followed by 4 digits selected from the digits 0 through 9:
(a) If letters and digits may be repeated?
(b) If letters may be repeated, but digits may not be repeated?
(c) If neither letters nor digits may be repeated?

47. Birthday Problem In how many ways can 2 people each have different birthdays? Assume that there are 365 days in a year.

48. Birthday Problem In how many ways can 5 people each have different birthdays? Assume that there are 365 days in a year.

49. Forming a Committee A student dance committee is to be formed consisting of 2 boys and 3 girls. If the membership is to be chosen from 4 boys and 8 girls, how many different committees are possible?

50. Forming a Committee The student relations committee of a college consists of 2 administrators, 3 faculty members, and 5 students. Four administrators, 8 faculty members, and 20 students are eligible to serve. How many different committees are possible?

51. **Forming Words** How many different 9-letter words (real or imaginary) can be formed from the letters in the word ECONOMICS?

52. **Forming Words** How many different 11-letter words (real or imaginary) can be formed from the letters in the word MATHEMATICS?

53. **Selecting Objects** An urn contains 7 white balls and 3 red balls. Three balls are selected. In how many ways can the 3 balls be drawn from the total of 10 balls:
    (a) If 2 balls are white and 1 is red?
    (b) If all 3 balls are white?
    (c) If all 3 balls are red?

54. **Selecting Objects** An urn contains 15 red balls and 10 white balls. Five balls are selected. In how many ways can the 5 balls be drawn from the total of 25 balls:
    (a) If all 5 balls are red?
    (b) If 3 balls are red and 2 are white?
    (c) If at least 4 are red balls?

55. **Senate Committees** The U.S. Senate has 100 members. Suppose that it is desired to place each senator on exactly 1 of 7 possible committees. The first committee has 22 members, the second has 13, the third has 10, the fourth has 5, the fifth has 16, and the sixth and seventh have 17 apiece. In how many ways can these committees be formed?

56. **Football Teams** A defensive football squad consists of 25 players. Of these, 10 are linemen, 10 are linebackers, and 5 are safeties. How many different teams of 5 linemen, 3 linebackers, and 3 safeties can be formed?

57. **Baseball** In the American Baseball League, a designated hitter may be used to hit for the pitcher. Assuming the designated hitter is used, how many batting orders is it possible for a manager to use? (There are 9 regular players on a team.)

58. **Baseball** In the National Baseball League, the pitcher usually bats ninth. If this is the case, how many batting orders is it possible for a manager to use?

59. **Baseball Teams** A baseball team has 15 members. Four of the players are pitchers, and the remaining 11 members can play any position. How many different teams of 9 players can be formed?

60. **World Series** In the World Series the American League team (*A*) and the National League team (*N*) play until one team wins four games. If the sequence of winners is designated by letters (for example, *NAAAA* means that the National League team won the first game and the American League won the next four), how many different sequences are possible?

61. **Basketball Teams** A basketball team has 6 players who play guard (2 of 5 starting positions). How many different teams are possible, assuming that the remaining 3 positions are filled and it is not possible to distinguish a left guard from a right guard?

62. **Basketball Teams** On a basketball team of 12 players, 2 only play center, 3 only play guard, and the rest play forward (5 players on a team: 2 forwards, 2 guards, and 1 center). How many different teams are possible, assuming that it is not possible to distinguish left and right guards and left and right forwards?

63. **Combination Locks** A combination lock displays 50 numbers. To open it, you turn to a number, then rotate clockwise to a second number, and then counterclockwise to the third number.
    (a) How many different lock combinations are there?
    (b) Comment on the description of such a lock as a *combination* lock.

Discussion and Writing

64. Create a problem different from any found in the text that requires a permutation to solve. Give it to a friend to solve and critique.

65. Create a problem different from any found in the text that requires a combination to solve. Give it to a friend to solve and critique.

66. Explain the difference between a permutation and a combination. Give an example to illustrate your explanation.

'Are You Prepared?' Answers

1. 1; 1   2. False

13.3 Probability

OBJECTIVES 1 Construct Probability Models (p. 864)
2 Compute Probabilities of Equally Likely Outcomes (p. 866)
3 Find Probabilities of the Union of Two Events (p. 868)
4 Use the Complement Rule to Find Probabilities (p. 869)

Probability is an area of mathematics that deals with experiments that yield random results, yet admit a certain regularity. Such experiments do not always produce the same result or outcome, so the result of any one observation is not predictable. However, the results of the experiment over a long period do produce regular patterns that enable us to predict with remarkable accuracy.

| EXAMPLE 1 | Tossing a Fair Coin |

In tossing a fair coin, we know that the outcome is either a head or a tail. On any particular throw, we cannot predict what will happen, but, if we toss the coin many times, we observe that the number of times that a head comes up is approximately equal to the number of times that we get a tail. It seems reasonable, therefore, to assign a probability of $\frac{1}{2}$ that a head comes up and a probability of $\frac{1}{2}$ that a tail comes up.

1 Construct Probability Models

The discussion in Example 1 illustrates the construction of a **probability model** for the experiment of tossing a fair coin once. A probability model has two components: a sample space and an assignment of probabilities. A **sample space** S is a set whose elements represent all the possibilities that might occur as a result of the experiment. Each element of S is called an **outcome.** To each outcome, we assign a number, called the **probability** of that outcome, which has two properties:

1. The probability assigned to each outcome is nonnegative.
2. The sum of all the probabilities equals 1.

DEFINITION   A **probability model** with the sample space

$$S = \{e_1, e_2, \ldots, e_n\}$$

where $e_1, e_2, \ldots, e_n$ are the possible outcomes and $P(e_1), P(e_2), \ldots, P(e_n)$ are the respective probabilities of these outcomes, requires that

$$P(e_1) \geq 0, P(e_2) \geq 0, \ldots, P(e_n) \geq 0 \tag{1}$$

$$\sum_{i=1}^{n} P(e_i) = P(e_1) + P(e_2) + \cdots + P(e_n) = 1 \tag{2}$$

| EXAMPLE 2 | Determining Probability Models |

In a bag of M&Ms,™ the candies are colored red, green, blue, brown, yellow, and orange. Suppose that a candy is drawn from the bag and the color is recorded. The sample space of this experiment is {red, green, blue, brown, yellow, orange}. Determine which of the following are probability models.

(a)

Outcome	Probability
red	0.3
green	0.15
blue	0
brown	0.15
yellow	0.2
orange	0.2

(b)

Outcome	Probability
red	0.1
green	0.1
blue	0.1
brown	0.4
yellow	0.2
orange	0.3

(c)

Outcome	Probability
red	0.3
green	−0.3
blue	0.2
brown	0.4
yellow	0.2
orange	0.2

(d)

Outcome	Probability
red	0
green	0
blue	0
brown	0
yellow	1
orange	0

Solution

(a) This model is a probability model since all the outcomes have probabilities that are nonnegative and the sum of the probabilities is 1.

(b) This model is not a probability model because the sum of the probabilities is not 1.

(c) This model is not a probability model because $P(\text{green})$ is less than 0. Recall, all probabilities must be nonnegative.

(d) This model is a probability model because all the outcomes have probabilities that are nonnegative, and the sum of the probabilities is 1. Notice that $P(\text{yellow}) = 1$, meaning that this outcome will occur with 100% certainty each time that the experiment is repeated. This means that the bag of M&Ms™ has only yellow candies.

Now Work PROBLEM 7

EXAMPLE 3 | **Constructing a Probability Model**

An experiment consists of rolling a fair die once. A die is a cube with each face having either 1, 2, 3, 4, 5, or 6 dots on it. See Figure 5. Construct a probability model for this experiment.

Solution

Figure 5

A sample space S consists of all the possibilities that can occur. Because rolling the die will result in one of six faces showing, the sample space S consists of

$$S = \{1, 2, 3, 4, 5, 6\}$$

Because the die is fair, one face is no more likely to occur than another. As a result, our assignment of probabilities is

$$P(1) = \frac{1}{6} \quad P(2) = \frac{1}{6}$$

$$P(3) = \frac{1}{6} \quad P(4) = \frac{1}{6}$$

$$P(5) = \frac{1}{6} \quad P(6) = \frac{1}{6}$$

Now suppose that a die is loaded (weighted) so that the probability assignments are

$$P(1) = 0, \quad P(2) = 0, \quad P(3) = \frac{1}{3}, \quad P(4) = \frac{2}{3}, \quad P(5) = 0, \quad P(6) = 0$$

This assignment would be made if the die were loaded so that only a 3 or 4 could occur and the 4 is twice as likely as the 3 to occur. This assignment is consistent with the definition, since each assignment is nonnegative and the sum of all the probability assignments equals 1.

═══► **Now Work** PROBLEM 23

EXAMPLE 4 **Constructing a Probability Model**

An experiment consists of tossing a coin. The coin is weighted so that heads (H) is three times as likely to occur as tails (T). Construct a probability model for this experiment.

Solution The sample space S is $S = \{H, T\}$. If x denotes the probability that a tail occurs,

$$P(T) = x \quad \text{and} \quad P(H) = 3x$$

Since the sum of the probabilities of the possible outcomes must equal 1, we have

$$P(T) + P(H) = x + 3x = 1$$
$$4x = 1$$
$$x = \frac{1}{4}$$

We assign the probabilities

$$P(T) = \frac{1}{4} \qquad P(H) = \frac{3}{4}$$

═══► **Now Work** PROBLEM 27

In working with probability models, the term **event** is used to describe a set of possible outcomes of the experiment. An event E is some subset of the sample space S. The **probability of an event** E, $E \neq \varnothing$, denoted by $P(E)$, is defined as the sum of the probabilities of the outcomes in E. We can also think of the probability of an event E as the likelihood that the event E occurs. If $E = \varnothing$, then $P(E) = 0$; if $E = S$, then $P(E) = P(S) = 1$.

2 Compute Probabilities of Equally Likely Outcomes

When the same probability is assigned to each outcome of the sample space, the experiment is said to have **equally likely outcomes.**

THEOREM **Probability for Equally Likely Outcomes**

If an experiment has n equally likely outcomes and if the number of ways that an event E can occur is m, then the probability of E is

$$P(E) = \frac{\text{Number of ways that } E \text{ can occur}}{\text{Number of possible outcomes}} = \frac{m}{n} \qquad (3)$$

If S is the sample space of this experiment,

$$P(E) = \frac{n(E)}{n(S)} \qquad (4)$$

EXAMPLE 5 | **Calculating Probabilities of Events Involving Equally Likely Outcomes**

Calculate the probability that in a 3-child family there are 2 boys and 1 girl. Assume equally likely outcomes.

Solution

We begin by constructing a tree diagram to help in listing the possible outcomes of the experiment. See Figure 6, where B stands for boy and G for girl. The sample space S of this experiment is

$$S = \{BBB, BBG, BGB, BGG, GBB, GBG, GGB, GGG\}$$

so $n(S) = 8$.

We wish to know the probability of the event E: "having two boys and one girl." From Figure 6, we conclude that $E = \{BBG, BGB, GBB\}$, so $n(E) = 3$. Since the outcomes are equally likely, the probability of E is

$$P(E) = \frac{n(E)}{n(S)} = \frac{3}{8}$$

Figure 6

1st child 2nd child 3rd child

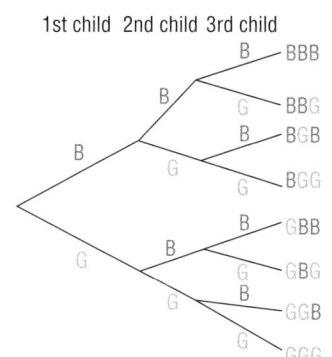

➞ **Now Work** PROBLEM 37

So far, we have calculated probabilities of single events. We will now compute probabilities of multiple events, called **compound probabilities.**

EXAMPLE 6 | **Computing Compound Probabilities**

Consider the experiment of rolling a single fair die. Let E represent the event "roll an odd number," and let F represent the event "roll a 1 or 2."

(a) Write the event E and F. What is $n(E \cap F)$?
(b) Write the event E or F. What is $n(E \cup F)$?
(c) Compute $P(E)$. Compute $P(F)$.
(d) Compute $P(E \cap F)$.
(e) Compute $P(E \cup F)$.

Solution

The sample space S of the experiment is $\{1, 2, 3, 4, 5, 6\}$, so $n(S) = 6$. Since the die is fair, the outcomes are equally likely. The event E: "roll an odd number" is $\{1, 3, 5\}$, and the event F: "roll a 1 or 2" is $\{1, 2\}$, so $n(E) = 3$ and $n(F) = 2$.

(a) The word *and* in probability means the intersection of two events. The event E and F is

$$E \cap F = \{1, 3, 5\} \cap \{1, 2\} = \{1\} \qquad n(E \cap F) = 1$$

(b) The word *or* in probability means the union of the two events. The event E or F is

$$E \cup F = \{1, 3, 5\} \cup \{1, 2\} = \{1, 2, 3, 5\} \qquad n(E \cup F) = 4$$

(c) We use formula (4). Then

$$P(E) = \frac{n(E)}{n(S)} = \frac{3}{6} = \frac{1}{2} \qquad P(F) = \frac{n(F)}{n(S)} = \frac{2}{6} = \frac{1}{3}$$

(d) $P(E \cap F) = \dfrac{n(E \cap F)}{n(S)} = \dfrac{1}{6}$

(e) $P(E \cup F) = \dfrac{n(E \cup F)}{n(S)} = \dfrac{4}{6} = \dfrac{2}{3}$

3 Find Probabilities of the Union of Two Events

The next formula can be used to find the probability of the union of two events.

THEOREM

For any two events E and F,

$$P(E \cup F) = P(E) + P(F) - P(E \cap F) \qquad (5)$$

This result is a consequence of the counting formula discussed earlier in Section 13.1.

For example, we can use formula (5) to find $P(E \cup F)$ in Example 6(e). Then

$$P(E \cup F) = P(E) + P(F) - P(E \cap F) = \frac{1}{2} + \frac{1}{3} - \frac{1}{6} = \frac{3}{6} + \frac{2}{6} - \frac{1}{6} = \frac{4}{6} = \frac{2}{3}$$

as before.

EXAMPLE 7   Computing Probabilities of the Union of Two Events

If $P(E) = 0.2$, $P(F) = 0.3$, and $P(E \cap F) = 0.1$, find the probability of E or F. That is, find $P(E \cup F)$.

Solution   We use formula (5).

$$\text{Probability of } E \text{ or } F = P(E \cup F) = P(E) + P(F) - P(E \cap F)$$

$$= 0.2 + 0.3 - 0.1 = 0.4$$

A Venn diagram can sometimes be used to obtain probabilities. To construct a Venn diagram representing the information in Example 7, we draw two sets E and F. We begin with the fact that $P(E \cap F) = 0.1$. See Figure 7(a). Then, since $P(E) = 0.2$ and $P(F) = 0.3$, we fill in E with $0.2 - 0.1 = 0.1$ and F with $0.3 - 0.1 = 0.2$. See Figure 7(b). Since $P(S) = 1$, we complete the diagram by inserting $1 - (0.1 + 0.1 + 0.2) = 0.6$ outside the circles. See Figure 7(c). Now it is easy to see, for example, that the probability of F, but not E, is 0.2. Also, the probability of neither E nor F is 0.6.

Figure 7

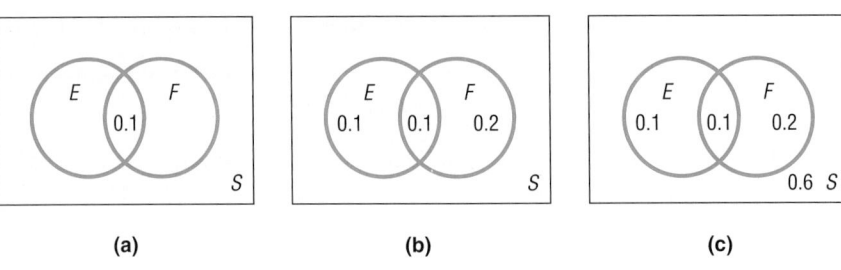

(a)　　　　　　　　(b)　　　　　　　　(c)

Now Work   PROBLEM 45

If events E and F are disjoint so that $E \cap F = \varnothing$, we say they are **mutually exclusive.** In this case, $P(E \cap F) = 0$, and formula (5) takes the following form:

THEOREM   **Mutually Exclusive Events**

If E and F are mutually exclusive events,

$$P(E \cup F) = P(E) + P(F) \qquad (6)$$

| EXAMPLE 8 | Computing Probabilities of the Union of Two Mutually Exclusive Events |

If $P(E) = 0.4$ and $P(F) = 0.25$, and E and F are mutually exclusive, find $P(E \cup F)$.

Solution   Since E and F are mutually exclusive, we use formula (6).

$$P(E \cup F) = P(E) + P(F) = 0.4 + 0.25 = 0.65$$

━━━━━▶ **Now Work** PROBLEM 47

4 Use the Complement Rule to Find Probabilities

Recall, if A is a set, the complement of A, denoted $\overline{A}$, is the set of all elements in the universal set U not in A. We similarly define the complement of an event.

DEFINITION   **Complement of an Event**

Let S denote the sample space of an experiment, and let E denote an event. The **complement of E,** denoted $\overline{E}$, is the set of all outcomes in the sample space S that are not outcomes in the event E.

The complement of an event E, that is, $\overline{E}$, in a sample space S has the following two properties:

$$E \cap \overline{E} = \varnothing \qquad E \cup \overline{E} = S$$

Since E and $\overline{E}$ are mutually exclusive, it follows from (6) that

$$P(E \cup \overline{E}) = P(S) = 1 \qquad P(E) + P(\overline{E}) = 1 \qquad P(\overline{E}) = 1 - P(E)$$

We have the following result:

THEOREM   **Computing Probabilities of Complementary Events**

If E represents any event and $\overline{E}$ represents the complement of E, then

$$P(\overline{E}) = 1 - P(E) \qquad\qquad (7)$$

| EXAMPLE 9 | Computing Probabilities Using Complements |

On the local news the weather reporter stated that the probability of rain tomorrow is 40%. What is the probability that it will not rain?

Solution   The complement of the event "rain" is "no rain."

$$P(\text{no rain}) = 1 - P(\text{rain}) = 1 - 0.4 = 0.6$$

There is a 60% chance of no rain tomorrow.

━━━━━▶ **Now Work** PROBLEM 51

| EXAMPLE 10 | Birthday Problem |

What is the probability that in a group of 10 people at least 2 people have the same birthday? Assume that there are 365 days in a year.

Solution   We assume that a person is as likely to be born on one day as another, so we have equally likely outcomes.

We first determine the number of outcomes in the sample space S. There are 365 possibilities for each person's birthday. Since there are 10 people in the group, there are 365^{10} possibilities for the birthdays. [For one person in the group, there are 365 days on which his or her birthday can fall; for two people, there are $(365)(365) = 365^2$ pairs of days; and, in general, using the Multiplication Principle, for n people there are 365^n possibilities.] So

$$n(S) = 365^{10}$$

We wish to find the probability of the event E: "at least two people have the same birthday." It is difficult to count the elements in this set; it is much easier to count the elements of the complementary event $\overline{E}$: "no two people have the same birthday."

We find $n(\overline{E})$ as follows: Choose one person at random. There are 365 possibilities for his or her birthday. Choose a second person. There are 364 possibilities for this birthday, if no two people are to have the same birthday. Choose a third person. There are 363 possibilities left for this birthday. Finally, we arrive at the tenth person. There are 356 possibilities left for this birthday. By the Multiplication Principle, the total number of possibilities is

$$n(\overline{E}) = 365 \cdot 364 \cdot 363 \cdot \cdots \cdot 356$$

The probability of the event $\overline{E}$ is

$$P(\overline{E}) = \frac{n(\overline{E})}{n(S)} = \frac{365 \cdot 364 \cdot 363 \cdot \cdots \cdot 356}{365^{10}} \approx 0.883$$

The probability of two or more people in a group of 10 people having the same birthday is then

$$P(E) = 1 - P(\overline{E}) \approx 1 - 0.883 = 0.117$$

The birthday problem can be solved for any group size. The following table gives the probabilities for two or more people having the same birthday for various group sizes. Notice that the probability is greater than $\dfrac{1}{2}$ for any group of 23 or more people.

	Number of People															
	5	10	15	20	21	22	23	24	25	30	40	50	60	70	80	90
Probability That Two or More Have the Same Birthday	0.027	0.117	0.253	0.411	0.444	0.476	0.507	0.538	0.569	0.706	0.891	0.970	0.994	0.99916	0.99991	0.99999

⎯ **Now Work** PROBLEM 71

Historical Feature

Blaise Pascal (1623–1662)

Set theory, counting, and probability first took form as a systematic theory in an exchange of letters (1654) between Pierre de Fermat (1601–1665) and Blaise Pascal (1623–1662). They discussed the problem of how to divide the stakes in a game that is interrupted before completion, knowing how many points each player needs to win. Fermat solved the problem by listing all possibilities and counting the favorable ones, whereas Pascal made use of the triangle that now bears his name. As mentioned in the text, the entries in Pascal's triangle are equivalent to $C(n, r)$. This recognition of the role of $C(n, r)$ in counting is the foundation of all further developments.

The first book on probability, the work of Christiaan Huygens (1629–1695), appeared in 1657. In it, the notion of mathematical expectation is explored. This allows the calculation of the profit or loss that a gambler might expect, knowing the probabilities involved in the game (see the Historical Problems that follow).

Although Girolamo Cardano (1501–1576) wrote a treatise on probability, it was not published until 1663 in Cardano's collected works, and this was too late to have any effect on the early development of the theory.

In 1713, the posthumously published *Ars Conjectandi* of Jakob Bernoulli (1654–1705) gave the theory the form it would have until 1900. Recently, both combinatorics (counting) and probability have undergone rapid development due to the use of computers.

A final comment about notation. The notations $C(n, r)$ and $P(n, r)$ are variants of a form of notation developed in England after 1830. The notation $\binom{n}{r}$ for $C(n, r)$ goes back to Leonhard Euler (1707–1783), but is now losing ground because it has no clearly related symbolism of the same type for permutations. The set symbols $\cup$ and $\cap$ were introduced by Giuseppe Peano (1858–1932) in 1888 in a slightly different context. The inclusion symbol $\subset$ was introduced by E. Schroeder (1841–1902) about 1890. The treatment of set theory in the text is due to George Boole (1815–1864), who wrote $A + B$ for $A \cup B$ and AB for $A \cap B$ (statisticians still use AB for $A \cap B$).

Historical Problems

1. *The Problem Discussed by Fermat and Pascal* A game between two equally skilled players, A and B, is interrupted when A needs 2 points to win and B needs 3 points. In what proportion would the stakes be divided?

   (a) *Fermat's solution* List all possible outcomes that can occur as a result of four more plays. The probabilities for A to win and B to win then determine how the stakes should be divided.

   (b) *Pascal's solution* Use combinations to determine the number of ways that the 2 points needed for A to win could occur in four plays. Then use combinations to determine the number of ways that the 3 points needed for B to win could occur. This is trickier than it looks, since A can win with 2 points in either two plays, three plays, or four plays. Compute the probabilities and compare with the results in part (a).

2. *Huygens's Mathematical Expectation* In a game with n possible outcomes with probabilities $p_1, p_2, \ldots, p_n$, suppose that the *net* winnings are $w_1, w_2, \ldots, w_n$, respectively. Then the mathematical expectation is

$$E = p_1 w_1 + p_2 w_2 + \cdots + p_n w_n$$

   The number E represents the profit or loss per game in the long run. The following problems are a modification of those of Huygens.

   (a) A fair die is tossed. A gambler wins \$3 if he throws a 6 and \$6 if he throws a 5. What is his expectation?

   [**Hint:** $w_1 = w_2 = w_3 = w_4 = 0$]

   (b) A gambler plays the same game as in part (a), but now the gambler must pay \$1 to play. This means that $w_5 = \$5, w_6 = \$2$, and $w_1 = w_2 = w_3 = w_4 = -\$1$. What is the expectation?

13.3 Assess Your Understanding

Concepts and Vocabulary

1. When the same probability is assigned to each outcome of a sample space, the experiment is said to have _____ _____ outcomes.

2. The _____ of an event E is the set of all outcomes in the sample space S that are not outcomes in the event E.

3. *True or False* The probability of an event can never equal 0.

4. *True or False* In a probability model, the sum of all probabilities is 1.

Skill Building

5. In a probability model, which of the following numbers could be the probability of an outcome?

$$0, \quad 0.01, \quad 0.35, \quad -0.4, \quad 1, \quad 1.4$$

6. In a probability model, which of the following numbers could be the probability of an outcome?

$$1.5, \quad \frac{1}{2}, \quad \frac{3}{4}, \quad \frac{2}{3}, \quad 0, \quad -\frac{1}{4}$$

7. Determine whether the following is a probability model.

Outcome	Probability
1	0.2
2	0.3
3	0.1
4	0.4

8. Determine whether the following is a probability model.

Outcome	Probability
Jim	0.4
Bob	0.3
Faye	0.1
Patricia	0.2

9. Determine whether the following is a probability model.

Outcome	Probability
Linda	0.3
Jean	0.2
Grant	0.1
Steve	0.3

10. Determine whether the following is a probability model.

Outcome	Probability
Donna	0.3
Joanne	0.2
Nelson	0.1
Elena	0.5
Patrick	−0.1

In Problems 11–16, construct a probability model for each experiment.

11. Tossing a fair coin twice

12. Tossing two fair coins once

13. Tossing two fair coins, then a fair die

14. Tossing a fair coin, a fair die, and then a fair coin

15. Tossing three fair coins once

16. Tossing one fair coin three times

In Problems 17–22, use the following spinners to construct a probability model for each experiment.

  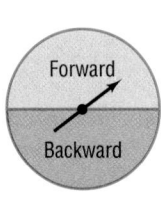

Spinner I
(4 equal areas)

Spinner II
(3 equal areas)

Spinner III
(2 equal areas)

17. Spin spinner I, then spinner II. What is the probability of getting a 2 or a 4, followed by Red?

18. Spin spinner III, then spinner II. What is the probability of getting Forward, followed by Yellow or Green?

19. Spin spinner I, then II, then III. What is the probability of getting a 1, followed by Red or Green, followed by Backward?

20. Spin spinner II, then I, then III. What is the probability of getting Yellow, followed by a 2 or a 4, followed by Forward?

21. Spin spinner I twice, then spinner II. What is the probability of getting a 2, followed by a 2 or a 4, followed by Red or Green?

22. Spin spinner III, then spinner I twice. What is the probability of getting Forward, followed by a 1 or a 3, followed by a 2 or a 4?

In Problems 23–26, consider the experiment of tossing a coin twice. The table lists six possible assignments of probabilities for this experiment. Using this table, answer the following questions.

Assignments	Sample Space			
	HH	**HT**	**TH**	**TT**
A	$\frac{1}{4}$	$\frac{1}{4}$	$\frac{1}{4}$	$\frac{1}{4}$
B	0	0	0	1
C	$\frac{3}{16}$	$\frac{5}{16}$	$\frac{5}{16}$	$\frac{3}{16}$
D	$\frac{1}{2}$	$\frac{1}{2}$	$-\frac{1}{2}$	$\frac{1}{2}$
E	$\frac{1}{4}$	$\frac{1}{4}$	$\frac{1}{4}$	$\frac{1}{8}$
F	$\frac{1}{9}$	$\frac{2}{9}$	$\frac{2}{9}$	$\frac{4}{9}$

23. Which of the assignments of probabilities is(are) consistent with the definition of a probability model?

24. Which of the assignments of probabilities should be used if the coin is known to be fair?

25. Which of the assignments of probabilities should be used if the coin is known to always come up tails?

26. Which of the assignments of probabilities should be used if tails is twice as likely as heads to occur?

27. Assigning Probabilities A coin is weighted so that heads is four times as likely as tails to occur. What probability should we assign to heads? to tails?

28. Assigning Probabilities A coin is weighted so that tails is twice as likely as heads to occur. What probability should we assign to heads? to tails?

29. Assigning Probabilities A die is weighted so that an odd-numbered face is twice as likely to occur as an even-numbered face. What probability should we assign to each face?

30. Assigning Probabilities A die is weighted so that a six cannot appear. The other faces occur with the same probability. What probability should we assign to each face?

For Problems 31–34, the sample space is $S = \{1, 2, 3, 4, 5, 6, 7, 8, 9, 10\}$. Suppose that the outcomes are equally likely.

31. Compute the probability of the event $E = \{1, 2, 3\}$.

32. Compute the probability of the event $F = \{3, 5, 9, 10\}$.

33. Compute the probability of the event E: "an even number."

34. Compute the probability of the event F: "an odd number."

For Problems 35 and 36, an urn contains 5 white marbles, 10 green marbles, 8 yellow marbles, and 7 black marbles.

35. If one marble is selected, determine the probability that it is white.

36. If one marble is selected, determine the probability that it is black.

In Problems 37–40, assume equally likely outcomes.

37. Determine the probability of having 3 boys in a 3-child family.

38. Determine the probability of having 3 girls in a 3-child family.

39. Determine the probability of having 1 girl and 3 boys in a 4-child family.

40. Determine the probability of having 2 girls and 2 boys in a 4-child family.

For Problems 41–44, two fair dice are rolled.

41. Determine the probability that the sum of the two dice is 7.

42. Determine the probability that the sum of the two dice is 11.

43. Determine the probability that the sum of the two dice is 3.

44. Determine the probability that the sum of the two dice is 12.

In Problems 45–48, find the probability of the indicated event if $P(A) = 0.25$ and $P(B) = 0.45$.

45. $P(A \cup B)$ if $P(A \cap B) = 0.15$

46. $P(A \cap B)$ if $P(A \cup B) = 0.6$

47. $P(A \cup B)$ if A, B are mutually exclusive

48. $P(A \cap B)$ if A, B are mutually exclusive

49. If $P(A) = 0.60$, $P(A \cup B) = 0.85$, and $P(A \cap B) = 0.05$, find $P(B)$.

50. If $P(B) = 0.30$, $P(A \cup B) = 0.65$, and $P(A \cap B) = 0.15$, find $P(A)$.

51. Automobile Theft According to the Insurance Information Institute, in 2004 there was a 13% probability that an automobile theft in the United States would result in an arrest. If an automobile theft case is randomly selected, what is the probability that it did not result in an arrest?

52. Pet Ownership According to the American Pet Products Manufacturers Association's *2005–2006 National Pet Owners Survey,* there is a 63% probability that a U.S. household owns a pet. If a U.S. household is randomly selected, what is the probability that it does not own a pet?

53. Cat Ownership According to the American Pet Products Manufacturers Association's *2005–2006 National Pet Owners Survey,* in 2004 there was a 34% probability that a U.S. pet owner owned a cat. If a U.S. pet owner is randomly selected, what is the probability that he or she does not own a cat?

54. Doctorate Degrees According to the National Science Foundation, in 2004 there was a 13.7% probability that a doctoral degree awarded at a U.S. university was awarded in engineering. If a 2004 U.S. doctoral recipient is randomly selected, what is the probability that his or her degree was not in engineering?

55. Online Gambling According to a Harris poll (January 12–17, 2006), 5% of U.S. adults admitted to having spent money gambling online. If a U.S. adult is selected at random, what is the probability that he or she has never spent any money gambling online?

56. Girl Scout Cookies According to the Girl Scouts of America, in March 2006, 9% of all Girl Scout cookies sold were shortbread/trefoils. If a box of Girl Scout cookies is selected at random, what is the probability that it is not shortbread/trefoils?

For Problems 57–60, a golf ball is selected at random from a container. If the container has 9 white balls, 8 green balls, and 3 orange balls, find the probability of each event.

57. The golf ball is white or green.

58. The golf ball is white or orange.

59. The golf ball is not white.

60. The golf ball is not green.

61. On the "Price Is Right" there is a game in which a bag is filled with 3 strike chips and 5 numbers. Let's say that the numbers in the bag are 0, 1, 3, 6, and 9. What is the probability of selecting a strike chip or the number 1?

62. Another game on the "Price Is Right" requires the contestant to spin a wheel with numbers 5, 10, 15, 20, . . . , 100. What is the probability that the contestant spins 100 or 30?

Problems 63–66 are based on a consumer survey of annual incomes in 100 households. The following table gives the data.

Income	$0–9999	$10,000–19,999	$20,000–29,999	$30,000–39,999	$40,000 or more
Number of households	5	35	30	20	10

63. What is the probability that a household has an annual income of $30,000 or more?

64. What is the probability that a household has an annual income between $10,000 and $29,999, inclusive?

65. What is the probability that a household has an annual income of less than $20,000?

66. What is the probability that a household has an annual income of $20,000 or more?

67. Surveys In a survey about the number of TV sets in a house, the following probability table was constructed:

Number of TV sets	0	1	2	3	4 or more
Probability	0.05	0.24	0.33	0.21	0.17

Find the probability of a house having:

(a) 1 or 2 TV sets

(b) 1 or more TV sets

(c) 3 or fewer TV sets

(d) 3 or more TV sets

(e) Fewer than 2 TV sets

(f) Fewer than 1 TV set

(g) 1, 2, or 3 TV sets

(h) 2 or more TV sets

68. Checkout Lines Through observation, it has been determined that the probability for a given number of people waiting in line at the "5 items or less" checkout register of a supermarket is as follows:

Number waiting in line	0	1	2	3	4 or more
Probability	0.10	0.15	0.20	0.24	0.31

Find the probability of:

(a) At most 2 people in line

(b) At least 2 people in line

(c) At least 1 person in line

69. In a certain Algebra and Trigonometry class, there are 18 freshmen and 15 sophomores. Of the 18 freshmen, 10 are male, and of the 15 sophomores, 8 are male. Find the probability that a randomly selected student is:

(a) A freshman or female

(b) A sophomore or male

70. The faculty of the mathematics department at Joliet Junior College is composed of 4 females and 9 males. Of the 4 females, 2 are under the age of 40, and of the males, 3 are under age 40. Find the probability that a randomly selected faculty member is:

(a) Female or under age 40

(b) Male or over age 40

71. Birthday Problem What is the probability that at least 2 people have the same birthday in a group of 12 people? Assume that there are 365 days in a year.

72. Birthday Problem What is the probability that at least 2 people have the same birthday in a group of 35 people? Assume that there are 365 days in a year.

73. Winning a Lottery In a certain lottery, there are ten balls, numbered 1, 2, 3, 4, 5, 6, 7, 8, 9, 10. Of these, five are drawn in order. If you pick five numbers that match those drawn in the correct order, you win $1,000,000. What is the probability of winning such a lottery?

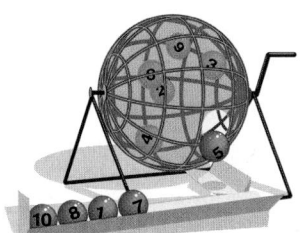

CHAPTER REVIEW

Things to Know

Counting formula (p. 851)	$n(A \cup B) = n(A) + n(B) - n(A \cap B)$
Addition Principle of Counting (p. 851)	If $A \cap B = \emptyset$, then $n(A \cup B) = n(A) + n(B)$.
Multiplication Principle of Counting (p. 853)	If a task consists of a sequence of choices in which there are p selections for the first choice, q selections for the second choice, and so on, the task of making these selections can be done in $p \cdot q \cdot \cdots$ different ways.
Permutation (p. 855)	An ordered arrangement of r objects chosen from n objects
Number of permutations: Distinct, with repetition (p. 856)	n^r The n objects are distinct (different), and repetition is allowed in the selection of r of them.
Number of permutations: Distinct, without repetition (p. 857)	$P(n, r) = n(n - 1) \cdot \cdots \cdot [n - (r - 1)] = \dfrac{n!}{(n - r)!}$ The n objects are distinct (different), and repetition is not allowed in the selection of r of them, where $r \le n$.
Combinations (p. 858)	An arrangement, without regard to order, of r objects selected from n distinct objects, where $r \le n$
Number of combinations (p. 859)	$C(n, r) = \dfrac{P(n, r)}{r!} = \dfrac{n!}{(n - r)!r!}$
Number of permutations: Not distinct (p. 861)	$\dfrac{n!}{n_1!n_2! \cdots n_k!}$ The number of permutations of n objects of which n_1 are of one kind, n_2 are of a second kind, ..., and n_k are of a kth kind, where $n = n_1 + n_2 + \cdots + n_k$
Sample space (p. 864)	Set whose elements represent the possible outcomes that can occur as a result of an experiment
Probability (p. 864)	A nonnegative number assigned to each outcome of a sample space; the sum of all the probabilities of the outcomes equals 1.
Probability for equally likely outcomes (p. 866)	$P(E) = \dfrac{n(E)}{n(S)}$ The same probability is assigned to each outcome.
Probability of the union of two events (p. 868)	$P(E \cup F) = P(E) + P(F) - P(E \cap F)$
Probability of the complement of an event (p. 869)	$P(\overline{E}) = 1 - P(E)$

Objectives

Section	You should be able to . . .	Example(s)	Review Exercises
13.1	**1** Find all the subsets of a set (p. 850)	1	1, 2
	2 Count the number of elements in a set (p. 850)	2, 3	3–10
	3 Solve counting problems using the Multiplication Principle (p. 852)	4, 5	15–18
13.2	**1** Solve counting problems using permutations involving n distinct objects (p. 855)	1–5	11, 12, 19, 20, 24–28, 33(a)
	2 Solve counting problems using combinations (p. 858)	6–9	13, 14, 21–23, 31, 32
	3 Solve counting problems using permutations involving n nondistinct objects (p. 860)	10, 11	29, 30
13.3	**1** Construct probability models (p. 864)	2–4	
	2 Compute probabilities of equally likely outcomes (p. 866)	5, 6	33(b), 34(a), 35(a), 36–39
	3 Find probabilities of the union of two events (p. 868)	7, 8	40
	4 Use the Complement Rule to find probabilities (p. 869)	9, 10	33(c), 34(b), 35(b), 36

Review Exercises

1. Write down all the subsets of the set {Dave, Joanne, Erica}.

2. Write down all the subsets of the set {Green, Blue, Red}.

3. If $n(A) = 8, n(B) = 12$, and $n(A \cap B) = 3$, find $n(A \cup B)$.

4. If $n(A) = 12, n(A \cup B) = 30$, and $n(A \cap B) = 6$, find $n(B)$.

In Problems 5–10, use the information supplied in the figure.

5. How many are in A?

6. How many are in A or B?

7. How many are in A and C?

8. How many are not in B?

9. How many are in neither A nor C?

10. How many are in B but not in C?

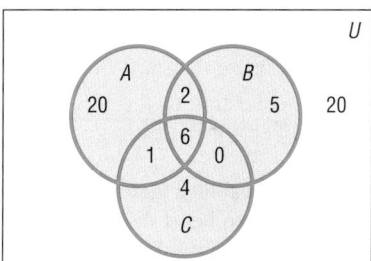

In Problems 11–14, compute the given expression.

11. $P(8, 3)$

12. $P(7, 3)$

13. $C(8, 3)$

14. $C(7, 3)$

---

15. Stocking a Store A clothing store sells pure wool and polyester–wool suits. Each suit comes in 3 colors and 10 sizes. How many suits are required for a complete assortment?

16. Wiring In connecting a certain electrical device, 5 wires are to be connected to 5 different terminals. How many different wirings are possible if 1 wire is connected to each terminal?

17. Baseball On a given day, the American Baseball League schedules 7 games. How many different outcomes are possible, assuming that each game is played to completion?

18. Baseball On a given day, the National Baseball League schedules 6 games. How many different outcomes are possible, assuming that each game is played to completion?

19. Choosing Seats If 4 people enter a bus having 9 vacant seats, in how many ways can they be seated?

20. Arranging Letters How many different arrangements are there of the letters in the word ROSE?

21. Choosing a Team In how many ways can a squad of 4 relay runners be chosen from a track team of 8 runners?

22. Writing a Test A professor has 10 similar problems to put on a test that has 3 problems. How many different tests can she design?

23. Baseball In how many ways can 2 teams from 14 teams in the American League be chosen without regard to which team is at home?

24. Arranging Books on a Shelf There are 5 different French books and 5 different Spanish books. How many ways are there to arrange them on a shelf if:
(a) Books of the same language must be grouped together, French on the left, Spanish on the right?
(b) French and Spanish books must alternate in the grouping, beginning with a French book?

25. Telephone Numbers Using the digits 0, 1, 2, ..., 9, how many 7-digit numbers can be formed if the first digit cannot be 0 or 9 and if the last digit is greater than or equal to 2 and less than or equal to 3? Repeated digits are allowed.

26. Home Choices A contractor constructs homes with 5 different choices of exterior finish, 3 different roof arrangements, and 4 different window designs. How many different types of homes can be built?

27. License Plate Possibilities A license plate consists of 1 letter, excluding O and I, followed by a 4-digit number that cannot have a 0 in the lead position. How many different plates are possible?

28. **Binary Codes**   Using the digits 0 and 1, how many different numbers consisting of 8 digits can be formed?

29. **Forming Different Words**   How many different words, real or imaginary, can be formed using all the letters in the word MISSING?

30. **Arranging Flags**   How many different vertical arrangements are there of 10 flags if 4 are white, 3 are blue, 2 are green, and 1 is red?

31. **Forming Committees**   A group of 9 people is going to be formed into committees of 4, 3, and 2 people. How many committees can be formed if:
   (a) A person can serve on any number of committees?
   (b) No person can serve on more than one committee?

32. **Forming Committees**   A group consists of 5 men and 8 women. A committee of 4 is to be formed from this group, and policy dictates that at least 1 woman be on this committee.
   (a) How many committees can be formed that contain exactly 1 man?
   (b) How many committees can be formed that contain exactly 2 women?
   (c) How many committees can be formed that contain at least 1 man?

33. **Birthday Problem**   For this problem, assume that a year has 365 days.
   (a) How many ways can 18 people have different birthdays?
   (b) What is the probability that nobody has the same birthday in a group of 18 people?
   (c) What is the probability in a group of 18 people that at least 2 people have the same birthday?

34. **Death Rates**   According to the U.S. National Center for Health Statistics, 28% of all deaths in 2003 were due to heart disease.
   (a) What is the probability that a randomly selected death in 2003 was due to heart disease?
   (b) What is the probability that a randomly selected death in 2003 was not due to heart disease?

35. **Unemployment**   According to the U.S. Bureau of Labor Statistics, 4.5% of the U.S. labor force was unemployed in May 2007.
   (a) What is the probability that a randomly selected member of the U.S. labor force was unemployed in May 2007?

(b) What is the probability that a randomly selected member of the U.S. labor force was not unemployed in May 2007?

36. From a box containing three 40-watt bulbs, six 60-watt bulbs, and eleven 75-watt bulbs, a bulb is drawn at random. What is the probability that the bulb is 40 watts? What is the probability that it is not a 75-watt bulb?

37. You have four $1 bills, three $5 bills, and two $10 bills in your wallet. If you pick a bill at random, what is the probability that it will be a $1 bill?

38. Each letter in the word ROSE is written on an index card and the cards are shuffled. When the cards are dealt, what is the probability that they spell the word ROSE?

39. Each of the numbers, 1, 2, ..., 100 is written on an index card and the cards are shuffled. If a card is selected at random, what is the probability that the number on the card is divisible by 5? What is the probability that the card selected is either a 1 or names a prime number?

40. At the Milex tune-up and brake repair shop, the manager has found that a car will require a tune-up with a probability of 0.6, a brake job with a probability of 0.1, and both with a probability of 0.02.
   (a) What is the probability that a car requires either a tune-up or a brake job?
   (b) What is the probability that a car requires a tune-up but not a brake job?
   (c) What is the probability that a car requires neither a tune-up nor a brake job?

CHAPTER TEST

In Problems 1–4, a survey of 70 college freshmen asked whether students planned to take biology, chemistry, or physics during their first year. Use the diagram to answer each question.

1. How many of the surveyed students plan to take physics during their first year?

2. How many of the surveyed students do not plan to take biology, chemistry, or physics during their first year?

3. How many of the surveyed students plan to take only biology and chemistry during their first year?

4. How many of the surveyed students plan to take physics or chemistry during their first year?

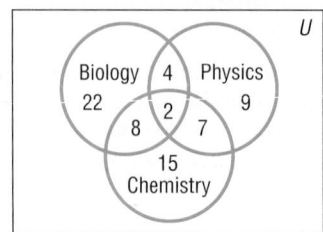

In Problems 5–7, compute the given expression.

5. $7!$ 6. $P(10, 6)$ 7. $C(11, 5)$

8. M&M's® offers customers the opportunity to create their own color mix of candy. There are 21 colors to choose from, and customers are allowed to select up to 6 different colors. How many different color mixes are possible, assuming that no color is selected more than once?

9. How many distinct 8-letter words (real or imaginary) can be formed from the letters in the word REDEEMED?

10. In horse racing, an exacta bet requires the bettor to pick the first two horses in the exact order. If there are 8 horses in a race, in how many ways could you make an exacta bet?

11. On February 20, 2004, the Ohio Bureau of Motor Vehicles unveiled the state's new license plate format. The plate consists of three letters (A–Z) followed by 4 digits (0–9). Assume that all letters and digits may be used except that the third letter cannot be O, I, or Z. If repetitions are allowed, how many different plates are possible?

12. Kiersten applies for admission to the University of Southern California (USC) and Florida State University (FSU). She estimates that she has a 60% chance of being admitted to USC, a 70% chance of being admitted to FSU, and a 35% chance of being admitted to both universities.
    (a) What is the probability that she will be admitted to either USC or FSU?
    (b) What is the probability that she will not be admitted to FSU?

13. A cooler contains 8 bottles of Pepsi, 5 bottles of Coke, 4 bottles of Mountain Dew, and 3 bottles of IBC.

(a) What is the probability that a bottle chosen at random is Coke?
(b) What is the probability that a bottle chosen at random is either Pepsi or IBC?

14. A study on the age distribution of a community college gave the following table:

Age	17 and under	18–20	21–24	25–34	35–64	65 and over
Probability	0.03	???	0.23	0.29	0.25	0.01

What must be the probability that a randomly selected student at the college is between 18 and 20 years old?

15. Powerball is a multistate lottery in which 5 white balls from a drum with 53 balls and 1 red ball from a drum with 42 red balls are selected. For a $1 ticket, players get one chance at winning the jackpot by matching all 6 numbers. What is the probability of selecting the winning numbers on a $1 play?

16. If you roll a die five times, what is the probability that you obtain exactly 2 fours?

CUMULATIVE REVIEW

1. Solve: $3x^2 - 2x = -1$

2. Graph $f(x) = x^2 + 4x - 5$ by determining whether the graph opens up or down and by finding the vertex, axis of symmetry, and intercepts.

3. Graph $f(x) = 2(x + 1)^2 - 4$ using transformations.

4. Solve: $|x - 4| \leq 0.01$

5. Find the complex zeros of
$$f(x) = 5x^4 - 9x^3 - 7x^2 - 31x - 6$$

6. Graph $g(x) = 3^{x-1} + 5$ using transformations. Determine the domain, the range, and horizontal asymptote of g.

7. What is the exact value of $\log_3 9$?

8. Solve: $\log_2(3x - 2) + \log_2 x = 4$

9. Solve the system: $\begin{cases} x - 2y + z = 15 \\ 3x + y - 3z = -8 \\ -2x + 4y - z = -27 \end{cases}$

10. What is the 33rd term in the sequence $-3, 1, 5, 9, \ldots$? What is the sum of the first 20 terms?

11. Graph: $y = 3\sin(2x + \pi)$

12. Solve the following triangle and determine its area.

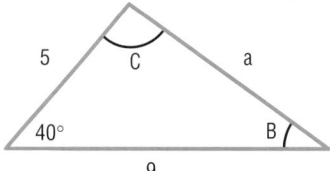

CHAPTER PROJECTS

I. **The Monty Hall Game** The *Monty Hall Game,* based on a segment from the game show *Let's Make a Deal,* is a classic probability problem that continues to stir debate. A more recent game show, *Deal or No Deal* (see the chapter opening vignette) has often been compared to the classic *Monty Hall Game.*

(a) Research the *Monty Hall Game* and *Deal or No Deal.*

(b) In the *Monty Hall Game,* what is the probability that a contestant wins if she does not switch? What is the probability of winning if she does switch? Perform a simulation to estimate the probabilities. Do the values agree with your research?

(c) Suppose the game *Deal or No Deal* is played with only three suitcases. Explain why this game is not the same as the *Monty Hall Game*.

(d) Suppose the game *Deal or No Deal* is played with 26 suitcases and the contestant is not allowed to switch at the end. What is the probability that the contestant will win the grand prize?

(e) Suppose the game *Deal or No Deal* is played with 26 suitcases and the contestant is allowed to switch at the end. Perform a simulation to estimate the probability that the contestant will win the grand prize if he does not switch at the end.

(f) Repeat part (e), but assume the contestant will always switch at the end.

The following projects are available at the Instructor's Resource Center (IRC):

II. Project at Motorola ***Probability of Error in Digital Wireless Communications*** Transmission errors in digital communications can often be detected by adding an extra digit of code to each transmitted signal. Investigate the probability of identifying an erroneous code using this simple coding method.

III. Surveys Polling (or taking a survey) is big business in the United States. Take and analyze a survey; then consider why different pollsters might get different results.

IV. Law of Large Numbers The probability that an event occurs, such as a head in a coin toss, is the proportion of heads you expect in the long run. A simulation is used to show that the more times a coin is flipped, the closer the probability that half of the outcomes is head.

V. Simulation Electronic simulation of an experiment is often an economical way to investigate a theoretical probability. Develop a theory without leaving your desk.

A Preview of Calculus: The Limit, Derivative, and Integral of a Function

14

Two hundred years ago the Rev. Thomas Robert Malthus, an English economist and mathematician, anonymously published an essay predicting that the world's burgeoning population would overwhelm Earth's capacity to sustain it.

Malthus's gloomy forecast was condemned by Karl Marx, Friedrich Engels, and many other theorists, and it was still striking sparks last week at a meeting in Philadelphia of the American Anthropological Society. Despite continuing controversy, it was clear that Malthus's conjectures are far from dead.

Among the scores of special conferences organized for the 5,000 participating anthropologists, many touched directly and indirectly on the Malthusian dilemma: Although global food supplies increase arithmetically, the population increases geometrically—a vastly faster rate.

Source: *"Will Humans Overwhelm the Earth? The Debate Continues," Malcolm W. Browne, New York Times, December 8, 1998.*

—*See Chapter Project I*—

A Look Back

In this book we have studied a variety of functions: polynomial functions (including linear and quadratic functions), rational functions, exponential and logarithmic functions, trigonometric functions, and the inverse trigonometric functions. For each of these, we found their domain and range, intercepts, symmetry, if any, and asymptotes, if any, and we graphed each. We also discussed whether these functions were even, odd, or neither and determined on what intervals they were increasing and decreasing. We also discussed the idea of their average rate of change.

A Look Ahead

In calculus, other properties are discussed, such as finding limits of functions, determining where functions are continuous, finding the derivative of functions, and finding the integral of functions. In this chapter, we give an introduction to these properties. By completing this chapter you will be well prepared for a first course in calculus.

Outline

14.1 Finding Limits Using Tables and Graphs

14.2 Algebra Techniques for Finding Limits

14.3 One-sided Limits; Continuous Functions

14.4 The Tangent Problem; The Derivative

14.5 The Area Problem; The Integral

Chapter Review

Chapter Test

Chapter Projects

14.1 Finding Limits Using Tables and Graphs

PREPARING FOR THIS SECTION   *Before getting started, review the following:*

- Piecewise–defined Functions (Section 2.4, pp. 95–96)

Now Work the 'Are You Prepared?' problems on page 883.

OBJECTIVES   1 Find a Limit Using a Table (p. 880)
2 Find a Limit Using a Graph (p. 881)

1 Find a Limit Using a Table

The idea of the limit of a function is what connects algebra and geometry to the mathematics of calculus. In working with the limit of a function, we encounter notation of the form

$$\lim_{x \to c} f(x) = N$$

This is read as "the limit of $f(x)$ as x approaches c equals the number N." Here f is a function defined on some open interval containing the number c; f need not be defined at c, however.

We may describe the meaning of $\lim_{x \to c} f(x) = N$ as follows:

For all x approximately equal to c, with $x \neq c$, the corresponding value $f(x)$ is approximately equal to N.

Another description of $\lim_{x \to c} f(x) = N$ is

As x gets closer to c, but remains unequal to c, the corresponding value of $f(x)$ gets closer to N.

Tables generated with the help of a calculator are useful for finding limits.

EXAMPLE 1   **Finding a Limit Using a Table**

Find: $\lim_{x \to 3} (5x^2)$

Solution   Here $f(x) = 5x^2$ and $c = 3$. We choose values of x close to 3, arbitrarily starting with 2.99. Then we select additional numbers that get closer to 3, but remain less than 3. Next we choose values of x greater than 3, starting with 3.01, that get closer to 3. Table 1 shows the value of f at each choice.

From Table 1, we infer that as x gets closer to 3 the value of $f(x) = 5x^2$ gets closer to 45. That is,

$$\lim_{x \to 3} (5x^2) = 45$$

Table 1

X	Y1
2.99	44.701
2.999	44.97
2.9999	44.997
3.0001	45.003
3.001	45.03
3.01	45.301

Y1 ■5X²

When choosing the values of x in a table, the number to start with and the subsequent entries are arbitrary. However, the entries should be chosen so that the table makes it clear what the corresponding values of f are getting close to.

Now Work PROBLEM 7

EXAMPLE 2   Finding a Limit Using a Table

Find: (a) $\displaystyle\lim_{x \to 2} \frac{x^2 - 4}{x - 2}$ (b) $\displaystyle\lim_{x \to 2}(x + 2)$

Solution   (a) Here $f(x) = \dfrac{x^2 - 4}{x - 2}$ and $c = 2$. Notice that the domain of f is $\{x | x \neq 2\}$, so f is not defined at 2. We proceed to choose values of x close to 2 and evaluate f at each choice, as shown in Table 2. We infer that as x gets closer to 2 the value of $f(x) = \dfrac{x^2 - 4}{x - 2}$ gets closer to 4. That is,

$$\lim_{x \to 2} \frac{x^2 - 4}{x - 2} = 4$$

(b) Here $g(x) = x + 2$ and $c = 2$. The domain of g is all real numbers. See Table 3. We infer that as x gets closer to 2 the value of $g(x)$ gets closer to 4. That is,

$$\lim_{x \to 2}(x + 2) = 4$$

Table 2

X	Y1
1.99	3.99
1.999	3.999
1.9999	3.9999
2.0001	4.0001
2.001	4.001
2.01	4.01

Y1 ◻(X²−4)/(X−2)

Table 3

X	Y1
1.99	3.99
1.999	3.999
1.9999	3.9999
2.0001	4.0001
2.001	4.001
2.01	4.01

Y1 ◻X+2

The conclusion that $\displaystyle\lim_{x \to 2}(x + 2) = 4$ could have been obtained without the use of Table 3; as x gets closer to 2, it follows that $x + 2$ will get closer to $2 + 2 = 4$.

Also, for part (a), you are right if you make the observation that, since $x \neq 2$, then

$$f(x) = \frac{x^2 - 4}{x - 2} = \frac{(x - 2)(x + 2)}{x - 2} = x + 2 \qquad x \neq 2$$

We conclude that

$$\lim_{x \to 2} \frac{x^2 - 4}{x - 2} = \lim_{x \to 2}(x + 2) = 4$$

Let's look at an example for which the factoring technique used above does not work.

EXAMPLE 3   Finding a Limit Using a Table

Find: $\displaystyle\lim_{x \to 0} \frac{\sin x}{x}$

Solution   First, we observe that the domain of the function $f(x) = \dfrac{\sin x}{x}$ is $\{x | x \neq 0\}$. We create Table 4, where x is measured in radians. We infer from Table 4 that

$$\lim_{x \to 0} \frac{\sin x}{x} = 1.$$

Table 4

X	Y1
−.05	.99958
−.02	.99993
−.01	.99998
.01	.99998
.02	.99993
.05	.99958

Y1 ◻sin(X)/X

2 Find a Limit Using a Graph

The graph of a function f can also be of help in finding limits. See Figure 1. In each graph, notice that, as x gets closer to c, the value of f gets closer to the number N. We conclude that

$$\lim_{x \to c} f(x) = N$$

This is the conclusion regardless of the value of f at c. In Figure 1(a), $f(c) = N$, and in Figure 1(b), $f(c) \neq N$. Figure 1(c) illustrates that $\lim\limits_{x \to c} f(x) = N$, even if f is not defined at c.

Figure 1

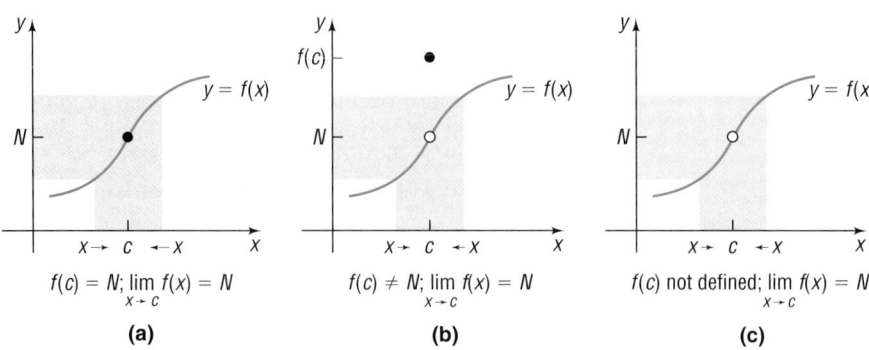

$f(c) = N$; $\lim\limits_{x \to c} f(x) = N$ $f(c) \neq N$; $\lim\limits_{x \to c} f(x) = N$ $f(c)$ not defined; $\lim\limits_{x \to c} f(x) = N$

(a)   (b)   (c)

| EXAMPLE 4 | **Finding a Limit by Graphing** |

Find: $\lim\limits_{x \to 2} f(x)$ if $f(x) = \begin{cases} 3x - 2 & \text{if } x \neq 2 \\ 3 & \text{if } x = 2 \end{cases}$

Solution The function f is a piecewise-defined function. Its graph is shown in Figure 2(a) drawn by hand. Figure 2(b) shows the graph using a graphing utility.

Figure 2

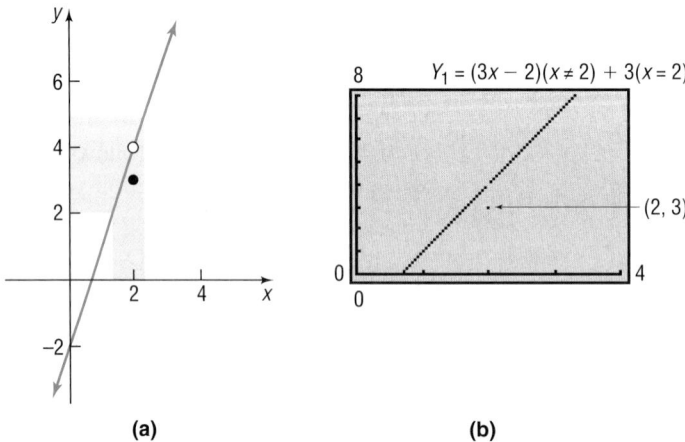

(a)   (b)

See Figure 3. By ZOOMing in around $x = 2$ and TRACEing, we conclude from the graph that $\lim\limits_{x \to 2} f(x) = 4$.

Figure 3

Notice in Example 4 that the value of f at 2, that is, $f(2) = 3$, plays no role in the conclusion that $\lim\limits_{x \to 2} f(x) = 4$. In fact, even if f were undefined at 2, it would still be the case that $\lim\limits_{x \to 2} f(x) = 4$.

▬▬▶ **Now Work** PROBLEM 23

Sometimes there is no *single* number that the values of f get closer to as x gets closer to c. In this case, we say that **f has no limit as x approaches c** or that $\lim\limits_{x \to c} f(x)$ **does not exist.**

| EXAMPLE 5 | A Function That Has No Limit at 0 |

Find: $\displaystyle\lim_{x\to 0} f(x)$ if $f(x) = \begin{cases} x & \text{if } x \le 0 \\ 1 & \text{if } x > 0 \end{cases}$

Figure 4

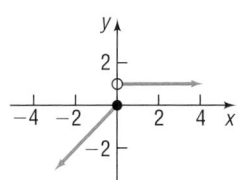

Solution See Figure 4. As x gets closer to 0, but remains negative, the value of f also gets closer to 0. As x gets closer to 0, but remains positive, the value of f always equals 1. Since there is no single number that the values of f are close to when x is close to 0, we conclude that $\displaystyle\lim_{x\to 0} f(x)$ does not exist.

➤ **Now Work** PROBLEMS 17 AND 37

| EXAMPLE 6 | Using a Graphing Utility to Find a Limit |

Find: $\displaystyle\lim_{x\to 2} \dfrac{x^3 - 2x^2 + 4x - 8}{x^4 - 2x^3 + x - 2}$

Solution Table 5 shows the solution, from which we conclude that

$$\lim_{x\to 2} \frac{x^3 - 2x^2 + 4x - 8}{x^4 - 2x^3 + x - 2} = 0.889$$

rounded to three decimal places.

Table 5

X	Y1		X	Y1
1	2.5		3	.46429
1.5	1.4286		2.5	.61654
1.8	1.0597		2.3	.70555
1.9	.96832		2.1	.81961
1.99	.89635		2.01	.88153
1.999	.88963		2.001	.88815
1.9999	.88896		2.0001	.88801
Y1■(X^3-2X²+4X-…			Y1■(X^3-2X²+4X-…	

➤ **Now Work** PROBLEM 43

In the next section, we will see how algebra can be used to obtain exact solutions to limits like the one in Example 6.

14.1 Assess Your Understanding

'Are You Prepared?' *Answers are given at the end of these exercises. If you get a wrong answer, read the pages listed in red.*

1. Graph $f(x) = \begin{cases} 3x - 2 & \text{if } x \ne 2 \\ 3 & \text{if } x = 2 \end{cases}$ (pp. 95–96)

2. If $f(x) = \begin{cases} x & \text{if } x \le 0 \\ 1 & \text{if } x > 0 \end{cases}$ what is $f(0)$? (pp. 95–96)

Concepts and Vocabulary

3. The limit of a function $f(x)$ as x approaches c is denoted by the symbol _____.

4. If a function f has no limit as x approaches c, then we say that $\displaystyle\lim_{x\to c} f(x)$ _____ _____ _____.

5. *True or False* $\displaystyle\lim_{x\to c} f(x) = N$ may be described by saying that the value of $f(x)$ gets closer to N as x gets closer to c but remains unequal to c.

6. *True or False* $\displaystyle\lim_{x\to c} f(x)$ exists and equals some number for any function f as long as c is in the domain of f.

Skill Building

In Problems 7–16, use a table to find the indicated limit.

7. $\lim\limits_{x \to 2} (4x^3)$

8. $\lim\limits_{x \to 3} (2x^2 + 1)$

9. $\lim\limits_{x \to 0} \dfrac{x + 1}{x^2 + 1}$

10. $\lim\limits_{x \to 0} \dfrac{2 - x}{x^2 + 4}$

11. $\lim\limits_{x \to 4} \dfrac{x^2 - 4x}{x - 4}$

12. $\lim\limits_{x \to 3} \dfrac{x^2 - 9}{x^2 - 3x}$

13. $\lim\limits_{x \to 0} (e^x + 1)$

14. $\lim\limits_{x \to 0} \dfrac{e^x - e^{-x}}{2}$

15. $\lim\limits_{x \to 0} \dfrac{\cos x - 1}{x}$ x in radians

16. $\lim\limits_{x \to 0} \dfrac{\tan x}{x}$ x in radians

In Problems 17–22, use the graph shown to determine if the limit exists. If it does, find its value.

17. $\lim\limits_{x \to 2} f(x)$

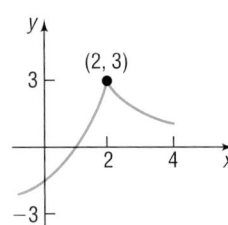

18. $\lim\limits_{x \to 4} f(x)$

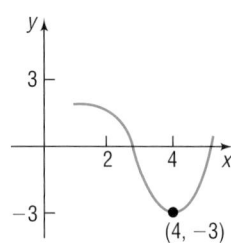

19. $\lim\limits_{x \to 2} f(x)$

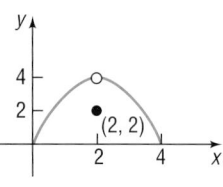

20. $\lim\limits_{x \to 2} f(x)$

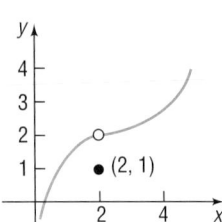

21. $\lim\limits_{x \to 3} f(x)$

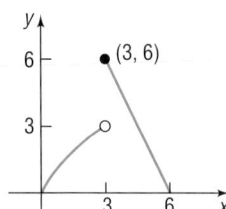

22. $\lim\limits_{x \to 4} f(x)$

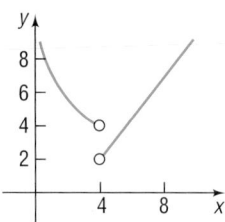

In Problems 23–42, graph each function. Use the graph to find the indicated limit, if it exists.

23. $\lim\limits_{x \to 4} f(x), \quad f(x) = 3x + 1$

24. $\lim\limits_{x \to -1} f(x), \quad f(x) = 2x - 1$

25. $\lim\limits_{x \to 2} f(x), \quad f(x) = 1 - x^2$

26. $\lim\limits_{x \to -1} f(x), \quad f(x) = x^3 - 1$

27. $\lim\limits_{x \to -3} f(x), \quad f(x) = |2x|$

28. $\lim\limits_{x \to 4} f(x), \quad f(x) = 3\sqrt{x}$

29. $\lim\limits_{x \to \pi/2} f(x), \quad f(x) = \sin x$

30. $\lim\limits_{x \to \pi} f(x), \quad f(x) = \cos x$

31. $\lim\limits_{x \to 0} f(x), \quad f(x) = e^x$

32. $\lim\limits_{x \to 1} f(x), \quad f(x) = \ln x$

33. $\lim\limits_{x \to -1} f(x), \quad f(x) = \dfrac{1}{x}$

34. $\lim\limits_{x \to 2} f(x), \quad f(x) = \dfrac{1}{x^2}$

35. $\lim\limits_{x \to 0} f(x), \quad f(x) = \begin{cases} x^2 & \text{if } x \geq 0 \\ 2x & \text{if } x < 0 \end{cases}$

36. $\lim\limits_{x \to 0} f(x), \quad f(x) = \begin{cases} x - 1 & \text{if } x < 0 \\ 3x - 1 & \text{if } x \geq 0 \end{cases}$

37. $\lim\limits_{x \to 1} f(x), \quad f(x) = \begin{cases} 3x & \text{if } x \leq 1 \\ x + 1 & \text{if } x > 1 \end{cases}$

38. $\lim\limits_{x \to 2} f(x), \quad f(x) = \begin{cases} x^2 & \text{if } x \leq 2 \\ 2x - 1 & \text{if } x > 2 \end{cases}$

39. $\lim\limits_{x \to 0} f(x), \quad f(x) = \begin{cases} x & \text{if } x < 0 \\ 1 & \text{if } x = 0 \\ 3x & \text{if } x > 0 \end{cases}$

40. $\lim\limits_{x \to 0} f(x), \quad f(x) = \begin{cases} 1 & \text{if } x < 0 \\ -1 & \text{if } x > 0 \end{cases}$

41. $\lim\limits_{x \to 0} f(x), \quad f(x) = \begin{cases} \sin x & \text{if } x \leq 0 \\ x^2 & \text{if } x > 0 \end{cases}$

42. $\lim\limits_{x \to 0} f(x), \quad f(x) = \begin{cases} e^x & \text{if } x > 0 \\ 1 - x & \text{if } x \leq 0 \end{cases}$

In Problems 43–48, use a graphing utility to find the indicated limit rounded to two decimal places.

43. $\lim\limits_{x \to 1} \dfrac{x^3 - x^2 + x - 1}{x^4 - x^3 + 2x - 2}$

44. $\lim\limits_{x \to -1} \dfrac{x^3 + x^2 + 3x + 3}{x^4 + x^3 + 2x + 2}$

45. $\lim\limits_{x \to 2} \dfrac{x^3 - 2x^2 + 4x - 8}{x^2 + x - 6}$

46. $\lim\limits_{x \to 1} \dfrac{x^3 - x^2 + 3x - 3}{x^2 + 3x - 4}$

47. $\lim\limits_{x \to -1} \dfrac{x^3 + 2x^2 + x}{x^4 + x^3 + 2x + 2}$

48. $\lim\limits_{x \to 3} \dfrac{x^3 - 3x^2 + 4x - 12}{x^4 - 3x^3 + x - 3}$

'Are You Prepared?' Answers

1. See Figure 2 on page 882. **2.** $f(0) = 0$

14.2 Algebra Techniques for Finding Limits

OBJECTIVES **1** Find the Limit of a Sum, a Difference, and a Product (p. 886)
   2 Find the Limit of a Polynomial (p. 888)
   3 Find the Limit of a Power or a Root (p. 888)
   4 Find the Limit of a Quotient (p. 889)
   5 Find the Limit of an Average Rate of Change (p. 890)

We mentioned in the previous section that algebra can sometimes be used to find the exact value of a limit. This is accomplished by developing two formulas involving limits and several properties of limits.

THEOREM

Two Formulas: $\lim\limits_{x \to c} b$ and $\lim\limits_{x \to c} x$

Limit of a Constant

For the constant function $f(x) = b$,

In Words
The limit of a constant is the constant.

$$\lim_{x \to c} f(x) = \lim_{x \to c} b = b \qquad (1)$$

where c is any number.

Limit of x

For the identity function $f(x) = x$,

In Words
The limit of x as x approaches c is c.

$$\lim_{x \to c} f(x) = \lim_{x \to c} x = c \qquad (2)$$

where c is any number.

We use graphs to establish formulas (1) and (2). Since the graph of a constant function is a horizontal line, it follows that, no matter how close x is to c, the corresponding value of $f(x)$ equals b. That is, $\lim\limits_{x \to c} b = b$. See Figure 5(a).

See Figure 5(b). For any choice of c, as x gets closer to c, the corresponding value of $f(x)$ is x, which is just as close to c. That is, $\lim\limits_{x \to c} x = c$.

Figure 5

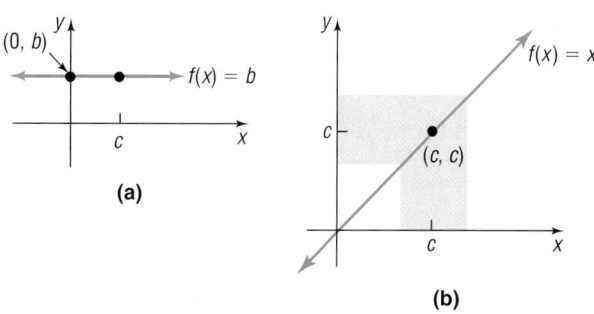

(a)

(b)

EXAMPLE 1   Using Formulas (1) and (2)

(a) $\lim\limits_{x \to 3} 5 = 5$ (b) $\lim\limits_{x \to 3} x = 3$ (c) $\lim\limits_{x \to 0} (-8) = -8$ (d) $\lim\limits_{x \to -1/2} x = -\dfrac{1}{2}$

Now Work PROBLEM 7

Formulas (1) and (2), when used with the properties that follow, enable us to evaluate limits of more complicated functions.

1 Find the Limit of a Sum, a Difference, and a Product

In the following properties, we assume that f and g are two functions for which both $\lim_{x \to c} f(x)$ and $\lim_{x \to c} g(x)$ exist.

THEOREM

Limit of a Sum

$$\lim_{x \to c}[f(x) + g(x)] = \lim_{x \to c} f(x) + \lim_{x \to c} g(x) \qquad (3)$$

In Words
The limit of the sum of two functions equals the sum of their limits.

EXAMPLE 2   Finding the Limit of a Sum

Find: $\lim_{x \to -3} (x + 4)$

Solution   The limit we seek is the sum of two functions $f(x) = x$ and $g(x) = 4$. From formulas (1) and (2), we know that

$$\lim_{x \to -3} f(x) = \lim_{x \to -3} x = -3 \quad \text{and} \quad \lim_{x \to -3} g(x) = \lim_{x \to -3} 4 = 4$$

From formula (3), it follows that

$$\lim_{x \to -3} (x + 4) = \lim_{x \to -3} x + \lim_{x \to -3} 4 = -3 + 4 = 1$$

THEOREM

Limit of a Difference

$$\lim_{x \to c}[f(x) - g(x)] = \lim_{x \to c} f(x) - \lim_{x \to c} g(x) \qquad (4)$$

In Words
The limit of the difference of two functions equals the difference of their limits.

EXAMPLE 3   Finding the Limit of a Difference

Find: $\lim_{x \to 4} (6 - x)$

Solution   The limit we seek is the difference of two functions $f(x) = 6$ and $g(x) = x$. From formulas (1) and (2), we know that

$$\lim_{x \to 4} f(x) = \lim_{x \to 4} 6 = 6 \quad \text{and} \quad \lim_{x \to 4} g(x) = \lim_{x \to 4} x = 4$$

From formula (4), it follows that

$$\lim_{x \to 4} (6 - x) = \lim_{x \to 4} 6 - \lim_{x \to 4} x = 6 - 4 = 2$$

THEOREM

Limit of a Product

$$\lim_{x \to c}[f(x) \cdot g(x)] = \left[\lim_{x \to c} f(x)\right]\left[\lim_{x \to c} g(x)\right] \qquad (5)$$

In Words
The limit of the product of two functions equals the product of their limits.

EXAMPLE 4	Finding the Limit of a Product

Find: $\lim\limits_{x \to -5}(-4x)$

Solution   The limit we seek is the product of two functions $f(x) = -4$ and $g(x) = x$. From formulas (1) and (2), we know that

$$\lim\limits_{x \to -5} f(x) = \lim\limits_{x \to -5}(-4) = -4 \quad \text{and} \quad \lim\limits_{x \to -5} g(x) = \lim\limits_{x \to -5} x = -5$$

From formula (5), it follows that

$$\lim\limits_{x \to -5}(-4x) = \left[\lim\limits_{x \to -5}(-4)\right]\left[\lim\limits_{x \to -5} x\right] = (-4)(-5) = 20$$

EXAMPLE 5	Finding Limits Using Algebraic Properties

Find: (a) $\lim\limits_{x \to -2}(3x - 5)$ (b) $\lim\limits_{x \to 2}(5x^2)$

Solution   (a) $\lim\limits_{x \to -2}(3x - 5) = \lim\limits_{x \to -2}(3x) - \lim\limits_{x \to -2} 5 = \left[\lim\limits_{x \to -2} 3\right]\left[\lim\limits_{x \to -2} x\right] - \lim\limits_{x \to -2} 5$
$$= (3)(-2) - 5 = -6 - 5 = -11$$

(b) $\lim\limits_{x \to 2}(5x^2) = \left[\lim\limits_{x \to 2} 5\right]\left[\lim\limits_{x \to 2} x^2\right] = 5\lim\limits_{x \to 2}(x \cdot x) = 5\left[\lim\limits_{x \to 2} x\right]\left[\lim\limits_{x \to 2} x\right]$
$$= 5 \cdot 2 \cdot 2 = 20$$

Now Work   PROBLEM 15

Notice in the solution to part (b) that $\lim\limits_{x \to 2}(5x^2) = 5 \cdot 2^2$.

THEOREM   **Limit of a Monomial**

If $n \geq 1$ is a positive integer and a is a constant,

$$\lim\limits_{x \to c}(ax^n) = ac^n \qquad (6)$$

for any number c.

Proof $\lim\limits_{x \to c}(ax^n) = [\lim\limits_{x \to c} a][\lim\limits_{x \to c} x^n] = a[\lim\limits_{x \to c} \underbrace{(x \cdot x \cdot x \cdot \ldots \cdot x)}_{n \text{ factors}}]$

$$= a\underbrace{[\lim\limits_{x \to c} x][\lim\limits_{x \to c} x][\lim\limits_{x \to c} x] \ldots [\lim\limits_{x \to c} x]}_{n \text{ factors}}$$

$$= a \cdot \underbrace{c \cdot c \cdot c \cdot \ldots \cdot c}_{n \text{ factors}} = ac^n$$

EXAMPLE 6	Finding the Limit of a Monomial

Find: $\lim\limits_{x \to 2}(-4x^3)$

Solution $\lim\limits_{x \to 2}(-4x^3) = -4 \cdot 2^3 = -4 \cdot 8 = -32$

2 Find the Limit of a Polynomial

Since a polynomial is a sum of monomials, we can use formula (6) and repeated use of formula (3) to obtain the following result:

THEOREM

Limit of a Polynomial

If P is a polynomial function, then

$$\lim_{x \to c} P(x) = P(c) \tag{7}$$

for any number c.

In Words
To find the limit of a polynomial as x approaches c all we need to do is evaluate the polynomial at c.

Proof If P is a polynomial function, that is, if

$$P(x) = a_n x^n + a_{n-1} x^{n-1} + \cdots + a_1 x + a_0$$

then

$$\lim_{x \to c} P(x) = \lim_{x \to c} [a_n x^n + a_{n-1} x^{n-1} + \cdots + a_1 x + a_0]$$

$$= \lim_{x \to c} (a_n x^n) + \lim_{x \to c} (a_{n-1} x^{n-1}) + \cdots + \lim_{x \to c} (a_1 x) + \lim_{x \to c} a_0$$

$$= a_n c^n + a_{n-1} c^{n-1} + \cdots + a_1 c + a_0$$

$$= P(c) \qquad \blacksquare$$

EXAMPLE 7 **Finding the Limit of a Polynomial**

Find: $\lim_{x \to 2} [5x^4 - 6x^3 + 3x^2 + 4x - 2]$

Solution $\lim_{x \to 2} [5x^4 - 6x^3 + 3x^2 + 4x - 2] = 5 \cdot 2^4 - 6 \cdot 2^3 + 3 \cdot 2^2 + 4 \cdot 2 - 2$

$$= 5 \cdot 16 - 6 \cdot 8 + 3 \cdot 4 + 8 - 2$$

$$= 80 - 48 + 12 + 6 = 50$$

Now Work PROBLEM 17

3 Find the Limit of a Power or a Root

THEOREM

Limit of a Power or Root

If $\lim_{x \to c} f(x)$ exists and if $n \geq 2$ is a positive integer,

$$\lim_{x \to c} [f(x)]^n = [\lim_{x \to c} f(x)]^n \tag{8}$$

and

$$\lim_{x \to c} \sqrt[n]{f(x)} = \sqrt[n]{\lim_{x \to c} f(x)} \tag{9}$$

In formula (9), we require that both $\sqrt[n]{f(x)}$ and $\sqrt[n]{\lim_{x \to c} f(x)}$ be defined.

Look carefully at equations (8) and (9) and compare each side.

889 Algebra Techniques for Finding Limits

EXAMPLE 8	**Finding the Limit of a Power or a Root**

Find: (a) $\lim\limits_{x \to 1} (3x - 5)^4$ (b) $\lim\limits_{x \to 0} \sqrt{5x^2 + 8}$ (c) $\lim\limits_{x \to -1} (5x^3 - x + 3)^{4/3}$

Solution   (a) $\lim\limits_{x \to 1} (3x - 5)^4 = [\lim\limits_{x \to 1} (3x - 5)]^4 = (-2)^4 = 16$

(b) $\lim\limits_{x \to 0} \sqrt{5x^2 + 8} = \sqrt{\lim\limits_{x \to 0} (5x^2 + 8)} = \sqrt{8} = 2\sqrt{2}$

(c) $\lim\limits_{x \to -1} (5x^3 - x + 3)^{4/3} = \sqrt[3]{\lim\limits_{x \to -1} (5x^3 - x + 3)^4}$

$$= \sqrt[3]{\left[\lim\limits_{x \to -1} (5x^3 - x + 3)\right]^4} = \sqrt[3]{(-1)^4} = \sqrt[3]{1} = 1$$

✏️ **Now Work** PROBLEM 27

4 Find the Limit of a Quotient

THEOREM	**Limit of a Quotient**

In Words
The limit of the quotient of two functions equals the quotient of their limits, provided that the limit of the denominator is not zero.

$$\lim_{x \to c}\left[\frac{f(x)}{g(x)}\right] = \frac{\lim\limits_{x \to c} f(x)}{\lim\limits_{x \to c} g(x)} \qquad \textbf{(10)}$$

provided that $\lim\limits_{x \to c} g(x) \neq 0$.

EXAMPLE 9	**Finding the Limit of a Quotient**

Find: $\lim\limits_{x \to 1} \dfrac{5x^3 - x + 2}{3x + 4}$

Solution   The limit we seek is the quotient of two functions: $f(x) = 5x^3 - x + 2$ and $g(x) = 3x + 4$. First, we find the limit of the denominator $g(x)$.

$$\lim_{x \to 1} g(x) = \lim_{x \to 1} (3x + 4) = 7$$

Since the limit of the denominator is not zero, we can proceed to use formula (10).

$$\lim_{x \to 1} \frac{5x^3 - x + 2}{3x + 4} = \frac{\lim\limits_{x \to 1}(5x^3 - x + 2)}{\lim\limits_{x \to 1}(3x + 4)} = \frac{6}{7}$$

✏️ **Now Work** PROBLEM 25

When the limit of the denominator is zero, formula (10) cannot be used. In such cases, other strategies need to be used. Let's look at two examples.

EXAMPLE 10	**Finding the Limit of a Quotient**

Find: (a) $\lim\limits_{x \to 3} \dfrac{x^2 - x - 6}{x^2 - 9}$ (b) $\lim\limits_{x \to 0} \dfrac{5x - \sin x}{x}$

Solution   (a) The limit of the denominator equals zero, so formula (10) cannot be used. Instead, we notice that the expression can be factored as

$$\frac{x^2 - x - 6}{x^2 - 9} = \frac{(x - 3)(x + 2)}{(x - 3)(x + 3)}$$

When we compute a limit as x approaches 3, we are interested in the values of the function when x is close to 3, but unequal to 3. Since $x \neq 3$, we can cancel the $(x - 3)$'s. Formula (10) can then be used.

$$\lim_{x \to 3} \frac{x^2 - x - 6}{x^2 - 9} = \lim_{x \to 3} \frac{(x - 3)(x + 2)}{(x - 3)(x + 3)} = \frac{\lim_{x \to 3}(x + 2)}{\lim_{x \to 3}(x + 3)} = \frac{5}{6}$$

(b) Again, the limit of the denominator is zero. In this situation, we perform the indicated operation and divide by x.

$$\lim_{x \to 0} \frac{5x - \sin x}{x} = \lim_{x \to 0} \left[\frac{5x}{x} - \frac{\sin x}{x} \right] = \lim_{x \to 0} \frac{5x}{x} - \lim_{x \to 0} \frac{\sin x}{x} = 5 - 1 = 4$$

↑
Limit of
a difference

↑
Refer to Example 3,
Section 14.1.

EXAMPLE 11 | **Finding Limits Using Algebraic Properties**

Find: $\displaystyle\lim_{x \to 2} \frac{x^3 - 2x^2 + 4x - 8}{x^4 - 2x^3 + x - 2}$

Solution   The limit of the denominator is zero, so formula (10) cannot be used. We factor the expression.

$$\frac{x^3 - 2x^2 + 4x - 8}{x^4 - 2x^3 + x - 2} = \frac{x^2(x - 2) + 4(x - 2)}{x^3(x - 2) + 1(x - 2)} = \frac{(x^2 + 4)(x - 2)}{(x^3 + 1)(x - 2)}$$

↑
Factor by grouping

Then

$$\lim_{x \to 2} \frac{x^3 - 2x^2 + 4x - 8}{x^4 - 2x^3 + x - 2} = \lim_{x \to 2} \frac{(x^2 + 4)(x - 2)}{(x^3 + 1)(x - 2)} = \frac{8}{9}$$

which is exact.

Compare the exact solution above with the approximate solution found in Example 6 of Section 14.1.

5 Find the Limit of an Average Rate of Change

EXAMPLE 12 | **Finding the Limit of an Average Rate of Change**

Find the limit as x approaches 2 of the average rate of change of the function

$$f(x) = x^2 + 3x$$

from 2 to x.

Solution   The average rate of change of f from 2 to x is

$$\frac{\Delta y}{\Delta x} = \frac{f(x) - f(2)}{x - 2} = \frac{(x^2 + 3x) - 10}{x - 2} = \frac{(x + 5)(x - 2)}{x - 2}$$

The limit of the average rate of change is

$$\lim_{x \to 2} \frac{f(x) - f(2)}{x - 2} = \lim_{x \to 2} \frac{(x^2 + 3x) - 10}{x - 2} = \lim_{x \to 2} \frac{(x + 5)(x - 2)}{x - 2} = 7$$

SUMMARY

To find exact values for $\lim_{x \to c} f(x)$, try the following:

1. If f is a polynomial function, $\lim_{x \to c} f(x) = f(c)$. (formula 7)
2. If f is a polynomial raised to a power or is the root of a polynomial, use formulas (8) and (9) with formula (7).
3. If f is a quotient and the limit of the denominator is not zero, use the fact that the limit of a quotient is the quotient of the limits. (formula 10)
4. If f is a quotient and the limit of the denominator is zero, use other techniques, such as factoring.

14.2 Assess Your Understanding

Concepts and Vocabulary

1. The limit of the product of two functions equals the _____ of their limits.

2. $\lim_{x \to 0} 5 = $ _____.

3. $\lim_{x \to 1} x = $ _____.

4. *True or False* The limit of a polynomial function as x approaches 5 equals the value of the polynomial at 5.

5. *True or False* The limit of a rational function at 5 equals the value of the rational function at 5.

6. *True or False* The limit of a quotient equals the quotient of the limits.

Skill Building

In Problems 7–42, find each limit algebraically.

7. $\lim_{x \to 1} 5$

8. $\lim_{x \to 1} (-3)$

9. $\lim_{x \to 4} x$

10. $\lim_{x \to -3} x$

11. $\lim_{x \to -2} (5x)$

12. $\lim_{x \to 4} (-3x)$

13. $\lim_{x \to 2} (5x^4)$

14. $\lim_{x \to -3} (2x^3)$

15. $\lim_{x \to 2} (3x + 2)$

16. $\lim_{x \to 3} (2 - 5x)$

17. $\lim_{x \to -1} (3x^2 - 5x)$

18. $\lim_{x \to 2} (8x^2 - 4)$

19. $\lim_{x \to 1} (5x^4 - 3x^2 + 6x - 9)$

20. $\lim_{x \to -1} (8x^5 - 7x^3 + 8x^2 + x - 4)$

21. $\lim_{x \to 1} (x^2 + 1)^3$

22. $\lim_{x \to 2} (3x - 4)^2$

23. $\lim_{x \to 1} \sqrt{5x + 4}$

24. $\lim_{x \to 0} \sqrt{1 - 2x}$

25. $\lim_{x \to 0} \dfrac{x^2 - 4}{x^2 + 4}$

26. $\lim_{x \to 2} \dfrac{3x + 4}{x^2 + x}$

27. $\lim_{x \to 2} (3x - 2)^{5/2}$

28. $\lim_{x \to -1} (2x + 1)^{5/3}$

29. $\lim_{x \to 2} \dfrac{x^2 - 4}{x^2 - 2x}$

30. $\lim_{x \to -1} \dfrac{x^2 + x}{x^2 - 1}$

31. $\lim_{x \to -3} \dfrac{x^2 - x - 12}{x^2 - 9}$

32. $\lim_{x \to -3} \dfrac{x^2 + x - 6}{x^2 + 2x - 3}$

33. $\lim_{x \to 1} \dfrac{x^3 - 1}{x - 1}$

34. $\lim_{x \to 1} \dfrac{x^4 - 1}{x - 1}$

35. $\lim_{x \to -1} \dfrac{(x + 1)^2}{x^2 - 1}$

36. $\lim_{x \to 2} \dfrac{x^3 - 8}{x^2 - 4}$

37. $\lim_{x \to 1} \dfrac{x^3 - x^2 + x - 1}{x^4 - x^3 + 2x - 2}$

38. $\lim_{x \to -1} \dfrac{x^3 + x^2 + 3x + 3}{x^4 + x^3 + 2x + 2}$

39. $\lim_{x \to 2} \dfrac{x^3 - 2x^2 + 4x - 8}{x^2 + x - 6}$

40. $\lim_{x \to 1} \dfrac{x^3 - x^2 + 3x - 3}{x^2 + 3x - 4}$

41. $\lim_{x \to -1} \dfrac{x^3 + 2x^2 + x}{x^4 + x^3 + 2x + 2}$

42. $\lim_{x \to 3} \dfrac{x^3 - 3x^2 + 4x - 12}{x^4 - 3x^3 + x - 3}$

In Problems 43–52, find the limit as x approaches c of the average rate of change of each function from c to x.

43. $c = 2$; $f(x) = 5x - 3$

44. $c = -2$; $f(x) = 4 - 3x$

45. $c = 3$; $f(x) = x^2$

46. $c = 3$; $f(x) = x^3$

47. $c = -1$; $f(x) = x^2 + 2x$

48. $c = -1$; $f(x) = 2x^2 - 3x$

49. $c = 0$; $f(x) = 3x^3 - 2x^2 + 4$

50. $c = 0$; $f(x) = 4x^3 - 5x + 8$

51. $c = 1$; $f(x) = \dfrac{1}{x}$

52. $c = 1$; $f(x) = \dfrac{1}{x^2}$

In Problems 53–56, use the properties of limits and the facts that

$$\lim_{x \to 0} \frac{\sin x}{x} = 1 \qquad \lim_{x \to 0} \frac{\cos x - 1}{x} = 0 \qquad \lim_{x \to 0} \sin x = 0 \qquad \lim_{x \to 0} \cos x = 1$$

where x is in radians, to find each limit.

53. $\lim_{x \to 0} \dfrac{\tan x}{x}$

54. $\lim_{x \to 0} \dfrac{\sin(2x)}{x}$

[Hint: Use a Double-angle Formula.]

55. $\lim_{x \to 0} \dfrac{3 \sin x + \cos x - 1}{4x}$

56. $\lim_{x \to 0} \dfrac{\sin^2 x + \sin x(\cos x - 1)}{x^2}$

14.3 One-sided Limits; Continuous Functions

PREPARING FOR THIS SECTION   *Before getting started, review the following:*

- Piecewise-defined Functions (Section 2.4, pp. 95–96)
- Library of Functions (Section 2.4, pp. 90–95)
- Polynomial Functions (Section 4.1, pp. 174–186)
- Properties of Rational Functions (Section 4.2, pp. 191–199)
- The Graph of a Rational Function (Section 4.3, pp. 202–209)

- Properties of the Exponential Function (Section 5.3, pp. 274 and 275)
- Properties of the Logarithmic Function (Section 5.4, p. 287)
- Properties of the Trigonometric Functions (Section 6.4, pp. 396 and 398, and Section 6.5, pp. 411–417)

Now Work the 'Are You Prepared?' problems on page 897.

OBJECTIVES   **1** Find the One-sided Limits of a Function (p. 892)
   2 Determine Whether a Function Is Continuous (p. 894)

1 Find the One-sided Limits of a Function

Earlier we described $\lim_{x \to c} f(x) = N$ by saying that as x gets closer to c, but remains unequal to c, the corresponding values of $f(x)$ get closer to N. Whether we use a numerical argument or the graph of the function f, the variable x can get closer to c in only two ways: either by approaching c from the left, through numbers less than c, or by approaching c from the right, through numbers greater than c.

If we only approach c from one side, we have a **one-sided limit.** The notation

$$\lim_{x \to c^-} f(x) = L$$

sometimes called the **left limit,** read as "the limit of $f(x)$ as x approaches c from the left equals L," may be described by the following statement:

As x gets closer to c, but remains less than c, the corresponding value of $f(x)$ gets closer to L.

In Words
$x \to c^-$ means x is approaching the value of c from the left, so $x < c$.

The notation $x \to c^-$ is used to remind us that x is less than c.

The notation

$$\lim_{x \to c^+} f(x) = R$$

sometimes called the **right limit,** read as "the limit of $f(x)$ as x approaches c from the right equals R," may be described by the following statement:

As x gets closer to c, but remains greater than c, the corresponding value of $f(x)$ gets closer to R.

The notation $x \to c^+$ is used to remind us that x is greater than c.

Figure 6 illustrates left and right limits.

Figure 6

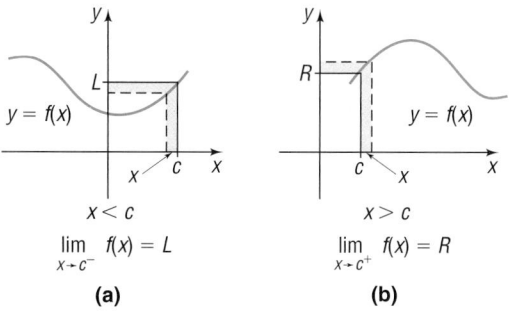

$$x < c$$
$$\lim_{x \to c^-} f(x) = L$$
(a)

$$x > c$$
$$\lim_{x \to c^+} f(x) = R$$
(b)

The left and right limits can be used to determine whether $\lim_{x \to c} f(x)$ exists. See Figure 7.

In Figure 7(a), $\lim_{x \to c} f(x)$ exists and equals the common value of the left limit and the right limit ($L = R$). In Figure 7(b), $\lim_{x \to c} f(x)$ does not exist because $L \neq R$.

Figure 7

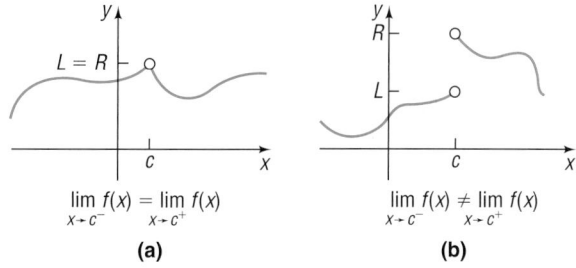

$$\lim_{x \to c^-} f(x) = \lim_{x \to c^+} f(x)$$
(a)

$$\lim_{x \to c^-} f(x) \neq \lim_{x \to c^+} f(x)$$
(b)

This leads us to the following result.

THEOREM

Suppose that $\lim_{x \to c^-} f(x) = L$ and $\lim_{x \to c^+} f(x) = R$. Then $\lim_{x \to c} f(x)$ exists if and only if $L = R$. Furthermore, if $L = R$, then $\lim_{x \to c} f(x) = L (= R)$.

Collectively, the left and right limits of a function are called **one-sided limits** of the function.

EXAMPLE 1   **Finding One-sided Limits of a Function**

For the function

$$f(x) = \begin{cases} 2x - 1 & \text{if } x < 2 \\ 1 & \text{if } x = 2 \\ x - 2 & \text{if } x > 2 \end{cases}$$

find: (a) $\lim_{x \to 2^-} f(x)$ (b) $\lim_{x \to 2^+} f(x)$ (c) $\lim_{x \to 2} f(x)$

Figure 8

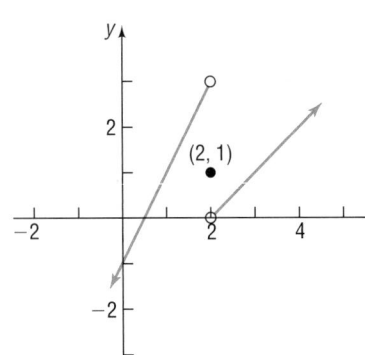

Solution   Figure 8 shows the graph of f.

(a) To find $\lim\limits_{x \to 2^-} f(x)$, we look at the values of f when x is close to 2, but less than 2. Since $f(x) = 2x - 1$ for such numbers, we conclude that

$$\lim_{x \to 2^-} f(x) = \lim_{x \to 2^-} (2x - 1) = 2(2) - 1 = 3$$

(b) To find $\lim\limits_{x \to 2^+} f(x)$, we look at the values of f when x is close to 2, but greater than 2. Since $f(x) = x - 2$ for such numbers, we conclude that

$$\lim_{x \to 2^+} f(x) = \lim_{x \to 2^+} (x - 2) = 2 - 2 = 0$$

(c) Since the left and right limits are unequal, $\lim\limits_{x \to 2} f(x)$ does not exist.

━━━━━ **Now Work** PROBLEMS 21 AND 35

2 Determine Whether a Function Is Continuous

We have observed that $f(c)$, the value of the function f at c, plays no role in determining the one-sided limits of f at c. What is the role of the value of a function at c and its one-sided limits at c? Let's look at some of the possibilities. See Figure 9.

Figure 9

Much earlier in this book, we said that a function f was *continuous* if its graph could be drawn without lifting pencil from paper. In looking at Figure 9, the only graph that has this characteristic is the graph in Figure 9(a), for which the one-sided limits at c each exist and are equal to the value of f at c. This leads us to the following definition.

DEFINITION

A function f is **continuous** at c if:

1. f is defined at c; that is, c is in the domain of f so that $f(c)$ equals a number.
2. $\lim\limits_{x \to c^-} f(x) = f(c)$
3. $\lim\limits_{x \to c^+} f(x) = f(c)$

In other words, a function f is continuous at c if

$$\lim_{x \to c} f(x) = f(c)$$

If f is not continuous at c, we say that f is **discontinuous at c.** Each function whose graph appears in Figures 9(b) to 9(f) is discontinuous at c.

Look again at formula (7) on page 888. Based on (7), we conclude that a polynomial function is continuous at every number.

Look at formula (10) on page 889. We conclude that a rational function is continuous at every number, except any at which it is not defined. At numbers where a rational function is not defined, either a hole appears in the graph or else an asymptote appears.

—————▶ **Now Work** PROBLEM 27

EXAMPLE 2	**Determining the Numbers at Which a Rational Function Is Continuous**

(a) Determine the numbers at which the rational function

$$R(x) = \frac{x-2}{x^2 - 6x + 8}$$

is continuous.

(b) Use limits to analyze the graph of R near 2 and near 4.

(c) Graph R.

Solution

(a) Since $R(x) = \dfrac{x-2}{(x-2)(x-4)}$, the domain of R is $\{x \mid x \neq 2, x \neq 4\}$.

Since R is a rational function, it is continuous at every number except 2 and 4. We conclude that R is discontinuous at both 2 and 4. (Condition 1 of the definition is violated.)

(b) To determine the behavior of the graph near 2 and near 4, we look at $\lim\limits_{x \to 2} R(x)$ and $\lim\limits_{x \to 4} R(x)$.

For $\lim\limits_{x \to 2} R(x)$, we have

$$\lim_{x \to 2} R(x) = \lim_{x \to 2} \frac{\cancel{x-2}}{\cancel{(x-2)}(x-4)} = \lim_{x \to 2} \frac{1}{x-4} = -\frac{1}{2}$$

As x gets closer to 2, the graph of R gets closer to $-\dfrac{1}{2}$. Since R is not defined at 2, the graph will have a hole at $\left(2, -\dfrac{1}{2}\right)$.

For $\lim\limits_{x \to 4} R(x)$, we have

$$\lim_{x \to 4} R(x) = \lim_{x \to 4} \frac{\cancel{x-2}}{\cancel{(x-2)}(x-4)} = \lim_{x \to 4} \frac{1}{x-4}$$

If $x < 4$ and x is getting closer to 4, the value of $\dfrac{1}{x-4}$ is negative and is becoming unbounded; that is, $\lim\limits_{x \to 4^-} R(x) = -\infty$.

If $x > 4$ and x is getting closer to 4, the value of $\dfrac{1}{x-4}$ is positive and is becoming unbounded; that is, $\lim\limits_{x \to 4^+} R(x) = \infty$.

Since $|R(x)| \to \infty$ for x close to 4, the graph of R will have a vertical asymptote at $x = 4$.

(c) It is easiest to graph R by observing that

$$\text{if } x \neq 2, \quad \text{then} \quad R(x) = \frac{\cancel{x-2}}{\cancel{(x-2)}(x-4)} = \frac{1}{x-4}$$

So the graph of R is the graph of $y = \dfrac{1}{x}$ shifted to the right 4 units with a hole at $\left(2, -\dfrac{1}{2}\right)$. See Figure 10.

Figure 10

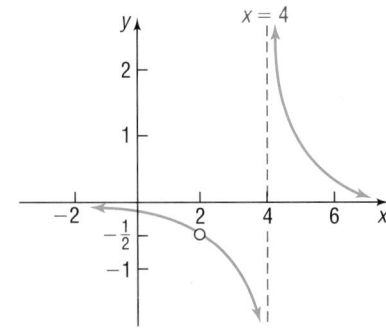

━━━ **Now Work** PROBLEM 73

The exponential, logarithmic, sine, and cosine functions are continuous at every number in their domain. The tangent, cotangent, secant, and cosecant functions are continuous except at numbers for which they are not defined, where asymptotes occur. The square root function and absolute value function are continuous at every number in their domain. The function $f(x) = \text{int}(x)$ is continuous except for $x =$ an integer, where a jump occurs in the graph.

Piecewise-defined functions require special attention.

| EXAMPLE 3 | **Determining Where a Piecewise-defined Function Is Continuous** |

Determine the numbers at which the following function is continuous.

$$f(x) = \begin{cases} x^2 & \text{if } x \le 0 \\ x + 1 & \text{if } 0 < x < 2 \\ 5 - x & \text{if } 2 \le x \le 5 \end{cases}$$

Solution   The "pieces" of f, that is, $y = x^2$, $y = x + 1$, and $y = 5 - x$, are each continuous for every number since they are polynomials. In other words, when we graph the pieces, we will not lift our pencil. When we graph the function f, however, we have to be careful, because the pieces change at $x = 0$ and at $x = 2$. So the numbers we need to investigate for f are $x = 0$ and $x = 2$.

$$\text{At } x = 0: \quad f(0) = 0^2 = 0$$

$$\lim_{x \to 0^-} f(x) = \lim_{x \to 0^-} x^2 = 0$$

$$\lim_{x \to 0^+} f(x) = \lim_{x \to 0^+} (x + 1) = 1$$

Since $\lim_{x \to 0^+} f(x) \ne f(0)$, we conclude that f is not continuous at $x = 0$.

$$\text{At } x = 2: \quad f(2) = 5 - 2 = 3$$

$$\lim_{x \to 2^-} f(x) = \lim_{x \to 2^-} (x + 1) = 3$$

$$\lim_{x \to 2^+} f(x) = \lim_{x \to 2^+} (5 - x) = 3$$

We conclude that f is continuous at $x = 2$.

The graph of f, given in Figure 11, demonstrates the conclusions drawn above.

Figure 11

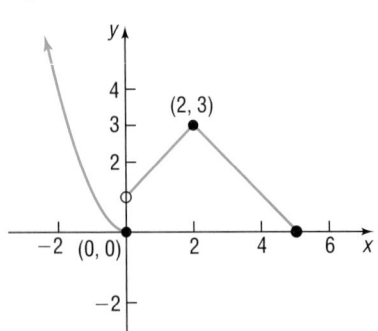

━━━ **Now Work** PROBLEMS 53 AND 61

SUMMARY   Library of Functions: Continuity Properties

Function	Domain	Property
Polynomial function	All real numbers	Continuous at every number in the domain
Rational function $R(x) = \dfrac{P(x)}{Q(x)}$, P, Q are polynomials	$\{x \mid Q(x) \neq 0\}$	Continuous at every number in the domain Hole or vertical asymptote where R is undefined
Exponential function	All real numbers	Continuous at every number in the domain
Logarithmic function	Positive real numbers	Continuous at every number in the domain
Sine and cosine functions	All real numbers	Continuous at every number in the domain
Tangent and secant functions	All real numbers, except odd integer multiples of $\dfrac{\pi}{2}$	Continuous at every number in the domain Vertical asymptotes at odd integer multiples of $\dfrac{\pi}{2}$
Cotangent and cosecant functions	All real numbers, except integer multiples of π	Continuous at every number in the domain Vertical asymptotes at integer multiples of π

14.3 Assess Your Understanding

'Are You Prepared?'   *Answers are given at the end of these exercises. If you get a wrong answer, read the pages listed in red.*

1. For the function $f(x) = \begin{cases} x^2 & \text{if } x \le 0 \\ x + 1 & \text{if } 0 < x < 2, \\ 5 - x & \text{if } 2 \le x \le 5 \end{cases}$ find $f(0)$ and $f(2)$. (pp. 95–96)

2. What are the domain and range of $f(x) = \ln x$? (p. 287)

3. **True or False** The exponential function $f(x) = e^x$ is increasing on the interval $(-\infty, \infty)$. (p. 274)

4. Name the trigonometric functions that have asymptotes. (pp. 411–417)

5. **True or False** Some rational functions have holes in their graph. (pp. 207–208)

6. **True or False** Every polynomial function has a graph that can be traced without lifting pencil from paper. (p. 175)

Concepts and Vocabulary

7. If we only approach c from one side, then we have a(n) _____ limit.

8. The notation _____ is used to describe the fact that as x gets closer to c, but remains greater than c, the value of $f(x)$ gets closer to R.

9. If $\lim\limits_{x \to c} f(x) = f(c)$, then f is _____ at _____.

10. **True or False** For any function f, $\lim\limits_{x \to c^-} f(x) = \lim\limits_{x \to c^+} f(x)$.

11. **True or False** If f is continuous at c, then $\lim\limits_{x \to c^+} f(x) = f(c)$.

12. **True or False** Every polynomial function is continuous at every real number.

Skill Building

In Problems 13–32, use the accompanying graph of $y = f(x)$.

13. What is the domain of f?

14. What is the range of f?

15. Find the x-intercept(s), if any, of f.

16. Find the y-intercept(s), if any, of f.

17. Find $f(-8)$ and $f(-4)$.

18. Find $f(2)$ and $f(6)$.

19. Find $\lim\limits_{x \to -6^-} f(x)$.

20. Find $\lim\limits_{x \to -6^+} f(x)$.

21. Find $\lim\limits_{x \to -4^-} f(x)$.

22. Find $\lim\limits_{x \to -4^+} f(x)$.

23. Find $\lim\limits_{x \to 2^-} f(x)$.

24. Find $\lim\limits_{x \to 2^+} f(x)$.

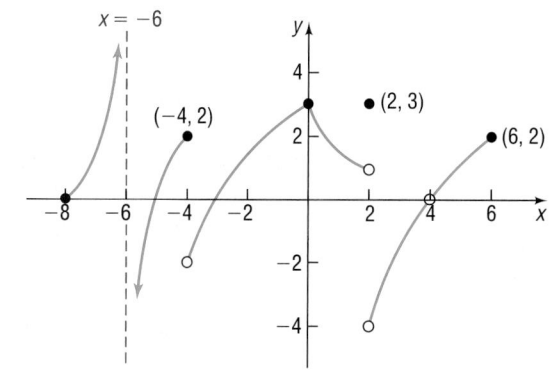

25. Does $\lim\limits_{x \to 4} f(x)$ exist? If it does, what is it?

26. Does $\lim\limits_{x \to 0} f(x)$ exist? If it does, what is it?

27. Is f continuous at -6?

28. Is f continuous at -4?

29. Is f continuous at 0?

30. Is f continuous at 2?

31. Is f continuous at 4?

32. Is f continuous at 5?

In Problems 33–44, find the one-sided limit.

33. $\lim\limits_{x \to 1^+} (2x + 3)$

34. $\lim\limits_{x \to 2^-} (4 - 2x)$

35. $\lim\limits_{x \to 1^-} (2x^3 + 5x)$

36. $\lim\limits_{x \to -2^+} (3x^2 - 8)$

37. $\lim\limits_{x \to \pi/2^+} \sin x$

38. $\lim\limits_{x \to \pi^-} (3 \cos x)$

39. $\lim\limits_{x \to 2^+} \dfrac{x^2 - 4}{x - 2}$

40. $\lim\limits_{x \to 1^-} \dfrac{x^3 - x}{x - 1}$

41. $\lim\limits_{x \to -1^-} \dfrac{x^2 - 1}{x^3 + 1}$

42. $\lim\limits_{x \to 0^+} \dfrac{x^3 - x^2}{x^4 + x^2}$

43. $\lim\limits_{x \to -2^+} \dfrac{x^2 + x - 2}{x^2 + 2x}$

44. $\lim\limits_{x \to -4^-} \dfrac{x^2 + x - 12}{x^2 + 4x}$

In Problems 45–60, determine whether f is continuous at c.

45. $f(x) = x^3 - 3x^2 + 2x - 6 \quad c = 2$

46. $f(x) = 3x^2 - 6x + 5 \quad c = -3$

47. $f(x) = \dfrac{x^2 + 5}{x - 6} \quad c = 3$

48. $f(x) = \dfrac{x^3 - 8}{x^2 + 4} \quad c = 2$

49. $f(x) = \dfrac{x + 3}{x - 3} \quad c = 3$

50. $f(x) = \dfrac{x - 6}{x + 6} \quad c = -6$

51. $f(x) = \dfrac{x^3 + 3x}{x^2 - 3x} \quad c = 0$

52. $f(x) = \dfrac{x^2 - 6x}{x^2 + 6x} \quad c = 0$

53. $f(x) = \begin{cases} \dfrac{x^3 + 3x}{x^2 - 3x} & \text{if } x \neq 0 \\ 1 & \text{if } x = 0 \end{cases} \quad c = 0$

54. $f(x) = \begin{cases} \dfrac{x^2 - 6x}{x^2 + 6x} & \text{if } x \neq 0 \\ -2 & \text{if } x = 0 \end{cases} \quad c = 0$

55. $f(x) = \begin{cases} \dfrac{x^3 + 3x}{x^2 - 3x} & \text{if } x \neq 0 \\ -1 & \text{if } x = 0 \end{cases} \quad c = 0$

56. $f(x) = \begin{cases} \dfrac{x^2 - 6x}{x^2 + 6x} & \text{if } x \neq 0 \\ -1 & \text{if } x = 0 \end{cases} \quad c = 0$

57. $f(x) = \begin{cases} \dfrac{x^3 - 1}{x^2 - 1} & \text{if } x < 1 \\ 2 & \text{if } x = 1 \\ \dfrac{3}{x + 1} & \text{if } x > 1 \end{cases} \quad c = 1$

58. $f(x) = \begin{cases} \dfrac{x^2 - 2x}{x - 2} & \text{if } x < 2 \\ 2 & \text{if } x = 2 \\ \dfrac{x - 4}{x - 1} & \text{if } x > 2 \end{cases} \quad c = 2$

59. $f(x) = \begin{cases} 2e^x & \text{if } x < 0 \\ 2 & \text{if } x = 0 \\ \dfrac{x^3 + 2x^2}{x^2} & \text{if } x > 0 \end{cases} \quad c = 0$

60. $f(x) = \begin{cases} 3 \cos x & \text{if } x < 0 \\ 3 & \text{if } x = 0 \\ \dfrac{x^3 + 3x^2}{x^2} & \text{if } x > 0 \end{cases} \quad c = 0$

In Problems 61–72, find the numbers at which f is continuous. At which numbers is f discontinuous?

61. $f(x) = 2x + 3$

62. $f(x) = 4 - 3x$

63. $f(x) = 3x^2 + x$

64. $f(x) = -3x^3 + 7$

65. $f(x) = 4 \sin x$

66. $f(x) = -2 \cos x$

67. $f(x) = 2 \tan x$

68. $f(x) = 4 \csc x$

69. $f(x) = \dfrac{2x + 5}{x^2 - 4}$

70. $f(x) = \dfrac{x^2 - 4}{x^2 - 9}$

71. $f(x) = \dfrac{x - 3}{\ln x}$

72. $f(x) = \dfrac{\ln x}{x - 3}$

In Problems 73–76, discuss whether R is continuous at c. Use limits to analyze the graph of R at c. Graph R.

73. $R(x) = \dfrac{x - 1}{x^2 - 1} \quad c = -1 \text{ and } c = 1$

74. $R(x) = \dfrac{3x + 6}{x^2 - 4} \quad c = -2 \text{ and } c = 2$

75. $R(x) = \dfrac{x^2 + x}{x^2 - 1} \quad c = -1 \text{ and } c = 1$

76. $R(x) = \dfrac{x^2 + 4x}{x^2 - 16} \quad c = -4 \text{ and } c = 4$

In Problems 77–82, (a) determine where each rational function is undefined. Determine whether an asymptote or a hole appears at such numbers. (b) Graph the function using a graphing utility and verify the solution found in part (a).

77. $R(x) = \dfrac{x^3 - x^2 + x - 1}{x^4 - x^3 + 2x - 2}$

78. $R(x) = \dfrac{x^3 + x^2 + 3x + 3}{x^4 + x^3 + 2x + 2}$

79. $R(x) = \dfrac{x^3 - 2x^2 + 4x - 8}{x^2 + x - 6}$

80. $R(x) = \dfrac{x^3 - x^2 + 3x - 3}{x^2 + 3x - 4}$

81. $R(x) = \dfrac{x^3 + 2x^2 + x}{x^4 + x^3 + 2x + 2}$

82. $R(x) = \dfrac{x^3 - 3x^2 + 4x - 12}{x^4 - 3x^3 + x - 3}$

Discussion and Writing

83. Name three functions that are continuous at every real number.

84. Create a function that is not continuous at the number 5.

'Are You Prepared?' Answers

1. $f(0) = 0; f(2) = 3$

2. Domain: $\{x \mid x > 0\}$; range $\{y \mid -\infty < y < \infty\}$

3. True

4. Secant, cosecant, tangent, cotangent

5. True

6. True

14.4 The Tangent Problem; The Derivative

PREPARING FOR THIS SECTION *Before getting started, review the following:*

- Point–Slope Form of a Line (Section 1.4, p. 33)
- Average Rate of Change (Section 2.3, pp. 84–86)

Now Work the 'Are You Prepared?' problems on page 905.

OBJECTIVES **1** Find an Equation of the Tangent Line to the Graph of a Function (p. 900)
2 Find the Derivative of a Function (p. 901)
3 Find Instantaneous Rates of Change (p. 902)
4 Find the Instantaneous Speed of a Particle (p. 903)

The Tangent Problem

One question that motivated the development of calculus was a geometry problem, the **tangent problem.** This problem asks, "What is the slope of the tangent line to the graph of a function $y = f(x)$ at a point P on its graph?" See Figure 12.

We first need to define what we mean by a *tangent* line. In high school geometry, the tangent line to a circle is defined as the line that intersects the circle at exactly one point. Look at Figure 13. Notice that the tangent line just touches the graph of the circle at P.

Figure 12

Figure 13

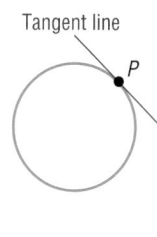

This definition, however, does not work in general. Look at Figure 14. The lines L_1 and L_2 only intersect the graph in one point P, but neither touches the graph at P. Additionally, the tangent line L_T shown in Figure 15 touches the graph of f at P, but also intersects the graph elsewhere. So how should we define the tangent line to the graph of f at a point P?

Figure 14

Figure 15

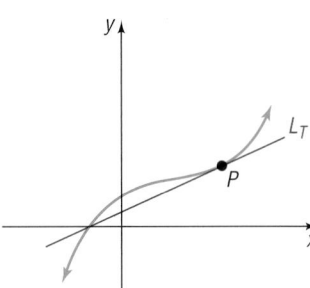

1 Find an Equation of the Tangent Line to the Graph of a Function

The tangent line L_T to the graph of a function $y = f(x)$ at a point P necessarily contains the point P. To find an equation for L_T using the point–slope form of the equation of a line, we need to find the slope m_{tan} of the tangent line.

Suppose that the coordinates of the point P are $(c, f(c))$. Locate another point $Q = (x, f(x))$ on the graph of f. The line containing P and Q is a secant line. (Refer to Section 2.3.) The slope m_{sec} of the secant line is

Figure 16

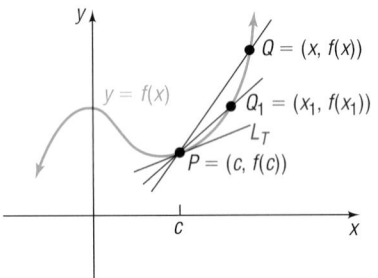

$$m_{\text{sec}} = \frac{f(x) - f(c)}{x - c}$$

Now look at Figure 16.

As we move along the graph of f from Q toward P, we obtain a succession of secant lines. The closer we get to P, the closer the secant line is to the tangent line L_T. The limiting position of these secant lines is the tangent line L_T. Therefore, the limiting value of the slopes of these secant lines equals the slope of the tangent line. But, as we move from Q toward P, the values of x get closer to c. Therefore,

$$m_{\text{tan}} = \lim_{x \to c} m_{\text{sec}} = \lim_{x \to c} \frac{f(x) - f(c)}{x - c}$$

DEFINITION

The **tangent line** to the graph of a function $y = f(x)$ at a point $P = (c, f(c))$ on its graph is defined as the line containing the point P whose slope is

$$m_{\text{tan}} = \lim_{x \to c} \frac{f(x) - f(c)}{x - c} \tag{1}$$

provided that this limit exists.

THEOREM

If m_{tan} exists, an equation of the tangent line is

$$y - f(c) = m_{\text{tan}}(x - c) \tag{2}$$

| EXAMPLE 1 | Finding an Equation of the Tangent Line |

Find an equation of the tangent line to the graph of $f(x) = \dfrac{x^2}{4}$ at the point $\left(1, \dfrac{1}{4}\right)$. Graph f and the tangent line.

Solution The tangent line contains the point $\left(1, \dfrac{1}{4}\right)$. The slope of the tangent line to the graph of $f(x) = \dfrac{x^2}{4}$ at $\left(1, \dfrac{1}{4}\right)$ is

$$m_{\tan} = \lim_{x \to 1} \frac{f(x) - f(1)}{x - 1} = \lim_{x \to 1} \frac{\dfrac{x^2}{4} - \dfrac{1}{4}}{x - 1} = \lim_{x \to 1} \frac{(x - 1)(x + 1)}{4(x - 1)}$$

$$= \lim_{x \to 1} \frac{x + 1}{4} = \frac{1}{2}$$

Figure 17

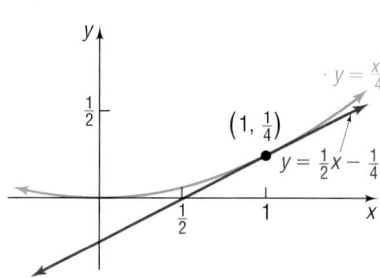

An equation of the tangent line is

$$y - \frac{1}{4} = \frac{1}{2}(x - 1) \qquad y - f(c) = m_{\tan}(x - c)$$

$$y = \frac{1}{2}x - \frac{1}{4}$$

Figure 17 shows the graph of $y = \dfrac{x^2}{4}$ and the tangent line at $\left(1, \dfrac{1}{4}\right)$.

─── **Now Work** PROBLEM 11

2 Find the Derivative of a Function

The limit in formula (1) has an important generalization: it is called the *derivative of f at c*.

DEFINITION

Let $y = f(x)$ denote a function f. If c is a number in the domain of f, the **derivative of f at c,** denoted by $f'(c)$, read "f prime of c," is defined as

$$f'(c) = \lim_{x \to c} \frac{f(x) - f(c)}{x - c} \tag{3}$$

provided that this limit exists.

| EXAMPLE 2 | Finding the Derivative of a Function |

Find the derivative of $f(x) = 2x^2 - 5x$ at 2. That is, find $f'(2)$.

Solution Since $f(2) = 2(4) - 5(2) = -2$, we have

$$\frac{f(x) - f(2)}{x - 2} = \frac{(2x^2 - 5x) - (-2)}{x - 2} = \frac{2x^2 - 5x + 2}{x - 2} = \frac{(2x - 1)(x - 2)}{x - 2}$$

The derivative of f at 2 is

$$f'(2) = \lim_{x \to 2} \frac{f(x) - f(2)}{x - 2} = \lim_{x \to 2} \frac{(2x - 1)(x - 2)}{x - 2} = 3$$

─── **Now Work** PROBLEM 21

Example 2 provides a way of finding the derivative at 2 analytically. Graphing utilities have built-in procedures to approximate the derivative of a function at any number c. Consult your owner's manual for the appropriate keystrokes.

EXAMPLE 3	Finding the Derivative of a Function Using a Graphing Utility

Use a graphing utility to find the derivative of $f(x) = 2x^2 - 5x$ at 2. That is, find $f'(2)$.

Solution   Figure 18 shows the solution using a TI-84 Plus graphing calculator. As shown, $f'(2) = 3$.

Figure 18

```
nDeriv(2X²-5X,X,
2)
                    3
```

━━━ **Now Work**   PROBLEM 33

EXAMPLE 4	Finding the Derivative of a Function

Find the derivative of $f(x) = x^2$ at c. That is, find $f'(c)$.

Solution   Since $f(c) = c^2$, we have

$$\frac{f(x) - f(c)}{x - c} = \frac{x^2 - c^2}{x - c} = \frac{(x + c)(x - c)}{x - c}$$

The derivative of f at c is

$$f'(c) = \lim_{x \to c} \frac{f(x) - f(c)}{x - c} = \lim_{x \to c} \frac{(x + c)(x - c)}{x - c} = 2c$$

As Example 4 illustrates, the derivative of $f(x) = x^2$ exists and equals $2c$ for any number c. In other words, the derivative is itself a function and, using x for the independent variable, we can write $f'(x) = 2x$. The function f' is called the **derivative function of f** or the **derivative of f.** We also say that f is **differentiable.** The instruction "differentiate f" means "find the derivative of f."

3 Find Instantaneous Rates of Change

The average rate of change of a function f from c to x is

$$\frac{\Delta y}{\Delta x} = \frac{f(x) - f(c)}{x - c}$$

The limit as x approaches c of the average rate of change of f, based on formula (3), is the derivative of f at c.

DEFINITION   The derivative of f at c is also called the **instantaneous rate of change of f with respect to x at c.** That is,

$$\left(\begin{array}{c} \text{Instantaneous rate of} \\ \text{change of } f \text{ with respect to } x \text{ at } c \end{array} \right) = f'(c) = \lim_{x \to c} \frac{f(x) - f(c)}{x - c} \qquad \textbf{(4)}$$

EXAMPLE 5	Finding the Instantaneous Rate of Change

The volume V of a right circular cone of height $h = 6$ feet and radius r feet is $V = V(r) = \frac{1}{3}\pi r^2 h = 2\pi r^2$. If r is changing, find the instantaneous rate of change of the volume V with respect to the radius r at $r = 3$.

Solution   The instantaneous rate of change of V with respect to r at $r = 3$ is the derivative $V'(3)$.

$$V'(3) = \lim_{r \to 3} \frac{V(r) - V(3)}{r - 3} = \lim_{r \to 3} \frac{2\pi r^2 - 18\pi}{r - 3} = \lim_{r \to 3} \frac{2\pi(r^2 - 9)}{r - 3}$$

$$= \lim_{r \to 3}[2\pi(r + 3)] = 12\pi$$

At the instant $r = 3$ feet, the volume of the cone is increasing with respect to r at a rate of $12\pi \approx 37.699$ cubic feet per 1-foot change in the radius.

■

 Now Work   PROBLEM 43

4 Find the Instantaneous Speed of a Particle

If $s = f(t)$ denotes the position of a particle at time t, the average speed of the particle from c to t is

$$\frac{\text{Change in position}}{\text{Change in time}} = \frac{\Delta s}{\Delta t} = \frac{f(t) - f(c)}{t - c} \tag{5}$$

DEFINITION   The limit as t approaches c of the expression in formula (5) is the **instantaneous speed of the particle at c** or the **velocity of the particle at c.** That is,

$$\left(\begin{array}{c}\text{Instantaneous speed of}\\ \text{a particle at time } c\end{array}\right) = f'(c) = \lim_{t \to c} \frac{f(t) - f(c)}{t - c} \tag{6}$$

EXAMPLE 6   **Finding the Instantaneous Speed of a Particle**

In physics it is shown that the height s of a ball thrown straight up with an initial speed of 80 feet per second (ft/sec) from a rooftop 96 feet high is

$$s = s(t) = -16t^2 + 80t + 96$$

Figure 19

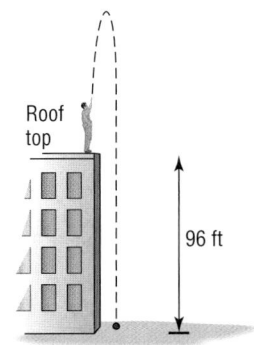

Roof top

96 ft

where t is the elapsed time that the ball is in the air. The ball misses the rooftop on its way down and eventually strikes the ground. See Figure 19.

(a) When does the ball strike the ground? That is, how long is the ball in the air?
(b) At what time t will the ball pass the rooftop on its way down?
(c) What is the average speed of the ball from $t = 0$ to $t = 2$?
(d) What is the instantaneous speed of the ball at time t_0?
(e) What is the instantaneous speed of the ball at $t = 2$?
(f) When is the instantaneous speed of the ball equal to zero?
(g) What is the instantaneous speed of the ball as it passes the rooftop on the way down?
(h) What is the instantaneous speed of the ball when it strikes the ground?

Solution   (a) The ball strikes the ground when $s = s(t) = 0$.

$$-16t^2 + 80t + 96 = 0$$
$$t^2 - 5t - 6 = 0$$
$$(t - 6)(t + 1) = 0$$
$$t = 6 \quad \text{or} \quad t = -1$$

We discard the solution $t = -1$. The ball strikes the ground after 6 sec.

(b) The ball passes the rooftop when $s = s(t) = 96$.

$$-16t^2 + 80t + 96 = 96$$
$$t^2 - 5t = 0$$
$$t(t - 5) = 0$$
$$t = 0 \quad \text{or} \quad t = 5$$

We discard the solution $t = 0$. The ball passes the rooftop on the way down after 5 sec.

(c) The average speed of the ball from $t = 0$ to $t = 2$ is

$$\frac{\Delta s}{\Delta t} = \frac{s(2) - s(0)}{2 - 0} = \frac{192 - 96}{2} = 48 \text{ ft/sec}$$

(d) The instantaneous speed of the ball at time t_0 is the derivative $s'(t_0)$; that is,

$$s'(t_0) = \lim_{t \to t_0} \frac{s(t) - s(t_0)}{t - t_0}$$

$$= \lim_{t \to t_0} \frac{(-16t^2 + 80t + 96) - (-16t_0^2 + 80t_0 + 96)}{t - t_0}$$

$$= \lim_{t \to t_0} \frac{-16[t^2 - t_0^2 - 5t + 5t_0]}{t - t_0}$$

$$= \lim_{t \to t_0} \frac{-16[(t + t_0)(t - t_0) - 5(t - t_0)]}{t - t_0}$$

$$= \lim_{t \to t_0} \frac{-16[(t + t_0 - 5)(t - t_0)]}{t - t_0} = \lim_{t \to t_0} [-16(t + t_0 - 5)]$$

$$= -16(2t_0 - 5) \text{ ft/sec}$$

Replace t_0 by t. The instantaneous speed of the ball at time t is

$$s'(t) = -16(2t - 5) \text{ ft/sec}$$

(e) At $t = 2$ sec, the instantaneous speed of the ball is

$$s'(2) = -16(-1) = 16 \text{ ft/sec}$$

(f) The instantaneous speed of the ball is zero when

$$s'(t) = 0$$
$$-16(2t - 5) = 0$$
$$t = \frac{5}{2} = 2.5 \text{ sec}$$

(g) The ball passes the rooftop on the way down when $t = 5$. The instantaneous speed at $t = 5$ is

$$s'(5) = -16(10 - 5) = -80 \text{ ft/sec}$$

At $t = 5$ sec, the ball is traveling -80 ft/sec. When the instantaneous rate of change is negative, it means that the direction of the object is downward. The ball is traveling 80 ft/sec in the downward direction when $t = 5$ sec.

(h) The ball strikes the ground when $t = 6$. The instantaneous speed when $t = 6$ is

$$s'(6) = -16(12 - 5) = -112 \text{ ft/sec}$$

The speed of the ball at $t = 6$ sec is -112 ft/sec. Again, the negative value implies that the ball is traveling downward.

Exploration

Determine the vertex of the quadratic function given in Example 6. What do you conclude about the velocity when $s(t)$ is a maximum?

SUMMARY

The derivative of a function $y = f(x)$ at c is defined as

$$f'(c) = \lim_{x \to c} \frac{f(x) - f(c)}{x - c}$$

In geometry, $f'(c)$ equals the slope of the tangent line to the graph of f at the point $(c, f(c))$.

In physics, $f'(c)$ equals the instantaneous speed (velocity) of a particle at time c, where $s = f(t)$ is the position of the particle at time t.

In applications, if two variables are related by the function $y = f(x)$, then $f'(c)$ equals the instantaneous rate of change of f with respect to x at c.

14.4 Assess Your Understanding

'Are You Prepared?'   *Answers are given at the end of these exercises. If you get a wrong answer, read the pages listed in red.*

1. Find an equation of the line with slope 5 containing the point $(2, -4)$. (p. 33)

2. *True or False*   The average rate of change of a function f from a to b is
$$\frac{f(b) + f(a)}{b + a} \quad \text{(p. 84)}$$

Concepts and Vocabulary

3. If $\lim\limits_{x \to c} \dfrac{f(x) - f(c)}{x - c}$ exists, it equals the slope of the _____ _____ to the graph of f at the point $(c, f(c))$.

4. If $\lim\limits_{x \to c} \dfrac{f(x) - f(c)}{x - c}$ exists, it is called the _____ of f at c.

5. If $s = f(t)$ denotes the position of a particle at time t, the derivative $f'(c)$ is the _____ of the particle at c.

6. *True or False*   The tangent line to a function is the limiting position of a secant line.

7. *True or False*   The slope of the tangent line to the graph of f at $(c, f(c))$ is the derivative of f at c.

8. *True or False*   The velocity of a particle whose position at time t is $s(t)$ is the derivative $s'(t)$.

Skill Building

In Problems 9–20, find the slope of the tangent line to the graph of f at the given point. Graph f and the tangent line.

9. $f(x) = 3x + 5$ at $(1, 8)$
10. $f(x) = -2x + 1$ at $(-1, 3)$
11. $f(x) = x^2 + 2$ at $(-1, 3)$
12. $f(x) = 3 - x^2$ at $(1, 2)$
13. $f(x) = 3x^2$ at $(2, 12)$
14. $f(x) = -4x^2$ at $(-2, -16)$
15. $f(x) = 2x^2 + x$ at $(1, 3)$
16. $f(x) = 3x^2 - x$ at $(0, 0)$
17. $f(x) = x^2 - 2x + 3$ at $(-1, 6)$
18. $f(x) = -2x^2 + x - 3$ at $(1, -4)$
19. $f(x) = x^3 + x$ at $(2, 10)$
20. $f(x) = x^3 - x^2$ at $(1, 0)$

In Problems 21–32, find the derivative of each function at the given number.

21. $f(x) = -4x + 5$ at 3
22. $f(x) = -4 + 3x$ at 1
23. $f(x) = x^2 - 3$ at 0
24. $f(x) = 2x^2 + 1$ at -1
25. $f(x) = 2x^2 + 3x$ at 1
26. $f(x) = 3x^2 - 4x$ at 2
27. $f(x) = x^3 + 4x$ at -1
28. $f(x) = 2x^3 - x^2$ at 2
29. $f(x) = x^3 + x^2 - 2x$ at 1
30. $f(x) = x^3 - 2x^2 + x$ at -1
31. $f(x) = \sin x$ at 0
32. $f(x) = \cos x$ at 0

In Problems 33–42, use a graphing utility to find the derivative of each function at the given number.

33. $f(x) = 3x^3 - 6x^2 + 2$ at -2
34. $f(x) = -5x^4 + 6x^2 - 10$ at 5

35. $f(x) = \dfrac{-x^3 + 1}{x^2 + 5x + 7}$ at 8
36. $f(x) = \dfrac{-5x^4 + 9x + 3}{x^3 + 5x^2 - 6}$ at -3

37. $f(x) = x \sin x$ at $\dfrac{\pi}{3}$
38. $f(x) = x \sin x$ at $\dfrac{\pi}{4}$
39. $f(x) = x^2 \sin x$ at $\dfrac{\pi}{3}$

40. $f(x) = x^2 \sin x$ at $\dfrac{\pi}{4}$
41. $f(x) = e^x \sin x$ at 2
42. $f(x) = e^{-x} \sin x$ at 2

Applications and Extensions

43. Instantaneous Rate of Change The volume V of a right circular cylinder of height 3 feet and radius r feet is $V = V(r) = 3\pi r^2$. Find the instantaneous rate of change of the volume with respect to the radius r at $r = 3$.

44. Instantaneous Rate of Change The surface area S of a sphere of radius r feet is $S = S(r) = 4\pi r^2$. Find the instantaneous rate of change of the surface area with respect to the radius r at $r = 2$.

45. Instantaneous Rate of Change The volume V of a sphere of radius r feet is $V = V(r) = \frac{4}{3}\pi r^3$. Find the instantaneous rate of change of the volume with respect to the radius r at $r = 2$.

46. Instantaneous Rate of Change The volume V of a cube of side x meters is $V = V(x) = x^3$. Find the instantaneous rate of change of the volume with respect to the side x at $x = 3$.

47. Instantaneous Speed of a Ball In physics it is shown that the height s of a ball thrown straight up with an initial speed of 96 ft/sec from ground level is

$$s = s(t) = -16t^2 + 96t$$

where t is the elapsed time that the ball is in the air.
(a) When does the ball strike the ground? That is, how long is the ball in the air?
(b) What is the average speed of the ball from $t = 0$ to $t = 2$?
(c) What is the instantaneous speed of the ball at time t?
(d) What is the instantaneous speed of the ball at $t = 2$?
(e) When is the instantaneous speed of the ball equal to zero?
(f) How high is the ball when its instantaneous speed equals zero?
(g) What is the instantaneous speed of the ball when it strikes the ground?

48. Instantaneous Speed of a Ball In physics it is shown that the height s of a ball thrown straight down with an initial speed of 48 ft/sec from a rooftop 160 feet high is

$$s = s(t) = -16t^2 - 48t + 160$$

where t is the elapsed time that the ball is in the air.
(a) When does the ball strike the ground? That is, how long is the ball in the air?
(b) What is the average speed of the ball from $t = 0$ to $t = 1$?
(c) What is the instantaneous speed of the ball at time t?
(d) What is the instantaneous speed of the ball at $t = 1$?
(e) What is the instantaneous speed of the ball when it strikes the ground?

49. Instantaneous Speed on the Moon Neil Armstrong throws a ball down into a crater on the moon. The height s (in feet)

of the ball from the bottom of the crater after t seconds is given in the following table:

Time, t (in Seconds)	Distance, s (in Feet)
0	1000
1	987
2	969
3	945
4	917
5	883
6	843
7	800
8	749

(a) Find the average speed from $t = 1$ to $t = 4$ seconds.
(b) Find the average speed from $t = 1$ to $t = 3$ seconds.
(c) Find the average speed from $t = 1$ to $t = 2$ seconds.
(d) Using a graphing utility, find the quadratic function of best fit.
(e) Using the function found in part (d), determine the instantaneous speed at $t = 1$ second.

50. Instantaneous Rate of Change The following data represent the total revenue R (in dollars) received from selling x bicycles at Tunney's Bicycle Shop.

Number of Bicycles, x	Total Revenue, R (in Dollars)
0	0
25	28,000
60	45,000
102	53,400
150	59,160
190	62,360
223	64,835
249	66,525

(a) Find the average rate of change in revenue from $x = 25$ to $x = 150$ bicycles.
(b) Find the average rate of change in revenue from $x = 25$ to $x = 102$ bicycles.
(c) Find the average rate of change in revenue from $x = 25$ to $x = 60$ bicycles.
(d) Using a graphing utility, find the quadratic function of best fit.
(e) Using the function found in part (d), determine the instantaneous rate of change of revenue at $x = 25$ bicycles.

'Are You Prepared?' Answers

1. $y = 5x - 14$ **2.** False

14.5 The Area Problem; The Integral

PREPARING FOR THIS SECTION *Before getting started, review the following:*

- Geometry Formulas (Appendix A, Section A.2, pp. A15–A16)

- Summation Notation (Section 12.1, pp. 808–811)

Now Work the 'Are You Prepared?' problems on page 912.

OBJECTIVES 1 Approximate the Area Under the Graph of a Function (p. 907)

2 Approximate Integrals Using a Graphing Utility (p. 911)

The Area Problem

The development of the integral, like that of the derivative, was originally motivated to a large extent by a problem in geometry: the *area problem*.

Figure 20

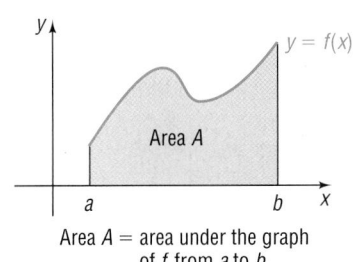

Area A = area under the graph of f from a to b

Area Problem

Suppose that $y = f(x)$ is a function whose domain is a closed interval $[a, b]$. We assume that $f(x) \geq 0$ for all x in $[a, b]$. Find the area enclosed by the graph of f, the x-axis, and the vertical lines $x = a$ and $x = b$.

Figure 20 illustrates the area problem. We refer to the area A shown in Figure 20 as **the area under the graph of f from a to b.**

For a constant function $f(x) = k$ and for a linear function $f(x) = mx + B$, we can solve the area problem using formulas from geometry. See Figures 21(a) and (b).

Figure 21

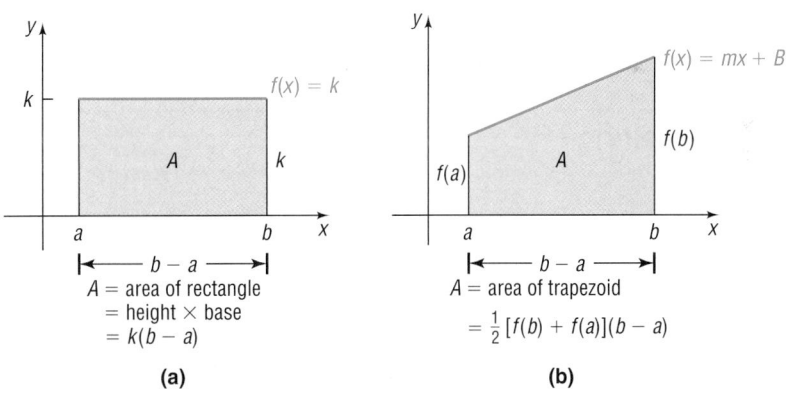

(a)

(b)

For most other functions, no formulas from geometry are available.

We begin by discussing a way to approximate the area under the graph of a function f from a to b.

1 Approximate the Area Under the Graph of a Function

We use rectangles to approximate the area under the graph of a function f. We do this by *partitioning* or dividing the interval $[a, b]$ into subintervals of equal length. On each subinterval, we form a rectangle whose base is the length of the subinterval and whose height is $f(u)$ for some number u in the subinterval. Look at Figure 22.

In Figure 22(a), the interval $[a, b]$ is partitioned into two subintervals, each of length $\dfrac{b - a}{2}$, and the number u is chosen as the left endpoint of each subinterval.

Figure 22

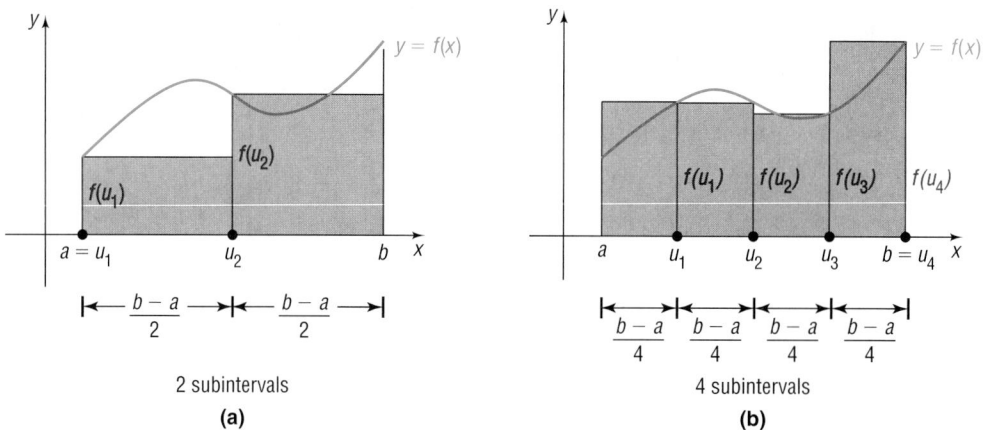

(a) 2 subintervals

(b) 4 subintervals

In Figure 22(b), the interval $[a, b]$ is partitioned into four subintervals, each of length $\dfrac{b-a}{4}$, and the number u is chosen as the right endpoint of each subinterval.

We approximate the area A under f from a to b by adding the areas of the rectangles formed by the partition.

Using Figure 22(a),

$$\text{Area } A \approx \text{area of first rectangle} + \text{area of second rectangle}$$

$$= f(u_1)\frac{b-a}{2} + f(u_2)\frac{b-a}{2}$$

Using Figure 22(b),

$$\text{Area } A \approx \text{area of first rectangle} + \text{area of second rectangle}$$

$$+ \text{area of third rectangle} + \text{area of fourth rectangle}$$

$$= f(u_1)\frac{b-a}{4} + f(u_2)\frac{b-a}{4} + f(u_3)\frac{b-a}{4} + f(u_4)\frac{b-a}{4}$$

In approximating the area under the graph of a function f from a to b, the choice of the number u in each subinterval is arbitrary. For convenience, we shall always pick u as either the left endpoint of each subinterval or the right endpoint. The choice of how many subintervals to use is also arbitrary. In general, the more subintervals used, the better the approximation will be. Let's look at a specific example.

EXAMPLE 1 **Approximating the Area under the Graph of $f(x) = 2x$ from 0 to 1**

Approximate the area A under the graph of $f(x) = 2x$ from 0 to 1 as follows:

(a) Partition $[0, 1]$ into two subintervals of equal length and choose u as the left endpoint.

(b) Partition $[0, 1]$ into two subintervals of equal length and choose u as the right endpoint.

(c) Partition $[0, 1]$ into four subintervals of equal length and choose u as the left endpoint.

(d) Partition $[0, 1]$ into four subintervals of equal length and choose u as the right endpoint.

(e) Compare the approximations found in parts (a)–(d) with the actual area.

Figure 23

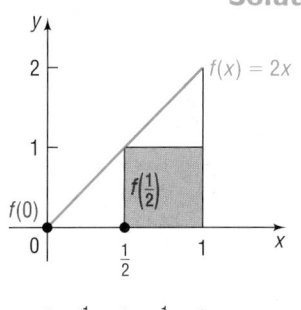

2 subintervals; u's are left endpoints

(a)

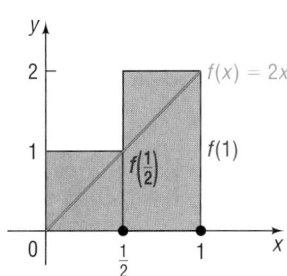

2 subintervals; u's are right endpoints

(b)

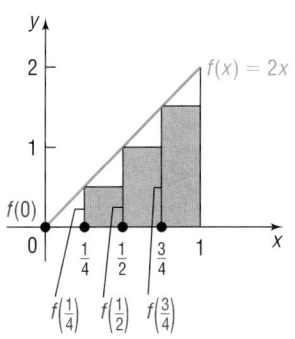

4 subintervals; u's are left endpoints

(c)

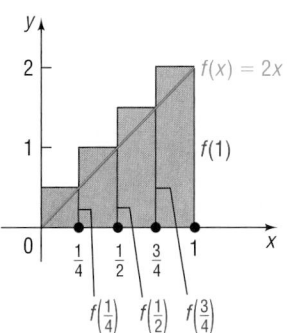

4 subintervals; u's are right endpoints

(d)

Solution

(a) We partition $[0, 1]$ into two subintervals, each of length $\frac{1}{2}$, and choose u as the left endpoint. See Figure 23(a). The area A is approximated as

$$A \approx f(0)\left(\frac{1}{2}\right) + f\left(\frac{1}{2}\right)\left(\frac{1}{2}\right)$$

$$= (0)\left(\frac{1}{2}\right) + (1)\left(\frac{1}{2}\right) \qquad f(0) = 2 \cdot 0 = 0; \ f\left(\frac{1}{2}\right) = 2 \cdot \frac{1}{2} = 1$$

$$= \frac{1}{2} = 0.5$$

(b) We partition $[0, 1]$ into two subintervals, each of length $\frac{1}{2}$, and choose u as the right endpoint. See Figure 23(b). The area A is approximated as

$$A \approx f\left(\frac{1}{2}\right)\left(\frac{1}{2}\right) + f(1)\left(\frac{1}{2}\right)$$

$$= (1)\left(\frac{1}{2}\right) + (2)\left(\frac{1}{2}\right)$$

$$= \frac{3}{2} = 1.5$$

(c) We partition $[0, 1]$ into four subintervals, each of length $\frac{1}{4}$, and choose u as the left endpoint. See Figure 23(c). The area A is approximated as

$$A \approx f(0)\left(\frac{1}{4}\right) + f\left(\frac{1}{4}\right)\left(\frac{1}{4}\right) + f\left(\frac{1}{2}\right)\left(\frac{1}{4}\right) + f\left(\frac{3}{4}\right)\left(\frac{1}{4}\right)$$

$$= (0)\left(\frac{1}{4}\right) + \left(\frac{1}{2}\right)\left(\frac{1}{4}\right) + (1)\left(\frac{1}{4}\right) + \left(\frac{3}{2}\right)\left(\frac{1}{4}\right)$$

$$= \frac{3}{4} = 0.75$$

(d) We partition $[0, 1]$ into four subintervals, each of length $\frac{1}{4}$, and choose u as the right endpoint. See Figure 23(d). The area A is approximated as

$$A \approx f\left(\frac{1}{4}\right)\left(\frac{1}{4}\right) + f\left(\frac{1}{2}\right)\left(\frac{1}{4}\right) + f\left(\frac{3}{4}\right)\left(\frac{1}{4}\right) + f(1)\left(\frac{1}{4}\right)$$

$$= \left(\frac{1}{2}\right)\left(\frac{1}{4}\right) + (1)\left(\frac{1}{4}\right) + \left(\frac{3}{2}\right)\left(\frac{1}{4}\right) + (2)\left(\frac{1}{4}\right)$$

$$= \frac{5}{4} = 1.25$$

(e) The actual area under the graph of $f(x) = 2x$ from 0 to 1 is the area of a right triangle whose base is of length 1 and whose height is 2. The actual area A is therefore

$$A = \frac{1}{2} \text{ base} \times \text{height} = \left(\frac{1}{2}\right)(1)(2) = 1$$

Now look at Table 6, which shows the approximations to the area under the graph of $f(x) = 2x$ from 0 to 1 for $n = 2, 4, 10$, and 100 subintervals. Notice that the approximations to the actual area improve as the number of subintervals increases.

Table 6

Using left endpoints:	n	2	4	10	100
	Area	0.5	0.75	0.9	0.99
Using right endpoints:	n	2	4	10	100
	Area	1.5	1.25	1.1	1.01

You are asked to confirm the entries in Table 6 in Problem 31.

There is another useful observation about Example 1. Look again at Figures 23(a)–(d) and at Table 6. Since the graph of $f(x) = 2x$ is increasing on $[0, 1]$, the choice of u as left endpoint gives a lower estimate to the actual area, while choosing u as the right endpoint gives an upper estimate. Do you see why?

Now Work PROBLEM 9

EXAMPLE 2

Approximating the Area Under the Graph of $f(x) = x^2$

Approximate the area under the graph of $f(x) = x^2$ from 1 to 5 as follows:

(a) Using four subintervals of equal length
(b) Using eight subintervals of equal length

In each case, choose the number u to be the left endpoint of each subinterval.

Solution

(a) See Figure 24. Using four subintervals of equal length, the interval $[1, 5]$ is partitioned into subintervals of length $\dfrac{5 - 1}{4} = 1$ as follows:

Figure 24

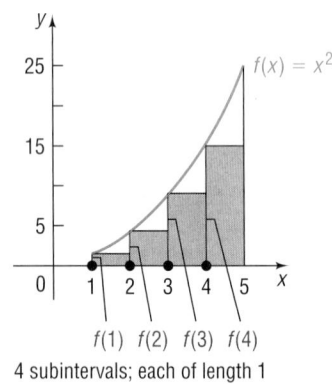

$f(1)$ $f(2)$ $f(3)$ $f(4)$
4 subintervals; each of length 1

$$[1, 2] \quad [2, 3] \quad [3, 4] \quad [4, 5]$$

Each of these subintervals is of length 1. Choosing u as the left endpoint of each subinterval, the area A under the graph of $f(x) = x^2$ is approximated by

$$\text{Area } A \approx f(1)(1) + f(2)(1) + f(3)(1) + f(4)(1)$$
$$= 1 + 4 + 9 + 16 = 30$$

(b) See Figure 25. Using eight subintervals of equal length, the interval $[1, 5]$ is partitioned into subintervals of length $\dfrac{5 - 1}{8} = 0.5$ as follows:

Figure 25

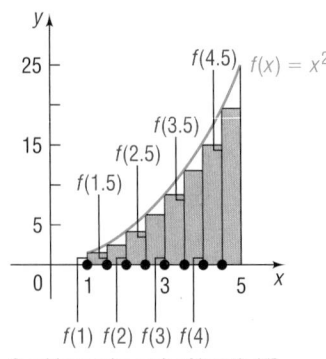

$f(1)$ $f(2)$ $f(3)$ $f(4)$
8 subintervals; each of length 1/2

$$[1, 1.5] \quad [1.5, 2] \quad [2, 2.5] \quad [2.5, 3] \quad [3, 3.5] \quad [3.5, 4] \quad [4, 4.5] \quad [4.5, 5]$$

Each of these subintervals is of length 0.5. Choosing u as the left endpoint of each subinterval, the area A under the graph of $f(x) = x^2$ is approximated by

$$\text{Area } A \approx f(1)(0.5) + f(1.5)(0.5) + f(2)(0.5) + f(2.5)(0.5)$$
$$+ f(3)(0.5) + f(3.5)(0.5) + f(4)(0.5) + f(4.5)(0.5)$$
$$= [f(1) + f(1.5) + f(2) + f(2.5) + f(3) + f(3.5) + f(4) + f(4.5)](0.5)$$
$$= [1 + 2.25 + 4 + 6.25 + 9 + 12.25 + 16 + 20.25](0.5)$$
$$= 35.5$$

In general, we approximate the area under the graph of a function $y = f(x)$ from a to b as follows:

1. Partition the interval $[a, b]$ into n subintervals of equal length. The length Δx of each subinterval is then

$$\Delta x = \frac{b - a}{n}$$

2. In each of these subintervals, pick a number u and evaluate the function f at each u. This results in n numbers $u_1, u_2, \ldots, u_n$ and n functional values $f(u_1), f(u_2), \ldots, f(u_n)$.

3. Form n rectangles with base equal to Δx, the length of each subinterval, and with height equal to the functional value $f(u_i), i = 1, 2, \ldots, n$. See Figure 26.

4. Add up the areas of the n rectangles.

$$A_1 + A_2 + \cdots + A_n = f(u_1)\,\Delta x + f(u_2)\,\Delta x + \cdots + f(u_n)\,\Delta x$$

$$= \sum_{i=1}^{n} f(u_i)\,\Delta x$$

This number is the approximation to the area under the graph of f from a to b.

Figure 26

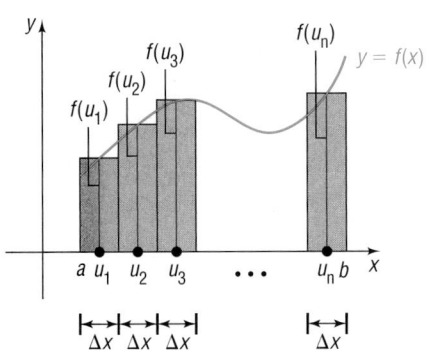

Definition of Area

We have observed that the larger the number n of subintervals used, the better the approximation to the area. If we let n become unbounded, we obtain the exact area under the graph of f from a to b.

DEFINITION

Area Under a Graph

Let f denote a function whose domain is a closed interval $[a, b]$ and suppose $f(x) \geq 0$ on $[a, b]$. Partition $[a, b]$ into n subintervals, each of length $\Delta x = \dfrac{b - a}{n}$. In each subinterval, pick a number $u_i, i = 1, 2, \ldots, n$, and evaluate $f(u_i)$. Form the products $f(u_i)\,\Delta x$ and add them up obtaining the sum

$$\sum_{i=1}^{n} f(u_i)\,\Delta x$$

If the limit of this sum exists as $n \to \infty$, that is,

if $\quad \lim_{n \to \infty} \sum_{i=1}^{n} f(u_i)\,\Delta x \quad$ exists

it is defined as the area under the graph of f from a to b. If this limit exists, it is denoted by the symbol

$$\int_a^b f(x)\,dx$$

read as "the integral from a to b of $f(x)$."

2 Approximate Integrals Using a Graphing Utility

We can use a graphing utility to approximate integrals.

| EXAMPLE 3 | Using a Graphing Utility to Approximate an Integral |

Use a graphing utility to approximate the area under the graph of $f(x) = x^2$ from 1 to 5. That is, evaluate the integral

$$\int_1^5 x^2 \, dx$$

Solution Figure 27 shows the result using a TI-84 Plus calculator. Consult your owner's manual for the proper keystrokes.

Figure 27

```
fnInt(X²,X,1,5)
        41.33333333
Ans▶Frac
            124/3
```

The value of the integral is $\dfrac{124}{3}$.

In calculus, techniques are given for evaluating integrals to obtain exact answers.

14.5 Assess Your Understanding

'Are You Prepared?' *Answers are given at the end of these exercises. If you get a wrong answer, read the pages listed in red.*

1. The formula for the area A of a rectangle of length l and width w is _____. (p. A15)

2. $\displaystyle\sum_{k=1}^{4} (2k + 1) =$ _____. (pp. 808–811)

Concepts and Vocabulary

3. The integral from a to b of $f(x)$ is denoted by the symbol _____.

4. The area under the graph of f from a to b is denoted by the symbol _____.

Skill Building

In Problems 5 and 6, refer to the illustration. The interval $[1, 3]$ is partitioned into two subintervals $[1, 2]$ and $[2, 3]$.

In Problems 7 and 8, refer to the illustration. The interval $[0, 8]$ is partitioned into four subintervals $[0, 2], [2, 4], [4, 6],$ and $[6, 8]$.

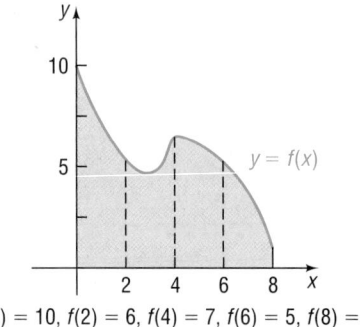

$f(1) = 1, f(2) = 2, f(3) = 4$

$f(0) = 10, f(2) = 6, f(4) = 7, f(6) = 5, f(8) = 1$

5. Approximate the area A choosing u as the left endpoint of each subinterval.

6. Approximate the area A choosing u as the right endpoint of each subinterval.

7. Approximate the area A choosing u as the left endpoint of each subinterval.

8. Approximate the area A choosing u as the right endpoint of each subinterval.

9. The function $f(x) = 3x$ is defined on the interval $[0, 6]$.
   (a) Graph f.
   In (b)–(e), approximate the area A under f from 0 to 6 as follows:
   (b) Partition $[0, 6]$ into three subintervals of equal length and choose u as the left endpoint of each subinterval.
   (c) Partition $[0, 6]$ into three subintervals of equal length and choose u as the right endpoint of each subinterval.
   (d) Partition $[0, 6]$ into six subintervals of equal length and choose u as the left endpoint of each subinterval.
   (e) Partition $[0, 6]$ into six subintervals of equal length and choose u as the right endpoint of each subinterval.
   (f) What is the actual area A?

10. Repeat Problem 9 for $f(x) = 4x$.

11. The function $f(x) = -3x + 9$ is defined on the interval $[0, 3]$.
   (a) Graph f.
   In (b)–(e), approximate the area A under f from 0 to 3 as follows:
   (b) Partition $[0, 3]$ into three subintervals of equal length and choose u as the left endpoint of each subinterval.
   (c) Partition $[0, 3]$ into three subintervals of equal length and choose u as the right endpoint of each subinterval.
   (d) Partition $[0, 3]$ into six subintervals of equal length and choose u as the left endpoint of each subinterval.
   (e) Partition $[0, 3]$ into six subintervals of equal length and choose u as the right endpoint of each subinterval.
   (f) What is the actual area A?

12. Repeat Problem 11 for $f(x) = -2x + 8$.

In Problems 13–22, a function f is defined over an interval $[a, b]$.
   (a) Graph f, indicating the area A under f from a to b.
   (b) Approximate the area A by partitioning $[a, b]$ into four subintervals of equal length and choosing u as the left endpoint of each subinterval.
   (c) Approximate the area A by partitioning $[a, b]$ into eight subintervals of equal length and choosing u as the left endpoint of each subinterval.
   (d) Express the area A as an integral.
   (e) Use a graphing utility to approximate the integral.

13. $f(x) = x^2 + 2$, $[0, 4]$
14. $f(x) = x^2 - 4$, $[2, 6]$
15. $f(x) = x^3$, $[0, 4]$
16. $f(x) = x^3$, $[1, 5]$
17. $f(x) = \dfrac{1}{x}$, $[1, 5]$
18. $f(x) = \sqrt{x}$, $[0, 4]$
19. $f(x) = e^x$, $[-1, 3]$
20. $f(x) = \ln x$, $[3, 7]$
21. $f(x) = \sin x$, $[0, \pi]$
22. $f(x) = \cos x$, $\left[0, \dfrac{\pi}{2}\right]$

In Problems 23–30, an integral is given.
   (a) What area does the integral represent?
   (b) Provide a graph that illustrates this area.
   (c) Use a graphing utility to approximate this area.

23. $\displaystyle\int_0^4 (3x + 1)\, dx$
24. $\displaystyle\int_1^3 (-2x + 7)\, dx$
25. $\displaystyle\int_2^5 (x^2 - 1)\, dx$
26. $\displaystyle\int_0^4 (16 - x^2)\, dx$
27. $\displaystyle\int_0^{\pi/2} \sin x\, dx$
28. $\displaystyle\int_{-\pi/4}^{\pi/4} \cos x\, dx$
29. $\displaystyle\int_0^2 e^x\, dx$
30. $\displaystyle\int_e^{2e} \ln x\, dx$

31. Confirm the entries in Table 6.

   [Hint: Review the formula for the sum of an arithmetic sequence.]

32. Consider the function $f(x) = \sqrt{1 - x^2}$ whose domain is the interval $[-1, 1]$.
   (a) Graph f.
   (b) Approximate the area under the graph of f from -1 to 1 by dividing $[-1, 1]$ into five subintervals, each of equal length.
   (c) Approximate the area under the graph of f from -1 to 1 by dividing $[-1, 1]$ into ten subintervals, each of equal length.
   (d) Express the area as an integral.
   (e) Evaluate the integral using a graphing utility.
   (f) What is the actual area?

'Are You Prepared?' Answers

1. $A = lw$
2. 24

CHAPTER REVIEW

Things to Know

Limit (p. 880)

$\displaystyle\lim_{x \to c} f(x) = N$
As x gets closer to c, $x \neq c$, the value of f gets closer to N.

Limit formulas (p. 885)

$\displaystyle\lim_{x \to c} b = b$
The limit of a constant is the constant.

$\displaystyle\lim_{x \to c} x = c$
The limit of x as x approaches c is c.

Limit properties (pp. 886, 888, 889)

$\lim\limits_{x \to c}[f(x) + g(x)] = \lim\limits_{x \to c} f(x) + \lim\limits_{x \to c} g(x)$ (p. 886)   The limit of a sum equals the sum of the limits.

$\lim\limits_{x \to c}[f(x) - g(x)] = \lim\limits_{x \to c} f(x) - \lim\limits_{x \to c} g(x)$ (p. 886)   The limit of a difference equals the difference of the limits.

$\lim\limits_{x \to c}[f(x) \cdot g(x)] = \lim\limits_{x \to c} f(x) \cdot \lim\limits_{x \to c} g(x)$ (p. 886)   The limit of a product equals the product of the limits.

$\lim\limits_{x \to c}\left[\dfrac{f(x)}{g(x)}\right] = \dfrac{\lim\limits_{x \to c} f(x)}{\lim\limits_{x \to c} g(x)}$

provided that $\lim\limits_{x \to c} g(x) \ne 0$ (p. 889)   The limit of a quotient equals the quotient of the limits, provided that the limit of the denominator is not zero.

$\lim\limits_{x \to c}[f(x)]^n = [\lim\limits_{x \to c} f(x)]^n$ (p. 888)   Provided $\lim\limits_{x \to c} f(x)$ exists, $n \ge 2$ an integer.

$\lim\limits_{x \to c} \sqrt[n]{f(x)} = \sqrt[n]{\lim\limits_{x \to c} f(x)}$ (p. 888)   Provided $\sqrt[n]{f(x)}$ and $\sqrt[n]{\lim\limits_{x \to c} f(x)}$ are both defined, $n \ge 2$ an integer.

Limit of a polynomial (p. 888)

$\lim\limits_{x \to c} P(x) = P(c)$, where P is a polynomial

Continuous function (p. 894)

$\lim\limits_{x \to c} f(x) = f(c)$

Derivative of a function (p. 901)

$f'(c) = \lim\limits_{x \to c} \dfrac{f(x) - f(c)}{x - c}$, provided that the limit exists

Area under a graph (p. 911)

$\displaystyle\int_a^b f(x)\, dx = \lim\limits_{n \to \infty} \sum_{i=1}^{n} f(u_i)\, \Delta x$, provided that the limit exists

Objectives

Section		You should be able to . . .	Example(s)	Review Exercises
14.1	1	Find a limit using a table (p. 880)	1–3, 6	1–22
	2	Find a limit using a graph (p. 881)	4, 5	43, 44
14.2	1	Find the limit of a sum, a difference, and a product (p. 886)	2–6	1, 2
	2	Find the limit of a polynomial (p. 888)	7	1–4
	3	Find the limit of a power or a root (p. 888)	8	3–6, 9, 10
	4	Find the limit of a quotient (p. 889)	9–11	11–16, 19–22
	5	Find the limit of an average rate of change (p. 890)	12	55–60
14.3	1	Find the one-sided limits of a function (p. 892)	1	7, 8, 17, 18, 37–42
	2	Determine whether a function is continuous (p. 894)	2, 3	23–30, 45–50, 51–54
14.4	1	Find an equation of the tangent line to the graph of a function (p. 900)	1	55–60
	2	Find the derivative of a function (p. 901)	2–4	61–70
	3	Find instantaneous rates of change (p. 902)	5	72, 73
	4	Find the instantaneous speed of a particle (p. 903)	6	71, 74
14.5	1	Approximate the area under the graph of a function (p. 907)	1, 2	75–80
	2	Approximate integrals using a graphing utility (p. 911)	3	77(e)–80(e); 81(c)–84(c)

Review Exercises

In Problems 1–22, find the limit.

1. $\lim\limits_{x \to 2}(3x^2 - 2x + 1)$ **2.** $\lim\limits_{x \to 1}(-2x^3 + x + 4)$ **3.** $\lim\limits_{x \to -2}(x^2 + 1)^2$ **4.** $\lim\limits_{x \to -2}(x^3 + 1)^2$

5. $\lim\limits_{x \to 3} \sqrt{x^2 + 7}$ **6.** $\lim\limits_{x \to -2} \sqrt[3]{x + 10}$ **7.** $\lim\limits_{x \to 1^-} \sqrt{1 - x^2}$ **8.** $\lim\limits_{x \to 2^+} \sqrt{3x - 2}$

9. $\lim\limits_{x \to 2}(5x + 6)^{3/2}$ **10.** $\lim\limits_{x \to -3}(15 - 3x)^{-3/2}$ **11.** $\lim\limits_{x \to -1} \dfrac{x^2 + x + 2}{x^2 - 9}$ **12.** $\lim\limits_{x \to 3} \dfrac{3x + 4}{x^2 + 1}$

13. $\lim\limits_{x \to 1} \dfrac{x - 1}{x^3 - 1}$ **14.** $\lim\limits_{x \to -1} \dfrac{x^2 - 1}{x^2 + x}$ **15.** $\lim\limits_{x \to -3} \dfrac{x^2 - 9}{x^2 - x - 12}$ **16.** $\lim\limits_{x \to -3} \dfrac{x^2 + 2x - 3}{x^2 - 9}$

17. $\lim\limits_{x \to -1^-} \dfrac{x^2 - 1}{x^3 - 1}$ **18.** $\lim\limits_{x \to 2^+} \dfrac{x^2 - 4}{x^3 - 8}$ **19.** $\lim\limits_{x \to 2} \dfrac{x^3 - 8}{x^3 - 2x^2 + 4x - 8}$

20. $\lim\limits_{x \to 1} \dfrac{x^3 - 1}{x^3 - x^2 + 3x - 3}$ **21.** $\lim\limits_{x \to 3} \dfrac{x^4 - 3x^3 + x - 3}{x^3 - 3x^2 + 2x - 6}$ **22.** $\lim\limits_{x \to -1} \dfrac{x^4 + x^3 + 2x + 2}{x^3 + x^2}$

In Problems 23–30, determine whether f is continuous at c.

23. $f(x) = 3x^4 - x^2 + 2 \quad c = 5$

24. $f(x) = \dfrac{x^2 - 9}{x + 10} \quad c = 2$

25. $f(x) = \dfrac{x^2 - 4}{x + 2} \quad c = -2$

26. $f(x) = \dfrac{x^2 + 6x}{x^2 - 6x} \quad c = 0$

27. $f(x) = \begin{cases} \dfrac{x^2 - 4}{x + 2} & \text{if } x \neq -2 \\ 4 & \text{if } x = -2 \end{cases} \quad c = -2$

28. $f(x) = \begin{cases} \dfrac{x^2 + 6x}{x^2 - 6x} & \text{if } x \neq 0 \\ 1 & \text{if } x = 0 \end{cases} \quad c = 0$

29. $f(x) = \begin{cases} \dfrac{x^2 - 4}{x + 2} & \text{if } x \neq -2 \\ -4 & \text{if } x = -2 \end{cases} \quad c = -2$

30. $f(x) = \begin{cases} \dfrac{x^2 + 6x}{x^2 - 6x} & \text{if } x \neq 0 \\ -1 & \text{if } x = 0 \end{cases} \quad c = 0$

In Problems 31–50, use the accompanying graph of $y = f(x)$.

31. What is the domain of f?

32. What is the range of f?

33. Find the x-intercept(s), if any, of f.

34. Find the y-intercept(s), if any, of f.

35. Find $f(-6)$ and $f(-4)$.

36. Find $f(-2)$ and $f(6)$.

37. Find $\lim\limits_{x \to -4^-} f(x)$.

38. Find $\lim\limits_{x \to -4^+} f(x)$.

39. Find $\lim\limits_{x \to -2^-} f(x)$.

40. Find $\lim\limits_{x \to -2^+} f(x)$.

41. Find $\lim\limits_{x \to 2^-} f(x)$.

42. Find $\lim\limits_{x \to 2^+} f(x)$.

43. Does $\lim\limits_{x \to 0} f(x)$ exist? If it does, what is it?

44. Does $\lim\limits_{x \to 2} f(x)$ exist? If it does, what is it?

45. Is f continuous at -2?

46. Is f continuous at -4?

47. Is f continuous at 0?

48. Is f continuous at 2?

49. Is f continuous at 4?

50. Is f continuous at 5?

In Problems 51 and 52, discuss whether R is continuous at c. Use limits to analyze the graph of R at c.

51. $R(x) = \dfrac{x + 4}{x^2 - 16}$ at $c = -4$ and $c = 4$

52. $R(x) = \dfrac{3x^2 + 6x}{x^2 - 4}$ at $c = -2$ and $c = 2$

In Problems 53 and 54, determine where each rational function is undefined. Determine whether an asymptote or a hole appears at such numbers.

53. $R(x) = \dfrac{x^3 - 2x^2 + 4x - 8}{x^2 - 11x + 18}$

54. $R(x) = \dfrac{x^3 + 3x^2 - 2x - 6}{x^2 + x - 6}$

In Problems 55–60, find the slope of the tangent line to the graph of f at the given point. Graph f and the tangent line.

55. $f(x) = 2x^2 + 8x$ at $(1, 10)$

56. $f(x) = 3x^2 - 6x$ at $(0, 0)$

57. $f(x) = x^2 + 2x - 3$ at $(-1, -4)$

58. $f(x) = 2x^2 + 5x - 3$ at $(1, 4)$

59. $f(x) = x^3 + x^2$ at $(2, 12)$

60. $f(x) = x^3 - x^2$ at $(1, 0)$

In Problems 61–66, find the derivative of each function at the number indicated.

61. $f(x) = -4x^2 + 5$ at 3

62. $f(x) = -4 + 3x^2$ at 1

63. $f(x) = x^2 - 3x$ at 0

64. $f(x) = 2x^2 + 4x$ at -1

65. $f(x) = 2x^2 + 3x + 2$ at 1

66. $f(x) = 3x^2 - 4x + 1$ at 2

In Problems 67–70, find the derivative of each function at the number indicated using a graphing utility.

67. $f(x) = 4x^4 - 3x^3 + 6x - 9$ at -2

68. $f(x) = \dfrac{-6x^3 + 9x - 2}{8x^2 + 6x - 1}$ at 5

69. $f(x) = x^3 \tan x$ at $\dfrac{\pi}{6}$

70. $f(x) = x \sec x$ at $\dfrac{\pi}{6}$

71. Instantaneous Speed of a Ball In physics it is shown that the height s of a ball thrown straight up with an initial speed of 96 ft/sec from a rooftop 112 feet high is

$$s = s(t) = -16t^2 + 96t + 112$$

where t is the elapsed time that the ball is in the air. The ball misses the rooftop on its way down and eventually strikes the ground.

(a) When does the ball strike the ground? That is, how long is the ball in the air?
(b) At what time t will the ball pass the rooftop on its way down?
(c) What is the average speed of the ball from $t = 0$ to $t = 2$?
(d) What is the instantaneous speed of the ball at time t?
(e) What is the instantaneous speed of the ball at $t = 2$?
(f) When is the instantaneous speed of the ball equal to zero?
(g) What is the instantaneous speed of the ball as it passes the rooftop on the way down?
(h) What is the instantaneous speed of the ball when it strikes the ground?

72. Finding an Instantaneous Rate of Change The area A of a circle is πr^2. Find the instantaneous rate of change of area with respect to r at $r = 2$ feet. What is the average rate of change from $r = 2$ to $r = 3$? What is the average rate of change from $r = 2$ to $r = 2.5$? From $r = 2$ to $r = 2.1$?

73. Instantaneous Rate of Change The following data represent the revenue R (in dollars) received from selling x wristwatches at Wilk's Watch Shop.

Wristwatches, x	Revenue, R
0	0
25	2340
40	3600
50	4375
90	6975
130	8775
160	9600
200	10,000
220	9900
250	9375

(a) Find the average rate of change of revenue from $x = 25$ to $x = 130$ wristwatches.
(b) Find the average rate of change of revenue from $x = 25$ to $x = 90$ wristwatches.
(c) Find the average rate of change of revenue from $x = 25$ to $x = 50$ wristwatches.
(d) Using a graphing utility, find the quadratic function of best fit.
(e) Using the function found in part (d), determine the instantaneous rate of change of revenue at $x = 25$ wristwatches.

74. Instantaneous Speed of a Parachutist The following data represent the distance s (in feet) that a parachutist has fallen over time t (in seconds).

Time, t (in Seconds)	Distance, s (in Feet)
1	16
2	64
3	144
4	256
5	400

(a) Find the average speed from $t = 1$ to $t = 4$ seconds.
(b) Find the average speed from $t = 1$ to $t = 3$ seconds.
(c) Find the average speed from $t = 1$ to $t = 2$ seconds.
(d) Using a graphing utility, find the power function of best fit.
(e) Using the function found in part (d), determine the instantaneous speed at $t = 1$ second.

75. The function $f(x) = 2x + 3$ is defined on the interval $[0, 4]$.
(a) Graph f.
    In (b)–(e), approximate the area A under f from $x = 0$ to $x = 4$ as follows:
(b) Partition $[0, 4]$ into four subintervals of equal length and choose u as the left endpoint of each subinterval.
(c) Partition $[0, 4]$ into four subintervals of equal length and choose u as the right endpoint of each subinterval.
(d) Partition $[0, 4]$ into eight subintervals of equal length and choose u as the left endpoint of each subinterval.
(e) Partition $[0, 4]$ into eight subintervals of equal length and choose u as the right endpoint of each subinterval.
(f) What is the actual area A?

76. Repeat Problem 75 for $f(x) = -2x + 8$.

In Problems 77–80, a function f is defined over an interval $[a, b]$.
(a) *Graph f, indicating the area A under f from a to b.*
(b) *Approximate the area A by partitioning $[a, b]$ into three subintervals of equal length and choosing u as the left endpoint of each subinterval.*
(c) *Approximate the area A by partitioning $[a, b]$ into six subintervals of equal length and choosing u as the left endpoint of each subinterval.*
(d) *Express the area A as an integral.*
(e) *Use a graphing utility to approximate the integral.*

77. $f(x) = 4 - x^2$, $[-1, 2]$ **78.** $f(x) = x^2 + 3$, $[0, 6]$

79. $f(x) = \dfrac{1}{x^2}$, $[1, 4]$ **80.** $f(x) = e^x$, $[0, 6]$

In Problems 81–84, an integral is given.
(a) *What area does the integral represent?*
(b) *Provide a graph that illustrates this area.*
(c) *Use a graphing utility to approximate this area.*

81. $\displaystyle\int_{-1}^{3} (9 - x^2)\, dx$ **82.** $\displaystyle\int_{1}^{4} \sqrt{x}\, dx$ **83.** $\displaystyle\int_{-1}^{1} e^x\, dx$ **84.** $\displaystyle\int_{\pi/3}^{2\pi/3} \sin x\, dx$

CHAPTER TEST

In Problems 1–6, find each limit.

1. $\lim\limits_{x\to 3} \left(-x^2 + 3x - 5\right)$

2. $\lim\limits_{x\to 2^+} \dfrac{|x - 2|}{3x - 6}$

3. $\lim\limits_{x\to -6} \sqrt{7 - 3x}$

4. $\lim\limits_{x\to -1} \dfrac{x^2 - 4x - 5}{x^3 + 1}$

5. $\lim\limits_{x\to 5} \left[(3x)(x - 2)^2\right]$

6. $\lim\limits_{x\to \frac{\pi}{4}} \dfrac{\tan x}{1 + \cos^2 x}$

---

7. Determine the value for k that will make the function continuous at $c = 4$.

$$f(x) = \begin{cases} \dfrac{x^2 - 9}{x + 3} & \text{if } x \le 4 \\ kx + 5 & \text{if } x > 4 \end{cases}$$

In Problems 8–12, use the accompanying graph of $y = f(x)$.

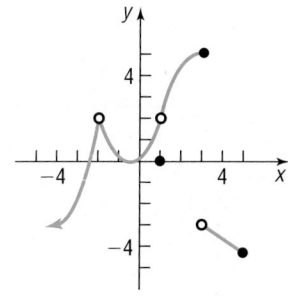

8. Find $\lim\limits_{x\to 3^+} f(x)$

9. Find $\lim\limits_{x\to 3^-} f(x)$

10. Find $\lim\limits_{x\to -2} f(x)$

11. Does $\lim\limits_{x\to 1} f(x)$ exist? If so, what is it? If not, explain why not.

12. Determine whether f is continuous at each of the following numbers. If it is not, explain why not.
(a) $x = -2$ (b) $x = 1$
(c) $x = 3$ (d) $x = 4$

13. Determine where the rational function

$$R(x) = \dfrac{x^3 + 6x^2 - 4x - 24}{x^2 + 5x - 14}$$

is undefined. Determine whether an asymptote or a hole appears at such numbers.

14. For the function $f(x) = 4x^2 - 11x - 3$:
(a) Find the derivative of f at $x = 2$.
(b) Find the equation of the tangent line to the graph of f at the point $(2, -9)$.
(c) Graph f and the tangent line.

15. The function $f(x) = \sqrt{16 - x^2}$ is defined on the interval $[0, 4]$.
(a) Graph f.
(b) Partition $[0, 4]$ into eight subintervals of equal length and choose u as the left endpoint of each subinterval. Use the partition to approximate the area under the graph of f and above the x-axis from $x = 0$ to $x = 4$.
(c) Find the exact area of the region and compare to the approximation in part (b).

16. Write the integral that represents the shaded area. Do not attempt to evaluate.

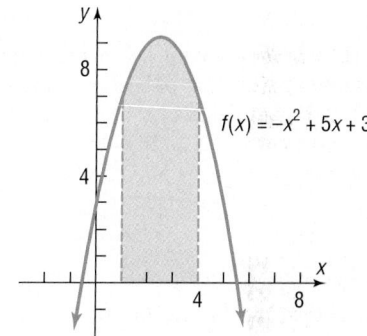

$f(x) = -x^2 + 5x + 3$

17. A particle is moving along a straight line according to some position function $s(t)$. The distance (in feet) of the particle, s, from its starting point after t seconds is given in the table. Find the average rate of change of distance from $t = 3$ to $t = 6$ seconds.

t	s
0	0
1	2.5
2	14
3	31
4	49
5	89
6	137
7	173
8	240

CHAPTER PROJECTS

I. **World Population** Thomas Malthus believed that "population, when unchecked, increases in a geometrical progression of such nature as to double itself every twenty-five years." However, the growth of population is limited because the resources available to us are limited in supply. If Malthus's conjecture were true, geometric growth of the world's population would imply that

$$\frac{P_t}{P_{t-1}} = r + 1, \text{ where } r \text{ is the growth rate}$$

1. Using *world population data* and a graphing utility, find the logistic growth function of best fit, treating the year as the independent variable. Let $t = 0$ represent 1950, $t = 1$ represent 1951, and so on, until you have entered all the years and the corresponding populations up to the current year.

2. Graph $Y_1 = f(t)$, where $f(t)$ represents the logistic growth function of best fit found in part (1).

3. Determine the instantaneous rate of growth of population in 1960 using the numerical derivative function on your graphing utility.

4. Use the result from part (3) to predict the population in 1961. What was the actual population in 1961?

5. Determine the instantaneous growth of population in 1970, 1980, 1990 and 2000. What is happening to the instantaneous growth rate as time passes? Is Malthus's contention of a geometric growth rate accurate?

6. Using the numerical derivative function on your graphing utility, graph $Y_2 = f'(t)$, where $f'(t)$ represents the derivative of $f(t)$ with respect to time. Y_2 is the growth rate of the population at any time t.

7. Using the MAXIMUM function on your graphing utility, determine the year in which the growth rate of the population is largest. What is happening to the growth rate in the years following the maximum? Find this point on the graph of $Y_1 = f(t)$.

8. Evaluate $\lim_{t \to \infty} f(t)$. This limiting value is the carrying capacity of Earth. What is the carrying capacity of Earth?

9. What do you think will happen if the population of Earth exceeds the carrying capacity? Do you think that agricultural output will continue to increase at the same rate as population growth? What effect will urban sprawl have on agricultural output?

The following projects are available on the Instructor's Resource Center (IRC):

II. **Project at Motorola** ***Curing Rates*** Engineers at Motorola use calculus to find the curing rate of a sealant.

III. **Finding the Profit-maximizing Level of Output** A manufacturer uses calculus to maximize profit.

Review

Outline

A.1 Algebra Essentials
A.2 Geometry Essentials
A.3 Polynomials
A.4 Synthetic Division
A.5 Rational Expressions
A.6 Solving Equations

A.7 Complex Numbers; Quadratic Equations in the Complex Number System
A.8 Problem Solving: Interest, Mixture, Uniform Motion, Constant Rate Job Applications
A.9 Interval Notation; Solving Inequalities
A.10 nth Roots; Rational Exponents

A.1 Algebra Essentials

PREPARING FOR THIS BOOK *Before getting started, read "To the Student" at the beginning of this book on page xiii.*

OBJECTIVES **1** Work with Sets (p. A1)

2 Graph Inequalities (p. A4)

3 Find Distance on the Real Number Line (p. A5)

4 Evaluate Algebraic Expressions (p. A6)

5 Determine the Domain of a Variable (p. A7)

6 Use the Laws of Exponents (p. A7)

7 Evaluate Square Roots (p. A9)

8 Use a Calculator to Evaluate Exponents (p. A10)

1 Work with Sets

A **set** is a well-defined collection of distinct objects. The objects of a set are called its **elements.** By **well-defined,** we mean that there is a rule that enables us to determine whether a given object is an element of the set. If a set has no elements, it is called the **empty set,** or **null set,** and is denoted by the symbol $\varnothing$.

For example, the set of *digits* consists of the collection of numbers 0, 1, 2, 3, 4, 5, 6, 7, 8, and 9. If we use the symbol D to denote the set of digits, then we can write

$$D = \{0, 1, 2, 3, 4, 5, 6, 7, 8, 9\}$$

In this notation, the braces $\{\ \}$ are used to enclose the objects, or **elements,** in the set. This method of denoting a set is called the **roster method.** A second way to denote a set is to use **set-builder notation,** where the set D of digits is written as

$$D = \{ \quad x \quad | \quad x \text{ is a digit}\}$$

Read as "D is the set of all x such that x is a digit."

EXAMPLE 1	Using Set-builder Notation and the Roster Method

(a) $E = \{x \mid x \text{ is an even digit}\} = \{0, 2, 4, 6, 8\}$

(b) $O = \{x \mid x \text{ is an odd digit}\} = \{1, 3, 5, 7, 9\}$

Because the elements of a set are distinct, we never repeat elements. For example, we would never write $\{1, 2, 3, 2\}$; the correct listing is $\{1, 2, 3\}$. Because a set is a collection, the order in which the elements are listed is immaterial. $\{1, 2, 3\}$, $\{1, 3, 2\}$, $\{2, 1, 3\}$, and so on, all represent the same set.

If every element of a set A is also an element of a set B, then we say that A is a **subset** of B and write $A \subseteq B$. If two sets A and B have the same elements, then we say that A **equals** B and write $A = B$.

For example, $\{1, 2, 3\} \subseteq \{1, 2, 3, 4, 5\}$ and $\{1, 2, 3\} = \{2, 3, 1\}$.

DEFINITION

If A and B are sets, the **intersection** of A with B, denoted $A \cap B$, is the set consisting of elements that belong to both A and B. The **union** of A with B, denoted $A \cup B$, is the set consisting of elements that belong to either A or B, or both.

EXAMPLE 2	Finding the Intersection and Union of Sets

Let $A = \{1, 3, 5, 8\}$, $B = \{3, 5, 7\}$, and $C = \{2, 4, 6, 8\}$. Find:

(a) $A \cap B$ (b) $A \cup B$ (c) $B \cap (A \cup C)$

Solution

(a) $A \cap B = \{1, 3, 5, 8\} \cap \{3, 5, 7\} = \{3, 5\}$

(b) $A \cup B = \{1, 3, 5, 8\} \cup \{3, 5, 7\} = \{1, 3, 5, 7, 8\}$

(c) $B \cap (A \cup C) = \{3, 5, 7\} \cap (\{1, 3, 5, 8\} \cup \{2, 4, 6, 8\})$
$= \{3, 5, 7\} \cap \{1, 2, 3, 4, 5, 6, 8\} = \{3, 5\}$

Now Work PROBLEM 13

Usually, in working with sets, we designate a **universal set** U, the set consisting of all the elements that we wish to consider. Once a universal set has been designated, we can consider elements of the universal set not found in a given set.

DEFINITION

If A is a set, the **complement** of A, denoted $\overline{A}$, is the set consisting of all the elements in the universal set that are not in A.*

EXAMPLE 3	Finding the Complement of a Set

If the universal set is $U = \{1, 2, 3, 4, 5, 6, 7, 8, 9\}$ and if $A = \{1, 3, 5, 7, 9\}$, then $\overline{A} = \{2, 4, 6, 8\}$.

It follows from the definition of complement that $A \cup \overline{A} = U$ and $A \cap \overline{A} = \varnothing$. Do you see why?

Now Work PROBLEM 17

It is often helpful to draw pictures of sets. Such pictures, called **Venn diagrams,** represent sets as circles enclosed in a rectangle, which represents the universal set. Such diagrams often help us to visualize various relationships among sets. See Figure 1.

Figure 1

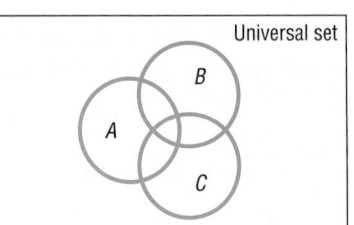

*Some books use the notation A' or A^c for the complement of A.

If we know that $A \subseteq B$, we might use the Venn diagram in Figure 2(a). If we know that A and B have no elements in common, that is, if $A \cap B = \varnothing$, we might use the Venn diagram in Figure 2(b). The sets A and B in Figure 2(b) are said to be **disjoint.**

Figure 2

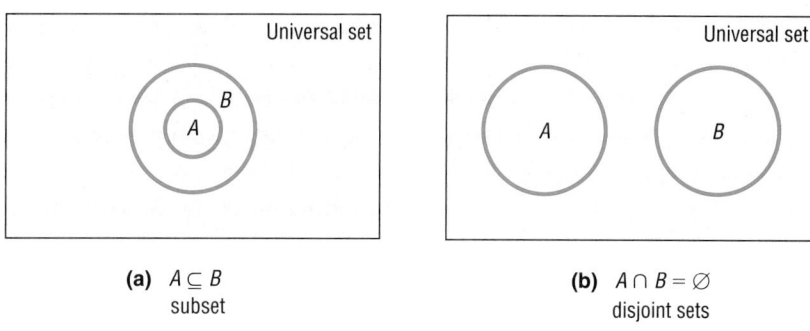

(a) $A \subseteq B$
subset

(b) $A \cap B = \varnothing$
disjoint sets

Figures 3(a), 3(b), and 3(c) use Venn diagrams to illustrate the definitions of intersection, union, and complement, respectively.

Figure 3

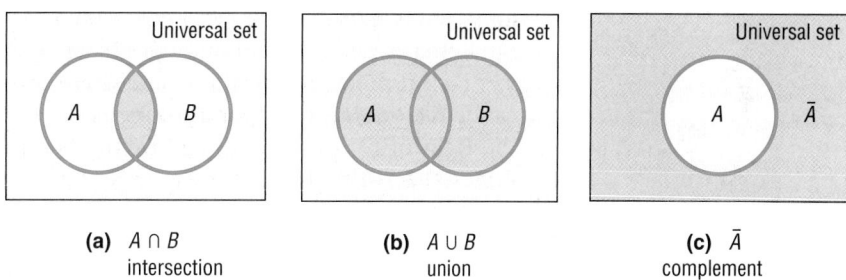

(a) $A \cap B$
intersection

(b) $A \cup B$
union

(c) $\bar{A}$
complement

Real Numbers

Real numbers are represented by symbols such as

$$25, \quad 0, \quad -3, \quad \frac{1}{2}, \quad -\frac{5}{4}, \quad 0.125, \quad \sqrt{2}, \quad \pi, \quad \sqrt[3]{-2}, \quad 0.666\ldots$$

The set of **counting numbers,** or **natural numbers,** contains the numbers in the set $\{1, 2, 3, 4, \ldots\}$. (The three dots, called an **ellipsis,** indicate that the pattern continues indefinitely.) The set of **integers** contains the numbers in the set $\{\ldots, -3, -2, -1, 0, 1, 2, 3, \ldots\}$. A **rational number** is a number that can be expressed as a *quotient* $\frac{a}{b}$ of two integers, where the integer b cannot be 0. Examples of rational numbers are $\frac{3}{4}, \frac{5}{2}, \frac{0}{4}$, and $-\frac{2}{3}$. Since $\frac{a}{1} = a$ for any integer a, every integer is also a rational number. Real numbers that are not rational are called **irrational.** Examples of irrational numbers are $\sqrt{2}$ and π (the Greek letter pi), which equals the constant ratio of the circumference to the diameter of a circle. See Figure 4.

Figure 4 $\pi = \dfrac{C}{d}$

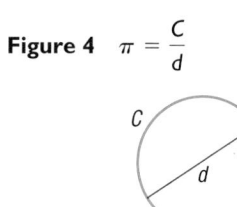

Real numbers can be represented as **decimals.** Rational real numbers have decimal representations that either **terminate** or are nonterminating with **repeating** blocks of digits. For example, $\frac{3}{4} = 0.75$, which terminates; and $\frac{2}{3} = 0.666\ldots$, in which the digit 6 repeats indefinitely. Irrational real numbers have decimal representations that neither repeat nor terminate. For example, $\sqrt{2} = 1.414213\ldots$ and $\pi = 3.14159\ldots$. In practice, the decimal representation of an irrational number is given as an approximation. We use the symbol $\approx$ (read as "approximately equal to") to write $\sqrt{2} \approx 1.4142$ and $\pi \approx 3.1416$.

Two properties of real numbers that we shall use often are given next. Suppose that a, b, and c are real numbers.

Distributive Property

$$a \cdot (b + c) = ab + ac$$

Zero-Product Property

If $ab = 0$, then either $a = 0$ or $b = 0$ or both equal 0.

The Distributive Property can be used to remove parentheses:

$$2(x + 3) = 2x + 2 \cdot 3 = 2x + 6$$

The Zero-Product Property will be used to solve equations (Section A.6). For example, if $2x = 0$, then $2 = 0$ or $x = 0$. Since $2 \neq 0$, it follows that $x = 0$.

The Real Number Line

The real numbers can be represented by points on a line called the **real number line.** There is a one-to-one correspondence between real numbers and points on a line. That is, every real number corresponds to a point on the line, and each point on the line has a unique real number associated with it.

Pick a point on the line somewhere in the center, and label it O. This point, called the **origin,** corresponds to the real number 0. See Figure 5. The point 1 unit to the right of O corresponds to the number 1. The distance between 0 and 1 determines the **scale** of the number line. For example, the point associated with the number 2 is twice as far from O as 1. Notice that an arrowhead on the right end of the line indicates the direction in which the numbers increase. Points to the left of the origin correspond to the real numbers -1, -2, and so on. Figure 5 also shows the points associated with the rational numbers $-\dfrac{1}{2}$ and $\dfrac{1}{2}$ and with the irrational numbers $\sqrt{2}$ and π.

Figure 5
Real number line

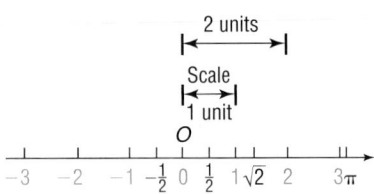

DEFINITION

The real number associated with a point P is called the **coordinate** of P, and the line whose points have been assigned coordinates is called the **real number line.**

The real number line consists of three classes of real numbers, as shown in Figure 6.

Figure 6

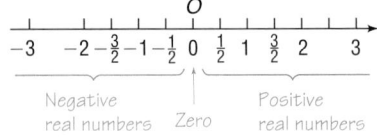

1. The **negative real numbers** are the coordinates of points to the left of the origin O.
2. The real number **zero** is the coordinate of the origin O.
3. The **positive real numbers** are the coordinates of points to the right of the origin O.

━━━━━ **Now Work** PROBLEM 21

2 Graph Inequalities

An important property of the real number line follows from the fact that, given two numbers (points) a and b, either a is to the left of b, or a is at the same location as b, or a is to the right of b. See Figure 7.

If a is to the left of b, we say that "a is less than b" and write $a < b$. If a is to the right of b, we say that "a is greater than b" and write $a > b$. If a is at the same location as b, then $a = b$. If a is either less than or equal to b, we write $a \leq b$. Similarly, $a \geq b$ means that a is either greater than or equal to b. Collectively, the symbols $<$, $>$, $\leq$, and $\geq$ are called **inequality symbols.**

Figure 7

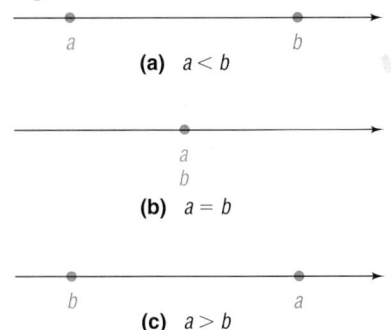

(a) $a < b$

(b) $a = b$

(c) $a > b$

Note that $a < b$ and $b > a$ mean the same thing. It does not matter whether we write $2 < 3$ or $3 > 2$.

Furthermore, if $a < b$ or if $b > a$, then the difference $b - a$ is positive. Do you see why?

An **inequality** is a statement in which two expressions are related by an inequality symbol. The expressions are referred to as the **sides** of the inequality. Statements of the form $a < b$ or $b > a$ are called **strict inequalities,** whereas statements of the form $a \leq b$ or $b \geq a$ are called **nonstrict inequalities.**

Based on the discussion so far, we conclude that

$$a > 0 \quad \text{is equivalent to } a \text{ is positive}$$
$$a < 0 \quad \text{is equivalent to } a \text{ is negative}$$

We sometimes read $a > 0$ by saying that "a is positive." If $a \geq 0$, then either $a > 0$ or $a = 0$, and we may read this as "a is nonnegative."

Now Work PROBLEMS **25** AND **35**

| EXAMPLE 4 | **Graphing Inequalities** |

(a) On the real number line, graph all numbers x for which $x > 4$.
(b) On the real number line, graph all numbers x for which $x \leq 5$.

Solution

(a) See Figure 8. Notice that we use a left parenthesis to indicate that the number 4 is *not* part of the graph.

(b) See Figure 9. Notice that we use a right bracket to indicate that the number 5 *is* part of the graph.

Figure 8

Figure 9

Now Work PROBLEM **41**

3 Find Distance on the Real Number Line

The *absolute value* of a number a is the distance from 0 to a on the number line. For example, -4 is 4 units from 0, and 3 is 3 units from 0. See Figure 10. Thus, the absolute value of -4 is 4, and the absolute value of 3 is 3.

A more formal definition of absolute value is given next.

Figure 10

DEFINITION

The **absolute value** of a real number a, denoted by the symbol $|a|$, is defined by the rules

$$|a| = a \quad \text{if } a \geq 0 \qquad \text{and} \qquad |a| = -a \quad \text{if } a < 0$$

For example, since $-4 < 0$, the second rule must be used to get $|-4| = -(-4) = 4$.

| EXAMPLE 5 | **Computing Absolute Value** |

(a) $|8| = 8$ (b) $|0| = 0$ (c) $|-15| = -(-15) = 15$

Look again at Figure 10. The distance from -4 to 3 is 7 units. This distance is the difference $3 - (-4)$, obtained by subtracting the smaller coordinate from the larger. However, since $|3 - (-4)| = |7| = 7$ and $|-4 - 3| = |-7| = 7$, we can use absolute value to calculate the distance between two points without being concerned about which is smaller.

DEFINITION

If P and Q are two points on a real number line with coordinates a and b, respectively, the **distance between P and Q,** denoted by $d(P, Q)$, is

$$d(P, Q) = |b - a|$$

Since $|b - a| = |a - b|$, it follows that $d(P, Q) = d(Q, P)$.

EXAMPLE 6 | **Finding Distance on a Number Line**

Let P, Q, and R be points on a real number line with coordinates -5, 7, and -3, respectively. Find the distance

(a) between P and Q (b) between Q and R

Solution See Figure 11.

Figure 11

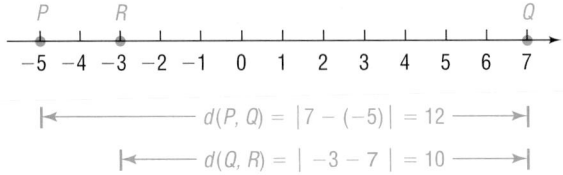

(a) $d(P, Q) = |7 - (-5)| = |12| = 12$
(b) $d(Q, R) = |-3 - 7| = |-10| = 10$

Now Work PROBLEM 47

4 Evaluate Algebraic Expressions

In algebra we use letters such as x, y, a, b, and c to represent numbers. If the letter used is to represent *any* number from a given set of numbers, it is called a **variable.** A **constant** is either a fixed number, such as 5 or $\sqrt{3}$, or a letter that represents a fixed (possibly unspecified) number.

Constants and variables are combined using the operations of addition, subtraction, multiplication, and division to form *algebraic expressions.* Examples of algebraic expressions include

$$x + 3 \qquad \frac{3}{1 - t} \qquad 7x - 2y$$

To evaluate an algebraic expression, substitute for each variable its numerical value.

EXAMPLE 7 | **Evaluating an Algebraic Expression**

Evaluate each expression if $x = 3$ and $y = -1$.

(a) $x + 3y$ (b) $5xy$ (c) $\dfrac{3y}{2 - 2x}$ (d) $|-4x + y|$

Solution (a) Substitute 3 for x and -1 for y in the expression $x + 3y$.

$$x + 3y = 3 + 3(-1) = 3 + (-3) = 0$$
$$\uparrow$$
$$x = 3, y = -1$$

(b) If $x = 3$ and $y = -1$, then
$$5xy = 5(3)(-1) = -15$$

(c) If $x = 3$ and $y = -1$, then
$$\frac{3y}{2 - 2x} = \frac{3(-1)}{2 - 2(3)} = \frac{-3}{2 - 6} = \frac{-3}{-4} = \frac{3}{4}$$

(d) If $x = 3$ and $y = -1$, then
$$\left|-4x + y\right| = \left|-4(3) + (-1)\right| = \left|-12 + (-1)\right| = \left|-13\right| = 13$$

─ **Now Work** PROBLEMS 49 AND 57

5 Determine the Domain of a Variable

In working with expressions or formulas involving variables, the variables may be allowed to take on values from only a certain set of numbers. For example, in the formula for the area A of a circle of radius r, $A = \pi r^2$, the variable r is restricted to the positive real numbers since a radius cannot be negative or zero. In the expression $\dfrac{1}{x}$, the variable x cannot take on the value 0, since division by 0 is not defined.

DEFINITION   The set of values that a variable may assume is called the **domain of the variable.**

EXAMPLE 8   Finding the Domain of a Variable

The domain of the variable x in the expression
$$\frac{5}{x - 2}$$

is $\{x \,|\, x \neq 2\}$, since, if $x = 2$, the denominator becomes 0, which is not defined.

EXAMPLE 9   Circumference of a Circle

In the formula for the circumference C of a circle of radius r,
$$C = 2\pi r$$

the domain of the variable r, representing the radius of the circle, is the set of positive real numbers. The domain of the variable C, representing the circumference of the circle, is also the set of positive real numbers.

In describing the domain of a variable, we may use either set notation or words, whichever is more convenient.

─ **Now Work** PROBLEM 67

6 Use the Laws of Exponents

Integer exponents provide a shorthand notation for representing repeated multiplications of a real number. For example,

$$2^3 = 2 \cdot 2 \cdot 2 = 8 \qquad 3^4 = 3 \cdot 3 \cdot 3 \cdot 3 = 81$$

DEFINITION If a is a real number and n is a positive integer, then the symbol a^n represents the product of n factors of a. That is,

$$a^n = \underbrace{a \cdot a \cdot \ldots \cdot a}_{n \text{ factors}} \qquad \text{(1)}$$

Here it is understood that $a^1 = a$.

Then $a^2 = a \cdot a$, $a^3 = a \cdot a \cdot a$, and so on. In the expression a^n, a is called the **base** and n is called the **exponent,** or **power.** We read a^n as "a raised to the power n" or as "a to the nth power." We usually read a^2 as "a squared" and a^3 as "a cubed."

In working with exponents, the operation of *raising to a power* is performed before any other operation. As examples,

$$4 \cdot 3^2 = 4 \cdot 9 = 36 \qquad 2^2 + 3^2 = 4 + 9 = 13$$
$$-2^4 = -16 \qquad 5 \cdot 3^2 + 2 \cdot 4 = 5 \cdot 9 + 2 \cdot 4 = 45 + 8 = 53$$

COMMENT Be careful with negatives and exponents.

$$-2^4 = -1 \cdot 2^4 = -16$$

whereas

$$(-2)^4 = (-2)(-2)(-2)(-2) = 16 \quad \blacksquare$$

Parentheses are used to indicate operations to be performed first. For example,

$$(-2)^4 = (-2)(-2)(-2)(-2) = 16 \qquad (2 + 3)^2 = 5^2 = 25$$

DEFINITION If $a \neq 0$, we define

$$a^0 = 1 \quad \text{if } a \neq 0$$

DEFINITION If $a \neq 0$ and if n is a positive integer, then we define

$$a^{-n} = \frac{1}{a^n} \quad \text{if } a \neq 0$$

Whenever you encounter a negative exponent, think "reciprocal."

EXAMPLE 10 Evaluating Expressions Containing Negative Exponents

(a) $2^{-3} = \dfrac{1}{2^3} = \dfrac{1}{8}$ (b) $-x^{-4} = \dfrac{-1}{x^4}$ (c) $\left(\dfrac{1}{5}\right)^{-2} = \dfrac{1}{\left(\dfrac{1}{5}\right)^2} = \dfrac{1}{\dfrac{1}{25}} = 25$

Now Work PROBLEMS 85 AND 105

The following properties, called the **Laws of Exponents,** can be proved using the preceding definitions. In the list, a and b are real numbers, and m and n are integers.

THEOREM **Laws of Exponents**

$$a^m a^n = a^{m+n} \qquad (a^m)^n = a^{mn} \qquad (ab)^n = a^n b^n$$
$$\frac{a^m}{a^n} = a^{m-n} = \frac{1}{a^{n-m}} \quad \text{if } a \neq 0 \qquad \left(\frac{a}{b}\right)^n = \frac{a^n}{b^n} \quad \text{if } b \neq 0$$

| EXAMPLE 11 | Using the Laws of Exponents |

Write each expression so that all exponents are positive.

(a) $\dfrac{x^5 y^{-2}}{x^3 y}$ $x \neq 0,\quad y \neq 0$ (b) $\left(\dfrac{x^{-3}}{3y^{-1}}\right)^{-2}$ $x \neq 0,\quad y \neq 0$

Solution   (a) $\dfrac{x^5 y^{-2}}{x^3 y} = \dfrac{x^5}{x^3} \cdot \dfrac{y^{-2}}{y} = x^{5-3} \cdot y^{-2-1} = x^2 y^{-3} = x^2 \cdot \dfrac{1}{y^3} = \dfrac{x^2}{y^3}$

(b) $\left(\dfrac{x^{-3}}{3y^{-1}}\right)^{-2} = \dfrac{(x^{-3})^{-2}}{(3y^{-1})^{-2}} = \dfrac{x^6}{3^{-2}(y^{-1})^{-2}} = \dfrac{x^6}{\dfrac{1}{9}y^2} = \dfrac{9x^6}{y^2}$

--- **Now Work** PROBLEMS 87 AND 97

7 Evaluate Square Roots

A real number is squared when it is raised to the power 2. The inverse of squaring is finding a **square root.** For example, since $6^2 = 36$ and $(-6)^2 = 36$, the numbers 6 and -6 are square roots of 36.

The symbol $\sqrt{}$, called a **radical sign,** is used to denote the **principal,** or nonnegative, square root. For example, $\sqrt{36} = 6$. We read $\sqrt{36}$ as "give me the nonnegative number whose square is 36."

DEFINITION   If a is a nonnegative real number, the nonnegative number b, for which $b^2 = a$, is the **principal square root** of a and is denoted by $b = \sqrt{a}$.

The following comments are noteworthy:

1. Negative numbers do not have square roots (in the real number system), because the square of any real number is *nonnegative.* For example, $\sqrt{-4}$ is not a real number, because there is no real number whose square is -4.

2. The principal square root of 0 is 0, since $0^2 = 0$. That is, $\sqrt{0} = 0$.

3. The principal square root of a positive number is positive.

4. If $c \geq 0$, then $(\sqrt{c})^2 = c$. For example, $(\sqrt{2})^2 = 2$ and $(\sqrt{3})^2 = 3$.

In Words
The symbol $\sqrt{a}$ means "give me the non-negative number whose square is a."

| EXAMPLE 12 | Evaluating Square Roots |

(a) $\sqrt{64} = 8$ (b) $\sqrt{\dfrac{1}{16}} = \dfrac{1}{4}$ (c) $\left(\sqrt{1.4}\right)^2 = 1.4$

Examples 12(a) and (b) are examples of square roots of perfect squares, since

$64 = 8^2$ and $\dfrac{1}{16} = \left(\dfrac{1}{4}\right)^2.$

Consider the expression $\sqrt{a^2}$. Since $a^2 \geq 0$, the principal square root of a^2 is defined whether $a > 0$ or $a < 0$. However, since the principal square root is nonnegative, we need an absolute value to ensure the nonnegative result. That is,

$$\sqrt{a^2} = |a| \qquad a \text{ any real number} \qquad (2)$$

> **EXAMPLE 13** Simplifying Expressions Using Equation 2
>
> (a) $\sqrt{(2.3)^2} = |2.3| = 2.3$ (b) $\sqrt{(-2.3)^2} = |-2.3| = 2.3$ (c) $\sqrt{x^2} = |x|$

Now Work PROBLEM 93

Calculators

Calculators are finite machines. As a result, they are incapable of displaying decimals that contain a large number of digits. For example, some calculators are capable of displaying only eight digits. When a number requires more than eight digits, the calculator either truncates or rounds. To see how your calculator handles decimals, divide 2 by 3. How many digits do you see? Is the last digit a 6 or a 7? If it is a 6, your calculator truncates; if it is a 7, your calculator rounds.

There are different kinds of calculators. An **arithmetic** calculator can only add, subtract, multiply, and divide numbers; therefore, this type is not adequate for this course. **Scientific** calculators have all the capabilities of arithmetic calculators and also contain **function keys** labeled ln, log, sin, cos, tan, x^y, inv, and so on. **Graphing** calculators have all the capabilities of scientific calculators and contain a screen on which graphs can be displayed.

8 Use a Calculator to Evaluate Exponents

Your calculator has a caret key, $\boxed{\wedge}$, which is used for computations involving exponents.

> **EXAMPLE 14** Exponents on a Graphing Calculator
>
> Evaluate: $(2.3)^5$
>
> **Solution** Figure 12 shows the result using a TI-84 graphing calculator.

Figure 12

Now Work PROBLEM 123

A.1 Assess Your Understanding

Concepts and Vocabulary

1. A(n) _____ is a letter used in algebra to represent any number from a given set of numbers.

2. On the real number line, the real number zero is the coordinate of the _____.

3. An inequality of the form $a > b$ is called a(n) _____ inequality.

4. In the expression 2^4, the number 2 is called the _____ and 4 is called the _____.

5. *True or False* The product of two negative real numbers is always greater than zero.

6. *True or False* The distance between two distinct points on the real number line is always greater than zero.

7. *True or False* The absolute value of a real number is always greater than zero.

8. *True or False* To multiply two expressions having the same base, retain the base and multiply the exponents.

Skill Building

In Problems 9–20, use U = universal set = $\{0, 1, 2, 3, 4, 5, 6, 7, 8, 9\}$, $A = \{1, 3, 4, 5, 9\}$, $B = \{2, 4, 6, 7, 8\}$, and $C = \{1, 3, 4, 6\}$ to find each set.

9. $A \cup B$ **10.** $A \cup C$ **11.** $A \cap B$ **12.** $A \cap C$

13. $(A \cup B) \cap C$ **14.** $(A \cap B) \cup C$ **15.** $\overline{A}$ **16.** $\overline{C}$

17. $\overline{A \cap B}$ **18.** $\overline{B \cup C}$ **19.** $\overline{A} \cup \overline{B}$ **20.** $\overline{B} \cap \overline{C}$

21. On the real number line, label the points with coordinates $0, 1, -1, \dfrac{5}{2}, -2.5, \dfrac{3}{4}$, and 0.25.

22. On the real number line, label the points with coordinates $0, -2, 2, -1.5, \dfrac{3}{2}, \dfrac{1}{3}$, and $\dfrac{2}{3}$.

In Problems 23–32, replace the question mark by $<$, $>$, or $=$, whichever is correct.

23. $\dfrac{1}{2} ? 0$ **24.** $5 ? 6$ **25.** $-1 ? -2$ **26.** $-3 ? -\dfrac{5}{2}$ **27.** $\pi ? 3.14$

28. $\sqrt{2} ? 1.41$ **29.** $\dfrac{1}{2} ? 0.5$ **30.** $\dfrac{1}{3} ? 0.33$ **31.** $\dfrac{2}{3} ? 0.67$ **32.** $\dfrac{1}{4} ? 0.25$

In Problems 33–38, write each statement as an inequality.

33. x is positive   **34.** z is negative   **35.** x is less than 2

36. y is greater than -5 **37.** x is less than or equal to 1   **38.** x is greater than or equal to 2

In Problems 39–42, graph the numbers x on the real number line.

39. $x \geq -2$ **40.** $x < 4$ **41.** $x > -1$ **42.** $x \leq 7$

In Problems 43–48, use the given real number line to compute each distance.

43. $d(C, D)$ **44.** $d(C, A)$ **45.** $d(D, E)$ **46.** $d(C, E)$ **47.** $d(A, E)$ **48.** $d(D, B)$

In Problems 49–56, evaluate each expression if $x = -2$ and $y = 3$.

49. $x + 2y$ **50.** $3x + y$ **51.** $5xy + 2$ **52.** $-2x + xy$

53. $\dfrac{2x}{x - y}$ **54.** $\dfrac{x + y}{x - y}$ **55.** $\dfrac{3x + 2y}{2 + y}$ **56.** $\dfrac{2x - 3}{y}$

In Problems 57–66, find the value of each expression if $x = 3$ and $y = -2$.

57. $|x + y|$ **58.** $|x - y|$ **59.** $|x| + |y|$ **60.** $|x| - |y|$ **61.** $\dfrac{|x|}{x}$

62. $\dfrac{|y|}{y}$ **63.** $|4x - 5y|$ **64.** $|3x + 2y|$ **65.** $\big||4x| - |5y|\big|$ **66.** $3|x| + 2|y|$

In Problems 67–74, determine which of the value(s) (a) through (d), if any, must be excluded from the domain of the variable in each expression:

  (a) $x = 3$ (b) $x = 1$ (c) $x = 0$ (d) $x = -1$

67. $\dfrac{x^2 - 1}{x}$ **68.** $\dfrac{x^2 + 1}{x}$ **69.** $\dfrac{x}{x^2 - 9}$ **70.** $\dfrac{x}{x^2 + 9}$

71. $\dfrac{x^2}{x^2 + 1}$ **72.** $\dfrac{x^3}{x^2 - 1}$ **73.** $\dfrac{x^2 + 5x - 10}{x^3 - x}$ **74.** $\dfrac{-9x^2 - x + 1}{x^3 + x}$

In Problems 75–78, determine the domain of the variable x in each expression.

75. $\dfrac{4}{x-5}$

76. $\dfrac{-6}{x+4}$

77. $\dfrac{x}{x+4}$

78. $\dfrac{x-2}{x-6}$

In Problems 79–82, use the formula $C = \dfrac{5}{9}(F-32)$ for converting degrees Fahrenheit into degrees Celsius to find the Celsius measure of each Fahrenheit temperature.

79. $F = 32°$

80. $F = 212°$

81. $F = 77°$

82. $F = -4°$

In Problems 83–94, simplify each expression.

83. $(-4)^2$

84. -4^2

85. 4^{-2}

86. -4^{-2}

87. $3^{-6} \cdot 3^4$

88. $4^{-2} \cdot 4^3$

89. $(3^{-2})^{-1}$

90. $(2^{-1})^{-3}$

91. $\sqrt{25}$

92. $\sqrt{36}$

93. $\sqrt{(-4)^2}$

94. $\sqrt{(-3)^2}$

In Problems 95–104, simplify each expression. Express the answer so that all exponents are positive. Whenever an exponent is 0 or negative, we assume that the base is not 0.

95. $(8x^3)^2$

96. $(-4x^2)^{-1}$

97. $(x^2 y^{-1})^2$

98. $(x^{-1}y)^3$

99. $\dfrac{x^2 y^3}{xy^4}$

100. $\dfrac{x^{-2}y}{xy^2}$

101. $\dfrac{(-2)^3 x^4 (yz)^2}{3^2 xy^3 z}$

102. $\dfrac{4x^{-2}(yz)^{-1}}{2^3 x^4 y}$

103. $\left(\dfrac{3x^{-1}}{4y^{-1}}\right)^{-2}$

104. $\left(\dfrac{5x^{-2}}{6y^{-2}}\right)^{-3}$

In Problems 105–116, find the value of each expression if $x = 2$ and $y = -1$.

105. $2xy^{-1}$

106. $-3x^{-1}y$

107. $x^2 + y^2$

108. $x^2 y^2$

109. $(xy)^2$

110. $(x+y)^2$

111. $\sqrt{x^2}$

112. $\left(\sqrt{x}\right)^2$

113. $\sqrt{x^2 + y^2}$

114. $\sqrt{x^2} + \sqrt{y^2}$

115. x^y

116. y^x

117. Find the value of the expression $2x^3 - 3x^2 + 5x - 4$ if $x = 2$. What is the value if $x = 1$?

118. Find the value of the expression $4x^3 + 3x^2 - x + 2$ if $x = 1$. What is the value if $x = 2$?

119. What is the value of $\dfrac{(666)^4}{(222)^4}$?

120. What is the value of $(0.1)^3 (20)^3$?

In Problems 121–128, use a calculator to evaluate each expression. Round your answer to three decimal places.

121. $(8.2)^6$

122. $(3.7)^5$

123. $(6.1)^{-3}$

124. $(2.2)^{-5}$

125. $(-2.8)^6$

126. $-(2.8)^6$

127. $(-8.11)^{-4}$

128. $-(8.11)^{-4}$

Applications and Extensions

In Problems 129–138, express each statement as an equation involving the indicated variables.

129. Area of a Rectangle The area A of a rectangle is the product of its length l and its width w.

131. Circumference of a Circle The circumference C of a circle is the product of π and its diameter d.

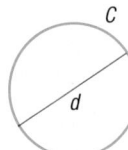

130. Perimeter of a Rectangle The perimeter P of a rectangle is twice the sum of its length l and its width w.

132. Area of a Triangle The area A of a triangle is one-half the product of its base b and its height h.

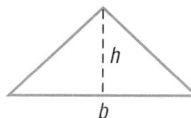

133. Area of an Equilateral Triangle The area A of an equilateral triangle is $\dfrac{\sqrt{3}}{4}$ times the square of the length x of one side.

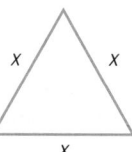

134. Perimeter of an Equilateral Triangle The perimeter P of an equilateral triangle is 3 times the length x of one side.

135. Volume of a Sphere The volume V of a sphere is $\dfrac{4}{3}$ times π times the cube of the radius r.

136. Surface Area of a Sphere The surface area S of a sphere is 4 times π times the square of the radius r.

137. Volume of a Cube The volume V of a cube is the cube of the length x of a side.

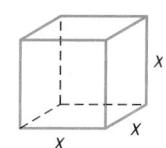

138. Surface Area of a Cube The surface area S of a cube is 6 times the square of the length x of a side.

139. Manufacturing Cost The weekly production cost C of manufacturing x watches is given by the formula $C = 4000 + 2x$, where the variable C is in dollars.
(a) What is the cost of producing 1000 watches?
(b) What is the cost of producing 2000 watches?

140. Balancing a Checkbook At the beginning of the month, Mike had a balance of $210 in his checking account. During the next month, he deposited $80, wrote a check for $120, made another deposit of $25, and wrote two checks: one for $60 and the other for $32. He was also assessed a monthly service charge of $5. What was his balance at the end of the month?

In Problems 141 and 142, write an inequality using an absolute value to describe each statement.

141. x is at least 6 units from 4.

142. x is more than 5 units from 2.

143. U.S. Voltage In the United States, normal household voltage is 110 volts. It is acceptable for the actual voltage x to differ from normal by at most 5 volts. A formula that describes this is

$$|x - 110| \leq 5$$

(a) Show that a voltage of 108 volts is acceptable.
(b) Show that a voltage of 104 volts is not acceptable.

144. Foreign Voltage In some countries, normal household voltage is 220 volts. It is acceptable for the actual voltage x to differ from normal by at most 8 volts. A formula that describes this is

$$|x - 220| \leq 8$$

(a) Show that a voltage of 214 volts is acceptable.
(b) Show that a voltage of 209 volts is not acceptable.

145. Making Precision Ball Bearings The FireBall Company manufactures ball bearings for precision equipment. One of its products is a ball bearing with a stated radius of 3 centimeters (cm). Only ball bearings with a radius within 0.01 cm of this stated radius are acceptable. If x is the radius of a ball bearing, a formula describing this situation is

$$|x - 3| \leq 0.01$$

(a) Is a ball bearing of radius $x = 2.999$ acceptable?
(b) Is a ball bearing of radius $x = 2.89$ acceptable?

146. Body Temperature Normal human body temperature is 98.6°F. A temperature x that differs from normal by at least 1.5°F is considered unhealthy. A formula that describes this is

$$|x - 98.6| \geq 1.5$$

(a) Show that a temperature of 97°F is unhealthy.
(b) Show that a temperature of 100°F is not unhealthy.

147. Does $\dfrac{1}{3}$ equal 0.333? If not, which is larger? By how much?

148. Does $\dfrac{2}{3}$ equal 0.666? If not, which is larger? By how much?

Discussion and Writing

149. Is there a positive real number "closest" to 0?

150. Number game I'm thinking of a number! It lies between 1 and 10; its square is rational and lies between 1 and 10. The number is larger than π. Correct to two decimal places (that is, truncated to two decimal places) name the number. Now think of your own number, describe it, and challenge a fellow student to name it.

151. Write a brief paragraph that illustrates the similarities and differences between "less than" ($<$) and "less than or equal to" ($\leq$).

152. Give a reason why the statement $5 < 8$ is true.

A.2 Geometry Essentials

OBJECTIVES 1 Use the Pythagorean Theorem and Its Converse (p. A14)
2 Know Geometry Formulas (p. A15)
3 Understand Congruent Triangles and Similar Triangles (p. A16)

In this section we review some topics studied in geometry that we shall need for our study of precalculus.

Figure 13

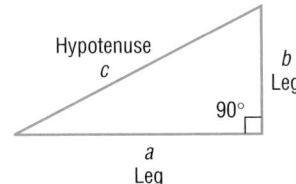

1 Use the Pythagorean Theorem and Its Converse

The *Pythagorean Theorem* is a statement about *right triangles*. A **right triangle** is one that contains a **right angle,** that is, an angle of 90°. The side of the triangle opposite the 90° angle is called the **hypotenuse;** the remaining two sides are called **legs.** In Figure 13 we have used c to represent the length of the hypotenuse and a and b to represent the lengths of the legs. Notice the use of the symbol ⌐ to show the 90° angle. We now state the Pythagorean Theorem.

PYTHAGOREAN THEOREM

In a right triangle, the square of the length of the hypotenuse is equal to the sum of the squares of the lengths of the legs. That is, in the right triangle shown in Figure 13,

$$c^2 = a^2 + b^2 \qquad \textbf{(1)}$$

A proof of the Pythagorean Theorem is given at the end of this section.

EXAMPLE 1 Finding the Hypotenuse of a Right Triangle

In a right triangle, one leg has length 4 and the other has length 3. What is the length of the hypotenuse?

Solution Since the triangle is a right triangle, we use the Pythagorean Theorem with $a = 4$ and $b = 3$ to find the length c of the hypotenuse. From equation (1), we have

$$c^2 = a^2 + b^2$$
$$c^2 = 4^2 + 3^2 = 16 + 9 = 25$$
$$c = \sqrt{25} = 5$$

━━━━ **Now Work** PROBLEM 13

The converse of the Pythagorean Theorem is also true.

CONVERSE OF THE PYTHAGOREAN THEOREM

In a triangle, if the square of the length of one side equals the sum of the squares of the lengths of the other two sides, the triangle is a right triangle. The 90° angle is opposite the longest side.

A proof is given at the end of this section.

EXAMPLE 2 Verifying That a Triangle Is a Right Triangle

Show that a triangle whose sides are of lengths 5, 12, and 13 is a right triangle. Identify the hypotenuse.

Solution We square the lengths of the sides.

$$5^2 = 25, \qquad 12^2 = 144, \qquad 13^2 = 169$$

Figure 14

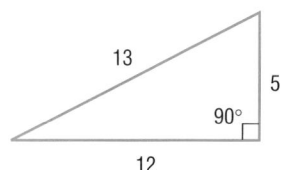

Notice that the sum of the first two squares (25 and 144) equals the third square (169). Hence, the triangle is a right triangle. The longest side, 13, is the hypotenuse. See Figure 14.

── **Now Work** PROBLEM 21

| EXAMPLE 3 | **Applying the Pythagorean Theorem** |

Excluding antenna, the tallest inhabited building in the world is Taipei 101 in Taipei, Taiwan. See Figure 15. If the indoor observation deck is 1437 feet above ground level, how far can a person standing on the observation deck see (with the aid of a telescope)? Use 3960 miles for the radius of Earth.

Source: Council on Tall Buildings and Urban Habitat, 2006.

Figure 15

Solution From the center of Earth, draw two radii: one through Taipei 101 and the other to the farthest point a person can see from the observation deck. See Figure 16. Apply the Pythagorean Theorem to the right triangle.

Since 1 mile = 5280 feet, then 1437 feet = $\dfrac{1437}{5280}$ mile. So we have

$$d^2 + (3960)^2 = \left(3960 + \frac{1437}{5280}\right)^2$$

$$d^2 = \left(3960 + \frac{1437}{5280}\right)^2 - (3960)^2 \approx 2155.57$$

$$d \approx 46.43$$

A person can see about 46 miles from the observation tower.

Figure 16

── **Now Work** PROBLEM 53

2 Know Geometry Formulas

Certain formulas from geometry are useful in solving precalculus problems. We list some of these next.

For a rectangle of length l and width w,

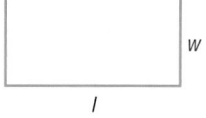

| Area = lw Perimeter = $2l + 2w$ |

For a triangle with base b and altitude h,

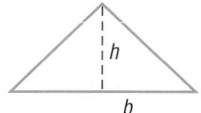

| Area = $\dfrac{1}{2}bh$ |

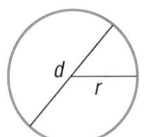

For a circle of radius r (diameter $d = 2r$),

$$\text{Area} = \pi r^2 \qquad \text{Circumference} = 2\pi r = \pi d$$

For a closed rectangular box of length l, width w, and height h,

$$\text{Volume} = lwh \qquad \text{Surface area} = 2lh + 2wh + 2lw$$

For a sphere of radius r,

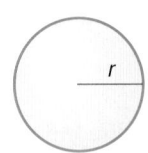

$$\text{Volume} = \frac{4}{3}\pi r^3 \qquad \text{Surface area} = 4\pi r^2$$

For a right circular cylinder of height h and radius r,

$$\text{Volume} = \pi r^2 h \qquad \text{Surface area} = 2\pi r^2 + 2\pi rh$$

━━━ **Now Work** PROBLEM 29

| EXAMPLE 4 | **Using Geometry Formulas** |

A Christmas tree ornament is in the shape of a semicircle on top of a triangle. How many square centimeters (cm) of copper is required to make the ornament if the height of the triangle is 6 cm and the base is 4 cm?

Solution

See Figure 17. The amount of copper required equals the shaded area. This area is the sum of the area of the triangle and the semicircle. The triangle has height $h = 6$ and base $b = 4$. The semicircle has diameter $d = 4$, so its radius is $r = 2$.

Figure 17

$$\text{Area} = \text{Area of triangle} + \text{Area of semicircle}$$
$$= \frac{1}{2}bh + \frac{1}{2}\pi r^2 = \frac{1}{2}(4)(6) + \frac{1}{2}\pi \cdot 2^2 \qquad b = 4; h = 6; r = 2$$
$$= 12 + 2\pi \approx 18.28 \text{ cm}^2$$

About 18.28 cm^2 of copper is required.

■

━━━ **Now Work** PROBLEM 47

3 Understand Congruent Triangles and Similar Triangles

Throughout the text we will make reference to triangles. We begin with a discussion of *congruent* triangles. According to dictionary.com, the word **congruent** means coinciding exactly when superimposed. For example, two angles are congruent if they have the same measure and two line segments are congruent if they have the same length.

In Words

Two triangles are congruent if they have the same size and shape.

DEFINITION

Two triangles are **congruent** if each of the corresponding angles is the same measure and each of the corresponding sides is the same length.

In Figure 18, corresponding angles are equal and the lengths of the corresponding sides are equal: $a = d$, $b = e$, and $c = f$. We conclude that these triangles are congruent.

Figure 18
Congruent triangles

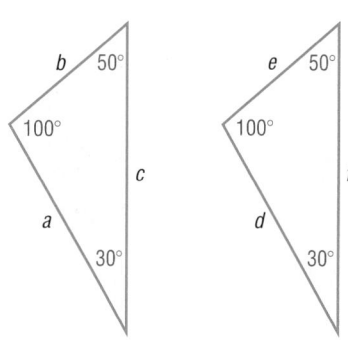

It is not necessary to verify that all three angles and all three sides are the same measure to determine whether two triangles are congruent.

Determining Congruent Triangles

1. **Angle–Side–Angle Case** Two triangles are congruent if two of the angles are equal and the lengths of the corresponding sides between the two angles are equal.

   For example, in Figure 19(a), the two triangles are congruent because two angles and the included side are equal.

2. **Side–Side–Side Case** Two triangles are congruent if the lengths of the corresponding sides of the triangles are equal.

   For example, in Figure 19(b), the two triangles are congruent because the three corresponding sides are all equal.

3. **Side–Angle–Side Case** Two triangles are congruent if the lengths of two corresponding sides are equal and the angles between the two sides are the same.

   For example, in Figure 19(c), the two triangles are congruent because two sides and the included angle are equal.

Figure 19

80° 80°	15 20 / 15 20	40° 8 / 40° 8
10 10	8 8	7 7
40° 40°		
(a)	(b)	(c)

We contrast congruent triangles with *similar* triangles.

DEFINITION Two triangles are **similar** if the corresponding angles are equal and the lengths of the corresponding sides are proportional.

In Words
Two triangles are similar if they have the same shape, but (possibly) different sizes.

For example, the triangles in Figure 20 on page A18 are similar because the corresponding angles are equal. In addition, the lengths of the corresponding sides are proportional because each side in the triangle on the right is twice as long as each corresponding side in the triangle on the left. That is, the ratio of the corresponding sides is a constant: $\dfrac{d}{a} = \dfrac{e}{b} = \dfrac{f}{c} = 2.$

Figure 20

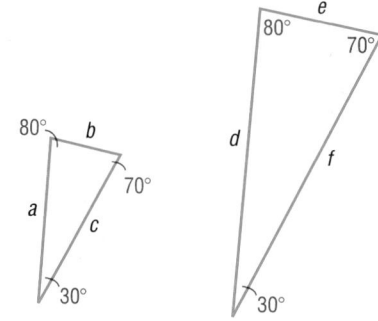

It is not necessary to verify that all three angles are equal and all three sides are proportional to determine whether two triangles are similar.

Determining Similar Triangles

1. **Angle–Angle Case**   Two triangles are similar if two of the corresponding angles are equal.

   For example, in Figure 21(a), the two triangles are similar because two angles are equal.

2. **Side–Side–Side Case**   Two triangles are similar if the lengths of all three sides of each triangle are proportional.

   For example, in Figure 21(b), the two triangles are similar because

$$\frac{10}{30} = \frac{5}{15} = \frac{6}{18} = \frac{1}{3}.$$

3. **Side–Angle–Side Case**   Two triangles are similar if two corresponding sides are proportional and the angles between the two sides are equal.

   For example, in Figure 21(c), the two triangles are similar because $\frac{4}{6} = \frac{12}{18} = \frac{2}{3}$ and the angles between the sides are equal.

Figure 21

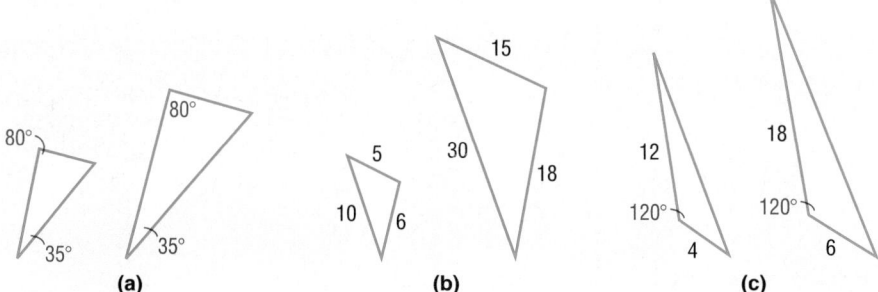

(a)   (b)   (c)

EXAMPLE 5   **Using Similar Triangles**

Given that the triangles in Figure 22 are similar, find the missing length x and the angles A, B, and C.

Figure 22

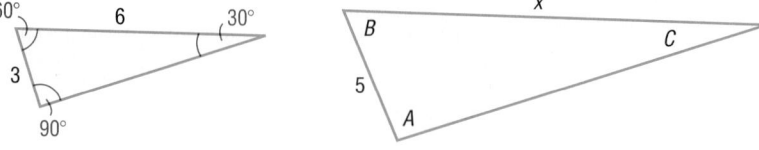

Solution   Because the triangles are similar, corresponding angles are equal. So $A = 90°$, $B = 60°$, and $C = 30°$. Also, the corresponding sides are proportional. That is, $\dfrac{3}{5} = \dfrac{6}{x}$. We solve this equation for x.

$$\frac{3}{5} = \frac{6}{x}$$

$$5x \cdot \frac{3}{5} = 5x \cdot \frac{6}{x} \qquad \text{Multiply both sides by 5x.}$$

$$3x = 30 \qquad \text{Simplify.}$$

$$x = 10 \qquad \text{Divide both sides by 3.}$$

The missing length is 10 units.

— **Now Work** PROBLEM 41

Proof of the Pythagorean Theorem   We begin with a square, each side of length $a + b$. In this square, we can form four right triangles, each having legs equal in length to a and b. See Figure 23. All these triangles are congruent (two sides and their included angle are equal). As a result, the hypotenuse of each is the same, say c, and the pink shading in Figure 23 indicates a square with an area equal to c^2.

Figure 23

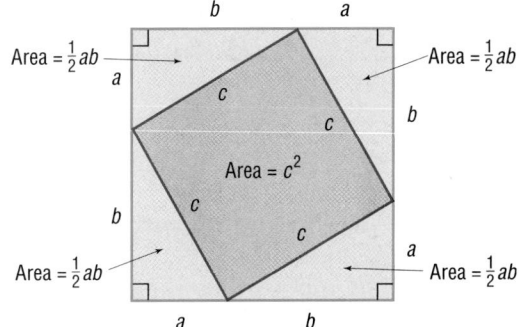

The area of the original square with sides $a + b$ equals the sum of the areas of the four triangles (each of area $\dfrac{1}{2}ab$) plus the area of the square with side c. That is,

$$(a + b)^2 = \frac{1}{2}ab + \frac{1}{2}ab + \frac{1}{2}ab + \frac{1}{2}ab + c^2$$

$$a^2 + 2ab + b^2 = 2ab + c^2$$

$$a^2 + b^2 = c^2$$

The proof is complete.   ∎

Proof of the Converse of the Pythagorean Theorem   We begin with two triangles: one a right triangle with legs a and b and the other a triangle with sides a, b, and c for which $c^2 = a^2 + b^2$. See Figure 24. By the Pythagorean Theorem, the length x of the third side of the first triangle is

$$x^2 = a^2 + b^2$$

But $c^2 = a^2 + b^2$. Hence,

$$x^2 = c^2$$

$$x = c$$

The two triangles have sides with the same length and are therefore congruent. This means corresponding angles are equal, so the angle opposite side c of the second triangle equals 90°.
    The proof is complete.   ∎

Figure 24

(a)

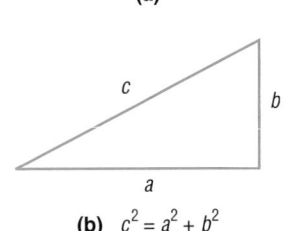

(b) $c^2 = a^2 + b^2$

A.2 Assess Your Understanding

Concepts and Vocabulary

1. A(n) _____ triangle is one that contains an angle of 90 degrees. The longest side is called the _____.

2. For a triangle with base b and altitude h, a formula for the area A is _____.

3. The formula for the circumference C of a circle of radius r is _____.

4. Two triangles are _____ if corresponding angles are equal and the lengths of the corresponding sides are proportional.

5. *True or False*   In a right triangle, the square of the length of the longest side equals the sum of the squares of the lengths of the other two sides.

6. *True or False*   The triangle with sides of length 6, 8, and 10 is a right triangle.

7. *True or False*   The volume of a sphere of radius r is $\dfrac{4}{3}\pi r^2$.

8. *True or False*   The triangles shown are congruent.

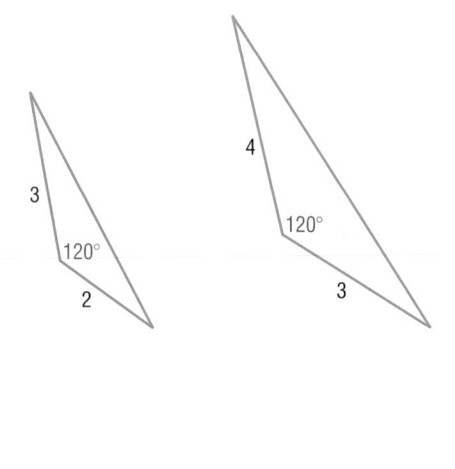

9. *True or False*   The triangles shown are similar.

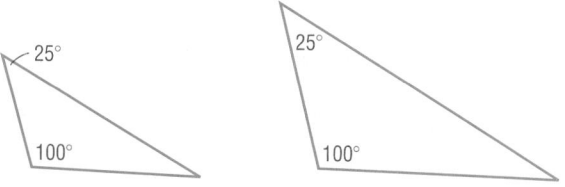

10. *True or False*   The triangles shown are similar.

Skill Building

In Problems 11–16, the lengths of the legs of a right triangle are given. Find the length of the hypotenuse.

11. $a = 5$, $b = 12$

12. $a = 6$, $b = 8$

13. $a = 10$, $b = 24$

14. $a = 4$, $b = 3$

15. $a = 7$, $b = 24$

16. $a = 14$, $b = 48$

In Problems 17–24, the lengths of the sides of a triangle are given. Determine which are right triangles. For those that are, identify the hypotenuse.

17. 3, 4, 5

18. 6, 8, 10

19. 4, 5, 6

20. 2, 2, 3

21. 7, 24, 25

22. 10, 24, 26

23. 6, 4, 3

24. 5, 4, 7

25. Find the area A of a rectangle with length 4 inches and width 2 inches.

26. Find the area A of a rectangle with length 9 centimeters and width 4 centimeters.

27. Find the area A of a triangle with height 4 inches and base 2 inches.

28. Find the area A of a triangle with height 9 centimeters and base 4 centimeters.

29. Find the area A and circumference C of a circle of radius 5 meters.

30. Find the area A and circumference C of a circle of radius 2 feet.

31. Find the volume V and surface area S of a rectangular box with length 8 feet, width 4 feet, and height 7 feet.

32. Find the volume V and surface area S of a rectangular box with length 9 inches, width 4 inches, and height 8 inches.

33. Find the volume V and surface area S of a sphere of radius 4 centimeters.

34. Find the volume V and surface area S of a sphere of radius 3 feet.

35. Find the volume V and surface area S of a right circular cylinder with radius 9 inches and height 8 inches.

36. Find the volume V and surface area S of a right circular cylinder with radius 8 inches and height 9 inches.

In Problems 37–40, find the area of the shaded region.

37.

38.

39.

40.
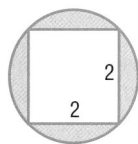

In Problems 41–44, each pair of triangles is similar. Find the missing length x and the missing angles A, B, and C.

41.

42.

43.

44.

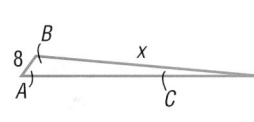

Applications and Extensions

45. How many feet does a wheel with a diameter of 16 inches travel after four revolutions?

46. How many revolutions will a circular disk with a diameter of 4 feet have completed after it has rolled 20 feet?

47. In the figure shown, *ABCD* is a square, with each side of length 6 feet. The width of the border (shaded portion) between the outer square *EFGH* and *ABCD* is 2 feet. Find the area of the border.

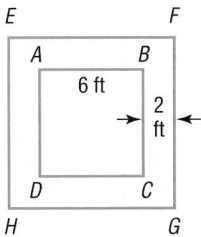

48. Refer to the figure. Square *ABCD* has an area of 100 square feet; square *BEFG* has an area of 16 square feet. What is the area of the triangle *CGF*?

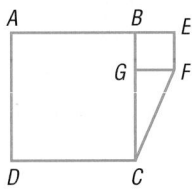

49. Architecture   A **Norman window** consists of a rectangle surmounted by a semicircle. Find the area of the Norman window shown in the illustration. How much wood frame is needed to enclose the window?

50. Construction   A circular swimming pool, 20 feet in diameter, is enclosed by a wooden deck that is 3 feet wide. What is the area of the deck? How much fence is required to enclose the deck?

51. How Tall Is the Great Pyramid? The ancient Greek philosopher Thales of Miletus is reported on one occasion to have visited Egypt and calculated the height of the Great Pyramid of Cheops by means of shadow reckoning. Thales knew that each side of the base of the pyramid was 252 paces and that his own height was 2 paces. He measured the length of the pyramid's shadow to be 114 paces and determined the length of his shadow to be 3 paces. See the illustration. Using similar triangles, determine the height of the Great Pyramid in terms of the number of paces.

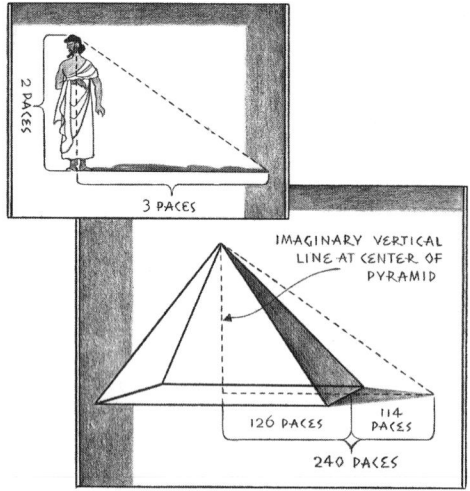

Source: www.anselm.edu/homepage/dbanach/ thales.htm. This site references another source: Selections, from Julia E. Diggins, *String, Straightedge, and Shadow,* Viking Press, New York, 1965, Illustrations by Corydon Bell.

52. The Bermuda Triangle Karen is doing research on the Bermuda Triangle which she defines roughly by Hamilton, Bermuda; San Juan, Puerto Rico; and Fort Lauderdale, Florida. On her atlas Karen measures the straight-line distances from Hamilton to Fort Lauderdale, Fort Lauderdale to San Juan, and San Juan to Hamilton to be approximately 57 millimeters (mm), 58 mm, and 53.5 mm respectively. If the actual distance from Fort Lauderdale to San Juan is 1046 miles, approximate the actual distances from San Juan to Hamilton and from Hamilton to Fort Lauderdale.

Source: www.worldatlas.com

Source: www.en.wikipedia.org/wiki/Bermuda_Triangle.

In Problems 53–55, use the facts that the radius of Earth is 3960 miles and 1 mile = 5280 feet.

53. How Far Can You See? The conning tower of the U.S.S. *Silversides,* a World War II submarine now permanently stationed in Muskegon, Michigan, is approximately 20 feet above sea level. How far can you see from the conning tower?

54. How Far Can You See? A person who is 6 feet tall is standing on the beach in Fort Lauderdale, Florida, and looks out onto the Atlantic Ocean. Suddenly, a ship appears on the horizon. How far is the ship from shore?

55. How Far Can You See? The deck of a destroyer is 100 feet above sea level. How far can a person see from the deck? How far can a person see from the bridge, which is 150 feet above sea level?

56. Suppose that m and n are positive integers with $m > n$. If $a = m^2 - n^2$, $b = 2mn$, and $c = m^2 + n^2$, show that a, b, and c are the lengths of the sides of a right triangle. (This formula can be used to find the sides of a right triangle that are integers, such as 3, 4, 5; 5, 12, 13; and so on. Such triplets of integers are called **Pythagorean triples.**)

Discussion and Writing

57. You have 1000 feet of flexible pool siding and wish to construct a swimming pool. Experiment with rectangular-shaped pools with perimeters of 1000 feet. How do their areas vary? What is the shape of the rectangle with the largest area? Now compute the area enclosed by a circular pool with a perimeter (circumference) of 1000 feet. What would be your choice of shape for the pool? If rectangular, what is your preference for dimensions? Justify your choice. If your only consideration is to have a pool that encloses the most area, what shape should you use?

58. The Gibb's Hill Lighthouse, Southampton, Bermuda, in operation since 1846, stands 117 feet high on a hill 245 feet high, so its beam of light is 362 feet above sea level. A brochure states that the light itself can be seen on the horizon about 26 miles distant. Verify the correctness of this information. The brochure further states that ships 40 miles away can see the light and planes flying at 10,000 feet can see it 120 miles away. Verify the accuracy of these statements. What assumption did the brochure make about the height of the ship?

A.3 Polynomials

OBJECTIVES 1 Recognize Monomials (p. A23)
2 Recognize Polynomials (p. A24)
3 Know Formulas for Special Products (p. A25)
4 Divide Polynomials Using Long Division (p. A26)
5 Factor Polynomials (p. A28)

We have described algebra as a generalization of arithmetic in which letters are used to represent real numbers. From now on, we shall use the letters at the end of the alphabet, such as x, y, and z, to represent variables and the letters at the beginning of the alphabet, such as a, b, and c, to represent constants. In the expressions $3x + 5$ and $ax + b$, it is understood that x is a variable and that a and b are constants, even though the constants a and b are unspecified. As you will find out, the context usually makes the intended meaning clear.

1 Recognize Monomials

DEFINITION

A **monomial** in one variable is the product of a constant and a variable raised to a nonnegative integer power. A monomial is of the form

$$ax^k$$

where a is a constant, x is a variable, and $k \geq 0$ is an integer. The constant a is called the **coefficient** of the monomial. If $a \neq 0$, then k is the **degree** of the monomial.

NOTE The nonnegative integers are the integers $0, 1, 2, 3, \ldots$. ∎

EXAMPLE 1   **Examples of Monomials**

Monomial	Coefficient	Degree	
(a) $6x^2$	6	2	
(b) $-\sqrt{2}x^3$	$-\sqrt{2}$	3	
(c) 3	3	0	Since $3 = 3 \cdot 1 = 3x^0, x \neq 0$
(d) $-5x$	-5	1	Since $-5x = -5x^1$
(e) x^4	1	4	Since $x^4 = 1 \cdot x^4$

Now let's look at some expressions that are not monomials.

EXAMPLE 2   **Examples of Nonmonomial Expressions**

(a) $3x^{1/2}$ is not a monomial, since the exponent of the variable x is $\dfrac{1}{2}$ and $\dfrac{1}{2}$ is not a nonnegative integer.

(b) $4x^{-3}$ is not a monomial, since the exponent of the variable x is -3 and -3 is not a nonnegative integer.

Now Work PROBLEM 11

2 Recognize Polynomials

Two monomials with the same variable raised to the same power are called **like terms.** For example, $2x^4$ and $-5x^4$ are like terms. In contrast, the monomials $2x^3$ and $2x^5$ are not like terms.

We can add or subtract like terms using the Distributive Property. For example,

$$2x^2 + 5x^2 = (2 + 5)x^2 = 7x^2 \quad \text{and} \quad 8x^3 - 5x^3 = (8 - 5)x^3 = 3x^3$$

The sum or difference of two monomials having different degrees is called a **binomial.** The sum or difference of three monomials with three different degrees is called a **trinomial.** For example,

$x^2 - 2$ is a binomial.

$x^3 - 3x + 5$ is a trinomial.

$2x^2 + 5x^2 + 2 = 7x^2 + 2$ is a binomial.

DEFINITION

A **polynomial** in one variable is an algebraic expression of the form

$$a_n x^n + a_{n-1} x^{n-1} + \cdots + a_1 x + a_0 \qquad (1)$$

In Words

A polynomial is a sum of monomials.

where $a_n, a_{n-1}, \ldots, a_1, a_0$ are constants,* called the **coefficients** of the polynomial, $n \geq 0$ is an integer, and x is a variable. If $a_n \neq 0$, it is the **leading coefficient,** and n is the **degree** of the polynomial.

The monomials that make up a polynomial are called its **terms.** If all the coefficients are 0, the polynomial is called the **zero polynomial,** which has no degree.

Polynomials are usually written in **standard form,** beginning with the nonzero term of highest degree and continuing with terms in descending order according to degree. If a power of x is missing, it is because its coefficient is zero.

EXAMPLE 3 | **Examples of Polynomials**

Polynomial	Coefficients	Degree
$-8x^3 + 4x^2 + 6x + 2$	$-8, 4, 6, 2$	3
$3x^2 - 5 = 3x^2 + 0 \cdot x + (-5)$	$3, 0, -5$	2
$8 - 2x + x^2 = 1 \cdot x^2 + (-2)x + 8$	$1, -2, 8$	2
$5x + \sqrt{2} = 5x^1 + \sqrt{2}$	$5, \sqrt{2}$	1
$3 = 3 \cdot 1 = 3 \cdot x^0$	3	0
0	0	No degree

Although we have been using x to represent the variable, letters such as y or z are also commonly used.

$3x^4 - x^2 + 2$ is a polynomial (in x) of degree 4.

$9y^3 - 2y^2 + y - 3$ is a polynomial (in y) of degree 3.

$z^5 + \pi$ is a polynomial (in z) of degree 5.

Algebraic expressions such as

$$\frac{1}{x} \quad \text{and} \quad \frac{x^2 + 1}{x + 5}$$

* The notation a_n is read as "a sub n." The number n is called a **subscript** and should not be confused with an exponent. We use subscripts to distinguish one constant from another when a large or undetermined number of constants is required.

are not polynomials. The first is not a polynomial because $\dfrac{1}{x} = x^{-1}$ has an exponent that is not a nonnegative integer. Although the second expression is the quotient of two polynomials, the polynomial in the denominator has degree greater than 0, so the expression cannot be a polynomial.

Now Work PROBLEM 21

3 Know Formulas for Special Products

Certain products, which we call **special products,** occur frequently in algebra. For example, we can find the product of two binomials using the **FOIL** (*First, Outer, Inner, Last*) method.

$$(ax + b)(cx + d) = ax(cx + d) + b(cx + d)$$
$$= ax \cdot cx + ax \cdot d + b \cdot cx + b \cdot d$$
$$= acx^2 + adx + bcx + bd$$
$$= acx^2 + (ad + bc)x + bd$$

EXAMPLE 4 | **Using FOIL**

(a) $(x - 3)(x + 3) = x^2 + 3x - 3x - 9 = x^2 - 9$

(b) $(x + 2)^2 = (x + 2)(x + 2) = x^2 + 2x + 2x + 4 = x^2 + 4x + 4$

(c) $(x - 3)^2 = (x - 3)(x - 3) = x^2 - 3x - 3x + 9 = x^2 - 6x + 9$

(d) $(x + 3)(x + 1) = x^2 + x + 3x + 3 = x^2 + 4x + 3$

(e) $(2x + 1)(3x + 4) = 6x^2 + 8x + 3x + 4 = 6x^2 + 11x + 4$

Now Work PROBLEM 41

Some products have been given special names because of their form. In the list that follows, x, a, and b are real numbers.

Difference of Two Squares

$$(x - a)(x + a) = x^2 - a^2 \qquad (2)$$

Squares of Binomials, or Perfect Squares

$$(x + a)^2 = x^2 + 2ax + a^2 \qquad (3a)$$
$$(x - a)^2 = x^2 - 2ax + a^2 \qquad (3b)$$

Cubes of Binomials, or Perfect Cubes

$$(x + a)^3 = x^3 + 3ax^2 + 3a^2x + a^3 \qquad (4a)$$
$$(x - a)^3 = x^3 - 3ax^2 + 3a^2x - a^3 \qquad (4b)$$

Difference of Two Cubes

$$(x - a)(x^2 + ax + a^2) = x^3 - a^3 \qquad \textbf{(5)}$$

Sum of Two Cubes

$$(x + a)(x^2 - ax + a^2) = x^3 + a^3 \qquad \textbf{(6)}$$

━━━━━ **Now Work** PROBLEMS 45, 49, AND 53

4 Divide Polynomials Using Long Division

The procedure for dividing two polynomials is similar to the procedure for dividing two integers.

EXAMPLE 5 | Dividing Two Integers

Divide 842 by 15.

Solution

$$
\begin{array}{r}
56 \quad \leftarrow \text{Quotient} \\
\text{Divisor} \rightarrow \quad 15\overline{)842} \quad \leftarrow \text{Dividend} \\
75 \quad \leftarrow 5 \cdot 15 \text{ (subtract)} \\
\hline
92 \\
90 \quad \leftarrow 6 \cdot 15 \text{ (subtract)} \\
\hline
2 \quad \leftarrow \text{Remainder}
\end{array}
$$

So, $\dfrac{842}{15} = 56 + \dfrac{2}{15}$.

In the long division process detailed in Example 5, the number 15 is called the **divisor,** the number 842 is called the **dividend,** the number 56 is called the **quotient,** and the number 2 is called the **remainder.**

To check the answer obtained in a division problem, multiply the quotient by the divisor and add the remainder. The answer should be the dividend.

$$\boxed{(\text{Quotient})(\text{Divisor}) + \text{Remainder} = \text{Dividend}}$$

For example, we can check the results obtained in Example 5 as follows:

$$(56)(15) + 2 = 840 + 2 = 842$$

To divide two polynomials, we first must write each polynomial in standard form. The process then follows a pattern similar to that of Example 5. The next example illustrates the procedure.

EXAMPLE 6 | Dividing Two Polynomials

Find the quotient and the remainder when

$$3x^3 + 4x^2 + x + 7 \quad \text{is divided by} \quad x^2 + 1$$

Solution

Each polynomial is in standard form. The dividend is $3x^3 + 4x^2 + x + 7$, and the divisor is $x^2 + 1$.

STEP 1: Divide the leading term of the dividend, $3x^3$, by the leading term of the divisor, x^2. Enter the result, $3x$, over the term $3x^3$, as follows:

$$
\begin{array}{r}
3x \\
x^2 + 1\overline{)3x^3 + 4x^2 + x + 7}
\end{array}
$$

STEP 2: Multiply $3x$ by $x^2 + 1$ and enter the result below the dividend.

$$
\begin{array}{r}
3x \qquad\qquad\quad \\
x^2 + 1 \overline{)3x^3 + 4x^2 + x + 7} \\
3x^3 \qquad\quad + 3x \qquad\quad
\end{array}
$$

$\leftarrow 3x \cdot (x^2 + 1) = 3x^3 + 3x$

Notice that we align the 3x term under the x to make the next step easier.

STEP 3: Subtract and bring down the remaining terms.

$$
\begin{array}{r}
3x \qquad\qquad\quad \\
x^2 + 1 \overline{)3x^3 + 4x^2 + x + 7} \\
3x^3 \qquad\quad + 3x \qquad\quad \\
\hline
4x^2 - 2x + 7
\end{array}
$$

$\leftarrow$ *Subtract (change the signs and add).*
$\leftarrow$ *Bring down the 4x² and the 7.*

STEP 4: Repeat Steps 1–3 using $4x^2 - 2x + 7$ as the dividend.

$$
\begin{array}{r}
3x + 4 \qquad\qquad \\
x^2 + 1 \overline{)3x^3 + 4x^2 + x + 7} \\
3x^3 \qquad\quad + 3x \qquad\quad \\
\hline
4x^2 - 2x + 7 \\
4x^2 \qquad\quad + 4 \\
\hline
-2x + 3
\end{array}
$$

$\leftarrow$ *Divide 4x² by x² to get 4.*
$\leftarrow$ *Multiply x² + 1 by 4; subtract.*

Since x^2 does not divide $-2x$ evenly (that is, the result is not a monomial), the process ends. The quotient is $3x + 4$, and the remainder is $-2x + 3$.

✓ **Check:** (Quotient)(Divisor) + Remainder

$$
\begin{aligned}
&= (3x + 4)(x^2 + 1) + (-2x + 3) \\
&= 3x^3 + 3x + 4x^2 + 4 + (-2x + 3) \\
&= 3x^3 + 4x^2 + x + 7 = \text{Dividend}
\end{aligned}
$$

Then

$$
\frac{3x^3 + 4x^2 + x + 7}{x^2 + 1} = 3x + 4 + \frac{-2x + 3}{x^2 + 1}
$$

The next example combines the steps involved in long division.

EXAMPLE 7   **Dividing Two Polynomials**

Find the quotient and the remainder when

$$x^4 - 3x^3 + 2x - 5 \quad \text{is divided by} \quad x^2 - x + 1$$

Solution   In setting up this division problem, it is necessary to leave a space for the missing x^2 term in the dividend.

$$
\begin{array}{r}
x^2 - 2x - 3 \qquad\qquad\quad \\
x^2 - x + 1 \overline{)x^4 - 3x^3 \qquad\quad + 2x - 5} \\
x^4 - x^3 + x^2 \qquad\qquad \\
\hline
-2x^3 - x^2 + 2x - 5 \\
-2x^3 + 2x^2 - 2x \qquad\quad \\
\hline
-3x^2 + 4x - 5 \\
-3x^2 + 3x - 3 \\
\hline
x - 2
\end{array}
$$

Divisor $\rightarrow$
Subtract $\rightarrow$
Subtract $\rightarrow$
Subtract $\rightarrow$

$\leftarrow$ Quotient
$\leftarrow$ Dividend
$\leftarrow$ Remainder

Check: (Quotient)(Divisor) + Remainder

$$= (x^2 - 2x - 3)(x^2 - x + 1) + x - 2$$
$$= x^4 - x^3 + x^2 - 2x^3 + 2x^2 - 2x - 3x^2 + 3x - 3 + x - 2$$
$$= x^4 - 3x^3 + 2x - 5 = \text{Dividend}$$

As a result,

$$\frac{x^4 - 3x^3 + 2x - 5}{x^2 - x + 1} = x^2 - 2x - 3 + \frac{x - 2}{x^2 - x + 1}$$

The process of dividing two polynomials leads to the following result:

THEOREM Let Q be a polynomial of positive degree and let P be a polynomial whose degree is greater than or equal to the degree of Q. The remainder after dividing P by Q is either the zero polynomial or a polynomial whose degree is less than the degree of the divisor Q.

Now Work PROBLEM 61

5 Factor Polynomials

Consider the following product:

$$(2x + 3)(x - 4) = 2x^2 - 5x - 12$$

The two polynomials on the left side are called **factors** of the polynomial on the right side. Expressing a given polynomial as a product of other polynomials, that is, finding the factors of a polynomial, is called **factoring.**

We shall restrict our discussion here to factoring polynomials in one variable into products of polynomials in one variable, where all coefficients are integers. We call this **factoring over the integers.**

Any polynomial can be written as the product of 1 times itself or as -1 times its additive inverse. If a polynomial cannot be written as the product of two other polynomials (excluding 1 and -1), then the polynomial is said to be **prime.** When a polynomial has been written as a product consisting only of prime factors, it is said to be **factored completely.** Examples of prime polynomials (over the integers) are

$$2, \quad 3, \quad 5, \quad x, \quad x + 1, \quad x - 1, \quad 3x + 4 \quad x^2 + 4$$

COMMENT Over the real numbers, $3x + 4$ factors into $3\left(x + \dfrac{4}{3}\right)$. It is the noninteger $\dfrac{4}{3}$ that causes $3x + 4$ to be prime over the integers. ∎

The first factor to look for in a factoring problem is a common monomial factor present in each term of the polynomial. If one is present, use the Distributive Property to factor it out.

| EXAMPLE 8 | Identifying Common Monomial Factors |

Polynomial	Common Monomial Factor	Remaining Factor	Factored Form
$2x + 4$	2	$x + 2$	$2x + 4 = 2(x + 2)$
$3x - 6$	3	$x - 2$	$3x - 6 = 3(x - 2)$
$2x^2 - 4x + 8$	2	$x^2 - 2x + 4$	$2x^2 - 4x + 8 = 2(x^2 - 2x + 4)$
$8x - 12$	4	$2x - 3$	$8x - 12 = 4(2x - 3)$
$x^2 + x$	x	$x + 1$	$x^2 + x = x(x + 1)$
$x^3 - 3x^2$	x^2	$x - 3$	$x^3 - 3x^2 = x^2(x - 3)$
$6x^2 + 9x$	$3x$	$2x + 3$	$6x^2 + 9x = 3x(2x + 3)$

Notice that, once all common monomial factors have been removed from a polynomial, the remaining factor is either a prime polynomial of degree 1 or a polynomial of degree 2 or higher. (Do you see why?)

The list of special products (2) through (6) given earlier provides a list of factoring formulas when the equations are read from right to left. For example, equation (2) states that if the polynomial is the difference of two squares, $x^2 - a^2$, it can be factored into $(x - a)(x + a)$. The following example illustrates several factoring techniques.

EXAMPLE 9   **Factoring Polynomials**

Factor completely each polynomial.

(a) $x^4 - 16$ (b) $x^3 - 1$ (c) $9x^2 - 6x + 1$

(d) $x^2 + 4x - 12$ (e) $3x^2 + 10x - 8$ (f) $x^3 - 4x^2 + 2x - 8$

Solution   (a) $x^4 - 16 = (x^2 - 4)(x^2 + 4) = (x - 2)(x + 2)(x^2 + 4)$

   Difference of squares   Difference of squares

(b) $x^3 - 1 = (x - 1)(x^2 + x + 1)$

   Difference of cubes

(c) $9x^2 - 6x + 1 = (3x - 1)^2$

   Perfect square

(d) $x^2 + 4x - 12 = (x + 6)(x - 2)$

   The product of 6 and -2 is -12, and the sum of 6 and -2 is 4.

   $12x - 2x = 10x$

(e) $3x^2 + 10x - 8 = (3x - 2)(x + 4)$

   $3x^2$ -8

NOTE The technique used in part (f) is called **factoring by grouping**. ■

(f) $x^3 - 4x^2 + 2x - 8 = (x^3 - 4x^2) + (2x - 8)$

   Group terms

$= x^2(x - 4) + 2(x - 4) = (x^2 + 2)(x - 4)$

   Distributive property   Distributive property

──── **Now Work** PROBLEMS 81, 97, AND 125

A.3 Assess Your Understanding

Concepts and Vocabulary

1. The polynomial $3x^4 - 2x^3 + 13x^2 - 5$ is of degree ____. The leading coefficient is ____.

2. $(x^2 - 4)(x^2 + 4) =$ ____.

3. $(x - 2)(x^2 + 2x + 4) =$ ____.

4. *True or False* $4x^{-2}$ is a monomial of degree -2.

5. *True or False* $(x + a)(x^2 + ax + a) = x^3 + a^3$.

6. To check division, the expression that is being divided, the dividend, should equal the product of the ____ and the ____ plus the ____.

7. If factored completely, $3x^3 - 12x =$ ____.

8. If a polynomial cannot be written as the product of two other polynomials (excluding 1 and -1), then the polynomial is said to be ____.

9. *True or False*   The polynomial $x^2 + 4$ is prime.

10. *True or False* $3x^3 - 2x^2 - 6x + 4 = (3x - 2)(x^2 + 2)$.

Skill Building

In Problems 11–20, tell whether the expression is a monomial. If it is, name the variable(s) and the coefficient and give the degree of the monomial. If it is not a monomial, state why not.

11. $2x^3$

12. $-4x^2$

13. $\dfrac{8}{x}$

14. $-2x^{-3}$

15. $-2x^3 + 5x^2$

16. $6x^5 - 8x^2$

17. $\dfrac{8x}{x^2 - 1}$

18. $-\dfrac{2x^2}{x^3 + 1}$

19. $x^2 + 2x - 5$

20. $3x^2 + 4$

In Problems 21–30, tell whether the expression is a polynomial. If it is, give its degree. If it is not, state why not.

21. $3x^2 - 5$

22. $1 - 4x$

23. 5

24. $-\pi$

25. $3x^2 - \dfrac{5}{x}$

26. $\dfrac{3}{x} + 2$

27. $2y^3 - \sqrt{2}$

28. $10z^2 + z$

29. $\dfrac{x^2 + 5}{x^3 - 1}$

30. $\dfrac{3x^3 + 2x - 1}{x^2 + x + 1}$

In Problems 31–56, add, subtract, or multiply, as indicated. Express your answer as a single polynomial in standard form.

31. $(x^2 + 4x + 5) + (3x - 3)$

32. $(x^3 + 3x^2 + 2) + (x^2 - 4x + 4)$

33. $(x^3 - 2x^2 + 5x + 10) - (2x^2 - 4x + 3)$

34. $(x^2 - 3x - 4) - (x^3 - 3x^2 + x + 5)$

35. $6(x^3 + x^2 - 3) - 4(2x^3 - 3x^2)$

36. $8(4x^3 - 3x^2 - 1) - 6(4x^3 + 8x - 2)$

37. $9(y^2 - 3y + 4) - 6(1 - y^2)$

38. $8(1 - y^3) + 4(1 + y + y^2 + y^3)$

39. $x(x^2 + x - 4)$

40. $4x^2(x^3 - x + 2)$

41. $(x + 2)(x + 4)$

42. $(x + 3)(x + 5)$

43. $(2x + 5)(x + 2)$

44. $(3x + 1)(2x + 1)$

45. $(x - 7)(x + 7)$

46. $(x - 1)(x + 1)$

47. $(2x + 3)(2x - 3)$

48. $(3x + 2)(3x - 2)$

49. $(x + 4)^2$

50. $(x - 5)^2$

51. $(2x - 3)^2$

52. $(3x - 4)^2$

53. $(x - 2)^3$

54. $(x + 1)^3$

55. $(2x + 1)^3$

56. $(3x - 2)^3$

In Problems 57–72, find the quotient and the remainder. Check your work by verifying that

$$(Quotient)(Divisor) + Remainder = Dividend$$

57. $4x^3 - 3x^2 + x + 1$ divided by $x + 2$

58. $3x^3 - x^2 + x - 2$ divided by $x + 2$

59. $4x^3 - 3x^2 + x + 1$ divided by x^2

60. $3x^3 - x^2 + x - 2$ divided by x^2

61. $5x^4 - 3x^2 + x + 1$ divided by $x^2 + 2$

62. $5x^4 - x^2 + x - 2$ divided by $x^2 + 2$

63. $4x^5 - 3x^2 + x + 1$ divided by $2x^3 - 1$

64. $3x^5 - x^2 + x - 2$ divided by $3x^3 - 1$

65. $2x^4 - 3x^3 + x + 1$ divided by $2x^2 + x + 1$

66. $3x^4 - x^3 + x - 2$ divided by $3x^2 + x + 1$

67. $-4x^3 + x^2 - 4$ divided by $x - 1$

68. $-3x^4 - 2x - 1$ divided by $x - 1$

69. $1 - x^2 + x^4$ divided by $x^2 + x + 1$

70. $1 - x^2 + x^4$ divided by $x^2 - x + 1$

71. $x^3 - a^3$ divided by $x - a$

72. $x^5 - a^5$ divided by $x - a$

In Problems 73–120, factor completely each polynomial. If the polynomial cannot be factored, say it is prime.

73. $x^2 - 36$

74. $x^2 - 9$

75. $2 - 8x^2$

76. $3 - 27x^2$

77. $x^2 + 11x + 10$

78. $x^2 + 5x + 4$

79. $x^2 - 10x + 21$

80. $x^2 - 6x + 8$

81. $4x^2 - 8x + 32$

82. $3x^2 - 12x + 15$

83. $x^2 + 4x + 16$

84. $x^2 + 12x + 36$

85. $15 + 2x - x^2$

86. $14 + 6x - x^2$

87. $3x^2 - 12x - 36$

88. $x^3 + 8x^2 - 20x$

89. $y^4 + 11y^3 + 30y^2$

90. $3y^3 - 18y^2 - 48y$

91. $4x^2 + 12x + 9$

92. $9x^2 - 12x + 4$

93. $6x^2 + 8x + 2$

94. $8x^2 + 6x - 2$

95. $x^4 - 81$

96. $x^4 - 1$

97. $x^6 - 2x^3 + 1$

98. $x^6 + 2x^3 + 1$

99. $x^7 - x^5$

100. $x^8 - x^5$

101. $16x^2 + 24x + 9$

102. $9x^2 - 24x + 16$

103. $5 + 16x - 16x^2$

104. $5 + 11x - 16x^2$

105. $4y^2 - 16y + 15$ **106.** $9y^2 + 9y - 4$ **107.** $1 - 8x^2 - 9x^4$ **108.** $4 - 14x^2 - 8x^4$

109. $x(x + 3) - 6(x + 3)$ **110.** $5(3x - 7) + x(3x - 7)$ **111.** $(x + 2)^2 - 5(x + 2)$ **112.** $(x - 1)^2 - 2(x - 1)$

113. $(3x - 2)^3 - 27$ **114.** $(5x + 1)^3 - 1$ **115.** $3(x^2 + 10x + 25) - 4(x + 5)$

116. $7(x^2 - 6x + 9) + 5(x - 3)$ **117.** $x^3 + 2x^2 - x - 2$ **118.** $x^3 - 3x^2 - x + 3$

119. $x^4 - x^3 + x - 1$ **120.** $x^4 + x^3 + x + 1$

Applications and Extensions

In Problems 121–130, expressions that occur in calculus are given. Factor completely each expression.

121. $2(3x + 4)^2 + (2x + 3) \cdot 2(3x + 4) \cdot 3$ **122.** $5(2x + 1)^2 + (5x - 6) \cdot 2(2x + 1) \cdot 2$

123. $2x(2x + 5) + x^2 \cdot 2$ **124.** $3x^2(8x - 3) + x^3 \cdot 8$

125. $2(x + 3)(x - 2)^3 + (x + 3)^2 \cdot 3(x - 2)^2$ **126.** $4(x + 5)^3(x - 1)^2 + (x + 5)^4 \cdot 2(x - 1)$

127. $(4x - 3)^2 + x \cdot 2(4x - 3) \cdot 4$ **128.** $3x^2(3x + 4)^2 + x^3 \cdot 2(3x + 4) \cdot 3$

129. $2(3x - 5) \cdot 3(2x + 1)^3 + (3x - 5)^2 \cdot 3(2x + 1)^2 \cdot 2$ **130.** $3(4x + 5)^2 \cdot 4(5x + 1)^2 + (4x + 5)^3 \cdot 2(5x + 1) \cdot 5$

131. Show that $x^2 + 4$ is prime.   **132.** Show that $x^2 + x + 1$ is prime.

Discussion and Writing

133. Explain why the degree of the product of two nonzero polynomials equals the sum of their degrees.

134. Explain why the degree of the sum of two polynomials of different degrees equals the larger of their degrees.

135. Give a careful statement about the degree of the sum of two polynomials of the same degree.

136. Do you prefer to memorize the rule for the square of a binomial $(x + a)^2$ or to use FOIL to obtain the product? Write a brief position paper defending your choice.

137. Make up a polynomial that factors into a perfect square.

138. Explain to a fellow student what you look for first when presented with a factoring problem. What do you do next?

A.4 Synthetic Division

OBJECTIVE 1 Divide Polynomials Using Synthetic Division (p. A31)

1 Divide Polynomials Using Synthetic Division

To find the quotient as well as the remainder when a polynomial of degree 1 or higher is divided by $x - c$, a shortened version of long division, called **synthetic division**, makes the task simpler.

To see how synthetic division works, we will use long division to divide the polynomial $2x^3 - x^2 + 3$ by $x - 3$.

$$
\begin{array}{r}
2x^2 + 5x + 15 \quad \leftarrow \text{Quotient} \\
x - 3 \overline{)\,2x^3 - x^2 + 3} \\
\underline{2x^3 - 6x^2} \\
5x^2 \\
\underline{5x^2 - 15x} \\
15x + 3 \\
\underline{15x - 45} \\
48 \quad \leftarrow \text{Remainder}
\end{array}
$$

✓CHECK: (Divisor) · (Quotient) + Remainder

$$
\begin{aligned}
&= (x - 3)(2x^2 + 5x + 15) + 48 \\
&= 2x^3 + 5x^2 + 15x - 6x^2 - 15x - 45 + 48 \\
&= 2x^3 - x^2 + 3
\end{aligned}
$$

The process of synthetic division arises from rewriting the long division in a more compact form, using simpler notation. For example, in the long division on page A31, the terms in blue are not really necessary because they are identical to the terms directly above them. With these terms removed, we have

$$
\begin{array}{r}
2x^2 + 5x\ + 15 \\
x-3\overline{)2x^3\ -\ x^2\qquad\qquad +\ \ 3} \\
-\,6x^2 \\ \hline
5x^2 \\
-\,15x \\ \hline
15x \\
-\,45 \\ \hline
48
\end{array}
$$

Most of the x's that appear in this process can also be removed, provided that we are careful about positioning each coefficient. In this regard, we will need to use 0 as the coefficient of x in the dividend, because that power of x is missing. Now we have

$$
\begin{array}{r}
2x^2 + 5x + 15 \\
x-3\overline{)2\quad -1\quad\ \ 0\quad\ \ 3} \\
-\,6 \\ \hline
5 \\
-\,15 \\ \hline
15 \\
-\,45 \\ \hline
48
\end{array}
$$

We can make this display more compact by moving the lines up until the numbers in blue align horizontally.

$$
\begin{array}{rllll}
 & 2x^2 + 5x + 15 & & & \text{Row 1}\\
x-3\overline{)2} & -1 & 0 & 3 & \text{Row 2}\\
 & -6 & -15 & -45 & \text{Row 3}\\ \hline
\bigcirc & 5 & 15 & 48 & \text{Row 4}
\end{array}
$$

Because the leading coefficient of the divisor is always 1, we know that the leading coefficient of the dividend will also be the leading coefficient of the quotient. So we place the leading coefficient of the quotient, 2, in the circled position. Now, the first three numbers in row 4 are precisely the coefficients of the quotient, and the last number in row 4 is the remainder. Thus, row 1 is not really needed, so we can compress the process to three rows, where the bottom row contains both the coefficients of the quotient and the remainder.

$$
\begin{array}{rllll}
x-3\overline{)2} & -1 & 0 & 3 & \text{Row 1}\\
 & -6 & -15 & -45 & \text{Row 2 (subtract)}\\ \hline
2 & 5 & 15 & 48 & \text{Row 3}
\end{array}
$$

Recall that the entries in row 3 are obtained by subtracting the entries in row 2 from those in row 1. Rather than subtracting the entries in row 2, we can change the sign of each entry and add. With this modification, our display will look like this:

$$
\begin{array}{rllll}
x-3\overline{)2} & -1 & 0 & 3 & \text{Row 1}\\
 & 6 & 15 & 45 & \text{Row 2 (add)}\\ \hline
2 & 5 & 15 & 48 & \text{Row 3}
\end{array}
$$

Notice that the entries in row 2 are three times the prior entries in row 3. Our last modification to the display replaces the $x - 3$ by 3. The entries in row 3 give the quotient and the remainder, as shown next.

$$3\overline{)\begin{array}{cccc} 2 & -1 & 0 & 3 \end{array}} \quad \text{Row 1}$$

$$\begin{array}{cccc} & 6 & 15 & 45 \end{array} \quad \text{Row 2 (add)}$$

$$\begin{array}{cccc} 2 & 5 & 15 & 48 \end{array} \quad \text{Row 3}$$

Quotient   Remainder

$$2x^2 + 5x + 15 \qquad 48$$

Let's go through an example step by step.

| EXAMPLE 1 | **Using Synthetic Division to Find the Quotient and Remainder** |

Use synthetic division to find the quotient and remainder when

$$x^3 - 4x^2 - 5 \quad \text{is divided by} \quad x - 3$$

Solution

STEP 1: Write the dividend in descending powers of x. Then copy the coefficients, remembering to insert a 0 for any missing powers of x.

$$\begin{array}{cccc} 1 & -4 & 0 & -5 \end{array} \quad \text{Row 1}$$

STEP 2: Insert the usual division symbol. In synthetic division, the divisor is of the form $x - c$, and c is the number placed to the left of the division symbol. Here, since the divisor is $x - 3$, we insert 3 to the left of the division symbol.

$$3\overline{)\begin{array}{cccc} 1 & -4 & 0 & -5 \end{array}} \quad \text{Row 1}$$

STEP 3: Bring the 1 down two rows, and enter it in row 3.

$$3\overline{)\begin{array}{cccc} 1 & -4 & 0 & -5 \end{array}} \quad \text{Row 1}$$
$$\downarrow \qquad\qquad\qquad \text{Row 2}$$
$$1 \qquad\qquad\qquad \text{Row 3}$$

STEP 4: Multiply the latest entry in row 3 by 3, and place the result in row 2, one column over to the right.

$$3\overline{)\begin{array}{cccc} 1 & -4 & 0 & -5 \end{array}} \quad \text{Row 1}$$
$$\begin{array}{cccc} & 3 \end{array} \qquad\qquad \text{Row 2}$$
$$1 \qquad\qquad\qquad \text{Row 3}$$

STEP 5: Add the entry in row 2 to the entry above it in row 1, and enter the sum in row 3.

$$3\overline{)\begin{array}{cccc} 1 & -4 & 0 & -5 \end{array}} \quad \text{Row 1}$$
$$\begin{array}{cccc} & 3 \end{array} \qquad\qquad \text{Row 2}$$
$$1 \quad -1 \qquad\qquad \text{Row 3}$$

STEP 6: Repeat Steps 4 and 5 until no more entries are available in row 1.

$$3\overline{)\begin{array}{cccc} 1 & -4 & 0 & -5 \end{array}} \quad \text{Row 1}$$
$$\begin{array}{cccc} & 3 & -3 & -9 \end{array} \quad \text{Row 2}$$
$$\begin{array}{cccc} 1 & -1 & -3 & -14 \end{array} \quad \text{Row 3}$$

STEP 7: The final entry in row 3, the -14, is the remainder; the other entries in row 3, the $1, -1,$ and -3, are the coefficients (in descending order) of a polynomial whose degree is 1 less than that of the dividend. This is the quotient. Thus,

$$\text{Quotient} = x^2 - x - 3 \qquad \text{Remainder} = -14$$

✓ Check: (Divisor)(Quotient) + Remainder

$$= (x - 3)(x^2 - x - 3) + (-14)$$
$$= (x^3 - x^2 - 3x - 3x^2 + 3x + 9) + (-14)$$
$$= x^3 - 4x^2 - 5 = \text{Dividend}$$

Let's do an example in which all seven steps are combined.

| EXAMPLE 2 | Using Synthetic Division to Verify a Factor |

Use synthetic division to show that $x + 3$ is a factor of

$$2x^5 + 5x^4 - 2x^3 + 2x^2 - 2x + 3$$

Solution   If the remainder is 0, then the divisor is a factor of the dividend, and the quotient is the other factor. The divisor is $x + 3 = x - (-3)$, so we place -3 to the left of the division symbol. Then the row 3 entries will be multiplied by -3, entered in row 2, and added to row 1.

$$
\begin{array}{r|rrrrrr}
-3) & 2 & 5 & -2 & 2 & -2 & 3 \quad \text{Row 1}\\
 & & -6 & 3 & -3 & 3 & -3 \quad \text{Row 2}\\
\hline
 & 2 & -1 & 1 & -1 & 1 & 0 \quad \text{Row 3}
\end{array}
$$

Because the remainder is 0, we have

$$\text{Dividend} = (\text{Divisor})(\text{Quotient}) + \text{Remainder}$$

$$2x^5 + 5x^4 - 2x^3 + 2x^2 - 2x + 3 = (x + 3)(2x^4 - x^3 + x^2 - x + 1)$$

As we see, $x + 3$ is a factor of $2x^5 + 5x^4 - 2x^3 + 2x^2 - 2x + 3$.

⬛

As Example 2 illustrates, the remainder after division gives information about whether the divisor is, or is not, a factor. We shall have more to say about this in Chapter 4.

➤ **Now Work** PROBLEMS **7** AND **17**

A.4 Assess Your Understanding

Concepts and Vocabulary

1. To check division, the expression that is being divided, the dividend, should equal the product of the _____ and the _____ plus the
   _____.

2. To divide $2x^3 - 5x + 1$ by $x + 3$ using synthetic division, the first step is to write _____$)\overline{}$.

3. **True or False** In using synthetic division, the divisor is always a polynomial of degree 1, whose leading coefficient is 1.

4. **True or False**
$$
\begin{array}{r|rrrr}
-2) & 5 & 3 & 2 & 1\\
 & & -10 & 14 & -32\\
\hline
 & 5 & -7 & 16 & -31
\end{array}
$$
means $\dfrac{5x^3 + 3x^2 + 2x + 1}{x + 2} = 5x^2 - 7x + 16 + \dfrac{-31}{x + 2}$.

Skill Building

In Problems 5–16, use synthetic division to find the quotient and remainder when:

5. $x^3 - x^2 + 2x + 4$ is divided by $x - 2$

6. $x^3 + 2x^2 - 3x + 1$ is divided by $x + 1$

7. $3x^3 + 2x^2 - x + 3$ is divided by $x - 3$

8. $-4x^3 + 2x^2 - x + 1$ is divided by $x + 2$

9. $x^5 - 4x^3 + x$ is divided by $x + 3$

10. $x^4 + x^2 + 2$ is divided by $x - 2$

11. $4x^6 - 3x^4 + x^2 + 5$ is divided by $x - 1$

12. $x^5 + 5x^3 - 10$ is divided by $x + 1$

13. $0.1x^3 + 0.2x$ is divided by $x + 1.1$

14. $0.1x^2 - 0.2$ is divided by $x + 2.1$

15. $x^5 - 1$ is divided by $x - 1$

16. $x^5 + 1$ is divided by $x + 1$

In Problems 17–26, use synthetic division to determine whether $x - c$ is a factor of the given polynomial.

17. $4x^3 - 3x^2 - 8x + 4$; $x - 2$

18. $-4x^3 + 5x^2 + 8$; $x + 3$

19. $3x^4 - 6x^3 - 5x + 10$; $x - 2$

20. $4x^4 - 15x^2 - 4$; $x - 2$

21. $3x^6 + 82x^3 + 27$; $x + 3$

22. $2x^6 - 18x^4 + x^2 - 9$; $x + 3$

23. $4x^6 - 64x^4 + x^2 - 15; \quad x + 4$

24. $x^6 - 16x^4 + x^2 - 16; \quad x + 4$

25. $2x^4 - x^3 + 2x - 1; \quad x - \dfrac{1}{2}$

26. $3x^4 + x^3 - 3x + 1; \quad x + \dfrac{1}{3}$

Applications and Extensions

27. Find the sum of $a, b, c,$ and d if

$$\frac{x^3 - 2x^2 + 3x + 5}{x + 2} = ax^2 + bx + c + \frac{d}{x + 2}$$

Discussion and Writing

28. When dividing a polynomial by $x - c$, do you prefer to use long division or synthetic division? Does the value of c make a difference to you in choosing? Give reasons.

A.5 Rational Expressions

OBJECTIVES 1 Reduce a Rational Expression to Lowest Terms (p. A35)

2 Multiply and Divide Rational Expressions (p. A36)

3 Add and Subtract Rational Expressions (p. A37)

4 Use the Least Common Multiple Method (p. A39)

5 Simplify Complex Rational Expressions (p. A41)

1 Reduce a Rational Expression to Lowest Terms

If we form the quotient of two polynomials, the result is called a **rational expression.** Some examples of rational expressions are

(a) $\dfrac{x^3 + 1}{x}$ (b) $\dfrac{3x^2 + x - 2}{x^2 + 5}$ (c) $\dfrac{x}{x^2 - 1}$ (d) $\dfrac{xy^2}{(x - y)^2}$

Expressions (a), (b), and (c) are rational expressions in one variable, x, whereas (d) is a rational expression in two variables, x and y.

Rational expressions are described in the same manner as rational numbers. In expression (a), the polynomial $x^3 + 1$ is called the **numerator,** and x is called the **denominator.** When the numerator and denominator of a rational expression contain no common factors (except 1 and -1), we say that the rational expression is **reduced to lowest terms,** or **simplified.**

The polynomial in the denominator of a rational expression cannot be equal to 0 because division by 0 is not defined. For example, for the expression $\dfrac{x^3 + 1}{x}$, x cannot take on the value 0. The domain of the variable x is $\{x \,|\, x \neq 0\}$.

A rational expression is reduced to lowest terms by factoring completely the numerator and the denominator and canceling any common factors by using the Cancellation Property:

$$\frac{a\cancel{c}}{b\cancel{c}} = \frac{a}{b} \qquad \text{if } b \neq 0, c \neq 0 \tag{1}$$

EXAMPLE 1 **Reducing a Rational Expression to Lowest Terms**

Reduce to lowest terms: $\dfrac{x^2 + 4x + 4}{x^2 + 3x + 2}$

Solution We begin by factoring the numerator and the denominator.

$$x^2 + 4x + 4 = (x + 2)(x + 2)$$
$$x^2 + 3x + 2 = (x + 2)(x + 1)$$

WARNING Apply the Cancellation Property only to rational expressions written in factored form. Be sure to cancel only common factors, not common terms! ■

Since a common factor, $x + 2$, appears, the original expression is not in lowest terms. To reduce it to lowest terms, we use the Cancellation Property:

$$\frac{x^2 + 4x + 4}{x^2 + 3x + 2} = \frac{\cancel{(x + 2)}(x + 2)}{\cancel{(x + 2)}(x + 1)} = \frac{x + 2}{x + 1} \qquad x \neq -2, -1$$

EXAMPLE 2   Reducing Rational Expressions to Lowest Terms

Reduce each rational expression to lowest terms.

(a) $\dfrac{x^3 - 8}{x^3 - 2x^2}$

(b) $\dfrac{8 - 2x}{x^2 - x - 12}$

Solution   (a) $\dfrac{x^3 - 8}{x^3 - 2x^2} = \dfrac{\cancel{(x - 2)}(x^2 + 2x + 4)}{x^2\cancel{(x - 2)}} = \dfrac{x^2 + 2x + 4}{x^2} \qquad x \neq 0, 2$

(b) $\dfrac{8 - 2x}{x^2 - x - 12} = \dfrac{2(4 - x)}{(x - 4)(x + 3)} = \dfrac{2(-1)\cancel{(x - 4)}}{\cancel{(x - 4)}(x + 3)} = \dfrac{-2}{x + 3} \qquad x \neq -3, 4$

Now Work PROBLEM 5

2 Multiply and Divide Rational Expressions

The rules for multiplying and dividing rational expressions are the same as the rules for multiplying and dividing rational numbers. If $\dfrac{a}{b}$ and $\dfrac{c}{d}$, $b \neq 0$, $d \neq 0$, are two rational expressions, then

$$\frac{a}{b} \cdot \frac{c}{d} = \frac{ac}{bd} \qquad \text{if } b \neq 0, d \neq 0 \tag{2}$$

$$\frac{\dfrac{a}{b}}{\dfrac{c}{d}} = \frac{a}{b} \cdot \frac{d}{c} = \frac{ad}{bc} \qquad \text{if } b \neq 0, c \neq 0, d \neq 0 \tag{3}$$

In using equations (2) and (3) with rational expressions, be sure first to factor each polynomial completely so that common factors can be canceled. Leave your answer in factored form.

EXAMPLE 3   Multiplying and Dividing Rational Expressions

Perform the indicated operation and simplify the result. Leave your answer in factored form.

(a) $\dfrac{x^2 - 2x + 1}{x^3 + x} \cdot \dfrac{4x^2 + 4}{x^2 + x - 2}$

(b) $\dfrac{\dfrac{x + 3}{x^2 - 4}}{\dfrac{x^2 - x - 12}{x^3 - 8}}$

Solution (a) $\dfrac{x^2 - 2x + 1}{x^3 + x} \cdot \dfrac{4x^2 + 4}{x^2 + x - 2} = \dfrac{(x-1)^2}{x(x^2+1)} \cdot \dfrac{4(x^2+1)}{(x+2)(x-1)}$

$$= \dfrac{(x-1)^2(4)\cancel{(x^2+1)}}{x\cancel{(x^2+1)}(x+2)\cancel{(x-1)}}$$

$$= \dfrac{4(x-1)}{x(x+2)} \qquad x \neq -2, 0, 1$$

(b) $\dfrac{\dfrac{x+3}{x^2-4}}{\dfrac{x^2-x-12}{x^3-8}} = \dfrac{x+3}{x^2-4} \cdot \dfrac{x^3-8}{x^2-x-12}$

$$= \dfrac{x+3}{(x-2)(x+2)} \cdot \dfrac{(x-2)(x^2+2x+4)}{(x-4)(x+3)}$$

$$= \dfrac{\cancel{(x+3)}\,\cancel{(x-2)}(x^2+2x+4)}{\cancel{(x-2)}(x+2)(x-4)\cancel{(x+3)}}$$

$$= \dfrac{x^2+2x+4}{(x+2)(x-4)} \qquad x \neq -3, -2, 2, 4$$

 Now Work PROBLEMS 17 AND 25

3 Add and Subtract Rational Expressions

The rules for adding and subtracting rational expressions are the same as the rules for adding and subtracting rational numbers. So, if the denominators of two rational expressions to be added (or subtracted) are equal, we add (or subtract) the numerators and keep the common denominator.

In Words

To add (or subtract) two rational expressions with the same denominator, keep the common denominator and add (or subtract) the numerators.

If $\dfrac{a}{b}$ and $\dfrac{c}{b}$ are two rational expressions, then

$$\boxed{\dfrac{a}{b} + \dfrac{c}{b} = \dfrac{a+c}{b} \qquad \dfrac{a}{b} - \dfrac{c}{b} = \dfrac{a-c}{b} \qquad \text{if } b \neq 0} \qquad \textbf{(4)}$$

EXAMPLE 4 **Adding and Subtracting Rational Expressions with Equal Denominators**

Perform the indicated operation and simplify the result. Leave your answer in factored form.

(a) $\dfrac{2x^2-4}{2x+5} + \dfrac{x+3}{2x+5} \qquad x \neq -\dfrac{5}{2}$ 　　(b) $\dfrac{x}{x-3} - \dfrac{3x+2}{x-3} \qquad x \neq 3$

Solution (a) $\dfrac{2x^2-4}{2x+5} + \dfrac{x+3}{2x+5} = \dfrac{(2x^2-4)+(x+3)}{2x+5}$

$$= \dfrac{2x^2+x-1}{2x+5} = \dfrac{(2x-1)(x+1)}{2x+5}$$

(b) $\dfrac{x}{x-3} - \dfrac{3x+2}{x-3} = \dfrac{x-(3x+2)}{x-3} = \dfrac{x-3x-2}{x-3}$

$$= \dfrac{-2x-2}{x-3} = \dfrac{-2(x+1)}{x-3}$$

EXAMPLE 5

Adding Rational Expressions Whose Denominators Are Additive Inverses of Each Other

Perform the indicated operation and simplify the result. Leave your answer in factored form.

$$\frac{2x}{x - 3} + \frac{5}{3 - x} \qquad x \neq 3$$

Solution

Notice that the denominators of the two rational expressions are different. However, the denominator of the second expression is the additive inverse of the denominator of the first. That is,

$$3 - x = -x + 3 = -1 \cdot (x - 3) = -(x - 3)$$

Then

$$\frac{2x}{x - 3} + \frac{5}{3 - x} \underset{\substack{\uparrow \\ 3 - x = -(x-3)}}{=} \frac{2x}{x - 3} + \frac{5}{-(x - 3)} \underset{\substack{\uparrow \\ \frac{a}{-b} = \frac{-a}{b}}}{=} \frac{2x}{x - 3} + \frac{-5}{x - 3}$$

$$= \frac{2x + (-5)}{x - 3} = \frac{2x - 5}{x - 3}$$

Now Work PROBLEMS 37 AND 43

If the denominators of two rational expressions to be added or subtracted are not equal, we can use the general formulas for adding and subtracting quotients.

$$\frac{a}{b} + \frac{c}{d} = \frac{a \cdot d}{b \cdot d} + \frac{b \cdot c}{b \cdot d} = \frac{ad + bc}{bd} \qquad \text{if } b \neq 0, d \neq 0 \qquad \textbf{(5a)}$$

$$\frac{a}{b} - \frac{c}{d} = \frac{a \cdot d}{b \cdot d} - \frac{b \cdot c}{b \cdot d} = \frac{ad - bc}{bd} \qquad \text{if } b \neq 0, d \neq 0 \qquad \textbf{(5b)}$$

EXAMPLE 6

Adding and Subtracting Rational Expressions with Unequal Denominators

Perform the indicated operation and simplify the result. Leave your answer in factored form.

(a) $\dfrac{x - 3}{x + 4} + \dfrac{x}{x - 2} \qquad x \neq -4, 2$

(b) $\dfrac{x^2}{x^2 - 4} - \dfrac{1}{x} \qquad x \neq -2, 0, 2$

Solution

(a) $\dfrac{x - 3}{x + 4} + \dfrac{x}{x - 2} = \dfrac{x - 3}{x + 4} \cdot \dfrac{x - 2}{x - 2} + \dfrac{x + 4}{x + 4} \cdot \dfrac{x}{x - 2}$

$\underset{\text{(5a)}}{\uparrow}$

$$= \frac{(x - 3)(x - 2) + (x + 4)(x)}{(x + 4)(x - 2)}$$

$$= \frac{x^2 - 5x + 6 + x^2 + 4x}{(x + 4)(x - 2)} = \frac{2x^2 - x + 6}{(x + 4)(x - 2)}$$

(b) $\dfrac{x^2}{x^2-4} - \dfrac{1}{x} = \dfrac{x^2}{x^2-4} \cdot \dfrac{x}{x} - \dfrac{x^2-4}{x^2-4} \cdot \dfrac{1}{x} = \dfrac{x^2(x) - (x^2-4)(1)}{(x^2-4)(x)}$

$\uparrow$

(5b)

$= \dfrac{x^3 - x^2 + 4}{x(x-2)(x+2)}$

Now Work PROBLEM 47

4 Use the Least Common Multiple Method

If the denominators of two rational expressions to be added (or subtracted) have common factors, we usually do not use the general rules given by equations (5a) and (5b). Just as with fractions, we apply the **least common multiple (LCM) method.** The LCM method uses the polynomial of least degree that has each denominator polynomial as a factor.

The LCM Method for Adding or Subtracting Rational Expressions

The Least Common Multiple (LCM) Method requires four steps:

STEP 1: Factor completely the polynomial in the denominator of each rational expression.

STEP 2: The LCM of the denominator is the product of each of these factors raised to a power equal to the greatest number of times that the factor occurs in the polynomials.

STEP 3: Write each rational expression using the LCM as the common denominator.

STEP 4: Add or subtract the rational expressions using equation (4).

Let's work an example that only requires Steps 1 and 2.

EXAMPLE 7   **Finding the Least Common Multiple**

Find the least common multiple of the following pair of polynomials:

$$x(x-1)^2(x+1) \quad \text{and} \quad 4(x-1)(x+1)^3$$

Solution   **STEP 1:** The polynomials are already factored completely as

$$x(x-1)^2(x+1) \quad \text{and} \quad 4(x-1)(x+1)^3$$

STEP 2: Start by writing the factors of the left-hand polynomial. (Or you could start with the one on the right.)

$$x(x-1)^2(x+1)$$

Now look at the right-hand polynomial. Its first factor, 4, does not appear in the polynomial above, so we insert it.

$$4x(x-1)^2(x+1)$$

The next factor, $x-1$, is already in our polynomial, so no change is necessary. The final factor is $(x+1)^3$. Since our polynomial has $x+1$ to the first power only, we replace $x+1$ in the polynomial by $(x+1)^3$. The LCM is

$$4x(x-1)^2(x+1)^3$$

Notice that the LCM is, in fact, the polynomial of least degree that contains $x(x - 1)^2(x + 1)$ and $4(x - 1)(x + 1)^3$ as factors.

━━━━━ **Now Work** PROBLEM 53

| EXAMPLE 8 | **Using the Least Common Multiple to Add Rational Expressions** |

Perform the indicated operation and simplify the result. Leave your answer in factored form.

$$\frac{x}{x^2 + 3x + 2} + \frac{2x - 3}{x^2 - 1} \qquad x \neq -2, -1, 1$$

Solution **STEP 1:** Factor completely the polynomials in the denominators.

$$x^2 + 3x + 2 = (x + 2)(x + 1)$$
$$x^2 - 1 = (x - 1)(x + 1)$$

STEP 2: The LCM is $(x + 2)(x + 1)(x - 1)$. Do you see why?

STEP 3: Write each rational expression using the LCM as the denominator.

$$\frac{x}{x^2 + 3x + 2} = \frac{x}{(x + 2)(x + 1)} = \frac{x}{(x + 2)(x + 1)} \cdot \frac{x - 1}{x - 1} = \frac{x(x - 1)}{(x + 2)(x + 1)(x - 1)}$$

Multiply numerator and denominator by x − 1 to get the LCM in the denominator.

$$\frac{2x - 3}{x^2 - 1} = \frac{2x - 3}{(x - 1)(x + 1)} = \frac{2x - 3}{(x - 1)(x + 1)} \cdot \frac{x + 2}{x + 2} = \frac{(2x - 3)(x + 2)}{(x - 1)(x + 1)(x + 2)}$$

Multiply numerator and denominator by x + 2 to get the LCM in the denominator

STEP 4: Now we can add by using equation (4).

$$\frac{x}{x^2 + 3x + 2} + \frac{2x - 3}{x^2 - 1} = \frac{x(x - 1)}{(x + 2)(x + 1)(x - 1)} + \frac{(2x - 3)(x + 2)}{(x + 2)(x + 1)(x - 1)}$$

$$= \frac{(x^2 - x) + (2x^2 + x - 6)}{(x + 2)(x + 1)(x - 1)}$$

$$= \frac{3x^2 - 6}{(x + 2)(x + 1)(x - 1)} = \frac{3(x^2 - 2)}{(x + 2)(x + 1)(x - 1)}$$ ■

| EXAMPLE 9 | **Using the Least Common Multiple to Subtract Rational Expressions** |

Perform the indicated operations and simplify the result. Leave your answer in factored form.

$$\frac{3}{x^2 + x} - \frac{x + 4}{x^2 + 2x + 1} \qquad x \neq -1, 0$$

Solution **STEP 1:** Factor completely the polynomials in the denominators.

$$x^2 + x = x(x + 1)$$
$$x^2 + 2x + 1 = (x + 1)^2$$

STEP 2: The LCM is $x(x + 1)^2$.

STEP 3: Write each rational expression using the LCM as the denominator.

$$\frac{3}{x^2 + x} = \frac{3}{x(x + 1)} = \frac{3}{x(x + 1)} \cdot \frac{x + 1}{x + 1} = \frac{3(x + 1)}{x(x + 1)^2}$$

$$\frac{x + 4}{x^2 + 2x + 1} = \frac{x + 4}{(x + 1)^2} = \frac{x + 4}{(x + 1)^2} \cdot \frac{x}{x} = \frac{x(x + 4)}{x(x + 1)^2}$$

STEP 4: Subtract, using equation (4).

$$\frac{3}{x^2 + x} - \frac{x + 4}{x^2 + 2x + 1} = \frac{3(x + 1)}{x(x + 1)^2} - \frac{x(x + 4)}{x(x + 1)^2}$$

$$= \frac{3(x + 1) - x(x + 4)}{x(x + 1)^2}$$

$$= \frac{3x + 3 - x^2 - 4x}{x(x + 1)^2}$$

$$= \frac{-x^2 - x + 3}{x(x + 1)^2}$$

---- **Now Work** PROBLEM 63

5 Simplify Complex Rational Expressions

When sums and/or differences of rational expressions appear as the numerator and/or denominator of a quotient, the quotient is called a **complex rational expression.*** For example,

$$\frac{1 + \dfrac{1}{x}}{1 - \dfrac{1}{x}} \quad \text{and} \quad \frac{\dfrac{x^2}{x^2 - 4} - 3}{\dfrac{x - 3}{x + 2} - 1}$$

are complex rational expressions. To **simplify** a complex rational expression means to write it as a rational expression reduced to lowest terms. This can be accomplished in either of two ways.

Simplifying a Complex Rational Expression

METHOD 1: Treat the numerator and denominator of the complex rational expression separately, performing whatever operations are indicated and simplifying the results. Follow this by simplifying the resulting rational expression.

METHOD 2: Find the LCM of the denominators of all rational expressions that appear in the complex rational expression. Multiply the numerator and denominator of the complex rational expression by the LCM and simplify the result.

We will use both methods in the next example. By carefully studying each method, you can discover situations in which one method may be easier to use than the other.

EXAMPLE 10   Simplifying a Complex Rational Expression

Simplify: $\dfrac{\dfrac{1}{2} + \dfrac{3}{x}}{\dfrac{x + 3}{4}}$ $x \neq -3, 0$

*Some texts use the term **complex fraction.**

Solution **Method 1:** First, we perform the indicated operation in the numerator, and then we divide.

$$\dfrac{\dfrac{1}{2} + \dfrac{3}{x}}{\dfrac{x+3}{4}} = \dfrac{\dfrac{1 \cdot x + 2 \cdot 3}{2 \cdot x}}{\dfrac{x+3}{4}} = \dfrac{\dfrac{x+6}{2x}}{\dfrac{x+3}{4}} = \dfrac{x+6}{2x} \cdot \dfrac{4}{x+3}$$

Rule for adding quotients   Rule for dividing quotients

$$= \dfrac{(x+6) \cdot 4}{2 \cdot x \cdot (x+3)} = \dfrac{2 \cdot 2 \cdot (x+6)}{2 \cdot x \cdot (x+3)} = \dfrac{2(x+6)}{x(x+3)}$$

Rule for multiplying quotients

Method 2: The rational expressions that appear in the complex rational expression are

$$\dfrac{1}{2} \qquad \dfrac{3}{x} \qquad \dfrac{x+3}{4}$$

The LCM of their denominators is $4x$. We multiply the numerator and denominator of the complex rational expression by $4x$ and then simplify.

$$\dfrac{\dfrac{1}{2} + \dfrac{3}{x}}{\dfrac{x+3}{4}} = \dfrac{4x \cdot \left(\dfrac{1}{2} + \dfrac{3}{x} \right)}{4x \cdot \left(\dfrac{x+3}{4} \right)} = \dfrac{4x \cdot \dfrac{1}{2} + 4x \cdot \dfrac{3}{x}}{\dfrac{4x \cdot (x+3)}{4}}$$

Multiply the   Use the Distributive Property
numerator and   in the numerator.
denominator by 4x.

$$= \dfrac{2 \cdot 2x \cdot \dfrac{1}{2} + 4x \cdot \dfrac{3}{x}}{\dfrac{4x \cdot (x+3)}{4}} = \dfrac{2x + 12}{x(x+3)} = \dfrac{2(x+6)}{x(x+3)}$$

Simplify   Factor

EXAMPLE 11   **Simplifying a Complex Rational Expression**

Simplify: $\dfrac{\dfrac{x^2}{x-4} + 2}{\dfrac{2x-2}{x} - 1} \qquad x \neq 0, 2, 4$

Solution   We will use Method 1.

$$\dfrac{\dfrac{x^2}{x-4} + 2}{\dfrac{2x-2}{x} - 1} = \dfrac{\dfrac{x^2}{x-4} + \dfrac{2(x-4)}{x-4}}{\dfrac{2x-2}{x} - \dfrac{x}{x}} = \dfrac{\dfrac{x^2 + 2x - 8}{x-4}}{\dfrac{2x-2-x}{x}}$$

$$= \dfrac{\dfrac{(x+4)(x-2)}{x-4}}{\dfrac{x-2}{x}} = \dfrac{(x+4)(x-2)}{x-4} \cdot \dfrac{x}{x-2} = \dfrac{(x+4) \cdot x}{x-4}$$

✏ **Now Work** PROBLEM 73

Application

EXAMPLE 12 | **Solving an Application in Electricity**

An electrical circuit contains two resistors connected in parallel, as shown in Figure 25. If the resistance of each is R_1 and R_2 ohms, respectively, their combined resistance R is given by the formula

Figure 25

$$R = \dfrac{1}{\dfrac{1}{R_1} + \dfrac{1}{R_2}}$$

Express R as a rational expression; that is, simplify the right-hand side of this formula. Evaluate the rational expression if $R_1 = 6$ ohms and $R_2 = 10$ ohms.

Solution We will use Method 2. If we consider 1 as the fraction $\dfrac{1}{1}$, then the rational expressions in the complex rational expression are

$$\dfrac{1}{1} \quad \dfrac{1}{R_1} \quad \dfrac{1}{R_2}$$

The LCM of the denominators is $R_1 R_2$. We multiply the numerator and denominator of the complex rational expression by $R_1 R_2$ and simplify.

$$R = \dfrac{1}{\dfrac{1}{R_1} + \dfrac{1}{R_2}} = \dfrac{1 \cdot R_1 R_2}{\left(\dfrac{1}{R_1} + \dfrac{1}{R_2}\right) \cdot R_1 R_2} = \dfrac{R_1 R_2}{\dfrac{1}{R_1} \cdot R_1 R_2 + \dfrac{1}{R_2} \cdot R_1 R_2} = \dfrac{R_1 R_2}{R_2 + R_1}$$

Thus,

$$R = \dfrac{R_1 R_2}{R_2 + R_1}$$

If $R_1 = 6$ and $R_2 = 10$, then

$$R = \dfrac{6 \cdot 10}{10 + 6} = \dfrac{60}{16} = \dfrac{15}{4} \quad \text{ohms}$$

A.5 Assess Your Understanding

Concepts and Vocabulary

1. When the numerator and denominator of a rational expression contain no common factors (except 1 and -1), the rational expression is in _____ _____.

2. LCM is an abbreviation for _____ _____ _____.

3. **True or False** The rational expression $\dfrac{2x^3 - 4x}{x - 2}$ is reduced to lowest terms.

4. **True or False** The LCM of $2x^3 + 6x^2$ and $6x^4 + 4x^3$ is $4x^3(x + 1)$.

Skill Building

In Problems 5–16, reduce each rational expression to lowest terms.

5. $\dfrac{3x + 9}{x^2 - 9}$

6. $\dfrac{4x^2 + 8x}{12x + 24}$

7. $\dfrac{x^2 - 2x}{3x - 6}$

8. $\dfrac{15x^2 + 24x}{3x^2}$

9. $\dfrac{24x^2}{12x^2 - 6x}$

10. $\dfrac{x^2 + 4x + 4}{x^2 - 4}$

11. $\dfrac{y^2 - 25}{2y^2 - 8y - 10}$

12. $\dfrac{3y^2 - y - 2}{3y^2 + 5y + 2}$

13. $\dfrac{x^2 + 4x - 5}{x^2 - 2x + 1}$

14. $\dfrac{x - x^2}{x^2 + x - 2}$

15. $\dfrac{x^2 + 5x - 14}{2 - x}$

16. $\dfrac{2x^2 + 5x - 3}{1 - 2x}$

In Problems 17–34, perform the indicated operation and simplify the result. Leave your answer in factored form.

17. $\dfrac{3x+6}{5x^2} \cdot \dfrac{x}{x^2-4}$

18. $\dfrac{3}{2x} \cdot \dfrac{x^2}{6x+10}$

19. $\dfrac{4x^2}{x^2-16} \cdot \dfrac{x^3-64}{2x}$

20. $\dfrac{12}{x^2+x} \cdot \dfrac{x^3+1}{4x-2}$

21. $\dfrac{4x-8}{-3x} \cdot \dfrac{12}{12-6x}$

22. $\dfrac{6x-27}{5x} \cdot \dfrac{2}{4x-18}$

23. $\dfrac{x^2-3x-10}{x^2+2x-35} \cdot \dfrac{x^2+4x-21}{x^2+9x+14}$

24. $\dfrac{x^2+x-6}{x^2+4x-5} \cdot \dfrac{x^2-25}{x^2+2x-15}$

25. $\dfrac{\dfrac{6x}{x^2-4}}{\dfrac{3x-9}{2x+4}}$

26. $\dfrac{\dfrac{12x}{5x+20}}{\dfrac{4x^2}{x^2-16}}$

27. $\dfrac{\dfrac{8x}{x^2-1}}{\dfrac{10x}{x+1}}$

28. $\dfrac{\dfrac{x-2}{4x}}{\dfrac{x^2-4x+4}{12x}}$

29. $\dfrac{\dfrac{4-x}{4+x}}{\dfrac{4x}{x^2-16}}$

30. $\dfrac{\dfrac{3+x}{3-x}}{\dfrac{x^2-9}{9x^3}}$

31. $\dfrac{\dfrac{x^2+7x+12}{x^2-7x+12}}{\dfrac{x^2+x-12}{x^2-x-12}}$

32. $\dfrac{\dfrac{x^2+7x+6}{x^2+x-6}}{\dfrac{x^2+5x-6}{x^2+5x+6}}$

33. $\dfrac{\dfrac{2x^2-x-28}{3x^2-x-2}}{\dfrac{4x^2+16x+7}{3x^2+11x+6}}$

34. $\dfrac{\dfrac{9x^2+3x-2}{12x^2+5x-2}}{\dfrac{9x^2-6x+1}{8x^2-10x-3}}$

In Problems 35–52, perform the indicated operation and simplify the result. Leave your answer in factored form.

35. $\dfrac{x}{2}+\dfrac{5}{2}$

36. $\dfrac{3}{x}-\dfrac{6}{x}$

37. $\dfrac{x^2}{2x-3}-\dfrac{4}{2x-3}$

38. $\dfrac{3x^2}{2x-1}-\dfrac{9}{2x-1}$

39. $\dfrac{x+1}{x-3}+\dfrac{2x-3}{x-3}$

40. $\dfrac{2x-5}{3x+2}+\dfrac{x+4}{3x+2}$

41. $\dfrac{3x+5}{2x-1}-\dfrac{2x-4}{2x-1}$

42. $\dfrac{5x-4}{3x+4}-\dfrac{x+1}{3x+4}$

43. $\dfrac{4}{x-2}+\dfrac{x}{2-x}$

44. $\dfrac{6}{x-1}-\dfrac{x}{1-x}$

45. $\dfrac{4}{x-1}-\dfrac{2}{x+2}$

46. $\dfrac{2}{x+5}-\dfrac{5}{x-5}$

47. $\dfrac{x}{x+1}+\dfrac{2x-3}{x-1}$

48. $\dfrac{3x}{x-4}+\dfrac{2x}{x+3}$

49. $\dfrac{x-3}{x+2}-\dfrac{x+4}{x-2}$

50. $\dfrac{2x-3}{x-1}-\dfrac{2x+1}{x+1}$

51. $\dfrac{x}{x^2-4}+\dfrac{1}{x}$

52. $\dfrac{x-1}{x^3}+\dfrac{x}{x^2+1}$

In Problems 53–60, find the LCM of the given polynomials.

53. $x^2-4,\ x^2-x-2$

54. $x^2-x-12,\ x^2-8x+16$

55. $x^3-x,\ x^2-x$

56. $3x^2-27,\ 2x^2-x-15$

57. $4x^3-4x^2+x,\ 2x^3-x^2,\ x^3$

58. $x-3,\ x^2+3x,\ x^3-9x$

59. $x^3-x,\ x^3-2x^2+x,\ x^3-1$

60. $x^2+4x+4,\ x^3+2x^2,\ (x+2)^3$

In Problems 61–72, perform the indicated operations and simplify the result. Leave your answer in factored form.

61. $\dfrac{x}{x^2-7x+6}-\dfrac{x}{x^2-2x-24}$

62. $\dfrac{x}{x-3}-\dfrac{x+1}{x^2+5x-24}$

63. $\dfrac{4x}{x^2-4}-\dfrac{2}{x^2+x-6}$

64. $\dfrac{3x}{x-1}-\dfrac{x-4}{x^2-2x+1}$

65. $\dfrac{3}{(x-1)^2(x+1)}+\dfrac{2}{(x-1)(x+1)^2}$

66. $\dfrac{2}{(x+2)^2(x-1)}-\dfrac{6}{(x+2)(x-1)^2}$

67. $\dfrac{x+4}{x^2-x-2}-\dfrac{2x+3}{x^2+2x-8}$

68. $\dfrac{2x-3}{x^2+8x+7}-\dfrac{x-2}{(x+1)^2}$

69. $\dfrac{1}{x}-\dfrac{2}{x^2+x}+\dfrac{3}{x^3-x^2}$

70. $\dfrac{x}{(x-1)^2}+\dfrac{2}{x}-\dfrac{x+1}{x^3-x^2}$

71. $\dfrac{1}{h}\left(\dfrac{1}{x+h}-\dfrac{1}{x}\right)$

72. $\dfrac{1}{h}\left[\dfrac{1}{(x+h)^2}-\dfrac{1}{x^2}\right]$

In Problems 73–84, perform the indicated operations and simplify the result. Leave your answer in factored form.

73. $\dfrac{1+\dfrac{1}{x}}{1-\dfrac{1}{x}}$

74. $\dfrac{4+\dfrac{1}{x^2}}{3-\dfrac{1}{x^2}}$

75. $\dfrac{2-\dfrac{x+1}{x}}{3+\dfrac{x-1}{x+1}}$

76. $\dfrac{1-\dfrac{x}{x+1}}{2-\dfrac{x-1}{x}}$

77. $\dfrac{\dfrac{x+4}{x-2}-\dfrac{x-3}{x+1}}{x+1}$

78. $\dfrac{\dfrac{x-2}{x+1}-\dfrac{x}{x-2}}{x+3}$

79. $\dfrac{\dfrac{x-2}{x+2}+\dfrac{x-1}{x+1}}{\dfrac{x}{x+1}-\dfrac{2x-3}{x}}$

80. $\dfrac{\dfrac{2x+5}{x}-\dfrac{x}{x-3}}{\dfrac{x^2}{x-3}-\dfrac{(x+1)^2}{x+3}}$

81. $1-\dfrac{1}{1-\dfrac{1}{x}}$

82. $1-\dfrac{1}{1-\dfrac{1}{1-x}}$

83. $\dfrac{2(x-1)^{-1}+3}{3(x-1)^{-1}+2}$

84. $\dfrac{4(x+2)^{-1}-3}{3(x+2)^{-1}-1}$

In Problems 85–92, expressions that occur in calculus are given. Reduce each expression to lowest terms.

85. $\dfrac{(2x+3)\cdot 3-(3x-5)\cdot 2}{(3x-5)^2}$

86. $\dfrac{(4x+1)\cdot 5-(5x-2)\cdot 4}{(5x-2)^2}$

87. $\dfrac{x\cdot 2x-(x^2+1)\cdot 1}{(x^2+1)^2}$

88. $\dfrac{x\cdot 2x-(x^2-4)\cdot 1}{(x^2-4)^2}$

89. $\dfrac{(3x+1)\cdot 2x-x^2\cdot 3}{(3x+1)^2}$

90. $\dfrac{(2x-5)\cdot 3x^2-x^3\cdot 2}{(2x-5)^2}$

91. $\dfrac{(x^2+1)\cdot 3-(3x+4)\cdot 2x}{(x^2+1)^2}$

92. $\dfrac{(x^2+9)\cdot 2-(2x-5)\cdot 2x}{(x^2+9)^2}$

Applications and Extensions

93. The Lensmaker's Equation The focal length f of a lens with index of refraction n is

$$\frac{1}{f}=(n-1)\left[\frac{1}{R_1}+\frac{1}{R_2}\right]$$

where R_1 and R_2 are the radii of curvature of the front and back surfaces of the lens. Express f as a rational expression. Evaluate the rational expression for $n=1.5$, $R_1=0.1$ meter, and $R_2=0.2$ meter.

94. Electrical Circuits An electrical circuit contains three resistors connected in parallel. If the resistance of each is R_1, R_2, and R_3 ohms, respectively, their combined resistance R is given by the formula

$$\frac{1}{R}=\frac{1}{R_1}+\frac{1}{R_2}+\frac{1}{R_3}$$

Express R as a rational expression. Evaluate R for $R_1=5$ ohms, $R_2=4$ ohms, and $R_3=10$ ohms.

Discussion and Writing

95. The following expressions are called **continued fractions:**

$$1+\frac{1}{x}\qquad 1+\frac{1}{1+\dfrac{1}{x}}\qquad 1+\frac{1}{1+\dfrac{1}{1+\dfrac{1}{x}}}\qquad 1+\frac{1}{1+\dfrac{1}{1+\dfrac{1}{1+\dfrac{1}{x}}}}\quad\cdots$$

Each simplifies to an expression of the form

$$\frac{ax+b}{bx+c}$$

Trace the successive values of a, b, and c as you "continue" the fraction. Can you discover the patterns that these values follow? Go to the library and research Fibonacci numbers. Write a report on your findings.

96. Explain to a fellow student when you would use the LCM method to add two rational expressions. Give two examples of adding two rational expressions, one in which you use the LCM and the other in which you do not.

97. Which of the two methods given in the text for simplifying complex rational expressions do you prefer? Write a brief paragraph stating the reasons for your choice.

A.6 Solving Equations

PREPARING FOR THIS SECTION *Before getting started, review the following:*

- Factoring Polynomials (Appendix A, Section A.3, pp. A28–A29)
- Zero-Product Property (Appendix A, Section A.1, p. A4)

- Square Roots (Appendix A, Section A.1, pp. A9–A10)
- Absolute Value (Appendix A, Section A.1, p. A5)
- Rational Expressions (Appendix A, Section A.5, pp. A35–A41)

Now Work the 'Are You Prepared?' problems on page A57.

OBJECTIVES
1 Solve Linear Equations (p. A47)
2 Solve Rational Equations (p. A49)
3 Solve Quadratic Equations by Factoring (p. A50)
4 Solve Quadratic Equations Using the Square Root Method (p. A51)
5 Solve Quadratic Equations by Completing the Square (p. A52)
6 Solve Quadratic Equations Using the Quadratic Formula (p. A53)
7 Solve Equations Quadratic in Form (p. A55)
8 Solve Absolute Value Equations (p. A56)
9 Solve Equations by Factoring (p. A57)

An **equation in one variable** is a statement in which two expressions, at least one containing the variable, are equal. The expressions are called the **sides** of the equation. Since an equation is a statement, it may be true or false, depending on the value of the variable. Unless otherwise restricted, the admissible values of the variable are those in the domain of the variable. Those admissible values of the variable, if any, that result in a true statement are called **solutions**, or **roots**, of the equation. To **solve an equation** means to find all the solutions of the equation.

For example, the following are all equations in one variable, x:

$$x + 5 = 9 \qquad x^2 + 5x = 2x - 2 \qquad \frac{x^2 - 4}{x + 1} = 0 \qquad \sqrt{x^2 + 9} = 5$$

The first of these statements, $x + 5 = 9$, is true when $x = 4$ and false for any other choice of x. Thus, 4 is a solution of the equation $x + 5 = 9$. We also say that 4 **satisfies** the equation $x + 5 = 9$, because, when we substitute 4 for x, a true statement results.

Sometimes an equation will have more than one solution. For example, the equation

$$\frac{x^2 - 4}{x + 1} = 0$$

has $x = -2$ and $x = 2$ as solutions.

Usually, we will write the solution of an equation in set notation. This set is called the **solution set** of the equation. For example, the solution set of the equation $x^2 - 9 = 0$ is $\{-3, 3\}$.

Some equations have no real solution. For example, $x^2 + 9 = 5$ has no real solution, because there is no real number whose square when added to 9 equals 5.

An equation that is satisfied for every choice of the variable for which both sides are defined is called an **identity**. For example, the equation

$$3x + 5 = x + 3 + 2x + 2$$

is an identity, because this statement is true for any real number x.

Solving Equations Algebraically

One method for solving equations algebraically requires that a series of *equivalent equations* be developed from the original equation until an obvious solution results.

For example, all the following equations are equivalent, because each has only the solution $x = 5$:

$$2x + 3 = 13$$
$$2x = 10$$
$$x = 5$$

The question, though, is "How do I obtain an equivalent equation?" In general, there are five ways to do so.

Procedures That Result in Equivalent Equations

1. Interchange the two sides of the equation:

Replace $3 = x$ by $x = 3$

2. Simplify the sides of the equation by combining like terms, eliminating parentheses, and so on:

Replace $x + 2 + 6 = 2x + 3(x + 1)$

by $x + 8 = 5x + 3$

3. Add or subtract the same expression on both sides of the equation:

Replace $3x - 5 = 4$

by $(3x - 5) + 5 = 4 + 5$

4. Multiply or divide both sides of the equation by the same nonzero expression:

Replace $\dfrac{3x}{x - 1} = \dfrac{6}{x - 1}$ $x \neq 1$

by $\dfrac{3x}{x - 1} \cdot (x - 1) = \dfrac{6}{x - 1} \cdot (x - 1)$

5. If one side of the equation is 0 and the other side can be factored, then we may use the Zero-Product Property and set each factor equal to 0:

Replace $x(x - 3) = 0$

by $x = 0$ or $x - 3 = 0$

WARNING Squaring both sides of an equation does not necessarily lead to an equivalent equation. ∎

Whenever it is possible to solve an equation in your head, do so. For example:

The solution of $2x = 8$ is $x = 4$.

The solution of $3x - 15 = 0$ is $x = 5$.

Now Work PROBLEM 13

We now introduce specific types of equations that can be solved algebraically to obtain exact solutions. We start with **linear equations.**

1 Solve Linear Equations

Linear equations are equations such as

$$3x + 12 = 0 \qquad \frac{3}{4}x - \frac{1}{5} = 0 \qquad 0.62x - 0.3 = 0$$

A **linear equation in one variable** is equivalent to an equation of the form

$$ax + b = 0$$

where a and b are real numbers and $a \neq 0$.

Sometimes a linear equation is called a **first-degree equation,** because the left side is a polynomial in x of degree 1.

EXAMPLE 1	Solving a Linear Equation

Solve the equation: $3(x - 2) = 5(x - 1)$

Solution

$$3(x - 2) = 5(x - 1)$$

$3x - 6 = 5x - 5$ Use the Distributive Property.

$3x - 6 - 5x = 5x - 5 - 5x$ Subtract 5x from each side.

$-2x - 6 = -5$ Simplify.

$-2x - 6 + 6 = -5 + 6$ Add 6 to each side.

$-2x = 1$ Simplify.

$\dfrac{-2x}{-2} = \dfrac{1}{-2}$ Divide each side by -2.

$x = -\dfrac{1}{2}$ Simplify.

✓ Check Let $x = -\dfrac{1}{2}$ in the expression in x on the left side of the equation and simplify. Let $x = -\dfrac{1}{2}$ in the expression in x on the right side of the equation and simplify. If the two expressions are equal, the solution checks.

$$3(x - 2) = 3\left(-\frac{1}{2} - 2\right) = 3\left(-\frac{5}{2}\right) = -\frac{15}{2}$$

$$5(x - 1) = 5\left(-\frac{1}{2} - 1\right) = 5\left(-\frac{3}{2}\right) = -\frac{15}{2}$$

Since the two expressions are equal, the solution $x = -\dfrac{1}{2}$ checks. The solution set is $\left\{-\dfrac{1}{2}\right\}$.

■

━━━ **Now Work** PROBLEM 23

The next example illustrates the solution of an equation that does not appear to be linear, but leads to a linear equation upon simplification.

EXAMPLE 2	Solving an Equation That Leads to a Linear Equation

Solve the equation: $(2x - 1)(x - 1) = (x - 5)(2x - 5)$

Solution

$$(2x - 1)(x - 1) = (x - 5)(2x - 5)$$

$2x^2 - 3x + 1 = 2x^2 - 15x + 25$ Multiply and combine like terms.

$2x^2 - 3x + 1 - 2x^2 = 2x^2 - 15x + 25 - 2x^2$ Subtract $2x^2$ from each side.

$-3x + 1 = -15x + 25$ Simplify.

$-3x + 1 - 1 = -15x + 25 - 1$ Subtract 1 from each side.

$-3x = -15x + 24$ Simplify.

$-3x + 15x = -15x + 24 + 15x$ Add 15x to each side.

$12x = 24$ Simplify.

$\dfrac{12x}{12} = \dfrac{24}{12}$ Divide each side by 12.

$x = 2$ Simplify.

✓Check $(2x - 1)(x - 1) = (2 \cdot 2 - 1)(2 - 1) = (3)(1) = 3$

$(x - 5)(2x - 5) = (2 - 5)(2 \cdot 2 - 5) = (-3)(-1) = 3$

Since the two expressions are equal, the solution checks. The solution set is $\{2\}$.

◼

➤ **Now Work** PROBLEM 33

2 Solve Rational Equations

We now introduce another type of equation, the *rational equation*. A **rational equation** is an equation that contains a rational expression. Examples of rational equations are

$$\frac{3}{x + 1} = \frac{2}{x - 1} + 7 \quad \text{and} \quad \frac{x - 5}{x - 4} = \frac{3}{x + 2}$$

To solve a rational equation, multiply both sides of the equation by the least common multiple of the denominators of the rational expressions that make up the rational equation.

| EXAMPLE 3 | Solving a Rational Equation |

Solve the equation: $\dfrac{3}{x - 2} = \dfrac{1}{x - 1} + \dfrac{7}{(x - 1)(x - 2)}$

Solution First, we note that the domain of the variable is $\{x \mid x \neq 1, x \neq 2\}$. We clear the equation of rational expressions by multiplying both sides by the least common multiple of the denominators of the three rational expressions, $(x - 1)(x - 2)$.

$$\frac{3}{x - 2} = \frac{1}{x - 1} + \frac{7}{(x - 1)(x - 2)}$$

$$(x - 1)(x - 2)\frac{3}{x - 2} = (x - 1)(x - 2)\left[\frac{1}{x - 1} + \frac{7}{(x - 1)(x - 2)}\right]$$

Multiply both sides by $(x - 1)(x - 2)$. Cancel on the left.

$$3x - 3 = (x - 1)(x - 2)\frac{1}{x - 1} + (x - 1)(x - 2)\frac{7}{(x - 1)(x - 2)}$$

Use the Distributive Property on each side; cancel on the right.

$$3x - 3 = (x - 2) + 7$$

$$3x - 3 = x + 5$$ Combine like terms.

$$2x = 8$$ Add 3 to each side; subtract x from each side.

$$x = 4$$ Divide by 2.

✓Check $\dfrac{3}{x - 2} = \dfrac{3}{4 - 2} = \dfrac{3}{2}$

$$\frac{1}{x - 1} + \frac{7}{(x - 1)(x - 2)} = \frac{1}{4 - 1} + \frac{7}{(4 - 1)(4 - 2)} = \frac{1}{3} + \frac{7}{3 \cdot 2} = \frac{2}{6} + \frac{7}{6} = \frac{9}{6} = \frac{3}{2}$$

Since the two expressions are equal, the solution $x = 4$ checks. The solution set is $\{4\}$.

◼

➤ **Now Work** PROBLEM 45

Quadratic Equations

Quadratic equations are equations such as

$$2x^2 + x + 8 = 0 \qquad 3x^2 - 5x = 0 \qquad x^2 - 9 = 0$$

A general definition is given next.

> A **quadratic equation** is an equation equivalent to one of the form
>
> $$ax^2 + bx + c = 0 \qquad\qquad\qquad \textbf{(1)}$$
>
> where a, b, and c are real numbers and $a \neq 0$.

A quadratic equation written in the form $ax^2 + bx + c = 0$ is said to be in **standard form.**

Sometimes, a quadratic equation is called a **second-degree equation,** because the left side is a polynomial of degree 2. We shall discuss three algebraic ways of solving quadratic equations: by factoring, by completing the square, and by using the quadratic formula.

3 Solve Quadratic Equations by Factoring

When a quadratic equation is written in standard form, $ax^2 + bx + c = 0$, it may be possible to factor the expression on the left side as the product of two first-degree polynomials. Then, by setting each factor equal to 0 and solving the resulting linear equations, we obtain the *exact* solutions of the quadratic equation. This approach leads us to a basic premise in mathematics. Whenever a problem is encountered, use techniques that reduce the problem to one you already know how to solve. In this instance, we are reducing quadratic equations to linear equations using the technique of factoring.

Let's look at an example.

EXAMPLE 4 | **Solving a Quadratic Equation by Factoring**

Solve the equation: $x^2 = 12 - x$

Solution   We put the equation in standard form by adding $x - 12$ to each side:

$$x^2 = 12 - x$$
$$x^2 + x - 12 = 0$$

The left side of the equation may now be factored as

$$(x + 4)(x - 3) = 0$$

Then, by the Zero-Product Property, we have

$$x + 4 = 0 \qquad \text{or} \qquad x - 3 = 0$$
$$x = -4 \qquad\qquad\qquad x = 3$$

We leave the check to you. The solution set is $\{-4, 3\}$.

 ✎══════ **Now Work** PROBLEM 67

When the left side factors into two linear equations with the same solution, the quadratic equation is said to have a **repeated solution.** We also call this solution a **root of multiplicity 2,** or a **double root.**

EXAMPLE 5 | **Solving a Quadratic Equation by Factoring**

Solve the equation: $x^2 - 6x + 9 = 0$

Solution   This equation is already in standard form, and the left side can be factored:

$$x^2 - 6x + 9 = 0$$
$$(x - 3)(x - 3) = 0$$

so

$$x = 3 \quad \text{or} \quad x = 3$$

This equation has only the repeated solution 3. The solution set is $\{3\}$.

4 Solve Quadratic Equations Using the Square Root Method

Suppose that we wish to solve the quadratic equation

$$x^2 = p \tag{2}$$

where $p \geq 0$ is a nonnegative number. We proceed as in the earlier examples:

$$x^2 - p = 0 \qquad \text{Put in standard form.}$$
$$(x - \sqrt{p})(x + \sqrt{p}) = 0 \qquad \text{Factor (over the real numbers).}$$
$$x = \sqrt{p} \quad \text{or} \quad x = -\sqrt{p} \qquad \text{Solve.}$$

We have the following result:

$$\text{If } x^2 = p \text{ and } p \geq 0, \text{ then } x = \sqrt{p} \text{ or } x = -\sqrt{p}. \tag{3}$$

When statement (3) is used, it is called the **Square Root Method.** In statement (3), note that if $p > 0$ the equation $x^2 = p$ has two solutions, $x = \sqrt{p}$ and $x = -\sqrt{p}$. We usually abbreviate these solutions as $x = \pm\sqrt{p}$, read as "x equals plus or minus the square root of p." For example, the two solutions of the equation

$$x^2 = 4$$

are

$$x = \pm\sqrt{4}$$

and, since $\sqrt{4} = 2$, we have

$$x = \pm 2$$

The solution set is $\{-2, 2\}$.

EXAMPLE 6	**Solving Quadratic Equations by Using the Square Root Method**

Solve each equation.

(a) $x^2 = 5$ (b) $(x - 2)^2 = 16$

Solution   (a) $x^2 = 5$

$$x = \pm\sqrt{5} \qquad \text{Use the Square Root Method.}$$
$$x = \sqrt{5} \quad \text{or} \quad x = -\sqrt{5}$$

The solution set is $\left\{-\sqrt{5}, \sqrt{5}\right\}$.

(b) $(x - 2)^2 = 16$

$$x - 2 = \pm\sqrt{16} \qquad \text{Use the Square Root Method.}$$
$$x - 2 = \sqrt{16} \quad \text{or} \quad x - 2 = -\sqrt{16}$$
$$x - 2 = 4 \qquad\qquad x - 2 = -4$$
$$x = 6 \qquad\qquad\quad x = -2$$

The solution set is $\{-2, 6\}$.

Now Work PROBLEM 95

5 Solve Quadratic Equations by Completing the Square

We now introduce the method of **completing the square.** The idea behind this method is to "adjust" the left side of a quadratic equation, $ax^2 + bx + c = 0$, so that it becomes a perfect square, that is, the square of a first-degree polynomial. For example, $x^2 + 6x + 9$ and $x^2 - 4x + 4$ are perfect squares because

$$x^2 + 6x + 9 = (x + 3)^2 \quad \text{and} \quad x^2 - 4x + 4 = (x - 2)^2$$

How do we "adjust" the left side? We do it by adding the appropriate number to create a perfect square. For example, to make $x^2 + 6x$ a perfect square, we add 9.

Let's look at several examples of completing the square when the coefficient of x^2 is 1.

Start	Add	Result
$x^2 + 4x$	4	$x^2 + 4x + 4 = (x + 2)^2$
$x^2 + 12x$	36	$x^2 + 12x + 36 = (x + 6)^2$
$x^2 - 6x$	9	$x^2 - 6x + 9 = (x - 3)^2$
$x^2 + x$	$\dfrac{1}{4}$	$x^2 + x + \dfrac{1}{4} = \left(x + \dfrac{1}{2}\right)^2$

Do you see the pattern? Provided that the coefficient of x^2 is 1, we complete the square by adding the square of one-half of the coefficient of x.

Start	Add	Result
$x^2 + mx$	$\left(\dfrac{m}{2}\right)^2$	$x^2 + mx + \left(\dfrac{m}{2}\right)^2 = \left(x + \dfrac{m}{2}\right)^2$

⊱──── **Now Work** PROBLEM 99

The next example illustrates how the procedure of completing the square can be used to solve a quadratic equation.

EXAMPLE 7 **Solving a Quadratic Equation by Completing the Square**

Solve by completing the square: $x^2 + 5x + 4 = 0$

Solution We always begin this procedure by rearranging the equation so that the constant is on the right side.

$$x^2 + 5x + 4 = 0$$
$$x^2 + 5x = -4$$

Since the coefficient of x^2 is 1, we can complete the square on the left side by adding $\left(\dfrac{1}{2} \cdot 5\right)^2 = \dfrac{25}{4}$. Of course, in an equation, whatever we add to the left side also must be added to the right side. We add $\dfrac{25}{4}$ to *both* sides.

$$x^2 + 5x + \frac{25}{4} = -4 + \frac{25}{4} \qquad \text{Add } \frac{25}{4} \text{ to both sides.}$$
$$\left(x + \frac{5}{2}\right)^2 = \frac{9}{4} \qquad \text{Factor; simplify.}$$

$$x + \frac{5}{2} = \pm\sqrt{\frac{9}{4}} \qquad \text{Use the Square Root Method.}$$

$$x + \frac{5}{2} = \pm\frac{3}{2}$$

$$x = -\frac{5}{2} \pm \frac{3}{2}$$

$$x = -\frac{5}{2} + \frac{3}{2} = -1 \quad \text{or} \quad x = -\frac{5}{2} - \frac{3}{2} = -4$$

The solution set is $\{-4, -1\}$.

> The solution of the equation in Example 7 can also be obtained by factoring. Rework Example 7 using factoring.

Now Work PROBLEM 105

6 Solve Quadratic Equations Using The Quadratic Formula

We can use the method of completing the square to obtain a general formula for solving the quadratic equation

$$ax^2 + bx + c = 0 \qquad a > 0$$

NOTE There is no loss in generality to assume that $a > 0$, since if $a < 0$ we can multiply both sides by -1 to obtain an equivalent equation with a positive leading coefficient. ∎

As in Example 7, we begin by rearranging the terms as

$$ax^2 + bx = -c$$

Since $a > 0$, we can divide both sides by a to get

$$x^2 + \frac{b}{a}x = -\frac{c}{a}$$

Now the coefficient of x^2 is 1. To complete the square on the left side, add the square of $\frac{1}{2}$ of the coefficient of x; that is, add

$$\left(\frac{1}{2} \cdot \frac{b}{a}\right)^2 = \frac{b^2}{4a^2}$$

to each side. Then

$$x^2 + \frac{b}{a}x + \frac{b^2}{4a^2} = \frac{b^2}{4a^2} - \frac{c}{a}$$

$$\left(x + \frac{b}{2a}\right)^2 = \frac{b^2 - 4ac}{4a^2} \qquad \frac{b^2}{4a^2} - \frac{c}{a} = \frac{b^2}{4a^2} - \frac{4ac}{4a^2} = \frac{b^2 - 4ac}{4a^2} \qquad \textbf{(4)}$$

Provided that $b^2 - 4ac \geq 0$, we now can use the Square Root Method to get

$$x + \frac{b}{2a} = \pm\sqrt{\frac{b^2 - 4ac}{4a^2}}$$

$$x + \frac{b}{2a} = \frac{\pm\sqrt{b^2 - 4ac}}{2a} \qquad \text{The square root of a quotient equals the quotient of the square roots. Also,} \sqrt{4a^2} = 2a \text{ since } a > 0.$$

$$x = -\frac{b}{2a} \pm \frac{\sqrt{b^2 - 4ac}}{2a} \qquad \text{Add } -\frac{b}{2a} \text{ to both sides.}$$

$$= \frac{-b \pm \sqrt{b^2 - 4ac}}{2a} \qquad \text{Combine the quotients on the right.}$$

What if $b^2 - 4ac$ is negative? Then equation (4) states that the left expression (a real number squared) equals the right expression (a negative number). Since this occurrence is impossible for real numbers, we conclude that if $b^2 - 4ac < 0$ the quadratic equation has no *real* solution.*

We now state the *quadratic formula*.

THEOREM

Quadratic Formula

Consider the quadratic equation

$$ax^2 + bx + c = 0 \qquad a \neq 0$$

If $b^2 - 4ac < 0$, this equation has no real solution.
If $b^2 - 4ac \geq 0$, the real solution(s) of this equation is (are) given by the **quadratic formula.**

$$x = \frac{-b \pm \sqrt{b^2 - 4ac}}{2a}$$

The quantity $b^2 - 4ac$ is called the **discriminant** of the quadratic equation, because its value tells us whether the equation has real solutions. In fact, it also tells us how many solutions to expect.

Discriminant of a Quadratic Equation

For a quadratic equation $ax^2 + bx + c = 0$:

1. If $b^2 - 4ac > 0$, there are two unequal real solutions.
2. If $b^2 - 4ac = 0$, there is a repeated real solution, a root of multiplicity 2.
3. If $b^2 - 4ac < 0$, there is no real solution.

When asked to find the real solutions, if any, of a quadratic equation, always evaluate the discriminant first to see how many real solutions there are.

EXAMPLE 8

Solving a Quadratic Equation by Using the Quadratic Formula

Find the real solutions, if any, of the equation $3x^2 - 5x + 1 = 0$.

Solution

The equation is in standard form, so we compare it to $ax^2 + bx + c = 0$ to find a, b, and c.

$$3x^2 - 5x + 1 = 0$$
$$ax^2 + bx + c = 0 \qquad a = 3, b = -5, c = 1$$

With $a = 3, b = -5$, and $c = 1$, we evaluate the discriminant $b^2 - 4ac$.

$$b^2 - 4ac = (-5)^2 - 4(3)(1) = 25 - 12 = 13$$

Since $b^2 - 4ac > 0$, there are two real solutions.

---

*We consider quadratic equations where $b^2 - 4ac$ is negative in the next section.

We use the quadratic formula with $a = 3$, $b = -5$, $c = 1$, and $b^2 - 4ac = 13$.

$$x = \frac{-b \pm \sqrt{b^2 - 4ac}}{2a} = \frac{-(-5) \pm \sqrt{13}}{2(3)} = \frac{5 \pm \sqrt{13}}{6}$$

The solution set is $\left\{ \dfrac{5 - \sqrt{13}}{6}, \dfrac{5 + \sqrt{13}}{6} \right\}$.

━━━ **Now Work** PROBLEM **111**

| **EXAMPLE 9** | **Solving a Quadratic Equation by Using the Quadratic Formula** |

Find the real solutions, if any, of the equation

$$3x^2 + 2 = 4x$$

Solution   The equation, as given, is not in standard form.

$$3x^2 + 2 = 4x$$

$$3x^2 - 4x + 2 = 0 \qquad \text{Subtract 4x from both sides to put the equation in standard form.}$$

$$ax^2 + bx + c = 0 \qquad \text{Compare to standard form.}$$

With $a = 3$, $b = -4$, and $c = 2$, we find that

$$b^2 - 4ac = (-4)^2 - 4(3)(2)$$

$$= 16 - 24$$

$$= -8$$

Since $b^2 - 4ac < 0$, the equation has no real solution.

━━━ **Now Work** PROBLEM **117**

SUMMARY   Procedure for Solving a Quadratic Equation Algebraically

To solve a quadratic equation, first put it in standard form:

$$ax^2 + bx + c = 0$$

Then:

STEP 1:   Identify a, b, and c.

STEP 2:   Evaluate the discriminant, $b^2 - 4ac$.

STEP 3:   (a) If the discriminant is negative, the equation has no real solution.

(b) If the discriminant is nonnegative, determine whether the left side can be factored. If you can easily spot factors, use the factoring method to solve the equation. Otherwise, use the quadratic formula or the method of completing the square.

7 Solve Equations Quadratic in Form

The equation $x^4 + x^2 - 12 = 0$ is not quadratic in x, but it is quadratic in x^2. That is, if we let $u = x^2$, we get $u^2 + u - 12 = 0$, a quadratic equation. This equation can be solved for u and, in turn, by using $u = x^2$, we can find the solutions x of the original equation.

In general, if an appropriate substitution u transforms an equation into one of the form

$$au^2 + bu + c = 0 \qquad a \neq 0$$

then the original equation is called an **equation of the quadratic type** or an **equation quadratic in form.**

The difficulty of solving such an equation lies in the determination that the equation is, in fact, quadratic in form. After you are told an equation is quadratic in form, it is easy enough to see it, but some practice is needed to enable you to recognize them on your own.

EXAMPLE 10	**Solving Equations That Are Quadratic in Form**

Find the real solutions of the equation: $(x + 2)^2 + 11(x + 2) - 12 = 0$

Solution For this equation, let $u = x + 2$. Then $u^2 = (x + 2)^2$, and the original equation,

$$(x + 2)^2 + 11(x + 2) - 12 = 0$$

becomes

$$u^2 + 11u - 12 = 0 \quad \text{Let } u = x + 2.$$
$$(u + 12)(u - 1) = 0 \quad \text{Factor.}$$
$$u = -12 \quad \text{or} \quad u = 1 \quad \text{Solve.}$$

But we want to solve for x. Because $u = x + 2$, we have

$$x + 2 = -12 \quad \text{or} \quad x + 2 = 1$$
$$x = -14 \qquad\qquad x = -1$$

✓Check $x = -14$: $(-14 + 2)^2 + 11(-14 + 2) - 12$
$$= (-12)^2 + 11(-12) - 12 = 144 - 132 - 12 = 0$$
$x = -1$: $(-1 + 2)^2 + 11(-1 + 2) - 12 = 1 + 11 - 12 = 0$

The original equation has the solution set $\{-14, -1\}$.

The idea should now be clear. If an equation contains an expression and that same expression squared, make a substitution for the expression. You may get a quadratic equation.

─═══ **Now Work** PROBLEM 85

8 Solve Absolute Value Equations

Recall that, on the real number line, the absolute value of a equals the distance from the origin to the point whose coordinate is a. For example, there are two points whose distance from the origin is 5 units, -5 and 5. Thus the equation $|x| = 5$ will have the solution set $\{-5, 5\}$. This leads to the following result:

Equations Involving Absolute Value

If a is a positive real number and if u is any algebraic expression, then

$|u| = a$ is equivalent to $u = a$ or $u = -a$	**(5)**

| EXAMPLE 11 | **Solving an Equation Involving Absolute Value** |

Solve the equation $|x + 4| = 13$.

Solution   This follows the form of equation (5), where $u = x + 4$. There are two possibilities.

$$x + 4 = 13 \quad \text{or} \quad x + 4 = -13$$
$$x = 9 \qquad\qquad x = -17$$

The solution set is $\{-17, 9\}$.

➤ **Now Work** PROBLEM 49

9 Solve Equations by Factoring

We have already solved certain quadratic equations using factoring. Let's look at examples of other kinds of equations that can be solved by factoring.

| EXAMPLE 12 | **Solving Equations by Factoring** |

Solve the equation: $x^3 - x^2 - 4x + 4 = 0$

Solution   Do you recall the method of factoring by grouping? (If not, review Example 9(f) on p. A29.) We group the terms of $x^3 - x^2 - 4x + 4 = 0$ as follows:

$$(x^3 - x^2) - (4x - 4) = 0$$

Factor out x^2 from the first grouping and 4 from the second.

$$x^2(x - 1) - 4(x - 1) = 0$$

This reveals the common factor $(x - 1)$, so we have

$$(x^2 - 4)(x - 1) = 0$$
$$(x - 2)(x + 2)(x - 1) = 0 \qquad\qquad \textit{Factor again.}$$
$$x - 2 = 0 \quad \text{or} \quad x + 2 = 0 \quad \text{or} \quad x - 1 = 0 \quad \textit{Set each factor equal to 0.}$$
$$x = 2 \qquad\qquad x = -2 \qquad\qquad x = 1 \quad \textit{Solve.}$$

The solution set is $\{-2, 1, 2\}$.

✓ **Check**

$x = -2$: $(-2)^3 - (-2)^2 - 4(-2) + 4 = -8 - 4 + 8 + 4 = 0$ -2 is a solution.

$x = 1$: $1^3 - 1^2 - 4(1) + 4 = 1 - 1 - 4 + 4 = 0$ 1 is a solution.

$x = 2$: $2^3 - 2^2 - 4(2) + 4 = 8 - 4 - 8 + 4 = 0$ 2 is a solution.

➤ **Now Work** PROBLEM 89

A.6 Assess Your Understanding

'Are You Prepared?' *Answers are given at the end of these exercises. If you get a wrong answer, read the pages listed in* red.

1. Find the least common denominator of
   $\dfrac{3}{x^2 - 4}$ and $\dfrac{5}{x^2 - 3x + 2}$. (pp. A39–A41)

2. Factor $2x^2 - x - 3$. (pp. A28–A29)

3. The solution set of the equation $(x - 3)(3x + 5) = 0$ is
   _____. (p. A4)

4. *True or False:* $\sqrt{x^2} = |x|$. (pp. A9–A10)

Concepts and Vocabulary

5. Two equations that have the same solution set are called _____.

6. An equation that is satisfied for every choice of the variable for which both sides are defined is called a(n) _____.

7. *True or False:* The solution of the equation $3x - 8 = 0$ is $\dfrac{3}{8}$.

8. *True or False:* Some equations have no solution.

9. To complete the square of the expression $x^2 + 5x$, you would _____ the number _____.

10. The quantity $b^2 - 4ac$ is called the _____ of a quadratic equation. If it is _____, the equation has no real solution.

11. *True or False:* Quadratic equations always have two real solutions.

12. *True or False:* If the discriminant of a quadratic equation is positive, then the equation has two solutions that are negatives of one another.

Skill Building

In Problems 13–92, solve each equation.

13. $3x = 21$

14. $3x = -24$

15. $5x + 15 = 0$

16. $3x + 18 = 0$

17. $2x - 3 = 5$

18. $3x + 4 = -8$

19. $\dfrac{1}{3}x = \dfrac{5}{12}$

20. $\dfrac{2}{3}x = \dfrac{9}{2}$

21. $6 - x = 2x + 9$

22. $3 - 2x = 2 - x$

23. $2(3 + 2x) = 3(x - 4)$

24. $3(2 - x) = 2x - 1$

25. $8x - (2x + 1) = 3x - 10$

26. $5 - (2x - 1) = 10$

27. $\dfrac{1}{2}x - 4 = \dfrac{3}{4}x$

28. $1 - \dfrac{1}{2}x = 5$

29. $0.9t = 0.4 + 0.1t$

30. $0.9t = 1 + t$

31. $\dfrac{2}{y} + \dfrac{4}{y} = 3$

32. $\dfrac{4}{y} - 5 = \dfrac{5}{2y}$

33. $(x + 7)(x - 1) = (x + 1)^2$

34. $(x + 2)(x - 3) = (x - 3)^2$

35. $z(z^2 + 1) = 3 + z^3$

36. $w(4 - w^2) = 8 - w^3$

37. $x^2 = 9x$

38. $x^3 = x^2$

39. $t^3 - 9t^2 = 0$

40. $4z^3 - 8z^2 = 0$

41. $\dfrac{3}{2x - 3} = \dfrac{2}{x + 5}$

42. $\dfrac{-2}{x + 4} = \dfrac{-3}{x + 1}$

43. $(x + 2)(3x) = (x + 2)(6)$

44. $(x - 5)(2x) = (x - 5)(4)$

45. $\dfrac{2}{x - 2} = \dfrac{3}{x + 5} + \dfrac{10}{(x + 5)(x - 2)}$

46. $\dfrac{1}{2x + 3} + \dfrac{1}{x - 1} = \dfrac{1}{(2x + 3)(x - 1)}$

47. $|2x| = 6$

48. $|3x| = 12$

49. $|2x + 3| = 5$

50. $|3x - 1| = 2$

51. $|1 - 4t| = 5$

52. $|1 - 2z| = 3$

53. $|-2x| = 8$

54. $|-x| = 1$

55. $|-2|x = 4$

56. $|3|x = 9$

57. $|x - 2| = -\dfrac{1}{2}$

58. $|2 - x| = -1$

59. $|x^2 - 4| = 0$

60. $|x^2 - 9| = 0$

61. $|x^2 - 2x| = 3$

62. $|x^2 + x| = 12$

63. $|x^2 + x - 1| = 1$

64. $|x^2 + 3x - 2| = 2$

65. $x^2 = 4x$

66. $x^2 = -8x$

67. $z^2 + 4z - 12 = 0$

68. $v^2 + 7v + 12 = 0$

69. $2x^2 - 5x - 3 = 0$

70. $3x^2 + 5x + 2 = 0$

71. $x(x - 7) + 12 = 0$

72. $x(x + 1) = 12$

73. $4x^2 + 9 = 12x$

74. $25x^2 + 16 = 40x$

75. $6x - 5 = \dfrac{6}{x}$

76. $x + \dfrac{12}{x} = 7$

77. $\dfrac{4(x - 2)}{x - 3} + \dfrac{3}{x} = \dfrac{-3}{x(x - 3)}$

78. $\dfrac{5}{x + 4} = 4 + \dfrac{3}{x - 2}$

79. $\dfrac{x}{x^2 - 1} - \dfrac{x + 3}{x^2 - x} = \dfrac{-3}{x^2 + x}$

80. $\dfrac{x + 1}{x^2 + 2x} - \dfrac{x + 4}{x^2 + x} = \dfrac{-3}{x^2 + 3x + 2}$

81. $x^4 - 5x^2 + 4 = 0$

82. $x^4 - 10x^2 + 25 = 0$

83. $(x + 2)^2 + 7(x + 2) + 12 = 0$

84. $(2x + 5)^2 - (2x + 5) - 6 = 0$

85. $2(s + 1)^2 - 5(s + 1) = 3$

86. $3(1 - y)^2 + 5(1 - y) + 2 = 0$

87. $x^3 + x^2 - 20x = 0$

88. $x^3 + 6x^2 - 7x = 0$

89. $x^3 + x^2 - x - 1 = 0$

90. $x^3 + 4x^2 - x - 4 = 0$

91. $2x^3 + 4 = x^2 + 8x$

92. $3x^3 + 4x^2 = 27x + 36$

In Problems 93–98, solve each equation by the Square Root Method.

93. $x^2 = 25$

94. $x^2 = 36$

95. $(x - 1)^2 = 4$

96. $(x + 2)^2 = 1$

97. $(2x + 3)^2 = 9$

98. $(3x - 2)^2 = 4$

In Problems 99–104, what number should be added to complete the square of each expression?

99. $x^2 + 8x$

100. $x^2 - 4x$

101. $x^2 + \dfrac{1}{2}x$

102. $x^2 - \dfrac{1}{3}x$

103. $x^2 - \dfrac{2}{3}x$

104. $x^2 - \dfrac{2}{5}x$

In Problems 105–110, solve each equation by completing the square.

105. $x^2 + 4x = 21$

106. $x^2 - 6x = 13$

107. $x^2 - \dfrac{1}{2}x - \dfrac{3}{16} = 0$

108. $x^2 + \dfrac{2}{3}x - \dfrac{1}{3} = 0$

109. $3x^2 + x - \dfrac{1}{2} = 0$

110. $2x^2 - 3x - 1 = 0$

In Problems 111–122, find the real solutions, if any, of each equation. Use the quadratic formula.

111. $x^2 - 4x + 2 = 0$

112. $x^2 + 4x + 2 = 0$

113. $x^2 - 5x - 1 = 0$

114. $x^2 + 5x + 3 = 0$

115. $2x^2 - 5x + 3 = 0$

116. $2x^2 + 5x + 3 = 0$

117. $4y^2 - y + 2 = 0$

118. $4t^2 + t + 1 = 0$

119. $4x^2 = 1 - 2x$

120. $2x^2 = 1 - 2x$

121. $x^2 + \sqrt{3}x - 3 = 0$

122. $x^2 + \sqrt{2}x - 2 = 0$

In Problems 123–128, use the discriminant to determine whether each quadratic equation has two unequal real solutions, a repeated real solution, or no real solution without solving the equation.

123. $x^2 - 5x + 7 = 0$

124. $x^2 + 5x + 7 = 0$

125. $9x^2 - 30x + 25 = 0$

126. $25x^2 - 20x + 4 = 0$

127. $3x^2 + 5x - 8 = 0$

128. $2x^2 - 3x - 4 = 0$

Problems 129–134 list some formulas that occur in applications. Solve each formula for the indicated variable.

129. Electricity $\dfrac{1}{R} = \dfrac{1}{R_1} + \dfrac{1}{R_2}$ for R

130. Finance $A = P(1 + rt)$ for r

131. Mechanics $F = \dfrac{mv^2}{R}$ for R

132. Chemistry $PV = nRT$ for T

133. Mathematics $S = \dfrac{a}{1 - r}$ for r

134. Mechanics $v = -gt + v_0$ for t

135. Show that the sum of the roots of a quadratic equation is $-\dfrac{b}{a}$.

136. Show that the product of the roots of a quadratic equation is $\dfrac{c}{a}$.

137. Find k so that the equation $kx^2 + x + k = 0$ has a repeated real solution.

138. Find k so that the equation $x^2 - kx + 4 = 0$ has a repeated real solution.

139. Show that the real solutions of the equation $ax^2 + bx + c = 0$ are the negatives of the real solutions of the equation $ax^2 - bx + c = 0$. Assume that $b^2 - 4ac \geq 0$.

140. Show that the real solutions of the equation $ax^2 + bx + c = 0$ are the reciprocals of the real solutions of the equation $cx^2 + bx + a = 0$. Assume that $b^2 - 4ac \geq 0$.

Discussion and Writing

141. Which of the following pairs of equations are equivalent? Explain.
  (a) $x^2 = 9$; $x = 3$
  (b) $x = \sqrt{9}$; $x = 3$
  (c) $(x - 1)(x - 2) = (x - 1)^2$; $x - 2 = x - 1$

142. The equation
$$\frac{5}{x + 3} + 3 = \frac{8 + x}{x + 3}$$
has no solution, yet when we go through the process of solving it we obtain $x = -3$. Write a brief paragraph to explain what causes this to happen.

143. Make up an equation that has no solution and give it to a fellow student to solve. Ask the fellow student to write a critique of your equation.

144. Describe three ways you might solve a quadratic equation. State your preferred method; explain why you chose it.

145. Explain the benefits of evaluating the discriminant of a quadratic equation before attempting to solve it.

146. Make up three quadratic equations: one having two distinct solutions, one having no real solution, and one having exactly one real solution.

147. The word *quadratic* seems to imply four (*quad*), yet a quadratic equation is an equation that involves a polynomial of degree 2. Investigate the origin of the term *quadratic* as it is used in the expression *quadratic equation*. Write a brief essay on your findings.

148. The equation $|x| = -2$ has no real solution. Why?

'Are You Prepared?' Answers

1. $(x - 2)(x + 2)(x - 1)$　　**2.** $(2x - 3)(x + 1)$　　**3.** $\left\{-\dfrac{5}{3}, 3\right\}$　　**4.** True

A.7　Complex Numbers; Quadratic Equations in the Complex Number System

PREPARING FOR THIS SECTION　*Before getting started, review the following:*

• Classification of Numbers (Appendix A, Section A.1, p. A3)

　Now Work the 'Are You Prepared?' problems on page A67.

OBJECTIVES　1　Add, Subtract, Multiply, and Divide Complex Numbers (p. A61)

　　　　　　　2　Solve Quadratic Equations in the Complex Number System (p. A65)

Complex Numbers

One property of a real number is that its square is nonnegative (greater than or equal to 0). For example, there is no real number x for which

$$x^2 = -1$$

To remedy this situation, we introduce a number called the **imaginary unit,** which we denote by i, whose square is -1; that is,

$$i^2 = -1$$

This should not surprise you. If our universe were to consist only of integers, there would be no number x for which $2x = 1$. This unfortunate circumstance was remedied by introducing numbers such as $\dfrac{1}{2}$ and $\dfrac{2}{3}$, the *rational numbers*. If our universe were to consist only of rational numbers, there would be no x whose square equals 2. That is, there would be no number x for which $x^2 = 2$. To remedy this, we introduced numbers such as $\sqrt{2}$ and $\sqrt[3]{5}$, the *irrational numbers*. The *real numbers,* you will recall, consist of the rational numbers and the irrational numbers. Now, if our universe were to consist only of real numbers, then there would be no number x whose square is -1. To remedy this, we introduce a number i, whose square is -1.

In the progression outlined, each time that we encountered a situation that was unsuitable, we introduced a new number system to remedy this situation. And each new number system contained the earlier number system as a subset. The number system that results from introducing the number i is called the **complex number system.**

Complex numbers are numbers of the form $a + bi$, where a and b are real numbers. The real number a is called the **real part** of the number $a + bi$; the real number b is called the **imaginary part** of $a + bi$.

For example, the complex number $-5 + 6i$ has the real part -5 and the imaginary part 6.

When a complex number is written in the form $a + bi$, where a and b are real numbers, we say it is in **standard form.** However, if the imaginary part of a complex number is negative, such as in the complex number $3 + (-2)i$, we agree to write it instead in the form $3 - 2i$.

Also, the complex number $a + 0i$ is usually written simply as a. This serves to remind us that the real numbers are a subset of the complex numbers. The complex number $0 + bi$ is usually written as bi. Sometimes the complex number bi is called a **pure imaginary number.**

1 Add, Subtract, Multiply, and Divide Complex Numbers

Equality, addition, subtraction, and multiplication of complex numbers are defined so as to preserve the familiar rules of algebra for real numbers. Thus, two complex numbers are equal if and only if their real parts are equal and their imaginary parts are equal. That is,

Equality of Complex Numbers

$$a + bi = c + di \quad \text{if and only if} \quad a = c \text{ and } b = d \qquad \textbf{(1)}$$

Two complex numbers are added by forming the complex number whose real part is the sum of the real parts and whose imaginary part is the sum of the imaginary parts. That is,

Sum of Complex Numbers

$$(a + bi) + (c + di) = (a + c) + (b + d)i \qquad \textbf{(2)}$$

To subtract two complex numbers, we use this rule:

Difference of Complex Numbers

$$(a + bi) - (c + di) = (a - c) + (b - d)i \qquad \textbf{(3)}$$

EXAMPLE 1 | **Adding and Subtracting Complex Numbers**

Figure 26

(a) $(3 + 5i) + (-2 + 3i) = [3 + (-2)] + (5 + 3)i = 1 + 8i$

(b) $(6 + 4i) - (3 + 6i) = (6 - 3) + (4 - 6)i = 3 + (-2)i = 3 - 2i$

Some graphing calculators have the capability of handling complex numbers. For example, Figure 26 shows the results of Example 1 using a TI-84 Plus graphing calculator.

Now Work PROBLEM 13

Products of complex numbers are calculated as illustrated in Example 2.

EXAMPLE 2 | **Multiplying Complex Numbers**

$$
\begin{aligned}
(5 + 3i) \cdot (2 + 7i) &= 5 \cdot (2 + 7i) + 3i(2 + 7i) && \text{Distributive Property} \\
&= 10 + 35i + 6i + 21i^2 && \text{Distributive Property} \\
&= 10 + 41i + 21(-1) && i^2 = -1 \\
&= -11 + 41i
\end{aligned}
$$

Based on the procedure of Example 2, we define the **product** of two complex numbers by the following formula:

Product of Complex Numbers

$$(a + bi) \cdot (c + di) = (ac - bd) + (ad + bc)i \qquad \textbf{(4)}$$

Figure 27

Do not bother to memorize formula (4). Instead, whenever it is necessary to multiply two complex numbers, follow the usual rules for multiplying two binomials, as in Example 2, remembering that $i^2 = -1$. For example,

$$(2i)(2i) = 4i^2 = -4$$

$$(2 + i)(1 - i) = 2 - 2i + i - i^2 = 3 - i$$

Graphing calculators may also be used to multiply complex numbers. Figure 27 shows the result obtained in Example 2 using a TI-84 Plus graphing calculator.

━━━━ **Now Work** PROBLEM 19

Algebraic properties for addition and multiplication, such as the Commutative, Associative, and Distributive Properties, hold for complex numbers. However, the property that every nonzero complex number has a multiplicative inverse, or reciprocal, requires a closer look.

Conjugates

If $z = a + bi$ is a complex number, then its **conjugate,** denoted by $\bar{z}$, is defined as

$$\bar{z} = \overline{a + bi} = a - bi$$

For example, $\overline{2 + 3i} = 2 - 3i$ and $\overline{-6 - 2i} = -6 + 2i$.

| EXAMPLE 3 | Multiplying a Complex Number by Its Conjugate |

Find the product of the complex number $z = 3 + 4i$ and its conjugate $\bar{z}$.

Solution Since $\bar{z} = 3 - 4i$, we have

$$z\bar{z} = (3 + 4i)(3 - 4i) = 9 - 12i + 12i - 16i^2 = 9 + 16 = 25$$

The result obtained in Example 3 has an important generalization.

THEOREM The product of a complex number and its conjugate is a nonnegative real number. That is, if $z = a + bi$, then

$$z\bar{z} = a^2 + b^2 \qquad \textbf{(5)}$$

Proof If $z = a + bi$, then

$$z\bar{z} = (a + bi)(a - bi) = a^2 - abi + abi - (bi)^2 = a^2 - b^2i^2 = a^2 + b^2 \quad ■$$

To express the reciprocal of a nonzero complex number z in standard form, multiply the numerator and denominator of $\dfrac{1}{z}$ by its conjugate $\bar{z}$. That is, if $z = a + bi$ is a nonzero complex number, then

$$\frac{1}{a + bi} = \frac{1}{z} = \frac{1}{z} \cdot \frac{\bar{z}}{\bar{z}} = \frac{\bar{z}}{z\bar{z}} \underset{\uparrow}{=} \frac{a - bi}{a^2 + b^2} = \frac{a}{a^2 + b^2} - \frac{b}{a^2 + b^2}i$$

Use (5).

| EXAMPLE 4 | **Writing the Reciprocal of a Complex Number in Standard Form** |

Write $\dfrac{1}{3 + 4i}$ in standard form $a + bi$; that is, find the reciprocal of $3 + 4i$.

Solution Multiply the numerator and denominator of $\dfrac{1}{3 + 4i}$ by the conjugate of $3 + 4i$, the complex number $3 - 4i$. The result is

Figure 28

$$\frac{1}{3 + 4i} = \frac{1}{3 + 4i} \cdot \frac{3 - 4i}{3 - 4i} = \frac{3 - 4i}{9 + 16} = \frac{3}{25} - \frac{4}{25}i$$

A graphing calculator can be used to verify the result of Example 4. See Figure 28. To express the quotient of two complex numbers in standard form, we multiply the numerator and denominator of the quotient by the conjugate of the denominator.

| EXAMPLE 5 | **Writing the Quotient of a Complex Number in Standard Form** |

Write each of the following in standard form.

(a) $\dfrac{1 + 4i}{5 - 12i}$ (b) $\dfrac{2 - 3i}{4 - 3i}$

Solution (a) $\dfrac{1 + 4i}{5 - 12i} = \dfrac{1 + 4i}{5 - 12i} \cdot \dfrac{5 + 12i}{5 + 12i} = \dfrac{5 + 12i + 20i + 48i^2}{25 + 144}$

$$= \frac{-43 + 32i}{169} = \frac{-43}{169} + \frac{32}{169}i$$

(b) $\dfrac{2 - 3i}{4 - 3i} = \dfrac{2 - 3i}{4 - 3i} \cdot \dfrac{4 + 3i}{4 + 3i} = \dfrac{8 + 6i - 12i - 9i^2}{16 + 9}$

$$= \frac{17 - 6i}{25} = \frac{17}{25} - \frac{6}{25}i$$

━━━━➤ **Now Work** PROBLEM 27

| EXAMPLE 6 | **Writing Other Expressions in Standard Form** |

If $z = 2 - 3i$ and $w = 5 + 2i$, write each of the following expressions in standard form.

(a) $\dfrac{z}{w}$ (b) $\overline{z + w}$ (c) $z + \overline{z}$

Solution (a) $\dfrac{z}{w} = \dfrac{z \cdot \overline{w}}{w \cdot \overline{w}} = \dfrac{(2 - 3i)(5 - 2i)}{(5 + 2i)(5 - 2i)} = \dfrac{10 - 4i - 15i + 6i^2}{25 + 4}$

$$= \frac{4 - 19i}{29} = \frac{4}{29} - \frac{19}{29}i$$

(b) $\overline{z + w} = \overline{(2 - 3i) + (5 + 2i)} = \overline{7 - i} = 7 + i$

(c) $z + \overline{z} = (2 - 3i) + (2 + 3i) = 4$

The conjugate of a complex number has certain general properties that we shall find useful later.

For a real number $a = a + 0i$, the conjugate is $\bar{a} = \overline{a + 0i} = a - 0i = a$. That is,

THEOREM

The conjugate of a real number is the real number itself.

Other properties that are direct consequences of the definition of the conjugate are given next. In each statement, z and w represent complex numbers.

THEOREM

The conjugate of the conjugate of a complex number is the complex number itself.

$$(\bar{\bar{z}}) = z \qquad (6)$$

The conjugate of the sum of two complex numbers equals the sum of their conjugates.

$$\overline{z + w} = \bar{z} + \bar{w} \qquad (7)$$

The conjugate of the product of two complex numbers equals the product of their conjugates.

$$\overline{z \cdot w} = \bar{z} \cdot \bar{w} \qquad (8)$$

We leave the proofs of equations (6), (7), and (8) as exercises. See Problems 88–90.

Powers of i

The powers of i follow a pattern that is useful to know.

$$i^1 = i \qquad\qquad i^5 = i^4 \cdot i = 1 \cdot i = i$$
$$i^2 = -1 \qquad\qquad i^6 = i^4 \cdot i^2 = -1$$
$$i^3 = i^2 \cdot i = -i \qquad\qquad i^7 = i^4 \cdot i^3 = -i$$
$$i^4 = i^2 \cdot i^2 = (-1)(-1) = 1 \qquad i^8 = i^4 \cdot i^4 = 1$$

And so on. The powers of i repeat with every fourth power.

EXAMPLE 7 **Evaluating Powers of i**

(a) $i^{27} = i^{24} \cdot i^3 = (i^4)^6 \cdot i^3 = 1^6 \cdot i^3 = -i$

(b) $i^{101} = i^{100} \cdot i^1 = (i^4)^{25} \cdot i = 1^{25} \cdot i = i$

EXAMPLE 8 **Writing the Power of a Complex Number in Standard Form**

Write $(2 + i)^3$ in standard form.

Solution We use the special product formula for $(x + a)^3$.

$$(x + a)^3 = x^3 + 3ax^2 + 3a^2x + a^3$$

Using this special product formula,

$$(2 + i)^3 = 2^3 + 3 \cdot i \cdot 2^2 + 3 \cdot i^2 \cdot 2 + i^3$$
$$= 8 + 12i + 6(-1) + (-i)$$
$$= 2 + 11i$$

NOTE If you did not remember the special product formula for $(x + a)^3$, you could find $(2 + i)^3$ by simplifying $(2 + i)^2 (2 + i)$. ∎

Now Work PROBLEMS 33 AND 41

2 Solve Quadratic Equations in the Complex Number System

Quadratic equations with a negative discriminant have no real number solution. However, if we extend our number system to allow complex numbers, quadratic equations will always have a solution. Since the solution to a quadratic equation involves the square root of the discriminant, we begin with a discussion of square roots of negative numbers.

DEFINITION
If N is a positive real number, we define the **principal square root of** $-N$, denoted by $\sqrt{-N}$, as

$$\sqrt{-N} = \sqrt{N}i$$

where i is the imaginary unit and $i^2 = -1$.

EXAMPLE 9

Evaluating the Square Root of a Negative Number

(a) $\sqrt{-1} = \sqrt{1}i = i$ (b) $\sqrt{-16} = \sqrt{16}i = 4i$

(c) $\sqrt{-8} = \sqrt{8}i = 2\sqrt{2}i$

EXAMPLE 10

Using the Square Root Method in the Complex Number System

Solve each equation in the complex number system.

(a) $x^2 = 4$ (b) $x^2 = -9$

Solution

(a) $x^2 = 4$

$$x = \pm\sqrt{4} = \pm 2$$

The equation has the solution set $\{-2, 2\}$.

WARNING When working with square roots of negative numbers, do not set the square root of a product equal to the product of the square roots (which can be done with positive numbers). To see why, look at this calculation: We know that $\sqrt{100} = 10$. However, it is also true that $100 = (-25)(-4)$, so

$$
\begin{aligned}
10 &= \sqrt{100} \\
&= \sqrt{(-25)(-4)} \\
&\neq \sqrt{-25}\,\sqrt{-4}
\end{aligned}
$$

because $\sqrt{-25}\cdot\sqrt{-4}$
$$
\begin{aligned}
&= \left(\sqrt{25}i\right)\left(\sqrt{4}i\right) \\
&= (5i)(2i) \\
&= 10i^2 = -10 \quad \blacksquare
\end{aligned}
$$

(b) $x^2 = -9$

$$x = \pm\sqrt{-9} = \pm\sqrt{9}i = \pm 3i$$

The equation has the solution set $\{-3i, 3i\}$.

Now Work PROBLEM 53

Because we have defined the square root of a negative number, we can now restate the quadratic formula without restriction.

THEOREM
In the complex number system, the solutions of the quadratic equation $ax^2 + bx + c = 0$, where a, b, and c are real numbers and $a \neq 0$, are given by the formula

$$x = \frac{-b \pm \sqrt{b^2 - 4ac}}{2a} \tag{9}$$

EXAMPLE 11

Solving a Quadratic Equation in the Complex Number System

Solve the equation $x^2 - 4x + 8 = 0$ in the complex number system.

Solution

Here $a = 1, b = -4, c = 8,$ and $b^2 - 4ac = 16 - 4(1)(8) = -16.$ Using equation (9), we find that

$$x = \frac{-(-4) \pm \sqrt{-16}}{2(1)} = \frac{4 \pm \sqrt{16}i}{2} = \frac{4 \pm 4i}{2} = 2 \pm 2i$$

The equation has the solution set $\{2 - 2i, 2 + 2i\}.$

✓ Check:

$2 + 2i:$ $(2 + 2i)^2 - 4(2 + 2i) + 8 = 4 + 8i + 4i^2 - 8 - 8i + 8$
$= 4 - 4 = 0$

$2 - 2i:$ $(2 - 2i)^2 - 4(2 - 2i) + 8 = 4 - 8i + 4i^2 - 8 + 8i + 8$
$= 4 - 4 = 0$

Figure 29

Figure 29 shows the check of the solution using a TI-84 Plus graphing calculator. Graph $Y_1 = x^2 - 4x + 8.$ How many x-intercepts are there?

Now Work PROBLEM 59

The discriminant $b^2 - 4ac$ of a quadratic equation still serves as a way to determine the character of the solutions.

Character of the Solutions of a Quadratic Equation

In the complex number system, consider a quadratic equation $ax^2 + bx + c = 0$ with real coefficients.

1. If $b^2 - 4ac > 0,$ the equation has two unequal real solutions.
2. If $b^2 - 4ac = 0,$ the equation has a repeated real solution, a double root.
3. If $b^2 - 4ac < 0,$ the equation has two complex solutions that are not real. The solutions are conjugates of each other.

The third conclusion in the display is a consequence of the fact that if $b^2 - 4ac = -N < 0$ then, by the quadratic formula, the solutions are

$$x = \frac{-b + \sqrt{b^2 - 4ac}}{2a} = \frac{-b + \sqrt{-N}}{2a} = \frac{-b + \sqrt{N}i}{2a} = \frac{-b}{2a} + \frac{\sqrt{N}}{2a}i$$

and

$$x = \frac{-b - \sqrt{b^2 - 4ac}}{2a} = \frac{-b - \sqrt{-N}}{2a} = \frac{-b - \sqrt{N}i}{2a} = \frac{-b}{2a} - \frac{\sqrt{N}}{2a}i$$

which are conjugates of each other.

EXAMPLE 12

Determining the Character of the Solutions of a Quadratic Equation

Without solving, determine the character of the solutions of each equation.

(a) $3x^2 + 4x + 5 = 0$ (b) $2x^2 + 4x + 1 = 0$

(c) $9x^2 - 6x + 1 = 0$

Solution   (a) Here $a = 3, b = 4$, and $c = 5$, so $b^2 - 4ac = 4^2 - 4(3)(5) = -44$. The solutions are two complex numbers that are not real and are conjugates of each other.

(b) Here $a = 2, b = 4$, and $c = 1$, so $b^2 - 4ac = 4^2 - 4(2)(1) = 8$. The solutions are two unequal real numbers.

(c) Here $a = 9, b = -6$, and $c = 1$, so $b^2 - 4ac = (-6)^2 - 4(9)(1) = 0$. The solution is a repeated real number, that is, a double root.

━━━▶ **Now Work** PROBLEM 73

A.7 Assess Your Understanding

'Are You Prepared?' *Answers are given at the end of these exercises. If you get a wrong answer, read the pages listed in red.*

1. Name the integers and the rational numbers in the set $\left\{-3, 0, \sqrt{2}, \dfrac{6}{5}, \pi\right\}$. (p. A3)

2. *True or False* Rational numbers and irrational numbers are in the set of real numbers. (p. A3)

3. *True or False* All integers are rational numbers. (p. A3)

Concepts and Vocabulary

4. In the complex number $5 + 2i$, the number 5 is called the _____ part; the number 2 is called the _____ part; the number i is called the _____ _____.

5. The equation $x^2 = -4$ has the solution set _____.

6. *True or False* The conjugate of $2 + 5i$ is $-2 - 5i$.

7. *True or False* All real numbers are complex numbers.

8. *True or False* If $2 - 3i$ is a solution of a quadratic equation with real coefficients, then $-2 + 3i$ is also a solution.

Skill Building

In Problems 9–46, write each expression in the standard form $a + bi$. Verify your results using a graphing utility.

9. $(2 - 3i) + (6 + 8i)$

10. $(4 + 5i) + (-8 + 2i)$

11. $(-3 + 2i) - (4 - 4i)$

12. $(3 - 4i) - (-3 - 4i)$

13. $(2 - 5i) - (8 + 6i)$

14. $(-8 + 4i) - (2 - 2i)$

15. $3(2 - 6i)$

16. $-4(2 + 8i)$

17. $2i(2 - 3i)$

18. $3i(-3 + 4i)$

19. $(3 - 4i)(2 + i)$

20. $(5 + 3i)(2 - i)$

21. $(-6 + i)(-6 - i)$

22. $(-3 + i)(3 + i)$

23. $\dfrac{10}{3 - 4i}$

24. $\dfrac{13}{5 - 12i}$

25. $\dfrac{2 + i}{i}$

26. $\dfrac{2 - i}{-2i}$

27. $\dfrac{6 - i}{1 + i}$

28. $\dfrac{2 + 3i}{1 - i}$

29. $\left(\dfrac{1}{2} + \dfrac{\sqrt{3}}{2}i\right)^2$

30. $\left(\dfrac{\sqrt{3}}{2} - \dfrac{1}{2}i\right)^2$

31. $(1 + i)^2$

32. $(1 - i)^2$

33. i^{23}

34. i^{14}

35. i^{-15}

36. i^{-23}

37. $i^6 - 5$

38. $4 + i^3$

39. $6i^3 - 4i^5$

40. $4i^3 - 2i^2 + 1$

41. $(1 + i)^3$

42. $(3i)^4 + 1$

43. $i^7(1 + i^2)$

44. $2i^4(1 + i^2)$

45. $i^6 + i^4 + i^2 + 1$

46. $i^7 + i^5 + i^3 + i$

In Problems 47–52, perform the indicated operations and express your answer in the form a + bi.

47. $\sqrt{-4}$

48. $\sqrt{-9}$

49. $\sqrt{-25}$

50. $\sqrt{-64}$

51. $\sqrt{(3 + 4i)(4i - 3)}$

52. $\sqrt{(4 + 3i)(3i - 4)}$

In Problems 53–72, solve each equation in the complex number system. Check your results using a graphing utility.

53. $x^2 + 4 = 0$

54. $x^2 - 4 = 0$

55. $x^2 - 16 = 0$

56. $x^2 + 25 = 0$

57. $x^2 - 6x + 13 = 0$

58. $x^2 + 4x + 8 = 0$

59. $x^2 - 6x + 10 = 0$

60. $x^2 - 2x + 5 = 0$

61. $8x^2 - 4x + 1 = 0$

62. $10x^2 + 6x + 1 = 0$

63. $5x^2 + 2x + 1 = 0$

64. $13x^2 + 6x + 1 = 0$

65. $x^2 + x + 1 = 0$

66. $x^2 - x + 1 = 0$

67. $x^3 - 8 = 0$

68. $x^3 + 27 = 0$

69. $x^4 - 16 = 0$

70. $x^4 - 1 = 0$

71. $x^4 + 13x^2 + 36 = 0$

72. $x^4 + 3x^2 - 4 = 0$

In Problems 73–78, without solving, determine the character of the solutions of each equation. Verify your answer using a graphing utility.

73. $3x^2 - 3x + 4 = 0$

74. $2x^2 - 4x + 1 = 0$

75. $2x^2 + 3x - 4 = 0$

76. $x^2 + 2x + 6 = 0$

77. $9x^2 - 12x + 4 = 0$

78. $4x^2 + 12x + 9 = 0$

Applications and Extensions

79. $2 + 3i$ is a solution of a quadratic equation with real coefficients. Find the other solution.

80. $4 - i$ is a solution of a quadratic equation with real coefficients. Find the other solution.

In Problems 81–84, z = 3 − 4i and w = 8 + 3i. Write each expression in the standard form a + bi.

81. $z + \bar{z}$

82. $w - \bar{w}$

83. $z\bar{z}$

84. $\overline{z - w}$

85. Electrical Circuits The impedance Z, in ohms, of a circuit element is defined as the ratio of the phasor voltage V, in volts, across the element to the phasor current I, in amperes, through the elements. That is, $Z = \dfrac{V}{I}$. If the voltage across a circuit element is $18 + i$ volts and the current through the element is $3 - 4i$ amperes, determine the impedance.

86. Parallel Circuits In an ac circuit with two parallel pathways, the total impedance Z, in ohms, satisfies the formula $\dfrac{1}{Z} = \dfrac{1}{Z_1} + \dfrac{1}{Z_2}$, where Z_1 is the impedance of the first pathway and Z_2 is the impedance of the second pathway. Determine the total impedance if the impedances of the two pathways are $Z_1 = 2 + i$ ohms and $Z_2 = 4 - 3i$ ohms.

87. Use $z = a + bi$ to show that $z + \bar{z} = 2a$ and that $z - \bar{z} = 2bi$.

88. Use $z = a + bi$ to show that $(\bar{\bar{z}}) = z$.

89. Use $z = a + bi$ and $w = c + di$ to show that $\overline{z + w} = \bar{z} + \bar{w}$.

90. Use $z = a + bi$ and $w = c + di$ to show that $\overline{z \cdot w} = \bar{z} \cdot \bar{w}$.

Discussion and Writing

91. Explain to a friend how you would add two complex numbers and how you would multiply two complex numbers. Explain any differences in the two explanations.

92. Write a brief paragraph that compares the method used to rationalize denominators and the method used to write the quotient of two complex numbers in standard form.

93. Use an Internet search engine to investigate the origins of complex numbers. Write a paragraph describing what you find and present it to the class.

94. Explain how the method of multiplying two complex numbers is related to multiplying two binomials.

95. What Went Wrong? A student multiplied $\sqrt{-9}$ and $\sqrt{-9}$ as follows:

$$\sqrt{-9} \cdot \sqrt{-9} = \sqrt{(-9)(-9)}$$
$$= \sqrt{81}$$
$$= 9$$

The instructor marked the problem incorrect. Why?

'Are You Prepared?' Answers

1. Integers: $\{-3, 0\}$; rational numbers: $\left\{-3, 0, \dfrac{6}{5}\right\}$

2. True

3. True

A.8 Problem Solving: Interest, Mixture, Uniform Motion, Constant Rate Jobs

OBJECTIVES   1 Translate Verbal Descriptions into Mathematical Expressions (p. A69)

2 Solve Interest Problems (p. A70)

3 Solve Mixture Problems (p. A71)

4 Solve Uniform Motion Problems (p. A72)

5 Solve Constant Rate Job Problems (p. A74)

 Applied (word) problems do not come in the form "Solve the equation. . . ." Instead, they supply information using words, a verbal description of the real problem. So, to solve applied problems, we must be able to translate the verbal description into the language of mathematics. We do this by using variables to represent unknown quantities and then finding relationships (such as equations) that involve these variables. The process of doing all this is called **mathematical modeling.** The equation or inequality that represents the relationship among the variables is called a **model.**

Any solution to the mathematical problem must be checked against the mathematical problem, the verbal description, and the real problem. See Figure 30 for an illustration of the **modeling process.**

Figure 30

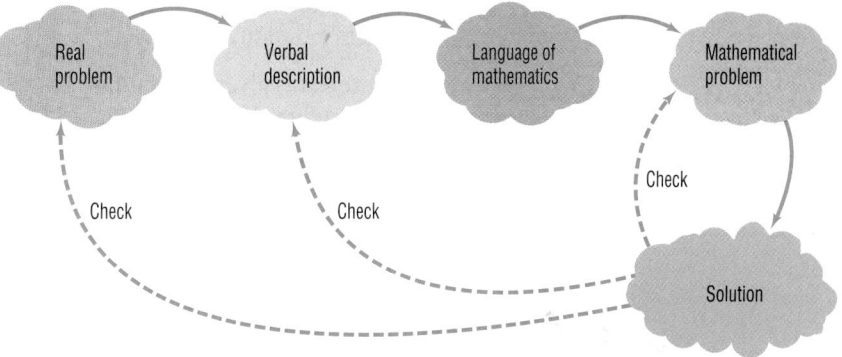

1 Translate Verbal Descriptions into Mathematical Expressions

Let's look at a few examples that will help you to translate certain words into mathematical symbols.

EXAMPLE 1   Translating Verbal Descriptions into Mathematical Expressions

(a) For uniform motion, the speed (rate) of an object equals the distance traveled divided by the time required.

Translation: If r is the speed (or rate), d the distance, and t the time, then $r = \dfrac{d}{t}$.

(b) Let x denote a number.

The number 5 times as large as x is $5x$.

The number 3 less than x is $x - 3$.

The number that exceeds x by 4 is $x + 4$.

The number that, when added to x, gives 5 is $5 - x$.

Now Work PROBLEM 7

Always check the units used to measure the variables of an applied problem. In Example 1(a), if r is measured in miles per hour, then the distance d must be expressed in miles and the time t must be expressed in hours. It is a good practice to check units to be sure that they are consistent and make sense.

2 Solve Interest Problems

Interest is money paid for the use of money. The total amount borrowed (whether by an individual from a bank in the form of a loan or by a bank from an individual in the form of a savings account) is called the **principal.** The **rate of interest,** expressed as a percent, is the amount charged for the use of the principal for a given period of time, usually on a yearly (that is, per annum) basis.

Simple Interest Formula

If a principal of P dollars is borrowed for a period of t years at a per annum interest rate r, expressed as a decimal, the interest I charged is

$$I = Prt \qquad\qquad (1)$$

Interest charged according to formula (1) is called **simple interest.** When using formula (1), be sure to express r as a decimal.

EXAMPLE 2 **Using the Simple Interest Formula: Computing Interest on a Loan**

Suppose that Juanita borrows $500 for 6 months at the simple interest rate of 9% per annum. What is the interest that Juanita will be charged on this loan? How much does Juanita owe after 6 months?

Solution The rate of interest is given per annum, so the actual time that the money is borrowed must be expressed in years. The interest charged would be the principal, $500, times the rate of interest ($9\% = 0.09$) times the time in years, $\dfrac{1}{2}$:

$$\text{Interest charged} = I = Prt = (500)(0.09)\left(\frac{1}{2}\right) = \$22.50$$

After 6 months, Juanita will owe what she borrowed plus the interest: $500 + $22.50 = $522.50.

∎

In the next example we illustrate the steps for solving applied problems.

EXAMPLE 3 **Financial Planning**

Candy has $70,000 to invest and requires an overall rate of return of 9%. She can invest in a safe, government-insured certificate of deposit, but it only pays 8%. To obtain 9%, she agrees to invest some of her money in noninsured corporate bonds paying 12%. How much should be placed in each investment to achieve her goal?

Solution **STEP 1:** *Determine the question being asked.* The question is asking for two dollar amounts: the principal to invest in the corporate bonds and the principal to invest in the certificate of deposit.

STEP 2: *Assign a variable to the unknown.* We let b represent the amount (in dollars) to be invested in the bonds. Then $70,000 - b$ is the amount that will be invested in the certificate. (Do you see why?)

NOTE Don't forget to choose variables that remind you of what they represent, as in b for bonds. ∎

STEP 3: *Build the model.* We set up a table:

	Principal ($)	Rate	Time (yr)	Interest ($)
Bonds	b	12% = 0.12	1	0.12b
Certificate	70,000 − b	8% = 0.08	1	0.08(70,000 − b)
Total	70,000	9% = 0.09	1	0.09(70,000) = 6300

Since the total interest from the investments is equal to $0.09(70,000) = 6300$, we have the equation

$$0.12b + 0.08(70,000 - b) = 6300 \quad \text{The Model}$$

(Note that the units are consistent: the unit is dollars on each side.)

STEP 4: *Solve the equation.*

$$0.12b + 5600 - 0.08b = 6300$$
$$0.04b = 700$$
$$b = 17,500$$

Candy should place $17,500 in the bonds and $70,000 - $17,500 = $52,500 in the certificate.

STEP 5: *Check your answer.* The interest on the bonds after 1 year is $0.12(\$17,500) = \$2100$; the interest on the certificate after 1 year is $0.08(\$52,500) = \$4200$. The total annual interest is $6300, the required amount.

Now Work PROBLEM 17

3 Solve Mixture Problems

Oil refineries sometimes produce gasoline that is a blend of two or more types of fuel; bakeries occasionally blend two or more types of flour for their bread. These problems are referred to as **mixture problems** because they combine two or more quantities to form a mixture.

| EXAMPLE 4 | **Blending Coffees** |

The manager of a Starbucks store decides to experiment with a new blend of coffee. She will mix some B grade Colombian coffee that sells for $5 per pound with some A grade Arabica coffee that sells for $10 per pound to get 100 pounds of the new blend. The selling price of the new blend is to be $7 per pound, and there is to be no difference in revenue from selling the new blend versus selling the other types. How many pounds of the B grade Colombian and A grade Arabica coffees are required?

Solution Let c represent the number of pounds of the B grade Colombian coffee. Then $100 - c$ equals the number of pounds of the A grade Arabica coffee. See Figure 31.

Figure 31

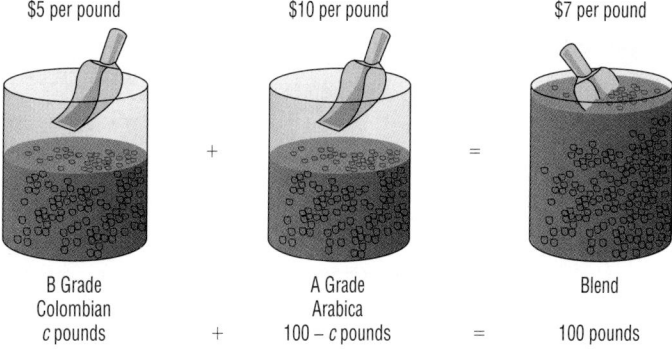

$5 per pound $10 per pound $7 per pound

B Grade   A Grade   Blend
Colombian   Arabica
c pounds   + $100 - c$ pounds   =   100 pounds

Since there is to be no difference in revenue between selling the A and B grades separately versus the blend, we have

$$\left\{ \begin{matrix} \text{Price per pound} \\ \text{of B grade} \end{matrix} \right\} \left\{ \begin{matrix} \text{No. pounds} \\ \text{B grade} \end{matrix} \right\} + \left\{ \begin{matrix} \text{Price per pound} \\ \text{of A grade} \end{matrix} \right\} \left\{ \begin{matrix} \text{No. pounds} \\ \text{A grade} \end{matrix} \right\} = \left\{ \begin{matrix} \text{Price per pound} \\ \text{of blend} \end{matrix} \right\} \left\{ \begin{matrix} \text{No. pounds} \\ \text{blend} \end{matrix} \right\}$$

$$\$5 \quad \cdot \quad c \quad + \quad \$10 \quad \cdot \quad (100 - c) \quad = \quad \$7 \quad \cdot \quad 100 \quad \text{The Model}$$

We have the equation

$$5c + 10(100 - c) = 7 \cdot (100)$$
$$5c + 1000 - 10c = 700$$
$$-5c = -300$$
$$c = 60$$

The manager should blend 60 pounds of B grade Colombian coffee with $100 - 60 = 40$ pounds of A grade Arabica coffee to get the desired blend.

✓ **Check:** The 60 pounds of B grade coffee would sell for $(\$5)(60) = \$300$, and the 40 pounds of A grade coffee would sell for $(\$10)(40) = \$400$; the total revenue, $700, equals the revenue obtained from selling the blend, as desired.

━━━━━━ **Now Work** PROBLEM 21

4 Solve Uniform Motion Problems

Objects that move at a constant speed are said to be in **uniform motion.** When the average speed of an object is known, it can be interpreted as its constant speed. For example, a bicyclist traveling at an average speed of 25 miles per hour is in uniform motion.

Uniform Motion Formula

If an object moves at an average speed (or rate) r, the distance d covered in time t is given by the formula

$$d = r \cdot t \qquad \qquad (2)$$

That is, Distance = Rate · Time.

EXAMPLE 5 | **Physics: Uniform Motion**

Tanya, who is a long-distance runner, runs at an average speed of 8 miles per hour (mi/hr). Two hours after Tanya leaves your house, you leave in your Honda and follow the same route. If your average speed is 40 mi/hr, how long will it be before you catch up to Tanya? How far will each of you be from your home?

Solution | Refer to Figure 32. We use t to represent the time (in hours) that it takes the Honda to catch up to Tanya. When this occurs, the total time elapsed for Tanya is $t + 2$ hours.

Figure 32

Set up the following table:

	Rate mi/hr	Time hr	Distance mi
Tanya	8	$t + 2$	$8(t + 2)$
Honda	40	t	$40t$

Since the distance traveled is the same, we are led to the following equation:

$$8(t + 2) = 40t \quad \text{The Model}$$
$$8t + 16 = 40t$$
$$32t = 16$$
$$t = \frac{1}{2} \text{ hour}$$

It will take the Honda $\frac{1}{2}$ hour to catch up to Tanya. Each will have gone 20 miles.

✓ Check: In 2.5 hours, Tanya travels a distance of $(2.5)(8) = 20$ miles. In $\frac{1}{2}$ hour, the Honda travels a distance of $\left(\frac{1}{2}\right)(40) = 20$ miles.

| EXAMPLE 6 | **Physics: Uniform Motion** |

A motorboat heads upstream a distance of 24 miles on a river whose current is running at 3 miles per hour (mi/hr). The trip up and back takes 6 hours. Assuming that the motorboat maintained a constant speed relative to the water, what was its speed?

Solution

Figure 33

See Figure 33. We use r to represent the constant speed of the motorboat relative to the water. Then the true speed going upstream is $r - 3$ mi/hr, and the true speed going downstream is $r + 3$ mi/hr. Since Distance = Rate × Time, then Time = $\dfrac{\text{Distance}}{\text{Rate}}$. We set up a table.

	Rate mi/hr	Distance mi	Time = $\dfrac{\text{Distance}}{\text{Velocity}}$
Upstream	$r - 3$	24	$\dfrac{24}{r - 3}$
Downstream	$r + 3$	24	$\dfrac{24}{r + 3}$

Since the total time up and back is 6 hours, we have

$$\frac{24}{r - 3} + \frac{24}{r + 3} = 6 \qquad \text{The Model}$$

$$\frac{24(r + 3) + 24(r - 3)}{(r - 3)(r + 3)} = 6 \qquad \text{Add the quotients on the left.}$$

$$\frac{48r}{r^2 - 9} = 6 \qquad \text{Simplify.}$$

$$48r = 6(r^2 - 9)$$

$$6r^2 - 48r - 54 = 0 \qquad \text{Place in standard form.}$$

$$r^2 - 8r - 9 = 0 \qquad \text{Divide by 6.}$$

$$(r - 9)(r + 1) = 0 \qquad \text{Factor.}$$

$$r = 9 \quad \text{or} \quad r = -1 \qquad \text{Apply the Zero-Product Property and solve.}$$

We discard the solution $r = -1$ mi/hr, so the speed of the motorboat relative to the water is 9 mi/hr.

Now Work PROBLEM 27

5 Solve Constant Rate Job Problems

This section involves jobs that are performed at a **constant rate.** Our assumption is that, if a job can be done in t units of time, $\frac{1}{t}$ of the job is done in 1 unit of time. So, if a job takes 4 hours, then $\frac{1}{4}$ of the job is done in 1 hour.

| EXAMPLE 7 | Working Together to Do a Job |

At 10 AM Danny is asked by his father to weed the garden. From past experience, Danny knows that this will take him 4 hours, working alone. His older brother, Mike, when it is his turn to do this job, requires 6 hours. Since Mike wants to go golfing with Danny and has a reservation for 1 PM, he agrees to help Danny. Assuming no gain or loss of efficiency, when will they finish if they work together? Can they make the tee time?

Solution   We set up Table 1. If it takes Danny 4 hours to do the entire job, and he works at a constant rate, then in 1 hour, Danny does $\frac{1}{4}$ of the job. In 1 hour, Mike does $\frac{1}{6}$ of the job. Let t be the time (in hours) that it takes them to do the job together. In 1 hour, then, $\frac{1}{t}$ of the job is completed. We reason as follows:

Table 1

	Hours to Do Job	Part of Job Done in 1 Hour
Danny	4	$\frac{1}{4}$
Mike	6	$\frac{1}{6}$
Together	t	$\frac{1}{t}$

$$\left(\begin{matrix}\text{Part done by Danny}\\ \text{in 1 hour}\end{matrix}\right) + \left(\begin{matrix}\text{Part done by Mike}\\ \text{in 1 hour}\end{matrix}\right) = \left(\begin{matrix}\text{Part done together}\\ \text{in 1 hour}\end{matrix}\right)$$

From Table 1,

$$\frac{1}{4} + \frac{1}{6} = \frac{1}{t} \qquad \text{The Model}$$

$$\frac{3}{12} + \frac{2}{12} = \frac{1}{t} \qquad \text{LCD} = 12$$

$$\frac{5}{12} = \frac{1}{t}$$

$$5t = 12 \qquad \text{Multiply both sides by } 12t.$$

$$t = \frac{12}{5} \qquad \text{Divide both sides by 5.}$$

Working together, the job can be done in $\frac{12}{5}$ hours, or 2 hours, 24 minutes. They should make the tee time, since they will finish at 12:24 PM.

◼

Now Work PROBLEM 29

A.8 Assess Your Understanding

Concepts and Vocabulary

1. Using variables to represent unknown quantities and then finding relationships that involve these variables is referred to as _____ _____.

2. The money paid for the use of money is _____.

3. Objects that move at a constant speed are said to be in _____ _____.

4. *True or False* The amount charged for the use of principal for a given period of time is called the rate of interest.

5. *True or False* If an object moves at an average rate r, the distance d covered in time t is given by the formula $d = r \cdot t$.

6. Suppose that you want to mix two coffees to obtain 100 pounds of the blend. If x represents the number of pounds of coffee A, write an algebraic expression that represents the number of pounds of coffee B.

Applications and Extensions

In Problems 7–16, translate each sentence into a mathematical equation. Be sure to identify the meaning of all symbols.

7. Geometry   The area of a circle is the product of the number π and the square of the radius.

8. Geometry   The circumference of a circle is the product of the number π and twice the radius.

9. Geometry   The area of a square is the square of the length of a side.

10. Geometry   The perimeter of a square is four times the length of a side.

11. Physics   Force equals the product of mass and acceleration.

12. Physics   Pressure is force per unit area.

13. Physics   Work equals force times distance.

14. Physics   Kinetic energy is one-half the product of the mass and the square of the velocity.

15. Business   The total variable cost of manufacturing x dishwashers is $150 per dishwasher times the number of dishwashers manufactured.

16. Business   The total revenue derived from selling x dishwashers is $250 per dishwasher times the number of dishwashers sold.

17. Financial Planning   Betsy, a recent retiree, requires $6000 per year in extra income. She has $84,000 to invest and can invest in B-rated bonds paying 8% per year or in a certificate of deposit (CD) paying 6% per year. How much money should be invested in each to realize exactly $6000 in interest per year?

18. Financial Planning   After 2 years, Betsy (see Problem 17) finds that she will now require $6400 per year. Assuming that the remaining information is the same, how should the money be reinvested?

19. Banking   A bank loaned out $120,000, part of it at the rate of 8% per year and the rest at the rate of 12% per year. If the interest received totaled $11,000, how much was loaned at 8%?

20. Banking   Wendy, a loan officer at a bank, has $1,000,000 to lend and is required to obtain an average return of 8% per year. If she can lend at the rate of 7% or at the rate of 11%, how much can she lend at the 7% rate and still meet her requirement?

21. Blending Teas   The manager of a store that specializes in selling tea decides to experiment with a new blend. She will mix some Earl Grey tea that sells for $5 per pound with some Orange Pekoe tea that sells for $3 per pound to get 100 pounds of the new blend. The selling price of the new blend is to be $4.50 per pound, and there is to be no difference in revenue from selling the new blend versus selling the other types. How many pounds of the Earl Grey tea and Orange Pekoe tea are required?

22. Business: Blending Coffee   A coffee manufacturer wants to market a new blend of coffee that sells for $3.90 per pound by mixing two coffees that sell for $2.75 and $5 per pound, respectively. What amounts of each coffee should be blended to obtain the desired mixture?

[Hint: Assume that the total weight of the desired blend is 100 pounds.]

23. Business: Mixing Nuts   A nut store normally sells cashews for $9.00 per pound and almonds for $3.50 per pound. But at the end of the month the almonds had not sold well, so, in order to sell 60 pounds of almonds, the manager decided to mix the 60 pounds of almonds with some cashews and sell the mixture for $7.50 per pound. How many pounds of cashews should be mixed with the almonds to ensure no change in the profit?

24. Business: Mixing Candy   A candy store sells boxes of candy containing caramels and cremes. Each box sells for $12.50 and holds 30 pieces of candy (all pieces are the same size). If the caramels cost $0.25 to produce and the cremes cost $0.45 to produce, how many of each should be in a box to make a profit of $3?

25. Physics: Uniform Motion   A motorboat can maintain a constant speed of 16 miles per hour relative to the water. The boat makes a trip upstream to a certain point in 20 minutes; the return trip takes 15 minutes. What is the speed of the current? (See the figure.)

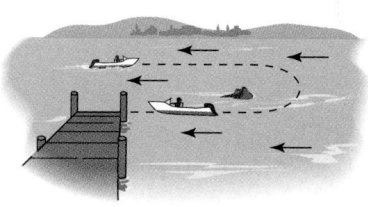

26. Physics: Uniform Motion   A motorboat heads upstream on a river that has a current of 3 miles per hour. The trip upstream takes 5 hours, and the return trip takes 2.5 hours. What is the speed of the motorboat? (Assume that the motorboat maintains a constant speed relative to the water.)

27. Physics: Uniform Motion   A motorboat maintained a constant speed of 15 miles per hour relative to the water in going 10 miles upstream and then returning. The total time for the trip was 1.5 hours. Use this information to find the speed of the current.

28. Physics: Uniform Motion   Two cars enter the Florida Turnpike at Commercial Boulevard at 8:00 AM, each heading for Wildwood. One car's average speed is 10 miles per hour more than the other's. The faster car arrives at Wildwood at 11:00 AM, $\frac{1}{2}$ hour before the other car. What is the average speed of each car? How far did each travel?

29. Working Together on a Job   Trent can deliver his newspapers in 30 minutes. It takes Lois 20 minutes to do the same route. How long will it take them to deliver the newspapers if they work together?

30. Working Together on a Job   Patrice, by himself, can paint four rooms in 10 hours. If he hires April to help, they can do the same job together in 6 hours. If he lets April work alone, how long will it take her to paint four rooms?

Mixed Practice

31. Enclosing a Garden A gardener has 46 feet of fencing to be used to enclose a rectangular garden that has a border 2 feet wide surrounding it (see the figure).
(a) If the length of the garden is to be twice its width, what are the dimensions of the garden?
(b) What is the area of the garden?
(c) If the length and width of the garden are to be the same, what are the dimensions of the garden?
(d) What is the area of the square garden?

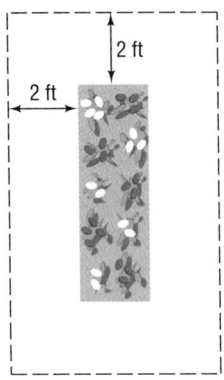

32. Construction A pond is enclosed by a wooden deck that is 3 feet wide. The fence surrounding the deck is 100 feet long.
(a) If the pond is square, what are its dimensions?
(b) If the pond is rectangular and the length of the pond is to be three times its width, what are its dimensions?
(c) If the pond is circular, what is its diameter?
(d) Which pond has the most area?

33. Football A tight end can run the 100-yard dash in 12 seconds. A defensive back can do it in 10 seconds. The tight end catches a pass at his own 20-yard line with the defensive back at the 15-yard line. (See the figure.) If no other players are nearby, at what yard line will the defensive back catch up to the tight end?

[**Hint:** At time $t = 0$, the defensive back is 5 yards behind the tight end.]

34. Computing Business Expense Therese, an outside salesperson, uses her car for both business and pleasure. Last year she traveled 30,000 miles, using 900 gallons of gasoline. Her car gets 40 miles per gallon on the highway and 25 in the city. She can deduct all highway travel, but no city travel, on her taxes. How many miles should Therese be allowed as a business expense?

35. Mixing Water and Antifreeze How much water should be added to 1 gallon of pure antifreeze to obtain a solution that is 60% antifreeze?

36. Mixing Water and Antifreeze The cooling system of a certain foreign-made car has a capacity of 15 liters. If the system is filled with a mixture that is 40% antifreeze, how much of this mixture should be drained and replaced by pure antifreeze so that the system is filled with a solution that is 60% antifreeze?

37. Moving Walkways The speed of a moving walkway is typically about 2.5 feet per second. Walking on such a moving walkway, it takes Karen a total of 40 seconds to travel 50 feet with the movement of the walkway and then back again against the movement of the walkway. What is Karen's normal walking speed?
Source: Answers.com

38. Moving Walkways The Gare Montparnasse train station in Paris has a high-speed version of a moving walkway. If Jean Claude walks while riding this moving walkway, he can travel 200 meters in 30 seconds less time than if he stands still on the moving walkway. If he walks at a normal rate of 1.5 meters per second, what is the speed of the Gare Montparnasse walkway?
Source: Answers.com

39. Laser Printers It takes an HP LaserJet 1300 laser printer 10 minutes longer to complete a 600-page print job by itself than it takes an HP LaserJet 2420 to complete the same job by itself. Together the two printers can complete the job in 12 minutes. How long does it take each printer to complete the print job alone? What is the speed of each printer?
Source: Hewlett-Packard

40. Tennis Anyone? A regulation doubles tennis court has an area of 2808 square feet. If it is 6 feet longer than twice its width, determine the dimensions of the court.
Source: United States Tennis Association

41. Chemistry: Salt Solutions How much water must be evaporated from 32 ounces of a 4% salt solution to make a 6% salt solution?

42. Chemistry: Salt Solutions How much water must be evaporated from 240 gallons of a 3% salt solution to produce a 5% salt solution?

43. Purity of Gold The purity of gold is measured in karats, with pure gold being 24 karats. Other purities of gold are expressed as proportional parts of pure gold. Thus, 18-karat gold is $\frac{18}{24}$, or 75% pure gold; 12-karat gold is $\frac{12}{24}$, or 50% pure gold; and so on. How much 12-karat gold should be mixed with pure gold to obtain 60 grams of 16-karat gold?

44. Chemistry: Sugar Molecules A sugar molecule has twice as many atoms of hydrogen as it does oxygen and one more atom of carbon than oxygen. If a sugar molecule has a total of 45 atoms, how many are oxygen? How many are hydrogen?

45. Running a Race Mike can run the mile in 6 minutes, and Dan can run the mile in 9 minutes. If Mike gives Dan a head start of 1 minute, how far from the start will Mike pass Dan? How long does it take?

46. Range of an Airplane An air rescue plane averages 300 miles per hour in still air. It carries enough fuel for 5 hours of flying time. If, upon takeoff, it encounters a head wind of 30 mi/hr, how far can it fly and return safely? (Assume that the wind remains constant.)

47. Emptying Oil Tankers An oil tanker can be emptied by the main pump in 4 hours. An auxiliary pump can empty the tanker in 9 hours. If the main pump is started at 9 AM, when should the auxiliary pump be started so that the tanker is emptied by noon?

48. Cement A 20-pound bag of Economy brand cement mix contains 25% cement and 75% sand. How much pure cement must be added to produce a cement mix that is 40% cement?

49. Emptying a Tub A bathroom tub fills in 15 minutes with both faucets open and the stopper in place. With both faucets closed and the stopper removed, the tub empties in 20 minutes. How long will it take for the tub to fill if both faucets are open and the stopper is removed?

50. Using Two Pumps A 5-horsepower (hp) pump can empty a pool in 5 hours. A smaller, 2-hp pump empties the same pool in 8 hours. The pumps are used together to begin emptying this pool. After 2 hours, the 2-hp pump breaks down. How long will it take the larger pump to empty the pool?

51. A Biathlon Suppose that you have entered an 87-mile biathlon that consists of a run and a bicycle race. During your run, your average speed is 6 miles per hour, and during your bicycle race, your average speed is 25 miles per hour. You finish the race in 5 hours. What is the distance of the run? What is the distance of the bicycle race?

52. Constructing a Coffee Can A 39-ounce can of Hills Bros.® coffee requires 188.5 square inches of aluminum. If its height is 7 inches, what is its radius? (The surface area S of a right cylinder is $S = 2\pi r^2 + 2\pi rh$, where r is the radius and h is the height.)

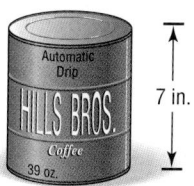

53. Comparing Olympic Heroes In the 1984 Olympics, Carl Lewis of the United States won the gold medal in the 100-meter race with a time of 9.99 seconds. In the 1896 Olympics, Thomas Burke, also of the United States, won the gold medal in the 100-meter race in 12.0 seconds. If they ran in the same race repeating their respective times, by how many meters would Lewis beat Burke?

Discussion and Writing

54. Critical Thinking You are the manager of a clothing store and have just purchased 100 dress shirts for $20.00 each. After 1 month of selling the shirts at the regular price, you plan to have a sale giving 40% off the original selling price. However, you still want to make a profit of $4 on each shirt at the sale price. What should you price the shirts at initially to ensure this? If, instead of 40% off at the sale, you give 50% off, by how much is your profit reduced?

55. Critical Thinking Make up a word problem that requires solving a linear equation as part of its solution. Exchange problems with a friend. Write a critique of your friend's problem.

56. Critical Thinking Without solving, explain what is wrong with the following mixture problem: How many liters of 25% ethanol should be added to 20 liters of 48% ethanol to obtain a solution of 58% ethanol? Now go through an algebraic solution. What happens?

57. Computing Average Speed In going from Chicago to Atlanta, a car averages 45 miles per hour, and in going from Atlanta to Miami, it averages 55 miles per hour. If Atlanta is halfway between Chicago and Miami, what is the average speed from Chicago to Miami? Discuss an intuitive solution. Write a paragraph defending your intuitive solution. Then solve the problem algebraically. Is your intuitive solution the same as the algebraic one? If not, find the flaw.

58. Speed of a Plane On a recent flight from Phoenix to Kansas City, a distance of 919 nautical miles, the plane arrived 20 minutes early. On leaving the aircraft, I asked the captain, "What was our tail wind?" He replied, "I don't know, but our ground speed was 550 knots." How can you determine if enough information is provided to find the tail wind? If possible, find the tail wind. (1 knot = 1 nautical mile per hour)

A.9 Interval Notation; Solving Inequalities

PREPARING FOR THIS SECTION   *Before getting started, review the following:*

- Algebra Essentials (Appendix A, Section A.1, pp. A4–A6)

Now Work the 'Are You Prepared?' problems on page A85.

OBJECTIVES **1** Use Interval Notation (p. A78)
  2 Use Properties of Inequalities (p. A79)
  3 Solve Inequalities (p. A81)
  4 Solve Combined Inequalities (p. A82)
  5 Solve Inequalities Involving Absolute Value (p. A83)

Suppose that a and b are two real numbers and $a < b$. We shall use the notation $a < x < b$ to mean that x is a number *between* a and b. The expression $a < x < b$ is equivalent to the two inequalities $a < x$ and $x < b$. Similarly, the expression $a \leq x \leq b$ is equivalent to the two inequalities $a \leq x$ and $x \leq b$. The remaining two possibilities, $a \leq x < b$ and $a < x \leq b$, are defined similarly.

Although it is acceptable to write $3 \geq x \geq 2$, it is preferable to reverse the inequality symbols and write instead $2 \leq x \leq 3$ so that, as you read from left to right, the values go from smaller to larger.

A statement such as $2 \leq x \leq 1$ is false because there is no number x for which $2 \leq x$ and $x \leq 1$. Finally, we never mix inequality symbols, as in $2 \leq x \geq 3$.

1 Use Interval Notation

Let a and b represent two real numbers with $a < b$.

DEFINITION

A **closed interval,** denoted by **[a, b]**, consists of all real numbers x for which $a \leq x \leq b$.

An **open interval,** denoted by **(a, b)**, consists of all real numbers x for which $a < x < b$.

The **half-open,** or **half-closed, intervals** are **(a, b]**, consisting of all real numbers x for which $a < x \leq b$, and **[a, b)**, consisting of all real numbers x for which $a \leq x < b$.

In each of these definitions, a is called the **left endpoint** and b the **right endpoint** of the interval.

The symbol ∞ (read as "infinity") is not a real number, but a notational device used to indicate unboundedness in the positive direction. The symbol $-\infty$ (read as "negative infinity") also is not a real number, but a notational device used to indicate unboundedness in the negative direction. Using the symbols ∞ and $-\infty$, we can define five other kinds of intervals:

$[a, \infty)$	Consists of all real numbers x for which $x \geq a$
(a, ∞)	Consists of all real numbers x for which $x > a$
$(-\infty, a]$	Consists of all real numbers x for which $x \leq a$
$(-\infty, a)$	Consists of all real numbers x for which $x < a$
$(-\infty, \infty)$	Consists of all real numbers x

Note that ∞ and $-\infty$ are never included as endpoints, since neither is a real number.

Table 2 summarizes interval notation, corresponding inequality notation, and their graphs.

Table 2

Interval	Inequality	Graph
The open interval (a, b)	$a < x < b$	
The closed interval $[a, b]$	$a \leq x \leq b$	
The half-open interval $[a, b)$	$a \leq x < b$	
The half-open interval $(a, b]$	$a < x \leq b$	
The interval $[a, \infty)$	$x \geq a$	
The interval (a, ∞)	$x > a$	
The interval $(-\infty, a]$	$x \leq a$	
The interval $(-\infty, a)$	$x < a$	
The interval $(-\infty, \infty)$	All real numbers	

EXAMPLE 1 | **Writing Inequalities Using Interval Notation**

Write each inequality using interval notation.

(a) $1 \leq x \leq 3$ (b) $-4 < x < 0$ (c) $x > 5$ (d) $x \leq 1$

Solution

(a) $1 \leq x \leq 3$ describes all numbers x between 1 and 3, inclusive. In interval notation, we write $[1, 3]$.

(b) In interval notation, $-4 < x < 0$ is written $(-4, 0)$.

(c) $x > 5$ consists of all numbers x greater than 5. In interval notation, we write $(5, \infty)$.

(d) In interval notation, $x \leq 1$ is written $(-\infty, 1]$.

EXAMPLE 2 | **Writing Intervals Using Inequality Notation**

Write each interval as an inequality involving x.

(a) $[1, 4)$ (b) $(2, \infty)$ (c) $[2, 3]$ (d) $(-\infty, -3]$

Solution

(a) $[1, 4)$ consists of all numbers x for which $1 \leq x < 4$.

(b) $(2, \infty)$ consists of all numbers x for which $x > 2$.

(c) $[2, 3]$ consists of all numbers x for which $2 \leq x \leq 3$.

(d) $(-\infty, -3]$ consists of all numbers x for which $x \leq -3$.

Now Work PROBLEMS 11, 23, AND 31

2 Use Properties of Inequalities

The product of two positive real numbers is positive, the product of two negative real numbers is positive, and the product of 0 and 0 is 0. For any real number a, the value of a^2 is 0 or positive; that is, a^2 is nonnegative. This is called the **nonnegative property.**

In Words

The square of a real number is never negative.

Nonnegative Property

For any real number a,

$$a^2 \geq 0 \qquad \qquad (1)$$

If we add the same number to both sides of an inequality, we obtain an equivalent inequality. For example, since $3 < 5$, then $3 + 4 < 5 + 4$ or $7 < 9$. This is called the **addition property** of inequalities.

Addition Property of Inequalities

For real numbers a, b, and c,

If $a < b$, then $a + c < b + c$.	**(2a)**
If $a > b$, then $a + c > b + c$.	**(2b)**

The addition property states that the sense, or direction, of an inequality remains unchanged if the same number is added to each side.

Now let's see what happens if we multiply each side of an inequality by a nonzero number. We begin with $3 < 7$ and multiply each side by 2. The numbers 6 and 14 that result obey the inequality $6 < 14$.

Now start with $9 > 2$ and multiply each side by -4. The numbers -36 and -8 that result obey the inequality $-36 < -8$.

Note that the effect of multiplying both sides of $9 > 2$ by the negative number -4 is that the direction of the inequality symbol is reversed. We are led to the following general **multiplication properties** for inequalities:

Multiplication Properties for Inequalities

For real numbers a, b, and c,

If $a < b$ and if $c > 0$, then $ac < bc$.	**(3a)**
If $a < b$ and if $c < 0$, then $ac > bc$.	
If $a > b$ and if $c > 0$, then $ac > bc$.	**(3b)**
If $a > b$ and if $c < 0$, then $ac < bc$.	

In Words

Multiplying by a negative number reverses the inequality.

The multiplication properties state that the sense, or direction, of an inequality *remains the same* if each side is multiplied by a *positive* real number, whereas the direction is *reversed* if each side is multiplied by a *negative* real number.

EXAMPLE 3 | **Multiplication Property of Inequalities**

(a) If $2x < 6$, then $\dfrac{1}{2}(2x) < \dfrac{1}{2}(6)$ or $x < 3$.

(b) If $\dfrac{x}{-3} > 12$, then $-3\left(\dfrac{x}{-3}\right) < -3(12)$ or $x < -36$.

(c) If $-4x < -8$, then $\dfrac{-4x}{-4} > \dfrac{-8}{-4}$ or $x > 2$.

(d) If $-x > 8$, then $(-1)(-x) < (-1)(8)$ or $x < -8$.

━━━━ **Now Work** PROBLEM 45

The **reciprocal property** states that the reciprocal of a positive real number is positive and that the reciprocal of a negative real number is negative.

Reciprocal Property for Inequalities

$$\text{If } a > 0, \text{ then } \frac{1}{a} > 0 \qquad \text{If } \frac{1}{a} > 0, \text{ then } a > 0 \qquad \textbf{(4a)}$$

$$\text{If } a < 0, \text{ then } \frac{1}{a} < 0 \qquad \text{If } \frac{1}{a} < 0, \text{ then } a < 0 \qquad \textbf{(4b)}$$

3 Solve Inequalities

An **inequality in one variable** is a statement involving two expressions, at least one containing the variable, separated by one of the inequality symbols $<$, $\leq$, $>$, or $\geq$. To **solve an inequality** means to find all values of the variable for which the statement is true. These values are called **solutions** of the inequality.

For example, the following are all inequalities involving one variable x:

$$x + 5 < 8 \qquad 2x - 3 \geq 4 \qquad x^2 - 1 \leq 3 \qquad \frac{x + 1}{x - 2} > 0$$

As with equations, one method for solving an inequality is to replace it by a series of equivalent inequalities until an inequality with an obvious solution, such as $x < 3$, is obtained. We obtain equivalent inequalities by applying some of the same properties as those used to find equivalent equations. The addition property and the multiplication properties form the basis for the following procedures.

Procedures That Leave the Inequality Symbol Unchanged

1. Simplify both sides of the inequality by combining like terms and eliminating parentheses:

   Replace $\qquad (x + 2) + 6 > 2x + 5(x + 1)$
   by $\qquad\qquad x + 8 > 7x + 5$

2. Add or subtract the same expression on both sides of the inequality:

   Replace $\qquad\qquad 3x - 5 < 4$
   by $\qquad (3x - 5) + 5 < 4 + 5$

3. Multiply or divide both sides of the inequality by the same positive expression:

   Replace $\quad 4x > 16$ by $\dfrac{4x}{4} > \dfrac{16}{4}$

Procedures That Reverse the Sense or Direction of the Inequality Symbol

1. Interchange the two sides of the inequality:

   Replace $\quad 3 < x$ by $x > 3$

2. Multiply or divide both sides of the inequality by the same *negative* expression:

   Replace $\quad -2x > 6$ by $\dfrac{-2x}{-2} < \dfrac{6}{-2}$

As the examples that follow illustrate, we solve inequalities using many of the same steps that we would use to solve equations. In writing the solution of an inequality, we may use either set notation or interval notation, whichever is more convenient.

| EXAMPLE 4 | **Solving an Inequality** |

Solve the inequality: $4x + 7 \geq 2x - 3$
Graph the solution set.

Solution

$$4x + 7 \geq 2x - 3$$

$$4x + 7 - 7 \geq 2x - 3 - 7 \qquad \text{Subtract 7 from both sides.}$$

$$4x \geq 2x - 10 \qquad \text{Simplify.}$$

$$4x - 2x \geq 2x - 10 - 2x \qquad \text{Subtract 2x from both sides.}$$

$$2x \geq -10 \qquad \text{Simplify.}$$

$$\frac{2x}{2} \geq \frac{-10}{2} \qquad \text{Divide both sides by 2. (The direction of the inequality symbol is unchanged.)}$$

$$x \geq -5 \qquad \text{Simplify.}$$

Figure 34

The solution set is $\{x | x \geq -5\}$ or, using interval notation, all numbers in the interval $[-5, \infty)$. See Figure 34 for the graph.

━━━━━ **Now Work** PROBLEM 57

4 Solve Combined Inequalities

| EXAMPLE 5 | **Solving Combined Inequalities** |

Solve the inequality: $-5 < 3x - 2 < 1$
Graph the solution set.

Solution

Recall that the inequality

$$-5 < 3x - 2 < 1$$

is equivalent to the two inequalities

$$-5 < 3x - 2 \quad \text{and} \quad 3x - 2 < 1$$

We will solve each of these inequalities separately.

$$-5 < 3x - 2 \qquad\qquad\qquad 3x - 2 < 1$$

$$-5 + 2 < 3x - 2 + 2 \quad \text{Add 2 to both sides.} \quad 3x - 2 + 2 < 1 + 2$$

$$-3 < 3x \qquad\qquad \text{Simplify.} \qquad\qquad 3x < 3$$

$$\frac{-3}{3} < \frac{3x}{3} \qquad\qquad \text{Divide both sides by 3.} \qquad \frac{3x}{3} < \frac{3}{3}$$

$$-1 < x \qquad\qquad \text{Simplify.} \qquad\qquad x < 1$$

The solution set of the original pair of inequalities consists of all x for which

$$-1 < x \quad \text{and} \quad x < 1$$

Figure 35

This may be written more compactly as $\{x | -1 < x < 1\}$. In interval notation, the solution is $(-1, 1)$. See Figure 35 for the graph.

We observe in the preceding process that the two inequalities we solved required exactly the same steps. A shortcut to solving the original inequality algebraically is to deal with the two inequalities at the same time, as follows:

$$-5 < \quad 3x - 2 \quad < 1$$
$$-5 + 2 < 3x - 2 + 2 < 1 + 2 \quad \text{Add 2 to each part.}$$
$$-3 < \quad 3x \quad < 3 \quad \text{Simplify.}$$
$$\frac{-3}{3} < \quad \frac{3x}{3} \quad < \frac{3}{3} \quad \text{Divide each part by 3.}$$
$$-1 < \quad x \quad < 1 \quad \text{Simplify.}$$

Now Work PROBLEM 73

| EXAMPLE 6 | **Using the Reciprocal Property to Solve an Inequality** |

Solve the inequality: $(4x - 1)^{-1} > 0$
Graph the solution set.

Solution Since $(4x - 1)^{-1} = \dfrac{1}{4x - 1}$ and since the Reciprocal Property states that when $\dfrac{1}{a} > 0$ then $a > 0$, we have

$$(4x - 1)^{-1} > 0$$
$$\frac{1}{4x - 1} > 0$$
$$4x - 1 > 0 \quad \text{Reciprocal Property}$$
$$4x > 1$$
$$x > \frac{1}{4}$$

Figure 36

The solution set is $\left\{ x \middle| x > \dfrac{1}{4} \right\}$, that is, all x in the interval $\left(\dfrac{1}{4}, \infty \right)$. Figure 36 illustrates the graph.

Now Work PROBLEM 83

5 Solve Inequalities Involving Absolute Value

| EXAMPLE 7 | **Solving an Inequality Involving Absolute Value** |

Solve the inequality $|x| < 4$, and graph the solution set.

Solution

Figure 37

We are looking for all points whose coordinate x is a distance less than 4 units from the origin. See Figure 37 for an illustration. Because any x between -4 and 4 satisfies the condition $|x| < 4$, the solution set consists of all numbers x for which $-4 < x < 4$, that is, all x in the interval $(-4, 4)$.

Less than 4 units
from origin 0

$$-5 \;-4 \;-3 \;-2 \;-1 \quad 0 \quad 1 \quad 2 \quad 3 \quad 4$$

| EXAMPLE 8 | **Solving an Inequality Involving Absolute Value** |

Solve the inequality $|x| > 3$, and graph the solution set.

Solution

Figure 38

$$-5 \;-4 \;-3 \;-2 \;-1 \quad 0 \quad 1 \quad 2 \quad 3 \quad 4$$

We are looking for all points whose coordinate x is a distance greater than 3 units from the origin. Figure 38 illustrates the situation. We conclude that any x less than -3 or greater than 3 satisfies the condition $|x| > 3$. Consequently, the solution set consists of all numbers x for which $x < -3$ or $x > 3$, that is, all x in $(-\infty, -3) \cup (3, \infty)$.*

We are led to the following results:

THEOREM

If a is any positive number, then

$$
\begin{array}{llll}
|u| < a & \text{is equivalent to} & -a < u < a & \textbf{(5)} \\
|u| \leq a & \text{is equivalent to} & -a \leq u \leq a & \textbf{(6)} \\
|u| > a & \text{is equivalent to} & u < -a \text{ or } u > a & \textbf{(7)} \\
|u| \geq a & \text{is equivalent to} & u \leq -a \text{ or } u \geq a & \textbf{(8)}
\end{array}
$$

| EXAMPLE 9 | **Solving an Inequality Involving Absolute Value** |

Solve the inequality $|2x + 4| \leq 3$, and graph the solution set.

Solution

$$
\begin{array}{ll}
|2x + 4| \leq 3 & \text{This follows the form of statement (6); the expression} \\
 & u = 2x + 4 \text{ is inside the absolute value bars.} \\
-3 \leq 2x + 4 \leq 3 & \text{Apply statement (6).} \\
-3 - 4 \leq 2x + 4 - 4 \leq 3 - 4 & \text{Subtract 4 from each part.} \\
-7 \leq 2x \leq -1 & \text{Simplify.} \\
\dfrac{-7}{2} \leq \dfrac{2x}{2} \leq \dfrac{-1}{2} & \text{Divide each part by 2.} \\
-\dfrac{7}{2} \leq x \leq -\dfrac{1}{2} & \text{Simplify.}
\end{array}
$$

Figure 39

The solution set is $\left\{ x \,\middle|\, -\dfrac{7}{2} \leq x \leq -\dfrac{1}{2} \right\}$, that is, all x in the interval $\left[-\dfrac{7}{2}, -\dfrac{1}{2} \right]$. See Figure 39 for a graph of the solution set.

 Now Work PROBLEM 89

| EXAMPLE 10 | **Solving an Inequality Involving Absolute Value** |

Solve the inequality $|2x - 5| > 3$, and graph the solution set.

Solution

$$|2x - 5| > 3 \quad \text{This follows the form of statement (7); the expression}$$
$$u = 2x - 5 \text{ is inside the absolute value bars.}$$

$$
\begin{array}{lll}
2x - 5 < -3 & \text{or} & 2x - 5 > 3 \qquad \text{Apply statement (7).} \\
2x - 5 + 5 < -3 & \text{or} & 2x - 5 + 5 > 3 + 5 \quad \text{Add 5 to each part.} \\
2x < 2 & \text{or} & 2x > 8 \qquad \text{Simplify.} \\
\dfrac{2x}{2} < \dfrac{2}{2} & \text{or} & \dfrac{2x}{2} > \dfrac{8}{2} \qquad \text{Divide each part by 2.} \\
x < 1 & \text{or} & x > 4 \qquad \text{Simplify.}
\end{array}
$$

Figure 40

The solution set is $\{x \,|\, x < 1 \text{ or } x > 4\}$, that is, all x in $(-\infty, 1) \cup (4, \infty)$. See Figure 40 for a graph of the solution set.

WARNING A common error to be avoided is to attempt to write the solution $x < 1$ or $x > 4$ as the combined inequality $1 > x > 4$, which is incorrect, since there are no numbers x for which $x < 1$ *and* $x > 4$. Another common error is to "mix" the symbols and write $1 < x > 4$, which makes no sense. ∎

Now Work PROBLEM 95

*The symbol $\cup$ stands for the union of two sets. Refer to page A2 if necessary.

A.9 Assess Your Understanding

'Are You Prepared?' *Answers are given at the end of these exercises. If you get a wrong answer, read the pages listed in red.*

1. Graph the inequality: $x \geq -2$. (pp. A4–A5)

2. *True or False* $-5 > -3$ (pp. A4–A5)

3. $|-2| = $ _____. (p. A5)

4. *True or False* $|x| \geq 0$ for any real number x. (pp. A5–A6)

Concepts and Vocabulary

5. If each side of an inequality is multiplied by a(n) _____ number, then the sense of the inequality symbol is reversed.

6. A(n) _____ _____, denoted $[a, b]$, consists of all real numbers x for which $a \leq x \leq b$.

7. The solution set of the equation $|x| = 5$ is { _____ }.

8. The solution set of the inequality $|x| < 5$ is $\{x|$ _____ $\}$

9. *True or False* The equation $|x| = -2$ has no solution.

10. *True or False* The inequality $|x| \geq -2$ has the set of real numbers as solution set.

Skill Building

In Problems 11–16, express the graph shown in blue using interval notation. Also express each as an inequality involving x.

11.

12.

13.

14.

15.

16.

In Problems 17–22, an inequality is given. Write the inequality obtained by:
  (a) Adding 3 to each side of the given inequality.
  (b) Subtracting 5 from each side of the given inequality.
  (c) Multiplying each side of the given inequality by 3.
  (d) Multiplying each side of the given inequality by −2.

17. $3 < 5$ 18. $2 > 1$ 19. $4 > -3$ 20. $-3 > -5$ 21. $2x + 1 < 2$ 22. $1 - 2x > 5$

In Problems 23–30, write each inequality using interval notation, and illustrate each inequality using the real number line.

23. $0 \leq x \leq 4$ 24. $-1 < x < 5$ 25. $4 \leq x < 6$ 26. $-2 < x < 0$

27. $x \geq 4$ 28. $x \leq 5$ 29. $x < -4$ 30. $x > 1$

In Problems 31–38, write each interval as an inequality involving x, and illustrate each inequality using the real number line.

31. $[2, 5]$ 32. $(1, 2)$ 33. $(-3, -2)$ 34. $[0, 1)$

35. $[4, \infty)$ 36. $(-\infty, 2]$ 37. $(-\infty, -3)$ 38. $(-8, \infty)$

In Problems 39–52, fill in the blank with the correct inequality symbol.

39. If $x < 5$, then $x - 5$ _____ 0.

40. If $x < -4$, then $x + 4$ _____ 0.

41. If $x > -4$, then $x + 4$ _____ 0.

42. If $x > 6$, then $x - 6$ _____ 0.

43. If $x \geq -4$, then $3x$ _____ -12.

44. If $x \leq 3$, then $2x$ _____ 6.

45. If $x > 6$, then $-2x$ _____ -12.

46. If $x > -2$, then $-4x$ _____ 8.

47. If $x \geq 5$, then $-4x$ _____ -20.

48. If $x \leq -4$, then $-3x$ _____ 12.

49. If $2x > 6$, then x _____ 3.

50. If $3x \leq 12$, then x _____ 4.

51. If $-\dfrac{1}{2}x \leq 3$, then x _____ -6.

52. If $-\dfrac{1}{4}x > 1$, then x _____ -4.

In Problems 53–100, solve each inequality. Express your answer using set notation or interval notation. Graph the solution set.

53. $x + 1 < 5$ 54. $x - 6 < 1$ 55. $1 - 2x \leq 3$

56. $2 - 3x \leq 5$ 57. $3x - 7 > 2$ 58. $2x + 5 > 1$

59. $3x - 1 \geq 3 + x$

60. $2x - 2 \geq 3 + x$

61. $-2(x + 3) < 8$

62. $-3(1 - x) < 12$

63. $4 - 3(1 - x) \leq 3$

64. $8 - 4(2 - x) \leq -2x$

65. $\frac{1}{2}(x - 4) > x + 8$

66. $3x + 4 > \frac{1}{3}(x - 2)$

67. $\frac{x}{2} \geq 1 - \frac{x}{4}$

68. $\frac{x}{3} \geq 2 + \frac{x}{6}$

69. $0 \leq 2x - 6 \leq 4$

70. $4 \leq 2x + 2 \leq 10$

71. $-5 \leq 4 - 3x \leq 2$

72. $-3 \leq 3 - 2x \leq 9$

73. $-3 < \frac{2x - 1}{4} < 0$

74. $0 < \frac{3x + 2}{2} < 4$

75. $1 < 1 - \frac{1}{2}x < 4$

76. $0 < 1 - \frac{1}{3}x < 1$

77. $(x + 2)(x - 3) > (x - 1)(x + 1)$

78. $(x - 1)(x + 1) > (x - 3)(x + 4)$

79. $x(4x + 3) \leq (2x + 1)^2$

80. $x(9x - 5) \leq (3x - 1)^2$

81. $\frac{1}{2} \leq \frac{x + 1}{3} < \frac{3}{4}$

82. $\frac{1}{3} < \frac{x + 1}{2} \leq \frac{2}{3}$

83. $(4x + 2)^{-1} < 0$

84. $(2x - 1)^{-1} > 0$

85. $0 < \frac{2}{x} < \frac{3}{5}$

86. $0 < \frac{4}{x} < \frac{2}{3}$

87. $0 < (2x - 4)^{-1} < \frac{1}{2}$

88. $0 < (3x + 6)^{-1} < \frac{1}{3}$

89. $|2x| < 8$

90. $|3x| < 12$

91. $|3x| > 12$

92. $|2x| > 6$

93. $|2x - 1| \leq 1$

94. $|2x + 5| \leq 7$

95. $|1 - 2x| > 3$

96. $|2 - 3x| > 1$

97. $|-4x| + |-5| \leq 9$

98. $|-x| - |4| \leq 2$

99. $|-2x| \geq |-4|$

100. $|-x - 2| \geq 1$

Applications and Extensions

101. Express the fact that x differs from 2 by less than $\frac{1}{2}$ as an inequality involving an absolute value. Solve for x.

102. Express the fact that x differs from -1 by less than 1 as an inequality involving an absolute value. Solve for x.

103. Express the fact that x differs from -3 by more than 2 as an inequality involving an absolute value. Solve for x.

104. Express the fact that x differs from 2 by more than 3 as an inequality involving an absolute value. Solve for x.

105. What is the domain of the variable in the expression $\sqrt{3x + 6}$?

106. What is the domain of the variable in the expression $\sqrt{8 + 2x}$?

107. A young adult may be defined as someone older than 21, but less than 30 years of age. Express this statement using inequalities.

108. Middle-aged may be defined as being 40 or more and less than 60. Express this statement using inequalities.

109. **Life Expectancy** The Social Security Administration determined that an average 30-year-old male in 2005 could expect to live at least 49.66 more years and an average 30-year-old female in 2005 could expect to live at least 53.58 more years.
(a) To what age can an average 30-year-old male expect to live? Express your answer as an inequality.

(b) To what age can an average 30-year-old female expect to live? Express your answer as an inequality.
(c) Who can expect to live longer, a male or a female? By how many years?

Source: Actuarial Study No. 120, August 2005

JAN 2005   JULY 2058   AUG 2054

110. **General Chemistry** For a certain ideal gas, the volume V (in cubic centimeters) equals 20 times the temperature T (in degrees Celsius). If the temperature varies from $80°$ to $120°$ C inclusive, what is the corresponding range of the volume of the gas?

111. **Real Estate** A real estate agent agrees to sell an apartment complex according to the following commission schedule: $45,000 plus 25% of the selling price in excess of $900,000. Assuming that the complex will sell at some price between $900,000 and $1,100,000 inclusive, over what range does the agent's commission vary? How does the commission vary as a percent of selling price?

112. Sales Commission A used car salesperson is paid a commission of $25 plus 40% of the selling price in excess of owner's cost. The owner claims that used cars typically sell for at least owner's cost plus $200 and at most owner's cost plus $3000. For each sale made, over what range can the salesperson expect the commission to vary?

113. Federal Tax Withholding The percentage method of withholding for federal income tax (2006) states that a single person whose weekly wages, after subtracting withholding allowances, are over $620, but not over $1409, shall have $78.30 plus 25% of the excess over $620 withheld. Over what range does the amount withheld vary if the weekly wages vary from $700 to $900 inclusive?

Source: Employer's Tax Guide. Department of the Treasury, Internal Revenue Service, Publication 2006.

114. Exercising Sue wants to lose weight. For healthy weight loss, the American College of Sports Medicine (ACSM) recommends 200 to 300 minutes of exercise per week. For the first six days of the week, Sue exercised 40, 45, 0, 50, 25, and 35 minutes. How long should Sue exercise on the seventh day in order to stay within the ACSM guidelines?

115. Electricity Rates Commonwealth Edison Company's charge for electricity in May 2006 is 8.275¢ per kilowatt-hour. In addition, each monthly bill contains a customer charge of $7.58. If last year's bills ranged from a low of $63.47 to a high of $214.53, over what range did usage vary (in kilowatt-hours)?

Source: Commonwealth Edison Co., Chicago, Illinois, 2006.

116. Water Bills The Village of Oak Lawn charges homeowners $28.84 per quarter-year plus $2.28 per 1000 gallons for water usage in excess of 12,000 gallons. In 2006 one homeowner's quarterly bill ranged from a high of $74.44 to a low of $42.52. Over what range did water usage vary?

Source: Village of Oak Lawn, Illinois, April 2006.

117. Markup of a New Car The markup over dealer's cost of a new car ranges from 12% to 18%. If the sticker price is $18,000, over what range will the dealer's cost vary?

118. IQ Tests A standard intelligence test has an average score of 100. According to statistical theory, of the people who take the test, the 2.5% with the highest scores will have scores of more than 1.96σ above the average, where σ (sigma, a number called the **standard deviation**) depends on the nature of the test. If $\sigma = 12$ for this test and there is (in principle) no upper limit to the score possible on the test, write the interval of possible test scores of the people in the top 2.5%.

119. Computing Grades In your Economics 101 class, you have scores of 68, 82, 87, and 89 on the first four of five tests. To get

a grade of B, the average of the first five test scores must be greater than or equal to 80 and less than 90.

(a) Solve an inequality to find the range of the score that you need on the last test to get a B.

(b) What score do you need if the fifth test counts double?

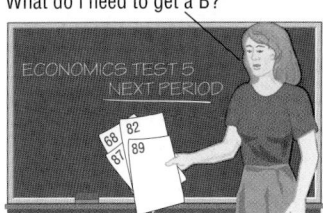
What do I need to get a B?

120. "Light" Foods For food products to be labeled "light," the U.S. Food and Drug Administration requires that the altered product must either contain one-third or fewer calories than the regular product or it must contain one-half or less fat than the regular product. If a serving of Miracle Whip® Light contains 20 calories and 1.5 grams of fat, then what must be true about either the number of calories or the grams of fat in a serving of regular Miracle Whip®?

121. Arithmetic Mean If $a < b$, show that $a < \dfrac{a + b}{2} < b$. The number $\dfrac{a + b}{2}$ is called the **arithmetic mean** of a and b.

122. Refer to Problem 121. Show that the arithmetic mean of a and b is equidistant from a and b.

123. Geometric Mean If $0 < a < b$, show that $a < 0\sqrt{ab} < b$. The number $\sqrt{ab}$ is called the **geometric mean** of a and b.

124. Refer to Problems 121 and 123. Show that the geometric mean of a and b is less than the arithmetic mean of a and b.

125. Harmonic Mean For $0 < a < b$, let h be defined by

$$\frac{1}{h} = \frac{1}{2}\left(\frac{1}{a} + \frac{1}{b}\right)$$

Show that $a < h < b$. The number h is called the **harmonic mean** of a and b.

126. Refer to Problems 121, 123, and 125. Show that the harmonic mean of a and b equals the geometric mean squared divided by the arithmetic mean.

127. Another Reciprocal Property Prove that if $0 < a < b$, then

$$0 < \frac{1}{b} < \frac{1}{a}.$$

Discussion and Writing

128. Make up an inequality that has no solution. Make up one that has exactly one solution.

129. The inequality $x^2 + 1 < -5$ has no real solution. Explain why.

130. Do you prefer to use inequality notation or interval notation to express the solution to an inequality? Give your reasons. Are there particular circumstances when you prefer one to the other? Cite examples.

131. How would you explain to a fellow student the underlying reason for the multiplication properties for inequalities (page A80), that is, the sense or direction of an inequality remains the same if each side is multiplied by a positive real number, whereas the direction is reversed if each side is multiplied by a negative real number.

'Are You Prepared?' Answers

1. ←———|———|————→
            −4   −2   0

2. False **3.** 2 **4.** True

A.10 *n*th Roots; Rational Exponents

PREPARING FOR THIS SECTION *Before getting started, review the following:*

- Exponents, Square Roots (Appendix A, Section A.1, pp. A7–A10)

Now Work the 'Are You Prepared?' problems on page A93.

OBJECTIVES 1 Work with *n*th Roots (p. A88)
2 Simplify Radicals (p. A89)
3 Rationalize Denominators (p. A90)
4 Simplify Expressions with Rational Exponents (p. A91)

1 Work with *n*th Roots

DEFINITION

The **principal *n*th root of a real number *a*,** $n \geq 2$ an integer, symbolized by $\sqrt[n]{a}$, is defined as follows:

$$\sqrt[n]{a} = b \quad \text{means} \quad a = b^n$$

where $a \geq 0$ and $b \geq 0$ if *n* is even and *a*, *b* are any real numbers if *n* is odd.

In Words
The symbol $\sqrt[n]{a}$ means "give me the number, when raised to the nth power, that results in *a*."

Notice that if *a* is negative and *n* is even then $\sqrt[n]{a}$ is not defined. When it is defined, the principal *n*th root of a number is unique.

The symbol $\sqrt[n]{a}$ for the principal *n*th root of *a* is called a **radical;** the integer *n* is called the **index,** and *a* is called the **radicand.** If the index of a radical is 2, we call $\sqrt[2]{a}$ the **square root** of *a* and omit the index 2 by writing $\sqrt{a}$. If the index is 3, we call $\sqrt[3]{a}$ the **cube root** of *a*.

EXAMPLE 1

Simplifying Principal *n*th Roots

(a) $\sqrt[3]{8} = \sqrt[3]{2^3} = 2$ The number whose cube is 8 is 2. (b) $\sqrt[3]{-64} = \sqrt[3]{(-4)^3} = -4$

(c) $\sqrt[4]{\dfrac{1}{16}} = \sqrt[4]{\left(\dfrac{1}{2}\right)^4} = \dfrac{1}{2}$ (d) $\sqrt[6]{(-2)^6} = |-2| = 2$

These are examples of **perfect roots,** since each simplifies to a rational number. Notice the absolute value in Example 1(d). If *n* is even, the principal *n*th root must be nonnegative.

In general, if $n \geq 2$ is an integer and *a* is a real number, we have

$\sqrt[n]{a^n} = a$	if $n \geq 3$ is odd	**(1a)**
$\sqrt[n]{a^n} = \|a\|$	if $n \geq 2$ is even	**(1b)**

Now Work PROBLEM 7

Radicals provide a way of representing many irrational real numbers. For example, there is no rational number whose square is 2. Using radicals, we can say that $\sqrt{2}$ is the positive number whose square is 2.

<table>
<tr><td>EXAMPLE 2</td></tr>
</table>

Using a Calculator to Approximate Roots

Use a calculator to approximate $\sqrt[5]{16}$.

Solution   Figure 41 shows the result using a TI-84 Plus graphing calculator.

Figure 41

Now Work PROBLEM 101

2 Simplify Radicals

Let $n \geq 2$ and $m \geq 2$ denote positive integers, and let a and b represent real numbers. Assuming that all radicals are defined, we have the following properties:

Properties of Radicals

$$\sqrt[n]{ab} = \sqrt[n]{a}\,\sqrt[n]{b} \tag{2a}$$

$$\sqrt[n]{\dfrac{a}{b}} = \dfrac{\sqrt[n]{a}}{\sqrt[n]{b}} \tag{2b}$$

$$\sqrt[n]{a^m} = \left(\sqrt[n]{a}\right)^m \tag{2c}$$

When used in reference to radicals, the direction to "simplify" will mean to remove from the radicals any perfect roots that occur as factors. Let's look at some examples of how the preceding rules are applied to simplify radicals.

<table>
<tr><td>EXAMPLE 3</td></tr>
</table>

Simplifying Radicals

(a) $\sqrt{32} = \sqrt{16 \cdot 2} = \sqrt{16} \cdot \sqrt{2} = 4\sqrt{2}$

        ↑   ↑

    Factor out 16,   (2a)
    a perfect square.

(b) $\sqrt[3]{16} = \sqrt[3]{8 \cdot 2} = \sqrt[3]{8} \cdot \sqrt[3]{2} = \sqrt[3]{2^3} \cdot \sqrt[3]{2} = 2\sqrt[3]{2}$

        ↑   ↑

    Factor out 8,   (2a)
    a perfect cube.

(c) $\sqrt[3]{-16x^4} = \sqrt[3]{-8 \cdot 2 \cdot x^3 \cdot x} = \sqrt[3]{(-8x^3)(2x)}$

        ↑   ↑

    Factor perfect   Group perfect
    cubes inside radical. cubes.

$$= \sqrt[3]{(-2x)^3 \cdot 2x} = \sqrt[3]{(-2x)^3} \cdot \sqrt[3]{2x} = -2x\sqrt[3]{2x}$$

               ↑

              (2a)

(d) $\sqrt[4]{\dfrac{16x^5}{81}} = \sqrt[4]{\dfrac{2^4 x^4 x}{3^4}} = \sqrt[4]{\left(\dfrac{2x}{3}\right)^4 \cdot x} = \sqrt[4]{\left(\dfrac{2x}{3}\right)^4} \cdot \sqrt[4]{x} = \left|\dfrac{2x}{3}\right|\sqrt[4]{x}$

Now Work PROBLEMS 11 AND 17

Two or more radicals can be combined, provided that they have the same index and the same radicand. Such radicals are called **like radicals.**

<table>
<tr><td>EXAMPLE 4</td></tr>
</table>

Combining Like Radicals

(a) $-8\sqrt{12} + \sqrt{3} = -8\sqrt{4 \cdot 3} + \sqrt{3}$

$$= -8 \cdot \sqrt{4}\,\sqrt{3} + \sqrt{3}$$

$$= -16\sqrt{3} + \sqrt{3} = -15\sqrt{3}$$

(b) $\sqrt[3]{8x^4} + \sqrt[3]{-x} + 4\sqrt[3]{27x} = \sqrt[3]{2^3 x^3 x} + \sqrt[3]{-1 \cdot x} + 4\sqrt[3]{3^3 x}$

$$= \sqrt[3]{(2x)^3} \cdot \sqrt[3]{x} + \sqrt[3]{-1} \cdot \sqrt[3]{x} + 4\sqrt[3]{3^3} \cdot \sqrt[3]{x}$$

$$= 2x\sqrt[3]{x} - 1 \cdot \sqrt[3]{x} + 12\sqrt[3]{x}$$

$$= (2x + 11)\sqrt[3]{x}$$

Now Work PROBLEM 33

3 Rationalize Denominators

When radicals occur in quotients, it is customary to rewrite the quotient so that the new denominator contains no radicals. This process is referred to as **rationalizing the denominator.**

The idea is to multiply by an appropriate expression so that the new denominator contains no radicals. For example:

If a Denominator Contains the Factor	Multiply by	To Obtain a Denominator Free of Radicals
$\sqrt{3}$	$\sqrt{3}$	$\left(\sqrt{3}\right)^2 = 3$
$\sqrt{3} + 1$	$\sqrt{3} - 1$	$\left(\sqrt{3}\right)^2 - 1^2 = 3 - 1 = 2$
$\sqrt{2} - 3$	$\sqrt{2} + 3$	$\left(\sqrt{2}\right)^2 - 3^2 = 2 - 9 = -7$
$\sqrt{5} - \sqrt{3}$	$\sqrt{5} + \sqrt{3}$	$\left(\sqrt{5}\right)^2 - \left(\sqrt{3}\right)^2 = 5 - 3 = 2$
$\sqrt[3]{4}$	$\sqrt[3]{2}$	$\sqrt[3]{4} \cdot \sqrt[3]{2} = \sqrt[3]{8} = 2$

In rationalizing the denominator of a quotient, be sure to multiply both the numerator and the denominator by the expression.

EXAMPLE 5 **Rationalizing Denominators**

Rationalize the denominator of each expression:

(a) $\dfrac{1}{\sqrt{3}}$ (b) $\dfrac{5}{4\sqrt{2}}$ (c) $\dfrac{\sqrt{2}}{\sqrt{3} - 3\sqrt{2}}$

Solution (a) The denominator contains the factor $\sqrt{3}$, so we multiply the numerator and denominator by $\sqrt{3}$ to obtain

$$\frac{1}{\sqrt{3}} = \frac{1}{\sqrt{3}} \cdot \frac{\sqrt{3}}{\sqrt{3}} = \frac{\sqrt{3}}{\left(\sqrt{3}\right)^2} = \frac{\sqrt{3}}{3}$$

(b) The denominator contains the factor $\sqrt{2}$, so we multiply the numerator and denominator by $\sqrt{2}$ to obtain

$$\frac{5}{4\sqrt{2}} = \frac{5}{4\sqrt{2}} \cdot \frac{\sqrt{2}}{\sqrt{2}} = \frac{5\sqrt{2}}{4\left(\sqrt{2}\right)^2} = \frac{5\sqrt{2}}{4 \cdot 2} = \frac{5\sqrt{2}}{8}$$

(c) The denominator contains the factor $\sqrt{3} - 3\sqrt{2}$, so we multiply the numerator and denominator by $\sqrt{3} + 3\sqrt{2}$ to obtain

$$\frac{\sqrt{2}}{\sqrt{3} - 3\sqrt{2}} = \frac{\sqrt{2}}{\sqrt{3} - 3\sqrt{2}} \cdot \frac{\sqrt{3} + 3\sqrt{2}}{\sqrt{3} + 3\sqrt{2}} = \frac{\sqrt{2}\left(\sqrt{3} + 3\sqrt{2}\right)}{\left(\sqrt{3}\right)^2 - \left(3\sqrt{2}\right)^2}$$

$$= \frac{\sqrt{2}\sqrt{3} + 3\left(\sqrt{2}\right)^2}{3 - 18} = \frac{\sqrt{6} + 6}{-15} = -\frac{6 + \sqrt{6}}{15}$$

Now Work PROBLEM 47

4 Simplify Expressions with Rational Exponents

Radicals are used to define rational exponents.

DEFINITION   If a is a real number and $n \geq 2$ is an integer, then

$$a^{1/n} = \sqrt[n]{a} \qquad \qquad \text{(3)}$$

provided that $\sqrt[n]{a}$ exists.

Note that if n is even and $a < 0$ then $\sqrt[n]{a}$ and $a^{1/n}$ do not exist.

EXAMPLE 6   **Writing Expressions Containing Fractional Exponents as Radicals**

(a) $4^{1/2} = \sqrt{4} = 2$ (b) $8^{1/2} = \sqrt{8} = 2\sqrt{2}$

(c) $(-27)^{1/3} = \sqrt[3]{-27} = -3$ (d) $16^{1/3} = \sqrt[3]{16} = 2\sqrt[3]{2}$

DEFINITION   If a is a real number and m and n are integers containing no common factors, with $n \geq 2$, then

$$a^{m/n} = \sqrt[n]{a^m} = (\sqrt[n]{a})^m \qquad \qquad \text{(4)}$$

provided that $\sqrt[n]{a}$ exists.

We have two comments about equation (4):

1. The exponent $\dfrac{m}{n}$ must be in lowest terms and n must be positive.

2. In simplifying the rational expression $a^{m/n}$, either $\sqrt[n]{a^m}$ or $(\sqrt[n]{a})^m$ may be used, the choice depending on which is easier to simplify. Generally, taking the root first, as in $(\sqrt[n]{a})^m$, is easier.

EXAMPLE 7   **Using Equation (4)**

(a) $4^{3/2} = (\sqrt{4})^3 = 2^3 = 8$ (b) $(-8)^{4/3} = (\sqrt[3]{-8})^4 = (-2)^4 = 16$

(c) $(32)^{-2/5} = (\sqrt[5]{32})^{-2} = 2^{-2} = \dfrac{1}{4}$ (d) $25^{6/4} = 25^{3/2} = (\sqrt{25})^3 = 5^3 = 125$

Now Work PROBLEM 55

It can be shown that the Laws of Exponents hold for rational exponents. The next example illustrates using the Law of Exponents to simplify.

EXAMPLE 8   **Simplifying Expressions Containing Rational Exponents**

Simplify each expression. Express your answer so that only positive exponents occur. Assume that the variables are positive.

(a) $(x^{2/3}y)(x^{-2}y)^{1/2}$ (b) $\left(\dfrac{2x^{1/3}}{y^{2/3}}\right)^{-3}$ (c) $\left(\dfrac{9x^2y^{1/3}}{x^{1/3}y}\right)^{1/2}$

Solution   (a) $(x^{2/3}y)(x^{-2}y)^{1/2} = (x^{2/3}y)[(x^{-2})^{1/2}y^{1/2}]$ $(ab)^n = a^n b^n$

$\qquad\qquad\qquad\qquad = x^{2/3}yx^{-1}y^{1/2}$ $(a^m)^n = a^{mn}$

$\qquad\qquad\qquad\qquad = (x^{2/3} \cdot x^{-1})(y \cdot y^{1/2})$

$\qquad\qquad\qquad\qquad = x^{-1/3}y^{3/2}$ $a^m \cdot a^n = a^{m+n}$

$\qquad\qquad\qquad\qquad = \dfrac{y^{3/2}}{x^{1/3}}$

(b) $\left(\dfrac{2x^{1/3}}{y^{2/3}}\right)^{-3} = \left(\dfrac{y^{2/3}}{2x^{1/3}}\right)^3 = \dfrac{(y^{2/3})^3}{(2x^{1/3})^3} = \dfrac{y^2}{2^3(x^{1/3})^3} = \dfrac{y^2}{8x}$

(c) $\left(\dfrac{9x^2y^{1/3}}{x^{1/3}y}\right)^{1/2} = \left(\dfrac{9x^{2-(1/3)}}{y^{1-(1/3)}}\right)^{1/2} = \left(\dfrac{9x^{5/3}}{y^{2/3}}\right)^{1/2} = \dfrac{9^{1/2}(x^{5/3})^{1/2}}{(y^{2/3})^{1/2}} = \dfrac{3x^{5/6}}{y^{1/3}}$

 Now Work PROBLEM 71

   The next two examples illustrate some algebra that you will need to know for certain calculus problems.

EXAMPLE 9   **Writing an Expression as a Single Quotient**

Write the following expression as a single quotient in which only positive exponents appear.

$$(x^2 + 1)^{1/2} + x \cdot \frac{1}{2}(x^2 + 1)^{-1/2} \cdot 2x$$

Solution $(x^2 + 1)^{1/2} + x \cdot \dfrac{1}{2}(x^2 + 1)^{-1/2} \cdot 2x = (x^2 + 1)^{1/2} + \dfrac{x^2}{(x^2 + 1)^{1/2}}$

$\qquad\qquad\qquad\qquad\qquad\qquad\qquad\qquad = \dfrac{(x^2 + 1)^{1/2}(x^2 + 1)^{1/2} + x^2}{(x^2 + 1)^{1/2}}$

$\qquad\qquad\qquad\qquad\qquad\qquad\qquad\qquad = \dfrac{(x^2 + 1) + x^2}{(x^2 + 1)^{1/2}}$

$\qquad\qquad\qquad\qquad\qquad\qquad\qquad\qquad = \dfrac{2x^2 + 1}{(x^2 + 1)^{1/2}}$

 Now Work PROBLEM 77

EXAMPLE 10   **Factoring an Expression Containing Rational Exponents**

Factor: $\dfrac{4}{3}x^{1/3}(2x + 1) + 2x^{4/3}$

Solution   We begin by writing $2x^{4/3}$ as a fraction with 3 as denominator.

$$\frac{4}{3}x^{1/3}(2x + 1) + 2x^{4/3} = \frac{4x^{1/3}(2x + 1)}{3} + \frac{6x^{4/3}}{3} = \frac{4x^{1/3}(2x + 1) + 6x^{4/3}}{3}$$

$\qquad\qquad\qquad\qquad\qquad\qquad\qquad\qquad\qquad\qquad$ ↑
$\qquad\qquad\qquad\qquad\qquad\qquad\qquad\qquad\qquad$ Add the two fractions

$$= \frac{2x^{1/3}[2(2x + 1) + 3x]}{3} = \frac{2x^{1/3}(7x + 2)}{3}$$

$\qquad\qquad\qquad\qquad$ ↑ $\qquad\qquad\qquad\qquad\qquad\qquad\qquad$ ↑
$\qquad\quad$ 2 and $x^{1/3}$ are common factors $\qquad\qquad\qquad$ Simplify

 Now Work PROBLEM 89

Historical Feature

The radical sign, $\sqrt{\ }$, was first used in print by Christoff Rudolff in 1525. It is thought to be the manuscript form of the letter r (for the Latin word *radix* = *root*), although this is not quite conclusively confirmed. It took a long time for $\sqrt{\ }$ to become the standard symbol for a square root and much longer to standardize $\sqrt[3]{\ }$, $\sqrt[4]{\ }$, $\sqrt[5]{\ }$, and so on. The indexes of the root were placed in every conceivable position, with

$$\sqrt[3]{8}, \quad \sqrt[3]{8}, \quad \text{and} \quad \underset{3}{\sqrt{}}8$$

all being variants for $\sqrt[3]{8}$. The notation $\sqrt{\ }\sqrt{16}$ was popular for $\sqrt[4]{16}$. By the 1700s, the index had settled where we now put it.

The bar on top of the present radical symbol, as follows,

$$\sqrt{a^2 + 2ab + b^2}$$

is the last survivor of the **vinculum,** a bar placed atop an expression to indicate what we would now indicate with parentheses. For example,

$$\overline{ab + c} = a(b + c)$$

A.10 Assess Your Understanding

'Are You Prepared?' *Answers are given at the end of these exercises. If you get a wrong answer, read the pages in* red.

1. $(-3)^2 =$ _____; $-3^2 =$ _____ (pp. A7–A8)

2. $\sqrt{16} =$ _____; $\sqrt{(-4)^2} =$ _____ (pp. A9–A10)

Concepts and Vocabulary

3. In the symbol $\sqrt[n]{a}$, the integer n is called the _____.

4. *True or False* $\sqrt[5]{-32} = -2$

5. We call $\sqrt[3]{a}$ the _____ _____ of a.

6. *True or False* $\sqrt[4]{(-3)^4} = -3$

Skill Building

In Problems 7–42, simplify each expression. Assume that all variables are positive when they appear.

7. $\sqrt[3]{27}$

8. $\sqrt[4]{16}$

9. $\sqrt[3]{-8}$

10. $\sqrt[3]{-1}$

11. $\sqrt{8}$

12. $\sqrt[3]{54}$

13. $\sqrt[3]{-8x^4}$

14. $\sqrt[4]{48x^5}$

15. $\sqrt[4]{x^{12}y^8}$

16. $\sqrt[5]{x^{10}y^5}$

17. $\sqrt[4]{\dfrac{x^9 y^7}{xy^3}}$

18. $\sqrt[3]{\dfrac{3xy^2}{81x^4 y^2}}$

19. $\sqrt{36x}$

20. $\sqrt{9x^5}$

21. $\sqrt{3x^2}\,\sqrt{12x}$

22. $\sqrt{5x}\,\sqrt{20x^3}$

23. $\left(\sqrt{5}\,\sqrt[3]{9}\right)^2$

24. $\left(\sqrt[3]{3}\,\sqrt{10}\right)^4$

25. $\left(3\sqrt{6}\right)\left(2\sqrt{2}\right)$

26. $\left(5\sqrt{8}\right)\left(-3\sqrt{3}\right)$

27. $3\sqrt{2} + 4\sqrt{2}$

28. $6\sqrt{5} - 4\sqrt{5}$

29. $-\sqrt{18} + 2\sqrt{8}$

30. $2\sqrt{12} - 3\sqrt{27}$

31. $\left(\sqrt{3} + 3\right)\left(\sqrt{3} - 1\right)$

32. $\left(\sqrt{5} - 2\right)\left(\sqrt{5} + 3\right)$

33. $5\sqrt[3]{2} - 2\sqrt[3]{54}$

34. $9\sqrt[3]{24} - \sqrt[3]{81}$

35. $\left(\sqrt{x} - 1\right)^2$

36. $\left(\sqrt{x} + \sqrt{5}\right)^2$

37. $\sqrt[3]{16x^4} - \sqrt[3]{2x}$

38. $\sqrt[4]{32x} + \sqrt[4]{2x^5}$

39. $\sqrt{8x^3} - 3\sqrt{50x}$

40. $3x\sqrt{9y} + 4\sqrt{25y}$

41. $\sqrt[3]{16x^4 y} - 3x\sqrt[3]{2xy} + 5\sqrt[3]{-2xy^4}$

42. $8xy - \sqrt{25x^2 y^2} + \sqrt[3]{8x^3 y^3}$

In Problems 43–54, rationalize the denominator of each expression. Assume that all variables are positive when they appear.

43. $\dfrac{1}{\sqrt{2}}$

44. $\dfrac{2}{\sqrt{3}}$

45. $\dfrac{-\sqrt{3}}{\sqrt{5}}$

46. $\dfrac{-\sqrt{3}}{\sqrt{8}}$

47. $\dfrac{\sqrt{3}}{5 - \sqrt{2}}$

48. $\dfrac{\sqrt{2}}{\sqrt{7} + 2}$

49. $\dfrac{2 - \sqrt{5}}{2 + 3\sqrt{5}}$

50. $\dfrac{\sqrt{3} - 1}{2\sqrt{3} + 3}$

51. $\dfrac{5}{\sqrt[3]{2}}$

52. $\dfrac{-2}{\sqrt[3]{9}}$

53. $\dfrac{\sqrt{x+h}-\sqrt{x}}{\sqrt{x+h}+\sqrt{x}}$

54. $\dfrac{\sqrt{x+h}+\sqrt{x-h}}{\sqrt{x+h}-\sqrt{x-h}}$

In Problems 55–66, simplify each expression.

55. $8^{2/3}$

56. $4^{3/2}$

57. $(-27)^{1/3}$

58. $16^{3/4}$

59. $16^{3/2}$

60. $25^{3/2}$

61. $9^{-3/2}$

62. $16^{-3/2}$

63. $\left(\dfrac{9}{8}\right)^{3/2}$

64. $\left(\dfrac{27}{8}\right)^{2/3}$

65. $\left(\dfrac{8}{9}\right)^{-3/2}$

66. $\left(\dfrac{8}{27}\right)^{-2/3}$

In Problems 67–74, simplify each expression. Express your answer so that only positive exponents occur. Assume that the variables are positive.

67. $x^{3/4}x^{1/3}x^{-1/2}$

68. $x^{2/3}x^{1/2}x^{-1/4}$

69. $(x^3y^6)^{1/3}$

70. $(x^4y^8)^{3/4}$

71. $\dfrac{(x^2y)^{1/3}(xy^2)^{2/3}}{x^{2/3}y^{2/3}}$

72. $\dfrac{(xy)^{1/4}(x^2y^2)^{1/2}}{(x^2y)^{3/4}}$

73. $\dfrac{(16x^2y^{-1/3})^{3/4}}{(xy^2)^{1/4}}$

74. $\dfrac{(4x^{-1}y^{1/3})^{3/2}}{(xy)^{3/2}}$

Applications and Extensions

In Problems 75–88, expressions that occur in calculus are given. Write each expression as a single quotient in which only positive exponents and/or radicals appear.

75. $\dfrac{x}{(1+x)^{1/2}}+2(1+x)^{1/2}$ $x>-1$

76. $\dfrac{1+x}{2x^{1/2}}+x^{1/2}$ $x>0$

77. $2x(x^2+1)^{1/2}+x^2\cdot\dfrac{1}{2}(x^2+1)^{-1/2}\cdot 2x$

78. $(x+1)^{1/3}+x\cdot\dfrac{1}{3}(x+1)^{-2/3}$ $x\neq -1$

79. $\sqrt{4x+3}\cdot\dfrac{1}{2\sqrt{x-5}}+\sqrt{x-5}\cdot\dfrac{1}{5\sqrt{4x+3}}$ $x>5$

80. $\dfrac{\sqrt[3]{8x+1}}{3\sqrt[3]{(x-2)^2}}+\dfrac{\sqrt[3]{x-2}}{24\sqrt[3]{(8x+1)^2}}$ $x\neq 2, x\neq -\dfrac{1}{8}$

81. $\dfrac{\sqrt{1+x}-x\cdot\dfrac{1}{2\sqrt{1+x}}}{1+x}$ $x>-1$

82. $\dfrac{\sqrt{x^2+1}-x\cdot\dfrac{2x}{2\sqrt{x^2+1}}}{x^2+1}$

83. $\dfrac{(x+4)^{1/2}-2x(x+4)^{-1/2}}{x+4}$ $x>-4$

84. $\dfrac{(9-x^2)^{1/2}+x^2(9-x^2)^{-1/2}}{9-x^2}$ $-3<x<3$

85. $\dfrac{\dfrac{x^2}{(x^2-1)^{1/2}}-(x^2-1)^{1/2}}{x^2}$ $x<-1$ or $x>1$

86. $\dfrac{(x^2+4)^{1/2}-x^2(x^2+4)^{-1/2}}{x^2+4}$

87. $\dfrac{\dfrac{1+x^2}{2\sqrt{x}}-2x\sqrt{x}}{(1+x^2)^2}$ $x>0$

88. $\dfrac{2x(1-x^2)^{1/3}+\dfrac{2}{3}x^3(1-x^2)^{-2/3}}{(1-x^2)^{2/3}}$ $x\neq -1, x\neq 1$

In Problems 89–98, expressions that occur in calculus are given. Factor each expression. Express your answer so that only positive exponents occur.

89. $(x+1)^{3/2}+x\cdot\dfrac{3}{2}(x+1)^{1/2}$ $x\geq -1$

90. $(x^2+4)^{4/3}+x\cdot\dfrac{4}{3}(x^2+4)^{1/3}\cdot 2x$

91. $6x^{1/2}(x^2 + x) - 8x^{3/2} - 8x^{1/2}$ $x \geq 0$

92. $6x^{1/2}(2x + 3) + x^{3/2} \cdot 8$ $x \geq 0$

93. $3(x^2 + 4)^{4/3} + x \cdot 4(x^2 + 4)^{1/3} \cdot 2x$

94. $2x(3x + 4)^{4/3} + x^2 \cdot 4(3x + 4)^{1/3}$

95. $4(3x + 5)^{1/3}(2x + 3)^{3/2} + 3(3x + 5)^{4/3}(2x + 3)^{1/2}$ $x \geq -\dfrac{3}{2}$

96. $6(6x + 1)^{1/3}(4x - 3)^{3/2} + 6(6x + 1)^{4/3}(4x - 3)^{1/2}$ $x \geq \dfrac{3}{4}$

97. $3x^{-1/2} + \dfrac{3}{2}x^{1/2}$ $x > 0$

98. $8x^{1/3} - 4x^{-2/3}$ $x \neq 0$

In Problems 99–106, use a calculator to approximate each radical. Round your answer to two decimal places.

99. $\sqrt{2}$ **100.** $\sqrt{7}$ **101.** $\sqrt[3]{4}$ **102.** $\sqrt[3]{-5}$

103. $\dfrac{2 + \sqrt{3}}{3 - \sqrt{5}}$ **104.** $\dfrac{\sqrt{5} - 2}{\sqrt{2} + 4}$ **105.** $\dfrac{3\sqrt[3]{5} - \sqrt{2}}{\sqrt{3}}$ **106.** $\dfrac{2\sqrt{3} - \sqrt[3]{4}}{\sqrt{2}}$

Applications and Extensions

107. Calculating the Amount of Gasoline in a Tank   A Shell station stores its gasoline in underground tanks that are right circular cylinders lying on their sides. See the illustration. The volume V of gasoline in the tank (in gallons) is given by the formula

$$V = 40h^2 \sqrt{\dfrac{96}{h} - 0.608}$$

where h is the height of the gasoline (in inches) as measured on a depth stick.

(a) If $h = 12$ inches, how many gallons of gasoline are in the tank?

(b) If $h = 1$ inch, how many gallons of gasoline are in the tank?

108. Inclined Planes   The final velocity v of an object in feet per second (ft/sec) after it slides down a frictionless inclined plane of height h feet is

$$v = \sqrt{64h + v_0^2}$$

where v_0 is the initial velocity (in ft/sec) of the object.

(a) What is the final velocity v of an object that slides down a frictionless inclined plane of height 4 feet? Assume that the initial velocity is 0.

(b) What is the final velocity v of an object that slides down a frictionless inclined plane of height 16 feet? Assume that the initial velocity is 0.

(c) What is the final velocity v of an object that slides down a frictionless inclined plane of height 2 feet with an initial velocity of 4 ft/sec?

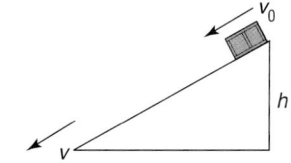

Problems 109–112 require the following information.

Period of a Pendulum   *The period T, in seconds, of a pendulum of length l, in feet, may be approximated using the formula*

$$T = 2\pi \sqrt{\dfrac{l}{32}}$$

In Problems 109–112, express your answer both as a square root and as a decimal.

109. Find the period T of a pendulum whose length is 64 feet.

110. Find the period T of a pendulum whose length is 16 feet.

111. Find the period T of a pendulum whose length is 8 inches.

112. Find the period T of a pendulum whose length is 4 inches.

Discussion and Writing

113. Give an example to show that $\sqrt{a^2}$ is not equal to a. Use it to explain why $\sqrt{a^2} = |a|$.

'Are You Prepared?' Answers

  1. 9; −9   **2.** 4; 4

The Limit of a Sequence; Infinite Series

The Limit of a Sequence

Consider the sequence $\{s_n\} = \left\{\dfrac{2n}{n+1}\right\}$. The terms of this sequence are

$$1, \frac{4}{3}, \frac{3}{2}, \frac{8}{5}, \frac{5}{3}, \ldots$$

Figure 1 shows the graph of the sequence.

Figure 1

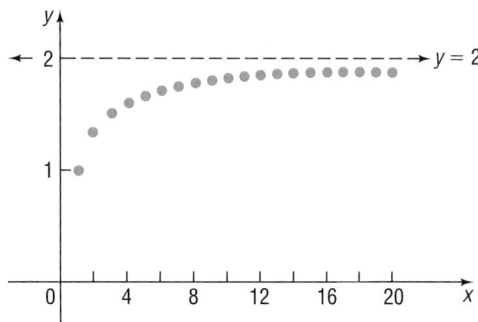

Notice that the points on the graph are getting closer to the line $y = 2$. To see why, consider the following:

$$\frac{2n}{n+1} = 2 \cdot \frac{n}{n+1}$$

$$= 2 \cdot \frac{1}{1 + \dfrac{1}{n}} \qquad \text{Divide the numerator and denominator by } n$$

As n gets larger and larger, the value of $\dfrac{1}{n}$ gets closer to zero so $\dfrac{2n}{n+1}$ gets closer to 2.

A graphing utility can be used to draw the same conclusion. See Table 1.

Table 1

n	$u(n)$
2	1.3333
5	1.6667
10	1.8182
50	1.9608
100	1.9802
1000	1.998
5000	1.9996

$u(n) = (2n)/(n+1)$

In calculus, we express this idea by saying that the sequence $\{s_n\}$ *converges* and we use limit notation to write

$$\lim_{n \to \infty} s_n = \lim_{n \to \infty} \frac{2n}{n+1} = 2$$

In general, we use the notation $\lim\limits_{n\to\infty} s_n = L$ to mean that as n gets larger and larger, the terms of the sequence $\{s_n\}$ get closer and closer to the number L. In such a case we say the sequence **converges** to L and call L the **limit** of the sequence.

EXAMPLE 1 **Finding the Limit of a Sequence**

Find the limit of each sequence:

(a) $\{a_n\} = \left\{\dfrac{6n^2}{n^2 - 4}\right\}$

(b) $\{b_n\} = \left\{\dfrac{3n^3 + 5n^2 - 2}{6n^3 + 10n + 8}\right\}$

Solution (a) We divide numerator and denominator by n^2. Then

$$\frac{6n^2}{n^2 - 4} = \frac{6}{1 - \dfrac{4}{n^2}}$$

As n gets larger and larger, the value of $\dfrac{4}{n^2}$ gets closer to 0. We conclude that

$$\lim_{n\to\infty} \frac{6n^2}{n^2 - 4} = 6$$

(b) We divide numerator and denominator by n^3. Then

$$\frac{3n^3 + 5n^2 - 2}{6n^3 + 10n + 8} = \frac{3 + \dfrac{5}{n} - \dfrac{2}{n^3}}{6 + \dfrac{10}{n^2} + \dfrac{8}{n^3}}$$

As n gets larger and larger, the terms $\dfrac{5}{n}, \dfrac{2}{n^3}, \dfrac{10}{n^2}$, and $\dfrac{8}{n^3}$ each get closer and closer to 0. We conclude that

$$\lim_{n\to\infty} \frac{3n^3 + 5n^2 - 2}{6n^3 + 10n + 8} = \frac{3}{6} = \frac{1}{2}$$

Some sequences do not converge. If a sequence does not converge, we say it is **divergent.**

EXAMPLE 2 **Examining a Divergent Sequence**

Discuss the sequence $\{s_n\} = \{2^n\}$.

Solution The terms of this sequence are

$$2, 4, 8, 32, 64, \ldots$$

Since each successive term is twice the preceding term, we conclude that the terms of the sequence are increasing without bound as n gets larger and larger. Since there is no number L that the terms get closer to, we conclude the sequence is divergent.

For the sequence of Example 2, since the terms of the sequence are increasing without bound, we write

$$\lim_{n\to\infty} s_n = \infty$$

A sequence can be divergent in other ways.

EXAMPLE 3	Examining Whether a Sequence Is Convergent or Divergent

Discuss the sequence $\{s_n\} = \begin{cases} 1 & \text{if } n \text{ is odd} \\ 2 & \text{if } n \text{ is even} \end{cases}$

Solution The terms of the sequence are

$$1,2,1,2,1,2,\ldots$$

As n gets larger and larger, the terms oscillate between 1 and 2, so the terms do not get closer to a single number L. We conclude the sequence is divergent.

EXAMPLE 4	Examining Whether a Sequence Is Convergent or Divergent

Determine whether the sequence $\{s_n\} = \left\{ \left(-\dfrac{1}{2} \right)^n \right\}$ converges or diverges. If it converges, find its limit.

Solution The terms of the sequence are

$$-\frac{1}{2}, \frac{1}{4}, -\frac{1}{8}, \frac{1}{16}, -\frac{1}{32}, \frac{1}{64}, \ldots$$

The terms alternate between being negative and being positive, but, as n gets larger and larger, the terms get closer to 0. Figure 2 illustrates this. We conclude the sequence converges. The limit of the sequence is 0.

Figure 2

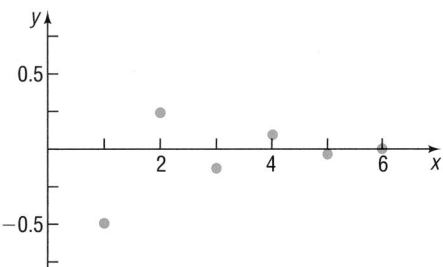

━━ **Now Work** PROBLEMS 9 AND 13

Infinite Series

Suppose you were asked to find the sum of an infinite collection of numbers. In particular, suppose you were asked to find the sum $\dfrac{1}{2} + \dfrac{1}{4} + \dfrac{1}{8} + \dfrac{1}{16} + \cdots$. To help find the answer, consider the square below in Figure 3.

Figure 3

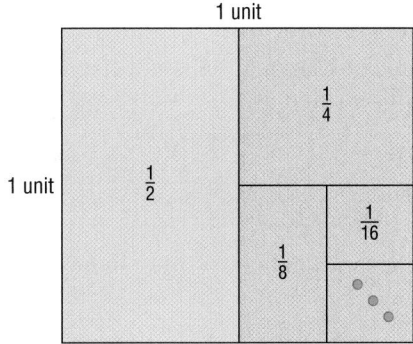

The square has each side of length 1 unit, so its area is 1 square unit. When we divide the square into two rectangles of equal area, each rectangle has an area of

$\frac{1}{2}$ square unit. Now divide the yellow rectangle into two smaller rectangles. If we continue this process indefinitely, we subdivide original square of area 1 unit, into rectangles of area $\frac{1}{2}, \frac{1}{4}, \frac{1}{8}, \frac{1}{16}$, and so forth. Adding up the areas of the rectangles, we find that,

$$1 = \underbrace{\frac{1}{2} + \frac{1}{4} + \frac{1}{8} + \frac{1}{16} + \cdots}$$

area of square = area of rectangles

Surprised?

Let's look at this result from an algebraic point of view by starting with the infinite sum

$$\frac{1}{2} + \frac{1}{4} + \frac{1}{8} + \frac{1}{16} + \cdots \tag{1}$$

One way we might add this up is by the use of *partial sums* to see whether a pattern develops. The first five partial sums are

$$\frac{1}{2} = 0.5 \qquad \text{First partial sum}$$

$$\frac{1}{2} + \frac{1}{4} = 0.75 \qquad \text{Second partial sum}$$

$$\frac{1}{2} + \frac{1}{4} + \frac{1}{8} = \frac{7}{8} = 0.875 \qquad \text{Third partial sum}$$

$$\frac{1}{2} + \frac{1}{4} + \frac{1}{8} + \frac{1}{16} = \frac{15}{16} = 0.9375 \qquad \text{Fourth partial sum}$$

$$\frac{1}{2} + \frac{1}{4} + \frac{1}{8} + \frac{1}{16} + \frac{1}{32} = \frac{31}{32} = 0.96875 \qquad \text{Fifth partial sum}$$

Each of these sums uses more of the terms in (1) and each sum seems to be getting closer to 1.

DEFINITION

If $a_1, a_2, \ldots, a_n, \ldots$ is some infinite collection of numbers, the expression

$$\sum_{k=1}^{\infty} a_k = a_1 + a_2 + \cdots + a_n + \cdots$$

is called an **infinite series.** The numbers $a_1, a_2, \ldots, a_n, \ldots$ are called **terms,** and the number a_n is called the **nth term** or **general term.**

The index of summation is not fixed for a given series. For example, the series in (1) may be written as

$$\frac{1}{2} + \frac{1}{2^2} + \frac{1}{2^3} + \cdots + \frac{1}{2^n} + \cdots = \sum_{k=1}^{\infty} \frac{1}{2^k}$$

This infinite series may be written in any of the following equivalent forms:

$$\sum_{k=1}^{\infty} \frac{1}{2}\left(\frac{1}{2^{k-1}}\right) \qquad \sum_{k=0}^{\infty} \frac{1}{2^{k+1}} \qquad \sum_{k=4}^{\infty} \frac{1}{2^{k-3}}$$

In most of our work, the index of summation will begin at 1.

To define the sum of an infinite series $\sum\limits_{k=1}^{\infty} a_k$, we make use of the sequence $\{S_n\}$ defined by

$$S_1 = a_1$$

$$S_2 = a_1 + a_2 = \sum_{k=1}^{2} a_k$$

$$\cdot$$
$$\cdot$$
$$\cdot$$

$$S_n = a_1 + a_2 + \cdots + a_n = \sum_{k=1}^{n} a_k$$

The sequence $\{S_n\}$ is called the **sequence of partial sums** of the series $\sum\limits_{k=1}^{\infty} a_k$.

For example, consider again the series

$$\sum_{k=1}^{\infty} \frac{1}{2^k} = \frac{1}{2} + \frac{1}{2^2} + \frac{1}{2^3} + \frac{1}{2^4} + \cdots = \frac{1}{2} + \frac{1}{4} + \frac{1}{8} + \frac{1}{16} + \cdots$$

As it turns out, the partial sums can be rewritten as 1 minus a power of $\frac{1}{2}$, as follows:

$$S_1 = \frac{1}{2} = 1 - \frac{1}{2}$$

$$S_2 = \frac{1}{2} + \frac{1}{4} = \frac{3}{4} = 1 - \frac{1}{4} = 1 - \frac{1}{2^2}$$

$$S_3 = \frac{1}{2} + \frac{1}{4} + \frac{1}{8} = \frac{7}{8} = 1 - \frac{1}{8} = 1 - \frac{1}{2^3}$$

$$S_4 = \frac{15}{16} = 1 - \frac{1}{16} = 1 - \frac{1}{2^4}$$

$$S_5 = \frac{31}{32} = 1 - \frac{1}{2^5}$$

$$\vdots$$

$$S_n = 1 - \frac{1}{2^n}$$

The nth partial sum is $S_n = 1 - \frac{1}{2^n}$. As n gets larger and larger, the sequence $\{S_n\}$ of partial sums approaches a fixed value or *limit*–namely,

$$\lim_{n \to \infty} S_n = \lim_{n \to \infty} \left(1 - \frac{1}{2^n}\right) = 1$$

We call this limit the *sum of the series,* and write

$$\sum_{k=1}^{\infty} \frac{1}{2^k} = \frac{1}{2} + \frac{1}{4} + \frac{1}{8} + \frac{1}{16} + \cdots = 1$$

DEFINITION

If the sequence $\{S_n\}$ of partial sums of an infinite series $\sum\limits_{k=1}^{\infty} a_k$ has a limit S, then the series **converges** and is said to have the **sum S**. That is, if $\lim\limits_{n \to \infty} S_n = S$, then

$$\sum_{k=1}^{\infty} a_k = a_1 + a_2 + \cdots + a_n + \cdots = S$$

An infinite series **diverges** if the sequence of partial sums diverges.

Geometric Series

DEFINITION

A special infinite series is the **geometric series**

$$\sum_{k=1}^{\infty} ar^{k-1} = a + ar + ar^2 + \cdots + ar^{n-1} + \cdots \quad r \neq 0 \qquad (2)$$

The first term in the series is a and the common ratio is r.

To determine the conditions for convergence of the geometric series, we examine the nth partial sum

$$S_n = a + ar + ar^2 + \cdots + ar^{n-1} \quad r \neq 0 \qquad (3)$$

If $r = 1$, $\sum_{k=1}^{\infty} a \cdot 1^{k-1} = a + a + a + \cdots + a + \cdots$ and the nth partial sum is

$$S_n = a + a + a + \cdots + a = na$$

In this case the sequence $\{S_n\}$ diverges (since $a \neq 0$, $\lim_{n \to \infty} S_n = \lim_{n \to \infty} (na) = \infty$), so the geometric series diverges.

If $r = -1$, the series becomes $\sum_{k=1}^{\infty} a(-1)^{k-1} = a - a + a - a + \cdots$ and the nth partial sum is

$$S_n = \begin{cases} 0 & \text{if } n \text{ is even} \\ a & \text{if } n \text{ is odd} \end{cases}$$

Since $a \neq 0$, the sequence $\{S_n\}$ diverges. We conclude that the geometric series diverges for $r = -1$.

Suppose that $r \neq 1$ and $r \neq -1$. To see what happens for other choices of r, $r \neq 0$, we multiply both sides of equation (3) by r, obtaining

$$rS_n = ar + ar^2 + ar^3 + \cdots + ar^n \qquad (4)$$

By subtracting (4) from the expression for S_n in (3), we have

$$S_n - rS_n = (a + ar + ar^2 + \cdots + ar^{n-1}) - (ar + ar^2 + ar^3 + \cdots + ar^n)$$
$$= a - ar^n$$
$$S_n(1 - r) = a(1 - r^n)$$

Since $r \neq 1$, we can express the nth partial sum of the geometric series as

$$S_n = \frac{a(1 - r^n)}{1 - r} = \frac{a - ar^n}{1 - r} = \frac{a}{1 - r} - \frac{ar^n}{1 - r}$$

Now

$$\lim_{n \to \infty} S_n = \lim_{n \to \infty} \left[\frac{a}{1 - r} - \frac{ar^n}{1 - r} \right]$$

The limit of a difference equals the difference of the limits.

$$= \lim_{n \to \infty} \frac{a}{1 - r} - \lim_{n \to \infty} \left[\frac{a}{1 - r} \cdot r^n \right]$$

The limit of a constant is the constant. The limit of the product of a constant and a function is the constant times the limit of the function.

$$= \frac{a}{1 - r} - \frac{a}{1 - r} \lim_{n \to \infty} r^n$$

If $-1 < r < 1$, then $\lim_{n \to \infty} r^n = 0$, so $\lim_{n \to \infty} S_n = \dfrac{a}{1 - r}$. For $-1 < r < 1$, the geometric series converges and its sum is $\dfrac{a}{1 - r}$.

If $r < -1$ or $r > 1$, then $\lim_{n \to \infty} r^n$ does not exist, so the geometric series diverges.

THEOREM **Sum of a Geometric Series**

If $-1 < r < 1$, the geometric series $\sum_{k=1}^{\infty} ar^{k-1}$ converges, and its sum is

$$\sum_{k=1}^{\infty} ar^{k-1} = \frac{a}{1-r}$$

If $r \leq -1$ or $r \geq 1$, the geometric series $\sum_{k=1}^{\infty} ar^{k-1}$ diverges.

Assess Your Understanding

Concepts and Vocabulary

1. If a sequence $\{s_n\}$ converges to L, we call L the _____ of the sequence.

2. If $a_1, a_2, \ldots, a_n, \cdots$ is some infinite collection of numbers, the expression

$$\sum_{k=1}^{\infty} a_k = a_1 + a_2 + \cdots + a_n + \cdots \text{ is}$$

called a(n) _____ _____.

3. If the sequence $\{S_n\}$ of partial sums of an infinite series $\sum_{k=1}^{\infty} a_k$ has a limit L, then the series _____.

4. An infinite series _____ if the sequence of partial sums diverges.

Skill Building

In Problems 5–28, determine whether each sequence converges or diverges. If it converges, find its limit.

5. $\{a_n\} = \left\{\dfrac{2n}{n+1}\right\}$

6. $\{a_n\} = \left\{\dfrac{5n}{2n+1}\right\}$

7. $\{b_n\} = \left\{\dfrac{5n^2}{4n+3}\right\}$

8. $\{b_n\} = \left\{\dfrac{n^2}{n+3}\right\}$

9. $\{b_n\} = \left\{\dfrac{2n^2 - 4n + 1}{4n^2 + 5}\right\}$

10. $\{c_n\} = \left\{\dfrac{4n^3 + 2n + 7}{8n^3 + n^2 - 2}\right\}$

11. $\{a_n\} = \left\{\dfrac{5n}{n^2+1}\right\}$

12. $\{a_n\} = \left\{\dfrac{12n^2}{n^3 - 3n + 1}\right\}$

13. $\{s_n\} = \{3^n\}$

14. $\{s_n\} = \{4^n\}$

15. $\{s_n\} = \left\{2\left(\dfrac{4}{5}\right)^n\right\}$

16. $\{s_n\} = \left\{3\left(\dfrac{3}{4}\right)^n\right\}$

17. $\{b_n\} = \left\{3 - \dfrac{2}{n}\right\}$

18. $\{a_n\} = \left\{10 + \dfrac{1}{n}\right\}$

19. $\{c_n\} = \left\{4 + \dfrac{(-1)^n}{n}\right\}$

20. $\{c_n\} = \left\{\dfrac{1 + (-1)^n}{n}\right\}$

21. $\{a_n\} = \left\{\dfrac{n + (-1)^n}{n}\right\}$

22. $\{b_n\} = \left\{\dfrac{2n^2 + (-1)^n}{n^2}\right\}$

23. $\{a_n\} = \left\{\dfrac{2^n}{n}\right\}$

24. $\{a_n\} = \left\{\dfrac{n}{e^n}\right\}$

25. $\{b_n\} = \left\{\sin\left(\dfrac{n\pi}{2}\right)\right\}$

26. $\{s_n\} = \left\{\cos\left(n\pi + \dfrac{\pi}{2}\right)\right\}$

27. $\{s_n\} = \{\cos(n\pi)\}$

28. $\{a_n\} = \left\{\sin\left(n\pi - \dfrac{\pi}{2}\right)\right\}$

In Problems 29–32, find the first five terms in the sequence of partial sums for each series.

29. $\sum_{k=1}^{\infty} \left(\dfrac{1}{3}\right)^{k-1}$

30. $\sum_{k=1}^{\infty} \left(\dfrac{1}{4}\right)^{k-1}$

31. $\sum_{k=1}^{\infty} k$

32. $\sum_{k=1}^{\infty} k^2$

Answers

CHAPTER 1 Graphs

1.1 Assess Your Understanding (page 14)

5. abscissa; ordinate **6.** quadrants **7.** midpoint **8.** F **9.** F **10.** T

11. (a) Quadrant II   **(d)** Quadrant I
(b) Positive x-axis   **(e)** Negative y-axis
(c) Quadrant III   **(f)** Quadrant IV

12. (a) Quadrant I   **(d)** Quadrant I
(b) Quadrant III   **(e)** Positive y-axis
(c) Quadrant II   **(f)** Negative x-axis

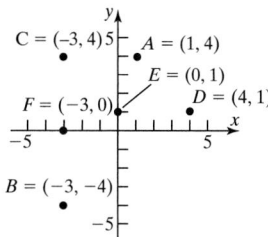

13. The points will be on a vertical line that is 2 units to the right of the y-axis.

14. The points will be on a horizontal line that is 3 units above the x-axis.

15. $(-1, 4)$; Quadrant II
16. $(3, 4)$; Quadrant I
17. $(3, 1)$; Quadrant I
18. $(-6, -4)$; Quadrant III
19. $X\min = -11, X\max = 5, X\mathrm{scl} = 1,$
$Y\min = -3, Y\max = 6, Y\mathrm{scl} = 1$
20. $X\min = -3, X\max = 7, X\mathrm{scl} = 1,$
$Y\min = -4, Y\max = 9, Y\mathrm{scl} = 1$
21. $X\min = -30, X\max = 50, X\mathrm{scl} = 10,$
$Y\min = -90, Y\max = 50, Y\mathrm{scl} = 10$

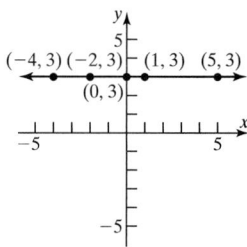

22. $X\min = -90, X\max = 30, X\mathrm{scl} = 10, Y\min = -50, Y\max = 70, Y\mathrm{scl} = 10$ **23.** $X\min = -10, X\max = 110, X\mathrm{scl} = 10, Y\min = -10,$
$Y\max = 160, Y\mathrm{scl} = 10$ **24.** $X\min = -20, X\max = 110, X\mathrm{scl} = 10, Y\min = -10, Y\max = 60, Y\mathrm{scl} = 10$ **25.** $X\min = -6, X\max = 6,$
$X\mathrm{scl} = 2, Y\min = -4, Y\max = 4, Y\mathrm{scl} = 2$ **26.** $X\min = -3, X\max = 3, X\mathrm{scl} = 1, Y\min = -2, Y\max = 2, Y\mathrm{scl} = 1$ **27.** $X\min = -6,$
$X\max = 6, X\mathrm{scl} = 2, Y\min = -1, Y\max = 3, Y\mathrm{scl} = 1$ **28.** $X\min = -9, X\max = 9, X\mathrm{scl} = 3, Y\min = -12, Y\max = 4, Y\mathrm{scl} = 4$
29. $X\min = 3, X\max = 9, X\mathrm{scl} = 1, Y\min = 2, Y\max = 10, Y\mathrm{scl} = 2$ **30.** $X\min = -22, X\max = -10, X\mathrm{scl} = 2, Y\min = 4,$
$Y\max = 8, Y\mathrm{scl} = 1$ **31.** $\sqrt{5}$ **32.** $\sqrt{5}$ **33.** $\sqrt{10}$ **34.** $\sqrt{10}$ **35.** $2\sqrt{17}$ **36.** 5 **37.** 20 **38.** 10 **39.** $\sqrt{53}$ **40.** $5\sqrt{5}$
41. $\sqrt{5.49} \approx 2.34$ **42.** $\sqrt{3.38} \approx 1.84$ **43.** $\sqrt{a^2 + b^2}$ **44.** $\sqrt{2}|a|$ **45.** $4\sqrt{10}$ **46.** $\sqrt{149}$ **47.** $2\sqrt{65}$ **48.** $\sqrt{205}$

49. $d(A, B) = \sqrt{13}$
$d(B, C) = \sqrt{13}$
$d(A, C) = \sqrt{26}$
$(\sqrt{13})^2 + (\sqrt{13})^2 = (\sqrt{26})^2$
Area $= \dfrac{13}{2}$ square units

50. $d(A, C) = 20$
$d(A, B) = 10\sqrt{2}$
$d(B, C) = 10\sqrt{2}$
$(10\sqrt{2})^2 + (10\sqrt{2})^2 = 20^2$
Area $= 100$ square units

51. $d(A, B) = \sqrt{130}$
$d(B, C) = \sqrt{26}$
$d(A, C) = 2\sqrt{26}$
$(\sqrt{26})^2 + (2\sqrt{26})^2 = (\sqrt{130})^2$
Area $= 26$ square units

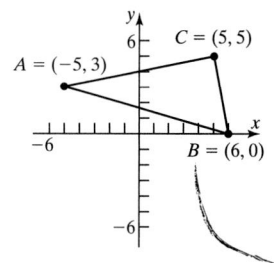

52. $d(A, B) = \sqrt{145}$
$d(A, C) = \sqrt{29}$
$d(B, C) = 2\sqrt{29}$
$(\sqrt{29})^2 + (2\sqrt{29})^2 = (\sqrt{145})^2$
Area = 29 square units

53. $d(A, B) = 4$
$d(A, C) = 5$
$d(B, C) = \sqrt{41}$
$4^2 + 5^2 = (\sqrt{41})^2$
Area = 10 square units

54. $d(A, B) = 4$
$d(A, C) = 2\sqrt{5}$
$d(B, C) = 2$
$4^2 + 2^2 = (2\sqrt{5})^2$
Area = 4 square units

55. $(4, 0)$ **56.** $(0, 2)$ **57.** $(3, 3)$ **58.** $(6, 0)$ **59.** $(5, -1)$ **60.** $\left(-1, -\dfrac{1}{2}\right)$ **61.** $(0.55, 1.2)$ **62.** $(0.35, 1.95)$ **63.** $\left(\dfrac{a}{2}, \dfrac{b}{2}\right)$

64. $\left(\dfrac{a}{2}, \dfrac{a}{2}\right)$ **65.** $(0, 0)$ is on the graph. **66.** $(0, 0)$ and $(1, -1)$ are on the graph. **67.** $(0, 3)$ is on the graph.

68. $(0, 1)$ and $(-1, 0)$ are on the graph. **69.** $(0, 2)$ and $(\sqrt{2}, \sqrt{2})$ are on the graph. **70.** $(0, 1)$ and $(2, 0)$ are on the graph.

71. $(-1, 0), (1, 0)$ **72.** $(0, 1)$ **73.** $\left(-\dfrac{\pi}{2}, 0\right), (0, 1), \left(\dfrac{\pi}{2}, 0\right)$ **74.** $(-2, 0), (0, -3), (2, 0)$ **75.** $(0, 2), (1, 0), (0, -2)$

76. $(-2, 0), (0, -2), (2, 0), (0, 2)$ **77.** $(-4, 0), (-1, 0), (0, -3), (4, 0)$ **78.** $(-2, 0), (0, 3), (2, 0)$

79.

80.

81.

82.

83.

84.

85.

86.

87.

88.

89.

90.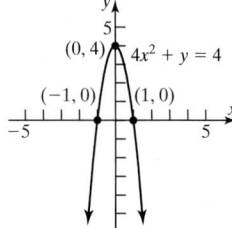

91. x-intercept: 6.5
y-intercept: -13

92. x-intercept: 4.67
y-intercept: 14

93. x-intercepts: $-2.74, 2.74$
y-intercept: -15

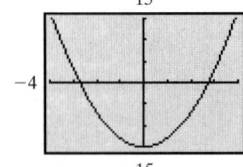

94. x-intercepts: $-2.52, 2.52$
y-intercept: 19

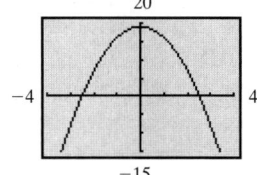

95. *x*-intercept: 14.33
y-intercept: −21.5

96. *x*-intercept: 20.5
y-intercept: 16.4

97. *x*-intercepts: −2.72, 2.72
y-intercept: 12.33

98. *x*-intercepts: −4.18, 4.18
y-intercept: −11.67

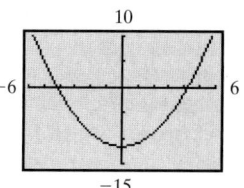

99. $\sqrt{17}; 2\sqrt{5}; \sqrt{29}$ **100.** Two triangles are possible. The third vertex is $(2\sqrt{3}, 2)$ or $(-2\sqrt{3}, 2)$. **101.** $d(P_1, P_2) = 6; d(P_2, P_3) = 4;$
$d(P_1, P_3) = 2\sqrt{13};$ right triangle **102.** $d(P_1, P_2) = \sqrt{53}; d(P_2, P_3) = \sqrt{53}; d(P_1, P_3) = \sqrt{106};$ isosceles right triangle **103.** $d(P_1, P_2) = 2\sqrt{17};$
$d(P_2, P_3) = \sqrt{34}; d(P_1, P_3) = \sqrt{34};$ isosceles right triangle **104.** $d(P_1, P_2) = 5\sqrt{5}; d(P_2, P_3) = 10; d(P_1, P_3) = 5;$ right triangle
105. $90\sqrt{2} \approx 127.28$ ft **106.** $60\sqrt{2} \approx 84.85$ ft **107. (a)** $(90, 0), (90, 90), (0, 90)$ **(b)** $5\sqrt{2161} \approx 232.43$ ft **(c)** $30\sqrt{149} \approx 366.20$ ft
108. (a) $(60, 0), (60, 60), (0, 60)$ **(b)** $40\sqrt{10} \approx 126.49$ ft **(c)** $20\sqrt{185} \approx 272.03$ ft **109.** $d = 50t$ **110.** $d = \sqrt{10,000 + 484t^2}$ **111. (a)** $(2.65, 1.6)$
(b) ≈ 1.285 units **112.** \$258 billion **113.** \$17,630.50 **114. (a)** $(5, 3)$ **(b)** $(0, 13)$ **115.** $B = (5, -2)$ **116. (a)** $y = \sqrt{x^2}$ and $y = |x|$ have the same
graph. **(b)** $\sqrt{x^2} = |x|$ **(c)** $x \geq 0$ for $y = (\sqrt{x})^2$, while x can be any real number for $y = x$. **(d)** $y \geq 0$ for $y = \sqrt{x^2}$

1.2 Assess Your Understanding (page 23)

3. $y = 0$ **4.** *y*-axis **5.** 4 **6.** $(-3, 4)$ **7.** T **8.** F

9. $(-2, 0), (0, 2)$

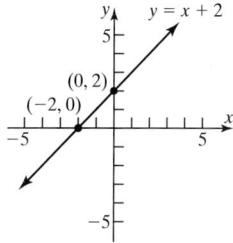

10. $(6, 0), (0, -6)$

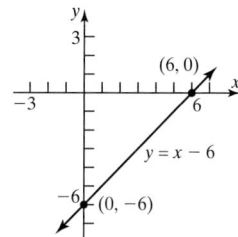

11. $(-4, 0), (0, 8)$

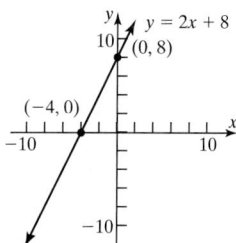

12. $(3, 0), (0, -9)$

13. $(-1, 0), (1, 0), (0, -1)$

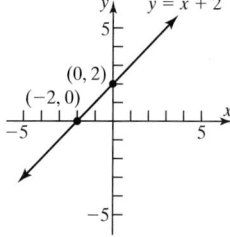

14. $(-3, 0), (3, 0), (0, -9)$

15. $(-2, 0), (2, 0), (0, 4)$

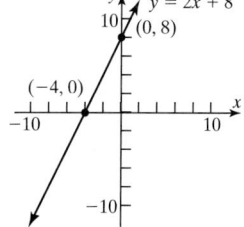

16. $(-1, 0), (1, 0), (0, 1)$

17. $(3, 0), (0, 2)$

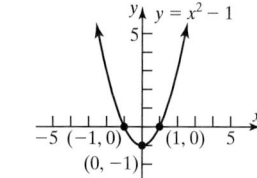

18. $(2, 0), (0, 5)$

19. $(-2, 0), (2, 0), (0, 9)$

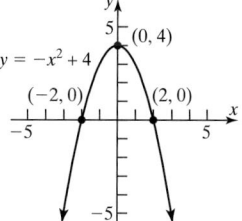

20. $(-1, 0), (1, 0), (0, 4)$

21.

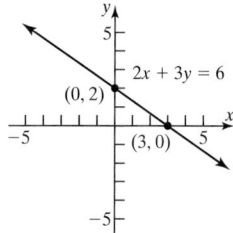

(b) = (−3, 4) (3, 4)
(c) = (−3, −4) (a) = (3, −4)

22.

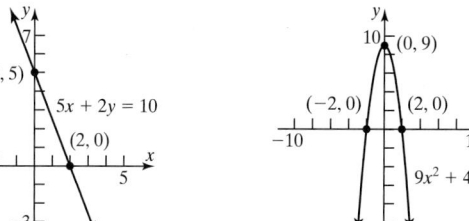

(b) = (−5, 3) (5, 3)
(c) = (−5, −3) (a) = (5, −3)

23.

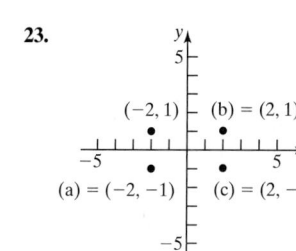

(−2, 1) (b) = (2, 1)
(a) = (−2, −1) (c) = (2, −1)

24.

25.

26.

27.

28.

29.

30.

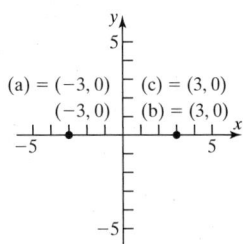

31. Symmetric with respect to the x-axis, the y-axis, and the origin   **32.** No symmetry   **33.** Symmetric with respect to the y-axis
34. Symmetric with respect to the y-axis   **35.** Symmetric with respect to the x-axis   **36.** Symmetric with respect to the x-axis, the y-axis, and the origin
37. Symmetric with respect to the origin   **38.** Symmetric with respect to the origin

39.

40.

41.

42.

43.

44.

45.

46.

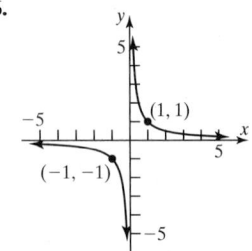

47. $(-4, 0)$, $(0, -2)$, $(0, 2)$; symmetric with respect to the x-axis   **48.** $(-9, 0)$, $(0, 3)$, $(0, -3)$; symmetric with respect to the x-axis   **49.** $(0, 0)$; symmetric with respect to the origin   **50.** $(0, 0)$; symmetric with respect to the origin   **51.** $(0, -9)$, $(3, 0)$, $(-3, 0)$; symmetric with respect to the y-axis
52. $(0, -8)$, $(-2, 0)$, $(2, 0)$; symmetric with respect to the y-axis   **53.** $(-2, 0)$, $(2, 0)$, $(0, -3)$, $(0, 3)$; symmetric with respect to the x-axis, y-axis, and origin
54. $(-1, 0)$, $(1, 0)$, $(0, -2)$, $(0, 2)$; symmetric with respect to the x-axis, y-axis, and origin   **55.** $(0, -9)$, $(3, 0)$, $(-3, 0)$, $(-1, 0)$; no symmetry
56. $(-2, 0)$, $(2, 0)$, $(0, -8)$; no symmetry   **57.** $(0, -4)$, $(4, 0)$, $(-4, 0)$; symmetric with respect to the y-axis   **58.** $(0, -2)$, $(-2, 0)$, $(2, 0)$; symmetric with respect to the y-axis   **59.** $(0, 0)$; symmetric with respect to the origin   **60.** $(2, 0)$, $(-2, 0)$; symmetric with respect to the origin   **61.** $(0, 0)$; symmetric with respect to the origin   **62.** no intercepts; symmetric with respect to the origin

63. **(a)** $(0, -5)$, $(-\sqrt{5}, 0)$, $(\sqrt{5}, 0)$
   (b) symmetric with respect to the y-axis
   (c)

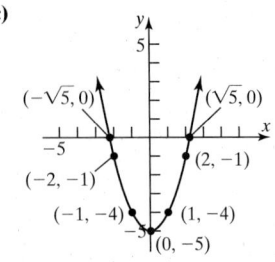

64. **(a)** $(0, -8)$, $(-2\sqrt{2}, 0)$, $(2\sqrt{2}, 0)$
   (b) symmetric with respect to the y-axis
   (c)

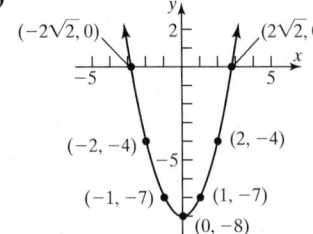

65. **(a)** $(-9, 0)$, $(0, -3)$, $(0, 3)$
   (b) symmetric with respect to the x-axis
   (c)

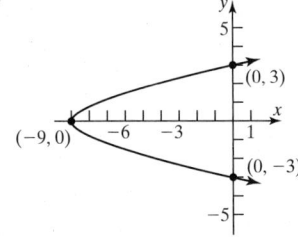

66. (a) $(4, 0), (0, -2), (0, 2)$

(b) symmetric with respect to the *x*-axis

(c)

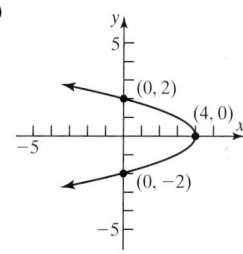

67. (a) $(0, 3), (0, -3), (-3, 0), (3, 0)$

(b) symmetric with respect to the *x*-axis, *y*-axis, and origin

(c)

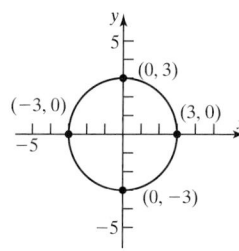

68. (a) $(0, 4), (0, -4), (-4, 0), (4, 0)$

(b) symmetric with respect to the *x*-axis, *y*-axis, and origin

(c)

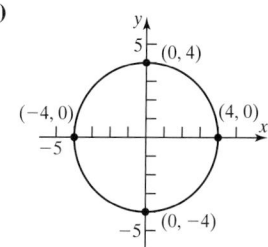

69. (a) $(0, 0), (-2, 0), (2, 0)$

(b) symmetric with respect to the origin

(c)

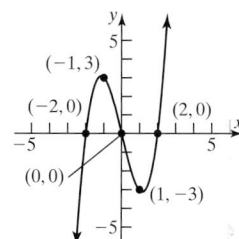

70. (a) $(0, 0), (-1, 0), (1, 0)$

(b) symmetric with respect to the origin

(c)

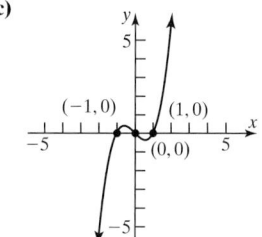

71. $(-1, -2)$

72. -6

73. 4

74. -2

75. (a) $(0, 0), (2, 0), (0, 1), (0, -1)$

(b) *x*-axis symmetry

76. (a) $\left(\dfrac{15}{8}, 0\right)$

(b) *x*-axis symmetry

1.3 Assess Your Understanding *(page 28)*

3. ZERO **4.** F **5.** $\{-2.21, 0.54, 1.68\}$ **6.** $\{-2.89, 0.13, 2.76\}$ **7.** $\{-1.55, 1.15\}$ **8.** $\{-1.11, 1.11\}$ **9.** $\{-1.12, 0.36\}$ **10.** $\{-0.85, 0.94\}$
11. $\{-2.69, -0.49, 1.51\}$ **12.** $\{-1.64, 0.31, 1.31, 3.02\}$ **13.** $\{-2.86, -1.34, 0.20, 1.00\}$ **14.** $\{-4.47, 0.80, 4.47\}$ **15.** No real solutions
16. No real solutions **17.** $\{-18\}$ **18.** $\left\{\dfrac{7}{5}\right\}$ **19.** $\{-4\}$ **20.** $\{-4\}$ **21.** $\left\{\dfrac{46}{5}\right\}$ **22.** $\{7\}$ **23.** $\{3\}$ **24.** $\{-1\}$ **25.** $\{2\}$ **26.** $\{3\}$
27. $\{-4, 7\}$ **28.** $\{-2, 9\}$ **29.** $\left\{-\dfrac{2}{3}, 2\right\}$ **30.** $\left\{-\dfrac{2}{5}, 3\right\}$ **31.** $\{-2, -1, 2\}$ **32.** $\{-3, -2, 3\}$ **33.** $\{15\}$ **34.** $\{11\}$ **35.** $\left\{-4, -\dfrac{1}{8}\right\}$ **36.** $\left\{-\dfrac{16}{21}, 3\right\}$

1.4 Assess Your Understanding *(page 40)*

1. undefined; 0 **2.** 3; 2 **3.** $y = b$; *y*-intercept **4.** T **5.** F **6.** T **7.** $m_1 = m_2$; *y*-intercepts; $m_1 m_2 = -1$ **8.** 2 **9.** $-\dfrac{1}{2}$ **10.** F

11. (a) Slope $= \dfrac{1}{2}$

(b) If *x* increases by 2 units, *y* will increase by 1 unit.

12. (a) Slope $= -\dfrac{1}{2}$

(b) If *x* increases by 2 units, *y* will decrease by 1 unit.

13. (a) Slope $= -\dfrac{1}{3}$

(b) If *x* increases by 3 units, *y* will decrease by 1 unit.

14. (a) Slope $= \dfrac{1}{3}$

(b) If *x* increases by 3 units, *y* will increase by 1 unit.

15. Slope $= -\dfrac{3}{2}$

16. Slope $= -2$

17. Slope $= -\dfrac{1}{2}$

18. Slope $= \dfrac{2}{3}$

19. Slope $= 0$

20. Slope $= 0$

21. Slope undefined

22. Slope undefined

23.

24.

25.

26.

27.

28.

29.

30.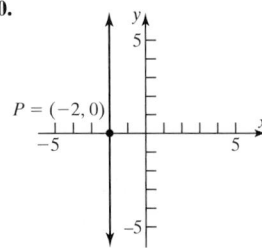

31. $(2, 6); (3, 10); (4, 14)$ **32.** $(-1, 5); (0, 7); (1, 9)$ **33.** $(4, -7); (6, -10); (8, -13)$ **34.** $(0, 6); (3, 10); (6, 14)$

35. $(-1, -5); (0, -7); (1, -9)$ **36.** $(5, 0); (6, -1); (7, -2)$ **37.** $x - 2y = 0$ or $y = \frac{1}{2}x$ **38.** $x + 2y = 0$ or $y = -\frac{1}{2}x$

39. $x + y = 2$ or $y = -x + 2$ **40.** $x - 3y = -4$ or $y = \frac{1}{3}x + \frac{4}{3}$ **41.** $2x - y = 3$ or $y = 2x - 3$ **42.** $x + y = 3$ or $y = -x + 3$

43. $x + 2y = 5$ or $y = -\frac{1}{2}x + \frac{5}{2}$ **44.** $x - y = -2$ or $y = x + 2$ **45.** $3x - y = -9$ or $y = 3x + 9$ **46.** $2x - y = 11$ or $y = 2x - 11$

47. $2x + 3y = -1$ or $y = -\frac{2}{3}x - \frac{1}{3}$ **48.** $x - 2y = 1$ or $y = \frac{1}{2}x - \frac{1}{2}$ **49.** $x - 2y = -5$ or $y = \frac{1}{2}x + \frac{5}{2}$ **50.** $x - 5y = -23$ or $y = \frac{1}{5}x + \frac{23}{5}$

51. $3x + y = 3$ or $y = -3x + 3$ **52.** $2x + y = -2$ or $y = -2x - 2$ **53.** $x - 2y = 2$ or $y = \frac{1}{2}x - 1$ **54.** $x - y = -4$ or $y = x + 4$

55. $x = 2$; no slope–intercept form   **56.** $x = 3$; no slope–intercept form   **57.** $y = 2$ **58.** $x = 4$; no slope–intercept form

59. $2x - y = -4$ or $y = 2x + 4$ **60.** $3x + y = -1$ or $y = -3x - 1$ **61.** $2x - y = 0$ or $y = 2x$ **62.** $x - 2y = 0$ or $y = \frac{1}{2}x$

63. $x = 4$; no slope–intercept form   **64.** $y = 2$ **65.** $2x + y = 0$ or $y = -2x$ **66.** $x + 2y = -3$ or $y = -\frac{1}{2}x - \frac{3}{2}$ **67.** $x - 2y = -3$ or $y = \frac{1}{2}x + \frac{3}{2}$

68. $2x + y = 4$ or $y = -2x + 4$ **69.** $y = 4$ **70.** $x = 3$; no slope–intercept form

71. Slope $= 2$; y-intercept $= 3$

72. Slope $= -3$; y-intercept $= 4$

73. Slope $= 2$; y-intercept $= -2$

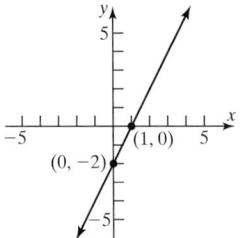

74. Slope $= -\frac{1}{3}$; y-intercept $= 2$

75. Slope $= \frac{1}{2}$; y-intercept $= 2$

76. Slope $= 2$; y-intercept $= \frac{1}{2}$

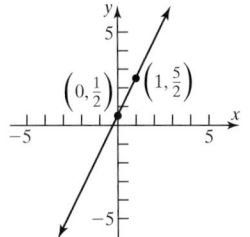

77. Slope $= -\dfrac{1}{2}$; y-intercept $= 2$

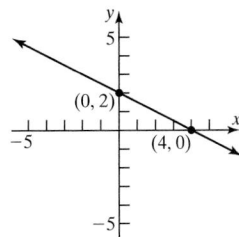

78. Slope $= \dfrac{1}{3}$; y-intercept $= 2$

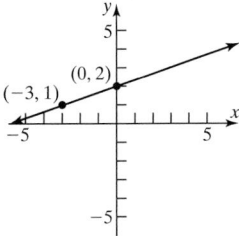

79. Slope $= \dfrac{2}{3}$; y-intercept $= -2$

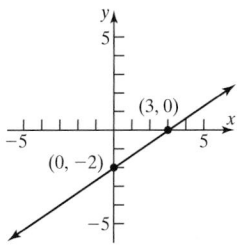

80. Slope $= -\dfrac{3}{2}$; y-intercept $= 3$

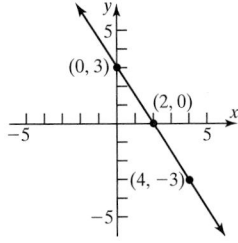

81. Slope $= -1$; y-intercept $= 1$

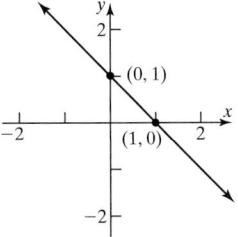

82. Slope $= 1$; y-intercept $= -2$

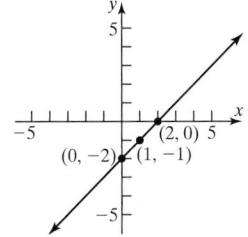

83. Slope undefined; no y-intercept

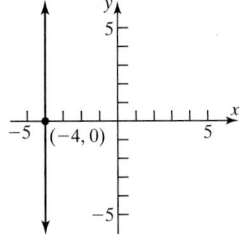

84. Slope $= 0$; y-intercept $= -1$

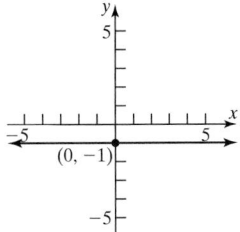

85. Slope $= 0$; y-intercept $= 5$

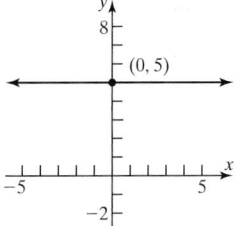

86. Slope undefined; no y-intercept

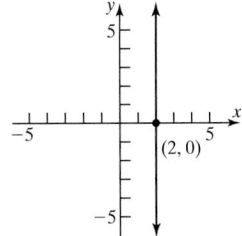

87. Slope $= 1$; y-intercept $= 0$

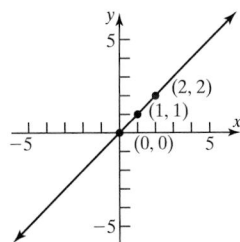

88. Slope $= -1$; y-intercept $= 0$

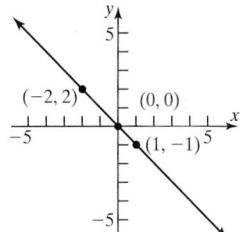

89. Slope $= \dfrac{3}{2}$; y-intercept $= 0$

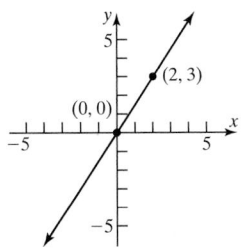

90. Slope $= -\dfrac{3}{2}$; y-intercept $= 0$

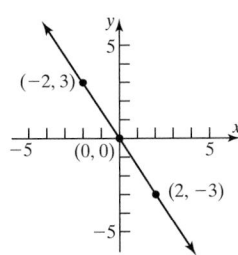

91. (a) x-intercept: 3; y-intercept: 2

(b)

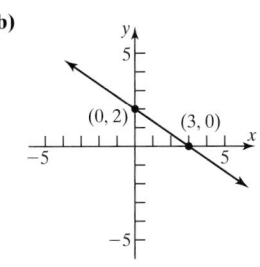

92. (a) x-intercept: 2; y-intercept: -3

(b)

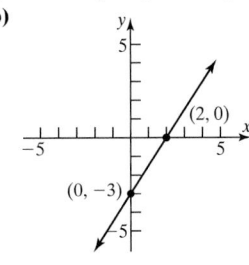

93. (a) x-intercept: -10; y-intercept: 8

(b)

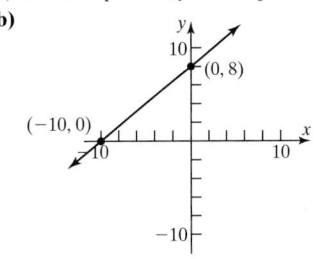

94. (a) x-intercept: 4; y-intercept: -6

(b)

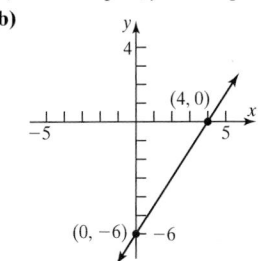

95. (a) x-intercept: 3; y-intercept: $\dfrac{21}{2}$

(b)

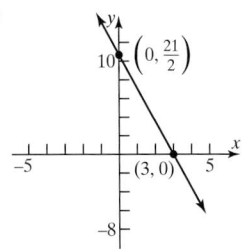

96. (a) x-intercept: $\dfrac{18}{5}$; y-intercept: 6

(b)

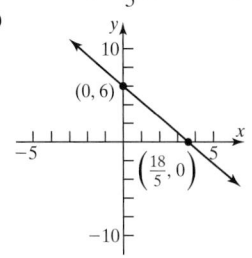

97. (a) x-intercept: 2; y-intercept: 3

(b)

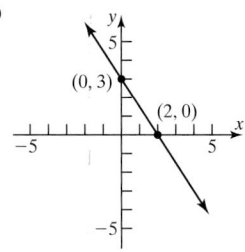

98. (a) x-intercept: 4; y-intercept: -6

(b)

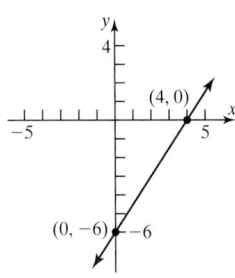

99. (a) x-intercept: 5; y-intercept: -2

(b)

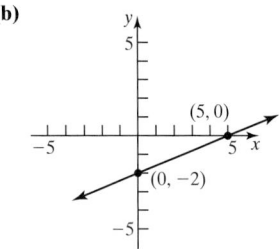

100. (a) x-intercept: -4; y-intercept: 3

(b)

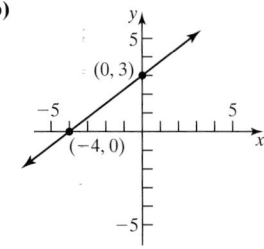

101. $y = 0$ **102.** $x = 0$ **103.** Parallel   **104.** Perpendicular   **105.** Neither   **106.** Neither   **107. (b)**   **108. (c)**   **109. (d)**   **110. (a)**

111. $P_1 = (-2, 5)$, $P_2 = (1, 3)$, $m_1 = -\dfrac{2}{3}$; $P_2 = (1, 3)$, $P_3 = (-1, 0)$, $m_2 = \dfrac{3}{2}$; because $m_1 m_2 = -1$, the lines are perpendicular and the points $(-2, 5)$, $(1, 3)$, and $(-1, 0)$ are the vertices of a right triangle; thus, the points P_1, P_2, and P_3 are the vertices of a right triangle.

112. $P_1 = (1, -1)$, $P_3 = (2, 2)$, $m = 3$; $P_2 = (4, 1)$, $P_4 = (5, 4)$, $m = 3$; $P_3 = (2, 2)$, $P_4 = (5, 4)$, $m = \dfrac{2}{3}$; $P_1 = (1, -1)$, $P_2 = (4, 1)$, $m = \dfrac{2}{3}$; opposite sides are parallel; the points are the vertices of a parallelogram.

113. $P_1 = (-1, 0)$, $P_2 = (2, 3)$, $m = 1$; $P_3 = (1, -2)$, $P_4 = (4, 1)$, $m = 1$; $P_1 = (-1, 0)$, $P_3 = (1, -2)$, $m = -1$; $P_2 = (2, 3)$, $P_4 = (4, 1)$, $m = -1$; opposite sides are parallel, and adjacent sides are perpendicular; the points are the vertices of a rectangle.

114. $P_1 = (0, 0)$, $P_2 = (1, 3)$, $m = 3$; $P_3 = (4, 2)$, $P_4 = (3, -1)$, $m = 3$; $P_2 = (1, 3)$, $P_3 = (4, 2)$, $m = -\dfrac{1}{3}$; $P_1 = (0, 0)$, $P_4 = (3, -1)$, $m = -\dfrac{1}{3}$; opposite sides are parallel; adjacent sides are perpendicular; $d(P_1, P_2) = \sqrt{10}$; $d(P_2, P_3) = \sqrt{10}$; $d(P_3, P_4) = \sqrt{10}$; $d(P_1, P_4) = \sqrt{10}$; all sides have equal lengths; the quadrilateral is a square.

115. $C = 0.20x + 29$; \$51.00; \$75.00   **116.** $C = 8x + 500$; \$3700; \$6420   **117.** $C = 0.53x + 1{,}070{,}000$ **118.** $S = 0.05x + 375$

119. (a) $C = 0.08275x + 7.58, 0 \le x \le 400$

(b)

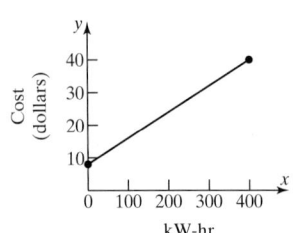

(c) \$15.86
(d) \$32.41
(e) Each additional kW-hr used adds \$0.08275 to the bill.

120. (a) $C = 0.1007x + 5.17, 0 \le x \le 1000$

(b)

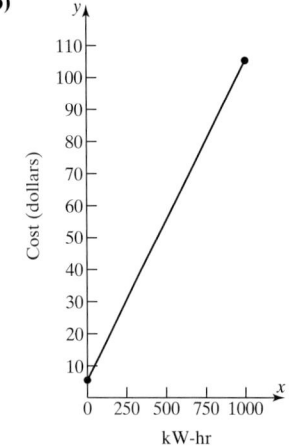

(c) \$25.31
(d) \$55.52
(e) Each additional kW-hr used adds \$0.1007 to the bill.

121. $^\circ C = \dfrac{5}{9}(^\circ F - 32)$; approximately $21.1^\circ C$ **122. (a)** $K = {^\circ C} + 273$ **(b)** $K = \dfrac{5}{9}{^\circ F} + \dfrac{2297}{9}$

123. (a) $y = -\dfrac{2}{25}x + 30$ **(b)** x-intercept: 375; the ramp meets the floor 375 in. (31.25 ft) from the base of the platform.

(c) The ramp does not meet design requirements. It has a run of 31.25 ft long.

(d) The only slope possible for the ramp to comply with the requirement is for it to drop 1 in. for every 12-in. run.

124. (a) $y = -\dfrac{20}{7}x + 42$ **(b)** $(0, 42), (14.7, 0)$

(c) The y-intercept represents the percentage of teens in 1998 who recently used cigarettes. The x-intercept represents the number of years after 1998 when 0% of teens recently used cigarettes.

(d) -18; the prediction is not reasonable because percents are not negative.

125. (a) $A = \dfrac{1}{5}x + 20{,}000$ **(b)** \$80,000 **(c)** Each additional box sold requires an additional \$0.20 in advertising.

126. Slope from (a, b) to (b, a) is $\dfrac{a - b}{b - a} = -1$. Slope of the line $y = x$ is 1. Since $-1 \cdot 1 = -1$, the line containing the points (a, b) and (b, a) is

perpendicular to the line $y = x$. The midpoint of (a, b) and $(b, a) = \left(\dfrac{a + b}{2}, \dfrac{b + a}{2}\right)$. Since $\dfrac{b + a}{2} = \dfrac{a + b}{2}$, the midpoint lies on the line $y = x$.

127. All have the same slope, 2; the lines are parallel.

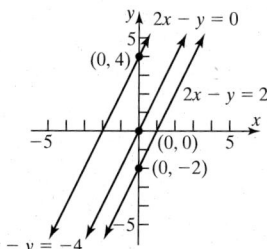

128. $m_1 m_2 = -1; d(A, B) = \sqrt{(m_2 - m_1)^2}; d(0, A) = \sqrt{1 + m_2^2}; d(0, B) = \sqrt{1 + m_1^2}$

$$[d(0, A)]^2 + [d(0, B)]^2 = \left(\sqrt{1 + m_2^2}\right)^2 + \left(\sqrt{1 + m_1^2}\right)^2$$
$$= 1 + m_2^2 + 1 + m_1^2$$
$$= m_2^2 + 2 + m_1^2$$
$$= m_2^2 - 2(-1) + m_1^2$$
$$= m_2^2 - 2(m_1 m_2) + m_1^2$$
$$= (m_2 - m_1)^2$$
$$= [d(A, B)]^2$$

Using the converse of the Pythagorean Theorem, the lines are perpendicular.

129. (b), (c), (e), (g) **130.** (a), (c), (g) **131.** (c) **132.** (d) **136.** No, consider vertical lines. **137.** No; no **138.** They are the same line.

139. They are the same line. **140.** No **141.** Yes, if the y-intercept is 0.

1.5 Assess Your Understanding *(page 49)*

3. F **4.** radius **5.** T **6.** F **7.** Center $(2, 1)$; radius $= 2$; $(x - 2)^2 + (y - 1)^2 = 4$ **8.** Center $(1, 2)$; radius $= 2$; $(x - 1)^2 + (y - 2)^2 = 4$

9. Center $\left(\dfrac{5}{2}, 2\right)$; radius $= \dfrac{3}{2}$; $\left(x - \dfrac{5}{2}\right)^2 + (y - 2)^2 = \dfrac{9}{4}$ **10.** Center $(1, 2)$; radius $= \sqrt{2}$; $(x - 1)^2 + (y - 2)^2 = 2$

11. $x^2 + y^2 = 4$;
$x^2 + y^2 - 4 = 0$

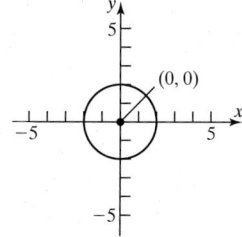

12. $x^2 + y^2 = 9$;
$x^2 + y^2 - 9 = 0$

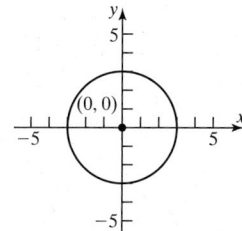

13. $x^2 + (y - 2)^2 = 4$;
$x^2 + y^2 - 4y = 0$

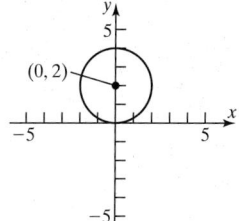

14. $(x - 1)^2 + y^2 = 9$;
$x^2 + y^2 - 2x - 8 = 0$

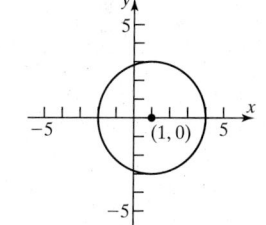

15. $(x - 4)^2 + (y + 3)^2 = 25$;
$x^2 + y^2 - 8x + 6y = 0$

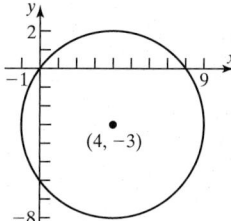

16. $(x - 2)^2 + (y + 3)^2 = 16$;
$x^2 + y^2 - 4x + 6y - 3 = 0$

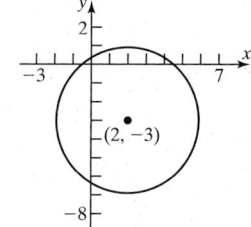

17. $(x + 2)^2 + (y - 1)^2 = 16$;
$x^2 + y^2 + 4x - 2y - 11 = 0$

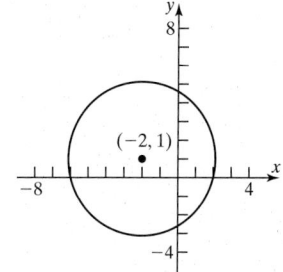

18. $(x + 5)^2 + (y + 2)^2 = 49$;
$x^2 + y^2 + 10x + 4y - 20 = 0$

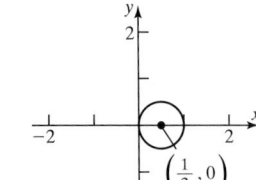

19. $\left(x - \frac{1}{2}\right)^2 + y^2 = \frac{1}{4}$;
$x^2 + y^2 - x = 0$

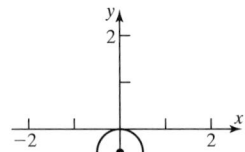

20. $x^2 + \left(y + \frac{1}{2}\right)^2 = \frac{1}{4}$;
$x^2 + y^2 + y = 0$

21. (a) $(h, k) = (0, 0); r = 2$
(b)

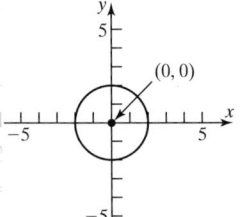

(c) $(\pm 2, 0); (0, \pm 2)$

22. (a) $(h, k) = (0, 1); r = 1$
(b)

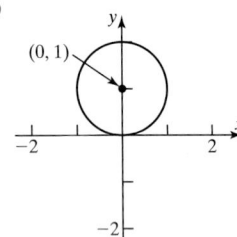

(c) $(0, 0); (0, 2)$

23. (a) $(h, k) = (3, 0); r = 2$
(b)

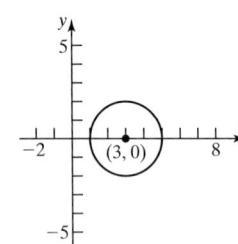

(c) $(1, 0); (5, 0)$

24. (a) $(h, k) = (-1, 1); r = \sqrt{2}$
(b)

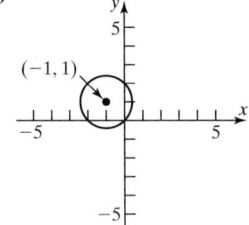

(c) $(0, 0); (0, 2); (-2, 0)$

25. (a) $(h, k) = (1, 2); r = 3$
(b)

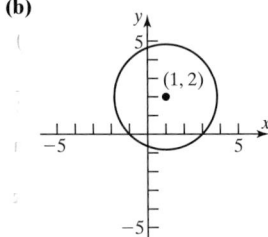

(c) $\left(1 \pm \sqrt{5}, 0\right); \left(0, 2 \pm 2\sqrt{2}\right)$

26. (a) $(h, k) = (-2, -1); r = 5$
(b)

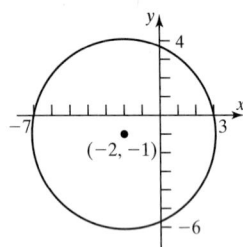

(c) $\left(-2 \pm 2\sqrt{6}, 0\right); \left(0, -1 \pm \sqrt{21}\right)$

27. (a) $(h, k) = (-2, 2); r = 3$
(b)

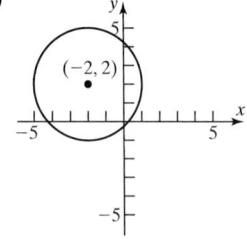

(c) $\left(-2 \pm \sqrt{5}, 0\right); \left(0, 2 \pm \sqrt{5}\right)$

28. (a) $(h, k) = (3, -1); r = 1$
(b)

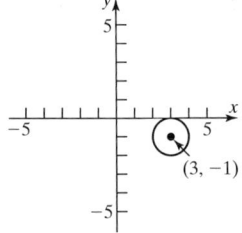

(c) $(3, 0)$

29. (a) $(h, k) = \left(\frac{1}{2}, -1\right); r = \frac{1}{2}$
(b)

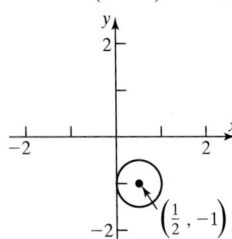

(c) $(0, -1)$

30. (a) $(h, k) = \left(-\frac{1}{2}, -\frac{1}{2}\right); r = 1$
(b)

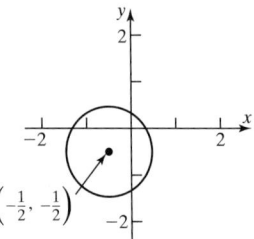

(c) $\left(\frac{-1 \pm \sqrt{3}}{2}, 0\right); \left(0, \frac{-1 \pm \sqrt{3}}{2}\right)$

31. (a) $(h, k) = (3, -2); r = 5$
(b)

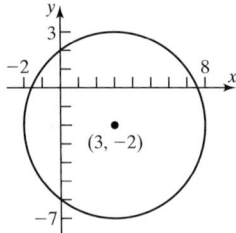

(c) $\left(3 \pm \sqrt{21}, 0\right); (0, -6), (0, 2)$

32. (a) $(h, k) = (-2, 0); r = \frac{\sqrt{2}}{2}$
(b)

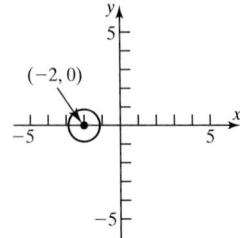

(c) $\left(-2 \pm \frac{\sqrt{2}}{2}, 0\right)$

33. (a) $(h, k) = (-2, 0); r = 2$
(b)

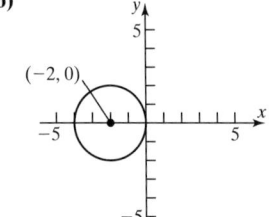

(c) $(0, 0), (-4, 0)$

34. (a) $(h, k) = (0, 2); r = 2$
(b)

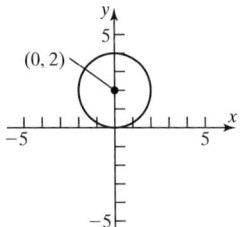

(c) $(0, 0), (0, 4)$

35. $x^2 + y^2 = 13$ **36.** $(x - 1)^2 + y^2 = 20$ **37.** $(x - 2)^2 + (y - 3)^2 = 9$ **38.** $(x + 3)^2 + (y - 1)^2 = 9$
39. $(x + 1)^2 + (y - 3)^2 = 5$ **40.** $(x - 2)^2 + (y - 2)^2 = 5$ **41.** $(x + 1)^2 + (y - 3)^2 = 1$ **42.** $(x - 4)^2 + (y + 2)^2 = 9$
43. (c) **44.** (d) **45.** (b) **46.** (a) **47.** 18 units^2 **48.** $36\pi - 72$ units^2 **49.** $x^2 + (y - 139)^2 = 15{,}625$ **50.** $x^2 + (y - 83.5)^2 = 5852.25$
51. $x^2 + y^2 + 2x + 4y - 4168.16 = 0$

52. (a) $x^2 + (mx + b)^2 = r^2$

$(1 + m^2)x^2 + 2mbx + b^2 - r^2 = 0$

One solution if and only if discriminant $= 0$

$(2mb)^2 - 4(1 + m^2)(b^2 - r^2) = 0$

$-4b^2 + 4r^2 + 4m^2r^2 = 0$

$r^2(1 + m^2) = b^2$

(b) $x = \dfrac{-2mb}{2(1 + m^2)} = \dfrac{-2mb}{2b^2/r^2} = \dfrac{-r^2m}{b}$

$y = m\left(\dfrac{-r^2m}{b}\right) + b = \dfrac{-r^2m^2}{b} + b = \dfrac{-r^2m^2 + b^2}{b} = \dfrac{r^2}{b}$

(c) Slope of tangent line $= m$

Slope of line joining center to point of tangency $= \dfrac{r^2/b}{-r^2m/b} = -\dfrac{1}{m}$

53. $\sqrt{2}x + 4y = 9\sqrt{2}$ **54.** $\sqrt{2}x + 4y = 11\sqrt{2} - 12$ **55.** $(1, 0)$ **56.** $x + 5y = -13$ **57.** $y = 2$ **58.** 3 **59.** (b), (c), (e), (g)
60. (b), (e), (g) **62.** The center is $(-3, 2)$.

Review Exercises (page 52)

1. (a) $2\sqrt{5}$ (b) $(2, 1)$ (c) $\dfrac{1}{2}$ (d) For each run of 2, there is a rise of 1. **2.** (a) $2\sqrt{13}$ (b) $(-2, 3)$ (c) $-\dfrac{3}{2}$

(d) For each run of 2, there is a rise of -3. **3.** (a) 5 (b) $\left(-\dfrac{1}{2}, 1\right)$ (c) $-\dfrac{4}{3}$ (d) For each run of 3, there is a rise of -4.

4. (a) $\sqrt{13}$ (b) $\left(-\dfrac{1}{2}, 3\right)$ (c) $\dfrac{2}{3}$ (d) For each run of 3, there is a rise of 2. **5.** (a) 12 (b) $(4, 2)$ (c) Undefined (d) No change in x

6. (a) 5 (b) $\left(-\dfrac{1}{2}, 4\right)$ (c) 0 (d) No change in y **7.** $(-4, 0), (0, 2), (0, 0), (0, -2), (2, 0)$

8.   ; $-3.87, 3.87$ **9.**   **10.**   **11.**

12.   **13.**   **14.**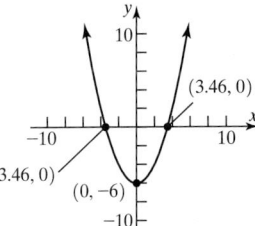

15. x-axis **16.** origin **17.** x-axis, y-axis, origin **18.** x-axis, y-axis, origin **19.** y-axis **20.** Origin **21.** no symmetry **22.** no symmetry

23.   **24.**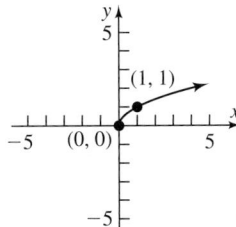

25. $\{-2.49, 0.66, 1.83\}$
26. $\{-1.53, -0.35, 1.88\}$
27. $\{-1.14, 1.64\}$
28. $\{-1.59, 1.59\}$

29. $2x + y = 5$ or $y = -2x + 5$ **30.** $y = 4$ **31.** $x = -3$; no slope–intercept form

    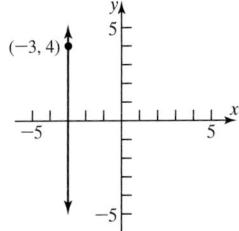

32. $5x + 2y = 10$ or $y = -\dfrac{5}{2}x + 5$

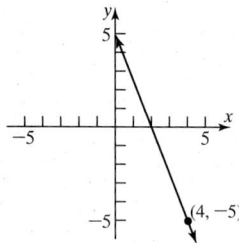

33. $x + 5y = -10$ or $y = -\dfrac{1}{5}x - 2$

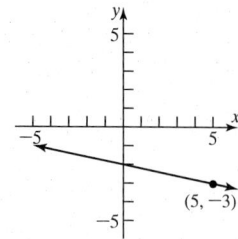

34. $5x + y = 11$ or $y = -5x + 11$

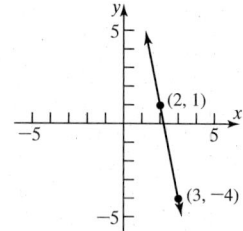

35. $2x - 3y = -19$ or $y = \dfrac{2}{3}x + \dfrac{19}{3}$

36. $x + y = -2$ or $y = -x - 2$

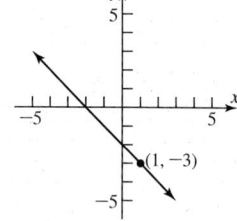

37. $x - y = 7$ or $y = x - 7$

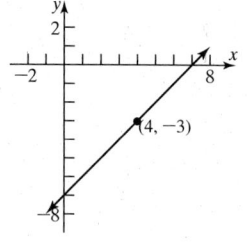

38. $x + 3y = 10$ or $y = -\dfrac{1}{3}x + \dfrac{10}{3}$

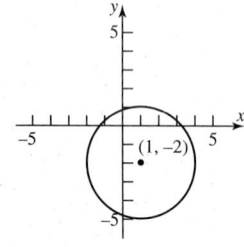

39. Slope $= -\dfrac{2}{3}$, y-intercept $= 6$

40. Slope $= \dfrac{7}{3}$, y-intercept $= -14$

41. Slope $= -\dfrac{1}{5}$, y-intercept $= 4$

42. Slope $= \dfrac{4}{3}$, y-intercept $= 4$

43. $(x + 2)^2 + (y - 3)^2 = 16$

44. $(x - 3)^2 + (y - 4)^2 = 16$

45. $(x + 1)^2 + (y + 2)^2 = 1$

46. $(x - 2)^2 + (y + 4)^2 = 9$

47. Center $(1, -2)$; radius $= 3$

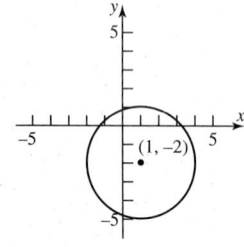

$\left(0, -2\pm2\sqrt{2}\right), \left(1\pm\sqrt{5}, 0\right)$

48. Center: $(-2, 2)$; radius $= 3$

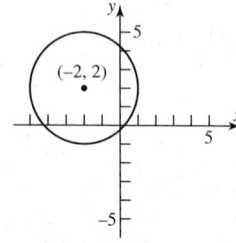

$\left(0, 2\pm\sqrt{5}\right), \left(-2\pm\sqrt{5}, 0\right)$

49. Center $(1, -2)$; radius $= \sqrt{5}$

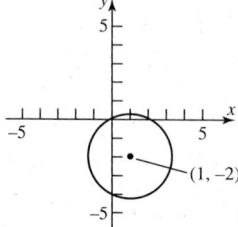

$(0, 0), (0, -4), (2, 0)$

50. Center: $(1, 0)$; radius $= 1$

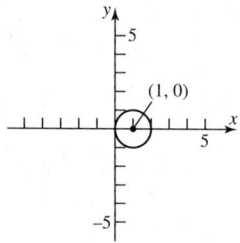

$(0, 0), (2, 0)$

51. $d(A, B) = \sqrt{13}$; $d(B, C) = \sqrt{13}$

52. **(a)** $d(A, B) = 2\sqrt{5}$; $d(B, C) = \sqrt{145}$; $d(A, C) = 5\sqrt{5}$; Since $d(A, B)^2 + d(A, C)^2 = d(B, C)^2$, by the converse of the Pythagorean Theorem, the points A, B, and C are vertices of a right triangle.

(b) Slope of $AB = -2$; Slope of $BC = \dfrac{1}{12}$; Slope of $AC = \dfrac{1}{2}$; Since $(-2)\left(\dfrac{1}{2}\right) = -1$, the lines AB and AC are perpendicular and hence form a right angle.

53. $m_{AB} = -1$; $m_{BC} = -1$

54. Let $D = (-1, 2)$. Then $d(A, D) = d(B, D) = d(C, D) = \sqrt{13}$.
A, B, and C lie on the circle $(x + 1)^2 + (y - 2)^2 = 13$ which has radius $\sqrt{13}$.

55. Center $(1, -2)$; radius $= 4\sqrt{2}$; $x^2 + y^2 - 2x + 4y - 27 = 0$

56. -4 and 8

57.

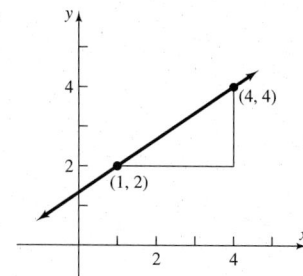

Chapter Test *(page 54)*

1. (a) $d = 10$ **(b)** $m = (1, 1)$

2.

3.

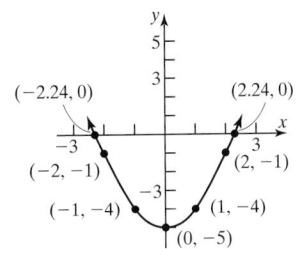

4. $-1, 0.5,$ and 1

5. -2.50 and 2.50

6. $-2.46, -0.24,$ and 1.70

7. (a) $m = -\dfrac{2}{3}$

(b) For every 3-unit change in x, y will change by -2 units.

8.

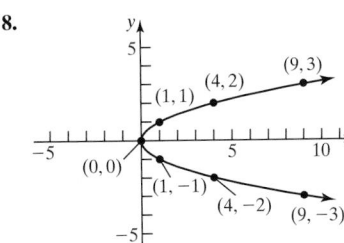

9. Intercepts: $(-3, 0), (3, 0), (0, 9)$; symmetric with respect to the y-axis

10. $y = -2x + 2$

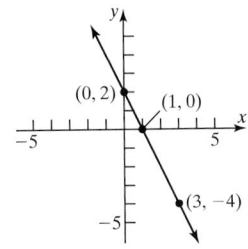

11. $x^2 + y^2 - 8x + 6y = 0$

12. Center: $(-2, 1)$; radius: 3

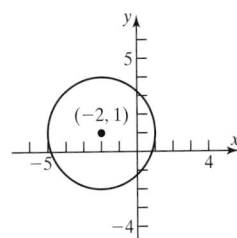

13. Parallel line: $y = -\dfrac{2}{3}x - \dfrac{1}{3}$;

perpendicular line: $y = \dfrac{3}{2}x + 3$

CHAPTER 2 Functions and Their Graphs

2.1 Assess Your Understanding *(page 67)*

5. independent; dependent **6.** range **7.** $[0, 5]$ **8.** image **9.** $(g - f)(x)$ **10.** F **11.** T **12.** T **13.** F **14.** F

15. Function; Domain: {Elvis, Colleen, Kaleigh, Marissa}, Range: {January 8, March 15, September 17} **16.** Not a function **17.** Not a function

18. Function; Domain: { Less than 9th grade, 9th–12th grade, High School Graduate, Some College, College Graduate};

Range: {$18,120, $23,251, $36,055, $45,810, $67,165} **19.** Not a function **20.** Function; Domain: $\{-2, -1, 3, 4\}$, Range: $\{3, 5, 7, 12\}$ **21.** Function;

Domain: $\{1, 2, 3, 4\}$; Range: $\{3\}$ **22.** Function; Domain: $\{0, 1, 2, 3\}$, Range: $\{-2, 3, 7\}$ **23.** Not a function **24.** Not a function **25.** Function;

Domain: $\{-2, -1, 0, 1\}$, Range: $\{0, 1, 4\}$ **26.** Function; Domain: $\{-2, -1, 0, 1\}$, Range: $\{3, 4, 16\}$ **27.** Function **28.** Function **29.** Function

30. Function **31.** Not a function **32.** Not a function **33.** Not a function **34.** Not a function **35.** Function **36.** Function **37.** Not a function

38. Not a function **39. (a)** -4 **(b)** 1 **(c)** -3 **(d)** $3x^2 - 2x - 4$ **(e)** $-3x^2 - 2x + 4$ **(f)** $3x^2 + 8x + 1$ **(g)** $12x^2 + 4x - 4$

(h) $3x^2 + 6xh + 3h^2 + 2x + 2h - 4$ **40. (a)** -1 **(b)** -2 **(c)** -4 **(d)** $-2x^2 - x - 1$ **(e)** $2x^2 - x + 1$ **(f)** $-2x^2 - 3x - 2$

(g) $-8x^2 + 2x - 1$ **(h)** $-2x^2 - 4xh - 2h^2 + x + h - 1$ **41. (a)** 0 **(b)** $\dfrac{1}{2}$ **(c)** $-\dfrac{1}{2}$ **(d)** $\dfrac{-x}{x^2 + 1}$ **(e)** $\dfrac{-x}{x^2 + 1}$ **(f)** $\dfrac{x + 1}{x^2 + 2x + 2}$

(g) $\dfrac{2x}{4x^2 + 1}$ **(h)** $\dfrac{x + h}{x^2 + 2xh + h^2 + 1}$ **42. (a)** $-\dfrac{1}{4}$ **(b)** 0 **(c)** 0 **(d)** $\dfrac{x^2 - 1}{-x + 4}$ **(e)** $\dfrac{-x^2 + 1}{x + 4}$ **(f)** $\dfrac{x^2 + 2x}{x + 5}$ **(g)** $\dfrac{4x^2 - 1}{2x + 4}$

(h) $\dfrac{x^2 + 2xh + h^2 - 1}{x + h + 4}$ **43. (a)** 4 **(b)** 5 **(c)** 5 **(d)** $|x| + 4$ **(e)** $-|x| - 4$ **(f)** $|x + 1| + 4$ **(g)** $2|x| + 4$ **(h)** $|x + h| + 4$

44. (a) 0 (b) $\sqrt{2}$ (c) 0 (d) $\sqrt{x^2 - x}$ (e) $-\sqrt{x^2 + x}$ (f) $\sqrt{x^2 + 3x + 2}$ (g) $\sqrt{4x^2 + 2x}$ (h) $\sqrt{x^2 + 2xh + h^2 + x + h}$ **45.** (a) $-\dfrac{1}{5}$

(b) $-\dfrac{3}{2}$ (c) $\dfrac{1}{8}$ (d) $\dfrac{2x - 1}{3x + 5}$ (e) $\dfrac{-2x - 1}{3x - 5}$ (f) $\dfrac{2x + 3}{3x - 2}$ (g) $\dfrac{4x + 1}{6x - 5}$ (h) $\dfrac{2x + 2h + 1}{3x + 3h - 5}$ **46.** (a) $\dfrac{3}{4}$ (b) $\dfrac{8}{9}$ (c) 0 (d) $1 - \dfrac{1}{(-x + 2)^2}$

(e) $-1 + \dfrac{1}{(x + 2)^2}$ (f) $1 - \dfrac{1}{(x + 3)^2}$ (g) $1 - \dfrac{1}{(2x + 2)^2}$ (h) $1 - \dfrac{1}{(x + h + 2)^2}$ **47.** All real numbers **48.** All real numbers

49. All real numbers **50.** All real numbers **51.** $\{x | x \neq -4, x \neq 4\}$ **52.** $\{x | x \neq -2, x \neq 2\}$ **53.** $\{x | x \neq 0\}$ **54.** $\{x | x \neq -2, x \neq 0, x \neq 2\}$

55. $\{x | x \geq 4\}$ **56.** $\{x | x \leq 1\}$ **57.** $\{x | x > 9\}$ **58.** $\{x | x > 4\}$ **59.** $\{x | x > 1\}$ **60.** $\{x | x \leq -2\}$ **61.** (a) $(f + g)(x) = 5x + 1$; All real numbers

(b) $(f - g)(x) = x + 7$; All real numbers (c) $(f \cdot g)(x) = 6x^2 - x - 12$; All real numbers (d) $\left(\dfrac{f}{g}\right)(x) = \dfrac{3x + 4}{2x - 3}$; $\left\{x \middle| x \neq \dfrac{3}{2}\right\}$ (e) 16 (f) 11

(g) 10 (h) -7 **62.** (a) $(f + g)(x) = 5x - 1$; All real numbers (b) $(f - g)(x) = -x + 3$; All real numbers (c) $(f \cdot g)(x) = 6x^2 - x - 2$;

All real numbers (d) $\left(\dfrac{f}{g}\right)(x) = \dfrac{2x + 1}{3x - 2}$; $\left\{x \middle| x \neq \dfrac{2}{3}\right\}$ (e) 14 (f) -1 (g) 20 (h) 3 **63.** (a) $(f + g)(x) = 2x^2 + x - 1$; All real numbers

(b) $(f - g)(x) = -2x^2 + x - 1$; All real numbers (c) $(f \cdot g)(x) = 2x^3 - 2x^2$; All real numbers (d) $\left(\dfrac{f}{g}\right)(x) = \dfrac{x - 1}{2x^2}$; $\{x | x \neq 0\}$ (e) 20

(f) -29 (g) 8 (h) 0 **64.** (a) $(f + g)(x) = 4x^3 + 2x^2 + 4$; All real numbers (b) $(f - g)(x) = -4x^3 + 2x^2 + 2$; All real numbers

(c) $(f \cdot g)(x) = 8x^5 + 12x^3 + 2x^2 + 3$; All real numbers (d) $\left(\dfrac{f}{g}\right)(x) = \dfrac{2x^2 + 3}{4x^3 + 1}$; $\left\{x \middle| x \neq -\dfrac{\sqrt[3]{2}}{2}\right\}$ (e) 130 (f) -222 (g) 363 (h) 1

65. (a) $(f + g)(x) = \sqrt{x} + 3x - 5$; $\{x | x \geq 0\}$ (b) $(f - g)(x) = \sqrt{x} - 3x + 5$; $\{x | x \geq 0\}$ (c) $(f \cdot g)(x) = 3x\sqrt{x} - 5\sqrt{x}$; $\{x | x \geq 0\}$

(d) $\left(\dfrac{f}{g}\right)(x) = \dfrac{\sqrt{x}}{3x - 5}$; $\left\{x \middle| x \geq 0, x \neq \dfrac{5}{3}\right\}$ (e) $\sqrt{3} + 4$ (f) -5 (g) $\sqrt{2}$ (h) $-\dfrac{1}{2}$ **66.** (a) $(f + g)(x) = |x| + x$; All real numbers

(b) $(f - g)(x) = |x| - x$; All real numbers (c) $(f \cdot g)(x) = x|x|$; All real numbers (d) $\left(\dfrac{f}{g}\right)(x) = \dfrac{|x|}{x}$; $\{x | x \neq 0\}$ (e) 6 (f) 0 (g) 4

(h) 1 **67.** (a) $(f + g)(x) = 1 + \dfrac{2}{x}$; $\{x | x \neq 0\}$ (b) $(f - g)(x) = 1$; $\{x | x \neq 0\}$ (c) $(f \cdot g)(x) = \dfrac{1}{x} + \dfrac{1}{x^2}$; $\{x | x \neq 0\}$

(d) $\left(\dfrac{f}{g}\right)(x) = x + 1$; $\{x | x \neq 0\}$ (e) $\dfrac{5}{3}$ (f) 1 (g) $\dfrac{3}{4}$ (h) 2 **68.** (a) $(f + g)(x) = \sqrt{x - 1} + \sqrt{4 - x}$; $\{x | 1 \leq x \leq 4\}$

(b) $(f - g)(x) = \sqrt{x - 1} - \sqrt{4 - x}$; $\{x | 1 \leq x \leq 4\}$ (c) $(f \cdot g)(x) = \sqrt{-x^2 + 5x - 4}$; $\{x | 1 \leq x \leq 4\}$

(d) $\left(\dfrac{f}{g}\right)(x) = \sqrt{\dfrac{x - 1}{4 - x}}$; $\{x | 1 \leq x < 4\}$ (e) $\sqrt{2} + 1$ (f) $\sqrt{3}$ (g) $\sqrt{2}$ (h) 0 **69.** (a) $(f + g)(x) = \dfrac{6x + 3}{3x - 2}$; $\left\{x \middle| x \neq \dfrac{2}{3}\right\}$

(b) $(f - g)(x) = \dfrac{-2x + 3}{3x - 2}$; $\left\{x \middle| x \neq \dfrac{2}{3}\right\}$ (c) $(f \cdot g)(x) = \dfrac{8x^2 + 12x}{(3x - 2)^2}$; $\left\{x \middle| x \neq \dfrac{2}{3}\right\}$ (d) $\left(\dfrac{f}{g}\right)(x) = \dfrac{2x + 3}{4x}$; $\left\{x \middle| x \neq 0; x \neq \dfrac{2}{3}\right\}$ (e) 3

(f) $-\dfrac{1}{2}$ (g) $\dfrac{7}{2}$ (h) $\dfrac{5}{4}$ **70.** (a) $(f + g)(x) = \sqrt{x + 1} + \dfrac{2}{x}$; $\{x | x \geq -1, x \neq 0\}$ (b) $(f - g)(x) = \sqrt{x + 1} - \dfrac{2}{x}$; $\{x | x \geq -1, x \neq 0\}$

(c) $(f \cdot g)(x) = \dfrac{2}{x}\sqrt{x + 1}$; $\{x | x \geq -1, x \neq 0\}$ (d) $\left(\dfrac{f}{g}\right)(x) = \dfrac{x\sqrt{x + 1}}{2}$; $\{x | x \geq -1, x \neq 0\}$ (e) $\dfrac{8}{3}$ (f) $\sqrt{5} - \dfrac{1}{2}$ (g) $\sqrt{3}$ (h) $\dfrac{\sqrt{2}}{2}$

71. $g(x) = 5 - \dfrac{7}{2}x$ **72.** $g(x) = \dfrac{x - 1}{x + 1}$ **73.** 4 **74.** -3 **75.** $2x + h - 1$ **76.** $2x + h + 5$ **77.** $6x + 3h - 2$ **78.** $8x + 4h + 5$

79. $3x^2 + 3xh + h^2$ **80.** $\dfrac{-1}{(x + h + 3)(x + 3)}$ **81.** $A = -\dfrac{7}{2}$ **82.** $B = 5$ **83.** $A = -4$ **84.** $B = -1$ **85.** $A = 8$; undefined at $x = 3$

86. $A = 1, B = 2$ **87.** $A(x) = \dfrac{1}{2}x^2$ **88.** $A(x) = \dfrac{1}{2}x^2$ **89.** $G(x) = 10x$ **90.** $G(x) = 10x + 100$ **91.** (a) P is the dependent variable; a is the

independent variable. (b) $P(20) = 197.34$; In 2005, there are 197.34 million people 20 years of age or older. (c) $P(0) = 290.580$;

In 2005, there are 290.580 million people. **92.** (a) N is the dependent variable; r is the independent variable. (b) $N(3) = 15.64$; In 2005, there are

15.64 million housing units having 3 rooms. **93.** (a) 15.1 m, 14.071 m, 12.944 m, 11.719 m (b) 1.01 s, 1.43 s, 1.75 s (c) 2.02 s

94. (a) 7 m, 4.27 m, 1.28 m (b) 0.62 s, 0.88 s, 1.07 s (c) 1.24 s **95.** (a) \$222 (b) \$225 (c) \$220 (d) \$230 **96.** (a) 1.26 ft^2

(b) 1.73 ft^2 (c) 1.99 ft^2 **97.** $R(x) = \dfrac{L(x)}{P(x)}$ **98.** $T(x) = V(x) + P(x)$ **99.** $H(x) = P(x) \cdot I(x)$ **100.** $N(x) = I(x) - T(x)$

101. (a) $P(x) = -0.05x^3 + 0.8x^2 + 155x - 500$ (b) $P(15) = \$1836.25$ (c) When 15 hundred cell phones are sold, the profit is \$1836.25.

102. (a) $P(x) = -0.1x^2 + 23x - 400$ (b) $P(30) = \$200$ (c) When 30 clocks are sold, the profit is \$200. **103.** Only $h(x) = 2x$ **104.** No; f has

a domain of all real numbers, while g has a domain of $\{x | x \neq -1\}$. **106.** $f(x) = \sqrt{3x + 5}$ **107.** Square the real number t and then subtract 2.

2.2 Assess Your Understanding (page 74)

3. vertical **4.** 5; −3 **5.** (−2, 7) **6.** F **7.** F **8.** T **9. (a)** $f(0) = 3$; $f(-6) = -3$ **(b)** $f(6) = 0$; $f(11) = 1$ **(c)** Positive **(d)** Negative
(e) −3, 6, and 10 **(f)** $-3 < x < 6$; $10 < x \leq 11$ **(g)** $\{x | -6 \leq x \leq 11\}$ **(h)** $\{y | -3 \leq y \leq 4\}$ **(i)** −3, 6, 10 **(j)** 3 **(k)** 3 times **(l)** Once
(m) 0, 4 **(n)** −5, 8 **10. (a)** $f(0) = 0$; $f(6) = 0$ **(b)** $f(2) = -2$; $f(-2) = 1$ **(c)** Negative **(d)** Positive **(e)** 0, 4, and 6 **(f)** $0 < x < 4$
(g) $\{x | -4 \leq x \leq 6\}$ **(h)** $\{y | -2 \leq y \leq 3\}$ **(i)** 0, 4, 6 **(j)** 0 **(k)** Twice **(l)** Once **(m)** 5 **(n)** 2 **11.** Not a function **12.** Function
(a) Domain: all real numbers; Range: $\{y | y > 0\}$ **(b)** (0, 1) **(c)** None **13.** Function **(a)** Domain: $\{x | -\pi \leq x \leq \pi\}$;

Range: $\{y | -1 \leq y \leq 1\}$ **(b)** $\left(-\dfrac{\pi}{2}, 0\right), \left(\dfrac{\pi}{2}, 0\right)$, (0, 1) **(c)** y-axis **14.** Function **(a)** Domain: $\{x | -\pi \leq x \leq \pi\}$; Range: $\{y | -1 \leq y \leq 1\}$

(b) $(-\pi, 0), (\pi, 0), (0, 0)$ **(c)** Origin **15.** Not a function **16.** Not a function **17.** Function **(a)** Domain: $\{x | x > 0\}$; Range: all real numbers
(b) (1, 0) **(c)** None **18.** Function **(a)** Domain: $\{x | 0 \leq x \leq 4\}$; Range: $\{y | 0 \leq y \leq 3\}$ **(b)** (0, 0) **(c)** None **19.** Function **(a)** Domain: all
real numbers; Range: $\{y | y \leq 2\}$ **(b)** $(-3, 0), (3, 0), (0, 2)$ **(c)** y-axis **20.** Function **(a)** Domain: $\{x | x \geq -3\}$; Range: $\{y | y \geq 0\}$
(b) $(-3, 0), (0, 2), (2, 0)$ **(c)** None **21.** Function **(a)** Domain: all real numbers; Range: $\{y | y \geq -3\}$ **(b)** $(1, 0), (3, 0), (0, 9)$ **(c)** None
22. Function **(a)** Domain: all real numbers: Range: $\{y | y \leq 5\}$ **(b)** $(-1, 0), (2, 0), (0, 4)$ **(c)** None **23. (a)** Yes **(b)** $f(-2) = 9$; $(-2, 9)$
(c) $0, \dfrac{1}{2}$; $(0, -1), \left(\dfrac{1}{2}, -1\right)$ **(d)** All real numbers **(e)** $-\dfrac{1}{2}, 1$ **(f)** −1 **24. (a)** No **(b)** $f(-2) = -22$; $(-2, -22)$ **(c)** $-\dfrac{1}{3}, 2$; $\left(-\dfrac{1}{3}, -2\right), (2, -2)$
(d) All real numbers **(e)** $0, \dfrac{5}{3}$ **(f)** 0 **25. (a)** No **(b)** $f(4) = -3$; $(4, -3)$ **(c)** 14; $(14, 2)$ **(d)** $\{x | x \neq 6\}$ **(e)** −2 **(f)** $-\dfrac{1}{3}$
26. (a) Yes **(b)** $f(0) = \dfrac{1}{2}$; $\left(0, \dfrac{1}{2}\right)$ **(c)** $0, \dfrac{1}{2}$; $\left(0, \dfrac{1}{2}\right), \left(\dfrac{1}{2}, \dfrac{1}{2}\right)$ **(d)** $\{x | x \neq -4\}$ **(e)** None **(f)** $\dfrac{1}{2}$ **27. (a)** Yes **(b)** $f(2) = \dfrac{8}{17}$; $\left(2, \dfrac{8}{17}\right)$
(c) $-1, 1$; $(-1, 1), (1, 1)$ **(d)** All real numbers **(e)** 0 **(f)** 0 **28. (a)** Yes **(b)** $f(4) = 4$; $(4, 4)$ **(c)** -2; $(-2, 1)$ **(d)** $\{x | x \neq 2\}$ **(e)** 0 **(f)** 0

29. (a) Approximately 10.4 ft high **(b)** Approximately 9.9 ft high **30. (a)** $v = 30$ ft/s **(b)** $h(x) = -\dfrac{34}{225}x^2 + 2.7x + 3.5$

(c)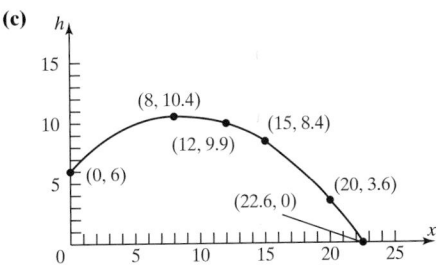

(c) $h(9) = 15.56$ ft
(d)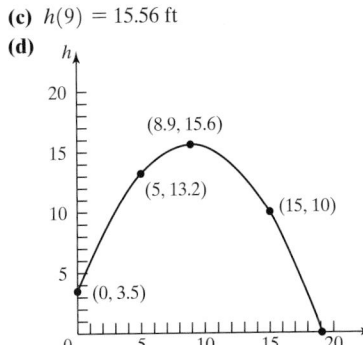

(d) The ball will not go through the hoop; $h(15) \approx 8.4$ ft.
If $v = 30$ ft/s, $h(15) = 10$ ft.

31. (a)

32. (a) $\{x | 0 < x < 1\}$
(b)

(b)

(c) 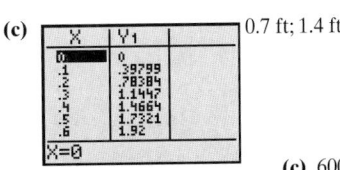 0.7 ft; 1.4 ft

(c) 600 mi/hr

33. (a) 3 **(b)** −2 **(c)** −1 **(d)** 1 **(e)** 2 **(f)** $-\dfrac{1}{3}$ **34. (a)** $5000; fixed costs of production **(b)** $19,000. It costs $19,000 to manufacture
10 computers in a day. **(c)** $51,000. It costs $51,000 to manufacture 50 computers in a day. **(d)** $\{q | 0 \leq q \leq 100\}$. Production capacity is limited to
100 computers per day. **35. (a)** $80; it costs $80 if you use 0 miniutes. **(b)** $80; it costs $80 if you use 1000 minutes. **(c)** $210; it costs $210 if you
use 2000 minutes. **(d)** $\{m | 0 \leq m \leq 14,400\}$. There are at most 14,400 anytime minutes in a month. **37.** The x-intercepts can number anywhere
from 0 to infinitely many. There is at most one y-intercept. **38.** Yes; $f(x) = 0$, domain $x = a$ **39. (a)** III **(b)** IV **(c)** I **(d)** V **(e)** II

40. (a) II **(b)** V **(c)** IV **(d)** III **(e)** I

41.

42.

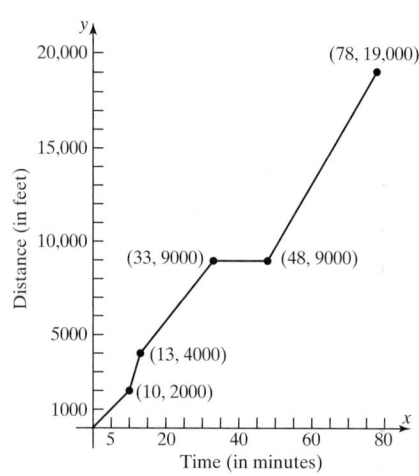

43. **(a)** 2 hr elapsed during which Kevin was between 0 and 3 mi from home. **(b)** 0.5 hr elapsed during which Kevin was 3 mi from home.
(c) 0.3 hr elapsed during which Kevin was between 0 and 3 mi from home. **(d)** 0.2 hr elapsed during which Kevin was 0 mi from home.
(e) 0.9 hr elapsed during which Kevin was between 0 and 2.8 mi from home. **(f)** 0.3 hr elapsed during which Kevin was 2.8 mi from home.
(g) 1.1 hr elapsed during which Kevin was between 0 and 2.8 mi from home. **(h)** 3 mi **(i)** 2 times
44. **(a)** $(7, 7.4)$ **(b)** $(4.2, 6)$ **(c)** Increasing from 0 to 30 mi/hr **(d)** 0 mi/hr **(e)** 50 mi/hr **(f)** $(2, 4), (4.2, 6), (7, 7.4), (7.6, 8)$
45. No points whose x-coordinate is 5 or whose y-coordinate is 0 can be on the graph. **46.** Yes. $f(x) = 0$ satisfies the condition that $f(x) = -f(x)$.

2.3 Assess Your Understanding (page 86)

6. increasing **7.** even; odd **8.** T **9.** T **10.** F **11.** Yes **12.** No **13.** No **14.** Yes **15.** $(-8, -2); (0, 2); (5, \infty)$ **16.** $(-\infty, -8), (-2, 0), (2, 5)$
17. Yes; 10 **18.** No **19.** $-2, 2; 6, 10$ **20.** $-8, 0, 5; -4, 0, 0$
21. **(a)** $(-2, 0), (0, 3), (2, 0)$ **(b)** Domain: $\{x | -4 \le x \le 4\}$ or $[-4, 4]$; Range: $\{y | 0 \le y \le 3\}$ or $[0, 3]$
   (c) Increasing on $(-2, 0)$ and $(2, 4)$; Decreasing on $(-4, -2)$ and $(0, 2)$ **(d)** Even
22. **(a)** $(-1, 0), (0, 2), (1, 0)$ **(b)** Domain: $\{x | -3 \le x \le 3\}$ or $[-3, 3]$; Range: $\{y | 0 \le y \le 3\}$ or $[0, 3]$
   (c) Increasing on $(-1, 0)$ and $(1, 3)$; Decreasing on $(-3, -1)$ and $(0, 1)$ **(d)** Even
23. **(a)** $(0, 1)$ **(b)** Domain: all real numbers; Range: $\{y | y > 0\}$ or $(0, \infty)$ **(c)** Increasing on $(-\infty, \infty)$ **(d)** Neither
24. **(a)** $(1, 0)$ **(b)** Domain: $\{x | x > 0\}$ or $(0, \infty)$; Range: all real numbers **(c)** Increasing on $(0, \infty)$ **(d)** Neither
25. **(a)** $(-\pi, 0), (0, 0), (\pi, 0)$ **(b)** Domain: $\{x | -\pi \le x \le \pi\}$ or $[-\pi, \pi]$; Range: $\{y | -1 \le y \le 1\}$ or $[-1, 1]$
   (c) Increasing on $\left(-\dfrac{\pi}{2}, \dfrac{\pi}{2}\right)$; Decreasing on $\left(-\pi, -\dfrac{\pi}{2}\right)$ and $\left(\dfrac{\pi}{2}, \pi\right)$ **(d)** Odd
26. **(a)** $\left(-\dfrac{\pi}{2}, 0\right), (0, 1), \left(\dfrac{\pi}{2}, 0\right)$ **(b)** Domain: $\{x | -\pi \le x \le \pi\}$ or $[-\pi, \pi]$; Range: $\{y | -1 \le y \le 1\}$ or $[-1, 1]$
   (c) Increasing on $(-\pi, 0)$; Decreasing on $(0, \pi)$ **(d)** Even
27. **(a)** $\left(0, \dfrac{1}{2}\right), \left(\dfrac{1}{3}, 0\right), \left(\dfrac{5}{2}, 0\right)$ **(b)** Domain: $\{x | -3 \le x \le 3\}$ or $[-3, 3]$; Range: $\{y | -1 \le y \le 2\}$ or $[-1, 2]$
   (c) Increasing on $(2, 3)$; Decreasing on $(-1, 1)$; Constant on $(-3, -1)$ and $(1, 2)$ **(d)** Neither
28. **(a)** $(-2.3, 0), (0, 1), (3, 0)$ **(b)** Domain: $\{x | -3 \le x \le 3\}$ or $[-3, 3]$; Range: $\{y | -2 \le y \le 2\}$ or $[-2, 2]$
   (c) Increasing on $(-3, -2)$ and $(0, 2)$; Decreasing on $(2, 3)$; Constant on $(-2, 0)$ **(d)** Neither **29.** **(a)** $0; 3$ **(b)** $-2, 2; 0, 0$
30. **(a)** $0; 2$ **(b)** $-1, 1; 0, 0$ **31.** **(a)** $\dfrac{\pi}{2}; 1$ **(b)** $-\dfrac{\pi}{2}; -1$ **32.** **(a)** $0; 1$ **(b)** $-\pi, \pi; -1, -1$ **33.** Odd **34.** Even **35.** Even **36.** Odd
37. Odd **38.** Neither **39.** Neither **40.** Even **41.** Even **42.** Odd **43.** Odd **44.** Odd

45.

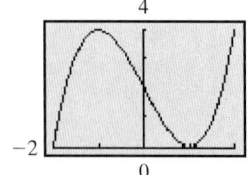

Increasing: $(-2, -1), (1, 2)$
Decreasing: $(-1, 1)$
Local maximum: 4 at $x = -1$
Local minimum: 0 at $x = 1$

46.

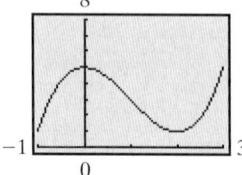

Increasing: $(-1, 0), (2, 3)$
Decreasing: $(0, 2)$
Local maximum: 5 at $x = 0$
Local minimum: 1 at $x = 2$

47.

Increasing: $(-2, -0.77), (0.77, 2)$
Decreasing: $(-0.77, 0.77)$
Local maximum: 0.19 at $x = -0.77$
Local minimum: -0.19 at $x = 0.77$

48.

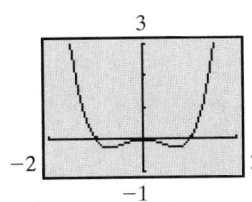

Increasing: $(-0.71, 0), (0.71, 2)$
Decreasing: $(-2, -0.71), (0, 0.71)$
Local maximum: 0 at $x = 0$
Local minimum: -0.25 at $x = -0.71$
Local minimum: -0.25 at $x = 0.71$

49.

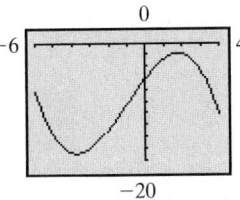

Increasing: $(-3.77, 1.77)$
Decreasing: $(-6, -3.77), (1.77, 4)$
Local maximum: -1.91 at $x = 1.77$
Local minimum: -18.89 at $x = -3.77$

50.

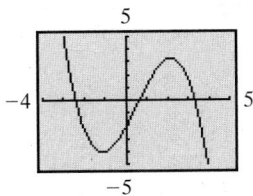

Increasing: $(-1.16, 2.16)$
Decreasing: $(-4, -1.16), (2.16, 5)$
Local maximum: 3.25 at $x = 2.16$
Local minimum: -4.05 at $x = -1.16$

51.

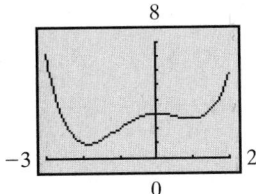

Increasing: $(-1.87, 0), (0.97, 2)$
Decreasing: $(-3, -1.87), (0, 0.97)$
Local maximum: 3 at $x = 0$
Local minimum: 0.95 at $x = -1.87$
Local minimum: 2.65 at $x = 0.97$

52.

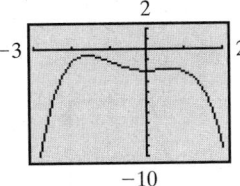

Increasing: $(-3, -1.57), (0, 0.64)$
Decreasing: $(-1.57, 0), (0.64, 2)$
Local maximum: -0.52 at $x = -1.57$
Local maximum: -1.87 at $x = 0.64$
Local minimum: -2 at $x = 0$

53. (a) -4 **(b)** -8 **(c)** -10 **54. (a)** -4 **(b)** -13 **(c)** -1 **55. (a)** 17 **(b)** -1 **(c)** 11 **56. (a)** -2 **(b)** 0 **(c)** 5

57. (a) 5 **(b)** $y = 5x - 2$ **58. (a)** -4 **(b)** $y = -4x + 1$ **59. (a)** -1; **(b)** $y = -x$ **60. (a)** 1 **(b)** $y = x + 3$ **61. (a)** 4 **(b)** $y = 4x - 8$

62. (a) -5
(b) $y = -5x$

63. (a) Odd
(b)

(c) Local minimum: -3.08 at $x = 1.15$
(d) Local maximum: 3.08 at $x = -1.15$

64. (a) Odd
(b)

(c) Local maximum: 5.66 at $x = 1.41$
(d) Local minimum: -5.66 at $x = -1.41$

65. (a) Even
(b)

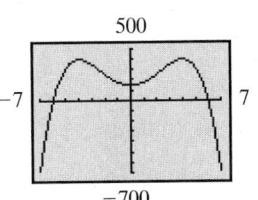

(c) Local maximum: 24 at $x = 2$
(d) Local maximum: 24 at $x = -2$
(e) 47.4 sq. units

66. (a) Even
(b)

(c) Local maximum: 400 at $x = 4$
(d) Local maximum: 400 at $x = -4$
(e) 1612.8 sq. units

67. (a)

(b) 10 riding lawn mowers/hr
(c) $239/mower

68. (a) 2.16 hr **(b)** 4.47 hr

69. (a) On average, the population is increasing at a rate of 0.036 g/hr from 0 to 2.5 hr.
(b) On average, from 4.5 to 6 hr, the population is increasing at a rate of 0.1 g/hr.
(c) The average rate of change is increasing over time.

70. (a) On average, the percentage of e-filers increased at a rate of 3.45%/yr from 1998 to 2000.
(b) On average, the percentage of e-filers increased at a rate of 4.75%/yr from 2001 to 2003.
(c) On average, from 2004 to 2006 the percentage of e-filers increased at a rate of 5.3%/yr.
(d) The average rate of change is increasing over time.

71. (a) 1 **(b)** 0.5 **(c)** 0.1 **(d)** 0.01 **(e)** 0.001
(f)

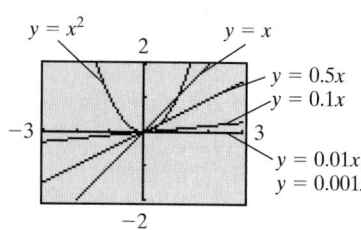

72. (a) 3 **(b)** 2.5 **(c)** 2.1 **(d)** 2.01 **(e)** 2.001
(f)

$y = 2.01(x - 1) + 1$
$y = 2.001(x - 1) + 1$
$y = 3(x - 1) + 1$
$y = 2.5(x - 1) + 1$
$y = 2.1(x - 1) + 1$

(g) They are getting closer to the tangent line at $(0, 0)$.
(h) They are getting closer to 0.

(g) They are getting closer to the tangent line at $(1, 1)$.
(h) They are getting closer to 2.

73. (a) 2 **(b)** $2; 2; 2; 2$
(c) $y = 2x + 5$
(d)

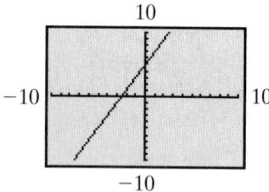

74. (a) -3 **(b)** $-3; -3; -3; -3$
(c) $y = -3x + 2$
(d)

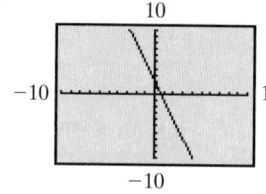

75. (a) $2x + h + 2$ **(b)** $4.5; 4.1; 4.01; 4$
(c) $y = 4.01x - 1.01$
(d)

76. (a) $4x + 2h + 1$ **(b)** $6; 5.2; 5.02; 5$
(c) $y = 5.02x - 2.02$
(d)

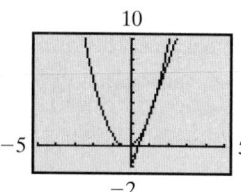

77. (a) $4x + 2h - 3$ **(b)** $2; 1.2; 1.02; 1$
(c) $y = 1.02x - 1.02$
(d)

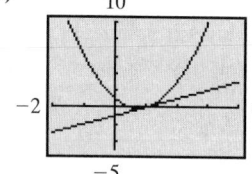

78. (a) $-2x - h + 3$ **(b)** $0.5; 0.9; 0.99; 1$
(c) $y = 0.99x - 0.99$
(d)

79. (a) $-\dfrac{1}{(x + h)x}$ **(b)** $-\dfrac{2}{3}; -\dfrac{10}{11}; -\dfrac{100}{101}; -1$ **(c)** $y = -\dfrac{100}{101}x + \dfrac{201}{101}$
(d)

80. (a) $\dfrac{-2x - h}{(x^2 + 2xh + h^2)x^2}$ **(b)** $-\dfrac{10}{9}; -\dfrac{210}{121}; -\dfrac{20,100}{10,201}; -2$
(c) $y = -1.9704x + 2.9704$ **(d)**

83. At most one **85.** Yes; the function $f(x) = 0$ is both even and odd.

2.4 Assess Your Understanding (page 96)

4. $(-\infty, 0)$ **5.** piecewise-defined **6.** T **7.** F **8.** F **9.** C **10.** A **11.** E **12.** G **13.** B **14.** D **15.** F **16.** H
17.

18.

19.

20.

21.

22.

23.

24.

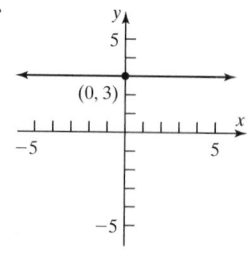

25. (a) 4 **(b)** 2 **(c)** 5 **26. (a)** 6 **(b)** 0 **(c)** 1 **27. (a)** -4 **(b)** -2 **(c)** 0 **(d)** 25 **28. (a)** -1 **(b)** 0 **(c)** 5 **(d)** 11

29. (a) All real numbers
(b) $(0, 1)$
(c)

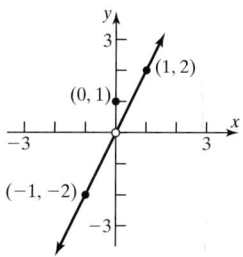

(d) $\{y \mid y \neq 0\}; (-\infty, 0) \cup (0, \infty)$
(e) Discontinuous at $x = 0$

30. (a) All real numbers
(b) $(0, 4)$
(c)

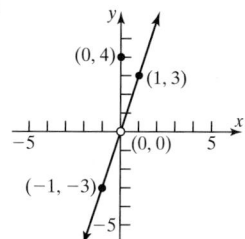

(d) $\{y \mid y \neq 0\}; (-\infty, 0) \cup (0, \infty)$
(e) Discontinuous at $x = 0$

31. (a) All real numbers
(b) $(0, 3)$
(c)

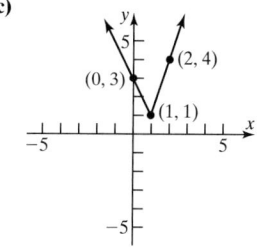

(d) $\{y \mid y \geq 1\}; [1, \infty)$
(e) Continuous

32. (a) All real numbers
(b) $(-3, 0), \left(-\dfrac{3}{2}, 0\right), (0, -3)$
(c)

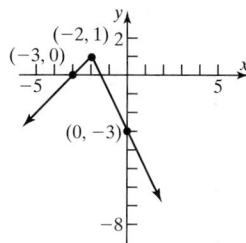

(d) $\{y \mid y \leq 1\}; (-\infty, 1]$
(e) Continuous

33. (a) $\{x \mid x \geq -2\}; [-2, \infty)$
(b) $(0, 3), (2, 0)$
(c)

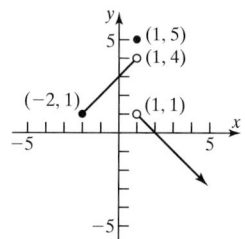

(d) $\{y \mid y < 4, y = 5\}; (-\infty, 4) \cup \{5\}$
(e) Discontinuous at $x = 1$

34. (a) $\{x \mid x \geq -3\}; [-3, \infty)$
(b) $\left(-\dfrac{5}{2}, 0\right), (0, -3)$
(c)

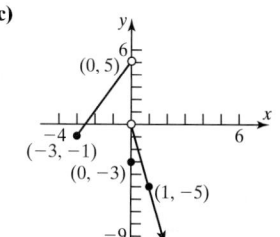

(d) $\{y \mid y < 5\}; (-\infty, 5)$
(e) Discontinuous at $x = 0$

35. (a) All real numbers
(b) $(-1, 0), (0, 0)$
(c)

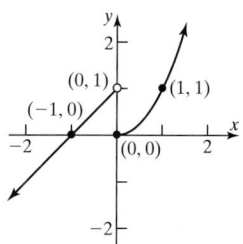

(d) All real numbers
(e) Discontinuous at $x = 0$

36. (a) All real numbers
(b) $(0, 0)$
(c)

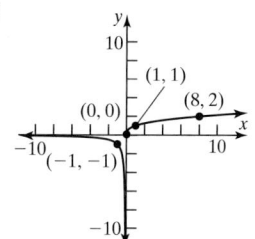

(d) All real numbers
(e) Discontinuous at $x = 0$

37. (a) $\{x \mid x \geq -2, x \neq 0\}; [-2, 0) \cup (0, \infty)$
(b) No intercepts
(c)

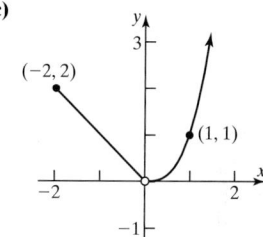

(d) $\{y \mid y > 0\}; (0, \infty)$
(e) Discontinuous at $x = 0$

38. (a) $\{x \mid x \geq -3, x \neq 1\}; [-3, 1) \cup (1, \infty)$
(b) $(0, 2)$
(c)

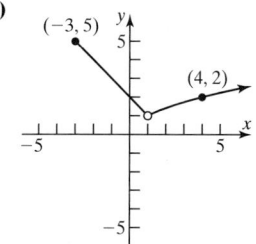

(d) $\{y \mid y > 1\}; (1, \infty)$

(e) Discontinuous at $x = 1$

39. (a) All real numbers
(b) $(x, 0)$ for $0 \leq x < 1$
(c)

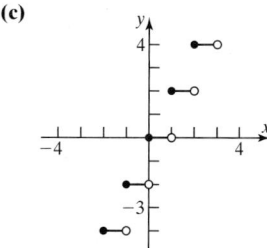

(d) Set of even integers

(e) Discontinuous at $\{x \mid x$ is an integer$\}$

40. (a) All real numbers
(b) $(x, 0)$ for $0 \leq x < \dfrac{1}{2}$
(c)

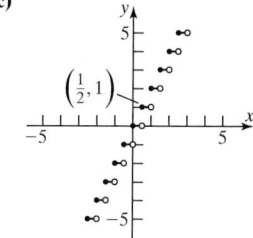

(d) Set of integers

(e) Discontinuous at $\left\{x \mid x = \dfrac{k}{2}, k \text{ is an integer}\right\}$

41. $f(x) = \begin{cases} -x & \text{if } -1 \leq x \leq 0 \\ \frac{1}{2}x & \text{if } 0 < x \leq 2 \end{cases}$ (Other answers are possible.)

42. $f(x) = \begin{cases} x & \text{if } -1 \leq x \leq 0 \\ 1 & \text{if } 0 < x \leq 2 \end{cases}$ (Other answers are possible.)

43. $f(x) = \begin{cases} -x & \text{if } x \leq 0 \\ -x + 2 & \text{if } 0 < x \leq 2 \end{cases}$ (Other answers are possible.)

44. $f(x) = \begin{cases} 2x + 2 & \text{if } -1 \leq x \leq 0 \\ x & \text{if } x > 0 \end{cases}$ (Other answers are possible.)

45. (a) 2   **(b)** 3   **(c)** -4 **46. (a)** 0   **(b)** 0   **(c)** -1 **47. (a)** $39.99   **(b)** $46.74   **(c)** $40.44   **48. (a)** $3   **(b)** $41   **(c)** $50   **(d)** $46

49. (a) $71.33   **(b)** $516.04

(c) $C(x) = \begin{cases} 1.23755x + 9.45 & \text{if } 0 \le x \le 50 \\ 0.98825x + 21.915 & \text{if } x > 50 \end{cases}$

50. (a) $39.75   **(b)** $156.76

(c) $C(x) = \begin{cases} 0.8173x + 8.85 & \text{if } 0 \le x \le 20 \\ 0.7279x + 10.638 & \text{if } 20 < x \le 50 \\ 0.7219x + 10.938 & \text{if } x > 50 \end{cases}$

(d)

(d)

51. For schedule X:

$$f(x) = \begin{cases} 0.10x & \text{if} & 0 < x \le 7825 \\ 782.50 + 0.15(x - 7825) & \text{if} & 7825 < x \le 31{,}850 \\ 4386.25 + 0.25(x - 31{,}850) & \text{if} & 31{,}850 < x \le 77{,}100 \\ 15{,}698.75 + 0.28(x - 77{,}100) & \text{if} & 77{,}100 < x \le 160{,}850 \\ 39{,}148.75 + 0.33(x - 160{,}850) & \text{if} & 160{,}850 < x \le 349{,}700 \\ 101{,}469.25 + 0.35(x - 349{,}700) & \text{if} & x > 349{,}700 \end{cases}$$

52. For schedule Y-1:

$$f(x) = \begin{cases} 0.10x & \text{if} & 0 < x \le 15{,}650 \\ 1565 + 0.15(x - 15{,}650) & \text{if} & 15{,}650 < x \le 63{,}700 \\ 8772.50 + 0.25(x - 63{,}700) & \text{if} & 63{,}700 < x \le 128{,}500 \\ 24{,}972.50 + 0.28(x - 128{,}500) & \text{if} & 128{,}500 < x \le 195{,}850 \\ 43{,}830.50 + 0.33(x - 195{,}850) & \text{if} & 195{,}850 < x \le 349{,}700 \\ 94{,}601 + 0.35(x - 349{,}700) & \text{if} & x > 349{,}700 \end{cases}$$

53. (a)

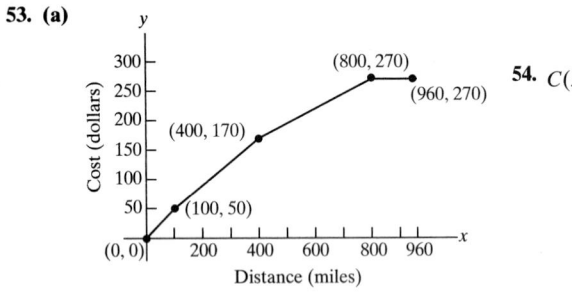

54. $C(x) = \begin{cases} 95 & \text{if } x = 7 \\ 119 & \text{if } 7 < x \le 8 \\ 143 & \text{if } 8 < x \le 9 \\ 167 & \text{if } 9 < x \le 10 \\ 190 & \text{if } 10 < x \le 14 \end{cases}$

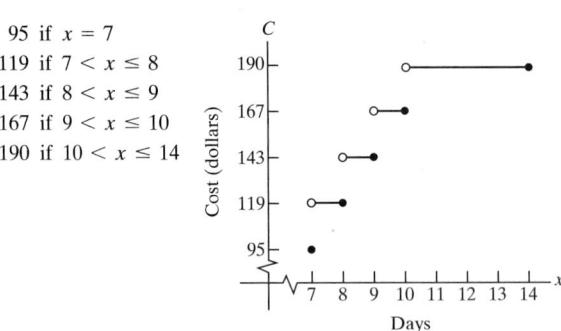

(b) $C(x) = 10 + 0.4x$
(c) $C(x) = 70 + 0.25x$

55. $f(x) = \begin{cases} x & \text{if} & 0 \le x < 10 \\ 10 & \text{if} & 10 \le x < 500 \\ 30 & \text{if} & 500 \le x < 1000 \\ 50 & \text{if} & 1000 \le x < 1500 \\ 70 & \text{if} & 1500 \le x \end{cases}$

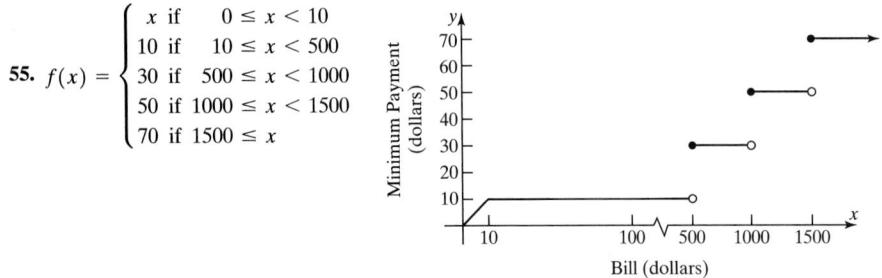

56. $g(x) = \begin{cases} 0.015x & \text{if } 0 \le x \le 1000 \\ 5 + 0.01x & \text{if } x > 1000 \end{cases}$

57. (a) 10°C   **(b)** 4°C   **(c)** -3°C   **(d)** -4°C   **(e)** The wind chill is equal to the air temperature.
    (f) At wind speed greater than 20 m/s, the wind chill factor depends only on the air temperature.

58. (a) $-10°C$
(b) $-21°C$
(c) $-34°C$
(d) $-36°C$

59.

$$C(x) = \begin{cases} 0.80 & 0 < x \le 1 \\ 0.97 & 1 < x \le 2 \\ 1.14 & 2 < x \le 3 \\ 1.31 & 3 < x \le 4 \\ 1.48 & 4 < x \le 5 \\ 1.65 & 5 < x \le 6 \\ 1.82 & 6 < x \le 7 \\ 1.99 & 7 < x \le 8 \\ 2.16 & 8 < x \le 9 \\ 2.33 & 9 < x \le 10 \\ 2.50 & 10 < x \le 11 \\ 2.67 & 11 < x \le 12 \\ 2.84 & 12 < x \le 13 \end{cases}$$

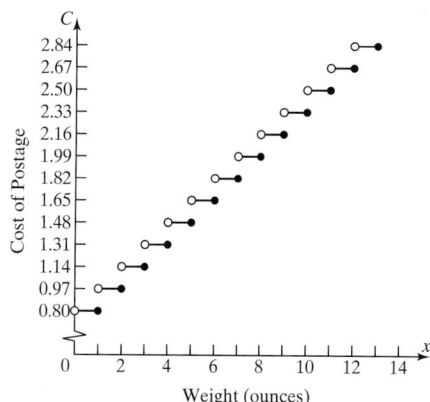

60. Each graph is that of $y = x^2$, but shifted vertically. If $y = x^2 + k, k > 0$, the shift is up k units; if $y = x^2 - k, k > 0$, the shift is down k units.
61. Each graph is that of $y = x^2$, but shifted horizontally. If $y = (x - k)^2, k > 0$, the shift is right k units; if $y = (x + k)^2, k > 0$, the shift is left k units.
62. Each graph is that of $y = |x|$, but either compressed or stretched. If $y = k|x|$ and $k > 1$, the graph is stretched vertically; if $y = k|x|, 0 < k < 1$, the graph is compressed vertically. **63.** The graph of $y = -f(x)$ is the reflection about the x-axis of the graph of $y = f(x)$. **64.** The graph of $y = f(-x)$ is the reflection about the y-axis of the graph of $y = f(x)$. **65.** Yes. The graph of $y = (x - 1)^3 + 2$ is the graph of $y = x^3$ shifted right 1 unit and up 2 units. **66.** They are all U-shaped and open upward. All three go through the points $(-1, 1), (0, 0)$ and $(1, 1)$. As the exponent increases, the steepness of the curve increases (except near $x = 0$). **67.** They all have the same general shape. All three go through the points $(-1, -1), (0, 0)$, and $(1, 1)$. As the exponent increases, the steepness of the curve increases (except near $x = 0$). **68.** y is a function. Domain: all real numbers; $(-\infty, \infty)$; range: $\{y | y = 0 \text{ or } y = 1\}$; y-intercept: 1; x-intercepts: $\{x | x \text{ is irrational}\}$. The function is even.

2.5 Assess Your Understanding *(page 108)*

1. horizontal; right **2.** y **3.** $-5; -2; 2$ **4.** T **5.** F **6.** T **7.** B **8.** E **9.** H **10.** D **11.** I **12.** A **13.** L **14.** C **15.** F **16.** J **17.** G
18. K **19.** $y = (x - 4)^3$ **20.** $y = (x + 4)^3$ **21.** $y = x^3 + 4$ **22.** $y = x^3 - 4$ **23.** $y = -x^3$ **24.** $y = -x^3$ **25.** $y = 4x^3$
26. $y = \left(\dfrac{1}{4}x\right)^3 = \dfrac{1}{64}x^3$ **27.** (1) $y = \sqrt{x} + 2$; (2) $y = -(\sqrt{x} + 2)$; (3) $y = -(\sqrt{-x} + 2)$
28. (1) $y = -\sqrt{x}$; (2) $y = -\sqrt{x - 3}$; (3) $y = -\sqrt{x - 3} - 2$ **29.** (1) $y = -\sqrt{x}$; (2) $y = -\sqrt{x} + 2$; (3) $y = -\sqrt{x + 3} + 2$
30. (1) $y = \sqrt{x} + 2$; (2) $y = \sqrt{-x} + 2$; (3) $y = \sqrt{-(x + 3)} + 2 = \sqrt{-x - 3} + 2$ **31.** (c) **32.** (d) **33.** (c) **34.** (c) **35. (a)** -7 and 1
(b) -3 and 5 **(c)** -5 and 3 **(d)** -3 and 5 **36. (a)** -12 and -3 **(b)** -5 and 4 **(c)** -8 and 1 **(d)** -1 and 8 **37 (a)** $(-3, 3)$ **(b)** $(4, 10)$
(c) Decreasing on $(-1, 5)$ **(d)** Decreasing on $(-5, 1)$ **38. (a)** $(-4, 5)$ **(b)** $(3, 12)$ **(c)** Increasing on $(-2, 7)$ **(d)** Increasing on $(-7, 2)$

39.

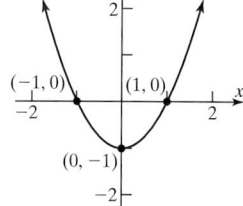

Domain: $(-\infty, \infty)$; Range: $[-1, \infty)$

40.

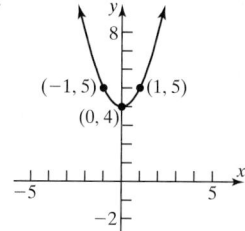

Domain: $(-\infty, \infty)$; Range: $[4, \infty)$

41.

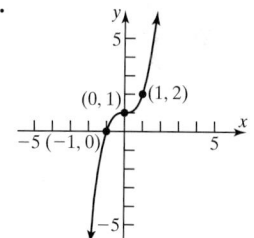

Domain: $(-\infty, \infty)$; Range: $(-\infty, \infty)$

42.

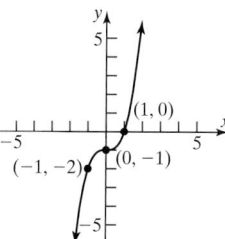

Domain: $(-\infty, \infty)$; Range: $(-\infty, \infty)$

43.

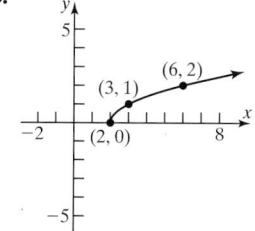

Domain: $[2, \infty)$; Range: $[0, \infty)$

44.

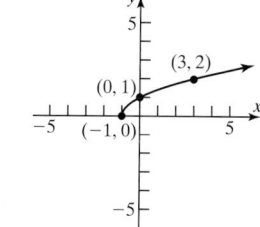

Domain: $[-1, \infty)$; Range: $[0, \infty)$

45.

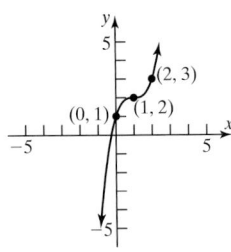

Domain: $(-\infty, \infty)$; Range: $(-\infty, \infty)$

46.

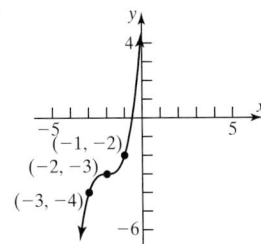

Domain: $(-\infty, \infty)$; Range: $(-\infty, \infty)$

47.

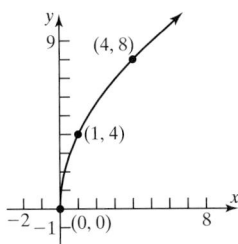

Domain: $[0, \infty)$; Range: $[0, \infty)$

48.

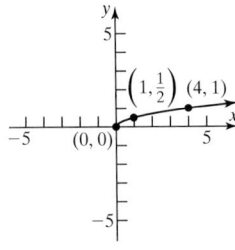

Domain: $[0, \infty)$; Range: $[0, \infty)$

49.

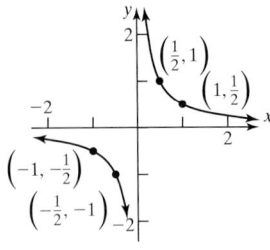

Domain: $(-\infty, 0) \cup (0, \infty)$
Range: $(-\infty, 0) \cup (0, \infty)$

50.

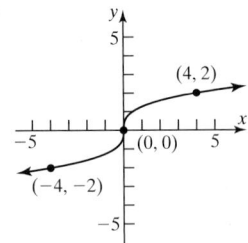

Domain: $(-\infty, \infty)$; Range: $(-\infty, \infty)$

51.

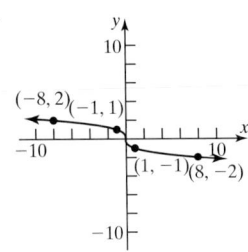

Domain: $(-\infty, \infty)$; Range: $(-\infty, \infty)$

52.

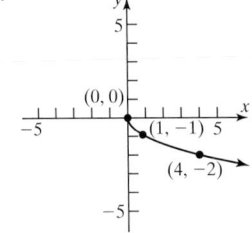

Domain: $[0, \infty)$; Range: $(-\infty, 0]$

53.

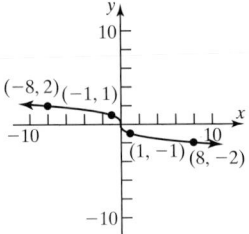

Domain: $(-\infty, \infty)$; Range: $(-\infty, \infty)$

54.

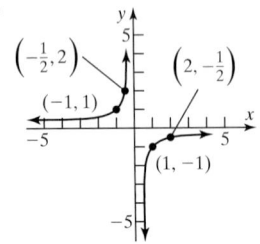

Domain: $(-\infty, 0) \cup (0, \infty)$;
Range: $(-\infty, 0) \cup (0, \infty)$

55.

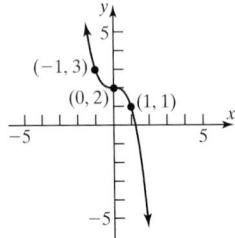

Domain: $(-\infty, \infty)$; Range: $(-\infty, \infty)$

56.

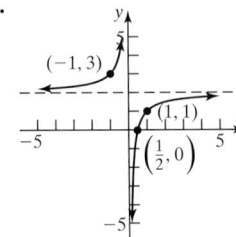

Domain: $(-\infty, 0) \cup (0, \infty)$
Range: $(-\infty, 2) \cup (2, \infty)$

57.

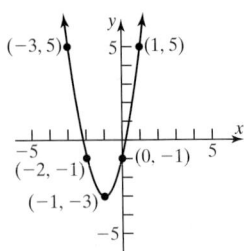

Domain: $(-\infty, \infty)$; Range: $[-3, \infty)$

58.

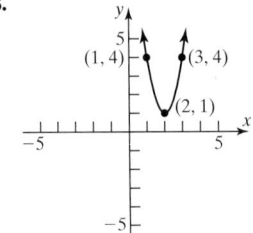

Domain: $(-\infty, \infty)$; Range: $[1, \infty)$

59.

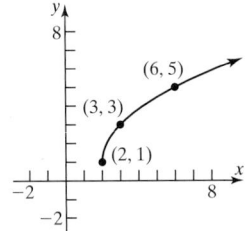

Domain: $[2, \infty)$; Range: $[1, \infty)$

60.

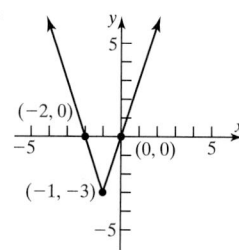

Domain: $(-\infty, \infty)$; Range: $[-3, \infty)$

61.

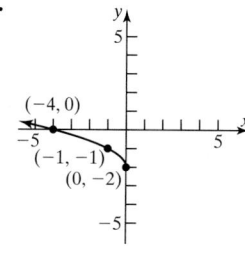

Domain: $(-\infty, 0]$; Range: $[-2, \infty)$

62.

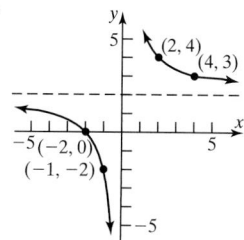

Domain: $(-\infty, 0) \cup (0, \infty)$;
Range: $(-\infty, 2) \cup (2, \infty)$

63.

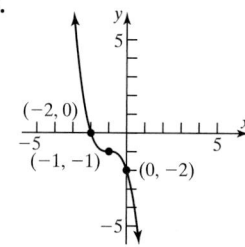

Domain: $(-\infty, \infty)$; Range: $(-\infty, \infty)$

64.

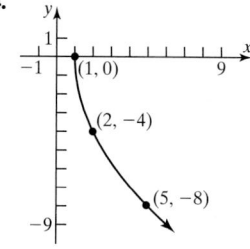

Domain: $[1, \infty)$; Range: $(-\infty, 0]$

65.

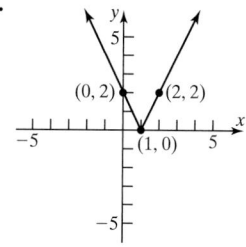

Domain: $(-\infty, \infty)$; Range: $[0, \infty)$

66.

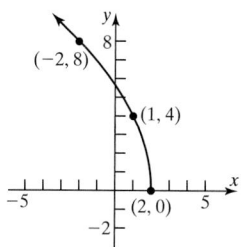

Domain: $(-\infty, 2]$; Range: $[0, \infty)$

67.

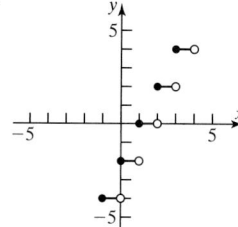

Domain: $(-\infty, \infty)$;
Range: $\left\{ y \mid y \text{ is an even integer} \right\}$

68.

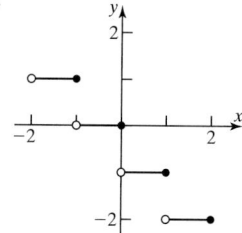

Domain: $(-\infty, \infty)$;
Range: $\left\{ y \mid y \text{ is an integer} \right\}$

69. (a) $F(x) = f(x) + 3$

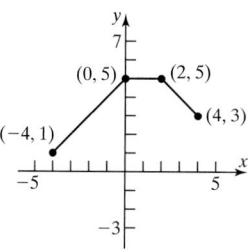

(b) $G(x) = f(x + 2)$

(c) $P(x) = -f(x)$

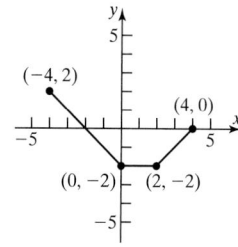

(d) $H(x) = f(x + 1) - 2$

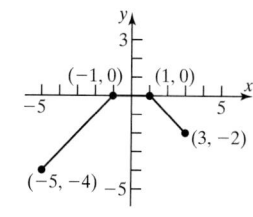

(e) $Q(x) = \dfrac{1}{2} f(x)$

(f) $g(x) = f(-x)$

(g) $h(x) = f(2x)$

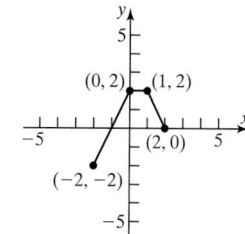

70. (a) $F(x) = f(x) + 3$

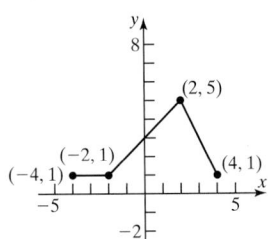

(b) $G(x) = f(x + 2)$

(c) $P(x) = -f(x)$

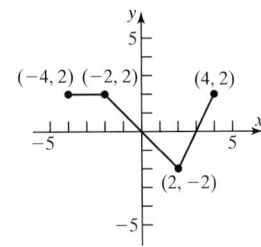

(d) $H(x) = f(x + 1) - 2$

(e) $Q(x) = \frac{1}{2}f(x)$

(f) $g(x) = f(-x)$

(g) $h(x) = f(2x)$

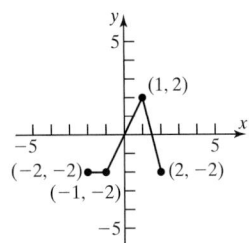

71. (a) $F(x) = f(x) + 3$

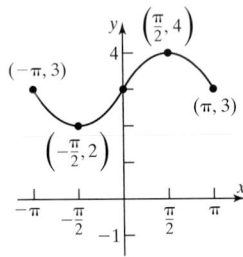

(b) $G(x) = f(x + 2)$

(c) $P(x) = -f(x)$

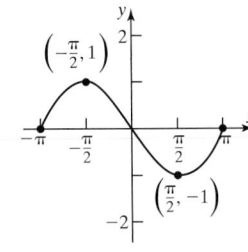

(d) $H(x) = f(x + 1) - 2$

(e) $Q(x) = \frac{1}{2}f(x)$

(f) $g(x) = f(-x)$

(g) $h(x) = f(2x)$

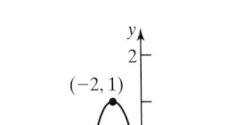

72. (a) $F(x) = f(x) + 3$

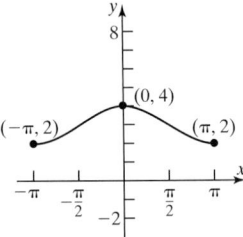

(b) $G(x) = f(x + 2)$

(c) $P(x) = -f(x)$

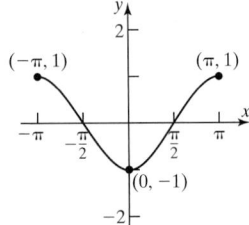

(d) $H(x) = f(x + 1) - 2$

(e) $Q(x) = \frac{1}{2}f(x)$

(f) $g(x) = f(-x)$

(g) $h(x) = f(2x)$

73. (a)

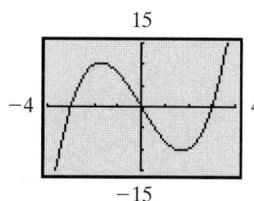

(b) $-3, 0, 3$

(c) Local maximum: 10.39 at $x = -1.73$
Local minimum: -10.39 at $x = 1.73$

(d) Increasing: $(-4, -1.73), (1.73, 4)$
Decreasing: $(-1.73, 1.73)$

(e) Intercepts: $-5, -2, 1$;
Local maximum: 10.39 at $x = -3.73$;
Local minimum: -10.39 at $x = -0.27$;
Increasing: $(-6, -3.73), (-0.27, 2)$;
Decreasing: $(-3.73, -0.27)$

(f) Intercepts: $-3, 0, 3$;
Local maximum: 20.78 at $x = -1.73$;
Local minimum: -20.78 at $x = 1.73$;
Increasing: $(-4, -1.73), (1.73, 4)$;
Decreasing: $(-1.73, 1.73)$

(g) Intercepts: $-3, 0, 3$;
Local maximum: 10.39 at $x = 1.73$;
Local minimum: -10.39 at $x = -1.73$;
Decreasing: $(-4, -1.73), (1.73, 4)$;
Increasing: $(-1.73, 1.73)$

74. (a)

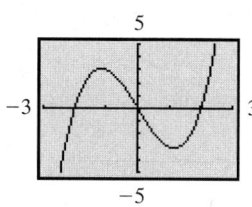

(b) $-2, 0, 2$

(c) Local maximum: 3.08 at $x = -1.15$
Local minimum: -3.08 at $x = 1.15$

(d) Increasing: $(-3, -1.15), (1.15, 3)$
Decreasing: $(-1.15, 1.15)$

(e) Intercepts: $2, 4, 6$;
Local maximum: 3.08 at $x = 2.85$;
Local minimum: -3.08 at $x = 5.15$;
Increasing: $(1, 2.85), (5.15, 7)$;
Decreasing: $(2.85, 5.15)$

(f) Intercepts: $-1, 0, 1$;
Local maximum: 3.08 at $x = -0.575$;
Local minimum: -3.08 at $x = 0.575$;
Increasing: $\left(-\frac{3}{2}, -0.575\right), \left(0.575, \frac{3}{2}\right)$;
Decreasing: $(-0.575, 0.575)$

(g) Intercepts: $-2, 0, 2$;
Local maximum: 3.08 at $x = 1.15$;
Local minimum: -3.08 at $x = -1.15$;
Decreasing: $(-3, -1.15), (1.15, 3)$;
Increasing: $(-1.15, 1.15)$

75. $f(x) = (x + 1)^2 - 1$

76. $f(x) = (x - 3)^2 - 9$

77. $f(x) = (x - 4)^2 - 15$

78. $f(x) = (x + 2)^2 - 2$

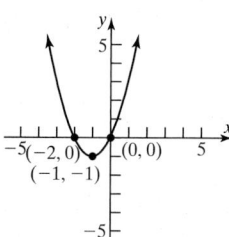

79. $f(x) = \left(x + \dfrac{1}{2}\right)^2 + \dfrac{3}{4}$

80. $f(x) = \left(x - \dfrac{1}{2}\right)^2 + \dfrac{3}{4}$

81. $f(x) = 2(x - 3)^2 + 1$

82. $f(x) = 3(x + 1)^2 - 2$

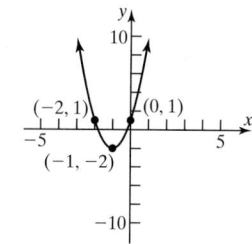

83. $f(x) = -3(x + 2)^2 - 5$

84. $f(x) = -2(x + 3)^2 + 5$

85.

86.

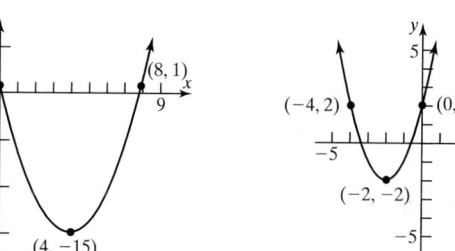

87. (a) 72°F; 65°F

   (b) The temperature decreases by 2° to 70°F during the day and 63°F overnight

(c) The time at which the temperature adjusts between the daytime and overnight settings is moved to 1 hr sooner. It begins warming up at 5:00 AM instead of 6:00 AM, and it begins cooling down at 8:00 PM in stead of 9:00 PM.

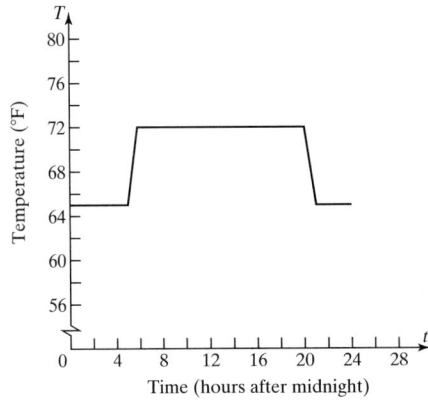

88. (a) $R(0) = 1080$; the estimated revenue in 2005 is $1080 million.

   $R(3) = 6735.3$; the estimated revenue in 2008 is $6735.3 million.

   $R(5) = 12{,}212.5$; the estimated revenue in 2010 is $12,212.5 million.

   (b) $r(x) = 170.7x^2 - 334x - 1517.5$

(c) $r(5) = 1080$; the estimated revenue in 2005 is $1080 million.

   $r(8) = 6735.3$; the estimated revenue in 2008 is $6735.3 million.

   $r(10) = 12{,}212.5$; the estimated revenue in 2010 is $12,212.5 million.

   (d) x is the number of years after 2000.

89.

90. (a)   **(b)**   **(d)**

91. (a)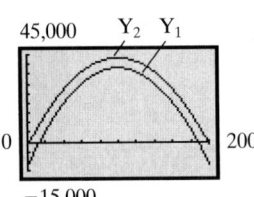

   (b) 10% tax

   (c) Y_1 is the graph of $p(x)$ shifted down vertically 10,000 units.

      Y_2 is the graph of $p(x)$ vertically compressed by a factor of 0.9.

   (d) 10% tax

92. (a)   **(b)**

93. (a)   **(b)**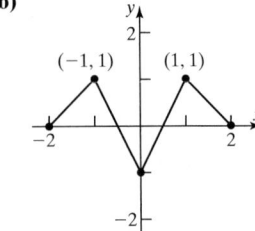

94. (a) $(-2, -2)$ **(b)** $(3, -5)$ **(c)** $(-1, 3)$ **95. (a)** $(-4, 2)$ **(b)** $(1, -12)$ **(c)** $(-4, 5)$

96. The graph of $y = 4f(x)$ is a vertical stretch by a factor of 4. The graph of $y = f(4x)$ is a horizontal compression by a factor of $\dfrac{1}{4}$.

97. $\dfrac{16}{3}$ square units

2.6 Assess Your Understanding *(page 115)*

1. (a) $d(x) = \sqrt{x^4 - 15x^2 + 64}$

(b) $d(0) = 8$

(c) $d(1) = \sqrt{50} \approx 7.07$

(d)

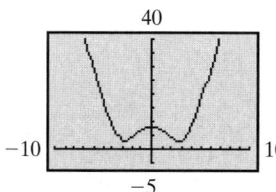

(e) d is smallest when $x \approx -2.74$
or $x \approx 2.74$.

2. (a) $d(x) = \sqrt{x^4 - 13x^2 + 49}$

(b) $d(0) = 7$

(c) $d(-1) = \sqrt{37} \approx 6.08$

(d)

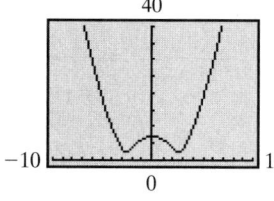

(e) d is smallest when $x \approx -2.55$
or $x \approx 2.55$.

3. (a) $d(x) = \sqrt{x^2 - x + 1}$

(b)

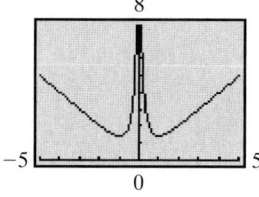

(c) d is smallest when $x = 0.5$.

4. (a) $d(x) = \sqrt{x^2 + \dfrac{1}{x^2}}$

(b)

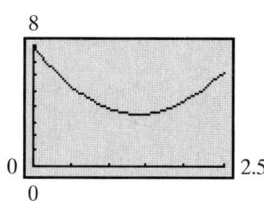

(c) d is smallest when $x = -1$ or $x = 1$.

5. $A(x) = \dfrac{1}{2}x^4$ **6.** $A(x) = \dfrac{9}{2}x - \dfrac{1}{2}x^3$

7. (a) $A(x) = x(16 - x^2)$

(b) Domain: $\{x \mid 0 < x < 4\}$

(c) The area is largest when $x \approx 2.31$.

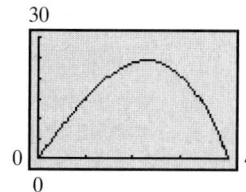

8. (a) $A(x) = 2x\sqrt{4 - x^2}$ **(b)** $p(x) = 4x + 2\sqrt{4 - x^2}$
(c) A is largest when $x \approx 1.41$.   **(d)** p is largest when $x \approx 1.79$.

9. (a) $A(x) = 4x\sqrt{4 - x^2}$ **(b)** $p(x) = 4x + 4\sqrt{4 - x^2}$
(c) A is largest when $x \approx 1.41$.   **(d)** p is largest when $x \approx 1.41$.

10. (a) $A(r) = 4r^2$ **(b)** $p(r) = 8r$

11. (a) $A(x) = x^2 + \dfrac{25 - 20x + 4x^2}{\pi}$

(b) Domain: $\{x \mid 0 < x < 2.5\}$

(c) A is smallest when $x \approx 1.40$ m.

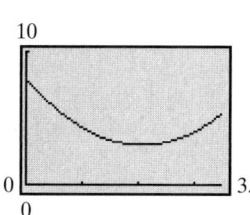

12. (a) $A(x) = \dfrac{\sqrt{3}}{4}x^2 + \dfrac{100 - 60x + 9x^2}{4\pi}$

(b) $0 < x < \dfrac{10}{3}$

(c) A is smallest when $x \approx 2.08$ m.

13. (a) $C(x) = x$ **(b)** $A(x) = \dfrac{x^2}{4\pi}$

14. (a) $p(x) = x$ **(b)** $A(x) = \dfrac{1}{16}x^2$

15. (a) $A(r) = 2r^2$ **(b)** $p(r) = 6r$

16. $C(x) = \dfrac{2\sqrt{3}}{3}\pi x$

17. $A(x) = \left(\dfrac{\pi}{3} - \dfrac{\sqrt{3}}{4}\right)x^2$

18. $d(t) = 50t$

19. (a) $d(t) = \sqrt{2500t^2 - 360t + 13}$

20. $V(h) = \pi h\left(R^2 - \dfrac{h^2}{4}\right)$

22. (a) $C(x) = 500x + 700\sqrt{x^2 - 10x + 29}, 0 \le x \le 5$

(b) d is smallest when $t \approx 0.07$ hr.

21. $V(r) = \dfrac{\pi H(R - r)r^2}{R}$

(b) $C(1) = \$3630.50$ **(c)** $C(3) = \$3479.90$

(d)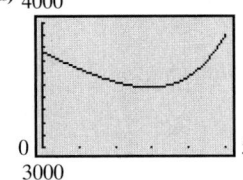

(e) The least cost occurs when $x \approx 2.96$ mi.

23. (a) $T(x) = \dfrac{12 - x}{5} + \dfrac{\sqrt{x^2 + 4}}{3}$ **(b)** $\{x | 0 \le x \le 12\}$ **(c)** 3.09 hr   **(d)** 3.55 hr

24. $V(h) = \dfrac{\pi}{48}h^3$

25. (a) $V(x) = x(24 - 2x)^2$ **(d)** V is largest when $x = 4$.

(b) 972 in.^{3} **(c)** 160 in.^{3}

26. (a) $A(x) = x^2 + \dfrac{40}{x}$ **(d)** A is smallest when $x \approx 2.71$ ft.

(b) 41 ft^2 **(c)** 24 ft^2

Review Exercises (page 119)

1. Function; domain $\{-1, 2, 4\}$, range $\{0, 3\}$ **2.** Not a function

3. (a) 2   **(b)** -2 **(c)** $-\dfrac{3x}{x^2 - 1}$ **(d)** $-\dfrac{3x}{x^2 - 1}$ **(e)** $\dfrac{3(x - 2)}{x^2 - 4x + 3}$ **(f)** $\dfrac{6x}{4x^2 - 1}$

4. (a) $\dfrac{4}{3}$ **(b)** -4 **(c)** $\dfrac{x^2}{-x + 1}$ **(d)** $-\dfrac{x^2}{x + 1}$ **(e)** $\dfrac{(x - 2)^2}{x - 1}$ **(f)** $\dfrac{4x^2}{2x + 1}$

5. (a) 0   **(b)** 0   **(c)** $\sqrt{x^2 - 4}$ **(d)** $-\sqrt{x^2 - 4}$ **(e)** $\sqrt{x^2 - 4x}$ **(f)** $2\sqrt{x^2 - 1}$

6. (a) 0   **(b)** 0   **(c)** $|x^2 - 4|$ **(d)** $-|x^2 - 4|$ **(e)** $|x^2 - 4x|$ **(f)** $4|x^2 - 1|$

7. (a) 0   **(b)** 0   **(c)** $\dfrac{x^2 - 4}{x^2}$ **(d)** $-\dfrac{x^2 - 4}{x^2}$ **(e)** $\dfrac{x(x - 4)}{(x - 2)^2}$ **(f)** $\dfrac{x^2 - 1}{x^2}$

8. (a) $-\dfrac{8}{5}$ **(b)** $\dfrac{8}{5}$ **(c)** $-\dfrac{x^3}{x^2 - 9}$ **(d)** $-\dfrac{x^3}{x^2 - 9}$ **(e)** $\dfrac{(x - 2)^3}{x^2 - 4x - 5}$ **(f)** $\dfrac{8x^3}{4x^2 - 9}$ **9.** $\{x | x \ne -3, x \ne 3\}$ **10.** $\{x | x \ne 2\}$

11. $\{x | x \le 2\}$ **12.** $\{x | x \ge -2\}$ **13.** $\{x | x > 0\}$ **14.** $\{x | x \ne 0\}$ **15.** $\{x | x \ne -3, x \ne 1\}$ **16.** $\{x | x \ne -1, x \ne 4\}$

17. $(f + g)(x) = 2x + 3$; Domain: all real numbers

$(f - g)(x) = -4x + 1$; Domain: all real numbers

$(f \cdot g)(x) = -3x^2 + 5x + 2$; Domain: all real numbers

$\left(\dfrac{f}{g}\right)(x) = \dfrac{2 - x}{3x + 1}$; Domain: $\left\{x \middle| x \ne -\dfrac{1}{3}\right\}$

18. $(f + g)(x) = 4x$; Domain: all real numbers

$(f - g)(x) = -2$; Domain: all real numbers

$(f \cdot g)(x) = 4x^2 - 1$; Domain: all real numbers

$\left(\dfrac{f}{g}\right)(x) = \dfrac{2x - 1}{2x + 1}$; Domain: $\left\{x \middle| x \ne -\dfrac{1}{2}\right\}$

19. $(f + g)(x) = 3x^2 + 4x + 1$; Domain: all real numbers

$(f - g)(x) = 3x^2 - 2x + 1$; Domain: all real numbers

$(f \cdot g)(x) = 9x^3 + 3x^2 + 3x$; Domain: all real numbers

$\left(\dfrac{f}{g}\right)(x) = \dfrac{3x^2 + x + 1}{3x}$; Domain: $\{x | x \ne 0\}$

20. $(f + g)(x) = 1 + 4x + x^2$; Domain: all real numbers

$(f - g)(x) = -1 + 2x - x^2$; Domain: all real numbers

$(f \cdot g)(x) = 3x + 3x^2 + 3x^3$; Domain: all real numbers

$\left(\dfrac{f}{g}\right)(x) = \dfrac{3x}{1 + x + x^2}$; Domain: all real numbers

21. $(f + g)(x) = \dfrac{x^2 + 2x - 1}{x(x - 1)}$; Domain: $\{x | x \ne 0, x \ne 1\}$

$(f - g)(x) = \dfrac{x^2 + 1}{x(x - 1)}$; Domain: $\{x | x \ne 0, x \ne 1\}$

$(f \cdot g)(x) = \dfrac{x + 1}{x(x - 1)}$; Domain: $\{x | x \ne 0, x \ne 1\}$

$\left(\dfrac{f}{g}\right)(x) = \dfrac{x(x + 1)}{x - 1}$; Domain: $\{x | x \ne 0, x \ne 1\}$

22. $(f + g)(x) = \dfrac{4x - 9}{x(x - 3)}$; Domain: $\{x | x \ne 0, x \ne 3\}$

$(f - g)(x) = \dfrac{-2x + 9}{x(x - 3)}$; Domain: $\{x | x \ne 0, x \ne 3\}$

$(f \cdot g)(x) = \dfrac{3}{x(x - 3)}$; Domain: $\{x | x \ne 0, x \ne 3\}$

$\left(\dfrac{f}{g}\right)(x) = \dfrac{x}{3(x - 3)}$; Domain: $\{x | x \ne 0, x \ne 3\}$

23. $-4x + 1 - 2h$ **24.** $6x - 2 + 3h$

25. (a) Domain: $\{x | -4 \le x \le 3\}$; Range: $\{y | -3 \le y \le 3\}$ **(b)** $(0, 0)$ **(c)** -1 **(d)** -4 **(e)** $\{x | 0 < x \le 3\}$

(f)   **(g)**   **(h)**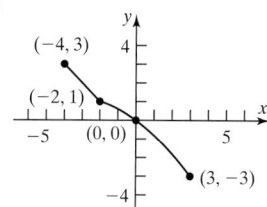

26. (a) Domain: $\{x | -5 \le x \le 4\}$; Range: $\{y | -3 \le y \le 1\}$ **(b)** 1 **(c)** $(0, 0), (4, 0)$ **(d)** 3 **(e)** $\{x | -5 \le x < 0\}$

(f)   **(g)**   **(h)**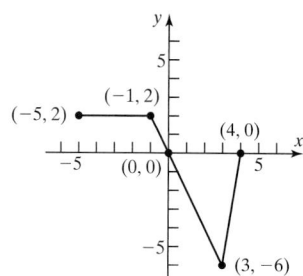

27. (a) Domain: $\{x | -4 \le x \le 4\}$ or $[-4, 4]$
Range: $\{y | -3 \le y \le 1\}$ or $[-3, 1]$
(b) Increasing on $(-4, -1)$ and $(3, 4)$
Decreasing on $(-1, 3)$
(c) Local maximum is 1 and occurs at $x = -1$.
Local minimum is -3 and occurs at $x = 3$.
(d) No symmetry
(e) Neither
(f) x-intercepts: $-2, 0, 4$; y-intercept: 0

28. (a) Domain: all real numbers or $(-\infty, \infty)$
Range: all real numbers or $(-\infty, \infty)$
(b) Increasing on $(-\infty, -2)$ and $(2, \infty)$
Decreasing on $(-2, 2)$
(c) Local maximum is 1 and occurs at $x = -2$.
Local minimum is -1 and occurs at $x = 2$.
(d) Origin
(e) Odd
(f) x-intercepts: $-3, 0, 3$; y-intercept: 0

29. Odd **30.** Even **31.** Even **32.** Neither **33.** Neither **34.** Neither **35.** Odd **36.** Odd

37.

Local maximum: 4.04 at $x = -0.91$

Local minimum: -2.04 at $x = 0.91$

Increasing: $(-3, -0.91)$; $(0.91, 3)$
Decreasing: $(-0.91, 0.91)$

38.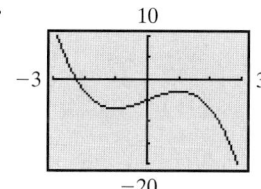

Local maximum: -3 at $x = 1$

Local minimum: -7 at $x = -1$

Increasing: $(-1, 1)$
Decreasing: $(-3, -1)$; $(1, 3)$

39.

Local maximum: 1.53 at $x = 0.41$

Local minima: 0.54 at $x = -0.34$
and -3.56 at $x = 1.80$
Increasing: $(-0.34, 0.41)$; $(1.80, 3)$
Decreasing: $(-2, -0.34)$; $(0.41, 1.80)$

40.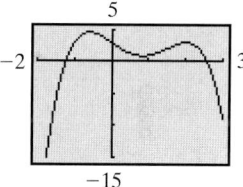

Local maxima: 4.62 at $x = -0.59$
and 3 at $x = 2$
Local minimum: 0.92 at $x = 0.84$

Increasing: $(-2, -0.59)$; $(0.84, 2)$
Decreasing: $(-0.59, 0.84)$; $(2, 3)$

41. (a) 23 **(b)** 7 **(c)** 47 **42. (a)** 15 **(b)** 3 **(c)** 57 **43.** -5 **44.** 10 **45.** -17 **46.** 2 **47.** No **48.** Yes **49.** Yes **50.** Yes

51.   **52.**   **53.**   **54.**

55.

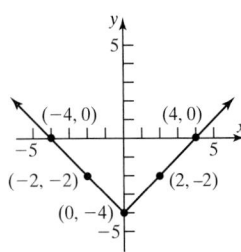

Intercepts: $(-4, 0)$, $(4, 0)$, $(0, -4)$
Domain: all real numbers
Range: $\{y \mid y \geq -4\}$ or $[-4, \infty)$

56.

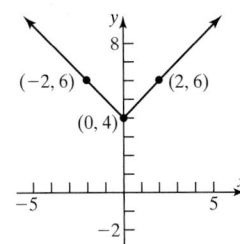

Intercept: $(0, 4)$
Domain: all real numbers
Range: $\{y \mid y \geq 4\}$ or $[4, \infty)$

57.

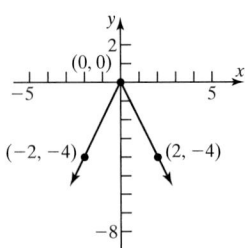

Intercept: $(0, 0)$
Domain: all real numbers
Range: $\{y \mid y \leq 0\}$ or $(-\infty, 0]$

58.

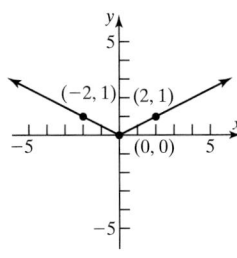

Intercept: $(0, 0)$
Domain: all real numbers
Range: $\{y \mid y \geq 0\}$ or $[0, \infty)$

59.

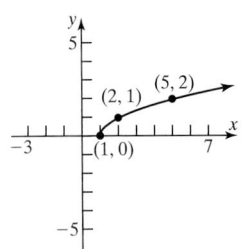

Intercept: $(1, 0)$
Domain: $\{x \mid x \geq 1\}$ or $[1, \infty)$
Range: $\{y \mid y \geq 0\}$ or $[0, \infty)$

60.

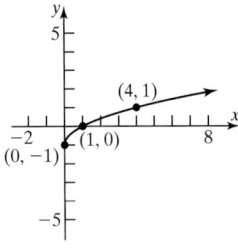

Intercepts: $(0, -1)$, $(1, 0)$
Domain: $\{x \mid x \geq 0\}$ or $[0, \infty)$
Range: $\{y \mid y \geq -1\}$ or $[-1, \infty)$

61.

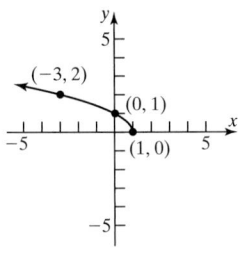

Intercepts: $(0, 1)$, $(1, 0)$
Domain: $\{x \mid x \leq 1\}$ or $(-\infty, 1]$
Range: $\{y \mid y \geq 0\}$ or $[0, \infty)$

62.

Intercepts: $\left(-3, 0\right)$, $\left(0, -\sqrt{3}\right)$
Domain: $\{x \mid x \geq -3\}$ or $[-3, \infty)$
Range: $\{y \mid y \leq 0\}$ or $(-\infty, 0]$

63.

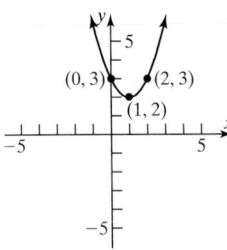

Intercept: $(0, 3)$

Domain: all real numbers

Range: $\{y \mid y \geq 2\}$ or $[2, \infty)$

64.

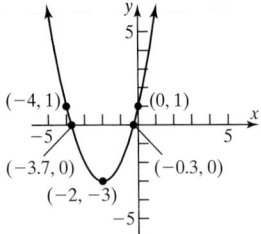

Intercepts: $\left(-2 - \sqrt{3}, 0\right)$,

$\left(-2 + \sqrt{3}, 0\right)$, $(0, 1)$

Domain: all real numbers
Range: $\{y \mid y \geq -3\}$ or $[-3, \infty)$

65.

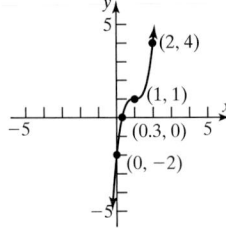

Intercepts: $(0, -2)$,

$\left(1 - \dfrac{\sqrt[3]{9}}{3}, 0\right)$ or about $(0.3, 0)$

Domain: all real numbers
Range: all real numbers

66.

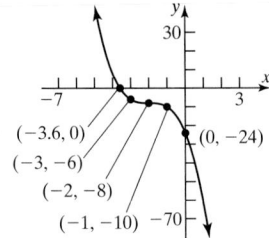

Intercepts: $(0, -24)$,

$\left(-2 - \sqrt[3]{4}, 0\right)$ or about $(-3.6, 0)$

Domain: all real numbers
Range: all real numbers

67. (a) $\{x \mid x > -2\}$ or $(-2, \infty)$

(b) $(0, 0)$

(c)

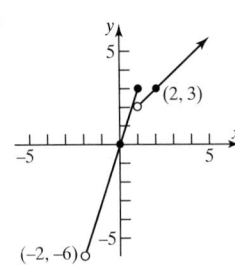

(d) $\{y \mid y > -6\}$ or $(-6, \infty)$

(e) Discontinuous at $x = 1$

68. (a) $\{x \mid x > -3\}$ or $(-3, \infty)$

(b) $(0, -1)$, $\left(\dfrac{1}{3}, 0\right)$

(c)

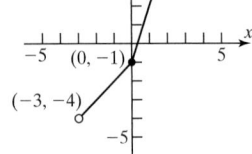

(d) $\{y \mid y > -4\}$ or $(-4, \infty)$

(e) Continuous

69. (a) $\{x \mid x \geq -4\}$ or $[-4, \infty)$

(b) $(0, 1)$

(c)

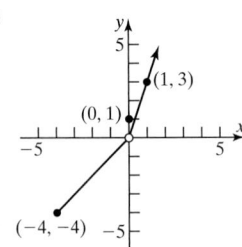

(d) $\{y \mid -4 \leq y < 0$ or $y > 0\}$
or $[-4, 0) \cup (0, \infty)$

(e) Discontinuous at $x = 0$

70. (a) $\{x \mid x \geq -2\}$ or $[-2, \infty)$

(b) $(0, 0)$

(c)

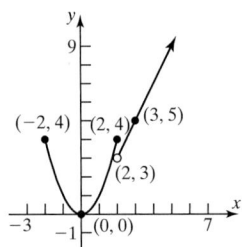

(d) $\{y \mid y \geq 0\}$ or $[0, \infty)$

(e) Discontinuous at $x = 2$

71. $A = 11$ **72.** $A = 8$

73. (a) $A(x) = (8.5 - 2x)(11 - 2x)$

(b) $0 \le x < 4.25, 0 < A \le 93.5$

(c) $A(1) = 58.5$ in.^{2}, $A(1.2) = 52.46$ in.^{2}, $A(1.5) = 44$ in.^{2}

(d)

74. (a) $A(x) = 2x^2 + \dfrac{40}{x}$

(b) 42 ft^2

(c) 28 ft^2

(d)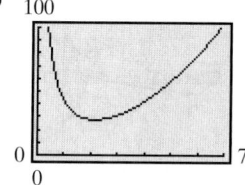

(e) $A(x) \approx 70$ when $x \approx 0.64$ in.; $A(x) \approx 50$ when $x \approx 1.28$ in. A is smallest when $x \approx 2.15$ ft.

75. (a) $A(x) = 10x - x^3$ **(b)** The largest area that can be enclosed by the rectangle is approximately 12.17 square units.

Chapter Test *(page 122)*

1. (a) Function; domain: $\{2, 4, 6, 8\}$; range: $\{5, 6, 7, 8\}$ **(b)** Not a function   **(c)** Not a function   **(d)** Function; domain: all real numbers;

range: $\{y | y \ge 2\}$ **2.** Domain: $\left\{ x \Big| x \le \dfrac{4}{5} \right\}$; $f(-1) = 3$ **3.** Domain: $\{x | x \ne -2\}$; $g(-1) = 1$ **4.** Domain: $\{x | x \ne -9, x \ne 4\}$; $h(-1) = \dfrac{1}{8}$

5. (a) Domain: $\{x | -5 \le x \le 5\}$; range: $\{y | -3 \le y \le 3\}$ **(b)** $(0, 2), (-2, 0)$, and $(2, 0)$ **(c)** $f(1) = 3$ **(d)** $x = -5$ and $x = 3$

(e) $\{x | -5 \le x < -2$ or $2 < x \le 5\}$ or $[-5, -2) \cup (2, 5]$ **6.** Local maxima: $f(-0.85) \approx -0.86$; $f(2.35) \approx 15.55$; local minima: $f(0) = -2$;

the function is increasing on the intervals $(-5, -0.85)$ and $(0, 2.35)$ and decreasing on the intervals $(-0.85, 0)$ and $(2.35, 5)$.

7. (a)

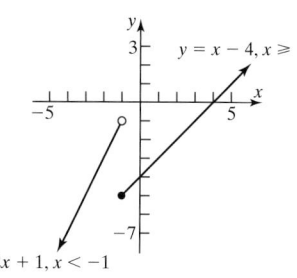

$y = x - 4, x \ge -1$

$y = 2x + 1, x < -1$

(b) $(0, -4), (4, 0)$

(c) $g(-5) = -9$

(d) $g(2) = -2$

8. 19

9. (a) $(f - g) = 2x^2 - 3x + 3$

(b) $(f \cdot g) = 6x^3 - 4x^2 + 3x - 2$

(c) $f(x + h) - f(x) = 4xh + 2h^2$

10. (a)

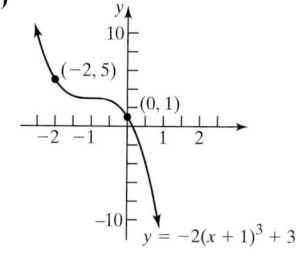

$(-2, 5)$

$(0, 1)$

$y = -2(x + 1)^3 + 3$

(b)

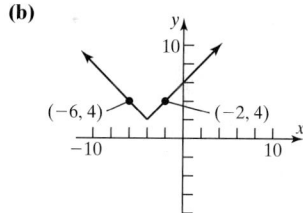

$(-6, 4)$ $(-2, 4)$

11. (a) 8.67% occurring in 1997 $(x \approx 5)$ **(b)** The model predicts that the interest rate will be -10.343%. This is not reasonable.

12. (a) $V(x) = \dfrac{x^2}{8} - \dfrac{5x}{4} + \dfrac{\pi x^2}{64}$ **(b)** 1297.61 ft^3

Cumulative Review *(page 123)*

1. $\left\{ \dfrac{4}{5} \right\}$ **2.** $\{3, 4\}$ **3.** $\left\{ -\dfrac{1}{3}, 2 \right\}$ **4.** $\left\{ -\dfrac{1}{2} \right\}$ **5.** No real solution   **6.** $\{-7\}$ **7.** $\{-31\}$ **8.** $\left\{ \dfrac{1}{3}, 1 \right\}$ **9.** $\left\{ \dfrac{1 - \sqrt{15}i}{4}, \dfrac{1 + \sqrt{15}i}{4} \right\}$

10. $\{x | 1 < x < 4\}$

11.

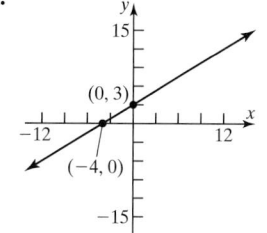

$(0, 3)$

$(-4, 0)$

12.

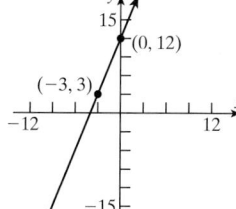

$(0, 12)$

$(-3, 3)$

13.

$(-1, 2)$

14.

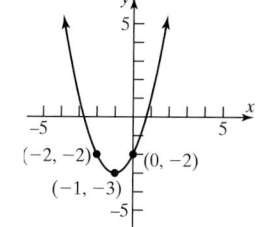

$(-2, -2)$ $(0, -2)$

$(-1, -3)$

15. (a) Domain: $\{x|-4 \le x \le 4\}$; range: $\{y|-1 \le y \le 3\}$ **(b)** $(-1,0), (0,-1), (1,0)$ **(c)** y-axis **(d)** 1 **(e)** -4 and 4 **(f)** $\{x|-1 < x < 1\}$

(g)

(h)

(i)

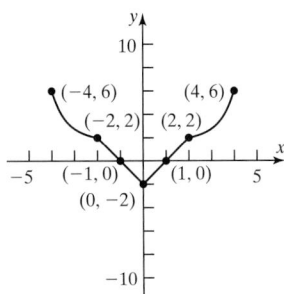

(j) even **(k)** $(0,4)$ **(l)** $(-4,0)$ **(m)** f has a local minimum of -1 at $x = 0$ **(n)** 1

16. $5\sqrt{2}$ **17.** $(-2,-1)$ and $(2,3)$ are on the graph. **18.** x-interce pts: $-5, \dfrac{1}{3}$; y-intercept: -5 **19.** $\{-1.10, 0.26, 1.48, 2.36\}$

20. $y = -\dfrac{1}{2}x + \dfrac{13}{2}$

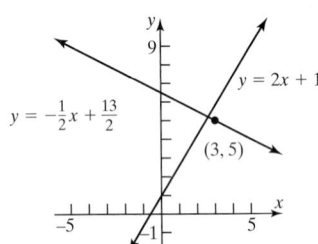

21. Yes, a function **22. (a)** -3 **(b)** $x^2 - 4x - 2$ **(c)** $x^2 + 4x + 1$ **(d)** $-x^2 + 4x - 1$

(e) $x^2 - 3$ **(f)** $2x + h - 4$ **23.** $\{z|z \ne -1, z \ne 7\}$ **24.** Yes, a function

25. (a) No **(b)** -1; $(-2,-1)$ is on the graph. **(c)** -8; $(-8, 2)$ is on the graph.

26. $2(x^2 + 1)^{1/2}(4x^2 + 1)$ **27.** $\dfrac{(3x + 10)(x + 5)^{1/2}}{x + 5}$

CHAPTER 3 Linear and Quadratic Functions

3.1 Assess Your Understanding (page 132)

7. slope; y-intercept **8.** $-4; 3$ **9.** positive **10.** T **11.** F **12.** F

13. (a) $m = 2; b = 3$

(b)

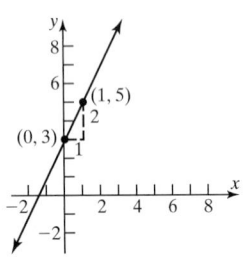

(c) Domain and Range: $(-\infty, \infty)$
(d) 2 **(e)** Increasing

14. (a) $m = 5; b = -4$

(b)

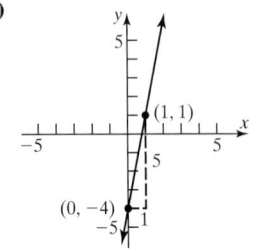

(c) Domain and Range: $(-\infty, \infty)$
(d) 5 **(e)** Increasing

15. (a) $m = -3; b = 4$

(b)

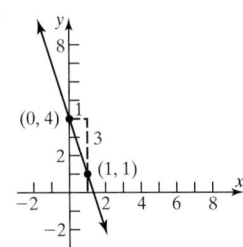

(c) Domain and Range: $(-\infty, \infty)$
(d) -3 **(e)** Decreasing

16. (a) $m = -1; b = 6$

(b)

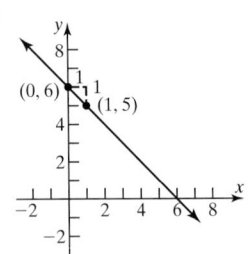

(c) Domain and Range: $(-\infty, \infty)$

(d) -1 **(e)** Decreasing

17. (a) $m = \dfrac{1}{4}; b = -3$

(b)

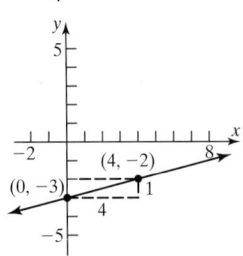

(c) Domain and Range: $(-\infty, \infty)$

(d) $\dfrac{1}{4}$ **(e)** Increasing

18. (a) $m = -\dfrac{2}{3}; b = 4$

(b)

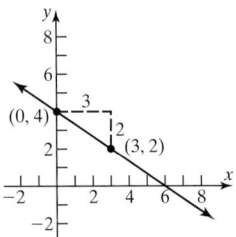

(c) Domain and Range: $(-\infty, \infty)$

(d) $-\dfrac{2}{3}$ **(e)** Decreasing

19. (a) $m = 0; b = 4$

(b)

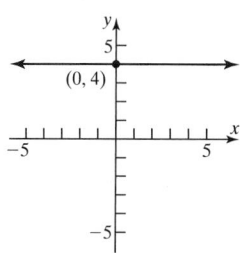

(c) Domain: $(-\infty, \infty)$

Range: $\{y \mid y = 4\}$

(d) 0 **(e)** Constant

20. (a) $m = 0; b = -2$

(b)

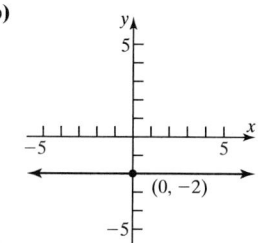

(c) Domain: $(-\infty, \infty)$

Range: $\{y \mid y = -2\}$

(d) 0 **(e)** Constant

21. Linear; $y = -3x - 2$
22. Nonlinear
23. Nonlinear
24. Linear; $y = 4x + 40$
25. Nonlinear
26. Linear; $y = 0.5x - 3$
27. Linear; $y = 8$
28. Nonlinear

29. (a) $\frac{1}{4}$ **(b)** $\left\{x \mid x > \frac{1}{4}\right\}$ or $\left(\frac{1}{4}, \infty\right)$

(c) 1 **(d)** $\{x \mid x \leq 1\}$ or $(-\infty, 1]$

(e)

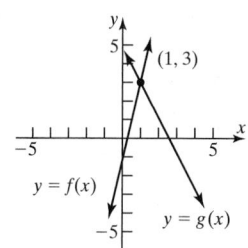

30. (a) $-\frac{5}{3}$ **(b)** $\left\{x \mid x < -\frac{5}{3}\right\}$ or $\left(-\infty, -\frac{5}{3}\right)$

(c) 2 **(d)** $\{x \mid x \geq 2\}$ or $[2, \infty)$

(e)

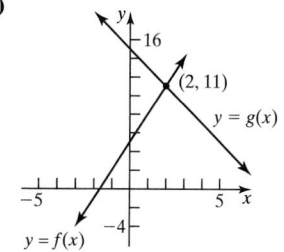

31. (a) 40 **(b)** 88 **(c)** -40 **(d)** $\{x \mid x > 40\}$ or $(40, \infty)$ **(e)** $\{x \mid x \leq 88\}$ or $(-\infty, 88]$ **(f)** $\{x \mid -40 < x < 88\}$ or $(-40, 88)$ **32. (a)** 5 **(b)** -15
(c) 15 **(d)** $\{x \mid x < 5\}$ or $(-\infty, 5)$ **(e)** $\{x \mid x \geq -15\}$ or $[-15, \infty)$ **(f)** $\{x \mid -15 < x < 15\}$ or $(-15, 15)$ **33. (a)** -4 **(b)** $\{x \mid x < -4\}$ or
$(-\infty, -4)$ **34. (a)** 2 **(b)** $\{x \mid x \leq 2\}$ or $(-\infty, 2]$ **35. (a)** -6 **(b)** $\{x \mid -6 \leq x < 5\}$ or $[-6, 5)$ **36. (a)** 7 **(b)** $\{x \mid -4 \leq x < 7\}$ or $[-4, 7)$
37. (a) \$45 **(b)** 180 mi **(c)** 260 mi **(d)** $\{x \mid x \geq 0\}$ or $[0, \infty)$ **38. (a)** \$24 **(b)** 64 min **(c)** 144 min **(d)** $\{x \mid 0 \leq x \leq 43,200\}$ or $[0, 43200]$
39. (a) \$16; 600 T-shirts **(b)** $\$0 \leq p < \$16$ **(c)** The price will increase. **40. (a)** \$3; 7000 hot dogs **(b)** $p > \$3$ **(c)** The price will decrease.
41. (a) $\{x \mid 7825 \leq x \leq 31,850\}$ or $[7825, 31,850]$ **(b)** \$2308.75 **42. (a)** $\{p \mid p > 136.5\}$ or $(136.5, \infty)$ **(b)** \$13.84 million
(c) The independent variable is adjusted gross income, x. **(c)**
The dependent variable is the tax bill, T.

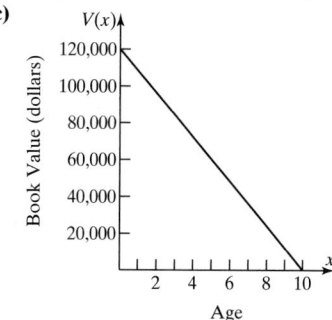

(e) \$25,000

(d) \$165.75 million

43. (a) $x = 5000$ **(b)** $x > 5000$ **44. (a)** $x = 7500$ **(b)** $x > 7500$
45. (a) $V(x) = -1000x + 3000$ **(b)** $\{x \mid 0 \leq x \leq 3\}$ or $[0, 3]$ **46. (a)** $V(x) = -12,000x + 120,000$ **(b)** $\{x \mid 0 \leq x \leq 10\}$ or $[0, 10]$
(c)

(c)

(d) \$1000 **(e)** After 1 year

(d) \$72,000 **(e)** After 4 years

47. (a) $C(x) = 90x + 1800$
(b)

(c) \$3060   **(d)** 22 bicycles

48. (a) \$1805   **(b)** $C(x) = 90x + 1805$
(c)

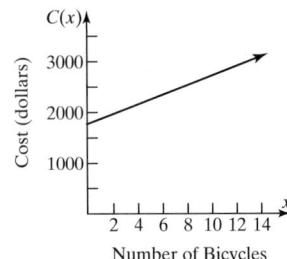

(d) \$3065   **(e)** 21 bicycles

49. (a) $C(x) = 0.07x + 29$ **(b)** \$36.70; \$45.10   **50. (a)** $C(x) = 0.05x + 5$ **(b)** \$10.25; \$14

51. (a)

(e)

(b) Since each input (price) corresponds to a single output (quantity demanded), we know that quantity demanded is a function of price. Also, because the average rate of change is a constant $-\$0.4$ per MP3 player, the function is linear.

(c) $q(p) = -0.4p + 160$

(d) $\{p \mid 0 \le p \le 400\}$ or $[0, 400]$

(f) If price increases by \$1, quantity demanded of MP3 players decreases by 0.4 player.

(g) q-intercept: When the price is \$0, 160 MP3 players will be demanded. p-intercept: There will be 0 MP3 players demanded when the price is \$400.

52. (a)

(e)

(b) Since each input (soda) corresponds to a single output (hot dogs), we know that number of hot dogs purchased is a function of number of sodas purchased. Also, because the average rate of change is a constant -0.6 hot dog per soda, the function is linear.

(c) $h(s) = -0.6s + 12$ **(d)** $\{s \mid 0 \le s \le 20\}$ or $[0, 20]$

(f) If the number of hot dogs purchased increases by 1, the number of sodas purchased decreases by 0.6.

(g) h-intercept: If 0 sodas are purchased, then 12 hot dogs may be purchased. s-intercept: If 0 hot dogs are purchased, then 20 sodas can be purchased.

53. (d), (e)   **54.** (b), (e)   **55.** $b = 0$; yes

3.2 Assess Your Understanding *(page 139)*

3. scatter diagram   **4.** T   **5.** Linear relation, $m > 0$ **6.** Nonlinear relation   **7.** Linear relation, $m < 0$ **8.** Linear relation, $m > 0$ **9.** Nonlinear relation
10. Nonlinear relation

11. (a)

(c)

(e)

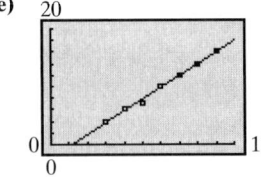

(b) Answers vary. Using $(4, 6)$ and $(8, 14)$, $y = 2x - 2$.

(d) $y = 2.0357x - 2.3571$

12. (a)   **(c)**   **(e)**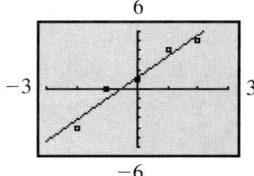

(b) Answers will vary. Using $(5, 2)$ and $(11, 9)$, $y = \frac{7}{6}x - \frac{23}{6}$.   **(d)** $y = 1.1286x - 3.8619$

13. (a)   **(c)**   **(e)**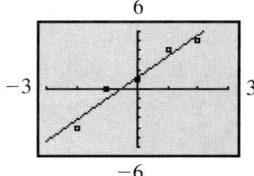

(b) Answers will vary. Using $(-2, -4)$ and $(2, 5)$, $y = \frac{9}{4}x + \frac{1}{2}$.   **(d)** $y = 2.2x + 1.2$

14. (a)   **(c)**   **(e)**

(b) Answers will vary. Using $(-2, 7)$ and $(2, 0)$, $y = -\frac{7}{4}x + \frac{7}{2}$.   **(d)** $y = -1.8x + 3.6$

15. (a)   **(c)**   **(e)**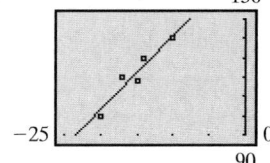

(b) Answers will vary. Using $(-20, 100)$ and $(-10, 140)$, $y = 4x + 180$ **(d)** $y = 3.8613x + 180.2920$

16. (a)   **(c)**   **(e)**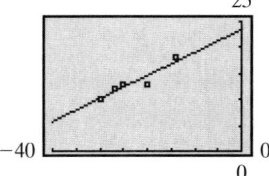

(b) Answers will vary. Using $(-30, 10)$ and $(-14, 18)$, $y = \frac{1}{2}x + 25$.   **(d)** $y = 0.4421x + 23.4559$

17. (a)

(b) Linear

(c) Answers will vary. Using the points $(39.52, 210)$ and $(66.45, 280)$, $y = 2.599x + 107.288$.

(d)

(e) 269 calories

(f) If the weight of a candy bar is increased by 1 gram, the number of calories will increase by 2.599.

18. (a) No

(b)

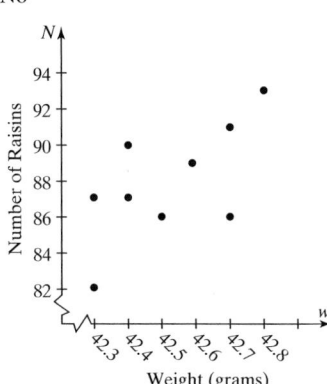

(c) Answers will vary. Using the points (42.3, 82) and (42.8, 93), $N = 22w - 848.6$.

(d)

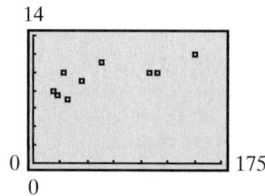

(e) $N(w) = 22w - 848.6$

(f) Approximately 86 raisins will be in a box weighing 42.5 grams.

(g) If the weight is increased by 1 gram, the number of raisins will increase by 22 raisins.

19. (a)

(b) $C(H) = 0.3734H + 7.3268$

(c) If height increases by 1 inch, head circumference increases by about 0.3734 inch.

(d) About 17.0 inches   **(e)** About 26.98 inches

20. (a)

(b) $L(G) = 0.0261G + 7.8738$

(c) If gestation period increases by 1 day, life expectancy increases by about 0.0261 year.

(d) About 10.2 years

21. (a) No

(b)

(c) $D = -1.3355p + 86.1974$

(d) If the price increases $1, the quantity sold per day decreases by about 1.34 pairs of jeans.

(e) $D(p) = -1.3355p + 86.1974$ **(f)** $\{p \mid 0 < p \le 64\}$

(g) About 49 pairs

22. (a) No

(b)

(c) $S = 2.0667A + 292.8869$

(d) As advertising increases by $1000, sales increase by about $2067.

(e) $S(A) = 2.0667A + 292.8869$

(f) $\{A \mid A \ge 0\}$ **(g)** Approximately $345 thousand

23.

No, the data do not follow a linear pattern.

24. $y = 1.5x + 3.5; r = 1$ **25.** No linear relation

3.3 Assess Your Understanding *(page 151)*

5. parabola   **6.** axis or axis of symmetry   **7.** $-\dfrac{b}{2a}$ **8.** T   **9.** T   **10.** T   **11.** C   **12.** E   **13.** F   **14.** A   **15.** G   **16.** B   **17.** H   **18.** D

19.

20.

21.

22.

23.

24.

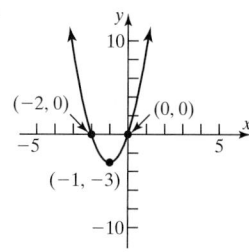

25. $f(x) = -(x + 1)^2 + 1$

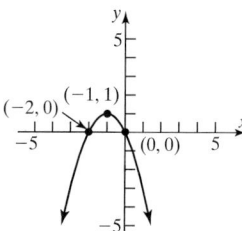

26. $f(x) = -2\left(x - \dfrac{3}{2}\right)^2 + \dfrac{13}{2}$

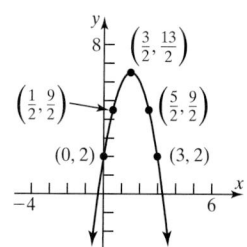

27. $f(x) = 2(x + 1)^2 - 4$

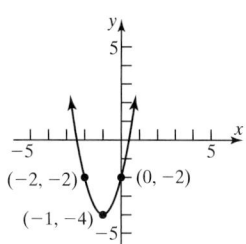

28. $f(x) = 3(x + 2)^2 - 7$

29. (a)

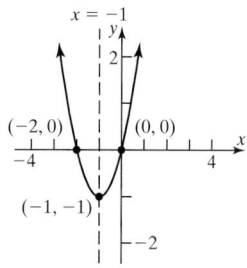

(b) Domain: $(-\infty, \infty)$
Range: $[-1, \infty)$
(c) Decreasing: $(-\infty, -1)$
Increasing: $(-1, \infty)$

30. (a)

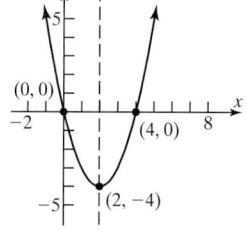

(b) Domain: $(-\infty, \infty)$
Range: $[-4, \infty)$
(c) Decreasing: $(-\infty, 2)$
Increasing: $(2, \infty)$

31. (a)

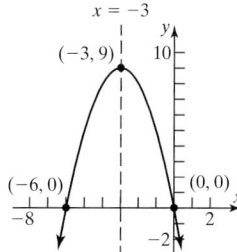

(b) Domain: $(-\infty, \infty)$
Range: $(-\infty, 9]$
(c) Increasing: $(-\infty, -3)$
Decreasing: $(-3, \infty)$

32. (a)

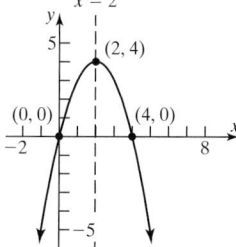

(b) Domain: $(-\infty, \infty)$
Range: $(-\infty, 4]$
(c) Increasing: $(-\infty, 2)$
Decreasing: $(2, \infty)$

33. (a)

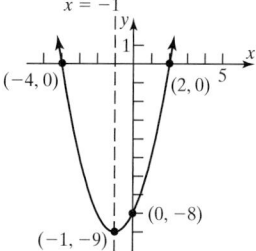

(b) Domain: $(-\infty, \infty)$
Range: $[-9, \infty)$
(c) Decreasing: $(-\infty, -1)$
Increasing: $(-1, \infty)$

34. (a)

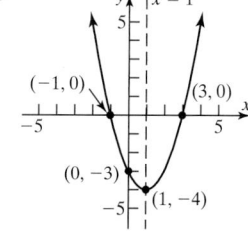

(b) Domain: $(-\infty, \infty)$
Range: $[-4, \infty)$
(c) Decreasing: $(-\infty, 1)$
Increasing: $(1, \infty)$

35. (a)

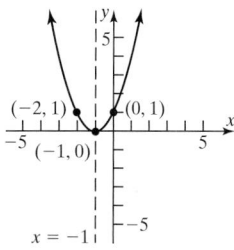

(b) Domain: $(-\infty, \infty)$
Range: $[0, \infty)$

(c) Decreasing: $(-\infty, -1)$

Increasing: $(-1, \infty)$

36. (a)

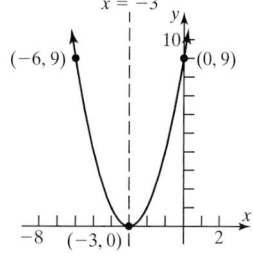

(b) Domain: $(-\infty, \infty)$
Range: $[0, \infty)$

(c) Decreasing: $(-\infty, -3)$

Increasing: $(-3, \infty)$

37. (a)

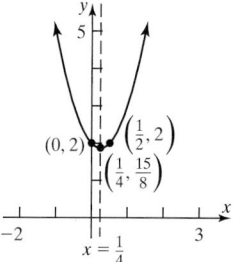

(b) Domain: $(-\infty, \infty)$

Range: $\left[\dfrac{15}{8}, \infty\right)$

(c) Decreasing: $\left(-\infty, \dfrac{1}{4}\right)$

Increasing: $\left(\dfrac{1}{4}, \infty\right)$

38. (a)

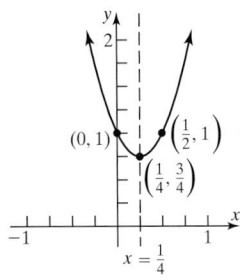

(b) Domain: $(-\infty, \infty)$

Range: $\left[\dfrac{3}{4}, \infty\right)$

(c) Decreasing: $\left(-\infty, \dfrac{1}{4}\right)$

Increasing: $\left(\dfrac{1}{4}, \infty\right)$

39. (a)

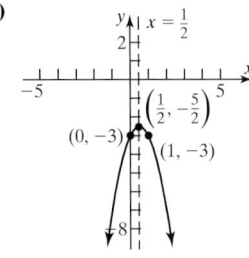

(b) Domain: $(-\infty, \infty)$

Range: $\left(-\infty, -\dfrac{5}{2}\right]$

(c) Increasing: $\left(-\infty, \dfrac{1}{2}\right)$

Decreasing: $\left(\dfrac{1}{2}, \infty\right)$

40. (a)

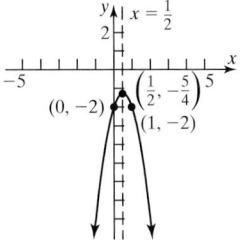

(b) Domain: $(-\infty, \infty)$

Range: $\left(-\infty, -\dfrac{5}{4}\right]$

(c) Increasing: $\left(-\infty, \dfrac{1}{2}\right)$

Decreasing: $\left(\dfrac{1}{2}, \infty\right)$

41. (a)

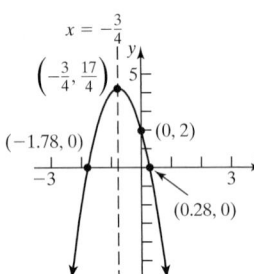

(b) Domain: $(-\infty, \infty)$

Range: $\left(-\infty, \dfrac{17}{4}\right]$

(c) Increasing: $\left(-\infty, -\dfrac{3}{4}\right)$

Decreasing: $\left(-\dfrac{3}{4}, \infty\right)$

42. (a)

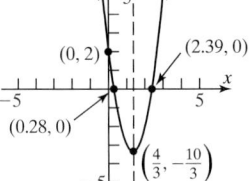

(b) Domain: $(-\infty, \infty)$

Range: $\left[-\dfrac{10}{3}, \infty\right)$

(c) Decreasing: $\left(-\infty, \dfrac{4}{3}\right)$

Increasing: $\left(\dfrac{4}{3}, \infty\right)$

43. $f(x) = (x + 1)^2 - 2 = x^2 + 2x - 1$ **44.** $f(x) = (x - 2)^2 + 1 = x^2 - 4x + 5$ **45.** $f(x) = -(x + 3)^2 + 5 = -x^2 - 6x - 4$

46. $f(x) = -(x - 2)^2 + 3 = -x^2 + 4x - 1$ **47.** $f(x) = 2(x - 1)^2 - 3 = 2x^2 - 4x - 1$ **48.** $f(x) = -2(x + 2)^2 + 6 = -2x^2 - 8x - 2$

49. Minimum value; -18 **50.** Maximum value; 18   **51.** Minimum value; -21 **52.** Minimum value; -1 **53.** Maximum value; 21

54. Maximum value; 11   **55.** Maximum value; 13   **56.** Minimum value; -1

57. (a)

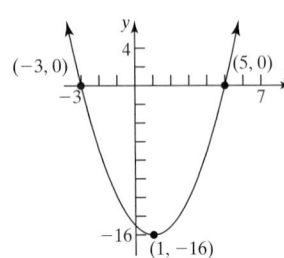

(b) Domain: $(-\infty, \infty)$

Range: $[-16, \infty)$

(c) Decreasing: $(-\infty, 1)$

Increasing: $(1, \infty)$

58. (a)

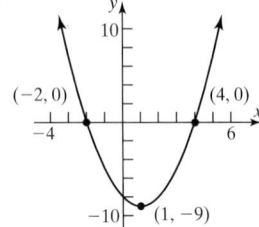

(b) Domain: $(-\infty, \infty)$

Range: $[-9, \infty)$

(c) Decreasing: $(-\infty, 1)$

Increasing: $(1, \infty)$

59. (a)

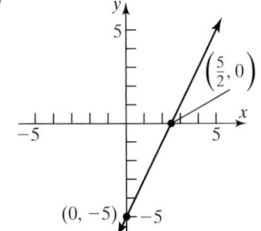

(b) Domain: $(-\infty, \infty)$

Range: $(-\infty, \infty)$

(c) Increasing: $(-\infty, \infty)$

60. (a)

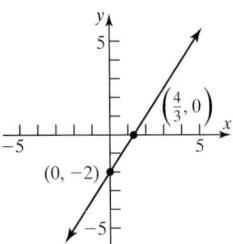

(b) Domain: $(-\infty, \infty)$

Range: $(-\infty, \infty)$

(c) Increasing: $(-\infty, \infty)$

61. (a)

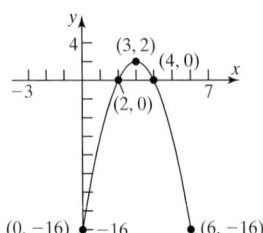

(b) Domain: $(-\infty, \infty)$

Range: $(-\infty, 2]$

(c) Increasing: $(-\infty, 3)$

Decreasing: $(3, \infty)$

62. (a)

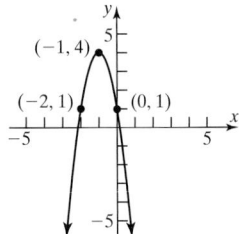

(b) Domain: $(-\infty, \infty)$

Range: $(-\infty, 4]$

(c) Increasing: $(-\infty, -1)$

Decreasing: $(-1, \infty)$

63. (a)

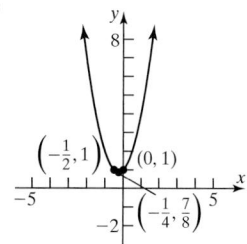

(b) Domain: $(-\infty, \infty)$

Range: $\left[\dfrac{7}{8}, \infty\right)$

(c) Decreasing: $\left(-\infty, -\dfrac{1}{4}\right)$

Increasing: $\left(-\dfrac{1}{4}, \infty\right)$

64. (a)

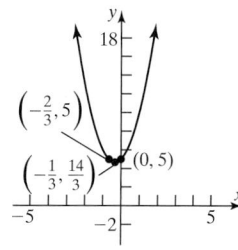

(b) Domain: $(-\infty, \infty)$

Range: $\left[\dfrac{14}{3}, \infty\right)$

(c) Decreasing: $\left(-\infty, -\dfrac{1}{3}\right)$

Increasing: $\left(-\dfrac{1}{3}, \infty\right)$

65. (a)

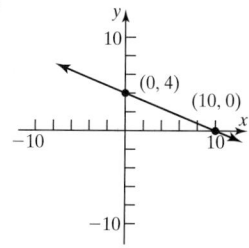

(b) Domain: $(-\infty, \infty)$

Range: $(-\infty, \infty)$

(c) Decreasing: $(-\infty, \infty)$

66. (a)

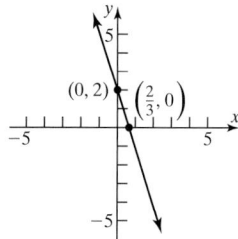

(b) Domain: $(-\infty, \infty)$

Range: $(-\infty, \infty)$

(c) Decreasing: $(-\infty, \infty)$

67. (a)

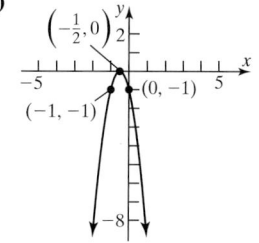

(b) Domain: $(-\infty, \infty)$

Range: $(-\infty, 0]$

(c) Increasing: $\left(-\infty, -\dfrac{1}{2}\right)$

Decreasing: $\left(-\dfrac{1}{2}, \infty\right)$

68. (a)

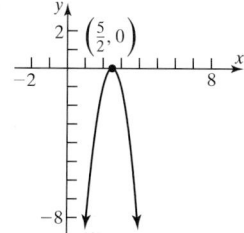

(b) Domain: $(-\infty, \infty)$

Range: $(-\infty, 0]$

(c) Increasing: $\left(-\infty, \dfrac{5}{2}\right)$

Decreasing: $\left(\dfrac{5}{2}, \infty\right)$

69. $a = 6, b = 0, c = 2$ **70.** $a = -3, b = 6, c = 1$

71. (a), (c), (d)

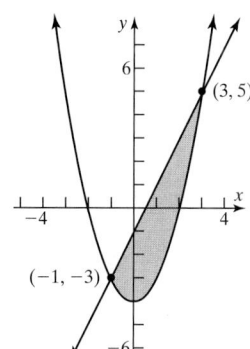

(b) $\{-1, 3\}$

72. (a), (c), (d)

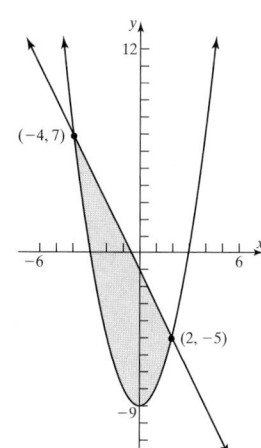

(b) $\{-4, 2\}$

73. (a), (c), (d)

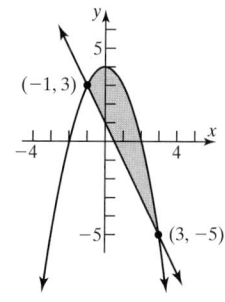

(b) $\{-1, 3\}$

74. (a), (c), (d)

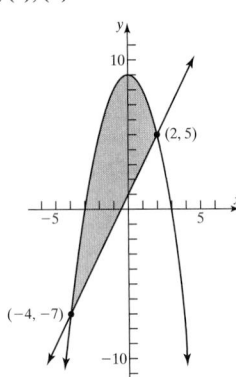

(b) $\{-4, 2\}$

75. (a), (c), (d)

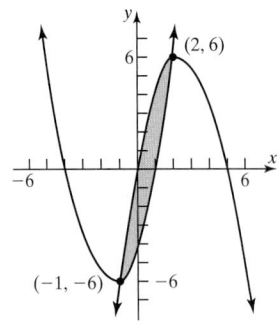

(b) $\{-1, 2\}$

76. (a), (c), (d)

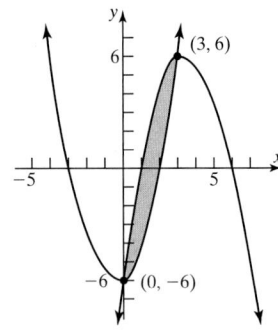

(b) $\{0, 3\}$

77. (a) $a = 1: f(x) = (x + 3)(x - 1) = x^2 + 2x - 3$
       $a = 2: f(x) = 2(x + 3)(x - 1) = 2x^2 + 4x - 6$
       $a = -2: f(x) = -2(x + 3)(x - 1) = -2x^2 - 4x + 6$
       $a = 5: f(x) = 5(x + 3)(x - 1) = 5x^2 + 10x - 15$

(b) The value of a does not affect the x-intercepts, but it changes
     the y-intercept by a factor of a.

(c) The value of a does not affect the axis of symmetry. It is $x = -1$
     for all values of a.

(d) The value of a does not affect the x-coordinate of the vertex.
     However, the y-coordinate of the vertex is multiplied by a.

(e) The mean of the x-intercepts is the x-coordinate of the vertex.

78. (a) $a = 1: f(x) = (x + 5)(x - 3) = x^2 + 2x - 15$
       $a = 2: f(x) = 2(x + 5)(x - 3) = 2x^2 + 4x - 30$
       $a = -2: f(x) = -2(x + 5)(x - 3) = -2x^2 - 4x + 30$
       $a = 5: f(x) = 5(x + 5)(x - 3) = 5x^2 + 10x - 75$

(b) The value of a does not affect the x-intercepts, but it changes
     the y-intercept by a factor of a.

(c) The value of a does not affect the axis of symmetry. It is $x = -1$
     for all values of a.

(d) The value of a does not affect the x-coordinate of the vertex.
     However, the y-coordinate of the vertex is multiplied by a.

(e) The mean of the x-intercepts is the x-coordinate of the vertex.

79. (a) $(-2, -25)$ (b) $-7, 3$
     (c) $-4, 0; (-4, -21), (0, -21)$
     (d)

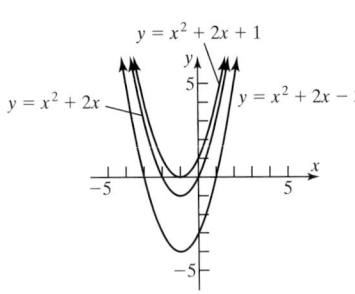

80. (a) $(-1, -9)$
     (b) $-4, 2$
     (c) $-2, 0; (-2, -8), (0, -8)$
     (d)

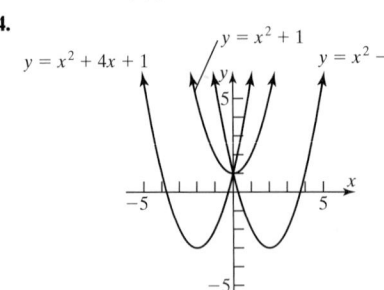

81. $(2, 2)$

82. $(2, 3)$

83. $500; 1,000,000

84. $1900; 1,805,000

85. (a) 70,000 mp3 players   (b) $2500

86. (a) 20,000 cell phones   (b) $2000

87. (a) 37.4 years old; 3784   (b) Decreasing

88. (a) 2149 victims   (b) 31.4 years old
     (c) The number of murder victims decreases.

89. (a) 187 or 188 watches; $7031.20
     (b) $P(x) = -0.2x^2 + 43x - 1750$
     (c) 107 or 108 watches; $561.20

90. (a) 119 boxes of candy; $564.06
     (b) $P(x) = -0.04x^2 + 8.25x - 250$
     (c) 103 boxes of candy; $175.39

91. If x is even, then ax^2 and bx are even and $ax^2 + bx$ is even, which means that $ax^2 + bx + c$ is odd. If x is odd, then ax^2 and bx are odd and $ax^2 + bx$ is even, which means that $ax^2 + bx + c$ is odd. In either case, $f(x)$ is odd.

93.

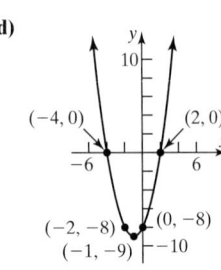

94.

95. $b^2 - 4ac < 0$

97. No

98. 0, 1, or 2

3.4 Assess Your Understanding (page 160)

3. (a) $R(x) = -\frac{1}{6}x^2 + 100x$ **(b)** $\{x \mid 0 \le x < 600\}$ **(c)** \$13,333.33 **(d)** 300; \$15,000 **(e)** \$50 **4. (a)** $R(x) = -\frac{1}{3}x^2 + 100x$

(b) $\{x \mid 0 \le x < 300\}$ **(c)** \$6666.67 **(d)** 150; \$7500 **(e)** \$50 **5. (a)** $R(x) = -\frac{1}{5}x^2 + 20x$ **(b)** \$255 **(c)** 50; \$500 **(d)** \$10

6. (a) $R(x) = -\frac{1}{20}x^2 + 25x$ **(b)** \$480 **(c)** 250; \$3125 **(d)** \$12.50 **7. (a)** $A(w) = -w^2 + 200w$ **(b)** A is largest when $w = 100$ yd. **(c)** 10,000 yd^2

8. (a) $A(x) = -x^2 + 1500x$ **(b)** A is largest when $x = 750$ ft. **(c)** 562,500 ft^2 **9.** 2,000,000 m^2 **10.** 500,000 m^2

11. (a) $\frac{625}{16} \approx 39$ ft **(b)** $\frac{7025}{32} \approx 219.5$ ft **12. (a)** 156.25 ft **(b)** 78.125 ft

(c) About 170 ft **(c)** 312.5 ft

(d)

(d)

(graph, axis labeled 80, 0, 0, 350)

(f) When the height is 100 ft, the projectile is about 135.7 ft from the cliff. **(f)** When the height is 50 ft, the projectile has traveled horizontally 62.5 ft or 250 ft.

13. 18.75 m **14.** Let the point $(0, 25)$ represent the vertex of the arch. Then the equation of the parabola is $h(x) = \frac{-25}{(60)^2}x^2 + 25$; $h(10) \approx 24.3$ ft;

$h(20) \approx 22.2$ ft; $h(40) \approx 13.9$ ft. **15.** 3 in. **16.** The width should be approximately 5.6 ft, and the total height of the window should be

approximately 5.6 ft. **17.** $\frac{750}{\pi} \approx 238.73$ m by 375 m **18.** $x = \frac{-16}{-6 + \sqrt{3}} \approx 3.75$ ft; total height $= 8 + \frac{24 - 8\sqrt{3}}{-6 + \sqrt{3}} \approx 5.62$ ft

19. (a) 171 ft **(b)** 49 mph **20. (a)** \$423.82 million **(b)** 2000 **21.** $x = \frac{a}{2}$

22. $\left.\begin{array}{r} ah^2 - bh + c = y_0 \\ c = y_1 \\ ah^2 + bh + c = y_2 \end{array}\right\}$ $\left.\begin{array}{r} y_0 + y_2 = 2ah^2 + 2c \\ 4y_1 = 4c \end{array}\right\}$ Area $= \frac{h}{3}(2ah^2 + 6c) = \frac{h}{3}(y_0 + 4y_1 + y_2)$ **23.** $\frac{38}{3}$ **24.** $\frac{128}{3}$ **25.** $\frac{248}{3}$ **26.** $\frac{22}{3}$

27. (a)

(graph, axis labeled 45,000, 15, 75, 0)

The data appear to follow a quadratic relation with $a < 0$.

(b) $I(x) = -43.384x^2 + 4089.654x - 53,244.570$

(c) About 47 years of age

(d) Approximately \$43,134

(e)

(graph, axis labeled 45,000, 15, 75, 0)

28. (a)

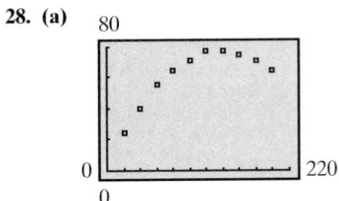

The data appear to follow a quadratic relation with $a < 0$.

(b) $h(x) = -0.0037x^2 + 1.0318x + 5.6667$

(c) 139.4 ft

(d) 77.6 ft

(e)

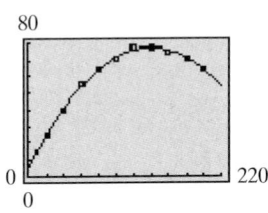

29. (a)

(graph, axis labeled 1800, 675, 925, 1550)

The data appear to be linearly related with positive slope.

(b) $R(x) = 0.836x + 1032.273$ **(c)** \$1743

30. (a)

The data appear to follow a quadratic relation with $a < 0$.

(b) $M(s) = -0.017s^2 + 1.935s - 25.341$ **(c)** 29.1 mph

31. (a)

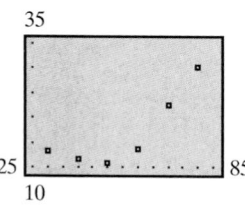

The data appear to follow a quadratic relation with $a > 0$.

(b) $P(a) = 0.015a^2 - 1.332a + 39.823$ **(c)** 11.6%

32. (a)

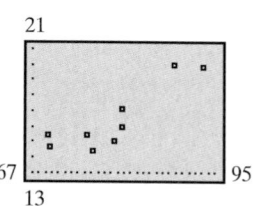

The data appear to be linearly related with a positive slope.

(b) $C(x) = 0.233x - 2.037$ **(c)** 16.6 chirps/sec

3.5 Assess Your Understanding (page 166)

3. (a) $\{x | x < -2 \text{ or } x > 2\}; (-\infty, -2) \cup (2, \infty)$ **(b)** $\{x | -2 \le x \le 2\}; [-2, 2]$ **4. (a)** $\{x | x < -1 \text{ or } x > 4\}; (-\infty, -1) \cup (4, \infty)$

(b) $\{x | -1 \le x \le 4\}; [-1, 4]$ **5. (a)** $\{x | -2 \le x \le 1\}; [-2, 1]$ **(b)** $\{x | x < -2 \text{ or } x > 1\}; (-\infty, -2) \cup (1, \infty)$

6. (a) $\{x | x < -3 \text{ or } x > 1\}; (-\infty, -3) \cup (1, \infty)$ **(b)** $\{x | -3 \le x \le 1\}; [-3, 1]$ **7.** $\{x | -2 \le x \le 5\}; [-2, 5]$

8. $\{x | x < -5 \text{ or } x > 2\}; (-\infty, -5) \cup (2, \infty)$ **9.** $\{x | x < 0 \text{ or } x > 4\}; (-\infty, 0) \cup (4, \infty)$ **10.** $\{x | -8 \le x \le 0\}; [-8, 0]$

11. $\{x | -3 < x < 3\}; (-3, 3)$ **12.** $\{x | -1 < x < 1\}; (-1, 1)$ **13.** $\{x | x < -4 \text{ or } x > 3\}; (-\infty, -4) \cup (3, \infty)$ **14.** $\{x | -4 < x < -3\}; (-4, -3)$

15. $\left\{x \left| -\dfrac{1}{2} \le x \le 3\right.\right\}; \left[-\dfrac{1}{2}, 3\right]$ **16.** $\left\{x \left| -\dfrac{2}{3} \le x \le \dfrac{3}{2}\right.\right\}; \left[-\dfrac{2}{3}, \dfrac{3}{2}\right]$ **17.** $\{x | x < -1 \text{ or } x > 8\}; (-\infty, -1) \cup (8, \infty)$

18. $\{x | x < -5 \text{ or } x > 4\}; (-\infty, -5) \cup (4, \infty)$ **19.** No real solution   **20.** No real solution   **21.** All real numbers; $(-\infty, \infty)$

22. All real numbers; $(-\infty, \infty)$ **23.** $\{x | x \le -4 \text{ or } x \ge 4\}; (-\infty, -4] \cup [4, \infty)$ **24.** $\left\{x \left| 0 \le x \le \dfrac{1}{3}\right.\right\}; \left[0, \dfrac{1}{3}\right]$ **25. (a)** $\{-1, 1\}$ **(b)** $\{-1\}$

(c) $\{-1, 4\}$ **(d)** $\{x | x < -1 \text{ or } x > 1\}; (-\infty, -1) \cup (1, \infty)$ **(e)** $\{x | x \le -1\}; (-\infty, -1]$ **(f)** $\{x | x < -1 \text{ or } x > 4\}; (-\infty, -1) \cup (4, \infty)$

(g) $\{x | x \le -\sqrt{2} \text{ or } x \ge \sqrt{2}\}; (-\infty, -\sqrt{2}] \cup [\sqrt{2}, \infty)$ **26. (a)** $\{-\sqrt{3}, \sqrt{3}\}$ **(b)** $\{1\}$ **(c)** $\{0, 3\}$ **(d)** $\{x | -\sqrt{3} < x < \sqrt{3}\}; (-\sqrt{3}, \sqrt{3})$

(e) $\{x | x \ge 1\} \text{ or } [1, \infty)$ **(f)** $\{x | 0 < x < 3\}; (0, 3)$ **(g)** $\{x | -\sqrt{2} \le x \le \sqrt{2}\}; [-\sqrt{2}, \sqrt{2}]$ **27. (a)** $\{-1, 1\}$ **(b)** $\left\{-\dfrac{1}{4}\right\}$ **(c)** $\{-4, 0\}$

(d) $\{x | -1 < x < 1\}; (-1, 1)$ **(e)** $\left\{x \left| x \le -\dfrac{1}{4}\right.\right\} \text{ or } \left(-\infty, -\dfrac{1}{4}\right]$ **(f)** $\{x | -4 < x < 0\}; (-4, 0)$ **(g)** $\{0\}$ **28. (a)** $\{-2, 2\}$ **(b)** $\{-2\}$

(c) $\{-2, 3\}$ **(d)** $\{x | -2 < x < 2\}; (-2, 2)$ **(e)** $\{x | x \ge -2\}; [-2, \infty)$ **(f)** $\{x | -2 < x < 3\}; (-2, 3)$ **(g)** $\{x | -\sqrt{3} \le x \le \sqrt{3}\}; [-\sqrt{3}, \sqrt{3}]$

29. (a) $\{-2, 2\}$ **(b)** $\{-2, 2\}$ **(c)** $\{-2, 2\}$ **(d)** $\{x | x < -2 \text{ or } x > 2\}; (-\infty, -2) \cup (2, \infty)$ **(e)** $\{x | x \le -2 \text{ or } x \ge 2\}; (-\infty, -2] \cup [2, \infty)$

(f) $\{x | x < -2 \text{ or } x > 2\}; (-\infty, -2) \cup (2, \infty)$ **(g)** $\{x | x \le -\sqrt{5} \text{ or } x \ge \sqrt{5}\}; (-\infty, -\sqrt{5}] \cup [\sqrt{5}, \infty)$ **30. (a)** $\{1\}$ **(b)** $\{-1, 1\}$

(c) $\{0, 1\}$ **(d)** $\{x | x < 1 \text{ or } x > 1\}; (-\infty, 1) \cup (1, \infty)$ **(e)** $\{x | x \le -1 \text{ or } x \ge 1\}; (-\infty, -1] \cup [1, \infty)$ **(f)** $\{x | x < 0 \text{ or } x > 1\}; (-\infty, 0) \cup (1, \infty)$

(g) $\{x | x \le 0 \text{ or } x \ge 2\}; (-\infty, 0] \cup [2, \infty)$ **31. (a)** $\{-1, 2\}$ **(b)** $\{-2, 1\}$ **(c)** $\{0\}$ **(d)** $\{x | x < -1 \text{ or } x > 2\}; (-\infty, -1) \cup (2, \infty)$

(e) $\{x | -2 \le x \le 1\}; [-2, 1]$ **(f)** $\{x | x < 0\}; (-\infty, 0)$ **(g)** $\left\{x \left| x \le \dfrac{1 - \sqrt{13}}{2} \text{ or } x \ge \dfrac{1 + \sqrt{13}}{2}\right.\right\}; \left(-\infty, \dfrac{1 - \sqrt{13}}{2}\right] \cup \left[\dfrac{1 + \sqrt{13}}{2}, \infty\right)$

32. (a) $\left\{\dfrac{-1 - \sqrt{5}}{2}, \dfrac{-1 + \sqrt{5}}{2}\right\}$ **(b)** $\{-2, 3\}$ **(c)** $\left\{-\dfrac{5}{2}\right\}$ **(d)** $\dfrac{-1 - \sqrt{5}}{2} < x < \dfrac{-1 + \sqrt{5}}{2}; \left(\dfrac{-1 - \sqrt{5}}{2}, \dfrac{-1 + \sqrt{5}}{2}\right)$

(e) $\{x | x \le -2 \text{ or } x \ge 3\}; (-\infty, -2] \cup [3, \infty)$ **(f)** $\left\{x \left| x < -\dfrac{5}{2}\right.\right\}; \left(-\infty, -\dfrac{5}{2}\right)$ **(g)** $\{x | -1 \le x \le 0\}; [-1, 0]$ **33. (a)** 5 sec   **(b)** The ball is

more than 96 ft above the ground from time t between 2 and 3 sec, $2 < t < 3$.   **34. (a)** 6 sec   **(b)** The ball is more than 128 ft above the ground from time t between 2 and 4 sec, $2 < t < 4$.   **35. (a)** \$0, \$1000   **(b)** The revenue is more than \$800,000 for prices between \$276.39 and \$723.61, \$276.39 $< p <$ \$723.61.   **36. (a)** \$0, \$3800   **(b)** The revenue is more than \$1,200,000 for prices between \$800 and \$3000, \$800 $< p <$ \$3000.

37. (a) $\{c | 0.112 < c < 81.907\}; (0.112, 81.907)$ **(b)** It is possible to hit a target 75 km away if $c = 0.651$ or $c = 1.536$.   **38.** The spring is required to be able to be compressed at least 4.3 feet.

Review Exercises (page 168)

1. (a) $m = 2; b = -5$

(b)

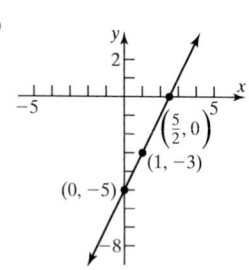

(c) Domain and Range: $(-\infty, \infty)$

(d) 2   **(e)** Increasing

2. (a) $m = -4; b = 7$

(b)

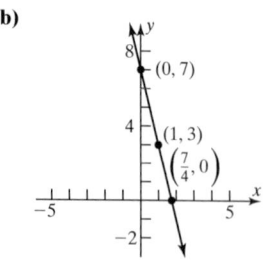

(c) Domain and Range: $(-\infty, \infty)$

(d) -4 **(e)** Decreasing

3. (a) $m = \dfrac{4}{5}; b = -6$

(b)

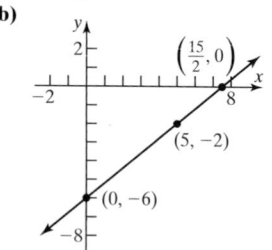

(c) Domain and Range: $(-\infty, \infty)$

(d) $\dfrac{4}{5}$ **(e)** Increasing

4. (a) $m = -\dfrac{1}{3}; b = 1$

(b)
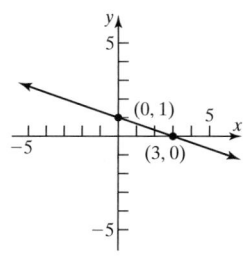

(c) Domain and Range: $(-\infty, \infty)$

(d) $-\dfrac{1}{3}$ **(e)** Decreasing

5. (a) $m = 0; b = 4$

(b)
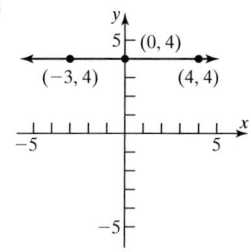

(c) Domain: $(-\infty, \infty)$

   Range: $\{y \mid y = 4\}$

(d) 0   **(e)** Constant

6. (a) $m = 0; b = -3$

(b)
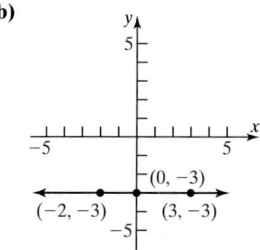

(c) Domain: $(-\infty, \infty)$

   Range: $\{y \mid y = -3\}$

(d) 0   **(e)** Constant

7. Linear; $y = 5x + 3$ **8.** Nonlinear

9.

10.

11.

12.

13.

14.

15. (a)
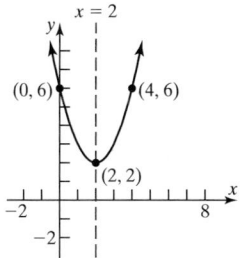

(b) Domain: $(-\infty, \infty)$

   Range: $[2, \infty)$

(c) Decreasing: $(-\infty, 2)$

   Increasing: $(2, \infty)$

16. (a)
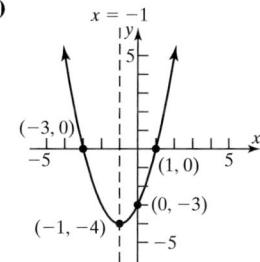

(b) Domain: $(-\infty, \infty)$

   Range: $[-4, \infty)$

(c) Decreasing: $(-\infty, -1)$

   Increasing: $(-1, \infty)$

17. (a)
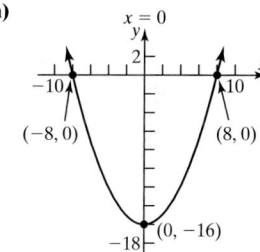

(b) Domain: $(-\infty, \infty)$

   Range: $[-16, \infty)$

(c) Decreasing: $(-\infty, 0)$

   Increasing: $(0, \infty)$

18. (a)
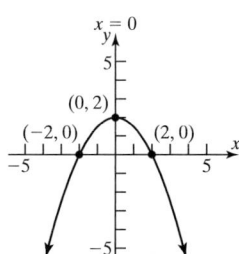

(b) Domain: $(-\infty, \infty)$

   Range: $(-\infty, 2]$

(c) Increasing: $(-\infty, 0)$

   Decreasing: $(0, \infty)$

19. (a)
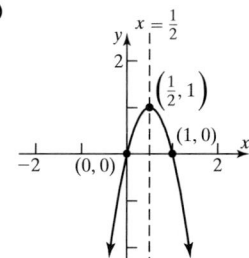

(b) Domain: $(-\infty, \infty)$

   Range: $(-\infty, 1]$

(c) Increasing: $\left(-\infty, \dfrac{1}{2}\right)$

   Decreasing: $\left(\dfrac{1}{2}, \infty\right)$

20. (a)
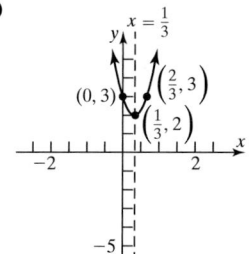

(b) Domain: $(-\infty, \infty)$

   Range: $[2, \infty)$

(c) Decreasing: $\left(-\infty, \dfrac{1}{3}\right)$

   Increasing: $\left(\dfrac{1}{3}, \infty\right)$

21. (a)

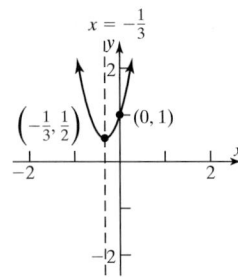

(b) Domain: $(-\infty, \infty)$

Range: $\left[\dfrac{1}{2}, \infty\right)$

(c) Decreasing: $\left(-\infty, -\dfrac{1}{3}\right)$

Increasing: $\left(-\dfrac{1}{3}, \infty\right)$

22. (a)

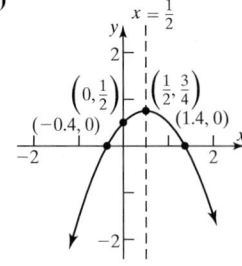

(b) Domain: $(-\infty, \infty)$

Range: $\left(-\infty, \dfrac{3}{4}\right]$

(c) Increasing: $\left(-\infty, \dfrac{1}{2}\right)$

Decreasing: $\left(\dfrac{1}{2}, \infty\right)$

23. (a)

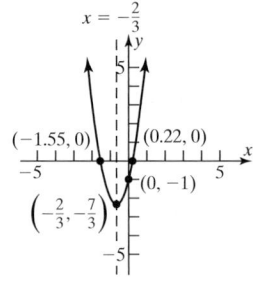

(b) Domain: $(-\infty, \infty)$

Range: $\left[-\dfrac{7}{3}, \infty\right)$

(c) Decreasing: $\left(-\infty, -\dfrac{2}{3}\right)$

Increasing: $\left(-\dfrac{2}{3}, \infty\right)$

24. (a)

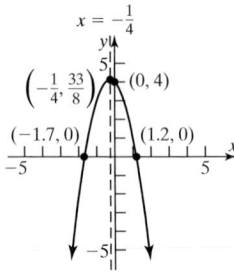

(b) Domain: $(-\infty, \infty)$

Range: $\left(-\infty, \dfrac{33}{8}\right]$

(c) Increasing: $\left(-\infty, -\dfrac{1}{4}\right)$

Decreasing: $\left(-\dfrac{1}{4}, \infty\right)$

25. Minimum value; 1   **26.** Minimum value; -3

27. Maximum value; 12   **28.** Maximum value; 22

29. Maximum value; 16   **30.** Maximum value; 4

31. $\{x | -8 < x < 2\}; (-8, 2)$

32. $\left\{x \,\middle|\, x \le -\dfrac{1}{3} \text{ or } x \ge 1\right\}; \left(-\infty, -\dfrac{1}{3}\right] \cup [1, \infty)$

33. $\left\{x \,\middle|\, x \le -\dfrac{1}{3} \text{ or } x \ge 5\right\}; \left(-\infty, -\dfrac{1}{3}\right] \cup [5, \infty)$

34. $\left\{x \,\middle|\, \dfrac{1}{4} < x < 3\right\}; \left(\dfrac{1}{4}, 3\right)$

35. (a) Company A: $C(x) = 0.06x + 7$; Company B: $C(x) = 0.08x$ **(b)** 350 min   **(c)** $0 \le x < 350$ **36. (a)** $S(x) = 0.01x + 15{,}000$ **(b)** \$25,000

(c) \$8,500,000   **(d)** $x > \$13{,}500{,}000$ **37. (a)** $R(x) = -\dfrac{1}{10}x^2 + 150x$ **(b)** \$14,000   **(c)** 750; \$56,250   **(d)** \$75   **38.** 50 ft by 50 ft

39. 4,166,666.7 m²   **40.** The side with the semicircles should be $\dfrac{50}{\pi}$ ft; the other side should be 25 ft.   **41. (a)** 63 clubs   **(b)** \$151.90

42. (a) 2004   **(b)** About 1,380,000 violent crimes   **(c)** Decreasing   **43.** $A(x) = -x^2 + 10x, 0 < x < 10; 25$ units²   **44.** 3.6 ft

45. (a)

(b) Yes; the two variables appear to be linearly related with positive slope.

(c) $y = 1.3902x + 1.1140$ **(d)** 37.95 mm

46. (a) Quadratic, $a < 0$

(b) $R(A) = -7.76A^2 + 411.88A + 942.72$

(c) About \$26.5 thousand

(d) \$6408 thousand

(e)

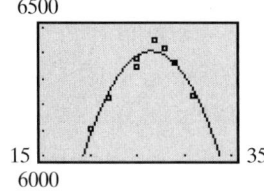

Chapter Test *(page 171)*

1. (a) Slope: -4; y-intercept: 3

(b) Decreasing

(c)

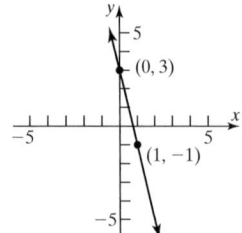

2. Linear; $y = -5x + 2$ **3.**

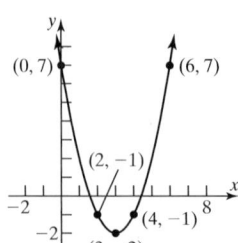

4. (a) Opens up

(b) $(2, -8)$

(c) $x = 2$

(d) x-intercepts: $\dfrac{6 - 2\sqrt{6}}{3}, \dfrac{6 + 2\sqrt{6}}{3}$;

y-intercept: 4

(e)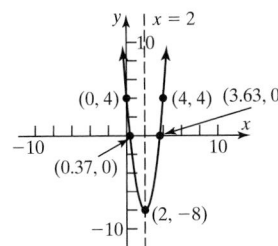

(f) Domain: All real numbers; $(-\infty, \infty)$

Range: $\{y \mid y \geq -8\}$; $[-8, \infty)$

(g) Decreasing: $(-\infty, 2)$; Increasing: $(2, \infty)$

5. (a) Opens down

(b) $(1, -3)$

(c) $x = 1$

(d) No x-intercepts: y-intercept: -5

(e)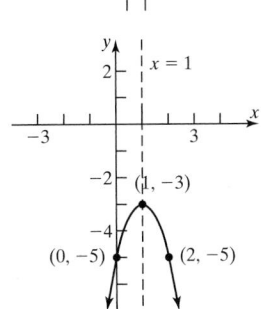

(f) Domain: All real numbers; $(-\infty, \infty)$

Range: $\{y \mid y \leq -3\}$; $(-\infty, -3]$

(g) Increasing: $(-\infty, 1)$; Decreasing: $(1, \infty)$

6. $f(x) = 2x^2 - 4x - 30$ **7.** Maximum value; 21 **8.** $\{x \mid x \leq 4 \text{ or } x \geq 6\}$; $(-\infty, 4] \cup [6, \infty)$

9. (a) $C(m) = 0.15m + 129.50$ **(b)** \$258.50 **(c)** 562 miles **10. (a)** $R(x) = -\dfrac{1}{10}x^2 + 1000x$ **(b)** \$384,000 **(c)** 5000 units; \$2,500,000 **(d)** \$500

11. (a)

Linear with negative slope   Quadratic that opens up

(b) $y = -4.234x - 2.362$ **(c)** $y = 1.993x^2 + 0.289x + 2.503$

Cumulative Review *(page 171)*

1. (a) -3 **(b)** $x^2 - 4x - 2$ **(c)** $x^2 + 4x + 1$ **(d)** $-x^2 + 4x - 1$ **(e)** $x^2 - 3$ **(f)** $2x + h - 4$ **2.** $\left\{z \mid z \neq \dfrac{7}{6}\right\}$ **3.** Yes **4. (a)** No

(b) -1; $(-2, -1)$ is on the graph. **(c)** -8; $(-8, 2)$ is on the graph. **5.** Neither **6.** Local maximum is 5.30 and occurs at $x = -1.29$.

Local minimum is -3.30 and occurs at $x = 1.29$. Increasing: $(-4, -1.29)$ and $(1.29, 4)$; Decreasing: $(-1.29, 1.29)$ **7. (a)** $\{-4\}$

(b) $\{x \mid x > -4\}$ or $(-4, \infty)$ **8. (a)** $\{-1, 3\}$ **(b)** $\{x \mid x < -1 \text{ or } x > 3\}$ or $(-\infty, -1) \cup (3, \infty)$

9. (a) Domain: $\{x \mid -4 \leq x \leq 4\}$ or $[-4, 4]$; **(b)** $(-1, 0), (0, -1), (1, 0)$ **(c)** y-axis **(d)** 1 **(e)** -4 and 4 **(f)** $\{x \mid -1 < x < 1\}$

Range: $\{y \mid -1 \leq y \leq 3\}$ or $[-1, 3]$

(g) **(h)** **(i)** 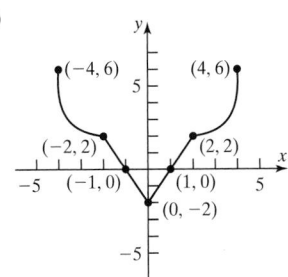 **(j)** Even **(k)** $(0, 4)$

CHAPTER 4 Polynomial and Rational Functions

4.1 Assess Your Understanding *(page 187)*

5. smooth; continuous **6.** zero or root **7.** touches **8.** T **9.** F **10.** F **11.** Yes; degree 3 **12.** Yes; degree 4 **13.** Yes; degree 2

14. Yes; degree 1 **15.** No; x is raised to the -1 power. **16.** Yes; degree 2 **17.** No; x is raised to the $\dfrac{3}{2}$ power. **18.** No; x is raised to the $\dfrac{1}{2}$ power.

19. Yes; degree 4 **20.** No; it is the ratio of two polynomials, and the polynomial in the denominator is of positive degree. **21.** Yes; degree 4

22. Yes; degree 5

23.

24.

25.

26.

27.

28.

29.

30.

31.

32.

33.

34.

35.

36.

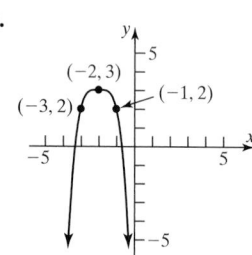

37. $f(x) = x^3 - 3x^2 - x + 3$ for $a = 1$
38. $f(x) = x^3 - 3x^2 - 4x + 12$ for $a = 1$
39. $f(x) = x^3 - x^2 - 12x$ for $a = 1$
40. $f(x) = x^3 + 2x^2 - 8x$ for $a = 1$
41. $f(x) = x^4 - 15x^2 + 10x + 24$ for $a = 1$
42. $f(x) = x^4 - 3x^3 - 15x^2 + 19x + 30$ for $a = 1$
43. $f(x) = x^3 - 5x^2 + 3x + 9$ for $a = 1$
44. $f(x) = x^3 - 12x - 16$ for $a = 1$

45. **(a)** 7, multiplicity 1; -3, multiplicity 2 **(b)** Graph touches the x-axis at -3 and crosses it at 7. **(c)** 2 **(d)** $y = 3x^3$

46. **(a)** -4, multiplicity 1; -3, multiplicity 3 **(b)** Graph crosses the x-axis at -4 and -3. **(c)** 3 **(d)** $y = 4x^4$ **47.** **(a)** 2, multiplicity 3

(b) Graph crosses the x-axis at 2 **(c)** 4 **(d)** $y = 4x^5$ **48.** **(a)** 3, multiplicity 1 **(b)** Graph crosses the x-axis at 3. **(c)** 6 **(d)** $y = 2x^7$

49. **(a)** $-\dfrac{1}{2}$, multiplicity 2; -4, multiplicity 3 **(b)** Graph touches the x-axis at $-\dfrac{1}{2}$ and crosses it at -4. **(c)** 4 **(d)** $y = -2x^5$

50. **(a)** $\dfrac{1}{3}$, multiplicity 2; 1, multiplicity 3 **(b)** Graph touches the x-axis at $\dfrac{1}{3}$ and crosses it at 1. **(c)** 4 **(d)** $y = x^5$ **51.** **(a)** 5, multiplicity 3; -4,

multiplicity 2 **(b)** Graph touches the x-axis at -4 and crosses it at 5. **(c)** 4 **(d)** $y = x^5$ **52.** **(a)** $-\sqrt{3}$, multiplicity 2; 2, multiplicity 4

(b) Graph touches the x-axis at $-\sqrt{3}$ and 2. **(c)** 5 **(d)** $y = x^6$ **53.** **(a)** No real zeros **(b)** Graph neither crosses nor touches the x-axis. **(c)** 5

(d) $y = 3x^6$ **54.** **(a)** No real zeros **(b)** Graph neither crosses nor touches the x-axis. **(c)** 5 **(d)** $y = -2x^6$ **55.** **(a)** 0, multiplicity 2; $-\sqrt{2}$, $\sqrt{2}$,

multiplicity 1 **(b)** Graph touches the x-axis at 0 and crosses it at $-\sqrt{2}$ and $\sqrt{2}$. **(c)** 3 **(d)** $y = -2x^4$ **56.** **(a)** 0, $-\sqrt{3}$, $\sqrt{3}$, multiplicity 1

(b) Graph crosses the x-axis at $-\sqrt{3}$, 0, and $\sqrt{3}$. **(c)** 2 **(d)** $y = 4x^3$ **57.** Could be; zeros: -1, 1, 2; least degree is 3. **58.** Could be; zeros: -1, 2;

least degree is 4. **59.** Cannot be the graph of a polynomial; gap at $x = -1$ **60.** Cannot be the graph of a polynomial; cusp at $x = 0$

61. $f(x) = x(x - 1)(x - 2)$ **62.** $f(x) = x(x - 1)^2(x - 2)$ **63.** $f(x) = -\dfrac{1}{2}(x + 1)(x - 1)(x - 2)$ **64.** $f(x) = -\dfrac{1}{2}(x + 1)(x - 1)^2(x - 2)$

65. Step 1: $y = x^3$

Step 2: x-intercepts: 0, 3; y-intercept: 0

Step 3: 0: multiplicity 2; touches;
3: multiplicity 1; crosses

Step 4:

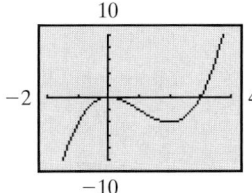

Step 5: $(2, -4)$; $(0, 0)$

Step 6:

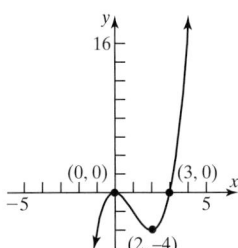

Step 7: Domain: $(-\infty, \infty)$;
Range: $(-\infty, \infty)$

Step 8: Increasing on $(-\infty, 0)$ and $(2, \infty)$
Decreasing on $(0, 2)$

66. Step 1: $y = x^3$

Step 2: x-intercepts: -2, 0; y-intercept: 0

Step 3: -2: multiplicity 2; touches; 0: multiplicity 1; crosses

Step 4:

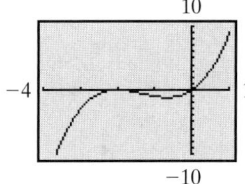

Step 5: $(-0.67, -1.19)$; $(-2, 0)$

Step 6:

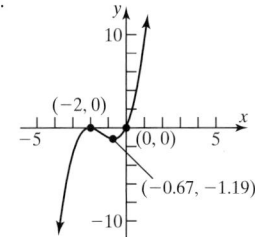

Step 7: Domain: $(-\infty, \infty)$;
Range: $(-\infty, \infty)$

Step 8: Increasing on $(-\infty, -2)$ and $(-0.67, \infty)$
Decreasing on $(-2, -0.67)$

67. Step 1: $y = x^3$

Step 2: x-intercepts: -4, 2

y-intercept: 16

Step 3: -4: multiplicity 1, crosses;

2: multiplicity 2, touches

Step 4:

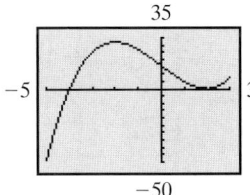

Step 5: $(-2, 32)$; $(2, 0)$

Step 6:

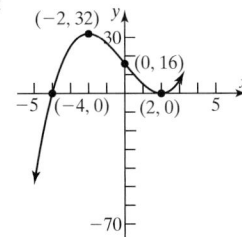

Step 7: Domain: $(-\infty, \infty)$; Range: $(-\infty, \infty)$

Step 8: Increasing on $(-\infty, -2)$ and $(2, \infty)$
Decreasing on $(-2, 2)$

68. Step 1: $y = x^3$

Step 2: x-intercepts: -3, 1

y-intercept: -9

Step 3: -3: multiplicity 2, touches;

1: multiplicity 1, crosses

Step 4:

Step 5: $(-3, 0)$; $(-0.33, -9.48)$

Step 6:

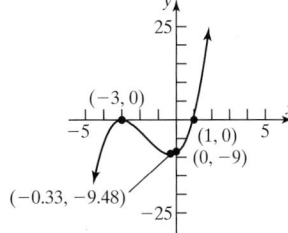

Step 7: Domain: $(-\infty, \infty)$; Range: $(-\infty, \infty)$

Step 8: Increasing on $(-\infty, -3)$ and $(-0.33, \infty)$
Decreasing on $(-3, -0.33)$

69. Step 1: $y = -2x^4$

Step 2: x-intercepts: -2, 2

y-intercept: 32

Step 3: -2: multiplicity 1, crosses;

2: multiplicity 3, crosses

Step 4:

Step 5: $(-1, 54)$

Step 6:

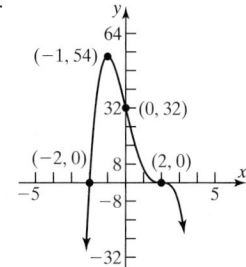

Step 7: Domain: $(-\infty, \infty)$; Range: $(-\infty, 54]$

Step 8: Increasing on $(-\infty, -1)$
Decreasing on $(-1, \infty)$

70. Step 1: $y = -\dfrac{1}{2}x^4$

Step 2: x-intercepts: $-4, 1$

    y-intercept: 2

Step 3: -4: multiplicity 1, crosses;

    1: multiplicity 3, crosses

Step 4:

Step 5: $(-2.75, 32.96)$

Step 6:

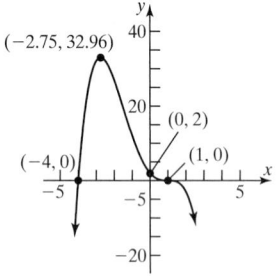

Step 7: Domain: $(-\infty, \infty)$; Range: $(-\infty, 32.96]$

Step 8: Increasing on $(-\infty, -2.75)$

    Decreasing on $(-2.75, \infty)$

71. Step 1: $y = x^3$

Step 2: x-intercepts: $-4, -1, 2$

    y-intercept: -8

Step 3: $-4, -1, 2$: multiplicity 1, crosses

Step 4:

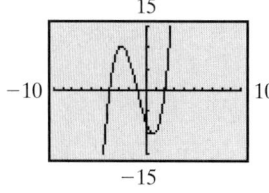

Step 5: $(-2.73, 10.39)$; $(0.73, -10.39)$

Step 6:

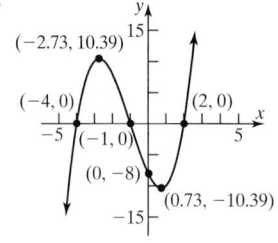

Step 7: Domain: $(-\infty, \infty)$; Range: $(-\infty, \infty)$

Step 8: Increasing on $(-\infty, -2.73)$

    and $(0.73, \infty)$

    Decreasing on $(-2.73, 0.73)$

72. Step 1: $y = x^3$

Step 2: x-intercepts: $-4, 1, 3$

    y-intercept: 12

Step 3: $-4, 1, 3$: multiplicity 1, crosses

Step 4:

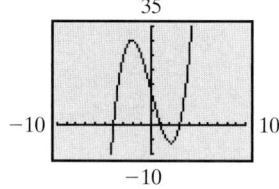

Step 5: $(-2.08, 30.04)$; $(2.08, -6.04)$

Step 6:

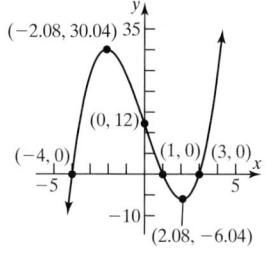

Step 7: Domain: $(-\infty, \infty)$; Range: $(-\infty, \infty)$

Step 8: Increasing on $(-\infty, -2.08)$

    and $(2.08, \infty)$

    Decreasing on $(-2.08, 2.08)$

73. Step 1: $y = x^4$

Step 2: x-intercepts: $-2, 0, 2$

    y-intercept: 0

Step 3: $-2, 2$: multiplicity 1, crosses;

    0: multiplicity 2, touches

Step 4:

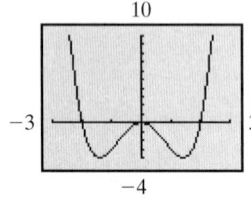

Step 5: $(-1.41, -4)$; $(1.41, -4)$; $(0, 0)$

Step 6:

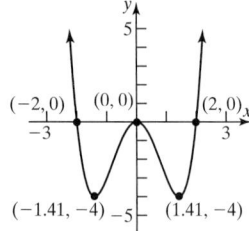

Step 7: Domain: $(-\infty, \infty)$; Range: $[-4, \infty)$

Step 8: Increasing on $(-1.41, 0)$ and $(1.41, \infty)$

    Decreasing on $(-\infty, -1.41)$ and $(0, 1.41)$

74. Step 1: $y = x^4$

Step 2: x-intercepts: $-4, 0, 3$

    y-intercept: 0

Step 3: $-4, 3$: multiplicity 1, crosses;

    0: multiplicity 2, touches

Step 4:

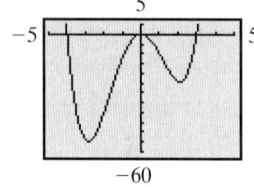

Step 5: $(-2.85, -54.64)$; $(2.1, -24.21)$; $(0, 0)$

Step 6:

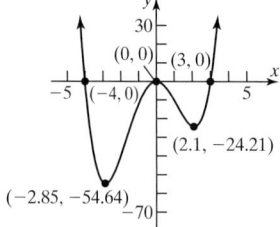

Step 7: Domain: $(-\infty, \infty)$; Range: $[-54.64, \infty)$

Step 8: Increasing on $(-2.85, 0)$ and $(2.1, \infty)$

    Decreasing on $(-\infty, -2.85)$ and $(0, 2.1)$

75. Step 1: $y = x^4$

Step 2: x-intercepts: $-1, 2$

    y-intercept: 4

Step 3: $-1, 2$: multiplicity 2, touches

Step 4:

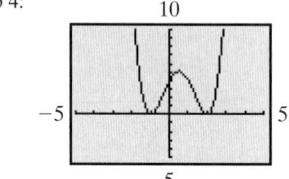

Step 5: $(-1, 0)$; $(2, 0)$; $(0.5, 5.06)$

Step 6:

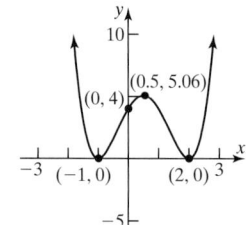

Step 7: Domain: $(-\infty, \infty)$; Range: $[0, \infty)$

Step 8: Increasing on $(-1, 0.5)$ and $(2, \infty)$

    Decreasing on $(-\infty, -1)$ and $(0.5, 2)$

76. Step 1: $y = x^4$

Step 2: x-intercepts: $-1, 3$; y-intercept: -3

Step 3: -1, multiplicity 3, crosses;
3, multiplicity 1, crosses

Step 4:

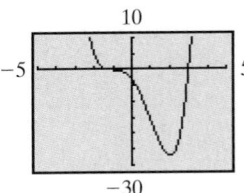

Step 5: $(2, -27)$

Step 6:

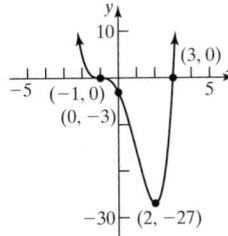

Step 7: Domain: $(-\infty, \infty)$; Range: $[-27, \infty)$

Step 8: Increasing on $(2, \infty)$
Decreasing on $(-\infty, 2)$

79. Step 1: $y = x^4$

Step 2: x-intercepts: $-2, 4$; y-intercept: 64

Step 3: $-2, 4$: multiplicity 2, touches

Step 4:

80. Step 1: $y = x^4$

Step 2: x-intercepts: $-4, -2, 2$; y-intercept: 32

Step 3: $-4, -2$: multiplicity 1, crosses;
2: multiplicity 2, touches

Step 4:

Step 5: $(-3.19, -25.96)$; $(2, 0)$; $(-0.31, 33.28)$

Step 6:

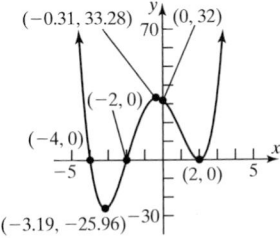

Step 7: Domain: $(-\infty, \infty)$; Range: $[-25.96, \infty)$

Step 8: Increasing on $(-3.19, -0.31)$ and $(2, \infty)$
Decreasing on $(-\infty, -3.19)$ and $(-0.31, 2)$

---

77. Step 1: $y = x^4$

Step 2: x-intercepts: $-1, 0, 3$; y-intercept: 0

Step 3: $-1, 3$: multiplicity 1, crosses;
0: multiplicity 2, touches

Step 4:

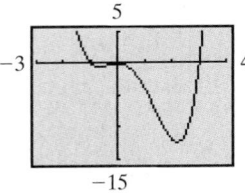

Step 5: $(-0.69, -0.54)$; $(2.19, -12.39)$; $(0, 0)$

Step 6:

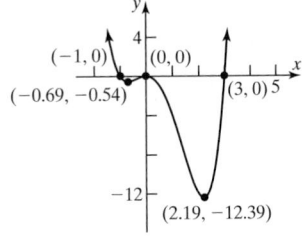

Step 7: Domain: $(-\infty, \infty)$; Range: $[-12.39, \infty)$

Step 8: Increasing on $(-0.69, 0)$ and $(2.19, \infty)$
Decreasing on $(-\infty, -0.69)$ and $(0, 2.19)$

Step 5: $(-2, 0)$; $(4, 0)$; $(1, 81)$

Step 6:

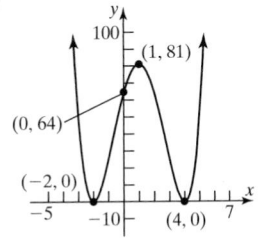

81. Step 1: $y = x^5$

Step 2: x-intercepts: $0, 2$; y-intercept: 0

Step 3: 0: multiplicity 2, touches;
2: multiplicity 1, crosses

Step 4:

Step 5: $(0, 0)$; $(1.48, -5.91)$

Step 6:

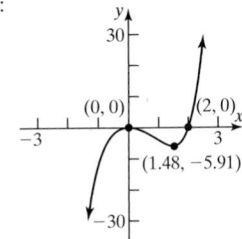

Step 7: Domain: $(-\infty, \infty)$; Range: $(-\infty, \infty)$

Step 8: Increasing on $(-\infty, 0)$ and $(1.48, \infty)$
Decreasing on $(0, 1.48)$

---

78. Step 1: $y = x^4$

Step 2: x-intercepts: $0, 1, 3$; y-intercept: 0

Step 3: 0: multiplicity 2, touches;
$1, 3$: multiplicity 1, crosses

Step 4:

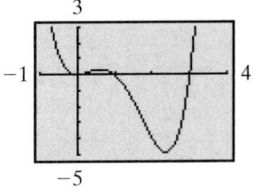

Step 5: $(0, 0)$; $(2.37, -4.85)$; $(0.63, 0.35)$

Step 6:

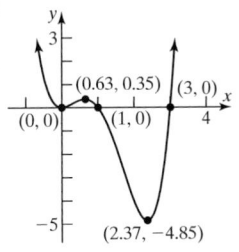

Step 7: Domain: $(-\infty, \infty)$; Range: $[-4.85, \infty)$

Step 8: Increasing on $(0, 0.63)$ and $(2.37, \infty)$
Decreasing on $(-\infty, 0)$ and $(0.63, 2.37)$

Step 7: Domain: $(-\infty, \infty)$; Range: $[0, \infty)$

Step 8: Increasing on $(-2, 1)$ and $(4, \infty)$
Decreasing on $(-\infty, -2)$ and $(1, 4)$

82. Step 1: $y = x^5$

Step 2: x-intercepts: $-4, 0$; y-intercept: 0

Step 3: -4: multiplicity 1, crosses;
0: multiplicity 2, touches

Step 4:

Step 5: $(-3.17, 92.15)$; $(0, 0)$

Step 6:

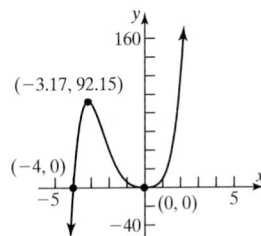

Step 7: Domain: $(-\infty, \infty)$; Range: $(-\infty, \infty)$

Step 8: Increasing on $(-\infty, -3.17)$ and $(0, \infty)$
Decreasing on $(-3.17, 0)$

83. Step 1: $y = x^3$

Step 2:

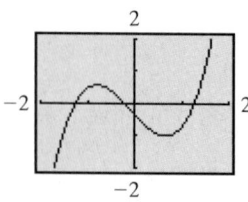

Step 3: x-intercepts: $-1.26, -0.20, 1.26$
   y-intercept: -0.31752

Step 4:

Step 5: $(-0.80, 0.57)$; $(0.66, -0.99)$

Step 6:

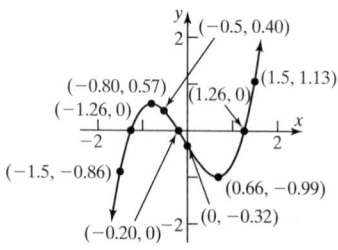

Step 7: Domain: $(-\infty, \infty)$; Range: $(-\infty, \infty)$

Step 8: Increasing on $(-\infty, -0.80)$ and $(0.66, \infty)$
   Decreasing on $(-0.80, 0.66)$

84. Step 1: $y = x^3$

Step 2:

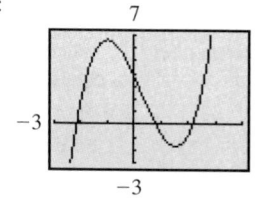

Step 3: x-intercepts: $-2.16, 0.8, 2.16$;
   y-intercept: 3.73248

Step 4:

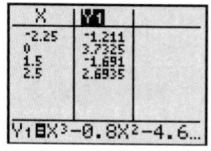

Step 5: $(-1.01, 6.60)$; $(1.54, -1.70)$

Step 6:

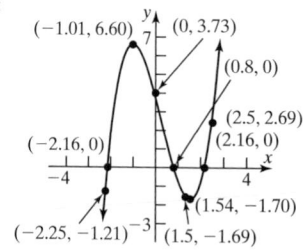

Step 7: Domain: $(-\infty, \infty)$; Range: $(-\infty, \infty)$

Step 8: Increasing on $(-\infty, -1.01)$ and $(1.54, \infty)$
   Decreasing on $(-1.01, 1.54)$

85. Step 1: $y = x^3$

Step 2:

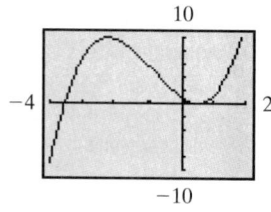

Step 3: x-intercepts: $-3.56, 0.50$
   y-intercept: 0.89

Step 4:

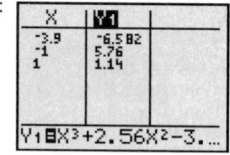

Step 5: $(-2.21, 9.91)$; $(0.50, 0)$

Step 6:

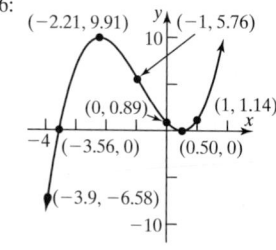

Step 7: Domain: $(-\infty, \infty)$; Range: $(-\infty, \infty)$

Step 8: Increasing on $(-\infty, -2.21)$ and $(0.50, \infty)$
   Decreasing on $(-2.21, 0.50)$

86. Step 1: $y = x^3$

Step 2:

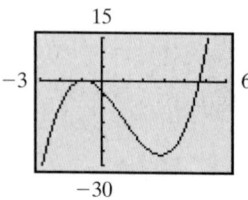

Step 3: x-intercepts: -0.9; 4.71
   y-intercept: -3.8151

Step 4:

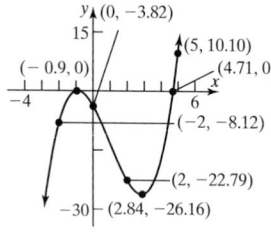

Step 5: $(-0.9, 0)$; $(2.84, -26.16)$

Step 6:

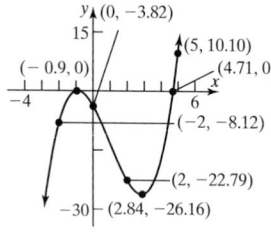

Step 7: Domain: $(-\infty, \infty)$; Range: $(-\infty, \infty)$

Step 8: Increasing on $(-\infty, -0.9)$ and $(2.84, \infty)$
   Decreasing on $(-0.9, 2.84)$

87. Step 1: $y = x^4$

Step 2:

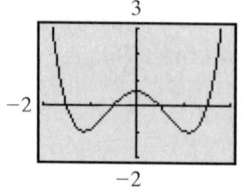

Step 3: x-intercepts: $-1.5, -0.5, 0.5, 1.5$
   y-intercept: 0.5625

Step 4:

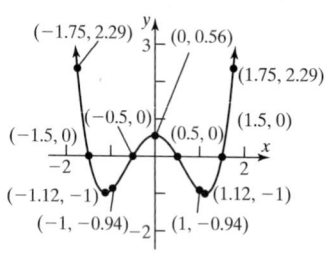

Step 5: $(-1.12, -1)$; $(1.12, -1)$; $(0, 0.56)$

Step 6:

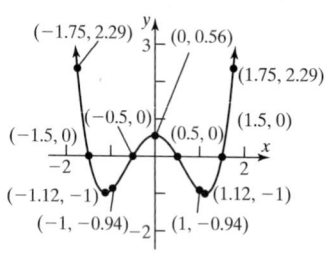

Step 7: Domain: $(-\infty, \infty)$; Range: $[-1, \infty)$

Step 8: Increasing on $(-1.12, 0)$ and $(1.12, \infty)$
   Decreasing on $(-\infty, -1.12)$ and $(0, 1.12)$

88. Step 1: $y = x^4$

Step 2:

Step 3: x-intercepts: $-3.90, -1.82$,
   $1.82, 3.90$; y-intercept: 50.2619

Step 4:

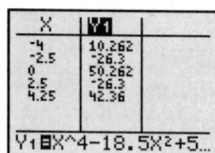

Step 5: $(-3.04, -35.30)$; $(3.04, -35.30)$; $(0, 50.26)$

Step 6:

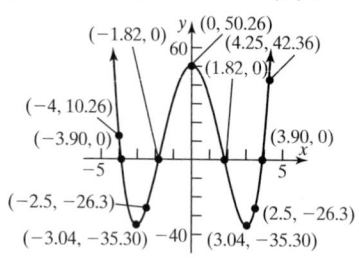

Step 7: Domain: $(-\infty, \infty)$; Range: $[-35.30, \infty)$

Step 8: Increasing on $(-3.04, 0)$ and $(3.04, \infty)$
   Decreasing on $(-\infty, -3.04)$ and $(0, 3.04)$

89. Step 1: $y = 2x^4$

Step 2:

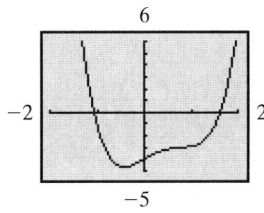

Step 3: x-intercepts: $-1.07, 1.62$
y-intercept: -4

Step 4:

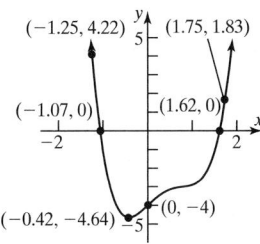

Step 5: $(-0.42, -4.64)$

Step 6:

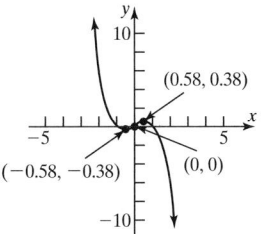

Step 7: Domain: $(-\infty, \infty)$;
Range: $[-4.64, \infty)$

Step 8: Increasing on $(-0.42, \infty)$
Decreasing on $(-\infty, -0.42)$

90. Step 1: $y = -1.2x^4$

Step 2:

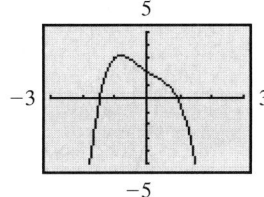

Step 3: x-intercepts: $-1.47, 0.91$
y-intercept: 2

Step 4:

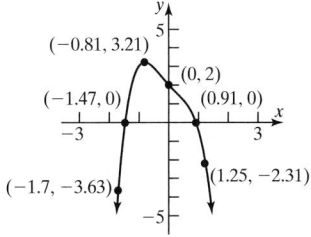

Step 5: $(-0.81, 3.21)$

Step 6:

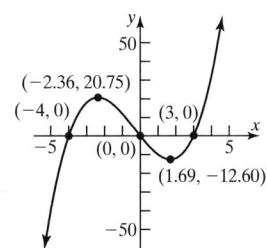

Step 7: Domain: $(-\infty, \infty)$;
Range: $(-\infty, 3.21]$

Step 8: Increasing on $(-\infty, -0.81)$
Decreasing on $(-0.81, \infty)$

91. $f(x) = -x(x + 2)(x - 2)$

Step 1: $y = -x^3$
Step 2: x-intercepts: $-2, 0, 2$; y-intercept: 0
Step 3: $-2, 0, 2$: multiplicity 1, crosses
Step 4:

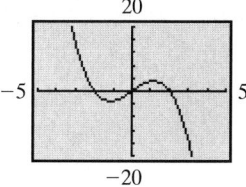

Step 5: $(-1.15, -3.08)$; $(1.15, 3.08)$
Step 6:

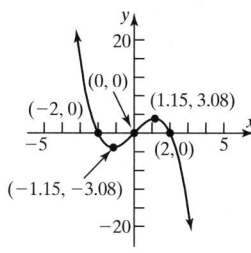

Step 7: Domain: $(-\infty, \infty)$; Range: $(-\infty, \infty)$
Step 8: Increasing on $(-1.15, 1.15)$
Decreasing on $(-\infty, -1.15)$ and $(1.15, \infty)$

92. $f(x) = -x(x + 1)(x - 1)$

Step 1: $y = -x^3$
Step 2: x-intercepts: $-1, 0, 1$; y-intercept: 0
Step 3: $-1, 0, 1$: multiplicity 1, crosses
Step 4:

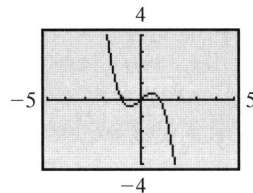

Step 5: $(-0.58, -0.38)$; $(0.58, 0.38)$

Step 6:

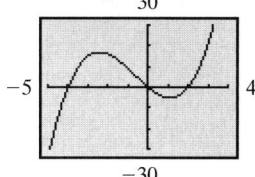

Step 7: Domain: $(-\infty, \infty)$; Range: $(-\infty, \infty)$
Step 8: Increasing on $(-0.58, 0.58)$
Decreasing on $(-\infty, -0.58)$
and $(0.58, \infty)$

93. $f(x) = x(x + 4)(x - 3)$

Step 1: $y = x^3$
Step 2: x-intercepts: $-4, 0, 3$; y-intercept: 0
Step 3: $-4, 0, 3$: multiplicity 1, crosses
Step 4:

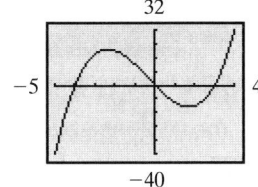

Step 5: $(-2.36, 20.75)$; $(1.69, -12.60)$

Step 6:

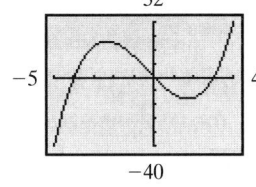

Step 7: Domain: $(-\infty, \infty)$; Range: $(-\infty, \infty)$
Step 8: Increasing on $(-\infty, -2.36)$ and $(1.69, \infty)$
Decreasing on $(-2.36, 1.69)$

94. $f(x) = x(x + 4)(x - 2)$

Step 1: $y = x^3$
Step 2: x-intercepts: $-4, 0, 2$; y-intercept: 0
Step 3: $-4, 0, 2$: multiplicity 1, crosses
Step 4:

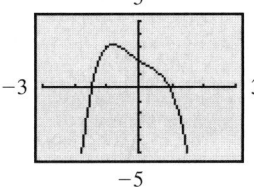

Step 5: $(-2.43, 16.90)$; $(1.10, -5.05)$

Step 6:

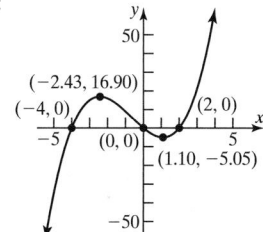

Step 7: Domain: $(-\infty, \infty)$; Range: $(-\infty, \infty)$
Step 8: Increasing on $(-\infty, -2.43)$ and $(1.10, \infty)$
Decreasing on $(-2.43, 1.10)$

95. $f(x) = 2x(x + 6)(x - 2)(x + 2)$

Step 1: $y = 2x^4$

Step 2: x-intercepts: $-6, -2, 0, 2$; y-intercept: 0

Step 3: $-6, -2, 0, 2$: multiplicity 1, crosses

Step 4:

Step 5: $(-4.65, -221.25)$; $(-1.06, 30.12)$; $(1.21, -44.25)$

Step 6:

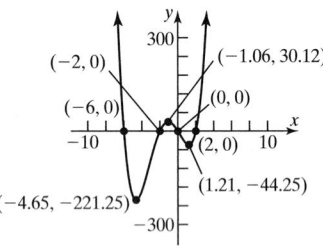

Step 7: Domain: $(-\infty, \infty)$; Range: $[-221.25, \infty)$

Step 8: Decreasing on $(-\infty, -4.65)$ and $(-1.06, 1.21)$

Increasing on $(-4.65, -1.06)$ and $(1.21, \infty)$

96. $f(x) = 2(x + 1)(x - 1)(2x + 5)$

Step 1: $y = 4x^3$

Step 2: x-intercepts: $-\dfrac{5}{2}, -1, 1$; y-intercept: -10

Step 3: $-\dfrac{5}{2}, -1, 1$: multiplicity 1, crosses

Step 4:

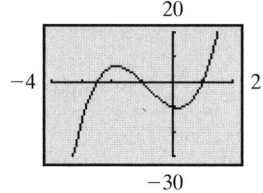

Step 5: $(-1.85, 6.30)$; $(0.18, -10.37)$

Step 6:

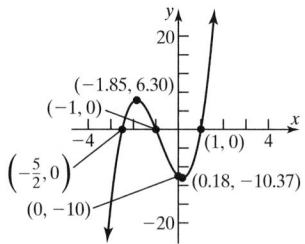

Step 7: Domain: $(-\infty, \infty)$; Range: $(-\infty, \infty)$

Step 8: Increasing on $(-\infty, -1.85)$ and $(0.18, \infty)$

Decreasing on $(-1.85, 0.18)$

97. $f(x) = -x^2(x + 1)^2(x - 1)$

Step 1: $y = -x^5$

Step 2: x-intercepts: $-1, 0, 1$; y-intercept: 0

Step 3: 1: multiplicity 1, crosses; $-1, 0$: multiplicity 2, touches

Step 4:

Step 5: $(-1, 0)$; $(-0.54, 0.10)$; $(0, 0)$; $(0.74, 0.43)$

Step 6:

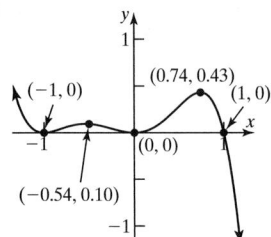

Step 7: Domain: $(-\infty, \infty)$; Range: $(-\infty, \infty)$

Step 8: Increasing on $(-1, -0.54)$ and $(0, 0.74)$

Decreasing on $(-\infty, -1)$, $(-0.54, 0)$ and $(0.74, \infty)$

98. $f(x) = -x^2(x - 2)(x + 2)(x - 5)$

Step 1: $y = -x^5$

Step 2: x-intercepts: $-2, 0, 2, 5$; y-intercept: 0

Step 3: 0: multiplicity 2, touches; $-2, 2, 5$: multiplicity 1, crosses

Step 4:

Step 5: $(-1.45, -25.73)$; $(0, 0)$; $(1.34, -14.49)$; $(4.11, 193.82)$

Step 6:

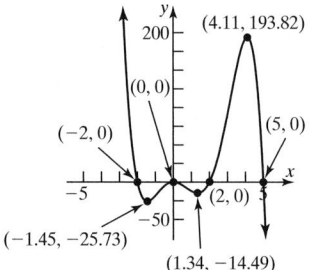

Step 7: Domain: $(-\infty, \infty)$; Range: $(-\infty, \infty)$

Step 8: Increasing on $(-1.45, 0)$ and $(1.34, 4.11)$

Decreasing on $(-\infty, -1.45)$, $(0, 1.34)$, and $(4.11, \infty)$

99. (a) $T(r) = \underbrace{500(1 + r)(1 + r)}_{\substack{\text{Account value of} \\ \text{deposit 1}}} + \underbrace{500(1 + r)}_{\substack{\text{Account value} \\ \text{of deposit 2}}} + \underbrace{500}_{\text{Deposit 3}}$

(b) $2155.06

$= 500(1 + 2r + r^2) + 500 + 500r + 500 = 500 + 1000r + 500r^2 + 500 + 500r + 500 = 500r^2 + 1500r + 1500$

100. (a)

(b)

(c)

(d) The values of the polynomial function get closer to the values of f. The approximations near 0 are better than those near -1 or 1.

101. (a) H

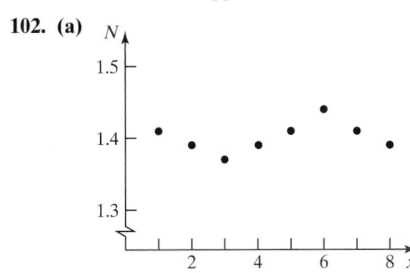

The relation appears to be cubic.

(b) $H(x) = 0.1591x^3 - 2.3203x^2 + 9.3301x - 2.2143$

(c) About 6 major hurricanes

(d) 12.5

(e) Approximately 10 major hurricanes

102. (a) N

The relation appears to be cubic.

(b) $N(x) = -0.0015x^3 + 0.0198x^2 - 0.0742x + 1.4671$

(c) Approximately 1.40 million people

(d) 1.5

1.3

103. (a) T

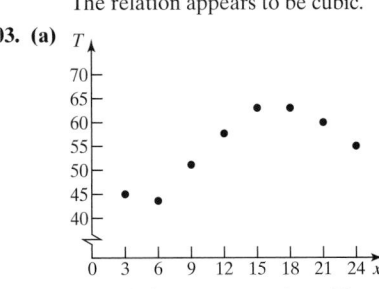

The relation appears to be cubic.

(b) Average rate of change: $2.27°$ /h

(c) Average rate of change: $0°$ /h

(d) $T(x) = -0.0103x^3 + 0.3174x^2 - 1.3742x + 45.3929$; The predicted temperature at 5 PM is $63.2°$F.

(e) 70

40

(f) The y-intercept, $45.4°$, is the predicted temperature at midnight.

104. No; yes **108.** $f(x) = \text{int}(x)$; $g(x) = |x|$ **109.** (a)–(d) **110. (a)** Even **(b)** Positive **(c)** Even **(d)** x^2 is a factor of the polynomial because $x = 0$ is a zero of even multiplicity. **(e)** Eight is the minimum degree of the polynomial.

4.2 Assess Your Understanding *(page 200)*

5. $y = 1$ **6.** $x = -1$ **7.** Proper **8.** F **9.** T **10.** T **11.** All real numbers except 3; $\{x | x \neq 3\}$ **12.** All real numbers except -3; $\{x | x \neq -3\}$

13. All real numbers except 2 and -4; $\{x | x \neq 2, x \neq -4\}$ **14.** All real numbers except -3 and 4; $\{x | x \neq -3, x \neq 4\}$ **15.** All real numbers except $-\dfrac{1}{2}$

and 3; $\left\{x \middle| x \neq -\dfrac{1}{2}, x \neq 3\right\}$ **16.** All real numbers except $\dfrac{1}{3}$ and -2; $\left\{x \middle| x \neq \dfrac{1}{3}, x \neq -2\right\}$ **17.** All real numbers except 2; $\{x | x \neq 2\}$ **18.** All real

numbers except -1 and 1; $\{x | x \neq -1, x \neq 1\}$ **19.** All real numbers **20.** All real numbers **21.** All real numbers except -3 and 3; $\{x | x \neq -3, x \neq 3\}$

22. All real numbers except -2; $\{x | x \neq -2\}$ **23. (a)** Domain: $\{x | x \neq 2\}$; Range: $\{y | y \neq 1\}$ **(b)** $(0, 0)$ **(c)** $y = 1$ **(d)** $x = 2$ **(e)** None

24. (a) Domain: $\{x \mid x \neq -1\}$; Range: $\{y \mid y > 0\}$ **(b)** $(0, 2)$ **(c)** $y = 0$ **(d)** $x = -1$ **(e)** None **25. (a)** Domain: $\{x \mid x \neq 0\}$; Range: all real numbers

(b) $(-1, 0), (1, 0)$ **(c)** None **(d)** $x = 0$ **(e)** $y = 2x$ **26. (a)** Domain: $\{x \mid x \neq 0\}$; Range: $\{y \mid y \leq -2, y \geq 2\}$ **(b)** None **(c)** None **(d)** $x = 0$

(e) $y = -x$ **27. (a)** Domain: $\{x \mid x \neq -2, x \neq 2\}$; Range: $\{y \mid y \leq 0, y > 1\}$ **(b)** $(0, 0)$ **(c)** $y = 1$ **(d)** $x = -2, x = 2$ **(e)** None

28. (a) Domain: $\{x \mid x \neq -1, x \neq 1\}$; Range: all real numbers **(b)** $(0, 0)$ **(c)** $y = 0$ **(d)** $x = -1, x = 1$ **(e)** None

29.

30.

31.

32.

33.

34.

35.

36.

37.

38.

39.

40.
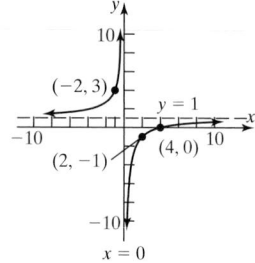

41. Vertical asymptote: $x = -4$; horizontal asymptote: $y = 3$ **42.** Vertical asymptote: $x = 6$; horizontal asymptote: $y = 3$

43. Vertical asymptote: $x = 3$; oblique asymptote: $y = x + 5$ **44.** Vertical asymptotes: $x = 2, x = 3$; oblique asymptote: $y = x + 5$

45. Vertical asymptotes: $x = 1, x = -1$; horizontal asymptote: $y = 0$ **46.** Vertical asymptote: $x = 1$; horizontal asymptote: $y = 0$

47. Vertical asymptote: $x = -\frac{1}{3}$; horizontal asymptote: $y = \frac{2}{3}$ **48.** Vertical asymptote: $x = -\frac{5}{2}$; horizontal asymptote: $y = \frac{1}{2}$

49. Vertical asymptote: none; oblique asymptote: $y = 2x - 1$ **50.** Vertical asymptotes: none; oblique asymptote: $y = 2x + 7$

51. Vertical asymptote: $x = 0$; no horizontal or oblique asymptotes **52.** Vertical asymptote: $x = 0$; no horizontal or oblique asymptotes

53. (a) 9.8208 m/sec^2 **(b)** 9.8195 m/sec^2 **(c)** 9.7936 m/sec^2 **(d)** h-axis **(e)** $\varnothing$ **54. (a)** 25 **(b)** Approximately 596 **(c)** $y = 2500; 2500$

55. (a)

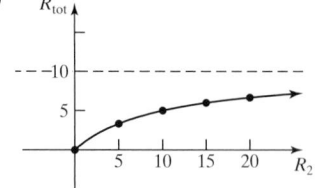

(b) Horizontal: $R_{\text{tot}} = 10$; as the resistance
of R_2 increases without bound, the total
resistance approaches 10 ohms, the resistance R_1.
(c) $R_1 \approx 103.5$ ohms

56. (a) $p(5) = 50; p(-3) = -46$
(b) We conclude that $p(x)$ has a zero in the interval $(-3, 5)$.
(c) $x = 4.0949$
(d)

(e) $p(4.0949) \approx -0.00017$

4.3 Assess Your Understanding *(page 210)*

3. in lowest terms **4.** F **5.** F **6.** T

7. Step 1: Domain: $\{x \mid x \neq 0, x \neq -4\}$
Step 2: $R(x)$ is in lowest terms.
Step 3: x-intercept: -1; no y-intercept
Step 4: No symmetry
Step 5: Vertical asymptotes: $x = 0, x = -4$
Step 6: Horizontal asymptote: $y = 0$, intersected at $(-1, 0)$

Step 7:

Step 8: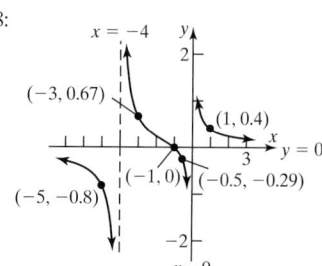

8. Step 1: Domain: $\{x \mid x \neq -2, x \neq 1\}$
Step 2: $R(x)$ is in lowest terms.
Step 3: Intercept: $(0, 0)$
Step 4: No symmetry
Step 5: Vertical asymptotes: $x = 1, x = -2$
Step 6: Horizontal asymptotes: $y = 0$, intersected at $(0, 0)$

Step 7:

Step 8: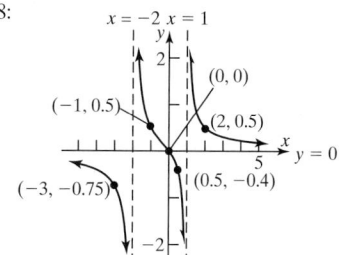

9. Step 1: $R(x) = \dfrac{3(x + 1)}{2(x + 2)}$; Domain: $\{x \mid x \neq -2\}$
Step 2: $R(x)$ is in lowest terms.
Step 3: x-intercept: -1; y-intercept: $\dfrac{3}{4}$
Step 4: No symmetry
Step 5: Vertical asymptote: $x = -2$
Step 6: Horizontal asymptote: $y = \dfrac{3}{2}$, not intersected

Step 7: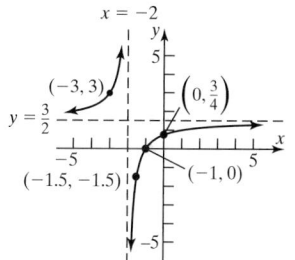

Step 8:

10. Step 1: $R(x) = \dfrac{2(x + 2)}{x - 1}$; Domain: $\{x \mid x \neq 1\}$
Step 2: $R(x)$ is in lowest terms.
Step 3: x-intercept: -2; y-intercept: -4
Step 4: No symmetry
Step 5: Vertical asymptote: $x = 1$
Step 6: Horizontal asymptote: $y = 2$, not intersected

Step 7:

Step 8: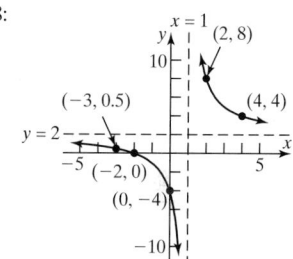

11. Step 1: $R(x) = \dfrac{3}{(x + 2)(x - 2)}$;
Domain: $\{x \mid x \neq -2, x \neq 2\}$
Step 2: $R(x)$ is in lowest terms.
Step 3: No x-intercept; y-intercept: $-\dfrac{3}{4}$
Step 4: Symmetric with respect to the y-axis
Step 5: Vertical asymptotes: $x = 2, x = -2$
Step 6: Horizontal asymptote: $y = 0$, not intersected

Step 7: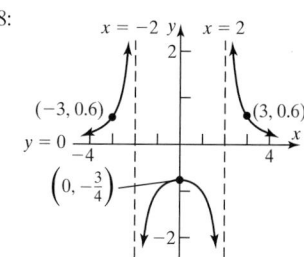

Step 8:

12. Step 1: $R(x) = \dfrac{6}{(x - 3)(x + 2)}$; X
Domain: $\{x \mid x \neq -2, x \neq 3\}$
Step 2: $R(x)$ is in lowest terms.
Step 3: No x-intercept; y-intercept: -1
Step 4: No symmetry
Step 5: Vertical asymptotes: $x = -2, x = 3$
Step 6: Horizontal asymptote: $y = 0$, not intersected

Step 7:

Step 8: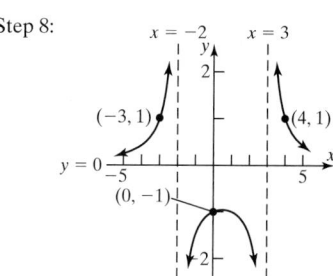

13. Step 1: $P(x) = \dfrac{x^4 + x^2 + 1}{(x + 1)(x - 1)}$; Domain: $\{x \mid x \neq -1, x \neq 1\}$

Step 2: $P(x)$ is in lowest terms.
Step 3: No x-intercept; y-intercept: -1
Step 4: Symmetric with respect to the y-axis
Step 5: Vertical asymptotes: $x = -1$, $x = 1$
Step 6: No horizontal or oblique asymptotes

Step 7:

Step 8: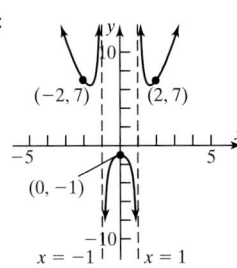

14. Step 1: $Q(x) = \dfrac{(x^2 + 1)(x - 1)(x + 1)}{(x + 2)(x - 2)}$;

Domain: $\{x \mid x \neq -2, x \neq 2\}$

Step 2: $Q(x)$ is in lowest terms.

Step 3: x-intercepts: -1, 1; y-intercept: $\dfrac{1}{4}$
Step 4: Symmetric with respect to the y-axis
Step 5: Vertical asymptotes: $x = -2$, $x = 2$
Step 6: No horizontal or oblique asymptotes

Step 7:

Step 8: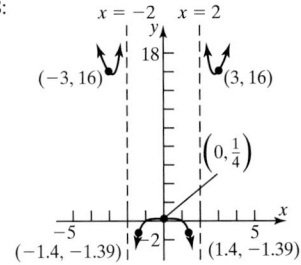

15. Step 1: $H(x) = \dfrac{(x - 1)(x^2 + x + 1)}{(x + 3)(x - 3)}$;

Domain: $\{x \mid x \neq -3, x \neq 3\}$

Step 2: $H(x)$ is in lowest terms.

Step 3: x-intercept: 1; y-intercept: $\dfrac{1}{9}$

Step 4: No symmetry

Step 5: Vertical asymptotes: $x = 3$, $x = -3$

Step 6: Oblique asymptote: $y = x$, intersected at $\left(\dfrac{1}{9}, \dfrac{1}{9}\right)$

Step 7:

Step 8: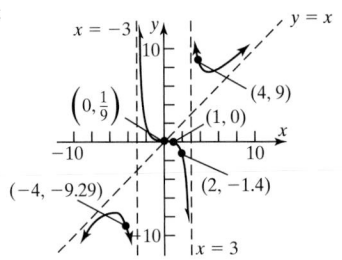

16. Step 1: $G(x) = \dfrac{(x + 1)(x^2 - x + 1)}{x(x + 2)}$;

Domain: $\{x \mid x \neq 0, x \neq -2\}$

Step 2: $G(x)$ is in lowest terms.
Step 3: x-intercept: -1; no y-intercept
Step 4: No symmetry
Step 5: Vertical asymptotes: $x = 0$, $x = -2$
Step 6: Oblique asymptote: $y = x - 2$,
intersected at $(-0.25, -2.25)$

Step 7:

Step 8: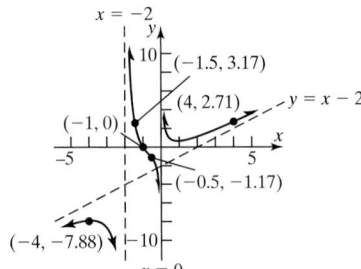

17. Step 1: $R(x) = \dfrac{x^2}{(x + 3)(x - 2)}$;

Domain: $\{x \neq -3, x \neq 2\}$
Step 2: $R(x)$ is in lowest terms.
Step 3: Intercept: $(0, 0)$
Step 4: No symmetry
Step 5: Vertical asymptotes: $x = 2$, $x = -3$
Step 6: Horizontal asymptote: $y = 1$, intersected at $(6, 1)$

Step 7:

Step 8: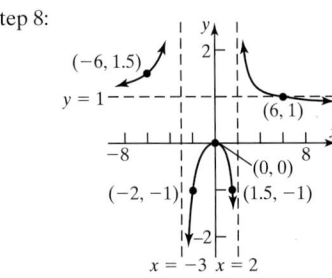

18. Step 1: $R(x) = \dfrac{(x + 4)(x - 3)}{(x + 2)(x - 2)}$; Domain: $\{x \mid x \neq -2, x \neq 2\}$

Step 2: $R(x)$ is in lowest terms.
Step 3: x-intercepts: 3, -4; y-intercept: 3
Step 4: No symmetry
Step 5: Vertical asymptotes: $x = -2$, $x = 2$
Step 6: Horizontal asymptote: $y = 1$, intersected at $(8, 1)$

Step 7:

Step 8:

19. Step 1: $G(x) = \dfrac{x}{(x+2)(x-2)}$; Domain: $\{x | x \neq -2, x \neq 2\}$ Step 7:

Step 2: $G(x)$ is in lowest terms.
Step 3: Intercept: $(0,0)$
Step 4: Symmetry with respect to the origin
Step 5: Vertical asymptotes: $x = -2, x = 2$
Step 6: Horizontal asymptote: $y = 0$, intersected at $(0,0)$

Step 8:

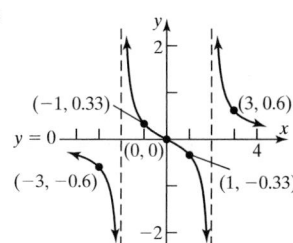

20. Step 1: $G(x) = \dfrac{3x}{(x+1)(x-1)}$; Domain: $\{x | x \neq -1, x \neq 1\}$ Step 7:

Step 2: $G(x)$ is in lowest terms.
Step 3: Intercept: $(0,0)$
Step 4: Symmetric with respect to the origin
Step 5: Vertical asymptotes: $x = -1, x = 1$
Step 6: Horizontal asymptote: $y = 0$, intersected at $(0,0)$

Step 8:

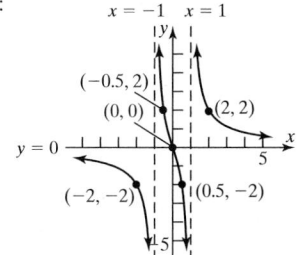

21. Step 1: $R(x) = \dfrac{3}{(x-1)(x-2)(x+2)}$; Step 7:

Domain: $\{x | x \neq 1, x \neq -2, x \neq 2\}$
Step 2: $R(x)$ is in lowest terms.
Step 3: No x-intercept; y-intercept: $\dfrac{3}{4}$
Step 4: No symmetry
Step 5: Vertical asymptotes: $x = -2, x = 1, x = 2$
Step 6: Horizontal asymptote: $y = 0$, not intersected

Step 8:

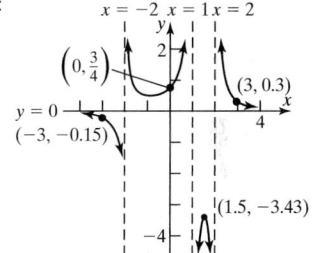

22. Step 1: $R(x) = \dfrac{-4}{(x+1)(x-3)(x+3)}$; Step 7:

Domain: $\{x | x \neq -1, x \neq -3, x \neq 3\}$
Step 2: $R(x)$ is in lowest terms.
Step 3: No x-intercept; y-intercept: $\dfrac{4}{9}$
Step 4: No symmetry
Step 5: Vertical asymptotes: $x = -1, x = -3, x = 3$
Step 6: Horizontal asymptote: $y = 0$, not intersected

Step 8:

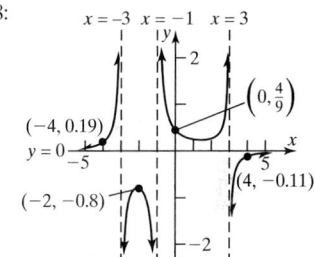

23. Step 1: $H(x) = \dfrac{4(x+1)(x-1)}{(x^2+4)(x+2)(x-2)}$; Step 7:

Domain: $\{x | x \neq -2, x \neq 2\}$
Step 2: $H(x)$ is in lowest terms.
Step 3: x-intercepts: $-1, 1$; y-intercept: $\dfrac{1}{4}$
Step 4: Symmetry with respect to the y-axis
Step 5: Vertical asymptotes: $x = -2, x = 2$
Step 6: Horizontal asymptote: $y = 0$,
intersected at $(-1, 0)$ and $(1, 0)$

Step 8:

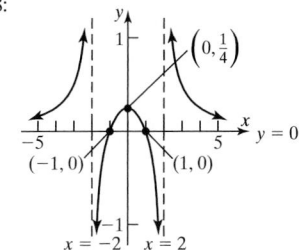

24. Step 1: $H(x) = \dfrac{x^2+4}{(x^2+1)(x+1)(x-1)}$; Step 7:

Domain: $\{x | x \neq -1, x \neq 1\}$
Step 2: $H(x)$ is in lowest terms.
Step 3: No x-intercept; y-intercept: -4
Step 4: Symmetric with respect to the y-axis
Step 5: Vertical asymptotes: $x = -1, x = 1$
Step 6: Horizontal asymptote: $y = 0$, not intersected

Step 8:

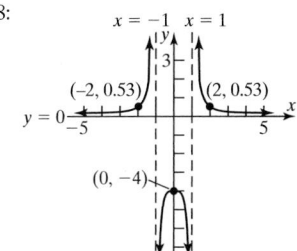

25. Step 1: $F(x) = \dfrac{(x-4)(x+1)}{x+2}$; Domain: $\{x|x \neq -2\}$
Step 2: $F(x)$ is in lowest terms.
Step 3: x-intercepts: $-1, 4$; y-intercept: -2
Step 4: No symmetry
Step 5: Vertical asymptote: $x = -2$
Step 6: Oblique asymptote: $y = x - 5$, not intersected

Step 7:

Step 8:

26. Step 1: $F(x) = \dfrac{(x+2)(x+1)}{x-1}$; Domain: $\{x|x \neq 1\}$
Step 2: $F(x)$ is in lowest terms.
Step 3: x-intercepts: $-2, -1$; y-intercept: -2
Step 4: No symmetry
Step 5: Vertical asymptote: $x = 1$
Step 6: Oblique asymptote: $y = x + 4$, not intersected

Step 7:

Step 8:

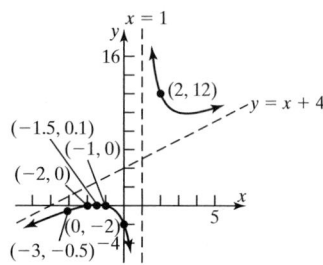

27. Step 1: $R(x) = \dfrac{(x+4)(x-3)}{x-4}$; Domain: $\{x|x \neq 4\}$
Step 2: $R(x)$ is in lowest terms.
Step 3: x-intercepts: $-4, 3$; y-intercept: 3
Step 4: No symmetry
Step 5: Vertical asymptote: $x = 4$
Step 6: Oblique asymptote: $y = x + 5$, not intersected

Step 7:

Step 8.

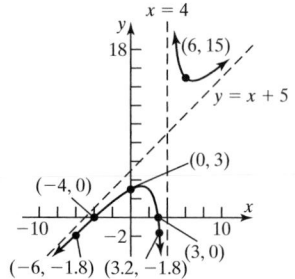

28. Step 1: $R(x) = \dfrac{(x-4)(x+3)}{x+5}$; Domain: $\{x|x \neq -5\}$
Step 2: $R(x)$ is in lowest terms.
Step 3: x-intercepts: $-3, 4$; y-intercept: $-\dfrac{12}{5}$
Step 4: No symmetry
Step 5: Vertical asymptote: $x = -5$
Step 6: Oblique asymptote: $y = x - 6$, not intersected

Step 7:

Step 8:

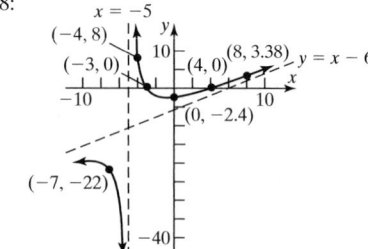

29. Step 1: $F(x) = \dfrac{(x+4)(x-3)}{x+2}$; Domain: $\{x|x \neq -2\}$
Step 2: $F(x)$ is in lowest terms.
Step 3: x-intercepts: $-4, 3$; y-intercept: -6
Step 4: No symmetry
Step 5: Vertical asymptote: $x = -2$
Step 6: Oblique asymptote: $y = x - 1$, not intersected

Step 7:

Step 8:

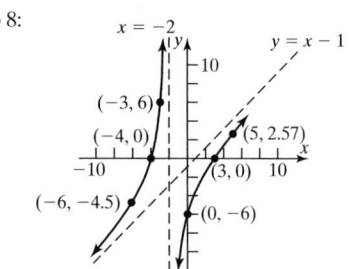

30. Step 1: $G(x) = \dfrac{(x-4)(x+3)}{x+1}$; Domain: $\{x|x \neq -1\}$
Step 2: $G(x)$ is in lowest terms.
Step 3: x-intercepts: $-3, 4$; y-intercept: -12
Step 4: No symmetry
Step 5: Vertical asymptote: $x = -1$
Step 6: Oblique asymptote: $y = x - 2$, not intersected

Step 7:

Step 8:

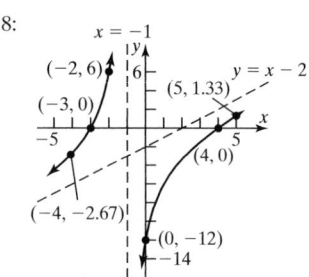

31. Step 1: Domain: $\{x | x \neq -3\}$

Step 2: $R(x)$ is in lowest terms.

Step 3: x-intercepts: 0, 1; y-intercept: 0

Step 4: No symmetry

Step 5: Vertical asymptote: $x = -3$

Step 6: Horizontal asymptote: $y = 1$, not intersected

Step 7:

Step 8:

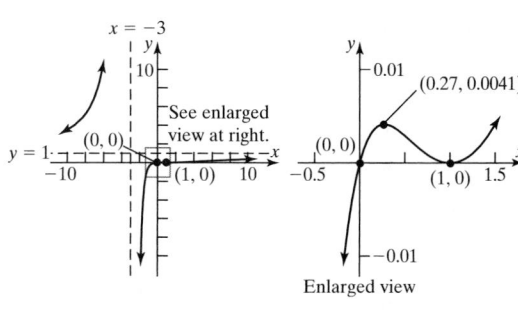

Enlarged view

32. Step 1: Domain: $\{x | x \neq 0, x \neq 4\}$

Step 2: $R(x)$ is in lowest terms.

Step 3: x-intercepts: 1, -2, 3; no y-intercept

Step 4: No symmetry

Step 5: Vertical asymptotes: $x = 0, x = 4$

Step 6: Horizontal asymptote: $y = 1$,
intersected at $(3.186, 1), (0.314, 1)$

Step 7:

Step 8:

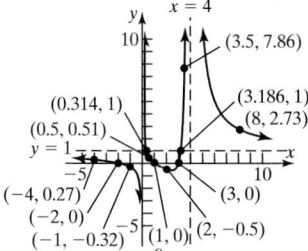

33. Step 1: $R(x) = \dfrac{(x + 4)(x - 3)}{(x + 2)(x - 3)}$;

Domain: $\{x | x \neq -2, x \neq 3\}$

Step 2: $R(x) = \dfrac{x + 4}{x + 2}$

Step 3: x-intercept: -4; y-intercept: 2

Step 4: No symmetry

Step 5: Vertical asymptote: $x = -2$; hole at $\left(3, \dfrac{7}{5}\right)$

Step 6: Horizontal asymptote: $y = 1$, not intersected

Step 7:

Step 8:

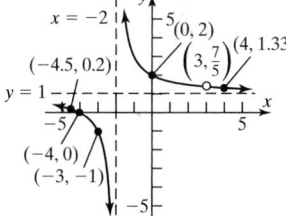

34. Step 1: $R(x) = \dfrac{(x - 2)(x + 5)}{(x + 3)(x + 5)}$;

Domain: $\{x | x \neq -3, x \neq -5\}$

Step 2: $R(x) = \dfrac{x - 2}{x + 3}$

Step 3: x-intercept: 2; y-intercept: $-\dfrac{2}{3}$

Step 4: No symmetry

Step 5: Vertical asymptote: $x = -3$; hole at $(-5, 3.5)$

Step 6: Horizontal asymptote: $y = 1$, not intersected

Step 7:

Step 8:

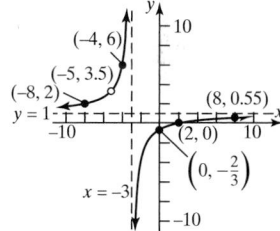

35. Step 1: $R(x) = \dfrac{(3x + 1)(2x - 3)}{(x - 2)(2x - 3)}$;

Domain: $\left\{x \middle| x \neq \dfrac{3}{2}, x \neq 2\right\}$

Step 2: $R(x) = \dfrac{3x + 1}{x - 2}$

Step 3: x-intercept: $-\dfrac{1}{3}$; y-intercept: $-\dfrac{1}{2}$

Step 4: No symmetry

Step 5: Vertical asymptote: $x = 2$; hole at $\left(\dfrac{3}{2}, -11\right)$

Step 6: Horizontal asymptote: $y = 3$, not intersected

Step 7:

Step 8:

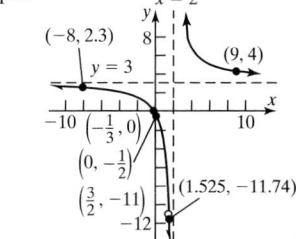

36. Step 1: $R(x) = \dfrac{(4x + 3)(2x + 5)}{(x - 3)(2x + 5)}$;

Domain: $\{x | x \neq -\dfrac{5}{2}, x \neq 3\}$

Step 2: $R(x) = \dfrac{4x + 3}{x - 3}$

Step 3: x-intercept: $-\dfrac{3}{4}$; y-intercept: -1

Step 4: No symmetry

Step 5: Vertical asymptote: $x = 3$; hole at $\left(-\dfrac{5}{2}, \dfrac{14}{11}\right)$

Step 6: Horizontal asymptote: $y = 4$, not intersected

Step 7:

Step 8:

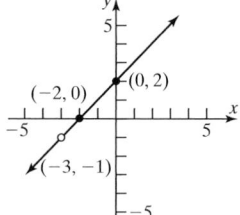

37. Step 1: $R(x) = \dfrac{(x + 2)(x + 3)}{(x + 3)}$; Domain: $\{x | x \neq -3\}$

Step 2: $R(x) = x + 2$
Step 3: x-intercept: -2; y-intercept: 2
Step 4: No symmetry
Step 5: Vertical asymptote: none; hole at $(-3, -1)$
Step 6: Oblique asymptote: $y = x + 2$, intersected over entire domain

Step 7:

Step 8:

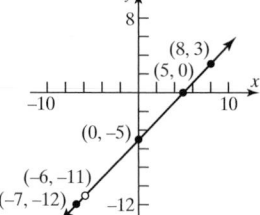

38. Step 1: $R(x) = \dfrac{(x + 6)(x - 5)}{(x + 6)}$; Domain: $\{x | x \neq -6\}$

Step 2: $R(x) = x - 5$
Step 3: x-intercept: 5; y-intercept: -5
Step 4: No symmetry
Step 5: Vertical asymptote: none; hole at $(-6, -11)$
Step 6: Oblique asymptote: $y = x - 5$, intersected over entire domain

Step 7:

Step 8:

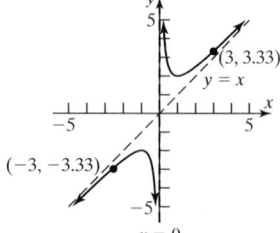

39. Step 1: $f(x) = \dfrac{x^2 + 1}{x}$; Domain: $\{x | x \neq 0\}$

Step 2: $f(x)$ is in lowest terms.
Step 3: No x-intercepts; no y-intercept
Step 4: Symmetric with respect to the origin
Step 5: Vertical asymptote: $x = 0$
Step 6: Oblique asymptote: $y = x$, not intersected

Step 7:

Step 8:

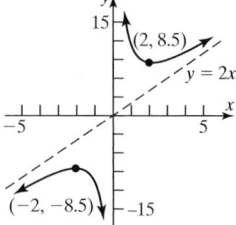

40. Step 1: $f(x) = \dfrac{2x^2 + 9}{x}$; Domain: $\{x | x \neq 0\}$

Step 2: $f(x)$ is in lowest terms.
Step 3: No x-intercepts; no y-intercept
Step 4: Symmetric with respect to the origin
Step 5: Vertical asymptote: $x = 0$
Step 6: Oblique asymptote: $y = 2x$, not intersected

Step 7:

Step 8:

41. Step 1: $f(x) = \dfrac{x^3 + 1}{x} = \dfrac{(x + 1)(x^2 - x + 1)}{x}$;

Domain: $\{x | x \neq 0\}$
Step 2: $f(x)$ is in lowest terms.
Step 3: x-intercept: -1; no y-intercept
Step 4: No symmetry
Step 5: Vertical asymptote: $x = 0$
Step 6: No horizontal or oblique asymptotes

Step 7:

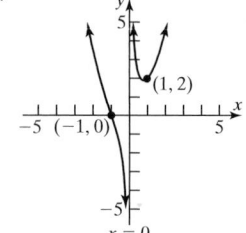

Step 8:

42. Step 1: $f(x) = \dfrac{2x^3 + 9}{x}$; Domain: $\{x | x \neq 0\}$

Step 2: $f(x)$ is in lowest terms.

Step 3: x-intercept: -1.65; no y-intercept

Step 4: No symmetry

Step 5: Vertical asymptote: $x = 0$

Step 6: No oblique or horizontal asymptotes

Step 7:

Step 8: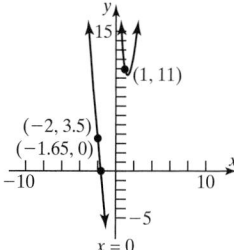

43. Step 1: $f(x) = \dfrac{x^4 + 1}{x^3}$; Domain: $\{x | x \neq 0\}$

Step 2: $f(x)$ is in lowest terms.

Step 3: No x-intercepts; no y-intercept

Step 4: Symmetric with respect to the origin

Step 5: Vertical asymptote: $x = 0$

Step 6: Oblique asymptote: $y = x$, not intersected.

Step 7:

Step 8: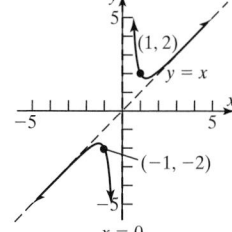

44. Step 1: $f(x) = \dfrac{2x^4 + 9}{x^3}$; Domain: $\{x | x \neq 0\}$

Step 2: $f(x)$ is in lowest terms.

Step 3: No x-intercepts; no y-intercept

Step 4: Symmetric with respect to the origin

Step 5: Vertical asymptote: $x = 0$

Step 6: Oblique asymptote: $y = 2x$, not intersected

Step 7:

Step 8: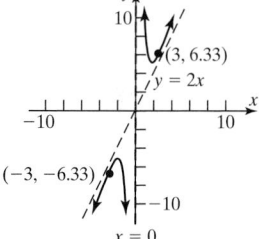

45. Minimum value: 2.00 at $x = 1.00$

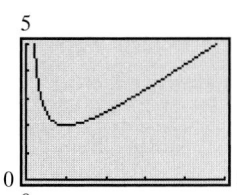

46. Minimum value: 8.49 at $x = 2.12$

47. Minimum value: 1.89 at $x = 0.79$

48. Minimum value: 10.30 at $x = 1.31$ **49.** Minimum value: 1.75 at $x = 1.32$ **50.** Minimum value: 5.11 at $x = 1.92$

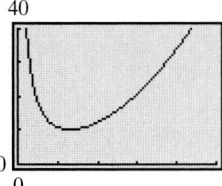

51. One possibility: $R(x) = \dfrac{x^2}{x^2 - 4}$ **52.** One possibility: $R(x) = -\dfrac{x}{x^2 - 1}$ **53.** One possibility: $R(x) = \dfrac{(x - 1)(x - 3)\left(x^2 + \frac{4}{3}\right)}{(x + 1)^2(x - 2)^2}$

54. One possibility: $R(x) = \dfrac{3(x + 2)(x - 1)^2}{(x + 3)(x - 4)^2}$

55. (a) t-axis; $C(t) \to 0$

(b)
0.4

0

0 12

(c) 0.71 h after injection

56. (a) t-axis; $C(t) \to 0$

(b)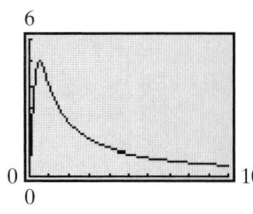
6

0

0 100

(c) 5 min after injection

57. (a) $C(x) = 16x + \dfrac{5000}{x} + 100$

(b) $x > 0$

(c)
10,000

0

0 300

(d) Approximately 17.7 ft by 56.6 ft
(longer side parallel to river)

58. (a) $f'(v_s) = 600\left(\dfrac{727.4}{772.4 - v_s}\right)$

(b) 68.5 mph

(c)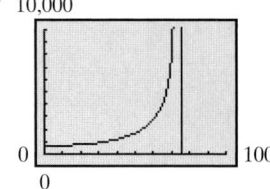
10,000

0

0 1000

59. (a) $S(x) = 2x^2 + \dfrac{40,000}{x}$

(b)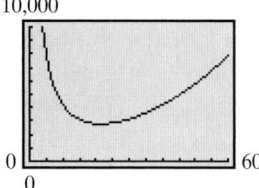
10,000

0

0 60

(c) 2784.95 in.^{2}

(d) 21.54 in. × 21.54 in. × 21.54 in.

(e) To minimize the cost of materials needed for construction

60. (a) $S(x) = x^2 + \dfrac{20,000}{x}$

(b)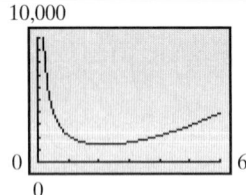
10,000

0

0 60

(c) 1392.48 in.^{2}

(d) 21.54 in. × 21.54 in. × 10.78 in.

(e) To minimize the cost of materials needed for construction

61. (a) $C(r) = 12\pi r^2 + \dfrac{4000}{r}$

(b)
6000

0

0 10

The cost is smallest when
$r = 3.76$ cm.

62. (a) $A(r) = 2\pi r^2 + \dfrac{200}{r}$

(b) Approximately 123.22 ft^2

(c) Approximately 150.53 ft^2

(d) Approximately 197.08 ft^2

(e)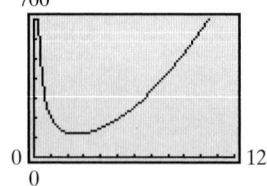
700

0

0 12

A is smallest when $r = 2.52$ ft.

63. No. Each function is a quotient of polynomials, but it is not written in lowest terms. Each function is undefined for $x = 1$; each graph has a hole at $x = 1$. **64.** All four graphs have a vertical asymptote at $x = 1$; $y = \dfrac{x^2}{x-1}$ has an oblique asymptote at $y = x + 1$.

4.4 Assess Your Understanding (page 217)

3. T **4.** F **5. (a)** $\{x | 0 < x < 1 \text{ or } x > 2\}$; $(0, 1) \cup (2, \infty)$ **(b)** $\{x | x \leq 0 \text{ or } 1 \leq x \leq 2\}$; $(-\infty, 0] \cup [1, 2]$

6. (a) $\{x | -1 < x < 1 \text{ or } x > 2\}$; $(-1, 1) \cup (2, \infty)$ **(b)** $\{x | x \leq -1 \text{ or } 1 \leq x \leq 2\}$; $(-\infty, -1] \cup [1, 2]$

7. (a) $\{x | -1 < x < 0 \text{ or } x > 1\}$; $(-1, 0) \cup (1, \infty)$ **(b)** $\{x | x < -1 \text{ or } 0 \leq x < 1\}$; $(-\infty, -1) \cup [0, 1)$

8. (a) $\{x | x < -1 \text{ or } -1 < x < 1 \text{ or } x > 3\}$; $(-\infty, -1) \cup (-1, 1) \cup (3, \infty)$ **(b)** $\{x | 1 \leq x < 2 \text{ or } 2 < x \leq 3\}$; $[1, 2) \cup (2, 3]$

9. $\{x | x < 0 \text{ or } 0 < x < 3\}$; $(-\infty, 0) \cup (0, 3)$ **10.** $\{x | x \leq 0\}$; $(-\infty, 0]$ **11.** $\{x | x \geq -4\}$; $[-4, \infty)$

12. $\{x | x > 1\}$; $(1, \infty)$ **13.** $\{x | x \leq -2 \text{ or } x \geq 2\}$; $(-\infty, -2] \cup [2, \infty)$ **14.** $\{x | x < -4 \text{ or } x > 1\}$; $(-\infty, -4) \cup (1, \infty)$

15. $\{x | -4 < x < -1 \text{ or } x > 0\}$; $(-4, -1) \cup (0, \infty)$ **16.** $\{x | x < -2 \text{ or } 0 < x < 1\}$; $(-\infty, -2) \cup (0, 1)$

17. $\{x | -2 < x \leq -1\}$; $(-2, -1]$ **18.** $\{x | x \leq -2 \text{ or } x > 1\}$; $(-\infty, -2] \cup (1, \infty)$ **19.** $\{x | x < -2\}$; $(-\infty, -2)$ **20.** $\{x | x > 5\}$; $(5, \infty)$

21. $\{x | x > 4\}$; $(4, \infty)$ **22.** $\{x | x < -8\}$; $(-\infty, -8)$ **23.** $\{x | -4 < x < 0 \text{ or } x > 0\}$; $(-4, 0) \cup (0, \infty)$ **24.** $\{x | x < -5\}$; $(-\infty, -5)$

25. $\{x | x \leq 1 \text{ or } 2 \leq x \leq 3\}$; $(-\infty, 1] \cup [2, 3]$ **26.** $\{x | x \leq -3 \text{ or } -2 \leq x \leq -1\}$; $(-\infty, -3] \cup [-2, -1]$

27. $\{x | -1 < x < 0 \text{ or } x > 3\}$; $(-1, 0) \cup (3, \infty)$ **28.** $\{x | -3 < x < 0 \text{ or } x > 1\}$; $(-3, 0) \cup (1, \infty)$ **29.** $\{x | x < -1 \text{ or } x > 1\}$; $(-\infty, -1) \cup (1, \infty)$

30. $\{x | -3 < x < 0 \text{ or } 0 < x < 3\}$; $(-3, 0) \cup (0, 3)$ **31.** $\{x | x < -1 \text{ or } x > 1\}$; $(-\infty, -1) \cup (1, \infty)$ **32.** $\{x | x > 1\}$; $(1, \infty)$

33. $\{x | x < -1 \text{ or } x > 1\}$; $(-\infty, -1) \cup (1, \infty)$ **34.** $\{x | x < -1 \text{ or } x > 3\}$; $(-\infty, -1) \cup (3, \infty)$ **35.** $\{x | x \le -1 \text{ or } 0 < x \le 1\}$; $(-\infty, -1] \cup (0, 1]$

36. $\{x | x \le -2 \text{ or } 1 < x \le 3\}$; $(-\infty, -2] \cup (1, 3]$ **37.** $\{x | x < -1 \text{ or } x > 1\}$; $(-\infty, -1) \cup (1, \infty)$ **38.** $\{x | x < -2 \text{ or } x > 2\}$; $(-\infty, -2) \cup (2, \infty)$

39. $\{x | x < 2\}$; $(-\infty, 2)$ **40.** $\{x | x > 4\}$; $(4, \infty)$ **41.** $\{x | -2 < x \le 9\}$; $(-2, 9]$ **42.** $\{x | -8 \le x < -2\}$; $[-8, -2)$

43. $\{x | x < 2 \text{ or } 3 < x < 5\}$; $(-\infty, 2) \cup (3, 5)$ **44.** $\{x | -7 < x < -1 \text{ or } x > 3\}$; $(-7, -1) \cup (3, \infty)$

45. $\{x | x < -5 \text{ or } -4 \le x \le -3 \text{ or } x = 0 \text{ or } x > 1\}$; $(-\infty, -5) \cup [-4, -3] \cup \{0\} \cup (1, \infty)$

46. $\{x | x < -1 \text{ or } 0 \le x < 1 \text{ or } x \ge 2\}$; $(-\infty, -1) \cup [0, 1) \cup [2, \infty)$ **47.** $\left\{x \left| -\dfrac{1}{2} < x < 1 \text{ or } x > 3\right.\right\}$; $\left(-\dfrac{1}{2}, 1\right) \cup (3, \infty)$

48. $\left\{x \left| -1 < x < \dfrac{2}{3} \text{ or } x > 2\right.\right\}$; $\left(-1, \dfrac{2}{3}\right) \cup (2, \infty)$ **49.** $\{x | -1 < x < 3 \text{ or } x > 5\}$; $(-1, 3) \cup (5, \infty)$

50. $\left\{x \left| x < -5 \text{ or } -2 < x < \dfrac{1}{2}\right.\right\}$; $(-\infty, -5) \cup \left(-2, \dfrac{1}{2}\right)$ **51.** $\left\{x \left| x \le -4 \text{ or } x \ge \dfrac{1}{2}\right.\right\}$; $(-\infty, -4] \cup \left[\dfrac{1}{2}, \infty\right)$

52. $\{x | x \le -5 \text{ or } x \ge 2\}$; $(-\infty, -5] \cup [2, \infty)$ **53.** $\{x | x < 3 \text{ or } x \ge 7\}$; $(-\infty, 3) \cup [7, \infty)$ **54.** $\{x | x < -2 \text{ or } x \ge -1\}$; $(-\infty, -2) \cup [-1, \infty)$

55. $\{x | x < 2\}$; $(-\infty, 2)$ **56.** $\left\{x \left| x > -\dfrac{11}{4}\right.\right\}$; $\left(-\dfrac{11}{4}, \infty\right)$ **57.** $\left\{x \left| x < -\dfrac{2}{3} \text{ or } 0 < x < \dfrac{3}{2}\right.\right\}$; $\left(-\infty, -\dfrac{2}{3}\right) \cup \left(0, \dfrac{3}{2}\right)$

58. $\{x | x < 0 \text{ or } 3 < x < 4\}$; $(-\infty, 0) \cup (3, 4)$ **59.** $\{x | x \le -3 \text{ or } 0 \le x \le 3\}$; $(-\infty, -3] \cup [0, 3]$

60. $\{x | -1 \le x \le 0 \text{ or } x \ge 1\}$; $[-1, 0] \cup [1, \infty)$ **61.** $\{x | x > 4\}$; $(4, \infty)$ **62.** $\{x | 0 < x < 1\}$; $(0, 1)$ **63.** $\{x | x \le -2 \text{ or } x \ge 2\}$; $(-\infty, -2] \cup [2, \infty)$

64. $\{x | x = 0 \text{ or } x \ge 3\}$; $\{0\} \cup [3, \infty)$ **65.** $\{x | x < -4 \text{ or } x \ge 2\}$; $(-\infty, -4) \cup [2, \infty)$ **66.** $\{x | x < -4 \text{ or } x \ge 1\}$; $(-\infty, -4) \cup [1, \infty)$

67.

$f(x) = x^4 - 1$ $g(x) = -2x^2 + 2$

$(-1, 0)$ $(1, 0)$

$f(x) \le g(x)$ if $-1 \le x \le 1$

68.

$f(x) = x^4 - 1$

$(1, 0)$

$(0, -1)$

$g(x) = x - 1$

$f(x) \le g(x)$ if $0 \le x \le 1$

69.

$g(x) = 3x^2$

$(-2, 12)$ $(2, 12)$

$f(x) = x^4 - 4$

$f(x) \le g(x)$ if $-2 \le x \le 2$

70.

$f(x) = x^4$

$(-1, 1)$ $(1, 1)$

$g(x) = 2 - x^2$

$f(x) \le g(x)$ if $-1 \le x \le 1$

71. Produce at least 250 bicycles

72. Produce at least 300 bicycles

73. (a) The stretch is less than 39 ft.
   (b) The ledge should be at least 84 ft above the ground for a 150-lb jumper.

74. When the object is more than $346,022$ km from Earth, the gravitational force of the moon is greater.

75. At least 50 students must attend.

Historical Problems *(page 231)*

1.
$$\left(x - \dfrac{b}{3}\right)^3 + b\left(x - \dfrac{b}{3}\right)^2 + c\left(x - \dfrac{b}{3}\right) + d = 0$$
$$x^3 - bx^2 + \dfrac{b^2 x}{3} - \dfrac{b^3}{27} + bx^2 - \dfrac{2b^2 x}{3} + \dfrac{b^3}{9} + cx - \dfrac{bc}{3} + d = 0$$
$$x^3 + \left(c - \dfrac{b^2}{3}\right)x + \left(\dfrac{2b^3}{27} - \dfrac{bc}{3} + d\right) = 0$$

Let $p = c - \dfrac{b^2}{3}$ and $q = \dfrac{2b^3}{27} - \dfrac{bc}{3} + d$. Then $x^3 + px + q = 0$.

2.
$$(H + K)^3 + p(H + K) + q = 0$$
$$H^3 + 3H^2 K + 3HK^2 + K^3 + pH + pK + q = 0$$
Let $3HK = -p$.
$$H^3 - pH - pK + K^3 + pH + pK + q = 0,$$
$$H^3 + K^3 = -q$$

3.
$$3HK = -p$$
$$K = -\dfrac{p}{3H}$$
$$H^3 + \left(-\dfrac{p}{3H}\right)^3 = -q$$
$$H^3 - \dfrac{p^3}{27H^3} = -q$$
$$27H^6 - p^3 = -27qH^3$$
$$27H^6 + 27qH^3 - p^3 = 0$$
$$H^3 = \dfrac{-27q \pm \sqrt{(27q)^2 - 4(27)(-p^3)}}{2 \cdot 27}$$
$$H^3 = \dfrac{-q}{2} \pm \sqrt{\dfrac{27^2 q^2}{2^2(27^2)} + \dfrac{4(27)p^3}{2^2(27^2)}}$$
$$H^3 = \dfrac{-q}{2} \pm \sqrt{\dfrac{q^2}{4} + \dfrac{p^3}{27}}$$
$$H = \sqrt[3]{\dfrac{-q}{2} + \sqrt{\dfrac{q^2}{4} + \dfrac{p^3}{27}}}$$

Choose the positive root for now.

4. $H^3 + K^3 = -q$

$K^3 = -q - H^3$

$K^3 = -q - \left[\dfrac{-q}{2} + \sqrt{\dfrac{q^2}{4} + \dfrac{p^3}{27}} \right]$

$K^3 = \dfrac{-q}{2} - \sqrt{\dfrac{q^2}{4} + \dfrac{p^3}{27}}$

$K = \sqrt[3]{\dfrac{-q}{2} - \sqrt{\dfrac{q^2}{4} + \dfrac{p^3}{27}}}$

5. $x = H + K$

$x = \sqrt[3]{\dfrac{-q}{2} + \sqrt{\dfrac{q^2}{4} + \dfrac{p^3}{27}}} + \sqrt[3]{\dfrac{-q}{2} - \sqrt{\dfrac{q^2}{4} + \dfrac{p^3}{27}}}$

(Note that had we used the negative root in 3 the result would be the same.)

6. $x = 3$ **7.** $x = 2$ **8.** $x = 2$

4.5 Assess Your Understanding (page 231)

5. Remainder; Dividend **6.** $f(c)$ **7.** -4 **8.** F **9.** F **10.** T **11.** $R = f(2) = 8$; no **12.** $R = f(-3) = 161$; no

13. $R = f(2) = 0$; yes; $f(x) = (x - 2)(3x^3 - 5)$ **14.** $R = f(2) = 0$; yes; $f(x) = (x - 2)(4x^3 + 8x^2 + x + 2)$

15. $R = f(-3) = 0$; yes; $f(x) = (x + 3)(3x^5 - 9x^4 + 27x^3 + x^2 - 3x + 9)$ **16.** $R = f(-3) = 0$; yes; $f(x) = (x + 3)(2x^5 - 6x^4 + x - 3)$

17. $R = f(-4) = 1$; no **18.** $R = f(-4) = 0$; yes; $f(x) = (x + 4)(x^5 - 4x^4 + x - 4)$ **19.** $R = f\left(\dfrac{1}{2}\right) = 0$; yes; $f(x) = \left(x - \dfrac{1}{2}\right)(2x^3 + 2)$

20. $R = f\left(-\dfrac{1}{3}\right) = 2$; no **21.** $4; \pm 1, \pm\dfrac{1}{3}$ **22.** $5; \pm 1, \pm 3$ **23.** $5; \pm 1, \pm 3$ **24.** $5; \pm 1, \pm\dfrac{1}{2}$ **25.** $3; \pm 1, \pm 2, \pm\dfrac{1}{4}, \pm\dfrac{1}{2}$ **26.** $4; \pm 1, \pm 2, \pm\dfrac{1}{2}, \pm\dfrac{1}{3}, \pm\dfrac{1}{6}, \pm\dfrac{2}{3}$

27. $4; \pm 1, \pm 3, \pm 9, \pm\dfrac{1}{2}, \pm\dfrac{1}{3}, \pm\dfrac{1}{6}, \pm\dfrac{3}{2}, \pm\dfrac{9}{2}$ **28.** $3; \pm 1, \pm 2, \pm 3, \pm 6, \pm\dfrac{1}{4}, \pm\dfrac{1}{2}, \pm\dfrac{3}{4}, \pm\dfrac{3}{2}$ **29.** $5; \pm 1, \pm 2, \pm 3, \pm 4, \pm 6, \pm 12, \pm\dfrac{1}{2}, \pm\dfrac{3}{2}$

30. $5; \pm 1, \pm 2, \pm 3, \pm 6, \pm 9, \pm 18, \pm\dfrac{1}{3}, \pm\dfrac{2}{3}$ **31.** $4; \pm 1, \pm 2, \pm 4, \pm 5, \pm 10, \pm 20, \pm\dfrac{1}{2}, \pm\dfrac{5}{2}, \pm\dfrac{1}{3}, \pm\dfrac{2}{3}, \pm\dfrac{4}{3}, \pm\dfrac{5}{3}, \pm\dfrac{10}{3}, \pm\dfrac{20}{3}, \pm\dfrac{1}{6}, \pm\dfrac{5}{6}$

32. $3; \pm 1, \pm 2, \pm 5, \pm 10, \pm\dfrac{1}{2}, \pm\dfrac{1}{3}, \pm\dfrac{1}{6}, \pm\dfrac{2}{3}, \pm\dfrac{5}{3}, \pm\dfrac{5}{2}, \pm\dfrac{5}{6}, \pm\dfrac{10}{3}$

33. -1 and 1

34. $-\dfrac{7}{3}$ and $\dfrac{7}{3}$

35. -12 and 12

36. $-\dfrac{13}{2}$ and $\dfrac{13}{2}$

37. -10 and 10

38. $-\dfrac{85}{4}$ and $\dfrac{85}{4}$

39. $-3, -1, 2; f(x) = (x + 3)(x + 1)(x - 2)$ **40.** $-5, -4, 1; f(x) = (x + 5)(x + 4)(x - 1)$ **41.** $\dfrac{1}{2}, 3, 3; f(x) = (2x - 1)(x - 3)^2$

42. $-\dfrac{3}{2}, 2, 2; f(x) = (2x + 3)(x - 2)^2$ **43.** $-\dfrac{1}{3}; f(x) = (3x + 1)(x^2 + x + 1)$ **44.** $\dfrac{7}{3}; f(x) = (3x - 7)(x^2 + 4)$

45. $3, \dfrac{5 + \sqrt{17}}{2}, \dfrac{5 - \sqrt{17}}{2}; f(x) = (x - 3)\left(x - \left(\dfrac{5 + \sqrt{17}}{2}\right)\right)\left(x - \left(\dfrac{5 - \sqrt{17}}{2}\right)\right)$

46. $-2, -2 + \sqrt{6}, -2 - \sqrt{6}; f(x) = (x + 2)(x + 2 - \sqrt{6})(x + 2 + \sqrt{6})$ **47.** $-2, -1, 1, 1; f(x) = (x + 2)(x + 1)(x - 1)^2$

48. $-2, -1, 2, 2; f(x) = (x + 2)(x + 1)(x - 2)^2$ **49.** $-5, -3, -\dfrac{3}{2}, 1; f(x) = (x + 5)(x + 3)(2x + 3)(x - 1)$

50. $-1, -\dfrac{1}{4}, 1, 4; f(x) = (x + 1)(4x + 1)(x - 1)(x - 4)$ **51.** $-2, -\dfrac{3}{2}, 1, 4; f(x) = (x + 2)(2x + 3)(x - 1)(x - 4)$

52. $-5, 1, \dfrac{-3 + \sqrt{65}}{4}, \dfrac{-3 - \sqrt{65}}{4}; f(x) = 2(x + 5)(x - 1)\left(x + \dfrac{3 - \sqrt{65}}{4}\right)\left(x + \dfrac{3 + \sqrt{65}}{4}\right)$ **53.** $-\dfrac{1}{2}, \dfrac{1}{2}; f(x) = (2x + 1)(2x - 1)(x^2 + 2)$

54. $-\dfrac{1}{2}, \dfrac{1}{2}; f(x) = (2x + 1)(2x - 1)(x^2 + 4)$ **55.** $\dfrac{\sqrt{2}}{2}, -\dfrac{\sqrt{2}}{2}, 2; f(x) = (x - 2)(\sqrt{2}x - 1)(\sqrt{2}x + 1)(2x^2 + 1)$

56. $-3, \dfrac{\sqrt{2}}{2}, -\dfrac{\sqrt{2}}{2}; f(x) = (x + 3)(\sqrt{2}x - 1)(\sqrt{2}x + 1)(2x^2 + 1)$ **57.** $-5.9, -0.3, 3$ **58.** $-4.5, -0.7, 2$ **59.** $-3.8, 4.5$ **60.** $-2.3, 1.7$

61. $-43.5, 1, 23$ **62.** $-54.82, 2.76, 9.87$ **63.** $\{-1, 2\}$ **64.** $\left\{-\dfrac{3}{2}\right\}$ **65.** $\left\{\dfrac{2}{3}, -1 + \sqrt{2}, -1 - \sqrt{2}\right\}$ **66.** $\left\{\dfrac{5}{2}\right\}$ **67.** $\left\{\dfrac{1}{3}, \sqrt{5}, -\sqrt{5}\right\}$ **68.** $\left\{-\dfrac{1}{2}, 2, 4\right\}$

69. $\{-3, -2\}$ **70.** $\{1\}$ **71.** $\left\{-\dfrac{1}{3}\right\}$ **72.** $\left\{\dfrac{2}{3}\right\}$ **73.** $f(0) = -1; f(1) = 10;$ Zero: 0.22 **74.** $f(-1) = -6; f(0) = 2;$ Zero: -0.6

75. $f(-5) = -58; f(-4) = 2;$ Zero: -4.05 **76.** $f(-3) = -42; f(-2) = 5;$ Zero: -2.17 **77.** $f(1.4) = -0.17536; f(1.5) = 1.40625;$ Zero: 1.41

78. $f(1.7) = 0.35627; f(1.8) = -1.02112;$ Zero: 1.73

79. Step 1: $y = x^3$
Step 2: x-intercepts: $-3, -1, 2$;
    y-intercept: -6
Step 3: $-3, -1, 2$: multiplicity 1, crosses

Step 4:

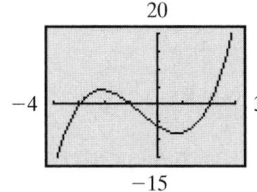

Step 5: $(-2.12, 4.06); (0.79, -8.21)$
Step 6:

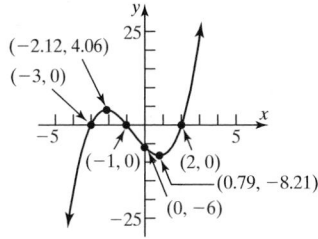

Step 7: Domain and Range: $(-\infty, \infty)$
Step 8: Increasing: $(-\infty, -2.12), (0.79, \infty)$;
    Decreasing: $(-2.12, 0.79)$

80. Step 1: $y = x^3$
Step 2: x-intercepts: $-5, -4, 1$;
    y-intercept: -20
Step 3: $-5, -4, 1$: multiplicity 1, crosses

Step 4:

Step 5: $(-4.52, 1.38); (-0.81, -24.19)$
Step 6:

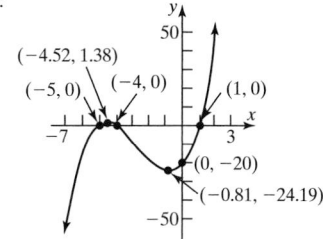

Step 7: Domain and Range: $(-\infty, \infty)$
Step 8: Increasing: $(-\infty, -4.52), (-0.81, \infty)$;
    Decreasing: $(-4.52, -0.81)$

81. Step 1: $y = x^4$
Step 2: x-intercepts: $-2, -1, 1$;
    y-intercept: 2
Step 3: $-2, -1$: multiplicity 1, crosses;
    1: multiplicity 2, touches

Step 4:

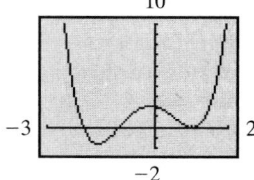

Step 5: $(-1.59, -1.62), (-0.16, 2.08), (1, 0)$
Step 6:

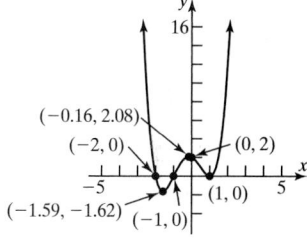

Step 7: Domain: $[-\infty, \infty)$; Range: $[-1.62, \infty)$
Step 8: Increasing: $(-1.59, -0.16), (1, \infty)$;
    Decreasing: $(-\infty, -1.59), (-0.16, 1)$

82. Step 1: $y = x^4$

Step 2: x-intercepts: $-2, -1, 2$;
    y-intercept: 8

Step 3: $-2, -1$: multiplicity 1, crosses;
    2: multiplicity 2, touches

Step 4:

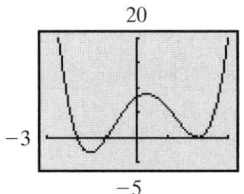

Step 5: $(-1.57, -3.12), (0.32, 8.64), (2, 0)$

Step 6:

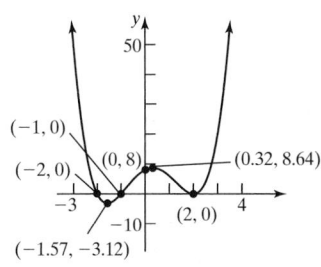

Step 7: Domain: $(-\infty, \infty)$; Range: $[-3.12, \infty)$
Step 8: Increasing: $(-1.57, 0.32), (2, \infty)$;
    Decreasing: $(-\infty, -1.57), (0.32, 2)$

83. Step 1: $y = 4x^5$

Step 2: x-intercepts: $-\dfrac{\sqrt{2}}{2}, \dfrac{\sqrt{2}}{2}, 2$;
    y-intercept: 2

Step 3: $-\dfrac{\sqrt{2}}{2}, \dfrac{\sqrt{2}}{2}, 2$: multiplicity 1, crosses

Step 4:

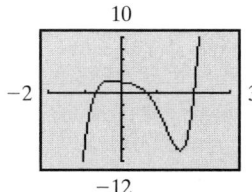

Step 5: $(-0.30, 2.23); (1.61, -10.09)$

Step 6:

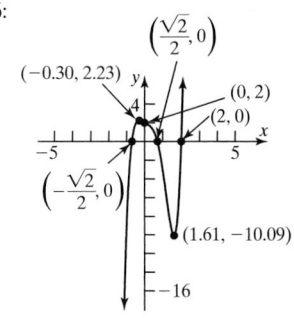

Step 7: Domain and range: $(-\infty, \infty)$
Step 8: Increasing: $(-\infty, -0.30), (1.61, \infty)$;
    Decreasing: $(-0.30, 1.61)$

84. Step 1: $y = 4x^5$

Step 2: x-intercepts: $-3, -\dfrac{\sqrt{2}}{2}, \dfrac{\sqrt{2}}{2}$;
    y-intercept: -3

Step 3: $-3, -\dfrac{\sqrt{2}}{2}, \dfrac{\sqrt{2}}{2}$: multiplicity 1, crosses

Step 4:

Step 5: $(-2.40, 79.03); (0.27, -3.20)$

Step 6:

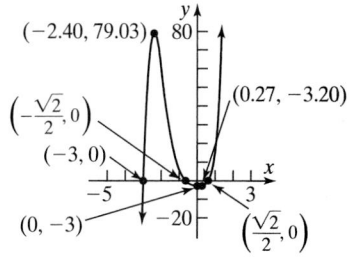

Step 7: Domain and range: $(-\infty, \infty)$
Step 8: Increasing: $(-\infty, -2.40), (0.27, \infty)$;
    Decreasing: $(-2.40, 0.27)$

85. $k = 5$ **86.** $k = -\dfrac{17}{12}$ **87.** -7 **88.** 1 **89.** If $f(x) = x^n - c^n$, then $f(c) = c^n - c^n = 0$; so $x - c$ is a factor of f.

90. If $n \geq 1$ is odd, $(-c)^n = -c^n$, then $f(-c) = (-c)^n + c^n = -c^n + c^n = 0$; so $x + c$ is a factor of f when n is odd. **91.** 5 **92.** -3 **93.** 7 in.

94. 6 cm or 12 cm **95.** All the potential rational zeros are integers, so r is either an integer or is not a rational zero (and is therefore irrational).

96. Let $\dfrac{p}{q}$, where p and q have no common factors except 1 and -1, be a solution of the polynomial $f(x) = a_n x^n + a_{n-1}x^{n-1} + \cdots + a_1 x + a_0$ whose coefficients are all integers. Then

$$f\left(\frac{p}{q}\right) = a_n\left(\frac{p}{q}\right)^n + a_{n-1}\left(\frac{p}{q}\right)^{n-1} + \cdots + a_1\left(\frac{p}{q}\right) + a_0 = 0$$
$$a_n p^n + a_{n-1}p^{n-1}q + \cdots + a_1 pq^{n-1} + a_0 q^n = 0$$

Because p is a factor of the first n terms of this equation, p must also be a factor of $a_0 q^n$. Since p is not a factor of q (p and q have no common factors except 1 and -1), p must be a factor of a_0. Similarly, q must be a factor of a_n.

97. 0.215 **98.** No; by the Rational Zeros Theorem, $\dfrac{1}{3}$ is not a potential rational zero.

99. No; by the Rational Zeros Theorem, $\dfrac{1}{3}$ is not a potential rational zero. **100.** No; by the Rational Zeros Theorem, $\dfrac{3}{5}$ is not a potential rational zero.

101. No; by the Rational Zeros Theorem, $\dfrac{2}{3}$ is not a potential rational zero.

4.6 Assess Your Understanding (page 238)

3. one **4.** $3 - 4i$ **5.** T **6.** F **7.** $4 + i$ **8.** $3 - i$ **9.** $-i, 1 - i$ **10.** $2 - i$ **11.** $-i, -2i$ **12.** $-i$ **13.** $-i$ **14.** $2 + i, i$ **15.** $2 - i, -3 + i$

16. $-i, 3 + 2i, -2 - i$ **17.** $f(x) = x^4 - 14x^3 + 77x^2 - 200x + 208; a = 1$ **18.** $f(x) = x^4 - 2x^3 + 6x^2 - 2x + 5; a = 1$

19. $f(x) = x^5 - 4x^4 + 7x^3 - 8x^2 + 6x - 4; a = 1$ **20.** $f(x) = x^6 - 12x^5 + 55x^4 - 120x^3 + 139x^2 - 108x + 85; a = 1$

21. $f(x) = x^4 - 6x^3 + 10x^2 - 6x + 9; a = 1$ **22.** $f(x) = x^5 - 5x^4 + 11x^3 - 13x^2 + 8x - 2; a = 1$ **23.** $-2i, 4$ **24.** $5i, -3$ **25.** $2i, -3, \dfrac{1}{2}$

26. $-3i, -2, \dfrac{1}{3}$ **27.** $3 + 2i, -2, 5$ **28.** $1 - 3i, -1, 6$ **29.** $4i, -\sqrt{11}, \sqrt{11}, -\dfrac{2}{3}$ **30.** $-3i, -3, 4, \dfrac{1}{2}$ **31.** $1, -\dfrac{1}{2} - \dfrac{\sqrt{3}}{2}i, -\dfrac{1}{2} + \dfrac{\sqrt{3}}{2}i$;

$f(x) = (x - 1)\left(x + \dfrac{1}{2} + \dfrac{\sqrt{3}}{2}i\right)\left(x + \dfrac{1}{2} - \dfrac{\sqrt{3}}{2}i\right)$ **32.** $-i, i, -1, 1; f(x) = (x + i)(x - i)(x + 1)(x - 1)$ **33.** $2, 3 - 2i, 3 + 2i$;

$f(x) = (x - 2)(x - 3 + 2i)(x - 3 - 2i)$ **34.** $-5, -4 + i, -4 - i; f(x) = (x + 5)(x + 4 - i)(x + 4 + i)$ **35.** $-i, i, -2i, 2i$;

$f(x) = (x + i)(x - i)(x + 2i)(x - 2i)$ **36.** $-2i, 2i, -3i, 3i; f(x) = (x + 2i)(x - 2i)(x + 3i)(x - 3i)$ **37.** $-5i, 5i, -3, 1$;

$f(x) = (x + 5i)(x - 5i)(x + 3)(x - 1)$ **38.** $-3i, 3i, -7, 4; f(x) = (x + 3i)(x - 3i)(x + 7)(x - 4)$ **39.** $-4, \dfrac{1}{3}, 2 - 3i, 2 + 3i$;

$f(x) = 3(x + 4)\left(x - \dfrac{1}{3}\right)(x - 2 + 3i)(x - 2 - 3i)$ **40.** $-3 - 2i, -3 + 2i, \dfrac{1}{2}, 5; f(x) = 2(x + 3 + 2i)(x + 3 - 2i)\left(x - \dfrac{1}{2}\right)(x - 5)$

41. Zeros that are complex numbers must occur in conjugate pairs; or a polynomial with real coefficients of odd degree must have at least one real zero. **42.** Zeros that are complex numbers must occur in conjugate pairs. **43.** If the remaining zero were a complex number, its conjugate would also be a zero, creating a polynomial of degree 5. **44.** A missing zero is $4 + i$. If the remaining zero were a complex number, its conjugate would also be a zero, creating a polynomial of degree 5.

Review Exercises (page 241)

1. Polynomial of degree 5 **2.** Not a polynomial; It is the ratio of two polynomials, and the polynomial in the denominator is of positive degree.

3. Not a polynomial; The variable x is raised to the $\dfrac{1}{2}$ power, which is not a nonnegative integer. **4.** Polynomial of degree 0

5.

6.

7.

8.

9.

10.
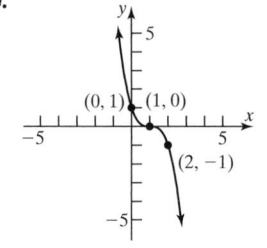

11. Step 1: $y = x^3$
Step 2: x-intercepts: $-4, -2, 0$; y-intercept: 0
Step 3: $-4, -2, 0$: multiplicity 1; crosses

Step 4:

Step 5: $(-3.15, 3.08), (-0.85, -3.08)$
Step 6:

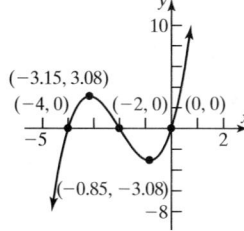

Step 7: Domain: $(-\infty, \infty)$; Range: $(-\infty, \infty)$
Step 8: Increasing on $(-\infty, -3.15)$ and $(-0.85, \infty)$
Decreasing on $(-3.15, -0.85)$

12. Step 1: $y = x^3$
Step 2: x-intercepts: $0, 2, 4$; y-intercept: 0
Step 3: $0, 2, 4$: multiplicity 1; crosses

Step 4:

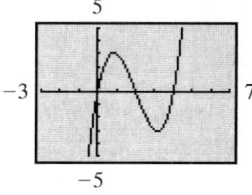

Step 5: $(0.85, 3.08), (3.15, -3.08)$
Step 6:

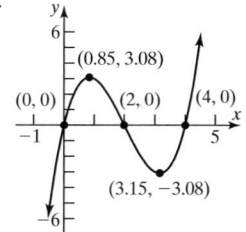

Step 7: Domain: $(-\infty, \infty)$; Range: $(-\infty, \infty)$
Step 8: Increasing on $(-\infty, 0.85)$ and $(3.15, \infty)$
Decreasing on $(0.85, 3.15)$

13. Step 1: $y = x^3$
Step 2: x-intercepts: $-4, 2$; y-intercept: 16
Step 3: -4: multiplicity 1; crosses;
2: multiplicity 2; touches

Step 4:

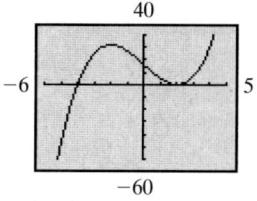

Step 5: $(-2, 32), (2, 0)$
Step 6:

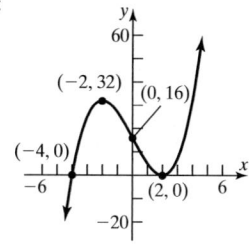

Step 7: Domain: $(-\infty, \infty)$; Range: $(-\infty, \infty)$
Step 8: Increasing on $(-\infty, -2)$ and $(2, \infty)$
Decreasing on $(-2, 2)$

14. Step 1: $y = x^3$
Step 2: x-intercepts: $-4, 2$; y-intercept: -32
Step 3: -4: multiplicity 2; touches;
2: multiplicity 1; crosses

Step 4:

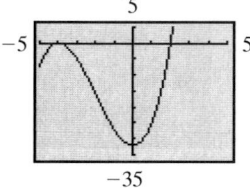

Step 5: $(-4, 0), (0, -32)$
Step 6:

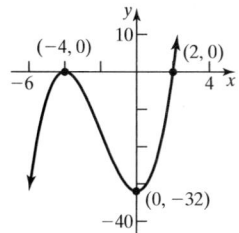

Step 7: Domain: $(-\infty, \infty)$; Range: $(-\infty, \infty)$
Step 8: Increasing on $(-\infty, -4)$ and $(0, \infty)$
Decreasing on $(-4, 0)$

15. Step 1: $y = x^3$
Step 2: x-intercepts: $0, 4$; y-intercept: 0
Step 3: 0: multiplicity 2; touches; 4:
multiplicity 1; crosses

Step 4:

Step 5: $(0, 0), (2.67, -9.48)$
Step 6:

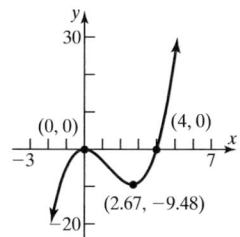

Step 7: Domain: $(-\infty, \infty)$; Range: $(-\infty, \infty)$
Step 8: Increasing on $(-\infty, 0)$ and $(2.67, \infty)$
Decreasing on $(0, 2.67)$

16. Step 1: $y = x^3$
Step 2: x-intercept: 0; y-intercept: 0
Step 3: 0: multiplicity 1; crosses

Step 4:

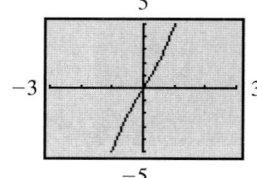

Step 5: No turning points
Step 6:

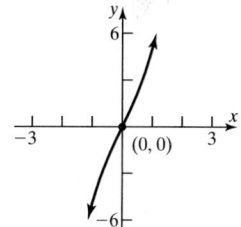

Step 7: Domain: $(-\infty, \infty)$; Range: $(-\infty, \infty)$
Step 8: Increasing on $(-\infty, \infty)$

17. Step 1: $y = x^4$
Step 2: x-intercepts: $-3, -1, 1$; y-intercept: 3
Step 3: $-3, -1$: multiplicity 1; crosses; 1:
multiplicity 2; touches

Step 4:

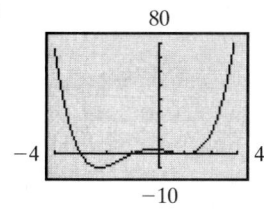

Step 5: $(-2.28, -9.91), (-0.22, 3.23), (1, 0)$
Step 6:

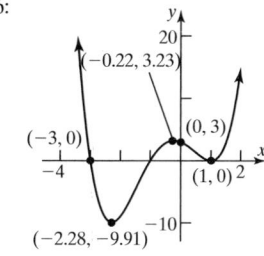

Step 7: Domain: $(-\infty, \infty)$; Range: $(-\infty, \infty)$
Step 8: Increasing on $(-2.28, -0.22)$ and $(1, \infty)$
Decreasing on $(-\infty, -2.28)$ and $(-0.22, 1)$

18. Step 1: $y = x^4$

Step 2: x-intercepts: $-2, 2, 4$; y-intercept: 32

Step 3: -2: multiplicity 2; touches;
2, 4: multiplicity 1; crosses

Step 4:

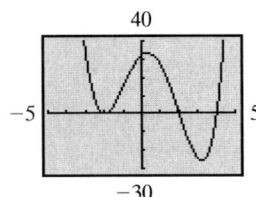

Step 5: $(-2, 0), (0.31, 33.28), (3.19, -25.96)$

Step 6:

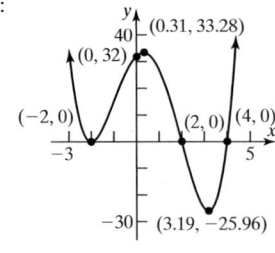

Step 7: Domain: $(-\infty, \infty)$;
Range: $(-25.96, \infty)$

Step 8: Increasing on $(-2, 0.31)$ and $(3.19, \infty)$
Decreasing on $(-\infty, -2)$ and $(0.31, 3.19)$

19. Domain: $\{x | x \neq -3, x \neq 3\}$; Horizontal asymptote: $y = 0$; Vertical asymptotes: $x = -3, x = 3$

20. Domain: $\{x | x \neq 2\}$; Oblique asymptote: $y = x + 2$; Vertical asymptote: $x = 2$

21. Domain: $\{x | x \neq -2\}$; Horizontal asymptote: $y = 2$; Vertical asymptote: $x = -2$

22. Domain: $\{x | x \neq 1\}$; Horizontal asymptote: $y = -4$; Vertical asymptote: $x = 1$

23. Step 1: $R(x) = \dfrac{2(x - 3)}{x}$; Domain: $\{x | x \neq 0\}$

Step 2: $R(x)$ is in lowest terms.

Step 3: x-intercept: 3; no y-intercept

Step 4: No symmetry

Step 5: Vertical asymptote: $x = 0$

Step 6: Horizontal asymptote: $y = 2$, not intersected

Step 7:

Step 8:

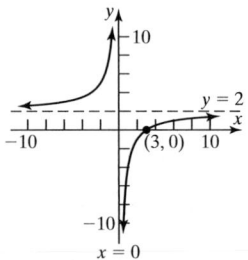

24. Step 1: Domain: $\{x | x \neq 0\}$

Step 2: $R(x)$ is in lowest terms.

Step 3: x-intercept: 4; no y-intercept

Step 4: No symmetry

Step 5: Vertical asymptote: $x = 0$

Step 6: Horizontal asymptote: $y = -1$, not intersected

Step 7:

Step 8:

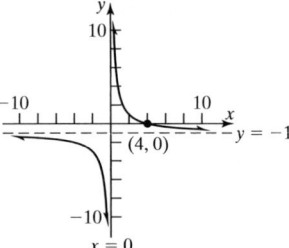

25. Step 1: Domain: $\{x | x \neq 0, x \neq 2\}$

Step 2: $H(x)$ is in lowest terms.

Step 3: x-intercept: -2; no y-intercept

Step 4: No symmetry

Step 5: Vertical asymptotes: $x = 0, x = 2$

Step 6: Horizontal asymptote: $y = 0$, intersected at $(-2, 0)$

Step 7:

Step 8:

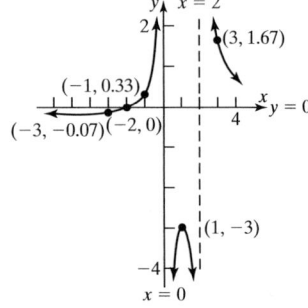

26. Step 1: $H(x) = \dfrac{x}{(x + 1)(x - 1)}$;

Domain: $\{x | x \neq -1, x \neq 1\}$

Step 2: $H(x)$ is in lowest terms.

Step 3: Intercept: $(0, 0)$

Step 4: Symmetric with respect to the origin

Step 5: Vertical asymptotes: $x = -1, x = 1$

Step 6: Horizontal asymptote: $y = 0$, intersected at $(0, 0)$

Step 7:

Step 8:

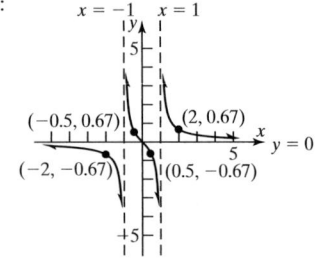

27. Step 1: $R(x) = \dfrac{(x+3)(x-2)}{(x-3)(x+2)};$

Domain: $\{x \mid x \neq -2, x \neq 3\}$

Step 2: $R(x)$ is in lowest terms.
Step 3: x-intercepts: $-3, 2$; y-intercept: 1
Step 4: No symmetry
Step 5: Vertical asymptotes: $x = -2, x = 3$
Step 6: Horizontal asymptote: $y = 1$, intersected at $(0, 1)$

Step 7:

Step 8: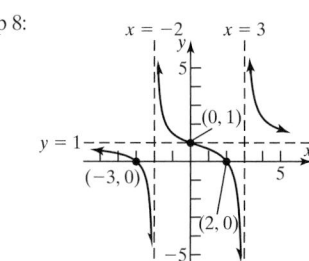

28. Step 1: $R(x) = \dfrac{(x-3)^2}{x^2};$ Domain: $\{x \mid x \neq 0\}$

Step 2: $R(x)$ is in lowest terms.
Step 3: x-intercept: 3; no y-intercept
Step 4: No symmetry
Step 5: Vertical asymptote: $x = 0$
Step 6: Horizontal asymptote: $y = 1$, intersected at $(1.5, 1)$

Step 7:

Step 8: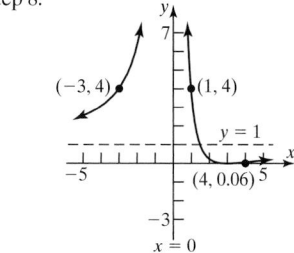

29. Step 1: $F(x) = \dfrac{x^3}{(x+2)(x-2)};$

Domain: $\{x \mid x \neq -2, x \neq 2\}$

Step 2: $F(x)$ is in lowest terms.
Step 3: Intercept: $(0, 0)$
Step 4: Symmetric with respect to the origin
Step 5: Vertical asymptotes: $x = -2, x = 2$
Step 6: Oblique asymptote: $y = x$, intersected at $(0, 0)$

Step 7:

Step 8: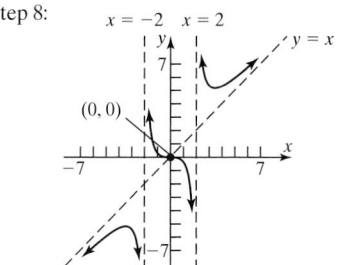

30. Step 1: Domain: $\{x \mid x \neq 1\}$
Step 2: $F(x)$ is in lowest terms.
Step 3: Intercept: $(0, 0)$
Step 4: No symmetry
Step 5: Vertical asymptote: $x = 1$
Step 6: Oblique asymptote: $y = 3x + 6$,

intersected at $\left(\dfrac{2}{3}, 8\right)$

Step 7:

Step 8: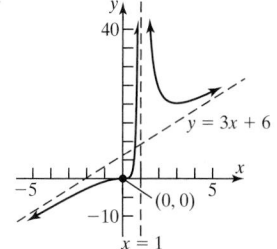

31. Step 1: Domain: $\{x \mid x \neq 1\}$
Step 2: $R(x)$ is in lowest terms.
Step 3: Intercept: $(0, 0)$
Step 4: No symmetry
Step 5: Vertical asymptote: $x = 1$
Step 6: No oblique or horizontal asymptote

Step 7:

Step 8: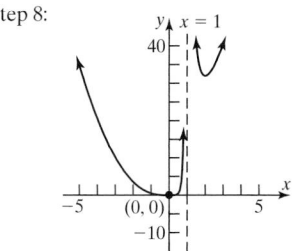

32. Step 1: $R(x) = \dfrac{x^4}{(x+3)(x-3)};$

Domain: $\{x \mid x \neq -3, x \neq 3\}$

Step 2: $R(x)$ is in lowest terms.
Step 3: Intercept: $(0, 0)$
Step 4: Symmetric with respect to the y-axis
Step 5: Vertical asymptotes: $x = -3, x = 3$
Step 6: No horizontal or oblique asymptotes

Step 7:

Step 8:

33. Step 1: $G(x) = \dfrac{(x + 2)(x - 2)}{(x + 1)(x - 2)}$;

Domain: $\{x | x \neq -1, x \neq 2\}$

Step 2: $G(x) = \dfrac{x + 2}{x + 1}$

Step 3: x-intercept: -2; y-intercept: 2

Step 4: No symmetry

Step 5: Vertical asymptote: $x = -1$; hole at $\left(2, \dfrac{4}{3}\right)$

Step 6: Horizontal asymptote: $y = 1$, not intersected

Step 7:

Step 8:

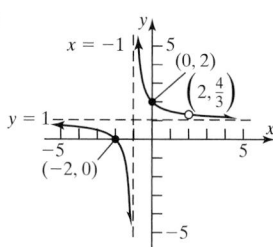

34. Step 1: $F(x) = \dfrac{(x - 1)^2}{(x + 1)(x - 1)}$; Domain: $\{x | x \neq -1, x \neq 1\}$

Step 2: $F(x) = \dfrac{x - 1}{x + 1}$

Step 3: No x-intercept; y-intercept: -1

Step 4: No symmetry

Step 5: Vertical asymptote: $x = -1$; hole at $(1, 0)$

Step 6: Horizontal asymptote: $y = 1$, not intersected

Step 7:

Step 8:

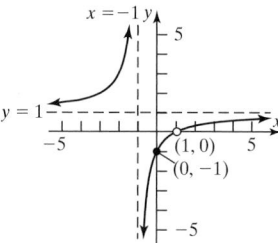

35. $\{x | x < -2 \text{ or } -1 < x < 2\}$;

$(-\infty, -2) \cup (-1, 2)$

36. $\{x | -4 \leq x \leq -1 \text{ or } x \geq 1\}$; $[-4, -1] \cup [1, \infty)$

37. $\{x | -3 < x \leq 3\}$; $(-3, 3]$

38. $\left\{x \left| x < \dfrac{1}{3} \text{ or } x > 1 \right.\right\}$; $\left(-\infty, \dfrac{1}{3}\right) \cup (1, \infty)$

39. $\{x | x < 1 \text{ or } x > 2\}$; $(-\infty, 1) \cup (2, \infty)$

40. $\left\{x \left| -\dfrac{5}{2} < x \leq -\dfrac{7}{6} \right.\right\}$; $\left(-\dfrac{5}{2}, -\dfrac{7}{6}\right]$

41. $\{x | 1 \leq x \leq 2 \text{ or } x > 3\}$; $[1, 2] \cup (3, \infty)$

42. $\{x | x \leq -1 \text{ or } 0 < x < 5\}$; $(-\infty, -1] \cup (0, 5)$

43. $\{x | x < -4 \text{ or } 2 < x < 4 \text{ or } x > 6\}$; $(-\infty, -4) \cup (2, 4) \cup (6, \infty)$

44. $\{x | x < -5 \text{ or } -4 < x \leq -2 \text{ or } 0 \leq x \leq 1\}$; $(-\infty, -5) \cup (-4, -2] \cup [0, 1]$

45. $R = 10$; g is not a factor of f. **46.** $R = 43$; g is not a factor of f.

47. $R = 0$; g is a factor of f. **48.** $R = 0$; g is a factor of f. **49.** $f(4) = 47{,}105$ **50.** $f(-2) = 204$ **51.** 8; $\pm 1, \pm 3, \pm\dfrac{1}{2}, \pm\dfrac{3}{2}, \pm\dfrac{1}{3}, \pm\dfrac{1}{4}, \pm\dfrac{3}{4}, \pm\dfrac{1}{6}, \pm\dfrac{1}{12}$

52. 5; $\pm 1, \pm\dfrac{1}{2}, \pm\dfrac{1}{3}, \pm\dfrac{1}{6}$ **53.** $-2, 1, 4$; $f(x) = (x + 2)(x - 1)(x - 4)$ **54.** $-1, 4, -2$; $f(x) = (x + 1)(x - 4)(x + 2)$

55. $\dfrac{1}{2}$, multiplicity 2; -2; $f(x) = 4\left(x - \dfrac{1}{2}\right)^2(x + 2)$ **56.** $-\dfrac{1}{2}$, multiplicity 2; 2; $f(x) = 4(x - 2)\left(x + \dfrac{1}{2}\right)^2$

57. 2, multiplicity 2; $f(x) = (x - 2)^2(x^2 + 5)$ **58.** -3, multiplicity 2; $f(x) = (x + 3)^2(x^2 + 2)$ **59.** $-2.5, 3.1, 5.32$ **60.** $-3.4, -0.25, 0.33$

61. $-11.3, -0.6, 4, 9.33$ **62.** $-10.33, -8.30, -3.56, -0.45$ **63.** $\{-3, 2\}$ **64.** $\{-3, 2\}$ **65.** $\left\{-3, -1, -\dfrac{1}{2}, 1\right\}$ **66.** $\left\{-3, -2, -\dfrac{1}{2}, 2\right\}$

67. -5 and 5 **68.** -11 and 11 **69.** $-\dfrac{37}{2}$ and $\dfrac{37}{2}$ **70.** $-\dfrac{17}{3}$ and $\dfrac{17}{3}$

71. $f(0) = -1; f(1) = 1$ **72.** $f(1) = -2; f(2) = 9$ **73.** $f(0) = -1; f(1) = 1$ **74.** $f(1) = -3, f(2) = 62$

75. $4 - i; f(x) = x^3 - 14x^2 + 65x - 102$ **76.** $3 - 4i; f(x) = x^3 - 11x^2 + 55x - 125$ **77.** $-i, 1 - i; f(x) = x^4 - 2x^3 + 3x^2 - 2x + 2$

78. $1 - i; f(x) = x^4 - 5x^3 + 10x^2 - 10x + 4$ **79.** $-2, 1, 4; f(x) = (x + 2)(x - 1)(x - 4)$ **80.** $-2, -1, 4; f(x) = (x + 2)(x + 1)(x - 4)$

81. $-2, \dfrac{1}{2}$ (multiplicity 2); $f(x) = 4(x + 2)\left(x - \dfrac{1}{2}\right)^2$ **82.** $-\dfrac{1}{2}$ (multiplicity 2), 2; $f(x) = 4\left(x + \dfrac{1}{2}\right)^2(x - 2)$

83. 2 (multiplicity 2), $-\sqrt{5}i, \sqrt{5}i; f(x) = \left(x + \sqrt{5}i\right)\left(x - \sqrt{5}i\right)(x - 2)^2$

84. -3 (multiplicity 2), $-\sqrt{2}i, \sqrt{2}i; f(x) = (x + 3)^2\left(x + \sqrt{2}i\right)\left(x - \sqrt{2}i\right)$

85. $-3, 2, -\dfrac{\sqrt{2}}{2}i, \dfrac{\sqrt{2}}{2}i; f(x) = 2(x + 3)(x - 2)\left(x + \dfrac{\sqrt{2}}{2}i\right)\left(x - \dfrac{\sqrt{2}}{2}i\right)$

86. $-3, 2, -\dfrac{\sqrt{3}}{3}i, \dfrac{\sqrt{3}}{3}i; f(x) = 3(x + 3)(x - 2)\left(x + \dfrac{\sqrt{3}}{3}i\right)\left(x - \dfrac{\sqrt{3}}{3}i\right)$

87. (a) $A(r) = 2\pi r^2 + \dfrac{500}{r}$

   (b) 223.22 cm^2

   (c) 257.08 cm^2

   (d)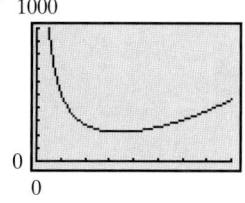

   A is smallest when $r \approx 3.41$ cm.

88. (a)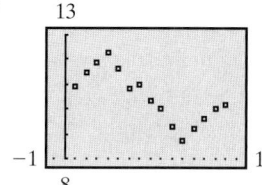

   Data appear to follow a cubic relation.

   (b) $P(t) = 0.0095x^3 - 0.2195x^2 + 1.1853x + 10.0078; 11.7\%$

   (c)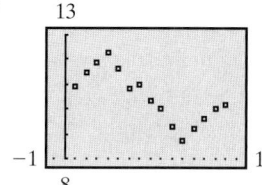

Chapter Test *(page 243)*

1.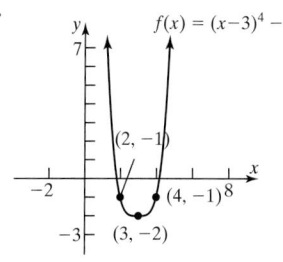

2. (a) 3   **(b)** Every zero of g lies between -15 and 15.

   (c) $\pm\dfrac{1}{2}, \pm 1, \pm\dfrac{3}{2}, \pm\dfrac{5}{2}, \pm 3, \pm 5, \pm\dfrac{15}{2}, \pm 15$

   (d) $-5, -\dfrac{1}{2}, 3; g(x) = (x + 5)(2x + 1)(x - 3)$

   (e) y-intercept: -15; x-intercepts: $-5, -\dfrac{1}{2}, 3$

   (f) Crosses at $-5, -\dfrac{1}{2}, 3$ **(g)** $y = 2x^3$

   (h) $(-3.15, 60.30), (1.48, -39.00)$

   (i)

3. $4, -5i, 5i$ **4.** $\left\{1, \dfrac{5 - \sqrt{61}}{6}, \dfrac{5 + \sqrt{61}}{6}\right\}$ **5.** Domain: $\{x | x \neq -10, x \neq 4\}$; asymptotes: $x = -10, y = 2$

6. Domain: $\{x | x \neq -1\}$; asymptotes: $x = -1, y = x + 1$

7.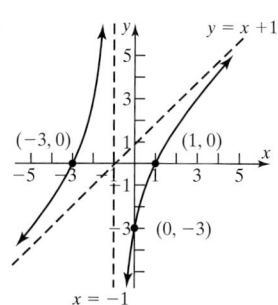

8. Answers may vary. One possibility is $f(x) = x^4 - 4x^3 - 2x^2 + 20x$.

9. Answers may vary. One possibility is $r(x) = \dfrac{2(x - 9)(x - 1)}{(x - 4)(x - 9)}$.

10. $f(0) = 8; f(4) = -36$

   Since $f(0) = 8 > 0$ and $f(4) = -36 < 0$, the Intermediate Value Theorem guarantees that there is at least one real zero between 0 and 4.

11. $\{x | x < 3 \text{ or } x > 8\}; (-\infty, 3) \cup (8, \infty)$

Cumulative Review *(page 243)*

1. $\sqrt{26}$

2. $\{x | x \leq 0 \text{ or } x \geq 1\}$; $(-\infty, 0]$ or $[1, \infty)$

3. $\{x | -1 < x < 4\}; (-1, 4)$

4. $f(x) = -3x + 1$

5. $y = 2x - 1$

6.

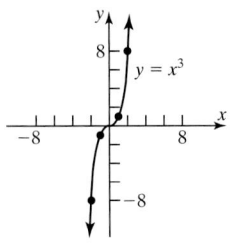

7. Not a function; 3 has two images. **8.** $\{0, 2, 4\}$ **9.** $\left\{x \middle| x \ge \dfrac{3}{2}\right\}$; $\left[\dfrac{3}{2}, \infty\right)$

10. Center: $(-2, 1)$; radius: 3

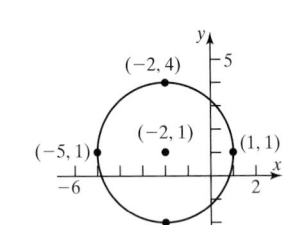

11. x-intercepts: $-3, 0, 3$; y-intercept: 0; symmetric with respect to the origin.

12. $y = -\dfrac{2}{3}x + \dfrac{17}{3}$

13. Not a function; it fails the vertical-line test.

14. (a) 22 **(b)** $x^2 - 5x - 2$ **(c)** $-x^2 - 5x + 2$ **(d)** $9x^2 + 15x - 2$ **(e)** $2x + h + 5$

15. (a) $\{x | x \ne 1\}$ **(b)** No; $(2, 7)$ is on the graph. **(c)** 4; $(3, 4)$ is on the graph.

(d) $\dfrac{7}{4}$; $\left(\dfrac{7}{4}, 9\right)$ is on the graph.

16.

17.

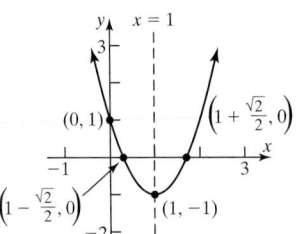

18. 6; $y = 6x - 1$
19. (a) x-intercepts: $-5, -1, 5$; y-intercept: -3
(b) No symmetry
(c) Neither
(d) Increasing: $(-\infty, -3)$ and $(2, \infty)$;
Decreasing: $(-3, 2)$
(e) Local maximum is 5 and occurs at $x = -3$.
(f) Local minimum is -6 and occurs at $x = 2$.
20. Odd

21. (a) Domain: $\{x | x > -3\}$ or $(-3, \infty)$

(b) x-intercept: $-\dfrac{1}{2}$; y-intercept: 1

(c)

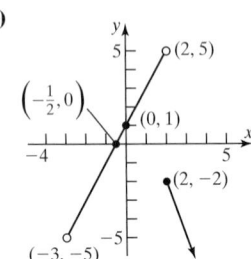

(d) Range: $\{y | y < 5\}$ or $(-\infty, 5)$

22.

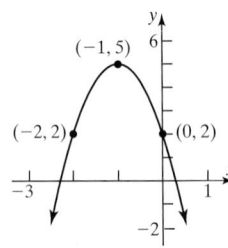

23. (a) $(f + g)(x) = x^2 - 9x - 6$; domain: all real numbers

(b) $\left(\dfrac{f}{g}\right)(x) = \dfrac{x^2 - 5x + 1}{-4x - 7}$; domain: $\left\{x \middle| x \ne -\dfrac{7}{4}\right\}$

24. (a) $R(x) = -\dfrac{1}{10}x^2 + 150x$

(b) \$14,000 **(c)** 750; \$56,250 **(d)** \$75

CHAPTER 5 Exponential and Logarithmic Functions

5.1 Assess Your Understanding *(page 253)*

4. $(g \circ f)(x)$ **5.** F **6.** F **7. (a)** -1 **(b)** -1 **(c)** 8 **(d)** 0 **(e)** 8 **(f)** -7 **8. (a)** 5 **(b)** 11 **(c)** 0 **(d)** 0 **(e)** 1 **(f)** 7 **9. (a)** 4 **(b)** 5
(c) -1 **(d)** -2 **10. (a)** 3 **(b)** 4 **(c)** 1 **(d)** -2 **11. (a)** 98 **(b)** 49 **(c)** 4 **(d)** 4 **12. (a)** 95 **(b)** 127 **(c)** 17 **(d)** 1 **13. (a)** 97
(b) $-\dfrac{163}{2}$ **(c)** 1 **(d)** $-\dfrac{3}{2}$ **14. (a)** 4418 **(b)** -191 **(c)** 8 **(d)** -2 **15. (a)** $2\sqrt{2}$ **(b)** $2\sqrt{2}$ **(c)** 1 **(d)** 0 **16. (a)** $\sqrt{13}$ **(b)** $3\sqrt{3}$
(c) $\sqrt{\sqrt{2} + 1}$ **(d)** 0 **17. (a)** $\dfrac{1}{17}$ **(b)** $\dfrac{1}{5}$ **(c)** 1 **(d)** $\dfrac{1}{2}$ **18. (a)** $\dfrac{11}{6}$ **(b)** $\dfrac{3}{2}$ **(c)** 1 **(d)** $\dfrac{12}{17}$ **19. (a)** $\dfrac{3}{\sqrt[3]{4} + 1}$ **(b)** 1 **(c)** $\dfrac{6}{5}$ **(d)** 0
20. (a) $\dfrac{2\sqrt{10}}{25}$ **(b)** $\dfrac{2}{2\sqrt{2} + 1}$ **(c)** 1 **(d)** $\dfrac{2}{3}$ **21.** $\{x | x \ne 0, x \ne 2\}$ **22.** $\left\{x \middle| x \ne 0, x \ne \dfrac{2}{3}\right\}$ **23.** $\{x | x \ne -4, x \ne 0\}$ **24.** $\left\{x \middle| x \ne -\dfrac{2}{3}, x \ne 0\right\}$
25. $\left\{x \middle| x \ge -\dfrac{3}{2}\right\}$ **26.** $\{x | x \le 1\}$ **27.** $\{x | x \ge 1\}$ **28.** $\{x | x \ge 2\}$ **29. (a)** $(f \circ g)(x) = 6x + 3$; all real numbers **(b)** $(g \circ f)(x) = 6x + 9$;
all real numbers **(c)** $(f \circ f)(x) = 4x + 9$; all real numbers **(d)** $(g \circ g)(x) = 9x$; all real numbers **30. (a)** $(f \circ g)(x) = -2x + 4$; all real
numbers **(b)** $(g \circ f)(x) = -2x - 4$; all real numbers **(c)** $(f \circ f)(x) = x$; all real numbers **(d)** $(g \circ g)(x) = 4x - 12$; all real numbers

31. (a) $(f \circ g)(x) = 3x^2 + 1$; all real numbers **(b)** $(g \circ f)(x) = 9x^2 + 6x + 1$; all real numbers **(c)** $(f \circ f)(x) = 9x + 4$; all real numbers
(d) $(g \circ g)(x) = x^4$; all real numbers **32. (a)** $(f \circ g)(x) = x^2 + 5$; all real numbers **(b)** $(g \circ f)(x) = x^2 + 2x + 5$; all real numbers
(c) $(f \circ f)(x) = x + 2$; all real numbers **(d)** $(g \circ g)(x) = x^4 + 8x^2 + 20$; all real numbers **33. (a)** $(f \circ g)(x) = x^4 + 8x^2 + 16$; all real numbers
(b) $(g \circ f)(x) = x^4 + 4$; all real numbers **(c)** $(f \circ f)(x) = x^4$; all real numbers **(d)** $(g \circ g)(x) = x^4 + 8x^2 + 20$; all real numbers
34. (a) $(f \circ g)(x) = 4x^4 + 12x^2 + 10$; all real numbers **(b)** $(g \circ f)(x) = 2x^4 + 4x^2 + 5$; all real numbers **(c)** $(f \circ f)(x) = x^4 + 2x^2 + 2$;
all real numbers **(d)** $(g \circ g)(x) = 8x^4 + 24x^2 + 21$; all real numbers **35. (a)** $(f \circ g)(x) = \dfrac{3x}{2 - x}$; $\{x | x \neq 0, x \neq 2\}$
(b) $(g \circ f)(x) = \dfrac{2(x - 1)}{3}$; $\{x | x \neq 1\}$ **(c)** $(f \circ f)(x) = \dfrac{3(x - 1)}{4 - x}$; $\{x | x \neq 1, x \neq 4\}$ **(d)** $(g \circ g)(x) = x$; $\{x | x \neq 0\}$
36. (a) $(f \circ g)(x) = \dfrac{x}{-2 + 3x}$; $\left\{x \middle| x \neq 0, x \neq \dfrac{2}{3}\right\}$ **(b)** $(g \circ f)(x) = -2(x + 3)$; $\{x | x \neq -3\}$ **(c)** $(f \circ f)(x) = \dfrac{x + 3}{3x + 10}$; $\left\{x \middle| x \neq -\dfrac{10}{3}, x \neq -3\right\}$
(d) $(g \circ g)(x) = x$; $\{x | x \neq 0\}$ **37. (a)** $(f \circ g)(x) = \dfrac{4}{4 + x}$; $\{x | x \neq -4, x \neq 0\}$ **(b)** $(g \circ f)(x) = \dfrac{-4(x - 1)}{x}$; $\{x | x \neq 0, x \neq 1\}$
(c) $(f \circ f)(x) = x$; $\{x | x \neq 1\}$ **(d)** $(g \circ g)(x) = x$; $\{x | x \neq 0\}$ **38. (a)** $(f \circ g)(x) = \dfrac{2}{2 + 3x}$; $\left\{x \middle| x \neq 0, x \neq -\dfrac{2}{3}\right\}$
(b) $(g \circ f)(x) = \dfrac{2(x + 3)}{x}$; $\{x | x \neq -3, x \neq 0\}$ **(c)** $(f \circ f)(x) = \dfrac{x}{4x + 9}$; $\left\{x \middle| x \neq -3, x \neq -\dfrac{9}{4}\right\}$ **(d)** $(g \circ g)(x) = x$; $\{x | x \neq 0\}$
39. (a) $(f \circ g)(x) = \sqrt{2x + 3}$; $\left\{x \middle| x \geq -\dfrac{3}{2}\right\}$ **(b)** $(g \circ f)(x) = 2\sqrt{x} + 3$; $\{x | x \geq 0\}$ **(c)** $(f \circ f)(x) = \sqrt[4]{x}$; $\{x | x \geq 0\}$
(d) $(g \circ g)(x) = 4x + 9$; all real numbers **40. (a)** $(f \circ g)(x) = \sqrt{-2x - 1}$; $\left\{x \middle| x \leq -\dfrac{1}{2}\right\}$ **(b)** $(g \circ f)(x) = 1 - 2\sqrt{x - 2}$; $\{x | x \geq 2\}$
(c) $(f \circ f)(x) = \sqrt{\sqrt{x - 2} - 2}$; $\{x | x \geq 6\}$ **(d)** $(g \circ g)(x) = -1 + 4x$; all real numbers **41. (a)** $(f \circ g)(x) = x$; $\{x | x \geq 1\}$
(b) $(g \circ f)(x) = |x|$; all real numbers **(c)** $(f \circ f)(x) = x^4 + 2x^2 + 2$; all real numbers **(d)** $(g \circ g)(x) = \sqrt{\sqrt{x - 1} - 1}$; $\{x | x \geq 2\}$
42. (a) $(f \circ g)(x) = x + 2$; $\{x | x \geq 2\}$ **(b)** $(g \circ f)(x) = \sqrt{x^2 + 2}$; all real numbers **(c)** $(f \circ f)(x) = x^4 + 8x^2 + 20$; all real numbers
(d) $(g \circ g)(x) = \sqrt{\sqrt{x - 2} - 2}$; $\{x | x \geq 6\}$ **43. (a)** $(f \circ g)(x) = \dfrac{4x - 17}{2x - 1}$; $\left\{x \middle| x \neq 3; \ x \neq \dfrac{1}{2}\right\}$
(b) $(g \circ f)(x) = -\dfrac{3x - 3}{2x + 8}$; $\{x | x \neq -4; \ x \neq -1\}$ **(c)** $(f \circ f)(x) = -\dfrac{2x + 5}{x - 2}$; $\{x | x \neq -1; \ x \neq 2\}$
(d) $(g \circ g)(x) = -\dfrac{3x - 4}{2x - 11}$; $\left\{x \middle| x \neq \dfrac{11}{2}; \ x \neq 3\right\}$ **44. (a)** $(f \circ g)(x) = -\dfrac{13}{3x - 14}$; $\left\{x \middle| x \neq \dfrac{5}{2}, \ x \neq \dfrac{14}{3}\right\}$
(b) $(g \circ f)(x) = -\dfrac{6x - 9}{x - 8}$; $\{x | x \neq 2; \ x \neq 8\}$ **(c)** $(f \circ f)(x) = x$; $\{x | x \neq 2\}$ **(d)** $(g \circ g)(x) = -\dfrac{9x - 16}{8x - 33}$; $\left\{x \middle| x \neq \dfrac{5}{2}; \ x \neq \dfrac{33}{8}\right\}$
45. $(f \circ g)(x) = f(g(x)) = f\left(\dfrac{1}{2}x\right) = 2\left(\dfrac{1}{2}x\right) = x$; $(g \circ f)(x) = g(f(x)) = g(2x) = \dfrac{1}{2}(2x) = x$
46. $(f \circ g)(x) = f(g(x)) = f\left(\dfrac{1}{4}x\right) = 4\left(\dfrac{1}{4}x\right) = x$; $(g \circ f)(x) = g(f(x)) = g(4x) = \dfrac{1}{4}(4x) = x$
47. $(f \circ g)(x) = f(g(x)) = f(\sqrt[3]{x}) = (\sqrt[3]{x})^3 = x$; $(g \circ f)(x) = g(f(x)) = g(x^3) = \sqrt[3]{x^3} = x$
48. $(f \circ g)(x) = f(g(x)) = f(x - 5) = x - 5 + 5 = x$; $(g \circ f)(x) = g(f(x)) = g(x + 5) = x + 5 - 5 = x$
49. $(f \circ g)(x) = f(g(x)) = f\left(\dfrac{1}{2}(x + 6)\right) = 2\left[\dfrac{1}{2}(x + 6)\right] - 6 = x + 6 - 6 = x$;
$\quad (g \circ f)(x) = g(f(x)) = g(2x - 6) = \dfrac{1}{2}(2x - 6 + 6) = \dfrac{1}{2}(2x) = x$
50. $(f \circ g)(x) = f(g(x)) = f\left(\dfrac{1}{3}(4 - x)\right) = 4 - 3\left[\dfrac{1}{3}(4 - x)\right] = 4 - (4 - x) = x$;
$\quad (g \circ f)(x) = g(f(x)) = g(4 - 3x) = \dfrac{1}{3}[4 - (4 - 3x)] = \dfrac{1}{3}(3x) = x$
51. $(f \circ g)(x) = f(g(x)) = f\left(\dfrac{1}{a}(x - b)\right) = a\left[\dfrac{1}{a}(x - b)\right] + b = x$; $(g \circ f)(x) = g(f(x)) = g(ax + b) = \dfrac{1}{a}(ax + b - b) = x$
52. $(f \circ g)(x) = f(g(x)) = f\left(\dfrac{1}{x}\right) = \dfrac{1}{\frac{1}{x}} = x$; $(g \circ f)(x) = g(f(x)) = g\left(\dfrac{1}{x}\right) = \dfrac{1}{\frac{1}{x}} = x$
53. $f(x) = x^4$; $g(x) = 2x + 3$ (Other answers are possible.) **54.** $f(x) = x^3$; $g(x) = 1 + x^2$ (Other answers are possible.)
55. $f(x) = \sqrt{x}$; $g(x) = x^2 + 1$ (Other answers are possible.) **56.** $f(x) = \sqrt{x}$; $g(x) = 1 - x^2$ (Other answers are possible.)
57. $f(x) = |x|$; $g(x) = 2x + 1$ (Other answers are possible.) **58.** $f(x) = |x|$; $g(x) = 2x^2 + 3$ (Other answers are possible.)
59. $(f \circ g)(x) = 11$; $(g \circ f)(x) = 2$ **60.** $(f \circ f)(x) = x$, $x \neq 1$ **61.** $-3, 3$ **62.** $-5, 5$ **63. (a)** $(f \circ g)(x) = acx + ad + b$
(b) $(g \circ f)(x) = acx + bc + d$ **(c)** The domains of both $f \circ g$ and $g \circ f$ are all real numbers. **(d)** $f \circ g = g \circ f$ when $ad + b = bc + d$
64. (a) $(f \circ g)(x) = \dfrac{amx + b}{cmx + d}$; **(b)** $(g \circ f)(x) = \dfrac{m(ax + b)}{cx + d}$; **(c)** The domain of $f \circ g$ is $\left\{x \middle| x \neq -\dfrac{d}{cm}\right\}$. The domain of $g \circ f$ is $\left\{x \middle| x \neq -\dfrac{d}{c}\right\}$.
(d) $f \circ g = g \circ f$ when $m = 1$. **65.** $S(t) = \dfrac{16}{9}\pi t^6$ **66.** $V(t) = \dfrac{32}{81}\pi t^9$ **67.** $C(t) = 15,000 + 800,000t - 40,000t^2$ **68.** $A(t) = 40,000\pi t$

69. $C(p) = \dfrac{2\sqrt{100 - p}}{25} + 600, 0 \le p \le 100$ **70.** $C(p) = \dfrac{\sqrt{1000 - 5p}}{10} + 400, 0 \le p \le 200$ **71.** $V(r) = 2\pi r^3$ **72.** $V(r) = \dfrac{2}{3}\pi r^3$

73. (a) $f(x) = 0.7480x$ **(b)** $g(x) = 158.7160x$ **(c)** $g(f(x)) = g(0.7480x) = 118.719568x$ **(d)** 118,719.568 yen **74. (a)** $K(C(F)) = \dfrac{5F + 2297}{9}$

(b) 299.7 kelvins **75. (a)** $f(p) = p - 200$ **(b)** $g(p) = 0.8p$ **(c)** $(f \circ g)(p) = 0.8p - 200$; $(g \circ f)(p) = 0.8p - 160$; The 20% discount followed by the $200 rebate is the better deal. **76.** f and g are odd functions, so $f(-x) = -f(x)$ and $g(-x) = -g(x)$. Then $(f \circ g)(-x) = f(g(-x))$ $= f(-g(x)) = -f(g(x)) = -(f \circ g)(x)$. So $f \circ g$ is also odd. **77.** f is an odd function, so $f(-x) = -f(x)$. g is an even function, so $g(-x) = g(x)$. Then $(f \circ g)(-x) = f(g(-x)) = f(g(x)) = (f \circ g)(x)$. So $f \circ g$ is even. Also, $(g \circ f)(-x) = g(f(-x)) = g(-f(x)) = g(f(x)) = (g \circ f)(x)$, so $g \circ f$ is even.

5.2 Assess Your Understanding (page 265)

4. one-to-one **5.** $y = x$ **6.** $[4, \infty)$ **7.** F **8.** T **9.** one-to-one **10.** one-to-one **11.** not one-to-one **12.** not one-to-one **13.** not one-to-one **14.** one-to-one **15.** one-to-one **16.** one-to-one **17.** one-to-one **18.** one-to-one **19.** not one-to-one **20.** not one-to-one **21.** one-to-one **22.** not one-to-one

23.

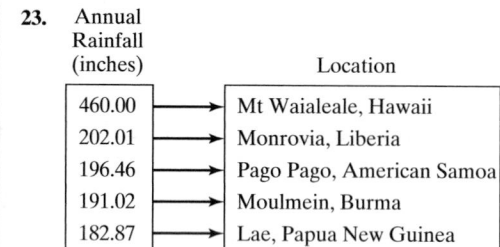

Domain: {460.00, 202.01, 196.46, 191.02, 182.87}
Range: {Mt Waialeale, Monrovia, Pago Pago, Moulmein, Lae}

24.

Domain: {$461, $431, $400, $357, $330}
Range: {Star Wars, The Phantom Menace, E.T., Jurassic Park, Forrest Gump}

25.

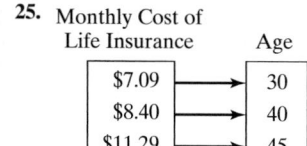

Domain: {$7.09, $8.40, $11.29}
Range: {30, 40, 45}

26.

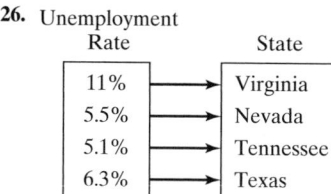

Domain: {11%, 5.5%, 5.1%, 6.3%}
Range: {Virginia, Nevada, Tennessee, Texas}

27. $\{(5, -3), (9, -2), (2, -1), (11, 0), (-5, 1)\}$
Domain: {5, 9, 2, 11, −5}
Range: {−3, −2, −1, 0, 1}

28. $\{(2, -2), (6, -1), (8, 0), (-3, 1), (9, 2)\}$
Domain: {2, 6, 8, −3, 9}
Range: {−2, −1, 0, 1, 2}

29. $\{(1, -2), (2, -3), (0, -10), (9, 1), (4, 2)\}$
Domain: {1, 2, 0, 9, 4}
Range: {−2, −3, −10, 1, 2}

30. $\{(-8, -2), (-1, -1), (0, 0), (1, 1), (8, 2)\}$
Domain: {−8, −1, 0, 1, 8}
Range: {−2, −1, 0, 1, 2}

31. $f(g(x)) = f\left(\dfrac{1}{3}(x - 4)\right) = 3\left[\dfrac{1}{3}(x - 4)\right] + 4 = (x - 4) + 4 = x$

$g(f(x)) = g(3x + 4) = \dfrac{1}{3}[(3x + 4) - 4] = \dfrac{1}{3}(3x) = x$

32. $f(g(x)) = f\left(-\dfrac{1}{2}(x - 3)\right) = 3 - 2\left(-\dfrac{1}{2}(x - 3)\right) = 3 + (x - 3) = x$

$g(f(x)) = g(3 - 2x) = -\dfrac{1}{2}[(3 - 2x) - 3] = -\dfrac{1}{2}(-2x) = x$

33. $f(g(x)) = f\left(\dfrac{x}{4} + 2\right) = 4\left[\dfrac{x}{4} + 2\right] - 8 = (x + 8) - 8 = x$

$g(f(x)) = g(4x - 8) = \dfrac{4x - 8}{4} + 2 = (x - 2) + 2 = x$

34. $f(g(x)) = f\left(\dfrac{1}{2}x - 3\right) = 2\left(\dfrac{1}{2}x - 3\right) + 6 = (x - 6) + 6 = x$

$g(f(x)) = g(2x + 6) = \dfrac{1}{2}(2x + 6) - 3 = (x + 3) - 3 = x$

35. $f(g(x)) = f\left(\sqrt[3]{x + 8}\right) = \left(\sqrt[3]{x + 8}\right)^3 - 8 = (x + 8) - 8 = x$

$g(f(x)) = g(x^3 - 8) = \sqrt[3]{(x^3 - 8) + 8} = \sqrt[3]{x^3} = x$

36. $f(g(x)) = f\left(\sqrt{x} + 2\right) = \left(\sqrt{x} + 2 - 2\right)^2 = \left(\sqrt{x}\right)^2 = x$

$g(f(x)) = g((x - 2)^2) = \sqrt{(x - 2)^2} + 2 = x - 2 + 2 = x$

37. $f(g(x)) = f\left(\dfrac{1}{x}\right) = \dfrac{1}{\left(\dfrac{1}{x}\right)} = x$; $g(f(x)) = g\left(\dfrac{1}{x}\right) = \dfrac{1}{\left(\dfrac{1}{x}\right)} = x$

38. $f(g(x)) = f(x) = x$

$g(f(x)) = g(x) = x$

39. $f(g(x)) = f\left(\dfrac{4x-3}{2-x}\right) = \dfrac{2\left(\dfrac{4x-3}{2-x}\right)+3}{\dfrac{4x-3}{2-x}+4}$

$= \dfrac{2(4x-3)+3(2-x)}{4x-3+4(2-x)} = \dfrac{5x}{5} = x, \ x \neq 2$

$g(f(x)) = g\left(\dfrac{2x+3}{x+4}\right) = \dfrac{4\left(\dfrac{2x+3}{x+4}\right)-3}{2-\dfrac{2x+3}{x+4}}$

$= \dfrac{4(2x+3)-3(x+4)}{2(x+4)-(2x+3)} = \dfrac{5x}{5} = x, \ x \neq -4$

40. $f(g(x)) = f\left(\dfrac{3x+5}{1-2x}\right) = \dfrac{\dfrac{3x+5}{1-2x}-5}{2\left(\dfrac{3x+5}{1-2x}\right)+3}$

$= \dfrac{3x+5-5(1-2x)}{2(3x+5)+3(1-2x)} = \dfrac{13x}{13} = x, \ x \neq \dfrac{1}{2}$

$g(f(x)) = g\left(\dfrac{x-5}{2x+3}\right) = \dfrac{3\left(\dfrac{x-5}{2x+3}\right)+5}{1-2\left(\dfrac{x-5}{2x+3}\right)}$

$= \dfrac{3(x-5)+5(2x+3)}{(2x+3)-2(x-5)} = \dfrac{13x}{13} = x, \ x \neq -\dfrac{3}{2}$

41.

42.

43.

44.

45.

46.

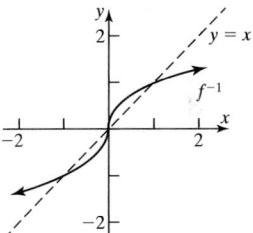

47. $f^{-1}(x) = \dfrac{1}{3}x$

$f(f^{-1}(x)) = f\left(\dfrac{1}{3}x\right) = 3\left(\dfrac{1}{3}x\right) = x$

$f^{-1}(f(x)) = f^{-1}(3x) = \dfrac{1}{3}(3x) = x$

48. $f^{-1}(x) = -\dfrac{1}{4}x$

$f(f^{-1}(x)) = f\left(-\dfrac{1}{4}x\right) = -4\left(-\dfrac{1}{4}x\right) = x$

$f^{-1}(f(x)) = f^{-1}(-4x) = -\dfrac{1}{4}(-4x) = x$

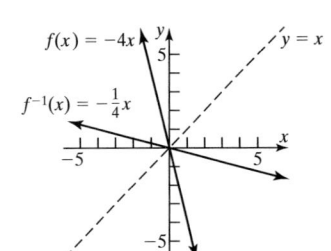

49. $f^{-1}(x) = \dfrac{x}{4} - \dfrac{1}{2}$

$f(f^{-1}(x)) = f\left(\dfrac{x}{4}-\dfrac{1}{2}\right) = 4\left(\dfrac{x}{4}-\dfrac{1}{2}\right)+2 = (x-2)+2 = x$

$f^{-1}(f(x)) = f^{-1}(4x+2) = \dfrac{4x+2}{4}-\dfrac{1}{2} = \left(x+\dfrac{1}{2}\right)-\dfrac{1}{2} = x$

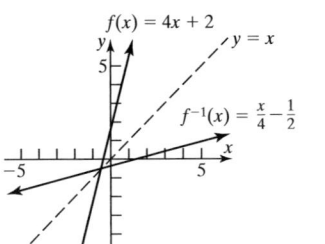

50. $f^{-1}(x) = \dfrac{1-x}{3}$

$f(f^{-1}(x)) = f\left(\dfrac{1-x}{3}\right) = 1-3\left(\dfrac{1-x}{3}\right) = 1-(1-x) = x$

$f^{-1}(f(x)) = f^{-1}(1-3x) = \dfrac{1-(1-3x)}{3} = \dfrac{3x}{3} = x$

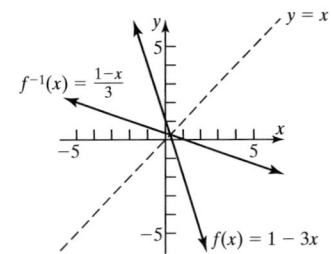

51. $f^{-1}(x) = \sqrt[3]{x+1}$

$f(f^{-1}(x)) = f(\sqrt[3]{x+1}) = (\sqrt[3]{x+1})^3 - 1 = x$

$f^{-1}(f(x)) = f^{-1}(x^3 - 1) = \sqrt[3]{(x^3-1)+1} = x$

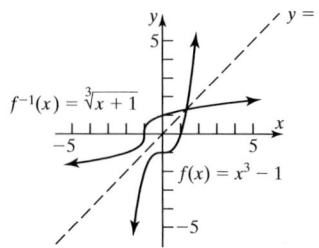

52. $f^{-1}(x) = \sqrt[3]{x-1}$

$f(f^{-1}(x)) = f(\sqrt[3]{x-1}) = (\sqrt[3]{x-1})^3 + 1 = x$

$f^{-1}(f(x)) = f^{-1}(x^3 + 1) = \sqrt[3]{(x^3+1)-1} = x$

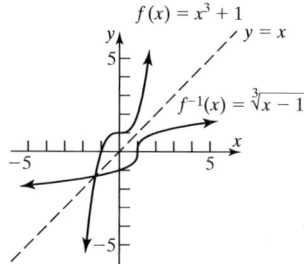

53. $f^{-1}(x) = \sqrt{x-4}, x \geq 4$

$f(f^{-1}(x)) = f(\sqrt{x-4}) = (\sqrt{x-4})^2 + 4 = x$

$f^{-1}(f(x)) = f^{-1}(x^2 + 4) = \sqrt{(x^2+4)-4} = \sqrt{x^2} = x, x \geq 0$

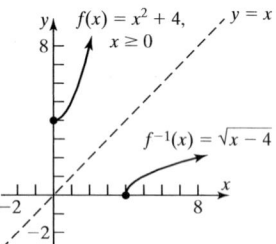

54. $f^{-1}(x) = \sqrt{x-9}, x \geq 9$

$f(f^{-1}(x)) = f(\sqrt{x-9}) = (\sqrt{x-9})^2 + 9 = x - 9 + 9 = x$

$f^{-1}(f(x)) = f^{-1}(x^2 + 9) = \sqrt{x^2 + 9 - 9} = \sqrt{x^2} = x, x \geq 0$

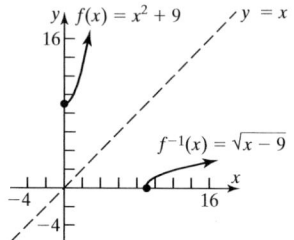

55. $f^{-1}(x) = \dfrac{4}{x}$

$f(f^{-1}(x)) = f\left(\dfrac{4}{x}\right) = \dfrac{4}{\left(\dfrac{4}{x}\right)} = x$

$f^{-1}(f(x)) = f^{-1}\left(\dfrac{4}{x}\right) = \dfrac{4}{\left(\dfrac{4}{x}\right)} = x$

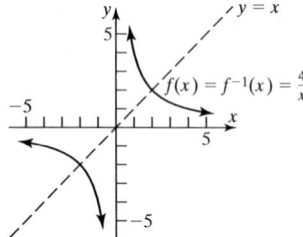

56. $f^{-1}(x) = -\dfrac{3}{x}$

$f(f^{-1}(x)) = f\left(-\dfrac{3}{x}\right) = -\dfrac{3}{\left(-\dfrac{3}{x}\right)} = x$

$f^{-1}(f(x)) = f^{-1}\left(-\dfrac{3}{x}\right) = -\dfrac{3}{\left(-\dfrac{3}{x}\right)} = x$

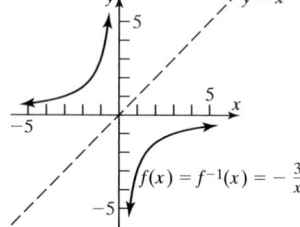

57. $f^{-1}(x) = \dfrac{2x+1}{x}$

$f(f^{-1}(x)) = f\left(\dfrac{2x+1}{x}\right) = \dfrac{1}{\dfrac{2x+1}{x} - 2} = \dfrac{x}{(2x+1)-2x} = x$

$f^{-1}(f(x)) = f^{-1}\left(\dfrac{1}{x-2}\right) = \dfrac{2\left(\dfrac{1}{x-2}\right)+1}{\dfrac{1}{x-2}} = \dfrac{2+(x-2)}{1} = x$

58. $f^{-1}(x) = \dfrac{4}{x} - 2$

$f(f^{-1}(x)) = f\left(\dfrac{4}{x} - 2\right) = \dfrac{4}{\left(\dfrac{4}{x}-2\right)+2} = \dfrac{4}{\left(\dfrac{4}{x}\right)} = x$

$f^{-1}(f(x)) = f^{-1}\left(\dfrac{4}{x+2}\right) = \dfrac{4}{\left(\dfrac{4}{x+2}\right)} - 2 = x + 2 - 2 = x$

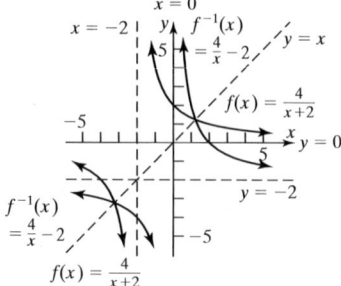

59. $f^{-1}(x) = \dfrac{2 - 3x}{x}$

$f(f^{-1}(x)) = f\left(\dfrac{2 - 3x}{x}\right) = \dfrac{2}{3 + \dfrac{2 - 3x}{x}} = \dfrac{2x}{3x + 2 - 3x} = \dfrac{2x}{2} = x$

$f^{-1}(f(x)) = f^{-1}\left(\dfrac{2}{3 + x}\right) = \dfrac{2 - 3\left(\dfrac{2}{3 + x}\right)}{\dfrac{2}{3 + x}} = \dfrac{2(3 + x) - 3 \cdot 2}{2} = \dfrac{2x}{2} = x$

Domain f = range of f^{-1} = all real numbers except -3

Range f = domain f^{-1} = all real numbers except 0

60. $f^{-1}(x) = 2 - \dfrac{4}{x}$

$f(f^{-1}(x)) = f\left(2 - \dfrac{4}{x}\right) = \dfrac{4}{2 - \left(2 - \dfrac{4}{x}\right)} = \dfrac{4}{\left(\dfrac{4}{x}\right)} = x$

$f^{-1}(f(x)) = f^{-1}\left(\dfrac{4}{2 - x}\right) = 2 - \dfrac{4}{\left(\dfrac{4}{2 - x}\right)}$

$= 2 - (2 - x) = x$

Domain f = range of f^{-1} = all real numbers except 2

Range f = domain f^{-1} = all real numbers except 0

61. $f^{-1}(x) = \dfrac{-2x}{x - 3}$

$f(f^{-1}(x)) = f\left(\dfrac{-2x}{x - 3}\right) = \dfrac{3\left(\dfrac{-2x}{x - 3}\right)}{\dfrac{-2x}{x - 3} + 2} = \dfrac{3(-2x)}{-2x + 2(x - 3)} = \dfrac{-6x}{-6} = x$

$f^{-1}(f(x)) = f^{-1}\left(\dfrac{3x}{x + 2}\right) = \dfrac{-2\left(\dfrac{3x}{x + 2}\right)}{\dfrac{3x}{x + 2} - 3} = \dfrac{-2(3x)}{3x - 3(x + 2)} = \dfrac{-6x}{-6} = x$

Domain f = range of f^{-1} = all real numbers except -2

Range f = domain f^{-1} = all real numbers except 3

62. $f^{-1}(x) = \dfrac{x}{x + 2}$

$f(f^{-1}(x)) = \dfrac{-2\left(\dfrac{x}{x + 2}\right)}{\dfrac{x}{x + 2} - 1} = \dfrac{-2x}{x - (x + 2)} = \dfrac{-2x}{-2} = x$

$f^{-1}(f(x)) = \dfrac{\dfrac{-2x}{x - 1}}{\dfrac{-2x}{x - 1} + 2} = \dfrac{-2x}{-2x + 2(x - 1)} = \dfrac{-2x}{-2} = x$

Domain f = range of f^{-1} = all real numbers except 1

Range f = domain f^{-1} = all real numbers except -2

63. $f^{-1}(x) = \dfrac{x}{3x - 2}$

$f(f^{-1}(x)) = f\left(\dfrac{x}{3x - 2}\right) = \dfrac{2\left(\dfrac{x}{3x - 2}\right)}{3\left(\dfrac{x}{3x - 2}\right) - 1} = \dfrac{2x}{3x - (3x - 2)} = \dfrac{2x}{2} = x$

$f^{-1}(f(x)) = f^{-1}\left(\dfrac{2x}{3x - 1}\right) = \dfrac{\dfrac{2x}{3x - 1}}{3\left(\dfrac{2x}{3x - 1}\right) - 2} = \dfrac{2x}{6x - 2(3x - 1)} = \dfrac{2x}{2} = x$

Domain f = range of f^{-1} = all real numbers except $\dfrac{1}{3}$

Range f = domain f^{-1} = all real numbers except $\dfrac{2}{3}$

64. $f^{-1}(x) = \dfrac{-1}{x + 3}$

$f(f^{-1}(x)) = f\left(\dfrac{-1}{x + 3}\right) = \dfrac{3\left(\dfrac{-1}{x + 3}\right) + 1}{-\left(\dfrac{-1}{x + 3}\right)}$

$= \dfrac{-3 + (x + 3)}{1} = x$

$f^{-1}(f(x)) = f^{-1}\left(\dfrac{3x + 1}{-x}\right) = \dfrac{-1}{\dfrac{3x + 1}{-x} + 3}$

$= \dfrac{x}{3x + 1 - 3x} = x$

Domain f = range of f^{-1} = all real numbers except 0

Range f = domain f^{-1} = all real numbers except -3

65. $f^{-1}(x) = \dfrac{3x + 4}{2x - 3}$

$f(f^{-1}(x)) = f\left(\dfrac{3x + 4}{2x - 3}\right) = \dfrac{3\left(\dfrac{3x + 4}{2x - 3}\right) + 4}{2\left(\dfrac{3x + 4}{2x - 3}\right) - 3}$

$= \dfrac{3(3x + 4) + 4(2x - 3)}{2(3x + 4) - 3(2x - 3)}$

$= \dfrac{17x}{17} = x$

$f^{-1}(f(x)) = f^{-1}\left(\dfrac{3x + 4}{2x - 3}\right) = \dfrac{3\left(\dfrac{3x + 4}{2x - 3}\right) + 4}{2\left(\dfrac{3x + 4}{2x - 3}\right) - 3}$

$= \dfrac{3(3x + 4) + 4(2x - 3)}{2(3x + 4) - 3(2x - 3)} = \dfrac{17x}{17} = x$

Domain f = range of f^{-1} = all real numbers except $\dfrac{3}{2}$

Range f = domain f^{-1} = all real numbers except $\dfrac{3}{2}$

66. $f^{-1}(x) = \dfrac{3 + 4x}{2 - x}$

$f(f^{-1}(x)) = f\left(\dfrac{3 + 4x}{2 - x}\right) = \dfrac{2\left(\dfrac{3 + 4x}{2 - x}\right) - 3}{\left(\dfrac{3 + 4x}{2 - x}\right) + 4}$

$= \dfrac{2(3 + 4x) - 3(2 - x)}{(3 + 4x) + 4(2 - x)} = \dfrac{11x}{11} = x$

$f^{-1}(f(x)) = f^{-1}\left(\dfrac{2x - 3}{x + 4}\right) = \dfrac{3 + 4\left(\dfrac{2x - 3}{x + 4}\right)}{2 - \left(\dfrac{2x - 3}{x + 4}\right)}$

$= \dfrac{3(x + 4) + 4(2x - 3)}{2(x + 4) - (2x - 3)} = \dfrac{11x}{11} = x$

Domain f = range of f^{-1} = all real numbers except -4

Range f = domain f^{-1} = all real numbers except 2

67. $f^{-1}(x) = \dfrac{-2x + 3}{x - 2}$

$$f(f^{-1}(x)) = f\left(\dfrac{-2x + 3}{x - 2}\right) = \dfrac{2\left(\dfrac{-2x + 3}{x - 2}\right) + 3}{\dfrac{-2x + 3}{x - 2} + 2}$$

$$= \dfrac{2(-2x + 3) + 3(x - 2)}{-2x + 3 + 2(x - 2)} = \dfrac{-x}{-1} = x$$

$$f^{-1}(f(x)) = f^{-1}\left(\dfrac{2x + 3}{x + 2}\right) = \dfrac{-2\left(\dfrac{2x + 3}{x + 2}\right) + 3}{\dfrac{2x + 3}{x + 2} - 2}$$

$$= \dfrac{-2(2x + 3) + 3(x + 2)}{2x + 3 - 2(x + 2)} = \dfrac{-x}{-1} = x$$

Domain f = range of f^{-1} = all real numbers except -2

Range f = domain f^{-1} = all real numbers except 2

68. $f^{-1}(x) = \dfrac{2x - 4}{x + 3}$

$$f(f^{-1}(x)) = f\left(\dfrac{2x - 4}{x + 3}\right) = \dfrac{-3\left(\dfrac{2x - 4}{x + 3}\right) - 4}{\left(\dfrac{2x - 4}{x + 3}\right) - 2}$$

$$= \dfrac{-3(2x - 4) - 4(x + 3)}{(2x - 4) - 2(x + 3)} = \dfrac{-10x}{-10} = x$$

$$f^{-1}(f(x)) = f^{-1}\left(\dfrac{-3x - 4}{x - 2}\right) = \dfrac{2\left(\dfrac{-3x - 4}{x - 2}\right) - 4}{\left(\dfrac{-3x - 4}{x - 2}\right) + 3}$$

$$= \dfrac{2(-3x - 4) - 4(x - 2)}{(-3x - 4) + 3(x - 2)} = \dfrac{-10x}{-10} = x$$

Domain f = range of f^{-1} = all real numbers except 2

Range f = domain f^{-1} = all real numbers except -3

69. $f^{-1}(x) = \dfrac{2}{\sqrt{1 - 2x}}$

$$f(f^{-1}(x)) = f\left(\dfrac{2}{\sqrt{1 - 2x}}\right) = \dfrac{\dfrac{4}{1 - 2x} - 4}{2 \cdot \dfrac{4}{1 - 2x}} = \dfrac{4 - 4(1 - 2x)}{2 \cdot 4}$$

$$= \dfrac{8x}{8} = x$$

$$f^{-1}(f(x)) = f^{-1}\left(\dfrac{x^2 - 4}{2x^2}\right) = \dfrac{2}{\sqrt{1 - 2\left(\dfrac{x^2 - 4}{2x^2}\right)}} = \dfrac{2}{\sqrt{\dfrac{4}{x^2}}} = \sqrt{x^2}$$

$$= x, \text{ since } x > 0$$

Domain f = range of f^{-1} = $(0, \infty)$

Range f = domain f^{-1} = $\left(-\infty, \dfrac{1}{2}\right)$

70. $f^{-1}(x) = \sqrt{\dfrac{3}{3x - 1}}$

$$f(f^{-1}(x)) = f\left(\sqrt{\dfrac{3}{3x - 1}}\right) = \dfrac{\dfrac{3}{3x - 1} + 3}{3\left(\dfrac{3}{3x - 1}\right)}$$

$$= \dfrac{3 + 3(3x - 1)}{9}$$

$$= \dfrac{9x}{9} = x$$

$$f^{-1}(f(x)) = f^{-1}\left(\dfrac{x^2 + 3}{3x^2}\right) = \sqrt{\dfrac{3}{3\left(\dfrac{x^2 + 3}{3x^2}\right) - 1}}$$

$$= \sqrt{\dfrac{3x^2}{(x^2 + 3) - x^2}} = \sqrt{\dfrac{3x^2}{3}}$$

$$= \sqrt{x^2} = x, \text{ since } x > 0$$

Domain f = range of f^{-1} = $(0, \infty)$

Range f = domain f^{-1} = $\left(\dfrac{1}{3}, \infty\right)$

71. (a) 0   **(b)** 2   **(c)** 0   **(d)** 1   **72. (a)** $\dfrac{1}{2}$ **(b)** 0   **(c)** 1   **(d)** 0   **73.** 7   **74.** -5 **75.** Domain of f^{-1}: $[-2, \infty)$; range of f^{-1}: $[5, \infty)$ **76.** Domain of f^{-1}: $[5, \infty)$; range of f^{-1}: $[0, \infty)$ **77.** Domain of g^{-1}: $[0, \infty)$; range of g^{-1}: all real numbers   **78.** Domain of g^{-1}: $(0, 8)$; range of g^{-1}: $[0, 15]$

79. Increasing on the interval $(f(0), f(5))$ **80.** Decreasing on the interval $(f(5), f(0))$ **81.** $f^{-1}(x) = \dfrac{1}{m}(x - b), m \neq 0$

82. $f^{-1}(x) = \sqrt{r^2 - x^2}, \; 0 \leq x \leq r$ **83.** Quadrant I   **84.** Quadrant IV   **85.** Possible answer: $f(x) = |x|, x \geq 0$, is one-to-one; $f^{-1}(x) = x, x \geq 0$

86. Possible answer: $f(x) = x^4, x \geq 0$, is one-to-one; $f^{-1}(x) = x^{1/4}, x \geq 0$

87. (a) $r(d) = \dfrac{d + 90.39}{6.97}$ **(b)** $r(d(r)) = \dfrac{6.97r - 90.39 + 90.39}{6.97} = \dfrac{6.97r}{6.97} = r$ **(c)** 56 miles per hour

$$d(r(d)) = 6.97\left(\dfrac{d + 90.39}{6.97}\right) - 90.39 = d + 90.39 - 90.39 = d$$

88. (a) $C(H) = \dfrac{H + 10.53}{2.15}$ **(b)** $H(C(H)) = 2.15\left(\dfrac{H + 10.53}{2.15}\right) - 10.53 = H + 10.53 - 10.53 = H$ **(c)** 17 inches

$$C(H(C)) = \dfrac{2.15C - 10.53 + 10.53}{2.15} = \dfrac{2.15C}{2.15} = C$$

89. (a) 77.6 kg   **(b)** $h(W) = \dfrac{W - 50}{2.3} + 60 = \dfrac{W + 88}{2.3}$ **(c)** $h(W(h)) = \dfrac{50 + 2.3(h - 60) + 88}{2.3} = \dfrac{2.3h}{2.3} = h$ **(d)** 73 inches

$$W(h(W)) = 50 + 2.3\left(\dfrac{W + 88}{2.3} - 60\right)$$

$$= 50 + W + 88 - 138 = W$$

90. (a) $C(F) = \dfrac{5}{9}(F - 32)$ **(b)** $C(F(C)) = \dfrac{5}{9}\left[\dfrac{9}{5}C + 32 - 32\right] = \dfrac{5}{9} \cdot \dfrac{9}{5}C = C$ **(c)** 21.1°C

$$F(C(F)) = \dfrac{9}{5}\left[\dfrac{5}{9}(F - 32)\right] + 32 = F - 32 + 32 = F$$

91. (a) $\{g|31{,}850 \le g \le 77{,}100\}$

(b) $\{T|4386.25 \le T \le 15{,}698.75\}$

(c) $g(T) = \dfrac{T - 4386.25}{0.25} + 31{,}850$

Domain: $\{T|4386.25 \le T \le 15{,}698.75\}$

Range: $\{g|31{,}850 \le g \le 77{,}100\}$

92. (a) $\{g|15{,}650 \le g \le 63{,}700\}$

(b) $\{T|1565 \le T \le 8772.50\}$

(c) $g(T) = \dfrac{T - 1565}{0.15} + 15{,}650$

Domain: $\{T|1565 \le T \le 8772.50\}$

Range: $\{g|15{,}650 \le g \le 63{,}700\}$

93. (a) t represents time, so $t \ge 0$.

(b) $t(H) = \sqrt{\dfrac{H - 100}{-4.9}} = \sqrt{\dfrac{100 - H}{4.9}}$

(c) 2.02 seconds

94. (a) $l(T) = \left(\dfrac{T}{2\pi}\right)^2 \cdot (32.2)$ **(b)** 7.34 feet

95. $f^{-1}(x) = \dfrac{-dx + b}{cx - a}$; $f = f^{-1}$ if $a = -d$ **96.** Yes, the graph must be symmetric about the line $y = x$; $y = \dfrac{1}{x}$ is an example.

98. Possible answer: $y = \begin{cases} \dfrac{1}{x}, & x < 0 \\ x, & x \ge 0 \end{cases}$ is neither an increasing nor a decreasing function on its domain, but is one-to-one.   **99.** No

100. The number of cars manufactured for $800,000

5.3 Assess Your Understanding (page 279)

6. $\left(-1, \dfrac{1}{a}\right), (0, 1), (1, a)$ **7.** 1   **8.** 4   **9.** F   **10.** F   **11. (a)** 11.212   **(b)** 11.587   **(c)** 11.664   **(d)** 11.665   **12. (a)** 15.426   **(b)** 16.189   **(c)** 16.241

(d) 16.242   **13. (a)** 8.815   **(b)** 8.821   **(c)** 8.824   **(d)** 8.825   **14. (a)** 6.498   **(b)** 6.543   **(c)** 6.580   **(d)** 6.581   **15. (a)** 21.217   **(b)** 22.217

(c) 22.440   **(d)** 22.459   **16. (a)** 21.738   **(b)** 22.884   **(c)** 23.119   **(d)** 23.141   **17.** 3.320   **18.** 0.273   **19.** 0.427   **20.** 8.166   **21.** Neither

22. Linear; $g(x) = 3x + 5$ **23.** Exponential; $H(x) = 4^x$ **24.** Exponential; $F(x) = \left(\dfrac{3}{2}\right)^x$ **25.** Exponential; $f(x) = 3(2^x)$ **26.** Neither

27. Linear; $H(x) = 2x + 4$ **28.** Exponential; $F(x) = \dfrac{1}{4}\left(\dfrac{1}{2}\right)^x$ **29.** B   **30.** A   **31.** D   **32.** H   **33.** F   **34.** C   **35.** E   **36.** G

37.

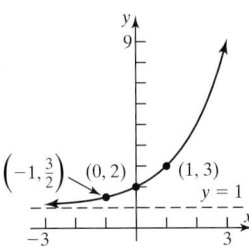

Domain: All real numbers
Range: $\{y|y > 1\}$ or $(1, \infty)$
Horizontal asymptote: $y = 1$

38.

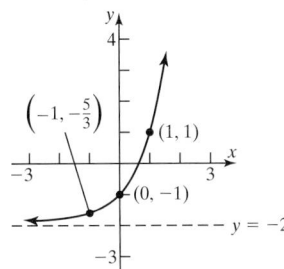

Domain: All real numbers
Range: $\{y|y > -2\}$ or $(-2, \infty)$
Horizontal asymptote: $y = -2$

39.

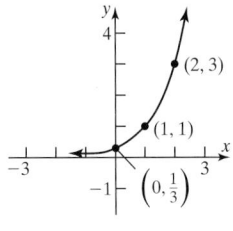

Domain: All real numbers
Range: $\{y|y > 0\}$ or $(0, \infty)$
Horizontal asymptote: $y = 0$

40.

Domain: All real numbers
Range: $\{y|y > 0\}$ or $(0, \infty)$
Horizontal asymptote: $y = 0$

41.

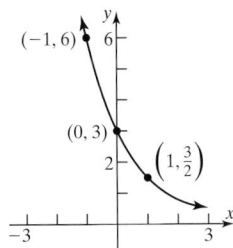

Domain: All real numbers
Range: $\{y|y > 0\}$ or $(0, \infty)$
Horizontal asymptote: $y = 0$

42.

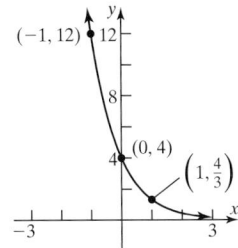

Domain: All real numbers
Range: $\{y|y > 0\}$ or $(0, \infty)$
Horizontal asymptote: $y = 0$

43.

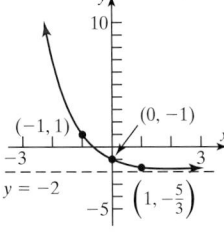

Domain: All real numbers
Range: $\{y|y > -2\}$ or $(-2, \infty)$
Horizontal asymptote: $y = -2$

44.

Domain: All real numbers
Range: $\{y|y < 1\}$ or $(-\infty, 1)$
Horizontal asymptote: $y = 1$

45.

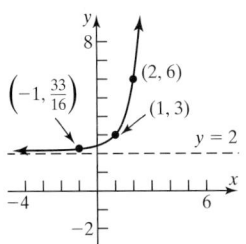

Domain: All real numbers
Range: $\{y|y > 2\}$ or $(2, \infty)$
Horizontal asymptote: $y = 2$

46.

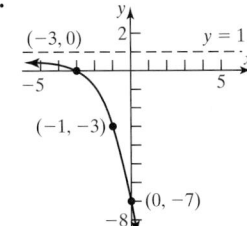

Domain: All real numbers
Range: $\{y|y < 1\}$ or $(-\infty, 1)$
Horizontal asymptote: $y = 1$

47.

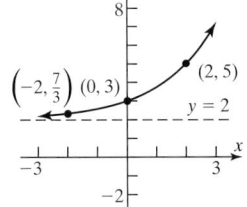

Domain: All real numbers
Range: $\{y|y > 2\}$ or $(2, \infty)$
Horizontal asymptote: $y = 2$

48.

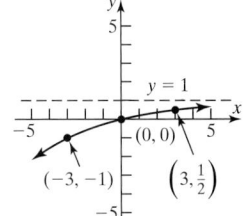

Domain: All real numbers
Range: $\{y|y < 1\}$ or $(-\infty, 1)$
Horizontal asymptote: $y = 1$

49.

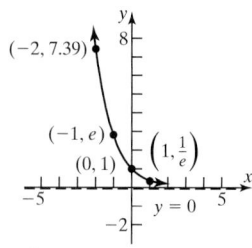

Domain: All real numbers
Range: $\{y | y > 0\}$ or $(0, \infty)$
Horizontal asymptote: $y = 0$

50.

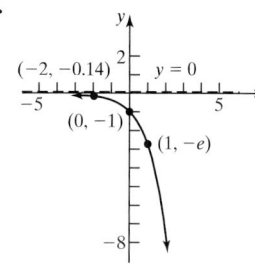

Domain: All real numbers
Range: $\{y | y < 0\}$ or $(-\infty, 0)$
Horizontal asymptote: $y = 0$

51.

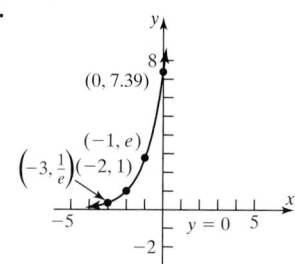

Domain: All real numbers
Range: $\{y | y > 0\}$ or $(0, \infty)$
Horizontal asymptote: $y = 0$

52.

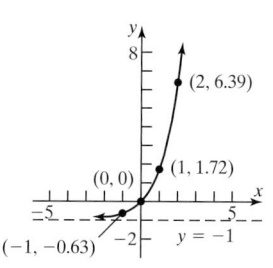

Domain: All real numbers
Range: $\{y | y > -1\}$ or $(-1, \infty)$
Horizontal asymptote: $y = -1$

53.

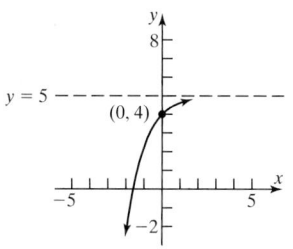

Domain: All real numbers
Range: $\{y | y < 5\}$ or $(-\infty, 5)$
Horizontal asymptote: $y = 5$

54.

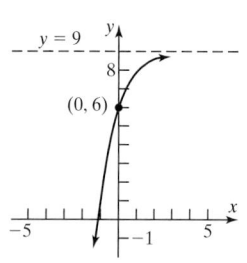

Domain: All real numbers
Range: $\{y | y < 9\}$ or $(-\infty, 9)$
Horizontal asymptote: $y = 9$

55.

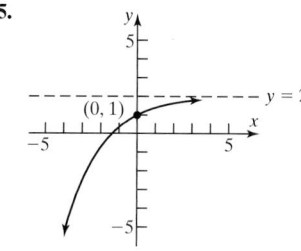

Domain: All real numbers
Range: $\{y | y < 2\}$ or $(-\infty, 2)$
Horizontal asymptote: $y = 2$

56.

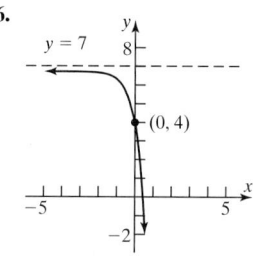

Domain: All real numbers
Range: $\{y | y < 7\}$ or $(-\infty, 7)$
Horizontal asymptote: $y = 7$

57. $\{3\}$ **58.** $\{-6\}$ **59.** $\{-4\}$ **60.** $\{-4\}$ **61.** $\{2\}$ **62.** $\{3\}$ **63.** $\left\{\dfrac{3}{2}\right\}$ **64.** $\{-4\}$ **65.** $\{-\sqrt{2}, 0, \sqrt{2}\}$ **66.** $\left\{0, \dfrac{1}{2}\right\}$ **67.** $\{6\}$ **68.** $\{6\}$

69. $\{-1, 7\}$ **70.** $\{2, 4\}$ **71.** $\{-4, 2\}$ **72.** $\left\{-1, -\dfrac{1}{3}\right\}$ **73.** $\{-4\}$ **74.** $\left\{\dfrac{1}{2}\right\}$ **75.** $\{1, 2\}$ **76.** $\{-6, 2\}$ **77.** $\dfrac{1}{49}$ **78.** $\dfrac{1}{9}$ **79.** $\dfrac{1}{4}$ **80.** $\dfrac{1}{27}$

81. $f(x) = 3^x$ **82.** $f(x) = 5^x$ **83.** $f(x) = -6^x$ **84.** $f(x) = -e^x$ **85. (a)** $16; (4, 16)$ **(b)** $-4; \left(-4, \dfrac{1}{16}\right)$ **86. (a)** $81; (4, 81)$ **(b)** $-2; \left(-2, \dfrac{1}{9}\right)$

87. (a) $\dfrac{9}{4}; \left(-1, \dfrac{9}{4}\right)$ **(b)** $3; (3, 66)$ **88. (a)** $-\dfrac{14}{5}; \left(-1, -\dfrac{14}{5}\right)$ **(b)** $3; (3, 122)$ **89. (a)** $60; (-6, 60)$ **(b)** $-4: (-4, 12)$ **(c)** -2

90. (a) $240; (-5, 240)$ **(b)** $-3; (-3, 24)$ **(c)** -1

91.

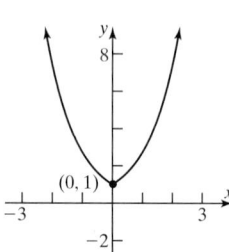

Domain: $(-\infty, \infty)$
Range: $[1, \infty)$
Intercept: $(0, 1)$

92.

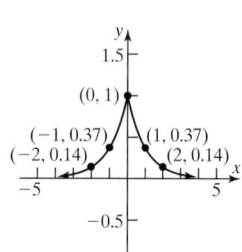

Domain: $(-\infty, \infty)$
Range: $(0, 1]$
Intercept: $(0, 1)$

93.

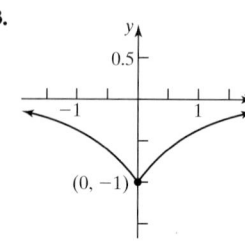

Domain: $(-\infty, \infty)$
Range: $[-1, 0)$
Intercept: $(0, -1)$

94.

Domain: $(-\infty, \infty)$
Range: $(-\infty, -1]$
Intercept: $(0, -1)$

95. (a) 74% **(b)** 47% **96. (a)** 568.68 mm Hg **(b)** 178.27 mm Hg **97. (a)** \$12,123 **(b)** \$6443 **98. (a)** 34.99 mm^2 **(b)** 3.02 mm^2

99. 3.35 mg; 0.45 mg **100.** 362 students **101. (a)** 0.632 **(b)** 0.982 **(c)** 1 **102. (a)** 0.895 **(b)** 0.989 **(c)** 1
(d) **(d)**

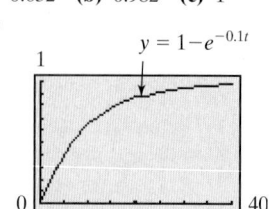

$y = 1 - e^{-0.1t}$

$y = 1 - e^{-0.15t}$

(e) About 7 min

(e) About 6 min

103. (a) 0.0516 **(b)** 0.0888 **104. (a)** 0.1563 **(b)** 0.0298 **105. (a)** 70.95% **(b)** 72.62% **(c)** 100% **106. (a)** 84 words **(b)** 153 words

107. (a) 5.41 amp, 7.59 amp, 10.38 amp **(b)** 12 amp **(d)** 3.34 amp, 5.31 amp, 9.44 amp **(e)** 24 amp

(c), (f)

108. (a) 0.06 amp; 0.0364 amp; 0.0134 amp **(d)** 0.12 amp; 0.0728 amp; 0.0268 amp **109.** $n = 4$: 2.7083; $n = 6$: 2.7181;
(b) 0.06 amp **(e)** 0.12 amp $n = 8$: 2.7182788; $n = 10$: 2.7182818

(c) **(f)**

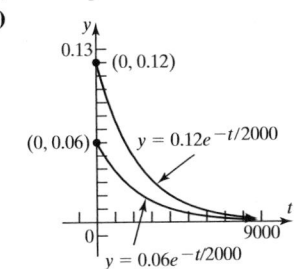

110.

Final Denominator	Value of Expression	Compare Value to $e \approx$ **2.718281828**
$1 + 1$	2.5	$2.5 < e$
$2 + 2$	2.8	$2.8 > e$
$3 + 3$	2.7	$2.7 < e$
$4 + 4$	2.721649485	$2.721649485 > e$
$5 + 5$	2.717770035	$2.717770035 < e$
$6 + 6$	2.718348855	$2.718348855 > e$

111. $\dfrac{f(x + h) - f(x)}{h} = \dfrac{a^{x+h} - a^x}{h} = \dfrac{a^x a^h - a^x}{h} = \dfrac{a^x(a^h - 1)}{h}$ **112.** $f(A + B) = a^{A+B} = a^A \cdot a^B = f(A) \cdot f(B)$

113. $f(-x) = a^{-x} = \dfrac{1}{a^x} = \dfrac{1}{f(x)}$ **114.** $f(\alpha x) = a^{\alpha x} = (a^x)^\alpha = [f(x)]^\alpha$

115. (a) $f(-x) = \dfrac{1}{2}(e^{-x} - e^{-(-x)})$

$= \dfrac{1}{2}(e^{-x} - e^x)$

$= -\dfrac{1}{2}(e^x - e^{-x})$

$= -f(x)$

(b)

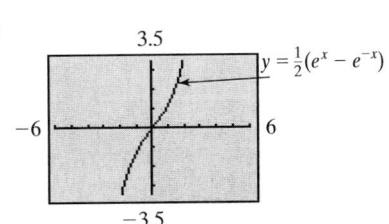

116. (a) $f(-x) = \dfrac{1}{2}(e^{-x} + e^{-(-x)})$

$= \dfrac{1}{2}(e^{-x} + e^x)$

$= \dfrac{1}{2}(e^x + e^{-x})$

$= f(x)$

(b)

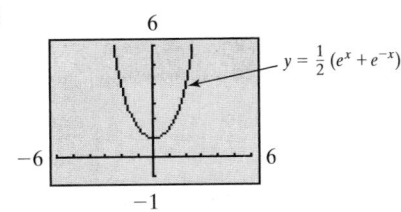

(c) $(\cosh x)^2 - (\sinh x)^2$

$= \left[\dfrac{1}{2}(e^x + e^{-x})\right]^2 - \left[\dfrac{1}{2}(e^x - e^{-x})\right]^2$

$= \dfrac{1}{4}[e^{2x} + 2 + e^{-2x} - e^{2x} + 2 - e^{-2x}]$

$= \dfrac{1}{4}(4) = 1$

117. $f(1) = 5, f(2) = 17, f(3) = 257, f(4) = 65{,}537$; $f(5) = 4{,}294{,}967{,}297 = 641 \times 6{,}700{,}417$ **118.** 59 minutes

5.4 Assess Your Understanding (page 293)

4. $\{x | x > 0\}$ or $(0, \infty)$ **5.** $\left(\dfrac{1}{a}, -1\right)$, $(1, 0), (a, 1)$ **6.** 1 **7.** F **8.** T **9.** $2 = \log_3 9$ **10.** $\log_4 16 = 2$ **11.** $2 = \log_a 1.6$ **12.** $\log_a 2.1 = 3$

13. $x = \log_2 7.2$ **14.** $\log_3 4.6 = x$ **15.** $x = \ln 8$ **16.** $\ln M = 2.2$ **17.** $2^3 = 8$ **18.** $3^{-2} = \dfrac{1}{9}$ **19.** $a^6 = 3$ **20.** $b^2 = 4$ **21.** $3^x = 2$ **22.** $2^x = 6$

23. $e^x = 4$ **24.** $e^4 = x$ **25.** 0 **26.** 1 **27.** 2 **28.** -2 **29.** -4 **30.** -2 **31.** $\dfrac{1}{2}$ **32.** $\dfrac{2}{3}$ **33.** 4 **34.** 4 **35.** $\dfrac{1}{2}$ **36.** 3 **37.** $\{x | x > 3\}$; $(3, \infty)$

38. $\{x | x > 1\}$; $(1, \infty)$ **39.** All real numbers except 0; $\{x | x \neq 0\}$ **40.** $\{x | x > 0\}$; $(0, \infty)$ **41.** $\{x | x > 10\}$; $(10, \infty)$ **42.** $\left\{x | x > -\dfrac{3}{2}\right\}$; $\left(-\dfrac{3}{2}, \infty\right)$

43. $\{x | x > -1\}$; $(-1, \infty)$ **44.** $\{x | x > 5\}$; $(5, \infty)$ **45.** $\{x | x < -1 \text{ or } x > 0\}$; $(-\infty, -1) \cup (0, \infty)$ **46.** $\{x | x < 0 \text{ or } x > 1\}$; $(-\infty, 0) \cup (1, \infty)$

47. $\{x | x \geq 1\}$; $[1, \infty)$ **48.** $\{x | x > 0, x \neq 1\}$; $(0, 1) \cup (1, \infty)$ **49.** 0.511 **50.** 0.536 **51.** 30.099 **52.** 4.055 **53.** 2.303 **54.** 0.434 **55.** -53.991

56. 1.110 **57.** $\sqrt{2}$ **58.** $2^{1/4} \approx 1.189$

59.

60.

61.

62.

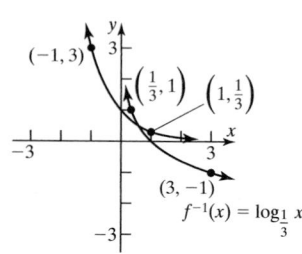

63. B **64.** F **65.** D **66.** H **67.** A **68.** C **69.** E **70.** G

71. (a) Domain: $(-4, \infty)$

(b)

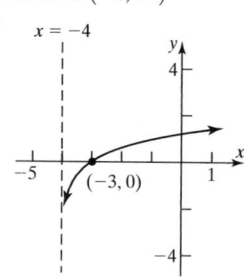

(c) Range: $(-\infty, \infty)$

Vertical asymptote: $x = -4$

(d) $f^{-1}(x) = e^x - 4$

(e) Range of f: $(-\infty, \infty)$

Range of f^{-1}: $(-4, \infty)$

(f)

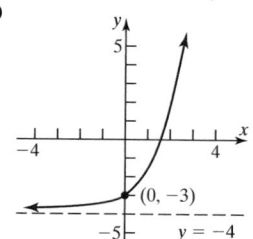

72. (a) Domain: $(3, \infty)$

(b)

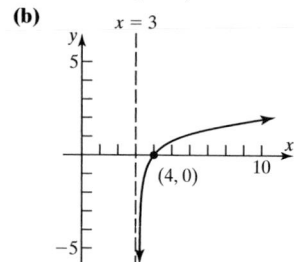

(c) Range: $(-\infty, \infty)$

Vertical asymptote: $x = 3$

(d) $f^{-1}(x) = e^x + 3$

(e) Range of f: $(-\infty, \infty)$

Range of f^{-1}: $(3, \infty)$

(f)

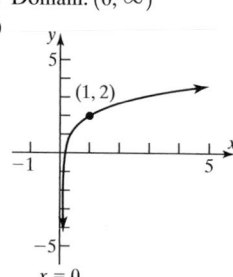

73. (a) Domain: $(0, \infty)$

(b)

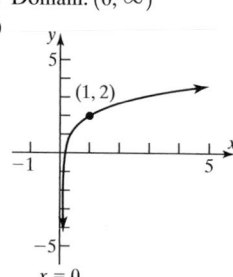

(c) Range: $(-\infty, \infty)$

Vertical asymptote: $x = 0$

(d) $f^{-1}(x) = e^{x-2}$

(e) Range of f: $(-\infty, \infty)$

Range of f^{-1}: $(0, \infty)$

(f)

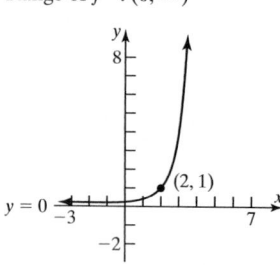

74. (a) Domain: $(-\infty, 0)$

(b)

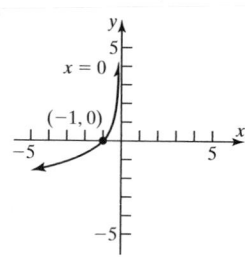

(c) Range: $(-\infty, \infty)$

Vertical asymptote: $x = 0$

(d) $f^{-1}(x) = -e^{-x}$

(e) Range of f: $(-\infty, \infty)$

Range of f^{-1}: $(-\infty, 0)$

(f)

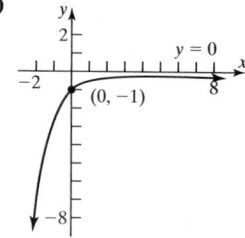

75. (a) Domain: $(0, \infty)$

(b)

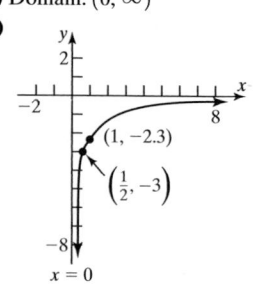

(c) Range: $(-\infty, \infty)$

Vertical asymptote: $x = 0$

(d) $f^{-1}(x) = \dfrac{1}{2} e^{x+3}$

(e) Range of f: $(-\infty, \infty)$

Range of f^{-1}: $(0, \infty)$

(f)

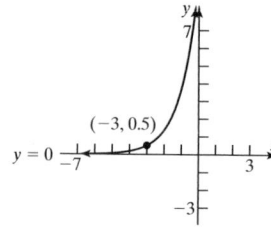

76. (a) Domain: $(-1, \infty)$

(b)

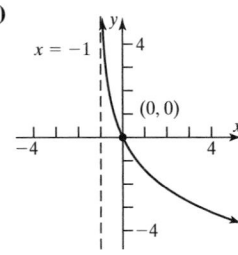

(c) Range: $(-\infty, \infty)$
Vertical asymptote: $x = -1$
(d) $f^{-1}(x) = e^{-x/2} - 1$
(e) Range of f: $(-\infty, \infty)$
Range of f^{-1}: $(-1, \infty)$

(f)

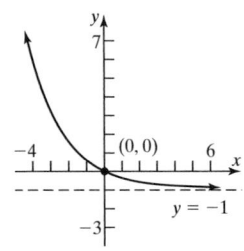

77. (a) Domain: $(4, \infty)$

(b)

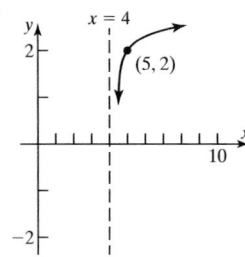

(c) Range: $(-\infty, \infty)$
Vertical asymptote: $x = 4$
(d) $f^{-1}(x) = 10^{x-2} + 4$
(e) Range of f: $(-\infty, \infty)$
Range of f^{-1}: $(4, \infty)$

(f)

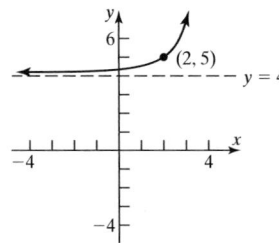

78. (a) Domain: $(0, \infty)$

(b)

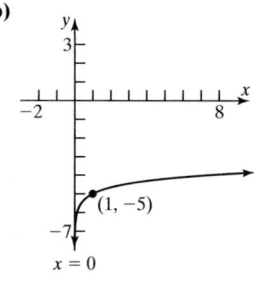

(c) Range: $(-\infty, \infty)$
Vertical asymptote: $x = 0$
(d) $f^{-1}(x) = 10^{2(x+5)}$
(e) Range of f: $(-\infty, \infty)$
Range of f^{-1}: $(0, \infty)$

(f)

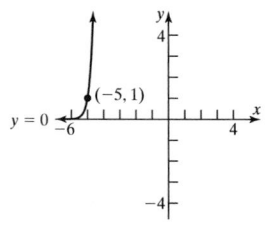

79. (a) Domain: $(0, \infty)$

(b)

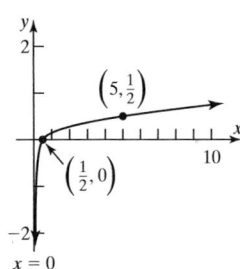

(c) Range: $(-\infty, \infty)$
Vertical asymptote: $x = 0$
(d) $f^{-1}(x) = \dfrac{1}{2} \cdot 10^{2x}$
(e) Range of f: $(-\infty, \infty)$
Range of f^{-1}: $(0, \infty)$

(f)

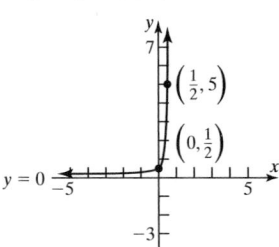

80. (a) Domain: $(-\infty, 0)$

(b)

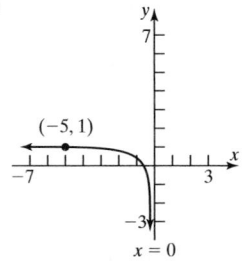

(c) Range: $(-\infty, \infty)$
Vertical asymptote: $x = 0$
(d) $f^{-1}(x) = -\dfrac{1}{2} \cdot 10^{x}$
(e) Range of f: $(-\infty, \infty)$
Range of f^{-1}: $(-\infty, 0)$

(f)

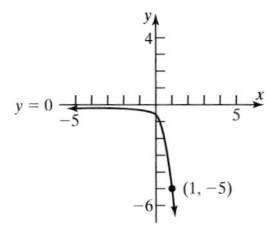

81. (a) Domain: $(-2, \infty)$

(b)

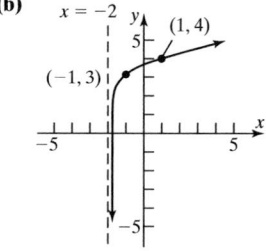

(c) Range: $(-\infty, \infty)$
Vertical asymptote: $x = -2$
(d) $f^{-1}(x) = 3^{x-3} - 2$
(e) Range of f: $(-\infty, \infty)$
Range of f^{-1}: $(-2, \infty)$

(f)

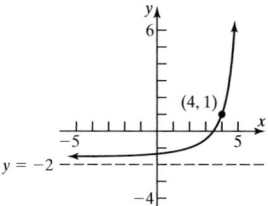

82. (a) Domain: $(-1, \infty)$

(b)

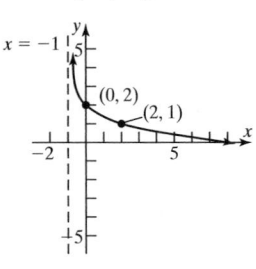

(c) Range: $(-\infty, \infty)$
Vertical asymptote: $x = -1$
(d) $f^{-1}(x) = 3^{2-x} - 1$

(e) Range of f: $(-\infty, \infty)$
Range of f^{-1}: $(-1, \infty)$

(f)

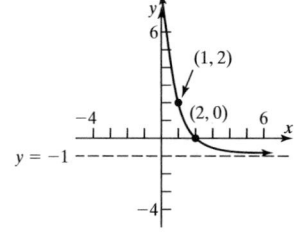

83. (a) Domain: $(-\infty, \infty)$
(b)

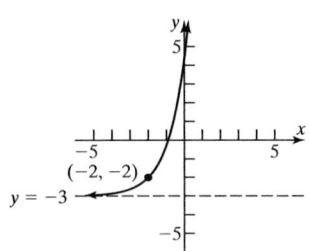

(c) Range: $(-3, \infty)$
Horizontal asymptote: $y = -3$

(d) $f^{-1}(x) = \ln(x + 3) - 2$

(e) Range of f: $(-3, \infty)$
Range of f^{-1}: $(-\infty, \infty)$

(f)

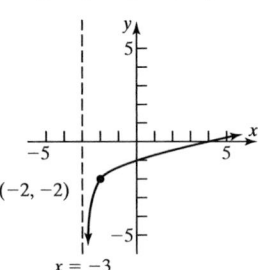

84. (a) Domain: $(-\infty, \infty)$
(b)

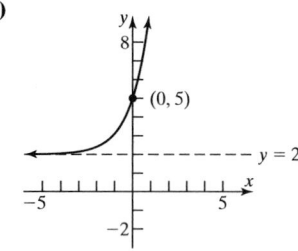

(c) Range: $(2, \infty)$
Horizontal asymptote: $y = 2$

(d) $f^{-1}(x) = \ln\left(\dfrac{x - 2}{3}\right)$

(e) Range of f: $(2, \infty)$
Range of f^{-1}: $(-\infty, \infty)$

(f)

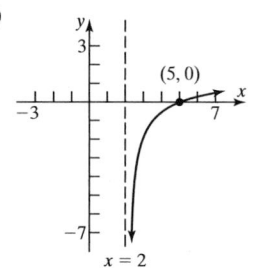

85. (a) Domain: $(-\infty, \infty)$
(b)

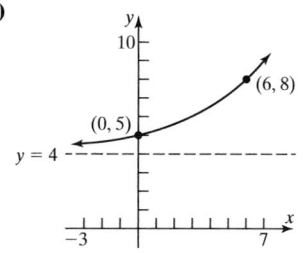

(c) Range: $(4, \infty)$
Horizontal asymptote: $y = 4$

(d) $f^{-1}(x) = 3 \log_2(x - 4)$

(e) Range of f: $(4, \infty)$
Range of f^{-1}: $(-\infty, \infty)$

(f)

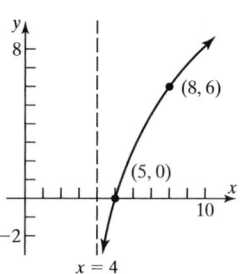

86. (a) Domain: $(-\infty, \infty)$
(b)

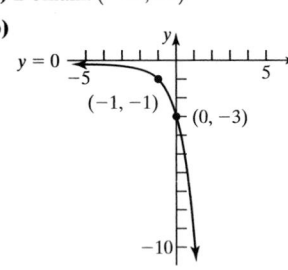

(c) Range: $(-\infty, 0)$
Horizontal asymptote: $y = 0$

(d) $f^{-1}(x) = \log_3(-x) - 1$

(e) Range of f: $(-\infty, 0)$
Range of f^{-1}: $(-\infty, \infty)$

(f)

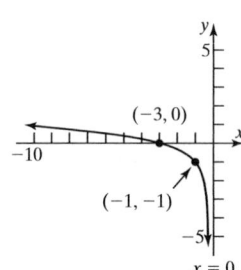

87. $\{9\}$ **88.** $\{125\}$ **89.** $\left\{\dfrac{7}{2}\right\}$ **90.** $\left\{\dfrac{11}{3}\right\}$

91. $\{2\}$ **92.** $\left\{\dfrac{1}{2}\right\}$ **93.** $\{5\}$ **94.** $\{-4\}$

95. $\{3\}$ **96.** $\{4\}$ **97.** $\{2\}$ **98.** $\left\{-\dfrac{1}{5}\right\}$

99. $\left\{\dfrac{\ln 10}{3}\right\}$ **100.** $\left\{\dfrac{\ln 3}{2}\right\}$ **101.** $\left\{\dfrac{\ln 8 - 5}{2}\right\}$

102. $\left\{\dfrac{1 - \ln 13}{2}\right\}$ **103.** $\{-2\sqrt{2}, 2\sqrt{2}\}$

104. $\left\{\dfrac{-1 + \sqrt{85}}{2}, \dfrac{-1 - \sqrt{85}}{2}\right\}$ **105.** $\{-1\}$

106. $\{-1\}$ **107.** $\left\{5 \ln \dfrac{7}{5}\right\}$ **108.** $\left\{\dfrac{1}{2}\left(7 + \log \dfrac{3}{8}\right)\right\}$ **109.** $\left\{2 - \log \dfrac{5}{2}\right\}$ **110.** $\left\{\ln \dfrac{5}{4} - 1\right\}$ **111. (a)** $\left\{x \mid x > -\dfrac{1}{2}\right\}; \left(-\dfrac{1}{2}, \infty\right)$

(b) $2; (40, 2)$ **(c)** $121; (121, 3)$ **(d)** 4 **112. (a)** $\{x \mid x > -1\}; (-1, \infty)$ **(b)** $0; (7, 0)$ **(c)** $3; (3, -1)$ **(d)** 7

113.

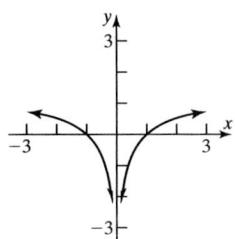

Domain: $\{x \mid x \neq 0\}$
Range: $(-\infty, \infty)$
Intercepts: $(-1, 0), (1, 0)$

114.

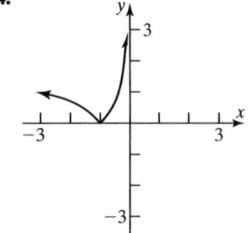

Domain: $\{x \mid x < 0\}$
Range: $\{y \mid y \geq 0\}$
Intercept: $(-1, 0)$

115.

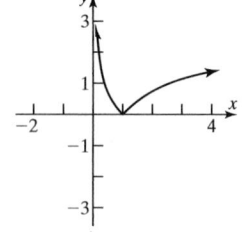

Domain: $\{x \mid x > 0\}$
Range: $\{y \mid y \geq 0\}$
Intercept: $(1, 0)$

116.

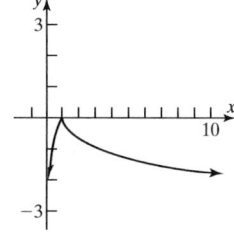

Domain: $\{x \mid x > 0\}$
Range: $\{y \mid y \leq 0\}$
Intercept: $(1, 0)$

117. (a) 1 **(b)** 2 **(c)** 3 **(d)** It increases. **(e)** 0.000316 **(f)** 3.981×10^{-8} **118. (a)** 0.4283 **(b)** 0.7782 **(c)** 0.5504 **119. (a)** 5.97 km
(b) 0.90 km **120. (a)** 1.98 days or slightly less than 2 days **(b)** 6.58 days or about 6 days and 14 h **121. (a)** 6.93 min **(b)** 16.09 min
122. (a) 4.62 min or about 4 min and 37 s **(b)** 10.73 min or about 10 min and 44 s
123. $h \approx 2.29$, so the time between injections is about 2 h, 17 min. **124.** 3.99 days or about 4 days

125. 0.2695 s

0.8959 s

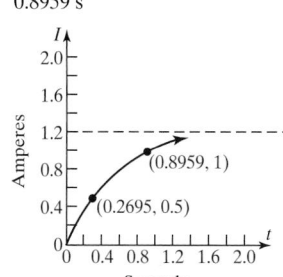

126. (a) $-\dfrac{\ln 0.9}{5} \approx 0.0211$ **(b)** 38 words **(c)** 54 words **(d)** 109.27 min

127. 50 decibels (dB)

128. 110 dB

129. 90 dB

130. 80 dB **131.** 8.1 **132.** 6.9

133. (a) $k \approx 11.216$ **(b)** 6.73 **(c)** 0.41% **(d)** 0.14%

135. Because $y = \log_1 x$ means $1^y = 1 = x$, which cannot be true for $x \neq 1$

5.5 Assess Your Understanding (page 304)

1. sum **2.** 7 **3.** $r \log_a M$ **4.** F **5.** F **6.** T **7.** 71 **8.** -13 **9.** -4 **10.** $\sqrt{2}$ **11.** 7 **12.** 8 **13.** 1 **14.** 2 **15.** 1 **16.** 1 **17.** 2 **18.** 2 **19.** $\dfrac{5}{4}$

20. 42 **21.** 4 **22.** 3 **23.** $a + b$ **24.** $a - b$ **25.** $b - a$ **26.** $-a$ **27.** $3a$ **28.** $3b$ **29.** $\dfrac{1}{5}(a + b)$ **30.** $\dfrac{1}{4}(a - b)$ **31.** $2 + \log_5 x$ **32.** $\log_3 x - 2$

33. $3 \log_2 z$ **34.** $5 \log_7 x$ **35.** $1 + \ln x$ **36.** $1 - \ln x$ **37.** $\ln x + x$ **38.** $\ln x - x$ **39.** $2 \log_a u + 3 \log_a v$ **40.** $\log_2 a - 2 \log_2 b$

41. $2 \ln x + \dfrac{1}{2}\ln(1 - x)$ **42.** $\ln x + \dfrac{1}{2}\ln(1 + x^2)$ **43.** $3 \log_2 x - \log_2(x - 3)$ **44.** $\dfrac{1}{3}\log_5(x^2 + 1) - \log_5(x + 1) - \log_5(x - 1)$

45. $\log x + \log(x + 2) - 2 \log(x + 3)$ **46.** $3 \log x + \dfrac{1}{2}\log(x + 1) - 2 \log(x - 2)$ **47.** $\dfrac{1}{3}\ln(x - 2) + \dfrac{1}{3}\ln(x + 1) - \dfrac{2}{3}\ln(x + 4)$

48. $\dfrac{4}{3}\ln(x - 4) - \dfrac{2}{3}\ln(x + 1) - \dfrac{2}{3}\ln(x - 1)$ **49.** $\ln 5 + \ln x + \dfrac{1}{2}\ln(1 + 3x) - 3 \ln(x - 4)$ **50.** $\ln 5 + 2 \ln x + \dfrac{1}{3}\ln(1 - x) - \ln 4 - 2 \ln(x + 1)$

51. $\log_5 u^3 v^4$ **52.** $\log_3\left(\dfrac{u^2}{v}\right)$ **53.** $\log_3\left(\dfrac{1}{x^{5/2}}\right)$ **54.** $\log_2\left(\dfrac{1}{x^3}\right)$ **55.** $\log_4\left[\dfrac{x - 1}{(x + 1)^4}\right]$ **56.** $\log\left(\dfrac{x + 2}{x + 1}\right)$ **57.** $-2 \ln(x - 1)$

58. $\log\left[\dfrac{(x + 3)(x - 1)}{(x - 2)(x + 6)(x + 1)}\right]$ **59.** $\log_2[x(3x - 2)^4]$ **60.** $\log_3 x^9$ **61.** $\log_a\left(\dfrac{25x^6}{\sqrt{2x + 3}}\right)$ **62.** $\log\left(\sqrt[3]{x^3 + 1}\sqrt{x^2 + 1}\right)$

63. $\log_2\left[\dfrac{(x + 1)^2}{(x + 3)(x - 1)}\right]$ **64.** $\log_5\left[\dfrac{(3x + 1)^3}{x(2x - 1)^2}\right]$ **65.** 2.771 **66.** 1.796 **67.** -3.880 **68.** -3.907 **69.** 5.615 **70.** 2.584 **71.** 0.874 **72.** 0.303

73. $y = \dfrac{\log x}{\log 4}$

74. $y = \dfrac{\log x}{\log 5}$

75. $y = \dfrac{\log(x + 2)}{\log 2}$

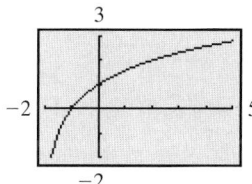

76. $y = \dfrac{\log(x - 3)}{\log 4}$

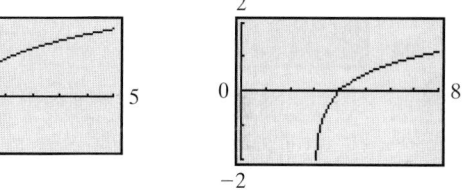

77. $y = \dfrac{\log(x + 1)}{\log(x - 1)}$

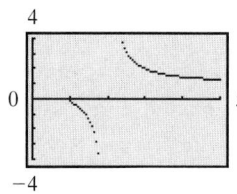

78. $y = \dfrac{\log(x - 2)}{\log(x + 2)}$

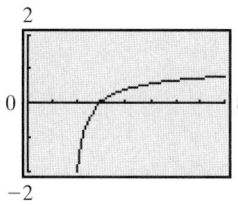

79. (a) $(f \circ g)(x) = x$; $\{x | x \text{ is any real number}\}$ or $(-\infty, \infty)$
  (b) $(g \circ f)(x) = x$; $\{x | x > 0\}$ or $(0, \infty)$ **(c)** 5
  (d) $(f \circ h)(x) = \ln x^2$; $\{x | x \neq 0\}$ or $(-\infty, 0) \cup (0, \infty)$ **(e)** 2
80. (a) $(f \circ g)(x) = x$; $\{x | x \text{ is any real number}\}$ or $(-\infty, \infty)$
  (b) $(g \circ f)(x) = x$; $\{x | x > 0\}$ or $(0, \infty)$ **(c)** 3
  (d) $(f \circ h)(x) = 2 + \log_2 x$; $\{x | x > 0\}$ or $(0, \infty)$ **(e)** 5

81. $y = Cx$ **82.** $y = x + C$ **83.** $y = Cx(x + 1)$ **84.** $y = \dfrac{Cx^2}{x + 1}$ **85.** $y = Ce^{3x}$ **86.** $y = Ce^{-2x}$ **87.** $y = Ce^{-4x} + 3$ **88.** $y = Ce^{5x} - 4$

89. $y = \dfrac{\sqrt[3]{C}(2x + 1)^{1/6}}{(x + 4)^{1/9}}$ **90.** $y = \dfrac{\sqrt{C}(x^2 + 1)^{1/6}}{x^{1/4}}$ **91.** 3 **92.** 3 **93.** 1 **94.** $n!$

95. $\log_a\left(x + \sqrt{x^2 - 1}\right) + \log_a\left(x - \sqrt{x^2 - 1}\right) = \log_a\left[\left(x + \sqrt{x^2 - 1}\right)\left(x - \sqrt{x^2 - 1}\right)\right] = \log_a[x^2 - (x^2 - 1)] = \log_a 1 = 0$

96. $\log_a\left(\sqrt{x} + \sqrt{x - 1}\right) + \log_a\left(\sqrt{x} - \sqrt{x - 1}\right) = \log_a\left[\left(\sqrt{x} + \sqrt{x - 1}\right)\left(\sqrt{x} - \sqrt{x - 1}\right)\right] = \log_a[x - (x - 1)] = \log_a 1 = 0$

97. $\ln(1 + e^{2x}) = \ln[e^{2x}(e^{-2x} + 1)] = \ln e^{2x} + \ln(e^{-2x} + 1) = 2x + \ln(1 + e^{-2x})$

98. $\dfrac{f(x + h) - f(x)}{h} = \dfrac{\log_a(x + h) - \log_a(x)}{h} = \dfrac{1}{h}\log_a\left(\dfrac{x + h}{x}\right) = \log_a\left(1 + \dfrac{h}{x}\right)^{1/h}, h \neq 0$

99. $y = f(x) = \log_a x; a^y = x$ implies $a^y = \left(\dfrac{1}{a}\right)^{-y} = x$, so $-y = \log_{1/a} x = -f(x)$.

100. $f(AB) = \log_a(AB) = \log_a(A) + \log_a(B) = f(A) + f(B)$ **101.** $f(x) = \log_a x; f\left(\dfrac{1}{x}\right) = \log_a\dfrac{1}{x} = \log_a 1 - \log_a x = -f(x)$

102. $f(x^\alpha) = \log_a(x^\alpha) = \alpha \log_a(x) = \alpha f(x)$

103. $\log_a\dfrac{M}{N} = \log_a(M \cdot N^{-1}) = \log_a M + \log_a N^{-1} = \log_a M - \log_a N$, since $a^{\log_a N^{-1}} = N^{-1}$ implies $a^{-\log_a N^{-1}} = N$; i.e., $\log_a N = -\log_a N^{-1}$.

104. $\log_a\dfrac{1}{N} = \log_a 1 - \log_a N = -\log_a N$

5.6 Assess Your Understanding *(page 310)*

5. $\{16\}$ **6.** $\{4\}$ **7.** $\left\{\dfrac{16}{5}\right\}$ **8.** $\left\{\dfrac{10}{3}\right\}$ **9.** $\{6\}$ **10.** $\{0\}$ **11.** $\{16\}$ **12.** $\left\{\dfrac{1}{3}\right\}$ **13.** $\left\{\dfrac{1}{3}\right\}$ **14.** $\{8\}$ **15.** $\{3\}$ **16.** $\{5\}$ **17.** $\{5\}$ **18.** $\{25\}$

19. $\left\{\dfrac{21}{8}\right\}$ **20.** $\left\{\dfrac{15}{4}\right\}$ **21.** $\{-6\}$ **22.** $\{-1\}$ **23.** $\{-2\}$ **24.** $\{2\}$ **25.** $\left\{-1 + \sqrt{1 + e^4}\right\} \approx \{6.456\}$

26. $\left\{\dfrac{1}{e^2 - 1}\right\} \approx \{0.157\}$ **27.** $\left\{\dfrac{-5 + 3\sqrt{5}}{2}\right\} \approx \{0.854\}$ **28.** $\left\{-4 + \sqrt{17}\right\} \approx \{0.123\}$ **29.** $\{2\}$ **30.** $\{67\}$ **31.** $\left\{\dfrac{9}{2}\right\}$ **32.** $\{4\}$

33. $\{8\}$ **34.** $\{-2\}$ **35.** $\left\{\log_2 10\right\} = \left\{\dfrac{\ln 10}{\ln 2}\right\} \approx \{3.322\}$ **36.** $\left\{\log_3 14\right\} = \left\{\dfrac{\ln 14}{\ln 3}\right\} \approx \{2.402\}$

37. $\left\{-\log_8 1.2\right\} = \left\{-\dfrac{\ln 1.2}{\ln 8}\right\} \approx \{-0.088\}$ **38.** $\left\{-\log_2 1.5\right\} = \left\{\dfrac{-\ln 1.5}{\ln 2}\right\} \approx \{-0.585\}$ **39.** $\left\{\dfrac{1}{3}\log_2\dfrac{8}{5}\right\} = \left\{\dfrac{\ln\frac{8}{5}}{3\ln 2}\right\} \approx \{0.226\}$

40. $\left\{\dfrac{\log_4\left(\frac{2}{3}\right)}{0.2}\right\} = \left\{\dfrac{\ln\left(\frac{2}{3}\right)}{0.2\ln 4}\right\} \approx \{-1.462\}$ **41.** $\left\{\dfrac{\ln 3}{2\ln 3 + \ln 4}\right\} \approx \{0.307\}$ **42.** $\left\{\dfrac{\ln 2.5}{\ln 50}\right\} \approx \{0.234\}$ **43.** $\left\{\dfrac{\ln 7}{\ln 0.6 + \ln 7}\right\} \approx \{1.356\}$

44. $\left\{\dfrac{\ln\left(\frac{4}{3}\right)}{\ln\left(\frac{20}{3}\right)}\right\} \approx \{0.152\}$ **45.** $\{0\}$ **46.** $\left\{\dfrac{\ln 0.51}{2\ln 1.7 - \ln 0.3}\right\} \approx \{-0.297\}$ **47.** $\left\{\dfrac{\ln \pi}{1 + \ln \pi}\right\} \approx \{0.534\}$ **48.** $\left\{\dfrac{3}{\ln \pi - 1}\right\} \approx \{20.728\}$

49. $\left\{\dfrac{\ln 3}{\ln 2}\right\} \approx \{1.585\}$ **50.** $\{0\}$ **51.** $\{0\}$ **52.** $\{1\}$ **53.** $\left\{\log_4\left(-2 + \sqrt{7}\right)\right\} \approx \{-0.315\}$

54. $\left\{\log_3\left(\dfrac{3 - \sqrt{5}}{2}\right), \log_3\left(\dfrac{3 + \sqrt{5}}{2}\right)\right\} \approx \{-0.876, 0.876\}$ **55.** $\{\log_5 4\} \approx \{0.861\}$ **56.** $\{\log_6 3\} \approx \{0.613\}$ **57.** No real solution

58. No real solution **59.** $\{\log_4 5\} \approx \{1.161\}$ **60.** $\{\log_3 7\} \approx \{1.771\}$ **61.** $\{2.79\}$ **62.** $\{12.15\}$ **63.** $\{-0.57\}$ **64.** $\{-1.98, 0.45\}$ **65.** $\{-0.70\}$

66. $\{1.86, 4.54\}$ **67.** $\{0.57\}$ **68.** $\{1.16\}$ **69.** $\{0.39, 1.00\}$ **70.** $\{0.65\}$ **71.** $\{1.32\}$ **72.** $\{0.05, 1.48\}$ **73.** $\{1.31\}$ **74.** $\{0.57\}$ **75.** $\{1\}$

76. $\left\{\dfrac{26 + 8\sqrt{10}}{9}, \dfrac{26 - 8\sqrt{10}}{9}\right\} \approx \{5.7, 0.078\}$ **77.** $\{16\}$ **78.** $\{81\}$ **79.** $\left\{-1, \dfrac{2}{3}\right\}$ **80.** $\left\{4, \dfrac{1}{4}\right\}$ **81.** $\{0\}$

82. $\left\{\ln\left(3 + 2\sqrt{2}\right), \ln\left(3 - 2\sqrt{2}\right)\right\} \approx \{1.763, -1.763\}$ **83.** $\left\{\ln\left(2 + \sqrt{5}\right)\right\} \approx \{1.444\}$ **84.** $\left\{\ln\left(-2 + \sqrt{5}\right)\right\} \approx \{-1.444\}$

85. $\left\{e^{\frac{\ln 5 \cdot \ln 3}{\ln 15}}\right\} \approx \{1.921\}$ **86.** $\left\{e^{\frac{3\ln 2 \cdot \ln 6}{\ln 12}}\right\} \approx \{4.479\}$ **87. (a)** $\{5\}; (5, 3)$ **(b)** $\{5\}; (5, 4)$ **(c)** $\{1\}$; yes, at $(1, 2)$ **(d)** $\{5\}$ **(e)** $\left\{-\dfrac{1}{11}\right\}$

88. (a) $\{4\}; (4, 2)$ **(b)** $\{28\}; (28, 3)$ **(c)** No real solution; no intersection **(d)** $\{4\}$ **(e)** $\left\{\dfrac{7}{4}\right\}$

89. (a)

(b) $(0.710, 6.541)$
(c) $\{x \mid x > 0.710\}$ or $(0.710, \infty)$

90. (a)

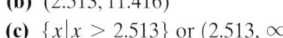

(b) $(2.513, 11.416)$
(c) $\{x \mid x > 2.513\}$ or $(2.513, \infty)$

91. (a), (b)

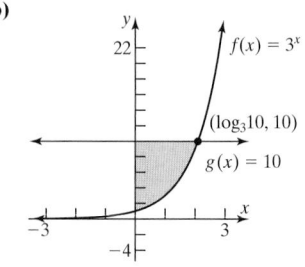

(c) $(\log_3 10, 10)$

92. (a), (b)

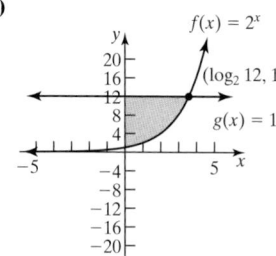

(c) $(\log_2 12, 12)$

93. (a), (b)

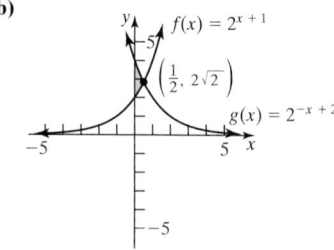

(c) $\left(\dfrac{1}{2}, 2\sqrt{2}\right)$

94. (a), (b)

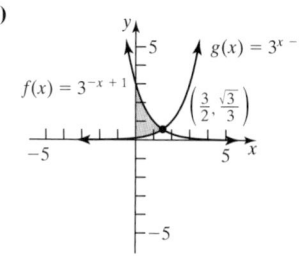

(c) $\left(\dfrac{3}{2}, \dfrac{\sqrt{3}}{3}\right)$

95. (a)

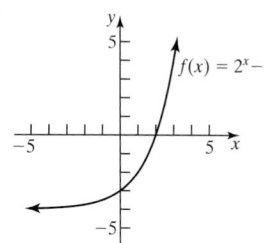

(b) 2

(c) $\{x | x < 2\}$ or $(-\infty, 2)$

96. (a)

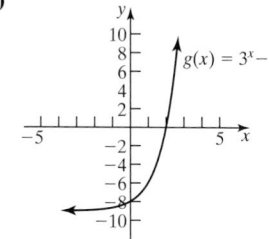

(b) 2

(c) $\{x | x > 2\}$ or $(2, \infty)$

97. (a) 2010 **(b)** 2027
98. (a) 2036 **(b)** 2057
99. (a) After 2.4 yr
   (b) After 6.5 yr
   (c) After 10 yr
100. (a) After 1.4 yr
   (b) After 5 yr
   (c) After 13 yr

5.7 Assess Your Understanding *(page 320)*

3. $108.29 **4.** $59.83 **5.** $609.50 **6.** $358.84 **7.** $697.09 **8.** $789.24 **9.** $12.46 **10.** $49.35 **11.** $125.23 **12.** $156.83 **13.** $88.72 **14.** $59.14
15. $860.72 **16.** $626.61 **17.** $554.09 **18.** $266.08 **19.** $59.71 **20.** $654.98 **21.** $361.93 **22.** $886.92 **23.** 5.095% **24.** 6.168% **25.** 5.127%
26. 6.184% **27.** $6\frac{1}{4}$% compounded annually **28.** 9% compounded quarterly **29.** 9% compounded monthly **30.** 7.9% compounded daily
31. 25.992% **32.** 12.246% **33.** 24.573% **34.** 11.612% **35. (a)** About 8.69 yr **(b)** About 8.66 yr **36. (a)** About 18.36 yr **(b)** About 18.31 yr
37. 6.823% **38.** 5.827% **39.** 5.09 yr; 5.07 yr **40.** 5.62 yr; 5.60 yr **41.** 15.27 yr or 15 yr, 3 mo **42.** 16.62 yr or 16 yr, 7 mo **43.** $104,335
44. $215.48 **45.** $12,910.62 **46.** $2955.39 **47.** About $30.17 per share or $3017 **48.** 9.35% **49.** Not quite. Jim will have $1057.60. The second bank
gives a better deal, since Jim will have $1060.62 after 1 yr. **50.** $1021.60 **51.** Will has $11,632.73; Henry has $10,947.89. **52.** It is better to be given
$1000 now for investment to earn $1349.86 in 3 yr. **53. (a)** $49,581 **(b)** $33,235 **54. (a)** Interest is $60,000 **(b)** Interest is $77,227 **(c)** Interest is
$75,505. Simple interest at 12% is best. **55.** Approximately $602 billion **56.** 2014 **57.** $940.90 **58.** $941.19 **59.** 2.53% **60.** 3.56% **61.** 34.31 yr
62. 16.98 yr **63. (a)** $1364.62 **(b)** $1353.35 **64.** $10,810.76 **65.** $4631.93 **66.** 9.07%

67. (a) 6.12 yr

(b) 18.45 yr

(c) $mP = P\left(1 + \dfrac{r}{n}\right)^{nt}$

$m = \left(1 + \dfrac{r}{n}\right)^{nt}$

$\ln m = \ln\left(1 + \dfrac{r}{n}\right)^{nt} = nt \ln\left(1 + \dfrac{r}{n}\right)$

$t = \dfrac{\ln m}{n \ln\left(1 + \dfrac{r}{n}\right)}$

68. (a) 20.79 yr **(b)** 7.74%

(c) $A = Pe^{rt}$

$\ln A = \ln P + rt$

$rt = \ln A - \ln P$

$t = \dfrac{\ln A - \ln P}{r}$

69. (a) 2.51% **(b)** In 2022 or after 27 yr
70. 268.9 **71.** 22.7 yr **72.** 1967

5.8 Assess Your Understanding *(page 331)*

1. (a) 500 insects
(b) 0.02 = 2%
(c)

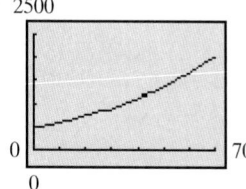

(d) About 611 insects
(e) After about 23.5 days
(f) After about 34.7 days

2. (a) 1000
(b) 0.01 = 1%
(c) 5000

(d) About 1041
(e) After about 53.1 h
(f) After about 69.3 h

3. (a) $-0.0244 = -2.44\%$
(b) 500

(c) About 391.7 g
(d) After about 9.1 yr
(e) 28.4 yr

4. (a) $-0.087 = -8.7\%$
(b)

100

0

0   25

(c) About 45.7 g
(d) After about 4.1 days
(e) About 7.97 days

5. (a) $N(t) = N_0 e^{kt}$
(b) 5832
(c) 3.9 days
7. (a) $N(t) = N_0 e^{kt}$
(b) 25,198
9. 9.797 g

6. (a) $N(t) = N_0 e^{kt}$
(b) About 5243
(c) About 7.85 h later
8. (a) $N(t) = N_0 e^{kt}, k < 0$
(b) 711,111
10. 9.999999467 g; 9.999994668 g

11. (a) 9727 yr ago
(b)

1

0

0   30,000

(c) 5600 yr

12. (a) 2882 yr old
(b)

1

0

0   10,000

(c) 5600 yr

13. (a) About 5:18 PM
(b)

450

0

0   60

(c) About 14.3 min
(d) The temperature of the pizza approaches 70°F.

14. (a) 45.41°F
(b) About 16.2 minutes
(c)

73

0   18
37

(d) About 7.26 min   **(e)** The temperature approaches 38°F.

15. (a) 18.63°C; 25.07°C
(b)

35

0

0   50

16. 45.69°F; 28.46 min
17. 1.7 ppm; 7.17 days or 172 h
18. 0.10 mol; 107 min
19. 0.26 mol; 6.58 h or 395 min
20. 7.34 kg; 76.6 h or 3.19 days
21. 26.6 days
22. At about 9:42 PM

23. (a) 1000 g **(b)** 43.9% **(c)** 30 g
(d)

1000

0   20
0

(e) 616.6 g **(f)** After 9.85 h
(g) About 7.9 h

24. (a) 500 eagles **(b)** 16.2%
(c)

500

0   60
0

(d) Almost 10 eagles **(e)** After 29.7 yr
(f) After 27.2 yr

25. (a) 9.23×10^{-3}, or about 0
(b) 0.81, or about 1
(c) 5.01, or about 5
(d) 57.91°, 43.99°, 30.07°

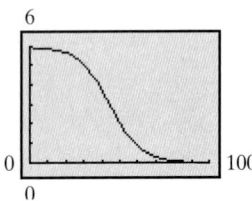
6

0   100
0

26. (a) 0.799
(b)

100

0   10
0

(c) 97.3% **(d)** During 1988

27. (a) In 1984, 91.8% of households
did not own a personal computer.
(b)

100

0   40
0

(c) 70.6% **(d)** During 2011

28. (a) In 1910, there were 13,840 farm workers.
(b)

15,000

0   100
0

(c) 2207 **(d)** In 1946 **(e)** $W \to 0$ as $t \to \infty$. No.

29. (a)

120

0   100
0

(b) 0.78 or 78% **(c)** 50 people
(d) As n increases, the probability decreases.

30. (a) In 1991 there were 130 bank failures.
(b)

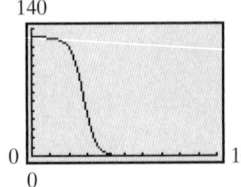
140

0   10
0

(c) 43 **(d)** 1995 **(e)** They go to zero.

5.9 Assess Your Understanding *(page 339)*

1. (a)

(d)

2. (a)

(d)

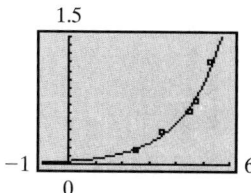

(b) $y = 0.0903(1.3384)^x$

(c) $N(t) = 0.0903e^{0.2915t}$

(e) 0.69

(f) After about 7.26 hr

(b) $y = 0.0339(1.9474)^x$

(c) $N(t) = 0.0339e^{0.6665t}$

(e) 1.85

(f) 6.19 hr

3. (a)

(b) $y = 100.326(0.8769)^x$

(c) $A(t) = 100.326e^{-0.1314t}$

(d)

(e) 5.3 weeks   **(f)** 0.14 g

(g) After about 12.3 weeks

4. (a)

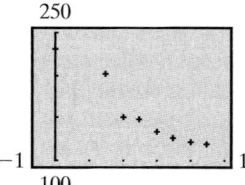

(b) $y = 228.437(0.92301)^x$

(c) $A(t) = 228.437e^{-0.08012t}$

(d)

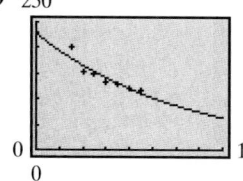

(e) Approximately 68.7 billion cigarettes

(f) In 2014 or about 19 yr after 1995

5. (a)

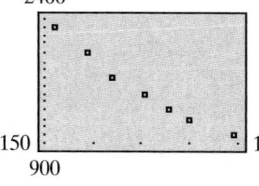

(b) $y = 32,741.02 - 6070.96 \ln x$

(c)

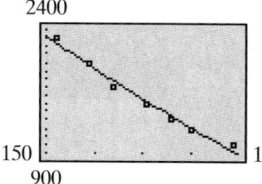

(d) Approximately 168 computers

6. (a)

7. (a)

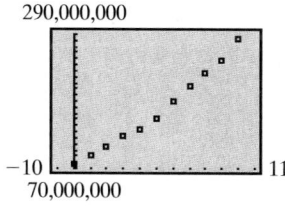

8. (a) $x = 1$ corresponds to 1993.

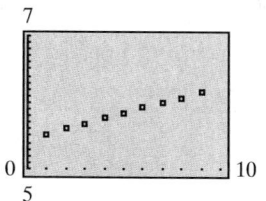

(b) $y = -11,850.72 + 2688.5 \ln x$

(b) $y = \dfrac{799,475,916.5}{1 + 9.1968e^{-0.0160x}}$

(b) $y = \dfrac{10.05267}{1 + 0.8439e^{-0.0320x}}$

(c)

(c)

(c)

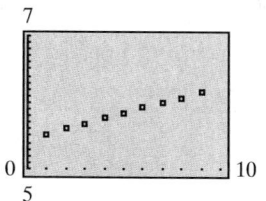

(d) Approximately 152 computers

(d) 799,475,917

(e) Approximately 291,599,733

(f) 2006

(d) 10.053 billion people

(e) Approximately 6.38 billion people

(f) 2012

9. (a) 76,100

0
150
38

(b) $y = \dfrac{68,684.8}{1 + 18.9416e^{-0.1974x}}$

(c) 76,100

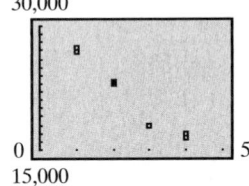

0
150
38

(d) About 68,685,000 subscribers
(e) About 68,505,000 subscribers

10. (a) $y = \dfrac{307.0202}{1 + 195.1148e^{-0.2866x}}$

(b) 260

0
0
25

(c) The predicted carrying capacity is about 307,020,200 subscribers.
(d) The model predicts there will be about 266,770,000 subscribers at the end of 2009.

11. (a) 225

20
175
90

12. (a) 60

0
0
100,000

13. (a) 30,000

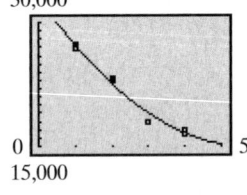

0
15,000
5

(b) Quadratic with $a < 0$ because of the "upside down U-shape" of the data
(c) $y = -0.0311x^2 + 3.4444x + 118.2493$

(b) Logarithmic
(c) $y = 130.9100 - 10.0800 \ln x$

(b) Exponential because depreciation of a car is described by exponential models in the theory of finance
(c) $y = 31,808.51\,(0.8474)^x$

(d) 225

20
175
90

(d) 60

0
0
100,000

(d) 30,000

0
15,000
5

(e) 201

(e) 20.9 crimes per 1000 population

(e) \$13,899

Review Exercises (page 344)

1. (a) -26 **(b)** -241 **(c)** 16 **(d)** -1 **2. (a)** -1 **(b)** 37 **(c)** 4 **(d)** 5 **3. (a)** $\sqrt{11}$ **(b)** 1 **(c)** $\sqrt{\sqrt{6}+2}$ **(d)** 19 **4. (a)** -5 **(b)** $\sqrt{15}$

(c) -6626 **(d)** $\sqrt{4 - \sqrt{5}}$ **5. (a)** e^4 **(b)** $3e^{-2} - 2$ **(c)** e^{e^4} **(d)** -17 **6. (a)** $\dfrac{2}{73}$ **(b)** $\dfrac{2}{3}$ **(c)** $\dfrac{2178}{1097}$ **(d)** -9

7. $(f \circ g)(x) = 1 - 3x$, all real numbers; $(g \circ f)(x) = 7 - 3x$, all real numbers; $(f \circ f)(x) = x$, all real numbers; $(g \circ g)(x) = 9x + 4$, all real numbers

8. $(f \circ g)(x) = 4x + 1$, all real numbers; $(g \circ f)(x) = 4x - 1$, all real numbers; $(f \circ f)(x) = 4x - 3$, all real numbers; $(g \circ g)(x) = 4x + 3$, all real numbers

9. $(f \circ g)(x) = 27x^2 + 3|x| + 1$, all real numbers; $(g \circ f)(x) = 3|3x^2 + x + 1|$, all real numbers; $(f \circ f)(x) = 27x^4 + 18x^3 + 24x^2 + 7x + 5$, all real numbers; $(g \circ g)(x) = 9|x|$, all real numbers

10. $(f \circ g)(x) = \sqrt{3 + 3x + 3x^2}$, all real numbers; $(g \circ f)(x) = 1 + \sqrt{3x} + 3x$, $\{x \mid x \geq 0\}$; $(f \circ f)(x) = \sqrt{3\sqrt{3x}}$, $\{x \mid x \geq 0\}$; $(g \circ g)(x) = 3 + 3x + 4x^2 + 2x^3 + x^4$, all real numbers

11. $(f \circ g)(x) = \dfrac{1 + x}{1 - x}$, $\{x \mid x \neq 0, x \neq 1\}$; $(g \circ f)(x) = \dfrac{x - 1}{x + 1}$, $\{x \mid x \neq -1, x \neq 1\}$; $(f \circ f)(x) = x$, $\{x \mid x \neq 1\}$; $(g \circ g)(x) = x$, $\{x \mid x \neq 0\}$

12. $(f \circ g)(x) = \sqrt{\dfrac{3 - 3x}{x}}$, $\{x \mid 0 < x \leq 1\}$; $(g \circ f)(x) = \dfrac{3}{\sqrt{x} - 3}$, $\{x \mid x > 3\}$; $(f \circ f)(x) = \sqrt{\sqrt{x} - 3} - 3$, $\{x \mid x \geq 12\}$; $(g \circ g)(x) = x$, $\{x \mid x \neq 0\}$

13. (a) one-to-one **(b)** $\{(2, 1), (5, 3), (8, 5), (10, 6)\}$ **14. (a)** one-to-one **(b)** $\{(4, -1), (2, 0), (5, 1), (7, 3)\}$

15.

16.

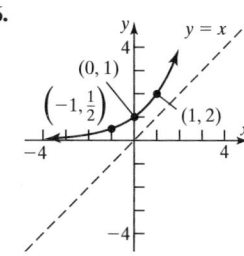

17. $f^{-1}(x) = \dfrac{2x + 3}{5x - 2}$

$$f(f^{-1}(x)) = \dfrac{2\left(\dfrac{2x + 3}{5x - 2}\right) + 3}{5\left(\dfrac{2x + 3}{5x - 2}\right) - 2} = x$$

$$f^{-1}(f(x)) = \dfrac{2\left(\dfrac{2x + 3}{5x - 2}\right) + 3}{5\left(\dfrac{2x + 3}{5x - 2}\right) - 2} = x$$

Domain of f = range of f^{-1} = all real numbers except $\dfrac{2}{5}$

Range of f = domain of f^{-1} = all real numbers except $\dfrac{2}{5}$

18. $f^{-1}(x) = \dfrac{2 - 3x}{x + 1}$

$$f(f^{-1}(x)) = \dfrac{2 - \dfrac{2 - 3x}{x + 1}}{3 + \dfrac{2 - 3x}{x + 1}} = x$$

$$f^{-1}(f(x)) = \dfrac{2 - 3\left(\dfrac{2 - x}{3 + x}\right)}{\dfrac{2 - x}{3 + x} + 1} = x$$

Domain of f = range of f^{-1} = all real numbers except -3
Range of f = domain of f^{-1} = all real numbers except -1

19. $f^{-1}(x) = \dfrac{x + 1}{x}$

$$f(f^{-1}(x)) = \dfrac{1}{\dfrac{x + 1}{x} - 1} = x$$

$$f^{-1}(f(x)) = \dfrac{\dfrac{1}{x - 1} + 1}{\dfrac{1}{x - 1}} = x$$

Domain of f = range of f^{-1} = all real numbers except 1
Range of f = domain of f^{-1} = all real numbers except 0

20. $f^{-1}(x) = x^2 + 2, \ x \geq 0$

$f(f^{-1}(x)) = \sqrt{x^2 + 2 - 2} = |x| = x, \ x \geq 0$
$f^{-1}(f(x)) = \left(\sqrt{x - 2}\right)^2 + 2 = x$
Domain of f = range of f^{-1} = $[2, \infty)$
Range of f = domain of f^{-1} = $[0, \infty)$

22. $f^{-1}(x) = (x - 1)^3$

$f(f^{-1}(x)) = ((x - 1)^3)^{1/3} + 1 = x$
$f^{-1}(f(x)) = (x^{1/3} + 1 - 1)^3 = x$
Domain of f = range of f^{-1} = $(-\infty, \infty)$
Range of f = domain of f^{-1} = $(-\infty, \infty)$

21. $f^{-1}(x) = \dfrac{27}{x^3}$

$$f(f^{-1}(x)) = \dfrac{3}{\left(\dfrac{27}{x^3}\right)^{1/3}} = x$$

$$f^{-1}(f(x)) = \dfrac{27}{\left(\dfrac{3}{x^{1/3}}\right)^3} = x$$

Domain of f = range of f^{-1} = all real numbers except 0
Range of f = domain of f^{-1} = all real numbers except 0

23. **(a)** 81   **(b)** 2   **(c)** $\dfrac{1}{9}$ **(d)** -3 **24. (a)** 3   **(b)** 4   **(c)** $\dfrac{1}{81}$ **(d)** -5 **25.** $\log_5 z = 2$ **26.** $\log_a m = 5$ **27.** $5^{13} = u$ **28.** $a^3 = 4$

29. $\left\{x \middle| x > \dfrac{2}{3}\right\}; \left(\dfrac{2}{3}, \infty\right)$ **30.** $\left\{x \middle| x > -\dfrac{1}{2}\right\}; \left(-\dfrac{1}{2}, \infty\right)$ **31.** $\{x | x < 1 \text{ or } x > 2\}; (-\infty, 1) \cup (2, \infty)$

32. $\{x | x < -3 \text{ or } x > 3\}; (-\infty, -3) \cup (3, \infty)$ **33.** -3 **34.** 4   **35.** $\sqrt{2}$ **36.** 0.1   **37.** 0.4   **38.** $\sqrt{3}$ **39.** $\log_3 u + 2 \log_3 v - \log_3 w$

40. $8 \log_2 a + 2 \log_2 b$ **41.** $2 \log x + \dfrac{1}{2}\log(x^3 + 1)$ **42.** $2 \log_5(x + 1) - 2 \log_5 x$ **43.** $\ln x + \dfrac{1}{3}\ln(x^2 + 1) - \ln(x - 3)$

44. $2 \ln(2x + 3) - 2 \ln(x - 1) - 2 \ln(x - 2)$ **45.** $\dfrac{25}{4}\log_4 x$ **46.** $\dfrac{13}{6}\log_3 x$ **47.** $-2 \ln(x + 1)$ **48.** $\log\left(\dfrac{x - 3}{x + 4}\right)$ **49.** $\log\left(\dfrac{4x^3}{[(x + 3)(x - 2)]^{1/2}}\right)$

50. $\ln\left[\dfrac{16\sqrt{x^2 + 1}}{\sqrt{x(x - 4)}}\right]$ **51.** 2.124   **52.** 4.392   **53.**

54.

55. (a) Domain of f: $(-\infty, \infty)$ **(e)** Range of f: $(0, \infty)$ **56. (a)** Domain of f: $(-\infty, \infty)$ **(e)** Range of f: $(-\infty, 3)$

(b)

(f)

(b)

(f)

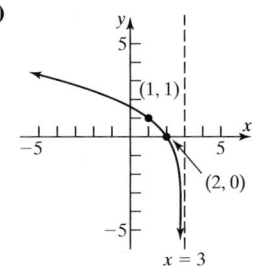

(c) Range of f: $(0, \infty)$
Horizontal asymptote: $y = 0$

(d) $f^{-1}(x) = 3 + \log_2 x$

(c) Range of f: $(-\infty, 3)$
Horizontal asymptote: $y = 3$

(d) $f^{-1}(x) = \log_2(3 - x)$

57. (a) Domain of f: $(-\infty, \infty)$ **(e)** Range of f: $(0, \infty)$ **58. (a)** Domain of f: $(-\infty, \infty)$ **(e)** Range of f: $(1, \infty)$

(b)

(f)

(b)

(f)

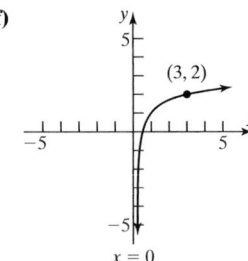

(c) Range of f: $(0, \infty)$
Horizontal asymptote: $y = 0$

(d) $f^{-1}(x) = -\log_3(2x)$

(c) Range of f: $(1, \infty)$
Horizontal asymptote: $y = 1$

(d) $f^{-1}(x) = -\log_3(x - 1)$

59. (a) Domain of f: $(-\infty, \infty)$ **(e)** Range of f: $(-\infty, 1)$ **60. (a)** Domain of: $(-\infty, \infty)$ **(e)** Range f: $(0, \infty)$

(b)

(f)

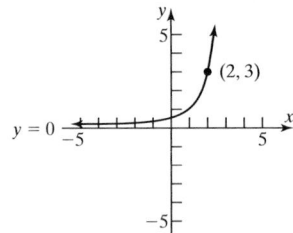

(b)

(f)

(c) Range of f: $(-\infty, 1)$
Horizontal asymptote: $y = 1$

(d) $f^{-1}(x) = -\ln(1 - x)$

(c) Range of f: $(0, \infty)$
Horizontal asymptote: $y = 0$

(d) $f^{-1}(x) = 2 + \ln\left(\dfrac{x}{3}\right)$

61. (a) Domain of f: $(-3, \infty)$ **(e)** Range of f: $(-\infty, \infty)$ **62. (a)** Domain of f: $(0, \infty)$ **(e)** Range of f: $(-\infty, \infty)$

(b)

(f)

(b)

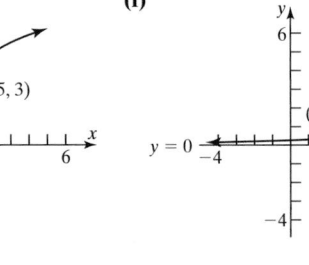

(f)

(c) Range of f: $(-\infty, \infty)$
Vertical asymptote: $x = -3$

(d) $f^{-1}(x) = e^{2x} - 3$

(c) Range of f: $(-\infty, \infty)$
Vertical asymptote: $x = 0$

(d) $f^{-1}(x) = \dfrac{1}{2}e^{x-3}$

63. $\left\{\dfrac{1}{4}\right\}$ **64.** $\left\{-\dfrac{16}{9}\right\}$ **65.** $\left\{\dfrac{-1 - \sqrt{3}}{2}, \dfrac{-1 + \sqrt{3}}{2}\right\} \approx \{-1.366, 0.366\}$ **66.** $\left\{\dfrac{1 - \sqrt{3}}{2}, \dfrac{1 + \sqrt{3}}{2}\right\} \approx \{-0.366, 1.366\}$ **67.** $\left\{\dfrac{1}{4}\right\}$ **68.** $\left\{\dfrac{1}{8}\right\}$

69. $\left\{\dfrac{2\ln 3}{\ln 5 - \ln 3}\right\} \approx \{4.301\}$ **70.** $\left\{\dfrac{2(\ln 7 + \ln 5)}{\ln 7 - \ln 5}\right\} \approx \{21.133\}$ **71.** $\left\{\dfrac{12}{5}\right\}$ **72.** $\{-2, 6\}$ **73.** $\{83\}$ **74.** $\left\{-\dfrac{1}{2}\right\}$ **75.** $\left\{\dfrac{1}{2}, -3\right\}$ **76.** $\{1\}$

77. $\{-1\}$ **78.** $\{3,4\}$ **79.** $\{1 - \ln 5\} \approx \{-0.609\}$ **80.** $\left\{\dfrac{1 - \ln 4}{2}\right\} \approx \{-0.193\}$ **81.** $\left\{\log_3\left(-2 + \sqrt{7}\right)\right\} = \left\{\dfrac{\ln\left(-2 + \sqrt{7}\right)}{\ln 3}\right\} \approx \{-0.398\}$

82. $\{\log_4 7\} = \left\{\dfrac{\ln 7}{\ln 4}\right\} \approx \{1.404\}$

83. (a), (e)

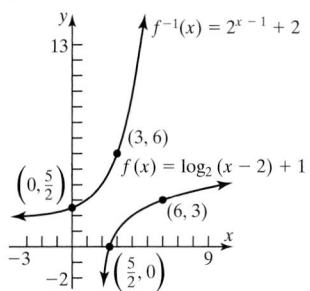

(b) $3; (6,3)$ **(c)** $10; (10,4)$
(d) $\left\{x \middle| x > \dfrac{5}{2}\right\}$ or $\left(\dfrac{5}{2}, \infty\right)$
(e) $f^{-1}(x) = 2^{x-1} + 2$

84. (a), (e)

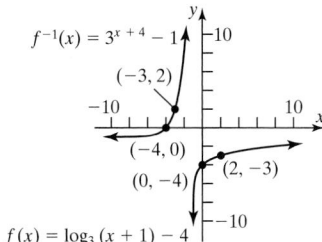

(b) $-2; (8, -2)$ **(c)** $2; (2, -3)$
(d) $\{x| -1 < x < 80\}$ or $(-1, 80)$
(e) $f^{-1}(x) = 3^{x+4} - 1$

85. 3229.5 m
86. 1482 m
87. (a) 37.3 W **(b)** 6.9 dB
88. (a) 11.77 **(b)** 9.56 in.
89. (a) 9.85 yr **(b)** 4.27 yr
90. \$20,398.87; 4.04%; 17.5 yr
91. \$41,668.97
92. (a) 10.436% **(b)** \$32,249.24
93. 24,203 yr ago
94. 55.22 min or 55 min and 13 s
95. 7,237,271,501
96. 7.204 g; 0.519 g **97.** \$483.67 billion

98. (a) 0.3 **(b)** 0.8
(c)

99. (a)

(c)

(b) $y = 165.73(0.9951)^x$ **(d)** Approximately 83 s

(d) In 2026

100. (a)

(c)

101. (a)

(c)

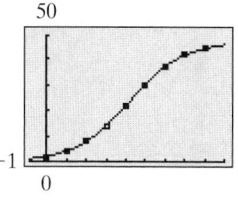

(b) $y = 18.921 - 7.096 \ln x$ **(d)** Approximately $-3°F$

(b) $C = \dfrac{46.93}{1 + 21.273e^{-0.7306t}}$

(d) About 47 people; 50 people
(e) 2.4 days; during the tenth hour of day 3
(f) 9.5 days

Chapter Test *(page 348)*

1. (a) $f \circ g = \dfrac{2x + 7}{2x + 3}$; domain: $\left\{x \middle| x \neq -\dfrac{3}{2}\right\}$ **(b)** $(g \circ f)(-2) = 5$ **(c)** $(f \circ g)(-2) = -3$

2. (a) The function is not one-to-one. **(b)** The function is one-to-one.

3. $f^{-1}(x) = \dfrac{2 + 5x}{3x}$; domain of $f = \left\{x \middle| x \neq \dfrac{5}{3}\right\}$, range of $f = \{y|y \neq 0\}$; domain of $f^{-1} = \{x|x \neq 0\}$; range of $f^{-1} = \left\{y \middle| y \neq \dfrac{5}{3}\right\}$

4. The point $(-5, 3)$ must be on the graph of f^{-1}. **5.** $x = 5$ **6.** $b = 4$ **7.** $x = 625$ **8.** $e^3 + 2 \approx 22.086$ **9.** $\log 20 \approx 1.301$

10. $\log_3 21 = \dfrac{\ln 21}{\ln 3} \approx 2.771$ **11.** $\ln 133 \approx 4.890$

12. (a) Domain of f: $\{x|-\infty < x < \infty\}$ **(e)** Range of f: $\{y|y > -2\}$ **13. (a)** Domain of f: $\{x|x > 2\}$ **(e)** Range of f: $\{y|-\infty < y < \infty\}$
or $(-\infty, \infty)$ or $(-2, \infty)$ or $(2, \infty)$ or $(-\infty, \infty)$

(b) **(f)** **(b)** **(f)**

   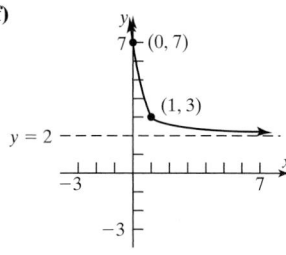

(c) Range of f: $\{y|y > -2\}$ or $(-2, \infty)$; **(c)** Range of f: $\{y|-\infty < y < \infty\}$
Horizontal asymptote: $y = -2$ or $(-\infty, \infty)$; vertical asymptote: $x = 2$

(d) $f^{-1}(x) = \log_4(x + 2) - 1$ **(d)** $f^{-1}(x) = 5^{1-x} + 2$

14. $\{1\}$ **15.** $\{91\}$ **16.** $\{-\ln 2\} \approx \{-0.693\}$ **17.** $\left\{\dfrac{1 - \sqrt{13}}{2}, \dfrac{1 + \sqrt{13}}{2}\right\} \approx \{-1.303, 2.303\}$ **18.** $\left\{\dfrac{3 \ln 7}{1 - \ln 7}\right\} \approx \{-6.172\}$ **19.** $\left\{2\sqrt{6}\right\} \approx \{4.899\}$

20. $2 + 3 \log_2 x - \log_2(x - 6) - \log_2(x + 3)$ **21.** About 250.39 days **22. (a)** \$1033.82 **(b)** \$963.42 **(c)** 11.9 yr
23. (a) About 83 dB **(b)** The pain threshold will be exceeded if 31,623 people shouted at the same time.

Cumulative Review *(page 348)*

1. Yes; no **2. (a)** 10 **(b)** $2x^2 + 3x + 1$ **(c)** $2x^2 + 4xh + 2h^2 - 3x - 3h + 1$ **3.** $\left(\dfrac{1}{2}, \dfrac{\sqrt{3}}{2}\right)$ is on the graph. **4.** $\{-26\}$

5. **6. (a)** **7.** $f(x) = 2(x - 4)^2 - 8 = 2x^2 - 16x + 24$

8.

(b) $\{x|-\infty < x < \infty\}$

9. $f(g(x)) = \dfrac{4}{(x - 3)^2} + 2;$ **10. (a)** Zeros: $-4, -\dfrac{1}{4}, 2$ **11. (a), (c)**
domain: $\{x|x \ne 3\}$; 3 **(b)** x-intercepts: $-4, -\dfrac{1}{4}, 2$; y-intercept: -8

(c) Local maximum of 60.75 occurs at $x = -2.5$.
Local minimum of -25 occurs at $x = 1$.

(d)

 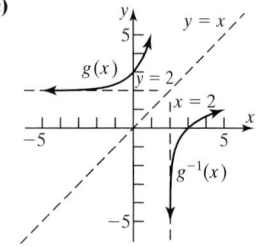

Domain g = range g^{-1} = $(-\infty, \infty)$
Range g = domain g^{-1} = $(2, \infty)$

(b) $g^{-1}(x) = \log_3(x - 2)$

12. $\left\{-\dfrac{3}{2}\right\}$ **13.** $\{2\}$ **14. (a)** $\{-1\}$ **(b)** $\{x|x > -1\}$ or $(-1, \infty)$ **(c)** $\{25\}$ **15. (a)**

CHAPTER 6 Trigonometric Functions

6.1 Assess Your Understanding (page 361)

3. standard position **4.** $r\theta; \frac{1}{2}r^2\theta$ **5.** $\frac{s}{t}; \frac{\theta}{t}$ **6.** F **7.** T **8.** T **9.** F **10.** F

11. **12.** **13.** **14.** **15.** **16.**

17. **18.** **19.** **20.** **21.** **22.**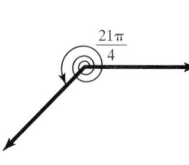

23. $40.17°$ **24.** $61.71°$ **25.** $1.03°$ **26.** $73.68°$ **27.** $9.15°$ **28.** $98.38°$ **29.** $40°19'12''$ **30.** $61°14'24''$ **31.** $18°15'18''$ **32.** $29°24'40''$

33. $19°59'24''$ **34.** $44°0'36''$ **35.** $\frac{\pi}{6}$ **36.** $\frac{2\pi}{3}$ **37.** $\frac{4\pi}{3}$ **38.** $\frac{11\pi}{6}$ **39.** $-\frac{\pi}{3}$ **40.** $-\frac{\pi}{6}$ **41.** π **42.** $\frac{3\pi}{2}$ **43.** $-\frac{3\pi}{4}$ **44.** $-\frac{5\pi}{4}$ **45.** $-\frac{\pi}{2}$ **46.** $-\pi$

47. $60°$ **48.** $150°$ **49.** $-225°$ **50.** $-120°$ **51.** $90°$ **52.** $720°$ **53.** $15°$ **54.** $75°$ **55.** $-90°$ **56.** $-180°$ **57.** $-30°$ **58.** $-135°$ **59.** 0.30

60. 1.27 **61.** -0.70 **62.** -0.89 **63.** 2.18 **64.** 6.11 **65.** $179.91°$ **66.** $42.97°$ **67.** $114.59°$ **68.** $171.89°$ **69.** $362.11°$ **70.** $81.03°$ **71.** 5 m

72. 12 ft **73.** 6 ft **74.** 24 cm **75.** 0.6 radian **76.** $\frac{4}{3} \approx 1.333$ radians **77.** $\frac{\pi}{3} \approx 1.047$ in. **78.** $2\pi \approx 6.283$ m **79.** 25 m^2 **80.** 36 ft^2

81. $2\sqrt{3} \approx 3.464$ ft **82.** $4\sqrt{3} \approx 6.928$ cm **83.** 0.24 radian **84.** $\frac{4}{9} \approx 0.444$ radian **85.** $\frac{\pi}{3} \approx 1.047$ in.^{2} **86.** $3\pi \approx 9.425$ m^2 **87.** $s = 2.094$ ft;

$A = 2.094$ ft^2 **88.** $s = 2.094$ m; $A = 4.189$ m^2 **89.** $s = 14.661$ yd; $A = 87.965$ yd^2 **90.** $s = 7.854$ cm; $A = 35.343$ cm^2 **91.** $3\pi \approx 9.42$ in;

$5\pi \approx 15.71$ in. **92.** $\frac{40\pi}{9} \approx 13.96$ in. **93.** $2\pi \approx 6.28$ m^2 **94.** $\frac{3\pi}{2} \approx 4.71$ cm^2 **95.** $\frac{675\pi}{2} \approx 1060.29$ ft^2 **96.** 0.89 radian $\approx 50.93°$

97. $\omega = \frac{1}{60}$ radian/s; $v = \frac{1}{12}$ cm/s **98.** $\omega = \frac{1}{8}$ radian/s; $v = \frac{1}{4}$ m/s **99.** Approximately 452.5 rpm **100.** Approximately 282.7 in./s;

approximately 16.1 mi/h **101.** Approximately 359 mi **102.** Approximately 554 mi **103.** Approximately 898 mi/h

104. Approximately 794 mi/h **105.** Approximately 2292 mi/h **106.** Approximately 66,633 mi/h **107.** $\frac{3}{4}$ rpm **108.** Approximately 2.69 ft/s;

approximately 0.09 radian/s **109.** Approximately 2.86 mi/h **110.** Approximately 37.13 mi/h; approximately 1034.26 rpm

111. Approximately 31.47 rpm **112.** Approximately 5.8 min **113.** Approximately 1037 mi/h **114.** Approximately 1.15 mi

115. Radius $\approx$ 3979 mi; circumference $\approx$ 25,000 mi **116.** **(a)** The fence is 335.1 ft long. **(b)** The area of the warning track is 3267.3 ft^2.

117. $v_1 = r_1\omega_1$, $v_2 = r_2\omega_2$, and $v_1 = v_2$, so $r_1\omega_1 = r_2\omega_2 \Rightarrow \frac{r_1}{r_2} = \frac{\omega_2}{\omega_1}$.

6.2 Assess Your Understanding (page 378)

7. $\frac{3}{2}$ **8.** 0.91 **9.** T **10.** F **11.** $\sin t = \frac{1}{2}$; $\cos t = \frac{\sqrt{3}}{2}$; $\tan t = \frac{\sqrt{3}}{3}$; $\csc t = 2$; $\sec t = \frac{2\sqrt{3}}{3}$; $\cot t = \sqrt{3}$ **12.** $\sin t = -\frac{\sqrt{3}}{2}$; $\cos t = \frac{1}{2}$;

$\tan t = -\sqrt{3}$; $\csc t = -\frac{2\sqrt{3}}{3}$; $\sec t = 2$; $\cot t = -\frac{\sqrt{3}}{3}$ **13.** $\sin t = \frac{\sqrt{21}}{5}$; $\cos t = -\frac{2}{5}$; $\tan t = -\frac{\sqrt{21}}{2}$; $\csc t = \frac{5\sqrt{21}}{21}$; $\sec t = -\frac{5}{2}$;

$\cot t = -\frac{2\sqrt{21}}{21}$ **14.** $\sin t = \frac{2\sqrt{6}}{5}$; $\cos t = -\frac{1}{5}$; $\tan t = -2\sqrt{6}$; $\csc t = \frac{5\sqrt{6}}{12}$; $\sec t = -5$; $\cot t = -\frac{\sqrt{6}}{12}$ **15.** $\sin t = \frac{\sqrt{2}}{2}$; $\cos t = -\frac{\sqrt{2}}{2}$;

$\tan t = -1$; $\csc t = \sqrt{2}$; $\sec t = -\sqrt{2}$; $\cot t = -1$ **16.** $\sin t = \frac{\sqrt{2}}{2}$; $\cos t = \frac{\sqrt{2}}{2}$; $\tan t = 1$; $\csc t = \sqrt{2}$; $\sec t = \sqrt{2}$; $\cot t = 1$

17. $\sin t = -\frac{1}{3}$; $\cos t = \frac{2\sqrt{2}}{3}$; $\tan t = -\frac{\sqrt{2}}{4}$; $\csc t = -3$; $\sec t = \frac{3\sqrt{2}}{4}$; $\cot t = -2\sqrt{2}$ **18.** $\sin t = -\frac{2}{3}$; $\cos t = -\frac{\sqrt{5}}{3}$; $\tan t = \frac{2\sqrt{5}}{5}$; $\csc t = -\frac{3}{2}$;

$\sec t = -\frac{3\sqrt{5}}{5}$; $\cot t = \frac{\sqrt{5}}{2}$ **19.** -1 **20.** -1 **21.** 0 **22.** 0 **23.** -1 **24.** 1 **25.** 0 **26.** 0 **27.** -1 **28.** 0 **29.** $\frac{1}{2}(\sqrt{2} + 1)$

30. $\frac{1}{2}(1 - \sqrt{2})$ **31.** 2 **32.** -1 **33.** $\frac{1}{2}$ **34.** $\frac{\sqrt{3}}{2}$ **35.** $\sqrt{6}$ **36.** $\frac{2\sqrt{3}}{3}$ **37.** 4 **38.** 8 **39.** 0 **40.** $\sqrt{2} + 3$

41. $2\sqrt{2} + \frac{4\sqrt{3}}{3}$ **42.** $2\sqrt{3} + 1$ **43.** 1 **44.** -2 **45.** $\sin\frac{2\pi}{3} = \frac{\sqrt{3}}{2}$; $\cos\frac{2\pi}{3} = -\frac{1}{2}$; $\tan\frac{2\pi}{3} = -\sqrt{3}$; $\csc\frac{2\pi}{3} = \frac{2\sqrt{3}}{3}$;

$\sec\frac{2\pi}{3} = -2$; $\cot\frac{2\pi}{3} = -\frac{\sqrt{3}}{3}$ **46.** $\sin\frac{5\pi}{6} = \frac{1}{2}$; $\cos\frac{5\pi}{6} = -\frac{\sqrt{3}}{2}$; $\tan\frac{5\pi}{6} = -\frac{\sqrt{3}}{3}$; $\csc\frac{5\pi}{6} = 2$; $\sec\frac{5\pi}{6} = -\frac{2\sqrt{3}}{3}$; $\cot\frac{5\pi}{6} = -\sqrt{3}$

47. $\sin 210° = -\frac{1}{2}$; $\cos 210° = -\frac{\sqrt{3}}{2}$; $\tan 210° = \frac{\sqrt{3}}{3}$; $\csc 210° = -2$; $\sec 210° = -\frac{2\sqrt{3}}{3}$; $\cot 210° = \sqrt{3}$

48. $\sin 240° = -\dfrac{\sqrt{3}}{2}$; $\cos 240° = -\dfrac{1}{2}$; $\tan 240° = \sqrt{3}$; $\csc 240° = -\dfrac{2\sqrt{3}}{3}$; $\sec 240° = -2$; $\cot 240° = \dfrac{\sqrt{3}}{3}$

49. $\sin\dfrac{3\pi}{4} = \dfrac{\sqrt{2}}{2}$; $\cos\dfrac{3\pi}{4} = -\dfrac{\sqrt{2}}{2}$; $\tan\dfrac{3\pi}{4} = -1$; $\csc\dfrac{3\pi}{4} = \sqrt{2}$; $\sec\dfrac{3\pi}{4} = -\sqrt{2}$; $\cot\dfrac{3\pi}{4} = -1$ **50.** $\sin\dfrac{11\pi}{4} = \dfrac{\sqrt{2}}{2}$; $\cos\dfrac{11\pi}{4} = -\dfrac{\sqrt{2}}{2}$;

$\tan\dfrac{11\pi}{4} = -1$; $\csc\dfrac{11\pi}{4} = \sqrt{2}$; $\sec\dfrac{11\pi}{4} = -\sqrt{2}$; $\cot\dfrac{11\pi}{4} = -1$ **51.** $\sin\dfrac{8\pi}{3} = \dfrac{\sqrt{3}}{2}$; $\cos\dfrac{8\pi}{3} = -\dfrac{1}{2}$; $\tan\dfrac{8\pi}{3} = -\sqrt{3}$; $\csc\dfrac{8\pi}{3} = \dfrac{2\sqrt{3}}{3}$; $\sec\dfrac{8\pi}{3} = -2$;

$\cot\dfrac{8\pi}{3} = -\dfrac{\sqrt{3}}{3}$ **52.** $\sin\dfrac{13\pi}{6} = \dfrac{1}{2}$; $\cos\dfrac{13\pi}{6} = \dfrac{\sqrt{3}}{2}$; $\tan\dfrac{13\pi}{6} = \dfrac{\sqrt{3}}{3}$; $\csc\dfrac{13\pi}{6} = 2$; $\sec\dfrac{13\pi}{6} = \dfrac{2\sqrt{3}}{3}$; $\cot\dfrac{13\pi}{6} = \sqrt{3}$

53. $\sin 405° = \dfrac{\sqrt{2}}{2}$; $\cos 405° = \dfrac{\sqrt{2}}{2}$; $\tan 405° = 1$; $\csc 405° = \sqrt{2}$; $\sec 405° = \sqrt{2}$; $\cot 405° = 1$

54. $\sin 390° = \dfrac{1}{2}$; $\cos 390° = \dfrac{\sqrt{3}}{2}$; $\tan 390° = \dfrac{\sqrt{3}}{3}$; $\csc 390° = 2$; $\sec 390° = \dfrac{2\sqrt{3}}{3}$; $\cot 390° = \sqrt{3}$

55. $\sin\left(-\dfrac{\pi}{6}\right) = -\dfrac{1}{2}$; $\cos\left(-\dfrac{\pi}{6}\right) = \dfrac{\sqrt{3}}{2}$; $\tan\left(-\dfrac{\pi}{6}\right) = -\dfrac{\sqrt{3}}{3}$; $\csc\left(-\dfrac{\pi}{6}\right) = -2$; $\sec\left(-\dfrac{\pi}{6}\right) = \dfrac{2\sqrt{3}}{3}$; $\cot\left(-\dfrac{\pi}{6}\right) = -\sqrt{3}$

56. $\sin\left(-\dfrac{\pi}{3}\right) = -\dfrac{\sqrt{3}}{2}$; $\cos\left(-\dfrac{\pi}{3}\right) = \dfrac{1}{2}$; $\tan\left(-\dfrac{\pi}{3}\right) = -\sqrt{3}$; $\csc\left(-\dfrac{\pi}{3}\right) = -\dfrac{2\sqrt{3}}{3}$; $\sec\left(-\dfrac{\pi}{3}\right) = 2$; $\cot\left(-\dfrac{\pi}{3}\right) = -\dfrac{\sqrt{3}}{3}$

57. $\sin(-135°) = -\dfrac{\sqrt{2}}{2}$; $\cos(-135°) = -\dfrac{\sqrt{2}}{2}$; $\tan(-135°) = 1$; $\csc(-135°) = -\sqrt{2}$; $\sec(-135°) = -\sqrt{2}$; $\cot(-135°) = 1$

58. $\sin(-240°) = \dfrac{\sqrt{3}}{2}$; $\cos(-240°) = -\dfrac{1}{2}$; $\tan(-240°) = -\sqrt{3}$; $\csc(-240°) = \dfrac{2\sqrt{3}}{3}$; $\sec(-240°) = -2$; $\cot(-240°) = -\dfrac{\sqrt{3}}{3}$

59. $\sin\dfrac{5\pi}{2} = 1$; $\cos\dfrac{5\pi}{2} = 0$; $\tan\dfrac{5\pi}{2}$ is undefined; $\csc\dfrac{5\pi}{2} = 1$; $\sec\dfrac{5\pi}{2}$ is undefined; $\cot\dfrac{5\pi}{2} = 0$ **60.** $\sin(5\pi) = 0$; $\cos(5\pi) = -1$; $\tan(5\pi) = 0$; $\csc(5\pi)$

is undefined; $\sec(5\pi) = -1$; $\cot(5\pi)$ is undefined **61.** $\sin 720° = 0$; $\cos 720° = 1$; $\tan 720° = 0$; $\csc 720°$ is undefined; $\sec 720° = 1$; $\cot 720°$ is

undefined **62.** $\sin 630° = -1$; $\cos 630° = 0$; $\tan 630°$ is undefined; $\csc 630° = -1$; $\sec 630°$ is undefined; $\cot 630° = 0$ **63.** 0.47 **64.** 0.97 **65.** 1.07

66. 0.36 **67.** 0.32 **68.** 0.38 **69.** 3.73 **70.** 1.07 **71.** 0.84 **72.** 1.56 **73.** 0.02 **74.** 0.02

75. $\sin\theta = \dfrac{4}{5}$; $\cos\theta = -\dfrac{3}{5}$; $\tan\theta = -\dfrac{4}{3}$; $\csc\theta = \dfrac{5}{4}$; $\sec\theta = -\dfrac{5}{3}$; $\cot\theta = -\dfrac{3}{4}$ **76.** $\sin\theta = -\dfrac{12}{13}$; $\cos\theta = \dfrac{5}{13}$; $\tan\theta = -\dfrac{12}{5}$; $\csc\theta = -\dfrac{13}{12}$; $\sec\theta = \dfrac{13}{5}$;

$\cot\theta = -\dfrac{5}{12}$ **77.** $\sin\theta = -\dfrac{3\sqrt{13}}{13}$; $\cos\theta = \dfrac{2\sqrt{13}}{13}$; $\tan\theta = -\dfrac{3}{2}$; $\csc\theta = -\dfrac{\sqrt{13}}{3}$; $\sec\theta = \dfrac{\sqrt{13}}{2}$; $\cot\theta = -\dfrac{2}{3}$ **78.** $\sin\theta = -\dfrac{2\sqrt{5}}{5}$; $\cos\theta = -\dfrac{\sqrt{5}}{5}$;

$\tan\theta = 2$; $\csc\theta = -\dfrac{\sqrt{5}}{2}$; $\sec\theta = -\sqrt{5}$; $\cot\theta = \dfrac{1}{2}$ **79.** $\sin\theta = -\dfrac{\sqrt{2}}{2}$; $\cos\theta = -\dfrac{\sqrt{2}}{2}$; $\tan\theta = 1$; $\csc\theta = -\sqrt{2}$; $\sec\theta = -\sqrt{2}$; $\cot\theta = 1$

80. $\sin\theta = \dfrac{\sqrt{2}}{2}$; $\cos\theta = -\dfrac{\sqrt{2}}{2}$; $\tan\theta = -1$; $\csc\theta = \sqrt{2}$; $\sec\theta = -\sqrt{2}$; $\cot\theta = -1$ **81.** $\sin\theta = \dfrac{3}{5}$; $\cos\theta = \dfrac{4}{5}$; $\tan\theta = \dfrac{3}{4}$; $\csc\theta = \dfrac{5}{3}$;

$\sec\theta = \dfrac{5}{4}$; $\cot\theta = \dfrac{4}{3}$ **82.** $\sin\theta = \dfrac{4}{5}$; $\cos\theta = \dfrac{3}{5}$; $\tan\theta = \dfrac{4}{3}$; $\csc\theta = \dfrac{5}{4}$; $\sec\theta = \dfrac{5}{3}$; $\cot\theta = \dfrac{3}{4}$ **83.** 0 **84.** $\dfrac{2\sqrt{3}}{3}$ **85.** 0 **86.** 0 **87.** −0.1

88. −0.3 **89.** 3 **90.** −2 **91.** 5 **92.** $\dfrac{3}{2}$ **93.** $\dfrac{\sqrt{3}}{2}$ **94.** $\dfrac{1}{2}$ **95.** $\dfrac{1}{2}$ **96.** $\dfrac{\sqrt{3}}{2}$ **97.** $\dfrac{3}{4}$ **98.** $\dfrac{1}{4}$ **99.** $\dfrac{\sqrt{3}}{2}$ **100.** $-\dfrac{1}{2}$ **101.** $\sqrt{3}$ **102.** 1

103. $-\dfrac{\sqrt{3}}{2}$ **104.** $\dfrac{1}{2}$ **105.** $\dfrac{1+\sqrt{3}}{2}$ **106.** $\dfrac{\sqrt{3}-1}{2}$ **107.** $-\dfrac{1}{2}$ **108.** $\dfrac{\sqrt{3}}{4}$ **109.** $\dfrac{\sqrt{3}}{2}$ **110.** $\dfrac{\sqrt{3}}{2}$ **111.** $\dfrac{\sqrt{2}}{4}$ **112.** 1

113. (a) $\dfrac{\sqrt{2}}{2}$; $\left(\dfrac{\pi}{4}, \dfrac{\sqrt{2}}{2}\right)$ (b) $\left(\dfrac{\sqrt{2}}{2}, \dfrac{\pi}{4}\right)$ (c) $\left(0, \dfrac{\sqrt{2}}{2} - 3\right)$ **114.** (a) $\dfrac{\sqrt{3}}{2}$; $\left(\dfrac{\pi}{6}, \dfrac{\sqrt{3}}{2}\right)$ (b) $\left(\dfrac{\sqrt{3}}{2}, \dfrac{\pi}{6}\right)$ (c) $\left(\dfrac{\pi}{3}, \sqrt{3}\right)$

115.

θ	0.5	0.4	0.2	0.1	0.01	0.001	0.0001	0.00001
$\sin\theta$	0.4794	0.3894	0.1987	0.0998	0.0100	0.0010	0.0001	0.00001
$\dfrac{\sin\theta}{\theta}$	0.9589	0.9735	0.9933	0.9983	1.0000	1.0000	1.0000	1.0000

$\dfrac{\sin\theta}{\theta}$ approaches 1 as θ approaches 0.

116.

θ	0.5	0.4	0.2	0.1	0.01	0.001	0.0001	0.00001
$\cos\theta - 1$	−0.1224	−0.0789	−0.0199	−0.0050	−0.00005	0.0000	0.0000	0.0000
$\dfrac{\cos\theta - 1}{\theta}$	−0.2448	−0.1973	−0.0997	−0.0500	−0.0050	−0.0005	−0.00005	−0.000005

$\dfrac{\cos\theta - 1}{\theta}$ approaches 0 as θ approaches 0.

117. $R \approx 310.56$ ft; $H \approx 77.64$ ft   **118.** $R \approx 1988.32$ m; $H \approx 286.99$ m   **119.** $R \approx 19{,}541.95$ m; $H \approx 2278.14$ m   **120.** $R \approx 1223.36$ ft; $H \approx 364.49$ ft
121. (a) 1.20 sec   **(b)** 1.12 sec   **(c)** 1.20 sec   **122.** 4.90 cm; 4.71 cm   **123. (a)** 1.9 hr; 0.57 hr   **(b)** 1.69 hr; 0.75 hr   **(c)** 1.63 hr; 0.86 hr   **(d)** 1.67 hr;
tan 90° is undefined   **124.** 251.42 cm³; 117.88 cm³; 75.4 cm³

125. (a) 16.56 ft   **(b)**

(c) 67.5°   **126.** Since L and M are parallel, $m_L = m_M = \dfrac{\sin\theta - 0}{\cos\theta - 0} = \tan\theta$.

127. (a) values estimated to the nearest tenth: sin 1 ≈ 0.8; cos 1 ≈ 0.5; tan 1 ≈ 1.6; csc 1 ≈ 1.3; sec 1 ≈ 2.0; cot 1 ≈ 0.6; actual values to the nearest tenth: sin 1 ≈ 0.8; cos 1 ≈ 0.5; tan 1 ≈ 1.6; csc 1 ≈ 1.2; sec 1 ≈ 1.9; cot 1 ≈ 0.6   **(b)** values estimated to the nearest tenth: sin 5.1 ≈ −0.9; cos 5.1 ≈ 0.4; tan 5.1 ≈ −2.3; csc 5.1 ≈ −1.1; sec 5.1 ≈ 2.5; cot 5.1 ≈ −0.4; actual values to the nearest tenth: sin 5.1 ≈ −0.9; cos 5.1 ≈ 0.4; tan 5.1 ≈ −2.4; csc 5.1 ≈ −1.1; sec 5.1 ≈ 2.6; cot 5.1 ≈ −0.4
128. (a) values estimated to the nearest tenth: sin 2 ≈ 0.9; cos 2 ≈ −0.4; tan 2 ≈ −2.3; csc 2 ≈ 1.1; sec 2 ≈ −2.5; cot 2 ≈ −0.4; actual values to the nearest tenth: sin 2 ≈ 0.9; cos 2 ≈ −0.4; tan 2 ≈ −2.2; csc 2 ≈ 1.1; sec 2 ≈ −2.4; cot 2 ≈ −0.5   **(b)** values estimated to the nearest tenth:
sin 4 ≈ −0.8; cos 4 ≈ −0.7; tan 4 ≈ 1.1; csc 4 ≈ −1.3; sec 4 ≈ −1.4; cot 4 ≈ 0.9; actual values to the nearest tenth: sin 4 ≈ −0.8; cos 4 ≈ −0.7;
tan 4 ≈ 1.2; csc 4 ≈ −1.3; sec 4 ≈ −1.5; cot 4 ≈ 0.9

6.3 Assess Your Understanding *(page 392)*

5. 2π; π **6.** all real numbers except odd multiples of $\dfrac{\pi}{2}$ **7.** $[-1, 1]$ **8.** T   **9.** F   **10.** F   **11.** $\dfrac{\sqrt{2}}{2}$ **12.** $\dfrac{1}{2}$ **13.** 1   **14.** $\dfrac{1}{2}$ **15.** 1   **16.** −1   **17.** $\sqrt{3}$
18. 2   **19.** $\dfrac{\sqrt{2}}{2}$ **20.** $\dfrac{\sqrt{2}}{2}$ **21.** 0   **22.** 1   **23.** $\sqrt{2}$ **24.** 1   **25.** $\dfrac{\sqrt{3}}{3}$ **26.** $\dfrac{2\sqrt{3}}{3}$ **27.** II   **28.** IV   **29.** IV   **30.** I   **31.** IV   **32.** III   **33.** II   **34.** II
35. $\tan\theta = -\dfrac{3}{4}$; $\cot\theta = -\dfrac{4}{3}$; $\sec\theta = \dfrac{5}{4}$; $\csc\theta = -\dfrac{5}{3}$ **36.** $\tan\theta = -\dfrac{4}{3}$; $\cot\theta = -\dfrac{3}{4}$; $\sec\theta = -\dfrac{5}{3}$; $\csc\theta = \dfrac{5}{4}$ **37.** $\tan\theta = 2$; $\cot\theta = \dfrac{1}{2}$; $\sec\theta = \sqrt{5}$;
$\csc\theta = \dfrac{\sqrt{5}}{2}$ **38.** $\tan\theta = \dfrac{1}{2}$; $\cot\theta = 2$; $\sec\theta = -\dfrac{\sqrt{5}}{2}$; $\csc\theta = -\sqrt{5}$ **39.** $\tan\theta = \dfrac{\sqrt{3}}{3}$; $\cot\theta = \sqrt{3}$; $\sec\theta = \dfrac{2\sqrt{3}}{3}$; $\csc\theta = 2$
40. $\tan\theta = \sqrt{3}$; $\cot\theta = \dfrac{\sqrt{3}}{3}$; $\sec\theta = 2$; $\csc\theta = \dfrac{2\sqrt{3}}{3}$ **41.** $\tan\theta = -\dfrac{\sqrt{2}}{4}$; $\cot\theta = -2\sqrt{2}$; $\sec\theta = \dfrac{3\sqrt{2}}{4}$; $\csc\theta = -3$ **42.** $\tan\theta = -2\sqrt{2}$;
$\cot\theta = -\dfrac{\sqrt{2}}{4}$; $\sec\theta = -3$; $\csc\theta = \dfrac{3\sqrt{2}}{4}$ **43.** $\cos\theta = -\dfrac{5}{13}$; $\tan\theta = -\dfrac{12}{5}$; $\csc\theta = \dfrac{13}{12}$; $\sec\theta = -\dfrac{13}{5}$; $\cot\theta = -\dfrac{5}{12}$ **44.** $\sin\theta = -\dfrac{4}{5}$; $\tan\theta = -\dfrac{4}{3}$;
$\csc\theta = -\dfrac{5}{4}$; $\sec\theta = \dfrac{5}{3}$; $\cot\theta = -\dfrac{3}{4}$ **45.** $\sin\theta = -\dfrac{3}{5}$; $\tan\theta = \dfrac{3}{4}$; $\csc\theta = -\dfrac{5}{3}$; $\sec\theta = -\dfrac{5}{4}$; $\cot\theta = \dfrac{4}{3}$ **46.** $\cos\theta = -\dfrac{12}{13}$; $\tan\theta = \dfrac{5}{12}$;
$\csc\theta = -\dfrac{13}{5}$; $\sec\theta = -\dfrac{13}{12}$; $\cot\theta = \dfrac{12}{5}$ **47.** $\cos\theta = -\dfrac{12}{13}$; $\tan\theta = -\dfrac{5}{12}$; $\csc\theta = \dfrac{13}{5}$; $\sec\theta = -\dfrac{13}{12}$; $\cot\theta = -\dfrac{12}{5}$ **48.** $\sin\theta = -\dfrac{3}{5}$;
$\tan\theta = -\dfrac{3}{4}$; $\csc\theta = -\dfrac{5}{3}$; $\sec\theta = \dfrac{5}{4}$; $\cot\theta = -\dfrac{4}{3}$ **49.** $\sin\theta = \dfrac{2\sqrt{2}}{3}$; $\tan\theta = -2\sqrt{2}$; $\csc\theta = \dfrac{3\sqrt{2}}{4}$; $\sec\theta = -3$; $\cot\theta = -\dfrac{\sqrt{2}}{4}$
50. $\cos\theta = -\dfrac{\sqrt{5}}{3}$; $\tan\theta = \dfrac{2\sqrt{5}}{5}$; $\csc\theta = -\dfrac{3}{2}$; $\sec\theta = -\dfrac{3\sqrt{5}}{5}$; $\cot\theta = \dfrac{\sqrt{5}}{2}$ **51.** $\cos\theta = -\dfrac{\sqrt{5}}{3}$; $\tan\theta = -\dfrac{2\sqrt{5}}{5}$; $\csc\theta = \dfrac{3}{2}$; $\sec\theta = -\dfrac{3\sqrt{5}}{5}$;
$\cot\theta = -\dfrac{\sqrt{5}}{2}$ **52.** $\sin\theta = -\dfrac{\sqrt{15}}{4}$; $\tan\theta = \sqrt{15}$; $\csc\theta = -\dfrac{4\sqrt{15}}{15}$; $\sec\theta = -4$; $\cot\theta = \dfrac{\sqrt{15}}{15}$ **53.** $\sin\theta = -\dfrac{\sqrt{3}}{2}$; $\cos\theta = \dfrac{1}{2}$; $\tan\theta = -\sqrt{3}$;
$\csc\theta = -\dfrac{2\sqrt{3}}{3}$; $\cot\theta = -\dfrac{\sqrt{3}}{3}$ **54.** $\sin\theta = \dfrac{1}{3}$; $\cos\theta = -\dfrac{2\sqrt{2}}{3}$; $\tan\theta = -\dfrac{\sqrt{2}}{4}$; $\sec\theta = -\dfrac{3\sqrt{2}}{4}$; $\cot\theta = -2\sqrt{2}$ **55.** $\sin\theta = -\dfrac{3}{5}$; $\cos\theta = -\dfrac{4}{5}$;
$\csc\theta = -\dfrac{5}{3}$; $\sec\theta = -\dfrac{5}{4}$; $\cot\theta = \dfrac{4}{3}$ **56.** $\sin\theta = -\dfrac{3}{5}$; $\cos\theta = -\dfrac{4}{5}$; $\tan\theta = \dfrac{3}{4}$; $\csc\theta = -\dfrac{5}{3}$; $\sec\theta = -\dfrac{5}{4}$ **57.** $\sin\theta = \dfrac{\sqrt{10}}{10}$; $\cos\theta = -\dfrac{3\sqrt{10}}{10}$;
$\csc\theta = \sqrt{10}$; $\sec\theta = -\dfrac{\sqrt{10}}{3}$; $\cot\theta = -3$ **58.** $\sin\theta = -\dfrac{\sqrt{3}}{2}$; $\cos\theta = -\dfrac{1}{2}$; $\tan\theta = \sqrt{3}$; $\csc\theta = -\dfrac{2\sqrt{3}}{3}$; $\cot\theta = \dfrac{\sqrt{3}}{3}$ **59.** $-\dfrac{\sqrt{3}}{2}$ **60.** $\dfrac{\sqrt{3}}{2}$
61. $-\dfrac{\sqrt{3}}{3}$ **62.** $-\dfrac{\sqrt{2}}{2}$ **63.** 2   **64.** −2   **65.** −1   **66.** 0   **67.** −1   **68.** 0   **69.** $\dfrac{\sqrt{2}}{2}$ **70.** $-\dfrac{\sqrt{3}}{2}$ **71.** 0   **72.** 1   **73.** $-\sqrt{2}$ **74.** −1   **75.** $\dfrac{2\sqrt{3}}{3}$
76. $-\dfrac{2\sqrt{3}}{3}$ **77.** 1   **78.** 1   **79.** 1   **80.** 1   **81.** 0   **82.** 0   **83.** 1   **84.** 1   **85.** −1   **86.** 1   **87.** 0   **88.** 0   **89.** 0.9   **90.** 0.6   **91.** 9   **92.** −6   **93.** 0
94. −1   **95.** All real numbers   **96.** All real numbers   **97.** Odd multiples of $\dfrac{\pi}{2}$ **98.** Multiples of π **99.** Odd multiples of $\dfrac{\pi}{2}$ **100.** Multiples of π
101. $-1 \le y \le 1$ **102.** $-1 \le y \le 1$ **103.** All real numbers   **104.** All real numbers   **105.** $|y| \ge 1$ **106.** $|y| \ge 1$ **107.** Odd; yes; origin
108. Even; yes; y-axis   **109.** Odd; yes; origin   **110.** Odd; yes; origin   **111.** Even; yes; y-axis   **112.** Odd; yes; origin   **113. (a)** $-\dfrac{1}{3}$ **(b)** 1
114. (a) $\dfrac{1}{4}$ **(b)** $\dfrac{3}{4}$ **115. (a)** −2   **(b)** 6   **116. (a)** 3   **(b)** −9   **117. (a)** −4   **(b)** −12   **118. (a)** −2   **(b)** 6   **119.** About 15.81 min

120. (a) About 2.75 hr   **121.** Let a be a real number and $P = (x, y)$ be the point on the unit circle that corresponds to t. Consider the equation
$\tan t = \dfrac{y}{x} = a$. Then $y = ax$. But $x^2 + y^2 = 1$, so $x^2 + a^2x^2 = 1$. So, $x = \pm\dfrac{1}{\sqrt{1 + a^2}}$ and $y = \pm\dfrac{a}{\sqrt{1 + a^2}}$; that is, for any real number a, there is
a point $P = (x, y)$ on the unit circle for which $\tan t = a$. In other ords, the range of the tangent function is the set of all real numbers.

122. Let a be a real number and $P = (x, y)$ be the point on the unit circle that corresponds to t. Consider the equation $\cot t = \dfrac{x}{y} = a$. Then $x = ay$. But $x^2 + y^2 = 1$, so $a^2 y^2 + y^2 = 1$. So, $y = \pm\dfrac{1}{\sqrt{1 + a^2}}$ and $x = \pm\dfrac{a}{\sqrt{1 + a^2}}$; that is, for any real number a, there is a point $P = (x, y)$ on the unit circle for which $\cot t = a$. In other words, the range of the cotangent function is the set of all real numbers. **123.** Suppose that there is a number $p, 0 < p < 2\pi$, for which $\sin(\theta + p) = \sin\theta$ for all θ. If $\theta = 0$, then $\sin(0 + p) = \sin p = \sin 0 = 0$, so $p = \pi$. If $\theta = \dfrac{\pi}{2}$, then $\sin\left(\dfrac{\pi}{2} + p\right) = \sin\left(\dfrac{\pi}{2}\right)$. But $p = \pi$. Thus, $\sin\left(\dfrac{3\pi}{2}\right) = -1 = \sin\left(\dfrac{\pi}{2}\right) = 1$. This is impossible. Therefore, the smallest positive number p for which $\sin(\theta + p) = \sin\theta$ for all θ is 2π. **124.** Suppose that there is a number $p, 0 < p < 2\pi$, for which $\cos(\theta + p) = \cos\theta$ for all θ. If $\theta = 0$, then $\cos(0 + p) = \cos p = \cos 0 = 1$. But on the interval $(0, 2\pi)$, $\cos p$ never equals 1. Therefore, the smallest positive number p for which $\cos(\theta + p) = \cos\theta$ for all θ is 2π. **125.** $\sec\theta = \dfrac{1}{\cos\theta}$; since $\cos\theta$ has period 2π, so does $\sec\theta$. **126.** $\csc\theta = \dfrac{1}{\sin\theta}$; since $\sin\theta$ has period 2π, so does $\csc\theta$. **127.** If $P = (a, b)$ is the point on the unit circle corresponding to θ, then $Q = (-a, -b)$ is the point on the unit circle corresponding to $\theta + \pi$. Thus, $\tan(\theta + \pi) = \dfrac{-b}{-a} = \dfrac{b}{a} = \tan\theta$. Suppose that there exists a number $p, 0 < p < \pi$, for which $\tan(\theta + p) = \tan\theta$ for all θ. Then, if $\theta = 0$, then $\tan p = \tan 0 = 0$. But this means that p is a multiple of π. Since no multiple of π exists in the interval $(0, \pi)$, this is a contradiction. Therefore, the period of $f(\theta) = \tan\theta$ is π. **128.** $\cot\theta = \dfrac{1}{\tan\theta}$; since $\tan\theta$ has period π, so does $\cot\theta$. **129.** Let $P = (a, b)$ be the point on the unit circle corresponding to θ. Then $\csc\theta = \dfrac{1}{b} = \dfrac{1}{\sin\theta}$; $\sec\theta = \dfrac{1}{a} = \dfrac{1}{\cos\theta}$; $\cot\theta = \dfrac{a}{b} = \dfrac{1}{b/a} = \dfrac{1}{\tan\theta}$.
130. If $P = (a, b)$ is the point on the unit circle corresponding to θ, then $\tan\theta = \dfrac{b}{a} = \dfrac{\sin\theta}{\cos\theta}$, and $\cot\theta = \dfrac{a}{b} = \dfrac{\cos\theta}{\sin\theta}$.
131. $(\sin\theta\cos\phi)^2 + (\sin\theta\sin\phi)^2 + \cos^2\theta = \sin^2\theta\cos^2\phi + \sin^2\theta\sin^2\phi + \cos^2\theta$
$$= \sin^2\theta(\cos^2\phi + \sin^2\phi) + \cos^2\theta = \sin^2\theta + \cos^2\theta = 1$$

6.4 Assess Your Understanding (page 406)

3. $1; \dfrac{\pi}{2} + 2\pi k, k$ any integer **4.** $3; \pi$ **5.** $3; \dfrac{\pi}{3}$ **6.** T **7.** F **8.** T **9.** 0 **10.** 1 **11.** $-\dfrac{\pi}{2} < x < \dfrac{\pi}{2}$ **12.** $0 < x < \pi$ **13.** 1 **14.** -1

15. $0, \pi, 2\pi$ **16.** $\dfrac{\pi}{2}, \dfrac{3\pi}{2}$ **17.** $\sin x = 1$ for $x = -\dfrac{3\pi}{2}, \dfrac{\pi}{2}$; $\sin x = -1$ for $x = -\dfrac{\pi}{2}, \dfrac{3\pi}{2}$ **18.** $\cos x = 1$ for $-2\pi, 0, 2\pi$; $\cos x = -1$ for $x = -\pi, \pi$

19. Amplitude $= 2$; period $= 2\pi$ **20.** Amplitude $= 3$; period $= 2\pi$ **21.** Amplitude $= 4$; period $= \pi$ **22.** Amplitude $= 1$; period $= 4\pi$

23. Amplitude $= 6$; period $= 2$ **24.** Amplitude $= 3$; period $= \dfrac{2\pi}{3}$ **25.** Amplitude $= \dfrac{1}{2}$; period $= \dfrac{4\pi}{3}$ **26.** Amplitude $= \dfrac{4}{3}$; period $= 3\pi$

27. Amplitude $= \dfrac{5}{3}$; period $= 3$ **28.** Amplitude $= \dfrac{9}{5}$; period $= \dfrac{4}{3}$ **29.** F **30.** E **31.** A **32.** I **33.** H **34.** B **35.** C **36.** G **37.** J

38. D **39.** A **40.** C **41.** B **42.** D

43.

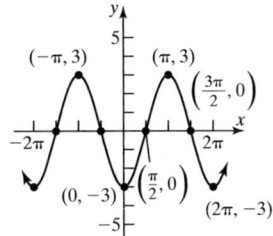

Domain: $(-\infty, \infty)$

Range: $[-4, 4]$

44.

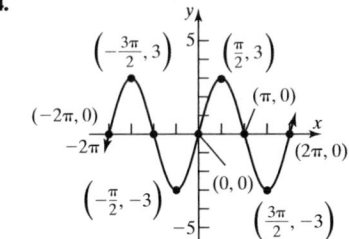

Domain: $(-\infty, \infty)$

Range: $[-3, 3]$

45.

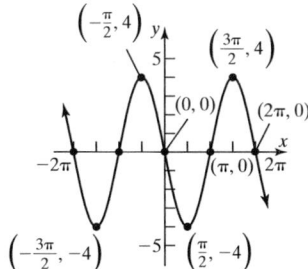

Domain: $(-\infty, \infty)$

Range: $[-4, 4]$

46.

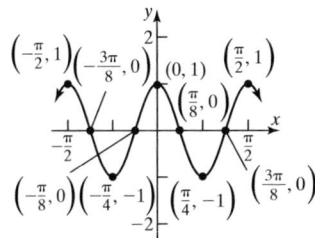

Domain: $(-\infty, \infty)$

Range: $[-3, 3]$

47.

Domain: $(-\infty, \infty)$

Range: $[-1, 1]$

48.

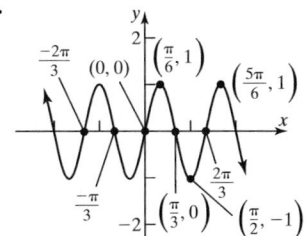

Domain: $(-\infty, \infty)$

Range: $[-1, 1]$

49.

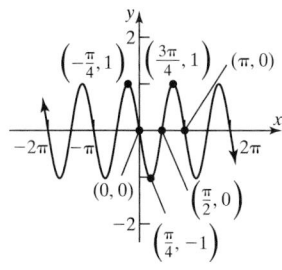

Domain: $(-\infty, \infty)$

Range: $[-1, 1]$

50.

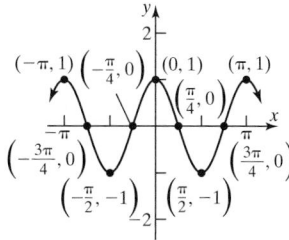

Domain: $(-\infty, \infty)$

Range: $[-1, 1]$

51.

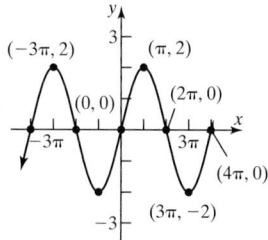

Domain: $(-\infty, \infty)$

Range: $[-2, 2]$

52.

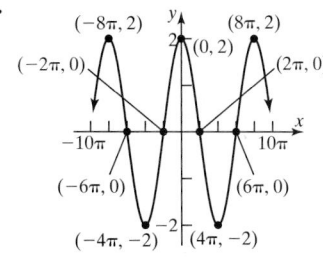

Domain: $(-\infty, \infty)$

Range: $[-2, 2]$

53.

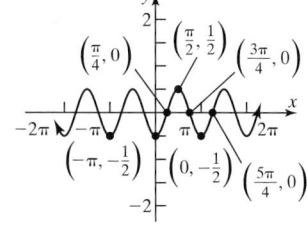

Domain: $(-\infty, \infty)$

Range: $\left[-\dfrac{1}{2}, \dfrac{1}{2}\right]$

54.

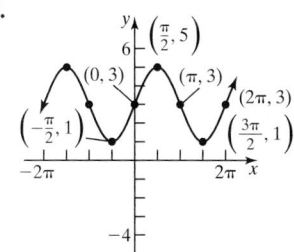

Domain: $(-\infty, \infty)$

Range: $[-4, 4]$

55.

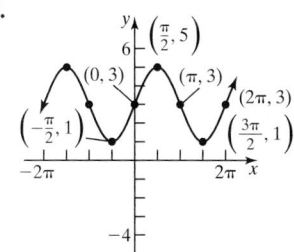

Domain: $(-\infty, \infty)$

Range: $[1, 5]$

56.

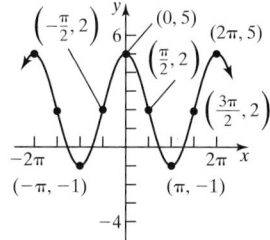

Domain: $(-\infty, \infty)$

Range: $[-1, 5]$

57.

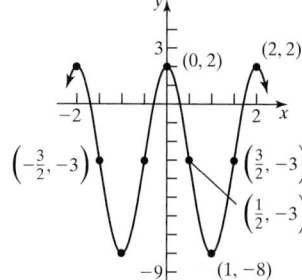

Domain: $(-\infty, \infty)$

Range: $[-8, 2]$

58.

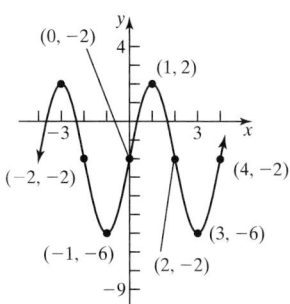

Domain: $(-\infty, \infty)$

Range: $[-6, 2]$

59.

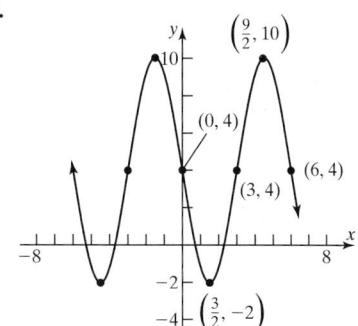

Domain: $(-\infty, \infty)$

Range: $[-2, 10]$

60.

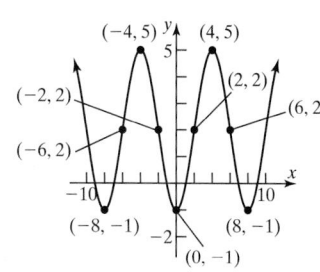

Domain: $(-\infty, \infty)$

Range: $[-1, 5]$

61.

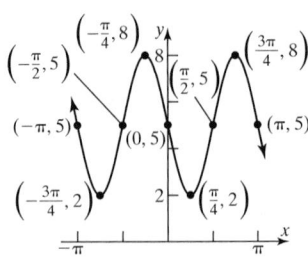

Domain: $(-\infty, \infty)$

Range: $[2, 8]$

62.

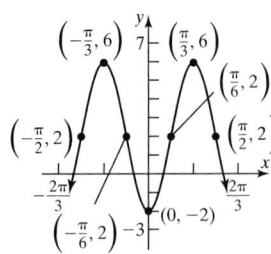

Domain: $(-\infty, \infty)$

Range: $[-2, 6]$

63.

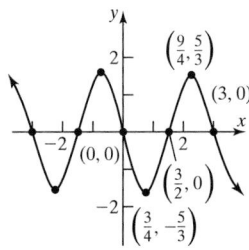

Domain: $(-\infty, \infty)$

Range: $\left[-\dfrac{5}{3}, \dfrac{5}{3}\right]$

64.

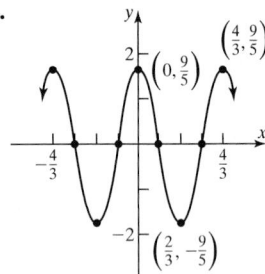

Domain: $(-\infty, \infty)$

Range: $\left[-\dfrac{9}{5}, \dfrac{9}{5}\right]$

65.

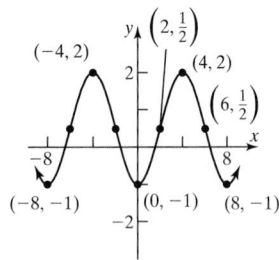

Domain: $(-\infty, \infty)$

Range: $[-1, 2]$

66.

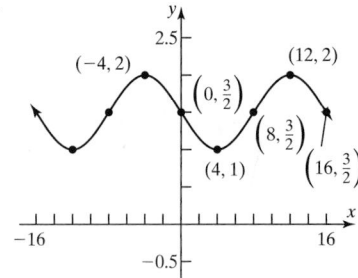

Domain: $(-\infty, \infty)$

Range: $[1, 2]$

67. $y = \pm 3 \sin(2x)$ **68.** $y = \pm 2 \sin\left(\dfrac{1}{2}x\right)$ **69.** $y = \pm 3 \sin(\pi x)$ **70.** $y = \pm 4 \sin(2\pi x)$ **71.** $y = 5 \cos\left(\dfrac{\pi}{4}x\right)$ **72.** $y = 4 \sin\left(\dfrac{1}{4}x\right)$

73. $y = -3 \cos\left(\dfrac{1}{2}x\right)$ **74.** $y = -2 \sin\left(\dfrac{\pi}{2}x\right)$ **75.** $y = \dfrac{3}{4}\sin(2\pi x)$ **76.** $y = -\dfrac{5}{2}\cos(\pi x)$ **77.** $y = -\sin\left(\dfrac{3}{2}x\right)$ **78.** $y = -\pi \cos x$

79. $y = -\cos\left(\dfrac{4\pi}{3}x\right) + 1$ **80.** $y = -\dfrac{1}{2}\sin\left(\dfrac{3}{2}x\right) - 1$ **81.** $y = 3 \sin\left(\dfrac{\pi}{2}x\right)$ **82.** $y = -2 \cos(\pi x)$ **83.** $y = -4 \cos(3x)$ **84.** $y = 4 \sin(2x)$

85. $\dfrac{2}{\pi}$ **86.** $-\dfrac{2}{\pi}$ **87.** $\dfrac{\sqrt{2}}{\pi}$ **88.** $-\dfrac{4}{\pi}$

89. $(f \circ g)(x) = \sin(4x)$

$(g \circ f)(x) = 4 \sin x$

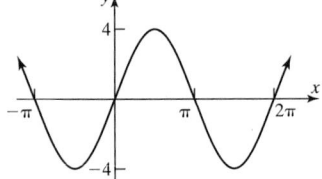

90. $(f \circ g)(x) = \cos\left(\dfrac{1}{2}x\right)$

$(g \circ f)(x) = \dfrac{1}{2}\cos x$

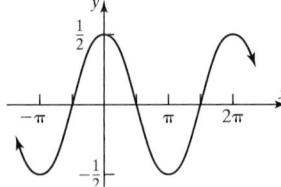

91. $(f \circ g)(x) = -2 \cos x$

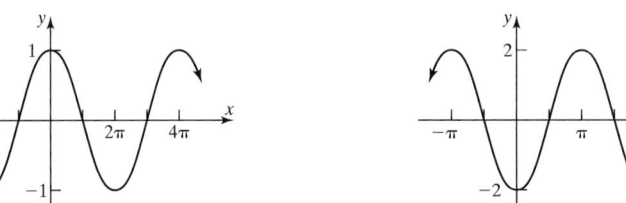

$(g \circ f)(x) = \cos(-2x)$

92. $(f \circ g)(x) = -3 \sin x$

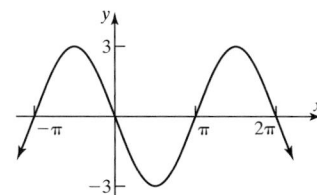

$(g \circ f)(x) = \sin(-3x)$

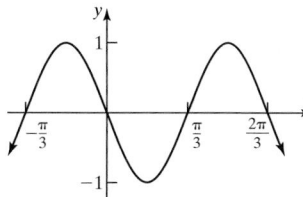

93. Period $= \dfrac{1}{30}$ s; amplitude $= 220$ amp

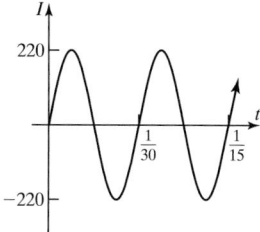

94. Period $= \dfrac{1}{15}$ s; amplitude $= 120$ amp

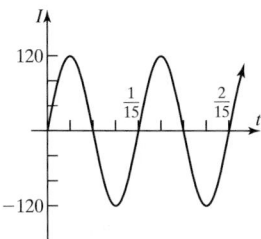

95. (a) Amplitude $= 220$ V; period $= \dfrac{1}{60}$ s

(b), (e)

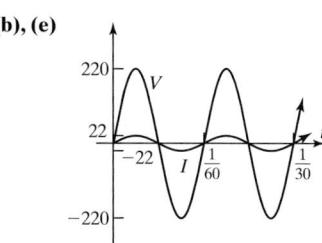

(c) $I(t) = 22 \sin(120\pi t)$

(d) Amplitude $= 22$ amp; period $= \dfrac{1}{60}$ s

96. (a) Amplitude $= 120$ V; period $= \dfrac{1}{60}$ s

(b), (e)

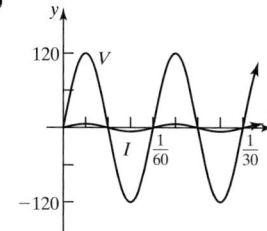

(c) $I(t) = 6 \sin(120\pi t)$

(d) Amplitude $= 6$ amp; period $= \dfrac{1}{60}$ s

97. (a) $P(t) = \dfrac{[V_0 \sin(2\pi ft)]^2}{R} = \dfrac{V_0^2}{R} \sin^2(2\pi ft)$ **(b)** Since the graph of P has amplitude $\dfrac{V_0^2}{2R}$ and period $\dfrac{1}{2f}$ and is of the form

$y = A \cos(\omega t) + B$, then $A = -\dfrac{V_0^2}{2R}$ and $B = \dfrac{V_0^2}{2R}$. Since $\dfrac{1}{2f} = \dfrac{2\pi}{\omega}$, then $\omega = 4\pi f$. Therefore, $P(t) = -\dfrac{V_0^2}{2R}\cos(4\pi ft) + \dfrac{V_0^2}{2R} = \dfrac{V_0^2}{2R}[1 - \cos(4\pi ft)]$.

98. (a) $y = 15 \sin\left(\dfrac{\pi}{28} x\right)$ **(b)** At the edge of the road the tunnel is 10.6 ft high.

99. (a) Physical potential: $\omega = \dfrac{2\pi}{23}$; emotional potential: $\omega = \dfrac{\pi}{14}$; intellectual potential: $\omega = \dfrac{2\pi}{33}$

(b)

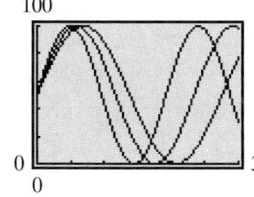

(c) No

(d) Physical potential peaks at 15 days after 20th birthday. Emotional potential is 50% at 17 days, with a maximum at 10 days and a minimum at 24 days. Intellectual potential starts fairly high, drops to a minimum at 13 days, and rises to a maximum at 29 days.

100.

101.

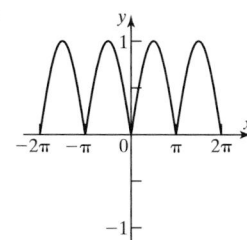

6.5 Assess Your Understanding *(page 417)*

3. origin; odd multiples of $\dfrac{\pi}{2}$ **4.** y-axis; odd multiples of $\dfrac{\pi}{2}$ **5.** $y = \cos x$ **6.** T **7.** 0 **8.** No y-intercept **9.** 1 **10.** No y-intercept

11. $\sec x = 1$ for $x = -2\pi, 0, 2\pi$; $\sec x = -1$ for $x = -\pi, \pi$ **12.** $\csc x = 1$ for $x = -\dfrac{3\pi}{2}, \dfrac{\pi}{2}$; $\csc x = -1$ for $x = -\dfrac{\pi}{2}, \dfrac{3\pi}{2}$ **13.** $-\dfrac{3\pi}{2}, -\dfrac{\pi}{2}, \dfrac{\pi}{2}, \dfrac{3\pi}{2}$

14. $-2\pi, -\pi, 0, \pi, 2\pi$ **15.** $-\dfrac{3\pi}{2}, -\dfrac{\pi}{2}, \dfrac{\pi}{2}, \dfrac{3\pi}{2}$ **16.** $-2\pi, -\pi, 0, \pi, 2\pi$

17.

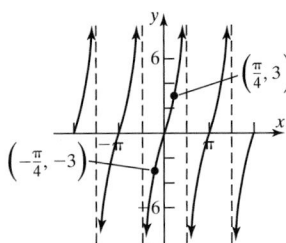

Domain: $\left\{x \mid x \neq \dfrac{k\pi}{2}, k \text{ is an odd integer}\right\}$
Range: $(-\infty, \infty)$

18.

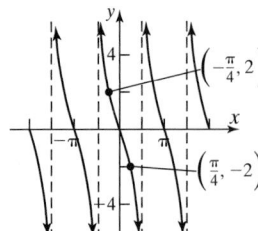

Domain: $\left\{x \mid x \neq \dfrac{k\pi}{2}, k \text{ is an odd integer}\right\}$
Range: $(-\infty, \infty)$

19.

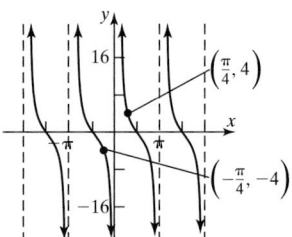

Domain: $\{x \mid x \neq k\pi, k \text{ is an integer}\}$
Range: $(-\infty, \infty)$

20.

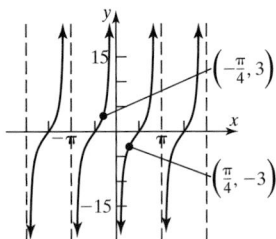

Domain: $\{x \mid x \neq k\pi, k \text{ is an integer}\}$
Range: $(-\infty, \infty)$

21.

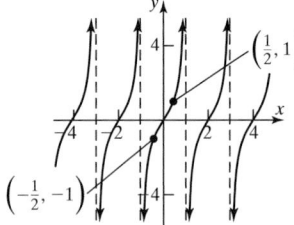

Domain: $\{x \mid x \text{ does not equal an odd integer}\}$
Range: $(-\infty, \infty)$

22.

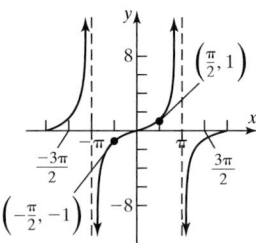

Domain: $\{x \mid x \neq k\pi, k \text{ is an integer}\}$
Range: $(-\infty, \infty)$

23.

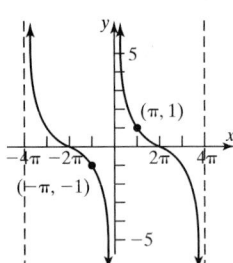

Domain: $\{x \mid x \neq 4k\pi, k \text{ is an integer}\}$
Range: $(-\infty, \infty)$

24.

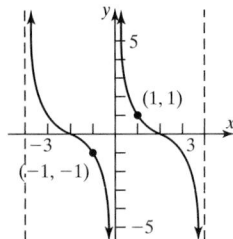

Domain: $\{x \mid x \neq 4k, k \text{ is an integer}\}$
Range: $(-\infty, \infty)$

25.

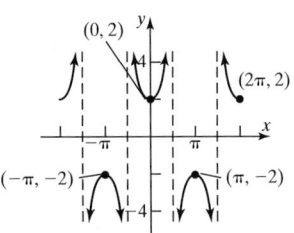

Domain: $\left\{x \mid x \neq \dfrac{k\pi}{2}, k \text{ is an odd integer}\right\}$

Range: $\{y \mid y \leq -2 \text{ or } y \geq 2\}$

26.

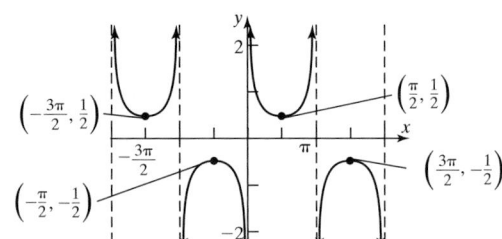

Domain: $\{x \mid x \neq k\pi, k \text{ is an integer}\}$

Range: $\left\{y \mid y \leq -\dfrac{1}{2} \text{ or } y \geq \dfrac{1}{2}\right\}$

27.

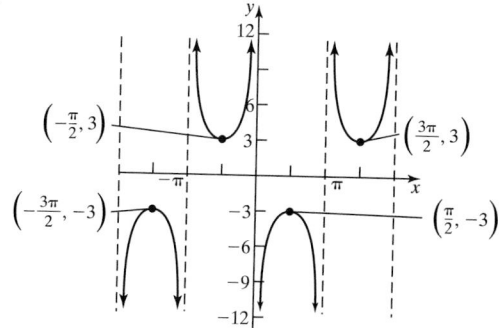

Domain: $\{x | x \neq k\pi, k \text{ is an integer}\}$

Range: $\{y | y \leq -3 \text{ or } y \geq 3\}$

28.

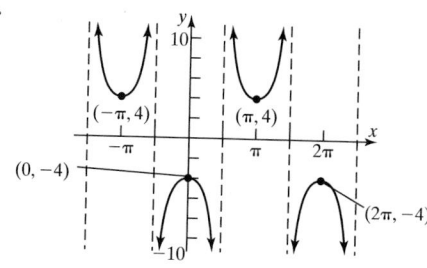

Domain: $\left\{x \middle| x \neq \dfrac{k\pi}{2}, k \text{ is an odd integer}\right\}$

Range: $\{y | y \leq -4 \text{ or } y \geq 4\}$

29.

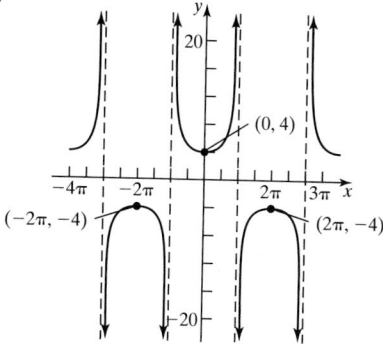

Domain: $\{x | x \neq k\pi, k \text{ is an odd integer}\}$

Range: $\{y | y \leq -4 \text{ or } y \geq 4\}$

30.

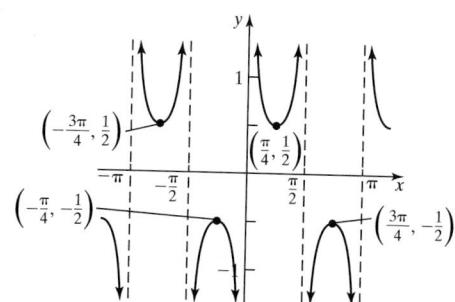

Domain: $\left\{x \middle| x \neq \dfrac{k\pi}{2}, k \text{ is an integer}\right\}$

Range: $\left\{y \middle| y \leq -\dfrac{1}{2} \text{ or } y \geq \dfrac{1}{2}\right\}$

31.

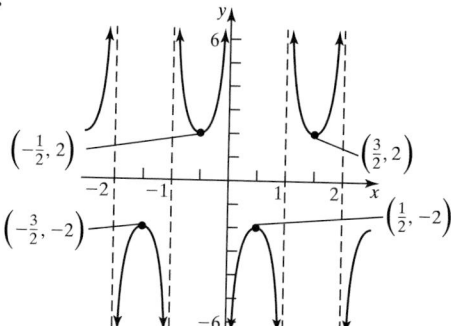

Domain: $\{x | x \text{ does not equal an integer}\}$

Range: $\{y | y \leq -2 \text{ or } y \geq 2\}$

32.

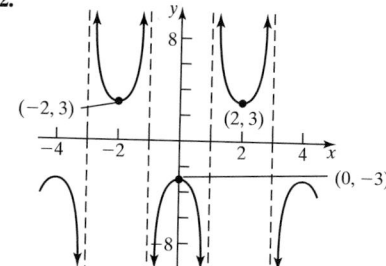

Domain: $\{x | x \text{ does not equal an odd integer}\}$

Range: $\{y | y \leq -3 \text{ or } y \geq 3\}$

33.

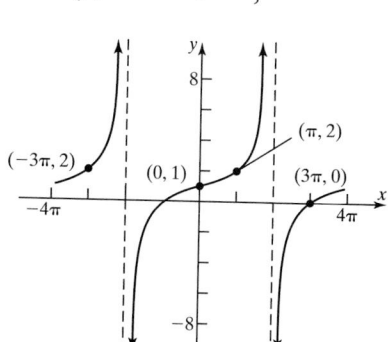

Domain: $\{x | x \neq 2\pi k, k \text{ is an odd integer}\}$

Range: $(-\infty, \infty)$

34.

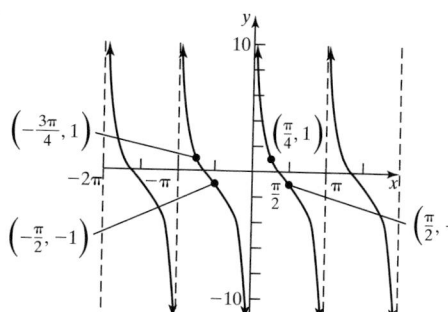

Domain: $\{x | x \neq k\pi, k \text{ is an integer}\}$

Range: $(-\infty, \infty)$

35.

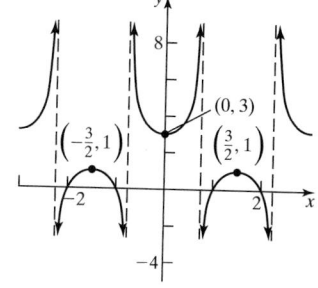

Domain: $\left\{x \middle| x \neq \dfrac{3}{4}k, k \text{ is an odd integer}\right\}$

Range: $\{y | y \leq 1 \text{ or } y \geq 3\}$

36.

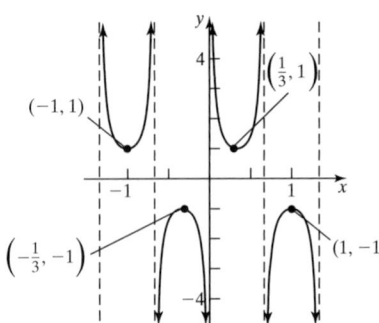

Domain: $\left\{x \middle| x \neq \dfrac{2}{3}k, k \text{ is an integer}\right\}$

Range: $\{y | y \leq -1 \text{ or } y \geq 1\}$

37.

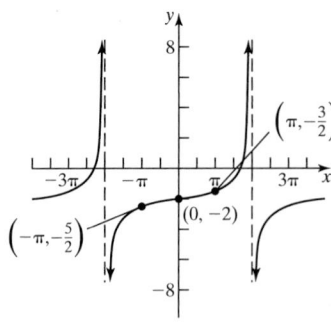

Domain: $\{x | x \neq 2\pi k, k \text{ is an odd integer}\}$

Range: $(-\infty, \infty)$

38.

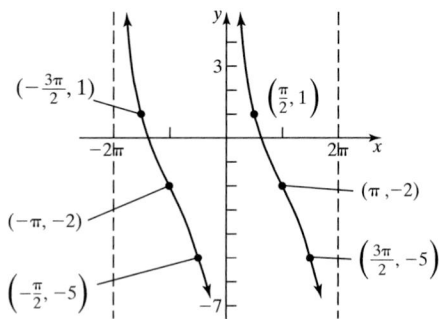

Domain: $\{x | x \neq 2\pi k, k \text{ is an integer}\}$

Range: $(-\infty, \infty)$

39.

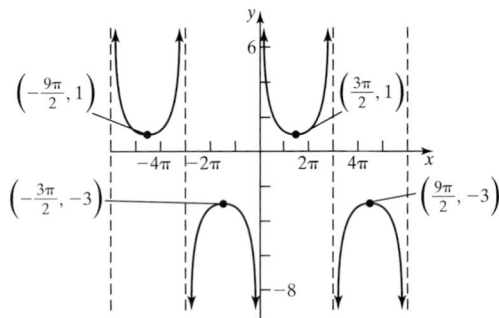

Domain: $\{x | x \neq 3\pi k, k \text{ is an integer}\}$

Range: $\{y | y \leq -3 \text{ or } y \geq 1\}$

40.

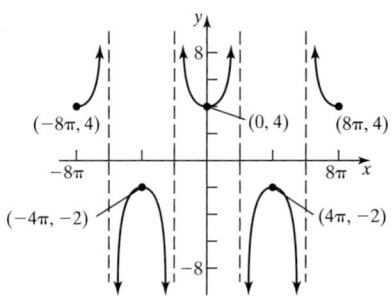

Domain: $\{x | x \neq 2\pi k, k \text{ is an odd integer}\}$

Range: $\{y | y \leq -2 \text{ or } y \geq 4\}$

41. $\dfrac{2\sqrt{3}}{\pi}$ **42.** $\dfrac{2\sqrt{3}}{\pi}(2 - \sqrt{3})$ **43.** $\dfrac{6\sqrt{3}}{\pi}$ **44.** $\dfrac{6}{\pi}$

45. $(f \circ g)(x) = \tan(4x)$ $(g \circ f)(x) = 4 \tan x$

          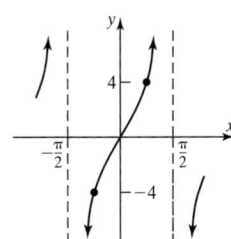

46. $(f \circ g)(x) = 2 \sec\left(\dfrac{1}{2}x\right)$ $(g \circ f)(x) = \sec x$

47. $(f \circ g)(x) = -2 \cot x$ $(g \circ f)(x) = \cot(-2x)$

          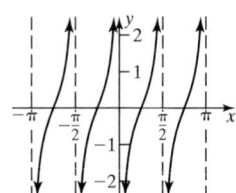

48. $(f \circ g)(x) = \csc x$ $(g \circ f)(x) = 2 \csc\left(\dfrac{1}{2}x\right)$

          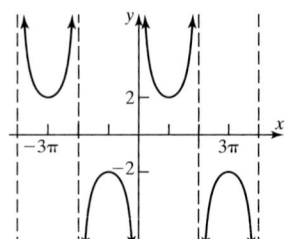

49. (a) $L(\theta) = \dfrac{3}{\cos\theta} + \dfrac{4}{\sin\theta}$ **(b)** 25 **(c)** Approximately 0.83 **(d)** Approximately 9.86 ft

$= 3\sec\theta + 4\csc\theta$

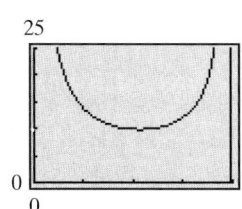

0

0 $\dfrac{\pi}{2}$

50. (a)

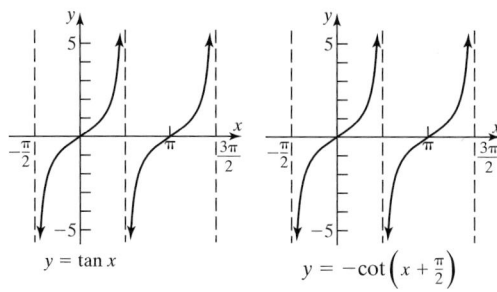

Time (Seconds)

(b) $d(t) = |10\tan(\pi t)|$ is undefined at $\left\{ t = \dfrac{k}{2} \Big| k \text{ is an odd integer} \right\}$. **(c)**

t	$d(t) = 10\tan(\pi t)$
0	0
0.1	3.2492
0.2	7.2654
0.3	13.764
0.4	30.777

(d) $\dfrac{d(0.1) - d(0)}{0.1} = 32.492;$ $\dfrac{d(0.2) - d(0.1)}{0.1} = 40.162;$ $\dfrac{d(0.3) - d(0.2)}{0.1} = 64.986;$ $\dfrac{d(0.4) - d(0.3)}{0.1} = 170.13$

(e) The first differences represent the average rate of change of the beam of light against the wall measured in feet per second. For example, between 0 and 0.1 second the beam of light is moving at 32.492 ft/s, on average. The speed increases from 0 to 0.4.

51.

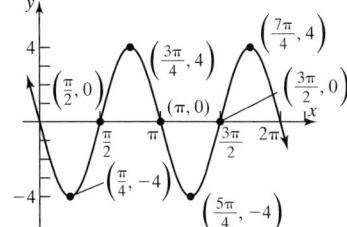

$y = \tan x$ $y = -\cot\left(x + \dfrac{\pi}{2}\right)$

6.6 Assess Your Understanding *(page 427)*

1. phase shift   **2.** F

3. Amplitude $= 4$

Period $= \pi$

Phase shift $= \dfrac{\pi}{2}$

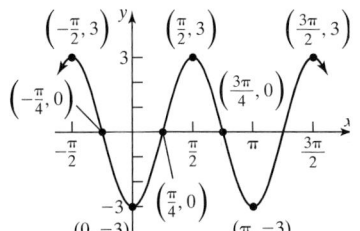

4. Amplitude $= 3$

Period $= \dfrac{2\pi}{3}$

Phase shift $= \dfrac{\pi}{3}$

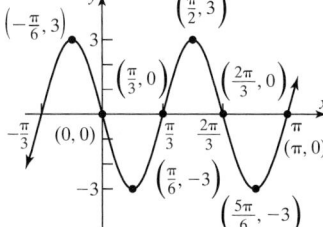

5. Amplitude $= 2$

Period $= \dfrac{2\pi}{3}$

Phase shift $= -\dfrac{\pi}{6}$

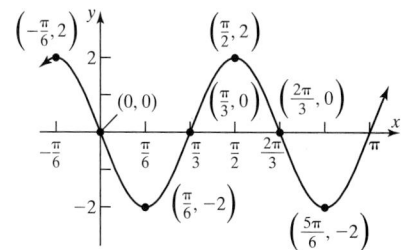

6. Amplitude $= 3$

Period $= \pi$

Phase shift $= -\dfrac{\pi}{2}$

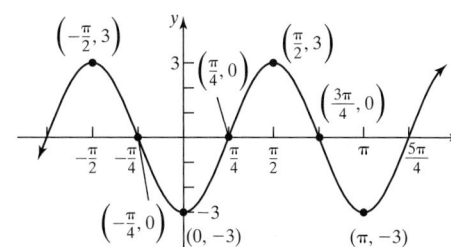

7. Amplitude $= 3$

Period $= \pi$

Phase shift $= -\dfrac{\pi}{4}$

8. Amplitude $= 2$

Period $= \pi$

Phase shift $= \dfrac{\pi}{4}$

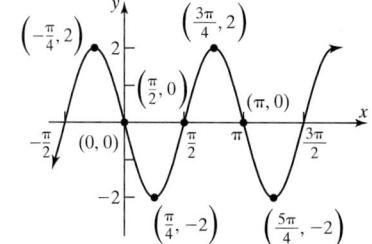

9. Amplitude = 4

Period = 2

Phase shift = $-\dfrac{2}{\pi}$

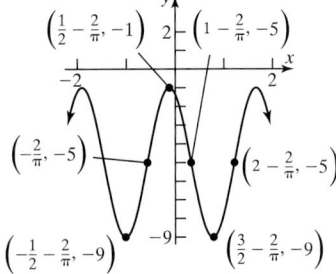

10. Amplitude = 2

Period = 1

Phase shift = $-\dfrac{2}{\pi}$

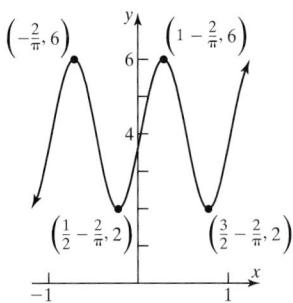

11. Amplitude = 3

Period = 2

Phase shift = $\dfrac{2}{\pi}$

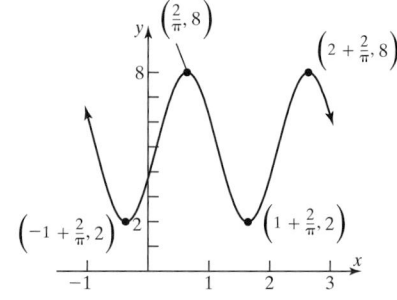

12. Amplitude = 2

Period = π

Phase shift = $\dfrac{2}{\pi}$

13. Amplitude = 3

Period = π

Phase shift = $\dfrac{\pi}{4}$

14. Amplitude = 3

Period = 1

Phase shift = $\dfrac{\pi}{4}$

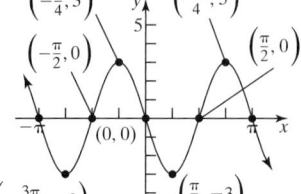

15. $y = 2\sin\left[2\left(x - \dfrac{1}{2}\right)\right]$ or $y = 2\sin(2x - 1)$

16. $y = 3\sin[4(x - 2)]$ or $y = 3\sin(4x - 8)$

17. $y = 3\sin\left[\dfrac{2}{3}\left(x + \dfrac{1}{3}\right)\right]$ or $y = 3\sin\left(\dfrac{2}{3}x + \dfrac{2}{9}\right)$

18. $y = 2\sin[2(x + 2)]$ or $y = 2\sin(2x + 4)$

19.

20.

21.

22.

23.

24.

25.

26.

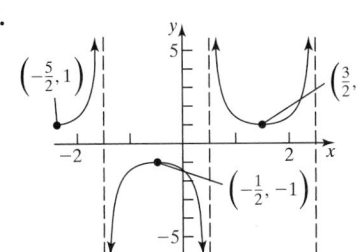

$\left(-\frac{5}{2}, 1\right)$ $\left(\frac{3}{2}, 1\right)$ $\left(-\frac{1}{2}, -1\right)$

27. Period $= \dfrac{1}{15}$ s;

amplitude $= 120$ amp;

phase shift $= \dfrac{1}{90}$ s

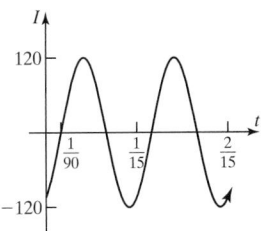

28. Period $= \dfrac{1}{30}$ s;

amplitude $= 220$ amp;

phase shift $= \dfrac{1}{360}$ s

29. (a)

(b) $y = 15.9 \sin\left[\dfrac{\pi}{6}(x - 4)\right] + 40.1$ or $y = 15.9 \sin\left(\dfrac{\pi}{6}x - \dfrac{2\pi}{3}\right) + 40.1$

(c)

(d) $y = 15.62 \sin(0.517x - 2.096) + 40.377$

(e)

30. (a)

(b) $y = 22.7 \sin\left[\dfrac{\pi}{6}(x - 4)\right] + 57.3$ or $y = 22.7 \sin\left(\dfrac{\pi}{6}x - \dfrac{2\pi}{3}\right) + 57.3$

(c)

(d) $y = 22.61 \sin(0.503x - 2.038) + 57.17$

(e)

31. (a)

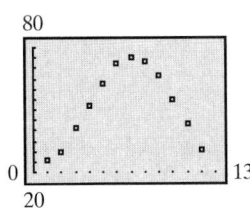

(b) $y = 24.95 \sin\left[\dfrac{\pi}{6}(x - 4)\right] + 50.45$ or $y = 24.95 \sin\left(\dfrac{\pi}{6}x - \dfrac{2\pi}{3}\right) + 50.45$

(c)

(d) $y = 25.693 \sin(0.476x - 1.814) + 49.854$

(e)

32. (a)

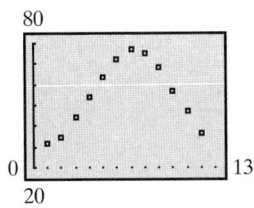

(b) $y = 22.6 \sin\left[\dfrac{\pi}{6}(x - 4)\right] + 54.4$ or $y = 22.6 \sin\left(\dfrac{\pi}{6}x - \dfrac{2\pi}{3}\right) + 54.4$

(c)

(d) $y = 22.46 \sin(0.506x - 2.060) + 54.35$

(e)

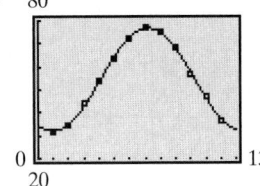

33. (a) 4:08 PM

(b) $y = 4.4 \sin\left[\frac{4\pi}{25}(x - 0.5083)\right] + 3.8$ or

$y = 4.4 \sin\left[\frac{4\pi}{25}x - 0.2555\right] + 3.8$

(c)

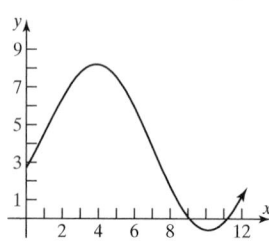

(d) 8.2 ft

34. (a) 8:41 PM

(b) $y = 5.5 \sin\left[\frac{4\pi}{25}(x - 5.0583)\right] + 7.7$ or

$y = 5.5 \sin\left(\frac{4\pi}{25}x - 2.5426\right) + 7.7$

(c)

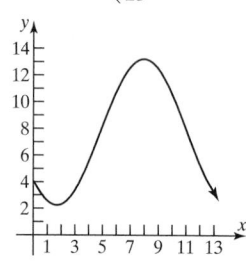

(d) 13.2 ft

35. (a) $y = 1.6 \sin\left(\frac{2\pi}{365}x - 1.39\right) + 12.15$

(b) 12.43 h

(c)

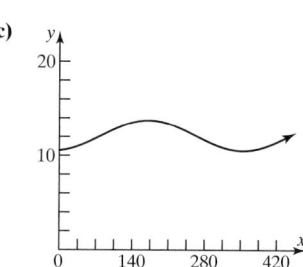

(d) The actual hours of sunlight on April 1, 2007, were 12.43 hours. This is the same as the predicted amount.

36. (a) $y = 3.1 \sin\left(\frac{2\pi}{365}x - 1.39\right) + 12.2$

(b) 12.74 h

(c)

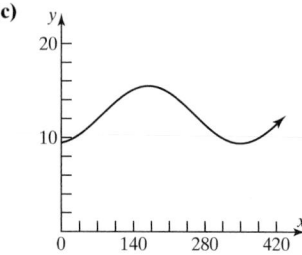

(d) The actual hours of sunlight, on April 1, 2007, were 12.72 hours. This is very close to the predicted amount of 12.74 hours.

37. (a) $y = 6.97 \sin\left(\frac{2\pi}{365}x - 1.39\right) + 12.45$

(b) 13.67 h

(c)

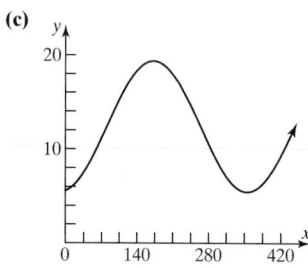

(d) The actual hours of sunlight on April 1, 2007, were 13.38 hours. This is close to the predicted amount of 13.67 hours.

38. (a) $y = 1.29 \sin\left(\frac{2\pi}{365}x - 1.39\right) + 12.14$

(b) 12.37 h

(c)

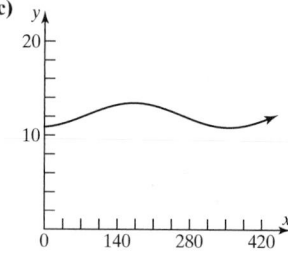

(d) The actual hours of sunlight on April 1, 2007, were 12.37 hours. This is the same as the predicted amount.

Review Exercises *(page 433)*

1. $\frac{3\pi}{4}$ **2.** $\frac{7\pi}{6}$ **3.** $\frac{\pi}{10}$ **4.** $\frac{\pi}{12}$ **5.** $135°$ **6.** $120°$ **7.** $-450°$ **8.** $-270°$ **9.** $\frac{1}{2}$ **10.** $\frac{3}{2}$ **11.** $\frac{3\sqrt{2}}{2} - \frac{4\sqrt{3}}{3}$ **12.** $2 + 3\sqrt{3}$ **13.** $-3\sqrt{2} - 2\sqrt{3}$

14. $\frac{3\sqrt{3}}{2}$ **15.** 3 **16.** $1 + 4\sqrt{2}$ **17.** 0 **18.** 1 **19.** 0 **20.** -2 **21.** 1 **22.** 1 **23.** 1 **24.** 1 **25.** 1 **26.** 1 **27.** -1 **28.** -1 **29.** 1 **30.** -1

31. $\cos\theta = \frac{3}{5}; \tan\theta = \frac{4}{3}; \csc\theta = \frac{5}{4}; \sec\theta = \frac{5}{3}; \cot\theta = \frac{3}{4}$ **32.** $\sin\theta = \frac{\sqrt{17}}{17}; \cos\theta = \frac{4\sqrt{17}}{17}; \csc\theta = \sqrt{17}; \sec\theta = \frac{\sqrt{17}}{4}; \cot\theta = 4$

33. $\sin\theta = -\frac{12}{13}; \cos\theta = -\frac{5}{13}; \csc\theta = -\frac{13}{12}; \sec\theta = -\frac{13}{5}; \cot\theta = \frac{5}{12}$ **34.** $\sin\theta = -\frac{5}{13}; \cos\theta = -\frac{12}{13}; \tan\theta = \frac{5}{12}; \csc\theta = -\frac{13}{5}; \sec\theta = -\frac{13}{12}$

35. $\sin\theta = \frac{3}{5}; \cos\theta = -\frac{4}{5}; \tan\theta = -\frac{3}{4}; \csc\theta = \frac{5}{3}; \cot\theta = -\frac{4}{3}$ **36.** $\sin\theta = -\frac{3}{5}; \cos\theta = \frac{4}{5}; \tan\theta = -\frac{3}{4}; \sec\theta = \frac{5}{4}; \cot\theta = -\frac{4}{3}$

37. $\cos\theta = -\frac{5}{13}; \tan\theta = -\frac{12}{5}; \csc\theta = \frac{13}{12}; \sec\theta = -\frac{13}{5}; \cot\theta = -\frac{5}{12}$ **38.** $\sin\theta = -\frac{4}{5}; \tan\theta = \frac{4}{3}; \csc\theta = -\frac{5}{4}; \sec\theta = -\frac{5}{3}; \cot\theta = \frac{3}{4}$

39. $\cos\theta = \frac{12}{13}; \tan\theta = -\frac{5}{12}; \csc\theta = -\frac{13}{5}; \sec\theta = \frac{13}{12}; \cot\theta = -\frac{12}{5}$ **40.** $\sin\theta = -\frac{5}{13}; \tan\theta = -\frac{5}{12}; \csc\theta = -\frac{13}{5}; \sec\theta = \frac{13}{12}; \cot\theta = -\frac{12}{5}$

41. $\sin\theta = -\frac{\sqrt{10}}{10}; \cos\theta = -\frac{3\sqrt{10}}{10}; \csc\theta = -\sqrt{10}; \sec\theta = -\frac{\sqrt{10}}{3}; \cot\theta = 3$ **42.** $\sin\theta = \frac{2\sqrt{13}}{13}; \cos\theta = -\frac{3\sqrt{13}}{13}; \csc\theta = \frac{\sqrt{13}}{2};$

$\sec\theta = -\frac{\sqrt{13}}{3}; \cot\theta = -\frac{3}{2}$ **43.** $\sin\theta = -\frac{2\sqrt{2}}{3}; \cos\theta = \frac{1}{3}; \tan\theta = -2\sqrt{2}; \csc\theta = -\frac{3\sqrt{2}}{4}; \cot\theta = -\frac{\sqrt{2}}{4}$ **44.** $\sin\theta = -\frac{1}{4}; \cos\theta = -\frac{\sqrt{15}}{4};$

$\tan\theta = \frac{\sqrt{15}}{15}; \sec\theta = -\frac{4\sqrt{15}}{15}; \cot\theta = \sqrt{15}$ **45.** $\sin\theta = \frac{\sqrt{5}}{5}; \cos\theta = -\frac{2\sqrt{5}}{5}; \tan\theta = -\frac{1}{2}; \csc\theta = \sqrt{5}; \sec\theta = -\frac{\sqrt{5}}{2}$

46. $\sin\theta = -\dfrac{2\sqrt{5}}{5}$; $\cos\theta = \dfrac{\sqrt{5}}{5}$; $\csc\theta = -\dfrac{\sqrt{5}}{2}$; $\sec\theta = \sqrt{5}$; $\cot\theta = -\dfrac{1}{2}$

47.

48.

49.

50.

51.

52.

53.

54.

55.

56.

57.

58.

59.

60.

61.

62.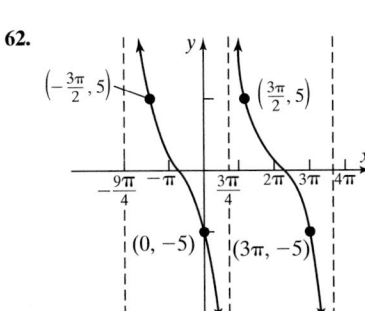

63. Amplitude = 4; period = 2π

64. Amplitude = 1; period = π

65. Amplitude = 8; period = 4

66. Amplitude = 2; period = $\dfrac{2}{3}$

67. Amplitude = 4

Period = $\dfrac{2\pi}{3}$

Phase shift = 0

68. Amplitude = 2

Period = 6π

Phase shift = 0

69. Amplitude = 2

Period = π

Phase shift = $\dfrac{\pi}{2}$

70. Amplitude = 1

Period = 4π

Phase shift = $-\pi$

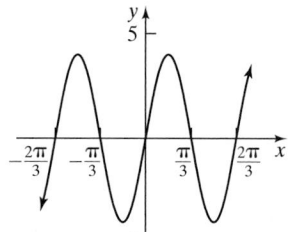

71. Amplitude = $\dfrac{1}{2}$

Period = $\dfrac{4\pi}{3}$

Phase shift = $\dfrac{2\pi}{3}$

72. Amplitude = $\dfrac{3}{2}$

Period = $\dfrac{\pi}{3}$

Phase shift = $-\dfrac{\pi}{2}$

73. Amplitude = $\dfrac{2}{3}$

Period = 2

Phase shift = $\dfrac{6}{\pi}$

74. Amplitude = 7

Period = 6

Phase shift = $-\dfrac{4}{\pi}$

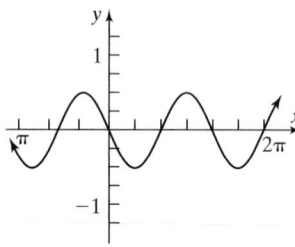

75. $y = 5 \cos \dfrac{x}{4}$ **76.** $y = 4 \sin \dfrac{x}{4}$ **77.** $y = -6 \cos\left(\dfrac{\pi}{4}x\right)$ **78.** $y = -7 \sin\left(\dfrac{\pi}{4}x\right)$ **79.** 0.38 **80.** 1.02

81. Sine, cosine, cosecant and secant: negative; tangent and cotangent: positive **82.** Quadrant IV

83. $\sin\theta = \dfrac{2\sqrt{2}}{3}$; $\cos\theta = -\dfrac{1}{3}$; $\tan\theta = -2\sqrt{2}$; $\csc\theta = \dfrac{3\sqrt{2}}{4}$; $\sec\theta = -3$; $\cot\theta = -\dfrac{\sqrt{2}}{4}$ **84.** $\sin t = \dfrac{5\sqrt{29}}{29}$, $\cos t = -\dfrac{2\sqrt{29}}{29}$, $\tan t = -\dfrac{5}{2}$

85. Domain: $\left\{x \mid x \neq \text{odd multiple of } \dfrac{\pi}{2}\right\}$; range: $\{y \mid |y| \geq 1\}$; period = $2(\pi)$ **86.** (a) 32.34° (b) 63°10′48″

87. $\dfrac{\pi}{3} \approx 1.05$ ft; $\dfrac{\pi}{3} \approx 1.05$ ft^2 **88.** $8\pi \approx 25.13$ in.; $\dfrac{16\pi}{3} \approx 16.76$ in. **89.** Approximately 114.59 revolutions/hr **90.** Approximately 5.24 ft/sec

91. 0.1 revolution/sec = $\dfrac{\pi}{5}$ radian/sec **92.** Approximately 945.38 rpm; yes; approximately 1080.43 rpm

93. (a) 120

(b) $\dfrac{1}{60}$

(c)

94. (a) $\dfrac{1}{15}$

(b) 220

(c) $-\dfrac{1}{180}$

(d)

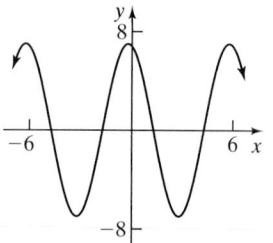

95. (a)

(c)

(e) 95

(b) $y = 19.5 \sin\left[\dfrac{\pi}{6}(x - 4)\right] + 70.5$ or

$y = 19.5 \sin\left(\dfrac{\pi}{6}x - \dfrac{2\pi}{3}\right) + 70.5$

(d) $y = 19.52 \sin(0.54x - 2.28) + 71.01$

96. (a) $y = 2.455 \sin\left(\dfrac{2\pi}{365} x - 1.39\right) + 12.175$ **97.**

(b) 12.61 h

(c)

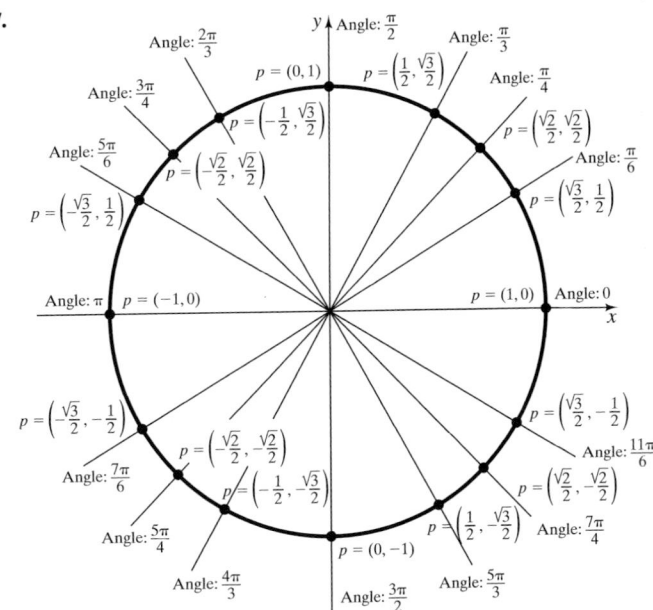

Chapter Test *(page 436)*

1. $\dfrac{13\pi}{9}$ **2.** $-\dfrac{20\pi}{9}$ **3.** $\dfrac{13\pi}{180}$ **4.** $-22.5°$ **5.** $810°$ **6.** $135°$ **7.** $\dfrac{1}{2}$ **8.** 0 **9.** $-\dfrac{1}{2}$ **10.** $-\dfrac{\sqrt{3}}{3}$ **11.** 2 **12.** $\dfrac{3(1 - \sqrt{2})}{2}$ **13.** 0.292 **14.** 0.309

15. -1.524 **16.** 2.747 **17.**

18. $-\dfrac{3}{5}$

	$\sin \theta$	$\cos \theta$	$\tan \theta$	$\sec \theta$	$\csc \theta$	$\cot \theta$
θ in QI	+	+	+	+	+	+
θ in QII	+	−	−	−	+	−
θ in QIII	−	−	+	−	−	+
θ in QIV	−	+	−	+	−	−

19. $\cos \theta = -\dfrac{2\sqrt{6}}{7}$; $\tan \theta = -\dfrac{5\sqrt{6}}{12}$; $\csc \theta = \dfrac{7}{5}$; $\sec \theta = -\dfrac{7\sqrt{6}}{12}$; $\cot \theta = -\dfrac{2\sqrt{6}}{5}$ **20.** $\sin \theta = -\dfrac{\sqrt{5}}{3}$; $\tan \theta = -\dfrac{\sqrt{5}}{2}$; $\csc \theta = -\dfrac{3\sqrt{5}}{5}$; $\sec \theta = \dfrac{3}{2}$;

$\cot \theta = -\dfrac{2\sqrt{5}}{5}$ **21.** $\sin \theta = \dfrac{12}{13}$; $\cos \theta = -\dfrac{5}{13}$; $\csc \theta = \dfrac{13}{12}$; $\sec \theta = -\dfrac{13}{5}$; $\cot \theta = -\dfrac{5}{12}$ **22.** $\dfrac{7\sqrt{53}}{53}$ **23.** $-\dfrac{5\sqrt{146}}{146}$ **24.** $-\dfrac{1}{2}$

25.

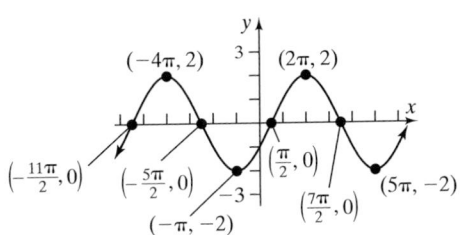

26. $y = \tan\left(-x + \dfrac{\pi}{4}\right) + 2$

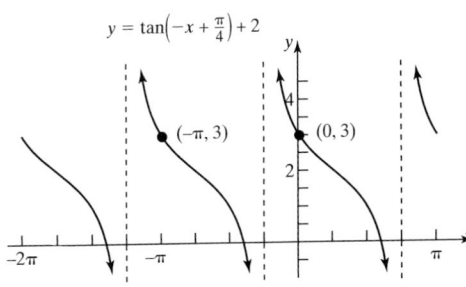

27. $y = -3 \sin\left(3x + \dfrac{3\pi}{4}\right)$

28. 78.93 ft^2 **29.** 143.5 rpm

Cumulative Review *(page 436)*

1. $\left\{-1, \dfrac{1}{2}\right\}$ **2.** $y - 5 = -3(x + 2)$ or $y = -3x - 1$ **3.** $x^2 + (y + 2)^2 = 16$

4. A line; slope $\dfrac{2}{3}$; intercepts $(6, 0)$ and $(0, -4)$ **5.** A circle; center $(1, -2)$; radius 3 **6.**

7. (a)

(b)

(c)

(d)

(e)

(f)

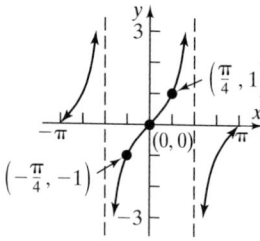

8. $f^{-1}(x) = \dfrac{1}{3}(x + 2)$

9. -2

10.

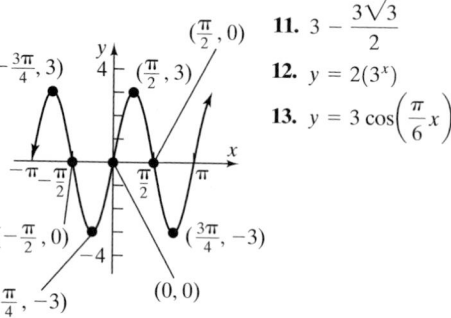

11. $3 - \dfrac{3\sqrt{3}}{2}$

12. $y = 2(3^x)$

13. $y = 3\cos\left(\dfrac{\pi}{6}x\right)$

14. (a) $f(x) = -3x - 3$;
   $m = -3; (-1, 0), (0, -3)$

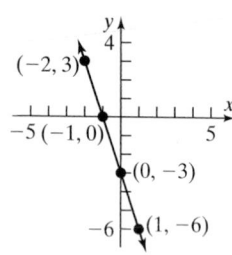

(b) $f(x) = (x - 1)^2 - 6; (0, -5),$
   $\left(-\sqrt{6} + 1, 0\right), \left(\sqrt{6} + 1, 0\right)$

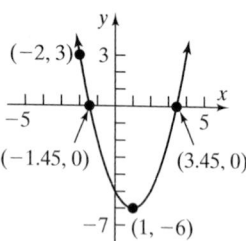

(c) We have that $y = 3$ when $x = -2$ and $y = -6$ when $x = 1$. Both points satisfy $y = ae^x$. Therefore, for $(-2, 3)$ we have $3 = ae^{-2}$, which implies that $a = 3e^2$. But for $(1, -6)$ we have $-6 = ae^1$, which implies that $a = -6e^{-1}$. Therefore, there is no exponential function $y = ae^x$ that contains $(-2, 3)$ and $(1, -6)$.

15. (a) $f(x) = \dfrac{1}{6}(x + 2)(x - 3)(x - 5)$

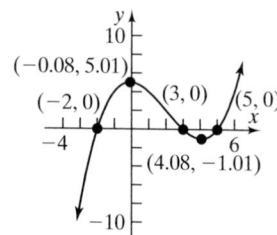

(b) $R(x) = -\dfrac{(x + 2)(x - 3)(x - 5)}{3(x - 2)}$

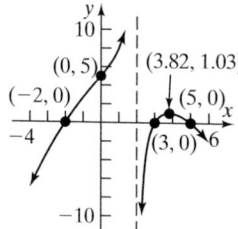

CHAPTER 7 Analytic Trigonometry

7.1 Assess Your Understanding (page 450)

7. $x = \sin y$ **8.** $\dfrac{\pi}{2}$ **9.** $\dfrac{\pi}{5}$ **10.** F **11.** T **12.** T **13.** 0 **14.** 0 **15.** $-\dfrac{\pi}{2}$ **16.** π **17.** 0 **18.** $-\dfrac{\pi}{4}$ **19.** $\dfrac{\pi}{4}$ **20.** $\dfrac{\pi}{6}$ **21.** $\dfrac{\pi}{3}$ **22.** $-\dfrac{\pi}{3}$ **23.** $\dfrac{5\pi}{6}$

24. $-\dfrac{\pi}{4}$ **25.** 0.10 **26.** 0.93 **27.** 1.37 **28.** 0.20 **29.** 0.51 **30.** 0.13 **31.** -0.38 **32.** -1.25 **33.** -0.12 **34.** 2.03 **35.** 1.08 **36.** 0.35 **37.** $\dfrac{4\pi}{5}$

38. $-\dfrac{\pi}{10}$ **39.** $-\dfrac{3\pi}{8}$ **40.** $-\dfrac{3\pi}{7}$ **41.** $-\dfrac{\pi}{8}$ **42.** $\dfrac{\pi}{3}$ **43.** $-\dfrac{\pi}{5}$ **44.** $\dfrac{\pi}{3}$ **45.** $\dfrac{1}{4}$ **46.** $-\dfrac{2}{3}$ **47.** 4 **48.** -2 **49.** Not defined **50.** Not defined

51. π **52.** Not defined

53. $f^{-1}(x) = \sin^{-1}\dfrac{x-2}{5}$

Domain of f = range of f^{-1}: $(-\infty, \infty)$

Domain of f^{-1} = range of f: $[-3, 7]$

54. $f^{-1}(x) = \tan^{-1}\dfrac{x+3}{2}$

Domain of f: $x \neq \dfrac{(2k+1)\pi}{2}$, k an integer

Range of f^{-1}: $y \neq \dfrac{(2k+1)\pi}{2}$, k an integer

Domain of f^{-1} = range of f: $(-\infty, \infty)$

55. $f^{-1}(x) = \dfrac{1}{3}\cos^{-1}\left(-\dfrac{x}{2}\right)$

Domain of f = range of f^{-1}: $(-\infty, \infty)$

Domain of f^{-1} = range of f: $[-2, 2]$

56. $f^{-1}(x) = \dfrac{1}{2}\sin^{-1}\dfrac{x}{3}$

Domain of f = range of f^{-1}: $(-\infty, \infty)$

Domain of f^{-1} = range of f: $[-3, 3]$

57. $f^{-1}(x) = -\tan^{-1}(x+3) - 1$

Domain of f: $x \neq \dfrac{(2k+1)\pi}{2} - 1$, k an integer

Range of f^{-1}: $y \neq \dfrac{(2k+1)\pi}{2} - 1$, k an integer

Domain of f^{-1} = range of f: $(-\infty, \infty)$

58. $f^{-1}(x) = \cos^{-1}(x-1) - 2$

Domain of f = range of f^{-1}: $(-\infty, \infty)$

Domain of f^{-1} = range of f: $[0, 2]$

59. $f^{-1}(x) = \dfrac{1}{2}\left[\sin^{-1}\left(\dfrac{x}{3}\right) - 1\right]$

Domain of f = range of f^{-1}: $(-\infty, \infty)$

Domain of f^{-1} = range of f: $[-3, 3]$

60. $f^{-1}(x) = \dfrac{1}{3}\left[\cos^{-1}\left(\dfrac{x}{2}\right) - 2\right]$

Domain of f = range of f^{-1}: $(-\infty, \infty)$

Domain of f^{-1} = range of f: $[-2, 2]$

61. $\left\{\dfrac{\sqrt{2}}{2}\right\}$ **62.** $\{0\}$ **63.** $\left\{-\dfrac{1}{4}\right\}$

64. $\left\{-\dfrac{1}{6}\right\}$ **65.** $\{\sqrt{3}\}$ **66.** $\{-1\}$

67. $\{-1\}$ **68.** $\left\{-\dfrac{\sqrt{3}}{2}\right\}$ **69. (a)** 13.92 h or 13 h, 55 min **(b)** 12 h **(c)** 13.85 h or 13 h, 51 min **70. (a)** 14.93 h or 14 h, 56 min **(b)** 12 h

(c) 14.83 h or 14 h, 50 min **71. (a)** 13.3 h or 13 h, 18 min **(b)** 12 h **(c)** 13.26 h or 13 h, 15 min **72. (a)** 18.96 h or 18 h, 57 min **(b)** 12 h

(c) 18.64 h or 18 h, 38 min **73. (a)** 12 h **(b)** 12 h **(c)** 12 h **(d)** It is 12 h. **74. (a)** 24 h **(b)** 12 h **(c)** 22.02 h or 22 h, 1 min

(d) 0 h; ranges from around-the-clock daylight to no daylight **75.** 3.28 min

76. (a) 42.6°; 44.4°; 42.8°

(b) fourth row

(c) 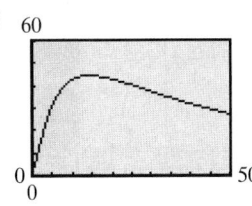 ; 14.3 ft

77. (a) $\dfrac{\pi}{3}$ square units

(b) $\dfrac{5\pi}{12}$ square units

78. (a) $\dfrac{\pi}{3}$ square units

(b) $\dfrac{\pi}{3}$ square units

79. 4250 mi

80. 5518 mi

7.2 Assess Your Understanding (page 457)

4. $x = \sec y; \geq 1; 0; \pi$ **5.** $\dfrac{\sqrt{2}}{2}$ **6.** F **7.** T **8.** T **9.** $\dfrac{\sqrt{2}}{2}$ **10.** $\dfrac{\sqrt{3}}{2}$ **11.** $-\dfrac{\sqrt{3}}{3}$ **12.** $-\dfrac{\sqrt{3}}{3}$ **13.** 2 **14.** $-\sqrt{3}$ **15.** $\sqrt{2}$ **16.** 2 **17.** $-\dfrac{\sqrt{2}}{2}$

18. $\dfrac{1}{2}$ **19.** $\dfrac{2\sqrt{3}}{3}$ **20.** 2 **21.** $\dfrac{3\pi}{4}$ **22.** $-\dfrac{\pi}{3}$ **23.** $\dfrac{\pi}{6}$ **24.** $\dfrac{\pi}{3}$ **25.** $\dfrac{\sqrt{2}}{4}$ **26.** $2\sqrt{2}$ **27.** $\dfrac{\sqrt{5}}{2}$ **28.** $\dfrac{\sqrt{7}}{3}$ **29.** $-\dfrac{\sqrt{14}}{2}$ **30.** $-\dfrac{\sqrt{5}}{2}$ **31.** $-\dfrac{3\sqrt{10}}{10}$

32. $-\dfrac{\sqrt{2}}{2}$ **33.** $\sqrt{5}$ **34.** $\sqrt{5}$ **35.** $-\dfrac{\pi}{4}$ **36.** $\dfrac{2\pi}{3}$ **37.** $\dfrac{\pi}{6}$ **38.** $\dfrac{\pi}{4}$ **39.** $-\dfrac{\pi}{2}$ **40.** $\dfrac{\pi}{4}$ **41.** $\dfrac{\pi}{6}$ **42.** $\dfrac{2\pi}{3}$ **43.** $\dfrac{2\pi}{3}$ **44.** $-\dfrac{\pi}{3}$ **45.** 1.32 **46.** 0.20

47. 0.46 **48.** 1.91 **49.** -0.34 **50.** 2.03 **51.** 2.72 **52.** 3.02 **53.** -0.73 **54.** 2.42 **55.** 2.55 **56.** 2.84 **57.** $\dfrac{1}{\sqrt{1+u^2}}$ **58.** $\sqrt{1-u^2}$

59. $\dfrac{u}{\sqrt{1-u^2}}$ **60.** $\dfrac{\sqrt{1-u^2}}{u}$ **61.** $\dfrac{\sqrt{u^2-1}}{|u|}$ **62.** $\dfrac{1}{\sqrt{1+u^2}}$ **63.** $\dfrac{\sqrt{u^2-1}}{u}$ **64.** $\dfrac{1}{u}$ **65.** $\dfrac{1}{u}$ **66.** $\sqrt{u^2-1}$ **67.** $\dfrac{5}{13}$ **68.** $\dfrac{12}{13}$ **69.** $\dfrac{3\pi}{4}$ **70.** $-\dfrac{\pi}{3}$

71. $-\dfrac{3}{4}$ **72.** $-\dfrac{3}{4}$ **73.** $\dfrac{5}{13}$ **74.** $\dfrac{5}{13}$ **75.** $\dfrac{\pi}{6}$ **76.** $\dfrac{2\pi}{3}$ **77.** $-\sqrt{15}$ **78.** $-\dfrac{2\sqrt{21}}{21}$ **79. (a)** $\theta = 31.89°$ **(b)** 54.64 ft in diameter **(c)** 37.96 ft high

80. (a) $\theta = 50.14°$ **(b)** 4.79 ft high **(c)** Tour grade 50/50; its angle of repose is 54.88°. **81. (a)** $\theta = 22.3°$ **(b)** $v_0 = 2940.23$ ft/s

82.

83.

84.

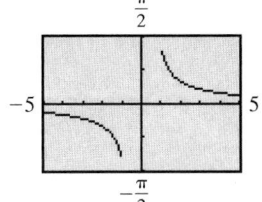

7.3 Assess Your Understanding *(page 463)*

3. identity; conditional **4.** -1 **5.** 0 **6.** T **7.** F **8.** T **9.** $\dfrac{1}{\cos\theta}$ **10.** $\dfrac{1}{\sin\theta}$ **11.** $\dfrac{1+\sin\theta}{\cos\theta}$ **12.** $\dfrac{1-\cos\theta}{\sin\theta}$ **13.** $\dfrac{1}{\sin\theta\cos\theta}$ **14.** $\dfrac{2}{\sin^2 v}$ **15.** 2

16. 2 **17.** $\dfrac{3\sin\theta+1}{\sin\theta+1}$ **18.** $\dfrac{\cos\theta+1}{\cos\theta}$ **19.** $\csc\theta\cdot\cos\theta=\dfrac{1}{\sin\theta}\cdot\cos\theta=\dfrac{\cos\theta}{\sin\theta}=\cot\theta$ **20.** $\sec\theta\cdot\sin\theta=\dfrac{1}{\cos\theta}\cdot\sin\theta=\dfrac{\sin\theta}{\cos\theta}=\tan\theta$

21. $1+\tan^2(-\theta)=1+(-\tan\theta)^2=1+\tan^2\theta=\sec^2\theta$ **22.** $1+\cot^2(-\theta)=1+(-\cot\theta)^2=1+\cot^2\theta=\csc^2\theta$

23. $\cos\theta(\tan\theta+\cot\theta)=\cos\theta\left(\dfrac{\sin\theta}{\cos\theta}+\dfrac{\cos\theta}{\sin\theta}\right)=\cos\theta\left(\dfrac{\sin^2\theta+\cos^2\theta}{\cos\theta\sin\theta}\right)=\cos\theta\left(\dfrac{1}{\cos\theta\sin\theta}\right)=\dfrac{1}{\sin\theta}=\csc\theta$

24. $\sin\theta(\cot\theta+\tan\theta)=\sin\theta\left(\dfrac{\cos\theta}{\sin\theta}+\dfrac{\sin\theta}{\cos\theta}\right)=\sin\theta\left(\dfrac{\cos^2\theta+\sin^2\theta}{\sin\theta\cos\theta}\right)=\sin\theta\left(\dfrac{1}{\sin\theta\cos\theta}\right)=\dfrac{1}{\cos\theta}=\sec\theta$

25. $\tan u\,\cot u-\cos^2 u=\tan u\cdot\dfrac{1}{\tan u}-\cos^2 u=1-\cos^2 u=\sin^2 u$ **26.** $\sin u\,\csc u-\cos^2 u=\sin u\cdot\dfrac{1}{\sin u}-\cos^2 u=1-\cos^2 u=\sin^2 u$

27. $(\sec\theta-1)(\sec\theta+1)=\sec^2\theta-1=\tan^2\theta$ **28.** $(\csc\theta-1)(\csc\theta+1)=\csc^2\theta-1=\cot^2\theta$

29. $(\sec\theta+\tan\theta)(\sec\theta-\tan\theta)=\sec^2\theta-\tan^2\theta=1$ **30.** $(\csc\theta+\cot\theta)(\csc\theta-\cot\theta)=\csc^2\theta-\cot^2\theta=1$

31. $\cos^2\theta(1+\tan^2\theta)=\cos^2\theta\sec^2\theta=\cos^2\theta\cdot\dfrac{1}{\cos^2\theta}=1$

32. $(1-\cos^2\theta)(1+\cot^2\theta)=\sin^2\theta\cdot\csc^2\theta=\sin^2\theta\cdot\dfrac{1}{\sin^2\theta}=1$

33. $(\sin\theta+\cos\theta)^2+(\sin\theta-\cos\theta)^2=\sin^2\theta+2\sin\theta\cos\theta+\cos^2\theta+\sin^2\theta-2\sin\theta\cos\theta+\cos^2\theta$
$$=\sin^2\theta+\cos^2\theta+\sin^2\theta+\cos^2\theta=1+1=2$$

34. $\tan^2\theta\cos^2\theta+\cot^2\theta\sin^2\theta=\dfrac{\sin^2\theta}{\cos^2\theta}\cdot\cos^2\theta+\dfrac{\cos^2\theta}{\sin^2\theta}\cdot\sin^2\theta=\sin^2\theta+\cos^2\theta=1$

35. $\sec^4\theta-\sec^2\theta=\sec^2\theta(\sec^2\theta-1)=(1+\tan^2\theta)\tan^2\theta=\tan^4\theta+\tan^2\theta$

36. $\csc^4\theta-\csc^2\theta=\csc^2\theta(\csc^2\theta-1)=(1+\cot^2\theta)\cot^2\theta=\cot^4\theta+\cot^2\theta$

37. $\sec u-\tan u=\dfrac{1}{\cos u}-\dfrac{\sin u}{\cos u}=\dfrac{1-\sin u}{\cos u}\cdot\dfrac{1+\sin u}{1+\sin u}=\dfrac{1-\sin^2 u}{\cos u(1+\sin u)}=\dfrac{\cos^2 u}{\cos u(1+\sin u)}=\dfrac{\cos u}{1+\sin u}$

38. $\csc u-\cot u=\dfrac{1}{\sin u}-\dfrac{\cos u}{\sin u}=\dfrac{1-\cos u}{\sin u}\cdot\dfrac{1+\cos u}{1+\cos u}=\dfrac{1-\cos^2 u}{\sin u(1+\cos u)}=\dfrac{\sin^2 u}{\sin u(1+\cos u)}=\dfrac{\sin u}{1+\cos u}$

39. $3\sin^2\theta+4\cos^2\theta=3\sin^2\theta+3\cos^2\theta+\cos^2\theta=3(\sin^2\theta+\cos^2\theta)+\cos^2\theta=3+\cos^2\theta$

40. $9\sec^2\theta-5\tan^2\theta=4\sec^2\theta+5\sec^2\theta-5\tan^2\theta=4\sec^2\theta+5(\sec^2\theta-\tan^2\theta)=5+4\sec^2\theta$

41. $1-\dfrac{\cos^2\theta}{1+\sin\theta}=1-\dfrac{1-\sin^2\theta}{1+\sin\theta}=1-\dfrac{(1+\sin\theta)(1-\sin\theta)}{1+\sin\theta}=1-(1-\sin\theta)=\sin\theta$

42. $1-\dfrac{\sin^2\theta}{1-\cos\theta}=1-\dfrac{1-\cos^2\theta}{1-\cos\theta}=1-\dfrac{(1+\cos\theta)(1-\cos\theta)}{1-\cos\theta}=1-(1+\cos\theta)=-\cos\theta$

43. $\dfrac{1+\tan v}{1-\tan v}=\dfrac{1+\dfrac{1}{\cot v}}{1-\dfrac{1}{\cot v}}=\dfrac{\dfrac{\cot v+1}{\cot v}}{\dfrac{\cot v-1}{\cot v}}=\dfrac{\cot v+1}{\cot v-1}$ **44.** $\dfrac{\csc v-1}{\csc v+1}=\dfrac{\dfrac{1}{\sin v}-1}{\dfrac{1}{\sin v}+1}=\dfrac{\dfrac{1-\sin v}{\sin v}}{\dfrac{1+\sin v}{\sin v}}=\dfrac{1-\sin v}{1+\sin v}$

45. $\dfrac{\sec\theta}{\csc\theta}+\dfrac{\sin\theta}{\cos\theta}=\dfrac{\dfrac{1}{\cos\theta}}{\dfrac{1}{\sin\theta}}+\tan\theta=\dfrac{\sin\theta}{\cos\theta}+\tan\theta=\tan\theta+\tan\theta=2\tan\theta$

46. $\dfrac{\csc\theta-1}{\cot\theta}=\dfrac{\csc\theta-1}{\cot\theta}\cdot\dfrac{\csc\theta+1}{\csc\theta+1}=\dfrac{\csc^2\theta-1}{\cot\theta(\csc\theta+1)}=\dfrac{\cot^2\theta}{\cot\theta(\csc\theta+1)}=\dfrac{\cot\theta}{\csc\theta+1}$

47. $\dfrac{1+\sin\theta}{1-\sin\theta}=\dfrac{1+\dfrac{1}{\csc\theta}}{1-\dfrac{1}{\csc\theta}}=\dfrac{\dfrac{\csc\theta+1}{\csc\theta}}{\dfrac{\csc\theta-1}{\csc\theta}}=\dfrac{\csc\theta+1}{\csc\theta-1}$ **48.** $\dfrac{\cos\theta+1}{\cos\theta-1}=\dfrac{\dfrac{1}{\sec\theta}+1}{\dfrac{1}{\sec\theta}-1}=\dfrac{\dfrac{1+\sec\theta}{\sec\theta}}{\dfrac{1-\sec\theta}{\sec\theta}}=\dfrac{1+\sec\theta}{1-\sec\theta}$

49. $\dfrac{1-\sin v}{\cos v}+\dfrac{\cos v}{1-\sin v}=\dfrac{(1-\sin v)^2+\cos^2 v}{\cos v(1-\sin v)}=\dfrac{1-2\sin v+\sin^2 v+\cos^2 v}{\cos v(1-\sin v)}=\dfrac{2-2\sin v}{\cos v(1-\sin v)}=\dfrac{2(1-\sin v)}{\cos v(1-\sin v)}=\dfrac{2}{\cos v}=2\sec v$

50. $\dfrac{\cos v}{1+\sin v}+\dfrac{1+\sin v}{\cos v}=\dfrac{\cos^2 v+(1+\sin v)^2}{\cos v(1+\sin v)}=\dfrac{\cos^2 v+1+2\sin v+\sin^2 v}{\cos v(1+\sin v)}=\dfrac{2+2\sin v}{\cos v(1+\sin v)}=\dfrac{2(1+\sin v)}{\cos v(1+\sin v)}=\dfrac{2}{\cos v}=2\sec v$

51. $\dfrac{\sin\theta}{\sin\theta-\cos\theta}=\dfrac{1}{\dfrac{\sin\theta-\cos\theta}{\sin\theta}}=\dfrac{1}{1-\dfrac{\cos\theta}{\sin\theta}}=\dfrac{1}{1-\cot\theta}$

52. $1-\dfrac{\sin^2\theta}{1+\cos\theta}=1-\dfrac{1-\cos^2\theta}{1+\cos\theta}=1-\dfrac{(1-\cos\theta)(1+\cos\theta)}{1+\cos\theta}=1-(1-\cos\theta)=\cos\theta$

53. $(\sec\theta-\tan\theta)^2=\sec^2\theta-2\sec\theta\tan\theta+\tan^2\theta=\dfrac{1}{\cos^2\theta}-\dfrac{2\sin\theta}{\cos^2\theta}+\dfrac{\sin^2\theta}{\cos^2\theta}=\dfrac{1-2\sin\theta+\sin^2\theta}{\cos^2\theta}=\dfrac{(1-\sin\theta)^2}{1-\sin^2\theta}=\dfrac{(1-\sin\theta)^2}{(1-\sin\theta)(1+\sin\theta)}$
$$=\dfrac{1-\sin\theta}{1+\sin\theta}$$

54. $(\csc\theta - \cot\theta)^2 = \csc^2\theta - 2\csc\theta\cot\theta + \cot^2\theta = \dfrac{1}{\sin^2\theta} - \dfrac{2\cos\theta}{\sin^2\theta} + \dfrac{\cos^2\theta}{\sin^2\theta} = \dfrac{1 - 2\cos\theta + \cos^2\theta}{\sin^2\theta} = \dfrac{(1-\cos\theta)^2}{1-\cos^2\theta} = \dfrac{(1-\cos\theta)^2}{(1-\cos\theta)(1+\cos\theta)}$

$= \dfrac{1-\cos\theta}{1+\cos\theta}$

55. $\dfrac{\cos\theta}{1-\tan\theta} + \dfrac{\sin\theta}{1-\cot\theta} = \dfrac{\cos\theta}{1 - \dfrac{\sin\theta}{\cos\theta}} + \dfrac{\sin\theta}{1 - \dfrac{\cos\theta}{\sin\theta}} = \dfrac{\cos\theta}{\dfrac{\cos\theta-\sin\theta}{\cos\theta}} + \dfrac{\sin\theta}{\dfrac{\sin\theta-\cos\theta}{\sin\theta}} = \dfrac{\cos^2\theta}{\cos\theta-\sin\theta} + \dfrac{\sin^2\theta}{\sin\theta-\cos\theta}$

$= \dfrac{\cos^2\theta - \sin^2\theta}{\cos\theta - \sin\theta} = \dfrac{(\cos\theta - \sin\theta)(\cos\theta + \sin\theta)}{\cos\theta - \sin\theta} = \sin\theta + \cos\theta$

56. $\dfrac{\cot\theta}{1-\tan\theta} + \dfrac{\tan\theta}{1-\cot\theta} = \dfrac{\cot\theta}{1 - \dfrac{\sin\theta}{\cos\theta}} + \dfrac{\tan\theta}{1 - \dfrac{\cos\theta}{\sin\theta}} = \dfrac{\cot\theta}{\dfrac{\cos\theta-\sin\theta}{\cos\theta}} + \dfrac{\tan\theta}{\dfrac{\sin\theta-\cos\theta}{\sin\theta}} = \dfrac{\dfrac{\cos\theta}{\sin\theta}\cdot\cos\theta}{\cos\theta-\sin\theta} - \dfrac{\dfrac{\sin\theta}{\cos\theta}\cdot\sin\theta}{\cos\theta-\sin\theta} = \dfrac{\dfrac{\cos^2\theta}{\sin\theta} - \dfrac{\sin^2\theta}{\cos\theta}}{\cos\theta-\sin\theta}$

$= \dfrac{\dfrac{\cos^3\theta - \sin^3\theta}{\sin\theta\cos\theta}}{\cos\theta-\sin\theta} = \dfrac{\dfrac{(\cos\theta-\sin\theta)(\cos^2\theta + \sin\theta\cos\theta + \sin^2\theta)}{\sin\theta\cos\theta}}{\cos\theta - \sin\theta} = \dfrac{\cos^2\theta + \sin\theta\cos\theta + \sin^2\theta}{\sin\theta\cos\theta} = \dfrac{\cos^2\theta}{\sin\theta\cos\theta} + \dfrac{\sin\theta\cos\theta}{\sin\theta\cos\theta} + \dfrac{\sin^2\theta}{\sin\theta\cos\theta}$

$= \cot\theta + 1 + \tan\theta$

57. $\tan\theta + \dfrac{\cos\theta}{1+\sin\theta} = \dfrac{\sin\theta}{\cos\theta} + \dfrac{\cos\theta}{1+\sin\theta} = \dfrac{\sin\theta(1+\sin\theta) + \cos^2\theta}{\cos\theta(1+\sin\theta)} = \dfrac{\sin\theta + \sin^2\theta + \cos^2\theta}{\cos\theta(1+\sin\theta)} = \dfrac{\sin\theta + 1}{\cos\theta(1+\sin\theta)} = \dfrac{1}{\cos\theta} = \sec\theta$

58. $\dfrac{\sin\theta\cos\theta}{\cos^2\theta - \sin^2\theta} = \dfrac{\dfrac{\sin\theta\cos\theta}{\cos^2\theta}}{\dfrac{\cos^2\theta - \sin^2\theta}{\cos^2\theta}} = \dfrac{\dfrac{\sin\theta}{\cos\theta}}{1 - \dfrac{\sin^2\theta}{\cos^2\theta}} = \dfrac{\tan\theta}{1 - \tan^2\theta}$

59. $\dfrac{\tan\theta + \sec\theta - 1}{\tan\theta - \sec\theta + 1} = \dfrac{\tan\theta + (\sec\theta - 1)}{\tan\theta - (\sec\theta - 1)} \cdot \dfrac{\tan\theta + (\sec\theta - 1)}{\tan\theta + (\sec\theta - 1)} = \dfrac{\tan^2\theta + 2\tan\theta(\sec\theta - 1) + \sec^2\theta - 2\sec\theta + 1}{\tan^2\theta - (\sec^2\theta - 2\sec\theta + 1)}$

$= \dfrac{\sec^2\theta - 1 + 2\tan\theta(\sec\theta - 1) + \sec^2\theta - 2\sec\theta + 1}{\sec^2\theta - 1 - \sec^2\theta + 2\sec\theta - 1} = \dfrac{2\sec^2\theta - 2\sec\theta + 2\tan\theta(\sec\theta - 1)}{-2 + 2\sec\theta}$

$= \dfrac{2\sec\theta(\sec\theta - 1) + 2\tan\theta(\sec\theta - 1)}{2(\sec\theta - 1)} = \dfrac{2(\sec\theta - 1)(\sec\theta + \tan\theta)}{2(\sec\theta - 1)} = \tan\theta + \sec\theta$

60. $\dfrac{\sin\theta - \cos\theta + 1}{\sin\theta + \cos\theta - 1} = \dfrac{\sin\theta - (\cos\theta - 1)}{\sin\theta + (\cos\theta - 1)} \cdot \dfrac{\sin\theta - (\cos\theta - 1)}{\sin\theta - (\cos\theta - 1)} = \dfrac{\sin^2\theta - 2\sin\theta(\cos\theta - 1) + \cos^2\theta - 2\cos\theta + 1}{\sin^2\theta - (\cos^2\theta - 2\cos\theta + 1)}$

$= \dfrac{1 - \cos^2\theta - 2\sin\theta(\cos\theta - 1) + \cos^2\theta - 2\cos\theta + 1}{\sin^2\theta - \cos^2\theta + 2\cos\theta - 1} = \dfrac{2 - 2\sin\theta(\cos\theta - 1) - 2\cos\theta}{1 - \cos^2\theta - \cos^2\theta + 2\cos\theta - 1}$

$= \dfrac{2(1 - \cos\theta) + 2\sin\theta(1 - \cos\theta)}{2\cos\theta - 2\cos^2\theta} = \dfrac{2(1 + \sin\theta)(1 - \cos\theta)}{2\cos\theta(1 - \cos\theta)} = \dfrac{\sin\theta + 1}{\cos\theta}$

61. $\dfrac{\tan\theta - \cot\theta}{\tan\theta + \cot\theta} = \dfrac{\dfrac{\sin\theta}{\cos\theta} - \dfrac{\cos\theta}{\sin\theta}}{\dfrac{\sin\theta}{\cos\theta} + \dfrac{\cos\theta}{\sin\theta}} = \dfrac{\dfrac{\sin^2\theta - \cos^2\theta}{\cos\theta\sin\theta}}{\dfrac{\sin^2\theta + \cos^2\theta}{\cos\theta\sin\theta}} = \dfrac{\sin^2\theta - \cos^2\theta}{1} = \sin^2\theta - \cos^2\theta$

62. $\dfrac{\sec\theta - \cos\theta}{\sec\theta + \cos\theta} = \dfrac{\dfrac{1}{\cos\theta} - \cos\theta}{\dfrac{1}{\cos\theta} + \cos\theta} = \dfrac{\dfrac{1 - \cos^2\theta}{\cos\theta}}{\dfrac{1 + \cos^2\theta}{\cos\theta}} = \dfrac{1 - \cos^2\theta}{1 + \cos^2\theta} = \dfrac{\sin^2\theta}{1 + \cos^2\theta}$

63. $\dfrac{\tan u - \cot u}{\tan u + \cot u} + 1 = \dfrac{\dfrac{\sin u}{\cos u} - \dfrac{\cos u}{\sin u}}{\dfrac{\sin u}{\cos u} + \dfrac{\cos u}{\sin u}} + 1 = \dfrac{\dfrac{\sin^2 u - \cos^2 u}{\cos u\sin u}}{\dfrac{\sin^2 u + \cos^2 u}{\cos u\sin u}} + 1 = \sin^2 u - \cos^2 u + 1 = \sin^2 u + (1 - \cos^2 u) = 2\sin^2 u$

64. $\dfrac{\tan u - \cot u}{\tan u + \cot u} + 2\cos^2 u = \dfrac{\dfrac{\sin u}{\cos u} - \dfrac{\cos u}{\sin u}}{\dfrac{\sin u}{\cos u} + \dfrac{\cos u}{\sin u}} + 2\cos^2 u = \dfrac{\dfrac{\sin^2 u - \cos^2 u}{\sin u\cos u}}{\dfrac{\sin^2 u + \cos^2 u}{\sin u\cos u}} + 2\cos^2 u = \sin^2 u - \cos^2 u + 2\cos^2 u = \sin^2 u + \cos^2 u = 1$

65. $\dfrac{\sec\theta + \tan\theta}{\cot\theta + \cos\theta} = \dfrac{\dfrac{1}{\cos\theta} + \dfrac{\sin\theta}{\cos\theta}}{\dfrac{\cos\theta}{\sin\theta} + \cos\theta} = \dfrac{\dfrac{1 + \sin\theta}{\cos\theta}}{\dfrac{\cos\theta + \cos\theta\sin\theta}{\sin\theta}} = \dfrac{1 + \sin\theta}{\cos\theta} \cdot \dfrac{\sin\theta}{\cos\theta(1 + \sin\theta)} = \dfrac{\sin\theta}{\cos\theta} \cdot \dfrac{1}{\cos\theta} = \tan\theta\sec\theta$

66. $\dfrac{\sec\theta}{1 + \sec\theta} = \dfrac{\dfrac{1}{\cos\theta}}{1 + \dfrac{1}{\cos\theta}} = \dfrac{\dfrac{1}{\cos\theta}}{\dfrac{\cos\theta + 1}{\cos\theta}} = \dfrac{1}{\cos\theta + 1} \cdot \dfrac{\cos\theta - 1}{\cos\theta - 1} = \dfrac{\cos\theta - 1}{\cos^2\theta - 1} = \dfrac{1 - \cos\theta}{1 - \cos^2\theta} = \dfrac{1 - \cos\theta}{\sin^2\theta}$

67. $\dfrac{1 - \tan^2\theta}{1 + \tan^2\theta} + 1 = \dfrac{1 - \tan^2\theta + 1 + \tan^2\theta}{1 + \tan^2\theta} = \dfrac{2}{1 + \tan^2\theta} = \dfrac{2}{\sec^2\theta} = 2\cos^2\theta$

68. $\dfrac{1 - \cot^2\theta}{1 + \cot^2\theta} + 2\cos^2\theta = \dfrac{1 - \cot^2\theta}{\csc^2\theta} + 2\cos^2\theta = \dfrac{1}{\csc^2\theta} - \dfrac{\cot^2\theta}{\csc^2\theta} + 2\cos^2\theta = \sin^2\theta - \dfrac{\dfrac{\cos^2\theta}{\sin^2\theta}}{\dfrac{1}{\sin^2\theta}} + 2\cos^2\theta$

$= \sin^2\theta - \cos^2\theta + 2\cos^2\theta = \sin^2\theta + \cos^2\theta = 1$

69. $\dfrac{\sec\theta - \csc\theta}{\sec\theta\csc\theta} = \dfrac{\sec\theta}{\sec\theta\csc\theta} - \dfrac{\csc\theta}{\sec\theta\csc\theta} = \dfrac{1}{\csc\theta} - \dfrac{1}{\sec\theta} = \sin\theta - \cos\theta$

70. $\dfrac{\sin^2\theta - \tan\theta}{\cos^2\theta - \cot\theta} = \dfrac{\sin^2\theta - \dfrac{\sin\theta}{\cos\theta}}{\cos^2\theta - \dfrac{\cos\theta}{\sin\theta}} = \dfrac{\dfrac{\sin^2\theta\cos\theta - \sin\theta}{\cos\theta}}{\dfrac{\sin\theta\cos^2\theta - \cos\theta}{\sin\theta}} = \dfrac{\sin\theta(\sin\theta\cos\theta - 1)}{\cos\theta} \cdot \dfrac{\sin\theta}{\cos\theta(\sin\theta\cos\theta - 1)} = \dfrac{\sin^2\theta}{\cos^2\theta} = \tan^2\theta$

71. $\sec\theta - \cos\theta = \dfrac{1}{\cos\theta} - \cos\theta = \dfrac{1 - \cos^2\theta}{\cos\theta} = \dfrac{\sin^2\theta}{\cos\theta} = \sin\theta \cdot \dfrac{\sin\theta}{\cos\theta} = \sin\theta\tan\theta$

72. $\tan\theta + \cot\theta = \dfrac{\sin\theta}{\cos\theta} + \dfrac{\cos\theta}{\sin\theta} = \dfrac{\sin^2\theta + \cos^2\theta}{\sin\theta\cos\theta} = \dfrac{1}{\sin\theta\cos\theta} = \dfrac{1}{\cos\theta} \cdot \dfrac{1}{\sin\theta} = \sec\theta\csc\theta$

73. $\dfrac{1}{1 - \sin\theta} + \dfrac{1}{1 + \sin\theta} = \dfrac{1 + \sin\theta + 1 - \sin\theta}{(1 + \sin\theta)(1 - \sin\theta)} = \dfrac{2}{1 - \sin^2\theta} = \dfrac{2}{\cos^2\theta} = 2\sec^2\theta$

74. $\dfrac{1 + \sin\theta}{1 - \sin\theta} - \dfrac{1 - \sin\theta}{1 + \sin\theta} = \dfrac{(1 + \sin\theta)^2 - (1 - \sin\theta)^2}{1 - \sin^2\theta} = \dfrac{1 + 2\sin\theta + \sin^2\theta - (1 - 2\sin\theta + \sin^2\theta)}{\cos^2\theta} = \dfrac{4\sin\theta}{\cos^2\theta} = 4 \cdot \dfrac{\sin\theta}{\cos\theta} \cdot \dfrac{1}{\cos\theta} = 4\tan\theta\sec\theta$

75. $\dfrac{\sec\theta}{1 - \sin\theta} = \dfrac{\sec\theta}{1 - \sin\theta} \cdot \dfrac{1 + \sin\theta}{1 + \sin\theta} = \dfrac{\sec\theta(1 + \sin\theta)}{1 - \sin^2\theta} = \dfrac{\sec\theta(1 + \sin\theta)}{\cos^2\theta} = \dfrac{1 + \sin\theta}{\cos^3\theta}$

76. $\dfrac{1 + \sin\theta}{1 - \sin\theta} = \dfrac{1 + \sin\theta}{1 - \sin\theta} \cdot \dfrac{1 + \sin\theta}{1 + \sin\theta} = \dfrac{(1 + \sin\theta)^2}{1 - \sin^2\theta} = \dfrac{(1 + \sin\theta)^2}{\cos^2\theta} = \left(\dfrac{1 + \sin\theta}{\cos\theta}\right)^2 = \left(\dfrac{1}{\cos\theta} + \dfrac{\sin\theta}{\cos\theta}\right)^2 = (\sec\theta + \tan\theta)^2$

77. $\dfrac{(\sec v - \tan v)^2 + 1}{\csc v(\sec v - \tan v)} = \dfrac{\sec^2 v - 2\sec v\tan v + \tan^2 v + 1}{\dfrac{1}{\sin v}\left(\dfrac{1}{\cos v} - \dfrac{\sin v}{\cos v}\right)} = \dfrac{2\sec^2 v - 2\sec v\tan v}{\dfrac{1}{\sin v}\left(\dfrac{1 - \sin v}{\cos v}\right)} = \dfrac{\dfrac{2}{\cos^2 v} - \dfrac{2\sin v}{\cos^2 v}}{\dfrac{1 - \sin v}{\sin v\cos v}} = \dfrac{2 - 2\sin v}{\cos^2 v} \cdot \dfrac{\sin v\cos v}{1 - \sin v}$

$= \dfrac{2(1 - \sin v)}{\cos v} \cdot \dfrac{\sin v}{1 - \sin v} = \dfrac{2\sin v}{\cos v} = 2\tan v$

78. $\dfrac{\sec^2 v - \tan^2 v + \tan v}{\sec v} = \dfrac{1 + \tan v}{\sec v} = \dfrac{1 + \dfrac{\sin v}{\cos v}}{\dfrac{1}{\cos v}} = \dfrac{\dfrac{\cos v + \sin v}{\cos v}}{\dfrac{1}{\cos v}} = \cos v + \sin v = \sin v + \cos v$

79. $\dfrac{\sin\theta + \cos\theta}{\cos\theta} - \dfrac{\sin\theta - \cos\theta}{\sin\theta} = \dfrac{\sin\theta}{\cos\theta} + 1 - 1 + \dfrac{\cos\theta}{\sin\theta} = \dfrac{\sin^2\theta + \cos^2\theta}{\cos\theta\sin\theta} = \dfrac{1}{\cos\theta\sin\theta} = \sec\theta\csc\theta$

80. $\dfrac{\sin\theta + \cos\theta}{\sin\theta} - \dfrac{\cos\theta - \sin\theta}{\cos\theta} = 1 + \dfrac{\cos\theta}{\sin\theta} - 1 + \dfrac{\sin\theta}{\cos\theta} = \dfrac{\cos^2\theta + \sin^2\theta}{\sin\theta\cos\theta} = \dfrac{1}{\sin\theta\cos\theta} = \sec\theta\csc\theta$

81. $\dfrac{\sin^3\theta + \cos^3\theta}{\sin\theta + \cos\theta} = \dfrac{(\sin\theta + \cos\theta)(\sin^2\theta - \sin\theta\cos\theta + \cos^2\theta)}{\sin\theta + \cos\theta} = \sin^2\theta + \cos^2\theta - \sin\theta\cos\theta = 1 - \sin\theta\cos\theta$

82. $\dfrac{\sin^3\theta + \cos^3\theta}{1 - 2\cos^2\theta} = \dfrac{(\sin\theta + \cos\theta)(\sin^2\theta - \sin\theta\cos\theta + \cos^2\theta)}{1 - \cos^2\theta - \cos^2\theta} = \dfrac{(\sin\theta + \cos\theta)(1 - \sin\theta\cos\theta)}{\sin^2\theta - \cos^2\theta} = \dfrac{(\sin\theta + \cos\theta)(1 - \sin\theta\cos\theta)}{(\sin\theta + \cos\theta)(\sin\theta - \cos\theta)}$

$= \dfrac{1 - \sin\theta\cos\theta}{\sin\theta - \cos\theta} \cdot \dfrac{\dfrac{1}{\cos\theta}}{\dfrac{1}{\cos\theta}} = \dfrac{\dfrac{1}{\cos\theta} - \sin\theta}{\dfrac{\sin\theta}{\cos\theta} - 1} = \dfrac{\sec\theta - \sin\theta}{\tan\theta - 1}$

83. $\dfrac{\cos^2\theta - \sin^2\theta}{1 - \tan^2\theta} = \dfrac{\cos^2\theta - \sin^2\theta}{1 - \dfrac{\sin^2\theta}{\cos^2\theta}} = \dfrac{\cos^2\theta - \sin^2\theta}{\dfrac{\cos^2\theta - \sin^2\theta}{\cos^2\theta}} = \cos^2\theta$

84. $\dfrac{\cos\theta + \sin\theta - \sin^3\theta}{\sin\theta} = \dfrac{\cos\theta}{\sin\theta} + \dfrac{\sin\theta(1 - \sin^2\theta)}{\sin\theta} = \cot\theta + (1 - \sin^2\theta) = \cot\theta + \cos^2\theta$

85. $\dfrac{(2\cos^2\theta - 1)^2}{\cos^4\theta - \sin^4\theta} = \dfrac{[2\cos^2\theta - (\sin^2\theta + \cos^2\theta)]^2}{(\cos^2\theta - \sin^2\theta)(\cos^2\theta + \sin^2\theta)} = \dfrac{(\cos^2\theta - \sin^2\theta)^2}{\cos^2\theta - \sin^2\theta} = \cos^2\theta - \sin^2\theta = (1 - \sin^2\theta) - \sin^2\theta = 1 - 2\sin^2\theta$

86. $\dfrac{1 - 2\cos^2\theta}{\sin\theta\cos\theta} = \dfrac{1 - \cos^2\theta - \cos^2\theta}{\sin\theta\cos\theta} = \dfrac{\sin^2\theta - \cos^2\theta}{\sin\theta\cos\theta} = \dfrac{\sin^2\theta}{\sin\theta\cos\theta} - \dfrac{\cos^2\theta}{\sin\theta\cos\theta} = \dfrac{\sin\theta}{\cos\theta} - \dfrac{\cos\theta}{\sin\theta} = \tan\theta - \cot\theta$

87. $\dfrac{1 + \sin\theta + \cos\theta}{1 + \sin\theta - \cos\theta} = \dfrac{(1 + \sin\theta) + \cos\theta}{(1 + \sin\theta) - \cos\theta} \cdot \dfrac{(1 + \sin\theta) + \cos\theta}{(1 + \sin\theta) + \cos\theta} = \dfrac{1 + 2\sin\theta + \sin^2\theta + 2(1 + \sin\theta)\cos\theta + \cos^2\theta}{1 + 2\sin\theta + \sin^2\theta - \cos^2\theta}$

$= \dfrac{1 + 2\sin\theta + \sin^2\theta + 2(1 + \sin\theta)(\cos\theta) + (1 - \sin^2\theta)}{1 + 2\sin\theta + \sin^2\theta - (1 - \sin^2\theta)} = \dfrac{2 + 2\sin\theta + 2(1 + \sin\theta)(\cos\theta)}{2\sin\theta + 2\sin^2\theta}$

$= \dfrac{2(1 + \sin\theta) + 2(1 + \sin\theta)(\cos\theta)}{2\sin\theta(1 + \sin\theta)} = \dfrac{2(1 + \sin\theta)(1 + \cos\theta)}{2\sin\theta(1 + \sin\theta)} = \dfrac{1 + \cos\theta}{\sin\theta}$

88. $\dfrac{1 + \cos\theta + \sin\theta}{1 + \cos\theta - \sin\theta} = \dfrac{(1 + \cos\theta) + \sin\theta}{(1 + \cos\theta) - \sin\theta} \cdot \dfrac{(1 + \cos\theta) + \sin\theta}{(1 + \cos\theta) + \sin\theta} = \dfrac{1 + 2\cos\theta + \cos^2\theta + 2(1 + \cos\theta)\sin\theta + \sin^2\theta}{1 + 2\cos\theta + \cos^2\theta - \sin^2\theta}$

$= \dfrac{1 + 2\cos\theta + \cos^2\theta + 2(1 + \cos\theta)\sin\theta + (1 - \cos^2\theta)}{1 + 2\cos\theta + \cos^2\theta - (1 - \cos^2\theta)} = \dfrac{2 + 2\cos\theta + 2(1 + \cos\theta)\sin\theta}{2\cos\theta + 2\cos^2\theta}$

$= \dfrac{2(1 + \cos\theta) + 2(1 + \cos\theta)\sin\theta}{2\cos\theta(1 + \cos\theta)} = \dfrac{2(1 + \sin\theta)(1 + \cos\theta)}{2\cos\theta(1 + \cos\theta)} = \dfrac{1 + \sin\theta}{\cos\theta} = \dfrac{1}{\cos\theta} + \dfrac{\sin\theta}{\cos\theta} = \sec\theta + \tan\theta$

89. $(a\sin\theta + b\cos\theta)^2 + (a\cos\theta - b\sin\theta)^2 = a^2\sin^2\theta + 2ab\sin\theta\cos\theta + b^2\cos^2\theta + a^2\cos^2\theta - 2ab\sin\theta\cos\theta + b^2\sin^2\theta$

$= a^2(\sin^2\theta + \cos^2\theta) + b^2(\cos^2\theta + \sin^2\theta) = a^2 + b^2$

90. $(2a\sin\theta\cos\theta)^2 + a^2(\cos^2\theta - \sin^2\theta)^2 = 4a^2\sin^2\theta\cos^2\theta + a^2(\cos^4\theta - 2\sin^2\theta\cos^2\theta + \sin^4\theta)$

$= a^2(\cos^4\theta + 2\sin^2\theta\cos^2\theta + \sin^4\theta) = a^2(\cos^2\theta + \sin^2\theta)^2 = a^2$

91. $\dfrac{\tan\alpha + \tan\beta}{\cot\alpha + \cot\beta} = \dfrac{\tan\alpha + \tan\beta}{\dfrac{1}{\tan\alpha} + \dfrac{1}{\tan\beta}} = \dfrac{\tan\alpha + \tan\beta}{\dfrac{\tan\beta + \tan\alpha}{\tan\alpha\tan\beta}} = (\tan\alpha + \tan\beta) \cdot \dfrac{\tan\alpha\tan\beta}{\tan\alpha + \tan\beta} = \tan\alpha\tan\beta$

92. $(\tan\alpha + \tan\beta)(1 - \cot\alpha\cot\beta) + (\cot\alpha + \cot\beta)(1 - \tan\alpha\tan\beta)$

$= \tan\alpha - \tan\alpha\cot\alpha\cot\beta + \tan\beta - \cot\alpha\cot\beta\tan\beta + \cot\alpha - \cot\alpha\tan\alpha\tan\beta + \cot\beta - \tan\alpha\tan\beta\cot\beta$

$= \tan\alpha - \cot\beta + \tan\beta - \cot\alpha + \cot\alpha - \tan\beta + \cot\beta - \tan\alpha$

$= (\tan\alpha - \tan\alpha) + (\cot\beta - \cot\beta) + (\tan\beta - \tan\beta) + (\cot\alpha - \cot\alpha) = 0$

93. $(\sin\alpha + \cos\beta)^2 + (\cos\beta + \sin\alpha)(\cos\beta - \sin\alpha) = (\sin^2\alpha + 2\sin\alpha\cos\beta + \cos^2\beta) + (\cos^2\beta - \sin^2\alpha)$

$= 2\cos^2\beta + 2\sin\alpha\cos\beta = 2\cos\beta(\cos\beta + \sin\alpha) = 2\cos\beta(\sin\alpha + \cos\beta)$

94. $(\sin\alpha - \cos\beta)^2 + (\cos\beta + \sin\alpha)(\cos\beta - \sin\alpha) = \sin^2\alpha - 2\sin\alpha\cos\beta + \cos^2\beta + \cos^2\beta - \sin^2\alpha = -2\sin\alpha\cos\beta + 2\cos^2\beta$

$= -2\cos\beta(\sin\alpha - \cos\beta)$

95. $\ln|\sec\theta| = \ln|\cos\theta|^{-1} = -\ln|\cos\theta|$ **96.** $\ln|\tan\theta| = \ln\left|\dfrac{\sin\theta}{\cos\theta}\right| = \ln|\sin\theta| - \ln|\cos\theta|$

97. $\ln|1 + \cos\theta| + \ln|1 - \cos\theta| = \ln(|1 + \cos\theta||1 - \cos\theta|) = \ln|1 - \cos^2\theta| = \ln|\sin^2\theta| = 2\ln|\sin\theta|$

98. $\ln|\sec\theta + \tan\theta| + \ln|\sec\theta - \tan\theta| = \ln(|\sec\theta + \tan\theta||\sec\theta - \tan\theta|) = \ln|\sec^2\theta - \tan^2\theta| = \ln|\tan^2\theta + 1 - \tan^2\theta| = \ln|1| = 0$

99. $g(x) = \sec x - \cos x = \dfrac{1}{\cos x} - \cos x = \dfrac{1}{\cos x} - \dfrac{\cos^2 x}{\cos x} = \dfrac{1 - \cos^2 x}{\cos x} = \dfrac{\sin^2 x}{\cos x} = \sin x \cdot \dfrac{\sin x}{\cos x} = \sin x \cdot \tan x = f(x)$

100. $g(x) = \csc x - \sin x = \dfrac{1}{\sin x} - \sin x = \dfrac{1}{\sin x} - \dfrac{\sin^2 x}{\sin x} = \dfrac{1 - \sin^2 x}{\sin x} = \dfrac{\cos^2 x}{\sin x} = \cos x \cdot \dfrac{\cos x}{\sin x} = \cos x \cdot \cot x = f(x)$

101. $f(\theta) = \dfrac{1 - \sin\theta}{\cos\theta} - \dfrac{\cos\theta}{1 + \sin\theta} = \dfrac{1 - \sin\theta}{\cos\theta} \cdot \dfrac{1 + \sin\theta}{1 + \sin\theta} - \dfrac{\cos\theta}{1 + \sin\theta} \cdot \dfrac{\cos\theta}{\cos\theta} = \dfrac{1 - \sin^2\theta}{\cos\theta(1 + \sin\theta)} - \dfrac{\cos^2\theta}{\cos\theta(1 + \sin\theta)}$

$= \dfrac{\cos^2\theta}{\cos\theta(1 + \sin\theta)} - \dfrac{\cos^2\theta}{\cos\theta(1 + \sin\theta)} = 0 = g(\theta)$

102. $g(\theta) = \dfrac{\cos\theta}{1 - \sin\theta} = \dfrac{\cos\theta}{1 - \sin\theta} \cdot \dfrac{1 + \sin\theta}{1 + \sin\theta} = \dfrac{\cos\theta(1 + \sin\theta)}{1 - \sin^2\theta} = \dfrac{\cos\theta(1 + \sin\theta)}{\cos^2\theta} = \dfrac{1 + \sin\theta}{\cos\theta} = \dfrac{1}{\cos\theta} + \dfrac{\sin\theta}{\cos\theta} = \sec\theta + \tan\theta = f(\theta)$

103. $1200\sec\theta(2\sec^2\theta - 1) = 1200\dfrac{1}{\cos\theta}\left(\dfrac{2}{\cos^2\theta} - 1\right) = 1200\dfrac{1}{\cos\theta}\left(\dfrac{2}{\cos^2\theta} - \dfrac{\cos^2\theta}{\cos^2\theta}\right) = 1200\dfrac{1}{\cos\theta}\left(\dfrac{2 - \cos^2\theta}{\cos^2\theta}\right) = \dfrac{1200(1 + 1 - \cos^2\theta)}{\cos^3\theta}$

$= \dfrac{1200(1 + \sin^2\theta)}{\cos^3\theta}$

104. $I_t = 4A^2\dfrac{(\csc\theta - 1)(\sec\theta + \tan\theta)}{\csc\theta\sec\theta} = 4A^2\dfrac{\csc\theta - 1}{\csc\theta} \cdot \dfrac{\sec\theta + \tan\theta}{\sec\theta} = 4A^2\left(1 - \dfrac{1}{\csc\theta}\right)\left(1 + \dfrac{\tan\theta}{\sec\theta}\right)$

$= 4A^2(1 - \sin\theta)(1 + \sin\theta) = 4A^2(1 - \sin^2\theta) = 4A^2\cos^2\theta = (2A\cos\theta)^2$

7.4 Assess Your Understanding *(page 473)*

4. – **5.** – **6.** F **7.** F **8.** F **9.** $\frac{1}{4}\left(\sqrt{6} + \sqrt{2}\right)$ **10.** $\frac{1}{4}\left(\sqrt{6} - \sqrt{2}\right)$ **11.** $\frac{1}{4}\left(\sqrt{2} - \sqrt{6}\right)$ **12.** $-2 - \sqrt{3}$ **13.** $-\frac{1}{4}\left(\sqrt{2} + \sqrt{6}\right)$

14. $\frac{1}{4}\left(\sqrt{6} + \sqrt{2}\right)$ **15.** $2 - \sqrt{3}$ **16.** $2 - \sqrt{3}$ **17.** $-\frac{1}{4}\left(\sqrt{6} + \sqrt{2}\right)$ **18.** $-2 - \sqrt{3}$ **19.** $\sqrt{6} - \sqrt{2}$ **20.** $-2 + \sqrt{3}$ **21.** $\frac{1}{2}$

22. $-\frac{\sqrt{3}}{2}$ **23.** 0 **24.** $\frac{\sqrt{3}}{2}$ **25.** 1 **26.** $\frac{\sqrt{3}}{3}$ **27.** -1 **28.** -1 **29.** $\frac{1}{2}$ **30.** $\frac{\sqrt{3}}{2}$ **31. (a)** $\frac{2\sqrt{5}}{25}$ **(b)** $\frac{11\sqrt{5}}{25}$ **(c)** $\frac{2\sqrt{5}}{5}$ **(d)** 2

32. (a) $\frac{2\sqrt{5}}{25}$ **(b)** $\frac{11\sqrt{5}}{25}$ **(c)** $\frac{2\sqrt{5}}{5}$ **(d)** -2 **33. (a)** $\frac{4 - 3\sqrt{3}}{10}$ **(b)** $\frac{-3 - 4\sqrt{3}}{10}$ **(c)** $\frac{4 + 3\sqrt{3}}{10}$ **(d)** $\frac{25\sqrt{3} + 48}{39}$

34. (a) $\frac{12 + 5\sqrt{3}}{26}$ **(b)** $\frac{-5 + 12\sqrt{3}}{26}$ **(c)** $\frac{-12 + 5\sqrt{3}}{26}$ **(d)** $\frac{240 - 169\sqrt{3}}{407}$

35. (a) $-\frac{5 + 12\sqrt{3}}{26}$ **(b)** $\frac{12 - 5\sqrt{3}}{26}$ **(c)** $\frac{-5 + 12\sqrt{3}}{26}$ **(d)** $\frac{-240 + 169\sqrt{3}}{69}$

36. (a) $\frac{1 - 2\sqrt{6}}{6}$ **(b)** $\frac{\sqrt{3} + 2\sqrt{2}}{6}$ **(c)** $\frac{-1 - 2\sqrt{6}}{6}$ **(d)** $\frac{-8\sqrt{2} - 9\sqrt{3}}{5}$

37. (a) $-\frac{2\sqrt{2}}{3}$ **(b)** $\frac{-2\sqrt{2} + \sqrt{3}}{6}$ **(c)** $\frac{-2\sqrt{2} + \sqrt{3}}{6}$ **(d)** $\frac{9 - 4\sqrt{2}}{7}$ **38. (a)** $-\frac{\sqrt{15}}{4}$ **(b)** $\frac{-1 - 3\sqrt{5}}{8}$ **(c)** $\frac{1 + 3\sqrt{5}}{8}$ **(d)** $\frac{8 + \sqrt{15}}{7}$

39. $\frac{1 - 2\sqrt{6}}{6}$ **40.** $\frac{\sqrt{3} + 2\sqrt{2}}{6}$ **41.** $\frac{\sqrt{3} - 2\sqrt{2}}{6}$ **42.** $\frac{1 + 2\sqrt{6}}{6}$ **43.** $\frac{8\sqrt{2} - 9\sqrt{3}}{5}$ **44.** $-\frac{8\sqrt{2} + 9\sqrt{3}}{5}$

45. $\sin\left(\frac{\pi}{2} + \theta\right) = \sin\frac{\pi}{2}\cos\theta + \cos\frac{\pi}{2}\sin\theta = 1\cdot\cos\theta + 0\cdot\sin\theta = \cos\theta$

46. $\cos\left(\frac{\pi}{2} + \theta\right) = \cos\frac{\pi}{2}\cos\theta - \sin\frac{\pi}{2}\sin\theta = 0\cdot\cos\theta - 1\cdot\sin\theta = -\sin\theta$

47. $\sin(\pi - \theta) = \sin\pi\cos\theta - \cos\pi\sin\theta = 0\cdot\cos\theta - (-1)\sin\theta = \sin\theta$

48. $\cos(\pi - \theta) = \cos\pi\cos\theta + \sin\pi\sin\theta = -1\cdot\cos\theta + 0\cdot\sin\theta = -\cos\theta$

49. $\sin(\pi + \theta) = \sin\pi\cos\theta + \cos\pi\sin\theta = 0\cdot\cos\theta + (-1)\sin\theta = -\sin\theta$

50. $\cos(\pi + \theta) = \cos\pi\cos\theta - \sin\pi\sin\theta = -1\cdot\cos\theta - 0\cdot\sin\theta = -\cos\theta$

51. $\tan(\pi - \theta) = \dfrac{\tan\pi - \tan\theta}{1 + \tan\pi\tan\theta} = \dfrac{0 - \tan\theta}{1 + 0\cdot\tan\theta} = -\tan\theta$ **52.** $\tan(2\pi - \theta) = \dfrac{\tan 2\pi - \tan\theta}{1 + \tan 2\pi\tan\theta} = \dfrac{0 - \tan\theta}{1 + 0\cdot\tan\theta} = -\tan\theta$

53. $\sin\left(\frac{3\pi}{2} + \theta\right) = \sin\frac{3\pi}{2}\cos\theta + \cos\frac{3\pi}{2}\sin\theta = (-1)\cos\theta + 0\cdot\sin\theta = -\cos\theta$

54. $\cos\left(\frac{3\pi}{2} + \theta\right) = \cos\frac{3\pi}{2}\cos\theta - \sin\frac{3\pi}{2}\sin\theta = 0\cdot\cos\theta - (-1)\sin\theta = \sin\theta$

55. $\sin(\alpha + \beta) + \sin(\alpha - \beta) = \sin\alpha\cos\beta + \cos\alpha\sin\beta + \sin\alpha\cos\beta - \cos\alpha\sin\beta = 2\sin\alpha\cos\beta$

56. $\cos(\alpha + \beta) + \cos(\alpha - \beta) = \cos\alpha\cos\beta - \sin\alpha\sin\beta + \cos\alpha\cos\beta + \sin\alpha\sin\beta = 2\cos\alpha\cos\beta$

57. $\dfrac{\sin(\alpha + \beta)}{\sin\alpha\cos\beta} = \dfrac{\sin\alpha\cos\beta + \cos\alpha\sin\beta}{\sin\alpha\cos\beta} = \dfrac{\sin\alpha\cos\beta}{\sin\alpha\cos\beta} + \dfrac{\cos\alpha\sin\beta}{\sin\alpha\cos\beta} = 1 + \cot\alpha\tan\beta$

58. $\dfrac{\sin(\alpha + \beta)}{\cos\alpha\cos\beta} = \dfrac{\sin\alpha\cos\beta + \cos\alpha\sin\beta}{\cos\alpha\cos\beta} = \dfrac{\sin\alpha\cos\beta}{\cos\alpha\cos\beta} + \dfrac{\cos\alpha\sin\beta}{\cos\alpha\cos\beta} = \tan\alpha + \tan\beta$

59. $\dfrac{\cos(\alpha + \beta)}{\cos\alpha\cos\beta} = \dfrac{\cos\alpha\cos\beta - \sin\alpha\sin\beta}{\cos\alpha\cos\beta} = \dfrac{\cos\alpha\cos\beta}{\cos\alpha\cos\beta} - \dfrac{\sin\alpha\sin\beta}{\cos\alpha\cos\beta} = 1 - \tan\alpha\tan\beta$

60. $\dfrac{\cos(\alpha - \beta)}{\sin\alpha\cos\beta} = \dfrac{\cos\alpha\cos\beta + \sin\alpha\sin\beta}{\sin\alpha\cos\beta} = \dfrac{\cos\alpha\cos\beta}{\sin\alpha\cos\beta} + \dfrac{\sin\alpha\sin\beta}{\sin\alpha\cos\beta} = \cot\alpha + \tan\beta$

61. $\dfrac{\sin(\alpha + \beta)}{\sin(\alpha - \beta)} = \dfrac{\sin\alpha\cos\beta + \cos\alpha\sin\beta}{\sin\alpha\cos\beta - \cos\alpha\sin\beta} = \dfrac{\dfrac{\sin\alpha\cos\beta + \cos\alpha\sin\beta}{\cos\alpha\cos\beta}}{\dfrac{\sin\alpha\cos\beta - \cos\alpha\sin\beta}{\cos\alpha\cos\beta}} = \dfrac{\dfrac{\sin\alpha\cos\beta}{\cos\alpha\cos\beta} + \dfrac{\cos\alpha\sin\beta}{\cos\alpha\cos\beta}}{\dfrac{\sin\alpha\cos\beta}{\cos\alpha\cos\beta} - \dfrac{\cos\alpha\sin\beta}{\cos\alpha\cos\beta}} = \dfrac{\tan\alpha + \tan\beta}{\tan\alpha - \tan\beta}$

62. $\dfrac{\cos(\alpha + \beta)}{\cos(\alpha - \beta)} = \dfrac{\cos\alpha\cos\beta - \sin\alpha\sin\beta}{\cos\alpha\cos\beta + \sin\alpha\sin\beta} = \dfrac{\dfrac{\cos\alpha\cos\beta - \sin\alpha\sin\beta}{\cos\alpha\cos\beta}}{\dfrac{\cos\alpha\cos\beta + \sin\alpha\sin\beta}{\cos\alpha\cos\beta}} = \dfrac{\dfrac{\cos\alpha\cos\beta}{\cos\alpha\cos\beta} - \dfrac{\sin\alpha\sin\beta}{\cos\alpha\cos\beta}}{\dfrac{\cos\alpha\cos\beta}{\cos\alpha\cos\beta} + \dfrac{\sin\alpha\sin\beta}{\cos\alpha\cos\beta}} = \dfrac{1 - \tan\alpha\tan\beta}{1 + \tan\alpha\tan\beta}$

63. $\cot(\alpha + \beta) = \dfrac{\cos(\alpha + \beta)}{\sin(\alpha + \beta)} = \dfrac{\cos\alpha\cos\beta - \sin\alpha\sin\beta}{\sin\alpha\cos\beta + \cos\alpha\sin\beta} = \dfrac{\dfrac{\cos\alpha\cos\beta - \sin\alpha\sin\beta}{\sin\alpha\sin\beta}}{\dfrac{\sin\alpha\cos\beta + \cos\alpha\sin\beta}{\sin\alpha\sin\beta}} = \dfrac{\dfrac{\cos\alpha\cos\beta}{\sin\alpha\sin\beta} - \dfrac{\sin\alpha\sin\beta}{\sin\alpha\sin\beta}}{\dfrac{\sin\alpha\cos\beta}{\sin\alpha\sin\beta} + \dfrac{\cos\alpha\sin\beta}{\sin\alpha\sin\beta}} = \dfrac{\cot\alpha\cot\beta - 1}{\cot\beta + \cot\alpha}$

64. $\cot(\alpha - \beta) = \dfrac{\cos(\alpha - \beta)}{\sin(\alpha - \beta)} = \dfrac{\cos \alpha \cos \beta + \sin \alpha \sin \beta}{\sin \alpha \cos \beta - \cos \alpha \sin \beta} = \dfrac{\dfrac{\cos \alpha \cos \beta + \sin \alpha \sin \beta}{\sin \alpha \sin \beta}}{\dfrac{\sin \alpha \cos \beta - \cos \alpha \sin \beta}{\sin \alpha \sin \beta}} = \dfrac{\dfrac{\cos \alpha \cos \beta}{\sin \alpha \sin \beta} + \dfrac{\sin \alpha \sin \beta}{\sin \alpha \sin \beta}}{\dfrac{\sin \alpha \cos \beta}{\sin \alpha \sin \beta} - \dfrac{\cos \alpha \sin \beta}{\sin \alpha \sin \beta}} = \dfrac{\cot \alpha \cot \beta + 1}{\cot \beta - \cot \alpha}$

65. $\sec(\alpha + \beta) = \dfrac{1}{\cos(\alpha + \beta)} = \dfrac{1}{\cos \alpha \cos \beta - \sin \alpha \sin \beta} = \dfrac{\dfrac{1}{\sin \alpha \sin \beta}}{\dfrac{\cos \alpha \cos \beta - \sin \alpha \sin \beta}{\sin \alpha \sin \beta}} = \dfrac{\dfrac{1}{\sin \alpha} \cdot \dfrac{1}{\sin \beta}}{\dfrac{\cos \alpha \cos \beta}{\sin \alpha \sin \beta} - \dfrac{\sin \alpha \sin \beta}{\sin \alpha \sin \beta}} = \dfrac{\csc \alpha \csc \beta}{\cot \alpha \cot \beta - 1}$

66. $\sec(\alpha - \beta) = \dfrac{1}{\cos(\alpha - \beta)} = \dfrac{1}{\cos \alpha \cos \beta + \sin \alpha \sin \beta} = \dfrac{\dfrac{1}{\cos \alpha \cos \beta}}{\dfrac{\cos \alpha \cos \beta + \sin \alpha \sin \beta}{\cos \alpha \cos \beta}} = \dfrac{\dfrac{1}{\cos \alpha} \cdot \dfrac{1}{\cos \beta}}{\dfrac{\cos \alpha \cos \beta}{\cos \alpha \cos \beta} + \dfrac{\sin \alpha \sin \beta}{\cos \alpha \cos \beta}} = \dfrac{\sec \alpha \sec \beta}{1 + \tan \alpha \tan \beta}$

67. $\sin(\alpha - \beta) \sin(\alpha + \beta) = (\sin \alpha \cos \beta - \cos \alpha \sin \beta)(\sin \alpha \cos \beta + \cos \alpha \sin \beta) = \sin^2 \alpha \cos^2 \beta - \cos^2 \alpha \sin^2 \beta$

$= (\sin^2 \alpha)(1 - \sin^2 \beta) - (1 - \sin^2 \alpha)(\sin^2 \beta) = \sin^2 \alpha - \sin^2 \beta$

68. $\cos(\alpha - \beta) \cos(\alpha + \beta) = (\cos \alpha \cos \beta + \sin \alpha \sin \beta)(\cos \alpha \cos \beta - \sin \alpha \sin \beta) = \cos^2 \alpha \cos^2 \beta - \sin^2 \alpha \sin^2 \beta$

$= \cos^2 \alpha(1 - \sin^2 \beta) - \sin^2 \alpha \sin^2 \beta = \cos^2 \alpha - \cos^2 \alpha \sin^2 \beta - \sin^2 \alpha \sin^2 \beta = \cos^2 \alpha - \sin^2 \beta(\cos^2 \alpha + \sin^2 \alpha) = \cos^2 \alpha - \sin^2 \beta$

69. $\sin(\theta + k\pi) = \sin \theta \cos k\pi + \cos \theta \sin k\pi = (\sin \theta)(-1)^k + (\cos \theta)(0) = (-1)^k \sin \theta, \; k$ any integer

70. $\cos(\theta + k\pi) = \cos \theta \cos k\pi - \sin \theta \sin k\pi = (\cos \theta)(-1)^k - (\sin \theta)(0) = (-1)^k \cos \theta, \; k$ any integer

71. $\dfrac{\sqrt{3}}{2}$ **72.** $\dfrac{\sqrt{3}}{2}$ **73.** $-\dfrac{24}{25}$ **74.** -1 **75.** $-\dfrac{33}{65}$ **76.** $\dfrac{33}{65}$ **77.** $\dfrac{63}{65}$ **78.** $\dfrac{16}{65}$ **79.** $\dfrac{48 + 25\sqrt{3}}{39}$ **80.** $-\dfrac{1}{7}$ **81.** $\dfrac{4}{3}$ **82.** $-\dfrac{4}{3}$

83. $u\sqrt{1 - v^2} - v\sqrt{1 - u^2} : \; -1 \le u \le 1; \; -1 \le v \le 1$ **84.** $uv - \sqrt{1 - u^2}\sqrt{1 - v^2} : -1 \le u \le 1; \; -1 \le v \le 1$

85. $\dfrac{u\sqrt{1 - v^2} - v}{\sqrt{1 + u^2}} : -\infty < u < \infty; -1 \le v \le 1$ **86.** $\dfrac{1 - uv}{\sqrt{1 + u^2}\sqrt{1 + v^2}} : \; -\infty < u < \infty; \; -\infty < v < \infty$

87. $\dfrac{uv - \sqrt{1 - u^2}\sqrt{1 - v^2}}{v\sqrt{1 - u^2} + u\sqrt{1 - v^2}} : -1 \le u \le 1; \; -1 \le v \le 1$ **88.** $\dfrac{\sqrt{1 + u^2}}{v - u\sqrt{1 - v^2}} : \; -\infty < u < \infty; \; -1 \le v \le 1$

89. Let $\alpha = \sin^{-1} v$ and $\beta = \cos^{-1} v$. Then $\sin \alpha = \cos \beta = v$, and since $\sin \alpha = \cos\left(\dfrac{\pi}{2} - \alpha\right)$, $\cos\left(\dfrac{\pi}{2} - \alpha\right) = \cos \beta$.

If $v \ge 0$, then $0 \le \alpha \le \dfrac{\pi}{2}$, so $\left(\dfrac{\pi}{2} - \alpha\right)$ and β both lie on $\left[0, \dfrac{\pi}{2}\right]$. If $v < 0$, then $-\dfrac{\pi}{2} \le \alpha < 0$, so $\left(\dfrac{\pi}{2} - \alpha\right)$ and β both lie on $\left(\dfrac{\pi}{2}, \pi\right]$.

Either way, $\cos\left(\dfrac{\pi}{2} - \alpha\right) = \cos \beta$ implies $\dfrac{\pi}{2} - \alpha = \beta$, or $\alpha + \beta = \dfrac{\pi}{2}$.

90. Let $\alpha = \tan^{-1} v$ and $\beta = \cot^{-1} v$. Then $\tan \alpha = \cot \beta = v$, and since $\tan \alpha = \cot\left(\dfrac{\pi}{2} - \alpha\right)$, $\cot\left(\dfrac{\pi}{2} - \alpha\right) = \cot \beta$.

If $v \ge 0$, then $0 \le \alpha < \dfrac{\pi}{2}$, so $\left(\dfrac{\pi}{2} - \alpha\right)$ and β both lie on $\left(0, \dfrac{\pi}{2}\right]$. If $v < 0$, then $-\dfrac{\pi}{2} < \alpha < 0$, so $\left(\dfrac{\pi}{2} - \alpha\right)$ and β both lie on $\left(\dfrac{\pi}{2}, \pi\right)$.

Either way, $\cot\left(\dfrac{\pi}{2} - \alpha\right) = \cot \beta$ implies $\dfrac{\pi}{2} - \alpha = \beta$, or $\alpha + \beta = \dfrac{\pi}{2}$.

91. Let $\alpha = \tan^{-1} \dfrac{1}{v}$ and $\beta = \tan^{-1} v$. Because $v \ne 0$, $\alpha, \beta \ne 0$. Then $\tan \alpha = \dfrac{1}{v} = \dfrac{1}{\tan \beta} = \cot \beta$, and since

$\tan \alpha = \cot\left(\dfrac{\pi}{2} - \alpha\right)$, $\cot\left(\dfrac{\pi}{2} - \alpha\right) = \cot \beta$. Because $v > 0, 0 < \alpha < \dfrac{\pi}{2}$, and so $\left(\dfrac{\pi}{2} - \alpha\right)$ and β both lie on $\left(0, \dfrac{\pi}{2}\right)$.

Then $\cot\left(\dfrac{\pi}{2} - \alpha\right) = \cot \beta$ implies $\dfrac{\pi}{2} - \alpha = \beta$, or $\alpha = \dfrac{\pi}{2} - \beta$.

92. Let $\theta = \tan^{-1} e^{-v}$. Then $\tan \theta = e^{-v}$, so $\cot \theta = \dfrac{1}{e^{-v}} = e^v$. Since $0 < \theta < \dfrac{\pi}{2}$ (because $e^{-v} > 0$), $\cot^{-1} e^v = \cot^{-1}(\cot \theta) = \theta = \tan^{-1} e^{-v}$.

93. $\sin(\sin^{-1} v + \cos^{-1} v) = \sin(\sin^{-1} v) \cos(\cos^{-1} v) + \cos(\sin^{-1} v) \sin(\cos^{-1} v) = (v)(v) + \sqrt{1 - v^2}\sqrt{1 - v^2} = v^2 + 1 - v^2 = 1$

94. $\cos(\sin^{-1} v + \cos^{-1} v) = \cos(\sin^{-1} v) \cos(\cos^{-1} v) - \sin(\sin^{-1} v) \sin(\cos^{-1} v) = \left(\sqrt{1 - v^2}\right)v - v\sqrt{1 - v^2} = 0$

95. $\dfrac{\sin(x + h) - \sin x}{h} = \dfrac{\sin x \cos h + \cos x \sin h - \sin x}{h} = \dfrac{\cos x \sin h - \sin x(1 - \cos h)}{h} = \cos x \cdot \dfrac{\sin h}{h} - \sin x \cdot \dfrac{1 - \cos h}{h}$

96. $\dfrac{\cos(x + h) - \cos x}{h} = \dfrac{\cos x \cos h - \sin x \sin h - \cos x}{h} = \dfrac{-\sin x \sin h - \cos x(1 - \cos h)}{h} = -\sin x \cdot \dfrac{\sin h}{h} - \cos x \cdot \dfrac{1 - \cos h}{h}$

97. (a) $\tan(\tan^{-1}1 + \tan^{-1}2 + \tan^{-1}3) = \tan((\tan^{-1}1 + \tan^{-1}2) + \tan^{-1}3) = \dfrac{\tan(\tan^{-1}1 + \tan^{-1}2) + \tan(\tan^{-1}3)}{1 - \tan(\tan^{-1}1 + \tan^{-1}2)\tan(\tan^{-1}3)}$

$= \dfrac{\dfrac{\tan(\tan^{-1}1) + \tan(\tan^{-1}2)}{1 - \tan(\tan^{-1}1)\tan(\tan^{-1}2)} + 3}{1 - \dfrac{\tan(\tan^{-1}1) + \tan(\tan^{-1}2)}{1 - \tan(\tan^{-1}1)\tan(\tan^{-1}2)} \cdot 3} = \dfrac{\dfrac{1+2}{1-1\cdot 2} + 3}{1 - \dfrac{1+2}{1-1\cdot 2}\cdot 3} = \dfrac{\dfrac{3}{-1} + 3}{1 - \dfrac{3}{-1}\cdot 3} = \dfrac{-3+3}{1+9} = \dfrac{0}{10} = 0$

(b) From the definition of the inverse tangent function $0 < \tan^{-1}1 < \dfrac{\pi}{2}$, $0 < \tan^{-1}2 < \dfrac{\pi}{2}$, and $0 < \tan^{-1}3 < \dfrac{\pi}{2}$, so $0 < \tan^{-1}1 + \tan^{-1}2 + \tan^{-1}3 < \dfrac{3\pi}{2}$.

On the interval $\left(0, \dfrac{3\pi}{2}\right)$, $\tan\theta = 0$ if and only if $\theta = \pi$. Therefore, from part (a), $\tan^{-1}1 + \tan^{-1}2 + \tan^{-1}3 = \pi$.

98. $\sin(\omega t)\sin(\omega t - \phi) = \sin(\omega t)[\sin(\omega t)\cos\phi - \cos(\omega t)\sin\phi] = [\sin(\omega t)]^2\cos\phi - \sin(\omega t)\cos(\omega t)\sin\phi = \cos\phi\sin^2(\omega t) - \sin\phi\sin(\omega t)\cos(\omega t)$

99. $\tan\theta = \tan(\theta_2 - \theta_1) = \dfrac{\tan\theta_2 - \tan\theta_1}{1 + \tan\theta_1\tan\theta_2} = \dfrac{m_2 - m_1}{1 + m_1 m_2}$

100. $\sin(\alpha - \theta) = \sin\alpha\cos\theta - \cos\alpha\sin\theta = \sin\theta[\sin\alpha\cot\theta - \cos\alpha] = \sin\theta\sin\alpha(\cot\theta - \cot\alpha) = \sin\theta\sin\alpha(\cot\beta + \cot\gamma)$

$= \sin\theta\sin\alpha\left(\dfrac{\cos\beta}{\sin\beta} + \dfrac{\cos\gamma}{\sin\gamma}\right) = \sin\theta\sin\alpha\left(\dfrac{\sin\gamma\cos\beta + \sin\beta\cos\gamma}{\sin\beta\sin\gamma}\right) = \sin\theta\sin\alpha\dfrac{\sin(\beta + \gamma)}{\sin\beta\sin\gamma} = \dfrac{\sin\theta\sin^2\alpha}{\sin\beta\sin\gamma}$

Similarly, $\sin(\beta - \theta) = \dfrac{\sin\theta\sin^2\beta}{\sin\alpha\sin\gamma}$ and $\sin(\gamma - \theta) = \dfrac{\sin\theta\sin^2\gamma}{\sin\alpha\sin\beta}$. Thus, $\sin(\alpha - \theta)\sin(\beta - \theta)\sin(\gamma - \theta)$

$= \dfrac{\sin\theta\sin^2\alpha}{\sin\beta\sin\gamma}\cdot\dfrac{\sin\theta\sin^2\beta}{\sin\alpha\sin\gamma}\cdot\dfrac{\sin\theta\sin^2\gamma}{\sin\alpha\sin\beta} = \sin^3\theta$.

101. $2\cot(\alpha - \beta) = \dfrac{2}{\tan(\alpha - \beta)} = 2\left(\dfrac{1 + \tan\alpha\tan\beta}{\tan\alpha - \tan\beta}\right) = 2\left(\dfrac{1 + (x+1)(x-1)}{(x+1) - (x-1)}\right) = 2\left(\dfrac{1 + x^2 - 1}{x + 1 - x + 1}\right) = \dfrac{2x^2}{2} = x^2$

102. No; $\tan\dfrac{\pi}{2}$ is undefined.   **103.** $\tan\dfrac{\pi}{2}$ is not defined; $\tan\left(\dfrac{\pi}{2} - \theta\right) = \dfrac{\sin\left(\dfrac{\pi}{2} - \theta\right)}{\cos\left(\dfrac{\pi}{2} - \theta\right)} = \dfrac{\cos\theta}{\sin\theta} = \cot\theta$.

7.5 Assess Your Understanding (page 482)

1. $\sin^2\theta$; $2\cos^2\theta$; $2\sin^2\theta$ **2.** $1 - \cos\theta$ **3.** $\sin\theta$ **4.** T   **5.** F   **6.** F   **7. (a)** $\dfrac{24}{25}$ **(b)** $\dfrac{7}{25}$ **(c)** $\dfrac{\sqrt{10}}{10}$ **(d)** $\dfrac{3\sqrt{10}}{10}$

8. (a) $\dfrac{24}{25}$ **(b)** $-\dfrac{7}{25}$ **(c)** $\dfrac{\sqrt5}{5}$ **(d)** $\dfrac{2\sqrt5}{5}$ **9. (a)** $\dfrac{24}{25}$ **(b)** $-\dfrac{7}{25}$ **(c)** $\dfrac{2\sqrt5}{5}$ **(d)** $-\dfrac{\sqrt5}{5}$ **10. (a)** $\dfrac{4}{5}$ **(b)** $\dfrac{3}{5}$ **(c)** $\sqrt{\dfrac{5 + 2\sqrt5}{10}}$ **(d)** $-\sqrt{\dfrac{5 - 2\sqrt5}{10}}$

11. (a) $-\dfrac{2\sqrt2}{3}$ **(b)** $\dfrac{1}{3}$ **(c)** $\sqrt{\dfrac{3 + \sqrt6}{6}}$ **(d)** $\sqrt{\dfrac{3 - \sqrt6}{6}}$ **12. (a)** $-\dfrac{2\sqrt2}{3}$ **(b)** $\dfrac{1}{3}$ **(c)** $\sqrt{\dfrac{3 - \sqrt6}{6}}$ **(d)** $-\sqrt{\dfrac{3 + \sqrt6}{6}}$

13. (a) $\dfrac{4\sqrt2}{9}$ **(b)** $-\dfrac{7}{9}$ **(c)** $\dfrac{\sqrt3}{3}$ **(d)** $\dfrac{\sqrt6}{3}$ **14. (a)** $\dfrac{4}{5}$ **(b)** $\dfrac{3}{5}$ **(c)** $\sqrt{\dfrac{5 + 2\sqrt5}{10}}$ **(d)** $-\sqrt{\dfrac{5 - 2\sqrt5}{10}}$

15. (a) $-\dfrac{4}{5}$ **(b)** $\dfrac{3}{5}$ **(c)** $\sqrt{\dfrac{5 + 2\sqrt5}{10}}$ **(d)** $\sqrt{\dfrac{5 - 2\sqrt5}{10}}$ **16. (a)** $-\dfrac{\sqrt3}{2}$ **(b)** $-\dfrac{1}{2}$ **(c)** $\dfrac{1}{2}$ **(d)** $-\dfrac{\sqrt3}{2}$

17. (a) $-\dfrac{3}{5}$ **(b)** $-\dfrac{4}{5}$ **(c)** $\dfrac{1}{2}\sqrt{\dfrac{10 - \sqrt{10}}{5}}$ **(d)** $-\dfrac{1}{2}\sqrt{\dfrac{10 + \sqrt{10}}{5}}$ **18. (a)** $\dfrac{3}{5}$ **(b)** $\dfrac{4}{5}$ **(c)** $\dfrac{1}{2}\sqrt{\dfrac{10 + 3\sqrt{10}}{5}}$ **(d)** $-\dfrac{1}{2}\sqrt{\dfrac{10 - 3\sqrt{10}}{5}}$

19. $\dfrac{\sqrt{2 - \sqrt2}}{2}$ **20.** $\dfrac{\sqrt{2 + \sqrt2}}{2}$ **21.** $1 - \sqrt2$ **22.** $-1 + \sqrt2$ **23.** $-\dfrac{\sqrt{2 + \sqrt3}}{2}$ **24.** $-\dfrac{\sqrt{2 - \sqrt3}}{2}$ **25.** $\dfrac{2}{\sqrt{2 + \sqrt2}} = (2 - \sqrt2)\sqrt{2 + \sqrt2}$

26. $\dfrac{2}{\sqrt{2 - \sqrt2}} = (2 + \sqrt2)\sqrt{2 - \sqrt2}$ **27.** $-\dfrac{\sqrt{2 - \sqrt2}}{2}$ **28.** $\dfrac{\sqrt{2 - \sqrt2}}{2}$ **29.** $-\dfrac{4}{5}$ **30.** $-\dfrac{3}{5}$ **31.** $\dfrac{\sqrt{10(5 - \sqrt5)}}{10}$ **32.** $\dfrac{\sqrt{10(5 + \sqrt5)}}{10}$

33. $\dfrac{4}{3}$ **34.** $\dfrac{1 + \sqrt5}{2}$ **35.** $-\dfrac{7}{8}$ **36.** $\dfrac{\sqrt{15}}{8}$ **37.** $\dfrac{\sqrt{10}}{4}$ **38.** $-\dfrac{\sqrt6}{4}$ **39.** $-\dfrac{\sqrt{15}}{3}$ **40.** $-\dfrac{\sqrt{15}}{7}$

41. $\sin^4\theta = (\sin^2\theta)^2 = \left(\dfrac{1 - \cos(2\theta)}{2}\right)^2 = \dfrac{1}{4}[1 - 2\cos(2\theta) + \cos^2(2\theta)] = \dfrac{1}{4} - \dfrac{1}{2}\cos(2\theta) + \dfrac{1}{4}\cos^2(2\theta)$

$= \dfrac{1}{4} - \dfrac{1}{2}\cos(2\theta) + \dfrac{1}{4}\left(\dfrac{1 + \cos(4\theta)}{2}\right) = \dfrac{1}{4} - \dfrac{1}{2}\cos(2\theta) + \dfrac{1}{8} + \dfrac{1}{8}\cos(4\theta) = \dfrac{3}{8} - \dfrac{1}{2}\cos(2\theta) + \dfrac{1}{8}\cos(4\theta)$

42. $\sin(4\theta) = \sin[2(2\theta)] = 2\sin(2\theta)\cos(2\theta) = (4\sin\theta\cos\theta)(1 - 2\sin^2\theta) = 4\sin\theta\cos\theta - 8\sin^3\theta\cos\theta = (\cos\theta)(4\sin\theta - 8\sin^3\theta)$

43. $\cos(3\theta) = 4\cos^3\theta - 3\cos\theta$ **44.** $\cos(4\theta) = 8\cos^4\theta - 8\cos^2\theta + 1$ **45.** $\sin(5\theta) = 16\sin^5\theta - 20\sin^3\theta + 5\sin\theta$

46. $\cos(5\theta) = 16\cos^5\theta - 20\cos^3\theta + 5\cos\theta$ **47.** $\cos^4\theta - \sin^4\theta = (\cos^2\theta + \sin^2\theta)(\cos^2\theta - \sin^2\theta) = \cos(2\theta)$

48. $\dfrac{\cot\theta - \tan\theta}{\cot\theta + \tan\theta} = \dfrac{\dfrac{\cos\theta}{\sin\theta} - \dfrac{\sin\theta}{\cos\theta}}{\dfrac{\cos\theta}{\sin\theta} + \dfrac{\sin\theta}{\cos\theta}} = \dfrac{\dfrac{\cos^2\theta - \sin^2\theta}{\sin\theta\cos\theta}}{\dfrac{\cos^2\theta + \sin^2\theta}{\sin\theta\cos\theta}} = \dfrac{\cos^2\theta - \sin^2\theta}{\cos^2\theta + \sin^2\theta} = \cos^2\theta - \sin^2\theta = \cos(2\theta)$

49. $\cot(2\theta) = \dfrac{1}{\tan(2\theta)} = \dfrac{1 - \tan^2\theta}{2\tan\theta} = \dfrac{1 - \dfrac{1}{\cot^2\theta}}{2\left(\dfrac{1}{\cot\theta}\right)} = \dfrac{\dfrac{\cot^2\theta - 1}{\cot^2\theta}}{\dfrac{2}{\cot\theta}} = \dfrac{\cot^2\theta - 1}{\cot^2\theta} \cdot \dfrac{\cot\theta}{2} = \dfrac{\cot^2\theta - 1}{2\cot\theta}$

50. $\cot(2\theta) = \dfrac{1}{\tan(2\theta)} = \dfrac{1 - \tan^2\theta}{2\tan\theta} = \dfrac{\dfrac{1}{\tan\theta} - \dfrac{\tan^2\theta}{\tan\theta}}{\dfrac{2\tan\theta}{\tan\theta}} = \dfrac{1}{2}(\cot\theta - \tan\theta)$

51. $\sec(2\theta) = \dfrac{1}{\cos(2\theta)} = \dfrac{1}{2\cos^2\theta - 1} = \dfrac{1}{\dfrac{2}{\sec^2\theta} - 1} = \dfrac{1}{\dfrac{2 - \sec^2\theta}{\sec^2\theta}} = \dfrac{\sec^2\theta}{2 - \sec^2\theta}$

52. $\csc(2\theta) = \dfrac{1}{\sin(2\theta)} = \dfrac{1}{2\sin\theta\cos\theta} = \dfrac{1}{2} \cdot \dfrac{1}{\sin\theta} \cdot \dfrac{1}{\cos\theta} = \dfrac{1}{2}\csc\theta\sec\theta$ **53.** $\cos^2(2u) - \sin^2(2u) = \cos[2(2u)] = \cos(4u)$

54. $\sin(4u) = \sin(2 \cdot 2u) = 2\sin(2u)\cos(2u) = 2(2\sin u\cos u)(1 - 2\sin^2 u) = (4\sin u\cos u)(1 - 2\sin^2 u)$

55. $\dfrac{\cos(2\theta)}{1 + \sin(2\theta)} = \dfrac{\cos^2\theta - \sin^2\theta}{1 + 2\sin\theta\cos\theta} = \dfrac{(\cos\theta - \sin\theta)(\cos\theta + \sin\theta)}{\sin^2\theta + \cos^2\theta + 2\sin\theta\cos\theta} = \dfrac{(\cos\theta - \sin\theta)(\cos\theta + \sin\theta)}{(\sin\theta + \cos\theta)(\sin\theta + \cos\theta)} = \dfrac{\cos\theta - \sin\theta}{\cos\theta + \sin\theta}$

$= \dfrac{\dfrac{\cos\theta - \sin\theta}{\sin\theta}}{\dfrac{\cos\theta + \sin\theta}{\sin\theta}} = \dfrac{\dfrac{\cos\theta}{\sin\theta} - \dfrac{\sin\theta}{\sin\theta}}{\dfrac{\cos\theta}{\sin\theta} + \dfrac{\sin\theta}{\sin\theta}} = \dfrac{\cot\theta - 1}{\cot\theta + 1}$

56. $\dfrac{1}{8}[1 - \cos(4\theta)] = \dfrac{1}{8}[1 - \cos(2 \cdot 2\theta)] = \dfrac{1}{8}[1 - (1 - 2\sin^2(2\theta))] = \dfrac{1}{4}\sin^2(2\theta) = \dfrac{1}{4}(2\sin\theta\cos\theta)^2 = \dfrac{1}{4}(4\sin^2\theta\cos^2\theta) = \sin^2\theta\cos^2\theta$

57. $\sec^2\dfrac{\theta}{2} = \dfrac{1}{\cos^2\left(\dfrac{\theta}{2}\right)} = \dfrac{1}{\dfrac{1 + \cos\theta}{2}} = \dfrac{2}{1 + \cos\theta}$ **58.** $\csc^2\dfrac{\theta}{2} = \dfrac{1}{\sin^2\left(\dfrac{\theta}{2}\right)} = \dfrac{1}{\dfrac{1 - \cos\theta}{2}} = \dfrac{2}{1 - \cos\theta}$

59. $\cot^2\dfrac{v}{2} = \dfrac{1}{\tan^2\left(\dfrac{v}{2}\right)} = \dfrac{1}{\dfrac{1 - \cos v}{1 + \cos v}} = \dfrac{1 + \cos v}{1 - \cos v} = \dfrac{1 + \dfrac{1}{\sec v}}{1 - \dfrac{1}{\sec v}} = \dfrac{\dfrac{\sec v + 1}{\sec v}}{\dfrac{\sec v - 1}{\sec v}} = \dfrac{\sec v + 1}{\sec v} \cdot \dfrac{\sec v}{\sec v - 1} = \dfrac{\sec v + 1}{\sec v - 1}$

60. $\tan\dfrac{v}{2} = \dfrac{1 - \cos v}{\sin v} = \dfrac{1}{\sin v} - \dfrac{\cos v}{\sin v} = \csc v - \cot v$

61. $\dfrac{1 - \tan^2\left(\dfrac{\theta}{2}\right)}{1 + \tan^2\left(\dfrac{\theta}{2}\right)} = \dfrac{1 - \dfrac{1 - \cos\theta}{1 + \cos\theta}}{1 + \dfrac{1 - \cos\theta}{1 + \cos\theta}} = \dfrac{\dfrac{1 + \cos\theta - (1 - \cos\theta)}{1 + \cos\theta}}{\dfrac{1 + \cos\theta + 1 - \cos\theta}{1 + \cos\theta}} = \dfrac{2\cos\theta}{1 + \cos\theta} \cdot \dfrac{1 + \cos\theta}{2} = \cos\theta$

62. $\dfrac{\sin^3\theta + \cos^3\theta}{\sin\theta + \cos\theta} = \sin^2\theta - \sin\theta\cos\theta + \cos^2\theta = 1 - \sin\theta\cos\theta = 1 - \dfrac{1}{2}(2\sin\theta\cos\theta) = 1 - \dfrac{1}{2}\sin(2\theta)$

63. $\dfrac{\sin(3\theta)}{\sin\theta} - \dfrac{\cos(3\theta)}{\cos\theta} = \dfrac{\sin(3\theta)\cos\theta - \cos(3\theta)\sin\theta}{\sin\theta\cos\theta} = \dfrac{\sin(3\theta - \theta)}{\dfrac{1}{2}(2\sin\theta\cos\theta)} = \dfrac{2\sin(2\theta)}{\sin(2\theta)} = 2$

64. $\dfrac{\cos\theta + \sin\theta}{\cos\theta - \sin\theta} - \dfrac{\cos\theta - \sin\theta}{\cos\theta + \sin\theta} = \dfrac{(\cos\theta + \sin\theta)^2 - (\cos\theta - \sin\theta)^2}{(\cos\theta - \sin\theta)(\cos\theta + \sin\theta)} = \dfrac{\cos^2\theta + 2\sin\theta\cos\theta + \sin^2\theta - \cos^2\theta + 2\sin\theta\cos\theta - \sin^2\theta}{\cos^2\theta - \sin^2\theta}$

$= \dfrac{4\sin\theta\cos\theta}{\cos^2\theta - \sin^2\theta} = 2\left(\dfrac{2\sin\theta\cos\theta}{\cos^2\theta - \sin^2\theta}\right) = 2\left(\dfrac{\sin(2\theta)}{\cos(2\theta)}\right) = 2\tan(2\theta)$

65. $\tan(3\theta) = \tan(\theta + 2\theta) = \dfrac{\tan\theta + \tan(2\theta)}{1 - \tan\theta\tan(2\theta)} = \dfrac{\tan\theta + \dfrac{2\tan\theta}{1 - \tan^2\theta}}{1 - \dfrac{\tan\theta(2\tan\theta)}{1 - \tan^2\theta}} = \dfrac{\tan\theta - \tan^3\theta + 2\tan\theta}{1 - \tan^2\theta - 2\tan^2\theta} = \dfrac{3\tan\theta - \tan^3\theta}{1 - 3\tan^2\theta}$

66. $\tan\theta + \tan(\theta + 120°) + \tan(\theta + 240°) = \tan\theta + \dfrac{\tan\theta + \tan 120°}{1 - \tan\theta\tan 120°} + \dfrac{\tan\theta + \tan 240°}{1 - \tan\theta\tan 240°}$

$= \tan\theta + \dfrac{\tan\theta - \sqrt{3}}{1 + \sqrt{3}\tan\theta} + \dfrac{\tan\theta + \sqrt{3}}{1 - \sqrt{3}\tan\theta} = \tan\theta + \dfrac{\left(\tan\theta - \sqrt{3}\right)\left(1 - \sqrt{3}\tan\theta\right) + \left(\tan\theta + \sqrt{3}\right)\left(1 + \sqrt{3}\tan\theta\right)}{1 - 3\tan^2\theta}$

$= \dfrac{\tan\theta - 3\tan^3\theta + \tan\theta - \sqrt{3}\tan^2\theta - \sqrt{3} + 3\tan\theta + \tan\theta + \sqrt{3}\tan^2\theta + \sqrt{3} + 3\tan\theta}{1 - 3\tan^2\theta}$

$= 3\left(\dfrac{3\tan\theta - \tan^3\theta}{1 - 3\tan^2\theta}\right) = 3\tan(3\theta)$ (from Problem 65)

67. $\dfrac{1}{2}(\ln|1 - \cos(2\theta)| - \ln 2) = \ln\left(\dfrac{|1 - \cos(2\theta)|}{2}\right)^{1/2} = \ln|\sin^2\theta|^{1/2} = \ln|\sin\theta|$

68. $\dfrac{1}{2}(\ln|1 + \cos(2\theta)| - \ln 2) = \ln\left(\dfrac{|1 + \cos(2\theta)|}{2}\right)^{1/2} = \ln|\cos^2\theta|^{1/2} = \ln|\cos\theta|$

69. $\dfrac{\sqrt{3}}{2}$ **70.** $\dfrac{\sqrt{3}}{2}$ **71.** $\dfrac{7}{25}$ **72.** $\dfrac{7}{25}$ **73.** $\dfrac{24}{7}$ **74.** $\dfrac{24}{7}$ **75.** $\dfrac{24}{25}$ **76.** $-\dfrac{7}{25}$ **77.** $\dfrac{1}{5}$ **78.** $\dfrac{9}{10}$ **79.** $\dfrac{25}{7}$ **80.** $-\dfrac{25}{24}$

81. (a) $W = 2D(\csc\theta - \cot\theta) = 2D\left(\dfrac{1}{\sin\theta} - \dfrac{\cos\theta}{\sin\theta}\right) = 2D\dfrac{1 - \cos\theta}{\sin\theta} = 2D\tan\dfrac{\theta}{2}$ **(b)** $\theta = 24.45°$

82. $I_{uv} = (I_x - I_y)\sin\theta\cos\theta + I_{xy}(\cos 2\theta) = \dfrac{I_x - I_y}{2}(2\sin\theta\cos\theta) + I_{xy}(\cos 2\theta) = \dfrac{I_x - I_y}{2}\sin 2\theta + I_{xy}\cos 2\theta$

83. (a) $R = \dfrac{v_0^2\sqrt{2}}{16}\cos\theta(\sin\theta - \cos\theta)$ **(b)**

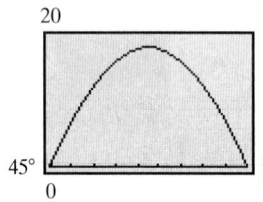

(c) $\theta = 67.5°$ makes R largest.

$= \dfrac{v_0^2\sqrt{2}}{32}(2\cos\theta\sin\theta - 2\cos^2\theta)$

$= \dfrac{v_0^2\sqrt{2}}{32}[\sin(2\theta) - \cos(2\theta) - 1]$

84. $y = \dfrac{1}{2}\sin(2\pi x) + \dfrac{1}{4}\sin(4\pi x) = \dfrac{1}{2}\sin(2\pi x) + \dfrac{1}{4}\sin(2\cdot 2\pi x) = \dfrac{1}{2}\sin(2\pi x) + \dfrac{1}{4}[2\sin(2\pi x)\cos(2\pi x)]$

$= \dfrac{1}{2}\sin(2\pi x) + \dfrac{1}{2}[\sin(2\pi x)\cdot\cos(2\cdot\pi x)] = \dfrac{1}{2}\sin(2\pi x) + \dfrac{1}{2}[\sin(2\pi x)\cdot(2\cos^2(\pi x) - 1)]$

$= \dfrac{1}{2}\sin(2\pi x) - \dfrac{1}{2}\sin(2\pi x) + \sin(2\pi x)\cos^2(\pi x) = \sin(2\pi x)\cos^2(\pi x)$

85. $A = \dfrac{1}{2}h(\text{base}) = h\left(\dfrac{1}{2}\text{base}\right) = s\cos\dfrac{\theta}{2}\cdot s\sin\dfrac{\theta}{2} = \dfrac{1}{2}s^2\sin\theta$ **86. (a)** $A = 2\sin\theta\cos\theta$ **(b)** $2\sin\theta\cos\theta = \sin(2\theta)$

(c) $\theta = 45°$ **(d)** $\sqrt{2}$ by $\dfrac{\sqrt{2}}{2}$ **87.** $\sin(2\theta) = \dfrac{4x}{4 + x^2}$ **88.** $\cos(2\theta) = \dfrac{4 - x^2}{4 + x^2}$ **89.** $-\dfrac{1}{4}$ **90.** $-\dfrac{1}{4}$

91. $\dfrac{2z}{1 + z^2} = \dfrac{2\tan\left(\dfrac{\alpha}{2}\right)}{1 + \tan^2\left(\dfrac{\alpha}{2}\right)} = \dfrac{2\tan\left(\dfrac{\alpha}{2}\right)}{\sec^2\left(\dfrac{\alpha}{2}\right)} = \dfrac{\dfrac{2\sin\left(\dfrac{\alpha}{2}\right)}{\cos\left(\dfrac{\alpha}{2}\right)}}{\dfrac{1}{\cos^2\left(\dfrac{\alpha}{2}\right)}} = 2\sin\left(\dfrac{\alpha}{2}\right)\cos\left(\dfrac{\alpha}{2}\right) = \sin\left(2\cdot\dfrac{\alpha}{2}\right) = \sin\alpha$

92. $\dfrac{1 - z^2}{1 + z^2} = \dfrac{1 - \tan^2\left(\dfrac{\alpha}{2}\right)}{1 + \tan^2\left(\dfrac{\alpha}{2}\right)} = \dfrac{1 - \dfrac{1 - \cos\alpha}{1 + \cos\alpha}}{1 + \dfrac{1 - \cos\alpha}{1 + \cos\alpha}} = \dfrac{\dfrac{1 + \cos\alpha - 1 + \cos\alpha}{1 + \cos\alpha}}{\dfrac{1 + \cos\alpha + 1 - \cos\alpha}{1 + \cos\alpha}} = \dfrac{2\cos\alpha}{2} = \cos\alpha$

93.

94.

95. $\sin\dfrac{\pi}{24} = \dfrac{\sqrt{2}}{4}\sqrt{4 - \sqrt{6} - \sqrt{2}}$

$\cos\dfrac{\pi}{24} = \dfrac{\sqrt{2}}{4}\sqrt{4 + \sqrt{6} + \sqrt{2}}$

96. $\cos\dfrac{\pi}{8} = \cos\left(\dfrac{\dfrac{\pi}{4}}{2}\right) = \sqrt{\dfrac{1 + \cos\dfrac{\pi}{4}}{2}} = \sqrt{\dfrac{1 + \dfrac{\sqrt{2}}{2}}{2}} = \sqrt{\dfrac{2 + \sqrt{2}}{4}} = \dfrac{\sqrt{2 + \sqrt{2}}}{2}$; $\sin\left(\dfrac{\pi}{16}\right) = \dfrac{\sqrt{2 - \sqrt{2 + \sqrt{2}}}}{2}$; $\cos\left(\dfrac{\pi}{16}\right) = \dfrac{\sqrt{2 + \sqrt{2 + \sqrt{2}}}}{2}$

97. $\sin^3\theta + \sin^3(\theta + 120°) + \sin^3(\theta + 240°) = \sin^3\theta + (\sin\theta\cos 120° + \cos\theta\sin 120°)^3 + (\sin\theta\cos 240° + \cos\theta\sin 240°)^3$

$= \sin^3\theta + \left(-\dfrac{1}{2}\sin\theta + \dfrac{\sqrt{3}}{2}\cos\theta\right)^3 + \left(-\dfrac{1}{2}\sin\theta - \dfrac{\sqrt{3}}{2}\cos\theta\right)^3$

$= \sin^3\theta + \dfrac{1}{8}\left(3\sqrt{3}\cos^3\theta - 9\cos^2\theta\sin\theta + 3\sqrt{3}\cos\theta\sin^2\theta - \sin^3\theta\right) - \dfrac{1}{8}\left(\sin^3\theta + 3\sqrt{3}\sin^2\theta\cos\theta + 9\sin\theta\cos^2\theta + 3\sqrt{3}\cos^3\theta\right)$

$= \dfrac{3}{4}\sin^3\theta - \dfrac{9}{4}\cos^2\theta\sin\theta = \dfrac{3}{4}[\sin^3\theta - 3\sin\theta(1 - \sin^2\theta)] = \dfrac{3}{4}(4\sin^3\theta - 3\sin\theta) = -\dfrac{3}{4}\sin(3\theta)$ (from Example 2)

98. $\tan\theta = \tan\left(3\cdot\dfrac{\theta}{3}\right) = \dfrac{3\tan\dfrac{\theta}{3} - \tan^3\dfrac{\theta}{3}}{1 - 3\tan^2\dfrac{\theta}{3}}$ (from Problem 65)

$a\tan\dfrac{\theta}{3} = \dfrac{\tan\dfrac{\theta}{3}\left(3 - \tan^2\dfrac{\theta}{3}\right)}{1 - 3\tan^2\dfrac{\theta}{3}} \Rightarrow a - 3a\tan^2\dfrac{\theta}{3} = 3 - \tan^2\dfrac{\theta}{3} \Rightarrow a - 3 = 3a\tan^2\dfrac{\theta}{3} - \tan^2\dfrac{\theta}{3} \Rightarrow a - 3 = \tan^2\dfrac{\theta}{3}(3a - 1)$

$\Rightarrow \tan^2\dfrac{\theta}{3} = \dfrac{a - 3}{3a - 1} \Rightarrow \tan\dfrac{\theta}{3} = \pm\sqrt{\dfrac{a - 3}{3a - 1}}$

7.6 Assess Your Understanding *(page 487)*

1. $\dfrac{1}{2}[\cos(2\theta) - \cos(6\theta)]$ **2.** $\dfrac{1}{2}[\cos(2\theta) + \cos(6\theta)]$ **3.** $\dfrac{1}{2}[\sin(6\theta) + \sin(2\theta)]$ **4.** $\dfrac{1}{2}[\cos(2\theta) - \cos(8\theta)]$ **5.** $\dfrac{1}{2}[\cos(2\theta) + \cos(8\theta)]$

6. $\dfrac{1}{2}[\sin(10\theta) - \sin(2\theta)]$ **7.** $\dfrac{1}{2}[\cos\theta - \cos(3\theta)]$ **8.** $\dfrac{1}{2}[\cos\theta + \cos(7\theta)]$ **9.** $\dfrac{1}{2}[\sin(2\theta) + \sin\theta]$ **10.** $\dfrac{1}{2}[\sin(3\theta) - \sin(2\theta)]$ **11.** $2\sin\theta\cos(3\theta)$

12. $2\sin(3\theta)\cos\theta$ **13.** $2\cos(3\theta)\cos\theta$ **14.** $-2\sin(4\theta)\sin\theta$ **15.** $2\sin(2\theta)\cos\theta$ **16.** $2\cos(2\theta)\cos\theta$ **17.** $2\sin\theta\sin\dfrac{\theta}{2}$ **18.** $-2\sin\dfrac{\theta}{2}\cos\theta$

19. $\dfrac{\sin\theta + \sin(3\theta)}{2\sin(2\theta)} = \dfrac{2\sin(2\theta)\cos\theta}{2\sin(2\theta)} = \cos\theta$ **20.** $\dfrac{\cos\theta + \cos(3\theta)}{2\cos(2\theta)} = \dfrac{2\cos(2\theta)\cos\theta}{2\cos(2\theta)} = \cos\theta$

21. $\dfrac{\sin(4\theta) + \sin(2\theta)}{\cos(4\theta) + \cos(2\theta)} = \dfrac{2\sin(3\theta)\cos\theta}{2\cos(3\theta)\cos\theta} = \dfrac{\sin(3\theta)}{\cos(3\theta)} = \tan(3\theta)$ **22.** $\dfrac{\cos\theta - \cos(3\theta)}{\sin(3\theta) - \sin\theta} = \dfrac{2\sin(2\theta)\sin\theta}{2\sin\theta\cos(2\theta)} = \dfrac{\sin(2\theta)}{\cos(2\theta)} = \tan(2\theta)$

23. $\dfrac{\cos\theta - \cos(3\theta)}{\sin\theta + \sin(3\theta)} = \dfrac{2\sin(2\theta)\sin\theta}{2\sin(2\theta)\cos\theta} = \dfrac{\sin\theta}{\cos\theta} = \tan\theta$ **24.** $\dfrac{\cos\theta - \cos(5\theta)}{\sin\theta + \sin(5\theta)} = \dfrac{2\sin(3\theta)\sin(2\theta)}{2\sin(3\theta)\cos(2\theta)} = \dfrac{\sin(2\theta)}{\cos(2\theta)} = \tan(2\theta)$

25. $\sin\theta[\sin\theta + \sin(3\theta)] = \sin\theta[2\sin(2\theta)\cos\theta] = \cos\theta[2\sin(2\theta)\sin\theta] = \cos\theta\left[2\cdot\dfrac{1}{2}[\cos\theta - \cos(3\theta)]\right] = \cos\theta[\cos\theta - \cos(3\theta)]$

26. $\sin\theta[\sin(3\theta) + \sin(5\theta)] = \sin\theta[2\sin(4\theta)\cos\theta] = \cos\theta[2\sin(4\theta)\sin\theta] = \cos\theta\left[2\cdot\dfrac{1}{2}[\cos(3\theta) - \cos(5\theta)]\right] = \cos\theta[\cos(3\theta) - \cos(5\theta)]$

27. $\dfrac{\sin(4\theta) + \sin(8\theta)}{\cos(4\theta) + \cos(8\theta)} = \dfrac{2\sin(6\theta)\cos(2\theta)}{2\cos(6\theta)\cos(2\theta)} = \dfrac{\sin(6\theta)}{\cos(6\theta)} = \tan(6\theta)$ **28.** $\dfrac{\sin(4\theta) - \sin(8\theta)}{\cos(4\theta) - \cos(8\theta)} = \dfrac{2\sin(-2\theta)\cos(6\theta)}{-2\sin(6\theta)\sin(-2\theta)} = -\dfrac{\cos(6\theta)}{\sin(6\theta)} = -\cot(6\theta)$

29. $\dfrac{\sin(4\theta) + \sin(8\theta)}{\sin(4\theta) - \sin(8\theta)} = \dfrac{2\sin(6\theta)\cos(-2\theta)}{2\sin(-2\theta)\cos(6\theta)} = \dfrac{\sin(6\theta)}{\cos(6\theta)}\cdot\dfrac{\cos(2\theta)}{-\sin(2\theta)} = \tan(6\theta)[-\cot(2\theta)] = -\dfrac{\tan(6\theta)}{\tan(2\theta)}$

30. $\dfrac{\cos(4\theta) - \cos(8\theta)}{\cos(4\theta) + \cos(8\theta)} = \dfrac{-2\sin(6\theta)\sin(-2\theta)}{2\cos(6\theta)\cos(-2\theta)} = \dfrac{\sin(2\theta)}{\cos(2\theta)}\cdot\dfrac{\sin(6\theta)}{\cos(6\theta)} = \tan(2\theta)\tan(6\theta)$

31. $\dfrac{\sin\alpha + \sin\beta}{\sin\alpha - \sin\beta} = \dfrac{2\sin\dfrac{\alpha+\beta}{2}\cos\dfrac{\alpha-\beta}{2}}{2\sin\dfrac{\alpha-\beta}{2}\cos\dfrac{\alpha+\beta}{2}} = \dfrac{\sin\dfrac{\alpha+\beta}{2}}{\cos\dfrac{\alpha+\beta}{2}}\cdot\dfrac{\cos\dfrac{\alpha-\beta}{2}}{\sin\dfrac{\alpha-\beta}{2}} = \tan\dfrac{\alpha+\beta}{2}\cot\dfrac{\alpha-\beta}{2}$

32. $\dfrac{\cos\alpha + \cos\beta}{\cos\alpha - \cos\beta} = \dfrac{2\cos\dfrac{\alpha+\beta}{2}\cos\dfrac{\alpha-\beta}{2}}{-2\sin\dfrac{\alpha+\beta}{2}\sin\dfrac{\alpha-\beta}{2}} = -\dfrac{\cos\dfrac{\alpha+\beta}{2}}{\sin\dfrac{\alpha+\beta}{2}}\cdot\dfrac{\cos\dfrac{\alpha-\beta}{2}}{\sin\dfrac{\alpha-\beta}{2}} = -\cot\dfrac{\alpha+\beta}{2}\cot\dfrac{\alpha-\beta}{2}$

33. $\dfrac{\sin\alpha + \sin\beta}{\cos\alpha + \cos\beta} = \dfrac{2\sin\dfrac{\alpha+\beta}{2}\cos\dfrac{\alpha-\beta}{2}}{2\cos\dfrac{\alpha+\beta}{2}\cos\dfrac{\alpha-\beta}{2}} = \dfrac{\sin\dfrac{\alpha+\beta}{2}}{\cos\dfrac{\alpha+\beta}{2}} = \tan\dfrac{\alpha+\beta}{2}$ **34.** $\dfrac{\sin\alpha - \sin\beta}{\cos\alpha - \cos\beta} = \dfrac{2\sin\dfrac{\alpha-\beta}{2}\cos\dfrac{\alpha+\beta}{2}}{-2\sin\dfrac{\alpha+\beta}{2}\sin\dfrac{\alpha-\beta}{2}} = -\dfrac{\cos\dfrac{\alpha+\beta}{2}}{\sin\dfrac{\alpha+\beta}{2}} = -\cot\dfrac{\alpha+\beta}{2}$

35. $1 + \cos(2\theta) + \cos(4\theta) + \cos(6\theta) = [1 + \cos(6\theta)] + [\cos(2\theta) + \cos(4\theta)] = 2\cos^2(3\theta) + 2\cos(3\theta)\cos(-\theta)$

$= 2\cos(3\theta)[\cos(3\theta) + \cos\theta] = 2\cos(3\theta)[2\cos(2\theta)\cos\theta] = 4\cos\theta\cos(2\theta)\cos(3\theta)$

36. $1 - \cos(2\theta) + \cos(4\theta) - \cos(6\theta) = [1 - \cos(6\theta)] + [\cos(4\theta) - \cos(2\theta)] = 2\sin^2(3\theta) + [-2\sin(3\theta)\sin\theta]$

$= 2\sin(3\theta)[\sin(3\theta) - \sin\theta] = 2\sin(3\theta)[2\sin\theta\cos(2\theta)] = 4\sin\theta\cos(2\theta)\sin(3\theta)$

37. (a) $y = 2\sin(2061\pi t)\cos(357\pi t)$ **(b)** $y_{max} = 2$ **38. (a)** $y = 2\sin(2418\pi t)\cos(536\pi t)$ **(b)** $y_{max} = 2$

(c)   **(c)**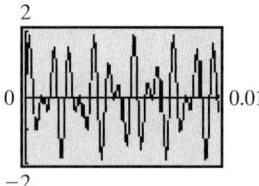

39. $I_u = I_x\cos^2\theta + I_y\sin^2\theta - 2I_{xy}\sin\theta\cos\theta = I_x\cos^2\theta + I_y\sin^2\theta - I_{xy}\sin 2\theta$

$= I_x\left(\dfrac{\cos 2\theta + 1}{2}\right) + I_y\left(\dfrac{1 - \cos 2\theta}{2}\right) - I_{xy}\sin 2\theta$

$= \dfrac{I_x}{2}\cos 2\theta + \dfrac{I_x}{2} + \dfrac{I_y}{2} - \dfrac{I_y}{2}\cos 2\theta - I_{xy}\sin 2\theta$

$= \dfrac{I_x + I_y}{2} + \dfrac{I_x - I_y}{2}\cos 2\theta - I_{xy}\sin 2\theta$

$I_v = I_x\sin^2\theta + I_y\cos^2\theta + 2I_{xy}\sin\theta\cos\theta = I_x\left(\dfrac{1 - \cos 2\theta}{2}\right) + I_y\left(\dfrac{\cos 2\theta + 1}{2}\right) + I_{xy}\sin 2\theta$

$= \dfrac{I_x}{2} - \dfrac{I_x}{2}\cos 2\theta + \dfrac{I_y}{2}\cos 2\theta + \dfrac{I_y}{2} + I_{xy}\sin 2\theta$

$= \dfrac{I_x + I_y}{2} - \dfrac{I_x - I_y}{2}\cos 2\theta + I_{xy}\sin 2\theta$

40. (a) Since ϕ and v_0 are fixed, we need to maximize $\sin\theta\cos(\theta - \phi)$.

$\sin\theta\cos(\theta - \phi) = \dfrac{1}{2}\left[\sin\left(\theta + (\theta - \phi)\right) + \sin\left(\theta - (\theta - \phi)\right)\right]$

$= \dfrac{1}{2}\left[\sin(2\theta - \phi) + \sin\phi\right]$

For fixed ϕ, this quantity will be maximized when $\sin(2\theta - \phi) = 1$. So

$\max R(\theta) = \dfrac{2v_0^2 \cdot \frac{1}{2} \cdot (1 + \sin\phi)}{g\cos^2\phi} = \dfrac{v_0^2(1 + \sin\phi)}{g(1 - \sin^2\phi)} = \dfrac{v_0^2(1 + \sin\phi)}{g(1 + \sin\phi)(1 - \sin\phi)} = \dfrac{v_0^2}{g(1 - \sin\phi)}$

(b) The maximum range is 598 m.

41. $\sin(2\alpha) + \sin(2\beta) + \sin(2\gamma) = 2\sin(\alpha + \beta)\cos(\alpha - \beta) + \sin(2\gamma) = 2\sin(\alpha + \beta)\cos(\alpha - \beta) + 2\sin\gamma\cos\gamma$

$= 2\sin(\pi - \gamma)\cos(\alpha - \beta) + 2\sin\gamma\cos\gamma = 2\sin\gamma\cos(\alpha - \beta) + 2\sin\gamma\cos\gamma = 2\sin\gamma[\cos(\alpha - \beta) + \cos\gamma]$

$= 2\sin\gamma\left(2\cos\dfrac{\alpha - \beta + \gamma}{2}\cos\dfrac{\alpha - \beta - \gamma}{2}\right) = 4\sin\gamma\cos\dfrac{\pi - 2\beta}{2}\cos\dfrac{2\alpha - \pi}{2} = 4\sin\gamma\cos\left(\dfrac{\pi}{2} - \beta\right)\cos\left(\alpha - \dfrac{\pi}{2}\right)$

$= 4\sin\gamma\sin\beta\sin\alpha = 4\sin\alpha\sin\beta\sin\gamma$

42. $\tan\alpha + \tan\beta + \tan\gamma = \dfrac{\sin\alpha}{\cos\alpha} + \dfrac{\sin\beta}{\cos\beta} + \dfrac{\sin\gamma}{\cos\gamma} = \dfrac{\sin\alpha\cos\beta\cos\gamma + \sin\beta\cos\alpha\cos\gamma + \sin\gamma\cos\alpha\cos\beta}{\cos\alpha\cos\beta\cos\gamma}$

$= \dfrac{\cos\gamma\sin(\alpha + \beta) + \sin\gamma\cos\alpha\cos\beta}{\cos\alpha\cos\beta\cos\gamma} = \dfrac{\sin\gamma(\cos\gamma + \cos\alpha\cos\beta)}{\cos\alpha\cos\beta\cos\gamma} = \dfrac{\sin\gamma[-\cos(\alpha + \beta) + \cos\alpha\cos\beta]}{\cos\alpha\cos\beta\cos\gamma} = \dfrac{\sin\gamma(\sin\alpha\sin\beta)}{\cos\alpha\cos\beta\cos\gamma}$

$= \tan\alpha\tan\beta\tan\gamma$ [Note that $\alpha + \beta = \pi - \gamma$, $\sin(\alpha + \beta) = \sin\gamma$, $\cos\gamma = \cos[\pi - (\alpha + \beta)] = -\cos(\alpha + \beta)$.]

43.
$$\sin(\alpha - \beta) = \sin\alpha\cos\beta - \cos\alpha\sin\beta$$
$$\sin(\alpha + \beta) = \sin\alpha\cos\beta + \cos\alpha\sin\beta$$
$$\sin(\alpha - \beta) + \sin(\alpha + \beta) = 2\sin\alpha\cos\beta$$
$$\sin\alpha\cos\beta = \dfrac{1}{2}[\sin(\alpha + \beta) + \sin(\alpha - \beta)]$$

44. $2\sin\dfrac{\alpha - \beta}{2}\cos\dfrac{\alpha + \beta}{2} = 2 \cdot \dfrac{1}{2}\left[\sin\left(\dfrac{\alpha - \beta}{2} + \dfrac{\alpha + \beta}{2}\right) + \sin\left(\dfrac{\alpha - \beta}{2} - \dfrac{\alpha + \beta}{2}\right)\right] = \sin\dfrac{2\alpha}{2} + \sin\left(-\dfrac{2\beta}{2}\right) = \sin\alpha - \sin\beta$

45. $2\cos\dfrac{\alpha + \beta}{2}\cos\dfrac{\alpha - \beta}{2} = 2 \cdot \dfrac{1}{2}\left[\cos\left(\dfrac{\alpha + \beta}{2} + \dfrac{\alpha - \beta}{2}\right) + \cos\left(\dfrac{\alpha + \beta}{2} - \dfrac{\alpha - \beta}{2}\right)\right] = \cos\dfrac{2\alpha}{2} + \cos\dfrac{2\beta}{2} = \cos\alpha + \cos\beta$

46. $-2\sin\dfrac{\alpha + \beta}{2}\sin\dfrac{\alpha - \beta}{2} = -2 \cdot \dfrac{1}{2}\left[\cos\left(\dfrac{\alpha + \beta}{2} - \dfrac{\alpha - \beta}{2}\right) - \cos\left(\dfrac{\alpha + \beta}{2} + \dfrac{\alpha - \beta}{2}\right)\right] = -\cos\dfrac{2\beta}{2} + \cos\dfrac{2\alpha}{2} = \cos\alpha - \cos\beta$

7.7 Assess Your Understanding (*page 492*)

3. $\dfrac{\pi}{6}; \dfrac{5\pi}{6}$ **4.** $\left\{\theta \,\middle|\, \theta = \dfrac{\pi}{6} + 2\pi k, \theta = \dfrac{5\pi}{6} + 2\pi k, k \text{ is any integer}\right\}$ **5.** F **6.** F **7.** $\left\{\dfrac{7\pi}{6}, \dfrac{11\pi}{6}\right\}$ **8.** $\left\{\dfrac{\pi}{3}, \dfrac{5\pi}{3}\right\}$ **9.** $\left\{\dfrac{\pi}{3}, \dfrac{2\pi}{3}, \dfrac{4\pi}{3}, \dfrac{5\pi}{3}\right\}$

10. $\left\{\dfrac{\pi}{6}, \dfrac{5\pi}{6}, \dfrac{7\pi}{6}, \dfrac{11\pi}{6}\right\}$ **11.** $\left\{\dfrac{\pi}{4}, \dfrac{3\pi}{4}, \dfrac{5\pi}{4}, \dfrac{7\pi}{4}\right\}$ **12.** $\left\{\dfrac{\pi}{6}, \dfrac{5\pi}{6}, \dfrac{7\pi}{6}, \dfrac{11\pi}{6}\right\}$ **13.** $\left\{\dfrac{\pi}{2}, \dfrac{7\pi}{6}, \dfrac{11\pi}{6}\right\}$ **14.** $\left\{\dfrac{2\pi}{3}\right\}$ **15.** $\left\{\dfrac{\pi}{3}, \dfrac{2\pi}{3}, \dfrac{4\pi}{3}, \dfrac{5\pi}{3}\right\}$

16. $\left\{\dfrac{3\pi}{8}, \dfrac{7\pi}{8}, \dfrac{11\pi}{8}, \dfrac{15\pi}{8}\right\}$ **17.** $\left\{\dfrac{4\pi}{9}, \dfrac{8\pi}{9}, \dfrac{16\pi}{9}\right\}$ **18.** $\left\{\dfrac{5\pi}{4}\right\}$ **19.** $\left\{\dfrac{7\pi}{6}, \dfrac{11\pi}{6}\right\}$ **20.** $\{\pi\}$ **21.** $\left\{\dfrac{3\pi}{4}, \dfrac{7\pi}{4}\right\}$ **22.** $\left\{\dfrac{2\pi}{3}, \dfrac{5\pi}{3}\right\}$ **23.** $\left\{\dfrac{2\pi}{3}, \dfrac{4\pi}{3}\right\}$

24. $\left\{\dfrac{\pi}{2}\right\}$ **25.** $\left\{\dfrac{3\pi}{4}, \dfrac{5\pi}{4}\right\}$ **26.** $\left\{\dfrac{4\pi}{3}, \dfrac{5\pi}{3}\right\}$ **27.** $\left\{\dfrac{3\pi}{4}, \dfrac{7\pi}{4}\right\}$ **28.** $\left\{\dfrac{4\pi}{27}, \dfrac{22\pi}{27}, \dfrac{40\pi}{27}\right\}$ **29.** $\left\{\dfrac{11\pi}{6}\right\}$ **30.** $\left\{\dfrac{7\pi}{4}\right\}$

31. $\left\{\theta \,\middle|\, \theta = \dfrac{\pi}{6} + 2k\pi, \theta = \dfrac{5\pi}{6} + 2k\pi\right\}; \dfrac{\pi}{6}, \dfrac{5\pi}{6}, \dfrac{13\pi}{6}, \dfrac{17\pi}{6}, \dfrac{25\pi}{6}, \dfrac{29\pi}{6}$ **32.** $\left\{\theta \,\middle|\, \theta = \dfrac{\pi}{4} + k\pi\right\}; \dfrac{\pi}{4}, \dfrac{5\pi}{4}, \dfrac{9\pi}{4}, \dfrac{13\pi}{4}, \dfrac{17\pi}{4}, \dfrac{21\pi}{4}$

33. $\left\{\theta \,\middle|\, \theta = \dfrac{5\pi}{6} + k\pi\right\}; \dfrac{5\pi}{6}, \dfrac{11\pi}{6}, \dfrac{17\pi}{6}, \dfrac{23\pi}{6}, \dfrac{29\pi}{6}, \dfrac{35\pi}{6}$ **34.** $\left\{\theta \,\middle|\, \theta = \dfrac{5\pi}{6} + 2k\pi, \theta = \dfrac{7\pi}{6} + 2k\pi\right\}; \dfrac{5\pi}{6}, \dfrac{7\pi}{6}, \dfrac{17\pi}{6}, \dfrac{19\pi}{6}, \dfrac{29\pi}{6}, \dfrac{31\pi}{6}$

35. $\left\{\theta \,\middle|\, \theta = \dfrac{\pi}{2} + 2k\pi, \theta = \dfrac{3\pi}{2} + 2k\pi\right\}; \dfrac{\pi}{2}, \dfrac{3\pi}{2}, \dfrac{5\pi}{2}, \dfrac{7\pi}{2}, \dfrac{9\pi}{2}, \dfrac{11\pi}{2}$ **36.** $\left\{\theta \,\middle|\, \theta = \dfrac{\pi}{4} + 2k\pi, \theta = \dfrac{3\pi}{4} + 2k\pi\right\}; \dfrac{\pi}{4}, \dfrac{3\pi}{4}, \dfrac{9\pi}{4}, \dfrac{11\pi}{4}, \dfrac{17\pi}{4}, \dfrac{19\pi}{4}$

37. $\left\{\theta \,\middle|\, \theta = \dfrac{\pi}{3} + k\pi, \theta = \dfrac{2\pi}{3} + k\pi\right\}; \dfrac{\pi}{3}, \dfrac{2\pi}{3}, \dfrac{4\pi}{3}, \dfrac{5\pi}{3}, \dfrac{7\pi}{3}, \dfrac{8\pi}{3}$ **38.** $\left\{\theta \,\middle|\, \theta = \dfrac{3\pi}{4} + k\pi\right\}; \dfrac{3\pi}{4}, \dfrac{7\pi}{4}, \dfrac{11\pi}{4}, \dfrac{15\pi}{4}, \dfrac{19\pi}{4}, \dfrac{23\pi}{4}$

39. $\left\{\theta \,\middle|\, \theta = \dfrac{8\pi}{3} + 4k\pi, \theta = \dfrac{10\pi}{3} + 4k\pi\right\}; \dfrac{8\pi}{3}, \dfrac{10\pi}{3}, \dfrac{20\pi}{3}, \dfrac{22\pi}{3}, \dfrac{32\pi}{3}, \dfrac{34\pi}{3}$ **40.** $\left\{\theta \,\middle|\, \theta = \dfrac{3\pi}{2} + 2k\pi\right\}; \dfrac{3\pi}{2}, \dfrac{7\pi}{2}, \dfrac{11\pi}{2}, \dfrac{15\pi}{2}, \dfrac{19\pi}{2}, \dfrac{23\pi}{2}$

41. $\{0.41, 2.73\}$ **42.** $\{0.93, 5.36\}$ **43.** $\{1.37, 4.51\}$ **44.** $\{0.46, 3.61\}$ **45.** $\{2.69, 3.59\}$ **46.** $\{3.34, 6.08\}$ **47.** $\{1.82, 4.46\}$ **48.** $\{3.48, 5.94\}$

49. $\{2.08, 5.22\}$ **50.** $\{2.47, 5.61\}$ **51.** $\{0.73, 2.41\}$ **52.** $\{2.42, 3.86\}$ **53.** $\dfrac{\pi}{3}, \dfrac{2\pi}{3}, \dfrac{4\pi}{3}, \dfrac{5\pi}{3}$ **54.** $\dfrac{2\pi}{9}, \dfrac{4\pi}{9}, \dfrac{8\pi}{9}$

55. (a) $-2\pi, -\pi, 0, \pi, 2\pi, 3\pi, 4\pi$

(b)

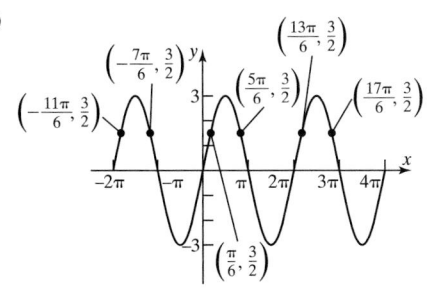

(c) $\left\{-\dfrac{11\pi}{6}, -\dfrac{7\pi}{6}, \dfrac{\pi}{6}, \dfrac{5\pi}{6}, \dfrac{13\pi}{6}, \dfrac{17\pi}{6}\right\}$

(d) $\left\{x \,\middle|\, -\dfrac{11\pi}{6} < x < -\dfrac{7\pi}{6} \text{ or } \dfrac{\pi}{6} < x < \dfrac{5\pi}{6} \text{ or } \dfrac{13\pi}{6} < x < \dfrac{17\pi}{6}\right\}$

56. (a) $-\dfrac{3\pi}{2}, -\dfrac{\pi}{2}, \dfrac{\pi}{2}, \dfrac{3\pi}{2}, \dfrac{5\pi}{2}, \dfrac{7\pi}{2}$

(b)

(c) $\left\{-\dfrac{7\pi}{6}, -\dfrac{5\pi}{6}, \dfrac{5\pi}{6}, \dfrac{7\pi}{6}, \dfrac{17\pi}{6}, \dfrac{19\pi}{6}\right\}$

(d) $\left\{x \,\middle|\, -\dfrac{7\pi}{6} < x < -\dfrac{5\pi}{6} \text{ or } \dfrac{5\pi}{6} < x < \dfrac{7\pi}{6} \text{ or } \dfrac{17\pi}{6} < x < \dfrac{19\pi}{6}\right\}$

57. (a) $\left\{x \,\middle|\, x = -\dfrac{\pi}{4} + k\pi, k \text{ is any integer}\right\}$ **58. (a)** $\left\{x \,\middle|\, x = \dfrac{5\pi}{6} + k\pi, k \text{ is any integer}\right\}$

(b) $-\dfrac{\pi}{2} < x < -\dfrac{\pi}{4} \text{ or } \left(-\dfrac{\pi}{2}, -\dfrac{\pi}{4}\right)$ **(b)** $0 < x < \dfrac{5\pi}{6} \text{ or } \left(0, \dfrac{5\pi}{6}\right)$

59. (a), (d)

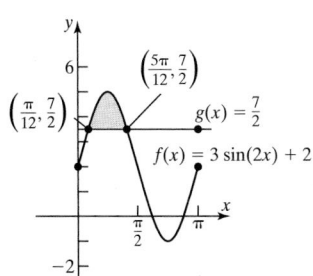

(b) $\left\{\dfrac{\pi}{12}, \dfrac{5\pi}{12}\right\}$

(c) $\left\{x \,\middle|\, \dfrac{\pi}{12} < x < \dfrac{5\pi}{12}\right\} \text{ or } \left(\dfrac{\pi}{12}, \dfrac{5\pi}{12}\right)$

60. (a), (d)

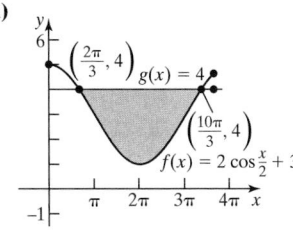

(b) $\left\{\dfrac{2\pi}{3}, \dfrac{10\pi}{3}\right\}$

(c) $\left\{x \,\middle|\, \dfrac{2\pi}{3} < x < \dfrac{10\pi}{3}\right\} \text{ or } \left(\dfrac{2\pi}{3}, \dfrac{10\pi}{3}\right)$

61. (a), (d)

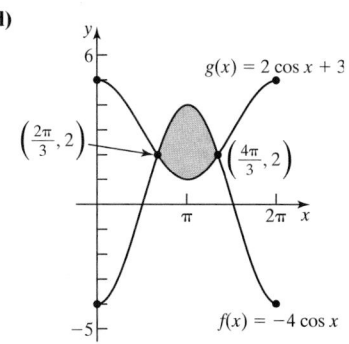

(b) $\left\{\dfrac{2\pi}{3}, \dfrac{4\pi}{3}\right\}$

(c) $\left\{x \,\middle|\, \dfrac{2\pi}{3} < x < \dfrac{4\pi}{3}\right\} \text{ or } \left(\dfrac{2\pi}{3}, \dfrac{4\pi}{3}\right)$

62. (a), (d)

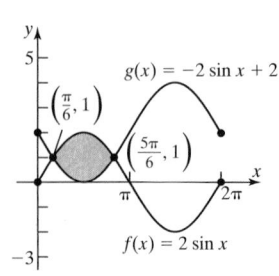

(b) $\left\{\dfrac{\pi}{6}, \dfrac{5\pi}{6}\right\}$ (c) $\left\{x \mid \dfrac{\pi}{6} < x < \dfrac{5\pi}{6}\right\}$ or $\left(\dfrac{\pi}{6}, \dfrac{5\pi}{6}\right)$

63. (a) 0 s, 0.43 s, 0.86 s (b) 0.21 s (c) $[0, 0.03] \cup [0.39, 0.43] \cup [0.86, 0.89]$

64. (a) 10 s; 30 s (b) 20 s; 60 s (c) $10 < x < 30$ or $(10, 30)$

65. (a) 150 mi (b) 6.06, 8.44, 15.72, 18.11 min
(c) Before 6.06 min, between 8.44 and 15.72 min, and after 18.11 min (d) No

66. (a) 21.02° or 68.98° (b) 26.74° or 63.26° (c) Between 22.79° and 67.21° (d) No

67. 28.90° **68.** 27.48° **69.** Yes; it varies from 1.25 to 1.34. **70.** 1.56 **71.** 1.47 **72.** 19.20°

73. If θ is the original angle of incidence and ϕ is the angle of refraction, then $\dfrac{\sin \theta}{\sin \phi} = n_2$.

The angle of incidence of the emerging beam is also ϕ, and the index of refraction is $\dfrac{1}{n_2}$.

Thus, θ is the angle of refraction of the emerging beam.

74. $\theta_B = 48.8°$

7.8 Assess Your Understanding (page 500)

5. $\left\{\dfrac{\pi}{2}, \dfrac{2\pi}{3}, \dfrac{4\pi}{3}, \dfrac{3\pi}{2}\right\}$ **6.** $\left\{\dfrac{\pi}{2}, \dfrac{3\pi}{2}\right\}$ **7.** $\left\{\dfrac{\pi}{2}, \dfrac{7\pi}{6}, \dfrac{11\pi}{6}\right\}$ **8.** $\left\{\dfrac{\pi}{3}, \pi, \dfrac{5\pi}{3}\right\}$ **9.** $\left\{0, \dfrac{\pi}{4}, \dfrac{5\pi}{4}\right\}$ **10.** $\left\{\dfrac{3\pi}{4}, \dfrac{7\pi}{4}\right\}$ **11.** $\left\{\dfrac{\pi}{2}, \dfrac{2\pi}{3}, \dfrac{4\pi}{3}, \dfrac{3\pi}{2}\right\}$

12. $\left\{\dfrac{\pi}{2}, \dfrac{7\pi}{6}, \dfrac{11\pi}{6}\right\}$ **13.** $\{\pi\}$ **14.** $\left\{0, \dfrac{\pi}{3}, \dfrac{5\pi}{3}\right\}$ **15.** $\left\{\dfrac{\pi}{3}, \dfrac{2\pi}{3}, \dfrac{4\pi}{3}, \dfrac{5\pi}{3}\right\}$ **16.** No real solution **17.** $\left\{\dfrac{\pi}{4}, \dfrac{5\pi}{4}\right\}$ **18.** $\left\{\dfrac{3\pi}{4}, \dfrac{7\pi}{4}\right\}$ **19.** $\left\{0, \dfrac{\pi}{3}, \pi, \dfrac{5\pi}{3}\right\}$

20. $\left\{\dfrac{\pi}{6}, \dfrac{\pi}{2}, \dfrac{5\pi}{6}, \dfrac{3\pi}{2}\right\}$ **21.** $\left\{\dfrac{\pi}{2}, \dfrac{3\pi}{2}\right\}$ **22.** $\left\{\dfrac{\pi}{4}, \dfrac{3\pi}{4}, \dfrac{5\pi}{4}, \dfrac{7\pi}{4}\right\}$ **23.** $\left\{0, \dfrac{2\pi}{3}, \dfrac{4\pi}{3}\right\}$ **24.** $\left\{\dfrac{\pi}{4}, \dfrac{\pi}{2}, \dfrac{3\pi}{4}, \dfrac{5\pi}{4}, \dfrac{3\pi}{2}, \dfrac{7\pi}{4}\right\}$ **25.** $\left\{0, \dfrac{\pi}{3}, \dfrac{\pi}{2}, \dfrac{2\pi}{3}, \pi, \dfrac{4\pi}{3}, \dfrac{3\pi}{2}, \dfrac{5\pi}{3}\right\}$

26. $\left\{\dfrac{\pi}{6}, \dfrac{\pi}{2}, \dfrac{5\pi}{6}, \dfrac{7\pi}{6}, \dfrac{3\pi}{2}, \dfrac{11\pi}{6}\right\}$ **27.** $\left\{0, \dfrac{\pi}{5}, \dfrac{2\pi}{5}, \dfrac{3\pi}{5}, \dfrac{4\pi}{5}, \pi, \dfrac{6\pi}{5}, \dfrac{7\pi}{5}, \dfrac{8\pi}{5}, \dfrac{9\pi}{5}\right\}$ **28.** $\left\{0, \dfrac{\pi}{10}, \dfrac{3\pi}{10}, \dfrac{\pi}{2}, \dfrac{7\pi}{10}, \dfrac{9\pi}{10}, \pi, \dfrac{11\pi}{10}, \dfrac{13\pi}{10}, \dfrac{3\pi}{2}, \dfrac{17\pi}{10}, \dfrac{19\pi}{10}\right\}$

29. $\left\{\dfrac{\pi}{6}, \dfrac{5\pi}{6}, \dfrac{3\pi}{2}\right\}$ **30.** $\{\pi\}$ **31.** $\left\{\dfrac{\pi}{2}\right\}$ **32.** $\left\{\dfrac{2\pi}{3}, \dfrac{4\pi}{3}\right\}$ **33.** $\{0\}$ **34.** $\left\{\dfrac{3\pi}{2}\right\}$ **35.** $\left\{\dfrac{\pi}{3}, \dfrac{5\pi}{3}\right\}$ **36.** $\left\{\dfrac{\pi}{4}, \dfrac{\pi}{2}, \dfrac{5\pi}{4}, \dfrac{3\pi}{2}\right\}$ **37.** No real solution

38. $\left\{\dfrac{2\pi}{3}, \dfrac{4\pi}{3}\right\}$ **39.** No real solution **40.** No real solution **41.** $\left\{\dfrac{\pi}{2}, \dfrac{7\pi}{6}\right\}$ **42.** $\left\{0, \dfrac{2\pi}{3}\right\}$ **43.** $\left\{0, \dfrac{\pi}{3}, \pi, \dfrac{5\pi}{3}\right\}$ **44.** $\left\{\dfrac{\pi}{2}, \dfrac{7\pi}{6}, \dfrac{3\pi}{2}, \dfrac{11\pi}{6}\right\}$

45. $\left\{\dfrac{\pi}{4}\right\}$ **46.** $\left\{\dfrac{5\pi}{4}\right\}$ **47.** $-1.31, 1.98, 3.84$ **48.** $-2.47, 0, 2.47$ **49.** 0.52 **50.** -0.30 **51.** 1.26 **52.** -1.26 **53.** $-1.02, 1.02$ **54.** $-1.72, 0$

55. $0, 2.15$ **56.** $-0.62, 0.81$ **57.** $0.76, 1.35$ **58.** 0.31 **59.** $\dfrac{\pi}{3}, \dfrac{2\pi}{3}, \dfrac{4\pi}{3}, \dfrac{5\pi}{3}$ **60.** $\dfrac{\pi}{3}, \dfrac{2\pi}{3}, \dfrac{4\pi}{3}, \dfrac{5\pi}{3}$ **61.** $0, \dfrac{\pi}{3}, \pi, \dfrac{5\pi}{3}$ **62.** $\dfrac{\pi}{3}, \pi, \dfrac{5\pi}{3}$ **63.** π **64.** $\dfrac{\pi}{2}, \dfrac{3\pi}{2}$

65. (a) 60° (b) 60°
(c) $A(60°) = 12\sqrt{3}$ in.²
(d)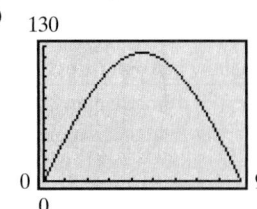
$\theta_{max} = 60°$
Maximum area $= 20.78$ in.²

66. (a) 67.5° (b) 67.5°
(c) $R = 32(2 - \sqrt{2})$ ft
(d)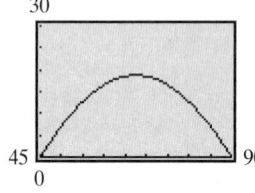
$\theta_{max} = 67.5°$
Maximum distance $= 18.75$ ft

67. 2.03, 4.91

68. (a) Let $L_1 =$ length of L in hallway with a 4-ft width.
Let $L_2 =$ length of L in hallway with a 3-ft width.
$L_1 = \dfrac{4}{\sin \theta} = 4 \csc \theta;\ L_2 = \dfrac{3}{\cos \theta} = 3 \sec \theta;$
$L(\theta) = L_1 + L_2 = 4 \csc \theta + 3 \sec \theta$
(b) 47.74° (c) 9.87 ft
(d)
$\theta_{min} = 47.74°$

69. (a) 30°, 60° (b) 123.6 m
(c)

70. (a) 21.2°, 68.8° (b) 163.3 m
(c)

Review Exercises (page 504)

1. $\dfrac{\pi}{2}$ **2.** $\dfrac{\pi}{2}$ **3.** $\dfrac{\pi}{4}$ **4.** $-\dfrac{\pi}{6}$ **5.** $\dfrac{5\pi}{6}$ **6.** $-\dfrac{\pi}{3}$ **7.** $\dfrac{\pi}{4}$ **8.** $\dfrac{3\pi}{4}$ **9.** $\dfrac{3\pi}{8}$ **10.** $\dfrac{3\pi}{4}$ **11.** $-\dfrac{\pi}{3}$ **12.** $-\dfrac{\pi}{8}$ **13.** $\dfrac{\pi}{7}$ **14.** $-\dfrac{\pi}{9}$ **15.** 0.9 **16.** 0.6 **17.** -0.3

18. 5 **19.** Not defined **20.** Not defined **21.** $-\dfrac{\pi}{6}$ **22.** π **23.** $-\dfrac{\pi}{4}$ **24.** $\dfrac{5\pi}{6}$ **25.** $-\sqrt{3}$ **26.** $-\sqrt{3}$ **27.** $\dfrac{2\sqrt{3}}{3}$ **28.** $\dfrac{2\sqrt{3}}{3}$ **29.** $\dfrac{4}{5}$ **30.** $\dfrac{4}{5}$

31. $-\dfrac{4}{3}$ **32.** $-\dfrac{4}{3}$ **33.** $f^{-1}(x) = \dfrac{1}{3}\sin^{-1}\left(\dfrac{x}{2}\right)$; Domain of f = range of f^{-1}: $(-\infty, \infty)$; Domain of f^{-1} = range of f: $[-2, 2]$

34. $f^{-1}(x) = \frac{1}{2}[\tan^{-1}(x+1) - 3]$; Domain of f: $x \neq \frac{(2k+1)\pi}{4} - \frac{3}{2}$, k an integer; Range of f^{-1}: $y \neq \frac{(2k+1)\pi}{4} - \frac{3}{2}$, k an integer;

Domain of f^{-1} = range of f: $(-\infty, \infty)$

35. $f^{-1}(x) = \cos^{-1}(3-x)$; Domain of f = range of f^{-1}: $(-\infty, \infty)$; Domain of f^{-1} = range of f: $[2, 4]$

36. $f^{-1}(x) = 1 - \sin^{-1}\frac{x}{2}$; Domain of f = range of f^{-1}: $(-\infty, \infty)$; Domain of f^{-1} = range of f: $[-2, 2]$ **37.** $\sqrt{1-u^2}$ **38.** $\frac{\sqrt{u^2-1}}{u}$ **39.** $\frac{1}{u}$

40. $\frac{1}{\sqrt{u^2-1}}$ **41.** $\tan\theta\cot\theta - \sin^2\theta = 1 - \sin^2\theta = \cos^2\theta$ **42.** $\sin\theta\csc\theta - \sin^2\theta = 1 - \sin^2\theta = \cos^2\theta$ **43.** $\sin^2\theta(1 + \cot^2\theta) = \sin^2\theta\csc^2\theta = 1$

44. $(1 - \sin^2\theta)(1 + \tan^2\theta) = \cos^2\theta\sec^2\theta = 1$ **45.** $5\cos^2\theta + 3\sin^2\theta = 2\cos^2\theta + 3(\cos^2\theta + \sin^2\theta) = 3 + 2\cos^2\theta$

46. $4\sin^2\theta + 2\cos^2\theta = 4(1 - \cos^2\theta) + 2\cos^2\theta = 4 - 4\cos^2\theta + 2\cos^2\theta = 4 - 2\cos^2\theta$

47. $\frac{1-\cos\theta}{\sin\theta} + \frac{\sin\theta}{1-\cos\theta} = \frac{(1-\cos\theta)^2 + \sin^2\theta}{\sin\theta(1-\cos\theta)} = \frac{1 - 2\cos\theta + \cos^2\theta + \sin^2\theta}{\sin\theta(1-\cos\theta)} = \frac{2(1-\cos\theta)}{\sin\theta(1-\cos\theta)} = 2\csc\theta$

48. $\frac{\sin\theta}{1+\cos\theta} + \frac{1+\cos\theta}{\sin\theta} = \frac{\sin^2\theta + (1+\cos\theta)^2}{\sin\theta(1+\cos\theta)} = \frac{\sin^2\theta + 1 + 2\cos\theta + \cos^2\theta}{\sin\theta(1+\cos\theta)} = \frac{2(1+\cos\theta)}{\sin\theta(1+\cos\theta)} = 2\csc\theta$

49. $\frac{\cos\theta}{\cos\theta - \sin\theta} = \frac{\dfrac{\cos\theta}{\cos\theta}}{\dfrac{\cos\theta - \sin\theta}{\cos\theta}} = \frac{1}{1 - \dfrac{\sin\theta}{\cos\theta}} = \frac{1}{1 - \tan\theta}$

50. $1 - \frac{\sin^2\theta}{1+\cos\theta} = 1 - \frac{1-\cos^2\theta}{1+\cos\theta} = 1 - \frac{(1+\cos\theta)(1-\cos\theta)}{1+\cos\theta} = 1 - (1 - \cos\theta) = \cos\theta$

51. $\frac{\csc\theta}{1+\csc\theta} = \frac{\dfrac{1}{\sin\theta}}{1 + \dfrac{1}{\sin\theta}} = \frac{1}{1+\sin\theta} = \frac{1}{1+\sin\theta}\cdot\frac{1-\sin\theta}{1-\sin\theta} = \frac{1-\sin\theta}{1-\sin^2\theta} = \frac{1-\sin\theta}{\cos^2\theta}$

52. $\frac{1+\sec\theta}{\sec\theta} = \frac{1 + \dfrac{1}{\cos\theta}}{\dfrac{1}{\cos\theta}} = (1+\cos\theta)\cdot\frac{1-\cos\theta}{1-\cos\theta} = \frac{1-\cos^2\theta}{1-\cos\theta} = \frac{\sin^2\theta}{1-\cos\theta}$

53. $\csc\theta - \sin\theta = \frac{1}{\sin\theta} - \sin\theta = \frac{1-\sin^2\theta}{\sin\theta} = \frac{\cos^2\theta}{\sin\theta} = \cos\theta\cdot\frac{\cos\theta}{\sin\theta} = \cos\theta\cot\theta$

54. $\frac{\csc\theta}{1-\cos\theta} = \frac{\dfrac{1}{\sin\theta}}{1-\cos\theta}\cdot\frac{1+\cos\theta}{1+\cos\theta} = \frac{1+\cos\theta}{\sin\theta(1-\cos^2\theta)} = \frac{1+\cos\theta}{\sin^3\theta}$ **55.** $\frac{1-\sin\theta}{\sec\theta} = \cos\theta(1-\sin\theta)\cdot\frac{1+\sin\theta}{1+\sin\theta} = \frac{\cos\theta(1-\sin^2\theta)}{1+\sin\theta} = \frac{\cos^3\theta}{1+\sin\theta}$

56. $\frac{1-\cos\theta}{1+\cos\theta} = \frac{1-\cos\theta}{1+\cos\theta}\cdot\frac{1-\cos\theta}{1-\cos\theta} = \frac{(1-\cos\theta)^2}{1-\cos^2\theta} = \frac{(1-\cos\theta)^2}{\sin^2\theta} = \left(\frac{1}{\sin\theta} - \frac{\cos\theta}{\sin\theta}\right)^2 = (\csc\theta - \cot\theta)^2$

57. $\cot\theta - \tan\theta = \frac{\cos\theta}{\sin\theta} - \frac{\sin\theta}{\cos\theta} = \frac{\cos^2\theta - \sin^2\theta}{\sin\theta\cos\theta} = \frac{1 - 2\sin^2\theta}{\sin\theta\cos\theta}$

58. $\frac{(2\sin^2\theta - 1)^2}{\sin^4\theta - \cos^4\theta} = \frac{(-\cos(2\theta))^2}{(\sin^2\theta + \cos^2\theta)(\sin^2\theta - \cos^2\theta)} = \frac{(\cos(2\theta))^2}{1(-\cos(2\theta))} = -\cos(2\theta) = 1 - 2\cos^2\theta$

59. $\frac{\cos(\alpha+\beta)}{\cos\alpha\sin\beta} = \frac{\cos\alpha\cos\beta - \sin\alpha\sin\beta}{\cos\alpha\sin\beta} = \frac{\cos\alpha\cos\beta}{\cos\alpha\sin\beta} - \frac{\sin\alpha\sin\beta}{\cos\alpha\sin\beta} = \cot\beta - \tan\alpha$

60. $\frac{\sin(\alpha-\beta)}{\sin\alpha\cos\beta} = \frac{\sin\alpha\cos\beta - \cos\alpha\sin\beta}{\sin\alpha\cos\beta} = \frac{\sin\alpha\cos\beta}{\sin\alpha\cos\beta} - \frac{\cos\alpha\sin\beta}{\sin\alpha\cos\beta} = 1 - \cot\alpha\tan\beta$

61. $\frac{\cos(\alpha-\beta)}{\cos\alpha\cos\beta} = \frac{\cos\alpha\cos\beta + \sin\alpha\sin\beta}{\cos\alpha\cos\beta} = \frac{\cos\alpha\cos\beta}{\cos\alpha\cos\beta} + \frac{\sin\alpha\sin\beta}{\cos\alpha\cos\beta} = 1 + \tan\alpha\tan\beta$

62. $\frac{\cos(\alpha+\beta)}{\sin\alpha\cos\beta} = \frac{\cos\alpha\cos\beta - \sin\alpha\sin\beta}{\sin\alpha\cos\beta} = \frac{\cos\alpha\cos\beta}{\sin\alpha\cos\beta} - \frac{\sin\alpha\sin\beta}{\sin\alpha\cos\beta} = \cot\alpha - \tan\beta$

63. $(1 + \cos\theta)\left(\tan\frac{\theta}{2}\right) = (1+\cos\theta)\cdot\frac{\sin\theta}{1+\cos\theta} = \sin\theta$ **64.** $\sin\theta\tan\frac{\theta}{2} = \sin\theta\cdot\frac{1-\cos\theta}{\sin\theta} = 1 - \cos\theta$

65. $2\cot\theta\cot 2\theta = 2\left(\frac{\cos\theta}{\sin\theta}\right)\left(\frac{\cos 2\theta}{\sin 2\theta}\right) = \frac{2\cos\theta(\cos^2\theta - \sin^2\theta)}{2\sin^2\theta\cos\theta} = \frac{\cos^2\theta - \sin^2\theta}{\sin^2\theta} = \cot^2\theta - 1$

66. $2\sin(2\theta)(1 - 2\sin^2\theta) = 2\sin(2\theta)\cdot\cos(2\theta) = \sin(4\theta)$ **67.** $1 - 8\sin^2\theta\cos^2\theta = 1 - 2(2\sin\theta\cos\theta)^2 = 1 - 2\sin^2(2\theta) = \cos(4\theta)$

68. $\frac{\sin(3\theta)\cos\theta - \sin\theta\cos(3\theta)}{\sin(2\theta)} = \frac{\sin(2\theta)}{\sin(2\theta)} = 1$ **69.** $\frac{\sin(2\theta) + \sin(4\theta)}{\cos(2\theta) + \cos(4\theta)} = \frac{2\sin(3\theta)\cos(-\theta)}{2\cos(3\theta)\cos(-\theta)} = \tan(3\theta)$

70. $\dfrac{\sin(2\theta) + \sin(4\theta)}{\sin(2\theta) - \sin(4\theta)} + \dfrac{\tan(3\theta)}{\tan\theta} = \dfrac{2\sin(3\theta)\cos(-\theta)}{2\sin(-\theta)\cos(3\theta)} + \dfrac{\tan(3\theta)}{\tan\theta} = -\dfrac{\tan(3\theta)}{\tan\theta} + \dfrac{\tan(3\theta)}{\tan\theta} = 0$

71. $\dfrac{\cos(2\theta) - \cos(4\theta)}{\cos(2\theta) + \cos(4\theta)} - \tan\theta\tan(3\theta) = \dfrac{-2\sin(3\theta)\sin(-\theta)}{2\cos(3\theta)\cos(-\theta)} - \tan\theta\tan(3\theta) = \tan(3\theta)\tan\theta - \tan\theta\tan(3\theta) = 0$

72. $\tan(4\theta)[\sin(2\theta) + \sin(10\theta)] = \tan(4\theta)[2\sin(6\theta)\cos(-4\theta)] = 2\sin(4\theta)\sin(6\theta) = 2\cdot\dfrac{1}{2}[\cos(-2\theta) - \cos(10\theta)] = \cos(2\theta) - \cos(10\theta)$

73. $\dfrac{1}{4}\left(\sqrt{6} - \sqrt{2}\right)$ **74.** $-2 - \sqrt{3}$ **75.** $\dfrac{1}{4}\left(\sqrt{6} - \sqrt{2}\right)$ **76.** $\dfrac{1}{4}\left(\sqrt{2} - \sqrt{6}\right)$ **77.** $\dfrac{1}{2}$ **78.** $\dfrac{1}{2}$ **79.** $\sqrt{2} - 1$ **80.** $\dfrac{\sqrt{2 + \sqrt{2}}}{2}$

81. (a) $-\dfrac{33}{65}$ **(b)** $-\dfrac{56}{65}$ **(c)** $-\dfrac{63}{65}$ **(d)** $\dfrac{33}{56}$ **(e)** $\dfrac{24}{25}$ **(f)** $\dfrac{119}{169}$ **(g)** $\dfrac{5\sqrt{26}}{26}$ **(h)** $\dfrac{2\sqrt{5}}{5}$ **82. (a)** $-\dfrac{33}{65}$ **(b)** $\dfrac{56}{65}$ **(c)** $\dfrac{63}{65}$ **(d)** $-\dfrac{33}{56}$ **(e)** $\dfrac{24}{25}$

(f) $-\dfrac{119}{169}$ **(g)** $-\dfrac{2\sqrt{13}}{13}$ **(h)** $\dfrac{3\sqrt{10}}{10}$ **83. (a)** $-\dfrac{16}{65}$ **(b)** $-\dfrac{63}{65}$ **(c)** $-\dfrac{56}{65}$ **(d)** $\dfrac{16}{63}$ **(e)** $\dfrac{24}{25}$ **(f)** $\dfrac{119}{169}$ **(g)** $\dfrac{\sqrt{26}}{26}$ **(h)** $-\dfrac{\sqrt{10}}{10}$

84. (a) $\dfrac{56}{65}$ **(b)** $\dfrac{33}{65}$ **(c)** $-\dfrac{16}{65}$ **(d)** $\dfrac{56}{33}$ **(e)** $-\dfrac{24}{25}$ **(f)** $-\dfrac{119}{169}$ **(g)** $\dfrac{3\sqrt{13}}{13}$ **(h)** $\dfrac{2\sqrt{5}}{5}$ **85. (a)** $-\dfrac{63}{65}$ **(b)** $\dfrac{16}{65}$ **(c)** $\dfrac{33}{65}$ **(d)** $-\dfrac{63}{16}$ **(e)** $\dfrac{24}{25}$

(f) $-\dfrac{119}{169}$ **(g)** $\dfrac{2\sqrt{13}}{13}$ **(h)** $-\dfrac{\sqrt{10}}{10}$ **86. (a)** $-\dfrac{33}{65}$ **(b)** $\dfrac{56}{65}$ **(c)** $-\dfrac{63}{65}$ **(d)** $-\dfrac{33}{56}$ **(e)** $-\dfrac{24}{25}$ **(f)** $\dfrac{119}{169}$ **(g)** $\dfrac{5\sqrt{26}}{26}$ **(h)** $\dfrac{\sqrt{5}}{5}$

87. (a) $\dfrac{-\sqrt{3} - 2\sqrt{2}}{6}$ **(b)** $\dfrac{1 - 2\sqrt{6}}{6}$ **(c)** $\dfrac{-\sqrt{3} + 2\sqrt{2}}{6}$ **(d)** $\dfrac{8\sqrt{2} + 9\sqrt{3}}{23}$ **(e)** $-\dfrac{\sqrt{3}}{2}$ **(f)** $-\dfrac{7}{9}$ **(g)** $\dfrac{\sqrt{3}}{3}$ **(h)** $\dfrac{\sqrt{3}}{2}$ **88. (a)** $\dfrac{-1 - 2\sqrt{6}}{6}$

(b) $\dfrac{\sqrt{3} - 2\sqrt{2}}{6}$ **(c)** $\dfrac{-1 + 2\sqrt{6}}{6}$ **(d)** $\dfrac{9\sqrt{3} + 8\sqrt{2}}{5}$ **(e)** $-\dfrac{\sqrt{3}}{2}$ **(f)** $-\dfrac{7}{9}$ **(g)** $\dfrac{\sqrt{6}}{3}$ **(h)** $\dfrac{\sqrt{2 - \sqrt{3}}}{2}$ **89. (a)** 1 **(b)** 0 **(c)** $-\dfrac{1}{9}$

(d) Not defined **(e)** $\dfrac{4\sqrt{5}}{9}$ **(f)** $-\dfrac{1}{9}$ **(g)** $\dfrac{\sqrt{30}}{6}$ **(h)** $-\dfrac{\sqrt{6}\sqrt{3} - \sqrt{5}}{6}$ **90. (a)** -1 **(b)** 0 **(c)** $-\dfrac{3}{5}$ **(d)** Not defined **(e)** $-\dfrac{4}{5}$ **(f)** $\dfrac{3}{5}$

(g) $\dfrac{\sqrt{10}\sqrt{5 + 2\sqrt{5}}}{10}$ **(h)** $\dfrac{\sqrt{10}\sqrt{5 - \sqrt{5}}}{10}$ **91.** $\dfrac{4 + 3\sqrt{3}}{10}$ **92.** $\dfrac{33}{65}$ **93.** $-\dfrac{48 + 25\sqrt{3}}{39}$ **94.** $-\dfrac{\sqrt{2}}{10}$ **95.** $-\dfrac{24}{25}$ **96.** $-\dfrac{7}{25}$ **97.** $\left\{\dfrac{\pi}{3}, \dfrac{5\pi}{3}\right\}$

98. $\left\{\dfrac{4\pi}{3}, \dfrac{5\pi}{3}\right\}$ **99.** $\left\{\dfrac{3\pi}{4}, \dfrac{5\pi}{4}\right\}$ **100.** $\left\{\dfrac{2\pi}{3}, \dfrac{5\pi}{3}\right\}$ **101.** $\left\{\dfrac{3\pi}{4}, \dfrac{7\pi}{4}\right\}$ **102.** $\left\{\dfrac{\pi}{4}, \dfrac{3\pi}{4}, \dfrac{5\pi}{4}, \dfrac{7\pi}{4}\right\}$ **103.** $\left\{0, \dfrac{\pi}{2}, \pi, \dfrac{3\pi}{2}\right\}$ **104.** $\left\{\dfrac{\pi}{6}, \dfrac{5\pi}{6}, \dfrac{3\pi}{2}\right\}$

105. $\left\{\dfrac{\pi}{3}, \dfrac{2\pi}{3}, \dfrac{4\pi}{3}, \dfrac{5\pi}{3}\right\}$ **106.** $\left\{\dfrac{\pi}{2}, \dfrac{3\pi}{2}\right\}$ **107.** $\{0, \pi\}$ **108.** $\{0, \pi\}$ **109.** $\left\{0, \dfrac{2\pi}{3}, \pi, \dfrac{4\pi}{3}\right\}$ **110.** $\left\{\dfrac{\pi}{6}, \dfrac{5\pi}{6}, \dfrac{3\pi}{2}\right\}$ **111.** $\left\{0, \dfrac{\pi}{6}, \dfrac{5\pi}{6}\right\}$ **112.** $\left\{\dfrac{\pi}{3}, \dfrac{\pi}{2}, \dfrac{5\pi}{3}\right\}$

113. $\left\{\dfrac{\pi}{6}, \dfrac{\pi}{2}, \dfrac{5\pi}{6}\right\}$ **114.** $\left\{\dfrac{\pi}{3}, \pi, \dfrac{5\pi}{3}\right\}$ **115.** $\left\{\dfrac{\pi}{3}, \dfrac{5\pi}{3}\right\}$ **116.** $\left\{\dfrac{\pi}{4}, \dfrac{3\pi}{4}, \dfrac{5\pi}{4}, \dfrac{7\pi}{4}\right\}$ **117.** $\left\{\dfrac{\pi}{4}, \dfrac{\pi}{2}, \dfrac{3\pi}{4}, \dfrac{3\pi}{2}\right\}$ **118.** $\left\{\dfrac{\pi}{2}, \dfrac{5\pi}{6}, \dfrac{7\pi}{6}, \dfrac{3\pi}{2}\right\}$ **119.** $\left\{\dfrac{\pi}{2}, \pi\right\}$

120. $\left\{\dfrac{5\pi}{6}\right\}$ **121.** 0.78 **122.** 0.64 **123.** -1.11 **124.** 1.77 **125.** 1.23 **126.** 2.90 **127.** $\{1.11\}$ **128.** $\{0, 2.13\}$ **129.** $\{0.87\}$ **130.** $\{1.89, 3.07\}$

131. $\{2.22\}$ **132.** $\{0.59, 3.10\}$ **133.** $\left\{-\dfrac{\sqrt{3}}{2}\right\}$ **134.** $\{0\}$

135. $\sin 15° = \sqrt{\dfrac{1 - \cos 30°}{2}} = \sqrt{\dfrac{1 - \dfrac{\sqrt{3}}{2}}{2}} = \sqrt{\dfrac{2 - \sqrt{3}}{4}} = \sqrt{\dfrac{2 - \sqrt{3}}{2}};$

$\sin 15° = \sin(45° - 30°) = \sin 45°\cos 30° - \cos 45°\sin 30° = \dfrac{\sqrt{2}}{2}\cdot\dfrac{\sqrt{3}}{2} - \dfrac{\sqrt{2}}{2}\cdot\dfrac{1}{2} = \dfrac{\sqrt{6}}{4} - \dfrac{\sqrt{2}}{4} = \dfrac{\sqrt{6} - \sqrt{2}}{4};$

$\left[\dfrac{\sqrt{2 - \sqrt{3}}}{2}\right]^2 = \dfrac{2 - \sqrt{3}}{4} = \dfrac{4(2 - \sqrt{3})}{4\cdot 4} = \dfrac{8 - 4\sqrt{3}}{16} = \dfrac{6 - 2\sqrt{12} + 2}{16} = \left(\dfrac{\sqrt{6} - \sqrt{2}}{4}\right)^2$

Chapter Test (page 506)

1. $\dfrac{\pi}{6}$ **2.** $-\dfrac{\pi}{4}$ **3.** $\dfrac{\pi}{5}$ **4.** $\dfrac{7}{3}$ **5.** 3 **6.** $-\dfrac{4}{3}$ **7.** 0.39 **8.** 0.78 **9.** 1.25 **10.** 0.20

11. $\dfrac{\csc\theta + \cot\theta}{\sec\theta + \tan\theta} = \dfrac{\csc\theta + \cot\theta}{\sec\theta + \tan\theta}\cdot\dfrac{\csc\theta - \cot\theta}{\csc\theta - \cot\theta} = \dfrac{\csc^2\theta - \cot^2\theta}{(\sec\theta + \tan\theta)(\csc\theta - \cot\theta)} = \dfrac{1}{(\sec\theta + \tan\theta)(\csc\theta - \cot\theta)}$

$= \dfrac{1}{(\sec\theta + \tan\theta)(\csc\theta - \cot\theta)}\cdot\dfrac{\sec\theta - \tan\theta}{\sec\theta - \tan\theta} = \dfrac{\sec\theta - \tan\theta}{(\sec^2\theta - \tan^2\theta)(\csc\theta - \cot\theta)} = \dfrac{\sec\theta - \tan\theta}{\csc\theta - \cot\theta}$

12. $\sin\theta\tan\theta + \cos\theta = \sin\theta\cdot\dfrac{\sin\theta}{\cos\theta} + \cos\theta = \dfrac{\sin^2\theta}{\cos\theta} + \dfrac{\cos^2\theta}{\cos\theta} = \dfrac{\sin^2\theta + \cos^2\theta}{\cos\theta} = \dfrac{1}{\cos\theta} = \sec\theta$

13. $\tan\theta + \cot\theta = \dfrac{\sin\theta}{\cos\theta} + \dfrac{\cos\theta}{\sin\theta} = \dfrac{\sin^2\theta}{\sin\theta\cos\theta} + \dfrac{\cos^2\theta}{\sin\theta\cos\theta} = \dfrac{\sin^2\theta + \cos^2\theta}{\sin\theta\cos\theta} = \dfrac{1}{\sin\theta\cos\theta} = \dfrac{2}{2\sin\theta\cos\theta} = \dfrac{2}{\sin(2\theta)} = 2\csc(2\theta)$

14. $\dfrac{\sin(\alpha+\beta)}{\tan\alpha + \tan\beta} = \dfrac{\sin\alpha\cos\beta + \cos\alpha\sin\beta}{\dfrac{\sin\alpha}{\cos\alpha} + \dfrac{\sin\beta}{\cos\beta}} = \dfrac{\sin\alpha\cos\beta + \cos\alpha\sin\beta}{\dfrac{\sin\alpha\cos\beta}{\cos\alpha\cos\beta} + \dfrac{\cos\alpha\sin\beta}{\cos\alpha\cos\beta}} = \dfrac{\sin\alpha\cos\beta + \cos\alpha\sin\beta}{\dfrac{\sin\alpha\cos\beta + \cos\alpha\sin\beta}{\cos\alpha\cos\beta}}$

$= \dfrac{\sin\alpha\cos\beta + \cos\alpha\sin\beta}{1} \cdot \dfrac{\cos\alpha\cos\beta}{\sin\alpha\cos\beta + \cos\alpha\sin\beta} = \cos\alpha\cos\beta$

15. $\sin(3\theta) = \sin(\theta + 2\theta) = \sin\theta\cos(2\theta) + \cos\theta\sin(2\theta) = \sin\theta\cdot(\cos^2\theta - \sin^2\theta) + \cos\theta\cdot 2\sin\theta\cos\theta = \sin\theta\cos^2\theta - \sin^3\theta + 2\sin\theta\cos^2\theta$
$= 3\sin\theta\cos^2\theta - \sin^3\theta = 3\sin\theta(1 - \sin^2\theta) - \sin^3\theta = 3\sin\theta - 3\sin^3\theta - \sin^3\theta = 3\sin\theta - 4\sin^3\theta$

16. $\dfrac{\tan\theta - \cot\theta}{\tan\theta + \cot\theta} = \dfrac{\dfrac{\sin\theta}{\cos\theta} - \dfrac{\cos\theta}{\sin\theta}}{\dfrac{\sin\theta}{\cos\theta} + \dfrac{\cos\theta}{\sin\theta}} = \dfrac{\dfrac{\sin^2\theta - \cos^2\theta}{\sin\theta\cos\theta}}{\dfrac{\sin^2\theta + \cos^2\theta}{\sin\theta\cos\theta}} = \dfrac{\sin^2\theta - \cos^2\theta}{\sin^2\theta + \cos^2\theta} = \dfrac{-\cos(2\theta)}{1} = -(2\cos^2\theta - 1) = 1 - 2\cos^2\theta$ **17.** $\dfrac{1}{4}\left(\sqrt{6} + \sqrt{2}\right)$

18. $2 + \sqrt{3}$ **19.** $\dfrac{\sqrt{5}}{5}$ **20.** $\dfrac{12\sqrt{85}}{49}$ **21.** $\dfrac{2\sqrt{13}\left(\sqrt{5}-3\right)}{39}$ **22.** $\dfrac{2+\sqrt{3}}{4}$ **23.** $\dfrac{\sqrt{6}}{2}$ **24.** $\dfrac{\sqrt{2}}{2}$ **25.** $\left\{\dfrac{\pi}{3}, \dfrac{2\pi}{3}, \dfrac{4\pi}{3}, \dfrac{5\pi}{3}\right\}$ **26.** $\{0, 1.911, \pi, 4.373\}$

27. $\left\{\dfrac{3\pi}{8}, \dfrac{7\pi}{8}, \dfrac{11\pi}{8}, \dfrac{15\pi}{8}\right\}$ **28.** $\{0.285, 3.427\}$ **29.** $\{0.253, 2.889\}$ **30.** The change in elevation during the time trial was about 1.18 km.

Cumulative Review *(page 506)*

1. $\left\{\dfrac{-1-\sqrt{13}}{6}, \dfrac{-1+\sqrt{13}}{6}\right\}$ **2.** $y + 1 = -1(x - 4)$ or $x + y = 3$; $6\sqrt{2}$; $(1, 2)$ **3.** x-axis symmetry; $(0, -3), (0, 3), (3, 0)$

4.

5.

6.

7. (a)

(b)

(c)

(d)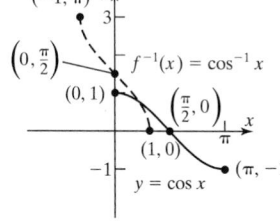

8. (a) $-\dfrac{2\sqrt{2}}{3}$ **(b)** $\dfrac{\sqrt{2}}{4}$ **(c)** $\dfrac{4\sqrt{2}}{9}$ **(d)** $\dfrac{7}{9}$ **(e)** $\sqrt{\dfrac{3+2\sqrt{2}}{6}}$ **(f)** $-\sqrt{\dfrac{3-2\sqrt{2}}{6}}$

9. $\dfrac{\sqrt{5}}{5}$ **10. (a)** $-\dfrac{2\sqrt{2}}{3}$ **(b)** $-\dfrac{2\sqrt{2}}{3}$ **(c)** $\dfrac{7}{9}$ **(d)** $\dfrac{4\sqrt{2}}{9}$ **(e)** $\dfrac{\sqrt{6}}{3}$

11. (a) $f(x) = (2x - 1)(x - 1)^2(x + 1)^2$; $\dfrac{1}{2}$ multiplicity 1; 1 and -1 multiplicity 2

(b) $(0, -1)$; $\left(\dfrac{1}{2}, 0\right)$; $(-1, 0)$; $(1, 0)$

(c) $y = 2x^5$

12. (a) $\left\{-1, -\dfrac{1}{2}\right\}$

(b) $\{-1, 1\}$

(c) $(-\infty, -1) \cup \left(-\dfrac{1}{2}, \infty\right)$

(d) $(-\infty, -1] \cup [1, \infty)$

(d)

(f)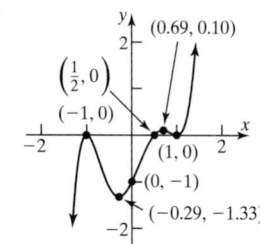

(e) Minima at $(-0.29, -1.33), (1, 0)$
    Maxima at $(-1, 0), (0.69, 0.10)$

(g) Increasing: $(-\infty, -1), (-0.29, 0.69), (1, \infty)$
    Decreasing: $(-1, -0.29), (0.69, 1)$

CHAPTER 8 Applications of Trigonometric Functions

8.1 Assess Your Understanding (page 517)

4. F **5.** T **6.** angle of elevation **7.** T **8.** F **9.** $\sin\theta = \dfrac{5}{13}$; $\cos\theta = \dfrac{12}{13}$; $\tan\theta = \dfrac{5}{12}$; $\cot\theta = \dfrac{12}{5}$; $\sec\theta = \dfrac{13}{12}$; $\csc\theta = \dfrac{13}{5}$

10. $\sin\theta = \dfrac{3}{5}$; $\cos\theta = \dfrac{4}{5}$; $\tan\theta = \dfrac{3}{4}$; $\cot\theta = \dfrac{4}{3}$; $\sec\theta = \dfrac{5}{4}$; $\csc\theta = \dfrac{5}{3}$

11. $\sin\theta = \dfrac{2\sqrt{13}}{13}$; $\cos\theta = \dfrac{3\sqrt{13}}{13}$; $\tan\theta = \dfrac{2}{3}$; $\cot\theta = \dfrac{3}{2}$; $\sec\theta = \dfrac{\sqrt{13}}{3}$; $\csc\theta = \dfrac{\sqrt{13}}{2}$

12. $\sin\theta = \dfrac{\sqrt{2}}{2}$; $\cos\theta = \dfrac{\sqrt{2}}{2}$; $\tan\theta = 1$; $\cot\theta = 1$; $\sec\theta = \sqrt{2}$; $\csc\theta = \sqrt{2}$

13. $\sin\theta = \dfrac{\sqrt{3}}{2}$; $\cos\theta = \dfrac{1}{2}$; $\tan\theta = \sqrt{3}$; $\cot\theta = \dfrac{\sqrt{3}}{3}$; $\sec\theta = 2$; $\csc\theta = \dfrac{2\sqrt{3}}{3}$

14. $\sin\theta = \dfrac{3}{4}$; $\cos\theta = \dfrac{\sqrt{7}}{4}$; $\tan\theta = \dfrac{3\sqrt{7}}{7}$; $\cot\theta = \dfrac{\sqrt{7}}{3}$; $\sec\theta = \dfrac{4\sqrt{7}}{7}$; $\csc\theta = \dfrac{4}{3}$

15. $\sin\theta = \dfrac{\sqrt{6}}{3}$; $\cos\theta = \dfrac{\sqrt{3}}{3}$; $\tan\theta = \sqrt{2}$; $\cot\theta = \dfrac{\sqrt{2}}{2}$; $\sec\theta = \sqrt{3}$; $\csc\theta = \dfrac{\sqrt{6}}{2}$

16. $\sin\theta = \dfrac{2\sqrt{7}}{7}$; $\cos\theta = \dfrac{\sqrt{21}}{7}$; $\tan\theta = \dfrac{2\sqrt{3}}{3}$; $\cot\theta = \dfrac{\sqrt{3}}{2}$; $\sec\theta = \dfrac{\sqrt{21}}{3}$; $\csc\theta = \dfrac{\sqrt{7}}{2}$

17. $\sin\theta = \dfrac{\sqrt{5}}{5}$; $\cos\theta = \dfrac{2\sqrt{5}}{5}$; $\tan\theta = \dfrac{1}{2}$; $\cot\theta = 2$; $\sec\theta = \dfrac{\sqrt{5}}{2}$; $\csc\theta = \sqrt{5}$

18. $\sin\theta = \dfrac{\sqrt{5}}{5}$; $\cos\theta = \dfrac{2\sqrt{5}}{5}$; $\tan\theta = \dfrac{1}{2}$; $\cot\theta = 2$; $\sec\theta = \dfrac{\sqrt{5}}{2}$; $\csc\theta = \sqrt{5}$

19. 0 **20.** 0 **21.** 1 **22.** 1 **23.** 0 **24.** 0 **25.** 0 **26.** 0 **27.** 1 **28.** 1 **29.** $a \approx 13.74, c \approx 14.62, A = 70°$ **30.** $a \approx 22.69, c \approx 23.04, A = 80°$
31. $b \approx 5.03, c \approx 7.83, A = 50°$ **32.** $b \approx 8.34, c \approx 10.89, A = 40°$ **33.** $a \approx 0.71, c \approx 4.06, B = 80°$ **34.** $a \approx 2.18, c \approx 6.39, B = 70°$ **35.** $b \approx 10.72, c \approx 11.83,$
$B = 65°$ **36.** $b \approx 7.15, c \approx 9.33, B = 50°$ **37.** $b \approx 3.08, a \approx 8.46, A = 70°$ **38.** $a \approx 6.43, b \approx 7.66, B = 50°$ **39.** $c \approx 5.83, A \approx 59.0°, B \approx 31.0°$
40. $c \approx 8.25, A \approx 14.0°, B \approx 76.0°$ **41.** $b \approx 4.58, A \approx 23.6°, B \approx 66.4°$ **42.** $a \approx 4.47, A \approx 48.2°, B \approx 41.8°$ **43.** 23.6° and 66.4° **44.** 19.5° and 70.5°
45. 4.59 in.; 6.55 in. **46.** 6.43 cm; 7.66 cm **47. (a)** 5.52 in. or 11.83 in. **48. (a)** 3.25 m or 7.84 m **49.** 70.02 ft **50.** 83.91 ft **51.** 985.91 ft **52.** 214.45 ft
53. 137.37 m **54.** 20.67 ft **55.** 80.5° **56.** 15.9° **57. (a)** 111.96 ft/sec or 76.3 mi/hr **(b)** 82.42 ft/sec or 56.2 mi/hr **(c)** Under 18.8° **58.** 14.0°
59. (a) 2.4898×10^{13} miles **(b)** 0.000214° **60. (a)** 6.5726×10^{13} miles **(b)** 0.00008° **61.** 554.52 ft **62.** 7524.67 ft **63.** S76.6°E **64.** S16.6°E
65. The embankment is 30.5 m high. **66. (a)** The surveyor is 2150 ft from the base. **(b)** The building is 1450 ft tall. **(c)** The angle of elevation is
38.4°. **(d)** The antenna is 253 ft tall. **67.** 3.83 mi **68.** No; move the tripod back about 1 foot. **69.** 1978.09 ft **70.** 580.61 ft **71.** 60.27 ft
72. 350.69 ft **73.** The buildings are 7984 ft apart. **74.** The river is 1650 ft wide. **75.** 69.0° **76.** 14.9° **77.** 38.9° **78. (a)** $\cos\dfrac{\theta}{2} = \dfrac{3960}{3960+h}$

(b) $d = 3960\,\theta$ **(c)** $\cos\dfrac{d}{7920} = \dfrac{3960}{3960+h}$ **(d)** 206 mi **(e)** 2990 mi **79.** The white ball should hit the top cushion 4.125 ft from the upper left corner.

80. (a) The office building is 2633 ft away from the Freedom Tower. **(b)** The office building is 818 ft tall.

8.2 Assess Your Understanding (page 529)

4. oblique **5.** $\dfrac{\sin A}{a} = \dfrac{\sin B}{b} = \dfrac{\sin C}{c}$ **6.** F **7.** T **8.** F **9.** $a \approx 3.23, b \approx 3.55, A = 40°$ **10.** $a \approx 2.84, b \approx 2.58, C = 95°$

11. $a \approx 3.25, c \approx 4.23, B = 45°$ **12.** $a \approx 8.45, c \approx 16.38, A = 25°$ **13.** $C = 95°, c \approx 9.86, a \approx 6.36$ **14.** $a \approx 3.35, b \approx 1.68, C = 165°$

15. $A = 40°, a = 2, c \approx 3.06$ **16.** $a \approx 11.82, c \approx 9.19, C = 50°$ **17.** $C = 120°, b \approx 1.06, c \approx 2.69$ **18.** $b \approx 3.68, c \approx 1.34, B = 110°$

19. $A = 100°, a \approx 5.24, c \approx 0.92$ **20.** $a \approx 4.91, b \approx 4.52, C = 50°$ **21.** $B = 40°, a \approx 5.64, b \approx 3.86$ **22.** $a \approx 10.82, c \approx 11.34, A = 70°$

23. $C = 100°, a \approx 1.31, b \approx 1.31$ **24.** $b \approx 0.34, c \approx 0.94, A = 90°$ **25.** One triangle; $B \approx 30.7°, C \approx 99.3°, c \approx 3.86$

26. One triangle; $a \approx 5.80, A \approx 111.2°, C \approx 28.8°$ **27.** One triangle; $C \approx 36.2°, A \approx 43.8°, a \approx 3.51$ **28.** One triangle; $b \approx 1.30, B \approx 34.3°,$
$C \approx 25.7°$ **29.** No triangle **30.** Two triangles; $a_1 \approx 2.83, A_1 \approx 65.4°, C_1 \approx 74.6°$ or $a_2 \approx 1.77, A_2 \approx 34.6°, C_2 \approx 105.4°$ **31.** Two triangles;
$C_1 \approx 30.9°, A_1 \approx 129.1°, a_1 \approx 9.07$ or $C_2 \approx 149.1°, A_2 \approx 10.9°, a_2 \approx 2.20$ **32.** No triangle **33.** No triangle **34.** No triangle
35. Two triangles; $A_1 \approx 57.7°, B_1 \approx 97.3°, b_1 \approx 2.35$ or $A_2 \approx 122.3°, B_2 \approx 32.7°, b_2 \approx 1.28$ **36.** Two triangles; $a_1 = 6.21, A_1 \approx 86.5°, C_1 \approx 53.5°$ or
$a_2 = 1.45, A_2 \approx 13.5°, C_2 \approx 126.5°$ **37. (a)** Station Able is about 143.33 mi from the ship: Station Baker is about 135.58 mi from the ship.
(b) Approximately 41 min **38.** 389,000 km **39.** 1490.48 ft **40.** 629.90 ft **41.** 381.69 ft **42.** 1053.15 ft **43.** The tree is 39.4 ft high. **44.** The new
ramp is 14.86 ft long. **45.** Adam receives 88.3 more frequent flyer miles. **46.** 18.7 s **47.** 84.7°; 183.72 ft **48.** 6.80 in. or 10.58 in. **49.** 2.64 mi
50. (a) 3.21 mi **(b)** 3.78 mi **(c)** 3.10 mi **51.** 38.5 in. **52.** 110.01 ft **53.** 449.36 ft **54.** 710.97 ft **55.** 187,600,000 km or 101,440,000 km
56. 42,300,000 km or 252,400,000 km **57.** The diameter is 252 ft.

58. $\dfrac{a+b}{c} = \dfrac{a}{c} + \dfrac{b}{c} = \dfrac{\sin A}{\sin C} + \dfrac{\sin B}{\sin C} = \dfrac{\sin A + \sin B}{\sin C} = \dfrac{2\sin\left(\dfrac{A+B}{2}\right)\cos\left(\dfrac{A-B}{2}\right)}{2\sin\dfrac{C}{2}\cos\dfrac{C}{2}} = \dfrac{\sin\left(\dfrac{\pi}{2} - \dfrac{C}{2}\right)\cos\left(\dfrac{A-B}{2}\right)}{\sin\dfrac{C}{2}\cos\dfrac{C}{2}} = \dfrac{\cos\left(\dfrac{A-B}{2}\right)}{\sin\dfrac{C}{2}}$

59. $\dfrac{a-b}{c} = \dfrac{a}{c} - \dfrac{b}{c} = \dfrac{\sin A}{\sin C} - \dfrac{\sin B}{\sin C} = \dfrac{\sin A - \sin B}{\sin C} = \dfrac{2\sin\left(\dfrac{A-B}{2}\right)\cos\left(\dfrac{A+B}{2}\right)}{2\sin\dfrac{C}{2}\cos\dfrac{C}{2}} = \dfrac{\sin\left(\dfrac{A-B}{2}\right)\cos\left(\dfrac{\pi}{2}-\dfrac{C}{2}\right)}{\sin\dfrac{C}{2}\cos\dfrac{C}{2}} = \dfrac{\sin\left(\dfrac{A-B}{2}\right)}{\cos\dfrac{C}{2}}$

60. $a = \dfrac{b\sin A}{\sin B} = \dfrac{b\sin[180° - (B+C)]}{\sin B} = \dfrac{b}{\sin B}(\sin B\cos C + \cos B\sin C) = b\cos C + \dfrac{b\sin C}{\sin B}\cos B = b\cos C + c\cos B$

61. $\dfrac{a-b}{a+b} = \dfrac{\dfrac{a-b}{c}}{\dfrac{a+b}{c}} = \dfrac{\dfrac{\sin\left[\dfrac{1}{2}(A-B)\right]}{\cos\dfrac{C}{2}}}{\dfrac{\cos\left[\dfrac{1}{2}(A-B)\right]}{\sin\dfrac{C}{2}}} = \dfrac{\tan\left[\dfrac{1}{2}(A-B)\right]}{\cot\dfrac{C}{2}} = \dfrac{\tan\left[\dfrac{1}{2}(A-B)\right]}{\tan\left(\dfrac{\pi}{2}-\dfrac{C}{2}\right)} = \dfrac{\tan\left[\dfrac{1}{2}(A-B)\right]}{\tan\left[\dfrac{1}{2}(A+B)\right]}$

62. $\sin B = \sin(\angle PQR) = \sin(\angle PP'R) = \dfrac{b}{2r}; \dfrac{\sin B}{b} = \dfrac{1}{2r};$ the result follows using the Law of Sines.

8.3 Assess Your Understanding *(page 537)*

3. Cosines **4.** Sines **5.** Cosines **6.** F **7.** F **8.** T **9.** $b \approx 2.95, A \approx 28.7°, C \approx 106.3°$ **10.** $a \approx 2.05, B \approx 46.9°, C \approx 103.1°$

11. $c \approx 3.75, A \approx 32.1°, B \approx 52.9°$ **12.** $b \approx 3.19, A \approx 12.4°, C \approx 147.6°$ **13.** $A \approx 48.5°, B \approx 38.6°, C \approx 92.9°$ **14.** $A \approx 125.1°, B \approx 30.8°,$

$C \approx 24.1°$ **15.** $A \approx 127.2°, B \approx 32.1°, C \approx 20.7°$ **16.** $A \approx 68.0°, B \approx 44.0°, C \approx 68.0°$ **17.** $c \approx 2.57, A \approx 48.6°, B \approx 91.4°$

18. $b \approx 1.03, A \approx 160.3°, C \approx 9.7°$ **19.** $a \approx 2.99, B \approx 19.2°, C \approx 80.8°$ **20.** $c \approx 5.29, A \approx 79.1°, B \approx 40.9°$ **21.** $b \approx 4.14, A \approx 43.0°, C \approx 27.0°$

22. $a \approx 4.58, B \approx 49.1°, C \approx 10.9°$ **23.** $c \approx 1.69, A = 65.0°, B = 65.0°$ **24.** $b \approx 3.61, A \approx 56.3°, C \approx 33.7°$ **25.** $A \approx 67.4°, B = 90°, C \approx 22.6°$

26. $A \approx 53.1°, B = 90°, C \approx 36.9°$ **27.** $A = 60°, B = 60°, C = 60°$ **28.** $A \approx 70.5°, B \approx 70.5°, C \approx 38.9°$ **29.** $A \approx 33.6°, B \approx 62.2°, C \approx 84.3°$

30. $A \approx 36.3°, B \approx 26.4°, C \approx 117.3°$ **31.** $A \approx 97.9°, B \approx 52.4°, C \approx 29.7°$ **32.** $A \approx 60.9°, B \approx 42.8°, C \approx 76.2°$

33. $A = 85°, a = 14.56, c = 14.12$ **34.** $C = 75°, a = 7.14, b = 7.63$ **35.** $A = 40.8°, B = 60.6°, C = 78.6°$

36. $B = 29.9°, C = 65.1°, c = 12.75$ **37.** $A = 80°, b = 8.74, c = 13.80$ **38.** $b = 4.25, A = 50.5°, C = 74.5°$

39. Two triangles: $B_1 = 35.4°, C_1 = 134.6°, c_1 = 12.29; B_2 = 144.6°, C_2 = 25.4°, c_2 = 7.40$ **40.** $C = 43°, a = 6.67, c = 5.02$

41. $B = 24.5°, C = 95.5°, a = 10.44$ **42.** $A = 41.4°, B = 41.4°, C = 97.2°$ **43.** 165 yd **44.** **(a)** 227.56 mi **(b)** N19.67°E **45.** **(a)** 26.4°

(b) 30.8 h **46.** **(a)** 12.0° **(b)** 220.8 mph **47.** **(a)** 63.7 ft **(b)** 66.8 ft **(c)** 92.8° **48.** **(a)** 42.58 ft **(b)** 38.85 ft **(c)** 85.2° **49.** **(a)** 492.6 ft

(b) 269.3 ft **50.** 501.28 ft, 518.38 ft **51.** 342.33 ft **52.** 241.33 ft **53.** The footings should be 7.65 ft apart.

54. Using the Law of Cosines: $L^2 = x^2 + r^2 - 2rx\cos\theta$; $x^2 - 2rx\cos\theta + r^2 - L^2 = 0$. Then, using the quadratic formula,

$x = r\cos\theta + \sqrt{r^2\cos^2\theta + L^2 - r^2}$.

55. Suppose $0 < \theta < \pi$. Then by the Law of Cosines, $d^2 = r^2 + r^2 - 2r^2\cos\theta = 4r^2\left(\dfrac{1-\cos\theta}{2}\right) \Rightarrow d = 2r\sqrt{\dfrac{1-\cos\theta}{2}} = 2r\sin\dfrac{\theta}{2}$. Since for any

angle in $(0, \pi)$, d is strictly less than the length of the arc subtended by θ, that is, $d < r\theta$, then $2r\sin\dfrac{\theta}{2} < r\theta$, or $2\sin\dfrac{\theta}{2} < \theta$. Since $\cos\dfrac{\theta}{2} < 1$, then,

for $0 < \theta < \pi, \sin\theta = 2\sin\dfrac{\theta}{2}\cos\dfrac{\theta}{2} < 2\sin\dfrac{\theta}{2} < \theta$. If $\theta \geq \pi$, then since $\sin\theta \leq 1, \sin\theta < \theta$. Thus $\sin\theta < \theta$ for all $\theta > 0$.

56. $\cos\dfrac{C}{2} = \sqrt{\dfrac{1+\cos C}{2}} = \sqrt{\dfrac{1+\dfrac{a^2+b^2-c^2}{2ab}}{2}} = \sqrt{\dfrac{2ab+a^2+b^2-c^2}{4ab}} = \sqrt{\dfrac{(a+b)^2-c^2}{4ab}} = \sqrt{\dfrac{(a+b+c)(a+b-c)}{4ab}}$

$= \sqrt{\dfrac{2s(2s-2c)}{4ab}} = \sqrt{\dfrac{s(s-c)}{ab}}$

57. $\sin\dfrac{C}{2} = \sqrt{\dfrac{1-\cos C}{2}} = \sqrt{\dfrac{1-\dfrac{a^2+b^2-c^2}{2ab}}{2}} = \sqrt{\dfrac{2ab-a^2-b^2+c^2}{4ab}} = \sqrt{\dfrac{c^2-(a-b)^2}{4ab}} = \sqrt{\dfrac{(c+a-b)(c+b-a)}{4ab}}$

$= \sqrt{\dfrac{(2s-2b)(2s-2a)}{4ab}} = \sqrt{\dfrac{(s-a)(s-b)}{ab}}$

58. $\dfrac{\cos A}{a} + \dfrac{\cos B}{b} + \dfrac{\cos C}{c} = \dfrac{b^2+c^2-a^2}{2abc} + \dfrac{a^2+c^2-b^2}{2abc} + \dfrac{a^2+b^2-c^2}{2abc} = \dfrac{b^2+c^2-a^2+a^2+c^2-b^2+a^2+b^2-c^2}{2abc} = \dfrac{a^2+b^2+c^2}{2abc}$

8.4 Assess Your Understanding *(page 542)*

2. Heron's **3.** F **4.** T **5.** 2.83 **6.** 3 **7.** 2.99 **8.** 1.71 **9.** 14.98 **10.** 8.18 **11.** 9.56 **12.** 5.56 **13.** 3.86 **14.** 0.17 **15.** 1.48 **16.** 10.39

17. 2.82 **18.** 1.73 **19.** 30 **20.** 6 **21.** 1.73 **22.** 2.83 **23.** 19.90 **24.** 5.33 **25.** $K = \dfrac{1}{2}ab\sin C = \dfrac{1}{2}a\sin C\left(\dfrac{a\sin B}{\sin A}\right) = \dfrac{a^2\sin B\sin C}{2\sin A}$

26. $K = \dfrac{1}{2}ab \sin C = \dfrac{1}{2}b \sin C\left(\dfrac{b \sin A}{\sin B}\right) = \dfrac{b^2 \sin A \sin C}{2 \sin B}$; $K = \dfrac{1}{2}bc \sin A = \dfrac{1}{2}c \sin A\left(\dfrac{c \sin B}{\sin C}\right) = \dfrac{c^2 \sin A \sin B}{2 \sin C}$ **27.** 0.92 **28.** 1.89 **29.** 2.27

30. 8.50 **31.** 5.44 **32.** 10.66 **33.** 9.03 sq ft **34.** 0.69 sq in. **35.** \$5446.38 **36.** 326.73 ft^2 **37.** The area of home plate is about 216.5 in^2.

38. 15.27 in^2 **39.** $K = \dfrac{1}{2}r^2(\theta + \sin \theta)$ **40.** 1645.14 ft^2 **41.** The ground area is 7517.4 ft^2. **42.** The area of the Bermuda triangle is 442,816 mi^2.

43. (a) Area $\triangle OAC = \dfrac{1}{2}|OC||AC| = \dfrac{1}{2}\cdot\dfrac{|OC|}{1}\cdot\dfrac{|AC|}{1} = \dfrac{1}{2}\sin \alpha \cos \alpha$

(e) Area $\triangle OAB = $ Area $\triangle OAC + $ Area $\triangle OCB$

$\dfrac{1}{2}|OB| \sin(\alpha + \beta) = \dfrac{1}{2}\sin \alpha \cos \alpha + \dfrac{1}{2}|OB|^2 \sin \beta \cos \beta$

(b) Area $\triangle OCB = \dfrac{1}{2}|BC||OC| = \dfrac{1}{2}|OB|^2\dfrac{|BC|}{|OB|}\cdot\dfrac{|OC|}{|OB|} = \dfrac{1}{2}|OB|^2 \sin \beta \cos \beta$

$\sin(\alpha + \beta) = \dfrac{1}{|OB|}\sin \alpha \cos \alpha + |OB| \sin \beta \cos \beta$

(c) Area $\triangle OAB = \dfrac{1}{2}|BD||OA| = \dfrac{1}{2}|OB|\dfrac{|BD|}{|OB|} = \dfrac{1}{2}|OB| \sin(\alpha + \beta)$

$\sin(\alpha + \beta) = \dfrac{\cos \beta}{\cos \alpha}\sin \alpha \cos \alpha + \dfrac{\cos \alpha}{\cos \beta}\sin \beta \cos \beta$

(d) $\dfrac{\cos \alpha}{\cos \beta} = \dfrac{\dfrac{|OC|}{1}}{\dfrac{|OC|}{|OB|}} = |OB|$

$\sin(\alpha + \beta) = \sin \alpha \cos \beta + \cos \alpha \sin \beta$

44. (a) The area of $\triangle OBC$ equals $\dfrac{\sin \theta}{2}$, since the length of the base is 1 and the height of the triangle is $\sin \theta$.

(b) The height of $\triangle OBD$ equals $\tan \theta$, so, since the base equals 1, the area of $\triangle OBD$ equals $\dfrac{\tan \theta}{2} = \dfrac{\sin \theta}{2 \cos \theta}$.

(c) Since area $\triangle OBC < $ area $\widehat{OBC} < $ area $\triangle OBD$, then, from parts (a) and (b), $\dfrac{\sin \theta}{2} < \dfrac{\theta}{2} < \dfrac{\sin \theta}{2 \cos \theta}$. Since θ is acute, then $\sin \theta > 0$,

so multiplying by $\dfrac{2}{\sin \theta}$ yields $1 < \dfrac{\theta}{\sin \theta} < \dfrac{1}{\cos \theta}$.

45. 31,145 ft^2 **46.** 30,973 ft^2 **47. (a)** The perimeter and area are both 36. **(b)** The perimeter and area are both 60.

48. $h_1 = 2\dfrac{K}{a}, h_2 = 2\dfrac{K}{b}, h_3 = 2\dfrac{K}{c}$. Then $\dfrac{1}{h_1} + \dfrac{1}{h_2} + \dfrac{1}{h_3} = \dfrac{a}{2K} + \dfrac{b}{2K} + \dfrac{c}{2K} = \dfrac{a + b + c}{2K} = \dfrac{2s}{2K} = \dfrac{s}{K}$.

49. $K = \dfrac{1}{2}ah = \dfrac{1}{2}ab \sin C \Rightarrow h = b \sin C = \dfrac{a \sin B \sin C}{\sin A}$

50. $\angle POQ = 180° - \left(\dfrac{A}{2} + \dfrac{B}{2}\right) = 180° - \dfrac{1}{2}(180° - C) = 90° + \dfrac{C}{2}$, and $\sin\left(90° + \dfrac{C}{2}\right) = \cos\left(-\dfrac{C}{2}\right) = \cos\dfrac{C}{2}$, since cosine is an

even function. Therefore, $r = \dfrac{c \sin\dfrac{A}{2}\sin\dfrac{B}{2}}{\sin\left(90° + \dfrac{C}{2}\right)} = \dfrac{c \sin\dfrac{A}{2}\sin\dfrac{B}{2}}{\cos\dfrac{C}{2}}$.

51. $\cot\dfrac{C}{2} = \dfrac{\cos\dfrac{C}{2}}{\sin\dfrac{C}{2}} = \dfrac{\dfrac{c \sin\dfrac{A}{2}\sin\dfrac{B}{2}}{r}}{\sqrt{\dfrac{(s - a)(s - b)}{ab}}} = \dfrac{c\sqrt{\dfrac{(s - b)(s - c)}{bc}}\sqrt{\dfrac{(s - a)(s - c)}{ac}}}{r\sqrt{\dfrac{(s - a)(s - b)}{ab}}} = \dfrac{c}{r}\sqrt{\dfrac{(s - c)^2}{c^2}} = \dfrac{s - c}{r}$

52. $\cot\dfrac{A}{2} + \cot\dfrac{B}{2} + \cot\dfrac{C}{2} = \dfrac{s - a}{r} + \dfrac{s - b}{r} + \dfrac{s - c}{r} = \dfrac{3s - (a + b + c)}{r} = \dfrac{3s - 2s}{r} = \dfrac{s}{r}$

53. $K = $ area of triangle $QOR + $ area of $ROP + $ area of $POQ = \dfrac{1}{2}ar + \dfrac{1}{2}br + \dfrac{1}{2}cr = r\dfrac{1}{2}(a + b + c) = rs$, so

$r = \dfrac{K}{s} = \dfrac{\sqrt{s(s - a)(s - b)(s - c)}}{s} = \sqrt{\dfrac{(s - a)(s - b)(s - c)}{s}}$.

8.5 Assess Your Understanding (page 552)

2. simple harmonic; amplitude **3.** simple harmonic; damped **4.** T **5.** $d = -5 \cos(\pi t)$ **6.** $d = -10 \cos\left(\dfrac{2\pi}{3}t\right)$

7. $d = -6 \cos(2t)$ **8.** $d = -4 \cos(4t)$ **9.** $d = -5 \sin(\pi t)$ **10.** $d = -10 \sin\left(\dfrac{2\pi}{3}t\right)$ **11.** $d = -6 \sin(2t)$ **12.** $d = -4 \sin(4t)$

13. (a) simple harmonic **(b)** 5 m **(c)** $\dfrac{2\pi}{3}$ s **(d)** $\dfrac{3}{2\pi}$ oscillation/s **14. (a)** simple harmonic **(b)** 4 m **(c)** π s **(d)** $\dfrac{1}{\pi}$ oscillation/s

15. (a) simple harmonic **(b)** 6 m **(c)** 2 s **(d)** $\dfrac{1}{2}$ oscillation/s **16. (a)** simple harmonic **(b)** 5 m **(c)** 4 s **(d)** $\dfrac{1}{4}$ oscillation/s

17. (a) simple harmonic **(b)** 3 m **(c)** 4π s **(d)** $\dfrac{1}{4\pi}$ oscillation/s **18. (a)** simple harmonic **(b)** 2 m **(c)** π s **(d)** $\dfrac{1}{\pi}$ oscillation/s

19. (a) simple harmonic **(b)** 2 m **(c)** 1 s **(d)** 1 oscillation/s **20. (a)** simple harmonic **(b)** 3 m **(c)** 2 s **(d)** $\dfrac{1}{2}$ oscillation/s

21. (a) $d = -10e^{-0.7t/50}\cos\left(\sqrt{\dfrac{4\pi^2}{25} - \dfrac{0.49}{2500}}\,t\right)$ **22. (a)** $d = -15e^{-0.75t/40}\cos\left(\sqrt{\dfrac{\pi^2}{9} - \dfrac{0.5625}{1600}}\,t\right)$ **23. (a)** $d = -18e^{-0.6t/60}\cos\left(\sqrt{\dfrac{\pi^2}{4} - \dfrac{0.36}{3600}}\,t\right)$

(b)

(b)

(b)

24. (a) $d = -16e^{-0.65t/30}\cos\left(\sqrt{\dfrac{4\pi^2}{25} - \dfrac{0.4225}{900}}\,t\right)$ **25. (a)** $d = -5e^{-0.8t/20}\cos\left(\sqrt{\dfrac{4\pi^2}{9} - \dfrac{0.64}{400}}\,t\right)$ **26. (a)** $d = -5e^{-0.7t/20}\cos\left(\sqrt{\dfrac{4\pi^2}{9} - \dfrac{0.49}{400}}\,t\right)$

(b)

(b)

(b)
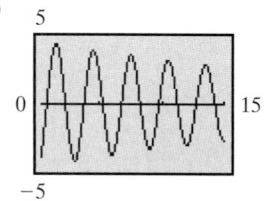

27. (a) The motion is damped.
The bob has mass $m = 20$ kg
with a damping factor of 0.7 kg/s.
(b) 20 m leftward
(c)

(d) 18.33 m leftward **(e)** $d \to 0$

28. (a) The motion is damped.
The bob has mass $m = 20$ kg
with a damping factor of 0.8 kg/s.
(b) 20 m leftward
(c)
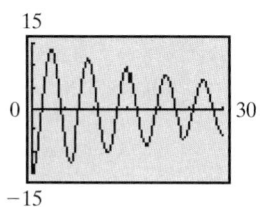
(d) 18.10 m leftward **(e)** $d \to 0$

29. (a) The motion is damped.
The bob has mass $m = 40$ kg
with a damping factor of 0.6 kg/s.
(b) 30 m leftward
(c)

(d) 28.47 m leftward **(e)** $d \to 0$

30. (a) The motion is damped.
The bob has mass $m = 35$ kg
with a damping factor of 0.5 kg/s.
(b) 30 m leftward
(c)
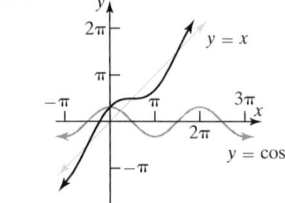
(d) 29.15 m leftward **(e)** $d \to 0$

31. (a) The motion is damped.
The bob has mass $m = 15$ kg
with a damping factor of 0.9 kg/s.
(b) 15 m leftward
(c)

(d) 12.53 m leftward **(e)** $d \to 0$

32. (a) The motion is damped.
The bob has mass $m = 25$ kg
with a damping factor of 0.8 kg/s.
(b) 10 m leftward
(c)
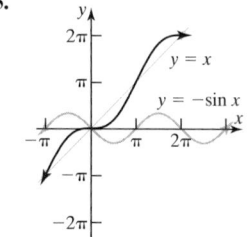
(d) 9.53 m leftward **(e)** $d \to 0$

33.

34.

35.

36.

37.

38.

39.

40.

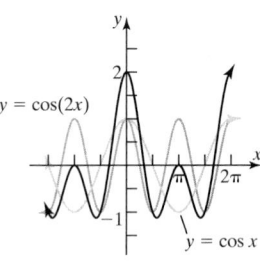

41. $\omega = 1040\pi$;

$d = 0.80 \cos(1040\pi t)$

42. $h = 97.5 - 82.5 \cos(3.2\pi t)$

43. $\omega = 880\pi$;

$d = 0.01 \sin(880\pi t)$

44. $\omega = 659.26\pi$;

$d = 0.025 \sin(659.26\pi t)$

45. (a)

46. (a)

(b)

(c)

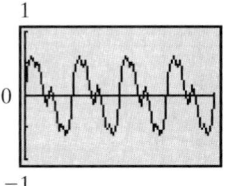

(b) At $t = 0, 2$; at $t = 1, t = 3$

(c) During the approximate intervals
$0.35 < t < 0.67, 1.29 < t < 1.75$,
and $2.19 < t \le 3$

47.

48.

51.

52. $y = x \sin x$

$y = x^2 \sin x$

$y = x^3 \sin x$

53. $y = \dfrac{1}{x} \sin x$

$y = \dfrac{1}{x^2} \sin x$

$y = \dfrac{1}{x^3} \sin x$

Review Exercises *(page 555)*

1. $\sin \theta = \dfrac{4}{3}$; $\cos \theta = \dfrac{3}{5}$; $\tan \theta = \dfrac{4}{3}$; $\cot \theta = \dfrac{3}{4}$; $\sec \theta = \dfrac{5}{3}$; $\csc \theta = \dfrac{5}{4}$

2. $\sin \theta = \dfrac{3\sqrt{34}}{34}$; $\cos \theta = \dfrac{5\sqrt{34}}{34}$; $\tan \theta = \dfrac{3}{5}$; $\cot \theta = \dfrac{5}{3}$; $\sec \theta = \dfrac{\sqrt{34}}{5}$; $\csc \theta = \dfrac{\sqrt{34}}{3}$

3. $\sin \theta = \dfrac{\sqrt{3}}{2}$; $\cos \theta = \dfrac{1}{2}$; $\tan \theta = \sqrt{3}$; $\cot \theta = \dfrac{\sqrt{3}}{3}$; $\sec \theta = 2$; $\csc \theta = \dfrac{2\sqrt{3}}{3}$

4. $\sin \theta = \dfrac{\sqrt{2}}{2}$; $\cos \theta = \dfrac{\sqrt{2}}{2}$; $\tan \theta = 1$; $\cot \theta = 1$; $\sec \theta = \sqrt{2}$; $\csc \theta = \sqrt{2}$ **5.** 0 **6.** 0 **7.** 1 **8.** 1 **9.** 1 **10.** -1 **11.** $A = 70°, b \approx 3.42, a \approx 9.40$

12. $b \approx 7.14, c \approx 8.72, B = 55°$ **13.** $a \approx 4.58, A \approx 66.4°, B \approx 23.6°$ **14.** $c \approx 3.16, A \approx 71.6°, B \approx 18.4°$ **15.** $C = 100°, b \approx 0.65, c \approx 1.29$

16. $a \approx 0.54, b \approx 2.38, B = 130°$ **17.** $B \approx 56.8°, C \approx 23.2°, b \approx 4.25$ **18.** No triangle **19.** No triangle **20.** No triangle **21.** $b \approx 3.32, A \approx 62.8°,$ $C \approx 17.2°$ **22.** $A \approx 36.2°, C \approx 63.8°, c \approx 4.55$ **23.** No triangle **24.** $A \approx 83.3°, B \approx 44.0°, C \approx 52.6°$ **25.** $c \approx 2.32, A \approx 16.1°, B \approx 123.9°$ **26.** $c \approx 4.29, A \approx 66.7°, B \approx 13.3°$ **27.** $B \approx 36.2°, C \approx 63.8°, c \approx 4.55$ **28.** Two triangles: $B_1 \approx 30.9°, C_1 \approx 129.1°, c_1 \approx 4.54$ or $B_2 \approx 149.1°,$ $C_2 \approx 10.9°, c_2 \approx 1.10$ **29.** $A \approx 39.6°, B \approx 18.6°, C \approx 121.9°$ **30.** $A \approx 97.2°, B \approx 41.4°, C \approx 41.4°$ **31.** Two triangles: $B_1 \approx 13.4°, C_1 \approx 156.6°,$ $c_1 \approx 6.86$ or $B_2 \approx 166.6°, C_2 \approx 3.4°, c_2 \approx 1.02$ **32.** $b \approx 11.52, c \approx 10.13, C = 60°$ **33.** $a \approx 5.23, B \approx 46.0°, C \approx 64.0°$ **34.** $c \approx 1.73, A = 30°,$ $B = 90°$ **35.** 1.93 **36.** 4.28 **37.** 18.79 **38.** 0.98 **39.** 6 **40.** 27.81 **41.** 3.80 **42.** 1.98 **43.** 0.32 **44.** 0.93 **45.** 1.92 in^2 **46.** 48.2° **47.** 23.32 ft **48.** 37.30 ft **49.** 2.15 mi **50.** 839.10 ft **51.** 132.55 ft/min **52.** 12.7° **53.** 29.97 ft **54.** (a) 2.59 mi (b) 2.92 mi (c) 2.53 mi **55.** 6.22 mi **56.** (a) 131.8 mi (b) 23.1° (c) 0.21 hr **57.** 71.12 ft **58.** 8798.67 sq ft **59.** \$222,983.51 **60.** S4.0°E **61.** 76.94 in. **62.** 79.69 in.

63. $d = -3 \cos\left(\dfrac{\pi}{2}t\right)$ **64.** $d = -5 \cos\left(\dfrac{\pi}{3}t\right)$ **65.** (a) Simple harmonic (b) 6 ft (c) π sec (d) $\dfrac{1}{\pi}$ oscillation/sec

66. (a) Simple harmonic (b) 2 ft (c) $\dfrac{\pi}{2}$ sec (d) $\dfrac{2}{\pi}$ oscillation/sec **67.** (a) Simple harmonic (b) 2 ft (c) 2 sec (d) $\dfrac{1}{2}$ oscillation/sec

68. (a) Simple harmonic

(b) 3 ft

(c) 4 sec

(d) $\dfrac{1}{4}$ oscillation/sec

69. (a) $d = -15e^{-0.75t/80}\cos\left(\sqrt{\dfrac{4\pi^2}{25} - \dfrac{0.5625}{6400}}\,t\right)$ **70.** (a) $d = -13e^{-0.65t/50}\cos\left(\sqrt{\dfrac{\pi^2}{4} - \dfrac{0.4225}{2500}}\,t\right)$

(b)

(b)

71. (a) The motion is damped. The bob has mass $m = 20$ kg with a damping factor of 0.6 kg/sec.

(b) 15 m leftward

(c)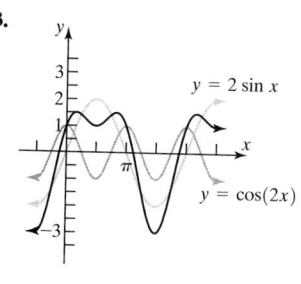

(d) 13.92 m leftward

(e) $d \to 0$

72. (a) The motion is damped. The bob has mass $m = 30$ kg with a damping factor of 0.5 kg/sec.

(b) 20 m leftward

(c)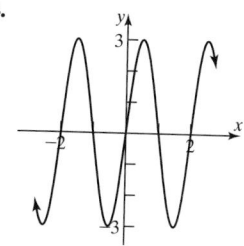

(d) 19.51 m leftward

(e) $d \to 0$

73.

74.

Chapter Test *(page 558)*

1. $\sin\theta = \dfrac{\sqrt{5}}{5}; \cos\theta = \dfrac{2\sqrt{5}}{5}; \tan\theta = \dfrac{1}{2}; \csc\theta = \sqrt{5}; \sec\theta = \dfrac{\sqrt{5}}{2}; \cot\theta = 2$ **2.** 0 **3.** $a = 15.88, B \approx 57.5°, C \approx 70.5°$
4. $b \approx 6.85, C = 117°, c \approx 16.30$ **5.** $A \approx 52.4°, B \approx 29.7°, C \approx 97.9°$ **6.** $b \approx 4.72, c \approx 1.67, B = 105°$ **7.** No triangle
8. $c \approx 7.62, A \approx 80.5°, B \approx 29.5°$ **9.** 15.04 square units **10.** 19.81 square units **11.** 61.0° **12.** 1.3° **13.** The area of the shaded region is 9.26 cm^2.
14. 54.15 square units **15.** Madison will have to swim about 2.23 miles. **16.** 12.63 square units **17.** The lengths of the sides are 15, 18, and 21.
18. $d = 5(\sin 42°)\sin\left(\dfrac{\pi t}{3}\right)$ or $d \approx 3.346\sin\left(\dfrac{\pi t}{3}\right)$

Cumulative Review *(page 559)*

1. $\left\{\dfrac{1}{3}, 1\right\}$ **2.** $(x + 5)^2 + (y - 1)^2 = 9$ **3.** $\{x \mid x \le -1 \text{ or } x \ge 4\}$ **4.**

5.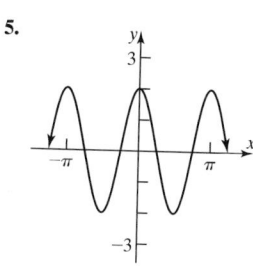

6. (a) $-\dfrac{2\sqrt{5}}{5}$ **(b)** $\dfrac{\sqrt{5}}{5}$ **(c)** $-\dfrac{4}{5}$ **(d)** $-\dfrac{3}{5}$ **(e)** $\sqrt{\dfrac{5-\sqrt{5}}{10}}$ **(f)** $-\sqrt{\dfrac{5+\sqrt{5}}{10}}$

7. (a) **(b)** **(c)** **(d)**

8. (a) **(b)** **(c)**

(d) **(e)** **(f)**

(g) **(h)** **(i)**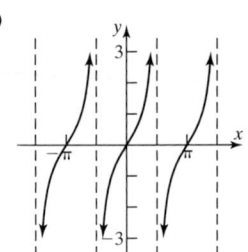

9. Two triangles: $A_1 \approx 59.0°$, $B_1 \approx 81.0°$, $b_1 \approx 23.05$ or $A_2 \approx 121.0°$, $B_2 \approx 19.0°$, $b_2 \approx 7.59$ **10.** $\left\{-2i, 2i, \dfrac{1}{3}, 1, 2\right\}$

11. $R(x) = \dfrac{(2x+1)(x-4)}{(x+5)(x-3)}$; domain: $\{x \mid x \neq -5, x \neq 3\}$

Intercepts: $\left(-\dfrac{1}{2}, 0\right)$, $(4, 0)$, $\left(0, \dfrac{4}{15}\right)$

No symmetry

Vertical asymptotes: $x = -5$, $x = 3$

Horizontal asymptote: $y = 2$

Intersects: $\left(\dfrac{26}{11}, 2\right)$

 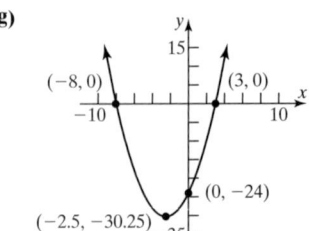

12. $\{2.26\}$ **13.** $\{1\}$ **14. (a)** $\left\{-\dfrac{5}{4}\right\}$ **(b)** $\{2\}$ **(c)** $\left\{\dfrac{-1-3\sqrt{13}}{2}, \dfrac{-1+3\sqrt{13}}{2}\right\}$ **(d)** $\left\{x \mid x > -\dfrac{5}{4}\right\}$ or $\left(-\dfrac{5}{4}, \infty\right)$

(e) $\left\{x \mid -8 \leq x \leq 3\right\}$ or $[-8, 3]$ **(f)** **(g)**

CHAPTER 9 Polar Coordinates; Vectors

9.1 Assess Your Understanding (page 569)

5. pole; polar axis **6.** -2 **7.** $\left(-\sqrt{3},-1\right)$ **8.** F **9.** T **10.** T **11.** A **12.** B **13.** C **14.** C **15.** B **16.** D **17.** A **18.** D

19.

20.

21.

22.

23.

24.

25.

26.

27.

28.

29.

30.

31.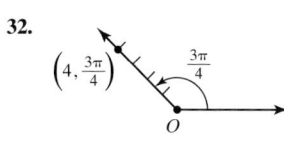

(a) $\left(5,-\dfrac{4\pi}{3}\right)$

(b) $\left(-5,\dfrac{5\pi}{3}\right)$

(c) $\left(5,\dfrac{8\pi}{3}\right)$

32.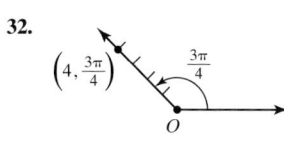

(a) $\left(4,-\dfrac{5\pi}{4}\right)$

(b) $\left(-4,\dfrac{7\pi}{4}\right)$

(c) $\left(4,\dfrac{11\pi}{4}\right)$

33.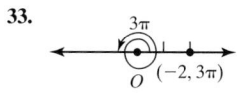

(a) $(2,-2\pi)$

(b) $(-2,\pi)$

(c) $(2,2\pi)$

34.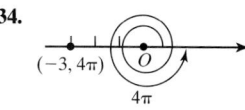

(a) $(3,-\pi)$

(b) $(-3,0)$

(c) $(3,3\pi)$

35.

(a) $\left(1,-\dfrac{3\pi}{2}\right)$

(b) $\left(-1,\dfrac{3\pi}{2}\right)$

(c) $\left(1,\dfrac{5\pi}{2}\right)$

36.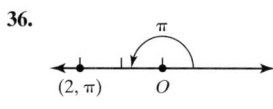

(a) $(2,-\pi)$

(b) $(-2,0)$

(c) $(2,3\pi)$

37.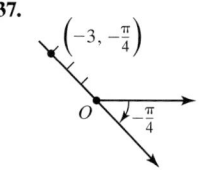

(a) $\left(3,-\dfrac{5\pi}{4}\right)$

(b) $\left(-3,\dfrac{7\pi}{4}\right)$

(c) $\left(3,\dfrac{11\pi}{4}\right)$

38.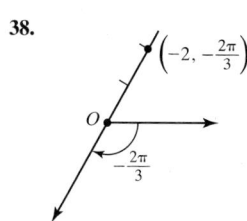

(a) $\left(2,-\dfrac{5\pi}{3}\right)$

(b) $\left(-2,\dfrac{4\pi}{3}\right)$

(c) $\left(2,\dfrac{7\pi}{3}\right)$

39. $(0,3)$ **40.** $(0,-4)$ **41.** $(-2,0)$ **42.** $(3,0)$ **43.** $\left(-3\sqrt{3},3\right)$ **44.** $\left(\dfrac{5}{2},-\dfrac{5\sqrt{3}}{2}\right)$ **45.** $\left(\sqrt{2},-\sqrt{2}\right)$ **46.** $\left(1,-\sqrt{3}\right)$ **47.** $\left(-\dfrac{1}{2},\dfrac{\sqrt{3}}{2}\right)$

48. $\left(\dfrac{3\sqrt{2}}{2},\dfrac{3\sqrt{2}}{2}\right)$ **49.** $(2,0)$ **50.** $(0,3)$ **51.** $(-2.57,7.05)$ **52.** $(3.10,0.11)$ **53.** $(-4.98,-3.85)$ **54.** $(3.79,-7.16)$ **55.** $(3,0)$ **56.** $\left(2,\dfrac{\pi}{2}\right)$

57. $(1, \pi)$ **58.** $\left(2, -\dfrac{\pi}{2}\right)$ **59.** $\left(\sqrt{2}, -\dfrac{\pi}{4}\right)$ **60.** $\left(3\sqrt{2}, \dfrac{3\pi}{4}\right)$ **61.** $\left(2, \dfrac{\pi}{6}\right)$ **62.** $\left(4, -\dfrac{2\pi}{3}\right)$ **63.** $(2.47, -1.02)$ **64.** $(2.25, -1.93)$ **65.** $(9.30, 0.47)$

66. $(2.31, 3.05)$ **67.** $r^2 = \dfrac{3}{2}$ or $r = \dfrac{\sqrt{6}}{2}$ **68.** $r = \cos\theta$ **69.** $r^2 \cos^2\theta - 4r\sin\theta = 0$ **70.** $r^2 \sin^2\theta - 2r\cos\theta = 0$ **71.** $r^2 \sin 2\theta = 1$

72. $r^3(\sin\theta)(\cos^2\theta) = \dfrac{1}{4}$ **73.** $r\cos\theta = 4$ **74.** $r\sin\theta = -3$ **75.** $x^2 + y^2 - x = 0$ or $\left(x - \dfrac{1}{2}\right)^2 + y^2 = \dfrac{1}{4}$ **76.** $x^2 + y^2 = y + \sqrt{x^2 + y^2}$

77. $(x^2 + y^2)^{3/2} - x = 0$ **78.** $x^2 + y^2 = y - x$ or $\left(x + \dfrac{1}{2}\right)^2 + \left(y - \dfrac{1}{2}\right)^2 = \dfrac{1}{2}$ **79.** $x^2 + y^2 = 4$ **80.** $x^2 + y^2 = 16$ **81.** $y^2 = 8(x + 2)$

82. $64\left(x - \dfrac{3}{8}\right)^2 + 72y^2 = 81$ **83. (a)** $(-10, 36)$ **(b)** $\left(2\sqrt{349}, 180° + \tan^{-1}\left(-\dfrac{18}{5}\right)\right) \approx (37.36, 105.5°)$ **(c)** $(-3, -35)$

(d) $\left(\sqrt{1234}, 180° + \tan^{-1}\left(\dfrac{35}{3}\right)\right)$ **84.** $d = \sqrt{(r_2\cos\theta_2 - r_1\cos\theta_1)^2 + (r_2\sin\theta_2 - r_1\sin\theta_1)^2}$
$\approx (35.13, 265.1°)$
$\qquad = \sqrt{(r_2^2\cos^2\theta_2 - 2r_2\cos\theta_2\, r_1\cos\theta_1 + r_1^2\cos^2\theta_1) + (r_2^2\sin^2\theta_2 - 2r_2\sin\theta_2\, r_1\sin\theta_1 + r_1^2\sin^2\theta_1)}$
$\qquad = \sqrt{r_1^2 + r_2^2 - 2r_1r_2(\cos\theta_2\cos\theta_1 + \sin\theta_2\sin\theta_1)}$
$\qquad = \sqrt{r_1^2 + r_2^2 - 2r_1r_2\cos(\theta_2 - \theta_1)}$

9.2 Assess Your Understanding *(page 586)*

7. polar equation **8.** $r = 2\cos\theta$ **9.** $-r$ **10.** F **11.** F **12.** F

13. $x^2 + y^2 = 16$; circle, radius 4, center at pole

14. $x^2 + y^2 = 4$; circle, radius 2, center at pole

15. $y = \sqrt{3}x$; line through pole, making an angle of $\dfrac{\pi}{3}$ with polar axis

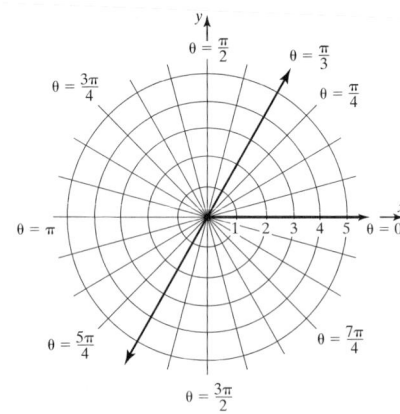

16. $y = -x$; line through pole, making an angle of $-\dfrac{\pi}{4}$ $\left(\text{or } \dfrac{3\pi}{4}\right)$ with polar axis

17. $y = 4$; horizontal line 4 units above the pole

18. $x = 4$; vertical line 4 units to the right of the pole

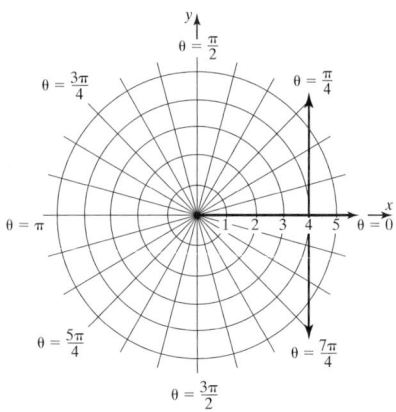

19. $x = -2$; vertical line 2 units to the left of the pole

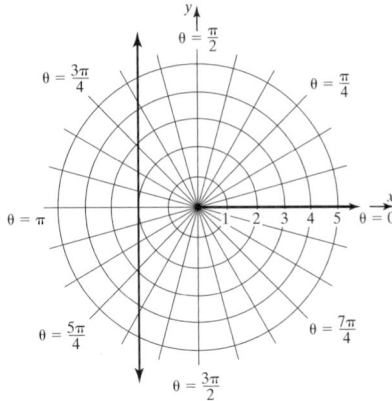

20. $y = -2$; horizontal line 2 units below the pole

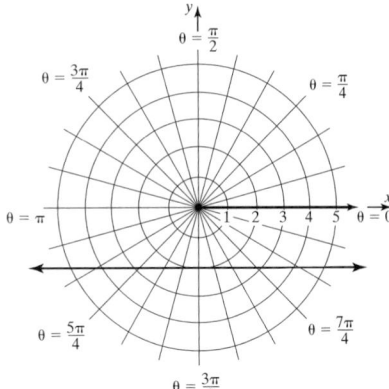

21. $(x - 1)^2 + y^2 = 1$; circle, radius 1, center $(1, 0)$ in rectangular coordinates

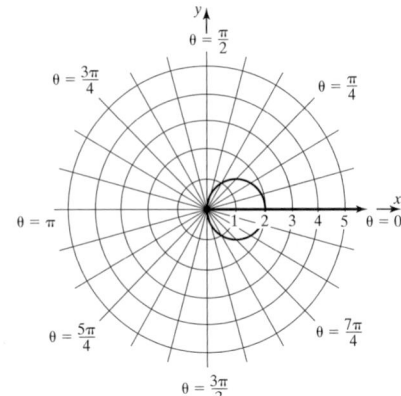

22. $x^2 + (y - 1)^2 = 1$; circle, radius 1, center $(0, 1)$ in rectangular coordinates

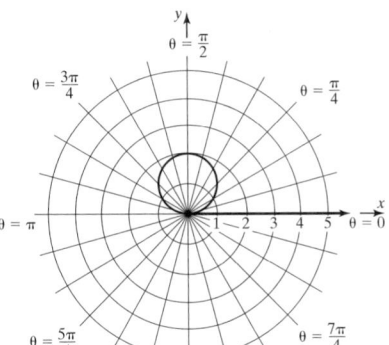

23. $x^2 + (y + 2)^2 = 4$; circle, radius 2, center at $(0, -2)$ in rectangular coordinates

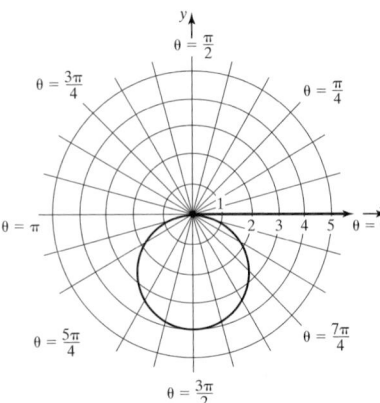

24. $(x + 2)^2 + y^2 = 4$; circle, radius 2, center $(-2, 0)$ in rectangular coordinates

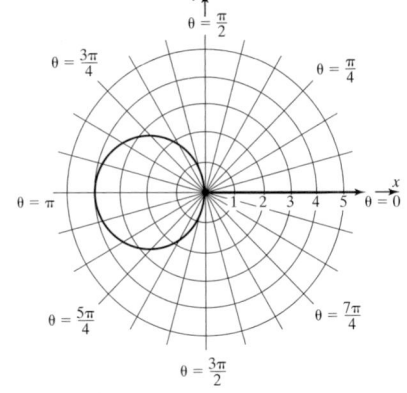

25. $(x - 2)^2 + y^2 = 4$; circle, radius 2, center at $(2, 0)$ in rectangular coordinates

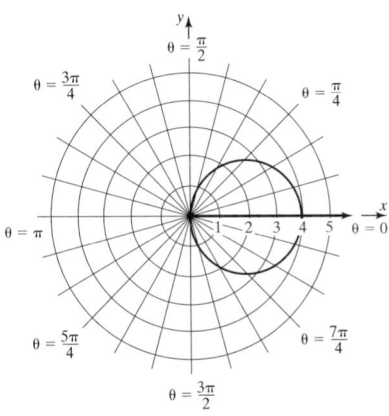

26. $x^2 + (y - 4)^2 = 16$; circle, radius 4, center $(0, 4)$ in rectangular coordinates

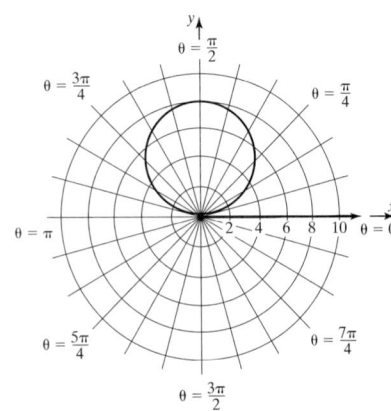

27. $x^2 + (y + 1)^2 = 1$; circle, radius 1, center at $(0, -1)$ in rectangular coordinates

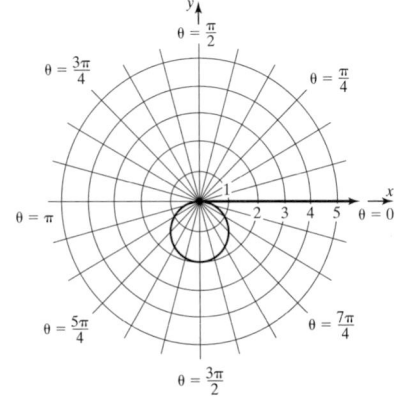

28. $(x + 2)^2 + y^2 = 4$; circle, radius 2, center $(-2, 0)$ in rectangular coordinates

29. *E* **30.** *A* **31.** *F* **32.** *B* **33.** *H* **34.** *G* **35.** *D* **36.** *C*

37. Cardioid

38. Cardioid

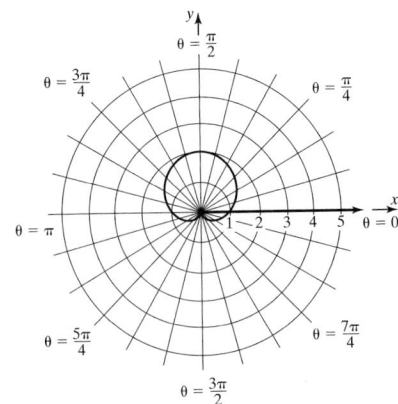

39. Cardioid

40. Cardioid

41. Limaçon without inner loop

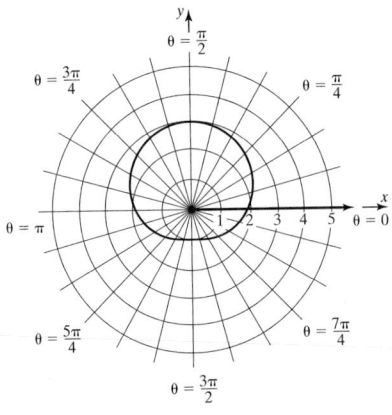

42. Limaçon without inner loop

43. Limaçon without inner loop

44. Limaçon without inner loop

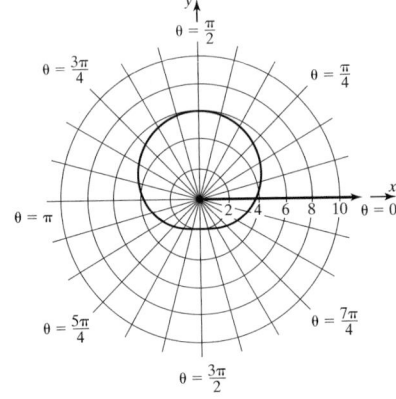

45. Limaçon with inner loop

46. Limaçon with inner loop

47. Limaçon with inner loop

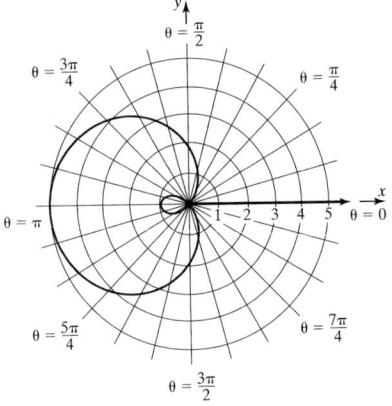

48. Limaçon with inner loop

49. Rose

50. Rose

51. Rose

52. Rose

53. Lemniscate

54. Lemniscate

55. Spiral

56. Spiral

57. Cardioid

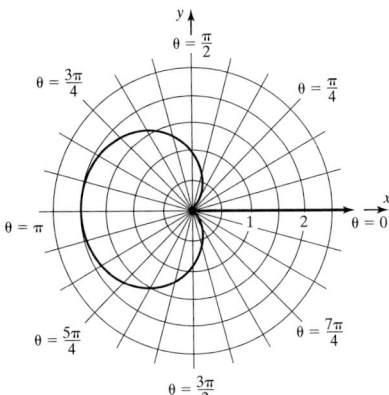

58. Limaçon without inner loop

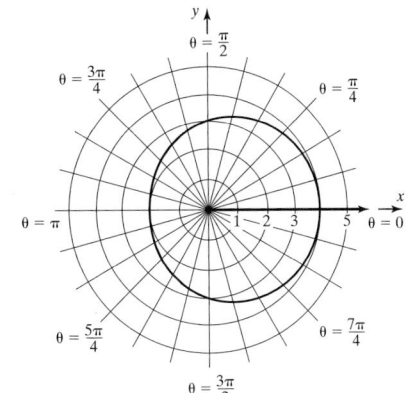

59. Limaçon with inner loop

60. Rose

61.

62.

63.

64.

65.

66.

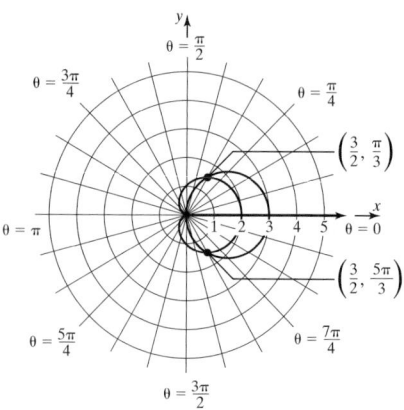

67. $r = 3 + 3\cos\theta$ **68.** $r = 3 - 3\cos\theta$ **69.** $r = 4 + \sin\theta$ **70.** $r = 1 + 4\sin\theta$

71.

72.

73.

74.

75.

76.

77.

78.

79.

80.

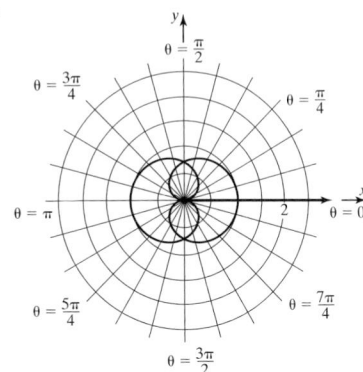

81. $r \sin \theta = a$
$y = a$

82. $r \cos \theta = a$
$x = a$

83.
$$r = 2a \sin \theta$$
$$r^2 = 2ar \sin \theta$$
$$x^2 + y^2 = 2ay$$
$$x^2 + y^2 - 2ay = 0$$
$$x^2 + (y - a)^2 = a^2$$
Circle, radius a, center at $(0, a)$
in rectangular coordinates

84.
$$r = -2a \sin \theta$$
$$r^2 = -2ar \sin \theta$$
$$x^2 + y^2 = -2ay$$
$$x^2 + y^2 + 2ay = 0$$
$$x^2 + (y + a)^2 = a^2$$
Circle, radius a, center at $(0, -a)$
in rectangular coordinates

85.
$$r = 2a \cos \theta$$
$$r^2 = 2ar \cos \theta$$
$$x^2 + y^2 = 2ax$$
$$x^2 - 2ax + y^2 = 0$$
$$(x - a)^2 + y^2 = a^2$$
Circle, radius a, center at $(a, 0)$
in rectangular coordinates

86.
$$r = -2a \cos \theta$$
$$r^2 = -2ar \cos \theta$$
$$x^2 + y^2 = -2ax$$
$$x^2 + 2ax + y^2 = 0$$
$$(x + a)^2 + y^2 = a^2$$
Circle, radius a, center at $(-a, 0)$
in rectangular coordinates

87. (a) $r^2 = \cos \theta : r^2 = \cos(\pi - \theta)$
$r^2 = -\cos \theta$
Not equivalent; test fails.
$(-r)^2 = \cos(-\theta)$
$r^2 = \cos \theta$
New test works.

(b) $r^2 = \sin \theta : r^2 = \sin(\pi - \theta)$
$r^2 = \sin \theta$
Test works.
$(-r)^2 = \sin(-\theta)$
$r^2 = -\sin \theta$
Not equivalent; new test fails.

Historical Problems *(page 595)*

1. (a) $1 + 4i, 1 + i$ **(b)** $-1, 2 + i.$

9.3 Assess Your Understanding (page 595)

5. magnitude; modulus; argument **6.** De Moivre's **7.** three **8.** T **9.** F **10.** T

11.
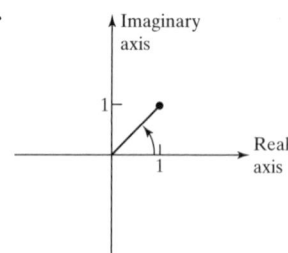
$\sqrt{2}(\cos 45° + i \sin 45°)$

12.
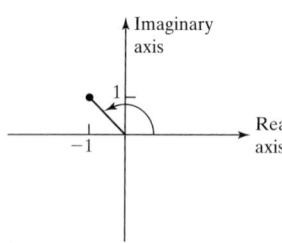
$\sqrt{2}(\cos 135° + i \sin 135°)$

13.
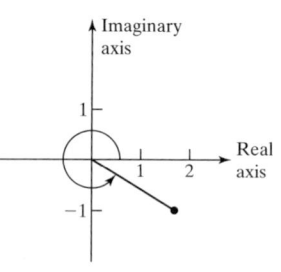
$2(\cos 330° + i \sin 330°)$

14.
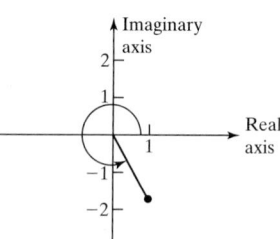
$2(\cos 300° + i \sin 300°)$

15.
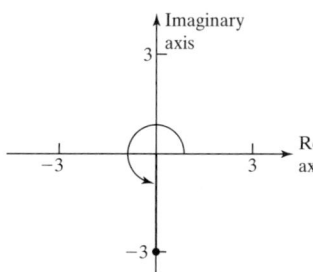
$3(\cos 270° + i \sin 270°)$

16.
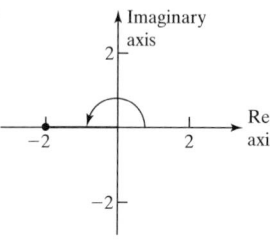
$2(\cos 180° + i \sin 180°)$

17.
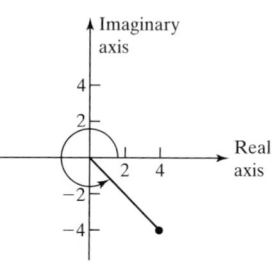
$4\sqrt{2}(\cos 315° + i \sin 315°)$

18.
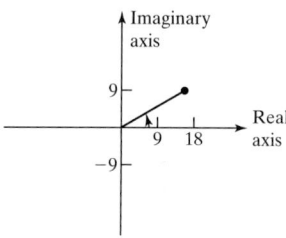
$18(\cos 30° + i \sin 30°)$

19.
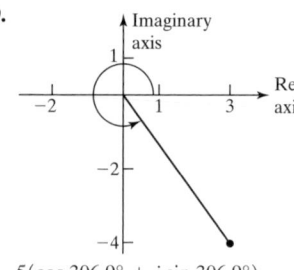
$5(\cos 306.9° + i \sin 306.9°)$

20.
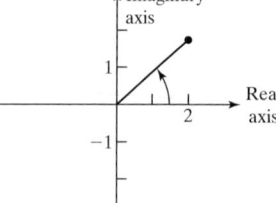
$\sqrt{7}(\cos 40.9° + i \sin 40.9°)$

21.

$\sqrt{13}(\cos 123.7° + i \sin 123.7°)$

22.
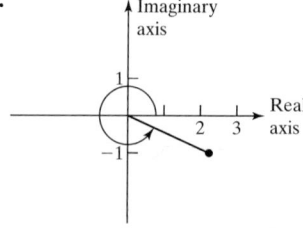
$\sqrt{6}(\cos 335.9° + i \sin 335.9°)$

23. $-1 + \sqrt{3}i$ **24.** $-\dfrac{3\sqrt{3}}{2} - \dfrac{3}{2}i$ **25.** $2\sqrt{2} - 2\sqrt{2}i$ **26.** $-\sqrt{3} + i$ **27.** $-3i$ **28.** $4i$ **29.** $-0.035 + 0.197i$ **30.** $-0.376 - 0.137i$

31. $1.970 + 0.347i$ **32.** $2.853 + 0.927i$ **33.** $zw = 8(\cos 60° + i \sin 60°); \dfrac{z}{w} = \dfrac{1}{2}(\cos 20° + i \sin 20°)$

34. $zw = \cos 220° + i \sin 220°; \dfrac{z}{w} = \cos 20° + i \sin 20°$ **35.** $zw = 12(\cos 40° + i \sin 40°); \dfrac{z}{w} = \dfrac{3}{4}(\cos 220° + i \sin 220°)$

36. $zw = 12(\cos 280° + i \sin 280°); \dfrac{z}{w} = \dfrac{1}{3}(\cos 240° + i \sin 240°)$ **37.** $zw = 4\left(\cos \dfrac{9\pi}{40} + i \sin \dfrac{9\pi}{40}\right); \dfrac{z}{w} = \cos \dfrac{\pi}{40} + i \sin \dfrac{\pi}{40}$

38. $zw = 8\left(\cos \dfrac{15\pi}{16} + i \sin \dfrac{15\pi}{16}\right); \dfrac{z}{w} = 2\left(\cos \dfrac{29\pi}{16} + i \sin \dfrac{29\pi}{16}\right)$ **39.** $zw = 4\sqrt{2}(\cos 15° + i \sin 15°); \dfrac{z}{w} = \sqrt{2}(\cos 75° + i \sin 75°)$

40. $zw = 2\sqrt{2}(\cos 255° + i \sin 255°); \dfrac{z}{w} = \dfrac{\sqrt{2}}{2}(\cos 15° + i \sin 15°)$ **41.** $-32 + 32\sqrt{3}i$ **42.** $-\dfrac{27}{2} - \dfrac{27\sqrt{3}}{2}i$ **43.** $32i$ **44.** $-2\sqrt{2} - 2\sqrt{2}i$

45. $\dfrac{27}{2} + \dfrac{27\sqrt{3}}{2}i$ **46.** $\dfrac{1}{32}$ **47.** $-\dfrac{25\sqrt{2}}{2} + \dfrac{25\sqrt{2}}{2}i$ **48.** $\dfrac{27}{2} - \dfrac{27\sqrt{3}}{2}i$ **49.** $-4 + 4i$ **50.** -64 **51.** $-23 + 14.142i$

52. $-1264 - 286.217i$ **53.** $\sqrt[6]{2}(\cos 15° + i \sin 15°), \sqrt[6]{2}(\cos 135° + i \sin 135°), \sqrt[6]{2}(\cos 255° + i \sin 255°)$

54. $\sqrt[4]{2}(\cos 82.5° + i \sin 82.5°), \sqrt[4]{2}(\cos 172.5° + i \sin 172.5°), \sqrt[4]{2}(\cos 262.5° + i \sin 262.5°), \sqrt[4]{2}(\cos 352.5° + i \sin 352.5°)$

55. $\sqrt[4]{8}(\cos 75° + i \sin 75°), \sqrt[4]{8}(\cos 165° + i \sin 165°), \sqrt[4]{8}(\cos 255° + i \sin 255°), \sqrt[4]{8}(\cos 345° + i \sin 345°)$

56. $2^{7/6}(\cos 75° + i \sin 75°), 2^{7/6}(\cos 195° + i \sin 195°), 2^{7/6}(\cos 315° + i \sin 315°)$

57. $2(\cos 67.5° + i \sin 67.5°), 2(\cos 157.5° + i \sin 157.5°), 2(\cos 247.5° + i \sin 247.5°), 2(\cos 337.5° + i \sin 337.5°)$

58. $2(\cos 60° + i \sin 60°), 2(\cos 180° + i \sin 180°), 2(\cos 300° + i \sin 300°)$

59. $\cos 18° + i \sin 18°, \cos 90° + i \sin 90°, \cos 162° + i \sin 162°, \cos 234° + i \sin 234°, \cos 306° + i \sin 306°$

60. $\cos 54° + i \sin 54°, \cos 126° + i \sin 126°, \cos 198° + i \sin 198°, \cos 270° + i \sin 270°, \cos 342° + i \sin 342°$

61. $1, i, -1, -i$

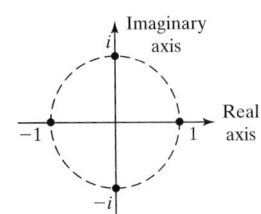

62. $1, \frac{1}{2} + \frac{\sqrt{3}}{2}i, -\frac{1}{2} + \frac{\sqrt{3}}{2}i, -1, -\frac{1}{2} - \frac{\sqrt{3}}{2}i, \frac{1}{2} - \frac{\sqrt{3}}{2}i$

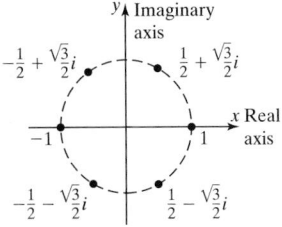

63. Look at formula (8); $|z_k| = \sqrt[n]{r}$ for all k.

64. The radius is $\sqrt[n]{|w|} = \sqrt[n]{r}$, where w is the original complex number.

65. Look at formula (8). The z_k are spaced apart by an angle of $\frac{2\pi}{n}$.

66. $\dfrac{z_1}{z_2} = \dfrac{r_1(\cos\theta_1 + i\sin\theta_1)}{r_2(\cos\theta_2 + i\sin\theta_2)} = \left(\dfrac{r_1}{r_2}\right)\dfrac{(\cos\theta_1 + i\sin\theta_1)(\cos\theta_2 - i\sin\theta_2)}{(\cos\theta_2 + i\sin\theta_2)(\cos\theta_2 - i\sin\theta_2)} = \left(\dfrac{r_1}{r_2}\right)\dfrac{\cos\theta_1\cos\theta_2 + \sin\theta_1\sin\theta_2 + i(\sin\theta_1\cos\theta_2 - \cos\theta_1\sin\theta_2)}{\cos^2\theta_2 + \sin^2\theta_2}$

$= \dfrac{r_1}{r_2}[\cos(\theta_1 - \theta_2) + i\sin(\theta_1 - \theta_2)]$

67. (a)

$z = a_0$	a_1	a_2	a_3	a_4	a_5	a_6
$0.1 - 0.4i$	$-0.05 - 0.48i$	$-0.13 - 0.35i$	$-0.01 - 0.31i$	$0.01 - 0.35i$	$0.2 - 0.41i$	$0.07 - 0.42i$
$0.5 + 0.8i$	$0.11 + 1.6i$	$-2.05 + 1.15i$	$3.37 - 3.92i$	$-3.52 - 25.6i$	$-641.9 + 181.1i$	$379290 - 232509i$
$-0.9 + 0.7i$	$-0.58 - 0.56i$	$0.87 + 1.35i$	$-1.95 - 1.67i$	$0.13 + 7.21i$	$-52.88 + 2.56i$	$2788.5 - 269.6i$
$-1.1 + 0.1i$	$0.1 - 0.12i$	$-1.10 + 0.76i$	$0.11 - 0.068i$	$-1.09 + 0.085i$	$0.085 - 0.85i$	$-1.10 + 0.086i$
$0 - 1.3i$	$-1.69 - 1.3i$	$1.17 + 3.09i$	$-8.21 + 5.92i$	$32.46 - 98.47i$	$-8643.6 - 6393.7i$	$33833744 + 110529134.4i$
$1 + 1i$	$1 + 3i$	$-7 + 7i$	$1 - 97i$	$-9407 - 193i$	$88454401 + 3631103i$	$7.8 \times 10^{15} + 6.4 \times 10^{14}i$

(b) z_1 and z_4 are in the Mandlebrot set. a_6 for the complex numbers not in the set have very large components.

(c)

z	$|z|$	$|a_6|$
$0.1 - 0.4i$	0.4	0.4
$0.5 + 0.8i$	0.9	444884
$-0.9 + 0.7i$	1.1	2802
$-1.1 + 0.1i$	1.1	1.1
$0 - 1.3i$	1.3	115591573
$1 + 1i$	1.4	7.8×10^{15}

The numbers that are in the Mandlebrot set satisfy the condition $|a_n| \le 2$.

9.4 Assess Your Understanding *(page 606)*

1. unit **2.** scalar **3.** horizontal; vertical **4.** T **5.** T **6.** F

7.

8.

9.

10.

NOT TO SCALE

11.

12.

13.

14.

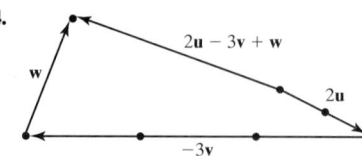

15. T **16.** F **17.** F **18.** T **19.** F **20.** F **21.** T **22.** T **23.** 12

24. 8 **25.** $\mathbf{v} = 3\mathbf{i} + 4\mathbf{j}$ **26.** $\mathbf{v} = -3\mathbf{i} - 5\mathbf{j}$ **27.** $\mathbf{v} = 2\mathbf{i} + 4\mathbf{j}$

28. $\mathbf{v} = 9\mathbf{i} + 3\mathbf{j}$ **29.** $\mathbf{v} = 8\mathbf{i} - \mathbf{j}$ **30.** $\mathbf{v} = 7\mathbf{i} - 2\mathbf{j}$

31. $\mathbf{v} = -\mathbf{i} + \mathbf{j}$ **32.** $\mathbf{v} = \mathbf{i} + \mathbf{j}$ **33.** 5 **34.** 13 **35.** $\sqrt{2}$ **36.** $\sqrt{2}$

37. $\sqrt{13}$ **38.** $2\sqrt{10}$ **39.** $-\mathbf{j}$ **40.** $13\mathbf{i} - 21\mathbf{j}$ **41.** $\sqrt{89}$ **42.** $\sqrt{5}$

43. $\sqrt{34} - \sqrt{13}$ **44.** $\sqrt{34} + \sqrt{13}$ **45.** $\mathbf{i}$ **46.** $-\mathbf{j}$

47. $\dfrac{3}{5}\mathbf{i} - \dfrac{4}{5}\mathbf{j}$ **48.** $-\dfrac{5}{13}\mathbf{i} + \dfrac{12}{13}\mathbf{j}$ **49.** $\dfrac{\sqrt{2}}{2}\mathbf{i} - \dfrac{\sqrt{2}}{2}\mathbf{j}$ **50.** $\dfrac{2\sqrt{5}}{5}\mathbf{i} - \dfrac{\sqrt{5}}{5}\mathbf{j}$ **51.** $\mathbf{v} = \dfrac{8\sqrt{5}}{5}\mathbf{i} + \dfrac{4\sqrt{5}}{5}\mathbf{j}$ or $\mathbf{v} = -\dfrac{8\sqrt{5}}{5}\mathbf{i} - \dfrac{4\sqrt{5}}{5}\mathbf{j}$

52. $\mathbf{v} = \dfrac{3\sqrt{2}}{2}\mathbf{i} + \dfrac{3\sqrt{2}}{2}\mathbf{j}$ or $\mathbf{v} = -\dfrac{3\sqrt{2}}{2}\mathbf{i} - \dfrac{3\sqrt{2}}{2}\mathbf{j}$ **53.** $\{-2 + \sqrt{21}, -2 - \sqrt{21}\}$ **54.** $\{-7, 1\}$ **55.** $\mathbf{v} = \dfrac{5}{2}\mathbf{i} + \dfrac{5\sqrt{3}}{2}\mathbf{j}$

56. $\mathbf{v} = 4\sqrt{2}\mathbf{i} + 4\sqrt{2}\mathbf{j}$ **57.** $\mathbf{v} = -7\mathbf{i} + 7\sqrt{3}\mathbf{j}$ **58.** $\mathbf{v} = -\dfrac{3}{2}\mathbf{i} - \dfrac{3\sqrt{3}}{2}\mathbf{j}$ **59.** $\mathbf{v} = \dfrac{25\sqrt{3}}{2}\mathbf{i} - \dfrac{25}{2}\mathbf{j}$ **60.** $\mathbf{v} = \dfrac{15\sqrt{2}}{2}\mathbf{i} - \dfrac{15\sqrt{2}}{2}\mathbf{j}$

61. (a) $(-1, 4)$

(b)

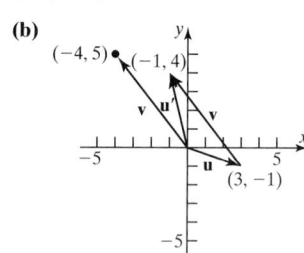

62. (a) $(0, -2), (2, -4), (6, -1), (4, 1)$

(b) $\left(-\dfrac{9}{2}, 1\right), \left(-\dfrac{5}{2}, -1\right), \left(\dfrac{3}{2}, 2\right), \left(-\dfrac{1}{2}, 4\right)$

63. $\mathbf{F} = 20\sqrt{3}\mathbf{i} + 20\mathbf{j}$

64. $\mathbf{F} = 100(\cos 20°\mathbf{i} + \sin 20°\mathbf{j})$

65. $\mathbf{F} = \left(20\sqrt{3} + 30\sqrt{2}\right)\mathbf{i} + \left(20 - 30\sqrt{2}\right)\mathbf{j}$

66. $\mathbf{F} = \left(15\sqrt{2} - 35\right)\mathbf{i} + \left(15\sqrt{2} + 35\sqrt{3}\right)\mathbf{j}$

67. Tension in right cable: 1000 lb; tension in left cable: 845.2 lb

68. Tension in right cable: 657.8 lb; tension in left cable: 516.2 lb

69. Tension in right part: 1088.4 lb; tension in left part: 1089.1 lb

70. Tension in right part: 1208.4 lb; tension in left part: 1209.9 lb

71. The truck must pull with a force of 4635. 2 lb.

72. (a) No, the two tractors will have a combined pull of only 11,757.4 lb, which is less than 6 tons.
  (b) Yes, the two tractors will have a combined pull of 12,208 lb, or more than 6 tons.

73.

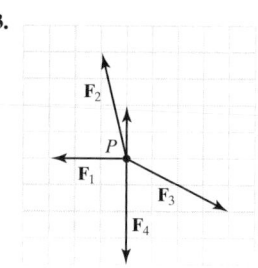

Historical Problem *(page 614)*

$(a\mathbf{i} + b\mathbf{j}) \cdot (c\mathbf{i} + d\mathbf{j}) = ac + bd$

Real part $[(\overline{a + bi})(c + di)] = $ real part$[(a - bi)(c + di)] = $ real part$[ac + adi - bci - bdi^2] = ac + bd$

9.5 Assess Your Understanding *(page 614)*

2. orthogonal **3.** parallel **4.** F **5.** T **6.** F **7. (a)** 0 **(b)** 90° **(c)** orthogonal **8. (a)** 0 **(b)** 90° **(c)** orthogonal **9. (a)** 0 **(b)** 90°

(c) orthogonal **10. (a)** 6 **(b)** 18.4° **(c)** neither **11. (a)** $\sqrt{3} - 1$ **(b)** 75° **(c)** neither **12. (a)** $1 - \sqrt{3}$ **(b)** 105° **(c)** neither

13. (a) -50 **(b)** 180° **(c)** parallel **14. (a)** 75 **(b)** 0° **(c)** parallel **15. (a)** 0 **(b)** 90° **(c)** orthogonal **16. (a)** 0 **(b)** 90° **(c)** orthogonal

17. $\dfrac{2}{3}$ **18.** -1 **19.** $\mathbf{v}_1 = \dfrac{5}{2}\mathbf{i} - \dfrac{5}{2}\mathbf{j}, \mathbf{v}_2 = -\dfrac{1}{2}\mathbf{i} - \dfrac{1}{2}\mathbf{j}$ **20.** $\mathbf{v}_1 = -\dfrac{8}{5}\mathbf{i} - \dfrac{4}{5}\mathbf{j}, \mathbf{v}_2 = -\dfrac{7}{5}\mathbf{i} + \dfrac{14}{5}\mathbf{j}$ **21.** $\mathbf{v}_1 = -\dfrac{1}{5}\mathbf{i} - \dfrac{2}{5}\mathbf{j}, \mathbf{v}_2 = \dfrac{6}{5}\mathbf{i} - \dfrac{3}{5}\mathbf{j}$

22. $\mathbf{v}_1 = \dfrac{4}{5}\mathbf{i} - \dfrac{8}{5}\mathbf{j}, \mathbf{v}_2 = \dfrac{6}{5}\mathbf{i} + \dfrac{3}{5}\mathbf{j}$ **23.** $\mathbf{v}_1 = \dfrac{14}{5}\mathbf{i} + \dfrac{7}{5}\mathbf{j}, \mathbf{v}_2 = \dfrac{1}{5}\mathbf{i} - \dfrac{2}{5}\mathbf{j}$ **24.** $\mathbf{v}_1 = \dfrac{28}{17}\mathbf{i} - \dfrac{7}{17}\mathbf{j}, \mathbf{v}_2 = -\dfrac{11}{17}\mathbf{i} - \dfrac{44}{17}\mathbf{j}$ **25.** 9 ft-lb

26. $1000\sqrt{3}$ ft-lb ≈ 1732 ft-lb **27. (a)** $\|\mathbf{I}\| = 0.022$; the intensity of the sun's rays is approximately 0.022 W/cm². $\|\mathbf{A}\| = 500$; the area of the solar panel is

500 cm². **(b)** $W = 10$; ten watts of energy is collected. **(c)** Vectors **I** and **A** should be parallel with the solar panels facing the sun.

28. (a) $\|\mathbf{R}\| \approx 1.90$; about 1.9 in. of rain fell. $\|\mathbf{A}\| \approx 1.04$; the area of the opening of the gauge is approximately 1.04 in.². **(b)** $V = 1.525$; the gauge

collected 1.525 in.³ of rain. **(c)** Vectors **R** and **A** should be parallel and oriented in opposite directions. **29.** 496.7 mi/h; 38.5° west of south

30. 6.5° north of east; 276.7 mi/h **31.** 8.6° off direct heading across the current, upstream; 1.52 min **32.** $\mathbf{v} = 3\mathbf{i} + 20\mathbf{j}$; 20.2 mi/h; N8.5°E (assuming

boat traveling north and current traveling east) **33.** Force required to keep Sienna from rolling down the hill: 737.6 lb; force perpendicular to the hill:

5248.4 lb **34.** Force required to keep Bonneville from rolling down the hill: 781.4 lb; force perpendicular to the hill: 4431.6 lb

35. $\mathbf{v} = \left(250\sqrt{2} - 30\right)\mathbf{i} + \left(250\sqrt{2} + 30\sqrt{3}\right)\mathbf{j}$; 518.8 km/h; N38.6°E **36.** $\mathbf{v} = \left(300 + 20\sqrt{2}\right)\mathbf{i} - \left(300\sqrt{3} + 20\sqrt{2}\right)\mathbf{j}$; 638.7 km/h; S30.9°E

37. Timmy must exert 85.5 lb.   **38.** 11.5°   **39.** 60°

40. Let $\mathbf{u} = a_1\mathbf{i} + b_1\mathbf{j}$, $\mathbf{v} = a_2\mathbf{i} + b_2\mathbf{j}$, $\mathbf{w} = a_3\mathbf{i} + b_3\mathbf{j}$.

$$\mathbf{u} \cdot (\mathbf{v} + \mathbf{w}) = (a_1\mathbf{i} + b_1\mathbf{j}) \cdot \left[(a_2 + a_3)\mathbf{i} + (b_2 + b_3)\mathbf{j}\right]$$

$$= a_1(a_2 + a_3) + b_1(b_2 + b_3) = a_1 a_2 + a_1 a_3 + b_1 b_2 + b_1 b_3 = (a_1 a_2 + b_1 b_2) + (a_1 a_3 + b_1 b_3) = \mathbf{u} \cdot \mathbf{v} + \mathbf{u} \cdot \mathbf{w}$$

41. Let $\mathbf{v} = a\mathbf{i} + b\mathbf{j}$. Then $\mathbf{0} \cdot \mathbf{v} = 0a + 0b = 0$.   **42.** $\cos \alpha = \dfrac{\mathbf{v} \cdot \mathbf{i}}{\|\mathbf{v}\|\|\mathbf{i}\|} = \mathbf{v} \cdot \mathbf{i}$; if $\mathbf{v} = x\mathbf{i} + y\mathbf{j}$, then $\mathbf{v} \cdot \mathbf{i} = x = \cos \alpha$ and $\mathbf{v} \cdot \mathbf{j} = y = \cos\left(\dfrac{\pi}{2} - \alpha\right) = \sin \alpha$.

43. $\mathbf{v} = \cos \alpha\mathbf{i} + \sin \alpha\mathbf{j}$, $0 \le \alpha \le \pi$; $\mathbf{w} = \cos \beta\mathbf{i} + \sin \beta\mathbf{j}$, $0 \le \beta \le \pi$. If θ is the angle between $\mathbf{v}$ and $\mathbf{w}$, then $\mathbf{v} \cdot \mathbf{w} = \cos\theta$, since $\|\mathbf{v}\| = 1$ and $\|\mathbf{w}\| = 1$.
Now $\theta = \alpha - \beta$ or $\theta = \beta - \alpha$. Since the cosine function is even, $\mathbf{v} \cdot \mathbf{w} = \cos(\alpha - \beta)$. Also, $\mathbf{v} \cdot \mathbf{w} = \cos \alpha \cos \beta + \sin \alpha \sin \beta$. So $\cos(\alpha - \beta)$
$= \cos \alpha \cos \beta + \sin \alpha \sin \beta$.

44. $\mathbf{v} = a\mathbf{i} + b\mathbf{j}$; the vector projection of $\mathbf{v}$ onto $\mathbf{i}$ is $\dfrac{\mathbf{v} \cdot \mathbf{i}}{\|\mathbf{i}\|^2}\mathbf{i} = (\mathbf{v} \cdot \mathbf{i})\mathbf{i}$; $\mathbf{v} \cdot \mathbf{i} = a$, $\mathbf{v} \cdot \mathbf{j} = b$, so $\mathbf{v} = (\mathbf{v} \cdot \mathbf{i})\mathbf{i} + (\mathbf{v} \cdot \mathbf{j})\mathbf{j}$.

45. (a) If $\mathbf{u} = a_1\mathbf{i} + b_1\mathbf{j}$ and $\mathbf{v} = a_2\mathbf{i} + b_2\mathbf{j}$, then, since $\|\mathbf{u}\| = \|\mathbf{v}\|$, $a_1^2 + b_1^2 = \|\mathbf{u}\|^2 = \|\mathbf{v}\|^2 = a_2^2 + b_2^2$, and

$$(\mathbf{u} + \mathbf{v}) \cdot (\mathbf{u} - \mathbf{v}) = (a_1 + a_2)(a_1 - a_2) + (b_1 + b_2)(b_1 - b_2) = (a_1^2 + b_1^2) - (a_2^2 + b_2^2) = 0.$$

(b) The legs of the angle can be made to correspond to vectors $\mathbf{u} + \mathbf{v}$ and $\mathbf{u} - \mathbf{v}$.

46. $(\mathbf{v} - \alpha\mathbf{w}) \cdot \mathbf{w} = \mathbf{v} \cdot \mathbf{w} - \alpha\mathbf{w} \cdot \mathbf{w} = \alpha\|\mathbf{w}\|^2 - \alpha\|\mathbf{w}\|^2 = 0$ since the dot product of any vector with itself is equal to the square of its magnitude.

47. $(\|\mathbf{w}\|\mathbf{v} + \|\mathbf{v}\|\mathbf{w}) \cdot (\|\mathbf{w}\|\mathbf{v} - \|\mathbf{v}\|\mathbf{w}) = \|\mathbf{w}\|^2\mathbf{v} \cdot \mathbf{v} - \|\mathbf{w}\|\|\mathbf{v}\|\mathbf{v} \cdot \mathbf{w} + \|\mathbf{v}\|\|\mathbf{w}\|\mathbf{w} \cdot \mathbf{v} - \|\mathbf{v}\|^2\mathbf{w} \cdot \mathbf{w} = \|\mathbf{w}\|^2\mathbf{v} \cdot \mathbf{v} - \|\mathbf{v}\|^2\mathbf{w} \cdot \mathbf{w} = \|\mathbf{w}\|^2\|\mathbf{v}\|^2 - \|\mathbf{v}\|^2\|\mathbf{w}\|^2 = 0$

48. $W = \mathbf{F} \cdot \overrightarrow{AB} = 0$ when $\mathbf{F}$ is orthogonal to $\overrightarrow{AB}$.

49. $\|\mathbf{u} + \mathbf{v}\|^2 - \|\mathbf{u} - \mathbf{v}\|^2 = (\mathbf{u} + \mathbf{v}) \cdot (\mathbf{u} + \mathbf{v}) - (\mathbf{u} - \mathbf{v}) \cdot (\mathbf{u} - \mathbf{v}) = (\mathbf{u} \cdot \mathbf{u} + \mathbf{u} \cdot \mathbf{v} + \mathbf{v} \cdot \mathbf{u} + \mathbf{v} \cdot \mathbf{v}) - (\mathbf{u} \cdot \mathbf{u} - \mathbf{u} \cdot \mathbf{v} - \mathbf{v} \cdot \mathbf{u} + \mathbf{v} \cdot \mathbf{v})$
$= 2(\mathbf{u} \cdot \mathbf{v}) + 2(\mathbf{v} \cdot \mathbf{u}) = 4(\mathbf{u} \cdot \mathbf{v})$

9.6 Assess Your Understanding (page 624)

2. xy-plane   **3.** components   **4.** 1   **5.** F   **6.** T   **7.** All points of the form $(x, 0, z)$ **8.** All points of the form $(0, y, z)$
9. All points of the form $(x, y, 2)$ **10.** All points of the form $(x, 3, z)$ **11.** All points of the form $(-4, y, z)$ **12.** All points of the form $(x, y, -3)$
13. All points of the form $(1, 2, z)$ **14.** All points of the form $(3, y, 1)$ **15.** $\sqrt{21}$ **16.** $\sqrt{14}$ **17.** $\sqrt{33}$ **18.** $2\sqrt{19}$ **19.** $\sqrt{26}$ **20.** $2\sqrt{6}$
21. $(2, 0, 0)$; $(2, 1, 0)$; $(0, 1, 0)$; $(2, 0, 3)$; $(0, 1, 3)$; $(0, 0, 3)$ **22.** $(4, 0, 0)$; $(0, 2, 0)$; $(0, 0, 2)$; $(4, 2, 0)$; $(0, 2, 2)$; $(4, 0, 2)$
23. $(1, 4, 3)$; $(3, 2, 3)$; $(3, 4, 3)$; $(3, 2, 5)$; $(1, 4, 5)$; $(1, 2, 5)$ **24.** $(5, 6, 2)$; $(5, 8, 1)$; $(3, 6, 1)$; $(3, 8, 1)$; $(3, 6, 2)$; $(5, 8, 2)$
25. $(-1, 2, 2)$; $(4, 0, 2)$; $(4, 2, 2)$; $(-1, 2, 5)$; $(4, 0, 5)$; $(-1, 0, 5)$ **26.** $(-2, -3, 1)$; $(-2, 7, 0)$; $(-6, -3, 0)$; $(-2, 7, 1)$; $(-6, -3, 1)$; $(-6, 7, 0)$
27. $\mathbf{v} = 3\mathbf{i} + 4\mathbf{j} - \mathbf{k}$ **28.** $\mathbf{v} = -3\mathbf{i} - 5\mathbf{j} + 4\mathbf{k}$ **29.** $\mathbf{v} = 2\mathbf{i} + 4\mathbf{j} + \mathbf{k}$ **30.** $\mathbf{v} = 9\mathbf{i} + 3\mathbf{j} - \mathbf{k}$ **31.** $\mathbf{v} = 8\mathbf{i} - \mathbf{j}$ **32.** $\mathbf{v} = 7\mathbf{i} - 2\mathbf{j} + 4\mathbf{k}$ **33.** 7
34. 14   **35.** $\sqrt{3}$ **36.** $\sqrt{3}$ **37.** $\sqrt{22}$ **38.** $2\sqrt{11}$ **39.** $-\mathbf{j} - 2\mathbf{k}$ **40.** $13\mathbf{i} - 21\mathbf{j} + 10\mathbf{k}$ **41.** $\sqrt{105}$ **42.** $\sqrt{5}$ **43.** $\sqrt{38} - \sqrt{17}$ **44.** $\sqrt{38} + \sqrt{17}$
45. $\mathbf{i}$ **46.** $-\mathbf{j}$ **47.** $\dfrac{3}{7}\mathbf{i} - \dfrac{6}{7}\mathbf{j} - \dfrac{2}{7}\mathbf{k}$ **48.** $-\dfrac{3}{7}\mathbf{i} + \dfrac{6}{7}\mathbf{j} + \dfrac{2}{7}\mathbf{k}$ **49.** $\dfrac{\sqrt{3}}{3}\mathbf{i} + \dfrac{\sqrt{3}}{3}\mathbf{j} + \dfrac{\sqrt{3}}{3}\mathbf{k}$ **50.** $\dfrac{\sqrt{6}}{3}\mathbf{i} - \dfrac{\sqrt{6}}{6}\mathbf{j} + \dfrac{\sqrt{6}}{6}\mathbf{k}$ **51.** $\mathbf{v} \cdot \mathbf{w} = 0$; $\theta = 90°$
52. $\mathbf{v} \cdot \mathbf{w} = 0$; $\theta = 90°$ **53.** $\mathbf{v} \cdot \mathbf{w} = -2$, $\theta \approx 100.3°$ **54.** $\mathbf{v} \cdot \mathbf{w} = 3$; $\theta \approx 74.5°$ **55.** $\mathbf{v} \cdot \mathbf{w} = 0$; $\theta = 90°$ **56.** $\mathbf{v} \cdot \mathbf{w} = 0$; $\theta = 90°$
57. $\mathbf{v} \cdot \mathbf{w} = 52$; $\theta = 0°$ **58.** $\mathbf{v} \cdot \mathbf{w} = 52$; $\theta = 0°$ **59.** $\alpha \approx 64.6°$; $\beta \approx 149.0°$; $\gamma \approx 106.6°$; $\mathbf{v} = 7(\cos 64.6°\mathbf{i} + \cos 149.0°\mathbf{j} + \cos 106.6°\mathbf{k})$
60. $\alpha \approx 115.4°$; $\beta \approx 31.0°$; $\gamma \approx 73.4°$; $\mathbf{v} = 14(\cos 115.4°\mathbf{i} + \cos 31.0°\mathbf{j} + \cos 73.4°\mathbf{k})$
61. $\alpha = \beta = \gamma \approx 54.7°$; $\mathbf{v} = \sqrt{3}(\cos 54.7°\mathbf{i} + \cos 54.7°\mathbf{j} + \cos 54.7°\mathbf{k})$
62. $\alpha = 54.7°$; $\beta = \gamma \approx 125.3°$; $\mathbf{v} = \sqrt{3}(\cos 54.7°\mathbf{i} + \cos 125.3°\mathbf{j} + \cos 125.3°\mathbf{k})$
63. $\alpha = \beta = 45°$; $\gamma = 90°$; $\mathbf{v} = \sqrt{2}(\cos 45°\mathbf{i} + \cos 45°\mathbf{j} + \cos 90°\mathbf{k})$ **64.** $\alpha = 90°$; $\beta = \gamma = 45°$; $\mathbf{v} = \sqrt{2}(\cos 90°\mathbf{i} + \cos 45°\mathbf{j} + \cos 45°\mathbf{k})$
65. $\alpha \approx 60.9°$; $\beta \approx 144.2°$; $\gamma \approx 71.1°$; $\mathbf{v} = \sqrt{38}(\cos 60.9°\mathbf{i} + \cos 144.2°\mathbf{j} + \cos 71.1°\mathbf{k})$
66. $\alpha \approx 68.2°$; $\beta \approx 56.1°$; $\gamma \approx 138.0°$; $\mathbf{v} = \sqrt{29}(\cos 68.2°\mathbf{i} + \cos 56.1°\mathbf{j} + \cos 138.0°\mathbf{k})$ **67.** (a) $\mathbf{d} = \mathbf{a} + \mathbf{b} + \mathbf{c} = \langle 7, 1, 5 \rangle$ (b) 8.66 ft
68. If the point $P = (x, y, z)$ is on the sphere with center $C = (x_0, y_0, z_0)$ and radius r, then the distance between P and C is
$r = \sqrt{(x - x_0)^2 + (y - y_0)^2 + (z - z_0)^2}$. Therefore, the equation for a sphere is $(x - x_0)^2 + (y - y_0)^2 + (z - z_0)^2 = r^2$.
69. $(x - 3)^2 + (y - 1)^2 + (z - 1)^2 = 1$ **70.** $(x - 1)^2 + (y - 2)^2 + (z - 2)^2 = 4$ **71.** Radius $= 2$, center $(-1, 1, 0)$
72. Radius $= 1$, center $(-1, 0, 1)$ **73.** Radius $= 3$, center $(2, -2, -1)$ **74.** Radius $= 2$, center $(2, 0, 0)$
75. Radius $= \dfrac{3\sqrt{2}}{2}$, center $(2, 0, -1)$ **76.** Radius $= \sqrt{3}$, center $(-1, 1, 0)$ **77.** 2 newton-meters $= 2$ joules   **78.** $\dfrac{8}{3}$ newton-meters $= \dfrac{8}{3}$ joules
79. 9 newton-meters $= 9$ joules

9.7 Assess Your Understanding (page 630)

1. T   **2.** T   **3.** T   **4.** F   **5.** F   **6.** T   **7.** 2   **8.** -4 **9.** 4   **10.** -12 **11.** $-11A + 2B + 5C$ **12.** $2A + 12B - 6C$ **13.** $-6A + 23B - 15C$
14. $10A + 2B + 2C$ **15.** (a) $5\mathbf{i} + 5\mathbf{j} + 5\mathbf{k}$ (b) $-5\mathbf{i} - 5\mathbf{j} - 5\mathbf{k}$ (c) 0   (d) 0   **16.** (a) $\mathbf{i} + 5\mathbf{j} - 7\mathbf{k}$ (b) $-\mathbf{i} - 5\mathbf{j} + 7\mathbf{k}$ (c) 0   (d) 0
17. (a) $\mathbf{i} - \mathbf{j} - \mathbf{k}$ (b) $-\mathbf{i} + \mathbf{j} + \mathbf{k}$ (c) 0   (d) 0   **18.** (a) $-8\mathbf{i} + 5\mathbf{j} + 14\mathbf{k}$ (b) $8\mathbf{i} - 5\mathbf{j} - 14\mathbf{k}$ (c) 0   (d) 0   **19.** (a) $-\mathbf{i} + 2\mathbf{j} + 2\mathbf{k}$
(b) $\mathbf{i} - 2\mathbf{j} - 2\mathbf{k}$ (c) 0   (d) 0   **20.** (a) $-\mathbf{i} + 6\mathbf{j} - \mathbf{k}$ (b) $\mathbf{i} - 6\mathbf{j} + \mathbf{k}$ (c) 0   (d) 0   **21.** (a) $3\mathbf{i} - \mathbf{j} + 4\mathbf{k}$ (b) $-3\mathbf{i} + \mathbf{j} - 4\mathbf{k}$ (c) 0   (d) 0

22. (a) $6\mathbf{i} + 4\mathbf{j} + 6\mathbf{k}$ **(b)** $-6\mathbf{i} - 4\mathbf{j} - 6\mathbf{k}$ **(c)** 0 **(d)** 0 **23.** $-9\mathbf{i} - 7\mathbf{j} - 3\mathbf{k}$ **24.** $7\mathbf{i} + 11\mathbf{j} - 6\mathbf{k}$ **25.** $9\mathbf{i} + 7\mathbf{j} + 3\mathbf{k}$ **26.** $-7\mathbf{i} - 11\mathbf{j} + 6\mathbf{k}$
27. 0 **28.** 0 **29.** $-27\mathbf{i} - 21\mathbf{j} - 9\mathbf{k}$ **30.** $28\mathbf{i} + 44\mathbf{j} - 24\mathbf{k}$ **31.** $-18\mathbf{i} - 14\mathbf{j} - 6\mathbf{k}$ **32.** $-21\mathbf{i} - 33\mathbf{j} + 18\mathbf{k}$ **33.** 0 **34.** 0
35. -25 **36.** -25 **37.** 25 **38.** 25 **39.** 0 **40.** 0 **41.** Any vector of the form $c(-9\mathbf{i} - 7\mathbf{j} - 3\mathbf{k})$, where c is a nonzero scalar
42. Any vector of the form $c(-10\mathbf{i} - 5\mathbf{j} + 5\mathbf{k})$, where c is a nonzero scalar **43.** Any vector of the form $c(-\mathbf{i} + \mathbf{j} + 5\mathbf{k})$, where c is a nonzero scalar
44. Any vector of the form $c(-4\mathbf{i} - 2\mathbf{j} + 2\mathbf{k})$, where c is a nonzero scalar **45.** $\sqrt{166}$ **46.** $\sqrt{213}$ **47.** $\sqrt{555}$ **48.** $\sqrt{217}$ **49.** $\sqrt{34}$ **50.** 8

51. $\sqrt{998}$ **52.** $\sqrt{89}$ **53.** $\dfrac{11\sqrt{19}}{57}\mathbf{i} + \dfrac{\sqrt{19}}{57}\mathbf{j} + \dfrac{7\sqrt{19}}{57}\mathbf{k}$ or $-\dfrac{11\sqrt{19}}{57}\mathbf{i} - \dfrac{\sqrt{19}}{57}\mathbf{j} - \dfrac{7\sqrt{19}}{57}\mathbf{k}$

54. $-\dfrac{13\sqrt{237}}{237}\mathbf{i} + \dfrac{8\sqrt{237}}{237}\mathbf{j} - \dfrac{2\sqrt{237}}{237}\mathbf{k}$ or $\dfrac{13\sqrt{237}}{237}\mathbf{i} - \dfrac{8\sqrt{237}}{237}\mathbf{j} + \dfrac{2\sqrt{237}}{237}\mathbf{k}$ **55.** 98 cubic units **56.** 226 cubic units

57. $\mathbf{u} \times \mathbf{v} = \begin{vmatrix} \mathbf{i} & \mathbf{j} & \mathbf{k} \\ a_1 & b_1 & c_1 \\ a_2 & b_2 & c_2 \end{vmatrix} = (b_1c_2 - b_2c_1)\mathbf{i} - (a_1c_2 - a_2c_1)\mathbf{j} + (a_1b_2 - a_2b_1)\mathbf{k}$

$\|\mathbf{u} \times \mathbf{v}\|^2 = \left(\sqrt{(b_1c_2 - b_2c_1)^2 + (a_1c_2 - a_2c_1)^2 + (a_1b_2 - a_2b_1)^2}\right)^2$
$= b_1^2c_2^2 - 2b_1b_2c_1c_2 + b_2^2c_1^2 + a_1^2c_2^2 - 2a_1a_2c_1c_2 + a_2^2c_1^2 + a_1^2b_2^2 - 2a_1a_2b_1b_2 + a_2^2b_1^2$
$\|\mathbf{u}\|^2 = a_1^2 + b_1^2 + c_1^2, \|\mathbf{v}\|^2 = a_2^2 + b_2^2 + c_2^2$
$\|\mathbf{u}\|^2\|\mathbf{v}\|^2 = (a_1^2 + b_1^2 + c_1^2)(a_2^2 + b_2^2 + c_2^2) = a_1^2a_2^2 + a_1^2b_2^2 + a_1^2c_2^2 + b_1^2a_2^2 + b_1^2b_2^2 + b_1^2c_2^2 + a_2^2c_1^2 + b_2^2c_1^2 + c_1^2c_2^2$
$(\mathbf{u} \cdot \mathbf{v})^2 = (a_1a_2 + b_1b_2 + c_1c_2)^2 = (a_1a_2 + b_1b_2 + c_1c_2)(a_1a_2 + b_1b_2 + c_1c_2)$
$= a_1^2a_2^2 + a_1a_2b_1b_2 + a_1a_2c_1c_2 + b_1b_2c_1c_2 + b_1b_2a_1a_2 + b_1^2b_2^2 + b_1b_2c_1c_2 + a_1a_2c_1c_2 + c_1^2c_2^2$
$= a_1^2a_2^2 + b_1^2b_2^2 + c_1^2c_2^2 + 2a_1a_2b_1b_2 + 2b_1b_2c_1c_2 + 2a_1a_2c_1c_2$
$\|\mathbf{u}\|^2\|\mathbf{v}\|^2 - (\mathbf{u} \cdot \mathbf{v})^2 = a_1^2b_2^2 + a_1^2c_2^2 + b_1^2a_2^2 + a_2^2c_1^2 + b_2^2c_1^2 + b_1^2c_2^2 - 2a_1a_2b_1b_2 - 2b_1b_2c_1c_2 - 2a_1a_2c_1c_2$, which equals $\|\mathbf{u} \times \mathbf{v}\|^2$.

58. We know for any two vectors that $\|\mathbf{u} \times \mathbf{v}\| = \|\mathbf{u}\|\|\mathbf{v}\| \sin \theta$, where θ is the angle between $\mathbf{u}$ and $\mathbf{v}$; so, if $\mathbf{u}$ and $\mathbf{v}$ are orthogonal, $\theta = 90°$, and so the result follows.

59. By Problem 58, since $\mathbf{u}$ and $\mathbf{v}$ are orthogonal, $\|\mathbf{u} \times \mathbf{v}\| = \|\mathbf{u}\|\|\mathbf{v}\|$. If, in addition, $\mathbf{u}$ and $\mathbf{v}$ are unit vectors, $\|\mathbf{u} \times \mathbf{v}\| = 1 \cdot 1 = 1$.

60. $\mathbf{u} \times \mathbf{v} = \begin{vmatrix} \mathbf{i} & \mathbf{j} & \mathbf{k} \\ a_1 & b_1 & c_1 \\ a_2 & b_2 & c_2 \end{vmatrix} = (b_1c_2 - b_2c_1)\mathbf{i} - (a_1c_2 - a_2c_1)\mathbf{j} + (a_1b_2 - a_2b_1)\mathbf{k} = -[(b_2c_1 - b_1c_2)\mathbf{i} - (a_2c_1 - a_1c_2)\mathbf{j} + (a_2b_1 - a_1b_2)\mathbf{k}]$

$= -\begin{vmatrix} \mathbf{i} & \mathbf{j} & \mathbf{k} \\ a_2 & b_2 & c_2 \\ a_1 & b_1 & c_1 \end{vmatrix} = -(\mathbf{v} \times \mathbf{u})$

61. Assume that $\mathbf{u} = a\mathbf{i} + b\mathbf{j} + c\mathbf{k}, \mathbf{v} = d\mathbf{i} + e\mathbf{j} + f\mathbf{k}$, and $\mathbf{w} = l\mathbf{i} + m\mathbf{j} + n\mathbf{k}$. Then $\mathbf{u} \times \mathbf{v} = (bf - ec)\mathbf{i} - (af - dc)\mathbf{j} + (ae - db)\mathbf{k}$,
$\mathbf{u} \times \mathbf{w} = (bn - mc)\mathbf{i} - (an - lc)\mathbf{j} + (am - lb)\mathbf{k}$, and $\mathbf{v} + \mathbf{w} = (d + l)\mathbf{i} + (e + m)\mathbf{j} + (f + n)\mathbf{k}$. Therefore,
$(\mathbf{u} \times \mathbf{v}) + (\mathbf{u} \times \mathbf{w}) = (bf - ec + bn - mc)\mathbf{i} - (af - dc + an - lc)\mathbf{j} + (ae - db + am - lb)\mathbf{k}$ and
$\mathbf{u} \times (\mathbf{v} + \mathbf{w}) = [b(f + n) - (e + m)c]\mathbf{i} - [a(f + n) - (d + l)c]\mathbf{j} + [a(e + m) - (d + l)b]\mathbf{k}$
$= (bf - ec + bn - mc)\mathbf{i} - (af - dc + an - lc)\mathbf{j} + (ae - db + am - lb)\mathbf{k}$, which equals $(\mathbf{u} \times \mathbf{v}) + (\mathbf{u} \times \mathbf{w})$.

62. By Problem 57, $\|\mathbf{u} \times \mathbf{v}\|^2 = \|\mathbf{u}\|^2\|\mathbf{v}\|^2 - (\mathbf{u} \cdot \mathbf{v})^2$. Since $\mathbf{u} \cdot \mathbf{v} = \|\mathbf{u}\|\|\mathbf{v}\| \cos \theta$, where θ is the angle between $\mathbf{u}$ and $\mathbf{v}$, then
$\|\mathbf{u} \times \mathbf{v}\|^2 = \|\mathbf{u}\|^2\|\mathbf{v}\|^2 - (\|\mathbf{u}\|\|\mathbf{v}\| \cos \theta)^2 = \|\mathbf{u}\|^2\|\mathbf{v}\|^2 - \|\mathbf{u}\|^2\|\mathbf{v}\|^2 \cos^2 \theta = \|\mathbf{u}\|^2\|\mathbf{v}\|^2(1 - \cos^2 \theta) = \|\mathbf{u}\|^2\|\mathbf{v}\|^2 \sin^2 \theta$. Since $0 \le \theta \le \pi$,
then $\sin \theta \ge 0$. Therefore, $\|\mathbf{u} \times \mathbf{v}\| = \|\mathbf{u}\|\|\mathbf{v}\| \sin \theta$.

Review Exercises *(page 632)*

1. $\left(\dfrac{3\sqrt{3}}{2}, \dfrac{3}{2}\right)$ **2.** $\left(-2, 2\sqrt{3}\right)$ **3.** $\left(1, \sqrt{3}\right)$ **4.** $\left(\dfrac{\sqrt{2}}{2}, \dfrac{\sqrt{2}}{2}\right)$ **5.** $(0, 3)$

6. $\left(-2\sqrt{2}, 2\sqrt{2}\right)$

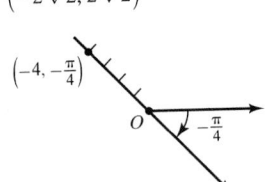

7. $\left(3\sqrt{2}, \dfrac{3\pi}{4}\right), \left(-3\sqrt{2}, -\dfrac{\pi}{4}\right)$ **10.** $(2, 0), (-2, \pi)$

8. $\left(\sqrt{2}, -\dfrac{\pi}{4}\right), \left(-\sqrt{2}, \dfrac{3\pi}{4}\right)$ **11.** $(5, 0.93), (-5, 4.07)$

9. $\left(2, -\dfrac{\pi}{2}\right), \left(-2, \dfrac{\pi}{2}\right)$ **12.** $(13, 1.97), (-13, 5.11)$

13. (a) $x^2 + (y - 1)^2 = 1$ **(b)** circle, radius 1,

center $(0, 1)$ in rectangular coordinates

14. (a) $x^2 + \left(y - \dfrac{1}{6}\right)^2 = \dfrac{1}{36}$ **(b)** circle, radius $\dfrac{1}{6}$,

center $\left(0, \dfrac{1}{6}\right)$ in rectangular coordinates

15. (a) $x^2 + y^2 = 25$ **(b)** circle, radius 5,

center at pole

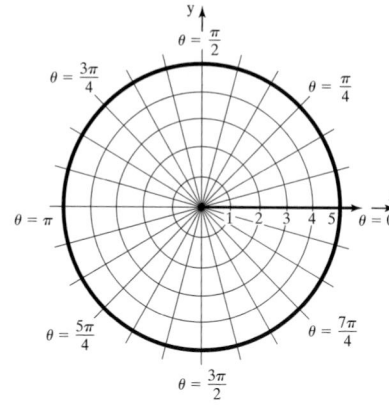

16. (a) $x - y = 0$ **(b)** line through pole, making

an angle of $\dfrac{\pi}{4}$ with polar axis

17. (a) $x + 3y = 6$ **(b)** line through $(6, 0)$

and $(0, 2)$ in rectangular coordinates

18. (a) $(x - 4)^2 + (y + 2)^2 = 25$ **(b)** circle, radius 5,

center $(4, -2)$ in rectangular coordinates

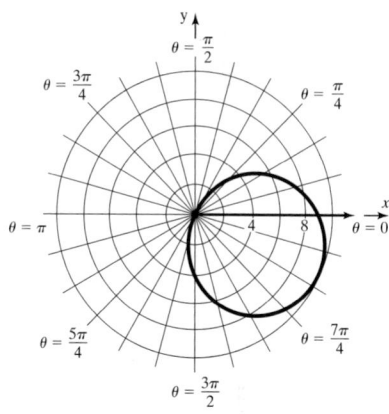

19. Circle; radius 2, center at $(2, 0)$ in

rectangular coordinates; symmetric

with respect to the polar axis

20. Circle; radius $\dfrac{3}{2}$, center at $\left(0, \dfrac{3}{2}\right)$

in rectangular coordinates; symmetric

with respect to the line $\theta = \dfrac{\pi}{2}$

21. Cardioid; symmetric with respect

to the line $\theta = \dfrac{\pi}{2}$

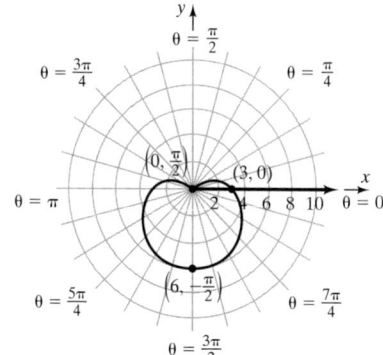

22. Limaçon without inner loop; symmetric with respect to the polar axis

23. Limaçon without inner loop; symmetric with respect to the polar axis

24. Limaçon with inner loop; symmetric with respect to the line $\theta = \dfrac{\pi}{2}$

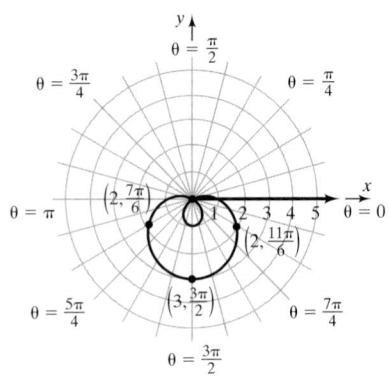

25. $\sqrt{2}(\cos 225° + i \sin 225°)$ **26.** $2(\cos 150° + i \sin 150°)$ **27.** $5(\cos 323.1° + i \sin 323.1°)$ **28.** $\sqrt{13}(\cos 326.3° + i \sin 326.3°)$

29. $-\sqrt{3} + i$

30. $\dfrac{3}{2} + \dfrac{3\sqrt{3}}{2}i$

31. $-\dfrac{3}{2} + \dfrac{3\sqrt{3}}{2}i$

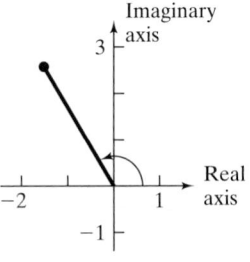

32. $-2\sqrt{2} + 2\sqrt{2}i$

33. $0.10 - 0.02i$

34. $-0.47 + 0.17i$

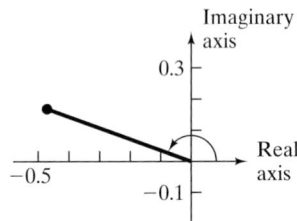

35. $zw = \cos 130° + i \sin 130°; \dfrac{z}{w} = \cos 30° + i \sin 30°$ **36.** $zw = \cos 290° + i \sin 290°; \dfrac{z}{w} = \cos 120° + i \sin 120°$

37. $zw = 6(\cos 0 + i \sin 0) = 6; \dfrac{z}{w} = \dfrac{3}{2}\left(\cos\dfrac{8\pi}{5} + i \sin\dfrac{8\pi}{5}\right)$ **38.** $zw = 6(\cos 0 + i \sin 0) = 6; \dfrac{z}{w} = \dfrac{2}{3}\left(\cos\dfrac{4\pi}{3} + i \sin\dfrac{4\pi}{3}\right)$

39. $zw = 5(\cos 5° + i \sin 5°); \dfrac{z}{w} = 5(\cos 15° + i \sin 15°)$ **40.** $zw = 4(\cos 30° + i \sin 30°); \dfrac{z}{w} = 4(\cos 70° + i \sin 70°)$ **41.** $\dfrac{27}{2} + \dfrac{27\sqrt{3}}{2}i$

42. $-4\sqrt{3} + 4i$ **43.** $4i$ **44.** $-8\sqrt{2} - 8\sqrt{2}i$ **45.** 64 **46.** 4096 **47.** $-527 - 336i$ **48.** $-7 + 24i$ **49.** $3, 3(\cos 120° + i \sin 120°),$

$3(\cos 240° + i \sin 240°)$ or $3, -\dfrac{3}{2} + \dfrac{3\sqrt{3}}{2}i, -\dfrac{3}{2} - \dfrac{3\sqrt{3}}{2}i$ **50.** $2(\cos 45° + i \sin 45°), 2(\cos 135° + i \sin 135°), 2(\cos 225° + i \sin 225°),$

$2(\cos 315° + i \sin 315°)$ or $\sqrt{2} + \sqrt{2}i, -\sqrt{2} + \sqrt{2}i, -\sqrt{2} - \sqrt{2}i, \sqrt{2} - \sqrt{2}i$

51.

52.

53.

54.

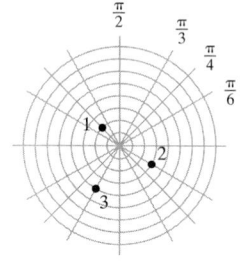

55. $\mathbf{v} = 2\mathbf{i} - 4\mathbf{j}$; $\|\mathbf{v}\| = 2\sqrt{5}$ **56.** $\mathbf{v} = 7\mathbf{i} - 3\mathbf{j}$; $\|\mathbf{v}\| = \sqrt{58}$ **57.** $\mathbf{v} = -\mathbf{i} + 3\mathbf{j}$; $\|\mathbf{v}\| = \sqrt{10}$

58. $\mathbf{v} = -5\mathbf{i} + 4\mathbf{j}$; $\|\mathbf{v}\| = \sqrt{41}$ **59.** $2\mathbf{i} - 2\mathbf{j}$ **60.** $-6\mathbf{i} + 4\mathbf{j}$ **61.** $-20\mathbf{i} + 13\mathbf{j}$ **62.** $10\mathbf{i} - 7\mathbf{j}$

63. $\sqrt{5}$ **64.** $2\sqrt{2}$ **65.** $\sqrt{5} + 5 \approx 7.24$ **66.** $2\sqrt{5} - 15 \approx -10.53$ **67.** $-\dfrac{2\sqrt{5}}{5}\mathbf{i} + \dfrac{\sqrt{5}}{5}\mathbf{j}$

68. $-\dfrac{4}{5}\mathbf{i} + \dfrac{3}{5}\mathbf{j}$ **69.** $\mathbf{v} = \dfrac{3}{2}\mathbf{i} + \dfrac{3\sqrt{3}}{2}\mathbf{j}$ **70.** $\mathbf{v} = -\dfrac{5\sqrt{3}}{2}\mathbf{i} + \dfrac{5}{2}\mathbf{j}$ **71.** $\sqrt{43} \approx 6.56$

72. $\sqrt{53} \approx 7.28$ **73.** $\mathbf{v} = 3\mathbf{i} - 5\mathbf{j} + 3\mathbf{k}$ **74.** $\mathbf{v} = 6\mathbf{i} - \mathbf{j} - 4\mathbf{k}$ **75.** $21\mathbf{i} - 2\mathbf{j} - 5\mathbf{k}$

76. $-9\mathbf{i} + 3\mathbf{j}$ **77.** $\sqrt{38}$ **78.** $3\sqrt{2}$ **79.** 0 **80.** $2\sqrt{14}$ **81.** $3\mathbf{i} + 9\mathbf{j} + 9\mathbf{k}$ **82.** 0

83. $\dfrac{3\sqrt{14}}{14}\mathbf{i} + \dfrac{\sqrt{14}}{14}\mathbf{j} - \dfrac{\sqrt{14}}{7}\mathbf{k}$; $-\dfrac{3\sqrt{14}}{14}\mathbf{i} - \dfrac{\sqrt{14}}{14}\mathbf{j} + \dfrac{\sqrt{14}}{7}\mathbf{k}$

84. $\dfrac{\sqrt{19}}{19}\mathbf{i} + \dfrac{3\sqrt{19}}{19}\mathbf{j} + \dfrac{3\sqrt{19}}{19}\mathbf{k}$ or $-\dfrac{\sqrt{19}}{19}\mathbf{i} - \dfrac{3\sqrt{19}}{19}\mathbf{j} - \dfrac{3\sqrt{19}}{19}\mathbf{k}$

85. $\mathbf{v} \cdot \mathbf{w} = -11$; $\theta \approx 169.7°$ **86.** $\mathbf{v} \cdot \mathbf{w} = 2$; $\theta \approx 63.4°$ **87.** $\mathbf{v} \cdot \mathbf{w} = -4$; $\theta \approx 153.4°$

88. $\mathbf{v} \cdot \mathbf{w} = -5$; $\theta \approx 109.7°$ **89.** $\mathbf{v} \cdot \mathbf{w} = 1$; $\theta \approx 70.5°$ **90.** $\mathbf{v} \cdot \mathbf{w} = 2$; $\theta \approx 61.9°$

91. $\mathbf{v} \cdot \mathbf{w} = 0$; $\theta = 90°$ **92.** $\mathbf{v} \cdot \mathbf{w} = -4$; $\theta \approx 101.9°$ **93.** Parallel **94.** Parallel

95. Parallel **96.** Neither **97.** Orthogonal **98.** Orthogonal **99.** $\mathbf{v}_1 = \dfrac{4}{5}\mathbf{i} - \dfrac{3}{5}\mathbf{j}$; $\mathbf{v}_2 = \dfrac{6}{5}\mathbf{i} + \dfrac{8}{5}\mathbf{j}$ **100.** $\mathbf{v}_1 = -\dfrac{16}{5}\mathbf{i} + \dfrac{8}{5}\mathbf{j}$; $\mathbf{v}_2 = \dfrac{1}{5}\mathbf{i} + \dfrac{2}{5}\mathbf{j}$

101. $\mathbf{v}_1 = \dfrac{9}{10}(3\mathbf{i} + \mathbf{j})$; $\mathbf{v}_2 = \dfrac{-7}{10}\mathbf{i} + \dfrac{21}{10}\mathbf{j}$ **102.** $\mathbf{v}_1 = -\dfrac{1}{2}(3\mathbf{i} - \mathbf{j})$; $\mathbf{v}_2 = \dfrac{1}{2}\mathbf{i} + \dfrac{3}{2}\mathbf{j}$ **103.** $\alpha \approx 56.1°$; $\beta \approx 138°$; $\gamma \approx 68.2°$ **104.** $\alpha \approx 65.9°$; $\beta \approx 114.1°$;

$\gamma \approx 35.3°$ **105.** $2\sqrt{83}$ **106.** $2\sqrt{43}$ **107.** $-2\mathbf{i} + 3\mathbf{j} - \mathbf{k}$ **108.** 0 **109.** $\sqrt{29} \approx 5.39$ mi/hr; 0.4 mi **110.** 459.54 km/hr, at an angle 5.3° east of north

111. Left cable: 1843.21 lb; right cable: 1630.41 lb **112.** 9.13 mi/hr; 13.4° east of south **113.** 50 foot-pounds

Chapter Test *(page 635)*

1–3.

4. $\left(4, \dfrac{\pi}{3}\right)$ **5.** $x^2 + y^2 = 49$ **6.** $\dfrac{y}{x} = 3$ or $y = 3x$

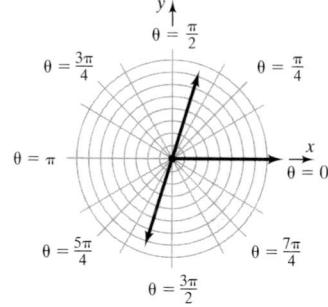

7. $8y = x^2$ or $4(2)y = x^2$

The graph is a parabola with vertex $(0, 0)$ and focus $(0, 2)$.

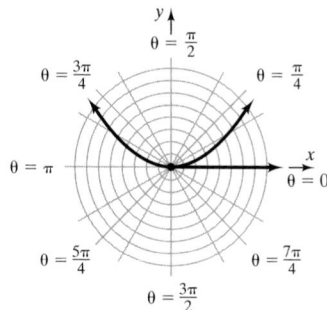

8. $r^2 \cos \theta = 5$ is symmetric about the pole, the polar axis, and the line $\theta = \dfrac{\pi}{2}$.

9. $r = 5 \sin \theta \cos^2 \theta$ is symmetric about the line $\theta = \dfrac{\pi}{2}$. The tests for symmetry about the pole and the polar axis fail, so the graph of $r = 5 \sin \theta \cos^2 \theta$ may or may not be symmetric about the pole or polar axis.

10. $z \cdot w = 6(\cos 107° + i \sin 107°)$

11. $\dfrac{w}{z} = \dfrac{3}{2}(\cos 297° + i \sin 297°)$

12. $w^5 = 243(\cos 110° + i \sin 110°)$

13. $z_0 = 2\sqrt[3]{2}(\cos 40° + i \sin 40°)$, $z_1 = 2\sqrt[3]{2}(\cos 160° + i \sin 160°)$, $z_2 = 2\sqrt[3]{2}(\cos 280° + i \sin 280°)$

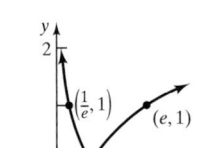

14. $\mathbf{v} = \langle 5\sqrt{2}, -5\sqrt{2} \rangle$ **15.** $\|\mathbf{v}\| = 10$

16. $\mathbf{u} = \dfrac{\mathbf{v}}{\|\mathbf{v}\|} = \left\langle \dfrac{\sqrt{2}}{2}, -\dfrac{\sqrt{2}}{2} \right\rangle$ **17.** 315° off the positive x-axis

18. $\mathbf{v} = 5\sqrt{2}\mathbf{i} - 5\sqrt{2}\mathbf{j}$ **19.** $\mathbf{v}_1 + 2\mathbf{v}_2 - \mathbf{v}_3 = \langle 6, -10 \rangle$

20. Vectors $\mathbf{v}_1$ and $\mathbf{v}_4$ are parallel.

21. Vectors $\mathbf{v}_2$ and $\mathbf{v}_3$ are orthogonal.

22. 172.87°   **23.** $-9\mathbf{i} - 5\mathbf{j} + 3\mathbf{k}$

24. $\alpha \approx 57.7°$, $\beta \approx 143.3°$, $\gamma \approx 74.5°$ **25.** $\sqrt{115}$

26. The cable must be able to endure a tension of approximately 670.82 lb.

Cumulative Review *(page 635)*

1. $\{-3, 3\}$

2. $y = \dfrac{\sqrt{3}}{3}x$

6.

7.

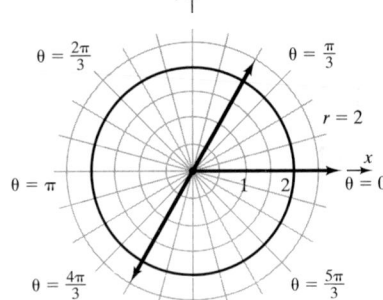

3. $x^2 + (y - 1)^2 = 9$

4. $\left\{ x \,\middle|\, x < \dfrac{1}{2} \right\}$ or $\left(-\infty, \dfrac{1}{2} \right)$

5. Symmetry with respect to the y-axis

8.

9. $-\dfrac{\pi}{6}$ **10.**

11.

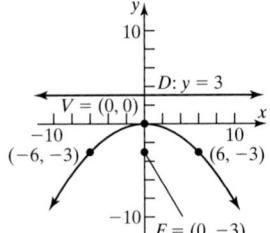

12. Amplitude: 4; period: 2

CHAPTER 10 Analytic Geometry

10.2 Assess Your Understanding *(page 646)*

6. parabola   **7.** paraboloid of revolution   **8.** T   **9.** T   **10.** T   **11.** B   **12.** G   **13.** E   **14.** D   **15.** H   **16.** A   **17.** C   **18.** F

19. $y^2 = 16x$

20. $x^2 = 8y$

21. $x^2 = -12y$

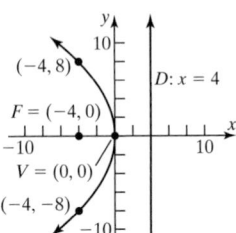

22. $y^2 = -16x$

23. $y^2 = -8x$

24. $x^2 = -4y$

25. $x^2 = 2y$

26. $y^2 = 2x$

27. $x^2 = \dfrac{4}{3}y$

28. $y^2 = \dfrac{9}{2}x$

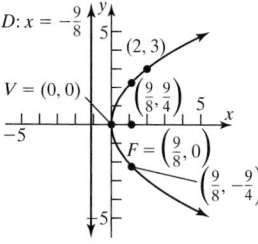

29. $(x - 2)^2 = -8(y + 3)$

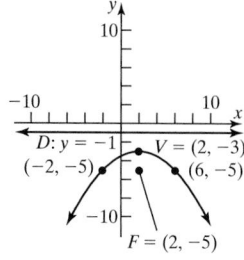

30. $(y + 2)^2 = 8(x - 4)$

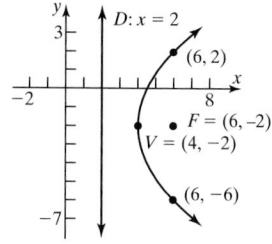

31. $(y + 2)^2 = 4(x + 1)$

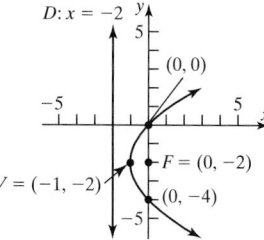

32. $(x - 3)^2 = -8y$

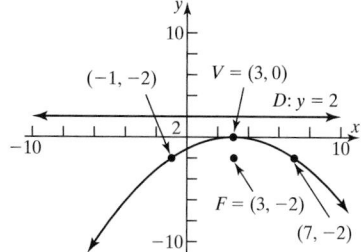

33. $(x + 3)^2 = 4(y - 3)$

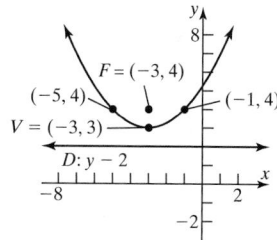

34. $(y - 4)^2 = 12(x + 1)$

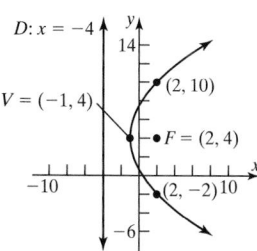

35. $(y + 2)^2 = -8(x + 1)$

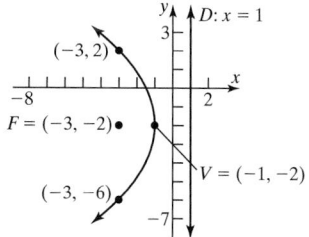

36. $(x + 4)^2 = 12(y - 1)$

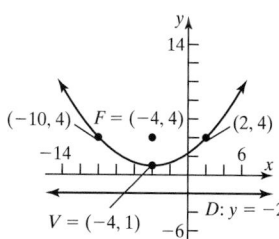

37. Vertex: $(0, 0)$; focus: $(0, 1)$;
directrix: $y = -1$

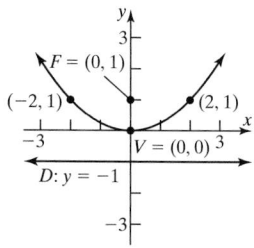

38. Vertex: $(0, 0)$; focus: $(2, 0)$;
directrix: $x = -2$

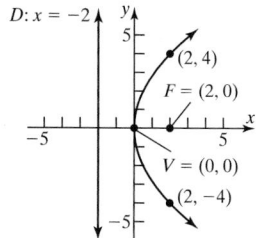

39. Vertex: $(0, 0)$; focus: $(-4, 0)$;
directrix: $x = 4$

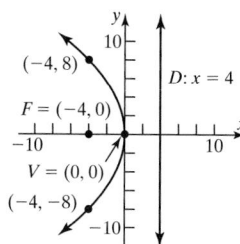

40. Vertex: $(0, 0)$; focus: $(0, -1)$;
directrix: $y = 1$

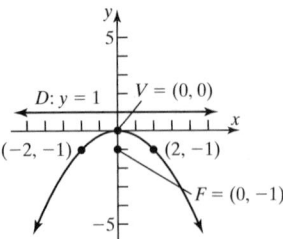

41. Vertex: $(-1, 2)$; focus: $(1, 2)$;
directrix: $x = -3$

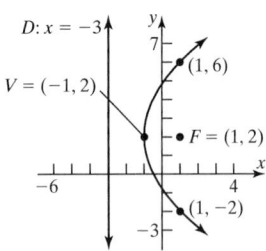

42. Vertex: $(-4, -2)$; focus: $(-4, 2)$;
directrix: $y = -6$

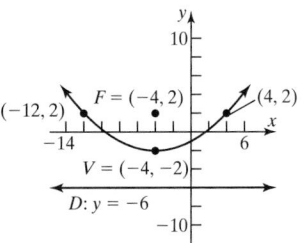

43. Vertex: $(3, -1)$; focus: $\left(3, -\dfrac{5}{4}\right)$;
directrix: $y = -\dfrac{3}{4}$

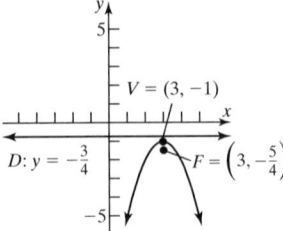

44. Vertex: $(2, -1)$; focus: $(1, -1)$;
directrix: $x = 3$

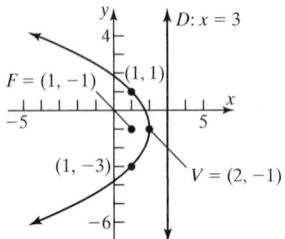

45. Vertex: $(2, -3)$; focus: $(4, -3)$;
directrix: $x = 0$

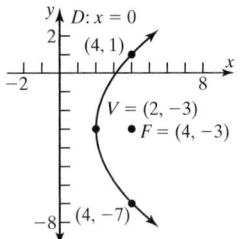

46. Vertex: $(2, 3)$; focus: $(2, 4)$;
directrix: $y = 2$

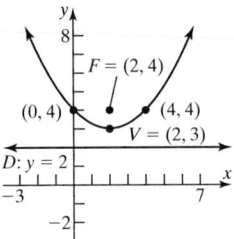

47. Vertex: $(0, 2)$; focus: $(-1, 2)$;
directrix: $x = 1$

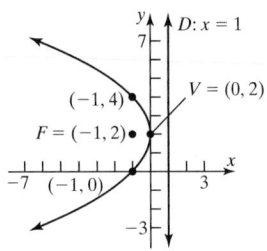

48. Vertex: $(-3, -2)$; focus: $(-3, -1)$;
directrix: $y = -3$

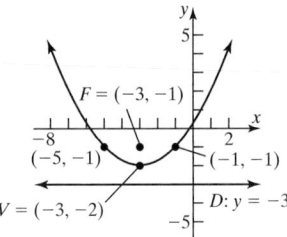

49. Vertex: $(-4, -2)$; focus: $(-4, -1)$;
directrix: $y = -3$

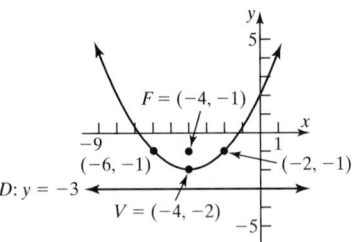

50. Vertex: $(0, 1)$; focus: $(2, 1)$;
directrix: $x = -2$

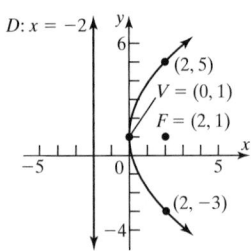

51. Vertex: $(-1, -1)$; focus: $\left(-\dfrac{3}{4}, -1\right)$;
directrix: $x = -\dfrac{5}{4}$

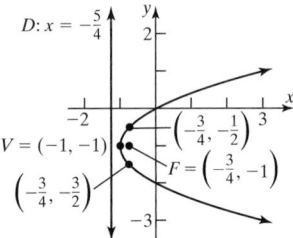

52. Vertex: $(2, -2)$; focus: $\left(2, -\dfrac{3}{2}\right)$;
directrix: $y = -\dfrac{5}{2}$

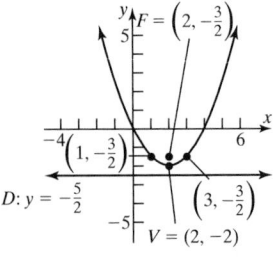

53. Vertex: $(2, -8)$; focus: $\left(2, -\dfrac{31}{4}\right)$;
directrix: $y = -\dfrac{33}{4}$

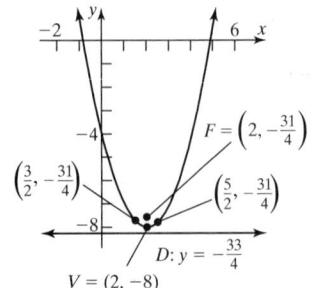

54. Vertex: $(37, -6)$; focus: $\left(\dfrac{147}{4}, -6\right)$;
directrix: $x = \dfrac{149}{4}$

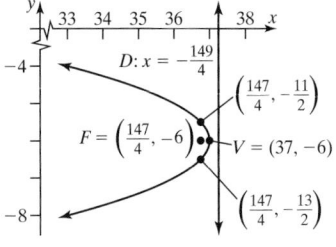

55. $(y-1)^2 = x$ **56.** $(x-1)^2 = -(y-2)$ **57.** $(y-1)^2 = -(x-2)$ **58.** $x^2 = 4(y+1)$ **59.** $x^2 = 4(y-1)$ **60.** $(x-1)^2 = \dfrac{1}{2}(y+1)$

61. $y^2 = \dfrac{1}{2}(x+2)$ **62.** $y^2 = -(x-1)$ **63.** 1.5625 ft from the base of the dish, along the axis of symmetry

64. 1.125 ft or 13.5 in. from the base of the dish, along the axis of symmetry **65.** 1 in. from the vertex, along the axis of symmetry

66. $4\sqrt{2} \approx 5.66$ in. **67.** 20 ft **68.** 15.625 ft **69.** 0.78125 ft **70.** $8\sqrt{2} \approx 11.31$ ft **71.** 4.17 ft from the base, along the axis of symmetry

72. $\dfrac{1}{3}$ in. from the base of the mirror, along the axis of symmetry **73.** 24.31 ft, 18.75 ft, 7.64 ft **74.** 27.78 ft **75.** **(a)** $y = -\dfrac{625}{(299)^2}x^2 + 625$

(b) 567 ft: 63.12 ft; 478 ft: 225.67 ft; 308 ft: 459.2 ft **(c)** No

76. $Ax^2 + Ey = 0, A \neq 0, E \neq 0$

$Ax^2 = -Ey$

$x^2 = -\dfrac{E}{A}y$

This is the equation of a parabola with vertex at $(0,0)$ and axis of symmetry the y-axis. The focus is $\left(0, -\dfrac{E}{4A}\right)$; the directrix is the line $y = \dfrac{E}{4A}$. The parabola opens up if $-\dfrac{E}{A} > 0$ and down if $-\dfrac{E}{A} < 0$.

77. $Cy^2 + Dx = 0, C \neq 0, D \neq 0$

$Cy^2 = -Dx$

$y^2 = -\dfrac{D}{C}x$

This is the equation of a parabola with vertex at $(0,0)$ and axis of symmetry the x-axis. The focus is $\left(-\dfrac{D}{4C}, 0\right)$; the directrix is the line $x = \dfrac{D}{4C}$. The parabola opens to the right if $-\dfrac{D}{C} > 0$ and to the left if $-\dfrac{D}{C} < 0$.

78. $Ax^2 + Dx + Ey + F = 0, A \neq 0$

$Ax^2 + Dx = -Ey - F$

$x^2 + \dfrac{D}{A}x = -\dfrac{E}{A}y - \dfrac{F}{A}$

$\left(x + \dfrac{D}{2A}\right)^2 = -\dfrac{E}{A}y - \dfrac{F}{A} + \dfrac{D^2}{4A^2}$

$\left(x + \dfrac{D}{2A}\right)^2 = -\dfrac{E}{A}y + \dfrac{D^2 - 4AF}{4A^2}$

(a) If $E \neq 0$, then the equation may be written as $\left(x + \dfrac{D}{2A}\right)^2 = -\dfrac{E}{A}\left(y - \dfrac{D^2 - 4AF}{4AE}\right)$.

This is the equation of a parabola with vertex at $\left(-\dfrac{D}{2A}, \dfrac{D^2 - 4AF}{4AE}\right)$ and axis of symmetry parallel to the y-axis.

(b)–(d) If $E = 0$, the graph of the equation contains no points if $D^2 - 4AF < 0$, is a single vertical line if $D^2 - 4AF = 0$, and is two vertical lines if $D^2 - 4AF > 0$.

79. $Cy^2 + Dx + Ey + F = 0, C \neq 0$

$Cy^2 + Ey = -Dx - F$

$y^2 + \dfrac{E}{C}y = -\dfrac{D}{C}x - \dfrac{F}{C}$

$\left(y + \dfrac{E}{2C}\right)^2 = -\dfrac{D}{C}x - \dfrac{F}{C} + \dfrac{E^2}{4C^2}$

$\left(y + \dfrac{E}{2C}\right)^2 = -\dfrac{D}{C}x + \dfrac{E^2 - 4CF}{4C^2}$

(a) If $D \neq 0$, then the equation may be written as $\left(y + \dfrac{E}{2C}\right)^2 = -\dfrac{D}{C}\left(x - \dfrac{E^2 - 4CF}{4CD}\right)$.

This is the equation of a parabola with vertex at $\left(\dfrac{E^2 - 4CF}{4CD}, -\dfrac{E}{2C}\right)$ and axis of symmetry parallel to the x-axis.

(b)–(d) If $D = 0$, the graph of the equation contains no points if $E^2 - 4CF < 0$, is a single horizontal line if $E^2 - 4CF = 0$, and is two horizontal lines if $E^2 - 4CF > 0$.

10.3 Assess Your Understanding (page 657)

7. ellipse **8.** major **9.** $(0, -5); (0, 5)$ **10.** F **11.** T **12.** T **13.** C **14.** D **15.** B **16.** A

17. Vertices: $(-5, 0), (5, 0)$

Foci: $\left(-\sqrt{21}, 0\right), \left(\sqrt{21}, 0\right)$

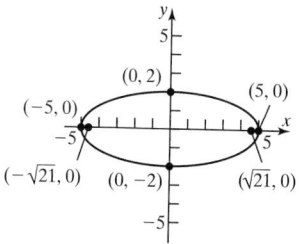

18. Vertices: $(-3, 0), (3, 0)$

Foci: $\left(-\sqrt{5}, 0\right), \left(\sqrt{5}, 0\right)$

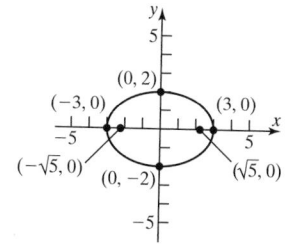

19. Vertices: $(0, -5), (0, 5)$

Foci: $(0, -4), (0, 4)$

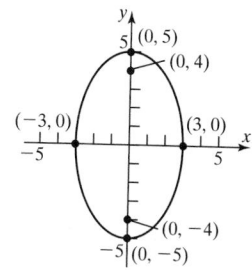

20. Vertices: $(0, -4), (0, 4)$

Foci: $\left(0, -\sqrt{15}\right), \left(0, \sqrt{15}\right)$

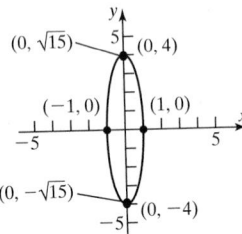

23. $\dfrac{x^2}{8} + \dfrac{y^2}{2} = 1$

Vertices: $\left(-2\sqrt{2}, 0\right), \left(2\sqrt{2}, 0\right)$

Foci: $\left(-\sqrt{6}, 0\right), \left(\sqrt{6}, 0\right)$

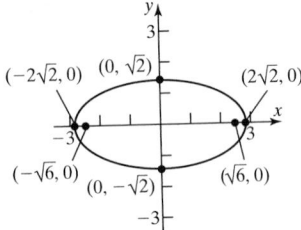

26. $\dfrac{x^2}{4} + \dfrac{y^2}{4} = 1$

Vertices: $(-2, 0), (2, 0), (0, -2), (0, 2)$

Focus: $(0, 0)$

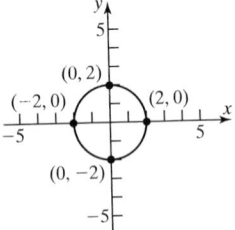

29. $\dfrac{x^2}{9} + \dfrac{y^2}{25} = 1$

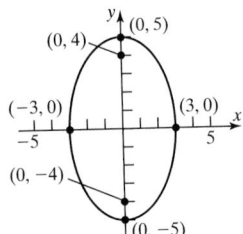

32. $\dfrac{x^2}{12} + \dfrac{y^2}{16} = 1$

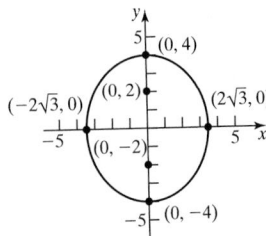

21. $\dfrac{x^2}{4} + \dfrac{y^2}{16} = 1$

Vertices: $(0, -4), (0, 4)$

Foci: $\left(0, -2\sqrt{3}\right), \left(0, 2\sqrt{3}\right)$

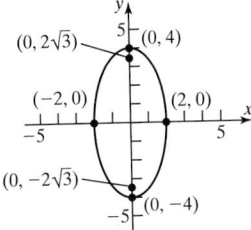

24. $\dfrac{x^2}{4} + \dfrac{y^2}{9} = 1$

Vertices: $(0, -3), (0, 3)$

Foci: $\left(0, -\sqrt{5}\right), \left(0, \sqrt{5}\right)$

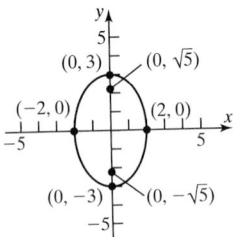

27. $\dfrac{x^2}{25} + \dfrac{y^2}{16} = 1$

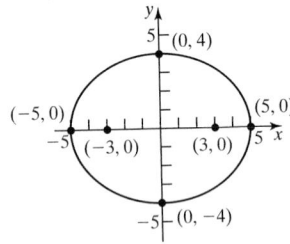

30. $\dfrac{x^2}{3} + \dfrac{y^2}{4} = 1$

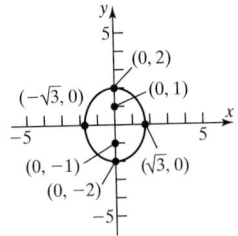

33. $\dfrac{x^2}{25} + \dfrac{y^2}{9} = 1$

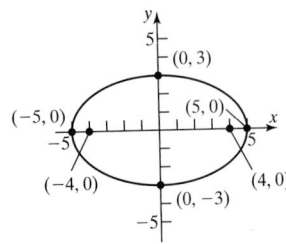

22. $\dfrac{x^2}{18} + \dfrac{y^2}{2} = 1$

Vertices: $\left(-3\sqrt{2}, 0\right), \left(3\sqrt{2}, 0\right)$

Foci: $(-4, 0), (4, 0)$

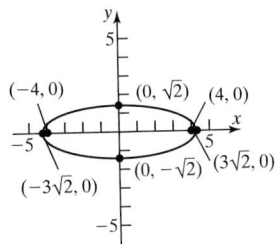

25. $\dfrac{x^2}{16} + \dfrac{y^2}{16} = 1$

Vertices: $(-4, 0), (4, 0), (0, -4), (0, 4)$

Focus: $(0, 0)$

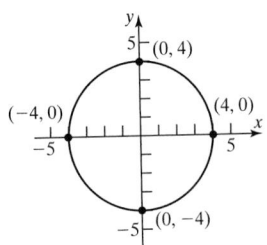

28. $\dfrac{x^2}{9} + \dfrac{y^2}{8} = 1$

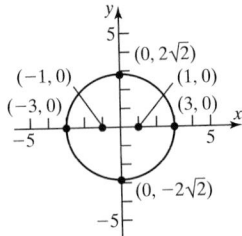

31. $\dfrac{x^2}{9} + \dfrac{y^2}{5} = 1$

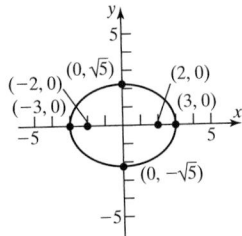

34. $\dfrac{x^2}{48} + \dfrac{y^2}{64} = 1$

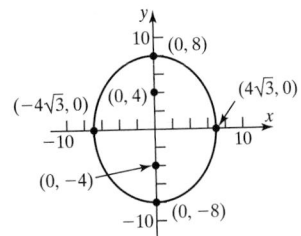

35. $\dfrac{x^2}{4} + \dfrac{y^2}{13} = 1$

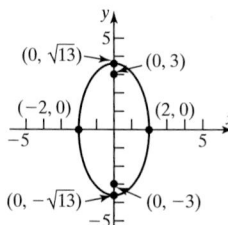

36. $\dfrac{x^2}{16} + y^2 = 1$

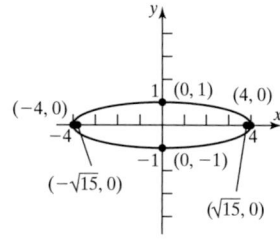

37. $x^2 + \dfrac{y^2}{16} = 1$

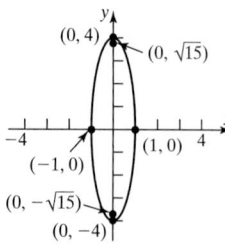

38. $\dfrac{x^2}{25} + \dfrac{y^2}{21} = 1$

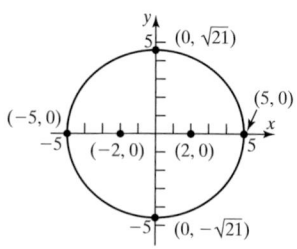

39. $\dfrac{(x+1)^2}{4} + (y-1)^2 = 1$

40. $(x+1)^2 + \dfrac{(y+1)^2}{4} = 1$

41. $(x-1)^2 + \dfrac{y^2}{4} = 1$

42. $\dfrac{x^2}{4} + (y-1)^2 = 1$

43. Center: $(3, -1)$; vertices: $(3, -4), (3, 2)$;

foci: $\left(3, -1 - \sqrt{5}\right), \left(3, -1 + \sqrt{5}\right)$

44. Center: $(-4, -2)$;

vertices: $(-7, -2), (-1, -2)$;

foci: $\left(-4 - \sqrt{5}, -2\right), \left(-4 + \sqrt{5}, -2\right)$

45. $\dfrac{(x+5)^2}{16} + \dfrac{(y-4)^2}{4} = 1$

Center: $(-5, 4)$; vertices: $(-9, 4), (-1, 4)$;

foci: $\left(-5 - 2\sqrt{3}, 4\right), \left(-5 + 2\sqrt{3}, 4\right)$

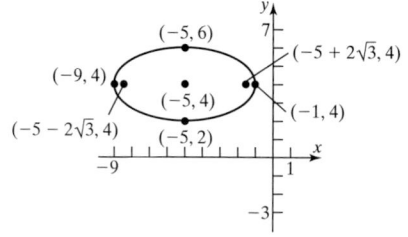

46. $\dfrac{(x-3)^2}{2} + \dfrac{(y+2)^2}{18} = 1$

Center: $(3, -2)$;

vertices: $\left(3, -2 - 3\sqrt{2}\right), \left(3, -2 + 3\sqrt{2}\right)$;

foci: $(3, -6), (3, 2)$

47. $\dfrac{(x+2)^2}{4} + (y-1)^2 = 1$

Center: $(-2, 1)$; vertices: $(-4, 1), (0, 1)$;

foci: $\left(-2 - \sqrt{3}, 1\right), \left(-2 + \sqrt{3}, 1\right)$

48. $\dfrac{x^2}{3} + (y-2)^2 = 1$

Center: $(0, 2)$;

vertices: $\left(-\sqrt{3}, 2\right), \left(\sqrt{3}, 2\right)$;

foci: $\left(-\sqrt{2}, 2\right), \left(\sqrt{2}, 2\right)$

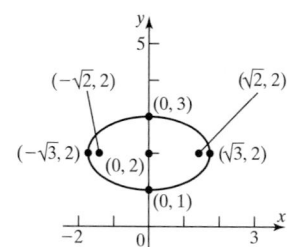

49. $\dfrac{(x-2)^2}{3} + \dfrac{(y+1)^2}{2} = 1$

Center: $(2, -1)$; vertices: $\left(2 - \sqrt{3}, -1\right)$;

$\left(2 + \sqrt{3}, -1\right)$; foci: $(1, -1), (3, -1)$

50. $\dfrac{(x+1)^2}{3} + \dfrac{(y-1)^2}{4} = 1$

Center: $(-1, 1)$; vertices: $(-1, -1), (-1, 3)$;

foci: $(-1, 0), (-1, 2)$

51. $\dfrac{(x-1)^2}{4} + \dfrac{(y+2)^2}{9} = 1$

Center: $(1, -2)$; vertices: $(1, -5), (1, 1)$;

foci: $\left(1, -2 - \sqrt{5}\right), \left(1, -2 + \sqrt{5}\right)$

52. $\dfrac{(x+3)^2}{9} + (y-1)^2 = 1$

Center: $(-3, 1)$; vertices: $(-6, 1)$, $(0, 1)$;
foci: $\left(-3 - 2\sqrt{2}, 1\right), \left(-3 + 2\sqrt{2}, 1\right)$

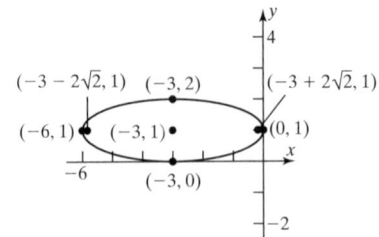

53. $x^2 + \dfrac{(y+2)^2}{4} = 1$

Center: $(0, -2)$; vertices: $(0, -4)$, $(0, 0)$;
foci: $\left(0, -2 - \sqrt{3}\right), \left(0, -2 + \sqrt{3}\right)$

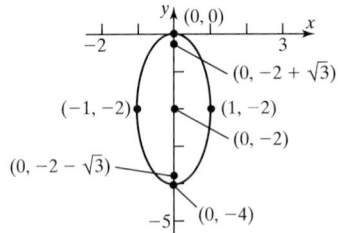

54. $(x-1)^2 + \dfrac{y^2}{9} = 1$

Center: $(1, 0)$; vertices: $(1, -3)$, $(1, 3)$;
foci: $\left(1, -2\sqrt{2}\right), \left(1, 2\sqrt{2}\right)$

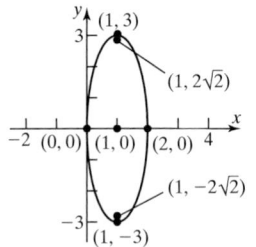

55. $\dfrac{(x-2)^2}{25} + \dfrac{(y+2)^2}{21} = 1$

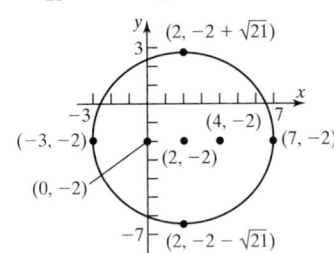

56. $\dfrac{(x+3)^2}{3} + \dfrac{(y-1)^2}{4} = 1$

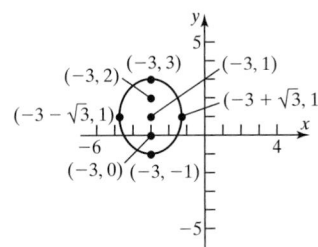

57. $\dfrac{(x-4)^2}{5} + \dfrac{(y-6)^2}{9} = 1$

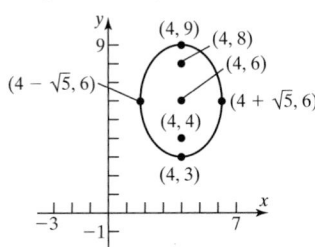

58. $\dfrac{(x+1)^2}{9} + \dfrac{(y-2)^2}{5} = 1$

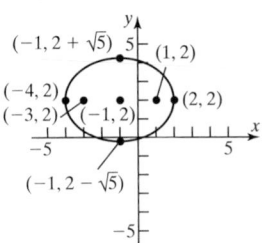

59. $\dfrac{(x-2)^2}{16} + \dfrac{(y-1)^2}{7} = 1$

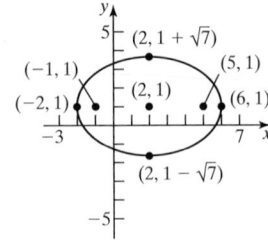

60. $\dfrac{(x-2)^2}{5} + \dfrac{(y-2)^2}{9} = 1$

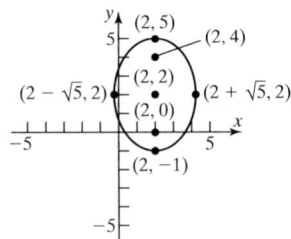

61. $\dfrac{(x-1)^2}{10} + (y-2)^2 = 1$

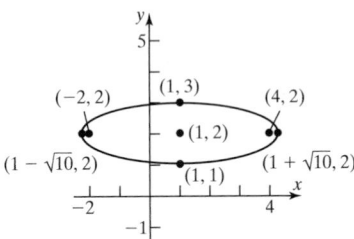

62. $(x-1)^2 + \dfrac{(y-2)^2}{5} = 1$

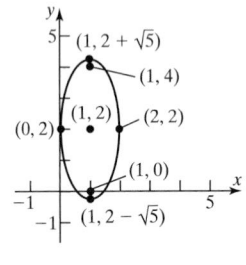

63. $\dfrac{(x-1)^2}{9} + (y-2)^2 = 1$

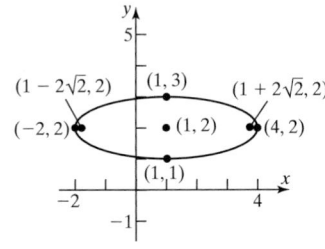

64. $(x-1)^2 + \dfrac{(y-2)^2}{4} = 1$

65.

66.

67.

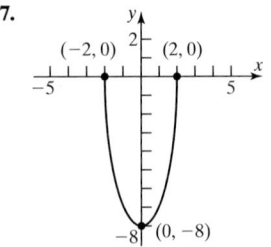

68.

69. $\dfrac{x^2}{100} + \dfrac{y^2}{36} = 1$ **70.** 5 ft from center of bridge, distance is 2.57 ft; 10 ft from center, distance is 4.55 ft;
15 ft from center, distance is 12 ft   **71.** 43.3 ft   **72.** 112 ft; 25.2 ft   **73.** 24.65 ft, 21.65 ft, 13.82 ft
74. 16.67 ft   **75.** 30 ft   **76.** 73.69 ft   **77.** The elliptical hole will have a major axis of length $2\sqrt{41}$ in. and
a minor axis of length 8 in.   **78.** Approximately 471 in.³

79. 91.5 million mi; $\dfrac{x^2}{8649} + \dfrac{y^2}{8646.75} = 1$ **80.** 155.5 million mi; $\dfrac{x^2}{20{,}164} + \dfrac{y^2}{19{,}981.75} = 1$

81. Perihelion: 460.6 million mi; mean distance: 483.8 million mi; $\dfrac{x^2}{233{,}482} + \dfrac{y^2}{233{,}524.2} = 1$

82. Aphelion: 6346 million mi; mean distance: 5448.5 million mi; $\dfrac{x^2}{29,686,152} + \dfrac{y^2}{28,880,646} = 1$

83. (a) $Ax^2 + Cy^2 + F = 0$ \qquad If A and C are of the same sign and F is of opposite sign, then the equation takes the form

$Ax^2 + Cy^2 = -F$ \qquad $\dfrac{x^2}{\left(-\dfrac{F}{A}\right)} + \dfrac{y^2}{\left(-\dfrac{F}{C}\right)} = 1$, where $-\dfrac{F}{A}$ and $-\dfrac{F}{C}$ are positive. This is the equation of an ellipse

with center at $(0,0)$.

(b) If $A = C$, the equation may be written as $x^2 + y^2 = \dfrac{-F}{A}$. This is the equation of a circle with center at $(0,0)$ and radius equal to $\sqrt{-\dfrac{F}{A}}$.

84. $Ax^2 + Cy^2 + Dx + Ey + F = 0 \quad A \neq 0, C \neq 0$

$Ax^2 + Dx + Cy^2 + Ey = -F$

$A\left(x^2 + \dfrac{D}{A}x\right) + C\left(y^2 + \dfrac{E}{C}y\right) = -F$

$A\left(x + \dfrac{D}{2A}\right)^2 + C\left(y + \dfrac{E}{2C}\right)^2 = -F + \dfrac{D^2}{4A} + \dfrac{E^2}{4C}$

(a) If $\dfrac{D^2}{4A} + \dfrac{E^2}{4C} - F$ is of the same sign as A (and C), this is the equation of an ellipse with center at $\left(\dfrac{-D}{2A}, \dfrac{-E}{2C}\right)$.

(b) If $\dfrac{D^2}{4A} + \dfrac{E^2}{4C} - F = 0$, the graph is the single point $\left(\dfrac{-D}{2A}, \dfrac{-E}{2C}\right)$.

(c) If $\dfrac{D^2}{4A} + \dfrac{E^2}{4C} - F$ is of the opposite sign to A (and C), the graph contains no points since, in this case, the left side has a sign opposite that of the right side.

10.4 Assess Your Understanding *(page 670)*

7. hyperbola \quad **8.** transverse axis \quad **9.** $y = \dfrac{3}{2}x; \; y = -\dfrac{3}{2}x$ \quad **10.** F \quad **11.** T \quad **12.** F \quad **13.** B \quad **14.** C \quad **15.** A \quad **16.** D

17. $x^2 - \dfrac{y^2}{8} = 1$

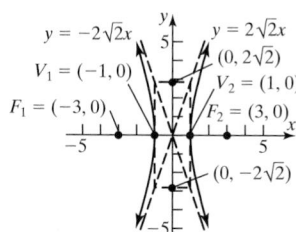

18. $\dfrac{y^2}{9} - \dfrac{x^2}{16} = 1$

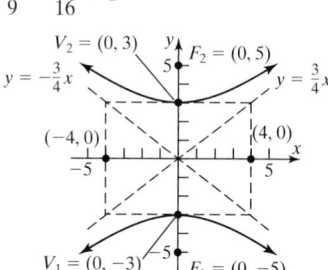

19. $\dfrac{y^2}{16} - \dfrac{x^2}{20} = 1$

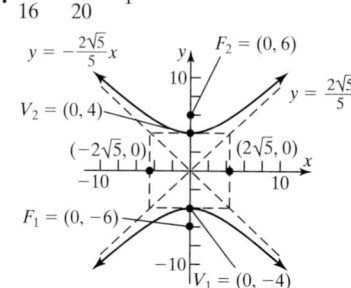

20. $\dfrac{x^2}{4} - \dfrac{y^2}{5} = 1$

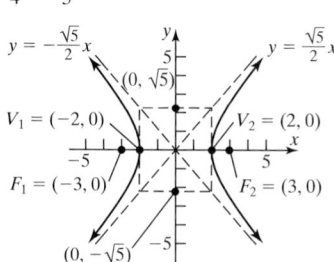

21. $\dfrac{x^2}{9} - \dfrac{y^2}{16} = 1$

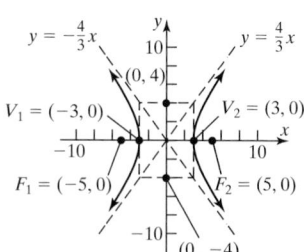

22. $\dfrac{y^2}{4} - \dfrac{x^2}{32} = 1$

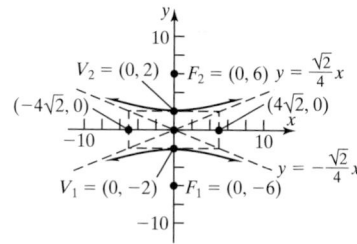

23. $\dfrac{y^2}{36} - \dfrac{x^2}{9} = 1$

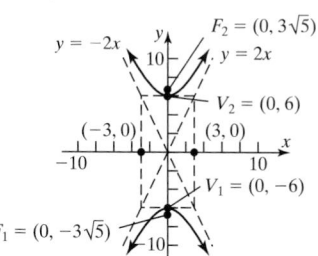

24. $\dfrac{x^2}{16} - \dfrac{y^2}{64} = 1$

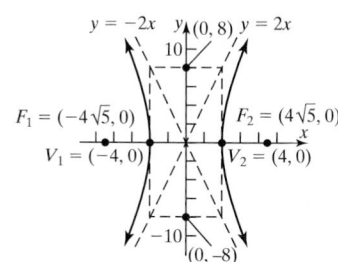

25. $\dfrac{x^2}{8} - \dfrac{y^2}{8} = 1$

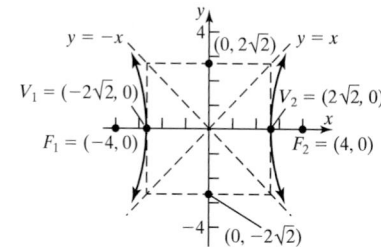

26. $\dfrac{y^2}{2} - \dfrac{x^2}{2} = 1$

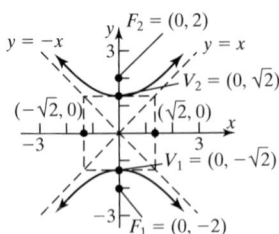

27. $\dfrac{x^2}{25} - \dfrac{y^2}{9} = 1$

Center: $(0, 0)$

Transverse axis: x-axis

Vertices: $(-5, 0), (5, 0)$

Foci: $\left(-\sqrt{34}, 0\right), \left(\sqrt{34}, 0\right)$

Asymptotes: $y = \pm \dfrac{3}{5} x$

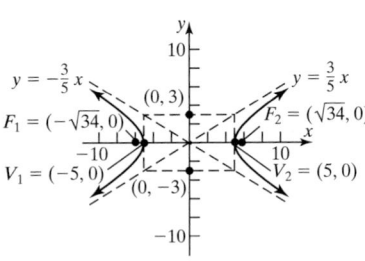

28. $\dfrac{y^2}{16} - \dfrac{x^2}{4} = 1$

Center: $(0, 0)$

Transverse axis: y-axis

Vertices: $(0, -4), (0, 4)$

Foci: $\left(0, -2\sqrt{5}\right), \left(0, 2\sqrt{5}\right)$

Asymptotes: $y = \pm 2x$

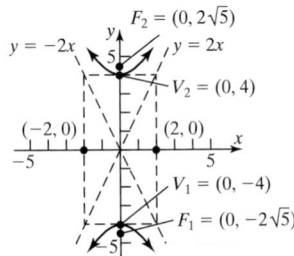

29. $\dfrac{x^2}{4} - \dfrac{y^2}{16} = 1$

Center: $(0, 0)$

Transverse axis: x-axis

Vertices: $(-2, 0), (2, 0)$

Foci: $\left(-2\sqrt{5}, 0\right), \left(2\sqrt{5}, 0\right)$

Asymptotes: $y = \pm 2x$

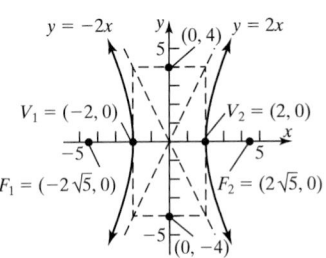

30. $\dfrac{y^2}{4} - \dfrac{x^2}{16} = 1$

Center: $(0, 0)$

Transverse axis: y-axis

Vertices: $(0, -2), (0, 2)$

Foci: $\left(0, -2\sqrt{5}\right), \left(0, 2\sqrt{5}\right)$

Asymptotes: $y = \pm \dfrac{1}{2} x$

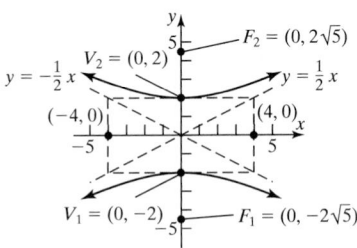

31. $\dfrac{y^2}{9} - x^2 = 1$

Center: $(0, 0)$

Transverse axis: y-axis

Vertices: $(0, -3), (0, 3)$

Foci: $\left(0, -\sqrt{10}\right), \left(0, \sqrt{10}\right)$

Asymptotes: $y = \pm 3x$

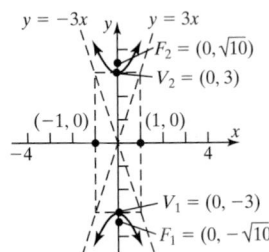

32. $\dfrac{x^2}{4} - \dfrac{y^2}{4} = 1$

Center: $(0, 0)$

Transverse axis: x-axis

Vertices: $(-2, 0), (2, 0)$

Foci: $\left(-2\sqrt{2}, 0\right), \left(2\sqrt{2}, 0\right)$

Asymptotes: $y = \pm x$

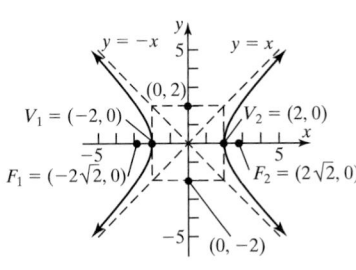

33. $\dfrac{y^2}{25} - \dfrac{x^2}{25} = 1$

Center: $(0, 0)$

Transverse axis: y-axis

Vertices: $(0, -5), (0, 5)$

Foci: $\left(0, -5\sqrt{2}\right), \left(0, 5\sqrt{2}\right)$

Asymptotes: $y = \pm x$

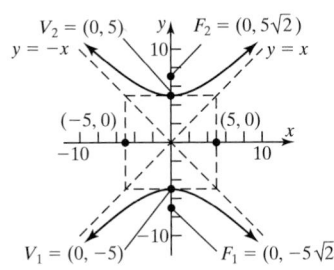

34. $\dfrac{x^2}{2} - \dfrac{y^2}{4} = 1$

Center: $(0, 0)$

Transverse axis: x-axis

Vertices: $\left(-\sqrt{2}, 0\right), \left(\sqrt{2}, 0\right)$

Foci: $\left(-\sqrt{6}, 0\right), \left(\sqrt{6}, 0\right)$

Asymptotes: $y = \pm \sqrt{2} x$

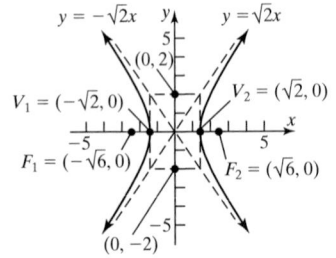

35. $x^2 - y^2 = 1$

36. $y^2 - x^2 = 1$

37. $\dfrac{y^2}{36} - \dfrac{x^2}{9} = 1$

38. $\dfrac{x^2}{4} - \dfrac{y^2}{16} = 1$

39. $\dfrac{(x-4)^2}{4} - \dfrac{(y+1)^2}{5} = 1$

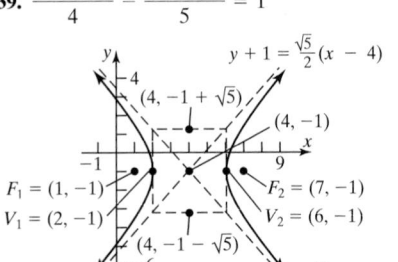

40. $\dfrac{(y-1)^2}{9} - \dfrac{(x+3)^2}{16} = 1$

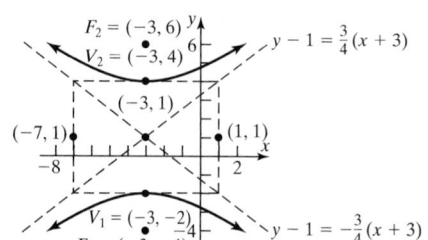

41. $\dfrac{(y+4)^2}{4} - \dfrac{(x+3)^2}{12} = 1$

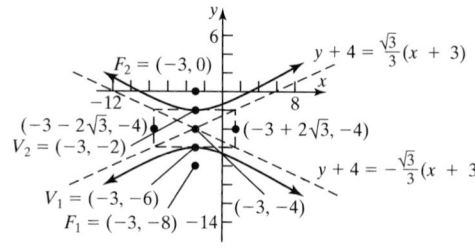

42. $(x-1)^2 - \dfrac{(y-4)^2}{8} = 1$

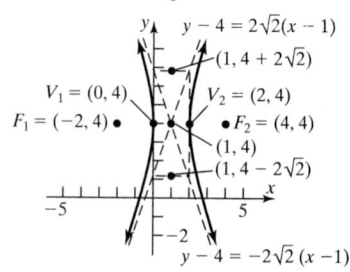

43. $(x-5)^2 - \dfrac{(y-7)^2}{3} = 1$

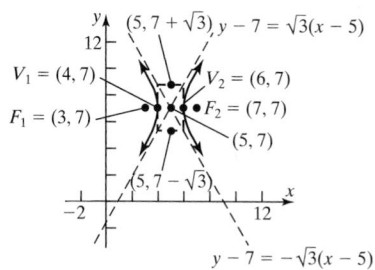

44. $(y-3)^2 - \dfrac{(x+4)^2}{8} = 1$

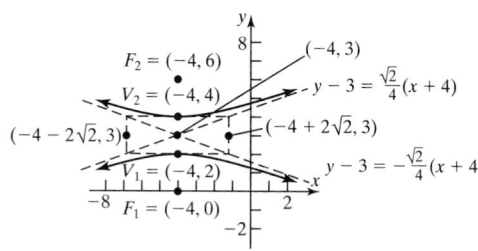

45. $\dfrac{(x-1)^2}{4} - \dfrac{(y+1)^2}{9} = 1$

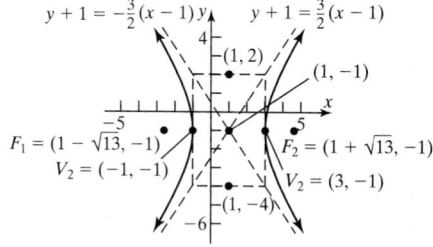

46. $\dfrac{(y+1)^2}{4} - \dfrac{9(x-1)^2}{16} = 1$

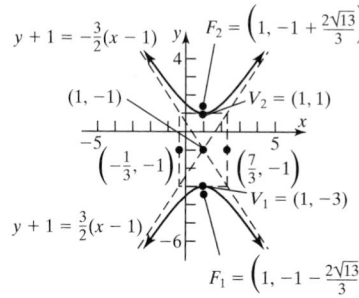

47. $\dfrac{(x-2)^2}{4} - \dfrac{(y+3)^2}{9} = 1$

Center: $(2, -3)$

Transverse axis: parallel to x-axis

Vertices: $(0, -3), (4, -3)$

Foci: $\left(2 - \sqrt{13}, -3\right), \left(2 + \sqrt{13}, -3\right)$

Asymptotes: $y + 3 = \pm\dfrac{3}{2}(x - 2)$

48. $\dfrac{(y+3)^2}{4} - \dfrac{(x-2)^2}{9} = 1$

Center: $(2, -3)$

Transverse axis: parallel to y-axis

Vertices: $(2, -5), (2, -1)$

Foci: $\left(2, -3 - \sqrt{13}\right), \left(2, -3 + \sqrt{13}\right)$

Asymptotes: $y + 3 = \pm\dfrac{2}{3}(x - 2)$

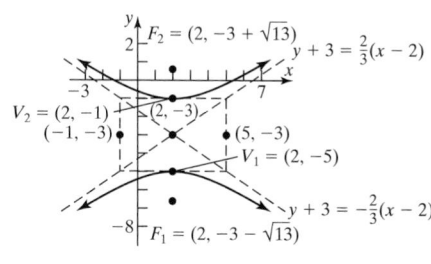

49. $\dfrac{(y-2)^2}{4} - (x+2)^2 = 1$

Center: $(-2, 2)$

Transverse axis: parallel to y-axis

Vertices: $(-2, 0), (-2, 4)$

Foci: $\left(-2, 2 - \sqrt{5}\right), \left(-2, 2 + \sqrt{5}\right)$

Asymptotes: $y - 2 = \pm 2(x + 2)$

50. $\dfrac{(x+4)^2}{9} - (y-3)^2 = 1$

Center: $(-4, 3)$

Transverse axis: parallel to x-axis

Vertices: $(-7, 3), (-1, 3)$

Foci: $\left(-4 - \sqrt{10}, 3\right), \left(-4 + \sqrt{10}, 3\right)$

Asymptotes: $y - 3 = \pm\dfrac{1}{3}(x + 4)$

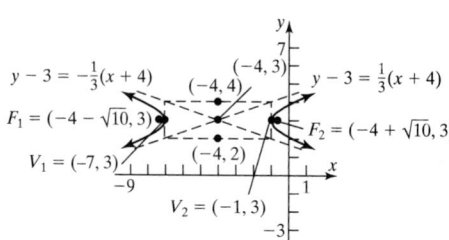

51. $\dfrac{(x+1)^2}{4} - \dfrac{(y+2)^2}{4} = 1$
Center: $(-1, -2)$
Transverse axis: parallel to x-axis
Vertices: $(-3, -2), (1, -2)$
Foci: $\left(-1 - 2\sqrt{2}, -2\right), \left(-1 + 2\sqrt{2}, -2\right)$
Asymptotes: $y + 2 = \pm(x + 1)$

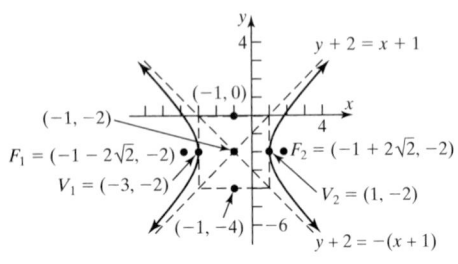

52. $\dfrac{(y-3)^2}{4} - \dfrac{(x+2)^2}{4} = 1$
Center: $(-2, 3)$
Transverse axis: parallel to y-axis
Vertices: $(-2, 1), (-2, 5)$
Foci: $\left(-2, 3 - 2\sqrt{2}\right), \left(-2, 3 + 2\sqrt{2}\right)$
Asymptotes: $y - 3 = \pm(x + 2)$

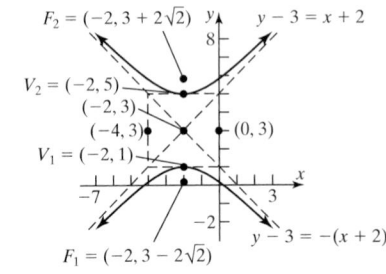

53. $(x-1)^2 - (y+1)^2 = 1$
Center: $(1, -1)$
Transverse axis: parallel to x-axis
Vertices: $(0, -1), (2, -1)$
Foci: $\left(1 - \sqrt{2}, -1\right), \left(1 + \sqrt{2}, -1\right)$
Asymptotes: $y + 1 = \pm(x - 1)$

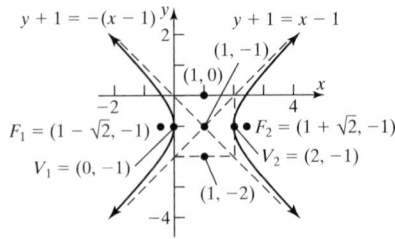

54. $(y-2)^2 - (x-2)^2 = 1$
Center: $(2, 2)$
Transverse axis: parallel to y-axis
Vertices: $(2, 1), (2, 3)$
Foci: $\left(2, 2 - \sqrt{2}\right), \left(2, 2 + \sqrt{2}\right)$
Asymptotes: $y - 2 = \pm(x - 2)$

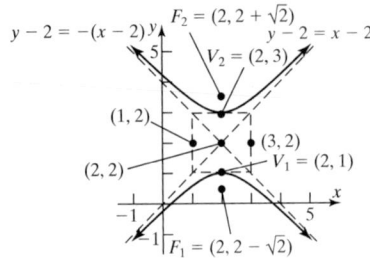

55. $\dfrac{(y-2)^2}{4} - (x+1)^2 = 1$
Center: $(-1, 2)$
Transverse axis: parallel to y-axis
Vertices: $(-1, 0), (-1, 4)$
Foci: $\left(-1, 2 - \sqrt{5}\right), \left(-1, 2 + \sqrt{5}\right)$
Asymptotes: $y - 2 = \pm 2(x + 1)$

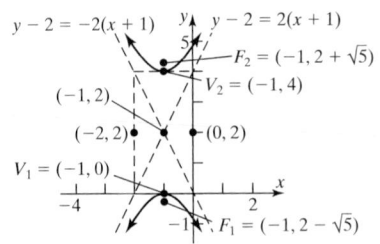

56. $(x+1)^2 - \dfrac{(y-2)^2}{2} = 1$
Center: $(-1, 2)$
Transverse axis: parallel to x-axis
Vertices: $(-2, 2), (0, 2)$
Foci: $\left(-1 - \sqrt{3}, 2\right), \left(-1 + \sqrt{3}, 2\right)$
Asymptotes: $y - 2 = \pm\sqrt{2}(x + 1)$

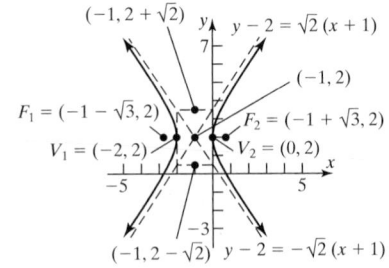

57. $\dfrac{(x-3)^2}{4} - \dfrac{(y+2)^2}{16} = 1$
Center: $(3, -2)$
Transverse axis: parallel to x-axis
Vertices: $(1, -2), (5, -2)$
Foci: $\left(3 - 2\sqrt{5}, -2\right), \left(3 + 2\sqrt{5}, -2\right)$
Asymptotes: $y + 2 = \pm 2(x - 3)$

58. $\dfrac{(y+2)^2}{2} - \dfrac{(x-1)^2}{4} = 1$
Center: $(1, -2)$
Transverse axis: parallel to y-axis
Vertices: $\left(1, -2 - \sqrt{2}\right), \left(1, -2 + \sqrt{2}\right)$
Foci: $\left(1, -2 - \sqrt{6}\right), \left(1, -2 + \sqrt{6}\right)$
Asymptotes: $y + 2 = \pm\dfrac{\sqrt{2}}{2}(x - 1)$

59. $\dfrac{(y-1)^2}{4} - (x+2)^2 = 1$
Center: $(-2, 1)$
Transverse axis: parallel to y-axis
Vertices: $(-2, -1), (-2, 3)$
Foci: $\left(-2, 1 - \sqrt{5}\right), \left(-2, 1 + \sqrt{5}\right)$
Asymptotes: $y - 1 = \pm 2(x + 2)$

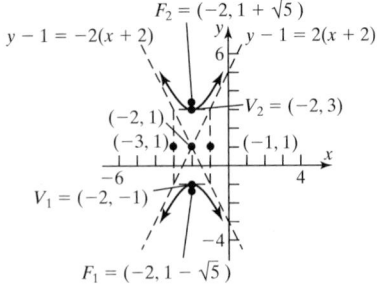

60. $\dfrac{(x+4)^2}{9} - \dfrac{(y+1)^2}{3} = 1$
Center: $(-4, -1)$
Transverse axis: parallel to x-axis
Vertices: $(-7, -1), (-1, -1)$
Foci: $\left(-4 - 2\sqrt{3}, -1\right), \left(-4 + 2\sqrt{3}, -1\right)$
Asymptotes: $y + 1 = \pm\dfrac{\sqrt{3}}{3}(x + 4)$

61.

62.

63.

64.

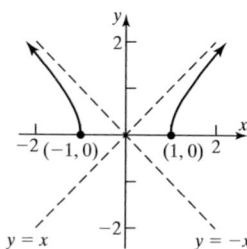

65. Center: $(3, 0)$

Transverse axis: parallel to x-axis

Vertices: $(1, 0), (5, 0)$

Foci: $\left(3 - \sqrt{29}, 0\right), \left(3 + \sqrt{29}, 0\right)$

Asymptotes: $y = \pm\dfrac{5}{2}(x - 3)$

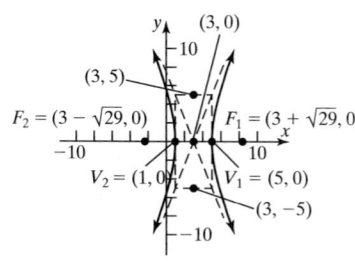

66. Center: $(2, -2)$

Transverse axis: parallel to y-axis

Vertices: $(2, 2), (2, -6)$

Foci: $\left(2, -2 - 2\sqrt{5}\right), \left(2, -2 + 2\sqrt{5}\right)$

Asymptotes: $y + 2 = \pm 2(x - 2)$

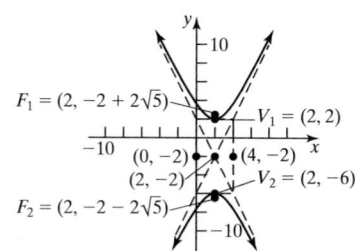

67. Vertex: $(0, 3)$; focus: $(0, 7)$; directrix: $y = -1$

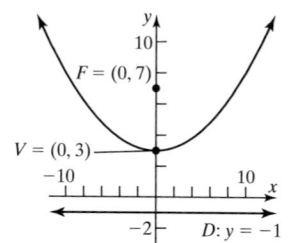

68. Vertex: $(-1, 0)$; focus: $(-4, 0)$; directrix: $x = 2$

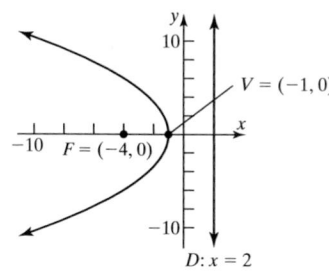

69. $\dfrac{(x - 5)^2}{9} + \dfrac{y^2}{25} = 1$

Center: $(5, 0)$; vertices: $(5, 5), (5, -5)$;

foci: $(5, -4), (5, 4)$

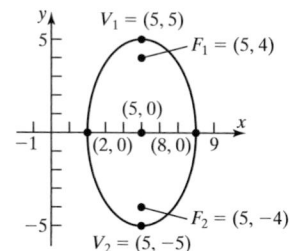

70. $\dfrac{(x - 1)^2}{36} + (y + 4)^2 = 1$

Center: $(1, -4)$; vertices: $(-5, -4), (7, -4)$;

foci: $\left(1 - \sqrt{35}, -4\right), \left(1 + \sqrt{35}, -4\right)$

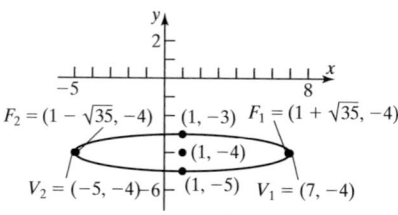

71. $(x - 3)^2 = 8(y + 5)$

Vertex: $(3, -5)$; foci: $(3, -3)$;

directrix: $y = -7$

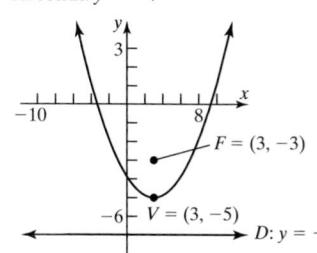

72. $\dfrac{(x - 1)^2}{9} - \dfrac{(y + 4)^2}{81} = 1$

Center: $(1, -4)$

Transverse axis: parallel to y-axis

Vertices: $(-2, -4), (4, -4)$

Foci: $\left(1 - 3\sqrt{10}, -4\right), \left(1 + 3\sqrt{10}, -4\right)$

Asymptotes: $y + 4 = \pm 3(x - 1)$

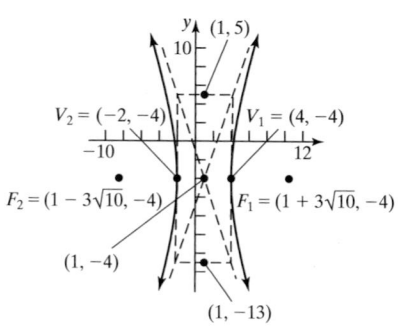

73. The fireworks display is 50,138 ft north of the person at point A.   **74.** The lightning strikes 5236 ft north of the person at point A.

75. The tower is 592.4 ft tall.   **76.** 700 ft   **77. (a)** $y = \pm x$ **(b)** $\dfrac{x^2}{100} - \dfrac{y^2}{100} = 1, x \geq 0$ **78.** $x^2 = 24(y + 1)$ or $y = \dfrac{1}{24}x^2 - 1$ **80.** $\sqrt{2}$

81. $\dfrac{x^2}{4} - y^2 = 1$: asymptotes $y = \pm\dfrac{1}{2}x$

$y^2 - \dfrac{x^2}{4} = 1$: asymptotes $y = \pm\dfrac{1}{2}x$

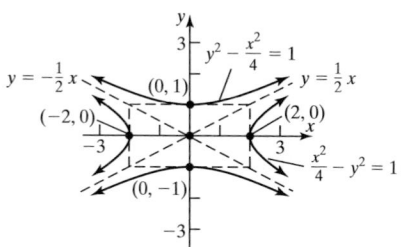

82. $\dfrac{y^2}{a^2} - \dfrac{x^2}{b^2} = 1$

$\dfrac{y^2}{a^2} = 1 + \dfrac{x^2}{b^2}$

$y^2 = a^2\left(1 + \dfrac{x^2}{b^2}\right)$

$y^2 = \dfrac{a^2 x^2}{b^2}\left(\dfrac{b^2}{x^2} + 1\right)$

$y = \pm\dfrac{ax}{b}\sqrt{\dfrac{b^2}{x^2} + 1}$

As $x \to -\infty$ or as $x \to \infty$, the term $\dfrac{b^2}{x^2}$ approaches 0, so the expression under the radical approaches 1.

Thus, the graph of the hyperbola approaches the lines $y = -\dfrac{a}{b}x$ and $y = \dfrac{a}{b}x$.

The lines are asymptotes of the hyperbola.

83. $Ax^2 + Cy^2 + F = 0$

$Ax^2 + Cy^2 = -F$

If A and C are of opposite sign and $F \neq 0$, this equation may be written as $\dfrac{x^2}{\left(-\dfrac{F}{A}\right)} + \dfrac{y^2}{\left(-\dfrac{F}{C}\right)} = 1$,

where $-\dfrac{F}{A}$ and $-\dfrac{F}{C}$ are opposite in sign. This is the equation of a hyperbola with center $(0,0)$.

The transverse axis is the x-axis if $-\dfrac{F}{A} > 0$; the transverse axis is the y-axis if $-\dfrac{F}{A} < 0$.

84. $Ax^2 + Cy^2 + Dx + Ey + F = 0$,

where A and C are of opposite sign

$Ax^2 + Dx + Cy^2 + Ey = -F$

$A\left(x^2 + \dfrac{D}{A}x\right) + C\left(y^2 + \dfrac{E}{C}y\right) = -F$

$A\left(x + \dfrac{D}{2A}\right)^2 + C\left(y + \dfrac{E}{2C}\right)^2 = -F + \dfrac{D^2}{4A} + \dfrac{E^2}{4C}$

(a) If $\dfrac{D^2}{4A} + \dfrac{E^2}{4C} - F \neq 0$, this is the equation of a hyperbola with

center at $\left(-\dfrac{D}{2A}, -\dfrac{E}{2C}\right)$.

(b) If $\dfrac{D^2}{4A} + \dfrac{E^2}{4C} - F = 0$, the graph is intersecting lines through the

point $\left(-\dfrac{D}{2A}, -\dfrac{E}{2C}\right)$ with slopes $\pm\sqrt{\left|\dfrac{A}{C}\right|}$.

10.5 Assess Your Understanding (page 679)

5. $\cot(2\theta) = \dfrac{A - C}{B}$ **6.** Hyperbola **7.** Ellipse **8.** T **9.** T **10.** F **11.** Parabola **12.** Parabola **13.** Ellipse **14.** Ellipse **15.** Hyperbola

16. Hyperbola **17.** Hyperbola **18.** Hyperbola **19.** Circle **20.** Circle **21.** $x = \dfrac{\sqrt{2}}{2}(x' - y'), y = \dfrac{\sqrt{2}}{2}(x' + y')$

22. $x = \dfrac{\sqrt{2}}{2}(x' - y'), y = \dfrac{\sqrt{2}}{2}(x' + y')$ **23.** $x = \dfrac{\sqrt{2}}{2}(x' - y'), y = \dfrac{\sqrt{2}}{2}(x' + y')$ **24.** $x = \dfrac{\sqrt{2}}{2}(x' - y'), y = \dfrac{\sqrt{2}}{2}(x' + y')$

25. $x = \dfrac{1}{2}(x' - \sqrt{3}y'), y = \dfrac{1}{2}(\sqrt{3}x' + y')$ **26.** $x = \dfrac{1}{2}(\sqrt{3}x' - y'), y = \dfrac{1}{2}(x' + \sqrt{3}y')$ **27.** $x = \dfrac{\sqrt{5}}{5}(x' - 2y'), y = \dfrac{\sqrt{5}}{5}(2x' + y')$

28. $x = \dfrac{\sqrt{5}}{5}(x' - 2y'), y = \dfrac{\sqrt{5}}{5}(2x' + y')$ **29.** $x = \dfrac{\sqrt{13}}{13}(3x' - 2y'), y = \dfrac{\sqrt{13}}{13}(2x' + 3y')$ **30.** $x = \dfrac{1}{5}(4x' - 3y'), y = \dfrac{1}{5}(3x' + 4y')$

31. $\theta = 45°$ (see Problem 21)

$x'^2 - \dfrac{y'^2}{3} = 1$

Hyperbola

Center at origin

Transverse axis is the x'-axis.

Vertices at $(\pm 1, 0)$

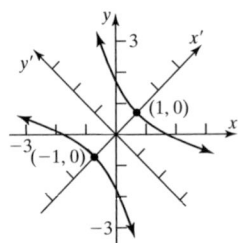

32. $\theta = 45°$ (see Problem 22)

$y'^2 - \dfrac{x'^2}{3} = 1$

Hyperbola

Center at origin

Transverse axis is the y'-axis.

Vertices at $(0, \pm 1)$

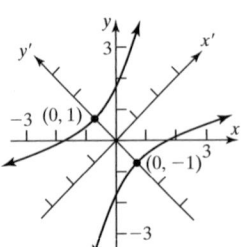

33. $\theta = 45°$ (see Problem 23)

$x'^2 + \dfrac{y'^2}{4} = 1$

Ellipse

Center at $(0, 0)$

Major axis is the y'-axis.

Vertices at $(0, \pm 2)$

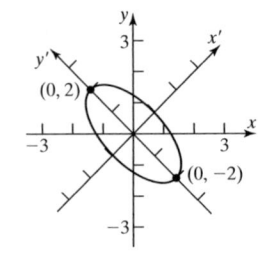

34. $\theta = 45°$ (see Problem 24)

$$\frac{y'^2}{4} - \frac{x'^2}{16} = 1$$

Hyperbola

Center at $(0, 0)$

Transverse axis is the y'-axis.

Vertices at $(0, \pm2)$

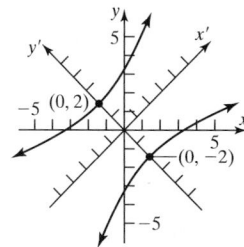

35. $\theta = 60°$ (see Problem 25)

$$\frac{x'^2}{4} + y'^2 = 1$$

Ellipse

Center at $(0, 0)$

Major axis is the x'-axis.

Vertices at $(\pm2, 0)$

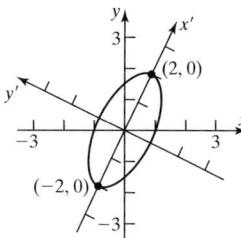

36. $\theta = 30°$ (see Problem 26)

$$4x'^2 - y'^2 = 1$$

Hyperbola

Center at $(0, 0)$

Transverse axis is the x'-axis.

Vertices at $\left(\pm\frac{1}{2}, 0\right)$

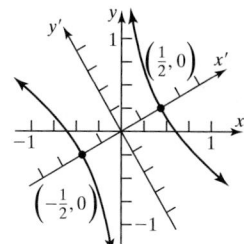

37. $\theta \approx 63°$ (see Problem 27)

$$y'^2 = 8x'$$

Parabola

Vertex at $(0, 0)$

Focus at $(2, 0)$

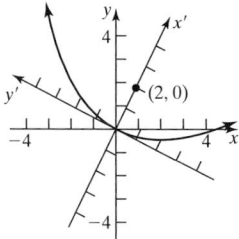

38. $\theta \approx 63°$ (see Problem 28)

$$(x' + 1)^2 = -y'$$

Parabola

Vertex at $(-1, 0)$

Focus at $\left(-1, -\frac{1}{4}\right)$

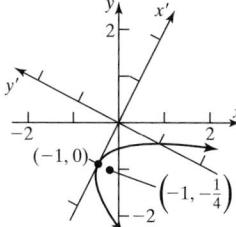

39. $\theta \approx 34°$ (see Problem 29)

$$\frac{(x' - 2)^2}{4} + y'^2 = 1$$

Ellipse

Center at $(2, 0)$

Major axis is the x'-axis.

Vertices at $(4, 0)$ and $(0, 0)$

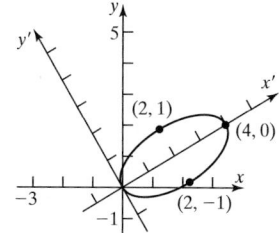

40. $\theta \approx 37°$ (see Problem 30)

$$x'^2 + 2y'^2 = 1$$

Ellipse

Center at $(0, 0)$

Major axis is the x'-axis.

Vertices at $(\pm1, 0)$

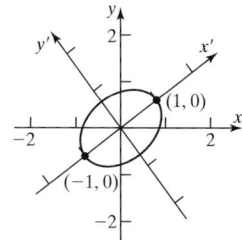

41. $\cot(2\theta) = \dfrac{7}{24}$;

$$\theta = \sin^{-1}\left(\frac{3}{5}\right) \approx 37°$$

$$(x' - 1)^2 = -6\left(y' - \frac{1}{6}\right)$$

Parabola

Vertex at $\left(1, \frac{1}{6}\right)$

Focus at $\left(1, -\frac{4}{3}\right)$

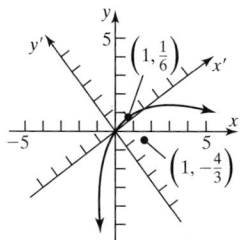

42. $\cot(2\theta) = \dfrac{7}{24}$;

$$\theta = \sin^{-1}\left(\frac{3}{5}\right) \approx 37°$$

$$x'^2 = -4y'$$

Parabola

Vertex at $(0, 0)$

Focus at $(0, -1)$

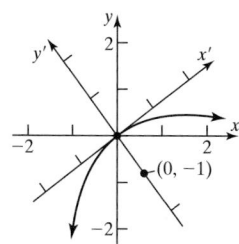

43. Hyperbola **44.** Ellipse **45.** Hyperbola **46.** Ellipse **47.** Parabola **48.** Ellipse **49.** Ellipse **50.** Parabola **51.** Ellipse **52.** Ellipse

53. Refer to equation (6): $A' = A\cos^2\theta + B\sin\theta\cos\theta + C\sin^2\theta$

$B' = B(\cos^2\theta - \sin^2\theta) + 2(C - A)(\sin\theta\cos\theta)$

$C' = A\sin^2\theta - B\sin\theta\cos\theta + C\cos^2\theta$

$D' = D\cos\theta + E\sin\theta$

$E' = -D\sin\theta + E\cos\theta$

$F' = F$

54. From equation (6), $A' + C' = (A \cos^2 \theta + B \sin \theta \cos \theta + C \sin^2 \theta) + (A \sin^2 \theta - B \sin \theta \cos \theta + C \cos^2 \theta)$
$$= A(\cos^2 \theta + \sin^2 \theta) + C(\sin^2 \theta + \cos^2 \theta)$$
$$= A + C$$

55. Use Problem 53 to find $B'^2 - 4A'C'$. After much cancellation, $B'^2 - 4A'C' = B^2 - 4AC$.

56. **(a)** $B^2 - 4AC$ is invariant under axes rotation (see Problem 55). But with an appropriate rotation, $B = 0$, so $B^2 - 4AC = 0$
only if, after rotation, $A = 0$ or $C = 0$. In either case, the equation becomes quadratic in one variable and linear in the other.
(b) After axes rotation to make $B = 0$, $B^2 - 4AC < 0$ means that A and C have the same sign.
(c) After axes rotation to make $B = 0$, $B^2 - 4AC > 0$ means that A and C have opposite signs.

57. The distance between P_1 and P_2 in the $x'y'$-plane equals $\sqrt{(x_2' - x_1')^2 + (y_2' - y_1')^2}$.
Assuming that $x' = x \cos \theta - y \sin \theta$ and $y' = x \sin \theta + y \cos \theta$, then
$$(x_2' - x_1')^2 = (x_2 \cos \theta - y_2 \sin \theta - x_1 \cos \theta + y_1 \sin \theta)^2$$
$$= \cos^2 \theta(x_2 - x_1)^2 - 2 \sin \theta \cos \theta(x_2 - x_1)(y_2 - y_1) + \sin^2 \theta(y_2 - y_1)^2, \text{ and}$$
$$(y_2' - y_1')^2 = (x_2 \sin \theta + y_2 \cos \theta - x_1 \sin \theta - y_1 \cos \theta)^2 = \sin^2 \theta(x_2 - x_1)^2 + 2 \sin \theta \cos \theta(x_2 - x_1)(y_2 - y_1) + \cos^2 \theta(y_2 - y_1)^2.$$
Therefore, $(x_2' - x_1')^2 + (y_2' - y_1')^2 = \cos^2 \theta(x_2 - x_1)^2 + \sin^2 \theta(x_2 - x_1)^2 + \sin^2 \theta(y_2 - y_1)^2 + \cos^2 \theta(y_2 - y_1)^2$
$$= (x_2 - x_1)^2(\cos^2 \theta + \sin^2 \theta) + (y_2 - y_1)^2(\sin^2 \theta + \cos^2 \theta) = (x_2 - x_1)^2 + (y_2 - y_1)^2.$$

58. With a 45° rotation, $x^{1/2} + y^{1/2} = a^{1/2}$ becomes $\left[\dfrac{\sqrt{2}}{2}(x' - y')\right]^{1/2} + \left[\dfrac{\sqrt{2}}{2}(x' + y')\right]^{1/2} = a^{1/2}$, which is equivalent to

$\sqrt{x' - y'} + \sqrt{x' + y'} = K$ with K a positive constant, which implies that $(x' - y') + 2\sqrt{(x' - y')(x' + y')} + (x' + y') = K^2$

$\Rightarrow 2\sqrt{x'^2 - y'^2} = K^2 - 2x' \Rightarrow 4x'^2 - 4y'^2 = 4x'^2 - 4K^2x' + K^4 \Rightarrow y'^2 = K^2x' - \dfrac{K^4}{4}$, which is a parabolic equation.

10.6 Assess Your Understanding *(page 685)*

3. $\dfrac{1}{2}$; ellipse; parallel; 4; below **4.** 1; <1; >1 **5.** T **6.** T **7.** Parabola; directrix is perpendicular to the polar axis 1 unit to the right of the pole.

8. Parabola; directrix is parallel to the polar axis 3 units below the pole. **9.** Hyperbola; directrix is parallel to the polar axis $\dfrac{4}{3}$ units below the pole.

10. Hyperbola; directrix is perpendicular to the polar axis 1 unit to the right of the pole. **11.** Ellipse; directrix is perpendicular to the polar axis $\dfrac{3}{2}$ units to the left of the pole. **12.** Ellipse; directrix is parallel to the polar axis 3 units above the pole.

13. Parabola; directrix is perpendicular to the polar axis 1 unit to the right of the pole; vertex is at $\left(\dfrac{1}{2}, 0\right)$.

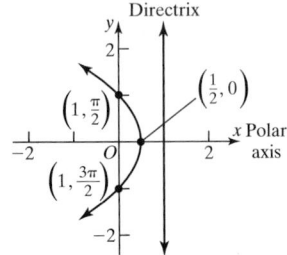

14. Parabola; directrix is parallel to the polar axis 3 units below the pole; vertex is at $\left(\dfrac{3}{2}, \dfrac{3\pi}{2}\right)$.

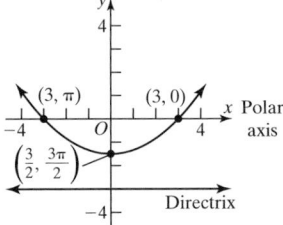

15. Ellipse; directrix is parallel to the polar axis $\dfrac{8}{3}$ units above the pole; vertices are at $\left(\dfrac{8}{7}, \dfrac{\pi}{2}\right)$ and $\left(8, \dfrac{3\pi}{2}\right)$.

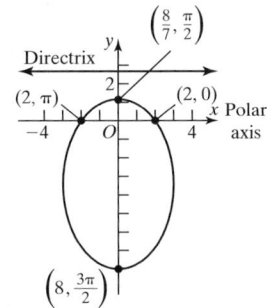

16. Ellipse; directrix is perpendicular to the polar axis $\dfrac{5}{2}$ units to the right of the pole; vertices are at $\left(\dfrac{10}{9}, 0\right)$ and $(10, \pi)$.

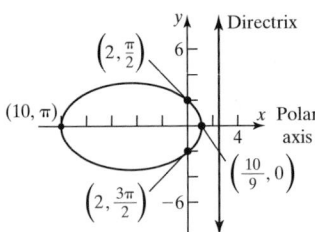

17. Hyperbola; directrix is perpendicular to the polar axis $\dfrac{3}{2}$ units to the left of the pole; vertices are at $(-3, 0)$ and $(1, \pi)$.

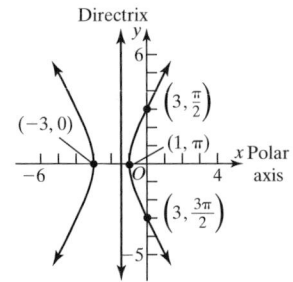

18. Hyperbola; directrix is parallel to the polar axis $\dfrac{3}{2}$ units above the pole; vertices are at $\left(-3, \dfrac{3\pi}{2}\right)$ and $\left(1, \dfrac{\pi}{2}\right)$.

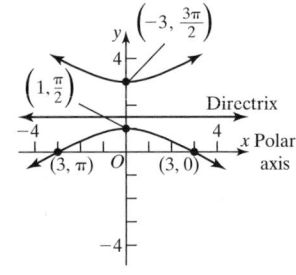

19. Ellipse; directrix is parallel to the polar axis 8 units below the pole; vertices are at $\left(8, \dfrac{\pi}{2}\right)$ and $\left(\dfrac{8}{3}, \dfrac{3\pi}{2}\right)$.

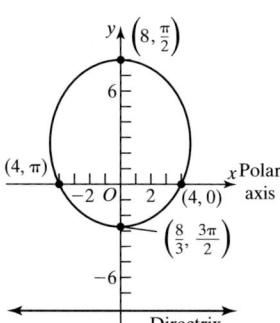

20. Hyperbola; directrix is perpendicular to the polar axis 2 units to the right of the pole; vertices are at $\left(\dfrac{4}{3}, 0\right)$ and $(-4, \pi)$.

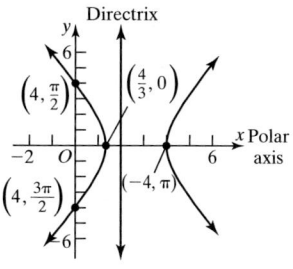

21. Ellipse; directrix is parallel to the polar axis 3 units below the pole; vertices are at $\left(6, \dfrac{\pi}{2}\right)$ and $\left(\dfrac{6}{5}, \dfrac{3\pi}{2}\right)$.

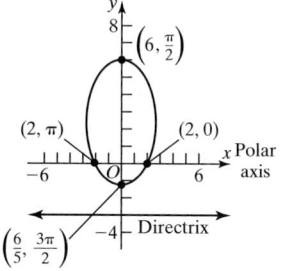

22. Ellipse; directrix is perpendicular to the polar axis 2 units to the left of the pole; vertices are at $\left(\dfrac{2}{3}, \pi\right)$ and $(2, 0)$.

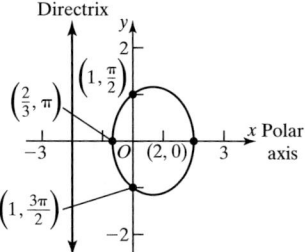

23. Ellipse; directrix is perpendicular to the polar axis 6 units to the left of the pole; vertices are at $(6, 0)$ and $(2, \pi)$.

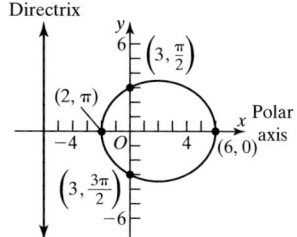

24. Parabola; directrix is parallel to the polar axis 3 units below the pole; vertex is at $\left(\dfrac{3}{2}, \dfrac{3\pi}{2}\right)$.

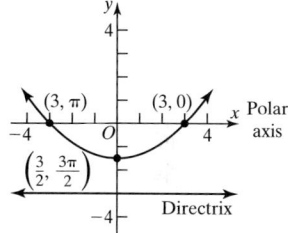

25. $y^2 + 2x - 1 = 0$ **26.** $x^2 - 6y - 9 = 0$ **27.** $16x^2 + 7y^2 + 48y - 64 = 0$ **28.** $9x^2 + 25y^2 + 80x - 100 = 0$

29. $3x^2 - y^2 + 12x + 9 = 0$ **30.** $x^2 - 3y^2 + 12y - 9 = 0$ **31.** $4x^2 + 3y^2 - 16y - 64 = 0$ **32.** $3x^2 - y^2 - 16x + 16 = 0$

33. $9x^2 + 5y^2 - 24y - 36 = 0$ **34.** $3x^2 + 4y^2 - 4x - 4 = 0$ **35.** $3x^2 + 4y^2 - 12x - 36 = 0$ **36.** $x^2 - 6y - 9 = 0$

37. $r = \dfrac{1}{1 + \sin\theta}$ **38.** $r = \dfrac{2}{1 - \sin\theta}$ **39.** $r = \dfrac{12}{5 - 4\cos\theta}$ **40.** $r = \dfrac{6}{3 + 2\sin\theta}$ **41.** $r = \dfrac{12}{1 - 6\sin\theta}$ **42.** $r = \dfrac{25}{1 + 5\cos\theta}$

43. Use $d(D, P) = p - r\cos\theta$ in the derivation of equation (a) in Table 5.

44. Use $d(D, P) = p - r\sin\theta$ in the derivation of equation (a) in Table 5.

45. Use $d(D, P) = p + r\sin\theta$ in the derivation of equation (a) in Table 5.

46. Aphelion: 4.335×10^7 mi; perihelion: 2.854×10^7 mi

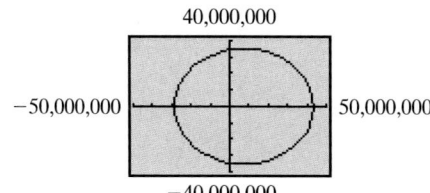

10.7 Assess Your Understanding *(page 697)*

2. plane curve; parameter   **3.** ellipse   **4.** cycloid   **5.** F   **6.** T

7.

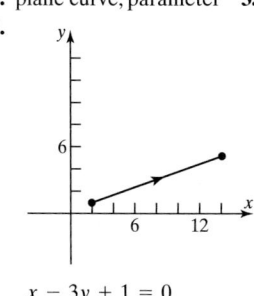

$x - 3y + 1 = 0$

8.

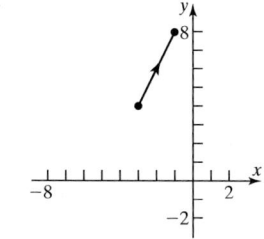

$2x - y + 10 = 0$

9.

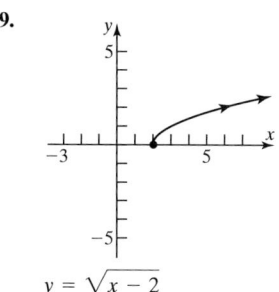

$y = \sqrt{x - 2}$

10.

$y = 4x^2$

11.

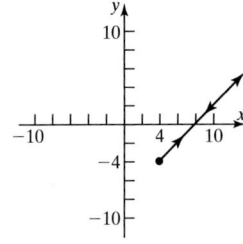

$y = x - 8$

12.

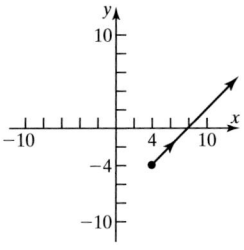

$y = x - 8$

13.

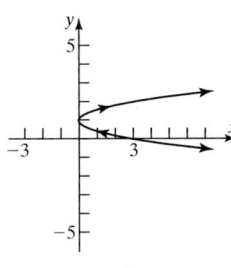

$x = 3(y - 1)^2$

14.

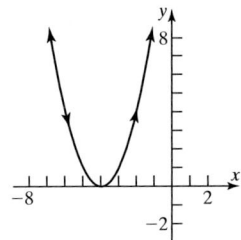

$y = (x + 4)^2$

15.

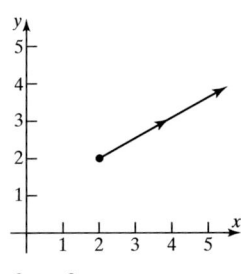

$2y = 2 + x$

16.

$y = \dfrac{1}{x}$

17.

$y = x^3$

18.

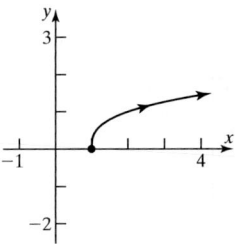

$x = y^3 + 1$

19.

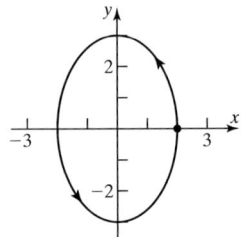

$\dfrac{x^2}{4} + \dfrac{y^2}{9} = 1$

20.

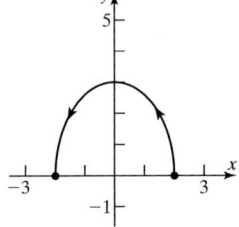

$\dfrac{x^2}{4} + \dfrac{y^2}{9} = 1$

21.

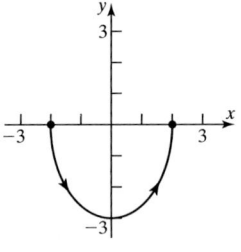

$\dfrac{x^2}{4} + \dfrac{y^2}{9} = 1$

22.

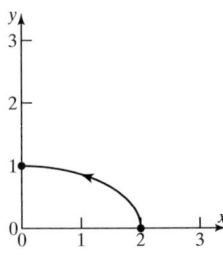

$\dfrac{x^2}{4} + y^2 = 1$

23.

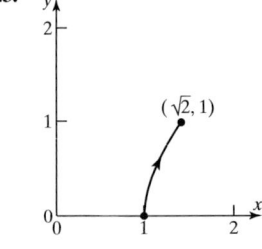

$x^2 - y^2 = 1$

24.

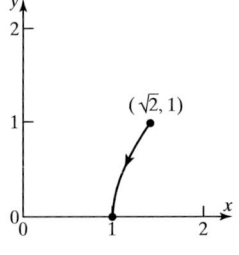

$x^2 - y^2 = 1$

25.

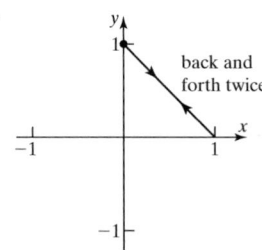

$x + y = 1$

26.

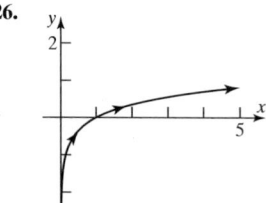

$y = \dfrac{1}{2}\ln x$

27. $x = t$ or $x = \dfrac{t + 1}{4}$

$y = 4t - 1$ $y = t$

28. $x = t$ or $x = \dfrac{3 - t}{8}$

$y = -8t + 3$ $y = t$

29. $x = t$ or $x = t^3$

$y = t^2 + 1$ $y = t^6 + 1$

30. $x = t$ or $x = t^3$

$y = -2t^2 + 1$ $y = -2t^6 + 1$

31. $x = t$ or $x = \sqrt[3]{t}$

$y = t^3$ $y = t$

32. $x = t$ or $x = t^3$

$y = t^4 + 1$ $y = t^{12} + 1$

33. $x = t$ or $x = t^3$

$y = t^{2/3}$ $y = t^2, t \geq 0$

34. $x = t$ or $x = \sqrt{t}$

$y = t^2, t \geq 0$ $y = t, t \geq 0$

35. $x = t + 2, y = t, 0 \leq t \leq 5$

36. $x = t - 1, y = -t + 2, 0 \leq t \leq 4$ **37.** $x = 3\cos t, y = 2\sin t, 0 \leq t \leq 2\pi$ **38.** $x = \cos\left(\dfrac{\pi}{2}(t - 1)\right), y = 4\sin\left(\dfrac{\pi}{2}(t - 1)\right), 0 \leq t \leq 2$

39. $x = 2\cos(\pi t), y = -3\sin(\pi t), 0 \leq t \leq 2$ **40.** $x = -2\sin(2\pi t), y = 3\cos(2\pi t), 0 \leq t \leq 1$

41. $x = 2\sin(2\pi t), y = 3\cos(2\pi t), 0 \leq t \leq 1$ **42.** $x = 2\cos\left(\dfrac{2}{3}\pi t\right), y = 3\sin\left(\dfrac{2}{3}\pi t\right), 0 \leq t \leq 3$

43.

44.

45.

46.

47.

48.

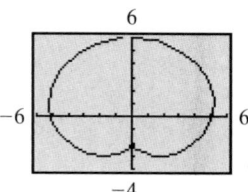

49. (a) $x = 3$

$y = -16t^2 + 50t + 6$

(b) 3.24 s

(c) 1.56 s; 45.06 ft

(d)

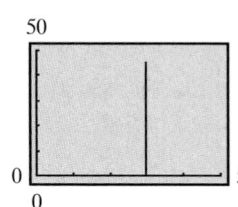

50. (a) $x = 3$

$y = -16t^2 + 40t + 5$

(b) 2.62 s

(c) 1.25 s; 30 ft

(d)

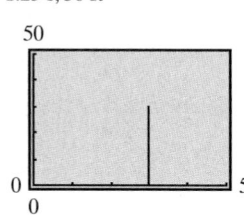

51. (a) Train: $x_1 = t^2, y_1 = 1$;

Bill: $x_2 = 5(t - 5), y_2 = 3$

(b) Bill won't catch the train.

(c)

52. (a) Bus: $x_1 = \dfrac{3}{2}t^2$ Jodi: $x_2 = 5(t-2)$

$\qquad\quad y_1 = 1 \qquad\qquad y_2 = 3$

(b) Jodi won't catch the bus.

(c)

53. (a) $x = (145\cos 20°)t$

$\qquad y = -16t^2 + (145\sin 20°)t + 5$

(b) 3.20 s **(c)** 435.61 ft

(d) 1.55 s; 43.43 ft

(e)

54. (a) $x = (125\cos 40°)t$

$\qquad y = -16t^2 + (125\sin 40°)t + 3$

(b) 5.06 s **(c)** 484.41 ft

(d) 2.51 s; 103.87 ft

(e)

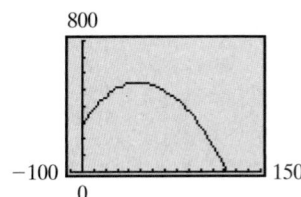

55. (a) $x = (40\cos 45°)t$

$\qquad y = -4.9t^2 + (40\sin 45°)t + 300$

(b) 11.23 s **(c)** 317.52 m

(d) 2.89 s; 340.82 m

(e)

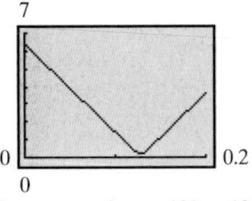

56. (a) $x = (40\cos 45°)t$

$\qquad y = -\dfrac{4.9}{6}t^2 + (40\sin 45°)t + 300$

(b) 43.15 s **(c)** 1220.35 m

(d) 17.32 s; 544.89 m

(e)

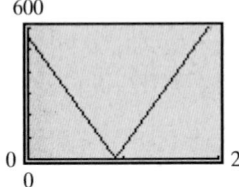

57. (a) Camry: $x = 40t - 5$, $y = 0$; Chevy Impala: $x = 0$, $y = 30t - 4$ **(d)** 0.2 mi; 7.68 min

(b) $d = \sqrt{(40t-5)^2 + (30t-4)^2}$ **(e)** Turn axes off to see the graph:

(c)

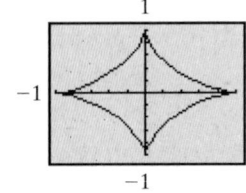

58. (a) Cessna: $x = 0$, $y = 100 - 120t$; 747: $x = 550 - 600t$, $y = 0$ **(d)** 9.81 mi; 54.81 min

(b) $d = \sqrt{(100 - 120t)^2 + (550 - 600t)^2}$ **(e)** Turn axes off to see the graph:

(c)

59. (a) $x = \dfrac{\sqrt{2}}{2}v_0 t$, $y = -16t^2 + \dfrac{\sqrt{2}}{2}v_0 t + 3$ **(b)** Maximum height is 139.1 ft. **(c)** The ball is 272.25 ft from home plate. **(d)** Yes, the ball will

clear the wall by about 99.5 ft. **60. (a)** $y = -\left(\dfrac{16}{v_0^2 \cos^2\theta}\right)x^2 + (\tan\theta)x$; parabola **(b)** $0 = (v_0\sin\theta)t - 16t^2 \Rightarrow t = 0$ or $t = \dfrac{1}{16}v_0\sin\theta$

(c) $\dfrac{1}{16}v_0^2\sin\theta\cos\theta$ **(d)** $t = 0$ or $t = \dfrac{1}{16}v_0(\sin\theta - \cos\theta)$; $x = y = \dfrac{1}{16}v_0^2\cos\theta(\sin\theta - \cos\theta)$; $\sqrt{x^2 + y^2} = \dfrac{\sqrt{2}}{16}v_0^2\cos\theta(\sin\theta - \cos\theta)$

61. The orientation is from (x_1, y_1) to (x_2, y_2). **62. (a)** **(b)** $x^{2/3} + y^{2/3} = 1$

Review Exercises *(page 701)*

1. Parabola; vertex $(0,0)$, focus $(-4,0)$, directrix $x = 4$ **2.** Parabola; vertex $(0,0)$, focus $\left(0, \dfrac{1}{64}\right)$, directrix $y = -\dfrac{1}{64}$

3. Hyperbola; center $(0,0)$, vertices $(5,0)$ and $(-5,0)$, foci $\left(\sqrt{26}, 0\right)$ and $\left(-\sqrt{26}, 0\right)$, asymptotes $y = \dfrac{1}{5}x$ and $y = -\dfrac{1}{5}x$

4. Hyperbola; center $(0,0)$, vertices $(0,5)$ and $(0,-5)$, foci $\left(0, \sqrt{26}\right)$ and $\left(0, -\sqrt{26}\right)$, asymptotes $y = 5x$ and $y = -5x$

5. Ellipse; center $(0, 0)$, vertices $(0, 5)$ and $(0, -5)$, foci $(0, 3)$ and $(0, -3)$ **6.** Ellipse; center $(0, 0)$, vertices $(0, 4)$ and $(0, -4)$, foci $\left(0, \sqrt{7}\right)$

and $\left(0, -\sqrt{7}\right)$ **7.** $x^2 = -4(y - 1)$: Parabola; vertex $(0, 1)$, focus $(0, 0)$, directrix $y = 2$ **8.** $\dfrac{y^2}{3} - \dfrac{x^2}{9} = 1$: Hyperbola; center $(0, 0)$, vertices $\left(0, \sqrt{3}\right)$

and $\left(0, -\sqrt{3}\right)$, foci $\left(0, 2\sqrt{3}\right)$ and $\left(0, -2\sqrt{3}\right)$, asymptotes $y = \dfrac{\sqrt{3}}{3}x, \; y = -\dfrac{\sqrt{3}}{3}x$ **9.** $\dfrac{x^2}{2} - \dfrac{y^2}{8} = 1$: Hyperbola; center $(0, 0)$, vertices $\left(\sqrt{2}, 0\right)$ and

$\left(-\sqrt{2}, 0\right)$, foci $\left(\sqrt{10}, 0\right)$ and $\left(-\sqrt{10}, 0\right)$, asymptotes $y = 2x$ and $y = -2x$ **10.** $\dfrac{x^2}{4} + \dfrac{y^2}{9} = 1$: Ellipse; center $(0, 0)$, vertices $(0, 3)$ and $(0, -3)$,

foci $\left(0, \sqrt{5}\right)$ and $\left(0, -\sqrt{5}\right)$ **11.** $(x - 2)^2 = 2(y + 2)$: Parabola; vertex $(2, -2)$, focus $\left(2, -\dfrac{3}{2}\right)$, directrix $y = -\dfrac{5}{2}$

12. $(y - 1)^2 = \dfrac{1}{2}x$: Parabola; vertex $(0, 1)$, focus $\left(\dfrac{1}{8}, 1\right)$, directrix $x = -\dfrac{1}{8}$

13. $\dfrac{(y - 2)^2}{4} - (x - 1)^2 = 1$: Hyperbola; center $(1, 2)$, vertices $(1, 4)$ and $(1, 0)$, foci $\left(1, 2 + \sqrt{5}\right)$ and $\left(1, 2 - \sqrt{5}\right)$, asymptotes $y - 2 = \pm 2(x - 1)$

14. $(x + 1)^2 + \dfrac{(y - 2)^2}{4} = 1$: Ellipse; center $(-1, 2)$, vertices $(-1, 0)$ and $(-1, 4)$, foci $\left(-1, 2 + \sqrt{3}\right)$ and $\left(-1, 2 - \sqrt{3}\right)$

15. $\dfrac{(x - 2)^2}{9} + \dfrac{(y - 1)^2}{4} = 1$: Ellipse; center $(2, 1)$, vertices $(5, 1)$ and $(-1, 1)$, foci $\left(2 + \sqrt{5}, 1\right)$ and $\left(2 - \sqrt{5}, 1\right)$

16. $\dfrac{(x - 2)^2}{9} + \dfrac{(y + 1)^2}{4} = 1$: Ellipse; center $(2, -1)$, vertices $(5, -1)$ and $(-1, -1)$, foci $\left(2 + \sqrt{5}, -1\right)$ and $\left(2 - \sqrt{5}, -1\right)$

17. $(x - 2)^2 = -4(y + 1)$: Parabola; vertex $(2, -1)$, focus $(2, -2)$, directrix $y = 0$ **18.** $(y - 2)^2 = -\dfrac{3}{4}(x + 1)$: Parabola; vertex $(-1, 2)$, focus

$\left(-\dfrac{19}{16}, 2\right)$, directrix $x = -\dfrac{13}{16}$ **19.** $\dfrac{(x - 1)^2}{4} + \dfrac{(y + 1)^2}{9} = 1$: Ellipse; center $(1, -1)$, vertices $(1, 2)$ and $(1, -4)$, foci $\left(1, -1 + \sqrt{5}\right)$ and

$\left(1, -1 - \sqrt{5}\right)$ **20.** $(x - 1)^2 - (y + 1)^2 = 1$: Hyperbola; center $(1, -1)$, vertices $(0, -1)$ and $(2, -1)$, foci $\left(1 + \sqrt{2}, -1\right)$ and $\left(1 - \sqrt{2}, -1\right)$,
asymptotes $y + 1 = x - 1$ and $y + 1 = -(x - 1)$

21. $y^2 = -8x$

22. $\dfrac{x^2}{16} + \dfrac{y^2}{25} = 1$

23. $\dfrac{y^2}{4} - \dfrac{x^2}{12} = 1$

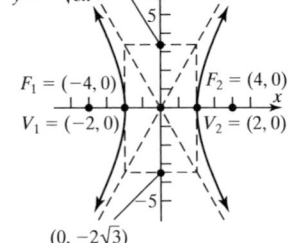

24. $x^2 = 12y$

25. $\dfrac{x^2}{16} + \dfrac{y^2}{7} = 1$

26. $\dfrac{x^2}{4} - \dfrac{y^2}{12} = 1$

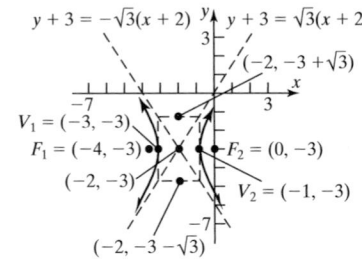

27. $(x - 2)^2 = -4(y + 3)$

28. $\dfrac{(x + 1)^2}{9} + \dfrac{(y - 2)^2}{8} = 1$

29. $(x + 2)^2 - \dfrac{(y + 3)^2}{3} = 1$

30. $(x - 3)^2 = -4(y - 7)$

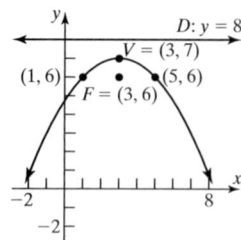

31. $\dfrac{(x + 4)^2}{16} + \dfrac{(y - 5)^2}{25} = 1$

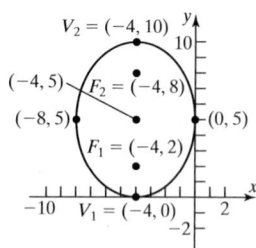

32. $\dfrac{(x - 1)^2}{16} - \dfrac{(y - 3)^2}{20} = 1$

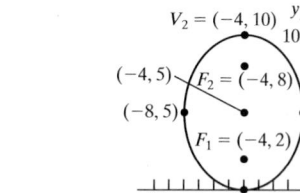

33. $\dfrac{(x + 1)^2}{9} - \dfrac{(y - 2)^2}{7} = 1$

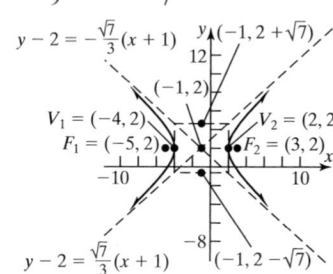

34. $(y + 2)^2 - \dfrac{(x - 4)^2}{15} = 1$

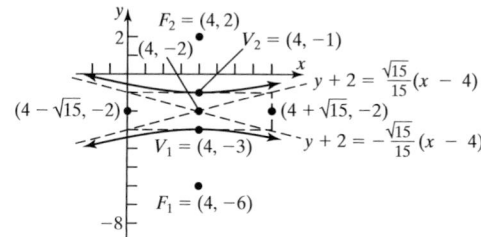

35. $\dfrac{(x - 3)^2}{9} - \dfrac{(y - 1)^2}{4} = 1$

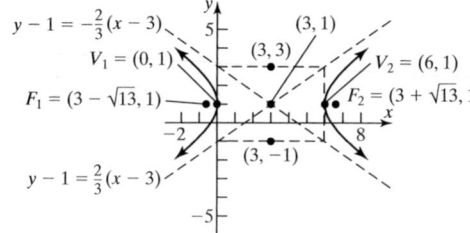

36. $\dfrac{(y - 2)^2}{4} - (x - 4)^2 = 1$

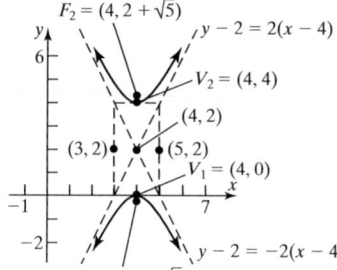

37. Parabola

38. Parabola

39. Ellipse

40. Hyperbola

41. Parabola

42. Parabola

43. Hyperbola

44. Hyperbola

45. Ellipse

46. Hyperbola

47. $x'^2 - \dfrac{y'^2}{9} = 1$

Hyperbola

Center at the origin

Transverse axis the x'-axis

Vertices at $(\pm 1, 0)$

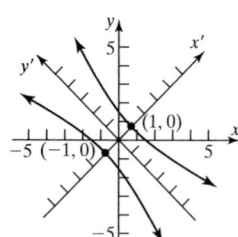

48. $y'^2 - \dfrac{x'^2}{9} = 1$

Hyperbola

Center at the origin

Transverse axis the y'-axis

Vertices at $(0, \pm 1)$

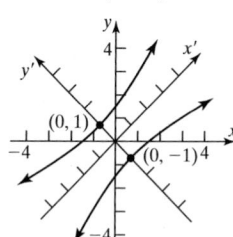

49. $\dfrac{x'^2}{2} + \dfrac{y'^2}{4} = 1$

Ellipse

Center at origin

Major axis the y'-axis

Vertices at $(0, \pm 2)$

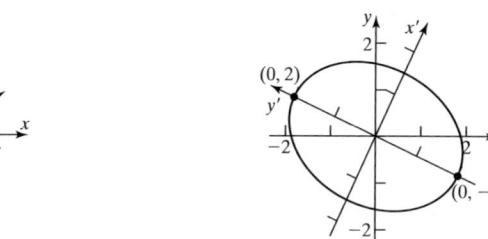

50. $x'^2 = 8y'$

Parabola

Vertex at the origin

Focus on the y'-axis at $(0, 2)$

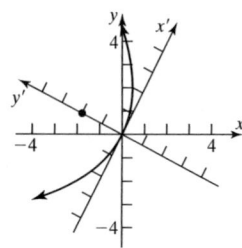

51. $y'^2 = -\dfrac{4\sqrt{13}}{13} x'$

Parabola

Vertex at the origin

Focus on the x'-axis at $\left(-\dfrac{\sqrt{13}}{13}, 0 \right)$

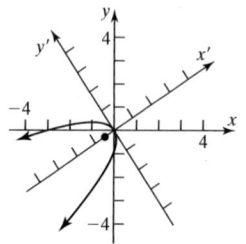

52. $y'^2 = -4x'$

Parabola

Vertex at the origin

Focus on the x'-axis at $(-1, 0)$

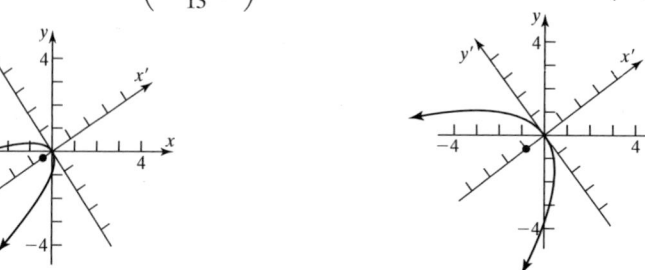

53. Parabola; directrix is perpendicular to the polar axis 4 units to the left of the pole; vertex is $(2, \pi)$.

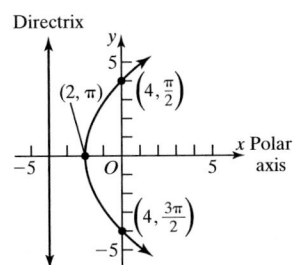

54. Parabola; directrix is parallel to the polar axis 6 units above the pole; vertex is $\left(3, \dfrac{\pi}{2}\right)$.

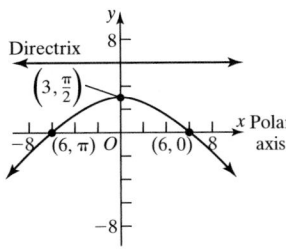

55. Ellipse; directrix is parallel to the polar axis 6 units below the pole; vertices are $\left(6, \dfrac{\pi}{2}\right)$ and $\left(2, \dfrac{3\pi}{2}\right)$.

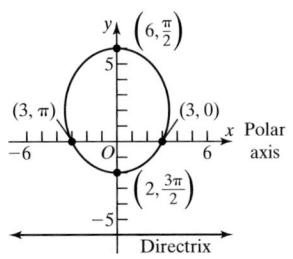

56. Ellipse; directrix is perpendicular to the polar axis 1 unit to the right of the pole; vertices are $\left(\dfrac{2}{5}, 0\right)$ and $(2, \pi)$.

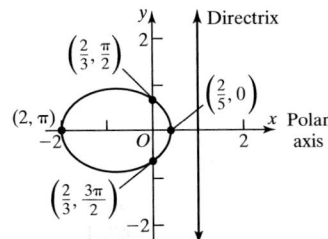

57. Hyperbola; directrix is perpendicular to the polar axis 1 unit to the right of the pole; vertices are $\left(\dfrac{2}{3}, 0\right)$ and $(-2, \pi)$.

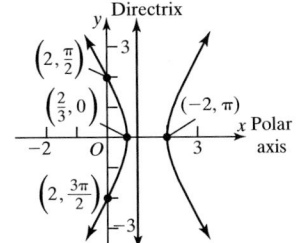

58. Hyperbola; directrix is parallel to the polar axis $\dfrac{1}{2}$ unit above the pole; vertices are $\left(-\dfrac{2}{3}, \dfrac{3\pi}{2}\right)$ and $\left(\dfrac{2}{5}, \dfrac{\pi}{2}\right)$.

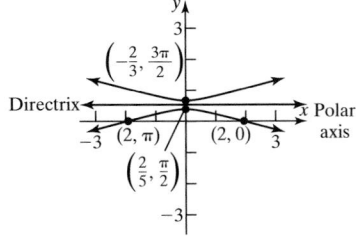

59. $y^2 - 8x - 16 = 0$ **60.** $4x^2 + 3y^2 - 12y - 36 = 0$ **61.** $3x^2 - y^2 - 8x + 4 = 0$ **62.** $5x^2 + 9y^2 + 8x - 4 = 0$

63.

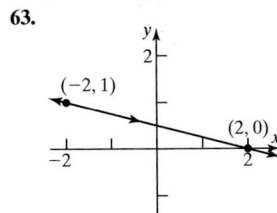

$x + 4y = 2$

64.

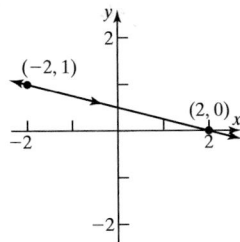

$x = 2(5 - y)^2 + 6$

65.

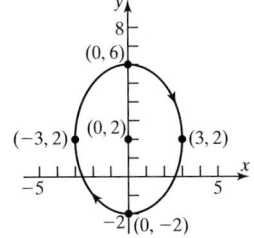

$\dfrac{x^2}{9} + \dfrac{(y - 2)^2}{16} = 1$

66.

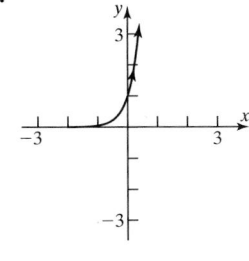

$x = \dfrac{1}{3}\ln y$

67.

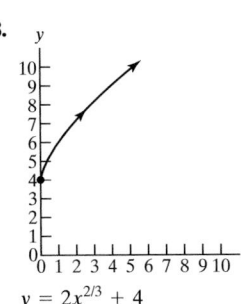

$1 + y = x$

68.

$y = 2x^{2/3} + 4$

69. $x = t, y = -2t + 4, -\infty < t < \infty$
$x = \dfrac{t - 4}{-2}, y = t, -\infty < t < \infty$

70. $x = t, y = 2t^2 - 8, -\infty < t < \infty$
$x = 2t, y = 8t^2 - 8, -\infty < t < \infty$

71. $x = 4\cos\left(\dfrac{\pi}{2}t\right), y = 3\sin\left(\dfrac{\pi}{2}t\right), 0 \le t \le 4$

72. $x = 4\sin\left(\dfrac{2\pi}{5}t\right), y = 3\cos\left(\dfrac{2\pi}{5}t\right), 0 \le t \le 5$

73. $\dfrac{x^2}{5} - \dfrac{y^2}{4} = 1$ **74.** $\dfrac{x^2}{20} + \dfrac{y^2}{4} = 1$ **75.** The ellipse $\dfrac{x^2}{16} + \dfrac{y^2}{7} = 1$ **76.** The hyperbola $\dfrac{x^2}{16} - \dfrac{y^2}{9} = 1$ **77.** $\dfrac{1}{4}$ ft or 3 in.

78. 19.44 ft, 17.78 ft, 11.11 ft **79.** 19.72 ft, 18.86 ft, 14.91 ft **80.** The foci are located 8.78 ft in from each wall. **81.** 450 ft

82. (a) Train: $x_1 = \dfrac{3}{2}t^2$ Mary: $x_2 = 6(t - 2)$
$y_1 = 1$ $y_2 = 3$
(b) Mary won't catch the train.
(c)

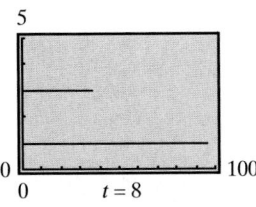

83. (a) $x = (80\cos 35°)t$
$y = -16t^2 + (80\sin 35°)t + 6$
(b) 2.9932 s **(c)** 1.4339 s; 38.9 ft
(d) 196.15 ft **(e)**

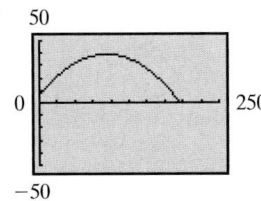

Chapter Test *(page 703)*

1. Hyperbola; center: $(-1, 0)$; vertices: $(-3, 0)$ and $(1, 0)$; foci: $\left(-1 - \sqrt{13}, 0\right)$ and $\left(-1 + \sqrt{13}, 0\right)$; asymptotes: $y = -\dfrac{3}{2}(x + 1)$ and $y = \dfrac{3}{2}(x + 1)$

2. Parabola; vertex: $\left(1, -\dfrac{1}{2}\right)$; focus: $\left(1, \dfrac{3}{2}\right)$; directrix: $y = -\dfrac{5}{2}$

3. Ellipse; center: $(-1, 1)$; foci: $\left(-1 - \sqrt{3}, 1\right)$ and $\left(-1 + \sqrt{3}, 1\right)$; vertices: $(-4, 1)$ and $(2, 1)$

4. $(x + 1)^2 = 6(y - 3)$

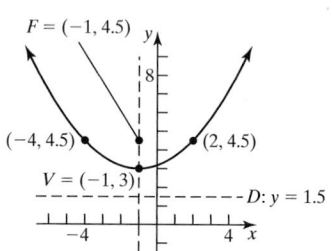

5. $\dfrac{x^2}{7} + \dfrac{y^2}{16} = 1$

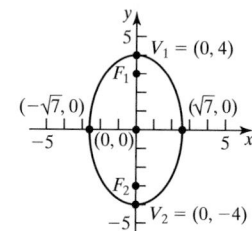

6. $\dfrac{(y - 2)^2}{4} - \dfrac{(x - 2)^2}{8} = 1$

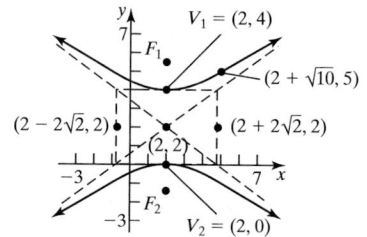

7. Hyperbola   8. Ellipse   9. Parabola

10. $x'^2 + 2y'^2 = 1$. This is the equation of an ellipse with center at $(0, 0)$ in the $x'y'$-plane. The vertices are at $(-1, 0)$ and $(1, 0)$ in the $x'y'$-plane.

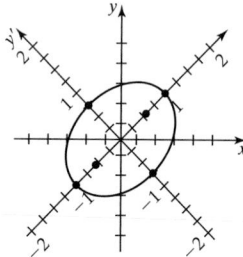

11. Hyperbola; $(x + 2)^2 - \dfrac{y^2}{3} = 1$

12. $y = 1 - \sqrt{\dfrac{x + 2}{3}}$

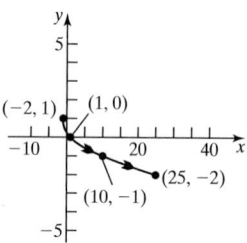

13. The microphone should be located $\dfrac{2}{3}$ ft from the base of the reflector, along its axis of symmetry.

Cumulative Review *(page 703)*

1. $-6x + 5 - 3h$ 2. $\left\{-5, -\dfrac{1}{3}, 2\right\}$ 3. $\{x \mid -3 \le x \le 2\}$ or $[-3, 2]$ 4. **(a)** Domain: $(-\infty, \infty)$; range: $(2, \infty)$

(b) $y = \log_3(x - 2)$; domain: $(2, \infty)$; range: $(-\infty, \infty)$ 5. **(a)** $\{18\}$ **(b)** $(2, 18]$ 6. **(a)** $y = 2x - 2$ **(b)** $(x - 2)^2 + y^2 = 4$ **(c)** $\dfrac{x^2}{9} + \dfrac{y^2}{4} = 1$

(d) $y = 2(x - 1)^2$ **(e)** $y^2 - \dfrac{x^2}{3} = 1$ **(f)** $y = 4^x$ 7. $\theta = \dfrac{\pi}{12} \pm \pi k$, k is any integer; $\theta = \dfrac{5\pi}{12} \pm \pi k$, k is any integer   8. $\theta = \dfrac{\pi}{6}$

9. $r = 8 \sin \theta$ 10. $\left\{x \mid x \ne \dfrac{3\pi}{4} \pm \pi k, k \text{ is an integer}\right\}$ 11. $\{22.5°\}$ 12. $y = \dfrac{x^2}{5} + 5$

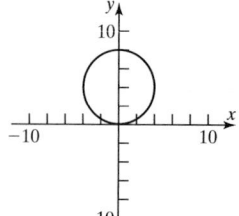

CHAPTER 11 Systems of Equations and Inequalities

11.1 Assess Your Understanding *(page 716)*

3. inconsistent **4.** consistent **5.** F **6.** T

7. $\begin{cases} 2(2) - (-1) = 5 \\ 5(2) + 2(-1) = 8 \end{cases}$ **8.** $\begin{cases} 3(-2) + 2(4) = 2 \\ (-2) - 7(4) = -30 \end{cases}$ **9.** $\begin{cases} 3(2) - 4\left(\dfrac{1}{2}\right) = 4 \\ \dfrac{1}{2}(2) - 3\left(\dfrac{1}{2}\right) = -\dfrac{1}{2} \end{cases}$ **10.** $\begin{cases} 2\left(-\dfrac{1}{2}\right) + \dfrac{1}{2}(2) = 0 \\ 3\left(-\dfrac{1}{2}\right) - 4(2) = -\dfrac{19}{2} \end{cases}$ **11.** $\begin{cases} 4 - 1 = 3 \\ \dfrac{1}{2}(4) + 1 = 3 \end{cases}$

12. $\begin{cases} (-2) - (-5) = 3 \\ -3(-2) + (-5) = 1 \end{cases}$ **13.** $\begin{cases} 3(1) + 3(-1) + 2(2) = 4 \\ 1 - (-1) - 2 = 0 \\ 2(-1) - 3(2) = -8 \end{cases}$ **14.** $\begin{cases} 4(2) - 1 = 7 \\ 8(2) + 5(-3) - 1 = 0 \\ -2 - (-3) + 5(1) = 6 \end{cases}$ **15.** $\begin{cases} 3(2) + 3(-2) + 2(2) = 4 \\ 2 - 3(-2) + 2 = 10 \\ 5(2) - 2(-2) - 3(2) = 8 \end{cases}$

16. $\begin{cases} 4(4) - 5(2) = 6 \\ 5(-3) - 2 = -17 \\ -4 - 6(-3) + 5(2) = 24 \end{cases}$ **17.** $x = 6, y = 2; (6, 2)$ **18.** $x = 1, y = -4; (1, -4)$ **19.** $x = 3, y = -6; (3, -6)$ **20.** $x = -1, y = 2; (-1, 2)$

21. $x = 8, y = -4; (8, -4)$ **22.** $x = -\dfrac{23}{4}, y = 4; \left(-\dfrac{23}{4}, 4\right)$ **23.** $x = \dfrac{1}{3}, y = -\dfrac{1}{6}; \left(\dfrac{1}{3}, -\dfrac{1}{6}\right)$ **24.** $x = -\dfrac{5}{3}, y = 1; \left(-\dfrac{5}{3}, 1\right)$ **25.** Inconsistent

26. Inconsistent **27.** $x = \dfrac{3}{2}, y = 3; \left(\dfrac{3}{2}, 3\right)$ **28.** $x = 1, y = -\dfrac{4}{3}; \left(1, -\dfrac{4}{3}\right)$

29. $\{(x, y) \mid x = 4 - 2y, y \text{ is any real number}\}$ or $\left\{(x, y) \mid y = \dfrac{4 - x}{2}, x \text{ is any real number}\right\}$

30. $\{(x, y) \mid y = 3x - 7, x \text{ is any real number}\}$ or $\left\{(x, y) \mid x = \dfrac{y + 7}{3}, y \text{ is any real number}\right\}$

31. $x = 1, y = 1; (1, 1)$ **32.** $x = \dfrac{1}{5}, y = \dfrac{3}{10}; \left(\dfrac{1}{5}, \dfrac{3}{10}\right)$ **33.** $x = \dfrac{3}{2}, y = 1; \left(\dfrac{3}{2}, 1\right)$ **34.** $x = 2, y = -3; (2, -3)$ **35.** $x = 4, y = 3; (4, 3)$

36. $x = 12, y = 6; (12, 6)$ **37.** $x = \dfrac{4}{3}, y = \dfrac{1}{5}; \left(\dfrac{4}{3}, \dfrac{1}{5}\right)$ **38.** $x = \dfrac{1}{2}, y = 2; \left(\dfrac{1}{2}, 2\right)$ **39.** $x = \dfrac{1}{5}, y = \dfrac{1}{3}; \left(\dfrac{1}{5}, \dfrac{1}{3}\right)$ **40.** $x = 4, y = 3; (4, 3)$

41. $x = 8, y = 2, z = 0; (8, 2, 0)$ **42.** $x = -3, y = 2, z = 1; (-3, 2, 1)$ **43.** $x = 2, y = -1, z = 1; (2, -1, 1)$

44. $x = \dfrac{56}{13}, y = -\dfrac{7}{13}, z = \dfrac{35}{13}; \left(\dfrac{56}{13}, -\dfrac{7}{13}, \dfrac{35}{13}\right)$ **45.** Inconsistent **46.** Inconsistent

47. $\{(x, y, z) \mid x = 5z - 2, y = 4z - 3; z \text{ is any real number}\}$ **48.** $\left\{(x, y, z) \mid x = \dfrac{4}{7}y + \dfrac{2}{7}, z = -\dfrac{13}{7}y + \dfrac{4}{7}; y \text{ is any real number}\right\}$

49. Inconsistent **50.** Inconsistent **51.** $x = 1, y = 3, z = -2; (1, 3, -2)$ **52.** $x = 1, y = 3, z = -2; (1, 3, -2)$

53. $x = -3, y = \dfrac{1}{2}, z = 1; \left(-3, \dfrac{1}{2}, 1\right)$ **54.** $x = 3, y = -\dfrac{8}{3}, z = \dfrac{1}{9}; \left(3, -\dfrac{8}{3}, \dfrac{1}{9}\right)$ **55.** Length 30 ft; width 15 ft **56.** 775 m by 725 m

57. There were 18 commercial launches and 37 noncommercial launches in 2005. **58.** 110 adults; 215 seniors **59.** 22.5 lb

60. (a) Invest $90,000 in AA bonds, $60,000 in bank certificate **(b)** Invest $130,000 in AA bonds, $20,000 in bank certificate **61.** Average wind speed 25 mph; average airspeed 175 mph **62.** 30 mph **63.** 80 $25 sets and 120 $45 sets **64.** A single hot dog: $2.75; a single soft drink: $1.50
65. $9.96 **66.** Pamela's average speed: 4 mph; the speed of the current: 1 mph **67.** Mix 50 mg of first compound with 75 mg of second.

68. First powder: 30 units; second powder: 15 units **69.** $a = \dfrac{4}{3}, b = -\dfrac{5}{3}, c = 1$ **70.** $a = 3, b = -1, c = -6$ **71.** $Y = 9000, r = 0.06$

72. $Y = 1200, r = 0.05$ **73.** $I_1 = \dfrac{10}{71}, I_2 = \dfrac{65}{71}, I_3 = \dfrac{55}{71}$ **74.** $I_1 = \dfrac{11}{13}, I_2 = \dfrac{6}{13}, I_3 = \dfrac{17}{13}$ **75.** 100 orchestra, 210 main, and 190 balcony seats

76. 110 adults; 220 children; 75 senior citizens **77.** 1.5 chicken, 1 corn, 2 milk

78. She should place $8000 in Treasury bills, $7000 in Treasury bonds, and $5000 in corporate bonds.

79. If $x =$ price of hamburgers, $y =$ price of fries, and $z =$ price of colas, then
$x = 2.75 - z, y = \dfrac{41}{60} + \dfrac{1}{3}z, \$0.60 \le z \le \$0.90$.
There is not sufficient information:

x	$2.13	$2.01	$1.86
y	$0.89	$0.93	$0.98
z	$0.62	$0.74	$0.89

80. Yes; hamburgers are $1.95, fries are $0.95, and cola is $0.80. **81.** It will take Beth 30 hr, Bill 24 hr, and Edie 40 hr.

11.2 Assess Your Understanding *(page 732)*

1. matrix **2.** augmented **3.** T **4.** T

5. $\begin{bmatrix} 1 & -5 & | & 5 \\ 4 & 3 & | & 6 \end{bmatrix}$ **6.** $\begin{bmatrix} 3 & 4 & | & 7 \\ 4 & -2 & | & 5 \end{bmatrix}$ **7.** $\begin{bmatrix} 2 & 3 & | & 6 \\ 4 & -6 & | & -2 \end{bmatrix}$ **8.** $\begin{bmatrix} 9 & -1 & | & 0 \\ 3 & -1 & | & 4 \end{bmatrix}$ **9.** $\begin{bmatrix} 0.01 & -0.03 & | & 0.06 \\ 0.13 & 0.10 & | & 0.20 \end{bmatrix}$ **10.** $\begin{bmatrix} \dfrac{4}{3} & -\dfrac{3}{2} & | & \dfrac{3}{4} \\ \dfrac{1}{4} & \dfrac{1}{3} & | & \dfrac{2}{3} \end{bmatrix}$

11. $\begin{bmatrix} 1 & -1 & 1 & | & 10 \\ 3 & 3 & 0 & | & 5 \\ 1 & 1 & 2 & | & 2 \end{bmatrix}$ **12.** $\begin{bmatrix} 5 & -1 & -1 & | & 0 \\ 1 & 1 & 0 & | & 5 \\ 2 & 0 & -3 & | & 2 \end{bmatrix}$ **13.** $\begin{bmatrix} 1 & 1 & -1 & | & 2 \\ 3 & -2 & 0 & | & 2 \\ 5 & 3 & -1 & | & 1 \end{bmatrix}$ **14.** $\begin{bmatrix} 2 & 3 & -4 & | & 0 \\ 1 & 0 & -5 & | & -2 \\ 1 & 2 & -3 & | & -2 \end{bmatrix}$ **15.** $\begin{bmatrix} 1 & -1 & -1 & | & 10 \\ 2 & 1 & 2 & | & -1 \\ -3 & 4 & 0 & | & 5 \\ 4 & -5 & 1 & | & 0 \end{bmatrix}$

16. $\begin{bmatrix} 1 & -1 & 2 & -1 & | & 5 \\ 1 & 3 & -4 & 2 & | & 2 \\ 3 & -1 & -5 & -1 & | & -1 \end{bmatrix}$ **17.** $\begin{cases} x - 3y = -2 & (1) \\ 2x - 5y = 5 & (2) \end{cases}$ $\begin{bmatrix} 1 & -3 & | & -2 \\ 0 & 1 & | & 9 \end{bmatrix}$ **18.** $\begin{cases} x - 3y = -3 & (1) \\ 2x - 5y = -4 & (2) \end{cases}$ $\begin{bmatrix} 1 & -3 & | & -3 \\ 0 & 1 & | & 2 \end{bmatrix}$

19. $\begin{cases} x - 3y + 4z = 3 & (1) \\ 3x - 5y + 6z = 6 & (2) \\ -5x + 3y + 4z = 6 & (3) \end{cases}$ **(a)** $\begin{bmatrix} 1 & -3 & 4 & | & 3 \\ 0 & 4 & -6 & | & -3 \\ -5 & 3 & 4 & | & 6 \end{bmatrix}$ **(b)** $\begin{bmatrix} 1 & -3 & 4 & | & 3 \\ 3 & -5 & 6 & | & 6 \\ 0 & -12 & 24 & | & 21 \end{bmatrix}$

20. $\begin{cases} x - 3y + 3z = -5 & (1) \\ -4x - 5y - 3z = -5 & (2) \\ -3x - 2y + 4z = 6 & (3) \end{cases}$ **(a)** $\begin{bmatrix} 1 & -3 & 3 & | & -5 \\ 0 & -17 & 9 & | & -25 \\ -3 & -2 & 4 & | & 6 \end{bmatrix}$ **(b)** $\begin{bmatrix} 1 & -3 & 3 & | & -5 \\ -4 & -5 & -3 & | & -5 \\ 0 & -11 & 13 & | & -9 \end{bmatrix}$

21. $\begin{cases} x - 3y + 2z = -6 & (1) \\ 2x - 5y + 3z = -4 & (2) \\ -3x - 6y + 4z = 6 & (3) \end{cases}$ **(a)** $\begin{bmatrix} 1 & -3 & 2 & | & -6 \\ 0 & 1 & -1 & | & 8 \\ -3 & -6 & 4 & | & 6 \end{bmatrix}$ **(b)** $\begin{bmatrix} 1 & -3 & 2 & | & -6 \\ 2 & -5 & 3 & | & -4 \\ 0 & -15 & 10 & | & -12 \end{bmatrix}$

22. $\begin{cases} x - 3y - 4z = -6 & (1) \\ 6x - 5y + 6z = -6 & (2) \\ -x + y + 4z = 6 & (3) \end{cases}$ **(a)** $\begin{bmatrix} 1 & -3 & -4 & | & -6 \\ 0 & 13 & 30 & | & 30 \\ -1 & 1 & 4 & | & 6 \end{bmatrix}$ **(b)** $\begin{bmatrix} 1 & -3 & -4 & | & -6 \\ 6 & -5 & 6 & | & -6 \\ 0 & -2 & 0 & | & 0 \end{bmatrix}$

23. $\begin{cases} 5x - 3y + z = -2 & (1) \\ 2x - 5y + 6z = -2 & (2) \\ -4x + y + 4z = 6 & (3) \end{cases}$ **(a)** $\begin{bmatrix} 1 & 7 & -11 & | & 2 \\ 2 & -5 & 6 & | & -2 \\ -4 & 1 & 4 & | & 6 \end{bmatrix}$ **(b)** $\begin{bmatrix} 1 & -2 & 5 & | & 4 \\ 2 & -5 & 6 & | & -2 \\ -4 & 1 & 4 & | & 6 \end{bmatrix}$

24. $\begin{cases} 4x - 3y - z = 2 & (1) \\ 3x - 5y + 2z = 6 & (2) \\ -3x - 6y + 4z = 6 & (3) \end{cases}$ **(a)** $\begin{bmatrix} 1 & 2 & -3 & | & -4 \\ 3 & -5 & 2 & | & 6 \\ -3 & -6 & 4 & | & 6 \end{bmatrix}$ **(b)** $\begin{bmatrix} 1 & -9 & 3 & | & 8 \\ 3 & -5 & 2 & | & 6 \\ -3 & -6 & 4 & | & 6 \end{bmatrix}$

25. $\begin{cases} x = 5 \\ y = -1 \end{cases}$ **26.** $\begin{cases} x = -4 \\ y = 0 \end{cases}$ **27.** $\begin{cases} x = 1 \\ y = 2 \\ 0 = 3 \end{cases}$ **28.** $\begin{cases} x = 0 \\ y = 0 \\ 0 = 2 \end{cases}$

Consistent; $x = 5$, $y = -1$ or $(5, -1)$ Consistent; $x = -4$, $y = 0$ or $(-4, 0)$ Inconsistent   Inconsistent

29. $\begin{cases} x + 2z = -1 \\ y - 4z = -2 \\ 0 = 0 \end{cases}$ **30.** $\begin{cases} x + 4z = 4 \\ y + 3z = 2 \\ 0 = 0 \end{cases}$ **31.** $\begin{cases} x_1 = 1 \\ x_2 + x_4 = 2 \\ x_3 + 2x_4 = 3 \end{cases}$ **32.** $\begin{cases} x_1 = 1 \\ x_2 + 2x_4 = 2 \\ x_3 + 3x_4 = 0 \end{cases}$

Consistent: Consistent: Consistent: Consistent:

$\begin{cases} x = -1 - 2z \\ y = -2 + 4z \\ z \text{ is any real number} \end{cases}$ or $\begin{cases} x = 4 - 4z \\ y = 2 - 3z \\ z \text{ is any real number} \end{cases}$ or $\begin{cases} x_1 = 1, x_2 = 2 - x_4 \\ x_3 = 3 - 2x_4 \\ x_4 \text{ is any real number} \end{cases}$ or $\begin{cases} x_1 = 1, x_2 = 2 - 2x_4 \\ x_3 = -3x_4 \\ x_4 \text{ is any real number} \end{cases}$ or

$\{(x, y, z) \mid x = -1 - 2z,$ $y = -2 + 4z, z \text{ is any real}$ number$\}$ $\{(x, y, z) \mid x = 4 - 4z, y = 2 - 3z,$ $z \text{ is any real number}\}$ $\{(x_1, x_2, x_3, x_4) \mid x_1 = 1,$ $x_2 = 2 - x_4, x_3 = 3 - 2x_4,$ $x_4 \text{ is any real number}\}$ $\{(x_1, x_2, x_3, x_4) \mid x_1 = 1,$ $x_2 = 2 - 2x_4, x_3 = -3x_4,$ $x_4 \text{ is any real number}\}$

33. $\begin{cases} x_1 + 4x_4 = 2 \\ x_2 + x_3 + 3x_4 = 3 \\ 0 = 0 \end{cases}$ **34.** $\begin{cases} x_1 = 1 \\ x_2 = 2 \\ x_3 + 2x_4 = 3 \end{cases}$ **35.** $\begin{cases} x_1 + x_4 = -2 \\ x_2 + 2x_4 = 2 \\ x_3 - x_4 = 0 \\ 0 = 0 \end{cases}$ **36.** $\begin{cases} x_1 = 1 \\ x_2 = 2 \\ x_3 = 3 \\ x_4 = 0 \end{cases}$

Consistent: Consistent: Consistent: Consistent:

$\begin{cases} x_1 = 2 - 4x_4 \\ x_2 = 3 - x_3 - 3x_4 \\ x_3, x_4 \text{ are any real numbers} \end{cases}$ or $\begin{cases} x_1 = 1 \\ x_2 = 2 \\ x_3 = 3 - 2x_4 \\ x_4 \text{ is any real number} \end{cases}$ or $\begin{cases} x_1 = -2 - x_4 \\ x_2 = 2 - 2x_4 \\ x_3 = x_4 \\ x_4 \text{ is any real number} \end{cases}$ or $\begin{cases} x_1 = 1 \\ x_2 = 2 \\ x_3 = 3 \\ x_4 = 0 \end{cases}$

$\{(x_1, x_2, x_3, x_4) \mid x_1 = 2 - 4x_4,$ $x_2 = 3 - x_3 - 3x_4, x_3, x_4 \text{ are}$ any real numbers$\}$ $\{(x_1, x_2, x_3, x_4) \mid x_1 = 1, x_2 = 2,$ $x_3 = 3 - 2x_4, x_4 \text{ is any real}$ number$\}$ $\{(x_1, x_2, x_3, x_4) \mid x_1 = -2 - x_4,$ $x_2 = 2 - 2x_4, x_3 = x_4, x_4 \text{ is any}$ real number$\}$ or $(1, 2, 3, 0)$

37. $x = 6$, $y = 2$; $(6, 2)$ **38.** $x = 1$, $y = 2$; $(1, 2)$ **39.** $x = \dfrac{1}{2}$, $y = \dfrac{3}{4}$; $\left(\dfrac{1}{2}, \dfrac{3}{4}\right)$ **40.** $x = \dfrac{1}{3}$, $y = \dfrac{2}{3}$; $\left(\dfrac{1}{3}, \dfrac{2}{3}\right)$ **41.** $x = 4 - 2y$, y is any real number;

$\{(x, y) \mid x = 4 - 2y, y \text{ is any real number}\}$ **42.** $y = 3x - 7$, x is any real number; $\{(x, y) \mid y = 3x - 7, x \text{ is any real number}\}$

43. $x = \dfrac{3}{2}$, $y = 1$; $\left(\dfrac{3}{2}, 1\right)$ **44.** $x = 2$, $y = -3$; $(2, -3)$ **45.** $x = \dfrac{4}{3}$, $y = \dfrac{1}{5}$; $\left(\dfrac{4}{3}, \dfrac{1}{5}\right)$ **46.** $x = \dfrac{1}{2}$, $y = 2$; $\left(\dfrac{1}{2}, 2\right)$ **47.** $x = 8$, $y = 2$, $z = 0$; $(8, 2, 0)$

48. $x = -3, y = 2, z = 1; (-3, 2, 1)$ **49.** $x = 2, y = -1, z = 1; (2, -1, 1)$ **50.** $x = \dfrac{56}{13}, y = -\dfrac{7}{13}, z = \dfrac{35}{13}; \left(\dfrac{56}{13}, -\dfrac{7}{13}, \dfrac{35}{13}\right)$ **51.** Inconsistent

52. Inconsistent **53.** $x = 5z - 2, y = 4z - 3$, where z is any real number; $\{(x, y, z) \mid x = 5z - 2, y = 4x - 3, z \text{ is any real number}\}$

54. $x = -\dfrac{4}{13}z + \dfrac{6}{13}, y = -\dfrac{7}{13}z + \dfrac{4}{13}$, where z is any real number; $\left\{(x, y, z) \mid x = -\dfrac{4}{13}z + \dfrac{6}{13}, y = -\dfrac{7}{13}z + \dfrac{4}{13}, z \text{ is any real number}\right\}$

55. Inconsistent **56.** Inconsistent **57.** $x = 1, y = 3, z = -2; (1, 3, -2)$ **58.** $x = 1, y = 3, z = -2; (1, 3, -2)$

59. $x = -3, y = \dfrac{1}{2}, z = 1; \left(-3, \dfrac{1}{2}, 1\right)$ **60.** $x = 3, y = -\dfrac{8}{3}, z = \dfrac{1}{9}; \left(3, -\dfrac{8}{3}, \dfrac{1}{9}\right)$ **61.** $x = \dfrac{1}{3}, y = \dfrac{2}{3}, z = 1; \left(\dfrac{1}{3}, \dfrac{2}{3}, 1\right)$

62. $x = \dfrac{1}{3}, y = \dfrac{2}{3}, z = 1; \left(\dfrac{1}{3}, \dfrac{2}{3}, 1\right)$ **63.** $x = 1, y = 2, z = 0, w = 1; (1, 2, 0, 1)$ **64.** $x = 2, y = 1, z = 0, w = 1; (2, 1, 0, 1)$

65. $y = 0, z = 1 - x, x$ is any real number; $\{(x, y, z) \mid y = 0, z = 1 - x, x \text{ is any real number}\}$ **66.** Inconsistent **67.** $x = 2, y = z - 3, z$ is any

real number; $\{(x, y, z) \mid x = 2, y = z - 3, z \text{ is any real number}\}$ **68.** $x = 1 + \dfrac{4}{3}z, y = 2 - \dfrac{5}{3}z$, where z is any real number;

$\left\{(x, y, z) \mid x = 1 + \dfrac{4}{3}z, y = 2 - \dfrac{5}{3}z, z \text{ is any real number}\right\}$ **69.** $x = \dfrac{13}{9}, y = \dfrac{7}{18}, z = \dfrac{19}{18}; \left(\dfrac{13}{9}, \dfrac{7}{18}, \dfrac{19}{18}\right)$ **70.** Inconsistent

71. $x = \dfrac{7}{5} - \dfrac{3}{5}z - \dfrac{2}{5}w, y = -\dfrac{8}{5} + \dfrac{7}{5}z + \dfrac{13}{5}w$, where z and w are any real numbers; $\left\{(x, y, z, w) \mid x = \dfrac{7}{5} - \dfrac{3}{5}z - \dfrac{2}{5}w, y = -\dfrac{8}{5} + \dfrac{7}{5}z + \dfrac{13}{5}w,\right.$

z and w are any real numbers $\Big\}$ **72.** $x = -3 - w, y = -7 - 4w, z = 4 - w$, where w is any real number; $\{(x, y, z, w) \mid x = -3 - w,$

$y = -7 - 4w, z = 4 - w, w \text{ is any real number}\}$ **73.** $y = -2x^2 + x + 3$ **74.** $y = x^2 - 4x + 2$ **75.** $f(x) = 3x^3 - 4x^2 + 5$

76. $f(x) = x^3 - 2x^2 + 6$ **77.** 1.5 salmon steak, 2 baked eggs, 1 acorn squash **78.** 1 serving of pork chop, 2 servings of corn on the cob, 2 servings of
2% milk **79.** \$4000 in Treasury bills, \$4000 in Treasury bonds, \$2000 in corporate bonds **80.** A tree costs \$19.95; labor costs \$13.75 an hour; delivery
costs \$250 per job. **81.** 8 Deltas, 5 Betas, 10 Sigmas **82.** 6 cases of orange juice, 20 cases of grapefruit juice, 12 cases of tomato juice

83. $I_1 = \dfrac{44}{23}, I_2 = 2, I_3 = \dfrac{16}{23}, I_4 = \dfrac{28}{23}$ **84.** $I_1 = 3.5, I_2 = 2.5, I_3 = 1$

85. (a)

Amount Invested At		
7%	**9%**	**11%**
0	10,000	10,000
1000	8000	11,000
2000	6000	12,000
3000	4000	13,000
4000	2000	14,000
5000	0	15,000

(b)

Amount Invested At		
7%	**9%**	**11%**
12,500	12,500	0
14,500	8500	2000
16,500	4500	4000
18,750	0	6250

(c) All the money invested at 7% provides \$2100, more than what is required.

86. (a) Investing all the money at 7% yields more than \$1500. **(b)**

7%	**9%**	**11%**
12,500	12,500	0
15,500	6500	3000
18,750	0	6250

(c)

7%	**9%**	**11%**
0	12,500	12,500
1000	10,500	13,500
6250	0	18,750

87.

First Supplement	Second Supplement	Third Supplement
50 mg	75 mg	0 mg
36 mg	76 mg	8 mg
22 mg	77 mg	16 mg
8 mg	78 mg	24 mg

88.

First Powder	Second Powder	Third Powder
30 units	15 units	0 units
20 units	14 units	8 units
10 units	13 units	16 units
0 units	12 units	24 units

11.3 Assess Your Understanding (page 743)

1. determinants **2.** $ad - bc$ **3.** F **4.** F **5.** 2 **6.** 7 **7.** 22 **8.** 28 **9.** -2 **10.** -2 **11.** 10 **12.** -169 **13.** -26 **14.** -119

15. $x = 6, y = 2; (6, 2)$ **16.** $x = \dfrac{11}{3}, y = \dfrac{2}{3}; \left(\dfrac{11}{3}, \dfrac{2}{3}\right)$ **17.** $x = 3, y = 2; (3, 2)$ **18.** $x = -1, y = 2; (-1, 2)$ **19.** $x = 8, y = -4; (8, -4)$

20. $x = -\dfrac{13}{4}, y = 2; \left(-\dfrac{13}{4}, 2\right)$ **21.** $x = 4, y = -2; (4, -2)$ **22.** $x = 2, y = 3; (2, 3)$ **23.** Not applicable **24.** Not applicable

25. $x = \dfrac{1}{2}, y = \dfrac{3}{4}; \left(\dfrac{1}{2}, \dfrac{3}{4}\right)$ **26.** $x = \dfrac{1}{3}, y = \dfrac{2}{3}; \left(\dfrac{1}{3}, \dfrac{2}{3}\right)$ **27.** $x = \dfrac{1}{10}, y = \dfrac{2}{5}; \left(\dfrac{1}{10}, \dfrac{2}{5}\right)$ **28.** $x = \dfrac{1}{5}, y = \dfrac{3}{10}; \left(\dfrac{1}{5}, \dfrac{3}{10}\right)$ **29.** $x = \dfrac{3}{2}, y = 1; \left(\dfrac{3}{2}, 1\right)$

30. $x = 2, y = -3; (2, -3)$ **31.** $x = \dfrac{4}{3}, y = \dfrac{1}{5}; \left(\dfrac{4}{3}, \dfrac{1}{5}\right)$ **32.** $x = \dfrac{1}{2}, y = 2; \left(\dfrac{1}{2}, 2\right)$ **33.** $x = 1, y = 3, z = -2; (1, 3, -2)$

34. $x = 1, y = 3, z = -2; (1, 3, -2)$ **35.** $x = -3, y = \dfrac{1}{2}, z = 1; \left(-3, \dfrac{1}{2}, 1\right)$ **36.** $x = 3, y = -\dfrac{8}{3}, z = \dfrac{1}{9}; \left(3, -\dfrac{8}{3}, \dfrac{1}{9}\right)$ **37.** Not applicable

38. Not applicable **39.** $x = 0, y = 0, z = 0; (0,0,0)$ **40.** $x = 0, y = 0, z = 0; (0, 0, 0)$ **41.** Not applicable **42.** Not applicable

43. -4 **44.** 8 **45.** 12 **46.** 4 **47.** 8 **48.** 4 **49.** 8 **50.** 12 **51.** -5 **52.** 1 or -1 **53.** $\dfrac{13}{11}$ **54.** $-\dfrac{7}{6}$ **55.** 0 or -9 **56.** 0 or $-\dfrac{1}{2}$

57.
$$(y_1 - y_2)x - (x_1 - x_2)y + (x_1 y_2 - x_2 y_1) = 0$$
$$(y_1 - y_2)x + (x_2 - x_1)y = x_2 y_1 - x_1 y_2$$
$$(x_2 - x_1)y - (x_2 - x_1)y_1 = (y_2 - y_1)x + x_2 y_1 - x_1 y_2 - (x_2 - x_1)y_1$$
$$(x_2 - x_1)(y - y_1) = (y_2 - y_1)x - (y_2 - y_1)x_1$$
$$y - y_1 = \frac{y_2 - y_1}{x_2 - x_1}(x - x_1)$$

58. From Problem 57 and substitution, we have $y_1 - y_2 = \dfrac{y_3 - y_2}{x_3 - x_2}(x_1 - x_2)$. The line containing (x_2, y_2) and (x_3, y_3) has the form
$y - y_2 = \dfrac{y_3 - y_2}{x_3 - x_2}(x - x_2)$. Any other point on this line can be substituted for (x, y) to get a true statement, and any point that
makes this a true statement is on the line. **59.** The triangle has an area of 5 square units.

60.
$$\begin{vmatrix} x^2 & x & 1 \\ y^2 & y & 1 \\ z^2 & z & 1 \end{vmatrix} = x^2 \begin{vmatrix} y & 1 \\ z & 1 \end{vmatrix} - x \begin{vmatrix} y^2 & 1 \\ z^2 & 1 \end{vmatrix} + \begin{vmatrix} y^2 & y \\ z^2 & z \end{vmatrix}$$
$$= x^2(y - z) - x(y^2 - z^2) + yz(y - z) = (y - z)[x^2 - x(y + z) + yz]$$
$$= (y - z)[(x^2 - xy) - (xz - yz)] = (y - z)[x(x - y) - z(x - y)]$$
$$= (y - z)(x - y)(x - z)$$

61. If $a = 0$, we have
$$by = s$$
$$cx + dy = t$$
Thus, $y = \dfrac{s}{b}$ and
$$x = \frac{t - dy}{c} = \frac{tb - ds}{bc}$$
Using Cramer's Rule, we get
$$x = \frac{sd - tb}{-bc} = \frac{tb - sd}{bc}$$
$$y = \frac{-sc}{-bc} = \frac{s}{b}$$

If $b = 0$, we have
$$ax = s$$
$$cx + dy = t$$
Since $D = ad \neq 0$, then
$a \neq 0$ and $d \neq 0$.
Thus, $x = \dfrac{s}{a}$ and
$$y = \frac{t - cx}{d} = \frac{ta - cs}{ad}$$
Using Cramer's Rule, we get
$$x = \frac{sd}{ad} = \frac{s}{a}$$
$$y = \frac{ta - cs}{ad}$$

If $c = 0$, we have
$$ax + by = s$$
$$dy = t$$
Since $D = ad \neq 0$, then
$a \neq 0$ and $d \neq 0$.
Thus, $y = \dfrac{t}{d}$ and
$$x = \frac{s - by}{a} = \frac{sd - bt}{ad}$$
Using Cramer's Rule, we get
$$x = \frac{sd - bt}{ad}$$
$$y = \frac{at}{ad} = \frac{t}{d}$$

If $d = 0$, we have
$$ax + by = s$$
$$cx = t$$
Since $D = -bc \neq 0$, then
$b \neq 0$ and $c \neq 0$.
Thus, $x = \dfrac{t}{c}$ and
$$y = \frac{s - ax}{b} = \frac{sc - at}{bc}$$
Using Cramer's Rule, we get
$$x = \frac{-tb}{-bc} = \frac{t}{c}$$
$$y = \frac{at - sc}{-bc} = \frac{sc - at}{bc}$$

62.
$$\begin{vmatrix} a_{13} & a_{12} & a_{11} \\ a_{23} & a_{22} & a_{21} \\ a_{33} & a_{32} & a_{31} \end{vmatrix} = a_{13}(a_{22}a_{31} - a_{32}a_{21}) - a_{12}(a_{23}a_{31} - a_{33}a_{21}) + a_{11}(a_{23}a_{32} - a_{33}a_{22})$$
$$= -[a_{11}(a_{22}a_{33} - a_{32}a_{23}) - a_{12}(a_{21}a_{33} - a_{31}a_{23}) + a_{13}(a_{21}a_{32} - a_{31}a_{22})] = - \begin{vmatrix} a_{11} & a_{12} & a_{13} \\ a_{21} & a_{22} & a_{23} \\ a_{31} & a_{32} & a_{33} \end{vmatrix}$$

63.
$$\begin{vmatrix} a_{11} & a_{12} & a_{13} \\ ka_{21} & ka_{22} & ka_{23} \\ a_{31} & a_{32} & a_{33} \end{vmatrix} = -ka_{21}(a_{12}a_{33} - a_{32}a_{13}) + ka_{22}(a_{11}a_{33} - a_{31}a_{13}) - ka_{23}(a_{11}a_{32} - a_{31}a_{12})$$
$$= k[-a_{21}(a_{12}a_{33} - a_{32}a_{13}) + a_{22}(a_{11}a_{33} - a_{31}a_{13}) - a_{23}(a_{11}a_{32} - a_{31}a_{12})] = k \begin{vmatrix} a_{11} & a_{12} & a_{13} \\ a_{21} & a_{22} & a_{23} \\ a_{31} & a_{32} & a_{33} \end{vmatrix}$$

64.
$$\begin{vmatrix} a_{11} & a_{12} & a_{11} \\ a_{21} & a_{22} & a_{21} \\ a_{31} & a_{32} & a_{31} \end{vmatrix} = a_{11}(a_{22}a_{31} - a_{32}a_{21}) - a_{12}(a_{21}a_{31} - a_{31}a_{21}) + a_{11}(a_{21}a_{32} - a_{31}a_{22})$$
$$= a_{11}a_{22}a_{31} - a_{11}a_{32}a_{21} - a_{12}(0) + a_{11}a_{21}a_{32} - a_{11}a_{31}a_{22} = 0$$

65.
$$\begin{vmatrix} a_{11} + ka_{21} & a_{12} + ka_{22} & a_{13} + ka_{23} \\ a_{21} & a_{22} & a_{23} \\ a_{31} & a_{32} & a_{33} \end{vmatrix} = (a_{11} + ka_{21})(a_{22}a_{33} - a_{32}a_{23}) - (a_{12} + ka_{22})(a_{21}a_{33} - a_{31}a_{23}) + (a_{13} + ka_{23})(a_{21}a_{32} - a_{31}a_{22})$$
$$= a_{11}a_{22}a_{33} - a_{11}a_{32}a_{23} + \overline{ka_{21}a_{22}a_{33}} - \overline{ka_{21}a_{32}a_{23}} - a_{12}a_{21}a_{33} + a_{12}a_{31}a_{23}$$
$$- \overline{ka_{22}a_{21}a_{33}} + \overline{ka_{22}a_{31}a_{23}} + a_{13}a_{21}a_{32} - a_{13}a_{31}a_{22} + \overline{ka_{23}a_{21}a_{32}} - \overline{ka_{23}a_{31}a_{22}}$$
$$= a_{11}a_{22}a_{33} - a_{11}a_{32}a_{23} - a_{12}a_{21}a_{33} + a_{12}a_{31}a_{23} + a_{13}a_{21}a_{32} - a_{13}a_{31}a_{22}$$
$$= a_{11}(a_{22}a_{33} - a_{32}a_{23}) - a_{12}(a_{21}a_{33} - a_{31}a_{23}) + a_{13}(a_{21}a_{32} - a_{31}a_{22})$$
$$= \begin{vmatrix} a_{11} & a_{12} & a_{13} \\ a_{21} & a_{22} & a_{23} \\ a_{31} & a_{32} & a_{33} \end{vmatrix}$$

Historical Problems *(page 759)*

1. (a) $2 - 5i \longleftrightarrow \begin{bmatrix} 2 & -5 \\ 5 & 2 \end{bmatrix}$, $1 + 3i \longleftrightarrow \begin{bmatrix} 1 & 3 \\ -3 & 1 \end{bmatrix}$ **(b)** $\begin{bmatrix} 2 & -5 \\ 5 & 2 \end{bmatrix}\begin{bmatrix} 1 & 3 \\ -3 & 1 \end{bmatrix} = \begin{bmatrix} 17 & 1 \\ -1 & 17 \end{bmatrix}$ **(c)** $17 + i$ **(d)** $17 + i$

2. $\begin{bmatrix} a & b \\ -b & a \end{bmatrix}\begin{bmatrix} a & -b \\ b & a \end{bmatrix} = \begin{bmatrix} a^2+b^2 & 0 \\ 0 & b^2+a^2 \end{bmatrix}$; the product is a real number.

3. (a) $x = k(ar + bs) + l(cr + ds) = r(ka + lc) + s(kb + ld)$
$y = m(ar + bs) + n(cr + ds) = r(ma + nc) + s(mb + nd)$

(b) $A = \begin{bmatrix} ka + lc & kb + ld \\ ma + nc & mb + nd \end{bmatrix}$

11.4 Assess Your Understanding *(page 759)*

1. inverse **2.** square **3.** identity **4.** F **5.** F **6.** F

7. $\begin{bmatrix} 4 & 4 & -5 \\ -1 & 5 & 4 \end{bmatrix}$ **8.** $\begin{bmatrix} -4 & 2 & -5 \\ 3 & -1 & 8 \end{bmatrix}$ **9.** $\begin{bmatrix} 0 & 12 & -20 \\ 4 & 8 & 24 \end{bmatrix}$ **10.** $\begin{bmatrix} -12 & -3 & 0 \\ 6 & -9 & 6 \end{bmatrix}$ **11.** $\begin{bmatrix} -8 & 7 & -15 \\ 7 & 0 & 22 \end{bmatrix}$ **12.** $\begin{bmatrix} 16 & 10 & -10 \\ -6 & 16 & 4 \end{bmatrix}$ **13.** $\begin{bmatrix} 28 & -9 \\ 4 & 23 \end{bmatrix}$

14. $\begin{bmatrix} 22 & 6 \\ 14 & -2 \end{bmatrix}$ **15.** $\begin{bmatrix} 1 & 14 & -14 \\ 2 & 22 & -18 \\ 3 & 0 & 28 \end{bmatrix}$ **16.** $\begin{bmatrix} 14 & 7 & -2 \\ 20 & 12 & -4 \\ -14 & 7 & -6 \end{bmatrix}$ **17.** $\begin{bmatrix} 15 & 21 & -16 \\ 22 & 34 & -22 \\ -11 & 7 & 22 \end{bmatrix}$ **18.** $\begin{bmatrix} 50 & -3 \\ 18 & 21 \end{bmatrix}$ **19.** $\begin{bmatrix} 25 & -9 \\ 4 & 20 \end{bmatrix}$ **20.** $\begin{bmatrix} 6 & 14 & -14 \\ 2 & 27 & -18 \\ 3 & 0 & 33 \end{bmatrix}$

21. $\begin{bmatrix} -13 & 7 & -12 \\ -18 & 10 & -14 \\ 17 & -7 & 34 \end{bmatrix}$ **22.** $\begin{bmatrix} 50 & -3 \\ 18 & 21 \end{bmatrix}$ **23.** $\begin{bmatrix} -2 & 4 & 2 & 8 \\ 2 & 1 & 4 & 6 \end{bmatrix}$ **24.** $\begin{bmatrix} -22 & 29 & 8 & -1 \\ -10 & 17 & 6 & -1 \end{bmatrix}$ **25.** $\begin{bmatrix} 5 & 14 \\ 9 & 16 \end{bmatrix}$ **26.** $\begin{bmatrix} -1 & 2 & -1 \\ 0 & -12 & 3 \\ 15 & 30 & 0 \end{bmatrix}$ **27.** $\begin{bmatrix} 9 & 2 \\ 34 & 13 \\ 47 & 20 \end{bmatrix}$

28. $\begin{bmatrix} 6 & 32 \\ 1 & 3 \\ -2 & -4 \end{bmatrix}$ **29.** $\begin{bmatrix} 1 & -1 \\ -1 & 2 \end{bmatrix}$ **30.** $\begin{bmatrix} 1 & 1 \\ 2 & 3 \end{bmatrix}$ **31.** $\begin{bmatrix} 1 & -\frac{5}{2} \\ -1 & 3 \end{bmatrix}$ **32.** $\begin{bmatrix} -1 & -\frac{1}{2} \\ -3 & -2 \end{bmatrix}$ **33.** $\begin{bmatrix} 1 & -\frac{1}{a} \\ -1 & \frac{2}{a} \end{bmatrix}$ **34.** $\begin{bmatrix} -\frac{2}{b} & \frac{3}{b} \\ 1 & -1 \end{bmatrix}$ **35.** $\begin{bmatrix} 3 & -3 & 1 \\ -2 & 2 & -1 \\ -4 & 5 & -2 \end{bmatrix}$

36. $\begin{bmatrix} 3 & -2 & -4 \\ 3 & -2 & -5 \\ -1 & 1 & 2 \end{bmatrix}$ **37.** $\begin{bmatrix} -\frac{5}{7} & \frac{1}{7} & \frac{3}{7} \\ \frac{9}{7} & \frac{1}{7} & -\frac{4}{7} \\ \frac{3}{7} & -\frac{2}{7} & \frac{1}{7} \end{bmatrix}$ **38.** $\begin{bmatrix} \frac{3}{7} & -\frac{4}{7} & \frac{1}{7} \\ \frac{1}{7} & \frac{1}{7} & -\frac{2}{7} \\ -\frac{5}{7} & \frac{9}{7} & \frac{3}{7} \end{bmatrix}$ **39.** $x = 3, y = 2; (3, 2)$ **40.** $x = 12, y = 28; (12, 28)$

41. $x = -5, y = 10; (-5, 10)$ **42.** $x = 9, y = 23; (9, 23)$ **43.** $x = 2, y = -1; (2, -1)$ **44.** $x = -7, y = -28; (-7, -28)$

45. $x = \frac{1}{2}, y = 2; \left(\frac{1}{2}, 2\right)$ **46.** $x = -\frac{1}{2}, y = 3; \left(-\frac{1}{2}, 3\right)$ **47.** $x = -2, y = 1; (-2, 1)$ **48.** $x = 2, y = 1; (2, 1)$

49. $x = \frac{2}{a}, y = \frac{3}{a}; \left(\frac{2}{a}, \frac{3}{a}\right)$ **50.** $x = \frac{2}{b}, y = 4; \left(\frac{2}{b}, 4\right)$ **51.** $x = -2, y = 3, z = 5; (-2, 3, 5)$ **52.** $x = 4, y = -2, z = 1; (4, -2, 1)$

53. $x = \frac{1}{2}, y = -\frac{1}{2}, z = 1; \left(\frac{1}{2}, -\frac{1}{2}, 1\right)$ **54.** $x = 1, y = -1, z = \frac{1}{2}; \left(1, -1, \frac{1}{2}\right)$ **55.** $x = -\frac{34}{7}, y = \frac{85}{7}, z = \frac{12}{7}; \left(-\frac{34}{7}, \frac{85}{7}, \frac{12}{7}\right)$

56. $x = \frac{8}{7}, y = \frac{5}{7}, z = \frac{17}{7}; \left(\frac{8}{7}, \frac{5}{7}, \frac{17}{7}\right)$ **57.** $x = \frac{1}{3}, y = 1, z = \frac{2}{3}; \left(\frac{1}{3}, 1, \frac{2}{3}\right)$ **58.** $x = 1, y = -1, z = 1; (1, -1, 1)$

59. $\left[\begin{array}{cc|cc} 4 & 2 & 1 & 0 \\ 2 & 1 & 0 & 1 \end{array}\right] \rightarrow \left[\begin{array}{cc|cc} 1 & \frac{1}{2} & \frac{1}{4} & 0 \\ 2 & 1 & 0 & 1 \end{array}\right] \rightarrow \left[\begin{array}{cc|cc} 1 & \frac{1}{2} & \frac{1}{4} & 0 \\ 0 & 0 & -\frac{1}{2} & 1 \end{array}\right]$ **60.** $\left[\begin{array}{cc|cc} -3 & \frac{1}{2} & 1 & 0 \\ 6 & -1 & 0 & 1 \end{array}\right] \rightarrow \left[\begin{array}{cc|cc} 1 & -\frac{1}{6} & -\frac{1}{3} & 0 \\ 6 & -1 & 0 & 1 \end{array}\right] \rightarrow \left[\begin{array}{cc|cc} 1 & -\frac{1}{6} & -\frac{1}{3} & 0 \\ 0 & 0 & 2 & 1 \end{array}\right]$

61. $\left[\begin{array}{cc|cc} 15 & 3 & 1 & 0 \\ 10 & 2 & 0 & 1 \end{array}\right] \rightarrow \left[\begin{array}{cc|cc} 1 & \frac{1}{5} & \frac{1}{15} & 0 \\ 10 & 2 & 0 & 1 \end{array}\right] \rightarrow \left[\begin{array}{cc|cc} 1 & \frac{1}{5} & \frac{1}{15} & 0 \\ 0 & 0 & -\frac{2}{3} & 1 \end{array}\right]$ **62.** $\left[\begin{array}{cc|cc} -3 & 0 & 1 & 0 \\ 4 & 0 & 0 & 1 \end{array}\right] \rightarrow \left[\begin{array}{cc|cc} 1 & 0 & -\frac{1}{3} & 0 \\ 4 & 0 & 0 & 1 \end{array}\right] \rightarrow \left[\begin{array}{cc|cc} 1 & 0 & -\frac{1}{3} & 0 \\ 0 & 0 & \frac{4}{3} & 1 \end{array}\right]$.

63. $\left[\begin{array}{ccc|ccc} -3 & 1 & -1 & 1 & 0 & 0 \\ 1 & -4 & -7 & 0 & 1 & 0 \\ 1 & 2 & 5 & 0 & 0 & 1 \end{array}\right] \rightarrow \left[\begin{array}{ccc|ccc} 1 & 2 & 5 & 0 & 0 & 1 \\ 1 & -4 & -7 & 0 & 1 & 0 \\ -3 & 1 & -1 & 1 & 0 & 0 \end{array}\right] \rightarrow \left[\begin{array}{ccc|ccc} 1 & 2 & 5 & 0 & 0 & 1 \\ 0 & -6 & -12 & 0 & 1 & -1 \\ 0 & 7 & 14 & 1 & 0 & 3 \end{array}\right]$

$\rightarrow \left[\begin{array}{ccc|ccc} 1 & 2 & 5 & 0 & 0 & 1 \\ 0 & 1 & 2 & 0 & -\frac{1}{6} & \frac{1}{6} \\ 0 & 1 & 2 & \frac{1}{7} & 0 & \frac{3}{7} \end{array}\right] \rightarrow \left[\begin{array}{ccc|ccc} 1 & 2 & 5 & 0 & 0 & 1 \\ 0 & 1 & 2 & 0 & -\frac{1}{6} & \frac{1}{6} \\ 0 & 0 & 0 & \frac{1}{7} & \frac{1}{6} & \frac{11}{42} \end{array}\right]$

64. $\begin{bmatrix} 1 & 1 & -3 & | & 1 & 0 & 0 \\ 2 & -4 & 1 & | & 0 & 1 & 0 \\ -5 & 7 & 1 & | & 0 & 0 & 1 \end{bmatrix} \rightarrow \begin{bmatrix} 1 & 1 & -3 & | & 1 & 0 & 0 \\ 0 & -6 & 7 & | & -2 & 1 & 0 \\ 0 & 12 & -14 & | & 5 & 0 & 1 \end{bmatrix} \rightarrow \begin{bmatrix} 1 & 1 & -3 & | & 1 & 0 & 0 \\ 0 & 1 & -\frac{7}{6} & | & \frac{1}{3} & -\frac{1}{6} & 0 \\ 0 & 1 & -\frac{7}{6} & | & \frac{5}{12} & 0 & \frac{1}{12} \end{bmatrix} \rightarrow \begin{bmatrix} 1 & 1 & -3 & | & 1 & 0 & 0 \\ 0 & 1 & -\frac{7}{6} & | & \frac{1}{3} & -\frac{1}{6} & 0 \\ 0 & 0 & 0 & | & \frac{1}{12} & \frac{1}{6} & \frac{1}{12} \end{bmatrix}$

65. $\begin{bmatrix} 0.01 & 0.05 & -0.01 \\ 0.01 & -0.02 & 0.01 \\ -0.02 & 0.01 & 0.03 \end{bmatrix}$ **66.** $\begin{bmatrix} 0.26 & -0.29 & -0.20 \\ -1.21 & 1.63 & 1.20 \\ -1.84 & 2.53 & 1.80 \end{bmatrix}$ **67.** $\begin{bmatrix} 0.02 & -0.04 & -0.01 & 0.01 \\ -0.02 & 0.05 & 0.03 & -0.03 \\ 0.02 & 0.01 & -0.04 & 0.00 \\ -0.02 & 0.06 & 0.07 & 0.06 \end{bmatrix}$ **68.** $\begin{bmatrix} 0.01 & 0.04 & 0.00 & 0.03 \\ 0.02 & -0.02 & 0.01 & 0.01 \\ -0.04 & 0.02 & 0.04 & 0.06 \\ 0.05 & -0.02 & 0.00 & -0.09 \end{bmatrix}$

69. $x = 4.57, y = -6.44, z = -24.07$ or $(4.57, -6.44, -24.07)$ **70.** $x = 4.56, y = -6.06, z = -22.55$ or $(4.56, -6.06, -22.55)$

71. $x = -1.19, y = 2.46, z = 8.27$ or $(-1.19, 2.46, 8.27)$ **72.** $x = -2.05, y = 3.88, z = 13.36$ or $(-2.05, 3.88, 13.36)$

73. $x = -5, y = 7; (-5, 7)$ **74.** $x = 8, y = -3; (8, -3)$ **75.** $x = -4, y = 2, z = \frac{5}{2}; (-4, 2, \frac{5}{2})$ **76.** $x = -\frac{3}{2}, y = \frac{5}{3}, z = 4; (-\frac{3}{2}, \frac{5}{3}, 4)$

77. Inconsistent; $\varnothing$ **78.** Inconsistent; $\varnothing$

79. $x = -\frac{1}{5}z + \frac{1}{5}, y = \frac{1}{5}z - \frac{6}{5}$, where z is any real number; $\left\{ (x, y, z) \,\middle|\, x = -\frac{1}{5}z + \frac{1}{5}, y = \frac{1}{5}z - \frac{6}{5}, z \text{ is any real number} \right\}$

80. $x = \frac{5}{13}z - \frac{12}{13}, y = -\frac{2}{13}z + \frac{10}{13}$, where z is any real number; $\left\{ (x, y, z) \,\middle|\, x = \frac{5}{13}z - \frac{12}{13}, y = -\frac{2}{13}z + \frac{10}{13}, z \text{ is any real number} \right\}$

81. (a) $A = \begin{bmatrix} 6 & 9 \\ 3 & 12 \end{bmatrix}; B = \begin{bmatrix} 71.00 \\ 158.60 \end{bmatrix}$ **(b)** $AB = \begin{bmatrix} 1853.40 \\ 2116.20 \end{bmatrix}$; Nikki's total tuition is $1853.40, and Joe's total tuition is $2116.20.

82. (a) $A = \begin{bmatrix} 4000 & 3000 \\ 2500 & 3800 \end{bmatrix}; B = \begin{bmatrix} 0.011 \\ 0.006 \end{bmatrix}$ **(b)** $AB = \begin{bmatrix} 62 \\ 50.3 \end{bmatrix}$ after 1 month Jamal's loans accrued $62.00 in interest, and Stephanie's loans accrued $50.30 in interest. **(c)** $A(C + B) = \begin{bmatrix} 7062 \\ 6350.3 \end{bmatrix}$ Jamal's loan balance after 1 month was $7062.00; Stephanie's was $6350.30.

83. (a) $\begin{bmatrix} 500 & 350 & 400 \\ 700 & 500 & 850 \end{bmatrix}; \begin{bmatrix} 500 & 700 \\ 350 & 500 \\ 400 & 850 \end{bmatrix}$ **(b)** $\begin{bmatrix} 15 \\ 8 \\ 3 \end{bmatrix}$ **(c)** $\begin{bmatrix} 11,500 \\ 17,050 \end{bmatrix}$ **(d)** $[0.10 \quad 0.05]$ **(e)** $2002.50

84. (a) January sales $\begin{bmatrix} 400 & 250 & 50 \\ 450 & 200 & 140 \end{bmatrix}$; February sales $\begin{bmatrix} 350 & 100 & 30 \\ 350 & 300 & 100 \end{bmatrix}$ **(b)** $\begin{bmatrix} 750 & 350 & 80 \\ 800 & 500 & 240 \end{bmatrix}$ **(c)** $\begin{bmatrix} 100 \\ 150 \\ 200 \end{bmatrix}$ **(d)** $\begin{bmatrix} 143,500 \\ 203,000 \end{bmatrix}$

85. (a) $K^{-1} = \begin{bmatrix} 1 & 0 & -1 \\ -1 & 1 & 1 \\ 0 & -1 & 1 \end{bmatrix}$ **(b)** $M = \begin{bmatrix} 13 & 1 & 20 \\ 8 & 9 & 19 \\ 6 & 21 & 14 \end{bmatrix}$ **(c)** Math is fun.

86. $P^2 = \begin{bmatrix} 0.27 & 0.22 & 0.18 \\ 0.55 & 0.56 & 0.55 \\ 0.18 & 0.22 & 0.27 \end{bmatrix}$; each entry represents the probability that a grandchild has a certain income level, given its grandparents' income level.

87. If $D = ad - bc \neq 0$, then $a \neq 0$ and $d \neq 0$, or $b \neq 0$ and $c \neq 0$. Assuming the former,

$$\begin{bmatrix} a & b & | & 1 & 0 \\ c & d & | & 0 & 1 \end{bmatrix} \rightarrow \begin{bmatrix} 1 & \frac{b}{a} & | & \frac{1}{a} & 0 \\ c & d & | & 0 & 1 \end{bmatrix} \rightarrow \begin{bmatrix} 1 & \frac{b}{a} & | & \frac{1}{a} & 0 \\ 0 & \frac{D}{a} & | & -\frac{c}{a} & 1 \end{bmatrix} \rightarrow \begin{bmatrix} 1 & \frac{b}{a} & | & \frac{1}{a} & 0 \\ 0 & 1 & | & -\frac{c}{D} & \frac{a}{D} \end{bmatrix} \rightarrow \begin{bmatrix} 1 & 0 & | & \frac{d}{D} & -\frac{b}{D} \\ 0 & 1 & | & -\frac{c}{D} & \frac{a}{D} \end{bmatrix}$$

$$R_1 = \frac{1}{a}r_1 \qquad R_2 = -cr_1 + r_2 \qquad R_2 = \frac{a}{D}r_2 \qquad R_1 = -\frac{b}{a}r_2 + r_1$$

11.5 Assess Your Understanding *(page 769)*

5. Proper **6.** Proper **7.** Improper; $1 + \dfrac{9}{x^2 - 4}$ **8.** Improper; $3 + \dfrac{1}{x^2 - 1}$ **9.** Improper; $5x + \dfrac{22x - 1}{x^2 - 4}$ **10.** Improper; $3x + \dfrac{x^2 - 24x - 2}{x^3 + 8}$

11. Improper; $1 + \dfrac{-2(x - 6)}{(x + 4)(x - 3)}$ **12.** Improper; $2x + \dfrac{6x}{x^2 + 1}$ **13.** $\dfrac{-4}{x} + \dfrac{4}{x - 1}$ **14.** $\dfrac{2}{x + 2} + \dfrac{1}{x - 1}$ **15.** $\dfrac{1}{x} + \dfrac{-x}{x^2 + 1}$

16. $\dfrac{\frac{1}{5}}{x + 1} + \dfrac{-\frac{1}{5}x + \frac{1}{5}}{x^2 + 4}$ **17.** $\dfrac{-1}{x - 1} + \dfrac{2}{x - 2}$ **18.** $\dfrac{1}{x + 2} + \dfrac{2}{x - 4}$ **19.** $\dfrac{\frac{1}{4}}{x + 1} + \dfrac{\frac{3}{4}}{x - 1} + \dfrac{\frac{1}{2}}{(x - 1)^2}$ **20.** $\dfrac{-\frac{3}{4}}{x} + \dfrac{\frac{1}{2}}{x^2} + \dfrac{\frac{3}{4}}{x - 2}$

21. $\dfrac{\frac{1}{12}}{x-2}+\dfrac{-\frac{1}{12}(x+4)}{x^2+2x+4}$ **22.** $\dfrac{2}{x-1}+\dfrac{-2x-2}{x^2+x+1}$ **23.** $\dfrac{\frac{1}{4}}{x-1}+\dfrac{\frac{1}{4}}{(x-1)^2}+\dfrac{-\frac{1}{4}}{x+1}+\dfrac{\frac{1}{4}}{(x+1)^2}$ **24.** $\dfrac{\frac{1}{2}}{x}+\dfrac{\frac{1}{4}}{x^2}+\dfrac{\frac{3}{4}}{(x-2)^2}+\dfrac{-\frac{1}{2}}{(x-2)}$

25. $\dfrac{-5}{x+2}+\dfrac{5}{x+1}+\dfrac{-4}{(x+1)^2}$ **26.** $\dfrac{\frac{2}{9}}{x+2}+\dfrac{\frac{7}{9}}{x-1}+\dfrac{\frac{2}{3}}{(x-1)^2}$ **27.** $\dfrac{\frac{1}{4}}{x}+\dfrac{1}{x^2}+\dfrac{-\frac{1}{4}(x+4)}{x^2+4}$ **28.** $\dfrac{\frac{14}{3}}{x-1}+\dfrac{4}{(x-1)^2}+\dfrac{-\frac{14}{3}x+\frac{4}{3}}{x^2+2}$

29. $\dfrac{\frac{2}{3}}{x+1}+\dfrac{\frac{1}{3}(x+1)}{x^2+2x+4}$ **30.** $\dfrac{-6}{x}+\dfrac{7x+7}{x^2+3x+3}$ **31.** $\dfrac{\frac{2}{7}}{3x-2}+\dfrac{\frac{1}{7}}{2x+1}$ **32.** $\dfrac{-\frac{1}{7}}{2x+3}+\dfrac{\frac{2}{7}}{4x-1}$ **33.** $\dfrac{\frac{3}{4}}{x+3}+\dfrac{\frac{1}{4}}{x-1}$

34. $\dfrac{-3}{x+1}+\dfrac{2}{x+2}+\dfrac{2}{x+3}$ **35.** $\dfrac{1}{x^2+4}+\dfrac{2x-1}{(x^2+4)^2}$ **36.** $\dfrac{x}{x^2+16}+\dfrac{-16x+1}{(x^2+16)^2}$ **37.** $\dfrac{-1}{x}+\dfrac{2}{x-3}+\dfrac{-1}{x+1}$ **38.** $\dfrac{-1}{x^2}+\dfrac{-1}{x^4}+\dfrac{1}{x-1}$

39. $\dfrac{4}{x-2}+\dfrac{-3}{x-1}+\dfrac{-1}{(x-1)^2}$ **40.** $\dfrac{\frac{3}{8}}{x-1}+\dfrac{\frac{1}{2}}{(x-1)^2}+\dfrac{\frac{5}{8}}{x+3}$ **41.** $\dfrac{x}{(x^2+16)^2}+\dfrac{-16x}{(x^2+16)^3}$ **42.** $\dfrac{1}{(x^2+4)^2}+\dfrac{-4}{(x^2+4)^3}$

43. $\dfrac{-\frac{8}{7}}{2x+1}+\dfrac{\frac{4}{7}}{x-3}$ **44.** $\dfrac{\frac{4}{5}}{2x-1}+\dfrac{\frac{8}{5}}{x+2}$ **45.** $\dfrac{\frac{2}{9}}{x}+\dfrac{-\frac{1}{3}}{x^2}+\dfrac{\frac{1}{6}}{x-3}+\dfrac{\frac{1}{18}}{x+3}$ **46.** $\dfrac{\frac{13}{24}}{x-2}+\dfrac{-\frac{13}{24}}{x+2}+\dfrac{-\frac{7}{6}}{x^2+2}$

Historical Problem (*page 776*)

$x = 6$ units, $y = 8$ units

11.6 Assess Your Understanding (*page 776*)

5.

6.

7.

8.

9.

10.

11.

12.

13.

14.

15.

16.

17.

18.

19.

20.

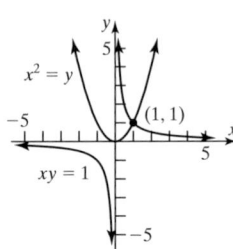

21. No points of intersection

22.

23.

24.

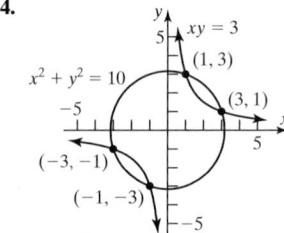

25. $x = 1, y = 4; x = -1, y = -4; x = 2\sqrt{2}, y = \sqrt{2}; x = -2\sqrt{2}, y = -\sqrt{2}$ or $(1, 4), (-1, -4), \left(2\sqrt{2}, \sqrt{2}\right), \left(-2\sqrt{2}, -\sqrt{2}\right)$

26. $x = 5, y = 2$ or $(5, 2)$　**27.** $x = 0, y = 1; x = -\dfrac{2}{3}, y = -\dfrac{1}{3}$ or $(0, 1), \left(-\dfrac{2}{3}, -\dfrac{1}{3}\right)$　**28.** $x = -5, y = -\dfrac{3}{2}$ or $\left(-5, -\dfrac{3}{2}\right)$

29. $x = 0, y = -1; x = \dfrac{5}{2}, y = -\dfrac{7}{2}$ or $(0, -1), \left(\dfrac{5}{2}, -\dfrac{7}{2}\right)$　**30.** $x = -2, y = -2; x = -\sqrt{2}, y = -2\sqrt{2}; x = \sqrt{2}, y = 2\sqrt{2}; x = 2, y = 2$ or

$(-2, -2), \left(-\sqrt{2}, -2\sqrt{2}\right), \left(\sqrt{2}, 2\sqrt{2}\right), (2, 2)$　**31.** $x = 2, y = \dfrac{1}{3}; x = \dfrac{1}{2}, y = \dfrac{4}{3}$ or $\left(2, \dfrac{1}{3}\right), \left(\dfrac{1}{2}, \dfrac{4}{3}\right)$　**32.** $x = -2, y = 0; x = 7, y = 6$ or $(-2, 0), (7, 6)$

33. $x = 3, y = 2; x = 3, y = -2; x = -3, y = 2; x = -3, y = -2$ or $(3, 2), (3, -2), (-3, 2), (-3, -2)$　**34.** $x = -1, y = -2; x = -1,$

$y = 2; x = 1, y = -2; x = 1, y = 2$ or $(-1, -2), (-1, 2), (1, -2), (1, 2)$　**35.** $x = \dfrac{1}{2}, y = \dfrac{3}{2}; x = \dfrac{1}{2}, y = -\dfrac{3}{2}; x = -\dfrac{1}{2}, y = \dfrac{3}{2}; x = -\dfrac{1}{2}, y = -\dfrac{3}{2}$

or $\left(\dfrac{1}{2}, \dfrac{3}{2}\right), \left(\dfrac{1}{2}, -\dfrac{3}{2}\right), \left(-\dfrac{1}{2}, \dfrac{3}{2}\right), \left(-\dfrac{1}{2}, -\dfrac{3}{2}\right)$　**36.** $x = -2\sqrt{2}, y = \sqrt{3}; x = 2\sqrt{2}, y = \sqrt{3}; x = 2\sqrt{2}, y = -\sqrt{3}; x = -2\sqrt{2}, y = -\sqrt{3}$ or

$\left(-2\sqrt{2}, \sqrt{3}\right), \left(2\sqrt{2}, \sqrt{3}\right), \left(2\sqrt{2}, -\sqrt{3}\right)\left(-2\sqrt{2}, -\sqrt{3}\right)$　**37.** $x = \sqrt{2}, y = 2\sqrt{2}; x = -\sqrt{2}, y = -2\sqrt{2}$ or $\left(\sqrt{2}, 2\sqrt{2}\right), \left(-\sqrt{2}, -2\sqrt{2}\right)$

38. $x = -5\sqrt{3}, y = \sqrt{3}; x = 5\sqrt{3}, y = -\sqrt{3}$ or $\left(-5\sqrt{3}, \sqrt{3},\right), \left(5\sqrt{3}, -\sqrt{3}\right)$　**39.** No real solution exists.　**40.** No real solution exists.

41. $x = \dfrac{8}{3}, y = \dfrac{2\sqrt{10}}{3}; x = -\dfrac{8}{3}, y = \dfrac{2\sqrt{10}}{3}; x = \dfrac{8}{3}, y = -\dfrac{2\sqrt{10}}{3}; x = -\dfrac{8}{3}, y = -\dfrac{2\sqrt{10}}{3}$ or $\left(\dfrac{8}{3}, \dfrac{2\sqrt{10}}{3}\right), \left(-\dfrac{8}{3}, \dfrac{2\sqrt{10}}{3}\right), \left(\dfrac{8}{3}, -\dfrac{2\sqrt{10}}{3}\right), \left(-\dfrac{8}{3}, -\dfrac{2\sqrt{10}}{3}\right)$

42. $x = -\dfrac{\sqrt{2}}{2}, y = -\dfrac{\sqrt{6}}{3}; x = -\dfrac{\sqrt{2}}{2}, y = \dfrac{\sqrt{6}}{3}; x = \dfrac{\sqrt{2}}{2}, y = -\dfrac{\sqrt{6}}{3}; x = \dfrac{\sqrt{2}}{2}, y = \dfrac{\sqrt{6}}{3}$ or $\left(-\dfrac{\sqrt{2}}{2}, -\dfrac{\sqrt{6}}{3}\right), \left(-\dfrac{\sqrt{2}}{2}, \dfrac{\sqrt{6}}{3}\right), \left(\dfrac{\sqrt{2}}{2}, -\dfrac{\sqrt{6}}{3}\right),$

$\left(\dfrac{\sqrt{2}}{2}, \dfrac{\sqrt{6}}{3}\right)$　**43.** $x = 1, y = \dfrac{1}{2}; x = -1, y = \dfrac{1}{2}; x = 1, y = -\dfrac{1}{2}; x = -1, y = -\dfrac{1}{2}$ or $\left(1, \dfrac{1}{2}\right), \left(-1, \dfrac{1}{2}\right), \left(1, -\dfrac{1}{2}\right), \left(-1, -\dfrac{1}{2}\right)$

44. $x = -2, y = -\sqrt{2}; x = -2, y = \sqrt{2}; x = 2, y = -\sqrt{2}; x = 2, y = \sqrt{2}$ or $\left(-2, -\sqrt{2}\right), \left(-2, \sqrt{2}\right), \left(2, -\sqrt{2}\right), \left(2, \sqrt{2}\right)$

45. No real solution exists. **46.** $x = -\sqrt[4]{\frac{2}{5}}, y = -\sqrt[4]{\frac{2}{3}}; x = -\sqrt[4]{\frac{2}{5}}, y = \sqrt[4]{\frac{2}{3}}; x = \sqrt[4]{\frac{2}{5}}, y = -\sqrt[4]{\frac{2}{3}}; x = \sqrt[4]{\frac{2}{5}}, y = \sqrt[4]{\frac{2}{3}}$ or

$\left(-\sqrt[4]{\frac{2}{5}}, -\sqrt[4]{\frac{2}{3}}\right), \left(-\sqrt[4]{\frac{2}{5}}, \sqrt[4]{\frac{2}{3}}\right), \left(\sqrt[4]{\frac{2}{5}}, -\sqrt[4]{\frac{2}{3}}\right), \left(\sqrt[4]{\frac{2}{5}}, \sqrt[4]{\frac{2}{3}}\right)$ **47.** $x = \sqrt{3}, y = \sqrt{3}; x = -\sqrt{3}, y = -\sqrt{3}; x = 2, y = 1; x = -2, y = -1$ or

$\left(\sqrt{3}, \sqrt{3}\right), \left(-\sqrt{3}, -\sqrt{3}\right), (2, 1), (-2, -1)$ **48.** $x = -2, y = 2; x = 3, y = -3$ or $(-2, 2), (3, -3)$ **49.** $x = 0, y = -2; x = 0, y = 1;$

$x = 2, y = -1$ or $(0, -2), (0, 1), (2, -1)$ **50.** $x = 2, y = 1$ or $(2, 1)$ **51.** $x = 2, y = 8$ or $(2, 8)$ **52.** $x = \frac{1}{2}, y = \frac{1}{16}$ or $\left(\frac{1}{2}, \frac{1}{16}\right)$

53. $x = 81, y = 3$ or $(81, 3)$ **54.** $x = 32, y = 2$ or $(32, 2)$

55.

56.

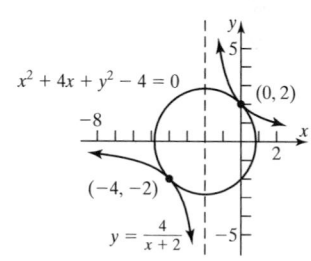

57. $x = 0.48, y = 0.62$ **58.** $x = 0.65, y = 0.52$ **59.** $x = -1.65, y = -0.89$ **60.** $x = -1.37, y = 2.14$

61. $x = 0.58, y = 1.86; x = 1.81, y = 1.05; x = 0.58, y = -1.86; x = 1.81, y = -1.05$

62. $x = 0.64, y = 1.55; x = -0.64, y = -1.55; x = 1.55, y = 0.64; x = -1.55, y = -0.64$ **63.** $x = 2.35, y = 0.85$

64. $x = 1.90, y = 0.64; x = 0.14, y = -2.00$

65.

66.

67.

68.

69.

70.

71. 3 and 1; -1 and -3 **72.** 5 and 2 **73.** 2 and 2; -2 and -2 **74.** 5 and 2; -5 and -2 **75.** $\frac{1}{2}$ and $\frac{1}{3}$

76. $\frac{1}{2}$ and -1 **77.** 5 **78.** $\frac{1}{7}$ **79.** 5 in. by 3 in. **80.** 4 ft and 6 ft **81.** 2 cm and 4 cm **82.** 8 cm **83.** tortoise: 7 m/hr, hare: $7\frac{1}{2}$ m/hr

84. 10.02 ft **85.** 12 cm by 18 cm **86.** 16.57 cm by 13.03 cm **87.** $x = 60$ ft; $y = 30$ ft **88.** It is not possible.

89. $l = \frac{P + \sqrt{P^2 - 16A}}{4}; w = \frac{P - \sqrt{P^2 - 16A}}{4}$ **90.** $b = P - \frac{4h^2 + P^2}{2P}, l = \frac{4h^2 + P^2}{4P}$ **91.** $y = 4x - 4$

92. $y = -\frac{1}{3}x + \frac{10}{3}$ **93.** $y = 2x + 1$ **94.** $y = 4x + 9$ **95.** $y = -\frac{1}{3}x + \frac{7}{3}$ **96.** $y = \frac{3}{2}x + \frac{7}{2}$ **97.** $y = 2x - 3$

98. $y = \frac{1}{3}x + \frac{7}{3}$ **99.** $r_1 = \frac{-b + \sqrt{b^2 - 4ac}}{2a}; r_2 = \frac{-b - \sqrt{b^2 - 4ac}}{2a}$ **101. (a)** 4.274 ft by 4.274 ft or 0.093 ft by 0.093 ft

11.7 Assess Your Understanding *(page 786)*

7. satisfied   **8.** half-plane   **9.** F   **10.** T

11.

$y \geq 0$

12.

$x \geq 0$

13.

$x \geq 4$

14.

$y \leq 2$

15.
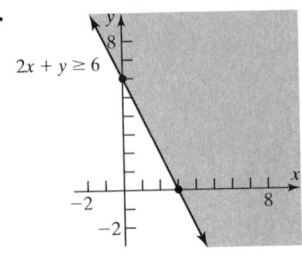
$2x + y \geq 6$

16.
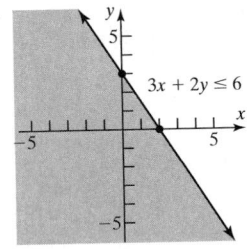
$3x + 2y \leq 6$

17.
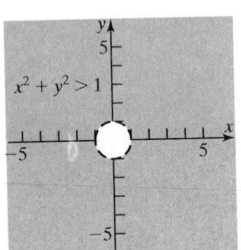
$x^2 + y^2 > 1$

18.
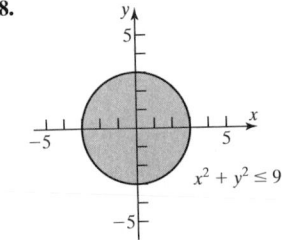
$x^2 + y^2 \leq 9$

19.
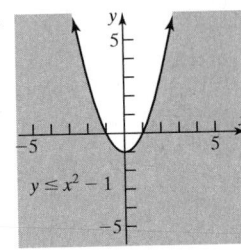
$y \leq x^2 - 1$

20.
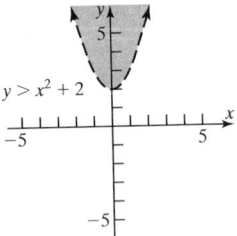
$y > x^2 + 2$

21.

$xy \geq 4$

22.

$xy \leq 1$

23.
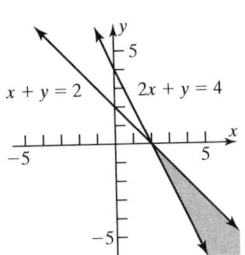
$x + y = 2$ $2x + y = 4$

24.
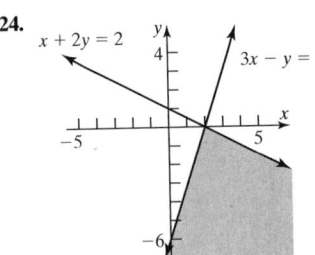
$x + 2y = 2$ $3x - y = 6$

25.
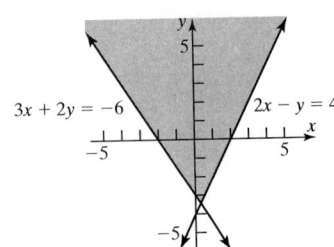
$3x + 2y = -6$ $2x - y = 4$

26.
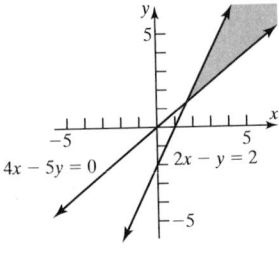
$4x - 5y = 0$ $2x - y = 2$

27.
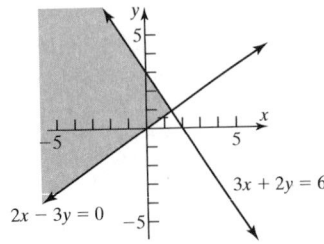
$2x - 3y = 0$ $3x + 2y = 6$

28.
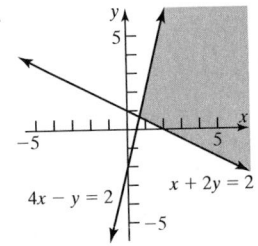
$4x - y = 2$ $x + 2y = 2$

29.

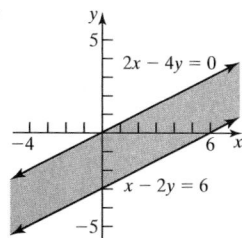

$2x - 4y = 0$

$x - 2y = 6$

30.

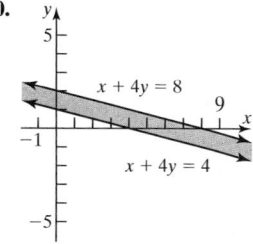

$x + 4y = 8$

$x + 4y = 4$

31.

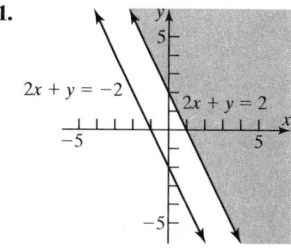

$2x + y = -2$

$2x + y = 2$

32.

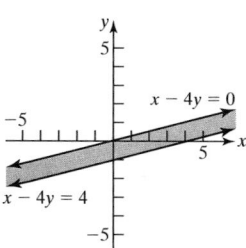

$x - 4y = 0$

$x - 4y = 4$

33. No solution

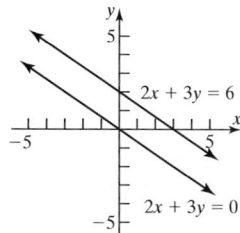

$2x + 3y = 6$

$2x + 3y = 0$

34.

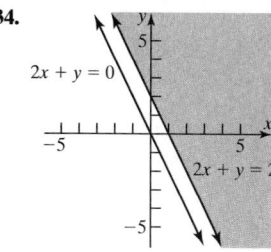

$2x + y = 0$

$2x + y = 2$

35.

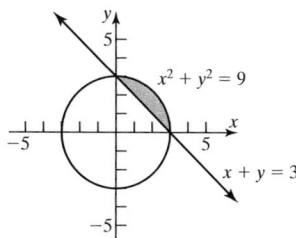

$x^2 + y^2 = 9$

$x + y = 3$

36.

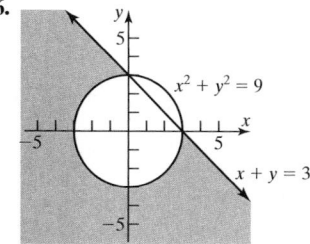

$x^2 + y^2 = 9$

$x + y = 3$

37.

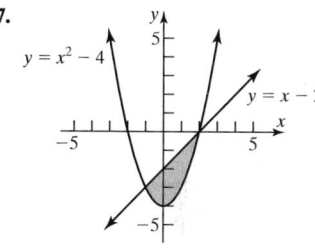

$y = x^2 - 4$

$y = x - 2$

38.

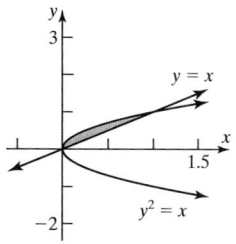

$y = x$

$y^2 = x$

39.

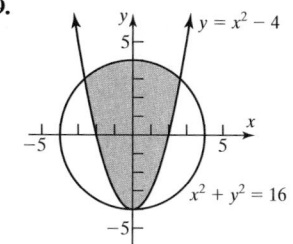

$y = x^2 - 4$

$x^2 + y^2 = 16$

40.

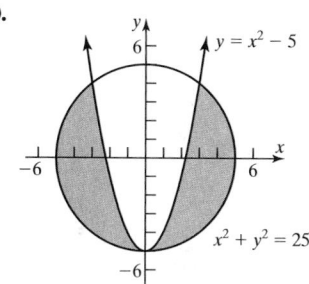

$y = x^2 - 5$

$x^2 + y^2 = 25$

41.

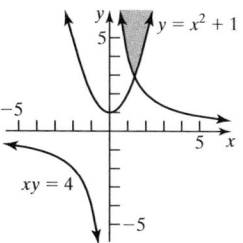

$y = x^2 + 1$

$xy = 4$

42.

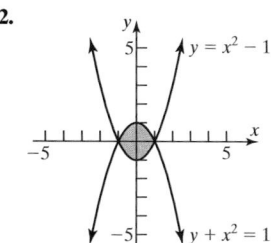

$y = x^2 - 1$

$y + x^2 = 1$

43. Bounded

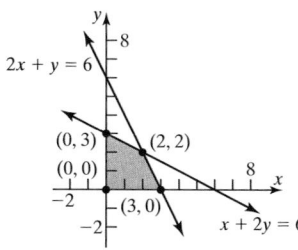

$2x + y = 6$

$(0, 3)$ $(2, 2)$

$(0, 0)$

$(3, 0)$ $x + 2y = 6$

44. Unbounded

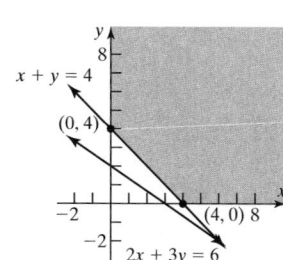

$x + y = 4$

$(0, 4)$

$(4, 0)$

$2x + 3y = 6$

45. Unbounded

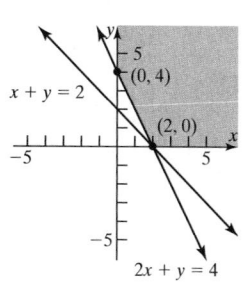

$x + y = 2$

$(0, 4)$

$(2, 0)$

$2x + y = 4$

46. Bounded

47. Bounded

48. Bounded

49. Bounded

50. Bounded

51. Bounded

52. Bounded

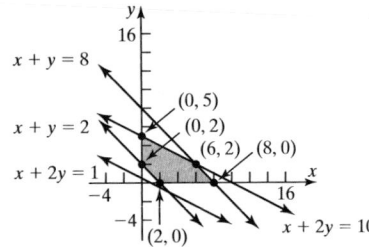

53. $\begin{cases} x \leq 4 \\ x + y \leq 6 \\ x \geq 0 \\ y \geq 0 \end{cases}$

54. $\begin{cases} y \leq 5 \\ x + y \geq 2 \\ x \leq 6 \\ x \geq 0 \\ y \geq 0 \end{cases}$

57. (a) $\begin{cases} x + y \leq 50{,}000 \\ x \geq 35{,}000 \\ y \leq 10{,}000 \\ y \geq 0 \end{cases}$

55. $\begin{cases} x \leq 20 \\ y \geq 15 \\ x + y \leq 50 \\ x - y \leq 0 \\ x \geq 0 \end{cases}$

56. $\begin{cases} y \leq 6 \\ x \leq 5 \\ 3x + 4y \geq 12 \\ y \geq 2x - 8 \\ x \geq 0 \end{cases}$

(b)

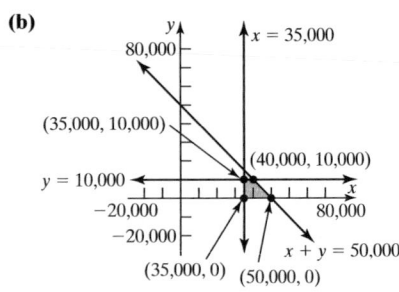

58. (a) $\begin{cases} x \geq 0 \\ y \geq 0 \\ 2x + 3y \leq 80 \\ 3x + 4y \leq 120 \end{cases}$

59. (a) $\begin{cases} x \geq 0 \\ y \geq 0 \\ x + 2y \leq 300 \\ 3x + 2y \leq 480 \end{cases}$

(b)

(b)

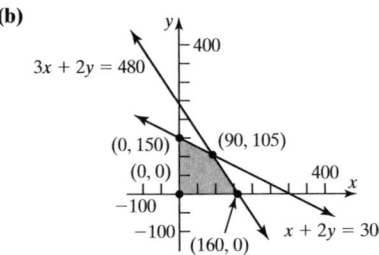

60. (a) $\begin{cases} 4x + 3y \leq 960 \\ 2x + 3y \leq 720 \\ x \geq 0 \\ y \geq 0 \end{cases}$

61. (a) $\begin{cases} 3x + 2y \leq 160 \\ 2x + 3y \leq 150 \\ x \geq 0 \\ y \geq 0 \end{cases}$

(b)

(b)

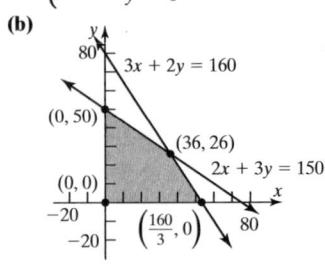

11.8 Assess Your Understanding (page 793)

1. objective function   **2.** T   **3.** Maximum value is 11; minimum value is 3.   **4.** Maximum value is 28; minimum value is 8.
5. Maximum value is 65; minimum value is 4.   **6.** Maximum value is 56; minimum value is 3.   **7.** Maximum value is 67; minimum value is 20.
8. Maximum value is 65; minimum value is 15.   **9.** The maximum value of z is 12, and it occurs at the point $(6, 0)$.
10. The maximum value is 26, and it occurs at the point $(5, 7)$.   **11.** The minimum value of z is 4, and it occurs at the point $(2, 0)$.
12. The minimum value of z is 8, and it occurs at the point $(0, 2)$.   **13.** The maximum value of z is 20, and it occurs at the point $(0, 4)$.
14. The maximum value of z is 28, and it occurs at the point $(2, 6)$.   **15.** The minimum value of z is 8, and it occurs at the point $(0, 2)$.

16. The minimum value of z is $\dfrac{15}{2}$, and it occurs at the point $\left(\dfrac{3}{2}, \dfrac{3}{2}\right)$.   **17.** The maximum value of z is 50, and it occurs at the point $(10, 0)$.

18. The maximum value of z is 36, and it occurs at the point $(0, 9)$.   **19.** Produce 8 downhill and 24 cross-country; \$1760; \$1920 which is the profit when producing 16 downhill and 16 cross-country.   **20.** Plant 24 acres of soybeans and 12 acres of wheat; \$5520; \$7200 which is the profit when planting 40 acres of soybeans and 0 acres of wheat.   **21.** Rent 15 rectangular tables and 16 round tables for a minimum cost of \$1252.
22. Rent 6 buses and 10 vans.   **23. (a)** \$10,000 in a junk bond and \$10,000 in Treasury bills   **(b)** \$12,000 in a junk bond
and \$8000 in Treasury bills   **24.** The combination that cost the least to operate is $\dfrac{1}{2}$ hr on machine 1 and $5\dfrac{1}{4}$ hr on machine 2.

25. 100 lb of ground beef should be mixed with 50 lb of pork.   **26.** Produce 400 gallons of regular ice cream and 100 gallons of premium ice cream.
27. Manufacture 10 racing skates and 15 figure skates.   **28.** \$20,000 in a AAA bond and \$30,000 in a CD   **29.** Order 2 metal samples and 4 plastic samples; \$34   **30.** Buy 15 cans of Gourmet Dog and 25 cans of Chow Hound.   **31. (a)** Configure with 10 first class seats and 120 coach seats.
(b) Configure with 15 first class seats and 120 coach seats.

Review Exercises (page 796)

1. $x = 2, y = -1$ or $(2, -1)$ **2.** $x = \dfrac{11}{23}, y = \dfrac{8}{23}$ or $\left(\dfrac{11}{23}, \dfrac{8}{23}\right)$ **3.** $x = 2, y = \dfrac{1}{2}$ or $\left(2, \dfrac{1}{2}\right)$ **4.** $x = -\dfrac{1}{2}, y = 1$ or $\left(-\dfrac{1}{2}, 1\right)$

5. $x = 2, y = -1$ or $(2, -1)$ **6.** $x = 0, y = \dfrac{5}{3}$ or $\left(0, \dfrac{5}{3}\right)$ **7.** $x = \dfrac{11}{5}, y = -\dfrac{3}{5}$ or $\left(\dfrac{11}{5}, -\dfrac{3}{5}\right)$ **8.** $x = -\dfrac{1}{2}, y = -\dfrac{1}{2}$ or $\left(-\dfrac{1}{2}, -\dfrac{1}{2}\right)$ **9.** Inconsistent

10. Inconsistent   **11.** $x = 2, y = 3$ or $(2, 3)$ **12.** $x = 84, y = -63$ or $(84, -63)$ **13.** Inconsistent   **14.** $y = -\dfrac{2}{5}x + 2$, where x is any real number or

$\left\{ (x, y) \mid y = -\dfrac{2}{5}x + 2, x \text{ is any real number} \right\}$ **15.** $x = -1, y = 2, z = -3$ or $(-1, 2, -3)$ **16.** $x = -1, y = 2, z = 7$ or $(-1, 2, 7)$

17. $x = \dfrac{7}{4}z + \dfrac{39}{4}, y = \dfrac{9}{8}z + \dfrac{69}{8}$, where z is any real number or $\left\{ (x, y, z,) \mid x = \dfrac{7}{4}z + \dfrac{39}{4}, y = \dfrac{9}{8}z + \dfrac{69}{8}, z \text{ is any real number} \right\}$ **18.** Inconsistent

19. $\begin{cases} 3x + 2y = 8 \\ x + 4y = -1 \end{cases}$ **20.** $\begin{cases} x + 2y + 5z = -2 \\ 5x \quad\; - 3z = 8 \\ 2x - y \quad\;\; = 0 \end{cases}$ **21.** $\begin{bmatrix} 4 & -4 \\ 3 & 9 \\ 4 & 4 \end{bmatrix}$ **22.** $\begin{bmatrix} -2 & 4 \\ 1 & -1 \\ -6 & 0 \end{bmatrix}$ **23.** $\begin{bmatrix} 6 & 0 \\ 12 & 24 \\ -6 & 12 \end{bmatrix}$ **24.** $\begin{bmatrix} -16 & 12 & 0 \\ -4 & -4 & 8 \end{bmatrix}$ **25.** $\begin{bmatrix} 4 & -3 & 0 \\ 12 & -2 & -8 \\ -2 & 5 & -4 \end{bmatrix}$

26. $\begin{bmatrix} -2 & -12 \\ 5 & 0 \end{bmatrix}$ **27.** $\begin{bmatrix} 8 & -13 & 8 \\ 9 & 2 & -10 \\ 22 & -13 & -4 \end{bmatrix}$ **28.** $\begin{bmatrix} 9 & -31 \\ -6 & -3 \end{bmatrix}$ **29.** $\begin{bmatrix} \dfrac{1}{2} & -1 \\ \dfrac{1}{6} & \dfrac{2}{3} \end{bmatrix}$ **30.** $\begin{bmatrix} -\dfrac{1}{2} & -\dfrac{1}{2} \\ \dfrac{1}{4} & \dfrac{3}{4} \end{bmatrix}$ **31.** $\begin{bmatrix} -\dfrac{5}{7} & \dfrac{9}{7} & \dfrac{3}{7} \\ \dfrac{1}{7} & \dfrac{1}{7} & \dfrac{2}{7} \\ \dfrac{3}{7} & -\dfrac{4}{7} & \dfrac{1}{7} \end{bmatrix}$ **32.** $\begin{bmatrix} \dfrac{3}{7} & \dfrac{1}{7} & \dfrac{5}{7} \\ -\dfrac{4}{7} & \dfrac{1}{7} & \dfrac{9}{7} \\ \dfrac{1}{7} & -\dfrac{2}{7} & \dfrac{3}{7} \end{bmatrix}$

33. Singular   **34.** Singular   **35.** $x = \dfrac{2}{5}, y = \dfrac{1}{10}$ or $\left(\dfrac{2}{5}, \dfrac{1}{10}\right)$ **36.** $x = 1, y = \dfrac{3}{2}$ or $\left(1, \dfrac{3}{2}\right)$ **37.** $x = 9, y = \dfrac{13}{3}, z = \dfrac{13}{3}$ or $\left(9, \dfrac{13}{3}, \dfrac{13}{3}\right)$

38. Inconsistent   **39.** $x = -\dfrac{1}{2}, y = -\dfrac{2}{3}, z = -\dfrac{3}{4}$ or $\left(-\dfrac{1}{2}, -\dfrac{2}{3}, -\dfrac{3}{4}\right)$ **40.** $x = \dfrac{1}{3}, y = \dfrac{4}{5}, z = -\dfrac{1}{15}$ or $\left(\dfrac{1}{3}, \dfrac{4}{5}, -\dfrac{1}{15}\right)$

41. $z = -1, x = y + 1$, where y is any real number or $\left\{ (x, y, z) \mid x = y + 1, z = -1, y \text{ is any real number} \right\}$

42. $y = z, x = -\dfrac{1}{2}z$, where z is any real number or $\left\{ (x, y, z) \mid x = -\dfrac{1}{2}z, y = z, z \text{ is any real number} \right\}$ **43.** $x = 4, y = 2, z = 3, t = -2$ or $(4, 2, 3, -2)$

44. $x = -\dfrac{17}{15}, y = -\dfrac{1}{5}, z = \dfrac{22}{15}, t = -\dfrac{2}{15}$ or $\left(-\dfrac{17}{15}, -\dfrac{1}{5}, \dfrac{22}{15}, -\dfrac{2}{15}\right)$ **45.** 5   **46.** -12 **47.** 108   **48.** -19 **49.** -100 **50.** 11

51. $x = 2, y = -1$ or $(2, -1)$ **52.** $x = 0, y = \dfrac{5}{3}$ or $\left(0, \dfrac{5}{3}\right)$ **53.** $x = 2, y = 3$ or $(2, 3)$ **54.** $x = 0, y = -3$ or $(0, -3)$

55. $x = -1, y = 2, z = -3$ or $(-1, 2, -3)$ **56.** $x = \dfrac{37}{9}, y = -\dfrac{19}{6}, z = \dfrac{13}{18}$ or $\left(\dfrac{37}{9}, -\dfrac{19}{6}, \dfrac{13}{18}\right)$ **57.** 16   **58.** -8 **59.** $\dfrac{-\dfrac{3}{2}}{x} + \dfrac{\dfrac{3}{2}}{x - 4}$

60. $\dfrac{\frac{2}{5}}{x + 2} + \dfrac{\frac{3}{5}}{x - 3}$ **61.** $\dfrac{-3}{x - 1} + \dfrac{3}{x} + \dfrac{4}{x^2}$ **62.** $\dfrac{4}{x - 2} + \dfrac{-2}{(x - 2)^2} + \dfrac{-4}{x - 1}$ **63.** $\dfrac{-\frac{1}{10}}{x + 1} + \dfrac{\frac{1}{10}x + \frac{9}{10}}{x^2 + 9}$ **64.** $\dfrac{\frac{6}{5}}{x - 2} + \dfrac{-\frac{6}{5}x + \frac{3}{5}}{x^2 + 1}$

65. $\dfrac{x}{x^2 + 4} + \dfrac{-4x}{(x^2 + 4)^2}$ **66.** $\dfrac{x}{x^2 + 16} + \dfrac{-16x + 1}{(x^2 + 16)^2}$ **67.** $\dfrac{\frac{1}{2}}{x^2 + 1} + \dfrac{\frac{1}{4}}{x - 1} + \dfrac{-\frac{1}{4}}{x + 1}$ **68.** $\dfrac{-\frac{4}{5}}{x^2 + 4} + \dfrac{-\frac{2}{5}}{x + 1} + \dfrac{\frac{2}{5}}{x - 1}$ **69.** $x = -\dfrac{2}{5}, y = -\dfrac{11}{5};$

$x = -2, y = 1$ or $\left(-\dfrac{2}{5}, -\dfrac{11}{5}\right), (-2, 1)$ **70.** $x = 2, y = -2\sqrt{3}; x = 2, y = 2\sqrt{3}; x = -4, y = 0$ or $\left(2, -2\sqrt{3}\right), \left(2, 2\sqrt{3}\right), (-4, 0)$

71. $x = 2\sqrt{2}, y = \sqrt{2}; x = -2\sqrt{2}, y = -\sqrt{2}$ or $\left(2\sqrt{2}, \sqrt{2}\right), \left(-2\sqrt{2}, -\sqrt{2}\right)$ **72.** $x = -\sqrt{3}, y = -2\sqrt{2}; x = -\sqrt{3}, y = 2\sqrt{2}; x = \sqrt{3},$

$y = -2\sqrt{2}; x = \sqrt{3}, y = 2\sqrt{2}$ or $\left(-\sqrt{3}, -2\sqrt{2}\right), \left(-\sqrt{3}, 2\sqrt{2}\right), \left(\sqrt{3}, -2\sqrt{2}\right), \left(\sqrt{3}, 2\sqrt{2}\right)$ **73.** $x = 0, y = 0; x = -3, y = 3; x = 3, y = 3$

or $(0, 0), (-3, 3), (3, 3)$ **74.** $x = 0, y = -3; x = 0, y = 3$ or $(0, -3), (0, 3)$ **75.** $x = \sqrt{2}, y = -\sqrt{2}; x = -\sqrt{2}, y = \sqrt{2};$

$x = \dfrac{4}{3}\sqrt{2}, y = -\dfrac{2}{3}\sqrt{2}; x = -\dfrac{4}{3}\sqrt{2}, y = \dfrac{2}{3}\sqrt{2}$ or $\left(\sqrt{2}, -\sqrt{2}\right), \left(-\sqrt{2}, \sqrt{2}\right), \left(\dfrac{4}{3}\sqrt{2}, -\dfrac{2}{3}\sqrt{2}\right), \left(-\dfrac{4}{3}\sqrt{2}, \dfrac{2}{3}\sqrt{2}\right)$

76. $x = -\dfrac{5}{21}\sqrt{42}, y = -\dfrac{2}{7}\sqrt{42}; x = \dfrac{5}{21}\sqrt{42}, y = \dfrac{2}{7}\sqrt{42}; x = -2, y = 1; x = 2, y = -1$ or $\left(-\dfrac{5}{21}\sqrt{42}, -\dfrac{2}{7}\sqrt{42}\right), \left(\dfrac{5}{21}\sqrt{42}, \dfrac{2}{7}\sqrt{42}\right),$

$(-2, 1) (2, -1)$ **77.** $x = 1, y = -1$ or $(1, -1)$ **78.** $x = -2, y = 0; x = 1, y = 0; x = -1, y = 2$ or $(-2, 0), (1, 0), (-1, 2)$

79.

80.

81.

82.

83. Unbounded

84. Unbounded

85. Bounded

86. Unbounded

87. Bounded

88. Bounded

89.

90.

91.   **92.**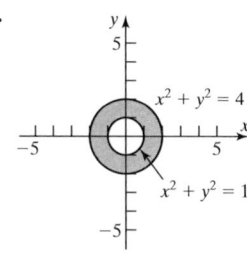

93. The maximum value is 32 when $x = 0$ and $y = 8$.   **94.** The maximum value is 20 when $x = 2$ and $y = 4$.

95. The minimum value is 3 when $x = 1$ and $y = 0$.   **96.** The minimum value is 4 when $x = 0$ and $y = 4$.

97. 10   **98.** A is any real number, $A \neq 10$.   **99.** $y = -\dfrac{1}{3}x^2 - \dfrac{2}{3}x + 1$ **100.** $x^2 + y^2 + 2x + 2y - 3 = 0$

101. Mix 70 lb of \$6.00 coffee and 30 lb of \$9.00 coffee.   **102.** Allocate 466.25 acres for corn and 533.75 acres for soybeans.

103. Buy 1 small, 5 medium, and 2 large.

104. (a) $x \geq 0$ **(b)**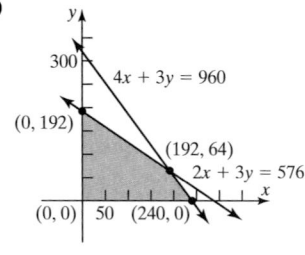
$$y \geq 0$$
$$4x + 3y \leq 960$$
$$2x + 3y \leq 576$$

105. Speedboat: 36.67 km/hr; Aguarico River: 3.33 km/hr

106. $\dfrac{475}{16} \approx 29.69$ mph

107. Bruce: 4hr; Bryce: 2hr; Marty: 8hr

108. Produce 12 mermaids and 12 dancing girls to have a profit of \$660; molding has 18 work-hours assigned that are not used.

109. Produce 35 gasoline engines and 15 diesel engines; the factory is producing an excess of 15 gasoline engines and 0 diesel engines.

Chapter Test *(page 799)*

1. $x = 3, y = -1$ or $(3, -1)$ **2.** Inconsistent.   **3.** $x = -z + \dfrac{18}{7}, y = z - \dfrac{17}{7}$, where z is any real number or

$\left\{(x, y, z) \mid x = -z + \dfrac{18}{7}, y = z - \dfrac{17}{7}, z \text{ is any real number}\right\}$ **4.** $x = \dfrac{1}{3}, y = -2, z = 0$ or $\left(\dfrac{1}{3}, -2, 0\right)$ **5.** $\begin{bmatrix} 4 & -5 & 1 & \mid & 0 \\ -2 & -1 & 0 & \mid & -25 \\ 1 & 5 & -5 & \mid & 10 \end{bmatrix}$

6. $\begin{cases} 3x + 2y + 4z = -6 \\ 1x + 0y + 8z = 2 \\ -2x + 1y + 3z = -11 \end{cases}$ or $\begin{cases} 3x + 2y + 4z = -6 \\ x + 8z = 2 \\ -2x + y + 3z = -11 \end{cases}$ **7.** $\begin{bmatrix} 6 & 4 \\ 1 & -11 \\ 5 & 12 \end{bmatrix}$ **8.** $\begin{bmatrix} -11 & -19 \\ -3 & 5 \\ 6 & -22 \end{bmatrix}$ **9.** The operation cannot be performed.   **10.** $\begin{bmatrix} 16 & 17 \\ 3 & -10 \end{bmatrix}$

11. $\begin{bmatrix} 2 & -1 \\ -\dfrac{5}{2} & \dfrac{3}{2} \end{bmatrix}$ **12.** $\begin{bmatrix} 3 & 3 & -4 \\ -2 & -2 & 3 \\ -4 & -5 & 7 \end{bmatrix}$ **13.** $x = \dfrac{1}{2}, y = 3$ or $\left(\dfrac{1}{2}, 3\right)$ **14.** $x = -\dfrac{1}{4}y + 7$, where y is any real number or

$\left\{(x, y) \mid x = -\dfrac{1}{4}y + 7, y \text{ is any real number}\right\}$ **15.** $x = 1, y = -2, z = 0$ or $(1, -2, 0)$ **16.** Inconsistent

17. -29 **18.** -12 **19.** $x = -2, y = -5$ or $(-2, -5)$ **20.** $x = 1, y = -1, z = 4$ or $(1, -1, 4)$ **21.** $(1, -3)$ and $(1, 3)$ **22.** $(3, 4)$ and $(1, 2)$

23.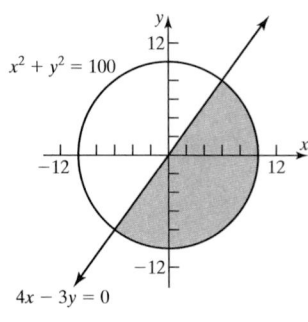

24. $\dfrac{3}{x + 3} + \dfrac{-2}{(x + 3)^2}$

25. $\dfrac{-\dfrac{1}{3}}{x} + \dfrac{\dfrac{1}{3}x}{(x^2 + 3)} + \dfrac{5x}{(x^2 + 3)^2}$

26. Unbounded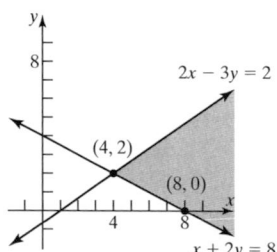

27. The maximum value of z is 64, and it occurs at the point $(0, 8)$.   **28.** Flare jeans cost \$24.50, camisoles cost \$8.50, and T-shirts cost \$6.00.

Cumulative Review *(page 800)*

1. $\left\{0, \dfrac{1}{2}\right\}$ **2.** $\{5\}$ **3.** $\left\{-1, -\dfrac{1}{2}, 3\right\}$ **4.** $\{-2\}$ **5.** $\left\{\dfrac{5}{2}\right\}$ **6.** $\left\{\dfrac{1}{\ln 3}\right\}$ **7.** Odd; symmetric with respect to the origin

8. Center: $(1, -2)$; radius $= 4$

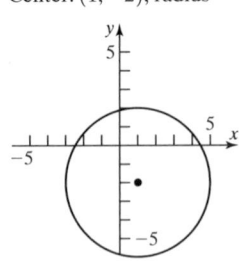

9. Domain: all real numbers
Range: $\{y|y > 1\}$
Horizontal asymptote: $y = 1$

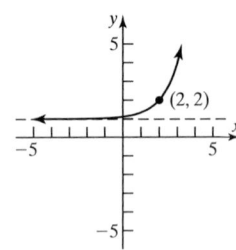

10. $f^{-1}(x) = \dfrac{5}{x} - 2$

Domain of f: $\{x|x \neq -2\}$
Range of f: $\{y|y \neq 0\}$
Domain of f^{-1}: $\{x|x \neq 0\}$
Range of f^{-1}: $\{y|y \neq -2\}$

11. (a)

(b)

(c)

(d)

(e)

(f)

(g)

(h)

(i)

(j)

(k)

(l)

12. (a)

$; -2.28$

(b) Local maximum of 7 at $x = -1$;
local minimum of 3 at $x = 1$

(c) $(-\infty, -1), (1, \infty)$

13. $\left\{ x \mid x = \pm \dfrac{\pi}{3} + 2\pi k, k \text{ any integer} \right\}$

CHAPTER 12 Sequences; Induction; the Binomial Theorem

12.1 Assess Your Understanding *(page 813)*

5. sequence **6.** 3; 15 **7.** 20 **8.** T **9.** T **10.** T **11.** 3,628,800 **12.** 362,880 **13.** 504 **14.** 132 **15.** 1260 **16.** 806,400

17. $s_1 = 1, s_2 = 2, s_3 = 3, s_4 = 4, s_5 = 5$ **18.** $s_1 = 2, s_2 = 5, s_3 = 10, s_4 = 17, s_5 = 26$ **19.** $a_1 = \frac{1}{3}, a_2 = \frac{1}{2}, a_3 = \frac{3}{5}, a_4 = \frac{2}{3}, a_5 = \frac{5}{7}$

20. $b_1 = \frac{3}{2}, b_2 = \frac{5}{4}, b_3 = \frac{7}{6}, b_4 = \frac{9}{8}, b_5 = \frac{11}{10}$ **21.** $c_1 = 1, c_2 = -4, c_3 = 9, c_4 = -16, c_5 = 25$ **22.** $d_1 = 1, d_2 = -\frac{2}{3}, d_3 = \frac{3}{5}, d_4 = -\frac{4}{7}, d_5 = \frac{5}{9}$

23. $s_1 = \frac{1}{2}, s_2 = \frac{2}{5}, s_3 = \frac{2}{7}, s_4 = \frac{8}{41}, s_5 = \frac{8}{61}$ **24.** $s_1 = \frac{4}{3}, s_2 = \frac{16}{9}, s_3 = \frac{64}{27}, s_4 = \frac{256}{81}, s_5 = \frac{1024}{243}$ **25.** $t_1 = -\frac{1}{6}, t_2 = \frac{1}{12}, t_3 = -\frac{1}{20}, t_4 = \frac{1}{30}, t_5 = -\frac{1}{42}$

26. $a_1 = 3, a_2 = \frac{9}{2}, a_3 = 9, a_4 = \frac{81}{4}, a_5 = \frac{243}{5}$ **27.** $b_1 = \frac{1}{e}, b_2 = \frac{2}{e^2}, b_3 = \frac{3}{e^3}, b_4 = \frac{4}{e^4}, b_5 = \frac{5}{e^5}$ **28.** $c_1 = \frac{1}{2}, c_2 = 1, c_3 = \frac{9}{8}, c_4 = 1, c_5 = \frac{25}{32}$

29. $a_n = \frac{n}{n+1}$ **30.** $a_n = \frac{1}{n(n+1)}$ **31.** $a_n = \frac{1}{2^{n-1}}$ **32.** $a_n = \left(\frac{2}{3}\right)^n$ **33.** $a_n = (-1)^{n+1}$ **34.** $a_n = \begin{cases} n & \text{if } n \text{ is odd} \\ \dfrac{1}{n} & \text{if } n \text{ is even} \end{cases}$ or $a_n = n^{(-1)^{n-1}}$

35. $a_n = (-1)^{n+1}n$ **36.** $a_n = (-1)^{n-1} \cdot 2n$ **37.** $a_1 = 2, a_2 = 5, a_3 = 8, a_4 = 11, a_5 = 14$ **38.** $a_1 = 3, a_2 = 1, a_3 = 3, a_4 = 1, a_5 = 3$

39. $a_1 = -2, a_2 = 0, a_3 = 3, a_4 = 7, a_5 = 12$ **40.** $a_1 = 1, a_2 = 1, a_3 = 2, a_4 = 2, a_5 = 3$ **41.** $a_1 = 5, a_2 = 10, a_3 = 20, a_4 = 40, a_5 = 80$

42. $a_1 = 2, a_2 = -2, a_3 = 2, a_4 = -2, a_5 = 2$ **43.** $a_1 = 3, a_2 = \frac{3}{2}, a_3 = \frac{1}{2}, a_4 = \frac{1}{8}, a_5 = \frac{1}{40}$ **44.** $a_1 = -2, a_2 = -4, a_3 = -9, a_4 = -23, a_5 = -64$

45. $a_1 = 1, a_2 = 2, a_3 = 2, a_4 = 4, a_5 = 8$ **46.** $a_1 = -1, a_2 = 1, a_3 = 2, a_4 = 9, a_5 = 47$ **47.** $a_1 = A, a_2 = A + d, a_3 = A + 2d, a_4 = A + 3d, a_5 = A + 4d$

48. $a_1 = A, a_2 = rA, a_3 = r^2A, a_4 = r^3A, a_5 = r^4A$

49. $a_1 = \sqrt{2}, a_2 = \sqrt{2 + \sqrt{2}}, a_3 = \sqrt{2 + \sqrt{2 + \sqrt{2}}}$,
$a_4 = \sqrt{2 + \sqrt{2 + \sqrt{2 + \sqrt{2}}}}$,
$a_5 = \sqrt{2 + \sqrt{2 + \sqrt{2 + \sqrt{2 + \sqrt{2}}}}}$

50. $a_1 = \sqrt{2}, a_2 = \sqrt{\frac{\sqrt{2}}{2}}, a_3 = \sqrt{\frac{\sqrt{\frac{\sqrt{2}}{2}}}{2}}, a_4 = \sqrt{\frac{\sqrt{\frac{\sqrt{\frac{\sqrt{2}}{2}}}{2}}}{2}}, a_5 = \sqrt{\frac{\sqrt{\frac{\sqrt{\frac{\sqrt{\frac{\sqrt{2}}{2}}}{2}}}{2}}}{2}}$

51. $3 + 4 + \cdots + (n + 2)$ **52.** $3 + 5 + 7 + \cdots + (2n + 1)$ **53.** $\frac{1}{2} + 2 + \frac{9}{2} + \cdots + \frac{n^2}{2}$ **54.** $4 + 9 + 16 + \cdots + (n + 1)^2$

55. $1 + \frac{1}{3} + \frac{1}{9} + \cdots + \frac{1}{3^n}$ **56.** $1 + \frac{3}{2} + \frac{9}{4} + \cdots + \left(\frac{3}{2}\right)^n$ **57.** $\frac{1}{3} + \frac{1}{9} + \frac{1}{27} + \cdots + \frac{1}{3^n}$ **58.** $1 + 3 + 5 + \cdots + (2n - 1)$

59. $\ln 2 - \ln 3 + \ln 4 - \cdots + (-1)^n \ln n$ **60.** $8 - 16 + 32 - \cdots + (-1)^{n+1} 2^n$ **61.** $\sum_{k=1}^{20} k$ **62.** $\sum_{k=1}^{8} k^3$ **63.** $\sum_{k=1}^{13} \frac{k}{k + 1}$ **64.** $\sum_{k=1}^{12}(2k - 1)$

65. $\sum_{k=0}^{6}(-1)^k\left(\frac{1}{3^k}\right)$ **66.** $\sum_{k=1}^{11}(-1)^{k+1}\left(\frac{2}{3}\right)^k$ **67.** $\sum_{k=1}^{n}\frac{3^k}{k}$ **68.** $\sum_{k=1}^{n}\frac{k}{e^k}$ **69.** $\sum_{k=0}^{n}(a + kd)$ or $\sum_{k=1}^{n+1}[a + (k - 1)d]$ **70.** $\sum_{k=0}^{n-1}ar^k$ or $\sum_{k=1}^{n}ar^{k-1}$ **71.** 200

72. 400 **73.** 820 **74.** −300 **75.** 1110 **76.** 871 **77.** 1560 **78.** 955 **79.** 3570 **80.** −2376 **81.** 44,000 **82.** 89,964

83. (a) $2930 (b) 14 payments have been made. (c) 36 payments; $3584.62 (d) $584.62

84. (a) $18,058.03 (b) 19 payments (c) After 39 payments; $20,364.31 (d) $1864.31 **85.** (a) 2162 (b) After 26 months

86. (a) 231 tons (b)   (c) 150 tons

n	$P_n = 0.9p_{n-1} + 15$ (tons)
1	240
2	231
3	222.9
4	215.61
5	209.05
6	203.14
7	197.83
8	193.05
9	188.74
10	184.87
11	181.38
12	178.24
13	175.42
14	172.88
15	170.59
16	168.53
17	166.68
18	165.01
19	163.51
20	162.16

87. (a) $a_0 = 0, a_n = (1.02)a_{n-1} + 500$
(b) After 82 quarters
(c) $156,116.15

88. (a) $A_n = (1.005)A_{n-1} + 45$
(b) 74 months or 6 years and 2 months
(c) $14,449.11

89. (a) $a_0 = 150,000$, $a_n = (1.005)a_{n-1} - 899.33$

(b) \$149,850.67   **(c)**

(d) After 58 payments or 4 years and 10 months later

(e) After 359 payments of \$899.33, plus last payment
of \$895.10

(f) \$173,754.57

(g) (a) $a_0 = 150,000$, $a_n = (1.005)a_{n-1} - 999.33$

(b) \$149,750.67   (c)

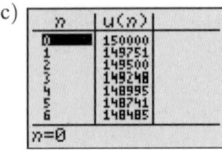

(d) After 37 payments or 3 years and 1 month later

(e) After 278 payments of \$999.33, plus last payment
of \$353.69(1.005) = \$355.46

(f) \$128,169.20

90. (a) $A_n = \left(1 + \dfrac{0.065}{12}\right)A_{n-1} - 758.48$, $A_0 = 120,000$

(b) \$119,891.52   **(c)**

(d) After 129 payments or 10 years and 9 months later

(e) After 359 monthly payments of \$758.48, plus last payment
of \$760.28

(f) \$153,054.60

(g) (a) $A_n = \left(1 + \dfrac{0.065}{12}\right)A_{n-1} - 858.48$, $A_0 = 120,000$

(b) \$119,791.52   (c)

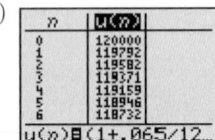

(d) After 78 payments or 6 years and 6 months later

(e) After 261 payments of \$858.48, plus last payment of \$855.84

(f) \$104,919.12

91. 21 pairs

92. (a) $u_1 = \dfrac{\left(1 + \sqrt{5}\right) - \left(1 - \sqrt{5}\right)}{2\sqrt{5}} = \dfrac{2\sqrt{5}}{2\sqrt{5}} = 1$

$u_2 = \dfrac{\left(1 + \sqrt{5}\right)^2 - \left(1 - \sqrt{5}\right)^2}{2^2\sqrt{5}}$

$= \dfrac{\left(1 + 2\sqrt{5} + 5\right) - \left(1 - 2\sqrt{5} + 5\right)}{4\sqrt{5}} = \dfrac{4\sqrt{5}}{4\sqrt{5}} = 1$

(b) Set $A = 1 + \sqrt{5}$, $B = 1 - \sqrt{5}$

$u_{n+2} = \dfrac{A^{n+2} - B^{n+2}}{2^{n+2}\sqrt{5}}$

$= \dfrac{A^2 \cdot A^n - B^2 \cdot B^n}{2^{n+2}\sqrt{5}}$

$= \dfrac{\left(1 + \sqrt{5}\right)^2 \cdot A^n - \left(1 - \sqrt{5}\right)^2 B^n}{2^{n+2}\sqrt{5}}$

$= \dfrac{\left(6 + 2\sqrt{5}\right) \cdot A^n - \left(6 - 2\sqrt{5}\right)B^n}{2^{n+2}\sqrt{5}}$

$= \dfrac{\left(3 + \sqrt{5}\right)A^n - \left(3 - \sqrt{5}\right)B^n}{2^{n+1}\sqrt{5}}$

$= \dfrac{\left(1 + \sqrt{5}\right)A^n - \left(1 - \sqrt{5}\right)B^n + 2A^n - 2B^n}{2^{n+1}\sqrt{5}}$

$= \dfrac{A^{n+1} - B^{n+1}}{2^{n+1}\sqrt{5}} + \dfrac{A^n - B^n}{2^n\sqrt{5}}$

$= u_{n+1} + u_n$

(c) This is a Fibonacci sequence since $u_1 = 1 = u_2$
and $u_{n+2} = u_{n+1} + u_n$.

93. Fibonacci sequence

94. (a) 1, 1, 2, 3, 5, 8, 13, 21, 34, 55, 89

(b) $1, 2, \dfrac{3}{2}, \dfrac{5}{3}, \dfrac{8}{5}, \dfrac{13}{8}, \dfrac{21}{13}, \dfrac{34}{21}, \dfrac{55}{34}, \dfrac{89}{55}$ **(c)** $\dfrac{1 + \sqrt{5}}{2}$

(d) $1, \dfrac{1}{2}, \dfrac{2}{3}, \dfrac{3}{5}, \dfrac{5}{8}, \dfrac{8}{13}, \dfrac{13}{21}, \dfrac{21}{34}, \dfrac{34}{55}, \dfrac{55}{89}$ **(e)** $\dfrac{2}{1 + \sqrt{5}}$

95. (a) 3.630170833   **(b)** 3.669060828   **(c)** 3.669296668   **(d)** 12

96. (a) -0.824 **(b)** 0.1602688   **(c)** 0.0907179533   **(d)** 17

97. (a) $a_1 = 0.4$; $a_2 = 0.7$; $a_3 = 1$; $a_4 = 1.6$; $a_5 = 2.8$; $a_6 = 5.2$; $a_7 = 10$; $a_8 = 19.6$

(b) Except for term 5, which has no match, Bode's formula provides
excellent approximations for the mean distances of the planets from
the sun.

(c) The mean distance of Ceres from the sun is approximated by $a_5 = 2.8$
and that of Uranus is $a_8 = 19.6$.

(d) $a_9 = 38.8$; $a_{10} = 77.2$

(e) Pluto's distance is approximated by a_9, but no term approximates
Neptune's mean distance from the sun.

(f) According to Bode's Law, the mean orbital distance of 2003 UB 313
will be 154 AU from the sun.

98. $a_0 = 2$; $a_5 = 2.236067977$; 2.236067977

99. $a_0 = 3$; $a_5 = 2.828427125$; 2.828427125

100. $a_0 = 4$; $a_5 = 4.582575695$; 4.582575695

101. $a_0 = 9$; $a_5 = 9.433981132$; 9.433981132

102. $2S = \underbrace{(1 + n) + (1 + n) + \cdots + (n + 1)}_{n \text{ terms}} = n(n + 1)$

$2S = n(n + 1)$

$S = \dfrac{1}{2}n(n + 1)$

12.2 Assess Your Understanding (page 821)

1. arithmetic **2.** F **3.** $s_n - s_{n-1} = (n + 4) - [(n - 1) + 4] = n + 4 - (n + 3) = n + 4 - n - 3 = 1$, a constant; $d = 1$; $s_1 = 5, s_2 = 6, s_3 = 7, s_4 = 8$

4. $s_n - s_{n-1} = (n - 5) - [(n - 1) - 5] = n - 5 - (n - 6) = n - 5 - n + 6 = 1$, a constant; $d = 1$; $s_1 = -4, s_2 = -3, s_3 = -2, s_4 = -1$

5. $a_n - a_{n-1} = (2n - 5) - [2(n - 1) - 5] = 2n - 5 - (2n - 2 - 5) = 2n - 5 - (2n - 7) = 2n - 5 - 2n + 7 = 2$, a constant; $d = 2$; $a_1 = -3, a_2 = -1, a_3 = 1, a_4 = 3$

6. $b_n - b_{n-1} = (3n + 1) - [3(n - 1) + 1] = 3n + 1 - (3n - 3 + 1) = 3n + 1 - (3n - 2) = 3n + 1 - 3n + 2 = 3$, a constant; $d = 3$; $b_1 = 4, b_2 = 7, b_3 = 10, b_4 = 13$

7. $c_n - c_{n-1} = (6 - 2n) - [6 - 2(n - 1)] = 6 - 2n - (6 - 2n + 2) = 6 - 2n - (8 - 2n) = 6 - 2n - 8 + 2n = -2$, a constant; $d = -2$; $c_1 = 4, c_2 = 2, c_3 = 0, c_4 = -2$

8. $d_n - d_{n-1} = (4 - 2n) - [4 - 2(n - 1)] = 4 - 2n - (4 - 2n + 2) = 4 - 2n - (6 - 2n) = 4 - 2n - 6 + 2n = -2$, a constant; $d = -2$; $d_1 = 2, d_2 = 0, d_3 = -2, d_4 = -4$

9. $t_n - t_{n-1} = \left(\dfrac{1}{2} - \dfrac{1}{3}n\right) - \left[\dfrac{1}{2} - \dfrac{1}{3}(n - 1)\right] = \dfrac{1}{2} - \dfrac{1}{3}n - \left(\dfrac{1}{2} - \dfrac{1}{3}n + \dfrac{1}{3}\right) = \dfrac{1}{2} - \dfrac{1}{3}n - \left(\dfrac{5}{6} - \dfrac{1}{3}n\right) = \dfrac{1}{2} - \dfrac{1}{3}n - \dfrac{5}{6} + \dfrac{1}{3}n = -\dfrac{1}{3}$, a constant; $d = -\dfrac{1}{3}$; $t_1 = \dfrac{1}{6}, t_2 = -\dfrac{1}{6}, t_3 = -\dfrac{1}{2}, t_4 = -\dfrac{5}{6}$

10. $t_n - t_{n-1} = \left(\dfrac{2}{3} + \dfrac{n}{4}\right) - \left(\dfrac{2}{3} + \dfrac{n - 1}{4}\right) = \dfrac{2}{3} + \dfrac{n}{4} - \left(\dfrac{2}{3} + \dfrac{n}{4} - \dfrac{1}{4}\right) = \dfrac{2}{3} + \dfrac{n}{4} - \left(\dfrac{5}{12} + \dfrac{n}{4}\right) = \dfrac{2}{3} + \dfrac{n}{4} - \dfrac{5}{12} - \dfrac{n}{4} = \dfrac{1}{4}$, a constant; $d = \dfrac{1}{4}$; $t_1 = \dfrac{11}{12}, t_2 = \dfrac{7}{6}, t_3 = \dfrac{17}{12}, t_4 = \dfrac{5}{3}$

11. $s_n - s_{n-1} = \ln 3^n - \ln 3^{n-1} = n \ln 3 - (n - 1) \ln 3 = n \ln 3 - (n \ln 3 - \ln 3) = n \ln 3 - n \ln 3 + \ln 3 = \ln 3$, a constant; $d = \ln 3$; $s_1 = \ln 3, s_2 = 2 \ln 3, s_3 = 3 \ln 3, s_4 = 4 \ln 3$

12. $s_n - s_{n-1} = e^{\ln n} - e^{\ln(n-1)} = n - (n - 1) = n - n + 1 = 1$, a constant; $d = 1$; $s_1 = 1, s_2 = 2, s_3 = 3, s_4 = 4$ **13.** $a_n = 3n - 1; a_{51} = 152$

14. $a_n = 4n - 6; a_{51} = 198$ **15.** $a_n = 8 - 3n; a_{51} = -145$ **16.** $a_n = 8 - 2n; a_{51} = -94$ **17.** $a_n = \dfrac{1}{2}(n - 1); a_{51} = 25$ **18.** $a_n = \dfrac{4}{3} - \dfrac{1}{3}n; a_{51} = -\dfrac{47}{3}$

19. $a_n = \sqrt{2}n; a_{51} = 51\sqrt{2}$ **20.** $a_n = (n - 1)\pi; a_{51} = 50\pi$ **21.** 200 **22.** 157 **23.** −266 **24.** −390 **25.** $\dfrac{83}{2}$

26. $140\sqrt{5}$ **27.** $a_1 = -13; d = 3; a_n = a_{n-1} + 3; a_n = -16 + 3n$ **28.** $a_1 = -3; d = 2; a_n = a_{n-1} + 2; a_n = -5 + 2n$

29. $a_1 = -53; d = 6; a_n = a_{n-1} + 6; a_n = -59 + 6n$ **30.** $a_1 = 74; d = -10; a_n = a_{n-1} - 10; a_n = 84 - 10n$

31. $a_1 = 28; d = -2; a_n = a_{n-1} - 2; a_n = 30 - 2n$ **32.** $a_1 = -18; d = 4; a_n = a_{n-1} + 4; a_n = -22 + 4n$

33. $a_1 = 25; d = -2; a_n = a_{n-1} - 2; a_n = 27 - 2n$ **34.** $a_1 = -40; d = 4; a_n = a_{n-1} + 4; a_n = -44 + 4n$ **35.** n^2 **36.** $n(n + 1)$ **37.** $\dfrac{n}{2}(9 + 5n)$

38. $n(2n - 3)$ **39.** 1260 **40.** 900 **41.** 324 **42.** 301 **43.** 30,919 **44.** −7592 **45.** 10,036 **46.** 4901 **47.** 6080 **48.** −7920 **49.** −1925 **50.** 1120

51. 15,960 **52.** −3013 **53.** $-\dfrac{3}{2}$ **54.** 1 **55.** 24 terms **56.** 13 or 27 terms **57.** 1185 seats **58.** 2160 seats **59.** 210 of beige and 190 blue

60. (a) 42 bricks **(b)** 2130 bricks **61.** $\{T_n\} = \{-5.5n + 67\}$; $T_5 = 39.5°F$ **62.** The ladder has 11 rungs, and 401.5 inches of material is needed.

63. The amphitheater has 1647 seats. **64.** 30 rows **65.** 8 yr

Historical Problems (page 830)

1. $1\dfrac{2}{3}$ loaves, $10\dfrac{5}{6}$ loaves, 20 loaves, $29\dfrac{1}{6}$ loaves, $38\dfrac{1}{3}$ loaves **2. (a)** 1 person **(b)** 2401 kittens **(c)** 2800

12.3 Assess Your Understanding (page 830)

1. geometric **2.** $\dfrac{a}{1 - r}$ **3.** annuity **4.** T **5.** F **6.** T **7.** $\dfrac{s_n}{s_{n-1}} = \dfrac{3^n}{3^{n-1}} = 3^{n-(n-1)} = 3$, a constant; $r = 3$; $s_1 = 3, s_2 = 9, s_3 = 27, s_4 = 81$

8. $\dfrac{s_n}{s_{n-1}} = \dfrac{(-5)^n}{(-5)^{n-1}} = (-5)^{n-(n-1)} = -5$, a constant; $r = -5$; $s_1 = -5, s_2 = 25, s_3 = -125, s_4 = 625$

9. $\dfrac{a_n}{a_{n-1}} = \dfrac{-3\left(\dfrac{1}{2}\right)^n}{-3\left(\dfrac{1}{2}\right)^{n-1}} = \left(\dfrac{1}{2}\right)^{n-(n-1)} = \dfrac{1}{2}$, a constant; $r = \dfrac{1}{2}$; $a_1 = -\dfrac{3}{2}, a_2 = -\dfrac{3}{4}, a_3 = -\dfrac{3}{8}, a_4 = -\dfrac{3}{16}$

10. $\dfrac{b_n}{b_{n-1}} = \dfrac{\left(\dfrac{5}{2}\right)^n}{\left(\dfrac{5}{2}\right)^{n-1}} = \left(\dfrac{5}{2}\right)^{n-(n-1)} = \dfrac{5}{2}$, a constant; $r = \dfrac{5}{2}$; $b_1 = \dfrac{5}{2}, b_2 = \dfrac{25}{4}, b_3 = \dfrac{125}{8}, b_4 = \dfrac{625}{16}$

11. $\dfrac{c_n}{c_{n-1}} = \dfrac{\dfrac{2^{n-1}}{4}}{\dfrac{2^{(n-1)-1}}{4}} = 2^{n-1-[(n-1)-1]} = 2$, a constant; $r = 2$; $c_1 = \dfrac{1}{4}, c_2 = \dfrac{1}{2}, c_3 = 1, c_4 = 2$

12. $\dfrac{d_n}{d_{n-1}} = \dfrac{\dfrac{3^n}{9}}{\dfrac{3^{n-1}}{9}} = 3^{n-(n-1)} = 3$, a constant; $r = 3$; $d_1 = \dfrac{1}{3}$, $d_2 = 1$, $d_3 = 3$, $d_4 = 9$

13. $\dfrac{e_n}{e_{n-1}} = \dfrac{2^{n/3}}{2^{(n-1)/3}} = 2^{n/3-(n-1)/3} = 2^{1/3}$, a constant; $r = 2^{1/3}$; $e_1 = 2^{1/3}$, $e_2 = 2^{2/3}$, $e_3 = 2$, $e_4 = 2^{4/3}$

14. $\dfrac{f_n}{f_{n-1}} = \dfrac{3^{2n}}{3^{2(n-1)}} = 3^{2n-2(n-1)} = 3^2 = 9$, a constant; $r = 9$; $f_1 = 9$, $f_2 = 81$, $f_3 = 729$, $f_4 = 6561$

15. $\dfrac{t_n}{t_{n-1}} = \dfrac{\dfrac{3^{n-1}}{2^n}}{\dfrac{3^{(n-1)-1}}{2^{n-1}}} = \dfrac{3^{n-1}}{2^n} \cdot \dfrac{2^{n-1}}{3^{(n-1)-1}} = 3^{n-1-[(n-1)-1]} \cdot 2^{n-1-n} = 3 \cdot 2^{-1} = \dfrac{3}{2}$, a constant; $r = \dfrac{3}{2}$; $t_1 = \dfrac{1}{2}$, $t_2 = \dfrac{3}{4}$, $t_3 = \dfrac{9}{8}$, $t_4 = \dfrac{27}{16}$

16. $\dfrac{u_n}{u_{n-1}} = \dfrac{\dfrac{2^n}{3^{n-1}}}{\dfrac{2^{n-1}}{3^{(n-1)-1}}} = \dfrac{2^n}{3^{n-1}} \cdot \dfrac{3^{(n-1)-1}}{2^{n-1}} = 2^{n-(n-1)} \cdot 3^{(n-1)-1-(n-1)} = 2 \cdot 3^{-1} = \dfrac{2}{3}$, a constant; $r = \dfrac{2}{3}$; $u_1 = 2$, $u_2 = \dfrac{4}{3}$, $u_3 = \dfrac{8}{9}$, $u_4 = \dfrac{16}{27}$

17. $a_5 = 162$; $a_n = 2 \cdot 3^{n-1}$ **18.** $a_5 = -512$; $a_n = -2 \cdot 4^{n-1}$ **19.** $a_5 = 5$; $a_n = 5 \cdot (-1)^{n-1}$ **20.** $a_5 = 96$; $a_n = 6 \cdot (-2)^{n-1}$ **21.** $a_5 = 0$; $a_n = 0$

22. $a_5 = \dfrac{1}{81}$; $a_n = \left(-\dfrac{1}{3}\right)^{n-1}$ **23.** $a_5 = 4\sqrt{2}$; $a_n = \left(\sqrt{2}\right)^n$ **24.** $a_5 = 0$; $a_n = 0$ **25.** $a_7 = \dfrac{1}{64}$ **26.** $a_8 = 2187$ **27.** $a_9 = 1$ **28.** $a_{10} = 512$

29. $a_8 = 0.00000004$ **30.** $a_7 = 100,000$ **31.** $a_n = 7 \cdot 2^{n-1}$ **32.** $a_n = 5 \cdot 2^{n-1}$ **33.** $a_n = -3 \cdot \left(-\dfrac{1}{3}\right)^{n-1} = \left(-\dfrac{1}{3}\right)^{n-2}$ **34.** $a_n = 4 \cdot \left(\dfrac{1}{4}\right)^{n-1} = \left(\dfrac{1}{4}\right)^{n-2}$

35. $a_n = -(-3)^{n-1}$ **36.** $a_n = 21 \cdot \left(\dfrac{1}{3}\right)^{n-1}$ **37.** $a_n = \dfrac{7}{15}(15)^{n-1} = 7 \cdot 15^{n-2}$ **38.** $a_n = 3 \cdot \left(\dfrac{1}{3}\right)^{n-1} = \left(\dfrac{1}{3}\right)^{n-2}$ **39.** $-\dfrac{1}{4}(1 - 2^n)$ **40.** $-\dfrac{1}{6}(1 - 3^n)$

41. $2\left[1 - \left(\dfrac{2}{3}\right)^n\right]$ **42.** $-2(1 - 3^n)$ **43.** $1 - 2^n$ **44.** $5\left[1 - \left(\dfrac{3}{5}\right)^n\right]$

45.   **46.**   **47.**   **48.**

49.   **50.**    **51.** Converges; $\dfrac{3}{2}$ **52.** Converges; 6   **53.** Converges; 16   **54.** Converges; 9

55. Converges; $\dfrac{8}{5}$ **56.** Converges; $\dfrac{4}{7}$ **57.** Diverges   **58.** Diverges

59. Converges; $\dfrac{20}{3}$ **60.** Converges; 12   **61.** Diverges   **62.** Diverges

63. Converges; $\dfrac{18}{5}$ **64.** Converges; $\dfrac{8}{3}$ **65.** Converges; 6   **66.** Converges; 6   **67.** Arithmetic; $d = 1$; 1375   **68.** Arithmetic; $d = 2$; 2300

69. Neither   **70.** Neither   **71.** Arithmetic; $d = -\dfrac{2}{3}$; -700 **72.** Arithmetic; $d = -\dfrac{3}{4}$; -556.25 **73.** Neither   **74.** Arithmetic; $d = 2$; 2550

75. Geometric; $r = \dfrac{2}{3}$; 1.999999997   **76.** Geometric; $r = \dfrac{5}{4}$; 350,319.6161   **77.** Geometric; $r = -2$; $3.752999689 \times 10^{14}$ **78.** Neither

79. Geometric; $r = 3^{1/2}$; $2.004706374 \times 10^{12}$ **80.** Geometric; $r = -1$; 0   **81.** -4 **82.** 2   **83.** $\$21,879.11$ **84.** $\$6655.58$ **85.** **(a)** 0.775 ft   **(b)** 8th swing

(c) 15.88 ft   **(d)** 20 ft   **86.** **(a)** 15.36 ft   **(b)** $30(0.8)^n$ **(c)** 19 times   **(d)** 270 ft   **87.** 1.845×10^{19} grains   **88.** $\dfrac{1}{3}$ **89.** 10   **90.** 20   **91.** $\$72.67$ per share

92. $\$39.64$ per share   **93.** December 20, 2007; $\$9999.92$ **94.** Option A results in a higher salary in year 5 ($\$25,250$ versus $\$24,761$); option B results in a higher 5-year total ($\$116,801$ versus $\$112,742$)   **95.** Option B results in more money ($\$524,287$ versus $\$500,500$).   **96.** Option 2 results in the most: $\$16,038,304$; option 1 results in the least: $\$14,700,000$.   **97.** Total pay: $\$41,943.03$; pay on day 22: $\$20,971.52$ **98.** Yes. A constant sequence is both arithmetic and geometric. For example, $3, 3, 3, \ldots$ is an arithmetic sequence with $a_1 = 3$ and $d = 0$ and is a geometric sequence with $a_1 = 3$ and $r = 1$.

12.4 Assess Your Understanding (page 836)

1. **(I)** $n = 1$: $2(1) = 2$ and $1(1 + 1) = 2$

(II) If $2 + 4 + 6 + \cdots + 2k = k(k + 1)$, then $2 + 4 + 6 + \cdots + 2k + 2(k + 1) = (2 + 4 + 6 + \cdots + 2k) + 2(k + 1)$
$= k(k + 1) + 2(k + 1) = k^2 + 3k + 2 = (k + 1)(k + 2) = (k + 1)[(k + 1) + 1]$.

2. (I) $n = 1$: $4(1) - 3 = 1$ and $1(2 - 1) = 1$

(II) If $1 + 5 + 9 + \cdots + (4k - 3) = k(2k - 1)$, then $1 + 5 + 9 + \cdots + (4k - 3) + [4(k + 1) - 3]$

$= [1 + 5 + 9 + \cdots + (4k - 3)] + (4k + 1) = k(2k - 1) + (4k + 1) = 2k^2 + 3k + 1 = (k + 1)(2k + 1)$

$= (k + 1)[2(k + 1) - 1]$.

3. (I) $n = 1$: $1 + 2 = 3$ and $\frac{1}{2}(1)(1 + 5) = \frac{1}{2}(6) = 3$

(II) If $3 + 4 + 5 + \cdots + (k + 2) = \frac{1}{2}k(k + 5)$, then $3 + 4 + 5 + \cdots + (k + 2) + [(k + 1) + 2]$

$= [3 + 4 + 5 + \cdots + (k + 2)] + (k + 3) = \frac{1}{2}k(k + 5) + k + 3 = \frac{1}{2}(k^2 + 7k + 6) = \frac{1}{2}(k + 1)(k + 6) = \frac{1}{2}(k + 1)[(k + 1) + 5]$.

4. (I) $n = 1$: $2(1) + 1 = 3$ and $1(1 + 2) = 3$

(II) If $3 + 5 + 7 + \cdots + (2k + 1) = k(k + 2)$, then $3 + 5 + 7 + \cdots + (2k + 1) + [2(k + 1) + 1]$

$= [3 + 5 + 7 + \cdots + (2k + 1)] + (2k + 3) = k(k + 2) + (2k + 3) = k^2 + 4k + 3 = (k + 1)(k + 3)$

$= (k + 1)[(k + 1) + 2]$.

5. (I) $n = 1$: $3(1) - 1 = 2$ and $\frac{1}{2}(1)[3(1) + 1] = \frac{1}{2}(4) = 2$

(II) If $2 + 5 + 8 + \cdots + (3k - 1) = \frac{1}{2}k(3k + 1)$, then $2 + 5 + 8 + \cdots + (3k - 1) + [3(k + 1) - 1]$

$= [2 + 5 + 8 + \cdots + (3k - 1)] + (3k + 2) = \frac{1}{2}k(3k + 1) + (3k + 2) = \frac{1}{2}(3k^2 + 7k + 4) = \frac{1}{2}(k + 1)(3k + 4)$

$= \frac{1}{2}(k + 1)[3(k + 1) + 1]$.

6. (I) $n = 1$: $3(1) - 2 = 1$ and $\frac{1}{2}(1)[3(1) - 1] = \frac{1}{2}(2) = 1$

(II) If $1 + 4 + 7 + \cdots + (3k - 2) = \frac{1}{2}k(3k - 1)$, then $1 + 4 + 7 + \cdots + (3k - 2) + [3(k + 1) - 2]$

$= [1 + 4 + 7 + \cdots + (3k - 2)] + (3k + 1) = \frac{1}{2}k(3k - 1) + (3k + 1) = \frac{1}{2}(3k^2 + 5k + 2) = \frac{1}{2}(k + 1)(3k + 2)$

$= \frac{1}{2}(k + 1)[3(k + 1) - 1]$.

7. (I) $n = 1$: $2^{1-1} = 1$ and $2^1 - 1 = 1$

(II) If $1 + 2 + 2^2 + \cdots + 2^{k-1} = 2^k - 1$, then $1 + 2 + 2^2 + \cdots + 2^{k-1} + 2^{(k+1)-1} = (1 + 2 + 2^2 + \cdots + 2^{k-1}) + 2^k$

$= 2^k - 1 + 2^k = 2(2^k) - 1 = 2^{k+1} - 1$.

8. (I) $n = 1$: $3^{1-1} = 1$ and $\frac{1}{2}(3^1 - 1) = 1$

(II) If $1 + 3 + 3^2 + \cdots + 3^{k-1} = \frac{1}{2}(3^k - 1)$, then $1 + 3 + 3^2 + \cdots + 3^{k-1} + 3^{(k+1)-1} = (1 + 3 + 3^2 + \cdots + 3^{k-1}) + 3^k$

$= \frac{1}{2}(3^k - 1) + 3^k = \frac{1}{2}[3^k - 1 + 2(3^k)] = \frac{1}{2}[3(3^k) - 1] = \frac{1}{2}(3^{k+1} - 1)$.

9. (I) $n = 1$: $4^{1-1} = 1$ and $\frac{1}{3}(4^1 - 1) = \frac{1}{3}(3) = 1$

(II) If $1 + 4 + 4^2 + \cdots + 4^{k-1} = \frac{1}{3}(4^k - 1)$, then $1 + 4 + 4^2 + \cdots + 4^{k-1} + 4^{(k+1)-1} = (1 + 4 + 4^2 + \cdots + 4^{k-1}) + 4^k$

$= \frac{1}{3}(4^k - 1) + 4^k = \frac{1}{3}[4^k - 1 + 3(4^k)] = \frac{1}{3}[4(4^k) - 1] = \frac{1}{3}(4^{k+1} - 1)$.

10. (I) $n = 1$: $5^{1-1} = 1$ and $\frac{1}{4}(5^1 - 1) = \frac{1}{4}(4) = 1$

(II) If $1 + 5 + 5^2 + \cdots + 5^{k-1} = \frac{1}{4}(5^k - 1)$, then $1 + 5 + 5^2 + \cdots + 5^{k-1} + 5^{(k+1)-1} = (1 + 5 + 5^2 + \cdots + 5^{k-1}) + 5^k$

$= \frac{1}{4}(5^k - 1) + 5^k = \frac{1}{4}[5^k - 1 + 4(5^k)] = \frac{1}{4}[5(5^k) - 1] = \frac{1}{4}(5^{k+1} - 1)$.

11. (I) $n = 1$: $\frac{1}{1 \cdot 2} = \frac{1}{2}$ and $\frac{1}{1 + 1} = \frac{1}{2}$

(II) If $\frac{1}{1 \cdot 2} + \frac{1}{2 \cdot 3} + \frac{1}{3 \cdot 4} + \cdots + \frac{1}{k(k + 1)} = \frac{k}{k + 1}$, then $\frac{1}{1 \cdot 2} + \frac{1}{2 \cdot 3} + \frac{1}{3 \cdot 4} + \cdots + \frac{1}{k(k + 1)} + \frac{1}{(k + 1)[(k + 1) + 1]}$

$= \left[\frac{1}{1 \cdot 2} + \frac{1}{2 \cdot 3} + \frac{1}{3 \cdot 4} + \cdots + \frac{1}{k(k + 1)} \right] + \frac{1}{(k + 1)(k + 2)} = \frac{k}{k + 1} + \frac{1}{(k + 1)(k + 2)} = \frac{k(k + 2) + 1}{(k + 1)(k + 2)}$

$= \frac{k^2 + 2k + 1}{(k + 1)(k + 2)} = \frac{(k + 1)^2}{(k + 1)(k + 2)} = \frac{k + 1}{k + 2} = \frac{k + 1}{(k + 1) + 1}$.

12. (I) $n = 1$: $\dfrac{1}{(2 \cdot 1 - 1)(2 \cdot 1 + 1)} = \dfrac{1}{3}$ and $\dfrac{1}{2 \cdot 1 + 1} = \dfrac{1}{3}$

(II) If $\dfrac{1}{1 \cdot 3} + \dfrac{1}{3 \cdot 5} + \dfrac{1}{5 \cdot 7} + \cdots + \dfrac{1}{(2k - 1)(2k + 1)} = \dfrac{k}{2k + 1}$, then

$\dfrac{1}{1 \cdot 3} + \dfrac{1}{3 \cdot 5} + \dfrac{1}{5 \cdot 7} + \cdots + \dfrac{1}{(2k - 1)(2k + 1)} + \dfrac{1}{[2(k + 1) - 1][2(k + 1) + 1]}$

$= \left[\dfrac{1}{1 \cdot 3} + \dfrac{1}{3 \cdot 5} + \dfrac{1}{5 \cdot 7} + \cdots + \dfrac{1}{(2k - 1)(2k + 1)} \right] + \dfrac{1}{(2k + 1)(2k + 3)}$

$= \dfrac{k}{2k + 1} + \dfrac{1}{(2k + 1)(2k + 3)} = \dfrac{k(2k + 3) + 1}{(2k + 1)(2k + 3)} = \dfrac{2k^2 + 3k + 1}{(2k + 1)(2k + 3)} = \dfrac{(2k + 1)(k + 1)}{(2k + 1)(2k + 3)} = \dfrac{k + 1}{2k + 3} = \dfrac{k + 1}{2(k + 1) + 1}$.

13. (I) $n = 1$: $1^2 = 1$ and $\dfrac{1}{6} \cdot 1 \cdot 2 \cdot 3 = 1$

(II) If $1^2 + 2^2 + 3^2 + \cdots + k^2 = \dfrac{1}{6}k(k + 1)(2k + 1)$, then $1^2 + 2^2 + 3^2 + \cdots + k^2 + (k + 1)^2$

$= (1^2 + 2^2 + 3^2 + \cdots + k^2) + (k + 1)^2 = \dfrac{1}{6}k(k + 1)(2k + 1) + (k + 1)^2 = \dfrac{1}{6}(k + 1)[k(2k + 1) + 6(k + 1)]$

$= \dfrac{1}{6}(k + 1)(2k^2 + 7k + 6) = \dfrac{1}{6}(k + 1)(k + 2)(2k + 3) = \dfrac{1}{6}(k + 1)[(k + 1) + 1][2(k + 1) + 1]$.

14. (I) $n = 1$: $1^3 = 1$ and $\dfrac{1}{4} \cdot 1^2(1 + 1)^2 = 1$

(II) If $1^3 + 2^3 + 3^3 + \cdots + k^3 = \dfrac{1}{4}k^2(k + 1)^2$, then $1^3 + 2^3 + 3^3 + \cdots + k^3 + (k + 1)^3 = (1^3 + 2^3 + 3^3 + \cdots + k^3) + (k + 1)^3$

$= \dfrac{1}{4}k^2(k + 1)^2 + (k + 1)^3 = (k + 1)^2\left(\dfrac{1}{4}k^2 + k + 1\right) = \dfrac{1}{4}(k + 1)^2(k^2 + 4k + 4) = \dfrac{1}{4}(k + 1)^2(k + 2)^2 = \dfrac{1}{4}(k + 1)^2[(k + 1) + 1]^2$.

15. (I) $n = 1$: $5 - 1 = 4$ and $\dfrac{1}{2}(1)(9 - 1) = \dfrac{1}{2} \cdot 8 = 4$

(II) If $4 + 3 + 2 + \cdots + (5 - k) = \dfrac{1}{2}k(9 - k)$, then $4 + 3 + 2 + \cdots + (5 - k) + [5 - (k + 1)]$

$= [4 + 3 + 2 + \cdots + (5 - k)] + 4 - k = \dfrac{1}{2}k(9 - k) + 4 - k = \dfrac{1}{2}(9k - k^2 + 8 - 2k) = \dfrac{1}{2}(-k^2 + 7k + 8)$

$= \dfrac{1}{2}(k + 1)(8 - k) = \dfrac{1}{2}(k + 1)[9 - (k + 1)]$.

16. (I) $n = 1$: $-(1 + 1) = -2$ and $-\dfrac{1}{2}(1)(1 + 3) = -2$

(II) If $-2 - 3 - 4 - \cdots - (k + 1) = -\dfrac{1}{2}k(k + 3)$, then $-2 - 3 - 4 - \cdots - (k + 1) - [(k + 1) + 1]$

$= [-2 - 3 - 4 - \cdots - (k + 1)] - (k + 2) = -\dfrac{1}{2}k(k + 3) - (k + 2) = -\dfrac{1}{2}(k^2 + 3k + 2k + 4) = -\dfrac{1}{2}(k^2 + 5k + 4)$

$= -\dfrac{1}{2}(k + 1)(k + 4) = -\dfrac{1}{2}(k + 1)[(k + 1) + 3]$.

17. (I) $n = 1$: $1 \cdot (1 + 1) = 2$ and $\dfrac{1}{3} \cdot 1 \cdot 2 \cdot 3 = 2$

(II) If $1 \cdot 2 + 2 \cdot 3 + 3 \cdot 4 + \cdots + k(k + 1) = \dfrac{1}{3}k(k + 1)(k + 2)$, then

$1 \cdot 2 + 2 \cdot 3 + 3 \cdot 4 + \cdots + k(k + 1) + (k + 1)[(k + 1) + 1] = [1 \cdot 2 + 2 \cdot 3 + 3 \cdot 4 + \cdots + k(k + 1)] + (k + 1)(k + 2)$

$= \dfrac{1}{3}k(k + 1)(k + 2) + \dfrac{1}{3} \cdot 3(k + 1)(k + 2) = \dfrac{1}{3}(k + 1)(k + 2)(k + 3) = \dfrac{1}{3}(k + 1)[(k + 1) + 1][(k + 1) + 2]$.

18. (I) $n = 1$: $(2 \cdot 1 - 1)(2 \cdot 1) = 2$ and $\dfrac{1}{3} \cdot 1 \cdot (1 + 1)(4 \cdot 1 - 1) = 2$

(II) If $1 \cdot 2 + 3 \cdot 4 + 5 \cdot 6 + \cdots + (2k - 1)(2k) = \dfrac{1}{3}k(k + 1)(4k - 1)$, then

$1 \cdot 2 + 3 \cdot 4 + 5 \cdot 6 + \cdots + (2k - 1)(2k) + [2(k + 1) - 1][2(k + 1)]$

$= [1 \cdot 2 + 3 \cdot 4 + 5 \cdot 6 + \cdots + (2k - 1)(2k)] + (2k + 1)(k + 1) \cdot 2$

$= \dfrac{1}{3}k(k + 1)(4k - 1) + 2(k + 1)(2k + 1) = (k + 1)\left[\dfrac{1}{3}k(4k - 1) + 2(2k + 1)\right]$

$= (k + 1)\left[\dfrac{4}{3}k^2 - \dfrac{1}{3}k + 4k + 2\right] = \dfrac{1}{3}(k + 1)\left(4k^2 - k + 12k + 6\right)$

$= \dfrac{1}{3}(k + 1)(4k^2 + 11k + 6) = \dfrac{1}{3}(k + 1)(k + 2)(4k + 3) = \dfrac{1}{3}(k + 1)[(k + 1) + 1][4(k + 1) - 1]$.

19. (I) $n = 1$: $1^2 + 1 = 2$, which is divisible by 2.

(II) If $k^2 + k$ is divisible by 2, then $(k + 1)^2 + (k + 1) = k^2 + 2k + 1 + k + 1 = (k^2 + k) + 2k + 2$. Since $k^2 + k$ is divisible by 2 and $2k + 2$ is divisible by 2, $(k + 1)^2 + (k + 1)$ is divisible by 2.

20. (I) $n = 1$: $1^3 + 2 \cdot 1 = 3$, which is divisible by 3.

(II) If $k^3 + 2k$ is divisible by 3, then $(k + 1)^3 + 2(k + 1) = k^3 + 3k^2 + 3k + 1 + 2k + 2 = (k^3 + 2k) + 3k^2 + 3k + 3$.

Since $k^3 + 2k$ is divisible by 3 and $3k^2 + 3k + 3$ is divisible by 3, $(k + 1)^3 + 2(k + 1)$ is divisible by 3.

21. (I) $n = 1$: $1^2 - 1 + 2 = 2$, which is divisible by 2.

(II) If $k^2 - k + 2$ is divisible by 2, then $(k + 1)^2 - (k + 1) + 2 = k^2 + 2k + 1 - k - 1 + 2 = (k^2 - k + 2) + 2k$. Since $k^2 - k + 2$ is divisible by 2 and $2k$ is divisible by 2, $(k + 1)^2 - (k + 1) + 2$ is divisible by 2.

22. (I) $n = 1$: $1(1 + 1)(1 + 2) = 6$, which is divisible by 6.

(II) If $k(k + 1)(k + 2)$ is divisible by 6, then $(k + 1)[(k + 1) + 1][(k + 1) + 2] = (k + 1)(k + 2)(k + 3)$

$= (k + 1)(k + 2)k + (k + 1)(k + 2)3 = k(k + 1)(k + 2) + 3(k + 1)(k + 2)$. Now, $k(k + 1)(k + 2)$ is divisible by 6, and since $k + 1$ and $k + 2$ are consecutive integers, either $k + 1$ or $k + 2$ is even (divisible by 2).

In either case, $3(k + 1)(k + 2)$ is divisible by 6, and so $(k + 1)[(k + 1) + 1][(k + 1) + 2]$ is divisible by 6.

23. (I) $n = 1$: If $x > 1$, then $x^1 = x > 1$.

(II) Assume, for an arbitrary natural number k, that if $x > 1$ then $x^k > 1$. Multiply both sides of the inequality $x^k > 1$ by x. If $x > 1$, then $x^{k+1} > x > 1$.

24. (I) $n = 1$: If $0 < x < 1$, then $x^1 = x$ and $0 < x^1 < 1$.

(II) Assume, for an arbitrary natural number k, that if $0 < x < 1$ then $0 < x^k < 1$. Multiply all sides of the inequalities $0 < x^k < 1$ by x. If $0 < x < 1$, then $0 < x^k x < x < 1$ and $0 < x^{k+1} < 1$.

25. (I) $n = 1$: $a - b$ is a factor of $a^1 - b^1 = a - b$.

(II) If $a - b$ is a factor of $a^k - b^k$, then $a^{k+1} - b^{k+1} = a(a^k - b^k) + b^k(a - b)$.

Since $a - b$ is a factor of $a^k - b^k$ and $a - b$ is a factor of $a - b$, then $a - b$ is a factor of $a^{k+1} - b^{k+1}$.

26. (I) $n = 1$: $a^{2 \cdot 1 + 1} + b^{2 \cdot 1 + 1} = a^3 + b^3 = (a + b)(a^2 - ab + b^2)$, so $a + b$ is a factor of $a^3 + b^3$.

(II) If $a + b$ is a factor of $a^{2k+1} + b^{2k+1}$, then $a^{2(k+1)+1} + b^{2(k+1)+1} = a^{2k+3} + b^{2k+3} = a^{2k+1}a^2 + b^{2k+1}b^2$

$= a^{2k+1}a^2 + b^{2k+1}a^2 - b^{2k+1}a^2 + b^{2k+1}b^2 = a^2(a^{2k+1} + b^{2k+1}) - b^{2k+1}(a^2 - b^2) = a^2(a^{2k+1} + b^{2k+1}) - b^{2k+1}(a + b)(a - b)$.

Since $a + b$ is a factor of $a^{2k+1} + b^{2k+1}$ and $a + b$ is a factor of $b^{2k+1}(a + b)(a - b)$, then $a + b$ is a factor of $a^{2(k+1)+1} + b^{2(k+1)+1}$.

27. (I) $n = 1$: $(1 + a)^1 = 1 + a \geq 1 + 1 \cdot a$

(II) Assume that there is an integer k for which the inequality holds. So $(1 + a)^k \geq 1 + ka$. We need to show that $(1 + a)^{k+1} \geq 1 + (k + 1)a$.

$(1 + a)^{k+1} = (1 + a)^k (1 + a) \geq (1 + ka)(1 + a) = 1 + ka^2 + a + ka = 1 + (k + 1)a + ka^2 \geq 1 + (k + 1)a$.

28. $n = 1$: $1^2 - 1 + 41 = 41$, which is a prime number.

$n = 41$: $41^2 - 41 + 41 = 1681 = 41^2$, which is not prime.

29. If $2 + 4 + 6 + \cdots + 2k = k^2 + k + 2$, then $2 + 4 + 6 + \cdots + 2k + 2(k + 1)$

$= (2 + 4 + 6 + \cdots + 2k) + 2k + 2 = k^2 + k + 2 + 2k + 2 = k^2 + 3k + 4 = (k^2 + 2k + 1) + (k + 1) + 2$

$= (k + 1)^2 + (k + 1) + 2$.

But $2 \cdot 1 = 2$ and $1^2 + 1 + 2 = 4$. The fact is that $2 + 4 + 6 + \cdots + 2n = n^2 + n$, not $n^2 + n + 2$ (Problem 1).

30. (I) $n = 1$: $ar^{1-1} = a \cdot 1 = a$ and $a \cdot \dfrac{1 - r^1}{1 - r} = a$, because $r \neq 1$.

(II) If $a + ar + ar^2 + \cdots + ar^{k-1} = a \cdot \dfrac{1 - r^k}{1 - r}$, then $a + ar + ar^2 + \cdots + ar^{k-1} + ar^{(k+1)-1} = (a + ar + ar^2 + \cdots + ar^{k-1}) + ar^k$

$= a \cdot \dfrac{1 - r^k}{1 - r} + ar^k = \dfrac{a(1 - r^k) + ar^k(1 - r)}{1 - r} = \dfrac{a - ar^k + ar^k - ar^{k+1}}{1 - r} = a \cdot \dfrac{1 - r^{k+1}}{1 - r}$.

31. (I) $n = 1$: $[a + (1 - 1)d] = a$ and $1 \cdot a + d \dfrac{1 \cdot (1 - 1)}{2} = a$.

(II) If $a + (a + d) + (a + 2d) + \cdots + [a + (k - 1)d] = ka + d \dfrac{k(k - 1)}{2}$, then

$a + (a + d) + (a + 2d) + \cdots + [a + (k - 1)d] + [a + ((k + 1) - 1)d] = ka + d \dfrac{k(k - 1)}{2} + a + kd$

$= (k + 1)a + d \dfrac{k(k - 1) + 2k}{2} = (k + 1)a + d \dfrac{(k + 1)(k)}{2} = (k + 1)a + d \dfrac{(k + 1)[(k + 1) - 1]}{2}$.

32. (I) $n = 4$: The number of diagonals in a convex polygon of 4 sides is 2 and $\dfrac{1}{2} \cdot 4 \cdot (4 - 3) = 2$.

(II) If the number of diagonals in a convex polygon of k sides is $\dfrac{1}{2}k(k - 3)$, then that of $(k + 1)$ sides is increased by $(k - 2) + 1 = k - 1$. Note all diagonals in a k-sided convex polygon correspond to a diagonal in a $(k + 1)$-sided convex polygon. In addition, the additional vertex of a $(k + 1)$-sided convex polygon makes a diagonal with $k - 2$ of the other vertices and the two vertices it does not make a diagonal with, make a diagonal with each other. Thus, the number of diagonals in a convex polygon of $(k + 1)$ sides is $\dfrac{1}{2}k(k - 3) + (k - 1)$

$= \dfrac{1}{2}[k^2 - 3k + 2k - 2] = \dfrac{1}{2}[k^2 - k - 2] = \dfrac{1}{2}(k + 1)(k - 2) = \dfrac{1}{2}(k + 1)[(k + 1) - 3]$.

33. (I) $n = 3$: The sum of the angles of a triangle is $(3 - 2) \cdot 180° = 180°$.

(II) Assume for some $k \geq 3$ that the sum of the angles of a convex polygon of k sides is $(k - 2) \cdot 180°$. A convex polygon of $k + 1$ sides consists of a convex polygon of k sides plus a triangle (see the illustration). The sum of the angles is

$$(k - 2) \cdot 180° + 180° = (k - 1) \cdot 180° = [(k + 1) - 2] \cdot 180°.$$

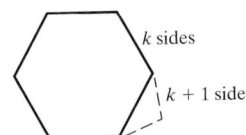

k sides

$k + 1$ sides

12.5 Assess Your Understanding (page 842)

1. Pascal triangle **2.** 15 **3.** F **4.** Binomial Theorem **5.** 10 **6.** 35 **7.** 21 **8.** 36 **9.** 50 **10.** 4950 **11.** 1 **12.** 1

13. $\approx 1.8664 \times 10^{15}$ **14.** $\approx 4.1918 \times 10^{15}$ **15.** $\approx 1.4834 \times 10^{13}$ **16.** $\approx 1.7673 \times 10^{10}$ **17.** $x^5 + 5x^4 + 10x^3 + 10x^2 + 5x + 1$

18. $x^5 - 5x^4 + 10x^3 - 10x^2 + 5x - 1$ **19.** $x^6 - 12x^5 + 60x^4 - 160x^3 + 240x^2 - 192x + 64$ **20.** $x^5 + 15x^4 + 90x^3 + 270x^2 + 405x + 243$

21. $81x^4 + 108x^3 + 54x^2 + 12x + 1$ **22.** $32x^5 + 240x^4 + 720x^3 + 1080x^2 + 810x + 243$ **23.** $x^{10} + 5x^8y^2 + 10x^6y^4 + 10x^4y^6 + 5x^2y^8 + y^{10}$

24. $x^{12} - 6x^{10}y^2 + 15x^8y^4 - 20x^6y^6 + 15x^4y^8 - 6x^2y^{10} + y^{12}$ **25.** $x^3 + 6\sqrt{2}x^{5/2} + 30x^2 + 40\sqrt{2}x^{3/2} + 60x + 24\sqrt{2}x^{1/2} + 8$

26. $x^2 - 4\sqrt{3}x^{3/2} + 18x - 12\sqrt{3}x^{1/2} + 9$ **27.** $a^5x^5 + 5a^4bx^4y + 10a^3b^2x^3y^2 + 10a^2b^3x^2y^3 + 5ab^4xy^4 + b^5y^5$

28. $a^4x^4 - 4a^3bx^3y + 6a^2b^2x^2y^2 - 4ab^3xy^3 + b^4y^4$ **29.** 17,010 **30.** $-262,440$ **31.** $-101,376$ **32.** 1760 **33.** 41,472 **34.** $-314,928$ **35.** $2835x^3$

36. $189x^5$ **37.** $314,928x^7$ **38.** $48,384x^3$ **39.** 495 **40.** -84 **41.** 3360 **42.** 252 **43.** 1.00501 **44.** 0.98806

45. $\binom{n}{n-1} = \dfrac{n!}{(n-1)! \, [n - (n-1)]!} = \dfrac{n!}{(n-1)! \, 1!} = \dfrac{n \cdot (n-1)!}{(n-1)!} = n; \binom{n}{n} = \dfrac{n!}{n! \, (n-n)!} = \dfrac{n!}{n!0!} = \dfrac{n!}{n!} = 1$

46. $\binom{n}{n-j} = \dfrac{n!}{(n-j)! \, [n-(n-j)]!} = \dfrac{n!}{(n-j)! \, j!} = \dfrac{n!}{j! \, (n-j)!} = \binom{n}{j}$

47. $2^n = (1+1)^n = \binom{n}{0}1^n + \binom{n}{1}(1)^{n-1}(1) + \cdots + \binom{n}{n}1^n = \binom{n}{0} + \binom{n}{1} + \cdots + \binom{n}{n}$

48. $0 = 0^n = (1-1)^n = \binom{n}{0}1^n + \binom{n}{1}(1)^{n-1}(-1) + \binom{n}{2}(1)^{n-2}(-1)^2 + \cdots + \binom{n}{n}(-1)^n = \binom{n}{0} - \binom{n}{1} + \binom{n}{2} - \cdots + (-1)^n\binom{n}{n}$

49. 1 **50.** $12! = 479,001,600 \approx 479,013,972.4$

$20! \approx 2.432902008 \times 10^{18} \approx 2.43292403 \times 10^{18}$

$25! \approx 1.551121004 \times 10^{25} \approx 1.551129917 \times 10^{25}$

Review Exercises (page 844)

1. $a_1 = -\dfrac{4}{3}, a_2 = \dfrac{5}{4}, a_3 = -\dfrac{6}{5}, a_4 = \dfrac{7}{6}, a_5 = -\dfrac{8}{7}$ **2.** $b_1 = 5, b_2 = -7, b_3 = 9, b_4 = -11, b_5 = 13$ **3.** $c_1 = 2, c_2 = 1, c_3 = \dfrac{8}{9}, c_4 = 1, c_5 = \dfrac{32}{25}$

4. $d_1 = e, d_2 = \dfrac{e^2}{2}, d_3 = \dfrac{e^3}{3}, d_4 = \dfrac{e^4}{4}, d_5 = \dfrac{e^5}{5}$ **5.** $a_1 = 3, a_2 = 2, a_3 = \dfrac{4}{3}, a_4 = \dfrac{8}{9}, a_5 = \dfrac{16}{27}$ **6.** $a_1 = 4, a_2 = -1, a_3 = \dfrac{1}{4}, a_4 = -\dfrac{1}{16}, a_5 = \dfrac{1}{64}$

7. $a_1 = 2, a_2 = 0, a_3 = 2, a_4 = 0, a_5 = 2$ **8.** $a_1 = -3, a_2 = 1, a_3 = 5, a_4 = 9, a_5 = 13$ **9.** $6 + 10 + 14 + 18 = 48$ **10.** $2 + (-1) + (-6) = -5$

11. $\displaystyle\sum_{k=1}^{13} (-1)^{k+1} \dfrac{1}{k}$ **12.** $\displaystyle\sum_{k=0}^{n} \dfrac{2^{k+1}}{3^k}$ **13.** Arithmetic; $d = 1; S_n = \dfrac{n}{2}(n + 11)$ **14.** Arithmetic; $d = 4; S_n = n(2n + 5)$ **15.** Neither **16.** Neither

17. Geometric; $r = 8; S_n = \dfrac{8}{7}(8^n - 1)$ **18.** Geometric; $r = 9; S_n = \dfrac{9}{8}(9^n - 1)$ **19.** Arithmetic; $d = 4; S_n = 2n(n - 1)$

20. Arithmetic; $d = -4; S_n = n(3 - 2n)$ **21.** Geometric; $r = \dfrac{1}{2}; S_n = 6\left[1 - \left(\dfrac{1}{2}\right)^n\right]$ **22.** Geometric; $r = -\dfrac{1}{3}; S_n = \dfrac{15}{4}\left[1 - \left(-\dfrac{1}{3}\right)^n\right]$

23. Neither **24.** Neither **25.** 3825 **26.** 9455 **27.** 1125 **28.** -1320 **29.** $\dfrac{1093}{2187} \approx 0.49977$ **30.** 682 **31.** 35 **32.** -13

33. $\dfrac{1}{10^{10}}$ **34.** 1024 **35.** $9\sqrt{2}$ **36.** $16\sqrt{2}$ **37.** $\{a_n\} = \{5n - 4\}$ **38.** $\{a_n\} = \{4 - 3n\}$ **39.** $\{a_n\} = \{n - 10\}$ **40.** $\{a_n\} = \{2n + 6\}$

41. Converges; $\dfrac{9}{2}$ **42.** Converges; 4 **43.** Converges; $\dfrac{4}{3}$ **44.** Converges; $\dfrac{18}{5}$ **45.** Diverges **46.** Diverges **47.** Converges; 8 **48.** Converges; $\dfrac{12}{7}$

49. (I) $n = 1: 3 \cdot 1 = 3$ and $\dfrac{3 \cdot 1}{2}(1 + 1) = 3$

(II) If $3 + 6 + 9 + \cdots + 3k = \dfrac{3k}{2}(k + 1)$, then $3 + 6 + 9 + \cdots + 3k + 3(k + 1) = (3 + 6 + 9 + \cdots + 3k) + (3k + 3)$

$= \dfrac{3k}{2}(k + 1) + (3k + 3) = \dfrac{3k}{2}(k + 1) + 3(k + 1) = 3(k + 1)\left(\dfrac{k}{2} + 1\right) = \dfrac{3}{2}(k + 1)(k + 2) = \dfrac{3(k + 1)}{2}[(k + 1) + 1].$

50. (I) $n = 1: (4 \cdot 1 - 2) = 2$ and $2 \cdot 1^2 = 2$

(II) If $2 + 6 + 10 + \cdots + (4k - 2) = 2k^2$, then $2 + 6 + 10 + \cdots + (4k - 2) + [4(k + 1) - 2]$

$= [2 + 6 + 10 + \cdots + (4k - 2)] + (4k + 2) = 2k^2 + (4k + 2) = 2(k + 1)^2.$

51. (I) $n = 1: 2 \cdot 3^{1-1} = 2$ and $3^1 - 1 = 2$

(II) If $2 + 6 + 18 + \cdots + 2 \cdot 3^{k-1} = 3^k - 1$, then $2 + 6 + 18 + \cdots + 2 \cdot 3^{k-1} + 2 \cdot 3^{(k+1)-1} = (2 + 6 + 18 + \cdots + 2 \cdot 3^{k-1}) + 2 \cdot 3^k$
$= 3^k - 1 + 2 \cdot 3^k = 3 \cdot 3^k - 1 = 3^{k+1} - 1.$

52. (I) $n = 1: 3 \cdot 2^{1-1} = 3$ and $3(2^1 - 1) = 3$

(II) If $3 + 6 + 12 + \cdots + 3 \cdot 2^{k-1} = 3(2^k - 1)$, then $3 + 6 + 12 + \cdots + 3 \cdot 2^{k-1} + 3 \cdot 2^{(k+1)-1}$
$= (3 + 6 + 12 + \cdots + 3 \cdot 2^{k-1}) + 3 \cdot 2^k = 3(2^k - 1) + 3 \cdot 2^k = 3(2 \cdot 2^k - 1) = 3(2^{k+1} - 1).$

53. (I) $n = 1: (3 \cdot 1 - 2)^2 = 1$ and $\frac{1}{2} \cdot 1 \cdot [6(1)^2 - 3(1) - 1] = 1$

(II) If $1^2 + 4^2 + 7^2 + \cdots + (3k - 2)^2 = \frac{1}{2} k(6k^2 - 3k - 1)$, then $1^2 + 4^2 + 7^2 + \cdots + (3k - 2)^2 + [3(k + 1) - 2]^2$

$= [1^2 + 4^2 + 7^2 + \cdots + (3k - 2)^2] + (3k + 1)^2 = \frac{1}{2} k(6k^2 - 3k - 1) + (3k + 1)^2 = \frac{1}{2}(6k^3 - 3k^2 - k) + (9k^2 + 6k + 1)$

$= \frac{1}{2}(6k^3 + 15k^2 + 11k + 2) = \frac{1}{2}(k + 1)(6k^2 + 9k + 2) = \frac{1}{2}(k + 1)[6(k + 1)^2 - 3(k + 1) - 1].$

54. (I) $n = 1: 1 \cdot (1 + 2) = 3$ and $\frac{1}{6}(1 + 1)(2 \cdot 1 + 7) = 3$

(II) If $1 \cdot 3 + 2 \cdot 4 + 3 \cdot 5 + \cdots + k(k + 2) = \frac{k}{6}(k + 1)(2k + 7)$, then
$1 \cdot 3 + 2 \cdot 4 + 3 \cdot 5 + \cdots + k(k + 2) + (k + 1)[(k + 1) + 2] = [1 \cdot 3 + 2 \cdot 4 + 3 \cdot 5 + \cdots + k(k + 2)] + (k + 1)(k + 3)$
$+ (k + 1)[(k + 1) + 2] = [1 \cdot 3 + 2 \cdot 4 + 3 \cdot 5 + \cdots + k(k + 2)] + (k + 1)(k + 3)$
$= \frac{k}{6}(k + 1)(2k + 7) + (k + 1)(k + 3) = (k + 1)\left[\frac{k}{6}(2k + 7) + k + 3\right] = \frac{1}{6}(k + 1)(2k^2 + 13k + 18)$
$= \frac{1}{6}(k + 1)(k + 2)(2k + 9) = \frac{k + 1}{6}[(k + 1) + 1][2(k + 1) + 7].$

55. 10 **56.** 28 **57.** $x^5 + 10x^4 + 40x^3 + 80x^2 + 80x + 32$ **58.** $x^4 - 12x^3 + 54x^2 - 108x + 81$ **59.** $32x^5 + 240x^4 + 720x^3 + 1080x^2 + 810x + 243$
60. $81x^4 - 432x^3 + 864x^2 - 768x + 256$ **61.** 144 **62.** $-13,608$ **63.** 84 **64.** 1792 **65.** (a) 8 bricks (b) 1100 bricks **66.** 360 tiles

67. (a) $20\left(\frac{3}{4}\right)^3 = \frac{135}{16}$ ft

(b) $20\left(\frac{3}{4}\right)^n$ ft

(c) 13 times

(d) 140 ft

68. (a) $A_0 = 190{,}000, A_n = \left(1 + \frac{0.0675}{12}\right)$
$A_n = \left(1 + \frac{0.0675}{12}\right)A_{n-1} - 1232.34$

(b) \$189,836.41

(c)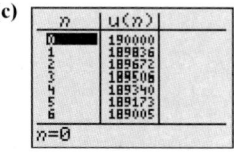

(d) After 252 months
(e) After 359 payments of \$1232.34, plus last payment of \$1228.14
(f) \$253,638.20

(g) (a) $A_0 = 190{,}000, A_n = \left(1 + \frac{0.0675}{12}\right)$
$A_n = \left(1 + \frac{0.0675}{12}\right)A_{n-1} - 1332.34$

(b) \$189,736.41

(c)

(d) After 192 months
(e) After 288 payments of \$1332.34, plus last payment of \$1149.23
(f) \$194,863.15

69. (a) \$4975
(b)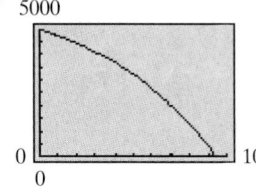

(c) At the beginning of the thirty-third month the balance is less than \$4000. At this time, 32 payments of \$100 each have been made.
(d) 93 payments of \$100 plus 1 payment of \$11.18; \$9311.18
(e) \$4311.18

70. \$23,397.17

Chapter Test *(page 846)*

1. $0, \frac{3}{10}, \frac{8}{11}, \frac{5}{4}, \frac{24}{13}$ **2.** 4, 14, 44, 134, 404 **3.** $2 - \frac{3}{4} + \frac{4}{9} = \frac{61}{36}$ **4.** $-\frac{1}{3} - \frac{14}{9} - \frac{73}{27} - \frac{308}{81} = -\frac{680}{81}$ **5.** $\sum_{k=1}^{10}(-1)^k\left(\frac{k + 1}{k + 4}\right)$ **6.** Neither

7. Geometric; $r = 4$; $S_n = \frac{2}{3}(1 - 4^n)$ **8.** Arithmetic: $d = -8$; $S_n = n(2 - 4n)$ **9.** Arithmetic; $d = -\frac{1}{2}$; $S_n = \frac{n}{4}(27 - n)$

10. Geometric; $r = \frac{2}{5}$ $S_n = \frac{125}{3}\left[1 - \left(\frac{2}{5}\right)^n\right]$ **11.** Neither **12.** Converges; $\frac{1024}{5}$ **13.** $243m^5 + 810m^4 + 1080m^3 + 720m^2 + 240m + 32$

14. First we show that the statement holds for $n = 1$. $\left(1 + \dfrac{1}{1}\right) = 1 + 1 = 2$. The equality is true for $n = 1$, so Condition I holds. Next we assume that

$$\left(1 + \frac{1}{1}\right)\left(1 + \frac{1}{2}\right)\left(1 + \frac{1}{3}\right)\cdots\left(1 + \frac{1}{n}\right) = n + 1 \text{ is true for some } k, \text{ and we show the formula then holds for } k + 1. \text{ We assume that}$$

$$\left(1 + \frac{1}{1}\right)\left(1 + \frac{1}{2}\right)\left(1 + \frac{1}{3}\right)\cdots\left(1 + \frac{1}{k}\right) = k + 1. \text{ Now we need to show that } \left(1 + \frac{1}{1}\right)\left(1 + \frac{1}{2}\right)\left(1 + \frac{1}{3}\right)\cdots\left(1 + \frac{1}{k}\right)\left(1 + \frac{1}{k+1}\right)$$

$= (k + 1) + 1 = k + 2$. We do this as follows:

$$\left(1 + \frac{1}{1}\right)\left(1 + \frac{1}{2}\right)\left(1 + \frac{1}{3}\right)\cdots\left(1 + \frac{1}{k}\right)\left(1 + \frac{1}{k+1}\right) = \left[\left(1 + \frac{1}{1}\right)\left(1 + \frac{1}{2}\right)\left(1 + \frac{1}{3}\right)\cdots\left(1 + \frac{1}{k}\right)\right]\left(1 + \frac{1}{k+1}\right) = (k + 1)\left(1 + \frac{1}{k+1}\right)$$

$$\text{(induction assumption)} = (k + 1)\cdot 1 + (k + 1)\cdot\frac{1}{k+1} = k + 1 + 1 = k + 2$$

Condition II also holds. Thus, the formula holds true for all natural numbers.

15. After 10 years, the Durango will be worth $6103.11.   **16.** The weight lifter will have lifted a total of 8000 pounds after 5 sets.

Cumulative Review *(page 847)*

1. $\{-3, 3, -3i, 3i\}$ **2. (a)**

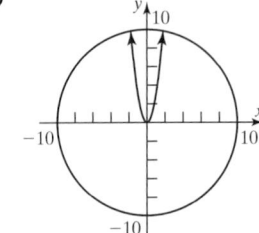

(b) $\left\{\left(\sqrt{\dfrac{-1 + \sqrt{3601}}{18}}, \dfrac{-1 + \sqrt{3601}}{6}\right), \left(-\sqrt{\dfrac{-1 + \sqrt{3601}}{18}}, \dfrac{-1 + \sqrt{3601}}{6}\right)\right\}$

(c) The circle and the parabola intersect at

$$\left(\sqrt{\frac{-1 + \sqrt{3601}}{18}}, \frac{-1 + \sqrt{3601}}{6}\right), \left(-\sqrt{\frac{-1 + \sqrt{3601}}{18}}, \frac{-1 + \sqrt{3601}}{6}\right).$$

3. $\left\{\ln\left(\dfrac{5}{2}\right)\right\}$ **4.** $y = 5x - 10$ **5.** $x^2 + y^2 + 2x - 4y - 20 = 0$

6. (a) 5   **(b)** 13   **(c)** $\dfrac{6x + 3}{2x - 1}$ **(d)** $\left\{x \mid x \neq \dfrac{1}{2}\right\}$ **(e)** $\dfrac{7x - 2}{x - 2}$ **(f)** $\{x \mid x \neq 2\}$ **(g)** $g^{-1}(x) = \dfrac{1}{2}(x-1)$; all reals   **(h)** $f^{-1}(x) = \dfrac{2x}{x - 3}$; $\{x \mid x \neq 3\}$

7. $\dfrac{x^2}{7} + \dfrac{y^2}{16} = 1$ **8.** $(x + 1)^2 = 4(y - 2)$ **9.** $r = 8 \sin\theta$; $x^2 + (y - 4)^2 = 16$ **10.** $\left\{\dfrac{3\pi}{2}\right\}$ **11.** $\dfrac{2\pi}{3}$

12. (a) $-\dfrac{\sqrt{15}}{4}$ **(b)** $-\dfrac{\sqrt{15}}{15}$ **(c)** $-\dfrac{\sqrt{15}}{8}$ **(d)** $\dfrac{7}{8}$ **(e)** $\sqrt{\dfrac{1 + \dfrac{\sqrt{15}}{4}}{2}} = \dfrac{\sqrt{4 + \sqrt{15}}}{2\sqrt{2}}$

CHAPTER 13 Counting and Probability

13.1 Assess Your Understanding *(page 854)*

5. $n(A) + n(B) - n(A \cap B)$ **6.** F   **7.** $\emptyset$, $\{a\}$, $\{b\}$, $\{c\}$, $\{d\}$, $\{a, b\}$, $\{a, c\}$, $\{a, d\}$, $\{b, c\}$, $\{b, d\}$, $\{c, d\}$, $\{a, b, c\}$, $\{a, b, d\}$, $\{a, c, d\}$, $\{b, c, d\}$, $\{a, b, c, d\}$ **8.** $\emptyset$, $\{a\}$, $\{b\}$, $\{c\}$, $\{d\}$, $\{e\}$, $\{a, b\}$, $\{a, c\}$, $\{a, d\}$, $\{a, e\}$, $\{b, c\}$, $\{b, d\}$, $\{b, e\}$, $\{c, d\}$, $\{c, e\}$, $\{d, e\}$, $\{a, b, c\}$, $\{a, b, d\}$, $\{a, b, e\}$, $\{a, c, d\}$, $\{a, c, e\}$, $\{a, d, e\}$, $\{b, c, d\}$, $\{b, c, e\}$, $\{b, d, e\}$, $\{c, d, e\}$, $\{a, b, c, d\}$, $\{a, b, c, e\}$, $\{a, b, d, e\}$, $\{a, c, d, e\}$, $\{b, c, d, e\}$, $\{a, b, c, d, e\}$
9. 25   **10.** 25   **11.** 40   **12.** 50   **13.** 25   **14.** 20   **15.** 37   **16.** 8   **17.** 18   **18.** 31   **19.** 5   **20.** 52   **21.** 15 different arrangements
22. 40 different outfits   **23.** 9000 numbers   **24.** 80,000 numbers   **25.** 175; 125   **26.** 550   **27. (a)** 15   **(b)** 15   **(c)** 15   **(d)** 25   **(e)** 40

28.

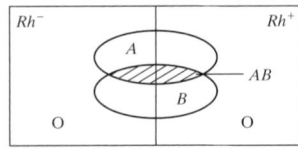

29. (a) 11,923 thousand
(b) 75,241 thousand
30. (a) 24,037 thousand   **31.** 480 portfolios.
(b) 88,008 thousand

13.2 Assess Your Understanding *(page 861)*

3. permutation   **4.** combination   **5.** T   **6.** T   **7.** 30   **8.** 42   **9.** 24   **10.** 40,320   **11.** 1   **12.** 1   **13.** 1680   **14.** 336   **15.** 28   **16.** 28   **17.** 35
18. 15   **19.** 1   **20.** 18   **21.** 10,400,600   **22.** 48,620   **23.** $\{abc, abd, abe, acb, acd, ace, adb, adc, ade, aeb, aec, aed, bac, bad, bae, bca, bcd, bce, bda,$
$bdc, bde, bea, bec, bed, cab, cad, cae, cba, cbd, cbe, cda, cdb, cde, cea, ceb, ced, dab, dac, dae, dba, dbc, dbe, dca, dcb, dce, dea, deb, dec, eab, eac, ead,$
$eba, ebc, ebd, eca, ecb, ecd, eda, edb, edc\}$; 60   **24.** $\{ab, ba, ac, ca, ad, da, ae, ea, bc, cb, bd, db, be, eb, cd, dc, ce, ec, de, ed\}$; 20

25. {123, 124, 132, 134, 142, 143, 213, 214, 231, 234, 241, 243, 312, 314, 321, 324, 341, 342, 412, 413, 421, 423, 431, 432}; 24   **26.** {123, 132, 213, 231, 312, 321, 124, 142, 214, 241, 412, 421, 125, 152, 215, 251, 512, 521, 126, 162, 216, 261, 612, 621, 134, 143, 314, 341, 413, 431, 135, 153, 315, 351, 513, 531, 136, 163, 316, 361, 613, 631, 145, 154, 415, 451, 514, 541, 146, 164, 416, 461, 614, 641, 156, 165, 516, 561, 615, 651, 234, 243, 324, 342, 423, 432, 235, 253, 325, 352, 523, 532, 236, 263, 326, 362, 623, 632, 245, 254, 425, 452, 524, 542, 246, 264, 426, 462, 624, 642, 256, 265, 526, 562, 625, 652, 345, 354, 435, 453, 534, 543, 346, 364, 436, 463, 634, 643, 356, 365, 536, 563, 635, 653, 456, 465, 546, 564, 645, 654}; 120   **27.** {abc, abd, abe, acd, ace, ade, bcd, bce, bde, cde}; 10   **28.** {ab, ac, ad, ae, bc, bd, be, cd, ce, de}; 10   **29.** {123, 124, 134, 234}; 4   **30.** {123, 124, 125, 126, 134, 135, 136, 145, 146, 156, 234, 235, 236, 245, 246, 256, 345, 346, 356, 456}; 20   **31.** 16   **32.** 25   **33.** 8   **34.** 1000 (allowing numbers with initial zeros such as 012)   **35.** 24   **36.** 120   **37.** 60   **38.** 360   **39.** 18,278   **40.** 12,338,352   **41.** 35   **42.** 56   **43.** 1024   **44.** 1024   **45.** 120   **46.** (a) 6,760,000   (b) 3,407,040   (c) 3,276,000   **47.** 132,860   **48.** 6,302,555,018,760   **49.** 336   **50.** 5,209,344   **51.** 90,720   **52.** 4,989,600   **53.** (a) 63   (b) 35   (c) 1   **54.** (a) 3003   (b) 20,475   (c) 16,653   **55.** 1.157×10^{76} **56.** 302,400   **57.** 362,880   **58.** 40,320   **59.** 660   **60.** 70   **61.** 15   **62.** 126   **63.** (a) 125,000   (b) A better name for a *combination* lock would be a *permutation* lock because the order of the numbers matters.

Historical Problems (page 871)

1. (a) {AAAA, AAAB, AABA, AABB, ABAA, ABAB, ABBA, ABBB, BAAA, BAAB, BABA, BABB, BBAA, BBAB, BBBA, BBBB};

$P(A \text{ wins}) = \dfrac{11}{16}$; $P(B \text{ wins}) = \dfrac{5}{16}$; A should get $\dfrac{11}{16}$ of the stakes and B should set $\dfrac{5}{16}$ of the stakes.

(b) $P(A \text{ wins}) = \dfrac{C(4,2) + C(4,3) + C(4,4)}{2^4} = \dfrac{6 + 4 + 1}{16} = \dfrac{11}{16}$; $P(B \text{ wins}) = \dfrac{C(4,3) + C(4,4)}{2^4} = \dfrac{4 + 1}{16} = \dfrac{5}{16}$

2. (a) $\$\dfrac{3}{2} = \$1.50$ **(b)** $\$\dfrac{1}{2} = \$0.50$

13.3 Assess Your Understanding (page 871)

1. equally likely   **2.** complement   **3.** F   **4.** T   **5.** $0, 0.01, 0.35, 1$ **6.** $\dfrac{1}{2}, \dfrac{3}{4}, \dfrac{2}{3}, 0$ **7.** Probability model   **8.** Probability model

9. Not a probability model   **10.** Not a probability model   **11.** $S = \{HH, HT, TH, TT\}$; $P(HH) = \dfrac{1}{4}, P(HT) = \dfrac{1}{4}, P(TH) = \dfrac{1}{4}, P(TT) = \dfrac{1}{4}$

12. $S = \{HH, HT, TH, TT\}$; $P(HH) = \dfrac{1}{4}, P(HT) = \dfrac{1}{4}, P(TH) = \dfrac{1}{4}, P(TT) = \dfrac{1}{4}$

13. $S = \{HH1, HH2, HH3, HH4, HH5, HH6, HT1, HT2, HT3, HT4, HT5, HT6, TH1, TH2, TH3, TH4, TH5, TH6, TT1, TT2, TT3, TT4, TT5, TT6\}$; each outcome has a probability of $\dfrac{1}{24}$.   **14.** $S = \{H1H, H2H, H3H, H4H, H5H, H6H, H1T, H2T, H3T, H4T, H5T, H6T, T1H, T2H, T3H, T4H, T5H, T6H, T1T, T2T, T3T, T4T, T5T, T6T\}$; each outcome has a probability of $\dfrac{1}{24}$.   **15.** $S = \{HHH, HHT, HTH, HTT, THH, THT, TTH, TTT\}$; each outcome has a probability of $\dfrac{1}{8}$.   **16.** $S = \{HHH, HHT, HTH, HTT, THH, THT, TTH, TTT\}$; each outcome has a probability of $\dfrac{1}{8}$.

17. $S = \{$1 Yellow, 1 Red, 1 Green, 2 Yellow, 2 Red, 2 Green, 3 Yellow, 3 Red, 3 Green, 4 Yellow, 4 Red, 4 Green$\}$; each outcome has a probability of $\dfrac{1}{12}$; thus, $P(2 \text{ Red}) + P(4 \text{ Red}) = \dfrac{1}{12} + \dfrac{1}{12} = \dfrac{1}{6}$.

18. $S = \{$Forward Yellow, Forward Green, Forward Red, Backward Yellow, Backward Green, Backward Red$\}$; each outcome has a probability of $\dfrac{1}{6}$; thus, $P(\text{Forward Yellow}) + P(\text{Forward Green}) = \dfrac{1}{6} + \dfrac{1}{6} = \dfrac{1}{3}$.

19. $S = \{$1 Yellow Forward, 1 Yellow Backward, 1 Red Forward, 1 Red Backward, 1 Green Forward, 1 Green Backward, 2 Yellow Forward, 2 Yellow Backward, 2 Red Forward, 2 Red Backward, 2 Green Forward, 2 Green Backward, 3 Yellow Forward, 3 Yellow Backward, 3 Red Forward, 3 Red Backward, 3 Green Forward, 3 Green Backward, 4 Yellow Forward, 4 Yellow Backward, 4 Red Forward, 4 Red Backward, 4 Green Forward, 4 Green Backward$\}$; each outcome has a probability of $\dfrac{1}{24}$; thus, $P(1 \text{ Red Backward}) + P(1 \text{ Green Backward}) = \dfrac{1}{24} + \dfrac{1}{24} = \dfrac{1}{12}$.

20. $S = \{$Yellow 1 Forward, Yellow 1 Backward, Yellow 2 Forward, Yellow 2 Backward, Yellow 3 Forward, Yellow 3 Backward, Yellow 4 Forward, Yellow 4 Backward, Green 1 Forward, Green 1 Backward, Green 2 Forward, Green 2 Backward, Green 3 Forward, Green 3 Backward, Green 4 Forward, Green 4 Backward, Red 1 Forward, Red 1 Backward, Red 2 Forward, Red 2 Backward, Red 3 Forward, Red 3 Backward, Red 4 Forward, Red 4 Backward$\}$; each outcome has a probability of $\dfrac{1}{24}$; thus, $P(\text{Yellow 2 Forward}) + P(\text{Yellow 4 Forward}) = \dfrac{1}{24} + \dfrac{1}{24} = \dfrac{1}{12}$.

21. $S = \{$11 Red, 11 Yellow, 11 Green, 12 Red, 12 Yellow, 12 Green, 13 Red, 13 Yellow, 13 Green, 14 Red, 14 Yellow, 14 Green, 21 Red, 21 Yellow, 21 Green, 22 Red, 22 Yellow, 22 Green, 23 Red, 23 Yellow, 23 Green, 24 Red, 24 Yellow, 24 Green, 31 Red, 31 Yellow, 31 Green, 32 Red, 32 Yellow, 32 Green, 33 Red, 33 Yellow, 33 Green, 34 Red, 34 Yellow, 34 Green, 41 Red, 41 Yellow, 41 Green, 42 Red, 42 Yellow, 42 Green, 43 Red, 43 Yellow, 43 Green, 44 Red, 44 Yellow, 44 Green$\}$; each outcome has a probability of $\dfrac{1}{48}$; thus, $P(22 \text{ Red}) + P(22 \text{ Green}) + P(24 \text{ Red}) + P(24 \text{ Green})$

$= \dfrac{1}{48} + \dfrac{1}{48} + \dfrac{1}{48} + \dfrac{1}{48} = \dfrac{1}{12}$.

22. $S = \{$Forward 11, Forward 12, Forward 13, Forward 14, Forward 21, Forward 22, Forward 23, Forward 24, Forward 31, Forward 32, Forward 33, Forward 34, Forward 41, Forward 42, Forward 43, Forward 44, Backward 11, Backward 12, Backward 13, Backward 14, Backward 21, Backward 22, Backward 23, Backward 24, Backward 31, Backward 32, Backward 33, Backward 34, Backward 41, Backward 42, Backward 43, Backward 44$\}$; each outcome

has a probability of $\frac{1}{32}$; thus, $P(\text{Forward } 12) + P(\text{Forward } 14) + P(\text{Forward } 32) + P(\text{Forward } 34) = \frac{1}{32} + \frac{1}{32} + \frac{1}{32} + \frac{1}{32} = \frac{1}{8}$.

23. A, B, C, F   **24.** A   **25.** B   **26.** F   **27.** $P(\text{H}) = \frac{4}{5}$; $P(\text{T}) = \frac{1}{5}$ **28.** $P(\text{H}) = \frac{1}{3}$; $P(\text{T}) = \frac{2}{3}$

29. $P(1) = P(3) = P(5) = \frac{2}{9}$; $P(2) = P(4) = P(6) = \frac{1}{9}$ **30.** $P(1) = P(2) = P(3) = P(4) = P(5) = \frac{1}{5}$; $P(6) = 0$ **31.** $\frac{3}{10}$ **32.** $\frac{2}{5}$ **33.** $\frac{1}{2}$

34. $\frac{1}{2}$ **35.** $\frac{1}{6}$ **36.** $\frac{7}{30}$ **37.** $\frac{1}{8}$ **38.** $\frac{1}{8}$ **39.** $\frac{1}{4}$ **40.** $\frac{3}{8}$ **41.** $\frac{1}{6}$ **42.** $\frac{1}{18}$ **43.** $\frac{1}{18}$ **44.** $\frac{1}{36}$ **45.** 0.55   **46.** 0.10   **47.** 0.70   **48.** 0   **49.** 0.30   **50.** 0.5

51. 0.87   **52.** 0.37   **53.** 0.66   **54.** 0.863   **55.** 0.95   **56.** 0.91   **57.** $\frac{17}{20}$ **58.** $\frac{3}{5}$ **59.** $\frac{11}{20}$ **60.** $\frac{3}{5}$ **61.** $\frac{1}{2}$ **62.** $\frac{1}{10}$ **63.** $\frac{3}{10}$ **64.** $\frac{13}{20}$ **65.** $\frac{2}{5}$ **66.** $\frac{3}{5}$

67. (a) 0.57   **(b)** 0.95   **(c)** 0.83   **(d)** 0.38   **(e)** 0.29   **(f)** 0.05   **(g)** 0.78   **(h)** 0.71   **68. (a)** 0.45   **(b)** 0.75   **(c)** 0.90   **69. (a)** $\frac{25}{33}$ **(b)** $\frac{25}{33}$

70. (a) $\frac{7}{13}$ **(b)** $\frac{11}{13}$ **71.** 0.167   **72.** 0.814   **73.** 0.000033069

Review Exercises *(page 875)*

1. $\emptyset$, {Dave}, {Joanne}, {Erica}, {Dave, Joanne}, {Dave, Erica}, {Joanne, Erica}, {Dave, Joanne, Erica}
2. $\emptyset$, {Green}, {Blue}, {Red}, {Green, Blue}, {Green, Red}, {Blue, Red}, {Green, Blue, Red}
3. 17   **4.** 24   **5.** 29   **6.** 34   **7.** 7   **8.** 45   **9.** 25   **10.** 7   **11.** 336   **12.** 210   **13.** 56   **14.** 35   **15.** 60   **16.** 120   **17.** 128   **18.** 64   **19.** 3024   **20.** 24
21. 1680   **22.** 120   **23.** 91   **24. (a)** 14,400   **(b)** 14,400   **25.** 1,600,000   **26.** 60   **27.** 216,000   **28.** 256 (allowing numbers with initial zeros, such as 011)
29. 1260   **30.** 12,600   **31. (a)** 381,024   **(b)** 1260   **32. (a)** 280   **(b)** 280   **(c)** 640   **33. (a)** $8.634628387 \times 10^{45}$ **(b)** 0.6531   **(c)** 0.3469
34. (a) 0.28   **(b)** 0.72   **35. (a)** 0.045   **(b)** 0.955   **36.** 0.15; 0.45   **37.** $\frac{4}{9}$ **38.** $\frac{1}{24}$ **39.** 0.2; 0.26   **40. (a)** 0.68   **(b)** 0.58   **(c)** 0.32

Chapter Test *(page 876)*

1. 22   **2.** 3   **3.** 8   **4.** 45   **5.** 5040   **6.** 151,200   **7.** 462   **8.** There are 54,264 ways to choose 6 colors from the 21 available colors.   **9.** There are 840 distinct arrangements of the letters in the word REDEEMED.   **10.** There are 56 different exacta bets for an 8-horse race.   **11.** There are 155,480,000 possible license plates using the new format.   **12. (a)** 0.95   **(b)** 0.30   **13. (a)** 0.25   **(b)** 0.55   **14.** 0.19

15. $P(\text{win on \$1 play}) = \frac{1}{120,526,770} \approx 0.0000000083$ **16.** $P(\text{exactly 2 fours}) = \frac{1250}{7776} \approx 0.1608$

Cumulative Review *(page 877)*

1. $\left\{\frac{1}{3} - \frac{\sqrt{2}}{3}i, \frac{1}{3} + \frac{\sqrt{2}}{3}i\right\}$

2.

3.

4. $\{x \mid 3.99 \leq x \leq 4.01\}$ or $[3.99, 4.01]$

5. $\left\{-\frac{1}{2} + \frac{\sqrt{7}}{2}i, -\frac{1}{2} - \frac{\sqrt{7}}{2}i, -\frac{1}{5}, 3\right\}$

6.

Domain: all real numbers or $(-\infty, \infty)$
Range: $\{y \mid y > 5\}$ or $(5, \infty)$
Horizontal asymptote: $y = 5$

7. 2

8. $\left\{\frac{8}{3}\right\}$

9. $x = 2, y = -5, z = 3$

10. 125; 700

11.

12.
Area $\approx$ 14.46 square units

CHAPTER 14 A Preview of Calculus:
The Limit, Derivative, and Integral of a Function

14.1 Assess Your Understanding (page 883)

3. $\lim_{x \to c} f(x)$ 4. does not exist 5. T 6. F 7. 32 8. 19 9. 1 10. $\frac{1}{2}$ 11. 4 12. 2 13. 2 14. 0 15. 0 16. 1 17. 3 18. -3 19. 4 20. 2
21. Does not exist 22. Does not exist

23.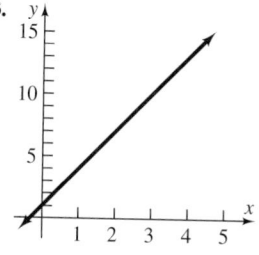

$\lim_{x \to 4} f(x) = 13$

24.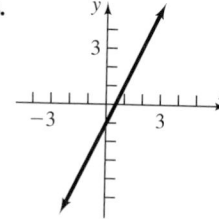

$\lim_{x \to -1} f(x) = -3$

25.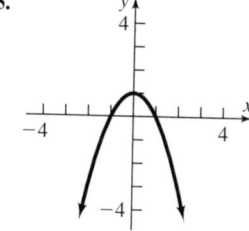

$\lim_{x \to 2} f(x) = -3$

26.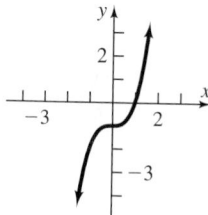

$\lim_{x \to -1} f(x) = -2$

27.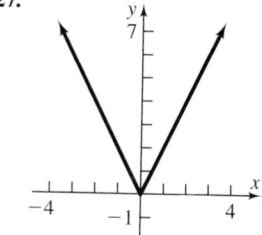

$\lim_{x \to -3} f(x) = 6$

28.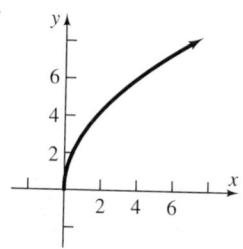

$\lim_{x \to 4} f(x) = 6$

29.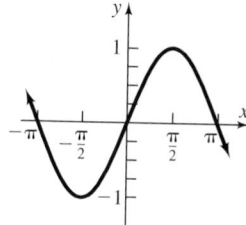

$\lim_{x \to \pi/2} f(x) = 1$

30.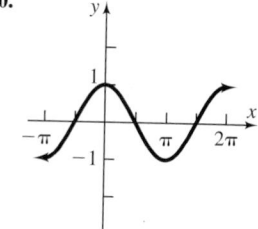

$\lim_{x \to \pi} f(x) = -1$

31.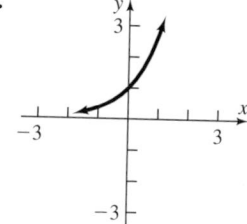

$\lim_{x \to 0} f(x) = 1$

32.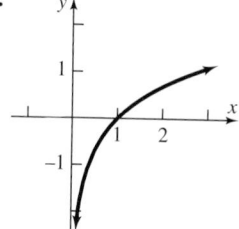

$\lim_{x \to 1} f(x) = 0$

33.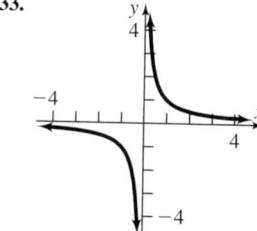

$\lim_{x \to -1} f(x) = -1$

34.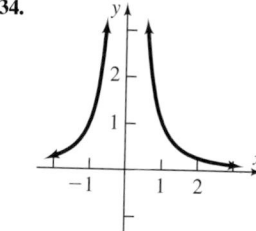

$\lim_{x \to 2} f(x) = \frac{1}{4}$

35.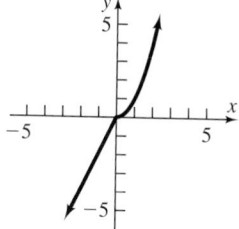

$\lim_{x \to 0} f(x) = 0$

36.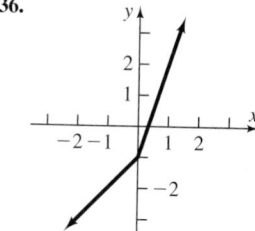

$\lim_{x \to 0} f(x) = -1$

37.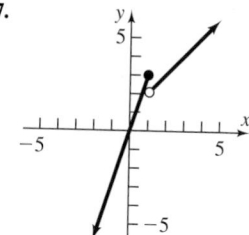

$\lim_{x \to 1} f(x)$ does not exist.

38.

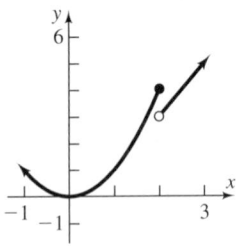

$\lim\limits_{x \to 2} f(x)$ does not exist.

39.

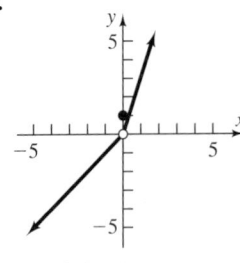

$\lim\limits_{x \to 0} f(x) = 0$

40.

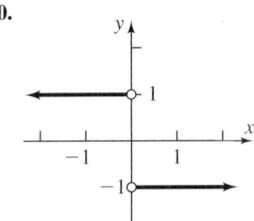

$\lim\limits_{x \to 0} f(x)$ does not exist.

41.

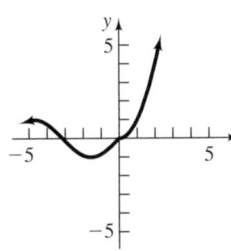

$\lim\limits_{x \to 0} f(x) = 0$

42.

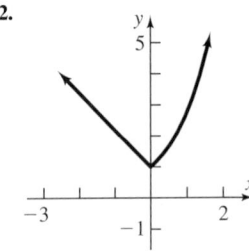

$\lim\limits_{x \to 0} f(x) = 1$

43. 0.67 **44.** 4 **45.** 1.6 **46.** 0.8 **47.** 0 **48.** 0.46

14.2 Assess Your Understanding *(page 891)*

1. product **2.** 5 **3.** 1 **4.** T **5.** F **6.** F **7.** 5 **8.** −3 **9.** 4 **10.** −3 **11.** −10 **12.** −12 **13.** 80 **14.** −54 **15.** 8 **16.** −13 **17.** 8 **18.** 28
19. −1 **20.** 2 **21.** 8 **22.** 4 **23.** 3 **24.** 1 **25.** −1 **26.** $\dfrac{5}{3}$ **27.** 32 **28.** −1 **29.** 2 **30.** $\dfrac{1}{2}$ **31.** $\dfrac{7}{6}$ **32.** $\dfrac{5}{4}$ **33.** 3 **34.** 4 **35.** 0 **36.** 3 **37.** $\dfrac{2}{3}$
38. 4 **39.** $\dfrac{8}{5}$ **40.** $\dfrac{4}{5}$ **41.** 0 **42.** $\dfrac{13}{28}$ **43.** 5 **44.** −3 **45.** 6 **46.** 27 **47.** 0 **48.** −7 **49.** 0 **50.** −5 **51.** −1 **52.** −2 **53.** 1 **54.** 2 **55.** $\dfrac{3}{4}$ **56.** 1

14.3 Assess Your Understanding *(page 897)*

7. one-sided **8.** $\lim\limits_{x \to c^+} f(x) = R$ **9.** continuous; c **10.** F **11.** T **12.** T **13.** $\{x | -8 \le x < -6 \text{ or } -6 < x < 4 \text{ or } 4 < x \le 6\}$ **14.** All real numbers
15. −8, −5, −3 **16.** 3 **17.** $f(-8) = 0; f(-4) = 2$ **18.** $f(2) = 3; f(6) = 2$ **19.** ∞ **20.** −∞ **21.** 2 **22.** −2 **23.** 1 **24.** −4 **25.** Limit exists; 0
26. Limit exists; 3 **27.** No **28.** No **29.** Yes **30.** No **31.** No **32.** Yes **33.** 5 **34.** 0 **35.** 7 **36.** 4 **37.** 1 **38.** −3 **39.** 4 **40.** 2 **41.** $-\dfrac{2}{3}$

42. −1 **43.** $\dfrac{3}{2}$ **44.** $\dfrac{7}{4}$ **45.** Continuous **46.** Continuous **47.** Continuous **48.** Continuous **49.** Not continuous **50.** Not continuous
51. Not continuous **52.** Not continuous **53.** Not continuous **54.** Not continuous **55.** Continuous **56.** Continuous **57.** Not continuous
58. Not continuous **59.** Continuous **60.** Continuous **61.** Continuous for all real numbers **62.** Continuous for all real numbers
63. Continuous for all real numbers **64.** Continuous for all real numbers **65.** Continuous for all real numbers **66.** Continuous for all real numbers
67. Continuous for all real numbers except $x = \dfrac{k\pi}{2}$, where k is an odd integer **68.** Continuous for all real numbers except $x = k\pi$, where k is an integer
69. Continuous for all real numbers except $x = -2$ and $x = 2$ **70.** Continuous for all real numbers except $x = 3$ and $x = -3$
71. Continuous for all positive real numbers except $x = 1$ **72.** Continuous for all positive real numbers except $x = 3$
73. Discontinuous at $x = -1$ and $x = 1$;

$\lim\limits_{x \to 1} R(x) = \dfrac{1}{2}$: Hole at $\left(1, \dfrac{1}{2}\right)$
$\lim\limits_{x \to -1^-} R(x) = -\infty; \lim\limits_{x \to -1^+} R(x) = \infty;$
vertical asymptote at $x = -1$

74. Discontinuous at $x = -2$ and $x = 2$;

$\lim\limits_{x \to -2} R(x) = -\dfrac{3}{4}$: Hole at $\left(-2, -\dfrac{3}{4}\right)$
$\lim\limits_{x \to 2^-} R(x) = -\infty; \lim\limits_{x \to 2^+} R(x) = \infty;$
vertical asymptote at $x = 2$

75. Discontinuous at $x = -1$ and $x = 1$;

$\lim\limits_{x \to -1} R(x) = \dfrac{1}{2}$: Hole at $\left(-1, \dfrac{1}{2}\right)$
$\lim\limits_{x \to 1^-} R(x) = -\infty; \lim\limits_{x \to 1^+} R(x) = \infty;$
vertical asymptote at $x = 1$

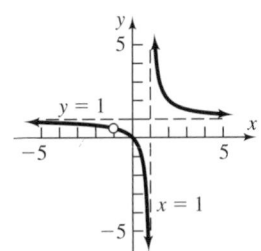

76. Discontinuous at $x = -4$ and $x = 4$;

$$\lim_{x \to -4} R(x) = \frac{1}{2}: \text{Hole at } \left(-4, \frac{1}{2}\right)$$

$$\lim_{x \to 4^-} R(x) = -\infty; \ \lim_{x \to 4^+} R(x) = \infty:$$

vertical asymptote at $x = 4$

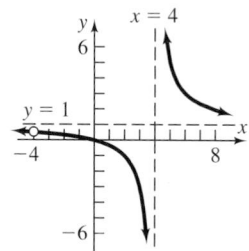

77. (a) $x = -\sqrt[3]{2}$: Asymptote; $x = 1$: Hole

(b)

78. (a) $x = -\sqrt[3]{2}$: Asymptote; $x = -1$: Hole

(b)

79. (a) $x = -3$: Asymptote; $x = 2$: Hole

(b)

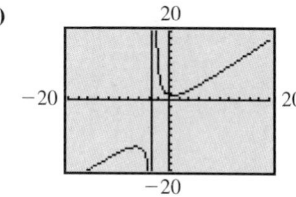

80. (a) $x = -4$: Asymptote; $x = 1$: Hole

(b)

81. (a) $x = -\sqrt[3]{2}$: Asymptote; $x = -1$: Hole

(b)

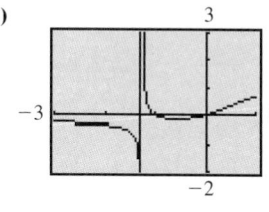

82. (a) $x = -1$: Asymptote; $x = 3$: Hole

(b)

14.4 Assess Your Understanding *(page 905)*

3. tangent line **4.** derivative **5.** velocity **6.** T **7.** T **8.** T

9. $m_{\text{tan}} = 3$

10. $m_{\text{tan}} = -2$

11. $m_{\text{tan}} = -2$

12. $m_{\text{tan}} = -2$

13. $m_{\text{tan}} = 12$

14. $m_{\text{tan}} = 16$

15. $m_{\tan} = 5$

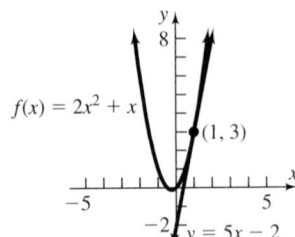

$f(x) = 2x^2 + x$
$(1, 3)$
$y = 5x - 2$

16. $m_{\tan} = -1$

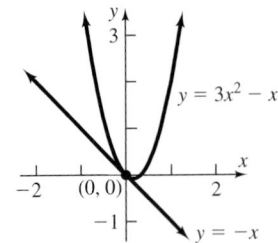

$y = 3x^2 - x$
$(0, 0)$
$y = -x$

17. $m_{\tan} = -4$

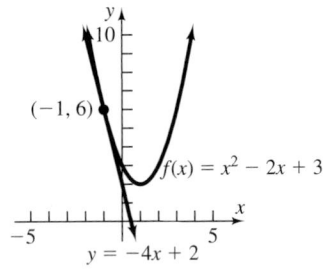

$(-1, 6)$
$f(x) = x^2 - 2x + 3$
$y = -4x + 2$

18. $m_{\tan} = -3$

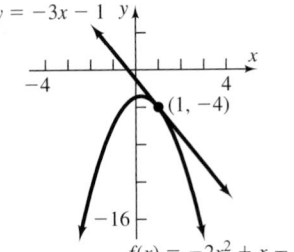

$y = -3x - 1$
$(1, -4)$
$f(x) = -2x^2 + x - 3$

19. $m_{\tan} = 13$

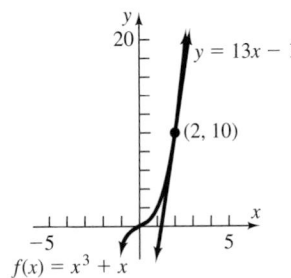

$y = 13x - 16$
$(2, 10)$
$f(x) = x^3 + x$

20. $m_{\tan} = 1$

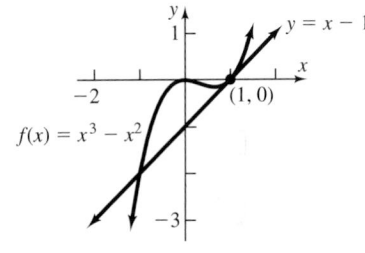

$y = x - 1$
$(1, 0)$
$f(x) = x^3 - x^2$

21. -4 **22.** 3   **23.** 0   **24.** -4 **25.** 7   **26.** 8   **27.** 7   **28.** 20   **29.** 3   **30.** 8   **31.** 1   **32.** 0   **33.** 60   **34.** -2440 **35.** -0.8587776956
36. 36.81251395   **37.** 1.389623659   **38.** 1.262466702   **39.** 2.362110222   **40.** 1.546899826   **41.** 3.643914112   **42.** -0.1793793526
43. 18π ft³/ft   **44.** 16π ft²/ft   **45.** 16π ft³/ft   **46.** 27 m³/m

47. (a) 6 sec   **(b)** 64 ft/sec   **(c)** $(-32t + 96)$ ft/sec   **(d)** 32 ft/sec
   (e) 3 sec   **(f)** 144 ft   **(g)** -96 ft/sec
48. (a) 2 sec   **(b)** -64 ft/sec   **(c)** $(-32t - 48)$ ft/sec
   (d) -80 ft/sec   **(e)** -112 ft/sec

49. (a) $-23\dfrac{1}{3}$ ft/sec   **(b)** -21 ft/sec   **(c)** -18 ft/sec
   (d) $s(t) = -2.631t^2 - 10.269t + 999.933$ **(e)** Approximately -15.531 ft/sec
50. (a) \$249.28 per bicycle   **(b)** Approximately \$329.87 per bicycle
   (c) Approximately \$485.71 per bicycle   **(d)** $R(x) = -1.522x^2 + 597.791x + 7944.450$
   (e) Approximately \$521.69 per bicycle

14.5 Assess Your Understanding *(page 912)*

3. $\displaystyle\int_a^b f(x)\,dx$ **4.** $\displaystyle\int_a^b f(x)\,dx$ **5.** 3   **6.** 6   **7.** 56   **8.** 38

9. (a)

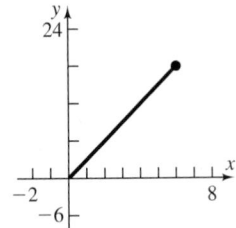

(b) 36   **(c)** 72

(d) 45   **(e)** 63   **(f)** 54

10. (a)

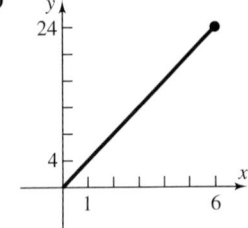

(b) 48   **(c)** 96

(d) 60   **(e)** 84   **(f)** 72

11. (a)

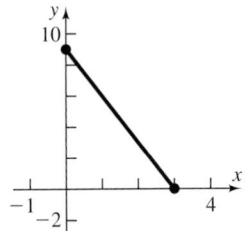

(b) 18   **(c)** 9

(d) $\dfrac{63}{4}$ **(e)** $\dfrac{45}{4}$ **(f)** $\dfrac{27}{2}$

12. (a)

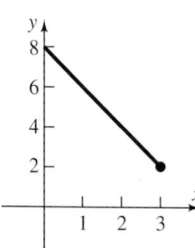

(b) 18 **(c)** 12

(d) $\dfrac{33}{2}$ **(e)** $\dfrac{27}{2}$ **(f)** 15

13. (a)

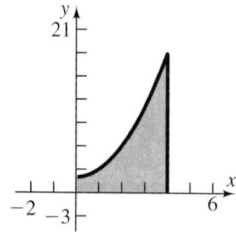

(b) 22 **(c)** $\dfrac{51}{2}$

(d) $\displaystyle\int_0^4 (x^2 + 2)\, dx$ **(e)** $\dfrac{88}{3}$

14. (a)

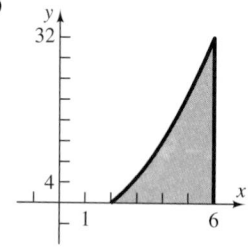

(b) 38 **(c)** $\dfrac{91}{2}$

(d) $\displaystyle\int_2^6 (x^2 - 4)\, dx$ **(e)** $\dfrac{160}{3}$

15. (a)

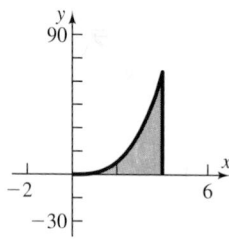

(b) 36 **(c)** 49

(d) $\displaystyle\int_0^4 x^3\, dx$ **(e)** 64

16. (a)

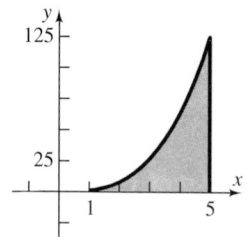

(b) 100 **(c)** $\dfrac{253}{2}$

(d) $\displaystyle\int_1^5 x^3\, dx$ **(e)** 156

17. (a)

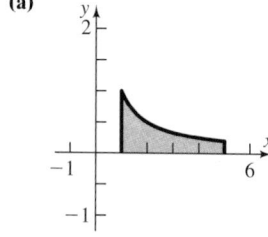

(b) $\dfrac{25}{12}$ **(c)** $\dfrac{4609}{2520}$

(d) $\displaystyle\int_1^5 \dfrac{1}{x}\, dx$ **(e)** 1.609

18. (a)

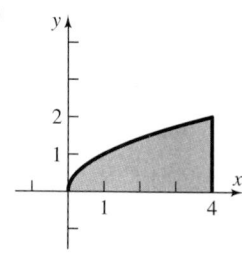

(b) 4.146 **(c)** 4.765

(d) $\displaystyle\int_0^4 \sqrt{x}\, dx$ **(e)** $\dfrac{16}{3}$

19. (a)

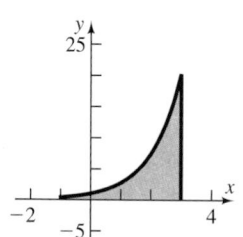

(b) 11.475 **(c)** 15.197

(d) $\displaystyle\int_{-1}^3 e^x\, dx$ **(e)** 19.718

20. (a)

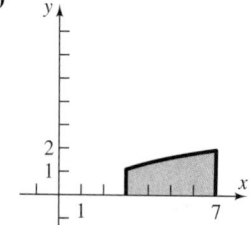

(b) 5.886 **(c)** 6.110

(d) $\displaystyle\int_3^7 \ln x\, dx$ **(e)** 6.326

21. (a)

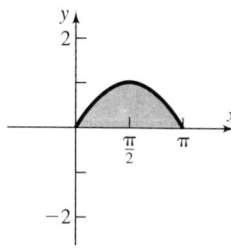

(b) 1.896 **(c)** 1.974

(d) $\displaystyle\int_0^\pi \sin x\, dx$ **(e)** 2

22. (a)

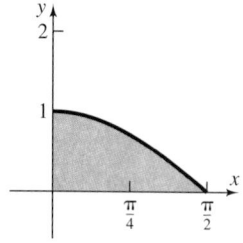

(b) 1.183 **(c)** 1.095

(d) $\displaystyle\int_0^{\pi/2} \cos x\, dx$ **(e)** 1

23. (a) Area under the graph of
$f(x) = 3x + 1$ from 0 to 4

(b)

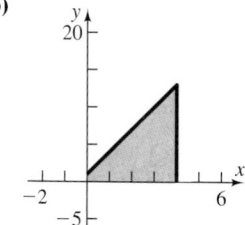

(c) 28

24. (a) Area under the graph of $f(x) = -2x + 7$ from 1 to 3

(b)

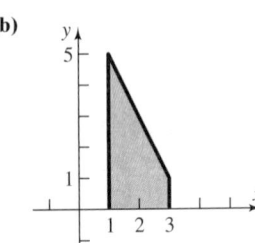

(c) 6

25. (a) Area under the graph of $f(x) = x^2 - 1$ from 2 to 5

(b)

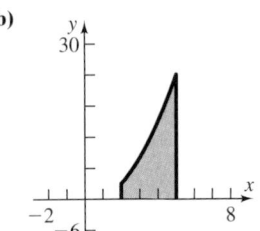

(c) 36

26. (a) Area under the graph of $f(x) = 16 - x^2$ from 0 to 4

(b)

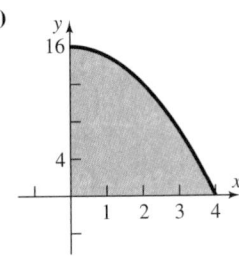

(c) $\dfrac{128}{3}$

27. (a) Area under the graph of $f(x) = \sin x$ from 0 to $\dfrac{\pi}{2}$

(b)

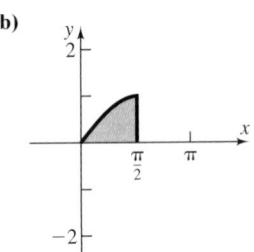

(c) 1

28. (a) Area under the graph of $f(x) = \cos x$ from $-\dfrac{\pi}{4}$ to $\dfrac{\pi}{4}$

(b)

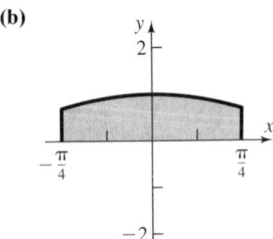

(c) 1.414

29. (a) Area under the graph of $f(x) = e^x$ from 0 to 2

(b)

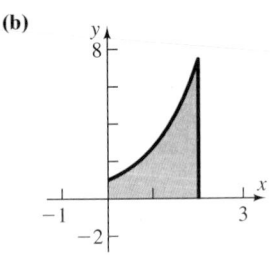

(c) 6.389

30. (a) Area under the graph of $f(x) = \ln x$ from e to $2e$

(b)

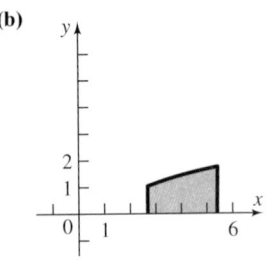

(c) 3.768

31. Using left endpoints: $n = 2: 0 + 0.5 = 0.5; n = 4: 0 + 0.125 + 0.25 + 0.375 = 0.75;$
$n = 10: 0 + 0.02 + 0.04 + 0.06 + \cdots + 0.18 = \dfrac{10}{2}(0 + 0.18) = 0.9;$

$n = 100: 0 + 0.0002 + 0.0004 + 0.0006 + \cdots + 0.0198 = \dfrac{100}{2}(0 + 0.0198) = 0.99;$

Using right endpoints: $n = 2: 0.5 + 1 = 1.5; n = 4: 0.125 + 0.25 + 0.375 + 0.5 = 1.25;$

$n = 10: 0.02 + 0.04 + 0.06 + \cdots + 0.20 = \dfrac{10}{2}(0.02 + 0.20) = 1.1;$

$n = 100: 0.0002 + 0.0004 + 0.0006 + \cdots + 0.02 = \dfrac{100}{2}(0.0002 + 0.02) = 1.01$

32. (a)

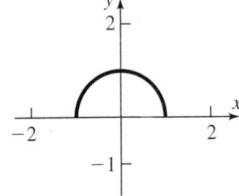

(b) 1.424   **(c)** 1.519   **(d)** $\displaystyle\int_{-1}^{1}\sqrt{1 - x^2}\,dx$ **(e)** 1.571   **(f)** $\dfrac{\pi}{2}$

Review Exercises *(page 914)*

1. 9 **2.** 3 **3.** 25 **4.** 49 **5.** 4 **6.** 2 **7.** 0 **8.** 2 **9.** 64 **10.** $\dfrac{\sqrt{6}}{288}$ **11.** $-\dfrac{1}{4}$ **12.** $\dfrac{13}{10}$ **13.** $\dfrac{1}{3}$ **14.** 2 **15.** $\dfrac{6}{7}$ **16.** $\dfrac{2}{3}$ **17.** 0 **18.** $\dfrac{1}{3}$ **19.** $\dfrac{3}{2}$ **20.** $\dfrac{3}{4}$

21. $\dfrac{28}{11}$ **22.** 1 **23.** Continuous **24.** Continuous **25.** Not continuous **26.** Not continuous **27.** Not continuous **28.** Not continuous

29. Continuous **30.** Continuous **31.** $\{x \mid -6 \le x < 2 \text{ or } 2 < x < 5 \text{ or } 5 < x \le 6\}$ **32.** All real numbers **33.** 1, 6 **34.** 4

35. $f(-6) = 2; f(-4) = 1$ **36.** $f(-2) = 2; f(6) = 0$ **37.** 4 **38.** -2 **39.** -2 **40.** 2 **41.** $-\infty$ **42.** ∞ **43.** Does not exist **44.** Does not exist

45. No **46.** No **47.** No **48.** No **49.** Yes **50.** No

51. R is discontinuous at $x = -4$ and $x = 4$.

$\displaystyle\lim_{x \to -4} R(x) = -\dfrac{1}{8}$: Hole at $\left(-4, -\dfrac{1}{8}\right)$

$\displaystyle\lim_{x \to 4^-} R(x) = -\infty; \ \lim_{x \to 4^+} R(x) = \infty$:

The graph of R has a vertical asymptote at $x = 4$.

52. R is discontinuous at $x = -2$ and $x = 2$.

$\displaystyle\lim_{x \to -2} R(x) = \dfrac{3}{2}$: Hole at $\left(-2, \dfrac{3}{2}\right)$

$\displaystyle\lim_{x \to 2^-} R(x) = -\infty; \ \lim_{x \to 2^+} R(x) = \infty$:

The graph of R has a vertical asymptote at $x = 2$.

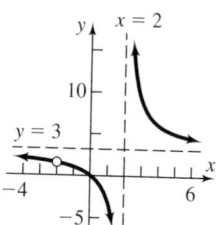

53. Undefined at $x = 2$ and $x = 9$; R has a hole at $x = 2$ and a vertical asymptote at $x = 9$.

54. Undefined at $x = -3$ and $x = 2$; R has a hole at $x = -3$ and a vertical asymptote at $x = 2$.

55. $m_{\tan} = 12$

56. $m_{\tan} = -6$

57. $m_{\tan} = 0$

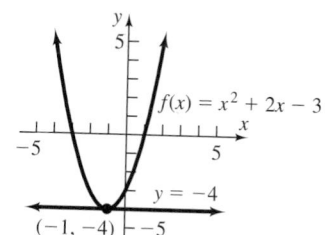

58. $m_{\tan} = 9$

59. $m_{\tan} = 16$

60. $m_{\tan} = 1$

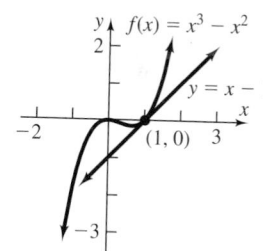

61. -24 **62.** 6 **63.** -3 **64.** 0 **65.** 7 **66.** 8 **67.** -158 **68.** -0.7663278737 **69.** 0.6662517653 **70.** 1.503767758 **71. (a)** 7 sec **(b)** 6 sec

(c) 64 ft/sec **(d)** $(-32t + 96)$ ft/sec **(e)** 32 ft/sec **(f)** At $t = 3$ sec **(g)** -96 ft/sec **(h)** -128 ft/sec **72.** 4π ft²/ft; 5π ft²/ft; 4.5π ft²/ft; 4.1π ft²/ft

73. (a) \$61.29/watch **(b)** \$71.31/watch **(c)** \$81.40/watch **(d)** $R(x) = -0.25x^2 + 100.01x - 1.24$ **(e)** Approximately \$87.51/watch

74. (a) 80 ft/sec **(b)** 64 ft/sec **(c)** 48 ft/sec **(d)** $y = 16x^2$ **(e)** 32 ft/sec

75. (a)

76. (a)

77. (a)

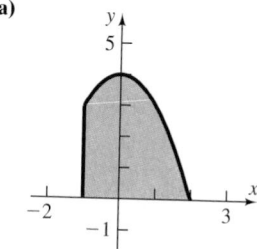

(b) 24 **(c)** 32

(d) 26 **(e)** 30 **(f)** 28

(b) 20 **(c)** 12

(d) 18 **(e)** 14 **(f)** 16

(b) 10 **(c)** $\dfrac{77}{8}$

(d) $\displaystyle\int_{-1}^{2} (4 - x^2)\, dx$ **(e)** 9

78. (a)

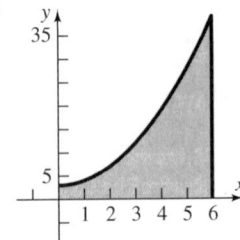

(b) 58 **(c)** 73

(d) $\int_0^6 (x^2 + 3)\, dx$ **(e)** 90

79. (a)

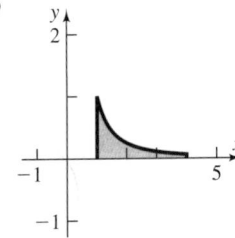

(b) $\dfrac{49}{36} \approx 1.36$ **(c)** 1.02

(d) $\int_1^4 \dfrac{1}{x^2}\, dx$ **(e)** 0.75

80. (a)

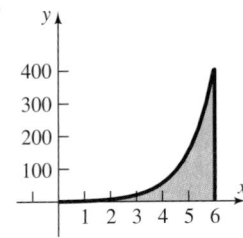

(b) 125.97 **(c)** 234.20

(d) $\int_0^6 e^x\, dx$ **(e)** 402.43

81. (a) Area under the graph of $f(x) = 9 - x^2$ from -1 to 3

(b)

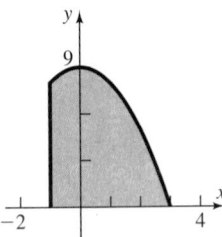

(c) $\dfrac{80}{3}$

82. (a) Area under the graph of $f(x) = \sqrt{x}$ from 1 to 4

(b)

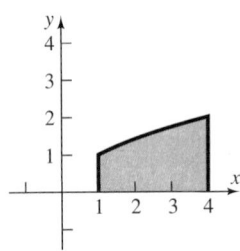

(c) $\dfrac{14}{3}$

83. (a) Area under the graph of $f(x) = e^x$ from -1 to 1

(b)

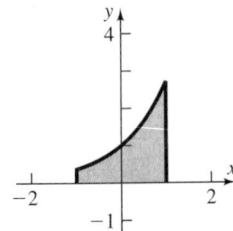

(c) 2.35

84. (a) Area under the graph of $f(x) = \sin x$ from $\dfrac{\pi}{3}$ to $\dfrac{2\pi}{3}$

(b)

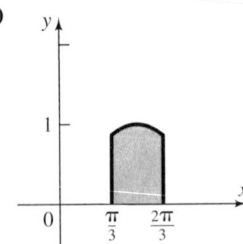

(c) 1

Chapter Test *(page 917)*

1. -5 **2.** $\dfrac{1}{3}$ **3.** 5 **4.** -2 **5.** 135 **6.** $\dfrac{2}{3}$ **7.** -1 **8.** -3 **9.** 5 **10.** 2 **11.** Limit exists; 2 **12. (a)** No; $f(-2)$ is not defined

(b) No; $\lim\limits_{x \to 1} f(x) \neq f(1)$ **(c)** No; $\lim\limits_{x \to 3^+} f(x) \neq f(3)$ **(d)** Yes **13.** $x = -7$: asymptote; $x = 2$: hole

14. (a) 5

(b) $y = 5x - 19$

(c)

15. (a)

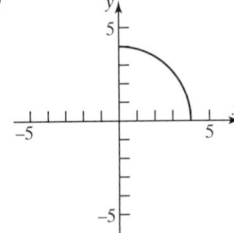

(b) 13.359 **(c)** $4\pi \approx 12.566$

16. $\int_1^4 (-x^2 + 5x + 3)\, dx$ **17.** $35\dfrac{1}{3}$ ft/sec

APPENDIX A

A.1 Assess Your Understanding *(page A10)*

1. variable **2.** origin **3.** strict **4.** base; exponent or power **5.** T **6.** T **7.** F **8.** F **9.** $\{1, 2, 3, 4, 5, 6, 7, 8, 9\}$
10. $\{1, 3, 4, 5, 6, 9\}$ **11.** $\{4\}$ **12.** $\{1, 3, 4\}$ **13.** $\{1, 3, 4, 6\}$ **14.** $\{1, 3, 4, 6\}$ **15.** $\{0, 2, 6, 7, 8\}$ **16.** $\{0, 2, 5, 7, 8, 9\}$
17. $\{0, 1, 2, 3, 5, 6, 7, 8, 9\}$ **18.** $\{0, 5, 9\}$ **19.** $\{0, 1, 2, 3, 5, 6, 7, 8, 9\}$ **20.** $\{0, 5, 9\}$

21. *(number line)* **22.** *(number line)* **23.** $>$ **24.** $<$ **25.** $>$ **26.** $<$ **27.** $>$ **28.** $>$

29. $=$ **30.** $>$ **31.** $<$ **32.** $=$ **33.** $x > 0$ **34.** $z < 0$ **35.** $x < 2$ **36.** $y > -5$ **37.** $x \leq 1$ **38.** $x \geq 2$ **39.** *(number line)*

40. *(number line)* **41.** *(number line)* **42.** *(number line)* **43.** 1 **44.** 3 **45.** 2 **46.** 3 **47.** 6 **48.** 2 **49.** 4 **50.** -3 **51.** -28

52. -2 **53.** $\frac{4}{5}$ **54.** $-\frac{1}{5}$ **55.** 0 **56.** $-\frac{7}{3}$ **57.** 1 **58.** 5 **59.** 5 **60.** 1 **61.** 1 **62.** -1 **63.** 22 **64.** 5 **65.** 2 **66.** 13 **67.** $x = 0$ **68.** $x = 0$
69. $x = 3$ **70.** None **71.** None **72.** $x = 1, x = -1$ **73.** $x = 0, x = 1, x = -1$ **74.** $x = 0$ **75.** $\{x | x \neq 5\}$ **76.** $\{x | x \neq -4\}$ **77.** $\{x | x \neq -4\}$
78. $\{x | x \neq 6\}$ **79.** $0°C$ **80.** $100°C$ **81.** $25°C$ **82.** $-20°C$ **83.** 16 **84.** -16 **85.** $\frac{1}{16}$ **86.** $-\frac{1}{16}$ **87.** $\frac{1}{9}$ **88.** 4 **89.** 9 **90.** 8 **91.** 5 **92.** 6

93. 4 **94.** 3 **95.** $64x^6$ **96.** $-\frac{1}{4x^2}$ **97.** $\frac{x^4}{y^2}$ **98.** $\frac{y^3}{x^3}$ **99.** $\frac{x}{y}$ **100.** $\frac{1}{x^3 y}$ **101.** $-\frac{8x^3 z}{9y}$ **102.** $\frac{1}{2x^6 y^2 z}$ **103.** $\frac{16x^2}{9y^2}$ **104.** $\frac{216x^6}{125y^6}$ **105.** -4 **106.** $\frac{3}{2}$

107. 5 **108.** 4 **109.** 4 **110.** 1 **111.** 2 **112.** 2 **113.** $\sqrt{5}$ **114.** 3 **115.** $\frac{1}{2}$ **116.** 1 **117.** 10; 0 **118.** 8; 44 **119.** 81 **120.** 8 **121.** 304,006.671
122. 693.440 **123.** 0.004 **124.** 0.019 **125.** 481.890 **126.** -481.890 **127.** 0.000 **128.** -0.000 **129.** $A = lw$ **130.** $P = 2(l + w)$ **131.** $C = \pi d$
132. $A = \frac{1}{2}bh$ **133.** $A = \frac{\sqrt{3}}{4}x^2$ **134.** $P = 3x$ **135.** $V = \frac{4}{3}\pi r^3$ **136.** $S = 4\pi r^2$ **137.** $V = x^3$ **138.** $S = 6x^2$ **139. (a)** $6000 **(b)** $8000
140. $98 **141.** $|x - 4| \geq 6$ **142.** $|x - 2| > 5$ **143. (a)** $2 \leq 5$ **(b)** $6 > 5$ **144. (a)** $6 \leq 8$ **(b)** $11 > 8$ **145. (a)** Yes **(b)** No **146. (a)** $1.6 \geq 1.5$
(b) $1.4 < 1.5$ **147.** No; $\frac{1}{3}$ is larger; 0.000333... **148.** No; $\frac{2}{3}$ is larger, 0.000666... **149.** No **150.** 3.14, 3.15, or 3.16

A.2 Assess Your Understanding *(page A20)*

1. right; hypotenuse **2.** $A = \frac{1}{2}bh$ **3.** $C = 2\pi r$ **4.** similar **5.** T **6.** T **7.** F **8.** T **9.** T **10.** F **11.** 13 **12.** 10 **13.** 26 **14.** 5

15. 25 **16.** 50 **17.** Right triangle; 5 **18.** Right triangle; 10 **19.** Not a right triangle **20.** Not a right triangle **21.** Right triangle; 25
22. Right triangle; 26 **23.** Not a right triangle **24.** Not a right triangle **25.** 8 in.^{2} **26.** 36 cm^2 **27.** 4 in.^{2} **28.** 18 cm^2
29. $A = 25\pi$ m^2; $C = 10\pi$ m **30.** $A = 4\pi$ ft^2; $C = 4\pi$ ft **31.** $V = 224$ ft^3; $S = 232$ ft^2 **32.** $V = 288$ in.^{3}; $S = 280$ in.^{2}
33. $V = \frac{256}{3}\pi$ cm^3; $S = 64\pi$ cm^2 **34.** $V = 36\pi$ ft^3; $S = 36\pi$ ft^2 **35.** $V = 648\pi$ in.^{3}; $S = 306\pi$ in.^{2} **36.** $V = 576\pi$ in.^{3}; $S = 272\pi$ in.^{2}
37. π square units **38.** $4 - \pi$ square units **39.** 2π square units **40.** $2\pi - 4$ square units **41.** $x = 4$ units; $A = 90°$; $B = 60°$; $C = 30°$
42. $x = 8$ units; $A = 30°$; $B = 75°$; $C = 75°$ **43.** $x = 67.5$ units; $A = 60°$; $B = 95°$; $C = 25°$
44. $x = 40$ units; $A = 50°$; $B = 125°$; $C = 5°$ **45.** About 16.8 ft **46.** About 1.6 revolutions **47.** 64 ft^2 **48.** 12 ft^2
49. $24 + 2\pi \approx 30.28$ ft^2; $16 + 2\pi \approx 22.28$ ft **50.** $69\pi \approx 216.77$ ft^2; $26\pi \approx 81.68$ ft **51.** 160 paces
52. San Juan to Hamilton ≈ 965 miles; Hamilton to Fort Lauderdale ≈ 1028 miles **53.** About 5.477 mi **54.** About 3.0 mi
55. From 100 ft: 12.2 mi; From 150 ft: 15.0 mi
56. $a^2 + b^2 = (m^2 - n^2)^2 + (2mn)^2 = m^4 - 2m^2 n^2 + n^4 + 4m^2 n^2 = m^4 + 2m^2 n^2 + n^4 = (m^2 + n^2)^2 = c^2$

A.3 Assess Your Understanding *(page A29)*

1. 4; 3 **2.** $x^4 - 16$ **3.** $x^3 - 8$ **4.** F **5.** F **6.** quotient; divisor; remainder **7.** $3x(x - 2)(x + 2)$ **8.** prime **9.** T **10.** F **11.** Monomial; variable:
x; coefficient: 2; degree: 3 **12.** Monomial; variable: x; coefficient: -4; degree: 2 **13.** Not a monomial; the exponent of the variable is not a nonnegative
integer **14.** Not a monomial; the exponent of the variable is not a nonnegative integer **15.** Not a monomial; it has more than one term
16. Not a monomial; it has more than one term **17.** Not a monomial; the exponent of one of the variables is not a nonnegative integer
18. Not a monomial; the exponent of one of the variables is not a nonnegative integer **19.** Not a monomial; it has more than one term
20. Not a monomial; it has more than one term **21.** Yes; 2 **22.** Yes; 1 **23.** Yes; 0 **24.** Yes; 0 **25.** No; the variable of one of the terms is not
a nonnegative integer **26.** No; the variable of one of the terms is not a nonnegative integer **27.** Yes; 3 **28.** Yes; 2 **29.** No; the polynomial of the
denominator has a degree greater than 0 **30.** No; the polymoial of the denominator has a degree greater than 0 **31.** $x^2 + 7x + 2$
32. $x^3 + 4x^2 - 4x + 6$ **33.** $x^3 - 4x^2 + 9x + 7$ **34.** $-x^3 + 4x^2 - 4x - 9$ **35.** $-2x^3 + 18x^2 - 18$ **36.** $8x^3 - 24x^2 - 48x + 4$
37. $15y^2 - 27y + 30$ **38.** $-4y^3 + 4y^2 + 4y + 12$ **39.** $x^3 + x^2 - 4x$ **40.** $4x^5 - 4x^3 + 8x^2$ **41.** $x^2 + 6x + 8$ **42.** $x^2 + 8x + 15$
43. $2x^2 + 9x + 10$ **44.** $6x^2 + 5x + 1$ **45.** $x^2 - 49$ **46.** $x^2 - 1$ **47.** $4x^2 - 9$ **48.** $9x^2 - 4$ **49.** $x^2 + 8x + 16$ **50.** $x^2 - 10x + 25$
51. $4x^2 - 12x + 9$ **52.** $9x^2 - 24x + 16$ **53.** $x^3 - 6x^2 + 12x - 8$ **54.** $x^3 + 3x^2 + 3x + 1$ **55.** $8x^3 + 12x^2 + 6x + 1$

56. $27x^3 - 54x^2 + 36x - 8$ **57.** $4x^2 - 11x + 23$; remainder -45 **58.** $3x^2 - 7x + 15$; remainder -32 **59.** $4x - 3$; remainder $x + 1$

60. $3x - 1$; remainder $x - 2$ **61.** $5x^2 - 13$; remainder $x + 27$ **62.** $5x^2 - 11$; remainder $x + 20$ **63.** $2x^2$; remainder $-x^2 + x + 1$

64. x^2; remainder $x - 2$ **65.** $x^2 - 2x + \dfrac{1}{2}$; remainder $\dfrac{5}{2}x + \dfrac{1}{2}$ **66.** $x^2 - \dfrac{2}{3}x - \dfrac{1}{9}$; remainder $\dfrac{16}{9}x - \dfrac{17}{9}$ **67.** $-4x^2 - 3x - 3$; remainder -7

68. $-3x^3 - 3x^2 - 3x - 5$; remainder -6 **69.** $x^2 - x - 1$; remainder $2x + 2$ **70.** $x^2 + x - 1$; remainder $-2x + 2$

71. $x^2 + ax + a^2$; remainder 0 **72.** $x^4 + ax^3 + a^2x^2 + a^3x + a^4$; remainder 0 **73.** $(x + 6)(x - 6)$ **74.** $(x - 3)(x + 3)$ **75.** $2(1 + 2x)(1 - 2x)$

76. $3(1 - 3x)(1 + 3x)$ **77.** $(x + 1)(x + 10)$ **78.** $(x + 1)(x + 4)$ **79.** $(x - 7)(x - 3)$ **80.** $(x - 4)(x - 2)$ **81.** $4(x^2 - 2x + 8)$

82. $3(x^2 - 4x + 5)$ **83.** Prime **84.** $(x + 6)^2$ **85.** $-(x - 5)(x + 3)$ **86.** Prime **87.** $3(x + 2)(x - 6)$ **88.** $x(x - 2)(x + 10)$

89. $y^2(y + 5)(y + 6)$ **90.** $3y(y - 8)(y + 2)$ **91.** $(2x + 3)^2$ **92.** $(3x - 2)^2$ **93.** $2(3x + 1)(x + 1)$ **94.** $2(x + 1)(4x - 1)$

95. $(x - 3)(x + 3)(x^2 + 9)$ **96.** $(x - 1)(x + 1)(x^2 + 1)$ **97.** $(x - 1)^2(x^2 + x + 1)^2$ **98.** $(x + 1)^2(x^2 - x + 1)^2$

99. $x^5(x - 1)(x + 1)$ **100.** $x^5(x - 1)(x^2 + x + 1)$ **101.** $(4x + 3)^2$ **102.** $(3x - 4)^2$ **103.** $-(4x - 5)(4x + 1)$ **104.** $-(x - 1)(16x + 5)$

105. $(2y - 5)(2y - 3)$ **106.** $(3y - 1)(3y + 4)$ **107.** $-(3x - 1)(3x + 1)(x^2 + 1)$ **108.** $-2(2x - 1)(2x + 1)(x^2 + 2)$

109. $(x + 3)(x - 6)$ **110.** $(x + 5)(3x - 7)$ **111.** $(x + 2)(x - 3)$ **112.** $(x - 3)(x - 1)$ **113.** $(3x - 5)(9x^2 - 3x + 7)$

114. $5x(25x^2 + 15x + 3)$ **115.** $(x + 5)(3x + 11)$ **116.** $(x - 3)(7x - 16)$ **117.** $(x - 1)(x + 1)(x + 2)$

118. $(x - 3)(x - 1)(x + 1)$ **119.** $(x - 1)(x + 1)(x^2 - x + 1)$ **120.** $(x + 1)^2(x^2 - x + 1)$ **121.** $2(3x + 4)(9x + 13)$

122. $(2x + 1)(30x - 19)$ **123.** $2x(3x + 5)$ **124.** $x^2(32x - 9)$ **125.** $5(x + 3)(x - 2)^2(x + 1)$ **126.** $6(x + 5)^3(x - 1)(x + 1)$

127. $3(4x - 3)(4x - 1)$ **128.** $3x^2(3x + 4)(5x + 4)$ **129.** $6(3x - 5)(2x + 1)^2(5x - 4)$ **130.** $2(4x + 5)^2(5x + 1)(50x + 31)$

131. The possibilities are $(x \pm 1)(x \pm 4) = x^2 \pm 5x + 4$ or $(x \pm 2)(x \pm 2) = x^2 \pm 4x + 4$, none of which equals $x^2 + 4$.

132. The possibilities are $(x \pm 1)^2 = x^2 \pm 2x + 1$, neither of which equals $x^2 + x + 1$.

A.4 Assess Your Understanding (page A34)

1. quotient; divisor; remainder **2.** $-3\overline{)2\ 0\ -5\ 1}$ **3.** T **4.** T **5.** $x^2 + x + 4$; remainder 12 **6.** $x^2 + x - 4$; remainder 5

7. $3x^2 + 11x + 32$; remainder 99 **8.** $-4x^2 + 10x - 21$; remainder 43 **9.** $x^4 - 3x^3 + 5x^2 - 15x + 46$; remainder -138

10. $x^3 + 2x^2 + 5x + 10$; remainder 22 **11.** $4x^5 + 4x^4 + x^3 + x^2 + 2x + 2$; remainder 7 **12.** $x^4 - x^3 + 6x^2 - 6x + 6$; remainder -16

13. $0.1x^2 - 0.11x + 0.321$; remainder -0.3531 **14.** $0.1x - 0.21$; remainder 0.241 **15.** $x^4 + x^3 + x^2 + x + 1$; remainder 0

16. $x^4 - x^3 + x^2 - x + 1$; remainder 0 **17.** No **18.** No **19.** Yes **20.** Yes **21.** Yes **22.** Yes **23.** No **24.** Yes **25.** Yes **26.** No **27.** -9

A.5 Assess Your Understanding (page A43)

1. lowest terms **2.** least common multiple **3.** T **4.** F **5.** $\dfrac{3}{x - 3}$ **6.** $\dfrac{x}{3}$ **7.** $\dfrac{x}{3}$ **8.** $\dfrac{5x + 8}{x}$ **9.** $\dfrac{4x}{2x - 1}$ **10.** $\dfrac{x + 2}{x - 2}$

11. $\dfrac{y + 5}{2(y + 1)}$ **12.** $\dfrac{y - 1}{y + 1}$ **13.** $\dfrac{x + 5}{x - 1}$ **14.** $-\dfrac{x}{x + 2}$ **15.** $-(x + 7)$ **16.** $-(x + 3)$ **17.** $\dfrac{3}{5x(x - 2)}$ **18.** $\dfrac{3x}{4(3x + 5)}$

19. $\dfrac{2x(x^2 + 4x + 16)}{x + 4}$ **20.** $\dfrac{6(x^2 - x + 1)}{x(2x - 1)}$ **21.** $\dfrac{8}{3x}$ **22.** $\dfrac{3}{5x}$ **23.** $\dfrac{x - 3}{x + 7}$ **24.** $\dfrac{(x - 5)(x - 2)(x + 3)}{(x - 3)(x - 1)(x + 5)}$ **25.** $\dfrac{4x}{(x - 2)(x - 3)}$

26. $\dfrac{3(x - 4)}{5x}$ **27.** $\dfrac{4}{5(x - 1)}$ **28.** $\dfrac{3}{x - 2}$ **29.** $-\dfrac{(x - 4)^2}{4x}$ **30.** $-\dfrac{9x^3}{(x - 3)^2}$ **31.** $\dfrac{(x + 3)^2}{(x - 3)^2}$ **32.** $\dfrac{(x + 1)(x + 2)}{(x - 2)(x - 1)}$ **33.** $\dfrac{(x - 4)(x + 3)}{(x - 1)(2x + 1)}$

34. $\dfrac{(2x - 3)(4x + 1)}{(3x - 1)(4x - 1)}$ **35.** $\dfrac{x + 5}{2}$ **36.** $-\dfrac{3}{x}$ **37.** $\dfrac{(x - 2)(x + 2)}{2x - 3}$ **38.** $\dfrac{3(x^2 - 3)}{2x - 1}$ **39.** $\dfrac{3x - 2}{x - 3}$ **40.** $\dfrac{3x - 1}{3x + 2}$ **41.** $\dfrac{x + 9}{2x - 1}$ **42.** $\dfrac{4x - 5}{3x + 4}$

43. $\dfrac{4 - x}{x - 2}$ **44.** $\dfrac{x + 6}{x - 1}$ **45.** $\dfrac{2(x + 5)}{(x - 1)(x + 2)}$ **46.** $-\dfrac{3x + 35}{(x - 5)(x + 5)}$ **47.** $\dfrac{3x^2 - 2x - 3}{(x + 1)(x - 1)}$ **48.** $\dfrac{x(5x + 1)}{(x - 4)(x + 3)}$ **49.** $\dfrac{-(11x + 2)}{(x + 2)(x - 2)}$

50. $-\dfrac{2}{(x - 1)(x + 1)}$ **51.** $\dfrac{2(x^2 - 2)}{x(x - 2)(x + 2)}$ **52.** $\dfrac{x^4 + x^3 - x^2 + x - 1}{x^3(x^2 + 1)}$ **53.** $(x - 2)(x + 2)(x + 1)$ **54.** $(x - 4)^2(x + 3)$

55. $x(x - 1)(x + 1)$ **56.** $3(x - 3)(x + 3)(2x + 5)$ **57.** $x^3(2x - 1)^2$ **58.** $x(x - 3)(x + 3)$ **59.** $x(x - 1)^2(x + 1)(x^2 + x + 1)$

60. $x^2(x + 2)^3$ **61.** $\dfrac{5x}{(x - 6)(x - 1)(x + 4)}$ **62.** $\dfrac{x^2 + 7x - 1}{(x - 3)(x + 8)}$ **63.** $\dfrac{2(2x^2 + 5x - 2)}{(x - 2)(x + 2)(x + 3)}$ **64.** $\dfrac{3x^2 - 4x + 4}{(x - 1)^2}$

65. $\dfrac{5x + 1}{(x - 1)^2(x + 1)^2}$ **66.** $\dfrac{-2(2x + 7)}{(x - 1)^2(x + 2)^2}$ **67.** $\dfrac{-x^2 + 3x + 13}{(x - 2)(x + 1)(x + 4)}$ **68.** $\dfrac{x^2 - 6x + 11}{(x + 7)(x + 1)^2}$ **69.** $\dfrac{x^3 - 2x^2 + 4x + 3}{x^2(x + 1)(x - 1)}$

70. $\dfrac{3x^3 - 5x^2 + 2x + 1}{x^2(x - 1)^2}$ **71.** $\dfrac{-1}{x(x + h)}$ **72.** $\dfrac{-(2x + h)}{x^2(x + h)^2}$ **73.** $\dfrac{x + 1}{x - 1}$ **74.** $\dfrac{4x^2 + 1}{3x^2 - 1}$ **75.** $\dfrac{(x - 1)(x + 1)}{2x(2x + 1)}$ **76.** $\dfrac{x}{(x + 1)^2}$

77. $\dfrac{2(5x - 1)}{(x - 2)(x + 1)^2}$ **78.** $\dfrac{-(5x - 4)}{(x - 2)(x + 1)(x + 3)}$ **79.** $\dfrac{-2x(x^2 - 2)}{(x + 2)(x^2 - x - 3)}$ **80.** $\dfrac{(x + 3)(x^2 - x - 15)}{x(4x^2 + 5x + 3)}$ **81.** $\dfrac{-1}{x - 1}$ **82.** $\dfrac{1}{x}$

83. $\dfrac{3x-1}{2x+1}$ **84.** $\dfrac{3x+2}{x-1}$ **85.** $\dfrac{19}{(3x-5)^2}$ **86.** $\dfrac{13}{(5x-2)^2}$ **87.** $\dfrac{(x+1)(x-1)}{(x^2+1)^2}$ **88.** $\dfrac{x^2+4}{(x+2)^2(x-2)^2}$ **89.** $\dfrac{x(3x+2)}{(3x+1)^2}$ **90.** $\dfrac{x^2(4x-15)}{(2x-5)^2}$

91. $-\dfrac{(x+3)(3x-1)}{(x^2+1)^2}$ **92.** $-\dfrac{2(x^2-5x-9)}{(x^2+9)^2}$ **93.** $f=\dfrac{R_1\cdot R_2}{(n-1)(R_1+R_2)};\dfrac{2}{15}$ m **94.** $R=\dfrac{R_1R_2R_3}{R_1R_2+R_1R_3+R_2R_3};\dfrac{20}{11}$ ohms

A.6 Assess Your Understanding (page A57)

5. equivalent equations **6.** identity **7.** F **8.** T **9.** add; $\dfrac{25}{4}$ **10.** discriminant; negative **11.** F **12.** F **13.** $\{7\}$ **14.** $\{-8\}$ **15.** $\{-3\}$ **16.** $\{-6\}$

17. $\{4\}$ **18.** $\{-4\}$ **19.** $\left\{\dfrac{5}{4}\right\}$ **20.** $\left\{\dfrac{27}{4}\right\}$ **21.** $\{-1\}$ **22.** $\{1\}$ **23.** $\{-18\}$ **24.** $\left\{\dfrac{7}{5}\right\}$ **25.** $\{-3\}$ **26.** $\{-2\}$ **27.** $\{-16\}$ **28.** $\{-8\}$ **29.** $\{0.5\}$

30. $\{-10\}$ **31.** $\{2\}$ **32.** $\left\{\dfrac{3}{10}\right\}$ **33.** $\{2\}$ **34.** $\{3\}$ **35.** $\{3\}$ **36.** $\{2\}$ **37.** $\{0,9\}$ **38.** $\{0,1\}$ **39.** $\{0,9\}$ **40.** $\{0,2\}$ **41.** $\{21\}$ **42.** $\{-10\}$

43. $\{-2,2\}$ **44.** $\{2,5\}$ **45.** $\{6\}$ **46.** $\left\{-\dfrac{1}{3}\right\}$ **47.** $\{-3,3\}$ **48.** $\{-4,4\}$ **49.** $\{-4,1\}$ **50.** $\left\{-\dfrac{1}{3},1\right\}$ **51.** $\left\{-1,\dfrac{3}{2}\right\}$ **52.** $\{-1,2\}$ **53.** $\{-4,4\}$

54. $\{-1,1\}$ **55.** $\{2\}$ **56.** $\{3\}$ **57.** No real solution **58.** No real solution **59.** $\{-2,2\}$ **60.** $\{-3,3\}$ **61.** $\{-1,3\}$ **62.** $\{-4,3\}$

63. $\{-2,-1,0,1\}$ **64.** $\{-4,-3,0,1\}$ **65.** $\{0,4\}$ **66.** $\{-8,0\}$ **67.** $\{-6,2\}$ **68.** $\{-3,-4\}$ **69.** $\left\{-\dfrac{1}{2},3\right\}$ **70.** $\left\{-1,-\dfrac{2}{3}\right\}$ **71.** $\{3,4\}$

72. $\{-4,3\}$ **73.** $\left\{\dfrac{3}{2}\right\}$ **74.** $\left\{\dfrac{4}{5}\right\}$ **75.** $\left\{-\dfrac{2}{3},\dfrac{3}{2}\right\}$ **76.** $\{3,4\}$ **77.** $\left\{-\dfrac{3}{4},2\right\}$ **78.** $\left\{-\dfrac{5}{2},1\right\}$ **79.** $\{-6\}$ **80.** $\{-7\}$ **81.** $\{-2,-1,1,2\}$

82. $\{-\sqrt{5},\sqrt{5}\}$ **83.** $\{-6,-5\}$ **84.** $\left\{-\dfrac{7}{2},-1\right\}$ **85.** $\left\{-\dfrac{3}{2},2\right\}$ **86.** $\left\{\dfrac{5}{3},2\right\}$ **87.** $\{-1,0,4\}$ **88.** $\{-7,0,1\}$ **89.** $\{-1,1\}$ **90.** $\{-4,-1,1\}$

91. $\left\{-2,\dfrac{1}{2},2\right\}$ **92.** $\left\{-3,-\dfrac{4}{3},3\right\}$ **93.** $\{-5,5\}$ **94.** $\{-6,6\}$ **95.** $\{-1,3\}$ **96.** $\{-3,-1\}$ **97.** $\{-3,0\}$ **98.** $\left\{0,\dfrac{4}{3}\right\}$ **99.** 16 **100.** 4

101. $\dfrac{1}{16}$ **102.** $\dfrac{1}{36}$ **103.** $\dfrac{1}{9}$ **104.** $\dfrac{1}{25}$ **105.** $\{-7,3\}$ **106.** $\{3-\sqrt{22},3+\sqrt{22}\}$ **107.** $\left\{-\dfrac{1}{4},\dfrac{3}{4}\right\}$ **108.** $\left\{-1,\dfrac{1}{3}\right\}$ **109.** $\left\{\dfrac{-1-\sqrt{7}}{6},\dfrac{-1+\sqrt{7}}{6}\right\}$

110. $\left\{\dfrac{3-\sqrt{17}}{4},\dfrac{3+\sqrt{17}}{4}\right\}$ **111.** $\{2-\sqrt{2},2+\sqrt{2}\}$ **112.** $\{-2-\sqrt{2},-2+\sqrt{2}\}$ **113.** $\left\{\dfrac{5-\sqrt{29}}{2},\dfrac{5+\sqrt{29}}{2}\right\}$

114. $\left\{\dfrac{-5-\sqrt{13}}{2},\dfrac{-5+\sqrt{13}}{2}\right\}$ **115.** $\left\{1,\dfrac{3}{2}\right\}$ **116.** $\left\{-\dfrac{3}{2},-1\right\}$ **117.** No real solution **118.** No real solution **119.** $\left\{\dfrac{-1-\sqrt{5}}{4},\dfrac{-1+\sqrt{5}}{4}\right\}$

120. $\left\{\dfrac{-1-\sqrt{3}}{2},\dfrac{-1+\sqrt{3}}{2}\right\}$ **121.** $\left\{\dfrac{-\sqrt{3}-\sqrt{15}}{2},\dfrac{-\sqrt{3}+\sqrt{15}}{2}\right\}$ **122.** $\left\{\dfrac{-\sqrt{2}-\sqrt{10}}{2},\dfrac{-\sqrt{2}+\sqrt{10}}{2}\right\}$ **123.** No real solution

124. No real solution **125.** Repeated real solution **126.** Repeated real solution **127.** Two unequal real solutions **128.** Two unequal real solutions

129. $R=\dfrac{R_1R_2}{R_1+R_2}$ **130.** $r=\dfrac{A-P}{Pt}$ **131.** $R=\dfrac{mv^2}{F}$ **132.** $T=\dfrac{PV}{nR}$ **133.** $r=\dfrac{S-a}{S}$ **134.** $t=\dfrac{v_0-v}{g}$

135. $\dfrac{-b+\sqrt{b^2-4ac}}{2a}+\dfrac{-b-\sqrt{b^2-4ac}}{2a}=\dfrac{-2b}{2a}=\dfrac{-b}{a}$

136. $\dfrac{-b+\sqrt{b^2-4ac}}{2a}\cdot\dfrac{-b-\sqrt{b^2-4ac}}{2a}=\dfrac{b^2-(b^2-4ac)}{4a^2}=\dfrac{b^2-b^2+4ac}{4a^2}=\dfrac{4ac}{4a^2}=\dfrac{c}{a}$

137. $k=-\dfrac{1}{2}$ or $\dfrac{1}{2}$ **138.** $k=-4$ or 4 **139.** The solutions of $ax^2-bx+c=0$ are $\dfrac{b+\sqrt{b^2-4ac}}{2a}$ and $\dfrac{b-\sqrt{b^2-4ac}}{2a}$.

140. The solution set of $ax^2+bx+c=0$ is $\left\{\dfrac{-b+\sqrt{b^2-4ac}}{2a},\dfrac{-b-\sqrt{b^2-4ac}}{2a}\right\}$,   **141.** (b)

The solution set of $cx^2+bx+a=0$ is $\left\{\dfrac{-b+\sqrt{b^2-4ca}}{2c},\dfrac{-b-\sqrt{b^2-4ca}}{2c}\right\}$

$\dfrac{-b+\sqrt{b^2-4ac}}{2a}\cdot\dfrac{-b-\sqrt{b^2-4ca}}{2c}=\dfrac{b^2-(b^2-4ac)}{4ac}=\dfrac{b^2-b^2+4ac}{4ac}=\dfrac{4ac}{4ac}=1$

$\dfrac{-b-\sqrt{b^2-4ac}}{2a}\cdot\dfrac{-b+\sqrt{b^2-4ca}}{2c}=\dfrac{b^2-(b^2-4ac)}{4ac}=\dfrac{b^2-b^2+4ac}{4ac}=\dfrac{4ac}{4ac}=1$

Since the product of each solution of $ax^2+bx+c=0$ with a corresponding solution of $cx^2+bx+a=0$ is 1, the solutions of the two equations are reciprocals.

A.7 Assess Your Understanding (page A67)

4. real; imaginary; imaginary unit **5.** $-2i,2i$ **6.** F **7.** T **8.** F **9.** $8+5i$ **10.** $-4+7i$ **11.** $-7+6i$ **12.** 6 **13.** $-6-11i$ **14.** $-10+6i$

15. $6-18i$ **16.** $-8-32i$ **17.** $6+4i$ **18.** $-12-9i$ **19.** $10-5i$ **20.** $13+i$ **21.** 37 **22.** -10 **23.** $\dfrac{6}{5}+\dfrac{8}{5}i$ **24.** $\dfrac{5}{13}+\dfrac{12}{13}i$ **25.** $1-2i$

26. $\dfrac{1}{2}+i$ **27.** $\dfrac{5}{2}-\dfrac{7}{2}i$ **28.** $-\dfrac{1}{2}+\dfrac{5}{2}i$ **29.** $-\dfrac{1}{2}+\dfrac{\sqrt{3}}{2}i$ **30.** $\dfrac{1}{2}-\dfrac{\sqrt{3}}{2}i$ **31.** $2i$ **32.** $-2i$ **33.** $-i$ **34.** -1 **35.** i **36.** i **37.** -6 **38.** $4-i$

39. $-10i$ **40.** $3 - 4i$ **41.** $-2 + 2i$ **42.** 82 **43.** 0 **44.** 0 **45.** 0 **46.** 0 **47.** $2i$ **48.** $3i$ **49.** $5i$ **50.** $8i$ **51.** $5i$ **52.** $5i$ **53.** $\{-2i, 2i\}$
54. $\{-2, 2\}$ **55.** $\{-4, 4\}$ **56.** $\{-5i, 5i\}$ **57.** $\{3 - 2i, 3 + 2i\}$ **58.** $\{-2 - 2i, -2 + 2i\}$ **59.** $\{3 - i, 3 + i\}$ **60.** $\{1 - 2i, 1 + 2i\}$
61. $\left\{\dfrac{1}{4} - \dfrac{1}{4}i, \dfrac{1}{4} + \dfrac{1}{4}i\right\}$ **62.** $\left\{-\dfrac{3}{10} - \dfrac{1}{10}i, -\dfrac{3}{10} + \dfrac{1}{10}i\right\}$ **63.** $\left\{-\dfrac{1}{5} - \dfrac{2}{5}i, -\dfrac{1}{5} + \dfrac{2}{5}i\right\}$ **64.** $\left\{-\dfrac{3}{13} - \dfrac{2}{13}i, -\dfrac{3}{13} + \dfrac{2}{13}i\right\}$
65. $\left\{-\dfrac{1}{2} - \dfrac{\sqrt{3}}{2}i, -\dfrac{1}{2} + \dfrac{\sqrt{3}}{2}i\right\}$ **66.** $\left\{\dfrac{1}{2} - \dfrac{\sqrt{3}}{2}i, \dfrac{1}{2} + \dfrac{\sqrt{3}}{2}i\right\}$ **67.** $\{2, -1 - \sqrt{3}i, -1 + \sqrt{3}i\}$ **68.** $\left\{-3, \dfrac{3}{2} - \dfrac{3\sqrt{3}}{2}i, \dfrac{3}{2} + \dfrac{3\sqrt{3}}{2}i\right\}$
69. $\{-2, 2, -2i, 2i\}$ **70.** $\{-1, 1, -i, i\}$ **71.** $\{-3i, -2i, 2i, 3i\}$ **72.** $\{-1, 1, -2i, 2i\}$ **73.** Two complex solutions
74. Two unequal real solutions **75.** Two unequal real solutions **76.** Two complex solutions **77.** A repeated real solution
78. A repeated real solution **79.** $2 - 3i$ **80.** $4 + i$ **81.** 6 **82.** $6i$ **83.** 25 **84.** $-5 + 7i$ **85.** $2 + 3i$ **86.** $\dfrac{7}{4} + \dfrac{1}{4}i$
87. $z + \bar{z} = (a + bi) + (a - bi) = 2a; z - \bar{z} = (a + bi) - (a - bi) = 2bi$ **88.** $\overline{(\bar{z})} = \overline{(a + bi)} = \overline{a - bi} = a + bi = z$
89. $\overline{z + w} = \overline{(a + bi) + (c + di)} = \overline{(a + c) + (b + d)i} = (a + c) - (b + d)i = (a - bi) + (c - di) = \bar{z} + \bar{w}$
90. $\overline{z \cdot w} = \overline{(a + bi)(c + di)} = \overline{ac - bd + (ad + bc)i} = ac - bd - (ad + bc)i = (a - bi)(c - di) = \bar{z} \cdot \bar{w}$
95. $\sqrt{a} \cdot \sqrt{b} = \sqrt{ab}$ only when $\sqrt{a}, \sqrt{b}$ are real numbers.

A.8 Assess Your Understanding (page A74)

1. mathematical modeling **2.** interest **3.** uniform motion **4.** F **5.** T **6.** $100 - x$ **7.** $A = \pi r^2; r$ = radius, A = area
8. $C = 2\pi r; r$ = radius, C = circumference **9.** $A = s^2; A$ = area, s = length of a side **10.** $P = 4s; s$ = length of a side, P = perimeter
11. $F = ma; F$ = force, m = mass, a = acceleration **12.** $P = \dfrac{F}{A}; P$ = pressure, F = force, A = area
13. $W = Fd; W$ = work, F = force, d = distance **14.** $K = \dfrac{1}{2}mv^2; K$ = kinetic energy, m = mass, v = velocity
15. $C = 150x; C$ = total variable cost, x = number of dishwashers **16.** $R = 250x; R$ = total revenue, x = number of dishwashers **17.** Invest
$48,000 in bonds and $36,000 in CDs. **18.** Invest $68,000 in bonds and $16,000 in CDs. **19.** $85,000 was loaned out at 8%. **20.** She can lend
$750,000 at 7%. **21.** Mix 75 lb of Earl Grey tea with 25 lb of Orange Pekoe tea. **22.** 49 lb of coffee I should be mixed with 51 lb of coffee II.
23. Mix 160 lb of cashews with the almonds. **24.** Each box should contain 20 carmels and 10 creams. **25.** The speed of the current is 2.286 mi/hr.
26. The speed of the boat is 9 mi/hr. **27.** The speed of the current is 5 mi/hr. **28.** The average speed of the slower car is 60 mi/hr; the average speed
of the faster car is 70 mi/hr. Each traveled 210 mi. **29.** Working together, it takes 12 min. **30.** April would take 15 hr. **31. (a)** The dimensions are
10 ft by 5 ft. **(b)** The area is 50 sq ft. **(c)** The dimensions would be 7.5 ft by 7.5 ft. **(d)** The area would be 56.25 sq ft. **32. (a)** Its dimensions are
19 ft by 19 ft. **(b)** Its dimensions are 28.5 ft by 9.5 ft. **(c)** The diameter is approximately 25.83 ft. **(d)** The circular one has the most area.
33. The defensive back catches up to the tight end at the tight end's 45-yd line. **34.** Therese should be allowed 20,000 mi as a business expense.
35. Add $\dfrac{2}{3}$ gal of water. **36.** 5 L should be drained. **37.** Approximately 4.05 ft/s. **38.** 2.5 m/s. **39.** hp 1300; 30 min; 20 pages/min; hp 2420;
20 min; 30 pages/min **40.** 36 ft by 78 ft **41.** Evaporate 10.67 oz of water. **42.** Evaporate 96 gal of water. **43.** 40 g of 12-karat gold should be mixed
with 20 g of pure gold. **44.** There are 11 atoms of oxygen and 22 atoms of hydrogen. **45.** Mike passes Dan $\dfrac{1}{3}$ mi from the start, 2 min from the time Mike
started to race. **46.** It can fly 742.5 mi. **47.** Start the auxiliary pump at 9:45 A.M. **48.** 5 lb of pure cement must be added. **49.** The tub will fill in 1 hr.
50. It will take 1 hr and 45 min more for the 5-hp pump to empty the pool. **51.** The distance of the run is 12 mi. The distance of the bicycle race
is 75 mi. **52.** The radius is 3 in. **53.** Lewis would beat Burke by 16.75 m. **54.** Set the original price at $40. At 50% off, there will be no profit.
57. The average speed is 49.5 mi/hr. **58.** The tail wind was 91.47 knots.

A.9 Assess Your Understanding (page A85)

5. negative **6.** closed interval **7.** $-5, 5$ **8.** $-5 < x < 5$ **9.** T **10.** T **11.** $[0, 2]; 0 \le x \le 2$ **12.** $(-1, 2); -1 < x < 2$ **13.** $[2, \infty); x \ge 2$
14. $(-\infty, 0]; x \le 0$ **15.** $[0, 3); 0 \le x < 3$ **16.** $(-1, 1]; -1 < x \le 1$ **17. (a)** $6 < 8$ **(b)** $-2 < 0$ **(c)** $9 < 15$ **(d)** $-6 > -10$
18. (a) $5 > 4$ **(b)** $-3 > -4$ **(c)** $6 > 3$ **(d)** $-4 < -2$ **19. (a)** $7 > 0$ **(b)** $-1 > -8$ **(c)** $12 > -9$ **(d)** $-8 < 6$
20. (a) $0 > -2$ **(b)** $-8 > -10$ **(c)** $-9 > -15$ **(d)** $6 < 10$ **21. (a)** $2x + 4 < 5$ **(b)** $2x - 4 < -3$ **(c)** $6x + 3 < 6$ **(d)** $-4x - 2 > -4$
22. (a) $4 - 2x > 8$ **(b)** $-4 - 2x > 0$ **(c)** $3 - 6x > 15$ **(d)** $-2 + 4x < -10$
23. $[0, 4]$

24. $(-1, 5)$

25. $[4, 6)$

26. $(-2, 0)$

27. $[4, \infty)$

28. $(-\infty, 5]$

29. $(-\infty, -4)$

30. $(1, \infty)$

31. $2 \le x \le 5$

32. $1 < x < 2$

33. $-3 < x < -2$

34. $0 \le x < 1$

35. $x \geq 4$

36. $x \leq 2$

37. $x < -3$

38. $x > -8$

39. $<$ **40.** $<$ **41.** $>$ **42.** $>$ **43.** $\geq$ **44.** $\leq$ **45.** $<$ **46.** $<$ **47.** $\leq$ **48.** $\geq$ **49.** $>$ **50.** $\leq$ **51.** $\geq$ **52.** $<$

53. $\{x | x < 4\}$ or $(-\infty, 4)$

54. $\{x | x < 7\}$ or $(-\infty, 7)$

55. $\{x | x \geq -1\}$ or $[-1, \infty)$

56. $\{x | x \geq -1\}$ or $[-1, \infty)$

57. $\{x | x > 3\}$ or $(3, \infty)$

58. $\{x | x > -2\}$ or $(-2, \infty)$

59. $\{x | x \geq 2\}$ or $[2, \infty)$

60. $\{x | x \geq 5\}$ or $[5, \infty)$

61. $\{x | x > -7\}$ or $(-7, \infty)$

62. $\{x | x < 5\}$ or $(-\infty, 5)$

63. $\left\{x \middle| x \leq \dfrac{2}{3}\right\}$ or $\left(-\infty, \dfrac{2}{3}\right]$

64. $\{x | x \leq 0\}$ or $(-\infty, 0]$

65. $\{x | x < -20\}$ or $(-\infty, -20)$

66. $\left\{x \middle| x > -\dfrac{7}{4}\right\}$ or $\left(-\dfrac{7}{4}, \infty\right)$

67. $\left\{x \middle| x \geq \dfrac{4}{3}\right\}$ or $\left[\dfrac{4}{3}, \infty\right)$

68. $\{x | x \geq 12\}$ or $[12, \infty)$

69. $\{x | 3 \leq x \leq 5\}$ or $[3, 5]$

70. $\{x | 1 \leq x \leq 4\}$ or $[1, 4]$

71. $\left\{x \middle| \dfrac{2}{3} \leq x \leq 3\right\}$ or $\left[\dfrac{2}{3}, 3\right]$

72. $\{x | -3 \leq x \leq 3\}$ or $[-3, 3]$

73. $\left\{x \middle| -\dfrac{11}{2} < x < \dfrac{1}{2}\right\}$ or $\left(-\dfrac{11}{2}, \dfrac{1}{2}\right)$

74. $\left\{x \middle| -\dfrac{2}{3} < x < 2\right\}$ or $\left(-\dfrac{2}{3}, 2\right)$

75. $\{x | -6 < x < 0\}$ or $(-6, 0)$

76. $\{x | 0 < x < 3\}$ or $(0, 3)$

77. $\{x | x < -5\}$ or $(-\infty, -5)$

78. $\{x | x < 11\}$ or $(-\infty, 11)$

79. $\{x | x \geq -1\}$ or $[-1, \infty)$

80. $\{x | x \leq 1\}$ or $(-\infty, 1]$

81. $\left\{x \middle| \dfrac{1}{2} \leq x < \dfrac{5}{4}\right\}$ or $\left[\dfrac{1}{2}, \dfrac{5}{4}\right)$

82. $\left\{x \middle| -\dfrac{1}{3} < x \leq \dfrac{1}{3}\right\}$ or $\left(-\dfrac{1}{3}, \dfrac{1}{3}\right]$

83. $\left\{x \middle| x < -\dfrac{1}{2}\right\}$ or $\left(-\infty, -\dfrac{1}{2}\right)$

84. $\left\{x \middle| x > \dfrac{1}{2}\right\}$ or $\left(\dfrac{1}{2}, \infty\right)$

85. $\left\{x \middle| x > \dfrac{10}{3}\right\}$ or $\left(\dfrac{10}{3}, \infty\right)$

86. $\{x | x > 6\}$ or $(6, \infty)$

87. $\{x | x > 3\}$ or $(3, \infty)$

88. $\{x | x > -1\}$ or $(-1, \infty)$

89. $\{x | -4 < x < 4\}$; $(-4, 4)$

90. $\{x | -4 < x < 4\}$; $(-4, 4)$

91. $\{x | x < -4 \text{ or } x > 4\}$; $(-\infty, -4) \cup (4, \infty)$

92. $\{x | x < -3 \text{ or } x > 3\}$; $(-\infty -3) \cup (3, \infty)$

93. $\{x|0 \le x \le 1\}; [0, 1]$

94. $\{x|-6 \le x \le 1\}; [-6, 1]$

95. $\{x|x < -1 \text{ or } x > 2\}; (-\infty -1) \cup (2, \infty)$

96. $\left\{x \left| x < \dfrac{1}{3} \text{ or } x > 1\right.\right\}; \left(-\infty, \dfrac{1}{3}\right) \cup (1, \infty)$

97. $\{x|-1 \le x \le 1\}; [-1, 1]$

98. $\{x|-6 \le x \le 6\}; [-6, 6]$

99. $\{x|x \le -2 \text{ or } x \ge 2\}; (-\infty, -2] \cup [2, \infty)$

100. $\{x|x \le -3 \text{ or } x \ge -1\}; (-\infty, -3] \cup [-1, \infty)$

101. $|x - 2| < \dfrac{1}{2}; \left\{x \left| \dfrac{3}{2} < x < \dfrac{5}{2}\right.\right\}$ **102.** $|x + 1| < 1; \{x|-2 < x < 0\}$ **103.** $|x + 3| > 2; \{x|x < -5 \text{ or } x > -1\}$

104. $|x - 2| > 3; \{x|x < -1 \text{ or } x > 5\}$ **105.** $\{x|x \ge -2\}$ **106.** $\{x|x \ge -4\}$ **107.** $21 < \text{Age} < 30$ **108.** $40 \le \text{Age} < 60$

109. (a) Male ≥ 79.66 years **(b)** Female ≥ 83.58 years **(c)** A female can expect to live 3.92 years longer. **110.** Volume ranges from 1600 to 2400 cm³, inclusive. **111.** The agent's commission ranges from \$45,000 to \$95,000, inclusive. As a percent of selling price, the commission ranges from 5% to 8.6%, inclusive. **112.** Commissions are at least \$105 and at most \$1225. **113.** The amount withheld varies from \$98.30 to \$148.30, inclusive.

114. Sue can exercise from 5 to 105 minutes. **115.** The usage varies from 675.41 kW · hr to 2500.91 kW · hr, inclusive.

116. The water usage ranged from 18,000 to 32,000 gal. **117.** The dealer's cost varies from \$15,254.24 to \$16,071.43, inclusive.

118. Test score > 123.52 or $(123.52, \infty)$ **119. (a)** You need at least a 74 on the fifth test. **(b)** You need at least a 77 on the fifth test.

120. A serving of regular Miracle Whip® contains at least 60 calories, or at least 3 grams of fat, or both.

121. $\dfrac{a + b}{2} - a = \dfrac{a + b - 2a}{2} = \dfrac{b - a}{2} > 0$; therefore, $a < \dfrac{a + b}{2}$.

$b - \dfrac{a + b}{2} = \dfrac{2b - a - b}{2} = \dfrac{b - a}{2} > 0$; therefore, $b > \dfrac{a + b}{2}$.

122. $d\left(a, \dfrac{a + b}{2}\right) = \left|a - \dfrac{a + b}{2}\right| = \dfrac{b - a}{2}$ since $b > a$.

$d\left(\dfrac{a + b}{2}, b\right) = \left|b - \dfrac{a + b}{2}\right| = \dfrac{b - a}{2}$ since $b > a$; thus $\dfrac{a + b}{2}$ is same distance from a and b.

123. $(\sqrt{ab})^2 - a^2 = ab - a^2 = a(b - a) > 0$; thus $(\sqrt{ab})^2 > a^2$ and $\sqrt{ab} > a$.

$b^2 - (\sqrt{ab})^2 = b^2 - ab = b(b - a) > 0$; thus $b^2 > (\sqrt{ab})^2$ and $b > \sqrt{ab}$.

124. $0 < (a - b)^2$

$0 < a^2 - 2ab + b^2$

$4ab < a^2 + 2ab + b^2$

$4ab < (a + b)^2$

$2\sqrt{ab} < a + b$

$\sqrt{ab} < \dfrac{a + b}{2}$.

125. $h - a = \dfrac{2ab}{a + b} - a = \dfrac{ab - a^2}{a + b} = \dfrac{a(b - a)}{a + b} > 0$; thus $h > a$.

$b - h = b - \dfrac{2ab}{a + b} = \dfrac{b^2 - ab}{a + b} = \dfrac{b(b - a)}{a + b} > 0$; thus $h < b$.

126. $\dfrac{1}{h} = \dfrac{1}{2}\left(\dfrac{1}{a} + \dfrac{1}{b}\right) = \dfrac{1}{2}\left(\dfrac{b + a}{ab}\right) = \dfrac{b + a}{2ab}$; thus $h = \dfrac{2ab}{b + a} = \dfrac{(\sqrt{ab})^2}{\left(\dfrac{b + a}{2}\right)}$.

127. Since $0 < a < b$, then $a - b < 0$ and $\dfrac{a - b}{ab} < 0$.

So $\dfrac{a}{ab} - \dfrac{b}{ab} < 0$, or $\dfrac{1}{b} - \dfrac{1}{a} < 0$. Therefore, $\dfrac{1}{b} < \dfrac{1}{a}$. And $0 < \dfrac{1}{b}$ because $b > 0$.

A.10 Assess Your Understanding (page A93)

3. index **4.** T **5.** cube root **6.** F **7.** 3 **8.** 2 **9.** -2 **10.** -1 **11.** $2\sqrt{2}$ **12.** $3\sqrt[3]{2}$ **13.** $-2x\sqrt[3]{x}$ **14.** $2x\sqrt[4]{3x}$ **15.** x^3y^2 **16.** x^2y **17.** x^2y

18. $\dfrac{1}{3x}$ **19.** $6\sqrt{x}$ **20.** $3x^2\sqrt{x}$ **21.** $6x\sqrt{x}$ **22.** $10x^2$ **23.** $15\sqrt[3]{3}$ **24.** $300\sqrt[3]{3}$ **25.** $12\sqrt{3}$ **26.** $-30\sqrt{6}$ **27.** $7\sqrt{2}$

28. $2\sqrt{5}$ **29.** $\sqrt{2}$ **30.** $-5\sqrt{3}$ **31.** $2\sqrt{3}$ **32.** $-1 + \sqrt{5}$ **33.** $-\sqrt[3]{2}$ **34.** $15\sqrt[3]{3}$ **35.** $x - 2\sqrt{x} + 1$ **36.** $x + 2\sqrt{5x} + 5$

37. $(2x - 1)\sqrt[3]{2x}$ **38.** $(x + 2)\sqrt[4]{2x}$ **39.** $(2x - 15)\sqrt{2x}$ **40.** $(9x + 20)\sqrt{y}$ **41.** $-(x + 5y)\sqrt[3]{2xy}$ **42.** $5xy$ **43.** $\dfrac{\sqrt{2}}{2}$ **44.** $\dfrac{2\sqrt{3}}{3}$

45. $-\dfrac{\sqrt{15}}{5}$ **46.** $-\dfrac{\sqrt{6}}{4}$ **47.** $\dfrac{(5+\sqrt{2})\sqrt{3}}{23}$ **48.** $\dfrac{(\sqrt{7}-2)\sqrt{2}}{3}$ **49.** $\dfrac{8\sqrt{5}-19}{41}$ **50.** $\dfrac{9-5\sqrt{3}}{3}$ **51.** $\dfrac{5\sqrt[3]{4}}{2}$ **52.** $-\dfrac{2\sqrt[3]{3}}{3}$

53. $\dfrac{2x+h-2\sqrt{x^2+xh}}{h}$ **54.** $\dfrac{x+\sqrt{x^2-h^2}}{h}$ **55.** 4 **56.** 8 **57.** -3 **58.** 8 **59.** 64 **60.** 125 **61.** $\dfrac{1}{27}$ **62.** $\dfrac{1}{64}$ **63.** $\dfrac{27\sqrt{2}}{32}$

64. $\dfrac{9}{4}$ **65.** $\dfrac{27\sqrt{2}}{32}$ **66.** $\dfrac{9}{4}$ **67.** $x^{7/12}$ **68.** $x^{11/12}$ **69.** xy^2 **70.** x^3y^6 **71.** $x^{2/3}y$ **72.** $\dfrac{y^{1/2}}{x^{1/4}}$ **73.** $\dfrac{8x^{5/4}}{y^{3/4}}$ **74.** $\dfrac{8}{x^3y}$ **75.** $\dfrac{3x+2}{(1+x)^{1/2}}$

76. $\dfrac{3x+1}{2x^{1/2}}$ **77.** $\dfrac{x(3x^2+2)}{(x^2+1)^{1/2}}$ **78.** $\dfrac{4x+3}{3(x+1)^{2/3}}$ **79.** $\dfrac{22x+5}{10\sqrt{(x-5)(4x+3)}}$ **80.** $\dfrac{65x+6}{24\sqrt[3]{(x-2)^2(8x+1)^2}}$ **81.** $\dfrac{2+x}{2(1+x)^{3/2}}$

82. $\dfrac{1}{(x^2+1)^{3/2}}$ **83.** $\dfrac{4-x}{(x+4)^{3/2}}$ **84.** $\dfrac{9}{(9-x^2)^{3/2}}$ **85.** $\dfrac{1}{x^2(x^2-1)^{1/2}}$ **86.** $\dfrac{4}{(x^2+4)^{3/2}}$ **87.** $\dfrac{1-3x^2}{2\sqrt{x}(1+x^2)^2}$ **88.** $\dfrac{2x(3-2x^2)}{3(1-x^2)^{4/3}}$

89. $\dfrac{1}{2}(5x+2)(x+1)^{1/2}$ **90.** $\dfrac{1}{3}(x^2+4)^{1/3}(11x^2+12)$ **91.** $2x^{1/2}(3x-4)(x+1)$ **92.** $2x^{1/2}(10x+9)$ **93.** $(x^2+4)^{1/3}(11x^2+12)$

94. $2x(3x+4)^{1/3}(5x+4)$ **95.** $(3x+5)^{1/3}(2x+3)^{1/2}(17x+27)$ **96.** $12(6x+1)^{1/3}(4x-3)^{1/2}(5x-1)$ **97.** $\dfrac{3(x+2)}{2x^{1/2}}$

98. $\dfrac{4(2x-1)}{x^{2/3}}$ **99.** 1.41 **100.** 2.65 **101.** 1.59 **102.** -1.71 **103.** 4.89 **104.** 0.04 **105.** 2.15 **106.** 1.33

107. (a) 15,660.4 gal **(b)** 390.7 gal **108. (a)** 16 ft/s **(b)** 32 ft/s **(c)** 12 ft/s **109.** $2\pi\sqrt{2}\approx 8.89$ s **110.** $\pi\sqrt{2}\approx 4.44$ s

111. $\dfrac{\pi\sqrt{3}}{6}\approx 0.91$ s **112.** $\dfrac{\pi\sqrt{6}}{12}\approx 0.64$ s

APPENDIX B

Assess Your Understanding (page A103)

1. limit **2.** infinite series **3.** converges **4.** diverges **5.** converges; 2 **6.** converges; $\dfrac{5}{2}$ **7.** diverges **8.** diverges **9.** converges; $\dfrac{1}{2}$

10. converges; $\dfrac{1}{2}$ **11.** converges; 0 **12.** converges; 0 **13.** diverges **14.** diverges **15.** converges; 0 **16.** converges; 0 **17.** converges; 3

18. converges; 10 **19.** converges; 4 **20.** converges; 0 **21.** converges; 1 **22.** converges; 2 **23.** diverges **24.** converges; 0 **25.** diverges

26. converges; 0 **27.** diverges **28.** diverges **29.** $1, \dfrac{4}{3}, \dfrac{13}{9}, \dfrac{40}{27}, \dfrac{121}{81}$ **30.** $1, \dfrac{5}{4}, \dfrac{21}{16}, \dfrac{85}{64}, \dfrac{341}{256}$ **31.** $1, 3, 6, 10, 15$ **32.** $1, 5, 14, 30, 55$

Index

Abel, Niels, 231, 842
Abscissa, 2
Absolute value, 590, A5
  solving equations involving,
    A56–A57
Absolute value function,
  91–92, 93–94
Acute angles, 510–12
Addition, A10. *See also* Sum
  of rational expressions, A37–A39
    least common multiple (LCM)
      method for, A39–A41
    triangular, 841
  of vectors, 598, 601–2
    in space, 619
Addition principle of counting, 851–52
Additive inverse, A28, A38
Ahmes (Egyptian scribe), 829
Airplane wings, 561
Algebra essentials, A1–A13
  distance on the real number
    line, A5–A6
  domain of variable, A7
  evaluating algebraic
    expressions, A6–A7
  evaluating exponents, A10
  graphing inequalities, A4–A5
  Laws of Exponents, A7–A9
  real number line, A4
  sets, A1–A4
  to simplify trigonometric
    expressions, 460
  to solve geometry problems, 6
  square roots, A9–A10
Algebraic functions, 247
Algebraic vector, 600
Algorithm, 220
Allergic rhinitis, 173
Alpha particles, 672
Altitude of triangle, A15
Ambiguous case, 525
Amortization, 812–13
Amount of annuity, 811
Amplitude
  of simple harmonic motion, 546
  of sinusoidal functions,
    400–401, 419–22
Analytic trigonometry, 439–507
  algebra to simplify trigonometric
    expressions, 460
  Double-angle Formulas, 476–79
    to establish identities, 477–79
    to find exact values, 476–77
  Half-angle Formulas, 479–82
    to find exact values, 479–82
    for tangent, 482
  inverse functions. *See* Inverse
    functions

Product-to-Sum Formulas, 485–86
Sum and Difference Formulas, 466–75
  for cosines, 466–67
  defined, 466
  to establish identities, 468–72
  to find exact values, 467–68, 469–70
  involving inverse trigonometric
    function, 472–73
  for sines, 469
  for tangents, 471
Sum-to-Product Formulas, 486–87
trigonometric equations, 488–502
  calculator for solving, 492
  graphing utility to solve, 500
  identities to solve, 496–98
  involving single trigonometric
    function, 489–92
  linear, 490
  linear in sine and cosine, 498–500
  quadratic in from, 495–96
  solutions of, defined, 489
trigonometric identities, 459–66
  basic, 460
  establishing, 461–63, 468–72, 477–79
  Even-Odd, 459
  Pythagorean, 459
  Quotient, 459
  Reciprocal, 459
Angle(s), 352–65. *See also* Trigonometric
  functions
  acute, 510–12
    trigonometric functions of. *See*
      Right triangle trigonometry
  central, 355
  converting between decimals and
    degrees, minutes, seconds,
    354–55
  converting between degrees and
    radians, 356–59
  of depression, 514, 515
  direction, 621–24
  drawing, 353–54
  of elevation, 514
  elongation, 532
  to find the linear speed of object
    traveling in circular
    motion, 360–61
  formation of, 352
  Greek letters to denote, 352
  historical feature on, 361
  of incidence, 494
  of inclination, 381, 395
  initial side of, 352
  measures for, 353–54, 355
  negative, 352
  optical (scanning), 484
  positive, 352
  quadrantal, 353, 368–70

  of refraction, 494
  of repose, 458
  right, 353, A14
  in standard position, 352
  straight, 353
  terminal side of, 352, 353
  between vectors, 609–11, 621
  viewing, 452
Angle-angle case of similar triangle, A18
Angle-side-angle case of congruent
    triangle, A17
Angular speed, 360
Annuity(ies), 811–12
  amount of, 811
  defined, 811
  formula for, 811
  ordinary, 811
Aphelion, 659, 686, 704
Apollonius of Perga, 637
Approaches infinity, 193
Approximate decimals, A3
Approximating area, 907–11
Araybhata the Elder, 377
Arc length of circle, 356
Area
  definition of, 911
  formulas for, A15
  under graph of function, 907–11
  of parallelogram, 629
  of sector of circle, 359
  of triangle, 540–45, A15
    SAS triangles, 540–41
    SSS triangles, 541–42
Argument
  of complex number, 590
  of function, 61
Arithmetic calculator, A10
Arithmetic sequences, 817–23
  common difference in, 817
  defined, 817
  determining, 817–18
  formula for, 818–19
  *n*th term of, 818
  recursive formula for, 819
  sum of, 819–21
Ars Conjectandi (Bernoulli), 871
Ars Magna (Cardano), 231
ASA triangles, 524
Associative property
  of matrix addition, 748
  of matrix multiplication, 753
  of vector addition, 598
Asymptote(s), 194–99, 664, 665–66
  horizontal (oblique), 194, 196–99
  vertical, 194–96
Atomic systems, 759
Augmented matrix, 721–22, 723
Average cost function, 74

Average rate of change, 30, 271–72
  of function, 84–86
    finding, 84–85
    secant line and, 85
  limit of, 890
  of linear functions, 126–29
Average speed, 360
Axis/axes
  of complex plane, 589
  of cone, 638
  coordinate, 2
  of ellipse, 649, 681
  of hyperbola
    conjugate, 660
    transverse, 660, 681
  polar, 562
  of quadratic function, 146–49
  rotation of, 674–78
    analyzing equation using, 676–78
    formulas for, 675
    identifying conic without, 678–79
  of symmetry
    of parabola, 144, 639
    of quadratic function, 146
Azimuth, 517

Babylonians, ancient, 829
Back substitution, 709
Barry, Rick, 76–77
Base of exponent, A8
Basic trigonometric identities, 460
Bearing (direction), 517
Bernoulli, Jakob, 586, 871
Bernoulli, Johann, 697
Bessel, Friedrich, 519
Bessel's Star, 519–20
Best fit
  line of, 138–39
  polynomial function of, 186–87
  quadratic functions of, 159
Beta of stock, 172
Bezout, Etienne, 776
Binomial(s), A24
  cubing, A25
  squares of (perfect squares), A25
Binomial coefficient, 839
Binomial Theorem, 837–41
  to evaluate $\binom{n}{j}$, 837–39
  expanding a binomial, 839–40
  historical feature on, 842
  proof of, 841
  using, 839–41
Bisection Method, 233
Blood alcohol concentration (BAC), 292
Bode, Johann, 816
Bode's Law, 816
Bonds, zero-coupon, 322
Book value, 130
Boole, George, 871
Bounded graphs, 786
Bounds on zeros, 227–30
Box, volume and surface area of, A16

Brachistochrone, 696–97
Brancazio, Peter, 76
Branches of hyperbola, 660
Break-even point, 134
Brewster's Law, 495
Briggs, Henry, 304
Bürgi, Joost, 304

Calculator(s), A10. *See also* Graphing
    utility(ies)
  converting between decimals and
    degrees, minutes, seconds forms
    for angles, 354
  converting from polar coordinates to
    rectangular coordinates, 566
  to evaluate powers of 2, 270
  functions on, 62
  inverse sine on, 443–44
  kinds of, A10
  logarithms on, 301
  trigonometric equations solved
    using, 492
Calculus, 501
  angles in, 355
  approximating e^x, 816
  area under curve, 452–53
  complicated functions in, 66
  composite functions in, 252
  derivative, 202
  difference quotient in, 62, 89, 284, 305, 475
  double-angle formulas in, 478
  e in, 276
  end behavior of graphs, 182
  exponential equations in, 310
  factoring problems occurring in, A31
  functions and
    exponential, 269, 816
    increasing, decreasing, or constant,
      81, 330
    local maxima and local
      minima in, 82
  graph of polynomial functions in, 175
  independent variable in, 395
  integral, 479, 911–12
    area under graph, 907–11
    graphing utility to
      approximate, 911–12
  Intermediate Value Theorem, 230
  limit notation, 827
  limits, 193
  logarithms and, 299, 310
  partial fraction decomposition and, 763
  polar equations and, 585–86
  projectile motion, 691
  secant line and, 85, 89
  Simpson's Rule, 162
  Snell's Law and, 494
  tangent line and, 544
  trigonometric functions and equations
    in, 478, 485, 493, 500, 501
  trigonometric identities useful in, 479
  turning points and, 180, 181
  of variations, 697

Cancellation Property, A35–A36
Carbon dating, 326
Cardano, Girolamo, 231, 595, 871
Cardioid, 578–79, 585
Carlson, Tor, 338
Carrying capacity, 329
Cartesian (rectangular)
    coordinates, 2–3
Cartesian (rectangular) form of
    complex number, 590
Catenary, 158*n*, 644
Cayley, Arthur, 705, 759
Ceilometer, 515
Cell division, 323, 328
Cellular Telecommunications and
    Internet Association
    (CTIA), 55
Center
  of circle, 44
  of hyperbolas, 660
  of sphere, 625
Central angle, 355
Change-of-Base Formula, 302
Chebyshëv, P.I., 478*n*
Chebyshëv polynomials, 478*n*
Chu Shih-chieh, 842
Circle(s), 44–51, 638
  arc length of, 356
  area of, A16
  area of sector of, 359
  center of, 44
  circumference of, A16
  defined, 44
  general form of equation of, 47–48
  graphing, 45–47, 584
  inscribed, 545
  intercepts of, 46–47
  polar equation of, 572, 575–76
  radius of, 44
  standard form of equation of, 45
  unit, 45, 366–81
Circular functions, 367
Circular motion
  linear speed of object
    traveling in, 360–61
  simple harmonic motion
    and, 546–47
Circumference, A16
Clark, William, 509
Clinton, Bill, 89
Clock, Huygens's, 697
Coefficient, A23, A24
  binomial, 839
  correlation, 139
  damping, 549
  leading, 234, A24
Coefficient matrix, 722
Cofactors, 740
Cofunctions, 512
  names of, 377
Coincident lines, 708
Column index, 721, 746
Column vector, 750

Combinations, 858–60
  defined, 858
  listing, 858–59
  of *n* distinct objects taken *r* at a
    time, 859
Combinatorics, 850, 871
Common difference, 817
Common logarithms (log), 289,
    301–2, 304
Common ratio, 823
Commutative property
  of dot products, 609, 621
  of matrix addition, 748
  of vector addition, 598
Complementary angle theorem, 512
Complement of event, 869
Complement of set, A2
Complement Rule, 869–70
Complete graph, 9
Completing the square
  identifying conics without, 673–74
Complex fraction, A41*n*
Complex function, 57
Complex number(s), 57, 605, 614
  argument of, 590
  conjugates of, 590
  De Moivre's Theorem and, 592–93
  geometric interpretation of, 589
  magnitude (modulus) of, 589
  in polar form
    converting from rectangular form
      to, 590–91
    converting to rectangular form, 591
    products and quotients of, 591–92
  product of, 591–92
  quotient of, 591–92
Complex plane, 589–92
  defined, 589
  imaginary axis of, 589
  plotting points in, 589–90
  real axis of, 589
Complex polynomial function, 234
Complex rational expressions, A41–A43
Complex roots, 593–94
Complex variable, 234
Complex zeros of polynomials, 234–39
  Conjugate Pairs Theorem, 235–36
  defined, 234
  finding, 237–38
  polynomial function with specified
    zeros, 236–37
Components of vectors, 600, 601, 618
Composite functions, 248–55
  calculus application of, 252
  components of, 252
  defined, 248
  domain of, 249–52
  equal, 251–52
  evaluating, 249
  finding, 249–52
  forming, 248–49
Compound interest
  computing, 314–15

continuous, 316–17
  defined, 314
  doubling or tripling time for
    money, 319
  effective rates of return, 317
  formula, 315
  present value of lump sum of
    money, 318
Compound probabilities, 867
Compressions, 102–4, 106
Conditional equation, 459
Cone
  axis of, 638
  generators of, 638
  right circular, 638
  vertex of, 638
Congruent triangles, A16–A19
Conics, 638
  defined, 681
  degenerate, 638
  directrix of, 681
  eccentricity of, 681
  ellipse, 638, 648–59
    with center at (*h*, *k*), 653–55
    with center at the origin, 649–53
    with center not at origin, 654–55
    center of, 649
    defined, 649, 681
    eccentricity of, 659, 681
    foci of, 649
    graphing of, 651–53
    length of major axis, 649
    major axis of, 649, 681
    minor axis of, 649
    solving applied problems
      involving, 656
    vertices of, 649
  focus of, 681
  general form of, 673–76
  hyperbolas, 637, 638, 659–72
    asymptotes of, 664, 665–66
    branches of, 660
    with center at (*h*, *k*), 666–68
    with center at the origin, 660–64
    with center not at the origin, 667–68
    center of, 660
    conjugate, 672
    conjugate axis of, 660
    defined, 659, 681
    eccentricity of, 672, 683–84
    equilateral, 672
    foci of, 659
    graphing equation of, 661–62
    solving applied problems
      involving, 668–70
    transverse axis of, 660, 681
    vertices of, 660
  identifying, 673–74
    without a rotation of axes, 678–79
  names of, 638
  parabola, 144–45, 638, 639–48
    axis of symmetry of, 144, 639
    defined, 639, 681

directrix of, 639
    focus of, 639
    graphing equation of, 640
    solving applied problems
      involving, 644–45
    with vertex at (*h*, *k*), 643–44
    with vertex at the origin, 639–43
    vertex of, 144, 639
  paraboloids of revolution, 637, 644–45
  parametric equations, 687–700
    applications to mechanics, 696–97
    for curves defined by rectangular
      equations, 694–97
    cycloid, 696
    defined, 687
    describing, 690–91
    graphing, 687–89
    rectangular equation for curve
      defined parametrically, 689–91
    time as parameter in, 691–94
  polar equations of, 681–86
    analyzing and graphing, 681–85
    converting to rectangular
      equation, 685
    focus at pole; eccentricity *e*, 682–85
  rotation of axes to transform
    equations of, 674–76
    analyzing equation using, 676–78
    formulas for, 675
Conjugate axis, 660
Conjugate golden ratio, 816
Conjugate hyperbola, 672
Conjugate of complex numbers, 590
Conjugate Pairs Theorem, 235–36
Connected mode, 94
Consistent systems of equations,
    707, 708, 712
Constant(s), A6, A23
Constant, limit of, 885
Constant functions, 81–82, 83, 92
Constant linear functions, 129
Constraints, 789
Consumer Price Index (CPI), 322
Continued fractions, A45
Continuous compounding, 316–17
Continuous function, 230, 894–96
Continuous graph, 175
Convergent geometric series, 827–29
Cooling, Newton's Law of, 327–28
Coordinates, 2, 4. *See also* Rectangular
    (Cartesian) coordinates
  of point on number line, A4
Copernicus, 361
Corner points, 786
Correlation coefficient, 139
Correspondence between two sets, 56
Cosecant, 368
  graph of, 415–17
  periodic properties of, 385
Cosecant function, 367
  continuous, 896, 897
  domain of, 383, 384
  inverse, 455

Cosecant function (*continued*)
approximate value of, 456
calculator to evaluate, 456
definition of, 455
exact value of, 455
range of, 384
Cosine(s), 368
direction, 622–24
exact value of, 467–68
Law of, 533–36
in applied problems, 536
defined, 534
historical feature on, 536
proof of, 534
Pythagorean Theorem as special
case of, 534
SAS triangles solved
using, 534–35
SSS triangles solved using, 535
periodic properties of, 385
Sum and Difference Formula
for, 466–67
trigonometric equations linear
in, 498–500
Cosine function, 367
continuous, 897
domain of, 382, 384, 398
graphs of, 395–410
amplitude and period, 400–401
equation for, 405–6
key points for, 401–5
hyperbolic, 284
inverse, 445–47
defined, 445
exact value of, 446–47
exact value of expressions
involving, 454
implicit form of, 445
properties of, 398
range of, 383, 384, 398
Cost(s)
fixed, 42
marginal, 153
variable, 42
Cotangent, 368
periodic properties of, 385
Cotangent function, 367
continuous, 896, 897
domain of, 383, 384
graph of, 414–15
inverse, 455
approximating the value of, 456
calculator to evaluate, 456
definition of, 455
range of, 384
Coubertin, Baron Pierre de, 1
Counting, 850–55
addition principle of, 851–52
combinations, 858–60
defined, 858
listing, 858–59
of *n* distinct objects taken *r* at
a time, 859

formula, 851
multiplication principle of, 852–54
number of possible meals, 853
permutations, 855–58
computing, 858
defined, 855
distinct objects without
repetition, 856–57
distinct objects with repetition, 856
involving *n* nondistinct objects,
860–61
Counting numbers (natural numbers),
833*n*, 835, A3
Cramer, Gabriel, 705
Cramer's Rule, 705, 736–39
for three equations containing three
variables, 741–42
for two equations containing two
variables, 736–39
Cross (vector) product, 605, 625–31
algebraic properties of, 627–28
area of parallelogram using, 629
defined, 626
geometric properties of, 628
of two vectors, 626–27
vector orthogonal to two given
vectors, 628–29
Cube(s)
of binomials (perfect cubes), A25
difference of two, A26
sum of two, A26
Cube function, 61, 93
Cube root, 90–91, 93
complex, 593–94
Cubic function of best fit, 187
Cubic models from data, 186–87
Curve(s)
defined by rectangular
equations, 694–97
defined parametrically, 689–91
of quickest descent, 696
sawtooth, 553
Curve fitting, 716
sinusoidal, 423–27
hours of daylight, 425–26
sine function of best fit, 427
temperature data, 423–25
Curvilinear motion, 691
Cycle of sinusoidal graph, 396, 401
Cycloid, 696
Cygni, 519–20

Damped motion, 546, 549–50
Damping factor (damping
coefficient), 549
Dantzig, George, 789*n*
Data
arrangement in matrix, 746
fitting exponential functions
to, 335–36
sinusoidal function from, 423–27
"Deal or No Deal" (TV show), 849,
877–78

Decay, Law of, 325–27. *See also*
Exponential growth and decay
Decimals, A3
approximate, A3
converting between degrees, minutes,
seconds forms for angles and,
354–55
Declination of the Sun, 451–52
Decomposition, 612–13
Decreasing functions, 81–82, 83
Decreasing linear functions, 129
Deflection, force of, 561
Degenerate conics, 638
Degree(s)
of monomial, A23
of polynomial, A24
Degree of polynomial, 174–77
odd, 227, 235–36
Degrees, 353
converting between decimals and, 354
converting between radians
and, 356–59
Demand equation, 155
De Moivre, Abraham, 592
De Moivre's Theorem, 592–93
Denominator, A35
Dependent systems of equations, 708
containing three variables, 715–16
containing two variables, 712
matrices to solve, 728–29
Dependent variable, 61
Depressed equation, 225
Depression, angle of, 514, 515
Derivative, 901–2
Descartes, René, 2*n*, 55, 494
Descartes's Law, 494
Determinants, 626–27, 705, 735–45
cofactors, 740
Cramer's Rule to solve a system of
three equations containing three
variables, 741–42
Cramer's Rule to solve a system of
two equations containing two
variables, 736–39
evaluating, 626–27
expanding across a row or
column, 740
to find cross products, 627
minors of, 739–40
properties of, 742–43
3 by 3, 739–40
2 by 2, 736, 742–43
Diagonal entries, 753
Difference(s). *See also* Subtraction
common, 817
first, 418
limits of, 886
of logarithms, 299–300
of two cubes, A26
of two functions, 65–66
of two matrices, 746–48
of two squares, A25
of vectors, 598

Difference quotient, 62, 89, 284, 305, 475
Diophantus, 829
Directed line segment, 597
Direction angles, 621–24
Direction (bearing), 517
Direction cosines, 622–24
Direction of vectors, 597, 603–4
Directrix, 681
  of parabola, 639
Dirichlet, Lejeune, 55, 57
Discontinuity, 94
Discontinuous function, 895
Disjoint sets, A3
Distance
  mean, 659, 704
Distance formula, 2–3, 4–6
  proof of, 5
  in space, 618
Distributive Property
  of dot products, 609, 621
  of matrix multiplication, 753
  of real numbers, A4
Divergent geometric series, 827–29
Dividend, 220, 221, A26
Division, A10. *See also* Quotient(s)
  of polynomials, A26–A28
    algorithm for, 220–21
    synthetic, A31–A35
  of rational expressions, A36–A37
  of two integers, A26
Divisor, 220, 221, A26
Domain, 57, 63–64
  of absolute value function, 94
  of composite function, 249–52
  of constant function, 92
  of cosecant function, 383, 384
  of cosine function, 382, 384, 398
  of cotangent function, 383, 384
  of cube function, 93
  of cube root function, 93
  of difference function, 65–66
  of greatest integer function, 94
  of identity function, 92
  of inverse function, 259
  of logarithmic function, 286
  of logistic models, 329
  of one-to-one function, 256
  of product function, 65
  of quotient function, 65
  of rational function, 192–95
  of reciprocal function, 93
  of secant function, 383, 384
  of sine function, 382, 384, 396
  of square function, 93
  of square root function, 93
  of sum function, 65–66
  of tangent function, 383, 384, 412
  of trigonometric functions, 382–84
  unspecified, 67
  of variable, A7
Domain-restricted function, 264
Doppler, Christian, 211

Doppler effect, 211
Dot mode, 94
Dot product, 602, 605, 608–15, 620–21
  angle between vectors using, 609–11
  to compute work, 613–14
  defined, 608, 620
  finding, 609
  historical feature on, 614
  orthogonal vectors and, 611–13
  parallel vectors and, 611
  properties of, 609, 621
  of two vectors, 608–9
Double-angle Formulas, 476–79
  to establish identities, 477–79
  to find exact values, 476–77
Double root (root of multiplicity 2), A50
Dry adiabatic lapse rate, 822

e, 276–78, 283–84
Earthquakes
  magnitude of, 297
Eccentricity, 681
  of ellipse, 659, 681, 682–85
  of hyperbola, 672, 683–84
Eddin, Nasir, 361, 536
Effective rates of return, 317
Egyptians, ancient, 829
Elements (Euclid), 536, 829
Elements of sets, 850–52, A1
Elevation, angle of, 514
Elimination, Gauss-Jordan, 727
Elimination method, 705, 710–11, 712
  systems of nonlinear equations
    solved using, 771–76
Ellipse, 638, 648–59
  with center at (h, k), 653–55
  with center at the origin, 649–53
    major axis along x-axis, 650
    major axis along y-axis, 652–53
  with center not at origin, 654–55
  center of, 649
  defined, 649, 681
  eccentricity of, 659, 681, 682–85
  foci of, 649
  graphing of, 651–53
  major axis of, 649, 681
    length of, 649
  minor axis of, 649
  solving applied problems
    involving, 656
  vertices of, 649
Ellipsis, A3
Elliptical orbits, 637
Elongation angle, 532
Empty (null) sets, 850, A1
End behavior, 182–83
Engels, Friedrich, 879
Entries of matrix, 721, 746
  diagonal, 753
Equality
  of sets, 850, A2
  of vectors, 597, 601
Equally likely outcomes, 866–67

Equation(s)
  algebraically solving, 27–28
  approximate solutions of, 26–27
  conditional, 459
  demand, 155
  depressed, 225
  equivalent, 10, A46–A47
  even and odd functions identified
    from, 80–81
  exponential, 278–79, 291–92, 308–10
    quadratic in form, 310
  in the form $y = \{$expression in $x\}$, 10
  as function, 60
  graphing utility to solve, 26–28
  intercepts from, 18–19
  inverse function defined by, 261–64
  linear. *See* Linear equation(s)
  in one variable, A46
  polar. *See* Polar equations
  satisfying the, 7
  sides of, 7, A46
  solutions (roots) of, A46
  solving, A46–A60
    algebraically, A46–A47
    by factoring, A50–A51
    involving absolute value,
      A56–A57
    linear equations, A47–A49
    quadratic equations, A50–A55
    rational equations, A49
  systems of. *See* Systems of equations
  in two variables, graphs of, 7–13
    intercepts from, 12–13
    by plotting points, 7–9
    symmetry test using, 19–21
    $x = y^2$, 22
    $y = 1 \div x$, 23
    $y = x^3$, 21–22
Equilateral hyperbola, 672
Equilateral triangle, 16
Equilibrium, static, 604–5
Equilibrium price, 131
Equilibrium quantity, 131
Equilibrium (rest) position, 546
Equivalent equations, 10, A46–A47
Equivalent systems of equations, 710
Error triangle, 17
Euclid, 536, 829, 842
Euler, Leonhard, 55, 361, 871
Even functions
  determining from graph, 79–80
  identifying from equation, 80–81
Evenness ratio, 296
Even-Odd identity, 459
Even-odd properties, 391–92
Events, 866
  complement of, 869
  mutually exclusive, 868–69
  probabilities of union of two, 868–69
Explicit form of function, 63
Exponent(s), A8
  Laws of, 270, 278, A7–A9
  logarithms related to, 285

Exponential equations, 278–79
  defined, 278
  solving, 278–79, 291–92, 308–10
    equations quadratic in form, 310
    using graphing utility, 310
Exponential expressions, changing
      between logarithmic expressions
      and, 285
Exponential functions, 269–84,
      439, 897
  continuous, 897
  defined, 270
  e, 276–78, 283–84
  evaluating, 269–72
  fitting to data, 335–36
  graph of, 273–76
    using transformations, 276–78
  identifying, 271–72
  power function vs., 271
  properties of, 274, 275, 279
Exponential growth and decay,
      270–72, 323–27
  law of decay, 325–27
  logistic models, 328–31
    defined, 328
    domain and range of, 329
    graph of, 329
    properties of, 329
  uninhibited growth, 323–25
Exponential law, 323
Extended Principle of Mathematical
      Induction, 836

Factored completely, A28
Factorial symbol, 806–7
Factoring
  defined, A28
  over the integers, A28
  polynomials, A28–A29
  solving equations by
      quadratic equations, A50–A51
Factors, A28
  linear, 763–67
    nonrepeated, 763–65
    repeated, 765–67
  quadratic, 227, 767–69
  synthetic division to verify, A34
Factor Theorem, 220–23
Family
  of lines, 43
  of parabolas, 111
Feasible point, 790
Fermat, Pierre de, 284, 870
Ferrari, Lodovico, 231
Ferris, George W., 50, 494
Fibonacci, 829
Fibonacci numbers, 808
Fibonacci sequences, 808, 815
Financial models, 313–22
  effective rates of return, 317
  future value of a lump sum of
      money, 313–17

present value of a lump sum of
      money, 318
  rate of interest or time required to
      double a lump sum of money, 319
Finck, Thomas, 361, 377
Finite sets, 850
First-degree equation. *See* Linear
      equation(s); Linear equation(s)
First differences, 418
Fixed costs, 42
Focus/foci, 681
  of ellipse, 649
  of hyperbola, 659
  of parabola, 639
FOIL method, A25
Foot-pounds, 613
Force, 546–47
  of deflection, 561
  resultant, 604
Force vector, 603
Formulas, geometry, A15–A16
Fractions
  complex, A41*n*
  continued, A45
  partial, 763
Frequency, 409
  in simple harmonic motion, 547
Frobenius, Georg, 759
Function(s), 55–124. *See also*
      Composite functions;
      Exponential functions; Inverse
      functions; Linear functions;
      Polynomial functions;
      Trigonometric functions
  absolute value, 91–92, 93–94
  area under graph of, 907–11
  argument of, 61
  average cost, 74
  average rate of change of, 84–86
    finding, 84–85
    secant line and, 85
  building and analyzing, 112–17
  on calculators, 62
  circular, 367
  complex, 57
  constant, 81–82, 83, 92
  continuous, 230, 894–96
  cube, 61, 93
  cube root, 90–91, 93
  decreasing, 81–82, 83
  defined, 57
  derivative of, 901–2
  difference of two, 65–66
  difference quotient of, 62
  discontinuous, 895
  domain of, 57, 63–64
    unspecified, 67
  domain-restricted, 264
  equation as, 60
  even and odd
    determining from graph, 79–80
    identifying from equation, 80–81

explicit form of, 63
  graph of, 70–79, 100–112
    combining procedures, 102, 107–8
    determining odd and even functions
      from, 79–80
    determining properties from, 81–82
    identifying, 71–72
    information from or about, 72–74
    using compressions and stretches,
      102–4, 106
    using reflections about the *x*-axis or
      y-axis, 104–8
    using vertical and horizontal shifts,
      100–102, 106
  greatest integer, 94
  identically equal, 459
  identity, 92
  implicit form of, 63
  important facts about, 63
  increasing, 81–82, 83
  library of, 90–95
  local maxima and local minima of, 82–83
  with no limit at 0, 883
  nonlinear, 127
  objective, 789
  one-to-one, 255–58
  periodic, 384
  piecewise-defined, 95–96, 896
  power, 175–77
    graph of, 176–77
    of odd degree, 176–77
    properties of, 176–77
  product of two, 65–66
  quotient of two, 65–66
  range of, 57
  reciprocal, 93, 415, 416. *See also*
      Cosecant function;
      Secant function
  relation as, 56–60
  square, 93
  square root, 90, 93
  step, 94
  sum of two, 65–66
    graph of, 550–51
  value (image) of, 57, 60–62
  zeros of, Bisection Method for
      approximating, 233
Function keys, A10
Function notation, 67
Fundamental identities of trigonometric
      functions, 386–88
  quotient, 387
  reciprocal, 387
Fundamental period, 384
Fundamental Theorem of Algebra, 234
  Conjugate Pairs Theorem and, 235–36
  proof of, 235
Future value, 313–17

Galois, Evariste, 231
Gauss, Karl Friedrich, 234, 595, 705
Gauss-Jordan method, 727

General addition principle of
　　counting, 852
General form
　　of conics, 673–76
　　of equation of circle, 47–48
　　linear equation in, 36–37
General term, 805
General term (nth term) of sequence, B4
Generators of cone, 638
Geometric progression. *See* Geometric
　　sequences
Geometric sequences, 823–26
　　common ratio of, 823
　　defined, 823
　　determining, 823–24
　　formula for, 824–25
　　nth term of, 825
　　sum of, 825–26
Geometric series, 827–29, B5–B6
　　infinite, 827–29
Geometric vectors, 597–98
Geometry essentials, A14–A22
　　congruent and similar triangles,
　　　A16–A19
　　formulas, A15–A16
　　Pythagorean Theorem and its
　　　converse, A14–A15
Geometry problems, algebra to solve, 6
George I of Greece, King, 1
Gibbs, Josiah, 605
Golden ratio, 816
　　conjugate, 816
Goodman, Peter S., 439
Grade, 44
Graph(s)/graphing
　　area under, 907–11
　　bounded, 786
　　of circles, 45–47, 584
　　complete, 9
　　of cosecant function, 415–17
　　　using transformations, 416
　　of the cosine function, 398
　　of cotangent function, 414–15
　　of ellipse, 651–53
　　of equations in two variables, 7–13
　　　intercepts from, 12–13
　　　by plotting points, 7–9
　　　symmetry test using, 19–21
　　　$x = y^2$, 22
　　　$y = 1 \div x$, 23
　　　$y = x^3$, 21–22
　　of exponential functions, 273–76
　　　using transformations, 276–78
　　of function, 70–79, 100–112
　　　combining procedures, 102, 107–8
　　　determining odd and even functions
　　　　from, 79–80
　　　determining properties from, 81–82
　　　identifying, 71–72
　　　information from or about, 72–74
　　　using compressions and stretches,
　　　　102–4, 106

using reflections about the x-axis
　　or y-axis, 104–8
　　using vertical and horizontal shifts,
　　　100–102, 106
　　of inequalities, 780–86, A4–A5
　　　linear inequalities, 782
　　　steps for, 781
　　of inverse functions, 260–61
　　of lines
　　　given a point and the slope, 31–32
　　　using intercepts, 36–37
　　of logarithmic functions, 287–90
　　　base not 10 or e, 303
　　　inverse, 288–89
　　of logistic models, 329
　　of parabola, 640
　　of parametric equations, 687–89
　　of piecewise-defined functions, 95–96
　　of polar equations, 571–88
　　　cardioid, 578–79, 585
　　　circles, 584
　　　of conics, 682–85
　　　by converting to rectangular
　　　　equations, 572–73
　　　defined, 572
　　　lemniscate, 582–83, 585
　　　limaçon with inner loop, 580–81, 585
　　　limaçon without inner loop,
　　　　579–80, 585
　　　by plotting points, 578–86
　　　polar grids for, 571–72
　　　rose, 581–82, 585
　　　sketching, 585–86
　　　spiral, 583–84
　　　using graphing utility, 573–77
　　of polynomial functions, 181–83
　　　analyzing, 183–86
　　　smooth and continuous, 175
　　　using bounds on zeros, 228–29
　　　using transformations, 177–78
　　of polynomial inequalities, 213–14
　　of quadratic functions
　　　properties of, 146
　　　steps for, 149
　　　using its vertex, axis, and intercepts,
　　　　146–49
　　　using transformations, 144–46
　　of rational functions, 202–13
　　　analyzing, 202–9
　　　constructing rational function
　　　　from, 208–9
　　　using transformations, 193–94
　　of rational inequalities, 215–17
　　of secant function, 415
　　of sequences, 804, 805
　　of sine and cosine functions, 395–410,
　　　421–23, 551
　　　amplitude and period, 400–401
　　　equation for, 405–6
　　　key points for, 401–5
　　to solve systems of equations, 708
　　of systems of nonlinear inequalities, 785

of vectors, 599
of $y = 1/x^2$, 192–93
Graphing calculator(s), A10
　　composite functions on, 249
Graphing utility(ies), 3–4
　　to analyze graph of polynomial
　　　function, 185–86
　　to approximate intercepts, 13
　　connected mode, 94
　　to convert between decimals and
　　　degrees, minutes, seconds forms
　　　for angles, 355
　　coordinates of a point on, 4
　　De Moivre's theorem on, 593
　　derivative of function using, 902
　　dot mode, 94
　　eVALUEate feature, 221
　　to find limit, 883
　　to find sum of arithmetic
　　　sequence, 819, 820
　　to fit exponential function to
　　　data, 335–36
　　to fit logarithmic function to
　　　data, 335–36
　　to fit logistic function to data, 338
　　functions on, 83–84
　　geometric sequences using, 825, 826
　　to graph a circle, 48
　　to graph equations, 10–11
　　to identify even and odd
　　　functions, 80–81
　　identity established with, 461
　　INTERSECT feature of, 26–27
　　line of best fit from, 138–39
　　matrix operations on, 747, 749,
　　　751–52, 757
　　MAXIMUM and MINIMUM
　　　features, 83–84, 146, 157
　　parametric equations on, 688–89
　　PARametric mode, 692, 693–94
　　polar equations on, 573–77
　　REGression options, 335
　　RREF command, 727
　　sequences on, 807, 809, 810–11
　　sine function of best fit on, 427
　　to solve equations, 26–28
　　to solve exponential equations,
　　　278, 308–10
　　to solve logarithmic and exponential
　　　equations, 307, 310
　　to solve systems of linear equations,
　　　726–27, 738–39
　　to solve systems of nonlinear
　　　equations, 770–75
　　to solve trigonometric equations, 500
　　square screens on, 30–31
　　TABLE feature, 805
　　TRACE feature, 805
　　turning points in, 180–81
　　ZERO (or ROOT) feature, 26, 157
　　Zoom-Fit feature, 11
　　Zoom-Standard feature, 11

Grassmann, Hermann, 605, 614
Greatest integer function, 94
Greek letters, angles denoted by, 352
Greeks, ancient, 361
Growth, exponential, 270–72
Growth, uninhibited, 323–25
Growth factor, 270

Half-angle Formulas, 479–82
  to find exact values, 479–82
  for tangent, 482
Half-life, 326
Half-line (ray), 352
Half-planes, 782
Hamilton, William Rowan, 605
Hay fever, 173
Heron of Alexandria, 541, 542, 829
Heron's Formula, 541–42
  historical feature on, 542
  proof of, 541–42
High tide, 437
Horizontal component of vector, 601
Horizontal compression or
    stretches, 104
Horizontal lines, 33–34, 573, 584
Horizontal-line test, 257–58
Horizontal (oblique) asymptote,
    194, 196–99
Horizontal shifts, 100–102, 106
Hurricane Ivan, 351
Huygens, Christiaan, 697, 870
Huygens's clock, 697
Hyperbolas, 637, 638, 659–72
  asymptotes of, 664, 665–66
  branches of, 660
  with center at (h, k), 666–68
  with center at the origin, 660–64
    transverse axis along x-axis, 661–62
    transverse axis along y-axis, 663–64
  with center not at the origin, 667–68
  center of, 660
  conjugate, 672
  conjugate axis of, 660
  defined, 659, 681
  eccentricity of, 672, 683–84
  equilateral, 672
  foci of, 659
  graphing equation of, 661–62
  solving applied problems
    involving, 668–70
  transverse axis of, 660, 681
  vertices of, 660
Hyperbolic cosine function, 284
Hyperbolic sine function, 284
Hyperboloid, 672
Hypocycloid, 700
Hypotenuse, A14

Identically equal functions, 459
Identity(ies)
  definition of, 459
  equation, A46
  polarization, 616

Pythagorean, 388, 459
trigonometric, 459–66
  basic, 460
  establishing, 461–63, 468–72,
    477–79
  Even-Odd, 459
  Pythagorean, 459
  Quotient, 387, 459
  Reciprocal, 387, 459
  trigonometric equations solved
    using, 496–98
Identity function, 92
Identity matrix, 753–54
Identity Properties, 754
Image (value) of function, 57, 60–62
Imaginary axis of complex plane, 589
Implicit form of function, 63
Improper rational expression, 763
Improper rational function, 197–99
Incidence, angle of, 494
Inclination, 395
Inconsistent systems of equations, 707,
    708, 713, 714–15
  containing three variables, 714–15
  containing two variables, 711–12
  matrices to solve, 729–30
Increasing functions, 81, 83
Increasing linear functions, 129
Independent systems of equations, 708
Independent variable, 61
  in calculus, 395
Index/indices
  of refraction, 494
  row and column, 721, 746
  of sum, 808
Induction, mathematical, 833–36
  Extended Principle of, 836
  principle of, 833, 836
  proving statements using, 833–35
Inequality(ies)
  graphing, 780–86
    linear inequalities, 782
    steps for, 781
  involving quadratic functions, 164–67
  nonstrict, A5
  polynomial, 213–15
    algebraically and graphically
      solving, 213–15
    steps for solving, 217
  rational
    algebraically and graphically
      solving, 215–17
    steps for solving, 217
  satisfying, 780
  sides of, A5
  strict, A5
  systems of, 780–88
    graphing, 783–86
  in two variables, 780
Inequality symbols, A4
Inertia
  moment of, 488
  product of, 484

Infinite series, 827–29, B3–B5
Infinite sets, 850
Infinity, approaches, 193
Inflation, 321
Inflection point, 329
Initial point of directed line
    segment, 597
Initial side of angle, 352
Initial value, 270
Input to relation, 56
Inscribed circle, 545
Instantaneous rate of change, 902–3
Integers, A3
  dividing, A26
  factoring over the, A28
  positive, 833n
Integrals, 479, 911–12
  area under graph, 907–11
  graphing utility to approximate,
    911–12
Intercept(s)
  of circle, 46–47
  from an equation, 18–19
  from a graph, 12–13
  graphing an equation in general
    form using, 36–37
  graphing utility to approximate, 13
  graph of lines using, 36–37
  of quadratic function, 146–49
Interest
  compound
    computing, 314–15
    continuous, 316–17
    defined, 314
    doubling or tripling time for
      money, 319
    effective rates of return, 317
    formula, 315
    present value of lump sum of
      money, 318
  rate of, 313
  simple, 313–14
Intermediate Value Theorem, 230
Internal Revenue Service
    Restructuring and Reform
    Act (RRA), 89
Intersection of sets, A2
Invariance, 680
Inverse
  additive, A28, A38
  of matrix, 754–57
    finding, 756–57
    multiplying matrix by, 754–55
    solving system of linear equations
      using, 757–58
Inverse functions, 258–65, 439, 440–53.
    See also Logarithmic functions
  cosine, 445–47
    defined, 445
    exact value of, 446–47
    exact value of expressions
      involving, 454
    implicit form of, 445

defined by a map or an ordered pair, 258–60
domain of, 259
of domain-restricted function, 264
finding, 258–60, 449–50
defined by an equation, 261–64
graph of, 260–61
range of, 259, 264
secant, cosecant, and cotangent, 455
approximating the value of, 456
calculator to evaluate, 456
definition of, 455
sine, 440–43
approximate value of, 443
defined, 441
exact value of, 441–42
exact value of expressions involving, 454, 472
implicit form of, 441
properties of, 443–44
solving equations involving, 450
Sum and Difference Formulas involving, 472
tangent, 447–49
defined, 448
exact value of, 448–49
exact value of expressions involving, 454
implicit form of, 448
verifying, 260
written algebraically, 456–57
Inverse trigonometric equations, 450
Irrational numbers, A3
decimal representation of, A3
Irreducible quadratic factor, 227, 767–69
Isosceles triangle, 16

Jaib, 377
Jība, 377
Jīva, 377
Jordan, Camille, 705
Joules (newton-meters), 613

Karmarkar, Narendra, 789n
Khayyám, Omar, 842
Kirchhoff's Rules, 719, 734
Koukounas, Teddy, 544
Kôwa, Takakazu Seki, 705

Lancaster, John, 439
Largent, Steve, 55
Latus rectum, 640
Law of Cosines, 533–36
in applied problems, 536
defined, 534
historical feature on, 536
proof of, 534
Pythagorean Theorem as special case of, 534
SAS triangles solved using, 534–35
SSS triangles solved using, 535
Law of Decay, 325–27. *See also* Exponential growth and decay

Law of Sines, 522–33
in applied problems, 527–29
defined, 523
historical feature on, 536
proof of, 528–29
SAA or ASA triangles solved using, 524
SSA triangles solved using, 525–27
Law of Tangents, 533, 536
Laws of Exponents, 270, 278, A7–A9
Leading coefficient, 234, A24
Least common multiple (LCM), A39–A41
Left limit, 892
Left stochastic transition matrix, 762
Legs of triangle, A14
Leibniz, Gottfried Wilhelm, 55, 705
Lemniscate, 582–83, 585
Lensmaker's equation, A45
Lewis, Meriwether, 509
Lexington, Ky., 173
Li, Doncheng, 351
Lift, 561
Light detector, 515
Light projector, 515
Like terms, A24
Limaçon
with inner loop, 580–81, 585
without inner loop, 579–80, 585
Limit(s), 193, 880–99
of average rate of change, 890
of constant, 885
of difference, 886
finding, 880–84
algebra techniques for, 885–92
by graphing, 882–83
using a table, 880–82
of monomial, 887
one-sided, 892–94
of polynomial, 888
of power or root, 888–89
of product, 886
of quotient, 889–90
of sequence, B1–B3
of sum, 886
of x, 885
Line(s), 29–44
of best fit, 138–39
coincident, 708
equations of. *See also* Linear equation(s); Systems of linear equations
perpendicular lines, 611n
secant, 85
family of, 43
graphing
given a point and the slope, 31–32
using intercepts, 36–37
horizontal, 33–34, 573, 584
point-slope form of, 33–34
polar equation of, 572–73, 584

slope of, 29–32, 35–36
containing two points, 30
from linear equation, 35–36
tangent, 50
vertical, 29, 574–75, 584
y-intercept of, 35–36
Linear algebra, 745
Linear equation(s). *See also* Line(s); Systems of linear equations
defined, 37
in general form, 36–37
given two points, 34
for horizontal line, 33–34
for parallel line, 37–38
for perpendicular line, 38–40
slope from, 35–36
in slope-intercept form, 34–35
solving, A47–A49
for vertical line, 32–33
Linear factors, 763–67
nonrepeated, 763–65
repeated, 765–67
Linear functions, 126–35
average rate of change of, 126–28
defined, 126
graphing utility to find the line of best fit, 138–39
graph of, 126
identifying, 271–72
increasing, decreasing, or constant, 129
models from data, 136–42
models from verbal descriptions, 130–32
scatter diagrams, 136–37
Linear programming problems, 705, 789–95
definition of, 790
maximum, 792–93
minimum, 791–92
setting up, 789–90
solution to, 791
location of, 791
solving, 790–93
in two variables, 790
Linear relations, nonlinear relations vs., 137–38
Linear speed of object traveling in circular motion, 360–61
Linear trigonometric equation, 490
Line segment, 597
length of, 5–6
midpoint of, 7
Local maxima and local minima of functions, 82–83
Logarithmic equations, 306–8
defined, 291
solving, 291–92, 306–8
Logarithmic functions, 284–97
changing between logarithmic expressions and exponential expressions, 285
continuous, 897

Logarithmic functions (*continued*)
  defined, 285
  domain of, 286
  evaluating, 285–86
  fitting to data, 336–37
  graph of, 287–90
  properties of, 287, 293
  range of, 286
Logarithmic spiral, 584
Logarithms, 297–305
  with bases other than 10 or *e*
    evaluating, 301–3
    graphing, 303
  on calculators, 301
  common (log), 289, 301–2, 304
  historical feature on, 304
  logarithmic expression as
      single, 300–301
  logarithmic expression as sum or
      difference of, 299–300
  natural (ln), 287, 301–2, 304
  properties of, 297–303
    establishing, 297–98
    proofs of, 298–99
    summary of, 303
  relating to exponents, 285
Logistic models, 328–31
  defined, 328
  domain and range of, 329
  graph of, 329
  growth models, 337–38
  properties of, 329
Loudness, 296
Louis, Spiridon, 1
Lowest terms
  rational expressions in,
      A35–A36
  rational function in, 192, 195
Low tide, 437

Magnitude
  of earthquake, 297
  of vectors, 597, 599, 601, 602,
      603–4, 623–24
    in space, 619
Magnitude (modulus), 589, 591
Major axis, 681
Malthus, Thomas Robert, 879, 918
Mandel, Howie, 849
Mapping, 56
Marathon, 1
Marginal cost, 153
Marginal propensity to consume, 832
Markov chains, 801
Marx, Karl, 879
Mathematical induction, 833–36
  Extended Principle of, 836
  principle of, 833, 836
  proving statements using, 833–35
Matrix/matrices, 705, 720–35, 745–62
  arranging data in, 746
  augmented, 721–22, 723
  coefficient, 722

defined, 721, 745
entries of, 721, 746, 753
equal, 746, 747
examples of, 746
graphing utilities for, 747
historical feature on, 759
identity, 753–54
inverse of, 754–57
  finding, 756–57
  multiplying matrix by, 754–55
  solving system of linear equations
      using, 757–58
left stochastic transition, 762
m by *n*, 746
nonsingular, 754, 756
product of two, 749–54
in reduced row echelon form, 727
row and column indices of, 721, 746
in row echelon form, 724–30
row operations on, 722–23
scalar multiples of, 748–49
singular, 754
to solve system of linear equations,
    724–35
square, 746
sum and difference of two, 746–48
transition, 801
zero, 748
Maxima of functions, local, 82–83
Mean distance, 659, 704
Mechanics, parametric equations
    applied to, 696–97
Medians of triangle, 16
Menelaus of Alexandria, 361
Metrica (Heron), 542
Midpoint formula, 7
Mile, nautical vs. statute, 364
Miller, Beth, 173
Minima of functions, local, 82–83
Minors, 739–40
Minutes, converting between
    decimals and, 354
Miranda, Kathleen, 544
Model(s)
  financial, 313–22
    effective rates of return, 317
    future value of a lump sum of
        money, 313–17
    present value of a lump sum of
        money, 318
    rate of interest or time required
        to double a lump sum of
        money, 319
  probability, 864–66
  quadratic, 155–60
    from data, 158–60
    from verbal descriptions, 155–58
  from verbal descriptions, 130–32
  wave, 351
Modulus (magnitude), 589, 591
Mollweide, Karl, 533
Mollweide's Formula, 533
Moment of inertia, 488

Monomial(s), A23
  degree of, A23
  examples of, A23
  recognizing, A23
Monomial, limit of, 887
Monter, 44
Monty Hall Game, 877–78
Motion
  circular, 546–47
  curvilinear, 691
  damped, 546, 549–50
  Newton's second law of, 599
  projectile, 691–93
  simple harmonic, 546–48
Multiple root, 179*n*
Multiplication, A10. See also Product(s)
  of rational expressions, A36–A37
  scalar, 748–49
  of vectors, by numbers, 598–99.
      See also Dot product
Multiplication principle of counting,
    852–54
Multiplier, 832
Mutually exclusive events, 868–69

Napier, John, 304
Nappes, 638
National Oceanic and Atmospheric
    Administration (NOAA), 351
Natural logarithms (ln), 287,
    301–2, 304
Natural numbers (counting numbers),
    833*n*, 835, A3
Nautical miles, 364
Negative angle, 352
Negative numbers
  real, A4
Neptune, 637
Newton, Isaac, 327
Newton-meters (joules), 613
Newton's Law of Cooling, 327–28, 332
Newton's Law of Heating, 332
Newton's Law of universal
    gravitation, 219
Newton's Method, 202
Newton's Second Law of Motion,
    546, 599
Niccolo of Brescia (Tartaglia),
    231, 595
Nonlinear equations, systems of, 770–80
  elimination method for
      solving, 771–76
  historical feature on, 776
  substitution method for
      solving, 770–71
Nonlinear functions, 127
Nonlinear inequalities, systems of, 785
Nonlinear relations, 137–38
Nonsingular matrix, 754, 756
Nonstrict inequalities, A5
Normal plane, 611*n*
*n*th term (general term) of sequence, B4
Null (empty) sets, 850, A1

Numbers
Fibonacci, 808
irrational, A3
natural (counting), 833*n*, 835, A3
rational, A3
Numerator, A35

Objective function, 789
Oblique (horizontal) asymptote, 194, 196–99
Oblique triangle, 522–23
Odd functions
determining from graph, 79–80
identifying from equation, 80–81
Olympics, first modern (1896), 1
One-sided limits, 892–94
One-to-one functions, 255–58
defined, 256
horizontal-line test for, 257–58
Opens down, 144
Opens up, 144
Optical (scanning) angle, 484
Optimization, quadratic functions and, 155
Orbits
elliptical, 637
planetary, 659
Ordered pair(s), 2
inverse function defined by, 258–60
as relations, 56–58
Ordinary annuity, 811
Ordinary (statute) miles, 364
Ordinate (*y*-coordinate), 2
Orientation, 687
Origin, 2
distance from point to, 112–13
of real number line, A4
in rectangular coordinates, 617
symmetry with respect to, 19–20
Orthogonal vectors, 611–13
Outcome of probability, 864
equally likely, 866–67
Output of relation, 56

Panchang, Vijay, 351
Parabola, 144–45, 638, 639–48
axis of symmetry of, 144, 639
defined, 639, 681
directrix of, 639
family of, 111
focus of, 639
graphing equation of, 640
solving applied problems involving, 644–45
with vertex at (h, k), 643–44
with vertex at the origin, 639–43
finding equation of, 640–41
focus at $(a, 0)$, $a > 0$, 640–41
vertex of, 144, 639
Paraboloids of revolution, 637, 644–45
Parallax, 519
Parallelepiped, 631
Parallel lines, 37–38

Parallelogram, area of, 629
Parallel vectors, 611
Parameter, 687
time as, 691–94
Parametric equations, 687–700
for curves defined by rectangular equations, 694–97
applications to mechanics, 696–97
cycloid, 696
defined, 687
describing, 690–91
graphing, 687–89
rectangular equation for curve defined parametrically, 689–91
time as parameter in, 691–94
Partial fraction decomposition, 705, 762–69
defined, 763
where denominator has nonrepeated irreducible quadratic factor, 767–68
where denominator has only nonrepeated linear factors, 763–65
where denominator has repeated irreducible quadratic factors, 768–69
where denominator has repeated linear factors, 765–67
Partial fractions, 763
Partial sums, sequence of, B5
Participation rate, 70
Partitioning, 907–13
Pascal, Blaise, 697, 839, 870
Pascal triangle, 839, 842
Payment period, 314
Peano, Giuseppe, 871
Perfect cubes, A25
Perfect squares, A25
Perfect triangle, 545
Perihelion, 659, 686, 704
Perimeter, formulas for, A15
Period
fundamental, 384
of simple harmonic motion, 546
of sinusoidal functions, 400–401, 419–22
of trigonometric functions, 384–85
Periodic functions, 384
Permutations, 855–58
computing, 858
defined, 855
distinct objects without repetition, 856–57
distinct objects with repetition, 856
involving *n* nondistinct objects, 860–61
Perpendicular line, 611*n*
Phase shift, 419–23
to graph $y = A \sin(\omega x - \phi)$, 419–23
Phones, portable, 55
Physics, vectors in, 597
Piecewise-defined functions, 95–96
continuous, 896
Pitch, 44
Pixels, 3

Plane(s)
complex, 589–92
defined, 589
imaginary axis of, 589
plotting points in, 589–90
real axis of, 589
normal, 611*n*
Plane curve, 687
Planets, orbit of, 659
Plotting points, 2, 562–64
graph equations by, 7–9
Pluto, 637
Point(s)
coordinate of, on number line, A4
coordinates of, 4
corner, 786
distance between two, 4
in space, 618
distance from the origin to, 112–13
feasible, 790
inflection, 329
initial, 597
plotting, 2, 562–64
graph equations by, 7–9
polar coordinates of, 563–64
of tangency, 50
terminal, 597
turning, 180–81
Point-slope form of equation of line, 33–34
Polar axis, 562
Polar coordinates, 562–71
conversion from rectangular coordinates, 566–68
conversion to rectangular coordinates, 564–66
defined, 562
plotting points using, 562–64
of a point, 563–64
polar axis of, 562
pole of, 562
rectangular coordinates vs., 562
Polar equations
calculus and, 585–86
classification of, 584–85
of conics, 681–86
analyzing and graphing, 682–85
converting to rectangular equation, 685
focus at pole; eccentricity *e*, 682–85
defined, 572
graph of, 571–88
cardioid, 578–79, 585
circles, 584
by converting to rectangular equations, 572–73
defined, 572
lemniscate, 582–83, 585
limaçon with inner loop, 580–81, 585
limaçon without inner loop, 579–80, 585
by plotting points, 578–86

Polar equations (*continued*)
    polar grids for, 571–72
    rose, 581–82, 585
    sketching, 585–86
    spiral, 583–84
    using graphing utility, 573–77
    historical feature on, 586
    identifying, 572–73
    testing for symmetry, 577
    transforming rectangular form to, 569
    transforming to rectangular
      form, 568–69
Polar form of complex number, 590
Polar grids, 571–72
Polarization identity, 616
Pole, 562
Pollen, 173, 244–45
Polynomial(s), A23–A31
    Chebyshëv, 478n
    degree of, 174–77, A24
      odd, 227, 235–36
    dividing, 220–21
      synthetic division, A31–A35
      using long division, A26–A28
    examples of, A24
    factoring, A28–A29
    limit of, 888
    monomials, 887, A23
    prime, A28
    recognizing, A23–A25
    solving, 226–27
    special products formulas, A25–A26
    in standard form, A24
    terms of, A24
    zero, A24
Polynomial functions, 174–91, 895
    of best fit, 186–87
    complex, 234
    complex zeros of, 234–39
      Conjugate Pairs Theorem, 235–36
      defined, 234
      finding, 237–38
      polynomial function with specified
        zeros, 236–37
    continuous, 895
    defined, 174
    end behavior of, 182–83
    graph of, 181–83
      analyzing, 183–86
      smooth and continuous, 175
      using bounds on zeros, 228–29
      using transformations, 177–78
    historical feature on, 231
    identifying, 174–77
    multiplicity of, 178–83
    real zeros (roots) of, 178–83, 220–33
      finding, 224–26
      Intermediate Value Theorem, 230
      number of, 223
      Rational Zeros Theorem,
        223–24, 237
      Remainder Theorem and Factor
        Theorem, 220–23

repeated, 179
    theorem for bounds on, 227–30
  solving, 224–26
Polynomial inequalities, 213–15
    algebraically and graphically
      solving, 213–15
    steps for solving, 217
Population increases, 879, 918
Portable phones, 55
Position vector, 600–601, 618–19
Positive angle, 352
Positive integers, 833n
Positive real numbers, A4
Power(s), 409. *See also* Exponent(s)
    limit of, 888–89
    log of, 299
Power functions, 175–77
    exponential function vs., 271
    graph of, 175–76
    of odd degree, 176–77
    properties of, 176–77
Present value, 315, 318
Price, equilibrium, 131
Prime polynomials, A28
Principal, 313
Principal square root, A9
Probability(ies), 801, 864–70
    Complement Rule to find, 869–70
    compound, 867
    constructing models, 864–66
    defined, 864
    of equally likely outcomes, 866–67
    of event, 866
      mutually exclusive, 868–69
    historical feature on, 870
    outcome of, 864
    sample space, 864
    of union of two events, 868–69
Product(s). *See also* Dot product;
    Multiplication
    of complex numbers
      in polar form, 591–92
    of inertia, 484
    limits of, 886–87
    log of, 299
    special, A25–A26, A29
    of two functions, 65–66
    of two matrices, 749–54
    vector (cross), 605
Product function, 65
Product-to-Sum Formulas, 485–86
Projectile motion, 691–93
Projection, vector, 612–13
Projection of P on the x-axis, 547
Projection of P on the y-axis, 547
Prolate spheroid, 658
Proper rational expressions, 763
Proper rational function, 197–99
Proper subsets, 850
Ptolemy, 494, 536
Pythagorean Identities, 388, 459
Pythagorean Theorem, A14–A15
    applying, A15

converse of, A14–A15, A19
    proof of, A19
    as special case of Law of Cosines, 534
Pythagorean triples, A22

Quadrantal angles, 353, 368–70
Quadrants, 2
Quadratic equations, A50–A55
    definition of, A50
    solving
      by completing the square, A52–A53
      by factoring, A50–A51
      using the quadratic formula,
        A53–A55
      using the Square Root Method, A51
    in standard form, A50
Quadratic factors, irreducible, 227, 767–69
Quadratic functions, 143–51
    applied problems involving, 155–58
    of best fit to data, 159
    defined, 143
    graph of
      properties of, 146
      steps for, 149
      using its vertex, axis, and
        intercepts, 146–49
      using transformations, 144–46
    inequalities involving, 164–67
    maximum or minimum value of,
      150–51
    optimizations and, 155
    vertex and axis of symmetry of,
      146–49
Quadratic models, 155–60
    from data, 158–60
    from verbal descriptions, 155–58
Quantity, equilibrium, 131
Quantity demanded, 131
Quantity supplied, 131
Quaternions, 605
Quotient(s), 220, 221, A26. *See also*
    Division
    of complex numbers
      in polar form, 591–92
    difference, 62, 89, 284, 475
    limit of, 889–90
    log of, 299
    synthetic division to find, A31–A35
    of two functions, 65–66
Quotient identity(ies), 459
    of trigonometric functions, 387

Radians, 353, 355
    converting between degrees
      and, 356–59
Radical sign, A9
Radioactive decay, 325
Radius, 44
    of sphere, 625
Range, 57
    of absolute value function, 94
    of constant function, 92
    of cosecant function, 384

of cosine function, 383, 384, 398
of cotangent function, 384
of cube function, 93
of cube root function, 93
of greatest integer function, 94
of identity function, 92
of inverse function, 259, 264
of logarithmic function, 286
of logistic models, 329
of one-to-one function, 256
of projectile, 479
of reciprocal function, 93
of secant function, 384
of sine function, 383, 384, 396
of square function, 93
of square root function, 93
of tangent function, 384, 412
of trigonometric functions, 382–84
Rate of change, average, 30, 271–72
of function, 84–86
finding, 84–85
linear functions, 126–29
secant line and, 85
limit of, 890
Rate of change, instantaneous, 902–3
Rate of interest, 313
Rates of return, effective, 317
Ratio
common, 823
evenness, 296
golden, 816
Rational equations, solving, A49
Rational expressions
adding and subtracting, A37–A39
least common multiple (LCM)
method for, A39–A41
complex, A41–A43
decomposing. *See* Partial fraction
decomposition
defined, A35
improper, 763
in lowest terms, A35–A36
multiplying and dividing, A36–A37
proper, 763
Rational functions, 173, 191–213
applied problems involving, 209–10
asymptotes of, 194–99
horizontal or oblique, 194
vertical, 194–96
continuous, 895–96
defined, 192
domain of, 192–95
examples of, 191
graph of, 202–13
analyzing, 202–9
constructing rational function
from, 208–9
using transformations, 193–94
with a hole, 207–8
improper, 197–99
in lowest terms, 192, 195
proper, 197–99
unbounded in positive direction, 193

Rational inequalities
algebraically and graphically
solving, 215–17
steps for solving, 217
Rational numbers, 191, A3
Rational Zeros Theorem, 223–24, 237
Ray (half-line), 352
Real axis of complex plane, 589
Real number(s), A3–A6
approximate decimals, A3
defined, A3
Real number line, A4
Real zeros (roots) of polynomial
functions, 220–33
finding, 224–26
Intermediate Value Theorem, 230
number of, 223
Rational Zeros Theorem, 223–24, 237
Remainder Theorem and Factor
Theorem, 220–23
repeated, 179
theorem for bounds on, 227–30
Reciprocal function, 93, 415, 416.
See also Cosecant function;
Secant function
Reciprocal identities, 387, 459
Rectangle, area and perimeter of, A15, A16
Rectangular (Cartesian) coordinates, 2–3
converted to polar coordinates,
566–68
polar coordinates converted to,
564–66
polar coordinates vs., 562
polar equations graphed by
converting to, 572–73
in space, 617
Rectangular (Cartesian) form of
complex number, 590, 591
Rectangular equations
for curve defined
parametrically, 689–91
polar equations converted to,
568–69, 685
transforming to polar equation, 569
Rectangular grid, 572
Recursive formula, 807–8
for arithmetic sequences, 819
terms of sequences defined by, 807–8
Reduced row echelon form, 727
Reflections about x-axis or
y-axis, 104–8
Refraction, 494
Regiomontanus, 361, 536
Relation(s), 56. *See also* Function(s)
defined, 56
as function, 56–60
input to, 56
linear vs. nonlinear, 137–38
ordered pairs as, 56–58
Remainder, 220, 221, A26
synthetic division to find, A31–A35
Remainder Theorem, 220–23
Repeated solution, A50

Repeated zeros (solutions), 179
Repeating decimals, A3
Repose, angle of, 458
Rest (equilibrium) position, 546
Resultant force, 604
Review, A1–A96
of algebra, A1–A13
distance on the real number
line, A5–A6
domain of variable, A7
evaluating algebraic
expressions, A6–A7
evaluating exponents, A10
graphing inequalities, A4–A5
Laws of Exponents, A7–A9
sets, A1–A4
square roots, A9–A10
of geometry, A14–A22
congruent and similar
triangles, A16–A19
formulas, A15–A16
Pythagorean theorem and its
converse, A14–A15
of polynomials, A23–A31
factoring, A28–A29
long division of, A26–A28
monomials, A23
recognizing, A23–A25
special products formulas, A25–A26
synthetic division of, A31–A35
of rational expressions, A35–A45
adding and subtracting, A37–A39
complex, A41–A43
in lowest terms, A35–A36
multiplying and dividing, A36–A37
solving equations, A46–A60
algebraically, A46–A47
by factoring, A50–A51
involving absolute value, A56–A57
linear equations, A47–A49
quadratic equations, A50–A55
rational equations, A49
Revolutions per unit of time, 360
Rhaeticus, 361
Rhind papyrus, 829
Richter scale, 297
Right angle, 353, A14
Right circular cone, 638
Right circular cylinder, volume
and surface area of, A16
Right-hand rule, 617
Right limit, 893
Right triangles, 510–22, A14
applications of, 513–17
solving, 512–13
Right triangle trigonometry, 510–22
Rise, 29
Root(s). *See also* Solution(s); Zeros
complex, 593–94
of equation, A46
limit of, 888–89
of multiplicity 2 (double root), A50
of multiplicity m, 179n

Rose, 581–82, 585
Roster method, A1
Rotation of axes, 674–78
  analyzing equation using, 676–78
  formulas for, 675
  identifying conic without, 678–79
Rounding, A10
Round-off errors, 513
Row echelon form, 724–30
  reduced, 727
Row index, 721, 746
Row operations, 722–23
Row vector, 750
Ruffini, P., 231
Rumsey, David, 509
Run, 29
Rutherford, Ernest, 672

SAA triangles, 524
Sample space, 864
SAS triangles, 523, 534–35, 540–41
Satisfying equations, 7
Satisfying inequalities, 780
Sawtooth curve, 553
Scalar, 598, 748
Scalar multiples of matrix, 748–49
Scalar product. *See* Dot product
Scale of number line, A4
Scanning (optical) angle, 484
Scatter diagrams, 136–37, 423
Schroeder, E., 871
Scientific calculators, A10
Secant, 368
  graph of, 415
  periodic properties of, 385
Secant function, 367
  continuous, 896, 897
  domain of, 383, 384
  inverse, 455
    approximating the value of, 456
    calculator to evaluate, 456
    definition of, 455
    range of, 384
Secant line, 85
Seconds, converting between decimals
  and, 354
Sequence(s), 804–26
  amortization, 812–13
  annuity problems, 811–12
  arithmetic, 817–23
    common difference in, 817
    defined, 817
    determining, 817–18
    formula for, 818–19
    nth term of, 818
    recursive formula for, 819
    sum of, 819–21
  convergent, B1
  defined, 804
  divergent, B2
  factorial symbol, 806–7
  Fibonacci, 808, 815–16
  geometric, 823–26

common ratio of, 823
  defined, 823
  determining, 823–24
  formula for, 824–25
  nth term of, 825
  sum of, 825–26
graph of, 804, 805
historical feature on, 829
limit of, B1–B3
of partial sums, B5
from a pattern, 806
properties of, 809
summation notation, 808
sum of, 809–11
terms of, 804–7
  alternating, 806
  defined by a recursive
    formula, 807–8
  general, 805
Series
  geometric, B5–B6
  infinite, B3–B5
Set(s), A1–A4
  complement of, A2
  correspondence between two, 56
  disjoint, A3
  elements of, 850–52, A1
  empty (null), 850, A1
  equal, 850, A2
  finite, 850
  infinite, 850
  intersection of, A2
  of numbers, A1–A4
  solution, A46
  subsets of, 850
    proper, 850
  union of, A2
  universal, 851, A2
Set-builder notation, A1–A2
Setting the viewing rectangle, 3
Shannon's diversity index, 295–96
Shifts, graphing functions using vertical
  and horizontal, 100–102, 106
Side-angle-side case of congruent
  triangle, A17
Side–angle–side case of similar
  triangle, A18
Sides
  of equation, 7, A46
  of inequality, A5
Side-side-side case of congruent
  triangle, A17
Side–side–side case of similar triangle, A18
Similar triangles, 523, A16–A19
Simple harmonic motion, 546–48
  amplitude of, 546
  analyzing, 548
  circular motion and, 546–47
  defined, 546
  equilibrium (rest) position, 546
  frequency of object in, 547
  model for an object in, 546–48
  period of, 546

Simple interest, 313–14
Simplex method, 789n
Simplifying
  complex rational expressions,
    A41–A43
Simpson's rule, 162
Sine, 368
  historical feature on, 377
  Law of, 522–33
    in applied problems, 527–29
    defined, 523
    historical feature on, 536
    proof of, 528–29
    SAA or ASA triangles solved
      using, 524
    SSA triangles solved using, 525–27
  periodic properties of, 385
  Sum and Difference Formula for, 469
  trigonometric equations linear
    in, 498–500
Sine function, 366
  of best fit, 427
  continuous, 897
  domain of, 382, 384, 396
  graphs of, 395–410
    amplitude and period, 400–401
    equation for, 405–6
    key points for, 401–5
  hyperbolic, 284
  inverse, 440–43
    approximate value of, 443
    defined, 441
    exact value of, 441–42
    exact value of expressions
      involving, 454
    implicit form of, 441
    properties of, 443–44
  properties of, 396
  range of, 383, 384, 396
Singular matrix, 754
Sinusoidal curve fitting, 423–27
  hours of daylight, 425–26
  sine function of best fit, 427
  temperature data, 423–25
Sinusoidal graphs, 395–410, 551
  amplitude and period, 400–401
  equation for, 405–6
  key points for, 401–5
  steps for, 421–23
Six trigonometric functions, 361
  of θ, 368. *See also* Trigonometric
    functions
  of t, 366–67
Slope, 29–32, 35–36
  containing two points, 30
  graphing lines given, 31–32
  from linear equation, 35–36
  of secant line, 85
Slope-intercept form of equation of
  line, 34–35
Smooth graph, 175
Snell, Willebrord, 494
Snell's Law of Refraction, 494

Solution(s), A46. *See also* Zeros
  of linear programming problems, 791
    location of, 791
  repeated, 179, A50
  of systems of equations, 707, 712
  of trigonometric equations, 489
Solution set, A46
Special products, A25–A26, A29
Speed
  angular, 360
  average, 360
  instantaneous, 903–4
  linear, of object traveling in circular
    motion, 360–61
Sphere, 625
  volume and surface area of, A16
Spheroid, prolate, 659
Spiral, 583–84
Square(s)
  of binomials (perfect squares), A25
  difference of two, A25
  perfect, A25
Square function, 93
Square matrix, 746
Square root(s), A9–A10
  complex, 593–94
  principal, A9
Square root function, 90, 93
SSA triangles, 525–27
SSS triangles, 523, 535, 541–42
Standard form
  of equation of circle, 45
  polynomials in, A24
  quadratic equation in, A50
Standard position, angle in, 352
Static equilibrium, 604–5
Statute (ordinary) miles, 364
Step function, 94
Stirling's formula, 843
Stock valuation, 125, 172
Straight angle, 353
Stretches, graphing functions using,
    102–4, 106
Strict inequalities, A5
Subscript, A24*n*
Subscripted letters, 804
Subsets, 850, A2
  proper, 850
Substitution method, 705, 708–9
  systems of nonlinear equations
    solved using, 770–71
Subtraction, A10. *See also* Difference(s)
  of rational expressions, A37–A39
    least common multiple (LCM)
      method for, A39–A41
  of vectors, 601–2
    in space, 619
Sum. *See also* Addition
  of arithmetic sequences, 819–21
  of geometric sequences, 825–26
  index of, 808
  of infinite geometric series, 827
  of infinite series, B4, B5

limits of, 886
  of logarithms, 299–300
  of sequences, 809–11
  of series, B5
  of two cubes, A26
  of two functions, 65–66
    graph of, 550–51
  of two matrices, 746–48
Sum and Difference Formulas, 466–75
  for cosines, 466–67
  defined, 466
  to establish identities, 468–72
  to find exact values, 467–68, 469–70
  involving inverse trigonometric
    function, 472–73
  for sines, 469
  for tangents, 471
Sum function, 65
Summation notation, 808
Sum-to-Product Formulas, 486–87
Sun, declination of, 451–52
Surface area, formulas for, A16
Sylvester, James J., 759
Symmetry, 19–21
  axis of
    of parabola, 144
    of quadratic function, 146
  axis of, of parabola, 639
  of polar equations, 577
  with respect to origin, 19–20
  with respect to the line $\theta = \pi/2$
    (*y*-axis), 577
  with respect to the polar axis
    (*x*-axis), 577
  with respect to the pole (origin), 577
  with respect to the *x*-axis, 19–20
  with respect to the *y*-axis, 19–20
Synthetic division, A31–A35
Systems of equations
  consistent, 707, 712
  dependent, 708
    containing three variables, 715–16
    containing two variables, 712
  equivalent, 710
  graphing, 708
  inconsistent, 707, 712–13, 714–15
    containing three variables, 714–15
    containing two variables, 711–12
  independent, 708
  solutions of, 707, 712
Systems of inequalities, 780–88
  graphing, 783–87
    bounded and unbounded
      graphs, 786
    vertices or corner points, 786
Systems of linear equations, 706–45
  consistent, 708, 712
  defined, 706
  dependent, 708
    containing three variables, 715–16
    containing two variables, 712
    matrices to solve, 728–29
  determinants, 735–45

cofactors, 740
  Cramer's Rule to solve a system of
    three equations containing three
    variables, 741–42
  Cramer's Rule to solve a system of
    two equations containing two
    variables, 736–39
  minors of, 739–40
  properties of, 742–43
  3 by 3, 739–40
  2 by 2, 736, 742–43
  elimination method of solving,
    710–11, 712
  equivalent, 710
  examples of, 706
  graphing, 708
  inconsistent, 708, 712–13, 714–15
    containing three variables, 714–15
    containing two variables, 711–12
    matrices to solve, 729–30
  independent, 708
  matrices. *See* Matrix/matrices
  partial fraction decomposition, 762–69
    defined, 763
    where denominator has a
      nonrepeated irreducible quadratic
      factor, 767–68
    where denominator has only
      nonrepeated linear factors,
      763–65
    where denominator has repeated
      irreducible quadratic factors,
      768–69
    where denominator has repeated
      linear factors, 765–67
  solution of, 707, 712
  solving, 707
  substitution method of, 708–9
  three equations containing three
    variables, 712–14
Systems of nonlinear equations, 770–80
  elimination method for solving,
    771–76
  historical feature on, 776
  substitution method for solving,
    770–71
Systems of nonlinear inequalities,
    graphing, 785

Tables, graphing utility to create, 12
Tangency, point of, 50
Tangent(s), 368
  graph of, 411–15
  Half-angle Formulas for, 482
  historical feature on, 377
  Law of, 533, 536
  periodic properties of, 385
  Sum and Difference Formulas
    for, 471
Tangent function, 367
  continuous, 896, 897
  domain of, 383, 384, 412
  inverse, 447–49

Tangent function (*continued*)
  defined, 448
    exact value of, 448–50
    exact value of expressions
      involving, 454
    implicit form of, 448
  properties of, 412–13
  range of, 384, 412
Tangent line, 50
  to the graph of a function, 900–901
  Greek method for finding, 50
Tangent problem, 899–900
Tartaglia (Niccolo of Brescia), 231, 595
Tautochrone, 696–97
Terminal point of directed line
      segment, 597
Terminal side of angle, 352, 353
Terminating decimals, A3
Terms
  of infinite series, B4
  like, A24
  of polynomial, A24
  of sequences, 804–7
    alternating, 806
    defined by a recursive
      formula, 807–8
    general, 805
3 by 3 determinants, 626, 739–40
TI-84 Plus, 10
Tides, 437
Time, as parameter, 691–94
Transcendental functions, 247
Transformations
  combining, 102, 107–8
  compressions and stretches, 102–4, 106
  cosecant and secant graphs using, 416
  of cosine function, 398–99
  defined, 100
  graphs using
    of exponential functions, 276–78
    of polynomial functions, 177–78
    of quadratic functions, 144–46
    of rational functions, 193–94
  reflections about the *x*-axis or
      y-axis, 104–8
  of sine function, 397–98
  vertical and horizontal shifts,
      100–102, 106
Transition matrix, 801
Transverse axis, 660, 681
Tree diagram, 853
Tree pollen, 173
Triangle(s). *See also* Law of Sines
  area of, 540–45, A15
  ASA, 524
  congruent, A16–A19
  equilateral, 16
  error, 17
  isosceles, 16
  legs of, A14
  medians of, 16
  oblique, 522–23
  Pascal, 839, 842

perfect, 545
  in the plane, 361
  right, 510–22, A14
    applied problems involving, 513–17
    solving, 512–13
  SAA, 524
  SAS, 523, 534–35, 540–41
  similar, 523, A16–A19
  on a sphere, 361
  SSA, 525–27
  SSS, 523, 535, 541–42
Triangular addition, 841
Trigonometric equations, 488–502
  calculator for solving, 492
  graphing utility to solve, 500
  identities to solve, 496–98
  involving single trigonometric
      function, 489–92
  linear, 490
  linear in sine and cosine, 498–500
  quadratic in from, 495–96
  solutions of, defined, 489
Trigonometric expressions, written
      algebraically, 456–57, 472–73
Trigonometric functions, 351–452
  of acute angles, 510–12
  applications of, 509–60
    damped motion, 546, 549–50
    graphing sum of two functions, 550–51
    involving right triangles, 513–17
    Law of Cosines, 533–36
    Law of Sines, 522–33, 536
    Law of Tangents, 533, 536
    simple harmonic motion, 546–48
  calculator to approximate values
      of, 375–76
  circle of radius *r* to evaluate, 376–77
  cosecant and secant graphs, 415–17
  fundamental identities of, 386–88
    quotient, 387
    reciprocal, 387
  for integer multiples of $\pi/6 = 30°$,
      $\pi/4 = 45°$, and $\pi/3 = 60°$, 374–75
  phase shift, 419–23
    to graph $y = A\sin(\omega x - \phi)$, 419–23
  of $\pi/4 = 45°$, 370–71
  of $\pi/6 = 30°$ and $\pi/3 = 60°$, 371–74
  properties of, 365–77, 382–95
    domain and range, 382–84
    even-odd, 391–92
    periodic, 384–85
  of quadrantal angles, 368–70
  right triangle trigonometry, 510–22
  signs of, in a given quadrant, 386
  sine and cosine graphs, 395–410
    amplitude and period,
      400–401, 419–22
    equation for, 405–6
    key points for, 401–5
  sinusoidal curve fitting, 423–27
  of *t*, 366–67
  tangent and cotangent
      graphs, 411–15

of θ, 368
    given one of the functions and the
      quadrant of the angle, 389–91
    unit circle approach to finding exact
      values of, 366–81
Trigonometric identities, 459–66
  basic, 460
  establishing, 461–63
    Double-angle Formulas for, 477–79
    Sum and Difference Formulas
      for, 468–72
  Even-Odd, 459
  Pythagorean, 459
  Quotient, 459
  Reciprocal, 459
Trigonometry, historical feature on, 361
Trinomials, A24
Truncation, A10
Tsunami, 351, 439
Turning points, 180–81
2 by 2 determinants, 626, 736
  proof for, 742–43

Umbra versa, 377
Unbounded graphs, 786
Unbounded in positive direction, 193
Uninhibited growth, 323–25
Union
  of sets, A2
  of two events, probabilities of, 868–69
Unit circle, 45, 366–81
  length wrapped around, 366
Unit vector, 599, 602–3, 618
  in direction of **v**, 620
Universal sets, 851, A2

Value (image) of function, 57, 60–62
Variable(s), A6, A23
  complex, 234
  dependent, 61
  domain of, A7
  independent, 61
    in calculus, 395
Variable costs, 42
Vector(s), 597–608
  adding, 598, 601–2
  algebraic, 600
  angle between, 609–11
  column, 750
  components of, 600, 618
    horizontal and vertical, 601
  cross product of, 626–27
  decomposing, 612–13
  defined, 597
  difference of, 598
  direction of, 597, 603–4
  dot product of two, 608–9
  equality of, 597, 601
  finding, 603–4
  force, 603
  geometric, 597–98
  graphing, 599
  historical feature on, 605

magnitudes of, 597, 599, 602, 603–4
multiplying by numbers, 598–99
objects in static equilibrium, 604–5
orthogonal, 611–13
parallel, 611
in physics, 597
position, 600–601
row, 750
scalar multiples of, 598, 602, 609
in space, 616–25
  angle between two vectors, 621
  direction angles of, 621–24
  distance between two points in
    space, 618
  dot product, 620–21
  operations on, 619–20
  position vectors, 618–19
subtracting, 601–2
unit, 599, 602–3, 618
  in direction of **v**, 620
velocity, 603
writing, 604
zero, 597
Vector product. *See* Cross (vector)
  product
Vector projection, 612–13
Velocity, instantaneous, 903–4
Velocity vector, 603
Venn diagrams, A2
Vertex/vertices, 786
  of cone, 638
  of ellipse, 649
  of hyperbola, 660
  of parabola, 144, 639
  of quadratic function, 146–49
  of ray, 352

Vertical asymptote, 194–96
Vertical component of vector, 601
Vertical line, 29, 574–75, 584
Vertical-line test, 71
Vertically compressed or stretched
    graphs, 102–4
Vertical shifts, 100–102, 106
Viète, François, 536
Viewing angle, 452
Viewing rectangle, 3
Volume, formulas for, A16

Wallis, John, 595
Ward, Steven N., 439
Waves. *See also* Simple harmonic
    motion
  model of, 351
  traveling speeds of, 494
Weed pollen, 244–45
Whispering galleries, 656
Wings, airplane, 561
Wireless communications, 55
Work, 625
  dot product to compute, 613–14
World population, 879, 918

x-axis, 2
  projection of *P* on the, 547
  reflections about, 104–8
  symmetry with respect to, 19–20
x-coordinate, 2
x-intercept, 12
  polynomial graphed using, 178–80
  of quadratic function, 147
xy-plane, 2, 617
xz-plane, 617

Yang Hui, 842
y-axis, 2
  projection of *P* on the, 547
  reflections about, 104–8
  symmetry with respect to, 19–20
y-coordinate (ordinate), 2
y-intercept, 12, 35–36
  from linear equation, 35–36
yz-plane, 617

Zero-coupon bonds, 322
Zero-level earthquake, 297
Zero matrix, 748
Zero polynomial, A24
Zero-Product Property, A4
Zeros
  bounds on, 227–30
  complex, of polynomials, 234–39
    Conjugate Pairs
      Theorem, 235–36
    defined, 234
    finding, 237–38
    polynomial function with specified
      zeros, 236–37
  real, of polynomials, 178–83,
    220–33
    finding, 224–26
    Intermediate Value Theorem, 230
    number of, 223
    Rational Zeros Theorem,
      223–24, 237
    Remainder Theorem and Factor
      Theorem, 220–23
    repeated, 179
    theorem for bounds on, 227–30
Zero vector, 597

LICENSING AGREEMENT
SULLIVAN / SULLIVAN, III

Chapter Test Prep Video CDs Precalculus: Enhanced with Graphing Utilities, 5e
ISBN: 0-13-235620-1/978-0-13-235620-6
© 2009 Pearson Education, Inc.
Pearson Prentice Hall
Pearson Education, Inc.
Upper Saddle River, NJ 07458
Pearson Prentice Hall™ is a trademark of Pearson Education, Inc

YOU SHOULD CAREFULLY READ THE TERMS AND CONDITIONS BEFORE USING THE CD-ROM PACKAGE. USING THIS CD-ROM PACKAGE INDICATES YOUR ACCEPTANCE OF THESE TERMS AND CONDITIONS.

Pearson Education, Inc. provides this program and licenses its use. You assume responsibility for the selection of the program to achieve your intended results, and for the installation, use, and results obtained from the program. This license extends only to use of the program in the United States or countries in which the program is marketed by authorized distributors.

LICENSE GRANT: You hereby accept a nonexclusive, nontransferable, permanent license to install and use the program ON A SINGLE COMPUTER at any given time. You may copy the program solely for backup or archival purposes in support of your use of the program on the single computer. You may not modify, translate, disassemble, decompile, or reverse engineer the program, in whole or in part.

TERM: The License is effective until terminated. Pearson Education, Inc. reserves the right to terminate this License automatically if any provision of the License is violated. You may terminate the License at any time. To terminate this License, you must return the program, including documentation, along with a written warranty stating that all copies in your possession have been returned or destroyed.

LIMITED WARRANTY: THE PROGRAM IS PROVIDED "AS IS" WITHOUT WARRANTY OF ANY KIND, EITHER EXPRESSED OR IMPLIED, INCLUDING, BUT NOT LIMITED TO, THE IMPLIED WARRANTIES OF MERCHANTABILITY AND FITNESS FOR APARTICULAR PURPOSE. THE ENTIRE RISK AS TO THE QUALITY AND PERFORMANCE OF THE PROGRAM IS WITH YOU. SHOULD THE PROGRAM PROVE DEFECTIVE, YOU (AND NOT PEARSON EDUCATION, INC. OR ANY AUTHORIZED DEALER) ASSUME THE ENTIRE COST OF ALL NECESSARY SERVICING, REPAIR, OR CORRECTION. NO ORAL OR WRITTEN INFORMATION OR ADVICE GIVEN BY PEARSON EDUCATION, INC., ITS DEALERS, DISTRIBUTORS, OR AGENTS SHALL CREATE A WARRANTY OR INCREASE THE SCOPE OF THIS WARRANTY. SOME STATES DO NOT ALLOW THE EXCLUSION OF IMPLIED WARRANTIES, SO THE ABOVE EXCLUSION MAY NOT APPLY TO YOU. THIS WARRANTY GIVES YOU SPECIFIC LEGAL RIGHTS AND YOU MAY ALSO HAVE OTHER LEGAL RIGHTS THAT VARY FROM STATE TO STATE.

Pearson Education, Inc. does not warrant that the functions contained in the program will meet your requirements or that the operation of the program will be uninterrupted or error-free. However, Pearson Education, Inc. warrants the CD-ROM(s) on which the program is furnished to be free from defects in material and workmanship under normal use for a period of ninety (90) days from the date of delivery to you as evidenced by a copy of your receipt. The program should not be relied on as the sole basis to solve a problem whose incorrect solution could result in injury to person or property. If the program is employed in such a manner, it is at the user's own risk and Pearson Education, Inc. explicitly disclaims all liability for such misuse.

LIMITATION OF REMEDIES: Pearson Education, Inc.'s entire liability and your exclusive remedy shall be:

1. the replacement of any CD-ROM not meeting Pearson Education, Inc.'s "LIMITED WARRANTY" and that is returned to Pearson Education, or
2. if Pearson Education is unable to deliver a replacement CD-ROM that is free of defects in materials or workmanship, you may terminate this agreement by returning the program.

IN NO EVENT WILL PEARSON EDUCATION, INC. BE LIABLE TO YOU FOR ANY DAMAGES, INCLUDING ANY LOST PROFITS, LOST SAVINGS, OR OTHER INCIDENTAL OR CONSEQUENTIAL DAMAGES ARISING OUT OF THE USE OR INABILITY TO USE SUCH PROGRAM EVEN IF PEARSON EDUCATION, INC. OR AN AUTHORIZED DISTRIBUTOR HAS BEEN ADVISED OF THE POSSIBILITY OF SUCH DAMAGES, OR FOR ANY CLAIM BY ANY OTHER PARTY.

SOME STATES DO NOT ALLOW FOR THE LIMITATION OR EXCLUSION OF LIABILITY FOR INCIDENTAL OR CONSEQUENTIAL DAMAGES, SO THE ABOVE LIMITATION OR EXCLUSION MAY NOT APPLY TO YOU.

GENERAL: You may not sublicense, assign, or transfer the license of the program. Any attempt to sublicense, assign or transfer any of the rights, duties, or obligations hereunder is void.

This Agreement will be governed by the laws of the State of New York. Should you have any questions concerning this Agreement, you may contact Pearson Education, Inc. by writing to:

ESM Media Development
Higher Education Division
Pearson Education, Inc.
1 Lake Street
Upper Saddle River, NJ 07458

Should you have any questions concerning technical support, you may write to:

New Media Production
Higher Education Division
Pearson Education, Inc.
1 Lake Street
Upper Saddle River, NJ 07458

YOU ACKNOWLEDGE THAT YOU HAVE READ THIS AGREEMENT, UNDERSTAND IT, AND AGREE TO BE BOUND BY ITS TERMS AND CONDITIONS. YOU FURTHER AGREE THAT IT IS THE COMPLETE AND EXCLUSIVE STATEMENT OF THE AGREEMENT BETWEEN US THAT SUPERSEDES ANY PROPOSAL OR PRIOR AGREEMENT, ORAL OR WRITTEN, AND ANY OTHER COMMUNICATIONS BETWEEN US RELATING TO THE SUBJECT MATTER OF THIS AGREEMENT.

System Requirements

Macintosh:
Power PC G3 233 MHz or better
Mac OS 10.x
64 MB RAM
19 MB available hard drive space for Mac OS X (optional – if QuickTime installation is needed)
800 × 600 resolution
8x or faster CD-ROM drive
QuickTime 6.x

Windows:
Pentium II 300 MHz processor
Windows 2000, XP, Vista Ultimate
64 MB RAM (128 MB RAM required for Windows XP)
4.3 MB available hard drive space (optional-for minimum QuickTime installation)
800 × 600 resolution
8x or faster CD-ROM drive
QuickTime 6.x
Sound Card

Support Information

If you are having problems with this software, you can get support by filling out the web form located at: http://247pearsoned.custhelp.com/

Our technical staff will need to know certain things about your system in order to help us solve your problems more quickly and efficiently. If possible, please be at your computer when you call for support. You should have the following information ready:

- ISBN
- CD-ROM ISBN
- corresponding product and title
- computer make and model
- Operating System (Windows or Macintosh) and Version
- RAM available
- hard disk space available
- Sound card? Yes or No
- printer make and model
- network connection
- detailed description of the problem, including the exact wording of any error messages.

NOTE: Pearson does not support and/or assist with the following:
- third-party software (i.e. Microsoft including Microsoft Office suite, Apple, Borland, etc.)
- homework assistance
- Textbooks and CD-ROMs purchased used are not supported and are non-replaceable. To purchase a new CD-ROM, contact Pearson Individual Order Copies at 1-800-282-0693.

CONICS

Parabola

  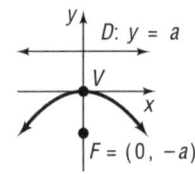

$$y^2 = 4ax \qquad\qquad y^2 = -4ax \qquad\qquad x^2 = 4ay \qquad\qquad x^2 = -4ay$$

Ellipse

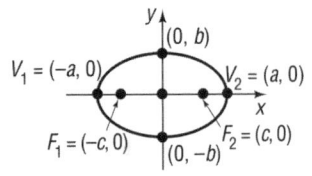

$$\frac{x^2}{a^2} + \frac{y^2}{b^2} = 1, \quad a > b, \quad c^2 = a^2 - b^2 \qquad\qquad \frac{x^2}{b^2} + \frac{y^2}{a^2} = 1, \quad a > b, \quad c^2 = a^2 - b^2$$

Hyperbola

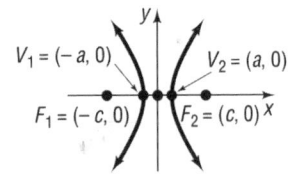

$$\frac{x^2}{a^2} - \frac{y^2}{b^2} = 1, \quad c^2 = a^2 + b^2 \qquad\qquad \frac{y^2}{a^2} - \frac{x^2}{b^2} = 1, \quad c^2 = a^2 + b^2$$

$$\text{Asymptotes:} \quad y = \frac{b}{a}x, \quad y = -\frac{b}{a}x \qquad\qquad \text{Asymptotes:} \quad y = \frac{a}{b}x, \quad y = -\frac{a}{b}x$$

PROPERTIES OF LOGARITHMS

$$\log_a(MN) = \log_a M + \log_a N$$

$$\log_a\left(\frac{M}{N}\right) = \log_a M - \log_a N$$

$$\log_a M^r = r \log_a M$$

$$\log_a M = \frac{\log M}{\log a} = \frac{\ln M}{\ln a}$$

PERMUTATIONS/COMBINATIONS

$$0! = 1 \qquad 1! = 1$$
$$n! = n(n-1) \cdot \ldots \cdot (3)(2)(1)$$

$$P(n,r) = \frac{n!}{(n-r)!}$$

$$C(n,r) = \binom{n}{r} = \frac{n!}{(n-r)!\,r!}$$

BINOMIAL THEOREM

$$(a+b)^n = a^n + \binom{n}{1}ba^{n-1} + \binom{n}{2}b^2a^{n-2}$$
$$+ \cdots + \binom{n}{n-1}b^{n-1}a + b^n$$

ARITHMETIC SEQUENCE

$$a_1 + (a_1 + d) + (a_1 + 2d) + \cdots + [a_1 + (n-1)d]$$
$$= \frac{n}{2}[2a_1 + (n-1)d] = \frac{n}{2}[a_1 + a_n]$$

GEOMETRIC SEQUENCE

$$a_1 + a_1 r + a_1 r^2 + \cdots + a_1 r^{n-1} = a_1 \cdot \frac{1 - r^n}{1 - r}$$

GEOMETRIC SERIES

$$\text{If } |r| < 1, \, a_1 + a_1 r + a_1 r^2 + \cdots = \sum_{k=1}^{\infty} a_1 r^{k-1}$$
$$= \frac{a_1}{1 - r}$$

LIBRARY OF FUNCTIONS

Identity Function
$f(x) = x$

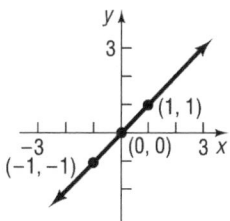

Square Function
$f(x) = x^2$

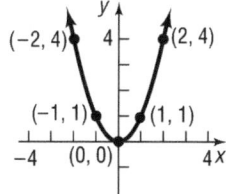

Cube Function
$f(x) = x^3$

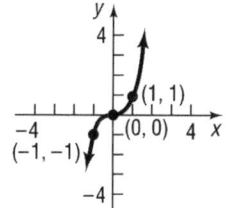

Square Root Function
$f(x) = \sqrt{x}$

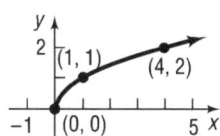

Reciprocal Function
$f(x) = \dfrac{1}{x}$

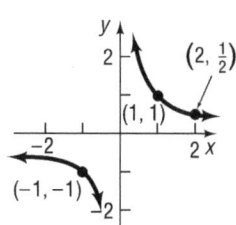

Cube Root Function
$f(x) = \sqrt[3]{x}$

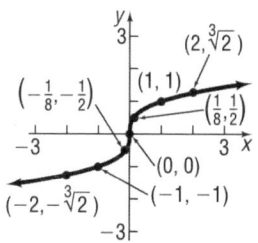

Absolute Value Function
$f(x) = |x|$

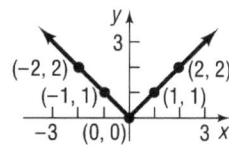

Exponential Function
$f(x) = e^x$

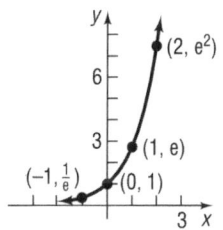

Natural Logarithm Function
$f(x) = \ln x$

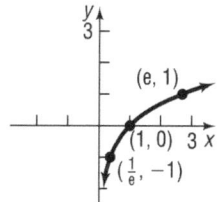

Sine Function
$f(x) = \sin x$

Cosine Function
$f(x) = \cos x$

Tangent Function
$f(x) = \tan x$

Cosecant Function
$f(x) = \csc x$

Secant Function
$f(x) = \sec x$

Cotangent Function
$f(x) = \cot x$

FORMULAS/EQUATIONS

Distance Formula

If $P_1 = (x_1, y_1)$ and $P_2 = (x_2, y_2)$, the distance from P_1 to P_2 is

$$d(P_1, P_2) = \sqrt{(x_2 - x_1)^2 + (y_2 - y_1)^2}$$

Standard Equation of a Circle

The standard equation of a circle of radius r with center at (h, k) is

$$(x - h)^2 + (y - k)^2 = r^2$$

Slope Formula

The slope m of the line containing the points $P_1 = (x_1, y_1)$ and $P_2 = (x_2, y_2)$ is

$$m = \frac{y_2 - y_1}{x_2 - x_1} \qquad \text{if } x_1 \neq x_2$$

$$m \text{ is undefined} \qquad \text{if } x_1 = x_2$$

Point–Slope Equation of a Line

The equation of a line with slope m containing the point (x_1, y_1) is

$$y - y_1 = m(x - x_1)$$

Slope–Intercept Equation of a Line

The equation of a line with slope m and y-intercept b is

$$y = mx + b$$

Quadratic Formula

The solutions of the equation $ax^2 + bx + c = 0, a \neq 0$, are

$$x = \frac{-b \pm \sqrt{b^2 - 4ac}}{2a}$$

If $b^2 - 4ac > 0$, there are two unequal real solutions.
If $b^2 - 4ac = 0$, there is a repeated real solution.
If $b^2 - 4ac < 0$, there are two complex solutions that are not real.

GEOMETRY FORMULAS

Circle

$r = $ Radius, $A = $ Area, $C = $ Circumference
$$A = \pi r^2 \qquad C = 2\pi r$$

Triangle

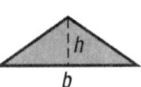

$b = $ Base, $h = $ Altitude (Height), $A = $ area
$$A = \tfrac{1}{2}bh$$

Rectangle

$l = $ Length, $w = $ Width, $A = $ area, $P = $ perimeter
$$A = lw \qquad P = 2l + 2w$$

Rectangular Box

$l = $ Length, $w = $ Width, $h = $ Height, $V = $ Volume, $S = $ Surface area
$$V = lwh \qquad S = 2lw + 2lh + 2wh$$

Sphere

$r = $ Radius, $V = $ Volume, $S = $ Surface area
$$V = \tfrac{4}{3}\pi r^3 \qquad S = 4\pi r^2$$

Right Circular Cylinder

$r = $ Radius, $h = $ Height, $V = $ Volume, $S = $ Surface area
$$V = \pi r^2 h \qquad S = 2\pi r^2 + 2\pi rh$$